A Wiley Publication in Psychology

HERBERT S. LANGFELD

Advisory Editor

Handbook of
EXPERIMENTAL
PSYCHOLOGY

Contributors

S. HOWARD BARTLEY

FRANK A. BEACH

HAROLD P. BECHTOLDT

GEORG von BÉKÉSY

FRANK BRINK, Jr.

W. J. BROGDEN

LEONARD CARMICHAEL

HALLOWELL DAVIS

EDWARD W. DEMPSEY

PAUL M. FITTS

C. H. GRAHAM

CALVIN S. HALL

ERNEST R. HILGARD

CARL I. HOVLAND

WILLIAM LEROY JENKINS

DEANE B. JUDD

ROBERT LEEPER

J. C. R. LICKLIDER

DONALD B. LINDSLEY

GEORGE A. MILLER

NEAL E. MILLER

CLIFFORD T. MORGAN

HENRY W. NISSEN

CARL PFAFFMANN

WALTER A. ROSENBLITH

T. C. RUCH

ROBERT H. SEASHORE

NATHAN W. SHOCK

KENNETH W. SPENCE

R. W. SPERRY

S. S. STEVENS

G. R. WENDT

DAEL WOLFLE

HERBERT WOODROW

Handbook of
EXPERIMENTAL
PSYCHOLOGY

Edited by

S. S. STEVENS

Professor of Psychology
Director of the Psychological Laboratories
Harvard University

JOHN WILEY & SONS, INC. · NEW YORK
LONDON · SYDNEY

BOOK BY STEVENS (S. S.) AND DAVIS (H.)
Hearing: Its Psychology and Physiology
ALSO BY STEVENS (S. S.)
Handbook of Experimental Psychology

There is a hierarchy of facts; some have no reach; they teach us nothing but themselves. The scientist who has ascertained them has learned nothing but a fact, and has not become more capable of foreseeing new facts. Such facts, it seems, come once, but are not destined to reappear.

There are, on the other hand, facts of great yield; each of them teaches us a new law. And since a choice must be made, it is to these that the scientist should devote himself.

HENRI POINCARÉ
The Foundations of Science, p. 544

Preface

In a very real sense this book was created by popular demand. Murchison's *Handbook of General Experimental Psychology*, published in 1934, went out of print before World War II, and by 1946 many psychologists were feeling a need for a technical survey that would systematize, digest, and appraise the mid-century state of experimental psychology.

This need for a handbook is a periodic occurrence. When the mass of new material in the journals becomes unmanageable, a secondary digest is called for, and psychology has had about half a dozen handbooks in the last century: Müller (1833), Wagner, Hermann, Schaefer, Nagel, and Murchison (1934). Of course other books have partially served the handbook function, and specialized handbooks have appeared in the various segments of psychology as the subject has expanded in the twentieth century.

In experimental psychology proper, then, a handbook was fully due. Among the official bodies of the American Psychological Association there was talk of preparing such a book—perhaps as an official venture of the APA. Meanwhile, however, several publishers were alive to the idea, and when one of them came forth with concrete plans the APA withdrew in favor of private enterprise.

It was immediately plain, in 1946, that this private enterprise would have to be highly public, for a modern handbook requires the collaborative efforts of a community of experts. No single specialist can marshal the erudition required for an inventory of experimental psychology's facts and findings. It was also plain that between the covers of a single volume it would be impossible to survey all of psychology that is truly experimental and that many limitations would be forced by circumstances. There would need to be arbitrary slicings made in a subject matter that is essentially continuous, and these slicings would need to coincide with the talents and interests of living experts. There would need to be compromise between the ideal of consistency throughout the volume and the democratic right of scientists to disagree and to correct one another's errors.

Equally clear was the fact that the handbook should address itself directly to the advanced scholar—to the graduate student who would use it as a textbook and to the specialist who would use it as a reference source and as a guide to matters outside his own specialty. Therefore it should be neither elementary nor esoteric.

These principles have indeed governed the writing and editing of this work. If an occasional practical exigency has forced us to content ourselves with less than our initial aspirations, other developments have certainly conspired in our favor. The chief beneficent conspirator has been the enthusiastic devotion of the contributors.

Let me say a little about the concrete circumstances of the labor. In the first place, the scramble of postwar reconversion was upon us and many of the authors were resuming their academic functions under conditions less than utopian. In the second place, the editor felt himself deficient in editorial wisdom. He tried to make up for this by seeking the advice of two wiser men, E. G. Boring and C. T. Morgan. The three of them argued about how the book should be organized and who should contribute chapters. The decisions were not always unanimous, but eventually a plan was adopted and contributors solicited. (Boring conducted most of the correspondence at this stage— and a lively correspondence it was.) Inevitably, of course, emendations of the original plan were necessary from time to time and the editor made them as the work progressed. Since neither the editor nor the authors had fully grasped the magnitude of the undertaking, the early optimistic deadlines had to be revised and it was November 1949 when 86 pounds of manuscript were finally shipped to the publisher. We then had hopes for publication in 1950. The authors had been patient with the editor. They had diligently revised the editor's revisions of their manuscripts and had gracefully put up with deletions and compressions of varying magnitudes.

But the end of the editing was still months away. The manuscript was carefully marked for the printer and the process uncovered many matters calling for revision. In the meantime, someone had counted the words and found them to run to more than a million, which was far more than had been bargained for. The entire manuscript was then returned to the editor who had another go at revision and compression. Several thousand words and a few figures were squeezed out on this final round.

The individual authors proofread their own galleys. Most of them faithfully suppressed the natural desire of authors to rewrite on the margins of the proof. Where the temptation proved too great the editor wielded his pencil with high censorial hand—which effectively makes him responsible for what may still be wrong with the text.

No one, of course, ever edits a work of this sort singlehanded. I have already mentioned the contributions of Boring and Morgan. But the person who did more work on this handbook than anyone else is Geraldine Stone. While I am writing this preface she is busy organizing the index.

The contributions of the authors speak for themselves in the pages that follow.

S. S. S.

January 29, 1951
Harvard University

Contents

CONTENTS

MOTIVATION

LEARNING AND ADJUSTMENT

SENSORY PROCESSES

Mathematics, Measurement, and Psychophysics

S. S. STEVENS
Harvard University

The stature of a science is commonly measured by the degree to which it makes use of mathematics. Yet mathematics is not itself a science, in the empirical sense, but a formal, logical, symbolic system — a game of signs and rules. The virtue that makes mathematics more than trivial is its capacity to serve as a model for events and relations in the empirical world. Like any model used to represent something other than itself, mathematics "fits" better in some places than in others, but at no place is there perfect correspondence between the mathematical model and the empirical variables of the material universe. Generally speaking, the fit is better to the degree that the dimensions and qualities of the things we study are measurable on well-founded scales. When description gives way to measurement, calculation replaces debate.

Measurement, then, is a concern of psychology. It is only remotely an aspiration in those fields of the discipline where uncharted complexity confronts the inquirer and where the cast of the basic topography

This chapter had the helpful criticism of several patient colleagues. E. G. Boring, G. A. Miller, F. C. Frick, and Frederick Mosteller gave it a most thorough combing, but theirs is not the responsibility for the errors it still contains.

Its production was carried through at the Psycho-Acoustic Laboratory, Harvard University, under contract with the U. S. Navy, Office of Naval Research (Contract N5ori-76, Project NR147-201, Report PNR-76).

is revealed only to men of bold insights. It is more immediately the goal in the experimental corner where the patient sifting of facts and relations has disentangled some of the relevant variables. Measurement is an especial preoccupation of psychophysics — not only of psychophysics in the narrow sense of the term, but of psychophysics in its older and broader spirit, which tries to discover rules relating the responses of organisms to the energetic configurations of the environment and which, as we shall see, resolves itself into seven basic problems.

But measurement is a relative matter. It varies in kind and degree, in type and precision. In its broadest sense measurement is the assignment of numerals to objects or events according to rules. And the fact that numerals can be assigned under different rules leads to different kinds of scales and different kinds of measurement. The rules themselves relate in part to the concrete empirical operations of our experimental procedures which, by their sundry degrees of precision, help to determine how snug is the fit between the mathematical model and what it stands for.

Measurement is possible in the first place only because there is a kind of isomorphism between (1) the empirical relations among objects and events and (2) the properties of the formal game in which numerals are the pawns, and operators the moves. When this correspondence between the formal model and its empirical counterpart is close and tight, we find ourselves able to discover truths about matters of fact by examining the model itself. Thus we calculate the flight of a bullet or the course of a comet without laying hands on either. And we are awed by the prodigious power of mathematics to see what is beyond our own vision.

In this mathematical puissance the ancients detected a mystical splendor — a proof that number rules the universe. The moderns see this as just another instance of man's creating his own gods, for mathematics is a human invention, like language, or like chess, and men not only play the game, they also make the rules. Of course the rules for much of mathematics (but by no means all of it) have been deliberately rigged to make the game isomorphic with common worldly experience, so that ten beans put with ten other beans to make a pile is mirrored in the symbolics: $10 + 10 = 20$. It is interesting to note, however, that a vast amount of what we call mathematics is not isomorphic with any known reality and is in this sense useless to the practice of science.

Nevertheless the structure of mathematics is studied by the scientist because it is the language in which he sets forth his precise propositions. Hogben oversimplifies it for the "million" by explaining that mathematics is the language of *size* as opposed to English which is a language of *sort*. In any case, mathematics is a specialized language with a rich and rigorous syntax — as every schoolboy knows. And, as every psychologist knows, there is no profit in trying to expound the technicalities of mathematical syntax in a single chapter. All we shall attempt here is an understanding of how it serves as a model to represent empirical operations. We can talk a little *about* mathematics without being skilled in the art of its use. For a book on the skills of mathematics applied to psychology, see D. Lewis (1948).

Syntactics, Semantics, and Pragmatics

When we discuss the nature and use of language — mathematical or otherwise — it is convenient to distinguish three regions of inquiry (Morris, 1938; see also Carnap, 1942):

1. Syntactics is the study of the relation of signs to signs.

2. Semantics is the study of the relation of signs to objects.

3. Pragmatics is the study of the relation of signs to the users of signs.

For examples, see Table 1.

TABLE 1

EXAMPLES FROM THE THREE LEVELS OF
LANGUAGE INQUIRY

Level	Examples
Syntactics	Rules of algebra:
	$a^2 = a \times a = \sqrt{a^4} = a^6 \times a^{-4}$, etc.
	Rules of punctuation:
	Unpunctuated: That that is is that that is not is not is that not it it is.
	Punctuated: That, that is, is; that, that is not, is not. Is that not it? It is.
Semantics	Geometry: Let h be the length of the hypotenuse of a right triangle.
	Objects: "Square" is the name for figures like this: □.
	Metalanguage: The word "horse" is a noun.
Pragmatics	Propaganda: "Progressive" is a "good" word in the view of most people.
	Usage: Educated people do not say "ain't."
	Idiom: The sentence, "We must rise equal to the occasion," is bad idiom.
	Insult: The word "nigger" is insulting to a negro.

Syntactics refers to the formal disciplines of logic, mathematics, and syntax, where the relations among signs are *abstracted* from the relation of the signs to objects and to the users or interpreters of signs. The propositions of syntactics are devoid of empirical content. They say nothing about the physical world. They are statements like the laws of algebra, which set the rules for the combining and arranging of the signs of algebra. In short, abstract mathematics is a branch of syntactics.

Of course, in order to *talk about* a syntactical system we have to get out of the system and into another language — a *metalanguage*. Thus, when the textbook describes in English the syntactical laws of algebra, English is the metalanguage, and the 'objects' to which the words of the textbook refer are the signs of algebra. In other words, the terms of the metalanguage are related by semantical rules to 'objects' that are themselves terms in another language. Or the 'objects' may even be terms in the same language, as when the grammar book discusses in English (metalanguage) the syntax of English (object language).

Semantics refers to the rules that relate signs to objects. What object do we call a chair, what a table? In our algebraic formula what does x stand for, and what do the other signs represent? Obviously, if a formula is to stand for something, its terms must be linked by semantical rules to objects or events; its terms must have a meaning. Semantical rules are basically arbitrary, in the sense that we make them up for our convenience, but the satisfactory definition of words and symbols is not always easy to come by. It is generally accepted that semantical rules should be in the nature of *operational* definitions (cf. Stevens, 1939a), but the problem of contriving definitions that meet the operational test of meaning is, as Bridgman showed in 1928, a serious, difficult business. It is easy enough to say, "Let x represent the ratio of responsibility to liberalism," but it is hard to know what, if anything, we are talking about.

Closely related to the problem of the operational definition of individual terms is the issue of the "truth" of empirical propositions. *Terms* have *applicability* to objects or events when the semantical rules governing their use satisfy operational criteria. The sentences or formulas created by combining these *semantically* significant terms into propositions are *empirically* significant (have truth value) when their assertions are confirmable by means of concrete operations. The operational definition of terms does not guarantee the operational validity of formulas. Thus H and W may stand unequivocally for a man's height in inches and weight in pounds, but the mathematical sentence reading $H = \sqrt{W}$ may be empirically false.

The confirmation of an empirical assertion, it should be remembered, is never absolute and final. Repeated tests can add to its *probability* but never clinch its certainty. Induction, as Hume said, is not a watertight method of proving anything empirical, and propositions about nature always have a degree of probability that is less than certainty (cf. Reichenbach, 1938). Not so with syntactic (mathematical) statements, however. There we find theorems and equations that are absolutely true or absolutely false. They are true if they are consistent with the rules laid down for playing the game; they are false if they break the law. But these absolutely true statements say nothing at all, unfortunately, about objects or events, and they reveal no secrets of nature.

It is by way of semantical rules that we tie the mathematical model to the empirical world, and it has already been pointed out that the model often fits as poorly as a borrowed hat. Some of the reasons for this lack of congruity can now be made more specific:

1. There are always empirical errors of measurement. We can calculate the area of a circle to far greater accuracy than physical operations can measure it. (Actually the irrationality of π precludes even an exact calculation of the area, but we can add on decimal places as long as we please.)

2. There are often uninterpretable mathematical terms for which we make no semantical rules. The length of the hypotenuse of a right triangle is gotten by solving: $h^2 = a^2 + b^2$. One solution is $+\sqrt{a^2 + b^2}$; the other is $-\sqrt{a^2 + b^2}$. We throw out the negative solution because negative lengths make no sense.

3. The rules of classical mathematics imply infinite divisibility, but matter, we have reason to believe, is not infinitely divisible.

4. Only a few of the many aspects of any natural phenomenon get themselves represented in a given mathematical formulation. Most aspects are neglected, deliberately or by oversight, and those that we try to depict may be ill chosen or ill defined. The shortcoming is then basically a matter of semantics.

Pragmatics refers to the relation of signs to scientists. Here belong the problems of how the scientist, as a behaving organism, uses signs, how he reacts to signs, how the choice of signs influences behavior. About this obviously fascinating problem no more will be said here, except to point out that the paralytic terror instilled by those clever souls who can calculate in those who cannot is a problem in applied pragmatics. It is the same terror that routed Diderot when Euler confronted him at the Russian court with a symbolic non sequitur to prove the existence of God (Bell, 1937).

THE MATHEMATICAL MODEL

The formal rules of mathematics are arbitrary conventions. Historically this fact was discovered late. The early mathematicians thought it proper to prove their mathematics empirically — to demonstrate that $2 + 2 = 4$ by sorting pebbles. The seeming success of this pebble counting as a test of many mathematical propositions still makes it hard for us to keep an understanding grip on the important truth that the "process of induction, which is basic in all experimental sciences, is *forever banned* from rigorous mathematics" (Dantzig, 1939, p. 67). Counting on the fingers may be a handy method of meeting computational emergencies, but all it proves about the nature of arithmetic is that the rules of number invented by our ancient ancestors are isomorphic with certain digital operations. We are not startled by this correspondence between fingers and arithmetic, because we know that in some dim era of the past somebody invented the system of natural numbers for precisely this purpose of providing a formal model to represent what he did with fingers and pebbles and enemies and cattle. That the forgotten genius of that historical day may have been unconscious of the *formal-empirical* dichotomy, which we now regard as so crucial, is beside the point. The fact is, he built a formal model to stand for an aspect of his empirical world, just as an architect draws a plan for a house.

The details of this primitive model making are lost to the record, but it is easy to imagine how it might have come about. Many things exist in obvious quantity, like fingers (in whose names we find the names of the numerals in many old languages, cf. Harkin) and pebbles (in whose Latin name we find our word *calculus*). To collections of these things primitive man applied the *principle of correspondence* — the basic mathematical process of setting things in one-to-one relation. He might have added one pebble to a pile for each fish in his cache, and if someone filched a fish he could have discovered the theft by *pairing* each of the remaining fish against a pebble.

This pairing of members until one or both groups is exhausted leads directly to the concept of *cardinal number*. If both fish and pebbles pair up evenly with none of either left over, the two groups have the same cardinal number. Which is why Frege in 1879 and Russell (independently) in 1901 defined number as the class of all classes that show a one-to-one correspondence with a given class (cf. Bell, 1937, p. 567). The cardinal number 3, for example, is the class of all trios; 2 is the class of all pairs, etc.

The ubiquity of the cardinal principle is evident in many systems of numeration, such as those of Rome and Egypt (Harkin). The Egyptians wrote the numeral nine thus: $111_{111}{}^{111}$. But cardinal number, resting solely on the principle of correspondence, implies *no counting*. Our primitive forebear who knew only cardinality had resort to a motley array of models, unsystematized and *ad hoc*. In order to create a counting process he had to devise a system: he had to arrange his set of models in an ordered sequence. This he probably accomplished in a few thousand years by setting successive piles of pebbles in an order such that any pile paired with its next-door neighbor would leave one pebble left over. In these ordered piles he had a model of a very tidy sort, one having ordinality, or succession. Next he named the successive piles (he made up semantical rules), and he remembered the order of the names. Then he was ready to *count* his fish. He simply paired them against the successive names until he ran out of fish. The name assigned to the last fish was the *ordinal number* of his catch.

This fanciful account of how our ancestors got from cardinal to ordinal numbers is intended to clarify the distinction between the two kinds of numbers. As history it is undoubtedly false. It is pleasant to surmise that cardinal number, based on matching, antedates ordinal number, which calls for both matching and ordering. "Yet the most careful investigations into primitive culture and philology fail to reveal any such precedence. Wherever any number technique exists at all, both aspects of number are found" (Dantzig, p. 9).

The reader should be alerted here and in what follows to the intensely controversial nature of some of the basic notions at the frontiers of mathematical inquiry. At these frontiers the mathematicians, like ordinary mortals, exchange incivilities and shout each other down. One of the noisiest of recent battles was that between the formalists, led by Hilbert, and the intuitionists, led by Weyl and Brouwer. The skirmish is vividly chronicled by Bell (1945, pp. 565–570) and I mention it here mainly because intuitionist Weyl does not agree that the cardinal (class) concept of number is primary. It seems to him "unquestionable that the concept of ordinal number is the primary one" (p. 35). The present account of things is more in line with the formalist tradition. Let us return to it.

The names for number we now call numerals, and the fact that they have a "natural" sequence — an ordered succession — makes possible an arithmetic, i.e. a set of rules for combining numerals. The rules, of course, are so chosen that the system can continue, as it began, to serve as a model for ordered piles of pebbles. Thus if two piles are pooled the result is a collection having the same cardinality as some one of the ordered piles. The model reflects these facts under the so-called rules of addition. Subtraction in the realm of numerals (e.g. $7 - 4 = 3$) reflects, with no change in the semantical rules originally laid down, the operation of taking one pile of pebbles from another. Multiplication is successive addition, and division is successive subtraction. Thus we arrive at whole-number arithmetic. And incidentally in the process we have achieved a scale of measurement — a scale for the measurement of "numerosity" — the cardinal attribute of physical collections of objects (Stevens, 1939*b*).

Numeration

The invention of ordered numerals was a momentous accomplishment. But how should they be written? A different numeral for each of the numbers represented by endless ordered piles of pebbles is a theoretical possibility but a psychological suicide. We could never remember them all. We must have a learnable set of different symbols and a learnable rule of succession. Given a numeral we must know how to produce its successor. Nearly all systems of numeration are based on a repetitive procedure that makes it possible to indicate large numbers by combining the symbols for smaller numbers (cf. Ore).

Many systems, like the Roman, are based on an obvious cardinal principle: I, II, and III, for 1, 2, and 3. This procedure is psychologically easy and obvious, provided the indication of magnitude is the only goal. But when we try to create an arithmetic we find it impossible to devise for Roman numerals a multiplication table that a human being can learn the way a fourth-grade pupil learns the Arabic table. To see what this means try multiplying MCDLVIII by XIX. The difficulty, we now know, is that the Roman system has no zero — no symbol for the empty column — and it can therefore make no use of the *principle of position*. The Greeks and the Romans, for all their intellectual brilliance, never hit upon the simple, powerful device of indicating *nothing* by means of a symbol. The Romans wrote DV where we write 505. Our numeration says explicitly: five hundreds, no tens, and five units. Our ability to say "no tens" in this manner is the secret of the power and simplicity of our reckoning. "When viewed in this light, the achievement of the unknown Hindu who some time in the first centuries of our era discovered the *principle of position* assumes the proportions of a world event" (Dantzig, p. 29). The Hindu called zero by the name *sunya,* which meant *empty* or *blank,* presumably because he used it to indicate that there were no marks in one of the columns of his counting board.

Most systems of numeration repeat on the base *ten.* The choice of this base is an anatomical accident and attests the anthropomorphic nature of our counting. If the three-toed horse had learned to calculate, he would probably have used the base six or twelve for his arithmetic. Contrary to popular belief, there is nothing sacred about the decimal base. Any base is possible, and other bases are sometimes used for special purposes. Modern binary computing machines use the base *two* because only two numerals are required, and they can be represented by a switch that is open for one numeral and closed for the other. In binary notation our number 22 is written 10110. For Leibniz the binary system had a mystic elegance because out of unity and nothing all numbers can be created!

Actually the base ten is an unhappy choice. It would have been better had we had no thumbs, for then the base would have been *eight.* The case for base-eight arithmetic has been argued by many (cf. Tingley). The advantage is allegedly psychological: it would make mental calculations easier because it more readily allows for successive halvings, and halving is psychologically the simplest of all numerical operations. On base ten and base eight the process of successive doubling gives:

Base Ten	Base Eight
1	1
2	2
4	4
8	10
16	20
32	40
64	100
128	200
256	400

Tingley points out that the world's moneys, weights, and measures try to follow the principle of successive doubling, but the base ten makes it impracticable. The coins and bills of our currency, for example, show the following ratios each to the one below it:

Coins (in cents)	Ratios
1	
5	5
10	2
25	2.5
50	2
100	2
200	2
500	2.5
1000	2
2000	2

If we used the base eight, all these ratios could be exactly two, and change counting would be vastly easier for both geniuses and morons. All the factors of base eight are twos, and in this age of binary computing machines it would be a happy economy if we could make this glorified binary the base of our counting.

But anatomy has chosen our base for us, and mere psychological advantage is probably not going to change it.

Extension of the Number Domain

The positive integers, which early in history became ordered into a system of ordinal numbers, are only a small part of what we now call the domain of number. And the story of mathematics discloses successive extensions of the domain, painfully and laboriously achieved.

The first accretion seems to have been the fractions, or, as we call them, the *positive rational numbers*. With these new elements added the mathematical model becomes adequate to the representation not only of things countable but also of things that vary in magnitude, like length. Unit fractions date back to Ahmes of Egypt (1700 B.C.), and Euclid considered commensurable ratios of the form *m/n*, but he did not himself regard these ratios as numbers (cf. Young, p. 101).

If later men were less conservative than Euclid in admitting new elements to the domain, the interesting question is why. This is not to inquire into Euclid's temperament, but to pose the problem of the rationale of new numbers. What should they be? What criteria must they satisfy? The answer to this question was not known to the ancients, who never mastered the distinction between the formal model and the empirical world of things and objects, and who put their trust in empirical induction. The possibility of syntactics (the study of signs and rules) divorced from any consideration of semantical definitions is a modern discovery. The notion of syntactics is *implicit* in the work of the early mathematicians, but it is only when we make *explicit* the nature of signs and rules that we are able to formulate criteria for the admission of new numbers to the number union.

Put crudely, the idea is this: any new number is admitted provided it obeys the old rules. It is analogous to the admission of a state to the union: the new state must agree to obey the federal laws. The laws of the number union have to do with addition, multiplication, subtraction, and division, and the new numbers must behave themselves when these operations are applied. Since rational fractions exhibit the proper decorum when they are added, multiplied, etc., we vote them in.

Actually, of course, new kinds of numbers do not step forth from nowhere to test themselves against the rules that were generated when the arithmetic of natural numbers was created. Rather the reverse is true. The attempt to apply the rules of arithmetic occasions these new numbers. Thus we subtract 4 from 7 and get 3; but suppose we subtract 7 from 4. In the system of natural numbers this subtraction is not possible, and until about the time of Descartes (1596–1650) operations of this sort were ruled out as "absurd" or "fictitious." But, if we admit *negative numbers* to the domain, subtraction is always possible, and after years of struggle and controversy these absurd new outlanders became naturalized citizens. In analogous fashion the rational fractions had wormed their way into citizenship because they made division always possible.

What we observe here is an involuntary tendency on the part of mathematicians "to employ rules under circumstances more general than are warranted by the special cases under which the rules were derived . . ." (Klein, p. 26). This tendency to generalize has become a highly respectable attribute among the moderns, and in 1867 Hankel gave it explicit dignity by claiming it to be a guiding principle in arithmetic. He called it the *principle of the permanence of the formal laws*, and by it he intended what we have already seen, namely, that in mathematics the rule's the thing. Unlike the ideal state where the laws are made for men, in mathematics the elements are made for the laws.

With the introduction of the negative numbers under this "principle of permanence" mathematics so changed its aspect that men began to see the reasonableness of the point on which we have been insisting: that mathematics is a syntactical sport. Faced with numbers generated by taking something large from something small (e.g. $4 - 7 = -3$) we find that it becomes harder to regard arithmetic as a system of concrete numerical magnitudes and that it becomes easier to see it as a formal symbolism. With the extension of the number domain so that there is *no least number* it becomes more obviously impossible to prove arithmetic empirically as the ancients tried to do.

With negative numbers admitted to the system an amusing thing happens. Felix Klein, one of the modern greats, quotes Max Simon to the effect that, "whereas negative numbers were created to make the operation of subtraction possible without any exception, subtraction as an independent operation ceased to exist by virture of that creation" (p. 24). Subtraction becomes merely the addition of a negative number.

Of course, once new formal elements have been introduced into the system it often becomes possible to relate them by semantical rules to objects or events, or even to the elements of other systems. Thus in bookkeeping the minus sign may mean that you owe the bank some money. And in geometry the minus sign can be interpreted as *rotation* through 180 degrees, so that negative numbers refer to distance in the direction opposite to that indicated by positive numbers (cf. Young, p. 114).

Again applying the principle of permanence (unconsciously perhaps) mathematicians introduced the *irrational numbers* into Western Europe in the sixteenth century (cf. Klein). Irrationals are necessary to the solution of equations like $x^2 - 2 = 0$. The solution, $\sqrt{2}$, is not a rational number like ⅗ because it is not expressible as the ratio of two integers. But irrational numbers fit into arithmetic and pay their way as useful, law-abiding tenants of the realm.

Actually the Greeks were aware of the existence of incommensurable ratios. They knew that the diagonals of most right triangles are irrational — incommensurable with the sides — a discovery celebrated by Pythagoras with the sacrifice of a hundred oxen. Furthermore the Greeks had a word for it — "unexpressible" — which tells us better than the Latin name that these ratios are not contrary to reason but merely undepictable by integers. But the Pythagoreans viewed the irrationals with mixed emotions. We are told that the members of the order were sworn to secrecy not to reveal to outsiders these "imperfections" in the number system, for number was supposed to rule the universe. Dantzig quotes Proclos: "It is told that those who first brought out the irrationals from concealment into the open perished in shipwreck, to a man."

As we have seen, the algebraic irrationals forced their way into the number domain, much as did the negatives, because they were useful in solving certain algebraic equations. An interesting question, one not settled until 1844, concerns the possibility that there exist irrational numbers that are not algebraic — that are the solution of no algebraic equation having rational numbers as coefficients. In 1873 Hermite astonished and delighted the mathematical world by proving that the number e, the base of the natural logarithms, whose value is 2.7182818 ⋯, is the root of no algebraic equation of this sort, and in 1882 Lindemann did the same for π. These numbers belong to the category known as *transcendental*, for, as Euler put it, they "transcend the power of algebraic methods" (Courant and Robbins, p. 104). Transcendental numbers comprise some of our most useful devices, for they include most logarithms and trigonometric ratios — functions that might well be called the work horses of applied mathematics.

With this latest enrichment, the addition of transcendentals, the realm of number becomes fatter and fuller by far than primitive man could have imagined it would ever be. All the numbers thus far discussed belong to what is called the *real domain,* and in this domain we can perform rich and varied calculations. But there are still some simple things we cannot do. For example, we cannot solve the equation: $x^2 + 1 = 0$, for a solution is $\sqrt{-1}$, which has the appearance of nonsense. For many centuries the impulse to write $x = \sqrt{-1}$ was inhibited by men's knowledge that there is no square root of a negative number. The Hindus and the Arabs resisted the temptation to write these numbers, although they were bold in other matters mathematical. It seems to have been the Italian, Cardan, who in 1545 first dared, albeit apologetically, to denote this "fiction" by a symbol. Once symbolized, however, these *imaginary numbers,* as we still call them, pushed their way to prominence. Denoted by the symbol i and combined with real numbers to make elements of the form $x + iy$, the imaginaries go to make up the complex numbers which are so essential to modern algebra. In fact it was with the aid of these numbers that the young Gauss was able, in his doctoral thesis in 1799, to prove what the mathematicians call the fundamental theorem of algebra, namely, that *every* algebraic equation in one unknown has a solution. And the prolific Euler had already in 1748 revealed the remarkable relation between integers, transcendentals, and imaginaries:

$$e^{\pi i} = -1$$

The creation of complex numbers is dramatic evidence of the validity of the distinction between the formal model and the empirical universe (cf. Stevens, 1939a). These numbers were originally developed from the purest of mathematical motives, and no application to concrete matters was even suspected when the rules for their addition and multiplication were first formulated. Complex numbers were simply abstract symbols, useless to the applied mathematician. True, there lurked an uneasiness in mathematical circles, for most men had not yet made peace with the notion that uninterpretable symbols need be no menace and that the justification of a formal system need not rest with its practical usefulness as a model of things

touchable. Nevertheless the formal system, the algebra of complex numbers, was born and elaborated in the vacuum of abstraction "without the approval, and even against the desires of individual mathematicians . . ." (Klein, p. 56).

As it turned out, these lingering doubts about the validity of complex numbers were set to rest early in the nineteenth century when a simple geometric interpretation of the operations with complex numbers was provided. Actually the fact that a geometric interpretation is possible proves neither the validity, nor the reality, nor the sanctity of complex numbers, but it does comfort the concrete-minded and the intuitionists, and it leads directly to the practical application of complex algebra in the physical sciences.

The geometric scheme consists simply in representing the number $x + iy$ as a point in the x, y plane. The abscissa of the point is x; the ordinate is y. And the relations among the points in the "number plane" are reflected in the algebra of complex numbers, just as the relations among the points on a line are mirrored by the algebra of real numbers. Furthermore the symbol i can be thought of as a *rotation*. The minus sign, it was noted above, corresponds in geometry to a rotation of 180 degrees, and in analogous fashion the sign i corresponds to a rotation of 90 degrees. Thus we get to the real part, x, of our complex number by marching x paces out along the reference line, and the addition of the imaginary part, iy, means: make a right-angle turn and proceed y paces.

This isomorphism between geometry and complex numbers makes skill in complex algebra a must for the engineer. For example, in treating problems that involve alternating currents the engineer can let x stand for resistance, iy for inductive reactance, and $-iy$ for capacitive reactance. These are his semantical rules. He can then turn the crank of the algebraic machine and grind out formulas that depict measurable aspects of electric circuits. In other words he can use this formal system as a model for the intricate theory of alternating currents. What began as an "empty play upon symbols" gets itself hitched by semantical rules to ohms, henries, and farads. And so well does it work that there are some electrical engineers, untutored in history, who think that complex algebra was invented expressly for the purpose of circuit analysis.

Not only were the inventors of complex numbers oblivious of electrical engineers and their practical problems; they were even convinced that no applications of these numbers would ever be possible. They were like a tailor in a compulsive fantasy who goes on designing garments for creatures whom he has never seen and can scarcely imagine. Occasionally a fellow shows up who fits one of the tailor's creations, and the world is filled with amazement and delight. But, as we noted near the beginning of this chapter, much of the mathematician's modern tailoring fits no known aspect of the physical world, and it seems certain that these symbolic tailors will go on creating new kinds of mathematics far faster than applications can possibly be found for them. Mathematics is not yet petrified in rigid completeness.*

This concludes our survey of numbers and how we came by them. Of course we could go on to show how still other kinds of numbers were added to the domain: numbers corresponding to points in space of three dimensions, quaternions, matrices, algebraic ideals, etc. It appears that once liberated from their fear of empty symbols the mathematicians produced a throng of new numbers, some useful, some useless. These new elements need not concern us here except in one particular: extensions of the domain beyond complex numbers call for a relaxation of the rules. The rule of the "permanence of the formal laws" must be shorn of its dominion if we are to add and multiply things like matrices — those "filing-cabinet" numbers

* See Bell (1945, p. 21) for four other dramatic examples of the generation of mathematical principles under the drive of intellectual curiosity, with no prospect then apparent of any possible practical application.

that consist of arrays of elements useful in factor analysis. For example, it was the revolutionary insight of Hamilton, the Irishman, that disclosed the necessity of revoking the commutative law of multiplication in order to extend complex algebra to "n-dimensional" numbers. The commutative law says what is intuitively so obvious, namely, that $a \times b = b \times a$, and it was a bold stroke when Hamilton proposed a system of quaternions in which a times b does not equal b times a.

If we are to point a moral in all this, it is that the rules and postulates of a formal system are arbitrary conventions. Under this conception of things, the "rule of permanence" turns out to be not so permanent. It has been demonstrated over and over again that the formal laws can be altered to the enrichment rather than the confusion of mathematics. Perhaps this is why Bell calls the rule of permanence a "notorious and discredited" principle. He sums up the modern attitude with an apt comparison: "In the same way that a novelist invents characters, dialogues and situations of which he is both author and master, the mathematician devises at will the postulates upon which he bases his mathematical systems" (1945, p. 330). Incidentally, Bell should know about the novelist. He writes science fiction under the name John Taine.

Summary of Number Domain

Leaving out the super complex numbers like quaternions, we can now summarize the number domain in a quotation and a table. The quotation is from Gauss, believed to be the greatest mathematician yet born, and is via Dantzig (pp. 189–190), the delightful expositor of number theory.

Wrote Gauss in 1831:

Our general arithmetic, far surpassing in extent the geometry of the ancients, is entirely the creation of modern times. Starting originally from the notion of absolute integers, it has gradually enlarged its domain.

TABLE 2

THE NUMBER SYSTEM

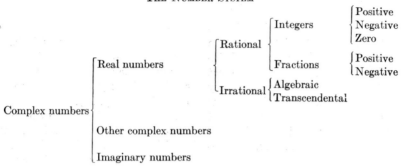

To integers have been added fractions, to rational quantities the irrational, to positive the negative, and to the real the imaginary. This advance, however, has always been made at first with timorous and hesitating steps. The early algebraists called the negative roots of equations false roots, and this is indeed the case when the problem to which they relate has been stated in such a form that the character of the quantity sought allows of no opposite. But just as no one would hesitate to admit fractions to general arithmetic, although there are so many countable things for which a fraction has no meaning, so we ought not deny to negative numbers the rights accorded to positive simply because innumerable things admit of no opposite. The reality of negative numbers is sufficiently justified, for in innumerable other cases they find an adequate interpretation. This has long been admitted, but the imaginary quantities — formerly and occasionally now improperly called impossible — are still rather tolerated than fully naturalized; they appear more like an empty play upon symbols, to which a thinkable substratum is unhesitatingly denied even by those who would not depreciate the rich contribution that this play upon symbols has made to the treasure of the relations of real quantities.

The table representing the number domain can be arranged as a breakdown of the complex number system into its subdivisions. This is possible because all real numbers are special cases of complex numbers, obtained

when the coefficient of i is zero. Similarly, when the real part of a complex number is zero we have a pure imaginary number.*

What this number system teaches us is that, given certain basic postulates or principles about relations within a formal system, the elements of the system generate themselves automatically. Or, as Dantzig says, "Arithmetic does not begin with numbers; it begins with criteria" (p. 208). These criteria (like one-to-one correspondence underlying the notion of cardinal number) existed only implicitly in the mathematics of a century or two ago, and the ferreting out of fundamental principles is a most modern phenomenon. The mathematicians are only lately becoming explicitly conscious of the rules that their predecessors followed unconsciously in their calculating.

Let us consider more fully some of these basic postulates that determine the nature of mathematics. And in doing so let us re-

* It should be pointed out, however, that Russell does not like this way of regarding the number domain. He says, "One of the mistakes that have delayed the discovery of correct definitions in this region is the common idea that each extension of number included the previous sorts as special cases" (1920, p. 63). To him negative numbers are relations, or instances of "relation-numbers," and are, therefore, not in the same universe with cardinal numbers, which are classes of classes. Nevertheless the "common idea," as he calls it, is a convenient if loose way of looking at the matter. "Although it is an error in theory, it is a convenience in practice" (p. 76).

member, as Young says, "that the starting point of any mathematical science must be a set of undefined terms and a set of unproved propositions (assumptions) concerning them. The science then consists of the formal logical implications of the latter" (p. 59). The elementary "objects" of mathematical inquiry, numbers, points, lines, etc., are not substantial "things in themselves," and they elude precise definition. The only relevant assertions concerning them are those that state their interrelations and the rules governing operations with them. Or, as Coutourat put it:

A mathematician never defines magnitudes in themselves, as a philosopher would be tempted to do; he defines their equality, their sum and their product, and these definitions determine, or rather constitute, all the mathematical properties of magnitudes. In a yet more abstract and more formal manner he *lays down* symbols and at the same time *prescribes* the rules according to which they must be combined; these rules suffice to characterize these symbols and to give them a mathematical value. Briefly, he creates mathematical entities by means of arbitrary conventions, in the same way that the several chessmen are defined by the conventions which govern their moves and the relations between them. [From Bell, 1937, p. 565.]

The rules create the game of chess, whether we play with ivory pieces or with collar buttons.

The practical utility of our inquiry into the foundations of formal mathematics may not be immediately obvious to the psychologist, but we undertake it here for the light it throws on our most fundamental problem: the creation of scales of measurement.

Attributes of Relations

As we have seen, the gist of mathematics lies in the *relations* among its elements. The recognition of this fact has led to an intricate and specialized *theory of relations,* which constitutes an important branch of modern logic (cf. Tarski, Chapter 5; also Reichen-

bach, 1947). Logic, incidentally, is not something apart from mathematics. In the modern view of things mathematics is a branch of logic, and it turns out that the notion of number and all other mathematical concepts are definable in the field of logic. "It follows that all pure mathematics, in so far as it is deducible from the theory of the natural numbers, is only a prolongation of logic" (Russell, 1920, p. 25).

The technicalities of the calculus of relations need not concern us here, but certain special attributes of relations merit our understanding. For convenience we may arrange these attributes in four groups of three attributes each. Then all the relations we shall be interested in are typified by some combination of four attributes drawn one from each of these four groups (see Table 3).

The four categories have to do with reflexivity, symmetry, transitivity, and connectedness. Table 3 tries to define these notions by means of examples. Examples probably suffice to convey the meaning of the first three categories. The import of the fourth category is clarified by Russell's definition which runs as follows: "A relation is *connected* when, given any two terms of its field, the relation holds between the first and the second or between the second and the first (not excluding the possibility that both may happen, though both cannot happen if the relation is asymmetrical)" (1920, p. 33). In other words, a relation is connected if it holds between all pairs of items in a specified field. Connected relations are necessary (but not sufficient) to the arrangement of things in a series.

It is an interesting exercise to think up examples and to assign them their proper attributes. In so doing, remember that it is essential to specify the "field" of the relation, i.e. the class of things related, whether natural numbers, real numbers, all people, some people, triangles, etc., before a proper assignment can be made. (For the examples in Table 3 the field is usually left to implication, but sometimes it is stated explicitly.)

TABLE 3

Some Attributes of Relations

Attribute	Examples
I	
Reflexive	Equal to ($x = x$ for all values of x), similar to, includes
Mesoreflexive	Reciprocal of (x may or may not be the reciprocal of x)
Irreflexive	Greater than (it is not true for any x that $x > x$), older than, not equal to
II	
Symmetrical	Equal to (if $x = y$ then $y = x$), not equal to, sibling of, proportional to, spouse of
Mesosymmetrical	Not greater than (if $x \not> y$ then y may be equal to or less than x), angry at, includes, brother of
Asymmetrical	Greater than (if $x > y$ then $y \not> x$), father of, successor to
III	
Transitive	Equal to (if $x = y$ and $y = z$ then $x = z$), greater than, ancestor of
Mesotransitive	Not equal to (if $x \neq y$ and $y \neq z$ then x may or may not equal z), angry at, in love with
Intransitive	Father of (if x is father of y and y is father of z, then x is not father of z), successor to
IV	
Connected	Greater than (in the series of natural numbers, if any two different items are selected, one of them is greater than the other), in telephonic link with (in the Bell system any subscriber can telephone each other subscriber)
Mesoconnected	Ancestor of (given any two people, one may or may not be the ancestor of the other), successor to
Unconnected	Alike (given any two fingerprints, neither is like the other)

Other attributes of relations are sometimes distinguished. For example, a relation may be *one-one* (square of, husband of); *one-many* (father of); *many-one* (relation of son to father, square root of); or *many-many* (grandparent of). For mathematics the one-one relation, which Russell sees as a special case of the one-many relation, is of great importance, because it is involved in all relations of the form, "the so-and-so of such-and-such," e.g. the king of Siam, the handle of the pump, the square of x, the log of y, etc. Relations of this sort are what Russell means by the term *function*. In the mathematical sense, the phrase "y is the so-and-so of x" defines a function in which x is the *argument* of the function and y is the *value*

of the function for the argument x. These are descriptive functions, and in this sense "the wife of Socrates" is as much a function as are the more mathematical formulations.

But confining our attention to the properties of relations listed in Table 3, we can single out certain combinations of attributes that are of especial moment. They are important because they characterize basic mathematical relations in the field of number. Thus the relation of *identity*, expressed by the sign =, is reflexive, symmetrical, transitive, and unconnected. The relation *successor to* is irreflexive, asymmetrical, intransitive, and mesoconnected.

One of the most interesting combinations of these attributes applies to relations that are irreflexive, asymmetrical, transitive, and connected. A little thought will show that a relation of this sort establishes a *serial order*. As a matter of fact, for the criterion of an ordering relation we would need to state only the three properties, *asymmetrical*, *transitive*, and *connected*, because if a relation is transitive and asymmetrical it is also irreflexive. (The properties of relations are not always independent.) Examples of relations having the three attributes that define order include such relations as *greater than* and *less than*.

The Postulates of Order

Since the business of setting things in rank order is important to many psychological inquiries, let us consider how we might characterize linear order by a set of *formal assumptions*. These assumptions, or postulates as they are often called, are due to Huntington (cf. Young, p. 68). When we make them we are laying down the conditions (the "demands") that any system must satisfy if it is to be classed as ordered. The word "postulate" is from the Latin *postulare*, meaning "to demand."

First we introduce a symbol, <, and we leave it completely undefined. It may stand for any one of a number of the relations, e.g. less than, precedes, older than, above, etc.

We also make use of the symmetrical relation expressed by the symbol $\neq$, meaning "is different from."

Then, given a class of elements, we let a, b, and c be any elements of the class. The relation $<$ is then assumed to obey the following rules:

O_1 If $a \neq b$, then either $a < b$ or $b < a$

O_2 If $a < b$, then $a \neq b$

O_3 If $a < b$ and $b < c$, then $a < c$.

These three demands are imposed upon the relations among the elements of an ordered series. If the three demands are met, the relations are of the sort that define what we mean by linear order. Now we have already seen that the relations defining order must have three attributes: they must be connected, asymmetrical, and transitive. And it is easy to see that these three attributes characterize the relations among elements that obey Huntington's three postulates.

Criteria for Postulates

Let us now digress a moment to discuss this business of postulation. Since postulates are merely the assumptions we make about relations, it is clear that initially they are very easy to come by. As Russell said when he was scolding those who postulate that an irrational number is the limit of the sequence of fractions that approach closer and closer to the irrational, "The method of 'postulating' what we want has many advantages; they are the same as the advantages of theft over honest toil" (1920, p. 71). But whether postulation is thievery depends upon circumstances. Russell objects to the process only when it is used to dodge a problem that honest toil could solve. In setting up the initial postulates of a mathematical system we are not trying to duck a difficulty; we are trying to pare away the irrelevant nonessentials in order to get a clear view of what constitutes the essence of the system. Generally we want to see how few notions we can leave undefined and still generate all the

propositions and theorems of the system. Consequently there are criteria that are applied to postulates in order to prove their fitness to serve. The most important of these criteria are *consistency*, *independence*, and *sufficiency*. The first of these is a must. The other two are in a sense optional.

Consistency is demonstrated if a system in which there are no known contradictions can be shown to fit the postulates. The postulates of order are consistent because systems like the natural numbers and the points on a line satisfy the postulates, provided, of course, that the proper interpretation is made of the symbol $<$. For the natural numbers this symbol may mean "less than"; for the points on a line it may mean "precedes."

Independence means that no one of the postulates can be derived from the others. The requirement of independence is not logically essential, because mere duplication or partial overlap among postulates does not invalidate the system they govern. But independence is economically and esthetically desirable. It furthers the cause of elegance.

The reader can test the independence of the postulates of order by thinking up interpretations of the symbol $<$ for which some one of the postulates is false while the others are true. Begin, for example, by letting $<$ mean "is the ancestor of."

Sufficiency is sometimes called *categoricalness*. It is a property that may or may not be required of a set of postulates, depending on our purpose. Sufficiency refers to the ability of the postulates to determine a single system, as opposed to several systems that are not mutually isomorphic. Two systems are isomorphic if the elements of one system can be paired off one-to-one with the elements of the other system. It turns out that the postulates of order are not sufficient to determine a single system. These postulates can be satisfied by a finite set of integers, say the numbers from 1 to 10, and by the infinite set of all integers. Obviously, these two sets cannot be put into one-to-one correspondence.

In contrast with the postulates of order, the fundamental postulates of algebra are sufficient to determine a single system. In this connection it is probably in order to call attention to a general principle: the negation of one of the postulates governing a system has the effect of making the system more general. In other words, it becomes easier to find instances that satisfy the postulates when their number is limited. Thus we have already seen how the suppression of the commutative law makes it possible to add quaternions to the number system. Another celebrated example is the creation of the numerous non-Euclidean geometries within the amplified elbow room of a curtailed set of postulates (e.g. a set in which the postulate of parallels is suppressed).

The Postulates of Algebra

It is a curious fact that, although the postulational method was applied to geometry two millenniums ago, only in modern times were the fundamental assumptions of algebra exhumed from the hodgepodge of rules by which algebraic manipulations are carried out. These basic postulates thus represent the distilled wisdom of more than 3000 years of algebraic juggling.

It should be pointed out at once that there is, strictly speaking, no one algebra — there are several. There is at least one for each major division of the number domain. In a certain sense all these algebras are included in the algebra of complex numbers, which is in many respects simpler than any of the more restricted algebras. The postulates of complex algebra as framed by Huntington are consistent, independent, and sufficient, and they are 27 in number, which means that we will not list them here. Instead we shall have a look at the postulates of ordinary algebra which Harkin sets forth in a scheme having a certain mnemonic merit. All that need be remembered is the word "scared," which the student of algebra will find quite natural.

First we assume a class or set of elements, $a, b, c, \cdots$. This class is ordered — it obeys the three postulates listed above. Next we assume two operations denoted by $+$ and $\times$, and finally we impose on these symbols the conditions listed in Table 4.

Out of the postulates we get the theorems of algebra. All the complicated propositions that fill the treatises on real algebra stem

TABLE 4

POSTULATES OF ORDINARY ALGEBRA

S (synthesis)	$a + b = c$ $a \times b = c$	The synthesis of any two elements produces another element that is in the set.
C (commutative)	$a + b = b + a$ $a \times b = b \times a$	The operations are commutative.
A (associative)	$a + (b + c) = (a + b) + c$ $a \times (b \times c) = (a \times b) \times c$	The operations are associative.
R (reversion)	$a + x = b$ $a \times x = b$	Reversion from a to b via some element x is always possible, provided $a \neq 0$ in multiplication.
E (existence)	$a + 0 = a$ $a \times 1 = a$	There exists an identity element for addition (0) and for multiplication (1).
D (distributive)	$a \times (b + c) = a \times b + a \times c$	Multiplication distributes over addition.

from this set of simple statements, and all
the algebraic theorems can be reduced to
the postulates S.C.A.R.E.D. Harkin shows
how the elementary rules of cancellation,
transposition, etc. — the rules we learn in
high school — follow directly from these
basic assumptions. These rules appear as
theorems, derivable from Table 4.

Definitions, Postulates, and Theorems

It is helpful to distinguish among *definitions, postulates,* and *theorems.* In a formal
system like algebra these distinctions are
clear enough. By means of definitions we
introduce new signs into the system, and the
definitions relate the new signs to the older
signs already explicated. Thus $a^n = a \times a
\times a \times \cdots$ (for n factors) is a definition
used to introduce the exponential sign into
the system. Postulates, then, are the statements we make, without proof, about the
signs and operators and their relations. And
theorems are the statements arrived at by
combining the signs in a manner consistent
with the postulates and definitions.

In an empirical science like psychology we
have a situation that is in some respects
analogous. What corresponds to formal definitions are the empirical definitions (semantical rules) invoked to relate words or
symbols to objects or events. What corresponds to formal postulates are usually
hypotheses — empirical statements relating
terms previously defined. And what corresponds to theorems are empirical propositions deduced from the hypotheses.

Unlike the theorems of a formal system,
which must pass only the test of consistency
with the postulates and definitions of the
system, the empirical propositions of science
are subject to the additional test of empirical
confirmation or refutation.

All this seems straightforward enough, but
the fact of the matter is that these distinctions are not always preserved in our textbooks. Many statements have the appearance of empirical propositions when they are
really definitions. And much confusion results. In the proper ordering of things we
might set up the illustrative paradigm:

Definition: An instinct is a stereotyped
   mode of response.
Definition: A cat is a four-legged mammal.
Hypothesis: Cats have instincts.
Empirical verification: Do cats show instances of stereotyped behavior?

Here the definitions are semantical rules.
They disclose an arbitrary convention concerning our use of words. Having arbitrarily
defined the words "cat" and "instinct," it is
in order for us to compose statements relating the two. These are empirical propositions, as distinct from formal theorems, and
their validity is a matter to be tested by
observation.

But consider what happens when an author begins with the statement, "Cats have
instincts." What is he really putting forth,
a definition or a proposition? It may be
either, and unless the author tells us more we
cannot be sure whether what he says is "true
by definition" or whether he is proposing
something that is amenable to operational
test.

It is astonishing how frequently we generate pseudo-problems in our science by confusing definitions (semantical and syntactical
statements) with empirical propositions. For
an analysis of a concrete instance in which
the scientist flounders in logomachy because
he hides his syntactical and semantical rules
in sentences that have the outward appearance of empirical propositions, see Stevens
(1939a, pp. 251f.).

In further pursuit of the analogy between
science and the postulational methods of algebra, let us consider the so-called *hypothetico-deductive method* of empirical inquiry, which has its vogue under the convic-
tion that science should be pursued in the
manner of Galileo rather than of Aristotle.
In the scientific method at its neatest we set
up hypotheses, we deduce consequences, and
we confirm or refute. For this purpose we

choose a formal model — mathematical, logical, or simply linguistic. We draw from the model an array of symbols. By means of semantical rules we relate these symbols to observable events or objects, and we arrange the symbols in the form of an equation or proposition (the hypothesis). Then we avail ourselves of the *syntactical* rules of the formal system of symbols and proceed to deduce. That is to say, we apply syntactical rules of transformation and convert the original equation or proposition (the hypothesis) into some other equation or proposition (the deduction) consistent with the original. Finally we relate the terms of the deduction to observable events by means of semantical rules, and having done this we are ready to put the deduction to experimental test.

The main difference between the postulational method of algebra and the hypothetico-deductive procedure in science lies in the fact that empirical considerations enter the latter. In science we can test our deductions against nature. In mathematics the facts of the natural universe are irrelevant. We cannot prove algebra with test tubes.

But a point to be noted is that in the process of scientific deduction from empirical hypotheses the process of deducing is carried out at the formal level. A deduction consists in a transformation of a sentence in accordance with syntactical rules. When the hypothesis is an equation and the syntactical rules are the laws of algebra, there can be no doubt that the procedure is as outlined here. When the hypothesis is a sentence in English, where the rules of syntax are less explicitly stated, we often make deductions without being fully aware of the "logic" we are using. Nevertheless, if we are consistent, we are using a logic of some sort, and it is the carrying out of the rules of this logic that is the process we call deduction.

Fortunately for the future of theory building in the nonquantitative reaches of science, the formalization of logic into a symbolic calculus is presently proceeding apace. This modern logic "provides explicit techniques for manipulating the most basic ingredients of discourse. Its yield for science may be expected to consist also in a contribution of rigor and clarity — a sharpening of the concepts of science" (Quine, p. 8). The well-read psychologist of the future may need to know both Russian and some universal language or pasigraphy like symbolic logic.

The Concept of Group

Let us return now to some further matters in what Russell likes to call the philosophy of mathematics, as opposed to its practice as an art. As we dig downward toward the lower strata of the subject in order to discover what notions are fundamental, we turn up, as we have already seen, some very simple but powerful ideas. The obviousness of some of these concepts does not detract from their importance. Rather we are reminded of what D'Arcy Thompson said of physics: "It behoves us to remember that . . . it has taken great men to discover simple things" (p. 13). The same can certainly be said of mathematics.

Two of the most fundamental concepts of mathematics have already been alluded to. They are the notion of a *class* of elements and the notion of one-to-one correspondence or *isomorphism*. A third concept is that of a mathematical *group*, and a fourth is the closely related concept of *invariance*. We shall first try to understand what the mathematician means by a group.

The theory of groups is little more than a century old, but it has already illuminated much of what goes on in geometry and algebra. Perhaps the theory is not the "Open sesame" it was thought to be in its heyday when the demonstration that a given theory obeyed the postulates of a group was considered a momentous accomplishment (cf. Bell, 1945, p. 445). Nevertheless the group is a very basic notion and one that we shall have use for when we consider the problem of devising scales of measurement.

A group in mathematics is a set of *operations*. The thing that makes these operations a group is the fact that one operation followed by another operation produces a result that is the same as what could have been produced by one or more different operations. This, of course, is a loose definition, and we will need to take up the slack as soon as we consider an example.

Take the batting order of a baseball team. There are nine players arranged in the sequence judged most effective by the divinations of the manager. Let the team lose a string of games, and the manager is apt to consult his oracle and shake up the batting order. Now, he operates on the order by interchanging (permuting) players. And it is plain that any one of the 362,880 possible orders could be achieved if, starting from any given order, the manager interchanged the players by successively substituting one for another in the order. He could put the lead-off man into the clean-up position (fourth place) by interchanging first and second, then second and third, and then third and fourth. That would get the lead-off man into fourth place. Then in order to move the clean-up man (now in third place) up to first place, the manager would interchange third and second, and then second and first. These five one-for-one substitutions produce the same batting order that would have resulted had the manager interchanged one and four in the first place. Hence we see that some combinations of operations are equivalent to other combinations of operations.

This always impresses the layman as a trivial and obvious matter, and he is astonished to learn that this simple notion, basic to the theory of *permutation groups*, was essential to Galois' solution of a long-standing riddle about the solvability of equations. These simple permutation groups even turn up in modern descriptions of atomic structure.

We generalize the group concept by doing what was just done for algebra: we lay down the postulates (demands) which a set of operations must satisfy in order to merit the title "group."

First we assume a set of elements (operations) $a, b, c, \cdots$ and a symbol, $\circ$, denoting their combination. Then we impose the four postulates of Table 5 (cf. Harkin, p. 98).*

TABLE 5

Postulates of a Group

Synthesis:	If a and b are members of the set of operations, then $a \circ b$ is also a member of the set.	(This postulate says that the group is closed.)
Associative:	For *any* three operations $(a \circ b) \circ c = a \circ (b \circ c)$.	(This postulate says that the group is associative.)
Existence:	There exists a unique "identity" operation, i, such that $a \circ i = i \circ a = a$.	(This postulate says that one of the operations must be the doing of nothing, or its equivalent.)
Reversion:	There is a unique "inverse" operation a' such that $a \circ a' = i$.	(This postulate says that we can always backtrack and undo the effect of a given operation.)

In the special case when $a \circ b = b \circ a$ the group is commutative, or Abelian, named after Abel who was Norway's gift to mathematics. With the commutative postulate imposed we find Table 5 looking very much like Table 4 (the postulates of ordinary algebra). The D is missing from S.C.A.R.E.D. because the distributive law is not needed to determine a group, Abelian or otherwise.

Actually there are at least two interesting groups in Table 4. For example, the real numbers form a group with respect to the process of addition. The sign $\circ$ in the group postulates becomes the $+$ sign in the addition group, and the numbers themselves may be regarded as the elements — the *opera-*

---

* The last two of these postulates are sometimes replaced by a single postulate in a different form, e.g. for every a, b there exist x, y such that $a \circ x = b$, $y \circ a = b$ (cf. Bell, 1945, p. 215).

tions. Thus $3 + 4 = 7$ may be interpreted to mean: if you first go 3 paces and then go another 4 paces, it is the same as going 7 paces; i.e. operations can be combined. In the addition group the identity element is 0, i.e. $a + 0 = a$, and the inverse element is $-a$, i.e. $a + (-a) = 0$. Since the commutative law (postulate C in Table 4) is in force, the addition group is Abelian.

Analogously, the real numbers (zero excepted) form an Abelian group under multiplication. In this case the identity element is 1, since $a \times 1 = a$ and the inverse element is the reciprocal, i.e. $a \times 1/a = 1$.

Curiously enough, some of the common operations of arithmetic do not form groups. Subtraction, for example, falls short of the demands listed in Table 5, because it is not associative. Division fails for the same reason. Had we only the positive numbers to work with, as in pre-Cartesian days, even the operations of addition would not form a group, for without the negatives reversion would be impossible.

Many different kinds of operations form groups (cf. Birkhoff and MacLane). There are groups of permutations on batting orders, on electrons hovering around an atomic nucleus, or on any other *arrangements* of things. There are rotations of objects in space, like those of a wheel with six spokes. Each operation of rotating by 60 degrees leaves the precise space occupied by rim and spokes unchanged (invariant), and these 60-degree rotations comprise a finite group in which a 360-degree rotation is equivalent to the identity operation of no rotation at all. On the other hand, all possible motions of a rigid body in space generate an infinite continuous group.

Perhaps the most interesting groups, from the point of view of measurement, are those whose sets of elements (operations) are algebraic transformations. The everyday process of multiplying by a constant, illustrated when we convert from inches to feet to yards to centimeters to miles, etc., is one of the simplest of these transformations. Such operations belong to the *similarity* group, and we note that when it is applied to distances the property that is preserved invariant is the *ratios* among the distances. Other transformation groups will be listed when we come to scales of measurement.

In the meantime a word is in order concerning this term "operation." In the foregoing paragraphs it has carried two different meanings: it has stood both for a mathematical manipulation (e.g. multiplying) and for a concrete empirical act (e.g. rotating a wheel through 60 degrees). We call both enterprises operations, but obviously they belong to different realms: one concerns a formal matter, the other a physical procedure. Perhaps the use of two different words would set the issue to rights, but usage is toughly ingrained, and the best we can do is to remember that operations in mathematics can serve as a model for physical events, but they are not the same thing.

The Concept of Invariance

It has already been hinted that the important thing about a transformation is what it does not transform, i.e., what it leaves invariant. Within the last hundred years the basic importance of invariance has proved itself in algebra, geometry, and theoretical physics, and we occasionally hear of it in psychology. Bell gives it a forty-eight page chapter in his *Development of Mathematics* (1945), and he begins with this quotation from Keyser:

> Invariance is changelessness in the midst of change, permanence in a world of flux, the persistence of configurations that remain the same despite the swirl and stress of countless hosts of curious transformations.

It took one of the greatest of self-taught mathematicians, George Boole, also a principal founder of symbolic logic, to call attention to the power of this simple principle (1841). It was with what is called *algebraic invariance* that Boole worked, and the gist of this stuff is a little beyond the grasp of those of us who are not mathematicians. But not too much for our intuitions are the displays of invariance in other fields like geometry and physics.

Draw a figure made up of intersecting lines and curves on a rubber sheet, and then stretch or distort the sheet in any way imaginable. Areas, lengths, and angles are obviously not left invariant, but something is. However we torture the rubber, the order of the intersections we must pass in tracing a path from one given part of the figure to another and the communality of boundaries between different areas are two of the properties that stay put. The study of invariance in "rubber-sheet" geometry is part of the vast, vigorous inquiry known as *topology*. It is geometry without a metric, and the fact that it seems to deal with relations stripped of the encumbrance of magnitude has struck up the hope in some psychologists that topology may answer the need for a formal model to represent things unmeasurable. Topology might well find a usefulness here, but it may be that more than metrical nakedness is needed to clothe a social dynamics. In any case, if something empirically verifiable is to issue from the application of mathematics, something empirically known must be put in.

The importance of invariance as a tool of thought is exemplified by the classical notion of the conservation of energy. The total amount of energy in a system stays the same under transformations from one form, such as heat, into other forms, such as electricity. Similarly, what we mean by *shape* and *size* of a rigid object are the properties that do not change when we alter or transform the coordinate system in terms of which we describe the object. It may be said in general that the task of physics is the description of natural phenomena in terms that remain invariant when the frame of reference is changed.

An example will help here. Newton's second law equates force to the time derivative of momentum. The physicist verifies this law in all sorts of reference systems and finds it true. The law would not be worth much if it worked only in Europe or only at sea level or only for circular motions or only for objects larger than elephants. The invariance of the law under a wide assortment of conditions is its source of power.

The scientist is usually looking for invariance whether he knows it or not. Whenever he discovers a functional relation between two variables his next question follows naturally: under what conditions does it hold? In other words, under what transformations is the relation invariant? The quest for invariant relations is essentially the aspiration toward generality, and in psychology, as in physics, the principles that have wide application are those we prize.

The conclusion, if we may venture one, is that the empirical scientist can emulate the attitude of the mathematicians who followed Boole and cultivate a love for invariance that leads him to seek uniformities in heterogeneity and to recognize invariance when he sees it.

Many psychological problems are already conceived as the deliberate search for invariances.* Perhaps all psychological problems ought to be so construed, at least when general principles are the goal. The "particularizing" mind may note that a visual stimulus has a threshold value, that two men look about the same size, and that flashing lights seem to move. The "generalizing" mind takes these matters into a wider frame and discovers (1) the luminosity or visibility curve — the threshold invariance under si-

---

* Note, for example, how explicitly Thurstone (1947, Chapter 16) makes "configurational invariance" a central issue in multiple factor analysis. And in a vastly different area, see how nicely the analysis of the determining factors in 'instinctive' behavior reduces to a problem of the invariance of a response under transformations of environmental conditions (cf. Chapter 12). For example, black-headed gulls continue to sit on the nest even though the eggs are painted a variety of colors or are replaced by wooden models of various sizes, shapes, and odors. Only if the 'eggs' have sharp contours does this invariant behavior break down.

multaneous transformations of frequency and intensity; (2) the size-constancy effect (the relative invariance of perceived size under transformations of distance, surrounds, etc.); and (3) the conditions for optimal phi phenomenon (the partial invariances of perceived movement known as Korte's laws).

In general, we enlarge the reach of invariance by exploring the effects of parameters. Thus we may start with a tonal threshold and find, for a given frequency, the intensity that can be heard as often as not. That is an invariant *point*. Then we change frequency and get the threshold *curve* for the whole audible range. That is the invariance under two parameters, frequency and intensity. Next we might vary another dimension, like the duration of the tone, and from the results we could construct in three dimensions the *surface* that gives the threshold invariance under three parameters. Age of the listener might be a fourth parameter, degree of the subject's training might be a fifth, and so on. In extending this process we encroach more and more on the no-man's land of what is usually pigeonholed in the catchall called variability. Not that variability is ever banished from empirical science, but successive expansions of the domain of invariance can reduce the dominion of variance to tractable proportions.

As an illustration in another field, consider the intelligence quotient — the IQ. Why is this such a capital concept in psychology and education? Surely if the IQ bobbed about like female fashions it would be just another incidental phenomenon in psychology. The fact that it stays relatively constant throughout the growing years is the reason for the ferment it has engendered. In this respect the IQ is analogous to the concept of the somatotype — the designation of human morphology by means of three variables, or components, whose values determine the basic character of a given physique. It is the apparent invariance of the somatotype under the transformation we call "aging" that makes this notion potentially useful in the characterization of human beings (cf. Sheldon, Stevens, and Tucker). *Absolute invariance* of the IQ and of the somatotype is not essential to the utility of these two concepts, but some degree of invariance seems requisite to their importance. The wider their limits of invariance, the more useful they become, for in his scientific account of humanity the scientist seeks measures that will stay put while his back is turned.

But, needless to say, the greater number of psychological studies seem not to result in the demonstration of significant invariance. It is obviously easy to say that the delineation of the conditions of invariance for any phenomenon would tell us all we want to know about the matter, but it is equally obvious that the experimental task itself is uphill work.

NUMERALS AND MEASUREMENT

Let us return now to the problem of measurement. Before the paraphernalia of mathematics can be of use to psychology, we must devise scales of measurement. I would spare the reader this platitude were it not for the fact that we sometimes talk the language of functional connections and speak in terms of "more" or "less" without seeming to diagnose the implications of our discourse. We might say, for example, that the more a man is frustrated the more aggressive he becomes. This is an easy sentence to translate into the language of proportionality, where it reads:

$$A = kF$$

i.e. aggression (A) is proportional (k) to frustration (F). This is an interesting notion and one we should like to test. The test would follow simply and automatically if we had a scale for the measurement of aggression and a different scale for the measurement of frustration. Each of these scales, as we shall see, would have to be a *ratio* scale if a relation of *proportionality* is to hold. If a less restrictive relation is what we want to establish, *ordinal* or *interval* scales might suffice.

The requirements for measurement are easier to state than to realize. But this does not mean that the meaning of measurement has always been clear. We have it from one of their own distinguished number that "The most distinguished physicists, when they attempt logical analysis, are apt to gibber; and probably more nonsense * is talked about measurement than about any other part of physics" (Campbell, 1938). With this sharp warning before us, let us tread gingerly.

It seems safe enough to say that measurement involves the process of linking the formal model called the number system to some discriminable aspect of objects or events. This notion was expressed near the beginning of this chapter: "Measurement is the assignment of numerals to objects or events according to rules" — a paraphrase of Campbell himself (1940; cf. Stevens, 1946). Russell (1937) seems to go along with this conception: "Measurement of magnitudes is, in its most general sense, any method by which a unique and reciprocal correspondence is established between all or some of the magnitudes of a kind and all or some of the numbers, integral, rational, or real, as the case may be. . . . Measurement demands some one-one relation between the numbers and magnitudes in question — a relation which may be direct or indirect, important or trivial, according to circumstances" (p. 176). Campbell's and Russell's definitions are both excellent, provided we take them at their face value, and they seem both to be saying the same thing except that one uses the term "numeral" where the other says "number." Both definitions are liberal

and generous — in fact, they show an open-handedness that both authors seem later to go back on, each in a different way. But these defections need not concern us here.

In using two different words, "numeral" and "number," for what gets related to objects by means of semantical rules, Campbell and Russell probably both intend the same meaning. Elsewhere I have sided with Campbell's usage because the meaning of the term "number" is often ambiguous: among other things, it refers sometimes to a physical attribute of a collection of discrete objects (a number of peanuts), sometimes to Frege's class of isomorphic classes (cardinal numbers), and sometimes to Russell's relational expressions (relation numbers, of which the ordinal numbers are a subclass). My guess would be that the numbers Russell intends for measurement are the relation numbers.

The term "numeral" has the defect that it sometimes means the physical ink mark on a piece of paper and it sometimes means the essentially *logical* relation that a numeral may stand for. This second meaning is in line with the formalist's view of mathematics, according to which arithmetic is regarded as the rules of a game played with numerical symbols "whose shape is recognizable by us with certainty independently of place and time, of the particular conditions of their manufacture, and of trifling differences in their execution" (quoted from Hilbert by Weyl, p. 35). Campbell seems to have this second meaning in mind, which is probably also Russell's meaning. In any case, two facts are plain. (1) There is a need for some new and univocal terms for these various meanings.† (But, the inertia of usage being what it is, the need will most likely persist.) (2) Whatever terms may be chosen, the essence of measurement is the as-

---

* The reader who would like to sample some of this nonsense — to which Campbell seems to contribute his fair share — will find it in the deliberations of a committee appointed by the British Association for the Advancement of Science to consider the measurability of sensation (for reference, see Campbell, 1940). For a more sensible analysis of the issues raised by this committee, see Reese (1943).

† In an attempt to distinguish between the cardinality attribute of groups of objects (number in the layman's sense) and the "subjective" aspect or attribute that we observe when we look at, but do not count, a collection of objects, I used the terms "numerosity" and "numerousness" (Stevens, 1939b). Taves (1941) did an experiment relating the visual perception of numerousness to physical numerosity.

signment (to aspects of objects or events) of elements drawn from the formal system to which the postulates of algebra (Table 4) apply. These assignments are made according to one or another of the rules that we will now discuss.

Scales of Measurement

A rule for the assignment of numerals (numbers) to aspects of objects or events creates a *scale*. Scales are possible in the first place only because there exists an isomorphism between the properties of the numeral series and the empirical operations that we can perform with the aspects of objects. This isomorphism, of course, is only partial. Not *all* the properties of number and not *all* the properties of objects can be paired off in a systematic correspondence. But *some* properties of objects can be related by semantical rules to *some* properties of the numeral series. In particular, in dealing with the aspects of objects we can invoke empirical operations for determining equality (the basis for classifying things), for rank ordering, and for determining when differences and when ratios between the aspects of objects are equal. The conventional series of numerals — the series in which by definition each member has a successor — yields to analogous operations: We can identify the members of the series and classify them. We know their order as given by convention. We can determine equal differences, as $7 - 5 = 4 - 2$, and equal ratios, as $10/5 = 6/3$. This isomorphism between the formal system and the empirical operations performable with material things justifies the use of the formal system as a *model* to stand for aspects of the empirical world.

The type of scale achieved when we deputize the numerals to serve as representatives for a state of affairs in nature depends upon the character of the basic empirical operations performed on nature. These operations are limited ordinarily by the peculiarities of the thing being scaled and by our choice of concrete procedures, but, once selected, the procedures determine that there will eventu-

ate one or another of four types of scale: *nominal, ordinal, interval,* or *ratio*. Each of these four classes of scales is best characterized by its range of invariance — by the kinds of transformations that leave the "structure" of the scale undistorted. And the nature of the invariance sets limits to the kinds of statistical manipulations that can legitimately be applied to the scaled data. This question of the applicability of the various statistics is of great practical concern to several of the sciences.

The principal facts about scales are summarized in Table 6.* It will be noted that the column listing the basic operations needed to create each type of scale is cumulative: to an operation listed opposite a particular scale must be added all those operations preceding it. Thus, an interval scale can be erected only provided we have an operation for determining equality of intervals, for determining greater or less, and for determining equality (not greater and not less). To these operations must be added a method for ascertaining equality of ratios if a ratio scale is to be achieved.

In the column that records the group structure of each scale are listed the mathematical transformations that leave the scale form invariant (see Fig. 1). Thus, any numeral x on a scale can be replaced by another numeral x', where x' is the function of x listed in this column. Each mathematical group in the column is contained in the group immediately above it.

The fourth column presents examples of the type of statistical operations appropriate to each scale. This column is cumulative in

---

* A classification essentially equivalent to that in Table 6 was presented by the author before the International Congress for the Unity of Science, September 1941. (The present discussion follows Stevens, 1946.) The gist of this notion of relating scales of measurement to transformation groups is also contained in the recent book by von Neumann and Morgenstern on games and economic behavior (pp. 22–23). They omit mention of the group corresponding to the nominal scale, and they call attention specifically to the group in which no transformation would be tolerated, i.e. where, under the similarity group, *a* would be limited to unity.

that *all* statistics listed are admissible for data scaled against a ratio scale. The criterion for the appropriateness of a statistic

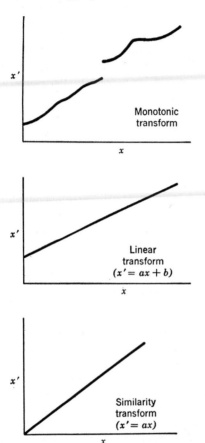

Monotonic transform

Linear transform
$(x' = ax + b)$

Similarity transform
$(x' = ax)$

Fɪɢ. 1. Graphical examples of three groups of transformations. The increasing monotonic function, which may have discontinuities of the type shown, belongs to the isotonic group and is a transformation applicable to ordinal scales. The linear transformation, intersecting the ordinate at the value *b*, is applicable to interval scales. Ratio scales allow only the similarity transformation (multiplication by a constant).

is *invariance* under the transformations in column 3. Thus the case that stands at the median (midpoint) of a distribution maintains its 'middleness' under all transformations that preserve order (isotonic group),

but an item located at the mean remains at the mean (retains its 'meanness'!) only under transformations as restricted as those of the linear group. The ratio expressed by the coefficient of variation remains invariant only under the similarity transformation (multiplication by a constant).

We note that there are two kinds of invariance involved here. If the statistic in question is dimensionless* (e.g. product-moment correlation coefficient, coefficient of variation, etc.), the numerical value of the statistic remains fixed when the scales are subjected to their permissible transformations. But when the statistic has a dimension (e.g. mean, median, etc.) its numerical value changes in accordance with the transformations applied to the scale. Thus the height of the *average man* in centimeters is numerically different from his height in inches. On the other hand, the man (or men) whose height is average remains the same man (or men) whether the measurements are made in inches or in centimeters. The invariance required of those statistics that have dimensions, then, is the identity of the object or event to which the given statistic corresponds.

The numerical value that a statistic assumes depends, of course, upon the statistic and upon the transformation. For example, a linear transformation, $x' = ax + b$, operating on the original scale values, produces for the mean $m' = am + b$, for the standard deviation $\sigma' = a\sigma$, and for the variance $\sigma'^2 = a^2\sigma^2$.

* Dimensions and the lack thereof figure prominently in the formulas of physics. The dimensionless factors are generally those that are formed of ratios in which the dimensions of the numerator cancel those of the denominator, as in the case of decibels. Measures having dimensions are those like velocity (having the dimensions of length divided by time), area (length times length), etc. In his *Dimensional Analysis*, Bridgman (1931) created a kind of algebra of dimensions which proves helpful in the investigation of physical relations. The basic notion is that the two sides of an equation must be dimensionally equivalent, and a discrepancy in dimensions may reveal an error that might be hard to detect by other means.

The last column in Table 6 lists some typical examples for each type of scale. It is an interesting fact that the measurement of many physical quantities has progressed from scale to scale. When men knew temperature only by sensation, when things were only "warmer" or "colder" than other things, temperature belonged to the ordinal class of scales. It became an interval scale with the development of thermometry, and after thermodynamics had used the expansion *ratio* of gases to extrapolate to zero it became a ratio scale.

Let us now consider each scale in turn.

Nominal Scale

The *nominal scale* represents the most unrestricted assignment of numerals. The numerals are used only as labels or type numbers, and words or letters would serve as well. Two types of nominal assignments are sometimes distinguished, as illustrated (type A) by the 'numbering' of football players for the identification of the individuals, and (type B) by the 'numbering' of types or classes, where each member of a class is assigned the same numeral. Actually, the first is a special case of the second, for when we label our football players we are dealing with unit

TABLE 6

SCALES OF MEASUREMENT

The basic operations needed to create a given scale are all those listed in the second column, down to and including the operation listed opposite the scale. The third column gives the mathematical transformations that leave the scale form invariant. Any numeral x on a scale can be replaced by another numeral x', where x' is the function of x listed in column 3. The fourth column lists, cumulatively downward, some of the statistics that show invariance under the transformations of column 3.

Scale	Basic Empirical Operations	Mathematical Group Structure	Permissible Statistics (invariantive)	Typical Examples
Nominal	Determination of equality	Permutation group $x' = f(x)$ [$f(x)$ means any one-to-one substitution]	Number of cases Mode Contingency correlation	"Numbering" of football players Assignment of type or model numbers to classes
Ordinal	Determination of greater or less	Isotonic group $x' = f(x)$ [$f(x)$ means any increasing monotonic function]	Median Percentiles Order correlation (type O)	Hardness of minerals Quality of leather, lumber, wool, etc. Pleasantness of odors
Interval	Determination of equality of intervals or differences	General linear group $x' = ax + b$	Mean Standard deviation Order correlation (type I) Product-moment correlation	Temperature (Fahrenheit and centigrade) Energy Calendar dates "Standard scores" on achievement tests (?)
Ratio	Determination of equality of ratios	Similarity group $x' = ax$	Geometric mean Coefficient of variation Decibel transformations	Length, weight, density, resistance, etc. Pitch scale (mels) Loudness scale (sones)

classes of one member each. Since the purpose is just as well served when any two designating numerals are interchanged, the structure of this scale remains invariant under the general substitution or permutation group (sometimes called the symmetric group of transformations). The only statistic relevant to nominal scales of type A is the number of cases, e.g. the number of players assigned numerals. But once classes containing several individuals have been formed (type B) we can determine the most numerous class (the mode), and under certain conditions we can test, by the contingency methods, hypotheses regarding the distribution of cases among the classes.

The nominal scale is a primitive form, and quite naturally there are many who will urge that it is absurd to attribute to this process of assigning numerals the dignity implied by the term measurement (cf. Campbell, 1938, p. 122). Certainly there can be no quarrel with this objection, for the naming of things is an arbitrary business. However we christen it, the use of numerals as names for classes is an example of the "assignment of numerals according to rule." The rule is: do not assign the same numeral to different classes or different numerals to the same class. Beyond that, anything goes with the nominal scale.

The formation of *classes* of objects or events is based on the demonstration of *equality* in respect of some trait or other. As an empirical problem the forming of classes is by no means trivial, and endless arguments have ensued over taxonomic standards. The definition of any common noun, like "horse," raises problems of classification — what animals are included, what excluded? (Cf. Stevens, 1939a, p. 233.) At the formal level, the logical (mathematical) definition of classes and of equality is the subject of much writing and arguing. Curiously enough, the relation of equality, which was described above as reflexive, symmetrical, and transitive, is so "obvious" that not until the 1930's did it become customary in

books on logic to include the postulates governing this basic relation (cf. Bell, 1945, p. 578). Mathematics has learned to pay attention to the obvious, and the empirical sciences need never apologize for following suit.

Ordinal Scale

The *ordinal scale* arises from the operation of rank ordering. Since any 'order-preserving' transformation will leave the scale form invariant, this scale has the structure of what may be called the isotonic or order-preserving group. This, of course, is a big group, for it includes transformations by all increasing monotonic functions, i.e., functions that never decrease and therefore do not have maxima. Thus the positive scale values on an ordinal scale may be replaced by their square or their logarithm or by a host of other functions, including in particular the "normalizing" transformation used in factor analysis (Thurstone, 1947, p. 368). All these transformations leave invariant the relation of "betweenness" for a given value with respect to its neighbors.

As a matter of fact, most of the scales used widely and effectively by psychologists are ordinal scales. In the strictest propriety the ordinary statistics involving means and standard deviations ought not to be used with these scales, for these statistics imply a knowledge of something more than the relative rank order of data. On the other hand, for this 'illegal' statisticizing there can be invoked a kind of pragmatic sanction: in numerous instances it leads to fruitful results. Although the outlawing of this procedure would probably serve no good purpose, it is proper to point out that means and standard deviations computed on an ordinal scale are in error to the extent that the successive intervals on the scale are unequal in size. When only the rank order of data is known, we should proceed cautiously with our statistics, and especially with the conclusions we draw from them.

Even in applying those statistics that are normally appropriate to ordinal scales, we sometimes find rigor compromised. Thus, although it is indicated in Table 6 that percentile measures may be applied to rank-ordered data, it should be pointed out that the customary procedure of assigning a value to a percentile by interpolating linearly within a class interval is, in all strictness, wholly out of bounds. Likewise, it is not strictly proper to determine the midpoint of a class interval by linear interpolation, because the linearity of an ordinal scale is precisely the property that is open to question.

Another matter also needs comment. In earlier discussions (e.g. Stevens, 1946) I expressed the opinion that rank-order correlation does not apply to ordinal scales because the derivation of the formula for this correlation involves the assumption that the differences between successive ranks are equal. My colleague, Frederick Mosteller, convinces me that this conservative view can be liberalized, provided the resulting coefficient (e.g. Spearman's ρ, or Kendall's τ) is *interpreted only* as a test function for a hypothesis about *order*. On the other hand, the interpretation of the coefficient as equivalent to r (the product-moment coefficient) would assume an underlying interval scale, and a bivariate normal distribution as well. In Table 6 I have allowed for these two interpretations by placing order correlation under both headings: type O for ordinal, type I for interval.

Interval Scale

With the interval scale we come to a form that is "quantitative" in the ordinary sense of the word. Almost all the usual statistical measures are applicable here, unless they are the kinds that imply a knowledge of a 'true' zero point. The zero point on an interval scale is a matter of convention or convenience, as is shown by the fact that the scale form remains invariant when a constant is added.

This point is illustrated by our two scales of temperature, centigrade and Fahrenheit. Equal intervals of temperature are scaled off by noting equal volumes of expansion; an arbitrary zero is agreed upon for each scale; and a numerical value on one of the scales is transformed into a value on the other by means of an equation of the form $x' = ax + b$. Similarly, energy is measured on an interval scale, for, as von Neumann and Morgenstern assert, "there is nothing in mechanics to fix a zero or a unit of energy" (p. 22). Our scales of *calendar time* offer another example. Dates on one calendar are transformed to those on another by way of this same equation. On these scales, of course, it is meaningless to say that one value is twice or some other proportion greater than another.

Periods of time, however, can be measured on ratio scales, and one period may be correctly defined as double another. In like manner, *differences* in energy (which is what we mean by *work*) may be considered ratio magnitudes, measurable on ratio scales. *Differences* between values on an interval scale become ratio scale measures for the simple reason that the process of determining a difference (i.e. subtraction) gets rid of the additive constant b.

Most psychological measurement aspires to create interval scales, and it sometimes succeeds. The problem usually is to devise operations for equalizing the units of the scales — a problem not always easy of solution but one for which there are several possible modes of attack. The determination of what we call equal sense distances is one obvious procedure. Only occasionally in psychological scaling is there concern for the location of a 'true' zero point. Intelligence, for example, is usefully assessed on ordinal scales that try to approximate interval scales, and it is not necessary to define what zero intelligence would mean. (Both Thorndike and Thurstone have tried it, however.)

The variability of a psychological measure is itself sometimes used to equalize the units of a scale. This process smacks of a kind of magic — a rope trick for climbing the hierarchy of scales. The rope in this case is the *assumption* that in the sample of individuals tested the trait in question has a canonical distribution (e.g. "normal"). Then it is a simple matter to adjust the units of the scale so that the assumed distribution is recovered when the individuals are measured. But this procedure is obviously no better than the gratuitous postulate behind it, and we are reminded of what Russell said about the larcenous aspects of postulation. There are those who believe that the psychologists who make assumptions whose validity is beyond test are hoist with their own petard, but the fact remains that the assumption of normality has the advocacy of a certain pragmatic usefulness in the measurement of many human traits. Forced to live up to certain criteria of internal consistency, as in the method of paired comparisons (cf. Thurstone, 1948), such assumptions make it possible to lay hold on problems of preferences and the like, which seem recalcitrant to other treatments.

Ratio Scale

Ratio scales are those most commonly encountered in physics, and they are possible only when there exist operations for determining all four relations: equality, rank order, equality of intervals, and equality of ratios. In the practical instance the determination of the last of these four relations — equal ratios — may take the form of the determination of successive equal intervals beginning at the zero value of the scale. This is *one* of the procedures by which we can assign numerals in such a way that equal ratios among them correspond to equal ratios of some attribute or other.

Once a ratio scale is erected, its numerical values can be transformed (as from inches to feet) only by multiplying each value by a constant. An absolute zero is always implied, even though the zero value on some scales (e.g. absolute temperature) may never be produced. All types of statistical measures are applicable to ratio scales, and only with these scales may we properly indulge in

the kind of transformations involved in the use of decibels where we take the logarithm of the ratio of two amounts of power.

Foremost among the ratio scales is the scale of "number" itself — number in the empirical sense — the scale we use when we count such things as eggs, pennies, and apples. This scale of the numerosity of aggregates is so basic and so common that it is ordinarily not even mentioned in discussions of measurement. This neglect might surprise us had we not already learned, in connection with the notion of equality, that it is often the most common and obvious things that are longest overlooked!

On the scale of numerosity we ordinarily admit only the transformation that involves multiplication by unity — the identity element of the similarity group. In other words we ordinarily count by ones. But it is plain that we could equally well count by twos, threes, tens, etc. We could assign numerals to collections of objects by the rule that would lead us to say that the numerosity of our toes is two and a half, in which case we would be counting by fours.

It is conventional in physics to distinguish between two types of ratio scales: *fundamental* and *derived*. Fundamental scales are represented by length, weight, and electrical resistance (and we should add numerosity), whereas derived scales are represented by density, velocity, and elasticity.

These latter are *derived* magnitudes in the sense that they are mathematical functions of certain fundamental magnitudes. They are actually more numerous in physics than are the fundamental magnitudes, which are commonly held to be basic because they permit a physical operation of addition analogous to the mathematical operation of addition. Weights, lengths, and resistances can be added in the physical sense, but this important empirical fact is generally accorded more prominence in the theory of measurement than it deserves. The so-called fundamental scales are important instances of ratio scales, but they are only instances.

As a matter of fact, it can be demonstrated that the fundamental scales can be set up even if the physical operation of addition is ruled out as impossible of performance. As an example, consider the scale of weight, and assume that we live in a world of explosive stuff, such that if we ever separate two blobs of it and then put them together in the same scale pan they will blow up. (There are such materials, we now know.) We will require three balances as follows: (1) a balance like the standard variety of the laboratory, (2) one like the standard variety (fulcrum at the center of the horizontal arm) but on which one pan hangs below the other when the pans are empty, and (3) one like the standard variety except that the fulcrum is not at the center of the arm. The first balance will suffice to determine equality and order, the second will determine equal differences, and the third equal ratios. We can then measure out with the second balance any required number of samples separated by equal intervals. Call these samples $a, b, c, d \cdots$. With the first balance we can find the order of this series from least to greatest. Then with the third balance we can get samples (A, B, C, D $\cdots$) related by equal, but unknown, ratios. At this point we apply the first balance to find which members of the one series are equal to which members of the other. Suppose it is

$$C = d, \quad D = j, \quad R = h, \quad S = p$$

Then C/D = R/S, and we can replace the capital letters by the letter d, plus the number of equal intervals between d and the other lower case letters corresponding to the appropriate capital letters. Then C/D = R/S becomes

$$\frac{d}{d+6} = \frac{d+4}{d+12}$$

Solving, we find $d = 12$. Then, since the intervals a–b–c–d–e $\cdots$ are equal, it follows that $c = 11$, $b = 10$, $a = 9$, and $e = 13$, $\cdots$ $h = 16$, $\cdots$, $j = 18$, $\cdots$, $p = 24$, etc. These

values form a true ratio scale, and the weights they attach to could serve as "standard" weights for measuring other things.

By this procedure we could achieve a set of weights whose properties would be completely isomorphic with the properties of a set determined by what the physicist calls fundamental measurement — built on the process of equating weights and of "adding" them.

This highly condensed description of a possible procedure is given here simply to show that *physical* addition is not necessarily the basis of all measurement. Valid measuring goes on where resort can never be had to the process of laying things end to end or of piling them up in a heap.

. . . .

We conclude, then, that the most liberal and useful definition of measurement is the assignment of numerals to things so as to represent facts and conventions about them. The problem of what is and what is not measurement then reduces to the simple question: what are the rules, if any, under which numerals are assigned? If we can point to a consistent set of rules, we are obviously concerned with measurement of some sort, and we can then proceed to the more interesting question: what kind of measurement is it? In most cases a formulation of the rules of assignment discloses directly the kind of measurement and hence the kind of scale involved. If there remains any ambiguity, we may seek the final and definitive answer in the mathematical group structure of the scale form: in what ways can we transform its values and still have it serve all the functions previously fulfilled? We know that the numerical values on all scales can be multiplied by a constant, which changes the numerical size of the unit (unless the multiplier is itself unity). If, in addition, a constant can be added (or a new zero point chosen), it is proof positive that we are not concerned with a ratio scale. Then, if the purpose of the scale is still served when its values are squared or cubed, it is not even an interval scale. And finally, if any two values may be interchanged at will, the ordinal scale is ruled out and the nominal scale is the sole remaining possibility.

This proposed solution to the problem of classifying scales is not meant to imply that all scales belonging to the same mathematical group are equally precise or accurate or useful or "fundamental," or even that in the practical instance it can always be decided into which category a given scale falls. Measurement is never better than the empirical operations by which it is carried out, and operations range from bad to good. Any particular scale, psychological or physical, may be objected to on the grounds of bias, low precision, restricted generality, and other factors, but the objector should remember that these are relative and practical matters and that no scale used by mortals is perfectly free of their taint.

PSYCHOPHYSICS

Scales of measurement find application in all domains of psychology, but in few quarters of the subject is the resort to measurement as deliberate as it is in psychophysics. There the formulation of the basic problems may be so worded that they read for all the world like the list of empirical operations in column 2 of Table 6. This follows from the fact that psychophysics, at least as it was conceived by its creator, is the exact science of the functional relations between "body and mind." It is beside the point that founder Fechner aimed to philosophize us into a panpsychism in which the distinction between mind and matter would be banished, or that his *Elemente der Psychophysik* of 1860 confined itself to the myopic view that sensation can be measured only "indirectly" (cf. Boring). What matters is that psychophysics was fashioned by an inventor who knew both the meaning of experiment and the essence of measurement.

Psychophysics, like mathematics, has had a curious history. Vastly younger than the "queen of the sciences," psychophysics has already stood long enough to contribute valid testimony to the invariance of human nature. Fechner, like his fellow mystic Pythagoras, advanced a science by trying to prove a theology. There followed a contentious clamor of complaint against the notion that sensations have units and magnitude. This clamor was no greater, and very little less, than the disquiet in the ranks when it was proposed that numbers may be incommensurable, or less than nothing, or the square roots of less than nothing. The sterility of the subtle wars occasioned by minutiae of method and interpretation in psychophysics is easily matched by the futility of the "vacuous logomachy" (to use Bell's name for it) that raged over such issues as the existence of points and lines and their role in geometry.

Both psychophysics and mathematics have been periodically enlivened by the clashes of those two polar temperaments — the analyzers and the synthesizers, the rigorous and the loose, the logicians and the geometers, the formalists and the intuitionists — call them what you will — there are dozens of names for them. The one is addicted to rigor and scorns what William James called the "more nutritious objects of attention." The other is irked by the demands of precision and seeks a swift road to the heart of things. Poincaré, the best psychologist among the great mathematicians, insists (pp. 210ff.) that every age has produced these two types of mind in mathematics. And the apparent victory has been now to the one, now to the other. In psychology it is the same, with the same pendular swings of opinion.

Perhaps this explains a lot about the pulling and hauling of the past ninety years in psychophysics. James, the intuitionist, could assess the published bickerings of the punctilious methodologists as a "dreadful literature" without in the least discouraging the invention of new methods and procedures and adhibitions. But, as with all such scientific tempests, the epithets are forgotten in the subsequent calm, and what lasts out the storm is the substantial residue of useful tools with which oncoming workers can build. That the tools of psychophysics have their uses is amply attested by the substance of many chapters of this handbook. And in the middle of the twentieth century psychophysics, like mathematics, finds itself incorporated into the applied disciplines of science, industry, and government.

Here we are viewing psychophysics in its broader aspects — as the science of the response of organisms to stimulating configurations. There are narrower ways of looking at it, and the parochial view is perhaps the more traditional.* The trouble with the narrow conception of psychophysics is that it mistakes procedures for problems, and precision for goals. Psychophysics then becomes synonymous with a few methods of determining thresholds, and the more meaty issues are lost in a concern for what amounts to a mere matter of sampling error. But the narrow view is fast fading as the applications of psychophysics are extended to such varied problems as telephone engineering and the assessment of attitudes.

We need belabor the narrow view no longer. Rather let us see what psychophysics is currently up to in the area of measurement and quantification. A factual inventory of current research would be one way of approaching this matter, but a better way perhaps is to search out the basic problems and methods.

We may confine our illustrations to the field of sensation. Not that sensory psychology is coextensive with psychophysics:

* As an example of a straitened definition of psychophysics, consider the ruling of the Colorimetric Committee of the Optical Society of America (Report of 1943–44), which reduces psychophysics to the employment of a human observer as a null instrument under a set of strictly specified conditions. See also H. Helson's complaint about the narrowness of this definition (*Psychol. Bull.*, 1949, **46**, 167–168).

it is merely a convenient backdrop against which to exhibit the sharper contours of the problem. If we succeed in delineating the generalities in one area, it should be a simple matter to transpose them to other areas. For example, Mosier (1940, 1941) elaborates a suggestive scheme for restating the theorems of psychophysics in the language of psychometrics (mental testing) by means of an appropriate transposition of the postulates and definitions. This is possible because both disciplines study the responses of individuals to stimulus situations. Psychophysics sees the response as an indicator of an attribute of the individual — an attribute that varies with the stimulus and is relatively invariant from person to person. Psychometrics regards the response as indicative of an attribute that varies from person to person but that is relatively invariant for different stimuli. Both psychophysics and psychometrics make it their business to display the conditions and limits of these invariances.

There is a kind of binary relation here — a relation between *responses* (sensations, perceptions, attitudes, judgments, preferences, and the like) and *organisms* (people and animals). On a given scale we can, for a single organism, or for a class of similar organisms, measure an aspect of a response. On the same scale we can also measure organisms. To take a simple example: in the laboratory we establish on a given scale the threshold for the response called hearing in a group of "normal" ears. In the hearing clinic we use the same scale to measure people — to sort them out in terms of their ability to hear.

Problems of Psychophysics

In a sense there is only one problem of psychophysics, namely, the definition of the stimulus. In this same sense there is only one problem in all of psychology — and it is the same problem. The definition of the stimulus is thus a bigger problem than it appears to be at first sight. The reason for equating psychology to the problem of defining stimuli can be stated thus: the complete definition of the stimulus to a given response involves the specification of all the transformations of the environment, both internal and external, that leave the response invariant. This specification of the conditions of invariance would entail, of course, a complete understanding of the factors that produce and that alter responses. It is easy enough, of course, to decide upon arbitrary definitions of "stimulus objects" (e.g. a given pattern of lines, a quantity of luminous flux, an acoustic waveform, etc.), but the question is: what properties of these objects do the stimulating? Viewed in this fashion, it is evident that for no response have we yet given a complete definition of the stimulus. At best we have only partially determined the conditions and limits of invariance.

Take, for example, a field like hearing, in which we think we know a lot. Under what transformations is the perception of a given pitch invariant? Can we change frequency? Yes, within limits, provided an appropriate change is made in intensity. Can we change phase? Yes, again, within limits. But we do not know precisely within what limits. What about waveform, power spectrum, duration, preceding stimuli, etc.? Actually we know only a little about the stimulus to pitch.

Consider next the perception of a given smell. Here it is probably safe to say that we can scarcely begin even to name the properties of gases that govern the invariance of odor. One theory suggests that the only transformation that will alter a smell is a change in the infrared absorption of a vapor, but this is far from settled.

When it comes to such complicated responses as hallucinations, attitudes, preferences, and the like, our ignorance of causes is even more impressive. Knowledge of the conditions and limits of invariance in these matters is only a remote aspiration.

These examples suffice to show that it is not unreasonable to subsume the problems of psychophysics under the quest for a defi-

nition of the stimulus, but they also reveal the practical futility of all-inclusive definitions. In order to get on with science we must break its problems into manageable sections. We cannot solve the universe at a stroke.

One manner of classifying the problems of psychophysics results in seven categories (Stevens, 1948). We may list them as follows:

1. *Absolute thresholds.* What are the stimulus values that mark the transition between response and no response on the part of an organism?

2. *Differential thresholds.* What is the resolving power of the organism; i.e. what is the smallest detectable change in a stimulus?

3. *Equality.* What values of two different stimuli produce the same response (e.g. appear equal on the scale of some attribute)?

4. *Order.* What different stimuli produce a set of responses or psychological impressions that can be set in serial order?

5. *Equality of intervals.* What stimuli produce a set of responses successively equidistant on the scale of some attribute?

6. *Equality of ratios.* What stimuli produce a set of responses bearing constant ratios to one another on the scale of some attribute?

7. *Stimulus rating.* With what accuracy (validity) and precision (reliability) can a person estimate the "physical" value of a stimulus?

These seven problems of psychophysics call for some additional comments. These comments must be brief, but we shall try to single out a few of the more interesting features of the psychophysical problems, especially as they relate to sensation. These are empirical issues. They are the working problems of the psychophysicist. Relative to the matters discussed in the early sections of this chapter they are practical problems. Relative to human engineering they are theoretical problems. Which proves the relativity of practicality.

Absolute Thresholds

The absolute threshold is a familiar notion to the psychologist. He is impressed by the fact that thresholds are universal among living organisms and that for each animal reaction there is a finite value of the stimulus below which nothing happens. The threshold is the value that divides the continuum * of stimuli into two classes: those to which the organism reacts and those to which it does not. Thus the threshold may be regarded as a 'cut' in the continuum of stimuli. This way of saying it is reminiscent of Dedekind's definition of an irrational number as the kind of "cut" in the domain of rational numbers that divides the domain into two classes, neither of which has a terminus in the region of the cut (see Young, p. 104).

One of the practical problems of psychophysics is to define the properties and limits of the two classes of stimuli into which the threshold cuts the energetic configurations of the environment. In solving this problem the psychophysicist addresses himself explicitly to the problem of invariance. Thus for any given attribute of sensation he asks what combinations of stimulus values (e.g. of frequency and intensity) will produce the threshold cut. In general the cut is invariant under the simultaneous transformation of several stimulus dimensions. The plot of the threshold contour, such as an "audiogram," is a common device for depicting an aspect of this invariance.

* Applied to the stimulus, the word "continuum" refers to a property of the various dimensions in terms of which stimuli may be ordered. Along these dimensions it is ordinarily possible to produce gradations that are small compared to the discriminative capacities of organisms. In this sense the dimensions of stimuli are continuous. Under certain special conditions, however, the ultimately discontinuous (quantal) nature of physical events may assert itself, e.g. when the visual threshold is made to appear dependent upon the absorption by the retina of a half-dozen light quanta. Unlike the continua of mathematics, physical continua are not infinitely divisible. Nevertheless, the mathematical continuum, although not perfectly isomorphic with the physical continuum, serves as a useful model for it.

In expounding the psychophysics of thresholds it is customary to bear down hard on the matter of variability. Ordinarily the threshold is not invariant with time. Rather it shifts about from moment to moment in a restless fashion, and we are forced to catch it on the fly. We manage this by procedures that are vaguely analogous to what the mathematician does when he traps the value of an irrational number by narrowing the gap between two rational numbers, one larger and one smaller than the irrational in question. We trap the threshold value of a stimulus by means of statistical devices for interpolating in the gap between stimuli that are definitely below threshold and stimuli that are definitely above threshold. What gets recorded as the threshold is then an arbitrary point within a range of variability.

This variability is a function of time. And, since we are forced to take time samples of it, the threshold takes on a fuzzy-edged appearance — as though the stimulus continuum had been cut with a wooden spoon. Nevertheless, there is reason to believe that at any instant the position of the threshold on the stimulus continuum is fixed, definite, and precise, and that adequate procedures would reveal the sharpness of the threshold 'cut.' Methods adequate to this revelation have not as yet been forthcoming for absolute thresholds, but for differential thresholds the outlook is more encouraging.

Differential Thresholds

Here the problem is to locate on the continuum of *stimulus increments* the point that divides the increments into two classes: those to which the organism reacts and those to which it does not. Thus the differential threshold, like the absolute threshold, is a cut that divides a physical continuum. And here again the location of the cut is obscured by its variability in time, so that resort must be had to sampling techniques and to interpolation. The traditional "psychophysical methods" are just such procedures for sampling and interpolating.

The fact that the discriminations of organisms depend on neural processes that are all-or-none in character suggests that the just noticeable difference between two stimuli ought, at a given instant, to be finite and definite, as we have assumed the value of the absolute threshold to be. This suggestion bore fruit when Békésy showed how the stimulating and the sampling of responses might be carried out so as to reveal the "quantal" nature of discrimination. Békésy's procedure was modified by Stevens and Volkmann (1940*a*) into a form that eliminated the "time error" and revealed more directly the size of the "neural quantum." This quantum has other theoretical implications, but our present interest in it stems from the lesson it teaches about mathematical models and their uses. Let us consider this matter more closely.

There are two basic models applicable to time samples of sensory discriminations of the type obtained when a subject tries to detect an increment added to a stimulus (cf. Stevens, Morgan, and Volkmann). Call them the 'normal' model and the rectangular model, in honor of the types of distributions into which the data are assumed to fall. The 'normal' model is invoked when it is assumed that the response to a stimulus increment depends upon the operation of a multitude of minute factors combining in random formation to help or hinder discrimination as chance might have it. This model makes use of an infinite, continuous mathematical function, the "normal curve," whose integral (the phi function of gamma) we fit to a plot of data: number of responses versus size of increment. This plot we call the *psychometric function.*

The rectangular model is used under the assumption that discrimination is discontinuous and proceeds by finite quantal jumps. The integral of the rectangular distribution is a straight-line function between two finite limits, and this integral we fit to the data as before.

Now we ask which of these two models fits the data on differential thresholds. The answer is that within reasonable limits of error both of them can be shown to fit. Which, if either, will fit a *given* psychometric plot depends upon the experimental procedure — upon the method used to collect the time sample of responses (see Fig. 2). As a matter of fact, several forms of psychometric function can be predictably obtained by various procedural devices (cf. Miller and Garner).

As is often the case, therefore, we cannot choose between two mathematical models simply by inspecting the fit of the data. Poincaré's famous dictum suggests itself in this connection: "If, then, a phenomenon admits of a complete mechanical explanation, it will admit of an infinity of others that will render an account equally well of all particulars revealed by experiment" (p. 181). We are not here concerned with a "mechanical phenomenon" or with the equations of which Poincaré spoke, but the ever-present possibility of alternative explanation — alternative models — is not something the psychologist can afford to lose sight of.

For the singling out of a preferred model the scientist likes to invoke the criteria (rationalizations?) of simplicity and power. Applied to the problem of sensory discrimination, these criteria would seem to favor the rectangular model — the quantal theory — because (1) another parameter than the mere form of the function is predicted by the theory, namely, the slope of the psychometric line, and (2) the phi function of gamma emerges as a special case of the quantal hypothesis: the phi function of gamma is commonly obtained when the experimental procedure leaves time for the organism to change its sensitivity between the presentations of the standard and the comparison stimuli.

One more point about differential thresholds.

The relation of the just noticeable difference to the size of the initial stimulus stands as a law of relativity in psychology: what must be added to produce a detectable difference is relative to what is already there. Weber proposed the principle that the ratio between the stimulus and the increment that

constancy fails.) The early psychophysicists, Fechner and Helmholtz, and others, knew about this small range of inconstancy, and they proposed to salvage "Weber's law" by a suggestion recently revived by G. A. Miller.

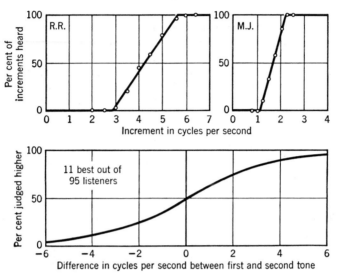

Fig. 2. Psychometric functions obtained with two different procedures. The two upper plots (for two different listeners) show the rectilinear functions obtained with the "quantal" procedure. Each point is based on 100 judgments of a brief increment added every 3 seconds to a 1000-cycle tone. The size of the quantum for R.R. is 2.8 cycles per second. For M.J. it is 1.1 cycle per second. Note that the slope of the line changes with the size of the quantum and reaches 100 per cent at the value of two quanta. (From Stevens, Morgan, and Volkmann, 1941.)

The lower plot is for the 11 best subjects out of 95 that were given the Seashore Test of pitch discrimination. This test employs the method of constant stimuli, with a short time interval between the standard and the comparison tone. If the 75-per-cent point is taken as the difference limen, its value for these 11 subjects is about 2 cycles per second. The psychometric function for the rest of the 95 listeners was even less steep than this one (cf. Stevens, 1948).

must be added to it is invariant with intensity, and to a good approximation he was right. It is fashionable to say that he was wrong, but in vision and hearing, where the measurement of these things is probably most satisfactory, the "Weber fraction" is apparently constant over more than 99.9 per cent of the usable range of stimulus intensities. (The customary plotting of this ratio against the *logarithm* of the stimulus magnifies the minute range of stimuli in which

Instead of saying $\Delta I = kI$, as Weber would have it, these gentlemen write

$$\Delta I = k(I + I_r)$$

where ΔI is the increment corresponding to a jnd, I is the stimulus intensity, I_r is a small addition to I, and k is a constant. Miller finds that this equation fits the data for the intensitive jnd measured with "white noise" when the procedure is such that the quantum of sensory discrimination can be assessed over a wide range of intensities. This modified equation reduces to Weber's law at high intensities, because I_r then becomes negligible, and at low intensities it makes the reasonable assumption that not all the effective stimulation is due to the "stimulus" that the experimenter measures. Some of it seems to be there as a residual background, and it is represented by the additive term in the equation, I_r.

If we now proceed one step further and write the modified equation in the form

$$\frac{\Delta I}{I + I_r} = k$$

we see that the invariant ratio between the increment and the stimulus is reestablished, provided we add a small residual I_r to the measured intensity I. This conception, if it can be made to stand up, is of prime interest to psychophysics, precisely because it hints at a basic invariance in sensory discrimination. These basic invariances are too precious few to be taken lightly.

Fechner, as we all know, used Weber's law to derive what he thought was a measure of the magnitude of a sensation. His procedure need not concern us here except for one particular. In order to make it come out, Fechner had not only to assume the validity of Weber's law, he had also to *postulate* the subjective equality of jnd's. This means that a stimulus 20 jnd's above threshold should produce a sensation twice as big as a stimulus 10 jnd's above threshold. Now Russell's words about postulation have already been quoted in this chapter, but here they are again: "The method of 'postulating' what we want has many advantages; they are the same as the advantages of theft over honest toil." Reasonably honest toil in several different laboratories has lately revealed that a tonal stimulus 20 jnd's above threshold sounds far more than twice as loud as a stimulus 10 jnd's above threshold (cf. Stevens and Davis, pp. 148ff.). Fechner's postulate has had to go, but its failure does not invalidate the notion that sensation is

measurable. Instead we now proceed to its measurement by a more direct route, forsaking Fechner's indirection.

It turns out, as we have seen, that the jnd's for loudness are unequal in subjective magnitude. The same appears to be true of other intensive attributes like subjective weight, brightness, and taste. On the other hand, for pitch, and possibly for saturation, the jnd's are subjectively equal; i.e. Fechner's postulate is apparently verified. Now the fact that there are two classes of jnd's, the equal and the unequal, suggests the hypothesis (Stevens, 1939*b*) that there may be two basic mechanisms of discrimination, illustrated by the mechanisms underlying our perception of loudness and of pitch. Presumably we discriminate an increase in loudness when neural excitation gets *added* to excitation already present, whereas we detect an increase in pitch when there is a change in the distribution of excitation — when new excitation gets *substituted* for old. The suggested generalization, then, is that for the *additive mechanism* the jnd's are subjectively unequal in size; for the *substitutive mechanism* they are equal. In this latter case it would seem legitimate to number the jnd's successively and to use them for an interval scale of the attribute in question.

In both cases, of course, the counting off of just noticeable differences produces at least an ordinal scale.

The Determination of Equality

The problem of equality (or of *equivalents*, as it has been called) is precisely the problem of finding alternative stimulus configurations for which some attribute of a response remains invariant. This problem shows up in many forms and in many fields of inquiry. As a matter of fact, an inventory would probably show it to be one of the commonest problems tackled by psychologists. An early and simple example of it is Weber's determination that a pressure of 4 ounces on the forehead feels approximately equal to a pressure of 1 ounce on the lips.

A later and not so simple example is Bruner and Postman's study of the apparent size of objects having different "symbolic values." Their observers found that a larger circle of light was needed to match a 1-inch disk with a dollar sign on it than to match a 1-inch disk bearing a neutral design. In this experiment the physical diameter of the circle of light provides an arbitrary yardstick for measuring the effect on perception of different symbolic values.

Other common examples of the determination of equivalents are the various isophonic contours: equal loudness, equal volume, etc.; and the isophotic contours: equal brightness (luminosity curve), equal hue (Bezold-Brücke phenomenon), etc. All these contours show the combinations of frequency and intensity for which the attribute in question is constant. A threshold contour, incidentally, may be regarded as a special case of equivalents; e.g. an audiogram may be thought of as the "highest" contour along which loudness is zero.

The problem of equality is ever with us, because it is in this problem that we most often land when we try to measure things for which there are no interval or ratio scales. My own induction into these mysteries was via the humble color mixer (Stevens, 1934). A combination of a red and a blue-green mixed to match a gray composed of black and white no longer matches the gray when we change the size of the field. Enlarge the field, and the mixture turns blue-green; narrow it, and the mixture turns red. For various changes in field size, then, how great is the change in saturation? With no scale to measure saturation, an alternative is to change the area and then to restore the match by inserting into the black-white mixture a sector of the necessary color. The size of this sector needed to restore equality then becomes an arbitrary "measure" of the change in saturation produced by the areal alteration.

Examples like this could be multiplied almost indefinitely. What we obtain from this procedure of mapping invariances is the chance to assess the change in a perception in terms of the stimulus configuration required to undo the change. The observer is used as a *null instrument*, and this is the way psychologists most often work with "illusions," so called. Sometimes this is the only practicable procedure, and often it gives results of major usefulness.

The Determination of Order

The setting of things in rank order is another pandemic activity among psychologists. This process presents itself explicitly as a problem whenever we confront a heterogeneous collection of stimuli having no obvious physical dimension that orders the stimuli in monotonic relation to the response in question. This sounds like a difficult notion; let us try to restate it. We usually resort to rank ordering when the psychological attribute connected with a group of stimuli is not a single-valued function of some measurable dimension of the stimuli.

Perhaps an example will help.

Consider the stimuli to be samples of handwriting, and the attribute of the observer's response to be his judgment of pleasingness. Admittedly there are many physical dimensions to handwriting, and against any one of them the handwriting could be "objectively" scaled: height of letters, length of words, width of lines, etc. But pleasingness is not a monotonic function of any of these physical measures in the same obvious way that pitch is a monotonic function of frequency. Consequently in order to set up an ordinal scale of pleasingness we resort to one or another of the several methods of ordering: paired comparisons, order-of-merit, rating scale, etc.

Once having set the specimens in a rank order, we may or may not find it possible to devise some physical measure, or a combination of measures, that correlates with the subjective order. If we find such a measure, we have probably advanced our understanding of the essential ingredient of pleasingness in handwriting. If not, we at least have an ordered set of examples against which to test various hypotheses.

It is interesting to note that in many practical problems of ranking we do not achieve a result that is completely isomorphic with a formal model obeying the three postulates of order listed in an earlier section. This is because two or more items are often tied for the same rank. In other words the relation in question (e.g. more pleasing than) is not always a *connected* relation in the field of samples under consideration. The result is what the mathematician would call a *partially ordered* system, a concept that figures prominently in lattice theory — the theory of structure — which is built on the relation "includes" or "is part of."

Whenever, as often happens, we try to order stimuli having multidimensional qualities, we are thrust into interesting problems of a different sweep. Given a large sample of odors, for example, the problem of ordering them may land us in the related problem of finding the dimensions or attributes along which olfactory sensations can vary. In general, the number of these attributes is the number of consistent orders in which the observer can set the stimuli. Normally the observer achieves these different orders by adopting for each ordering task a different "set," or attitude, and with the aid of this analytic approach the various attributes of sensation have been sorted out: hue, brightness, and saturation for vision; pitch, loudness, volume, and density for tones, etc. For odors there is in wide commercial use a set of four scales, each for a separate attribute, by means of which experienced judges are able to characterize an odor by assigning it a value on each scale separately (cf. Crocker and Henderson; also Beebe-Center). An analogous problem was faced by Sheldon in the initial phases of the somatotype development. For each of the three most obvious "components" of human physique, judges sorted photographs of 4000 individuals into three separate rank orders, one for each

of the visually distinguishable components: endomorphy, mesomorphy, and ectomorphy (cf. Sheldon, Stevens, and Tucker).

It is not always possible, of course, for subjects to analyze out a single subjective dimension, e.g. when they are asked to rate the *seriousness* of various criminal offenses. This means that different subjects will then produce incompatible rank orders that cannot be plotted on a single ordinal scale without resort to more than one dimension. When such judgments are made on the basis of multidimensional criteria, it is sometimes possible, under the method of paired comparisons, to infer the number of dimensions the subjects have used and to "scale" these dimensions in the appropriate number of "spaces" (cf. Gulliksen).

As a rule the psychophysicist does not feel obliged to undertake the rank ordering of stimuli that have convenient physical dimensions when one of these dimensions is clearly a monotonic function of the attribute under investigation. He skips the issue because the rank order is obvious and he takes it for granted. Thus he does not bother to rank-order a series of luminous stimuli in terms of subjective brightness because the order is readily apparent and his interest is in more fertile tasks. But the neglect of the obvious has its hazards, and some relations that are assumed to be monotonic might, under closer scrutiny, reach a maximum and double back on themselves. The possibility at least demands our alertness. In any case, it is clearly impossible to set up any scale above the nominal unless the order of the items scaled is determinable.

One further point. The fact that we most often resort to rank ordering when the stimuli have no common dimension that is a monotonic function of our responses to them does not mean that we are limited to rank ordering. Not at all. We might in addition select from the stimuli those that are separated by equal-appearing intervals or even by equal-appearing ratios, if such proves practicable. No logic forbids it. It is simply an observable fact that in such cases the psychologist usually determines rank orders and stops. Quite possibly he ought to go on. For, as Reese points out, "the operations for measurement in psychology do not necessarily depend upon the prior measurement of any other magnitude." What is required is that we have some means of *identifying* the objects, situations, or events that we are trying to scale. When physical scales exist, they usually provide the most convenient means of identifying stimuli, but any other identification would serve as well.

The availability of a physical scale enables us to determine the functional relation between it and the subjective scale — which relation is mighty interesting by itself — but, theoretically at least, we could deposit with the National Bureau of Standards the appropriate samples of handwriting that would define known values on a ratio scale of pleasingness without ever having measured the handwriting on any physical scale.

Equal Intervals

The equalizing of differences is the next step beyond ordering. The determination of equal intervals becomes a problem in psychophysics whenever we aspire to measurement of the sort that makes the mean a meaningful measure — whenever it is a question of *units* in the ordinary sense of the term.

This problem got its first explicit recognition in psychology when Plateau provided a group of artists with a black and a white piece of paper and had each of them paint a gray that seemed to lie halfway between (cf. Boring, p. 42). This determination of two equal sense distances, as Titchener called them, by the procedure of bisection is probably the easiest approach to equal intervals. The operation of "halving," as we noted when we considered base-eight arithmetic, is apparently one of the simplest of psychological operations. The 'simultaneous' adjustment of several stimuli to produce more than two equal intervals is possible, but harder. Stevens and Volkmann (1940*b*)

used five stimuli to produce four equal intervals of pitch. Their experiment confirmed, incidentally, the results of Münsterberg, who equated two pitch extents that were not adjacent, i.e. intervals that had no point in common.

These examples suffice to show that the equalization of sense distances has had its uses in psychophysics.* Other instances could be cited, but it is fair to state that the procedure has not been vigorously exploited by psychologists, despite the fact that it is essential to the creation of equal units on sensory scales. True, the solution of the problem of equal intervals is not in itself sufficient to determine the zero point of a psychological scale, but in the strict logic of the matter the equalizing of differences is a prerequisite to the erection not only of an interval scale but of a ratio scale as well. We shall return to this matter in a moment.

Meanwhile it is of interest to note that the problem of equalizing intervals gets a bigger play from the mental testers and other psychometricians than it does from the sensory psychologists. In psychometrics the need for equal units is distressingly acute, because the paraphernalia of metric statistics (means, standard deviations, coefficients of correlation, etc.) seem to be essential tools of the trade. The assessor of human abilities is usually knee deep in statistical problems to which most statistics do not apply unless his units can be equalized. Out of this quandary he hoists himself by an act of faith in the "normal distribution" of nature's errors. If this faith is firmly founded — if in truth it is legitimate to use the distribution of scores as a criterion for the sizes of units — then the equalization of units is pos-

* The meteorologists and other students of climate have experimented rather extensively with scales of subjective temperatures, humidity, and general climatic excellence. They have based these scales on equal-appearing intervals as well as on other psychophysical measures. As Titchener pointed out in 1909, here is rich sod for the cultivation of an applied branch of psychophysics.

sible. It is certainly not unreasonable to
believe that this faith is often justified.
What haunts us is the difficulty of knowing
when it isn't.

Equal Ratios

The problem of determining equal ratios
has had a long but spotty history in psychophysics. As early as 1888 Merkel tried setting visual intensities so that they appeared
to be in the ratio of two to one. He seems
not to have advanced, however, to the creation of a workable ratio scale, which is the
raison d'être for equalizing ratios. And it
was not until the 1930's that a full-dress
ratio scale for a sensory attribute (loudness)
was achieved. Since then ratio scales for
subjective magnitudes have blossomed out
in startling profusion. Scales have been attempted for:

> Loudness (several workers; cf. Boring,
>   p. 44).
> Pitch (Stevens and Volkmann, 1940*b*).
> Visual numerousness (Taves, 1941).
> Warmth (Herget, Granath, and Hardy,
>   1941).
> Visual flash rate, subjective difficulty of
>   digit memorization, subjective diffi-
>   culty of words in a vocabulary test
>   (all three by Reese, 1943).
> Pain (Hardy, Wolff, and Goodell, 1948).
> Sweetness, sourness, saltiness, bitterness
>   (all four by D. R. Lewis, 1948).
> Subjective weight (Harper and Stevens,
>   1948).
> Visual brightness (Hanes, 1949).

Of all these scales only the first two, loudness and pitch, have thus far been subjected
to the kind of cross-checking that might
justly be demanded by the skeptic. The
pitch scale, of which the unit is called a *mel*,
has been determined by "fractionation" judgments, in which the listener adjusts one tone
until it sounds half as high in pitch as some
standard tone, and by judgments of equal
sense distances, in which the listener equal-
izes a series of adjacent pitch extents, or

pitch differences. The pitch scale also agrees
with the prediction that we would make if
we assumed that pitch is 'spread' evenly
along the basilar membrane, in such a manner that the pitch that bisects the audible
range corresponds to the frequency that
stimulates the midpoint along the basilar
extent.

The loudness scale, based on fractionation
judgments and measured in *sones*, has been
tested against equal sense distances only to
a very limited extent, but it has been shown
to agree with a number of other reasonable
assumptions. (1) It confirms the prediction
that, for a given sound, the loudness heard
with two ears is just twice the loudness heard
with one ear. (2) It endorses the assumption that the loudness of two or more equally
loud tones equals the sum of the loudnesses
of the individual tones, provided the tones
do not stimulate overlapping regions of the
basilar membrane (cf. Howes). These are
perhaps the most important checks. There
are others.

Curiously enough, however, in all this work
on ratio scales the psychophysical problem
of equating sense ratios has not been faced.
It has been dodged by what appears to be
a happy expedient (until someone shall prove
it a sad one). Instead of adjusting pairs of
stimuli until the members of each pair appear to stand in some fixed (but unknown)
ratio to each other, the subject adjusts the
stimuli until they appear to stand in some
prescribed ratio, usually two to one. Or,
alternatively, a pair of stimuli are given, and
the subject estimates the numerical value of
their apparent ratio. (More properly stated,
he estimates the numerical ratio between the
two magnitudes of an attribute of the sensation aroused by the two stimuli, but for
the sake of brevity we say simply that he
estimates the apparent ratio of the stimuli.)
These are the procedures we label "fractionation."

When we proceed in this fashion, we make
an assumption that calls for scrutiny. We
postulate, among other things, that the sub-

ject knows what a given numerical ratio is and that he can make a valid judgment of the numerical relation between two values of a psychological attribute. If this postulate is thievery, it is certainly no petty larceny, for among the precious loot we find all the relations that we need in order to proceed directly to the construction of a ratio scale. This looks like larceny in the grand manner. If a series of items have been found that stand in a *known* ratio, each to its neighbor, it is a straightforward matter to assign a numeral to one of the items and then to assign to the other items numerals exhibiting the appropriate ratios to the first numeral. If the assumption is valid, the result is a ratio scale.

Actually there is persuasive evidence to attest the empirical validity and reliability of the judgment of ratios, especially of the ratio two to one. Halving, as we have already noted twice, is a wonderfully simple psychological operation. If we are to build a structure on psychological operations, this looks like a sturdy stone for the foundation.

Reese expounds the defensible opinion that this operation of finding a stimulus that appears half as great as a standard stimulus is merely a special case of the bisection of an interval, one end of which has the value zero. This view of the matter gets added support from the discovery of Stevens and Volkmann (1940*b*) that the subject does better when he is allowed to experience a stimulus that is very near zero. Apparently he can then tie the lower end of the interval to an anchor more solid than an imagined zero.

Needless to say, however, for the problem of scaling it matters little whether the subject bisects the interval between some value and zero, or whether he sets two stimuli to produce a known sensory ratio. In either case the empirical outcome is isomorphic with what we might call the ratio properties of the number system.

But it is important, theoretically at least, to consider what happens if we forsake the assumption that the subject can interpret a given numerical ratio in terms of relations between experiences, or that given two experiences he can name the numerical ratio between them. Having denied this postulate, we would need to retain the assumption that the subject can judge equality and order (e.g. greater than). We would also need to assume that he can determine the equality of two intervals, or sense distances, and the equality of two sense ratios. On the basis of these postulates we could then proceed precisely as we did in the example cited earlier (p. 29), where the problem was to erect a scale of weight without resort to "addition." This construction of a weight scale is an adequate paradigm for the building of a ratio scale when the empirical operations are limited to the determination of equality, rank order, equal intervals, and equal ratios.

This paradigm reveals in explicit fashion the full logic of ratio-scale measurement. In practical instances short cuts of one sort or another are usually possible, but the by-passing of any step in the procedure implies assumptions that need to be probed. Consequently it would be interesting, at least as an essay in method, to construct a psychological ratio scale by requesting a subject to equate intervals of arbitrary extent and to equate ratios of arbitrary size. This procedure ought to corroborate the scale gotten by fractionation, although I should predict that it would show less precision (reliability) than the short-cut method of "fractionation" displays.

Stimulus Rating

In this world of gadgets and gimmicks we are often more interested, as a practical matter, in the correct judgment of the physical measures of things than we are in the nature of subjective scales. The policeman tries to assess correctly the objective speed of passing cars; the aviator tries to judge his altitude in feet above the ground; the grocer tries to estimate the weight of a bag of beans; and the tailor tries to guess the size of the coat that will fit the customer. The common problem in these activities and the thousands like them is the utilization of a subjective impression to predict the result that would be obtained by an objective measurement. To perceive the stature of a man is one thing; to measure him with a yardstick is another. It is the business of many of us to correlate "subjective" and "objective" operations such as these and to predict the second from the first. In one way or another, we are constantly guessing at the physical values or relations of stimuli. We are doing deliberately what we just as deliberately try not to do when we study our sensations and perceptions: we are committing what Titchener called the "stimulus error." It would seem that more of the world's business depends on the successful commission of this "error" than on its successful avoidance.

Especially in military combat, where shells and missiles are hurled about by men who have no time for measurement, is the estimation of stimulus values a matter of great issue. There the gravity of the problem calls for programs of systematic training and procedures for gauging expertness. The excellence of an individual's performance in "free gunnery" and the like, where the close estimation of objective relations is vital, turns out to be compounded, as we might expect, of native ability and learning.

In distinguishing the problem of stimulus rating as a separate problem of psychophysics, we probably impute to it a dignity that its general untidiness belies. Actually it is a jumble of separate problems, each solvable *ad hoc*, perhaps, but no net of principles seems to bind these problems together. Conceivably, future insights might change all this, but for the present, at least, we must seek out the separate facts as we need them.

It can even be argued that the problem of stimulus rating, except for what it might teach us about individual skills in the matter, and the manner of their acquisition, is logically reducible to the other six problems we have discussed. If, for example, the policeman tends to make a systematic error in naming the speed of a Sunday driver, this fact reveals something about the relation between his psychological scale of apparent speed and the objective scale of miles per hour. Presumably the form of the subjective scale is the primary fact, and the policeman's skill at committing the "stimulus error" is merely a measure of his ability to compensate for the nonlinearity of his subjective scale.

On the other hand, the problem of stimulus rating assumes major dimensions if we see it as including the problem of the rating or judging of stimuli for which there are no objective measures, e.g., such elusive complexes as human traits. When we use one human being as an 'instrument' for the assessment of qualities in other human beings, we hope that the 'instrument' will commit the stimulus error 100 per cent and not return a verdict that tells us more about the 'instrument' than it does about the 'stimulus.' This hope, we know, is partly vain, but its degree of fulfillment is adequate to put rating-scale procedures in the category of the indispensable in some parts of psychology (cf. Guilford, Chapter 9). Perhaps there seems to be little in common between the judging of velocity on the highway and the rating of traits of leadership, but, if there are any common principles governing the estimation of the objective qualities of things, they ought to apply to both these instances.

But we are wandering far into speculation. Let us return to problems of exactitude.

PSYCHOPHYSICAL METHODS

With the seven problems of psychophysics before us, it is time to worry about methods for solving them. We shall not worry long, however, for methods have a way of being tedious. Moreover, the prescription of method is as antiscientific as the scientific method is receptive of innovation. When better psychophysical methods are devised, psychologists will use them, regardless of historical precedents.

Some of the psychophysical methods have already had incidental mention in previous sections. Here we shall try to call their roll in a more complete but still far from exhaustive fashion. The unabridged listing of methods is at best a fugacious goal, because for any method invented for one problem variations on it promptly suggest themselves for others. Three of the methods we shall list are styled "classical" (1, 2, and 4 in Table 7), but there is no reason to suppose that these, or any others, are better or worse than what may be devised by tomorrow's genius.

The reason for the traditional emphasis on method in psychophysics is simple enough: the responses of organisms vary from moment to moment. Forced to take time samples of a fluctuating process, we find ourselves thrown on the tender mercies of statistical procedures whenever we try to draw stable conclusions. It is a frustrating business. And in order to temper their frustration the psychophysicists have elaborated subtle measures that try to transcend the inconstancy of the mercurial response.

Seven of these methods are listed in Table 7. The listing of seven methods is sheerly arbitrary. We could easily list many more. But these are the main species of which most

TABLE 7

Some Methods of Psychophysics

Method	Brief Characterization	Usual Statistical Index	Problems to Which Most Applicable
1. Adjustment (average error)	Observer adjusts stimulus until it is subjectively equal to or in some desired relation to a criterion.	Average of settings (average error of settings measures precision).	Absolute threshold Equality Equal intervals Equal ratios
2. Minimal change (limits)	Experimenter varies stimulus upward and/or downward. Observer signals its apparent relation to a criterion.	Average value of stimulus at transition point of observer's judgment.	All thresholds Equality
3. Paired comparison	Stimuli are presented in pairs. Each stimulus is paired with each other stimulus. The observer indicates which of each pair is greater in respect of a given attribute.	Proportion of judgments calling one stimulus greater than another. (These proportions are sometimes translated into scale values via the assumption of a normal distribution of judgments.)	Order Equal intervals (under 'distribution' assumption)
4. Constant stimuli	Several comparison stimuli are paired at random with a fixed standard. Observer says whether each comparison is greater or less than the standard. (A special case of paired comparisons.)	Size of difference limen equals stimulus distance between 50- and 75- percent points on psychometric function.	All thresholds Equality Equal intervals Equal ratios
5. Quantal	Various fixed increments are added to a standard, with no time interval between. Each increment is added several times in succession. Observer indicates apparent presence or absence of the increment.	Size of sensory quantum equals distance between intercepts of rectilinear psychometric function.	Differential thresholds
6. Order of merit	Group of stimuli, presented simultaneously, are set in apparent rank order by the observer.	Average or median rank assigned by observers.	Order
7. Rating scale (single stimuli)	Each of a set of stimuli is given an "absolute" rating in terms of some attribute. Rating may be numerical or descriptive.	Average or median rating assigned by observers.	Order Equal intervals Stimulus rating

others are varieties. For a fuller discussion of all but method 5, see Guilford. For method 5, see Stevens, Morgan, and Volkmann.

The last column of Table 7 suggests that more than one method may be applicable to the solution of a given problem. Generally speaking, the empirical nature of the stimulus and the manner in which it can be manipulated will decide the method, but other considerations may well arise. Thus it has been rightly urged that of two alternative procedures the more direct is the better.

Now all the psychophysical methods give a distribution of scores from which may be obtained a measure of location (sometimes ill-advisedly called central tendency) and a measure of dispersion. Use might be made of either or both of these measures, but, other things being equal, the measure of location is the more solidly rooted in reality. It would seem defensible to argue, therefore, that the best method to use in a given instance is the one that gives the location of the observer's responses to the aspect or attribute in question. Then the measure of dispersion can be used to assess the precision of the observer's judgment. In general, we do well to keep clear of indirect measurements when direct measurements are possible.

A single example will suffice to illustrate this principle. The method of adjustment, which permits the observer to set the stimulus directly to the value that meets the criterion of his task, is the favored method for determining equivalents. But it is not so suitable for differential thresholds, because it forces us to estimate the limen by way of some arbitrary measure of dispersion.

This criterion of directness is not, however, the sole guide in these matters. Far from it. Considerations both practical and theoretical interact to mold our choice of method, and the manner of their give-and-take is too intricate to untangle here. An example of the problem of method as it applies to the hypothesis of the "neural quantum" has already been discussed above. For a discussion that makes a distinction between mean jnd's determined by the method of minimal changes, and jnd's derived as "variational indices" from dispersions of judgments, see Holway and Pratt.

PROBABILITY

In the foregoing sections the concept of probability has been latent in much of the discussion. The superstructure of statistics has the theory of probability in its basement, and without statistics there would be little measurement in psychology. As a matter of fact, the problem of quantification in most of the biological sciences has two chief facets: measurement and sampling. And the problem of sampling is one aspect of probability.

Now, everyone talks about probability, but no one explains it to the satisfaction of everybody else.* This is not the place nor is your author the person to rectify the crosscurrents of contention in this field, but two points ought to be made here — points that suggest themselves as lessons to be learned from the history of mathematics and from the theory of signs (syntactics, semantics, and pragmatics). These two points concern (1) the meanings of the word "probability" and (2) the formal-empirical dichotomy.

For the substance of probability theory in its modern technical forms the reader must go to the texts and treatises of the mathematicians. Perhaps a good place to start is with Wilks. And for an up-to-date sampling of the philosophical furor over basic issues and interpretations the reader should go to the *Journal of Philosophy and Phenomenological Research*, where a distinguished galaxy of scholars produced papers and counter-papers in "A Symposium on Probability," beginning in 1945. The two points

---

* Russell once told his lecture audience that "probability is the most important concept in modern science, especially as nobody has the slightest notion what it means" (see Bell, 1945, p. 587).

that follow may help the reader steer an orderly course through this symposium.

First of all there is the semantical problem: to what kinds of phenomena shall we apply the word probability? Ample precedent exists for many different semantical rules, and, theoretically at least, we could keep the record straight by using different words or, as is sometimes done, by appending subscripts.

Thus we might define probability$_1$ as degree of belief — what a man is willing to wager. This is the psychological or subjective feeling of probability known to all of us who make guesses before the fact.

Probability$_2$ could stand for the degree of confirmation of a proposition or hypothesis — the likelihood that an empirical statement is true in the operational sense. This is the concept for which Carnap tries to develop an inductive logic (see Carnap, 1947).

Probability$_3$ could be the a priori notion of probability: the probability induced from the "principle of indifference" which says that if we have no means of choosing among several alternatives then they are regarded as being equally likely. This is the principle we invoke when we assign the probability of $\frac{1}{6}$ to the upturn of a given face on the symmetrical die that is thrown on the carpet.

Probability$_4$ could stand for the frequency theory of probability — the notion that the probability of an event is the relative frequency of its occurrence in a large sample. This is the concept of probability that underlies most of statistics. And it is rightly argued that probability$_4$ is the operational test of probability$_3$. If without the one we could never know about the other, perhaps the two reduce to the same thing.*

These, then, are four possible kinds of probability. There are others, but these are sufficient to apprise us of the diversity of notions to which the word probability is linked. These are four semantical rules for relating this term to some aspect or other

* For a modern elaboration of the frequency theory of probability, see Reichenbach (1949).

of the empirical world. Quite naturally, therefore, there is no one theory of probability: there are as many as there are meanings for the word.

The second point to be made in this discussion concerns mainly the last two of these four varieties, because it is for them that the elaborate models of mathematical probability have been invented, and they are what we talk about in statistics.

Part of the cure (if there is one) for the confusion about the nature of statistical probability 'probably' lies in a strict adherence to the formalistic conception of mathematics. It behooves us to keep solidly in mind the distinction between a formal system that we might use as a model and the empirical reality for which the model might serve as a more or less isomorphic map. Consistent devotion to this distinction is hard enough to maintain in ordinary mathematical discussion. In talk about probability theory it seems to be doubly difficult. But it is precisely when we argue about chance expectations that it is most misleading to reason from the relations within the *mathematical model* of probability to the *necessity* of physical events. Under certain empirical conditions the mathematical model appears to "fit" the collection of empirical events, but the isomorphism is seldom if ever perfect, point for point.

The records compiled through the years at the Casino of Monte Carlo display a remarkable agreement between the properties of the frequency distributions of the winning numbers on the roulette wheels and the predictions of combinatorial analysis — the so-called laws of chance. But even here the coincidence between model and reality is not perfect. We are told that an English engineer patiently tabulated thousands of winning numbers for a particular wheel, and then alarmed the management by running up a long series of wins. In desperation the Casino spoiled his game by interchanging the parts from one wheel to another. This interchange is still a daily precaution. And most likely it helps to insure the futility of any gambling rule that the persevering system makers concoct.

Given a roulette wheel that is "mechanically perfect" — one with no physical irregularities — we get from it a *random* series of numbers fitting the mathematical expectation only provided we put this randomness into the throw of the ball. This the experienced croupier seems to manage. In much the same way we get the runs of heads predicted by the binomial expansion provided we put the right kind of randomness into the flip of a coin. But there is nothing in the pure mathematics of the binomial expansion that determines the behavior of the coin. In fact, it would not be particularly difficult to build a mechanical coin-tosser that would flip heads almost every time.

Our tendency to confuse a formal calculus of probability with the empirical properties of certain kinds of events is partly determined by the fact that, like most of the rest of mathematics, this formal calculus had its beginnings in empirical problems (cf. Bell, 1937, p. 86). It was originated by Pascal and Fermat to answer the query of a professional gambler, and never since that time have we entirely succeeded in separating the empirical and the formal aspects of the issue.

The trouble usually begins on the first page of the chapter on probability in any textbook on college algebra, where we find it duly recorded that the probability p of a success s is the ratio of the number of ways in which an *event* can succeed to the total number of ways in which it can happen, $s + f$. This gives the formula

$$p = \frac{s}{s + f}$$

So far so good, for the word "event" is undefined, as it should be in a purely mathematical statement, and what we have is a formula that is true by definition — a postulate, as it were. But, before the paragraph is out, s has been identified with a face on

an "unbiased" die, or with one side of a symmetrical coin, or with a white ball in a bag with some black ones. From then on we seldom know whether the author is talking about mathematics or about the actual tosses of actual coins. We even get the impression that it might be possible to *test* the mathematical model by empirical manipulations, as the ancients once thought they could test the rest of arithmetic.

If the history of mathematics teaches anything, it is that all we can ever test is the degree of isomorphism between the formal model — the calculus of probability — and some particular collection of empirical events. That the isomorphism is often good is a fortunate circumstance, for it permits us to predict the behavior of molecules and death rates and election votes. But the existence of this isomorphism proves nothing more than our good fortune. It certainly proves nothing about the necessity of things, nor does our belief in any particular variety of necessity guarantee that the formal model will fit the resulting events.

Let us consider, as an example of a formal system, the mathematical model proposed by von Mises for the frequency theory of probability. In the English edition of his book von Mises does not always make explicit the formal-empirical distinction, but some of his oral statements lead me to conclude that he believes in it. Central to von Mises' formal system is the concept of the "collective," which he defines by two postulates: (1) the ratio of one kind of element to the total number in the collective approaches a limit as the number becomes infinite; and (2) every "place selection" (the drawing of elements according to any fixed rule) results in another collective having the same limit. This second postulate is equivalent to saying that, by definition, there is no gambling rule that will guarantee success if a true collective is involved. From these two postulates a formal calculus is derived, and, as is always the case, the question whether physical systems will be found that fit these postulates is a matter for empirical test to decide. The roulette numbers of our earlier example approximate a collective, as is attested by the perennial solvency of the Prince of Monaco, and throughout many interesting pages von Mises examines still other concrete cases in which his calculus of collectives suffices for the statistical dissection of natural phenomena.

It is of incidental interest to us that Fechner, the psychophysicist, invented what von Mises calls the "useful concept of the 'Kollectivgegenstand'" (p. 98). Fechner did not go on, however, to develop a theory of probability on the basis of this notion of a "finite collective." Instead he developed, in what became posthumously a book, his theory of finite populations (Kollektivmasslehre) which is closely related to the frequency theory of probability, and which von Mises acknowledges as a "stimulus" to his own developments (p. 123). The missing notion in Fechner's treatment of the collective is the concept of randomness — the notion covered by the second postulate of von Mises.

One virtue of this frequency theory of probability is that it sets us straight about which comes first, the properties of the collective or the probability of the event. The collective is the prior concept, and events get their probabilities by belonging to collectives. Then the assignment of a probability to a single event is one of two things: either it is a meaningless procedure, or it is a backhanded way of saying that the event belongs to a particular collective.

It follows from this conception of probability that one of the first tasks in mathematical statistics is to determine whether a given collection of statistical data forms a collective. If it does not, then von Mises' formal calculus of probability is not the proper model for it. But the quality of probability that balks and baffles us lies in just this feature of it: for no *finite* set of data can we ever be quite sure either that the model fits or that it does not. In the strict sense this difficulty plagues every scientific indagation, but in matters of probability it founders our intent with a distressing regularity.

MEASURES AND INDICANTS

One final point and we are through.

Although psychologists devote much of their enthusiasm to the measurement of the psychological dimensions of people, they squander more of it in an effort to assess the various aspects of behavior by means of what we may call *indicants*. These are *effects* or *correlates* related to psychological dimensions by *unknown* laws. This process is inevitable in the present stage of our progress, and it is not to be counted a blemish. We know about psychological phenomena only through effects, and the measuring of the effects themselves is a first trudge on the road to understanding.

The end of the trail is measurement, which we reach when we solve the relation between our fortuitous indicants and the proper dimensions of the thing in question.

In the meantime we take hold of our problems by whatever handles nature provides. We count the number of pellets hoarded by a rat in order to assess its hoarding drive. We count the number of trials required for a man to learn a task, and use this number as an index of his ability. We measure changes in the resistance of the skin and call it an indicant of emotion. In short, we are far more frequently engaged, as the following chapters will demonstrate, in the measurement of indicants than we are in devising scales for the direct assessment of physiological and psychological phenomena, or of "intervening variables," as they are sometimes called.

Occasionally the measurement of an indicant is sufficient for the task at hand; e.g. when we gauge a worker's ability by his productivity we may be interested in no more than the relation between his production and that of his neighbor. But more often we would like to measure his ability, intelligence, drive, emotion, hunger, etc., on a scale of the attribute in question rather than by effects that bear a dubious relation to it.

The difference, then, between an indicant and a measure is just this: the indicant is a presumed effect or correlate bearing an unknown (but usually monotonic) relation to some underlying phenomenon, whereas a measure is a scaled value of the phenomenon itself. Indicants have the advantage of convenience. Measures have the advantage of validity. We aspire to measures, but we are often forced to settle for less.

This distinction between measures and indicants disappears, of course, as soon as we learn the quantitative relation between the indicant and the object of our interest, for then the indicant can be calibrated and used to measure the phenomenon at issue. We measure electric current by means of a calibrated indicant composed of a coil of wire suspended by a spring in a magnetic field. We measure psychological pitch with a frequency meter after we have established a scale relating pitch in mels to frequency in cycles per second. The more mature a science, the more it uses *calibrated* indicants.

REFERENCES

Beebe-Center, J. G. Standards for use of the gust scale. *J. Psychol.*, 1949, **28**, 411–419.

Békésy, G. von. Über das Fechner'sche Gesetz und seine Bedeutung für die Theorie der akustischen Beobachtungsfehler und die Theorie des Hörens. *Ann. Physik*, 1930, **7**, 329–359.

Bell, E. T. *Men of mathematics*. New York: Simon and Schuster, 1937.

Bell, E. T. *The development of mathematics*. (2nd Ed.) New York: McGraw-Hill, 1945.

Birkhoff, G., and S. MacLane. *A survey of modern algebra*. New York: Macmillan, 1941.

Boring, E. G. *Sensation and perception in the history of experimental psychology*. New York: Appleton-Century-Crofts, 1942.

Bridgman, P. W. *The logic of modern physics*. New York: Macmillan, 1928.

Bridgman, P. W. *Dimensional analysis*. (2nd Ed.) New Haven: Yale University Press, 1931.

Bruner, J. S., and L. Postman. Symbolic value as an organizing factor in perception. *J. soc. Psychol.*, 1948, **27**, 203–208.

Campbell, N. R. *Symposium: Measurement and its importance for philosophy*. Aristotelian

Society, Suppl. Vol. 17. London: Harrison, 1938.

Campbell, N. R., with others. Final report. *Advanc. Sci.*, 1940, No. 2, 331–349.

Carnap, R. *Introduction to semantics*. Cambridge: Harvard University Press, 1942.

Carnap, R. Probability as a guide in life. *J. Phil.*, 1947, **44**, 141–148.

Courant, R., and H. Robbins. *What is mathematics?* New York: Oxford University Press, 1941.

Crocker, F. C., and L. F. Henderson. Analysis and classification of odors. *Amer. Perfum.*, 1927, **22**, 325–327.

Dantzig, T. *Number: The language of science*. New York: Macmillan, 1939.

Guilford, J. P. *Psychometric methods*. New York: McGraw-Hill, 1936.

Gulliksen, H. Paired comparisons and the logic of measurement. *Psychol. Rev.*, 1946, **53**, 199–213.

Hanes, R. M. The construction of subjective brightness scales from fractionation data: A validation. *J. exp. Psychol.*, 1949, **39**, 719–728.

Hardy, J. D., H. G. Wolff, and H. Goodell. Studies on pain: an investigation of some quantitative aspects of the dol scale of pain intensity. *J. clin. Invest.*, 1948, **27**, 380–386.

Harkin, D. *Fundamental mathematics*. New York: Prentice-Hall, 1941.

Harper, R. S., and S. S. Stevens. A psychological scale of weight and a formula for its derivation. *Amer. J. Psychol.*, 1948, **61**, 343–351.

Herget, C. M., L. P. Granath, and J. D. Hardy. Thermal sensation and discriminations in relation to intensity of stimulus. *Amer. J. Physiol.*, 1941, **134**, 645–655.

Hogben, L. *Mathematics for the million*. (2nd Ed.) New York: Norton, 1940.

Holway, A. H., and C. C. Pratt. The Weber-ratio for intensive discrimination. *Psychol. Rev.*, 1936, **43**, 322–340.

Howes, D. H. The loudness of multicomponent tones. *Amer. J. Psychol.*, 1950, **63**, 1–30.

Huntington, E. V. The fundamental propositions of algebra. In J. W. A. Young (Ed.) *Monographs on modern mathematics*. New York: Longmans, Green, 1911. Reprinted by Galois Institute Press, Brooklyn, 1941.

Klein, F. *Elementary mathematics from an advanced standpoint*. New York: Dover, 1945. (Translation of 3rd ed., 1924.)

Lewis, D. *Quantitative methods in psychology*. Iowa City, 1948.

Lewis, D. R. Psychological scales of taste. *J. Psychol.*, 1948, **26**, 437–446.

Miller, G. A. Sensitivity to changes in the intensity of white noise and its relation to masking and loudness. *J. acoust. Soc. Amer.*, 1947, **19**, 609–619.

Miller, G. A., and W. R. Garner. Effect of random presentation on the psychometric function: implications for a quantal theory of discrimination. *Amer. J. Psychol.*, 1944, **57**, 451–467.

Mises, R. von. *Probability, statistics and truth.* New York: Macmillan, 1939.

Morris, C. W. Foundations of the theory of signs. *Int. Encycl. unif. Sci.,* 1938, No. 1, 63–75.

Mosier, C. I. Psychophysics and mental test theory: Fundamental postulates and elementary theorems. *Psychol. Rev.,* 1940, **47,** 355–366.

Mosier, C. I. Psychophysics and mental test theory. II. The constant process. *Psychol. Rev.,* 1941, **48,** 235–249.

Neumann, J. von, and O. Morgenstern. *Theory of games and economic behavior.* (2nd Ed.) Princeton: Princeton University Press, 1947.

Ore, O. *Number theory and its history.* New York: McGraw-Hill, 1948.

Poincaré, H. *The foundations of science.* New York: Science Press, 1913.

Quine, W. V. O. *Mathematical logic.* Cambridge: Harvard University Press, 1947.

Reese, T. W. The application of the theory of physical measurement to the measurement of psychological magnitudes, with three experimental examples. *Psychol. Monogr.,* 1943, **55,** No. 3, 1–88.

Reichenbach, H. *Experience and prediction.* Chicago: University of Chicago Press, 1938.

Reichenbach, H. *Elements of symbolic logic.* New York: Macmillan, 1947.

Reichenbach, H. *The theory of probability.* (2nd Ed.) Berkeley: University of California Press, 1949.

Riess, Anita. *Number readiness in research.* New York: Scott, Foresman, 1947.

Russell, B. *Introduction to mathematical philosophy.* (2nd Ed.) New York: Macmillan, 1920.

Russell, B. *The principles of mathematics.* (2nd Ed.) New York: Norton, 1937.

Sheldon, W. H., S. S. Stevens, and W. B. Tucker. *The varieties of human physique.* New York: Harper, 1940.

Stevens, S. S. The relation of saturation to the size of the retinal image. *Amer. J. Psychol.,* 1934, **46,** 70–79.

Stevens, S. S. Psychology and the science of science. *Psychol. Bull.,* 1939a, **36,** 221–263.

Stevens, S. S. On the problem of scales for the measurement of psychological magnitudes. *J. unif. Sci.,* 1939b, **9,** 94–99.

Stevens, S. S. On the theory of scales of measurement. *Science,* 1946, **103,** 677–680.

Stevens, S. S. Sensation and psychological measurement. Chapter 11 in E. G. Boring, H. S. Langfeld, and H. P. Weld. (Eds.), *Foundations of Psychology.* New York: Wiley, 1948.

Stevens, S. S., and H. Davis. *Hearing: Its psychology and physiology.* New York: Wiley, 1938.

Stevens, S. S., C. T. Morgan, and J. Volkmann. Theory of the neural quantum in the discrimination of loudness and pitch. *Amer. J. Psychol.,* 1941, **54,** 315–335.

Stevens, S. S., and J. Volkmann. The quantum of sensory discrimination. *Science,* 1940a, **92,** 583–585.

Stevens, S. S., and J. Volkmann. The relation of pitch to frequency: A revised scale. *Amer. J. Psychol.,* 1940b, **53,** 329–353.

Tarski, A. *Introduction to logic.* New York: Oxford University Press, 1941.

Taves, E. H. Two mechanisms for the perception of visual numerousness. *Arch. Psychol.,* 1941, **37,** No. 265.

Thompson, D'Arcy W. *On growth and form.* New York: Macmillan, 1942.

Thurstone, L. L. *Multiple factor analysis.* Chicago: Chicago University Press, 1947.

Thurstone, L. L. Psychophysical methods Chapter 5 in T. G. Andrews (Ed.), *Methods of Psychology.* New York: Wiley, 1948.

Tingley, E. M. Base eight arithmetic and money. *Sch. Sci. Math.,* June 1940.

Titchener, E. B. The psychophysics of climate. *Amer. J. Psychol.,* 1909, **20,** 1–14.

Weyl, H. *Philosophy of mathematics and natural science.* Princeton: Princeton University Press, 1949.

Wilks, S. S. *Mathematical statistics.* Princeton: Princeton University Press, 1943.

Young, J. W. *Lectures on the fundamental concepts of algebra and geometry.* New York: Macmillan, 1911.

2.

Excitation and Conduction
in the Neuron

FRANK BRINK, Jr.

The Johns Hopkins University

The essential fact about a single nerve cell, as a component of the nervous system, is that a response to a stimulus at one part of its surface can spread to distant parts of the cell and act as a stimulus to other nerve cells (or effector organs). The evolutionary specialization of the nerve cell for this purpose is manifested in its geometrical form and in its highly developed sensitivity. For example, the cell body of a motor neuron lies in the spinal cord, and its axon may extend for a distance of many feet to reach the muscle cells (Fig. 1). Stimulation of this neuron at any point produces a response that spreads to the periphery, as a nerve impulse, and causes some muscle cells to contract.

The impulse propagated along a nerve is itself a transient change in cellular structure revealed by various physical signs. The ability to propagate an impulse is a property of the neuron that is fundamental to its functioning as an element of the nervous system. This chapter begins, therefore, with a discussion of the physical properties of the communication line of the nervous system — the axon of the single neuron.

I wish to express my sincere thanks to Dr. D. W. Bronk, Dr. H. K. Hartline, and Dr. M. G. Larrabee for their constructive criticism of Chapters 2 and 3. They were prepared while the author was on the staff of the Johnson Foundation for Medical Physics, University of Pennsylvania.

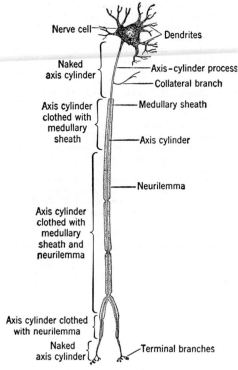

FIG. 1. Diagram of a motor neuron. The indentations in the myelin sheath, the nodes of Ranvier, may be 2 millimeters apart. The axon may be several feet long. (Stöhr.)

The Concept of Structure

In the physical sense the word "structure" implies a spatial distribution of the molecular components and larger particles of a system, in other than the random arrangement produced by the thermal motion of noninteracting particles. Such orderly arrays require forces between adjacent molecules that are sufficiently strong to overcome thermal agitation and to insure the cohesion of the structure. There are many ways of detecting and mapping the spatial arrangements of the constituents of a structure as complex as that of a neuron. Obviously, shapes and overall dimensions are given by microscopic observation. Polarized light, by interacting with some arrangements of molecules, reveals structure in a molecular system, and, by comparison with models having similar properties, the spatial arrangements of the molecular constituents can be specified. X-rays, too, are scattered by molecular structures to produce characteristic patterns which can be analyzed into spatial maps of molecular arrangements. An electrical potential difference is evidence for a particular aspect of structure: the spatial distribution of charged particles. All these and several other physical methods for detecting structure and for following the rate and degree of change in particular structures have been employed in the study of neurons.

Optically defined structure of the axon. Historically the study of neurons became divided into several categories, defined largely by the experimental procedures employed. First there were the studies with the microscope that revealed a considerable range of detailed structure (Fig. 1) and indicated the complex organization and the range of size of the conducting units of the nervous system. This was supplemented by more detailed probing of the spatial arrangement of the constituent molecules by means of X-ray diffraction methods (Schmitt, 1941) and, in single fibers, by means of analyses, with polarized light, of the spatial arrangement of protein and lipoid molecules at the surfaces of axons (Schmitt and Bear, 1939) and of cell bodies (Chinn, 1938).

Microscopic observation of living axons reveals the axis cylinder to be covered by several sheaths that are not part of the neuron. In the fibers of crustacea these sheaths seem to cover directly the cytoplasm of the axis cylinder (Fig. 2). In the large myelinated fibers of vertebrates thick layers of myelin intervene between the axis cylinder and these outer sheaths, except at the nodes of Ranvier. The sheath around the myelin is formed from Schwann cells and is in turn surrounded by a sheath of connective tissue. In the giant fiber of the squid (*Loligo pealii*) the Schwann cells are inside the myelin sheath (Bear, Schmitt, and Young, 1937a). In addition to these observable external investments the axis cylinder presumably has a plasma membrane at its surface, as do other living cells.

The structure of the myelin sheath has been extensively studied by means of polarized light (see Fig. 3). There are layers of oriented lipoid molecules alternating with layers of protein (Bear and Schmitt, 1936–37). The spatial arrangements of the constituents of this structure have been confirmed by X-ray studies. By means of polarized light the presence of similar myelin structures has been detected in the so-called unmyelinated nerves of crustacea (Schmitt and Bear, 1936–37: Chinn and Schmitt, 1936–37). The available evidence suggests that around all axons there is such a lamellar arrangement of protein and lipoid molecules. This membrane may extend over the entire axon and cell body (Chinn, 1938). However, this is not true for cells in the ventral horn of the spinal cord where the surface of the cells seems to be the plasma membrane.

The axis cylinder is made up of a viscous cytoplasm that flows slowly from the cut end of a giant axon of a squid (Fig. 2) but is apparently a stiff gel in heavily myelinated mature axons of vertebrates (de Renyi, 1929). The presence of oriented protein particles in the axis cylinder of the giant axon has been detected with polarized light (Bear, Schmitt, and Young, 1937b). These are rodlike and are oriented parallel to the long axis of the axon.

One outstanding fact about the axon is that it can persist only as long as it is con-

outside of the cell has been directly measured (Hodgkin and Huxley, 1945; Curtis and Cole, 1942). This is evidence for an orderly spatial arrangement of electrically charged

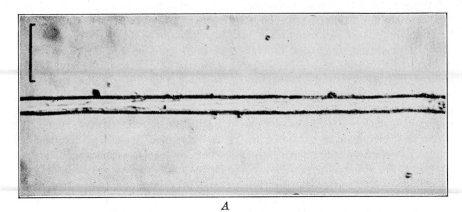

A

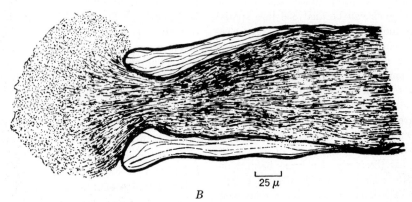

B

Fig. 2*A*. Living axon from *Carcinus* in seawater. The light intensity was adjusted to produce the maximum contrast between the opaque connective tissue and the transparent axis cylinder. Calibration line is 100 microns. (Hodgkin, 1938*b*.)

B. The viscous contents of the axis cylinder flow slowly from the cut end of a giant axon from a squid, *Loligo pealii*. The sheath structures are readily separated from the cytoplasm in this neuron. (Young, 1935.)

nected to the cell body. Another is that a cell body can regenerate this complex structure if the axon is destroyed.

Electrically defined structure of the axon. The relatively constant electrical properties of the resting cell are regarded as evidence of special arrangements of molecules within the cell structure. In one type of axon the potential difference between the inside and

molecules and for nonelectrical forces that create the electric field by maintaining a spatial separation of these oppositely charged particles. The spatial arrangement is such that the outside of the cell is positive, relative to the inside. This requires that positively charged molecules are on the average somewhat separated in a radial direction from an equal number of opposite charges.

The structure involved is the highly organized surface of the cell, which may be referred to as the nerve membrane. (The latter designation does not refer to a particular histological structure.)

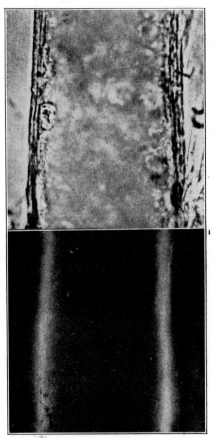

FIG. 3. The surface of a nerve has a special molecular structure revealed by its interaction with transmitted polarized light. The upper picture is a microscopic view of a single axon dissected from a crayfish claw nerve. The lower picture shows that the surface structure transmits polarized light that is not transmitted by the axis cylinder. Diameter of axon is 60 microns. (Bear and Schmitt, 1936–37.)

ter designation does not refer to a particular histological structure.)

In addition, studies of the way in which the membrane conducts electricity suggest that it may be composed of ion-permeable, or conducting, areas, and of ion-impermeable areas where electric charges accumulate, as on a condenser (Cole, 1940). Current flowing radially across the membrane then increases or decreases the potential difference between the inside and the outside of the nerve. This aspect of the nerve structure can therefore be studied by measuring the intensity and time course of the polarization potentials, or passive changes in membrane potential, created by passing current radially into or out of the cell.

The optically defined structures of the axon are not identical with the structures detected by electrical methods. For example, there is no change in structure detectable by polarized light during activity (Schmitt, 1939; Schmitt and Schmitt, 1940). Nevertheless there are profound structural changes accompanying the nerve impulse that can be detected by electrical methods (Cole and Curtis, 1938–39). The accumulated evidence suggests that the optically revealable structures are a stable molecular framework upon which are superimposed the more labile spatial arrays of molecules associated with excitation, response, and recovery. In particular, the principal electrical properties have been assigned to the regions near the surface, though it is not known how many of the observable membranes contribute significantly to these properties.

Physical Aspects of the Nerve Impulse

An impulse in a motor nerve can be conveniently detected by its physiological effect, the contraction of the attached muscle. It has been experimentally demonstrated that the conduction of such a nerve impulse along an axon is associated with an action potential. This is measured as an electrical potential difference longitudinally distributed along the fiber (Figs. 4 and 5). Since the magnitude of this electrical signal, measured by electrodes in contact with moist surface of the nerve, is a few millivolts or less, it is amplified by an electronic amplifier, which then drives a suitable recording instrument (Fig. 6).

There is a finite time between the application of a stimulus to the nerve and the contraction of the muscle. This time interval is longer, the greater the distance from the point of stimulation to the muscle. Accordingly, one physical characteristic of the nerve impulse is that it travels at a finite measurable velocity (Helmholtz, 1852). This velocity was originally measured by stimulating a motor nerve at two points a known

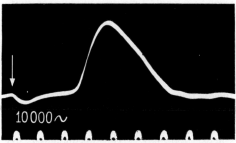

FIG. 4. Potential changes during the passage of a conducted impulse, recorded between an electrode on an active part of the nerve and another on the inactive end of the nerve. This is the spike component of the action potential in a single fiber. Stimulus artifact at arrow marks time of stimulation. Time marks separated by 0.1 millisecond. (Gasser, 1939.)

distance (L) apart and measuring the two time intervals between stimulation and muscle response. The difference in these time intervals (Δt) represents the conduction time between the two points of stimulation, and the velocity of the impulse is $L/\Delta t$. Later, by stimulating an axon at two points that are at different distances from a pair of recording electrodes, the conduction velocity of the action potential was measured (Bernstein, 1866). The velocity of conduction of the physiologically effective impulse that excites a muscle is the same as that of the action potential.

The action potential is now regarded as an essential physical accompaniment of the nerve impulse. In most experiments on nerves the action potential is the primary criterion of activity in an axon, and its presence is employed to distinguish an active nerve from a resting one.

As previously mentioned, potential gradients are created in the fluid surrounding active axons. The two electrodes attached to a suitable amplifier and placed in contact with this external fluid register this differ-

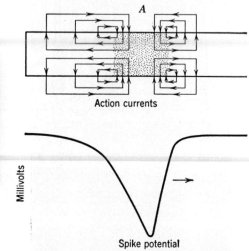

Action currents

Spike potential

FIG. 5. Diagram of instantaneous current distribution (upper diagram) around the depolarized area A during propagation of a nerve impulse. The potential change shown below becomes the recorded action potential when it is propagated past a recording electrode. In front of the depolarized area the currents flow outward from the membrane electromotive force and return by flowing inward in the depolarized region. This reversal of radial current flow occurs at the point of inflection on the rising phase of the action potential. The radial current again reverses direction at the inflection point on the descending phase of the action potential. (Modified from Howell's *Textbook of Physiology*. 15th Ed. Philadelphia: Saunders, 1946.)

ence of potential which varies in time as an impulse passes along the nerve. The moist film on the nerve is thin when the nerve is suspended in air in a moist chamber, and radial potential gradients in the external fluid are negligible. Under these conditions, as the activated area approaches the electrodes, the first recording electrode becomes negative with respect to the second. Later this potential difference passes through zero, and the first electrode becomes positive with respect to the second until the nerve is re-polarized. The result is a diphasic action potential.

is followed by smaller and slower changes of potential, designated the after-potentials. These are readily observed at high amplification only. The first observable after-potential is negative, as is the spike, but subsequently the potential at the first electrode becomes positive, and thereafter the

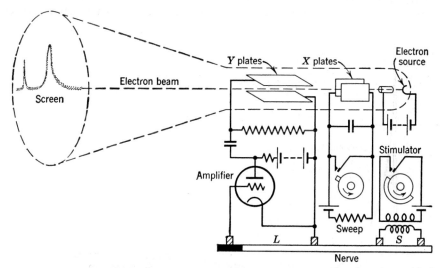

FIG. 6. Diagram of instruments for exciting a nerve and for observing the rapid electrical changes associated with a nerve impulse. One recording electrode is on a killed end of the nerve so that the recorded potential change is an undistorted representation of the sequence of changes under the other electrode. The sweep circuit causes the electron beam to move from left to right over the screen of the cathode-ray tube. The time of stimulation is marked by the first deflection on the screen. The action potential travels down the nerve and causes the second deflection when it reaches the first recording electrode. (Erlanger and Gasser, 1937.)

In order to observe the sequence of potential changes as the impulse passes one region of a nerve, it is desirable to prevent the potential changes at the second electrode. This is accomplished by placing the second electrode on a killed or otherwise inactivated part of the nerve, usually at the cut end of an excised nerve. The potential record now reflects the time course of changes at the first recording electrode, and the result is a monophasic action potential (Fig. 4).

The monophasic action potential is composed of an initial large and rapid change of potential, designated the spike. The spike

original isopotential condition is established as the nerve recovers from the activity. This total sequence of potential changes associated with a nerve impulse is called the action potential (Fig. 7).

The spike component of the action potential is not so easily modified by imposed environmental factors as are the after-potentials. This differential sensitivity to modification has been employed to establish that the spike is followed by a positive after-potential, or P_1 process. In the presence of a large negative after-potential this P_1 process is obscured. The negative after-potential is also followed by a prolonged positive wave, designated the P_2 process. This analysis is indicated in Fig. 7.

The action potential is by no means the only physical accompaniment of the propagated nerve impulse. It is possible in some axons to detect the arrival of an impulse at a given region by the changes in the electrical resistance of the membrane, by

electrical current flowing through the nerve; i.e. a nerve is sensitive to such current flow. (2) The conduction of the physiologically effective nerve impulse along an axon is always associated with an action potential. These two facts led to the hypothesis that propagation of the impulse is mediated by the electrical current flowing out of an inactive area and into the active area of the

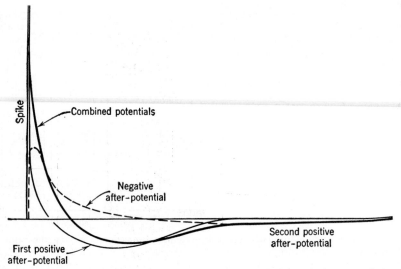

Fig. 7. Diagram depicting a theoretical series of potentials that, summed together, would reproduce the action potential. (Erlanger and Gasser, 1937.)

changes in the utilization of oxygen, and by the production of heat. The nerve impulse is thus a complex cycle of electrochemical changes in the nerve structure and is propagated at finite velocity from one part of a nerve cell to all other parts (the cell body may be an exception). In this sequence of events the initial part of the action potential is the earliest physical sign of the approach of the nerve impulse.

Mechanism of Conduction

There are two generalizations from experiments on isolated axons that underlie our present concepts of the physical process of conduction in nerve cells: (1) A propagated nerve impulse can be initiated by an

nerve. An obvious corollary to this proposition is that these currents are sufficiently intense to excite adjacent regions of the axon. The critical experiment was not performed until 1938 when Hodgkin presented clear evidence for the hypothesis that conduction is mediated by the electrical currents associated with the action potential.

In this experiment a few millimeters of the nerve were cooled so that a nerve impulse could not pass through the region (Fig. 8). There was then no propagated action potential in the fibers at points beyond the blocked region. When the recording electrodes were placed just beyond the blocked region, there was a change of potential correlated in time with each blocked action potential arriving at the other side of the cooled region. The maximum amplitude of this postblock change of potential decreased with distance from the edge of the blocked region (Fig. 9). Thus the transient

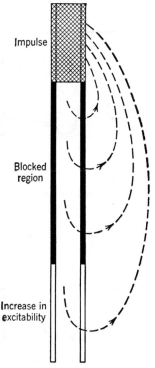

Impulse

Blocked region

Increase in excitability

FIG. 8.   Current from the membrane electromotive force flows into the depolarized area of the axon at the edge of the blocked region. The outwardly directed currents beyond the block make the nerve more excitable there. Such current flow provides the mechanism for propagation of the action potential associated with a nerve impulse. (Hodgkin, 1937.)

loss of potential difference across the membrane at the site of the impulse caused current to flow from the areas of nerve on the far side of the blocked region.

Such changes of potential along the nerve merely indicate the longitudinal flow of current due to the intrinsic electromotive force of the nerve. The current flows through the external fluid and back into the axon at the depolarized area. When this current is not intense enough to initiate a local response or a propagated impulse, as in this instance, the change in membrane potential is said to be a passive polarization in order to distinguish it from the membrane changes associated with an active response, such as a propagated wave of depolarization. These passive polarization potentials modify the excitability of a nerve and are often referred to as electrotonic potentials. Correspondingly, the associated current is described as electrotonic current and the change in excitability of the nerve is called electrotonus.

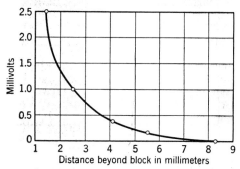

FIG. 9.   The maximum potential change due to a blocked impulse decreases with distance beyond the blocked region of the nerve, as does an electrotonic potential change. (Hodgkin, 1937.)

The fact that conduction was blocked indicates that the electrotonic current on the far side of the block was insufficient to insure propagation of the impulse. However, the excitability of the nerve beyond the blocked region was increased during the transient flow of current (Fig. 8). This electrotonus was measured by the least intensity of imposed current from an external source required to initiate an action potential beyond the blocked region. In this way Hodgkin showed that the postblock changes of potential were temporally correlated with changes in excitability (Fig. 10). Quantitative studies of the changes of excitability produced in motor nerves of a frog at different distances ahead of a blocked impulse indicated that at about 3 millimeters in front of the active area of an axon the current was sufficient to excite the region and thus insure propagation.

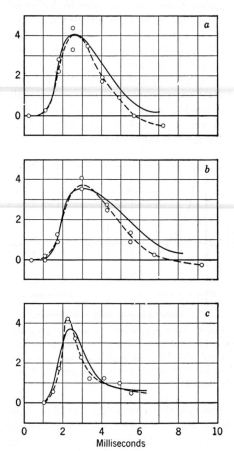

FIG. 10. The excitability changes (dotted curves), produced by the current flow ahead of a blocked impulse, parallel the electrotonic potential (solid curves) recorded at the same region. Thus the intensity of the excitation is related to the strength of the electrotonic currents shown in Fig. 8. Plots *a* and *b* are for cold block; *c* is for pressure block. Frog nerve. (Hodgkin, 1937.)

The strength of an action current is decreased by an increase in the electrical resistance of the external fluid through which it flows. Therefore the distance in front of an active region in an axon at which the

action current can excite is shorter, the greater the external resistance. If propagation is by means of the action currents, then the velocity should be reduced when the resistance to the flow of current in the external fluid is increased. This phenomenon has been experimentally demonstrated (Fig. 11), and it supports the hypothesis that the conduction process is electrical in nature.

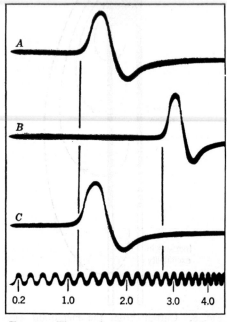

FIG. 11. The conduction velocity of the action potential is reduced when the electrical resistance of the solutions bathing the nerve is increased. The time interval from the beginning of the trace to the first deflection measures the conduction time from the stimulating electrodes to the recording electrodes. *A* and *C* are for nerve bathed in seawater. *B* is for nerve bathed in oil to increase the resistance of the outside solution conducting the action currents. Time scale: milliseconds. (Hodgkin, 1938–39.)

No experiment has yet contradicted the hypothesis that propagation of the nerve impulse within a single neuron is by excitation of successive portions of the cell by the action currents.

It is possible to construct an electrochemical model having conduction properties analogous to those of a nerve (Lillie, 1936). Thus an iron wire in strong nitric acid becomes coated by a layer of oxide that prevents further dissolution of the wire into the acid. The coating on this so-called passive iron wire can be destroyed at a given place, and between the bare iron thus produced and an adjacent coated area there is a difference of potential. The current flowing between the bare areas and the coated areas is such that the coating at the boundary of the two areas is removed. Hence the electrochemical reaction is propagated along the wire, and the acid solution later restores the coating. As with the nerve fiber, this system (1) is sensitive to current flow and (2) contains an internal source of current. To this extent the structure is an electrochemical model of the axon. The analogy is even more extended in that such systems are capable of rhythmic electrical processes similar to the oscillatory local response in nerve (see below; and Bartlett, 1948). Attempts have also been made to formulate a mathematical representation of excitation and conduction in this model (Bonhoeffer, 1948). This is a promising approach to the theoretical study of the properties of metastable structures resembling those in neurons.

Velocity of conduction and types of fibers. The velocity of conduction of the action potential varies widely in different types of axons. One of the principal criteria used in classifying nerve fibers is the average velocity of conduction of the members of each class. The group of fibers of highest conduction velocity in peripheral nerves has been designated the A-group. However, there are subdivisions of the A-group defined by the average velocity of conduction of the members of the subgroup. Thus, if the A-fibers in the sciatic nerve of a frog are simultaneously excited, the time of arrival of the compound action potential at various points along the nerve can be measured and the velocity of propagation determined (Fig.

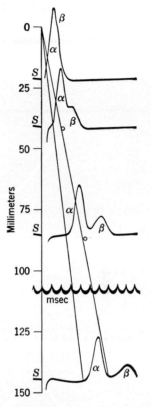

FIG. 12. Demonstration of the linearity of the velocity of propagation in α- and β-fibers. The distance from the stimulating to the recording electrodes is indicated along the vertical line, which also indicates the time of stimulation (S) for each test. "A straight line drawn through the start of the lowermost action potential and the point marking zero distance of conduction exactly intersects the starts of all of the other records. The start of *beta* is obvious only in the lowermost record where it is practically out in the clear. Another line has been drawn connecting the start of this *beta* with the zero of conduction distance. The positions of the starts of *beta* of the two intermediate records have been located by calculation and are indicated by the circles. In this way it becomes clear that the second straight line intersects reasonably closely the starts of all of the *betas.*" (Erlanger and Gasser, 1937, pp. 13–14.)

12). If all the impulses traveled at the same velocity, this compound action potential would retain its size and duration as it traveled. At the longest conduction distance,

are designated the α- and β-fibers. If all the A-fibers in the sciatic nerve of a frog are excited and the conduction distance is long enough, two more subgroups of somewhat

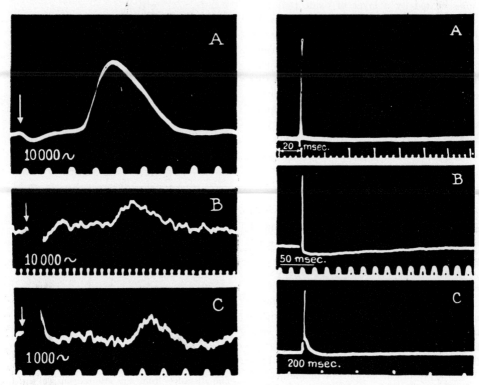

FIG. 13. *Left-hand column:* spike potentials of A-, B-, and C-fibers. The duration of the spike component of the action potential is shorter, the faster the conduction velocity. The A-fiber spike (cat) has a duration of 0.4 millisecond, that of the B-fiber (rabbit) is about 1 millisecond, and the C-fiber spike (cat) lasts about 2 milliseconds.

Right-hand column: complete action potentials of A-, B-, and C-fibers (cat). The spike is followed by an after-potential that varies in form, size, and duration, depending on the kind of fiber. In A- and C-fibers the complete sequence is a negative after-potential (upward deflection) followed by a positive potential (downward deflection). In B-fibers the negative after-potential is not detected in single responses. (Gasser, 1941.)

however, two distinct maxima are observed in the recorded action potential. The first is compounded from action potentials, of a subgroup of fibers, that travel faster than those represented by the second peak in the compound action potential. The degree of separation of the two sets of impulses increases, the longer the distance traveled. These two subgroups of the A-group of fibers

slower average velocity of conduction are found. Thus the A-group of nerve fibers is composed of α-, β-, γ-, and δ-fibers. The average velocities of conduction decrease in that order (Erlanger and Gasser, 1937).

When conduction velocities are measured in a variety of nerves, other types of fibers are recognized (Fig. 13). One such group is the B-fibers having an average conduction velocity much less than that for the A-fibers. However, the range of velocities of A-fibers overlaps that of the B-fibers (Table 1). Consequently other criteria are used to make a more complete distinction between these types. Both A- and B-fibers are myelinated and segmented by the nodes of Ranvier, as in Fig. 1. However, the diameter of B-fibers is less than 3 microns, whereas A-fibers can be as large as 20 microns, with an average diameter of about 10 microns. Other important distinguishing properties, such as the duration of the spike component of the action potential, are given in Table 1.

size determine conduction velocity. For example, a giant axon of a squid, which is not segmented and which is 500 microns in diameter, may have a conduction velocity equal to that of a segmented motor fiber of a frog, only 10 microns in diameter.

The differences in conduction velocity among A-, B-, and C-fibers are reflected in the speed of other processes in these cells. Thus the refractory period of an A-fiber is much less than that of a C-fiber. Indeed, the entire recovery cycle following a response is shorter in A-fibers than in C-fibers (Fig. 25). Furthermore, the after-potentials

TABLE 1

PROPERTIES OF THREE GROUPS OF MAMMALIAN NERVE FIBERS

Group	A	B	C
Diameters of fibers, μ	20 to 1	<3	Unmyelinated
Conduction velocity, mps	100 to <5	14 to <3	<2
Spike duration, msec	0.4 to 0.5	1.2	2.0
Negative after-potential			
Amount, per cent of spike	3 to 5	None	3 to 5
Duration, msec	12 to 20		50 to 80
Positive after-potential			
Amount, per cent of spike	0.2	1.5 to 4.0	1.5
Duration, msec	40 to 60	100 to 300	300 to >1000
Absolutely refractory period, msec	0.4 α	1.2	2.0
	0.6 δ, cat		
	1.0 δ, rabbit		
Period of latent addition, msec	0.2	0.2	2.5
Order of susceptibility to asphyxia	2	1	3

The fibers of slowest conduction are the C-group. They are not myelinated so heavily (see p. 51) as are A- and B-fibers, and all processes seem to be more prolonged. The complete classification of mammalian fibers is given in Table 1 (Grundfest, 1940). This division of the fibers into groups is particularly useful to an understanding of the neurological function of the components of a peripheral nerve.

In fibers of the same group there is a correlation between size and conduction velocity (Fig. 14). This is particularly striking if the conduction velocity is measured at various stages in the growth of fibers of the same type. However, other factors besides

of the three kinds of axons differ as shown in Fig. 13. The slower the conduction velocity, the longer the after-potential.

The initiation of the impulse. Impulses are normally initiated in the endings of sensory nerves or in the cell body and dendrites of postsynaptic neurons. On the other hand, most of the detailed information about the sequence of physical events that lead from stimulus to conducted impulse has been derived from the electrical excitation of excised axons. In these experiments the time course of the imposed electrical current is known, and the conducted action potential provides an index of the time of response of the cell. This response always occurs an appreciable time after the onset of the imposed stimulating current. It occurs at the cathode where the electric force causes positive ions to migrate outward across the membrane and negative ions to move inward. These spatial redistributions of ions lead to the physical events that finally develop into the propagated action potential.

stimulus is terminated, until a propagated impulse spreads over the entire axon. The significant fact that processes of excitation continue to grow after the termination of the stimulus was observed in motor nerves of the frog by Erlanger and Blair (1931a, 1936). A brief induction shock of a few microseconds duration is followed in about half a

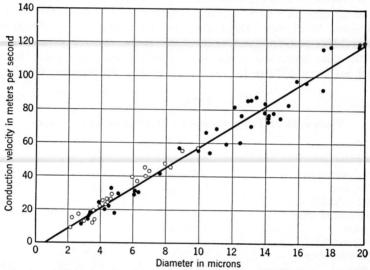

FIG. 14. Linear relation between diameter and conduction velocity of mammalian nerve fibers. Each point represents a determination of the maximum conduction velocity in meters per second and of the diameter in microns of the largest fiber of an individual nerve. Dots: adult nerves. Circles: immature nerves. Cats and kittens. (Hursh, 1939.)

The time interval between the onset of the stimulus and the conducted action potential is called the response time. If the stimulus imposed upon a crab nerve is a prolonged direct current, the response time is shorter, the greater the intensity of the current. In addition, at each intensity of current the time of response is longer, the shorter the duration of the imposed current. However, at each intensity of current there is a minimum duration that can excite the nerve. A plot of this last relation results in the classical intensity-duration curve shown in Fig. 15, curve A.

Clearly the processes of excitation initiated by the stimulus at one region of the nerve can continue to develop after the

millisecond by a conducted impulse arising in the nerve at the cathode of the stimulator. If a stimulus of opposite polarity is imposed during this interval, the development of excitation can be stopped and no impulse occurs. This is further evidence, in another type of nerve, for the independent development of the process of excitation after the termination of the stimulatory current.

A consideration of the time relations in the development of excitation led Rushton (1937) to the idea of the localized response. He proposed that a finite length of nerve must become depolarized by current flow from adjacent parts of the membrane into the area initially depolarized by the imposed current. This process of spreading depolarization can proceed after termination of the imposed stimulus. If the depolarized area thus created becomes large enough, the process of depolarization by circulating currents moves away from the point of imposed excitation and generates the action po-

Thus the state of excitation developed by a stimulus and the associated local electrical signs are both composite effects. One component is derived from the imposed current and is described as the direct effect of the stimulus. The other component is the self-

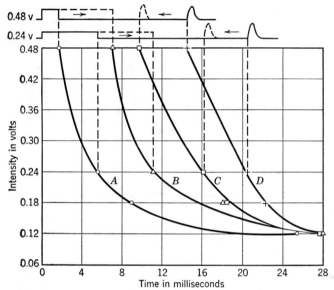

Fig. 15. The response time for a crab nerve depends upon the intensity and duration of a direct current stimulation. Stimuli and responses for two different intensities and durations are shown schematically at the top of the figure.

Curve *A:* Least duration (abscissa) at each intensity (ordinate) that will produce a response. The response at each intensity occurs at a time indicated by curve *D* (maximum latency of response).

Curve *B:* Least duration of stimulus at each intensity that will produce a response with a minimum latency (curve *C*). Longer durations produce no further reduction of the response time. (Arvanitaki, 1938.)

tential of the nerve impulse. Otherwise, processes of repolarization restore the nerve structure to its original polarized state, and the local action currents disappear.

If the imposed stimulatory current is sufficiently intense, the critical area of depolarization is created unaided by local circulating currents. The response time is then minimal. Only when the stimulating currents are weaker do the local action currents aid the imposed current in the creation of the area of depolarization required for conduction of the impulse.

excitation by current flow from intrinsic sources of electromotive force and is described as an active participation of the nerve in the growth of the local excited state. This dual nature of the excitatory process was recognized by Cremer in 1909 and is now incorporated in Rushton's theory of the growth of a nerve impulse.

The Local Electrical Response

The local electrical response has been detected in experiments on single motor axons excised from crabs (Hodgkin, 1938a) and from squid (Arvanitaki, 1939; Pumphrey, Schmitt, and Young, 1940). It is most clearly revealed if the stimulus is of brief duration so that the imposed current does not continue to contribute to the recorded changes in potential. A weak pulse of current changes the difference of potential across the membrane by a passive redistribution of positive and negative ions. Under the cathode the potential difference across

(however, see Lorente de Nó, 1947, Vol. 132).

This active contribution of the nerve to the process of spreading depolarization at the cathode is attributed to the local response. The local response is a change in the electromotive force and impedance of one area of the membrane that permits current to flow from adjacent areas of the membrane. As previously mentioned, it con-

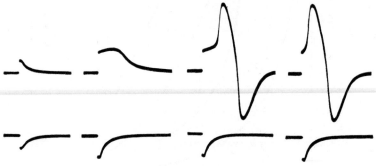

Fig. 16. Outward flow of current at the cathode (upper line) causes a local electrical response. A positive electrotonic potential change occurs at the anode (lower line). The polarizing current was weak for the first test, at the left, and the anodal and cathodal potential changes are similar. The stronger current used in the second test produced a local response as revealed by comparing the potential change at the cathode (upper) with that at the anode (lower). The last two testing currents produced local responses from which propagated action potentials developed. (Hodgkin, 1938b.)

the membrane is reduced, whereas at the anode it is increased. These polarization potentials decay exponentially in time at the cathode and at the anode (Fig. 16). The phenomenon resembles the passive charging and discharging of a condenser. When the brief stimulating current is of greater strength, the repolarization of the membrane under the cathode does not proceed in such a simple fashion. Some process intervenes that tends to maintain or even to increase the depolarization of the membrane (Fig. 16). This phenomenon occurs only in the area of the nerve under the cathode of the stimulator. It is the first sign of the local process of depolarization that is contributed by processes inherent in the nerve. At the anode a similar stimulus produces only the passively decaying polarization potential

tributes to the spreading of depolarization along the axon by means of minute local action currents. When the area of axon involved in the local response is great enough, this intrinsic process of depolarization spreads faster than the opposing processes of repolarization. Thus a conducted action potential grows out of the local response initiated by a threshold stimulus (Fig. 16). If the stimulus is greater than threshold value, it produces the critical size of local response earlier, and the impulse occurs sooner. The development of the action potential from the local potential change caused by the local response is shown quite clearly in Fig. 17.

The time course and the magnitude of the local electrical response are obtained by subtracting the component of potential change caused by the passive polarization of the nerve membrane from the recorded potential change. It is assumed that the passive polarization changes at the cathode are equal to those recorded at the anode. Thus the recorded anodal polarization is subtracted from the recorded cathodal potential change to obtain the cathodal component that is the

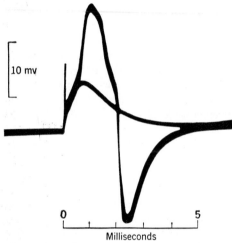

FIG. 17. Relation between a just subthreshold local electrical response and the action potential in a single crab nerve, recorded at the cathode of the stimulating current. The action potential rises out of the local response and is diphasic because it is propagated to the second recording electrode on a distant part of the axon. The two responses were produced in succession on the cathode-ray screen and were superimposed by double exposure of the same photographic plate. (Hodgkin, 1937.)

local electrical response of the nerve (Fig. 18). The expression "local electrical response" thus refers to the changes of potential associated with the local action currents created by the occurrence of a localized response in part of the axon.

The local response may be thought of as a change in structure of the membrane similar to that occurring during the action potential. However, it is not known to what extent the local response exhibits all the characteristics of the nerve impulse. For example, the local response could be graded

in magnitude in each tiny area of the axon, or it could be complete in each area. In the latter case it would have the all-or-nothing character of the spike component of the action potential, and its observed variation in intensity would merely measure the total area of axon that has responded.

The local electrical response is physical evidence of the changes occurring during the interval between the application of the stimulus and the occurrence of the action potential. These changes in the structure of a nerve have been investigated in another way. This method depends upon the use of a brief electric current to bring the existing state of excitation immediately to threshold intensity (Bishop, 1928; Erlanger and Blair,

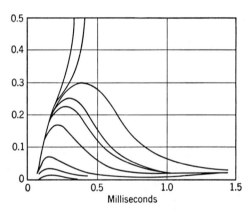

FIG. 18. Time course of local electrical responses in a single crab nerve, after subtraction of the electrotonic potential produced by the cathodal current. The size of the local response increases with the intensity of the stimulating current. The two upper traces show how, with a strong stimulus, the conducted action potential develops from the local electrical response. (Hodgkin, 1938b.)

1931a). The required intensity of this test shock is a measure of the difference between the existing state of excitation and that critical degree of excitation needed to initiate an impulse.

In this way the intensity of the local excitatory effect created by a subthreshold stimulus can be measured spatially and temporally. Thus it has been shown that the local electrical response recorded in some nerves is the physical sign of the subthreshold state of excitation created by a stimulus.

A local electrical response graded in magnitude has not been unequivocally demonstrated in motor nerves of vertebrates. A local segmental response has been observed to occur at one node of a motor nerve of a frog (Tasaki and Mizuguchi, 1948), and this may be the counterpart of the graded local response of invertebrate nerves. However, the changes in excitability following a brief stimulus have been mapped in segmented axons by means of the test-shock method (Katz, 1937). When the stimulus creates a moderate increase of excitability at the cathodal region, the excitability decays exponentially. The decay of the excitation after a stronger stimulus is distorted, and the heightened state of excitation tends to be maintained. The development and decay of this additional process of excitation are similar to those of the local electrical response in crab nerve. It has been inferred, therefore, that a local response occurs in the motor nerves of frogs. The excitability that decays exponentially, in cathodal or anodal areas, is correlated with the passive polarization changes. The processes of self-excitation that appear only at the cathode have been correlated with the local electrical response. Hence they are attributed to the spread of excitation by the local action currents.

There is another point of view regarding the action of an imposed current on a nerve. This interpretation was developed recently by Lorente de Nó and is based primarily upon his studies of the electrical properties of nerve bundles, principally the sciatic nerve of the frog and the motor roots of the bull frog. This analysis suggests that the state of excitation at the cathodal region is created entirely by the action of the imposed current. The response of the nerve is to oppose this enforced change in the potential difference across the membrane. This active process is called the nerve reaction, and it resembles in some respects the classical accommodation process (Lorente de Nó, 1947, Vol. 132, p. 143).

It seems to be generally agreed that such processes of accommodation, opposing the excitatory action of a current, do occur. Accommodation is found in all nerves, but to varying degrees. Therefore the principal point at issue seems to be whether or not there is developed, in a partially depolarized area, a process of self-excitation that aids in developing a propagated action potential.

There is no doubt that action potentials can be developed in nerves without the aid of an imposed electrical current. Thus the removal of calcium by diffusion from a limited region of nerve makes that region very sensitive to electrical stimuli (Brink, Bronk, and Larrabee, 1946). Even without the aid of an external stimulating current, such a region develops successive action potentials. Consequently self-excitation by processes inherent in the nerve can initiate the electrical events leading to a propagated impulse. This has been observed in motor nerves of the frog, of crabs, and in the giant nerve fiber of the squid. In this last preparation it is possible to record the electrical events occurring after the removal of calcium ions and preceding the first conducted impulse. There is developed between the calcium-deficient area and the adjacent areas of the axon a fluctuating difference of potential (Fig. 32). This potential difference may increase in magnitude, presumably as a result of increase in the area of axon taking part in the process. The process clearly involves, between adjacent areas of axon, an interaction that is mediated by the associated current flow. In addition it is probable that local processes of repolarization in each area are active. Thus the entire excitatory process leading to the action potentials may develop from processes inherent in the axon. The action potentials arise near the negative peaks of the recorded local electrical response. Similar oscillatory local responses to imposed electrical currents have been observed (Arvanitaki, 1939; Cole, 1941–42).

It appears then that processes of self-excitation can initiate nerve impulses in all these nerves under some conditions. The only question seems to be how much contribution to excitation initiated by imposed currents is made by the potentially self-excitatory processes? If the imposed stimulating current must continue to act until the conducted action potential occurs, then the processes of excitation inherent in the nerve must be weak and easily suppressed by the processes of repolarization. This seems to be the case in the motor nerves of the frog, where the utilization time is about equal to the response time (Lorente de Nó, 1947). However, single fibers of the frog clearly show a fluctuation in the response time to brief shocks at threshold intensity (Blair and Erlanger, 1936), and the response may occur as much as 1.5 millisecond after the end of the stimulus (Lorente de Nó, 1947, Vol. 132). If the response occurs after the termination of the imposed current, there must have been local processes of excitation that were gradually developing in the nerve. Furthermore this growth of self-excitation must have been great enough to overcome those processes in the nerve that tend to restore the initial state of the nerve.

In frog nerve then, under some conditions, there are processes of excitation within the nerve that aid an imposed current in initiating an action potential. However, the evidence is not so unequivocal as that obtained from experiments on nerves of the crab and of the squid. The reason for this seems to be that the time between the beginning of the local excitatory process and the initiation of the action potential is, in general, much shorter in frog nerve than in the nerves of the invertebrates. In addition there is some evidence that only the nodes are involved in the excitation and in the response of segmented nerves. Thus local electrical response and nodal response may be identical because of the small area of a nodal region. Since the area involved in a nodal response is very small, prolonged growth of the incipient action potential would not occur. It may be that an area of axon the size of a node responds almost as a unit.

Accommodation to an Imposed Stimulus

The change in excitability of a nerve during the flow of a direct current can be studied by determining the least intensity of a superimposed brief shock that is required to initiate an impulse immediately. This is the test shock method previously mentioned. In the type of experiment under discussion it is desirable to stop the direct current that is conditioning the nerve just after the test shock is imposed. In this way the further development of excitation by the direct current is reduced to a minimum, and the specification of the time at which the test shock measured the excitability is more precise. This kind of study, made on motor nerves of the frog by Rushton (1932), reveals the interaction between the accommodation process, opposing excitation by the imposed current, and the development of this excitation.

The threshold of the nerve tested in a cathodally polarized area decreases at a gradually declining rate (Fig. 19). The decline in the rate of decrease of threshold is attributed to an accommodation process that opposes excitation by the direct current. If the direct current is of subthreshold intensity, the interaction of the processes of excitation and of accommodation leads to a minimum in the threshold. Thereafter the accommodation process predominates, and the threshold rises toward the initial value. If the direct current flows long enough, the nerve may become fully accommodated; i.e. the final threshold equals the initial value.

When the direct current is strong enough to excite the nerve, the initial interplay between excitation by the imposed current and the accommodation process also occurs. This is indicated, at a relative intensity of

25 units marked on a curve in Fig. 19, by the initial part of this curve having a change in slope similar to that created by a sub-threshold direct current. However, there is no minimum threshold achieved because the accommodation process is itself opposed by processes of self-excitation. These predomi-

The acceleration in the development of a response that occurs after the point of inflection on the curves in Fig. 19 is attributed to the local excitatory process. It may arise in the nerve as the local action currents aid the imposed current in creating the necessary area of depolarization.

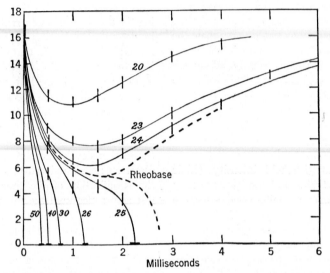

FIG. 19. During a subthreshold constant current there is a decrease in the threshold strength of a brief testing shock required to excite the nerve. After 1 or 2 milliseconds this decrease in threshold gradually disappears as the nerve adjusts to the disturbing action of the constant current (accommodation process). The relative strengths of the direct currents are given by the numbers on the curves. The strengths of the testing shocks are given on an arbitrary scale on the ordinate. When the direct current is above rheobase, the state of excitation develops at an accelerating rate. The stronger the current, the earlier the impulse is initiated, as indicated by the termination of the curves on the abscissa. (Rushton, 1932.)

nate after the point of inflection on the curve, and the threshold reaches zero on the ordinate scale. Then the impulse is initiated.

The intensity of direct current that is just sufficient to excite a nerve is called the rheobase. At the rheobase there is an unstable situation in which either accommodation or the local excitatory process may predominate. If accommodation predominates, there is no response and the usual decline of excitatory state occurs. This situation is indicated by the dotted lines in Fig. 19.

The accommodation process was postulated by Nernst to account for experimental deviations from his theory of nerve excitation. It is a prominent feature of the theories proposed later by Monnier (1934), Rashevsky (1936), and Hill (1936).

The complete time course of accommodation was first outlined by Erlanger and Blair (1931b). After the termination of the current flow in an accommodated nerve a test shock indicates that the threshold for excitation is very high (Blair and Erlanger,

1936b). It has, therefore, become the custom to speak of the process of accommodation as a rise of threshold for excitation, produced as the result of a change in the initial state of excitation. At the anodal region a corresponding increased excitability, or lowered threshold, occurs after the anodal current is terminated.

The relation of these complex transient changes in excitability to the associated changes in electrical polarization of the membrane has been studied for many years by many investigators (Katz, 1939). Studies by Lorente de Nó (1947) have led him to the conclusion that, within limits, a change in the potential difference across a nerve membrane will change the excitability. Though the evidence to prove the notion is not available, he proposes further that any increase in excitability is associated with a decrease in the potential difference across the membrane, and any decrease in excitability, with an increase in this potential difference. This conjecture should be considered a tentative hypothesis restricted to changes in excitability produced by an imposed electrical current.

Origin and Properties of the Action Potential

The spike is evidence for a transient change in membrane potential occupying a finite length of axon at any instant. At a particular area there is sequence of electrochemical changes which starts with the flow of current outward across the membrane. If the flow is sufficiently intense, there is rapid decrease of membrane electromotive force and a drop in membrane resistance (Fig. 20). The onset of the structural change indicated by the altered resistance is signaled by a reversal of the current flow so that adjacent areas of the axon now discharge into and through this region of the membrane where the resistance is low and the electromotive force reduced. This reversal of current flow occurs at the point of inflection on the rising phase of the action potential. The restoration of the original

potential difference and resistance of the membrane then begins. At the inflection point on the descending phase of the action potential the current is again flowing outward across the membrane. During this period of depolarization a second stimulus is ineffective. This period is therefore called the absolutely refractory period. In A-fibers

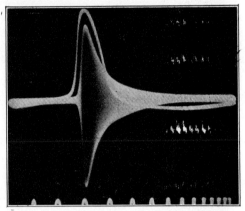

FIG. 20. During the action potential the membrane resistance to current flow suddenly decreases. Thereafter both the potential difference and the resistance are restored to their original values. The earliest deflection from the base line is the action potential, as in Fig. 4. The other trace measures the degree and duration of the associated change in resistance to current flow. Time marks are milliseconds. (Cole and Curtis, 1938–39.)

all these events occur in about a millisecond. The termination of the spike component of the action potential is obscured by afterpotentials representing further adjustments in the membrane structure as the cell processes slowly restore the original conditions at the membrane. (In so far as the phenomenon of conduction is concerned, the spike component is the essential electrical change in the membrane potential difference.)

The electrical characteristics of the nerve impulse direct attention to the nerve membrane as the fundamental structure underlying the functional properties of neurons. The membrane theory of the nerve impulse originated by Bernstein has undergone several modifications. In one interpretation the membrane potential is attributed to the selective permeability of a membrane which allows potassium ions to pass through but holds back the negative ion of a potassium

membrane potential difference to a lower value characteristic of a free diffusion potential (Höber, 1945, Chapter 17).

This theory has been proved inadequate by direct measurements of the membrane potential between an electrode inside the

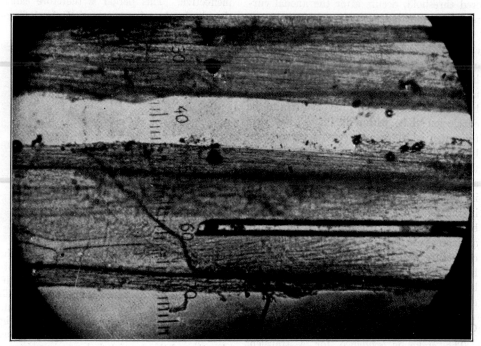

Fig. 21A. Microphotograph of the tip of a fluid-filled glass pipette that acts as an electrical connection to the inside of the axon. Upper view, at right angles to lower, was obtained by reflection from a mirror. The needle is near the center of the axon. The penetration of the needle into the fluid axoplasm does not interfere with the action potential, which depends only upon intact membrane structures. Giant fiber of the squid. Scale divisions, 25 microns. (Hodgkin and Huxley, 1945.)

salt inside the cell. This restraint on the free diffusion of the negative ion at the membrane separates it from the positive potassium ion which tends to diffuse out because of its thermal motion. The electric field created by this minute separation of charge restrains the movement of the potassium ion, and the membrane potential difference is thereby created. The action potential, according to this theory, is supposed to be a transient change in selective permeability, causing a reduction of the

squid giant axon and one on the outside surface (Fig. 21A). The resting potential was about 45 millivolts, and, when an impulse passed over the cell, the membrane potential did not just drop to a lower value, but reversed its sign and rose to 40 millivolts in the opposite direction. The action potential, about 100 millivolts, was thus almost twice the size of the resting membrane potential (Fig. 21B). The foregoing simple membrane theory is inadequate to explain this effect. According to Hodgkin, the reversal may be caused by the inward diffusion of sodium ions previously stopped by the membrane. Decreasing the external concentration of sodium ions reduces the magnitude of the reversed potential, which supports the hypothesis that the nerve

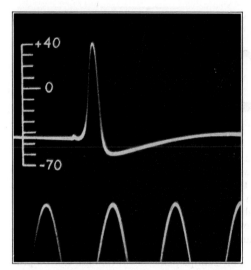

FIG. 21B. Resting potential and action potential measured across the membrane between the inside and outside of an axon, as in Fig. 21A. In the resting state the inside electrode is 45 millivolts negative relative to the outside electrode. During the action potential the inner electrode becomes 40 millivolts positive with respect to the outer one, showing that the membrane potential has been reversed. Time marks are milliseconds. (Hodgkin and Huxley, 1945.)

surface becomes permeable to sodium ions during the action potential (Hodgkin and Katz, 1949). However, an adequate theory of the potential difference across the membrane must explicitly state that the membrane contains a source of electromotive force, where chemical energy of oxidative reactions is converted ultimately into electrical energy.

Another theory (Nachmansohn, 1946) states that the depolarization is caused by the release of acetylcholine from a bound form. The supposed sequence of events is: (1) outward flow of current across the nerve membrane acts as a stimulus; (2) the release of acetylcholine is the response; (3) the free acetylcholine depolarizes the nerve and causes the sudden drop of resistance characteristic of the active area of nerve; and (4) acetylcholine is destroyed by the choline esterase, permitting repolarization of the axon. This hypothesis was originally based upon the observation that the esterase occurs in all parts of a neuron and that it is a very rapidly acting enzyme. Conceivably it could destroy free acetylcholine quickly enough for repolarization to occur during the declining phrase of the action potential. The biggest gap in the evidence for this view is the lack of a direct demonstration of the release of free acetylcholine during the development of the action potential. Furthermore acetylcholine has been shown to be a highly specific stimulator for certain types of neurons. This fact argues against its being universally utilized in the conduction process, which is common to all neurons.

The all-or-nothing character of the nerve impulse. The formulation of an adequate electrochemical explanation of the action potential in specific molecular and ionic terms consistent with the recognized lipoid and protein character of the cell structure is one of the principal problems in experimental neurology at the cellular level. But this phase of the problem may not be of great concern to the experimental psychologist at the present time. Nevertheless the fact that the nerve impulse is an electrochemical signal having the same physical character in all nerve cells presents the psychologist with an equally fundamental problem — that of understanding psychological phenomena in terms of a communication system in which the signals in the individual elements are transient changes of structure, or pulses, that can occur more or less frequently but have a relatively constant magnitude.

The last statement refers in part to the all-or-nothing character of the nerve impulse that was revealed by experiments on multifiber preparations (Adrian, 1914, 1933). The law states that the intensity of the conducted response is independent of the intensity of the stimulus by which it is initiated and depends only upon the physical state of the reacting cell.

But it must not be supposed that the all-or-nothing law precludes all changes in the magnitude of response in a particular part of the nerve cell. On the contrary, a change in the local physical state of any part of the nerve cell will produce just such an effect.

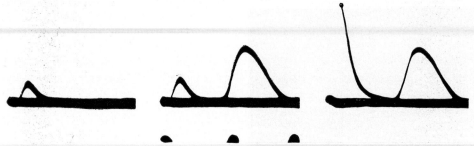

Fig. 22. The conducted action potential in a single fiber is independent of the intensity of the stimulus initiating it. First trace shows deflection produced by escape of stimulating current into the amplifier; it is called the stimulus artifact. The second stimulus was stronger and produced a conducted action potential. In the last record the stimulus was much stronger, as indicated by the height of the stimulus artifact, but the action potential was unchanged. Time in milliseconds. (C. Pfaffmann, unpublished record, Johnson Foundation, University of Pennsylvania, 1940).

If the action potential is taken as a measure of the response, the foregoing proposition is clearly demonstrated by recording the action potential of a single fiber as the strength of the stimulus is varied. For weak

For example, since such changes can be produced by previous activity, the magnitude of an action potential associated with an impulse late in a train may be quite different from that of earlier ones (Fig. 23).

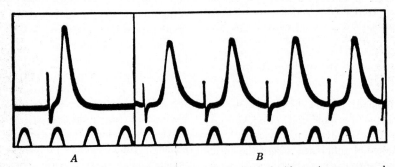

A   *B*

Fig. 23. Action potential measured between an electrode inside a giant axon and one on the outside. During repetitive response (*B*) the action potentials are smaller than for a single response (*A*) in a rested nerve. Time in milliseconds. (Hodgkin, 1938*b*.)

stimuli no conducted response occurs, whereas for stronger ones there is a conducted action potential of a magnitude independent of further increases in the strength of the stimulus (Fig. 22).

The functional significance of the intensity of response in a particular region of a cell must be measured (1) by its stimulating or inhibiting influence on adjacent cells or parts of the same cell or (2) by its associated after-effects, which may modify the action of the next incoming impulse. The response of one region of a nerve cell always brings a stimulus to bear upon other regions of the same cell or upon adjacent cells, and the intensity of the response becomes, in turn, a measure of the intensity of its stimulating action. But the stimulating effectiveness of such a decrease in the flow of electric current outward across the membrane (Fig. 24). A period of partial refractoriness is not peculiar to the conducted response, as is the absolutely refractory period, but can follow after even a subthreshold electrical stimulus. These neuronal processes, giving rise to periods of depressed excitability, are like the accommo-

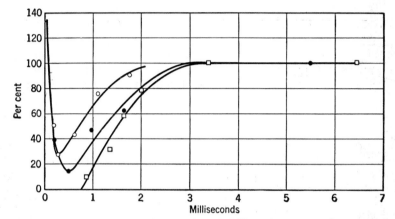

FIG. 24. There is a transient change of excitability of a nerve after a subthreshold stimulus or after a conducted impulse. The excitability is inversely related to the strength of a test shock required to initiate an action potential at various times after the conditioning stimulus. Ordinates present change of initial excitability where normal level is expressed as 100 per cent. The solid dots show the excitability of a nerve following a brief shock just below threshold; the circles are for a much weaker shock. The squares show relative refractoriness following a conducted impulse. (Erlanger and Gasser, 1937.)

response depends also upon the excitability of the part of a cell to be stimulated. Consequently the all-or-nothing character of the propagated response of a nerve does not necessarily produce an all-or-nothing stimulating effect. It can produce subthreshold states of excitation that are graded in magnitude.

The irritability cycle associated with recovery from an impulse. The irritability cycle, following an impulse is far from complete at the end of the absolutely refractory period. There follows a relatively refractory period during which a second impulse can be initiated by a strong stimulus. This relatively refractory period has been identified with the postcathodal depression, the period of reduced excitability that always follows a dation process, or nerve reaction, that occurs during the flow of current at a cathode on the nerve.

Usually the irritability cycle of an axon is even more complex because of the irritability changes associated with the after-potentials (Erlanger and Gasser, 1937). The after-potentials arise from processes in the nerve that are slow compared to the spike component of the action potential. Since they are initiated at each part of the nerve by the rapidly conducted spike, these processes begin at about the same time in rather long sections of a nerve. Therefore considerable lengths of the axon are in about the same phase of the after-potential at the same time. These slow after-potentials are significant as electrical signs of changes in the membrane that modify its excitability.

The negative after-potential is associated with a period of increased excitability called the supernormal period (Fig. 25). The excitability is reduced during the subsequent positive after-potentials. Such correlations between changes of membrane potential and

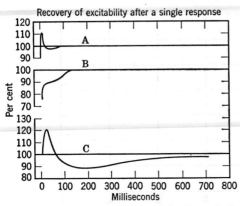

FIG. 25. Excitability curves of A-, B-, and C-fibers. During the negative after-potential the fibers have supernormal excitability, and during the subsequent positive potential there is subnormal excitability. The sequence of changes in the C-fibers resembles those for the A-fibers except in duration. In keeping with the absence of negative after-potential (Fig. 13), there is no supernormal period in the B-fibers. (Gasser, 1939.)

excitability are generally found (Fig. 26). Every change in membrane potential is associated with a change of excitability, whenever the latter can be tested. The functional significance of these phenomena is that they may occur at synapses and in receptors where they may determine the summation of excitatory effects.

Repetitive activity of neurons. The first direct information about the functional properties of the single neuron was obtained by recording action potentials in the individual axon. This method of investigation has been successfully applied to nerve fibers stimulated through sensory receptors *in situ.*

Thus the physical aspects of the signals entering the central nervous system from visual sense cells (Hartline and Graham, 1932), from muscle-stretch receptors (Matthews, 1933), from sense organs for taste (Pumphrey, 1935; Pfaffmann, 1941), from pressure receptors in the carotid sinus (Bronk and Stella, 1932), and from pain fibers in the skin (Adrian, 1932) have been directly examined. Two fundamental facts are evident: (1) though the primary stimuli to the sense organs are physically different, the signals communicated to the nervous system are alike in that they consist of a train of action potentials; (2) an increase in the intensity of the stimulus is reflected in an increase in the frequency of transmission of impulses into the central nervous system, without significant change in the magnitude of the individual action potentials (Adrian, 1928; see chapters on receptors for illustrations).

Thus the signals conducted into the nervous system, as revealed by action potentials in a single axon coming from a sense organ, consist of brief pulselike electrochemical changes in the cell structure as each part responds.

When, by similar methods, the output from the central nervous system is examined, as in a single motor fiber, the signals are also found to be trains of impulses (Adrian and Bronk, 1928). By examining the degree of contraction of a single motor unit as a function of frequency, we observe that muscular response increases with the frequency of the nerve impulses driving the muscle cells. These observations reveal the fundamental importance of impulse frequency as the functionally significant measure (1) of the intensity of response and (2) of the stimulating effectiveness of activity in a single neuron.

The maximum frequency of impulses in a nerve cell measures the range of the functionally significant activity it can manifest. Measurements have shown, in general, that axons stimulated experimentally are capable of responding much more frequently than neurons that are stimulated through sense organs or across a synapse. In the living organism the axon seems to be protected by a factor of safety in the sense that it cannot be overloaded readily by stimulation through the normal channels of the nervous system.

second. However, this rate can be achieved for only very short times, because each impulse causes changes in the nerve cell which will prolong the absolutely refractory period unless sufficient time is allowed for complete recovery after each response (Field and Brücke, 1926; Bugnard and Hill, 1935).

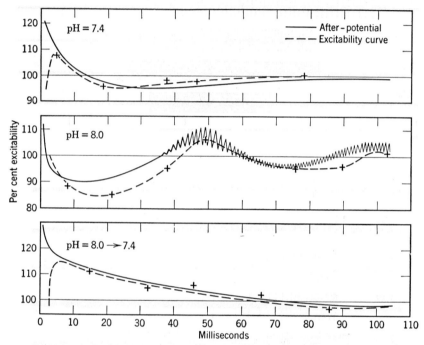

FIG. 26. The excitability of a nerve after passage of an impulse is correlated with the after-potential. Negative after-potential implies hyperexcitability, and positive after-potential implies subnormal excitability. These relations are preserved when changes in the time course are caused by changes in pH of the nerve. (Lehmann, 1937.)

The factors limiting the frequency of response of a given part of a neuron have been clearly revealed by studies on excised axons. As mentioned previously, following each conducted impulse there is a recovery period during which a second conducted impulse cannot be initiated. This absolutely refractory period measures the least interval between impulses and is approximately equal to the duration of the spike component of the action potential, about 1 millisecond in A-fibers. The upper frequency limit in motor nerves is, therefore, about 1000 impulses per

It has been observed that the absolutely refractory period can increase nine times in duration if a nerve responds at 85 impulses per second for some minutes. After termination of the activity there is a prolonged period of recovery to the original refractory period.

The cause of this lengthening refractoriness as a result of rapidly repeated impulses is not known. However, the oxygen uptake of a nerve after a single volley continues for a minute or more, and after a short burst of impulses at 100 per second the motor nerves

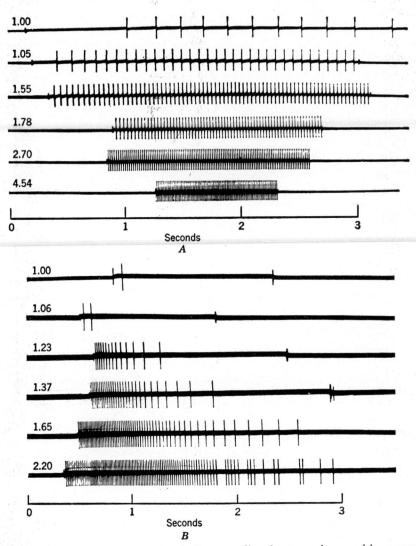

Fig. 27A. Repetitive response of a single motor fiber from a crab, caused by a constant current. The frequency of response increases with the strength of the current (proportional to numbers on curves). The onset and termination of the current is indicated by the small deflections of the baseline. The utilization time for the weakest current was almost 1 second. (Hodgkin, 1948.)

B. Some fibers accommodate to a direct current and cease responding after an interval that is longer when the current is stronger. Conditions as in A but for a different single fiber. (Hodgkin, 1948.)

of a frog have an increased oxygen uptake for as long as 45 minutes. This is evidence for long-lasting effects of previous activity and suggests that functional after-effects of activity, and limitations on rate of recovery, may be traceable to limitations on the rate of oxidation. If this is true, these functional limitations are intimately dependent upon some enzyme concentration in the cell.

Rhythmic Excitatory Processes in Axons

Because rhythmic response is a prominent characteristic of nerve-cell activity, its physi-trasts with the former notion that rhythmic response to a constant stimulus was necessarily related to highly specialized parts of the neuron or of the sense organs (Fessard, 1936; Brink, Sjöstrand, and Bronk, 1938).

Another method, based on chemical excitation, also has revealed a rhythmic excitatory process that is latent in all parts of a neuron. These methods for studying rhythmicity involve experimental conditions to which an axon is ordinarily not exposed. They must be regarded as special procedures for uncovering latent properties inherent in axon structure.

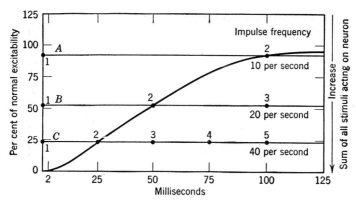

FIG. 28. The curve indicates the per cent recovery of excitability (left ordinate) as a function of time (abscissa) after a previous response. Line A indicates strength of a weak continuously acting stimulus that initiates a second impulse (2) after the nerve has almost recovered its normal excitability. For a stronger stimulus, line B, the repetition, indicated by the numbered dots, is more frequent. Thus the interval between impulses is attributed to the rate of recovery of the neuron. (Diagram by Pitts, 1946.)

cal origins have been studied extensively in isolated single axons. In the classical studies of the response of an axon to a direct current it was emphasized that a nerve responded only once when the current began. This has been proved to be an erroneous impression, and it is now recognized that repetitive response to sufficiently intense current is a reproducible characteristic of axons (Fessard, 1936; Arvanitaki, 1939; Katz, 1936; Erlanger and Blair, 1936; Hodgkin, 1948) (Fig. 27). Processes that regulate the frequency of response in its relation to the intensity of the stimulus are inherent in all parts of the axon. This revised view con-It is by analogy, supported by a few indirect experiments, that the mechanisms thus revealed are supposed to underly the rhythmic activity occurring normally in the nervous system. Indeed it should be emphasized that the axon, as the principal connector between one cell and another, is specialized so that it has a finite threshold. This insures that it does not respond to casual environmental changes but is always ready to conduct an impulse when excited through proper channels.

There are several prevailing explanations of the intervals between impulses in a train that is initiated by a constant stimulus. The first, designated the recovery-cycle hypothesis, attributes the interval between impulses to the time course of the relatively refractory

Thus a weak stimulus would excite late in the relatively refractory period, and the interval between responses would be long. A

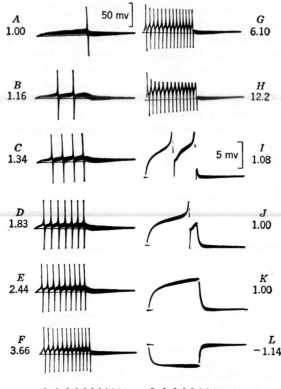

Fɪɢ. 29. Responses of a single motor nerve of a crab to direct current of different intensities, given by the numbers on each record. *A:* A single action potential occurs after a utilization time of about 0.1 second. During this time there was a slow local depolarization, indicated by the heavy trace. *B:* A stronger current initiates an impulse after a shorter utilization time, and this is followed by a second impulse. The slow depolarization develops to a critical degree as a preliminary process preceding each impulse. The frequency of impulses is determined by the rate of development of this local electrical response.

The development of the slow component of the local depolarization is shown clearly by the higher amplification in records *I* and *J*. This slow component of depolarization occurs only at the cathode (record *K*) and not at the anode (record *L*). (Hodgkin, 1948.)

period (Adrian, 1930). In this explanation it is supposed that a given intensity of stimulus creates a constant degree of excitation in the axon and that a second response occurs as soon as the nerve recovers sufficiently from the effects of the first response.

strong stimulus would excite at the beginning of the relatively refractory period, and the interval between responses would be short (Fig. 28). The upper limit of frequency would be that corresponding to an interval between impulses that is equal to the absolute refractory period. In order to account for the long intervals observed in naturally occurring trains of impulses it would be necessary to attribute extremely prolonged relatively refractory periods to the regions of the cell in which the impulses originate.

A second explanation attributes the rate at which impulses recur to the periodic character of the excitatory process. One version of this explanation is based upon the observation that in some axons the depolarizing action of a direct current develops progressively after each response at a rate determined by the strength of the stimulating current. It is observed that this depolarization must proceed to a critical level in order to excite. Thus the interval between impulses is the time required for the imposed current to recreate the critical degree of depolarization (Fig. 29; Hodgkin, 1948).

For this mechanism to operate in the nervous system it would be necessary for direct currents to be created that lasted as long as the observed trains of impulses. No such prolonged steady current flow in the region of the sense organs has been correlated with the duration of the train of impulses. Thus the retinal potential in a *Limulus* eye rapidly falls off to very low values, despite the continuation of the train of impulses in the optic nerve (Hartline, 1948).

Direct-current flow in some axons can cause repetitive responses by a somewhat different mechanism. The local electrical response previously described can become oscillatory under some conditions (Arvanitaki, 1939). Then successive impulses may arise at intervals determined by the successive negative peaks of this local potential change. This kind of rhythmic response may occur as a result of a constant current flow (Fig. 30) or as an after-effect of an impulse started by a single electric shock. Therefore, if a stimulus initiates the first impulse in a train, the temporal pattern of the successive impulses may be determined by this oscillatory local response. Studies of chemical excitation of single axons have shown

that such oscillatory local electric responses can develop merely as the result of a modified chemical environment (Brink and Bronk, 1941). An imposed external current is not a necessary part of this mechanism, nor is the process a part of the recovery cycle of a previous action potential.

In the giant axon of the squid this process of self-excitation is revealed by the local electrical response recorded as a difference of potential between the chemically modified

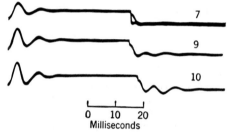

FIG. 30. Damped rhythmic variations of membrane potential at onset and termination of a subthreshold constant current. Recorded from the cathodal region, giant fiber of squid. Relative strength of current given by numbers on records. (Arvanitaki, 1939.)

region of the axon and the adjacent normal areas. The self-excitation is developed by internal processes as a result of the removal of calcium from a part of the axon. The calcium-deficient area first becomes hyperexcitable to electric currents (Fig. 31). When the threshold is very low there is developed a rhythmic local electrical response at high frequency. The amplitude increases, with a small decrease in frequency, until conducted action potentials are developed near the negative peaks of these local electrical responses (Fig. 32). The intervals between the conducted impulses are determined by the intervals between the peaks of the local electrical response.

When the stimulating effectiveness of a local response is below a certain critical value, a conducted action potential does not occur for each wave of the local response. If an action potential occurs for every other wave of the local response, the interval between successive impulses is twice the least interval. Other multiples of the least interval occur

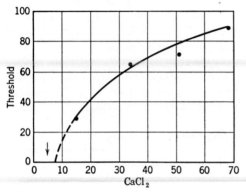

Fig. 31. The strength of current required to excite an isolated giant axon of the squid is less, the lower the concentration of calcium chloride in the fluid bathing the axon. Ordinate: threshold strength of direct current, or rheobase, as per cent of threshold of nerve in seawater. Abscissa: concentration of calcium chloride in millimoles per liter. The arrow indicates concentration at which spontaneous activity began. (Brink, Bronk, and Larrabee, 1946.)

as a result (1) of decreasing intensity of the local response and (2) of changes in the sensitivity of adjacent areas of axon to which depolarization must spread if conduction is to occur. The long intervals between im-

pulses in a train are thus multiples of the least interval and are due to changes in the stimulating effectiveness of the rhythmic excitatory process (Fig. 33).

Since the frequency-determining process is evident before the first conducted impulse occurs, it cannot be attributed to the after-effect of a previous response. Indeed, the rhythmic local response can exist for long periods of time without initiating an impulse. These local responses can be recorded electrically or their presence detected as a random fluctuation in excitability to test shocks.

Areas of frog axons deficient in calcium also develop trains of conducted impulses. Attempts to record local electrical oscillations at the origin of the impulses have not been successful. Furthermore the activity can occur without any constant potential difference between the treated and the normal regions of the axon. There is thus no direct current acting, as in the second mechanism of rhythmicity.

The properties of the periodic processes in axons of the frog can be deduced from a statistical analysis of the intervals between the recorded action potentials (Brink, Bronk, and Larrabee, 1946). The successive intervals in a long train of impulses in a single fiber are measured (Fig. 34). Then the frequency of occurrence of each interval is plotted as a function of the duration of the

Fig. 32. Local electrical response, recorded from a chemically excited region of the giant axon of a squid, is oscillatory and precedes the conducted impulses. The last ten oscillations on the right of the record initiated propagated impulses which were much larger in amplitude than shown. Stimulation was by topical application of isotonic sodium chloride. The frequency of the local oscillations is about 350 per second. (Brink and Bronk, 1941.)

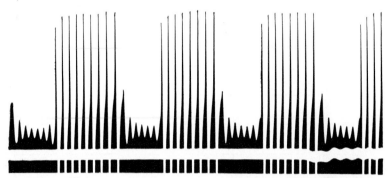

FIG. 33. The amplitude of the local electrical response in a giant axon (squid) deficient in calcium waxes and wanes spontaneously. During the period of increasing amplitude a series of diphasic impulses is initiated. Finally these action potentials cease, even though the local response remains large. Presumably refractoriness developed by nine action potentials makes the large local response ineffective. The frequency of the action potentials is clearly determined by that of the local response, and the long intervals between groups are multiples of the period of the local excitatory process. (Brink and Bronk, unpublished records, 1939.)

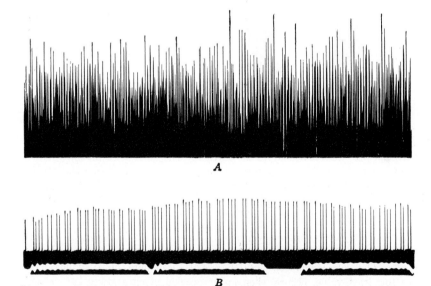

A

B

FIG. 34*A*. Impulses recorded from a branch of the sciatic nerve of a frog stimulated by topical application of isotonic sodium citrate. *B*. Impulses recorded from single fiber dissected from this nerve. (In the original record these spikes were all the same size.) Time in ⅕-second intervals. (Brink, Bronk, and Larrabee, 1946.)

interval. In this way it is observed that certain intervals occur much more frequently than others, as shown in Fig. 35. These peak values are multiples of the set of least intervals thus measured. Accordingly we may assume that the set of least intervals measures occurrence of a conducted impulse per cycle. Furthermore this excitatory process has a variable intensity, which may decrease to subthreshold value, without significant change in the rhythm of the process.

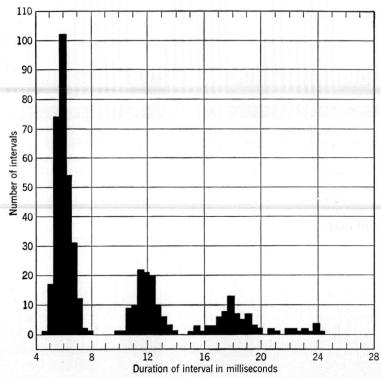

Fig. 35. The frequency of occurrence of intervals between impulses in a train (as in Fig. 34B) having values indicated on the abscissa. The set of least intervals measures the period of the rhythmic excitatory process initiating these impulses. The other sets of intervals are approximately two and three times as long as the most probable value of the least interval. Stimulation was by topical application of sodium citrate. Intervals longer than 24 milliseconds not shown. (Brink, Bronk, and Larrabee, 1946.)

assume that the set of least intervals measures the average period of a rhythmic excitatory process. The next longer set of intervals, twice this least value, occurs when an intervening cycle of the excitatory process fails to initiate an impulse. A similar explanation applies to the higher multiples of the least interval.

From these data it is concluded that in the frog, as in the squid, the rhythmic excitatory process exists independently of the

By a similar analysis of the discharge of impulses from single receptor organs, the existence there of a similar mechanism is revealed. Such a study has been made on a Pacinian corpuscle excited by constant pressure (Scott, 1948). The measured intervals in the train of impulses are distributed about multiples of a basic value, in a manner similar to that just reported (Fig. 36). Therefore in the Pacinian corpuscle there seems to be a rhythmic excitatory process that determines the frequency of the impulses sent into the nervous system from this receptor. The

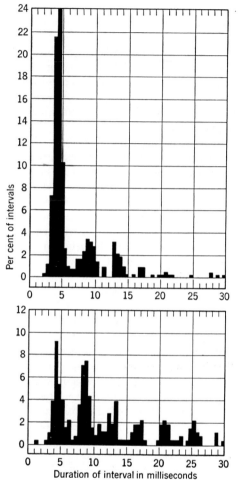

FIG. 36. The average number of impulses per second from a Pacinian corpuscle, stimulated by pressure, increases without any change in the period of the rhythmic excitatory process regulating the intervals between impulses. Records were analyzed as in Figs. 35 and 37 for chemical excitation of isolated axons. (D. Scott, Jr., unpublished records, Johnson Foundation, University of Pennsylvania, 1948.)

study has not been extended to other receptors, although published records of response of nerves in taste buds in a frog's tongue (Pfaffmann, 1941) strongly suggest its presence there.

The existence of a periodic excitatory process makes it necessary to distinguish two characteristic frequencies of neuronal action. The rhythm of the excitatory process seems to be a relatively fixed characteristic, related, perhaps, to the specific structure of the nerve. On the other hand, the average number of conducted impulses per second varies widely in response to the strength of the imposed stimulation. It is significant to note, then, that the average number of impulses per unit time can change without a change in the average period of the excitatory process (Fig. 37). As previously mentioned, this is possible because only those cycles of the local response that are of sufficient intensity can initiate conducted impulses. The intensity of the stimulus determines the average amplitude per cycle of this rhythmic excitatory process. The average amplitude, in turn, determines the average number of conducted impulses per second. Thus there is revealed in some detail one mechanism by which the average frequency of impulses in a neuron is determined by the intensity of the stimulus.

Origin of rhythmic processes in axons. The rhythmic properties of axons are inherent in the axon structure, as revealed by reactions to current flow. When a current penetrates the nerve membrane, there is a translation and redistribution of the charged molecules that would occur at any interface between dissimilar electrolytic conductors. A distinguishing characteristic of the living nerve cell is its tendency to oppose the disturbing effects upon its structure of the electric fields imposed upon it. There are, at present, two general views regarding the interpretation of the physical phenomena associated with the flow of subthreshold currents. It is generally agreed that the membrane can conduct electricity, and this property can be represented, for purposes of analysis, as an electrical resistance. Furthermore ions can accumulate at interfaces in a way that simulates the

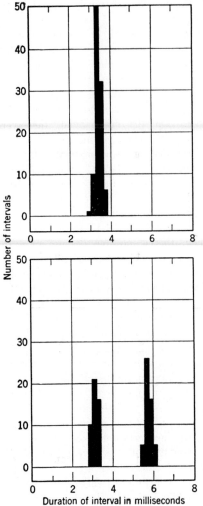

Fig. 37. The average number of impulses in a single fiber (frog) can be markedly increased without much change in the fundamental period. Lower: frequency of occurrence of intervals having values indicated on the abscissa. Stimulation by topical application of a solution containing sodium citrate. The average number of conducted impulses per second was about 220. Upper: similar analysis of a consecutive series of impulses recorded at height of increased response evoked by cathodal polarization of chemically treated region. The average number per second of conducted impulses was about 305. (Brink, Bronk, and Larrabee, 1946.)

charging of a condenser. Therefore the establishment of a current through the membrane will be opposed by changes of membrane potential, related to the charging of the condenser, and there will be leakage of this charge through the membrane resistance. On the other hand, when the membrane structure is disturbed by a varying electric current, there is evidence of opposition to changes in current that are not accounted for by a passive circuit containing only capacitance and resistance.

In pursuing the physical analysis of these phenomena, one group of investigators has described the results in terms of an inductive element in the membrane (Cole and Baker, 1941). In this representation certain aspects of the opposition of the membrane to changes in membrane current are attributed to a structural element (an inductance) of an equivalent electric circuit. However, in analyzing similar reactions of nerve to electric currents, other investigators have emphasized the importance of the membrane electromotive force (Lorente de Nó, 1947). According to this hypothesis, flow of current of any magnitude calls forth a nerve reaction that is a modification of the membrane electromotive force. This view emphasizes the importance of the electromotive force in opposing current flow and thus links the oscillatory phenomena to metabolic processes; i.e. it directs attention to the energy sources within the nerve.

Obviously the foregoing studies reveal important aspects of axon structure. But what is their functional significance in neuron activity? Their importance is that they offer alternative physical explanations of the origin of the rhythmic character of nervous activity. As discussed, the temporal pattern of impulses in a neuron is traceable in some instances to a rhythmic process of excitation. This rhythmic process can be called forth by a current imposed on the nerve, or by a chemical modification of the nerve. In the latter case the oscillatory changes in membrane potential are entirely due to current flow from sources of electrical energy inside the cell. But the rhythm itself could be imposed in at least two ways.

First, a cellular source of constant electromotive force could cause oscillations in membrane potential by discharging through a membrane structure that behaved like a circuit composed of capacity, resistance, and inductance. According to this view the frequency of the self-excitation process, revealed by removal of calcium from a squid axon, should be predictable from impedance measurements across the nerve membrane made with alternating current. Indeed, the undamped natural frequency of the membrane circuit as measured by Cole and Baker (1941) is about equal to the observed frequency of the oscillatory local response initiated by chemical means (Brink, Bronk, and Larrabee, 1946).

The second interpretation emphasizes the labile character of the electromotive force in the membrane. It states that rhythmic activity is a resultant of an interplay between the changes in membrane potential caused by passive polarization and the active changes in membrane electromotive force elicited thereby (Lorente de Nó, 1947). The latter view brings to the fore the chemical reactions underlying the electromotive force of the nerve cell. Future studies of the kinetics of these metabolic events in relation to changes in membrane potential may lead to a rephrasing of these hypotheses by interpreting the "inductive" element as a convenient symbol for the overall electrical aspect of the nerve reaction to current flow.

Source of Energy in Neurons

Like other living cells, the nerve cell is an assemblage of molecules maintained in an organized state by the continual transformation of energy normally derived from oxidative reactions. There are no significant properties of the nerve cell that have the permanence associated with a system of molecules in thermodynamic equilibrium. On the contrary, when the nerve cell ceases to dissipate oxidative energy it loses its function and its electrical properties. The cell is restored to its original state when the oxidative reactions begin again. Therefore the structures underlying the electrical properties of nerve and its excitability are the resultant of opposing processes, leading on the one hand to disorganization, and on the other to an ordered arrangement of the cellular constituents. A molecular system maintained in a relatively constant state of organization by the continuous flux of matter and transformation of energy is defined as a steady-state system.

These ideas focus attention upon the organized metabolic processes of nerve which, like those of other living cells, depend upon an orderly sequence of chemical reactions controlled by enzymes. This sequence of molecular transformations of glucose and other metabolites into their final products provides the continuous production of energy used to maintain the organized state of the cell. Underlying these material transformations is a set of molecules, the enzymes, which may be regarded as a relatively stable aspect of the cell structure. For example, this enzyme structure persists during anoxia, as evidenced by the prompt restoration of the metabolic reactions when oxygen is restored. The oxidative enzymes are not static entities, however, but operate in cycles, being first oxidized and then reduced.

The enzymes are not uniformly distributed through the cell structure (Nachmansohn, 1946). In the giant axon of the squid the oxidative enzymes are located in the cytoplasm. Other enzymes, such as choline esterase, are found only in the sheath. The experimental separation of the sites of specific chemical reactions was possible in this single cell because the fluid cytoplasm, though highly viscous, can be made to flow out, leaving the sheath structures (Fig. 2). This spatial arrangement of specific enzymes suggests that molecules produced by oxidative metabolism affect the electrical properties of the membrane by diffusing there from some other cytoplasmic region. These observations are the beginnings of the experimental demonstration of a spatial distribution of sites for specific chemical reactions related to the specialized functions of neurons.

The cycle of change in structure associated with the action potential can take place many times without the immediate use of

tion of molecules in this energy reservoir, and the rate of oxygen utilization that are mutually self-regulating. For example, a series of action potentials can reduce the amount of creatine phosphate in a nerve. In the presence of oxygen this is restored by phosphorylations that are associated with in-

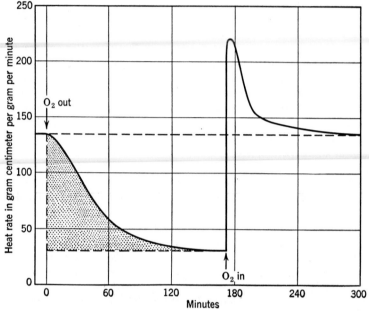

FIG. 38. The heat production of a nerve continues for some time after oxygen consumption is terminated. There is a greater than normal rate of heat production for some time after oxygen is again supplied. (After Beresina, 1932, modified from Feng, 1936.)

oxygen, apparently at the expense of energy stored in specific molecules by previous oxidations. The energy dissipated by the nerve impulse is thus derived from a reservoir that, in turn, is refilled by oxidation reactions. It is thought, at present, that creatine phosphate and adenosine triphosphate represent these energy stores. The supposition is that the hydrolysis of these molecules, releasing 10,000 calories of energy per mole, is somehow used to maintain the membrane potential difference (cf. Shanes and Brown, 1942).

There are connections between the structural changes during activity, the concentra-

creased velocity of oxidative reactions (Gerard, 1932).

Oxygen requirements at rest. An isolated nerve at rest uses oxygen at a constant rate, determined in part by the chemical constitution of the solution bathing it. There is also a constant output of carbon dioxide (Tashiro, 1917; Gerard, 1932). This steady flux of chemical change is correlated with a constant rate of heat production (Feng, 1936) Most of the heat production of a resting nerve is dependent upon a continuous supply of oxygen (Fig. 38). These are the essential facts that suggest that the oxidative metabolism of a resting nerve is in a steady state.

The rate of oxidative metabolism is different in the various types of nerves and does not seem to be directly correlated with the rates of other nerve processes. For example, the motor nerves of a crab have a high resting respiration compared with frog nerves, but the conduction velocity and the capacity for sustained repetitive activity are less in the nerves of the crab than in those of the frog. Furthermore the resting respiration of frog sciatic nerves can vary widely from one preparation to the next without corresponding variation of functional properties.

Since the rate of oxidation in nerve is regulated by enzymes, any modification of the effective enzyme concentration changes the rate of oxidation. Thus sodium azide progressively reduces the rate of respiration of a resting nerve. It is probable that the affected enzyme is cytochrome oxidase. Chloretone and some other narcotics also reduce the oxidation rate. These studies show that the resting respiration may be slowed as much as 30 per cent without rendering the nerve inexcitable. However, further slowing of the oxidative processes, as by anoxia or strong azide solution, will suppress all function.

The action of many chemical agents upon the properties of nerve cells can be traced to interference by the substance with some one of the numerous enzymes. For example, the time course of changes of excitability under the action of strong azide solutions is similar to that following the removal of oxygen. In this instance the sequence of events seems to be (1) slowed metabolism, (2) modification of essential structures, (3) loss of function. As in anoxia, a nerve poisoned with azide can continue to respond to stimuli for about an hour. This time may represent that required to use molecules previously prepared by the oxidative metabolism. However, not all chemical agents affecting the nervous system do so by impeding oxidative metabolism. Some, like cocaine, make a nerve inexcitable without modifying oxygen uptake. Others, like potassium chloride, can make a nerve inexcitable at concentrations that actually increase the oxygen metabolism (Fig. 39).

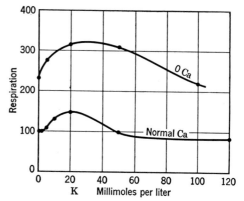

FIG. 39. The rate of oxygen uptake by a nerve depends on the ionic content of the solutions bathing the nerve. The rate of respiration is always higher in the absence of calcium ions (upper curve) in the bathing fluid than it is in Ringer's solution. Small increments in potassium (K) concentration increase the respiration above that in Ringer's solution, but greater increases depress the respiration. In each test the nerve (frog) was exposed to the test solution for 30 minutes or less, and the respiration seemed to have reached a relatively constant rate. At concentrations above 10 millimolar the nerve is inexcitable at this time. (Bronk, Brink, and Davies, 1941.)

The rate of respiration in a resting nerve is regulated also by the concentration of ionized calcium in the fluid bathing it. As previously mentioned, this normal constituent of body fluids affects the excitability of nerves. Thus the threshold value of electrical current decreases with a decrease in concentration of ionized calcium. Over the same range of concentration there has been measured, in frog nerve, an increase in oxygen uptake (Fig. 40). However, there is no general correlation between rate of respiration and threshold.

The rate of oxygen utilization in a resting nerve thus serves to maintain structural re-

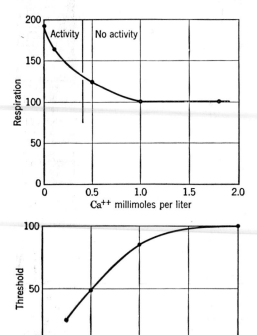

FIG. 40. The rate of respiration (as per cent of value in Ringer's fluid) of a frog sciatic nerve increases when the concentration of calcium chloride in the bathing fluid is below 1.0 millimolar. There is an appreciable increase at a concentration that is not low enough to initiate impulses. Lower figure: The excitability of a nerve to electric current depends upon the concentration of calcium ions in the bathing fluid. The changes in threshold occur over the same range of calcium concentrations as do the changes in oxygen uptake. Threshold of α-fibers of sciatic nerve of frog as per cent of rheobase of nerve in Ringer's fluid. Concentrations in millimoles per liter. (Brink, Bronk, and Larrabee, 1946.)

lations in the nerve that are essential to function. The progressive loss during anoxia of the potential difference across the membrane, and its restoration in a few minutes after restitution of oxygen, are the most direct evidence of this fundamental relation of oxidative rate to the functional state of the nerve membrane (Fig. 41). It has been assumed that the delayed loss of function and of polarization during anoxia is, in part, due to the continuation of energy-yielding reactions in the anoxic nerve. The prolonged decay of heat production (cf. Fig. 38) supports this view. One of the most obscure aspects of neuronal physiology is the molecular mechanism through which oxidative reactions are used to maintain the functional properties of nerves.

Relation of Metabolism to Structure and Function in Neurons

The nerve cell has often been discussed as though the significant properties were located in a membrane at the surface and as though the role of metabolism was to maintain and restore these structures after a period of activity. An alternative view would be that the oxidative metabolism is directly and concomitantly concerned in the phenomena of excitation and conduction. A significant adjustment of our views on this matter has been made possible recently. Many years ago Thörner (1922) discovered that anodal polarization of a length of nerve by an imposed current could delay the loss of excitability during anoxia. This was important evidence for the ability of an inwardly directed current to maintain the excitable structures despite the absence of oxidative metabolism. This initial observation has been remarkably extended in significance through the recent studies by Lorente de Nó (1947). He has demonstrated that a nerve depolarized by the use of metabolic inhibitors, and also made anoxic, can be repolarized by a current flowing inward across the nerve membrane (Fig. 42). When the repolarization is of sufficient magnitude, the repolarized part of the nerve can conduct trains of impulses, even at high frequencies. This restoration of function in the absence of oxidative metabolism has shown that an excitable structure can be formed, provided the potential difference across the membrane is of the correct direction and magnitude. The molecular elements of the structure must

concerned with establishing and maintaining the normal potential difference across the membrane.

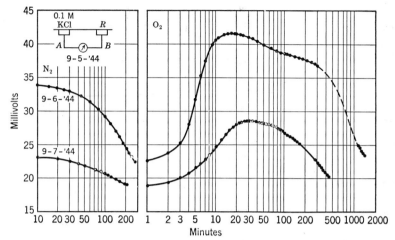

Fig. 41. The membrane potential slowly decreases in the absence of oxygen and is restored when oxygen is again supplied. Compare time course of changes with that of anoxic heat production (Fig. 38). One end of the nerve, electrode A, was previously depolarized by KCl to produce the initial demarcation potential. The other electrode, B, made contact with an area of nerve bathed in Ringer's fluid (R). N_2 indicates that the nerve was in nitrogen, and O_2 indicates that the nerve was in oxygen. The rate of depolarization and recovery was somewhat different in the two successive tests on the same nerve. Second test 24 hours after end of first period of anoxia. (Lorente de Nó, 1947.)

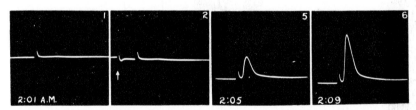

Fig. 42. A nerve depolarized by anoxia can be repolarized at an anode by an imposed current from an external source, and can produce an action potential as shown in record 5. As the repolarization progresses, the number of active fibers is increased, as shown by the larger compound action potentials in record 6. The height of the baseline in record 1 measures the resting membrane potential of the depolarized anoxic nerve. The arrow in record 2 indicates onset of anodal polarization. There is no action potential following the stimulus artifact at this time. Four minutes later, in record 5, the lowered baseline indicates marked repolarization. (Lorente de Nó, 1947.)

exist for a time in the absence of internal sources of energy. Presumably they are organized by the electric field of force existing in the polarized membrane. On the other hand, the oxidative metabolism is directly

This experiment suggests that there are at least two distinct, but coordinated, membrane structures. One is involved in maintaining the membrane potential difference by converting chemical energy into an electrical energy, as previously suggested. The other, only indirectly related to oxidative metabolism, is a molecular organization in the membrane that is imposed by the electric field

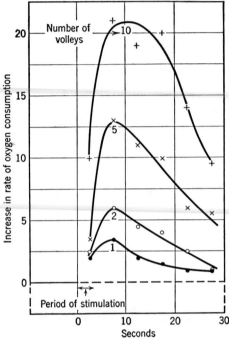

FIG. 43. The oxygen utilization of the leg nerve of a crab increases after a period of activity. The maximum rate is reached about 8 seconds after a single volley of impulses (lower curve). The maximum rate is higher, the greater the number of volleys produced during the indicated period of stimulation. Numbers on the curves give the number of volleys of impulses. The increase in rate above the resting level was measured by means of an oxygen electrode pressed against the nerve. (Unpublished research by C. M. Connelly, Johnson Foundation, University of Pennsylvania, 1948.)

across the membrane. The latter is the metastable structure whose cycle of change constitutes the nerve impulse. Thus the convenient distinction between the functional and metabolic aspects of nerve processes has experimental justification. The connecting link between the two aspects is the structure in

the nerve membrane that gives it the properties of a battery, i.e. an electromotive force generated from oxidative energy.

Increased oxygen requirements during activity. For a period of time after a nerve has conducted an action potential, the oxygen uptake is increased. In the leg nerve of a crab this increase is large enough to be detected after a single volley of impulses (Fig. 43). In the sciatic nerve of a frog repeated volleys are needed in order that the small amounts of extra oxygen required

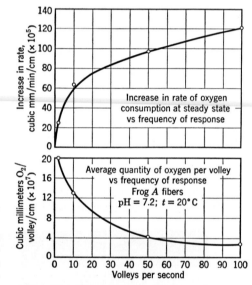

FIG. 44. The steady-state rate of oxygen consumption of an active frog nerve increases with the frequency of the conducted impulses but finally reaches a maximum rate. The average quantity of oxygen per volley of impulses decreases over this same frequency range. (Brink, Carlson, and Bronk, unpublished, 1947.) More recent experiments have indicated a more gradual rise in the rate, over the lower frequency range.

be measurable. When a nerve is excited at a constant frequency, the respiration changes to a new constant rate that is greater than that of the resting nerve. The higher the frequency of response, the higher this steady-state rate of respiration. However, at some upper frequency, usually about 100 per second for frog nerve, the increase in respiration reaches a maximum value (Fig. 44). This limitation on the maximum possible increase in respiration during activity is probably imposed by the limited concentration of enzymes within the fibers.

The increased metabolism of an active nerve is also revealed by the increased output of heat, during and after a period of

changes in the neuron last longer than any hitherto reported changes in the electrical properties. Even the prolonged positive after-potential is over in about one-half hour. However, repetitive activity lengthens the absolutely refractory period; i.e. the rate of recovery after an impulse is slowed. This slowed rate of recovery from a test impulse persists for many minutes after a series of impulses has been conducted along a frog

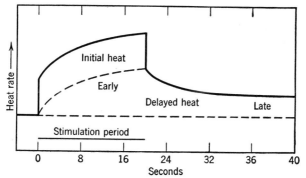

Fig. 45. The rate of heat production increases when a nerve is stimulated. At the end of stimulation there is an abrupt change in this increased rate. Thus an initial heat associated with the actual period of activity is distinguished from a delayed heat. The latter builds up during the activity (the early phase) and decays slowly after the activity stops (the late phase of the delayed heat). (After Hill, modified from Feng, 1936.)

activity (Fig. 45). Obviously the electrochemical events in the membrane of a nerve can, in turn, cause an increase in the rates of certain chemical reactions in the nerve.

This extra respiration is probably utilized to reverse the structural changes associated with the nerve impulses. However, under the action of sodium azide (10^{-4} molar) this extra respiration of activity is suppressed in frog axons for many hours with no interference with the ability to respond repetitively nor with the resting rate of oxygen utilization. Therefore, the relation of the extra respiration associated with activity to the capacity for sustained function is not clear at present.

Long-lasting metabolic effects of activity. After a short period of repetitive activity the respiration of frog nerve is increased for as long as three-quarters of an hour. These

nerve. Thus the longest known after-effects of activity in isolated nerves are increased rate of oxidation and decreased rate of recovery from a test response. Such persistent physical changes are potentially significant for long-lasting functional changes produced by activity in the intact nervous system.

REFERENCES

Adrian, E. D. The all-or-none principle in nerve. *J. Physiol.*, 1914, **47**, 450–474.

Adrian, E. D. *The basis of sensation.* London: Christophers, 1928.

Adrian, E. D. The effects of injury on mammalian nerve fibers. *Proc. roy. Soc.*, 1930, **B106**, 596.

Adrian, E. D. The mechanism of nervous action. Johnson Foundation Lectures, University of Pennsylvania, 1932.

Adrian, E. D. The all-or-nothing reaction. *Ergebn. Physiol.*, 1933, **35**, 744–755.

Adrian, E. D., and D. W. Bronk. The discharge of impulses in motor nerve fibers. Part I. *J. Physiol.*, 1928, **66**, 81.

Adrian, E. D., and Y. Zotterman. The impulses produced by sensory nerve-endings. Part II. The response of a single end-organ. *J. Psysiol.*, 1926, **61**, 151.

Arvanitaki, A. *Les variations graduées de la polarisation des systèmes excitables*. Paris: Herman, 1938.

Arvanitaki, A. Recherches sur la réponse oscillatoire locale de l'axone géant isolé de Sepia. *Arch. int. Physiol.*, 1939, **49**, 209–255.

Bartlett, J. H. Comparison of transients in inorganic systems with those in plant and nerve cells. *J. cell. comp. Physiol.*, 1948, **32**, 1.

Bear, R. S., and F. O. Schmitt. Optical properties of axon sheaths of crustacean nerves. *J. cell. comp. Physiol.*, 1936–37, **9**, 275.

Bear, R. S., F. O. Schmitt, and J. Z. Young. The sheath components of the giant nerve fibers of the squid. *Proc. roy. Soc.*, 1937a, **B123**, 496.

Bear, R. S., F. O. Schmitt, and J. Z. Young. The ultrastructure of nerve axoplasm. *Proc. roy. Soc.*, 1937b, **B123**, 496.

Bernstein, J. Die Fortpflanzungsgeschwindigkeit der negativen Schwankung in Nerven. *Zbl. med. Wiss.*, 1866, p. 597.

Bernstein, J. *Electrobiologie*. Braunschweig: Vieweg, 1912. Chapter 3.

Bishop, G. H. Relation between the threshold of nerve response and polarization by galvanic current stimuli. *Amer. J. Physiol.*, 1928, **84**, 417.

Blair, E. A., and J. Erlanger. On the process of excitation by brief shocks in axons. *Amer. J. Physiol.*, 1936a, **114**, 309.

Blair, E. A., and J. Erlanger. On excitation and depression in axons at the cathode of the constant current. *Amer. J. Physiol.*, 1936b, **114**, 317.

Bonhoeffer, K. F. Activation of passive iron as a model for the excitation of nerve. *J. gen. Physiol.*, 1948, **32**, 69.

Brink, F., and D. W. Bronk. Chemical initiation of rhythmic local responses in nerve preceding trains of propagated impulses. *Amer. J. Physiol.*, 1941, **133**, 222.

Brink, F., D. W. Bronk, and M. G. Larrabee. Chemical excitation of nerve. *Ann. N. Y. Acad. Sci.*, 1946, **47**, 457–485.

Brink, F., T. Sjöstrand, and D. W. Bronk. Chemically induced rhythmicity in peripheral axons. *Amer. J. Physiol.*, 1938, **123**, 22.

Bronk, D. W., F. Brink, and P. W. Davies. Chemical control of respiration and activity in peripheral nerve. *Amer. J. Physiol.*, 1941, **133**, 225.

Bronk, D. W., and G. Stella. Afferent impulses in the carotid sinus nerve. I. The relation of the discharge from single end organs to arterial blood pressure. *J. cell. comp. Physiol.*, 1932, **1**, 113.

Bugnard, L., and A. V. Hill. The effect of frequency of excitation on the total electric response of medullated nerve. *J. Physiol.*, 1935, **83**, 394.

Chinn, Priscilla. Polarization optical studies of the structure of nerve cells. *J. cell. comp. Physiol.*, 1938, **12**, 1.

Chinn, Priscilla, and F. O. Schmitt. On the birefringence of nerve sheaths as studied in cross sections. *J. cell. comp. Physiol.*, 1936–37, **9**, 289.

Cole, K. S. Permeability and impermeability of cell membranes for ions. *Cold Spr. Harb. Sympos. Quant. Biol.*, 1940, **8**.

Cole, K. S. Rectification and inductance in the squid giant axon. *J. gen. Physiol.*, 1941–42, **25**, 29.

Cole, K. S., and R. F. Baker. Longitudinal impedance of the squid giant axon. *J. gen. Physiol.*, 1941, **24** 771.

Cole, K. S., and H. J. Curtis. Electrical impedance of the squid giant axon during activity. *J. gen. Physiol.*, 1938–39, **22**, 649–670.

Curtis, H. J., and K. S. Cole. Membrane resting and action potentials from the squid giant axon. *J. cell. comp. Physiol.*, 1942, **19**, 135–144.

Erlanger, J., and E. A. Blair. The irritability changes in nerve in response to subthreshold induction shocks and related phenomena including the relatively refractory period. *Amer. J. Physiol.*, 1931a, **99**, 108.

Erlanger, J., and E. A. Blair. The irritability changes in nerve in response to subthreshold constant currents, and related phenomena. *Amer. J. Physiol.*, 1931b, **99**, 129–155.

Erlanger, J., and E. A. Blair. Observations on repetitive responses in axons. *Amer. J. Physiol.*, 1936, **114**, 328.

Erlanger, J., and H. S. Gasser. *Electrical signs of nervous activity*. Philadelphia: University of Pennsylvania Press, 1937.

Feng, T. P. The heat production of nerve. *Ergebn. Physiol.*, 1936, **38**, 73.

Fessard, A. *L'activité rythmique des nerfs isolés*. Paris: Herman, 1936.

Field, H., and E. T. Brücke. Prolongation of refractory period. *Pflüg. Arch. ges. Physiol.*, 1926, **214**, 103.

Fries, B. A., H. Schachner, and I. L. Chaikoff. The *in vitro* formation of phospholipid by brain and nerve with radioactive phosphorus as indicator. *J. biol. Chem.*, 1942, **144**, 59.

Gasser, H. S. Electrical signs of biological activity. *J. appl. Physics*, 1938, **9**, 88–96.

Gasser, H. S. Axons as samples of nervous tissue. *J. Neurophysiol.*, 1939, **2**, 361.

Gasser, H. S. The classification of nerve fibers. *Ohio J. Sci.*, 1941, **41**, 145.

Gerard, R. W. Studies on nerve metabolism. I. The influence of oxygen lack on heat production and action current. *J. Physiol.*, 1927, **63**, 280.

Gerard, R. W. Nerve metabolism. *Physiol. Rev.*, 1932, **12**, 469.

Grundfest, H. Bioelectric potentials. *Amer. Rev. Physiol.*, 1940, **2**, 213–242.

Hartline, H. K. Retinal action potentials of photoreceptor cells and the discharge of nerve impulses in their axons. *Amer. J. Physiol.,* 1948, Proc.

Hartline, H. K., and C. H. Graham. Nerve impulses from single receptors in the eye. *J. cell. comp. Physiol.,* 1932, **1,** 277.

Helmholtz, H. von. *Müllers Archiv,* 1852. Page 330.

Hill, A. V. Excitation and accommodation in nerve. *Proc. roy. Soc.,* 1936, **B119,** 305–355.

Höber, R. *Physical chemistry of cells and tissues.* Philadelphia : Blakiston, 1945.

Höber, R. The membrane theory. *Ann. N. Y. Acad. Sci.,* 1946, **47,** 381–394.

Hodgkin, A. L. Evidence for electrical transmission in nerve. Part I. *J. Physiol.,* 1937, **90,** 183–210. Part II. *J. Physiol.,* 1937, **90,** 211–232.

Hodgkin, A. L. A local electric response in crustacean nerve. *J. Physiol.,* 1938*a*, **91,** 5.

Hodgkin, A. L. The subthreshold potentials in crustacean nerve fibre. *Proc. roy. Soc.,* 1938*b*, **B126,** 87–121.

Hodgkin, A. L. The relation between conduction velocity and the electrical resistance outside a nerve fibre. *J. Physiol.,* 1938–39, **94,** 560–570.

Hodgkin, A. L. The local electric changes associated with repetitive action in non-medullated axon. *J. Physiol.,* 1948, **107,** 165–181.

Hodgkin, A. L., and A. F. Huxley. Resting and action potentials in single nerve fibers. *J. Physiol.,* 1945, **104,** 176.

Hodgkin, A. L., and B. Katz. The effect of sodium ions on the electrical activity of the giant axon of the squid. *J. Physiol.,* 1949, **108,** 37.

Hursh, J. B. Conduction velocity and diameter of nerve fibers. *Amer. J. Physiol.,* 1939, **127,** 131–139.

Katz, B. Multiple response to constant current in frog's medullated nerve. *J. Physiol.,* 1936, **88,** 239.

Katz, B. Experimental evidence for a non-conducted response of nerve to subthreshold stimulation. *Proc. roy. Soc.,* 1937, **B124,** 244–276.

Katz, B. *Electric excitation of nerve.* London : Oxford University Press, 1939.

Lehmann, J. E. The effect of changes in pH on the action potential of mammalian A nerve fibers. *Amer. J. Physiol.,* 1937, **118,** 600–612.

Lillie, R. S. The passive iron wire model of photoplasmic and nervous transmission and its physiological analogues. *Biol. Rev.,* 1936, **11,** 181.

Lorente de Nó, R. A study of nerve physiology. *Studies from Rockefeller Institute for Medical Research,* 1947, **131** and **132.**

Matthews, B. H. C. Nerve endings in mammalian muscle. *J. Physiol.,* 1933, **78,** 1.

Monnier, A. M. *L'excitation électrique des tissus.* Paris, 1934.

Nachmansohn, D. Chemical mechanism of nerve activity. *Ann. N. Y. Acad. Sci.,* 1946, 47, 395–428.

Pfaffmann, C. Gustatory afferent impulses. *J. cell. comp. Physiol.,* 1941, **17,** 243.

Pitts, R. F. *Howell's textbook of physiology.* (15th Ed.) Philadelphia : Saunders, 1946.

Pumphrey, R. J. Nerve impulses from receptors in the mouth of the frog. *J. cell. comp. Physiol.,* 1935, **6,** 445.

Pumphrey, R. J., O. H. Schmitt, and J. Z. Young. Correlation of local excitability with local physiological response in the giant axon of the squid (*Loligo*). *J. Physiol.,* 1940, **98,** 47.

Rashevsky, N. Physico-mathematical aspects of excitation and conduction in nerves. *Cold Spr. Harb. Sympos. Quant. Biol.,* 1936, **4,** 90.

de Renyi, G. S. The structure of cells in tissues as revealed by microdissection. II. The physical properties of the living axis cylinder in the myelinated nerve fiber of the frog. *J. comp. Neurol.,* 1929, **47,** 405.

Rushton, W. A. H. A new observation on the excitation of nerve and muscle. *J. Physiol.,* 1932, **75,** 16P.

Rushton, W. A. H. Initiation of the propagated disturbance. *Proc. roy. Soc.,* 1937, **B124,** 201.

Schmitt, F. O. Optical studies of the molecular organization of living systems. *J. appl. Physics,* 1938, **9,** 109–117.

Schmitt, F. O. The ultrastructure of protoplasmic constituents. *Physiol. Rev.,* 1939, **19,** 270.

Schmitt, F. O. X-ray diffraction studies on the structure of the nerve myelin sheath. *J. cell. comp. Physiol.,* 1941, **18,** 31.

Schmitt, F. O., and R. S. Bear. The optical properties of vertebrate nerve axons as related to fiber size. *J. cell. comp. Physiol.,* 1936–37, **9,** 261.

Schmitt, F. O., and R. S. Bear. The ultrastructure of the nerve axon sheath. *Biol. Rev.,* 1939, **14,** 27.

Schmitt, F. O., and O. H. Schmitt. Partial excitation and variable conduction in the squid giant axon. *J. Physiol.,* 1940, **98,** 26.

Shanes, A. M., and D. E. S. Brown. The effect of metabolic inhibitors on the resting potential of frog nerve. *J. cell comp. Physiol.,* 1942, **19,** 1.

Tasaki, I., K. Ishii, and H. Ito. On the relation between the conduction-rate, the fibre-diameter, and the internodal distance of medullated nerve fibre. *Jap. J. med. Sci.,* 1943, **9,** 189.

Tasaki, I., and K. Mizuguchi. Response of single Ranvier nodes to electrical stimuli. *J. Neurophysiol.,* 1948, **11,** 295.

Tashiro, S. *A chemical sign of life.* Chicago : University of Chicago Press, 1917.

Thörner, W. Elektrophysiologische Untersuchungen am alterierten Nerven. I. Die überlegene Erregungswirkung der aufsteigenden konstanten und Induktionsströme infolge Zunahme der anodischen Öffnungserregbarkeit und kathodischen Depression während der Erstickung. *Arch. ges. Physiol.,* 1922, **197,** 159.

Young, J. Z. Structure of nerve fibers in *Sepia. J. Physiol.,* 1935, **83,** 27.

3.

Synaptic Mechanisms

FRANK BRINK, JR.

The Johns Hopkins University

The functional connections between two nerve cells occur at synapses where the terminations of one cell end upon the cell body and dendrites of a second cell (see **Fig. 1**). Generally speaking, more than one cell has terminations on a particular neuron, which makes it possible for the effects of activity in two or more neuron pathways to converge and summate (see **Fig. 2**). Furthermore one neuron may have endings on more than one cell, providing the possibility for distributing the activity of a particular neuronal pathway (**Fig. 3**). Of importance to the orderly operation of such junctions in the nervous system is the one-way transmission of impulses. Thus a postsynaptic cell excited over one presynaptic pathway cannot, in general, stimulate other presynaptic cells having terminations on it. On the contrary, the stimulating action of a cell is directed solely toward those cells upon which its axon terminates.

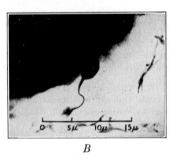

B

Fig. 1*A*. Histological preparation of a neuron from the spinal cord of a cat, showing the cell body, or perikaryon, the dendrites, and many terminal knobs of the presynaptic axons. *B*. An enlarged view of a single ending on the cell surface. (Hoff, 1932.)

A

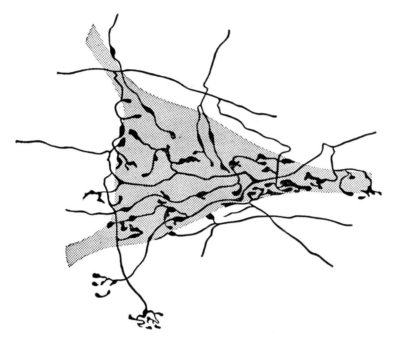

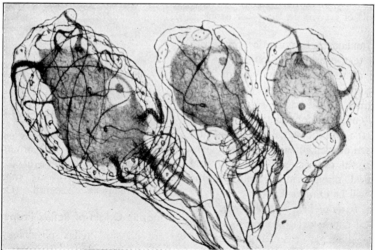

Fig. 2. Upper: Camera-lucida drawing of a motor nerve cell showing that many pre-synaptic fibers have endings on the same cell. (From Lorente de Nó, 1938b.) **Lower:** Three neurons from a stellate ganglion and the tortuous net of presynaptic fibers in their vicinity. (From de Castro, 1932.)

The transsynaptic excitatory effect of a presynaptic impulse may be sufficiently prolonged so that the stimulating actions of more than one impulse in the same presynaptic neuron can contribute to the state of excitation in the postsynaptic cell. At some synapses one presynaptic impulse is not enough to initiate an impulse in the postsynaptic cell; then summation of the effects of several presynaptic impulses is necessary.

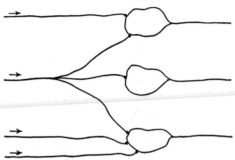

Fig. 3. Diagram of a variety of connections between individual presynaptic axons and the postsynaptic cells. Impulses in the branched axon can enhance the stimulating effectiveness in some cells of activity in the other axons.

These fundamental synaptic properties determine, to a considerable extent, the potentialities of the nervous system for integrated activity. It is the purpose of this section to indicate the extent to which these various potentialities for functions have been utilized in the evolutionary development and specialization of such junctions between cells. In addition, the experiments on the physical and chemical mechanism of transsynaptic excitation will be examined.

Neuronal basis of behavior patterns. The experimental psychologist has resolved many complex behavior patterns of organisms into component processes that are employed repeatedly in the functional organization of the nervous system. For example, there is the reflex in which stable functional relations between receptor and effector are based upon rather simple anatomical connections (Fig. 4). The studies of reflex phenomena have

defined clearly several problems requiring analysis in the study of the physical basis of behavior: the physical mechanism * or transducer system, employed to convert environmental forces into neuronal signals; the origin of the time delays in the reflex path; the mechanism for transsynaptic excitation and one-way transmission at a synapse; and, finally, the conversion of nerve impulses into the action of effectors, such as muscle, that is graded in relation to the intensity of the specific stimulus at the receptor.

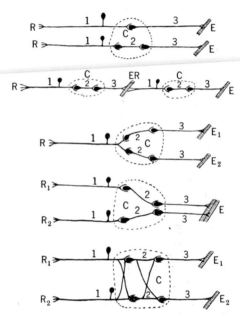

Fig. 4. The simplest reflex connection between a receptor (R) and an effector (E) involves one neural synapse at C. Other possible connections involving cross-connections and interneurons are shown. (Cowdry, 1932.)

Synaptic Origin of Reflex Properties

In classical reflex physiology there was developed a group of concepts from experiments in which receptors were stimulated and the responses of muscle observed (Creed et al., 1932). These concepts can be defined by the experimental operations by which

* The word physical is considered to include the idea of chemical (molecular) events.

they are demonstrated. A single stimulation of a small group of receptors is often not sufficient to elicit a particular reflex response, but rapidly repeated stimuli of the same strength to the same receptors may succeed in provoking the response. This phenomenon is defined as temporal summation of stimuli. Such temporal summation can be demonstrated not only by stimulating the receptors but also by direct excitation of afferent nerve trunks. Thus, if a small number of sensory (afferent) nerve fibers are directly stimulated by electrical shocks, synchronized volleys of impulses are conducted into the central nervous system. If one volley does not elicit a certain reflex response, repeated volleys may. Therefore temporal summation is not dependent upon the properties of the receptor mechanism. Instead of using the muscle response as the indicator of the reflex effect, we may employ the action potential in the motor (efferent) nerves. It is then found that repeated volleys of impulses in the same afferent nerve may be necessary to elicit a discharge of impulses in the efferent motor fibers. Thus temporal summation, as revealed in reflexes, occurs within the central nervous system. It is a property of the synaptic regions where nerve cells are functionally connected.

In the study of reflex phenomena the electrical excitation of afferent nerves and the recording of action potentials in the efferent nerve have been of great importance. In this way the receptor mechanism and the myoneural junction have been eliminated from the reflex circuit, and the unique dependence of the properties of certain stereotyped reflex patterns upon synaptic mechanisms has been revealed. In this method the intensity of the electric shock determines the number of afferent nerve fibers activated, and the number of motor nerve cells responding is measured by the amplitude of the compound action potential.

This procedure has been employed in the study of spatial summation, another basic property of reflex mechanisms. The possibility of spatial summation depends upon the anatomical fact that, in general, more than one presynaptic cell has endings upon each postsynaptic cell. Thus a volley of impulses in a few afferent fibers may excite some motor cells. A volley in another group of afferent fibers to the same group of motor cells may also excite some of them. When these two volleys of impulses, over two different afferent pathways, arrive simultaneously at the motor cells, the number responding may be greater than the sum of the separate responses. Some motor cells that do not respond to either of the separate afferent volleys are activated by both of them (cf. Fig. 23). This is spatial summation of the stimulating effects of afferent impulses.

A third phenomenon of reflex physiology that is a property of synaptic mechanisms is facilitation. This concept of facilitation at a synapse is derived from observations in which the number of postsynaptic cells responding to a given afferent volley of impulses is increased in number over some previous control level established after a long period of inactivity. Accordingly facilitation at synapses is based upon a combination of temporal and spatial summation of excitatory processes resulting from the previous activity of presynaptic endings; also, it depends on the recovery cycle of the pre- and postsynaptic neurons.

Spatial or temporal summation of presynaptic volleys are merely mechanisms for the activation of a postsynaptic cell. Consequently the physical basis of these phenomena is but one aspect of the processes of transsynaptic excitation.

In principle, the properties of reflexes mentioned above can be deduced (1) from anatomical knowledge of cellular connections and (2) from detailed information about the time course and the intensity of all the processes underlying synaptic excitation.

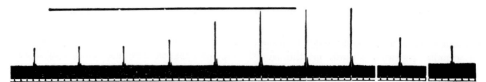

FIG. 5. More postsynaptic cells respond to a volley of impulses in a fixed number of presynaptic cells when a sympathetic ganglion is perfused with a solution containing acetylcholine. The number of cells responding is measured by the height of the action potential. Horizontal black line marks period of injection of acetylcholine into perfusion fluid. Second record: 15 seconds later. Third record: 35 seconds later. Time: 0.2-second intervals. (Bronk et al., 1938.)

Factors in Transsynaptic Excitation

In synaptic excitation we are always concerned with the properties of two or more neurons. The response of the presynaptic endings produces a sequence of physico-chemical events that modify the immediate environment of the postsynaptic cell. A priori it is to be expected that all these environmental changes affect the postsynaptic cell; they increase or decrease its state of excitation. One environmental factor is the action current of the presynaptic impulses; others include the chemical substances liberated in the surrounding fluid by the incident impulses. For example, in the sympathetic ganglia of the cat presynaptic activity leads to the release of potassium ions (Vogt, 1936) and of acetylcholine into the fluids bathing the postsynaptic cells (Dale, 1936a, b; Feldberg and Vartianen, 1935; Mac-Intosh, 1938). The excitatory effect is dependent upon the intensity of each of these environmental changes and the specific sensitivity of the postganglionic cell to each kind of change.

In the stellate ganglion small amounts of acetylcholine or potassium chloride perfused through the ganglion cause an increase in the number of postganglionic cells responding to a standard preganglionic volley of nerve impulses (Fig. 5). This increase is probably due to a change in the postganglionic neurons; indeed, larger concentrations of acetylcholine or of potassium chloride can excite these cells without the additional action of preganglionic impulses (Fig. 6). Corre-

spondingly the frequency of response of a postganglionic cell to a constant frequency of preganglionic impulses depends upon the

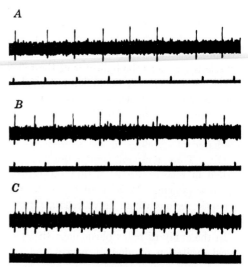

FIG. 6. Postganglionic cells respond repetitively to an adequate concentration of acetylcholine perfused through a sympathetic ganglion. The frequency of impulses in a single fiber increases with the concentration of acetylcholine. Concentration in micrograms per cubic centimeter are: A, 25; B, 50; and C, 100. (Bronk, 1939.)

concentration of calcium ions in the solution bathing the cells (Fig. 7). Hence it is clear that the stimulating effects of impulses and of local chemical changes can summate at synapses.

The stimulating action of acetylcholine is restricted to the postsynaptic cell, for even large concentrations do not excite the presynaptic axons. But other chemical changes are not so specific. For example, a sufficient lowering of the calcium ion concentration, by increase in calcium ion concentration reduces the frequency of response to acetylcholine (Fig. 8). The change of sensitivity to this chemical agent is parallel to the

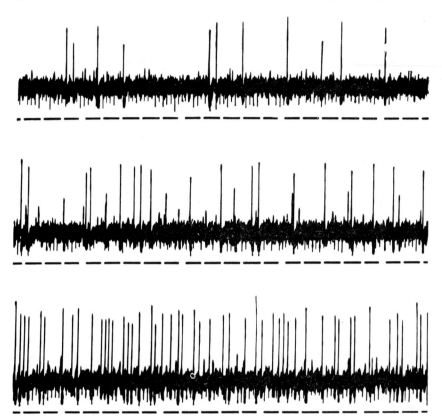

FIG. 7. The frequency of response of a postsynaptic cell to a constant frequency of presynaptic volleys is reduced by increasing the calcium concentration in the perfusion fluid. Impulses discharged by a few sympathetic ganglion cells in response to stimulation of the preganglionic nerve at a frequency of 50 per second. The ganglion was perfused with a modified Ringer's solution containing various amounts of calcium chloride: Upper record, 4.4 millimolar; middle record, 2.2 millimolar; bottom record, 1.1 millimolar. The middle record represents the normal level of calcium. Time: 0.1-second intervals. (Brink, Bronk, and Larrabee, 1946.)

means of sodium citrate, leads to changes that initiate impulses in both the pre- and postsynaptic cells.

The frequency of response of a postganglionic neuron to a given concentration of acetylcholine depends upon other chemical constituents of the perfusion fluid that influence the excitability of the cell. Thus an change in sensitivity to electrical currents exhibited by axons when the calcium ion in the bathing fluid is varied (Chapter 2, Fig. 31). Similarly a postganglionic cell exposed to high concentrations of potassium ion and acetylcholine will respond more frequently than when the potassium concentration is lowered. Thus the stimulating and inhibiting actions of chemical substances are compounded to determine the response of a neuron.

The flow of action currents associated with presynaptic impulses, the release of chemical substances, the state of excitation of the postsynaptic cell determined by the prevailing environmental influences, all combine to determine whether or not transsynaptic ex-

currents of the presynaptic terminals, the effectiveness of this stimulus depending upon the excitability of the postsynaptic cell as determined in part by chemical products of previous presynaptic activity. This proposition suggests that the specific chemical events contribute mainly to facilitation and after-discharge. It seems probable, however, that at some junctions between cells the

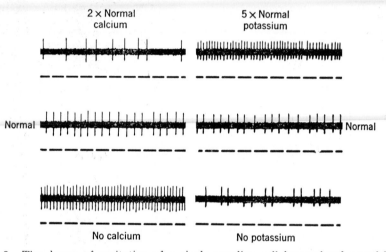

FIG. 8. The degree of excitation of a single ganglion cell by perfused acetylcholine, measured by the frequency of the action potentials, depends upon the concentration of other ions in the perfusion fluid. Time: 0.1-second intervals. (Bronk, 1939.)

citation initiates an impulse (Bronk, 1939). Therefore the physical explanation of synaptic excitation consists of a quantitative evaluation of the intensity, time course, and stimulating effectiveness of potentially significant changes in at least these component processes which, in turn, are modified by other changes that reduce the stimulating effectiveness of presynaptic volleys.

Studies of particular synaptic mechanisms have confirmed this multiple-factor hypothesis. There are, however, differences of opinion concerning the quantitative significance of the effects of electrical fields at synapses as contrasted with the actions of specific chemicals. An important phase of this discussion is the thesis that the immediate transmitter agent is always the action

action currents are the most significant aspect of the transmitter action of presynaptic impulses, whereas at others the chemical events predominate.

Analysis of Transmission at Synapses

The essential fact for which a physical explanation is sought is that a sufficient amount of activity in presynaptic endings can initiate a nerve impulse in the postsynaptic cell. The excitatory effectiveness of presynaptic activity depends upon the number of active endings on a particular cell, the intensity of the transsynaptic stimulus developed at each ending, the excitability of the postsynaptic cell near each ending, and the area of the cell that must respond to insure the initiation of a postsynaptic impulse.

The detailed analysis of these components of the synaptic mechanism is far from complete.

As in the study of axons, some preparations are more favorable than others for revealing particular aspects of synaptic transmission. For example, a desirable simplification is obtained if the amount of activity in the presynaptic fibers is directly controlled and the activity of the postsynaptic cells directly measured. This is accomplished in studies of synaptic transmission in the sympathetic ganglia where the presynaptic fibers end on cell bodies of the postsynaptic axons in which the response is measured. This is also true of monosynaptic reflex pathways through the spinal cord. In these preparations the properties of synapses are revealed without undue interference from more complicated phenomena caused by interneurons that form additional pathways leading to the postsynaptic cells in which the response is measured.

The most favorable experimental arrangement for some studies is a preparation in which a single presynaptic fiber excites a single postsynaptic neuron. A simple synapse of this sort has been discovered in the nervous system of the squid.

In the giant fiber system of the squid it is possible to record the electrical changes near the junction between two fibers. The initiation of a conducted action potential in the postsynaptic axon by an impulse in the presynaptic axon is preceded by a local electrical change in the postsynaptic cell (Fig. 9). Thus initiation of the postsynaptic activity seems to occur by way of the same physical mechanism that is responsible for direct excitation of an axon by an electric current (see Chapter 2, Fig. 17). The time relations between the postsynaptic local response and the presynaptic impulse are such that the action current of the latter could be the primary stimulus to the postsynaptic axon.

This conclusion is further supported by the fact that artificial synapses between two

fibers have similar properties. These artificial synapses can be made by appropriate contact between two axons; specialized parts

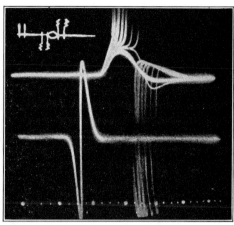

Fig. 9. Potential changes near the synapse between a pair of giant fibers in the stellate ganglion of a squid. The presynaptic fiber was excited by electrodes shown as vertical lines at the left of the inset diagram. The lower trace is the action potential of the presynaptic fiber recorded at the middle pair of electrodes in inset diagram. The upper trace is the simultaneous record from the postsynaptic axon near its exit from the ganglion at the right-hand pair of electrodes in inset. The upward trace (going off the record) is due to the first electrode becoming negative, and the subsequent downward trace signals the arrival of the impulse at the last recording electrode. Responses to repeated volleys are superimposed. The conducted diphasic action potential occurs later and later and seems to arise from the top of a monophasic potential, which persists even when the conducted response finally fails. This monophasic potential is the local electrical response to the stimulatory action of the presynaptic impulse. (Bullock, 1948.)

are not essential (Jasper and Monnier, 1938; Arvanitaki, 1942). At this artificial junction the electric current from the electromotive force in the presynaptic axon seems to be the principal transmitter agent responsible for the functional connection between the two neurons. We are left, however, without a satisfactory explanation of the one-way transmission across natural synapses between giant fibers.

A local depolarization and a reduction of impedance (Katz, 1942) also occurs at the

13). Temporal summation of the stimulating effects of the nerve impulses thus takes place in the muscle cell. When the electrotonic potential at the endplate is great enough, an action potential is initiated in the muscle cell.

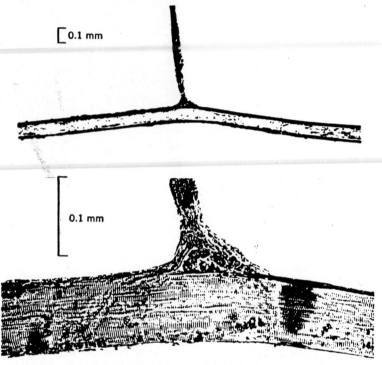

0.1 mm

0.1 mm

Fig. 10. Termination of a motor nerve on a single muscle fiber of a frog. The enlarged ending is the endplate. One recording electrode makes contact with the muscle near this endplate region, while the other is placed at a distance on the muscle. (Kuffler, 1942a.)

endplate in muscle cells following an impulse in the motor nerve endings (Figs. 10, 11, and 12). The associated flow of current from adjacent areas of the muscle membrane creates electrotonic changes of potential along the muscle membrane near the endplate. The duration of this change of potential is revealed by partially curarizing the preparation so that one nerve impulse is not sufficient to cause an action potential in the muscle (Fig. 12). In a curarized preparation repeated nerve impulses will increase the electrotonic potential in the muscle (Fig.

The action current of the presynaptic ending precedes by a short time this endplate potential in the muscle cell (Kuffler, 1948). And the local electrical change is the earliest known transsynaptic response to the presynaptic activity. The short time interval between them may represent the time required for the development of the changes in the muscle that lead to a local response — like the utilization time following a short shock to a motor nerve of a crab. On the other hand, this time interval may be in part the time required for the production and action of a transmitter agent that is physically distinct from the action currents of the motor nerve ending.

The existence of such a transmitter agent has been demonstrated. This agent is pro-

the local endplate potential can reappear after the muscle action current has passed the endplate. Therefore an agent that initiates the local electrotonic potential in the muscle was still present after the action cur-

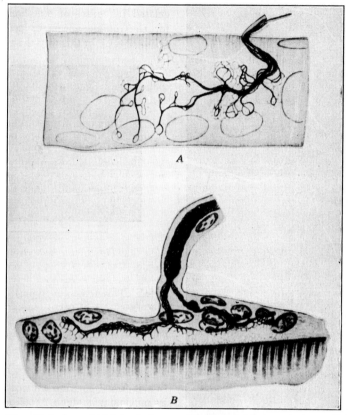

FIG. 11. Magnified view of histological preparation of endplate region. *A:* The terminations of a single fiber (bat) are spread diffusely on the muscle. *B:* The endplate (cat) is a complex structure containing the end of the motor nerve. (Cowdry, 1932.)

duced by motor nerve impulses but acts longer than the associated action currents (Kuffler, 1948). It initiates the local electrotonic potential by depolarizing the muscle cell at the endplate. Proof of its duration depends upon two facts: (1) when the muscle cell is stimulated directly, the action potential sweeping over the endplate region wipes out the local electrical change in the muscle; (2) if this occurs shortly after the action current in the motor nerve, part of

rents in the motor nerve had ceased. On the other hand, if the muscle response to direct excitation wipes out the endplate potential at a later stage of its development, then this potential does not reappear. The duration of the action of the active transmitter agent is thereby measured and is found to be about 5 milliseconds (Kuffler, 1942b).

The measured period of active depolarization by the transmitter agent is brief compared to the duration of the recorded elec-

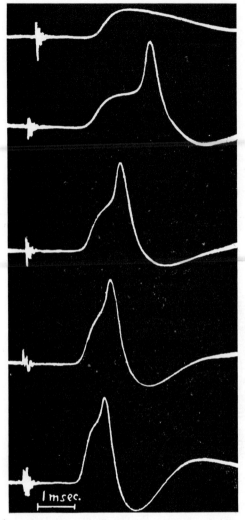

FIG. 12. A single impulse in a motor nerve (frog) produces an electrotonic potential in the muscle that is confined to the neighborhood of the endplate. The muscle action potential is in turn produced by this endplate potential. Under curare only the local electrical change occurs in the muscle (top record). As the curare action is reduced, the successive traces show the development of the conducted muscle action potential. This action potential occurs earlier, the lower the concentration of curare. In a normal muscle all but the beginning of the endplate potential is obscured by the action potential (bottom record). There is a delay of about 0.5 to 1.0 millisecond between the arrival of the nerve action potential and the beginning of the electrical change in the muscle. Temperature, 22 degrees C. (Kuffler, 1942a.)

trotonic endplate potential in the muscle. This is indicated also by an analysis of the time course of the recorded electrotonic endplate potential. The time course of the stimulus causing the redistribution of charge on the membrane of the muscle can be calculated by means of equations worked out for electrotonic effects in peripheral nerve (Hill, 1936). In this way the transmitter ac-

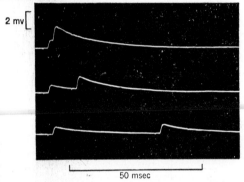

FIG. 13. In a curarized myoneural junction the local electrical changes produced in the muscle by two successive nerve impulses are added. This temporal summation of the excitatory effects of nerve impulses can increase the endplate potential so that a muscle action potential is finally produced, if the concentration of curare is not too great. (Eccles, Katz, and Kuffler, 1941.)

tion is found to have a rapid rise, reaching its maximum in about 2 milliseconds and decaying by the end of 5 milliseconds (Fig. 14). Hence the calculated duration of the transmitter action agrees with the measured value.

The duration of the transmitter action is increased by eserine (Eccles, Katz, and Kuffler, 1942) and decreased by curarine (Kuffler, 1942b; Eccles, Katz, and Kuffler, 1941). These chemical facts suggest that the agent depolarizing the muscle cell at the endplate is acetylcholine.

According to a recent interpretation of the available facts (Kuffler, 1948; Acheson, 1948), the significant transmitter agent in the normal myoneural junction of frogs and of cats is acetylcholine. However, at synapses in the central nervous system the chemical component of the transmitter action is thought to be of negligible importance compared to the direct effect of the action currents from the presynaptic nerve endings (Eccles, 1947). Indeed, the properties of all myoneural junctions are not readily explained either by the acetylcholine

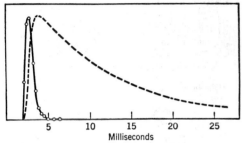

FIG. 14. The local electrical change in a muscle lasts for about 25 milliseconds (dotted line) and is produced by a transmitter (solid line), or depolarizing agent at the endplate, that achieves its maximum action in 2 milliseconds and is finished in about 5 to 8 milliseconds. These events begin 0.5 to 1.0 millisecond after the arrival of the nerve action potential. (Eccles, Katz, and Kuffler, 1941.)

mechanism of transmission or by the direct effects of the action currents. The possibility of a dual mechanism, involving both kinds of transmitter agents, has been discussed (Monnier, 1936). The proper emphasis is probably attained if the previous evidence is considered to indicate merely the predominant role of acetylcholine in transmission at neuromuscular junctions of skeletal muscle in cats and frogs. This leaves open the possibility that other substances, or the action currents themselves, may play the significant role at other neuromuscular junctions (Pantin, 1937).

To summarize, neuromuscular transmission involves four steps: (1) the response of the nerve terminals, (2) the production of a chemical transmitter agent, (3) the development of a local depolarization and change of

impedance (the local response) in the muscle, and (4) the initiation of a conducted action potential by the electrotonic current developed from the local response.

Anatomically, the usual connections between nerve cells do not resemble the two kinds of intercellular junction just discussed. There are many terminations on each postsynaptic cell, and the terminal enlargements, or knobs, are contributed by several presynaptic neurons. There is considerable evidence that the combined action of single impulses in each of several presynaptic fibers is required to excite a postsynaptic cell. Nevertheless it is probable that electrochemical events similar to those described for the simpler junctions occur at each region of contact between the terminal knobs and the dendrites or cell body of the postsynaptic neuron. According to this hypothesis, the principal additional factor to be considered in this complex synaptic mechanism is how the local responses at each junction add to produce excitation in the postsynaptic axon.

If local responses occur in the postsynaptic cell, electrotonic potential changes would spread along the postsynaptic axons. In the cardiac nerve of the stellate ganglion, or in a ventral root of the spinal cord, such axons are compactly arranged in bundles a short distance from the cell bodies. This part of the nerve should be negative to more distal parts whenever the cell bodies are partly depolarized. As a matter of fact, such electrotonic signs of local electrical responses have been measured in motor neurons (Bonnet and Bremer, 1938; Barron and Matthews, 1936, 1938; Eccles, 1946; Brooks and Eccles, 1947a) and in ganglion cells (Eccles, 1943, 1944).

Since the conducted response of a postganglionic cell, like that in muscle tissue, will obliterate the local response, it is necessary to prevent the postsynaptic action potential. Mild curarization is employed for this purpose in the stellate ganglion. In the absence of the postsynaptic action potential there is only the prolonged local electrotonic potential in the postsynaptic neuron (Fig. 15, curve *B*). This occurs with an estimated latency of about 4 milliseconds after the arrival of the presynaptic volley at the synapses. The maximum amplitude is reached

preganglionic volley produces only a subthreshold postsynaptic local response. Repeated volleys will, however, add to the local potential change, and finally the summated electrical changes cause a postsynaptic ac-

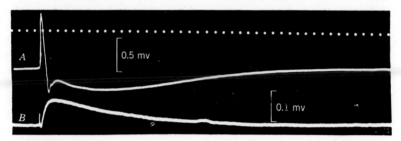

Fig. 15. The upper trace, *A*, is the potential recorded from a stellate ganglion of a cat at the point of emergence of the postsynaptic nerves when they are excited by a single presynaptic volley of impulses. The conducted action potential spike is followed by a prolonged positive after-potential. When the preparation is curarized only an electrotonic potential, *B*, originating in or near the cell bodies of the ganglionic neurons, occurs in response to a preganglionic volley. This local electrotonic potential is called the synaptic potential. Time marks: 10-millisecond intervals. (Eccles, 1943.)

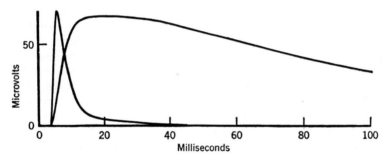

Fig. 16. The calculated transmitter action in the stellate ganglion, reaching its maximum in about 2 milliseconds, decays rapidly at first and then slowly over a period of 50 milliseconds. The recorded synaptic potential in the muscle lasts much longer. Ordinate for the transmitter action is arbitrary. (Eccles, 1943.)

in 10 to 20 milliseconds, and it drops to half-value in 90 more milliseconds (Fig. 16). Thus the time course of this electrotonic potential in a cat's stellate ganglion is longer than the similar physical changes at the endplate in a muscle of a cat.

The postsynaptic action potential occurs whenever this synaptic potential is of sufficient magnitude (Eccles, 1943). In the curarized stellate ganglion a single maximal

tion potential. Thus the temporal summation of preganglionic volleys shows up as the addition of electrical changes in the postsynaptic cell. Since the local synaptic potential lasts about 0.2 second, this is the longest permissible interval between volleys if they are to add their effects by this mechanism.

There are no direct experiments to indicate how long the transmitter agent producing the local electrical response acts. By indirect procedures, based upon Hill's excitation theory, it has been calculated that the local electrotonic changes are produced by an agent that acts upon the postsynaptic cell for 50 milliseconds (Fig. 16). The physical nature of this transmitter action is unknown, but it is composed of a rapid intense part that decays in about 20 milliseconds and a small slow component lasting as long as 50 milliseconds (Fig. 16). Eccles (1944) has suggested that the initial phase, reaching a maximum in 2.5 milliseconds, is the stimulus due to action currents in the presynaptic terminals. (The action currents arising in different fibers are assumed to be asynchronous and hence more prolonged than that of a single impulse.) He further suggests that the slow component of the transmitter action is due to the chemical products of presynaptic activity that depolarize the postsynaptic neuron.

The synaptic potentials and the associated transmitter action that have just been described occur after one or two impulses. However, if a train of presynaptic impulses at high frequency (50 per second) impinges upon the ganglion cells, the electrotonic potential is more prolonged and may persist for several seconds. Analysis of this prolonged synaptic potential indicates that an additional transmitter agent is accumulated under these conditions. This component of the transmitter agent is greatly prolonged when the cells are bathed in solutions containing eserine to inhibit the cholinesterase. It seems, therefore, that the accumulation of acetylcholine, as a result of frequent presynaptic impulses, causes this prolonged depolarization of the ganglion cells. In contrast, the transmitter action occurring after a single volley of presynaptic impulses is not changed by eserine. Thus there seem to be several transmitters of transynaptic excitation in sympathetic ganglia.

In résumé, synaptic transmission after a single presynaptic volley of impulses in the stellate ganglion seems to occur in four principal steps, each having a characteristic time course. (1) The presynaptic action potentials arrive asynchronously at the terminals, and action currents flow for 20 milliseconds or less, leading to excitatory effects in the postsynaptic cells. (2) The chemical component of the synaptic transmitter action persists for at least 50 milliseconds, having a prolonged excitatory effect. (3) Under the action of these combined excitatory processes there occurs a local response at each active synapse on a postsynaptic cell, causing an electrotonic potential change that rises slowly to a maximum at 20 milliseconds. (4) However, if the total excitation is adequate, the conducted action potential develops early, in response to the rapid phase of the transmitter action, and the synaptic potential is barely measurable.

Further considerations concerning acetylcholine. Another set of facts seems to place a rather different emphasis upon the significance of acetylcholine as a component of the transmitter action in sympathetic ganglia. As Dale (1939) has emphasized, the facts to be enumerated must be either controverted by further experiments or encompassed by the electrical hypothesis of transmission.

1. Acetylcholine is released in significant amounts by nerve activity in sympathetic ganglia as well as at myoneural junctions.

2. The stimulating action of a presynaptic volley of impulses is blocked by curarine at the same concentration at which the postsynaptic cells become insensitive to applied acetylcholine. At this time the cells can be excited by applied potassium chloride.

3. In the prolonged absence of metabolic substrates the synthesis of acetylcholine stops and transmission is also blocked. Both transmission and acetylcholine synthesis are restored when glucose, or other substrate, is added to the perfusion fluid.

4. In the absence of calcium ions in the perfusion fluid the release of acetylcholine by presynaptic activity is stopped and so is transmission.

The second of these observations can be adversely criticized. In order to offer such an experiment as controverting the electrical hypothesis, it would be necessary to show that curarine does not decrease the sensitivity of postsynaptic cells to electrical currents. The response to potassium chloride is an unsatisfactory control in this connection, for this agent can excite axons, and the curarine may act only at the synaptic regions. A rather similar experiment was reported by Bronk, Larrabee, and Gaylor (1948). In this instance anoxia caused a failure of transmission through the stellate ganglion at the same time that the direct excitation of ganglion cells by acetylcholine failed. However, this result could be caused by the cells becoming insensitive to all stimuli.

The third and fourth observations are also open to analogous criticism, for it is possible that the imposed environmental changes eliminate all response of the presynaptic nerve endings, including the action potential as well as acetylcholine liberation.

Hence the difficult and provocative question of the importane of acetylcholine in synaptic transmission in sympathetic ganglia remains unanswered. Nevertheless the ingenious experimentation that has been devoted to this problem has uncovered many important facts about nerve cells and synapses.

Nachmansohn (1946) has recently proposed an hypothesis, regarding nerve conduction and transmission, that attempts to unify the chemical and electrical theories. This hypothesis proposes acetylcholine as a depolarizing agent that is released from the postsynaptic cell by the action currents of the presynaptic terminals. The free acetylcholine then causes the local electrical response by its depolarizing action on the cell membrane. Subsequently it is resynthesized into a bound form, but some of it inevitably diffuses away from the reaction site. It is this latter portion that is detected in a perfusate, provided its destruction by cholinesterase is prevented.

Summation of Stimuli in Sympathetic Ganglia

Only under the action of a substance like curare has the full time course of the local electrotonic potential been directly demonstrated in ganglionic cells and the dual transmitter action deduced therefrom. However, the operation of several excitatory processes in normal ganglia can be indirectly revealed by studies of subliminally excited ganglion cells (Eccles, 1944). The time course of such excitation processes is revealed by facilitation developed through temporal and spatial summation of the effects of presynaptic impulses.

Of the several electrical processes occurring after the arrival of a preganglionic volley that does not initiate an impulse in a postganglionic cell, the synaptic potential is the most prolonged. The total duration of this physical effect in the postganglionic cell is less than 200 milliseconds in cells of the stellate ganglion of a cat. Therefore these local electrical changes show no significant overlapping when the preganglionic volleys occur at five per second or less. But temporal summation of individually ineffective afferent volleys occurs at much lower frequencies (Larrabee and Bronk, 1947).

The quantitative aspects of this summation can be studied particularly well if a response of a single postsynaptic cell is recorded. Thus in a sympathetic ganglion an occasional volley of impulses in a restricted group of presynaptic fibers may be unable to excite a particular postsynaptic cell. However, if the frequency of the impulses over the same presynaptic pathways is increased, their stimulating effects are summated until one of them finally causes a response in the postsynaptic neuron. At higher frequencies the first response of the postsynaptic cell occurs sooner and after fewer presynaptic volleys (Fig. 17). In such an experiment each response of the single cell is related in time to a particular volley of presynaptic impulses. It seems that each volley contributed a transient change at some part of the synaptic mechanism. If a second volley occurs before this change has subsided, it adds its effect. Finally, a particular volley causes the discharge of an impulse.

located in the endings of presynaptic fibers.

In support of this view, the detailed study of prolonged facilitation in stellate ganglia has suggested that the stimulating effectiveness of a preganglionic volley can be enhanced as an after-effect of a previous volley (Larrabee and Bronk, 1947). Such prolonged facilitation can be revealed only by

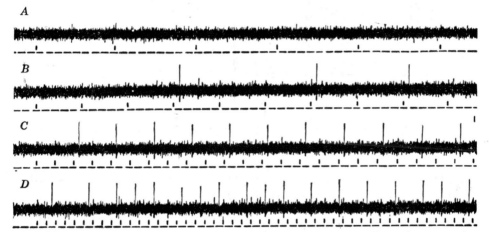

FIG. 17. Impulses discharged by a ganglion cell in response to volleys of presynaptic impulses repeated at various frequencies. The presynaptic impulses were initiated by supramaximal stimulation of the thoracic sympathetic trunk, between the fourth and fifth roots, at instants indicated by the short vertical lines above the time marks (0.1 second). The first stimulus in each record was applied after a long period of rest. In *A* the postsynaptic cell did not respond to any of the presynaptic volleys. Temporal summation of four volleys at 0.5-second intervals was required to produce the first response, shown in *B*. At higher frequencies of preganglionic volleys, fewer were needed to initiate the first impulse in the postsynaptic cell. (Larrabee and Bronk, 1947.)

Consequently either the after-effects of a single volley must produce subthreshold excitatory changes in the postsynaptic cell that persist more than 0.5 second, or else the stimulating effectiveness of successive preganglionic volleys at these low frequencies must increase. The first explanation is excluded because a prolonged after-effect due to a volley cannot be demonstrated by the spatial summation of impulses in preganglionic fibers. In order to demonstrate this prolonged subthreshold effect it is necessary that the successive volleys enter the ganglion over the same presynaptic fibers. It is very probable, therefore, that the persisting change is

the changes in the response to a standard testing volley that enters the ganglion over the same preganglionic fibers used to condition the synaptic mechanism (Fig. 18).

These latent modifications of the synaptic mechanism occur even after a single supramaximal stimulus to a given group of preganglionic axons. Such a stimulus insures that a constant number of preganglionic fibers are stimulated in conditioning and in testing. The changes in the excitatory effectiveness of these fixed volleys of presynaptic impulses are measured by the number of ganglion cells responding, i.e. by the height of the postganglionic compound action poten-

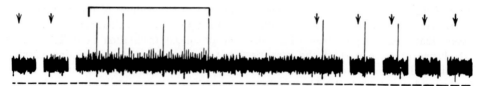

Fig. 18. Impulses from a ganglion cell in response to single and to rapidly repeated volleys in a constant number of preganglionic fibers. Arrows indicate application of single supramaximal stimuli to the preganglionic nerve, once every 5 seconds. No impulses were discharged when these stimuli were applied for more than a minute. The lack of response to the last two stimuli is shown at the beginning of the figure. The preganglionic stimuli were then repeated at the rate of 50 per second for about a second (indicated by bracket), causing one of the cells to discharge six impulses. The facilitating effects of this high-frequency stimulation did not disappear at once, for the cell was able to respond to a single volley after as long as 10 seconds. After 15 seconds it was no longer possible to excite the cell by single volleys at 5-second intervals. Time: 0.1-second intervals. (Larrabee and Bronk, 1947.)

tial. At short intervals after the conditioning volley there is an increased number of ganglion cells activated by the testing volley. After 0.2 second there is a period of depression, and fewer cells respond. Then from 0.4 second onward the period of prolonged facilitation occurs (Fig. 19).

The conditioning volley obviously excited some cells to activity and others to a subthreshold degree. A testing volley imposed in less than 0.2 second is thus able to excite more ganglion cells when those responding to the conditioning volley have recovered their excitability. This summation of subthreshold effects at these short intervals has been correlated with the previously described local electrical changes in the ganglion cells (Eccles, 1944). At longer summation intervals the reduced excitability associated with the positive after-potential develops in the cells responding to the conditioning volley (Eccles, 1935). Then there are fewer cells responding to a test volley, because the number depressed by this after-effect of postsynaptic activity is greater than the number recruited by temporal summation of subliminal excitatory processes. Thereafter, the period of prolonged facilitation can be traced for as much as 10 seconds after a single conditioning volley.

This facilitation process, which can last for minutes after a prolonged period of stimula-

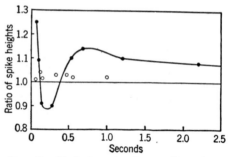

Fig. 19. Variations in the number of ganglion cells responding to a preganglionic volley following a single conditioning volley of preganglionic impulses. Both conditioning and test volleys were initiated by a single supramaximal shock to the third preganglionic ramus. Ordinate: ratio of postganglionic spike height in test response to the spike height in conditioning response. Abscissa: intervals between conditioning and test responses. Open circles show that there is little difference in height of spike in response to test and conditioning volleys when both are applied directly to the postganglionic nerve. (Larrabee and Bronk, 1947.)

tion (Figs. 20 and 21), does not seem to be associated with any electrical change. Nor is there direct evidence for its exact location within the synaptic mechanism. However, Larrabee and Bronk (1947) have eliminated as explanations (1) persisting chemical activators and (2) persisting changes in the state of excitation of the postganglionic cell. The

When facilitation is caused by changes in the postsynaptic neuron, then both spatial and temporal summation can be effective in increasing the number of cells responding to successive presynaptic volleys. This circum-

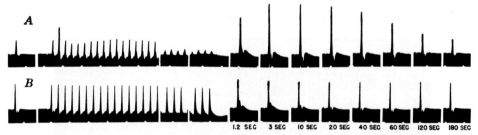

FIG. 20. Action potentials recorded from the postganglionic nerve trunk before, during, and at the indicated times following a 10-second period of repetitive activity. In *A*, supramaximal stimuli were applied to a preganglionic root; in *B*, to the postganglionic nerve. The larger spike potentials following the train of repetitive activity in *A* are due to the response of a larger number of ganglion cells. Time marks on lower edge of record indicate 0.2-second intervals. (Larrabee and Bronk, 1947.)

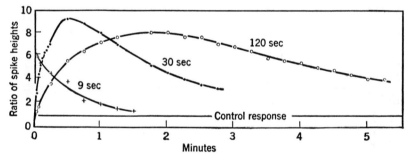

FIG. 21. Time course of prolonged facilitation after various durations of repetitive stimulation of a preganglionic nerve at a frequency of 24 per second. Ratio of spike height of postganglionic action potential to height of response to a similar preganglionic volley after a long period of rest (control response) is plotted against time after the final conditioning volley. All testing and conditioning volleys were initiated by supramaximal stimuli to a preganglionic root. (Larrabee and Bronk, 1947.)

authors suggest that prolonged facilitation is caused by a change in the preganglionic terminals whereby the stimulating effectiveness of an impulse is enhanced as a result of previous responses.*

This view emphasizes the importance of temporal summation in synaptic facilitation.

* Since the completion of this chapter this same type of facilitation has been discovered in the monosynaptic pathways through the spinal cord (Lloyd, 1949).

stance provides a unique experimental differentiation between pre- and postsynaptic mechanisms of facilitation. If the facilitation can be obtained by the spatial summation of two volleys in each of two separate presynaptic pathways, then it can not be caused by changes in the presynaptic cell terminations.

All the known components of the synaptic mechanism have thus been introduced to explain one or another aspect of synaptic function. The early period of facilitation is mainly attributed to summation of subthreshold excitatory processes in postsynaptic units and to the addition of transmitter actions. The period of depression is attributed to the reduced excitability of the post-

nisms, inhibition occurred only as an after-effect of a response of the postsynaptic neurons. It was part of a recovery cycle. To explain central inhibition, based on only this kind of inhibitory mechanism, elaborate schemes have been devised involving complex neuron networks. Now it is known that

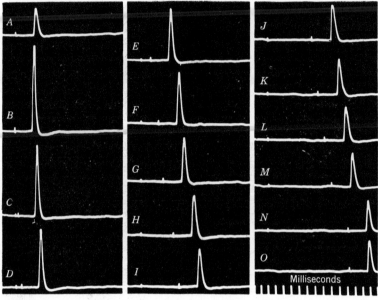

Fig. 22. Facilitation of the biceps reflex by an afferent (conditioning) volley from a small branch of the biceps nerve. *A* and *O*: Biceps reflex in response to test shock, applied to large branch only. *B* to *N*: Biceps reflex when the volley in the large branch occurs coincident with and at various intervals after the arrival of the conditioning volley in the small branch. The conditioning volley by itself evokes no reflex response. (Lloyd, 1946a.)

synaptic cells during the recovery cycle. The prolonged facilitation is attributed to residual changes in the presynaptic terminals and is an after-effect of previous activity therein.

Facilitation and Inhibition in the Spinal Cord

A prominent feature of coordinated neuronal events in the central nervous system is the inhibition of activity in one group of neurons during excitatory action in another group. Thus the motor neurons to a flexor muscle are inhibited during excitation of neuron pathways to an extensor muscle. In the previous discussion of synaptic mecha-

presynaptic activity can have a direct transsynaptic inhibitory action on a postsynaptic cell that is not an after-effect of an impulse in this cell (Lloyd, 1941).

The motor cells of a monosynaptic reflex pathway are innervated by excitatory afferent nerve endings. The synapses involved have some properties similar to those described in the general discussion of synaptic mechanisms except that, in the central nervous system, processes occur faster than in sympathetic ganglia. Thus the early facilitation (Lloyd, 1946a) related to electrical events in the postsynaptic cell (Brooks and

Eccles, 1947b) is over in about 13 milliseconds (Figs. 22 and 23). In addition there

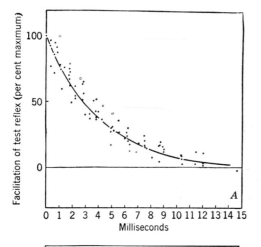

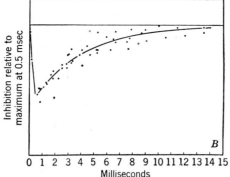

FIG. 23A. Facilitation of motor neurons by impulses in primary afferent fibers. Data from seven experiments (four for flexor and three for extensor nuclei) are scaled on the ordinate to coincide at the time of maximum facilitation. An individual experiment on facilitation is shown in Fig. 22.

B. Inhibition of motor neuron by impulses in primary afferent fibers. Points from four experiments are scaled to coincide at an interval of 0.5 millisecond between the conditioning volley and the test volley. Three experiments were concerned with flexor nuclei, the remaining with an extensor nucleus. (Lloyd, 1946a.)

are types of inhibitory nerves that end on motor neurons where they supply impulses that make the postsynaptic cell less sensitive to presynaptic activity of the excitatory endings. The time course of this inhibitory action has a finite rising phase and then declines along a time course similar to that for the decline of facilitation (Fig. 23).

The combination of the excitatory and inhibitory effects probably occurs on the postsynaptic neuron. Although the physical nature of the inhibition is not so well known as is that of excitation, an electrical mechanism has been proposed (Brooks and Eccles, 1947). Many experiments are suggested by analogy with studies of the excitatory mechanism. For example, it is not known whether the inhibitory afferents will suppress activity of a motor neuron excited directly by chemicals or whether the inhibition affects primarily the transsynaptic excitatory processes. Here we are definitely on the frontier of the science of neuronal action.

Transmitter Actions at Different Synapses

The transmitter agent is the immediate stimulus causing the response in the postsynaptic neuron. The duration and intensity of the action of the transmitter is deduced from the time course of the electrotonic potentials recorded from the postsynaptic cell. As previously discussed, when this method is employed, the effects of the response of the postsynaptic cell must be eliminated, for the action potential of this neuron obscures the recorded synaptic potential.

In the stellate ganglion of a cat the transmitter action is composed of a brief intense part associated with the asynchronous action currents of the many presynaptic endings. Thereafter there is a slower component that outlasts these action currents. This second phase of the transmitter action is attributed to chemicals, released by the presynaptic activity, that can depolarize the postsynaptic cell. The dual nature of the transmitter action is deduced from the time course of the electrotonic potential in postsynaptic axons. Another interpretation of the form of this synaptic potential is that the local electrical response of the postsynaptic cell has a slow component caused by the stimulating effect of the presynaptic action currents. Such slow changes of membrane potential difference following brief pulses of current have been observed in peripheral nerve (Lorente de Nó, 1939). If this is the explanation, the transmitter agent is solely the brief flow of electric current from the electromotive force in the presynaptic terminals. Then the prolonged component of early facilitation is entirely attributed to the addition of long-lasting local changes in the postsynaptic cell.

At some synapses of the central nervous system spatial summation of afferent volleys is not possible unless these volleys arrive at the neuron within 0.5 millisecond of each other. Both the transmitter action and the postsynaptic local response must be of very brief duration. This seems to be a response that lasts for less time than the spike component of the presynaptic action potential. At such synapses temporal summation of effects is impossible, for the absolute refractory period of the presynaptic fibers is longer than the stimulating effect of the previous impulse. Such synapses have been demonstrated in the oculomotor nucleus (Lorente de Nó, 1939).

Other synapses of the central nervous system, as described previously, exhibit spatial summation for as long as 13 milliseconds. This is correlated with the duration of the prolonged local electrotonic potentials in the postsynaptic neurons.

Early facilitation at all synapses is composed of a very brief component attributed to the summation of the effects of the action currents in the many presynaptic terminals. In some central synapses and in sympathetic ganglia there is a second component to the early phase of facilitation. This is attributed to the time course of the postsynaptic local electrical response or perhaps to a second slow component of the transmitter action. Finally, at synapses in sympathetic ganglia there is a third very prolonged component to facilitation that is attributed to persisting changes in the presynaptic endings. These changes are such that the transmitter action of the next volley of impulses is enhanced. How the transmitter action is thereby increased has not been determined (cf., however, Lloyd, 1949).

These observations support the previous statement that experimental studies are required to discover how many of the potentially significant synaptic processes are utilized in the functioning of each synaptic region.

The relation of irritability cycle to facilitation and inhibition. Thus far in the study of facilitation and inhibition the proposed mechanisms have emphasized events preliminary to the occurrence of a postsynaptic response. However, the irritability changes associated with the recovery of the postsynaptic cells from activity are potentially important to facilitation and inhibition. Suppose, for example, that a subthreshold stimulus is acting upon a cell when this cell is excited through other channels. We might expect that during the negative after-potential following the response the previously subthreshold stimulus would become effective. In this way the weak stimulus would keep the cell active until accumulated subnormal excitability again drops it out of action (Erlanger and Gasser, 1936). The period of subnormal excitability following a response can also prevent excitation by a stimulus of threshold intensity, as previously discussed.

In the experimental search for the operation in the spinal cord of these mechanisms, the cord potentials have been examined in relation to facilitation and inhibition of reflex action (Gasser, 1939; Hughes and Gasser, 1934; Hughes, McCouch, and Stewart, 1937). Following a response the motor cells undergo a period of reduced excitability correlated with a positive after-potential. This is sufficient in degree to inhibit reflex responses mediated by these motor cells. The attempts to demonstrate reflex facilitation related to a supernormal period and the negative after-potential in the motor neuron have not been successful (cf. Bernhard, 1947).

Temporal Pattern of Impulses at Synapses

Activity in the single neuron has been resolved into trains of conducted nerve impulses. The functional significance of the temporal pattern of the impulses in an afferent nerve can be evaluated, in part, by observing how these impulses, in combination with those from other cells, are transformed at a synapse into a train of impulses in the postsynaptic neuron. In general, the temporal pattern of the presynaptic impulses is not preserved in the responses of the postsynaptic cell (Bronk, 1939; Bronk and Larrabee, 1940). On the contrary, each impulse arriving at the termination of a presynaptic neuron contributes a transient increment to the state of excitation of a postsynaptic cell. The state of excitation in the postsynaptic cell thus builds up to a degree determined by the frequency of impinging impulses and by the rate of decay of this state of excitation in the postsynaptic cell (cf. Fig. 17). The degree of excitation required to initiate impulses is determined by the specific physical state of the postsynaptic cell.

This summation of excitatory effects is illustrated by studies of synaptic transmission in a sympathetic ganglion. The frequency of response of a postsynaptic cell depends upon the number of active presynaptic fibers. A few presynaptic fibers, stimulated ten times per second, cause a repetitive response of a postsynaptic neuron at about one per second. When more presynaptic fibers are stimulated at the same frequency, this ganglion cells responds at a higher frequency (Fig. 24). The state of excitation developed by presynaptic impulses of a certain frequency in a given number of presynaptic fibers, in conjunction with the contemporary local physical state of the cell (cf. Fig. 7), determines the frequency of conducted impulses in the postsynaptic unit. Since each impulse in one cell does not, in general, produce one impulse in each of the cells on which it terminates, the detail of

the temporal pattern of impulses in one nerve may not be preserved in a multineuronal pathway through the nervous system. However, when the number of active presynaptic cells is great enough, each volley may produce one response in a postsynaptic neuron (Fig. 25).

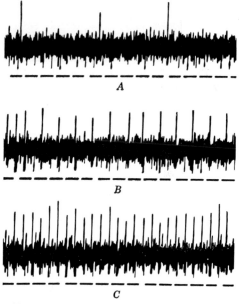

Fig. 24. The frequency of response of a postsynaptic neuron depends upon the number of active presynaptic fibers. A: Stimulation of a few presynaptic fibers at 10 per second. B: Stimulation of more presynaptic fibers at 10 per second. C: Stimulation of all the presynaptic fibers at 10 per second. Time: 0.1-second intervals. (Larrabee and Bronk, unpublished.)

Other properties depend upon the anatomical fact that many presynaptic cells are functionally connected to each postsynaptic cell. If a few preganglionic fibers are excited at low frequency, conducted impulses may appear in a certain number of postsynaptic axons (Fig. 26). However, if additional preganglionic fibers are simultaneously excited at a higher frequency, then more cells respond to the volleys at the low frequency (Fig. 26). Hence the state of excitation of some cells was raised by spatial summation of the stimulatory effects in many presynaptic terminals. Since the frequency of impulses in the several presynaptic neurons will, in general, be different, it is obvious that the nerve cell. There is no possibility of spatial summation of the excitatory effect in the muscle of impulses in several neurons. It is observed, furthermore, that each nerve impulse produces one action potential in each

Fig. 25. Each preganglionic volley of impulses initiated at a time marked by the higher vertical line excited one ganglion cell. (Bronk, 1939.)

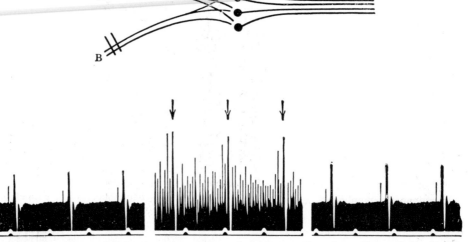

Fig. 26. Above: Schematic representation of the innervation of ganglion cells by fibers from different roots. Below: First record, postganglionic responses to preganglionic volleys in root A; second record, arrows indicate responses to similar volleys during concurrent repetitive stimulation of root B; last record, stimulation of root A alone. Time: 0.2-second intervals. (Bronk, 1939.)

frequency of response in a postsynaptic axon excited by spatial summation cannot be like that of more than one presynaptic cell.

There are systems, however, in which a change in the temporal pattern of impulses does not always occur. At the neuromuscular junction in mammals one axon branches and terminates on many muscle cells, and each striated muscle cell is innervated by one muscle cell, and the temporal pattern of action potentials in skeletal muscle is usually a faithful reproduction of the temporal pattern of impulses in the motor nerve. This kind of transsynaptic relation of neuronal impulses may also occur in some parts of the central nervous system. In that case the temporal pattern of impulses is transmitted unchanged.

After-Discharge and Rhythmic Activity of Neurons

When volleys of impulses in many presynaptic fibers impinge at high frequency upon a ganglion cell, the discharge of impulses in this cell may continue after termination of the presynaptic volleys. This continued discharge of postsynaptic impulses is called an after-discharge. The quantitative aspects of this phenomenon are revealed by recording from a single postsynaptic axon. The impulses may be developed for such a

but they traverse different pathways of interneurons before reaching the motor nerve cell (Forbes, 1922; Lorente de Nó, 1938c). Thus the first response of a motor cell is caused by impulses traversing a monosynaptic pathway through the spinal cord, and the subsequent responses are initiated by impulses arriving later over longer pathways.

The pathways of interneurons thus convert a synchronized volley of afferent impulses into a temporally dispersed series of impulses that impinge at different times upon

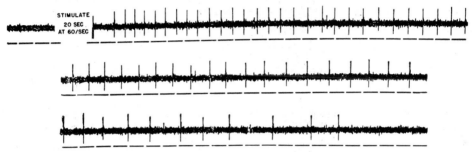

Fig. 27. Repetitive after-discharge from a ganglion cell following 20 seconds of preganglionic stimulation at 60 per second. Continuous record. The last impulse occurred 27 seconds after the stimulation ceased. Time: 0.5-second intervals. (Bronk, 1939.)

long time after the last preganglionic volley (about 30 seconds) that none of the known electrical signs of synaptic activity can be evoked as evidence of the underlying physical process (Fig. 27). It is highly probable that some excitatory substance accumulated by the repetitive activity is the causal agent (Bronk, 1939; Eccles, 1944). The prolonged repetitive response of ganglion cells to continued perfusion by acetylcholine shows that accommodation to such a chemical activator is slow or absent.

The prolonged discharge of impulses in an efferent nerve, after termination of the primary stimulus to the afferent nerve, is a common property of reflex mechanisms. Here the after-discharge occurs because impulses in many different neurons continue to bombard the motor nerve cell. These impulses are all initiated by the primary afferent volley of impulses in the sensory fibers,

a motor neuron. These delayed impulses may serve not to initiate an impulse in the motor cell but merely to increase its state of excitation. Since these impulses arrive during a considerable period of time, a prolonged state of enhanced excitability can be created in this way. This is the prevailing view of the origin of the central excitatory state first observed by Sherrington.

At the time this hypothesis was proposed it was thought that excitatory states created in a neuron by a synchronized volley of presynaptic impulses could not last more than a millisecond. Since then Lloyd (1946a) has shown that, in the cord, such a state of excitation can last at least 13 milliseconds. In addition, Larrabee and Bronk (1947) have shown prolonged facilitation at synapses in a sympathetic ganglion that endures for minutes. It seems, therefore, that the central excitatory state may in some cases be like that of the synaptic mechanism of a sympathetic ganglion during the period of prolonged facilitation (see footnote, p. 111).

The prolonged states of enhanced excitability and of after-discharge following a primary stimulus are prominent characteristics of chains of neurons in the central nervous system. In addition, some aggregates of neurons in the brain exhibit rhythmic changes of electrical potential (Berger, 1929; cf. Davis, 1936). These changes of potential, arising within the brain, can be recorded from the skull (electroencephalogram) or from the exposed cortex (electrocorticogram). The cortex is electrically active even in the absence of sensory impulses (Bremer, 1935). Hence some brain cells must be spontaneously active (Adrian, 1931).

In the occipital cortex the waves occur at about ten per second, the α-rhythm (Adrian and Yamagiwa, 1935). Impulses in the optic nerve, initiated by a flash of light on the retina, penetrate to the cortex and modify this rhythm (Jasper, 1936; Bishop, 1936). Furthermore, periodic flashes of light on the retina can produce periodic changes in the α-rhythm of the occipital cortex (Adrian and Matthews, 1934). The α-rhythm is, therefore, a state of activity of the visual cortex that is affected by sensory stimulation.

The exact function of these rhythmic electrical processes in aggregates of neurons is not known, but it has been suggested that they determine, in some manner, the neurons in the sensory cortex that will be excited by an incoming volley of impulses (Bishop, 1933 and 1936; Bremer, 1947a; Adrian, 1947). According to this hypothesis, these rhythmic processes would determine the pattern of cortical activity created by sensory stimuli.

There are slow potential waves in the motor cortex, too. Here the function is somewhat clearer because the discharge of groups of impulses down the pyramidal tracts is related to the period of the cortical waves (Adrian and Moruzzi, 1939).

It is probable that variations of the electromotive force in the membranes of individual neurons are the source of this rhythmic current flow through the brain (Adrian and Buytendijk, 1931). Furthermore it seems likely that the rhythm depends, in part, upon organized interaction between groups of neurons in the brain (cf. Gerard, 1936; Bishop, 1936). Moreover, as mentioned in Chapter 2, chemical agents can develop rhythmic fluctuations of potential across the membrane of a single axon. It is not impossible, therefore, that the cortical rhythm may arise from electrochemical processes inherent within a neuron (Jasper, 1936, 1948).

REFERENCES

Acheson, G. H. Physiology of neuro-muscular junction: chemical aspects. *Fed. Proc. Amer. Soc. exp. Biol.*, 1948, **7**, 447.

Adrian, E. D. Potential changes in the isolated nervous system of *Dytiscus marginalis*. *J. Physiol.*, 1931, **72**, 132.

Adrian, E. D. General principles of nervous activity. Hughlings Jackson Lecture, January 2, 1947. *Brain*, 1947, **70**, 1.

Adrian, E. D., and F. J. Buytendijk. Potential changes in the isolated brain stem of the goldfish. *J. Physiol.*, 1931, **71**, 121.

Adrian, E. D., and B. H. C. Matthews. The Berger rhythm: potential changes from the occipital lobes in man. *Brain*, 1934, **57**, 355.

Adrian, E. D., and G. Moruzzi. Impulses in the pyramidal tract. *J. Physiol.*, 1939, **97**, 153.

Adrian, E. D., and K. Yamagiwa. Origin of Berger rhythm. *Brain*, 1935, **58**, 323.

Arvanitaki, A. Effects evoked in an axon by the activity of a contiguous one. *J. Neurophysiol.*, 1942, **5**, 89–108.

Barron, D. H., and B. H. C. Matthews. Electrotonus in ventral roots of the spinal cord. *J. Physiol.*, 1936, **87**, 26P–27P.

Barron, D. H., and B. H. C. Matthews. The interpretation of potential changes in the spinal cord. *J. Physiol.*, 1938, **92**, 276.

Bartley, S. H., and G. H. Bishop. The cortical response to stimulation of the optic nerve in the rabbit. *Amer. J. Physiol.*, 1933, **103**, 159.

Berger, H. Über das Elektrenkephalogramm des Menschen. *Arch. Psychiat. Nervenkr.*, 1929, **87**, 527.

Bernhard, C. G. Slow cord potentials of opposite sign correlated to reciprocal function. *Acta Physiol. Scand.*, 1947, **14**, Suppl. 47, 6.

Bishop, G. H. Cyclic changes in excitability of the optic pathway of the rabbit. *Amer. J. Physiol.*, 1933, **103**, 213.

Bishop, G. H. The interpretation of cortical potentials. *Cold Spr. Harb. Sympos. quant. Biol.*, 1936, **4**, 305–319.

Bonnet, V., and F. Bremer. Étude des potentiels électriques de la moëlle épiniere faisant suite chez la grenouille spinale à une ou deux volées d'influx centripètes. *C. R. Soc. Biol. Paris,* 1938, **127,** 806.

Bremer, F. Recherches sur le mécanisme de l'action de la strychnine sur le système nerveux central. II. Étude des modifications, par la strychnine, des électromyogrammes des réflexes du chat et de la grenouille. *Mem. Cour. Acad. Med. Belg.,* 1926, **22,** 1.

Bremer, F. Quelques propriétés de l'activité électrique du cortex cérébral "isolé." *C. R. Soc. Biol. Paris,* 1935, **118,** 1241.

Bremer, F. L'activité électrique spontanée des centres nerveux et l'électroencéphalogramme; Essai d'interprétation. *J. belge Neurol. Psychiat.,* 1947a, **47,** Fasc. 9.

Bremer, F. Nerve and synaptic conduction. *Ann. Rev. Physiol.,* 1947b, **9,** 457.

Brink, F., Jr., D. W. Bronk, and M. G. Larrabee. Chemical excitation of nerve. *Ann. N. Y. Acad. Sci.,* 1946, **47,** 457.

Bronk, D. W. Synaptic mechanisms in sympathetic ganglia. *J. Neurophysiol.,* 1939, **2,** 380.

Bronk, D. W., and M. G. Larrabee. Neural factors determining the frequency of impulses discharged from a ganglion cell. *Amer. J. Physiol.,* 1940, **121,** 320.

Bronk, D. W., M. G. Larrabee, and J. B. Gaylor. The effects of circulatory arrest and oxygen lack on synaptic transmission in a sympathetic ganglion. *J. cell. comp. Physiol.,* 1948, **31,** 193.

Bronk, D. W., S. S. Tower, D. Y. Solandt, and M. G. Larrabee. The transmission of trains of impulses through a sympathetic ganglion and in its postganglionic nerves. *Amer. J. Physiol.,* 1938, **122,** 1–15.

Brooks, C. McC., and J. C. Eccles. Electrical investigation of the monosynaptic pathway through the spinal cord. *J. Neurophysiol.,* 1947a, **10,** 251.

Brooks, C. McC., and J. C. Eccles. An electrical hypothesis of central inhibition. *Nature, Lond.,* 1947b, **159,** 760.

Bullock, T. H. Properties of a single synapse in the stellate ganglion of squid. *J. Neurophysiol.,* 1948, **11,** 343.

de Castro, F. *Cytology and cellular pathology of the nervous system.* New York: Hoeber, 1932.

Cowdry, E. V. *Textbook of histology.* Philadelphia: Lea and Febiger, 1932.

Creed, R. S., D. Denny-Brown, J. C. Eccles, E. G. T. Liddell, and C. S. Sherrington. *Reflex activity of the spinal cord.* Oxford: Clarendon Press, 1932.

Dale, H. H. Transmission of nervous effects by acetylcholine. *Harvey Lect.,* 1936a, 229.

Dale, H. H. Some recent extensions of chemical transmission. *Cold Spr. Harb. Sympos. quant. Biol.,* 1936b.

Dale, H. H. Physiology of the nervous system. *Science,* 1939, **90,** 393.

Davis, H. Some aspects of the electrical activity of the cerebral cortex. *Cold Spr. Harb. Sympos. quant. Biol.,* 1936, **4,** 285.

Eccles, J. C. Slow potential waves in the superior cervical ganglion. *J. Physiol.,* 1935, **85,** 464.

Eccles, J. C. Synaptic potentials and transmission in sympathetic ganglion. *J. Physiol.,* 1943, **101,** 465–483.

Eccles, J. C. The nature of synaptic transmission in a sympathetic ganglion. *J. Physiol.,* 1944, **103,** 27–54.

Eccles, J. C. Synaptic potentials of motoneurones. *J. Neurophysiol.,* 1946, **9,** 87–120.

Eccles, J. C. Acetylcholine and synaptic transmission in the spinal cord. *J. Neurophysiol.,* 1947, **10,** 197–204.

Eccles, J. C., B. Katz, and S. W. Kuffler. Nature of the "endplate potential" in curarized muscle. *J. Neurophysiol.,* 1941, **4,** 362.

Eccles, J. C., B. Katz, and S. W. Kuffler. The effect of eserine on neuromuscular transmission. *J. Neurophysiol.,* 1942, **5,** 211.

Erlanger, J., and H. S. Gasser. *Electrical signs of nervous action.* Philadelphia: University of Pennsylvania Press, 1936.

Feldberg, W., and A. Vartianen. Further observations on the physiology and pharmacology of a sympathetic ganglion. *J. Physiol.,* 1935, **83,** 103.

Forbes, A. The interpretation of spinal reflexes in terms of present knowledge of nerve conduction. *Physiol. Rev.,* 1922, **2,** 361.

Forbes, A., H. Davis, and E. Lambert. The conflict between excitatory and inhibitory effects in a spinal center. *Amer. J. Physiol.,* 1930, **95,** 142.

Gasser, H. S. Axons as samples of nervous tissue. *J. Neurophysiol.,* 1939, **2,** 361.

Gerard, R. W. Factors controlling brain potentials. *Cold Spr. Harb. Sympos. quant. Biol.,* 1936, **4,** 292.

Hill, A. V. Excitation and accommodation in nerve. *Proc. roy. Soc.,* 1936, **B119,** 305.

Hoff, E. C. Central nerve terminals in the mammalian spinal cord and their examination by experimental degeneration. *Proc. roy. Soc.,* 1932, **B111,** 175–188.

Householder, A. S., and H. D. Landahl. *Mathematical biophysics of the central nervous system.* Bloomington, Ill.: Principia Press, 1945.

Hughes, J., and H. S. Gasser. Some properties of the cord potential evoked by a single afferent volley. *Amer. J. Physiol.,* 1934, **108,** 295.

Hughes, J., G. P. McCouch, and W. B. Stewart. Cord potentials in the spinal cat. *Amer. J. Physiol.,* 1937, **118,** 411.

Jasper, H. H. Cortical excitatory state and synchronism in the control of bioelectric autonomous rhythms. *Cold Spr. Harb. Sympos. quant. Biol.,* 1936, **4,** 320.

Jasper, H. H. Charting the sea of brain waves. *Science,* 1948, **108,** 343.

Jasper, H. H., and A. M. Monnier. Transmission of excitation between excised non-myelinated nerves. An artificial synapse. *J. cell. comp. Physiol.*, 1938, **11**, 259–277.

Katz, B. Impedance changes in frogs muscle associated with electrotonic and "endplate" potentials. *J. Neurophysiol.*, 1942, **5**, 169.

Kuffler, S. W. Electric potential changes at an isolated nerve-muscle junction. *J. Neurophysiol.*, 1942a, **5**, 18.

Kuffler, S. W. Further study on transmission in an isolated nerve-muscle fibre preparation. *J. Neurophysiol.*, 1942b, **5**, 309.

Kuffler, S. W. Physiology of neuro-muscular junctions. Electrical aspects. *Fed. Proc. Amer. Soc. exp. Biol.*, 1948, **7**, 447.

Larrabee, M. G., and D. W. Bronk. Prolonged facilitation of synaptic excitation in sympathetic ganglia. *J. Neurophysiol.*, 1947, **10**, 139–154.

Lloyd, D. P. C. A direct central inhibitory action of dromically conducted impulses. *J. Neurophysiol.*, 1941, **4**, 184–190.

Lloyd, D. P. C. Facilitation and inhibition of spinal motoneurons. *J. Neurophysiol.*, 1946a, **9**, 421.

Lloyd, D. P. C. Integrative pattern of excitation and inhibition in two-neuron reflex arcs. *J. Neurophysiol.*, 1946b, **9**, 439.

Lloyd, D. P. C. Post-tetanic potentiation of presynaptic actions in the spinal cord. *Fed. Proc. Amer. Soc. exp. Biol.*, 1949, **8**, 99.

Lorente de Nó, R. Vestibulo-ocular reflex arc. *Arch. Neurol. Psychiat., Chicago*, 1933, **30**, 245.

Lorente de Nó, R. Limits of variation of the synaptic delay of motoneurons. *J. Neurophysiol.*, 1938a, **1**, 187.

Lorente de Nó, R. Synaptic stimulation as a local process. *J. Neurophysiol.*, 1938b, **1**, 194.

Lorente de Nó, R. Analysis of the activity of the chains of internuncial neurons. *J. Neurophysiol.*, 1938c, **1**, 207.

Lorente de Nó, R. *Transmission of impulses through cranial motor nuclei. Symposium on the synapse.* Springfield, Ill.: Thomas, 1939.

Lorente de Nó, R., and H. T. Graham. Recovery cycle of motoneurons. *Amer. J. Physiol.*, 1938, **123**, 388–399.

MacIntosh, F. C. Liberation of acetylcholine by the perfused superior cervical ganglion. *J. Physiol.*, 1938, **94**, 155.

Monnier, A. M. Physical and chemical aspects of neuromuscular transmission. *Cold Spr. Harb. Sympos. quant. Biol.*, 1936, **4**, 111.

Nachmansohn, D. Chemical mechanism of nerve activity. *Ann. N. Y. Acad. Sci.*, 1946, **47**, 395.

Pantin, C. F. A. Functional transmission of stimuli in lower animals. *Proc. roy. Soc.*, 1937, **B123**, 397.

Renshaw, B. Activity in the simplest spinal reflex pathways. *J. Neurophysiol.*, 1940, **3**, 373.

Vogt, M. Potassium changes in the stimulated superior cervical ganglion. *J. Physiol.*, 1936, **86**, 258.

4

Sensory Mechanisms

T. C. RUCH
University of Washington

The physiology of the sensory systems was, until shortly before World War II, mainly concerned with the problem of localization. The localization or "where" problem is the province of anatomy, and much that has passed for physiology has been functional anatomy. The ultimate concern of physiology is "how," not where. Yet little, except behavioristic studies (e.g. correlation of stimulus and response), can be accomplished until the where is known. This is axiomatic. Moreover, only when physiological analysis penetrates deeper than the morphological level to the cellular level (e.g. single-unit analysis) and to the cytological level (e.g. histochemistry, membrane phenomena, synaptic transmission, etc.) do the where and how problems merge. In relatively simple structures in which cells and their processes are geometrically organized, as in peripheral nerve, this order of progression has brought innumerable successes. One may venture the prediction that structures that are not so arranged, such as the cerebral cortex, will not readily yield to single-unit analysis. And, if analysis is accomplished, synthesis will probably not be realized by mere multiplication. Methods of physiological analysis must be devised to deal with manifold structures and with circular rather than parallelolinear organizations. Electronics is a double-edged sword; it provides the instruments for stimulation and recording, and it provides the analogies and, with its mathematics, the analysis. The outlines of things to come are now discernible. With the analysis of perception and judgment being undertaken on a physiological basis (Marshall and Talbot, 1942; Pitts and McCulloch, 1947), there is new hope for the convergence of physiology and psychology.

SURVEY OF NEUROLOGICAL TECHNIQUES

Early neurophysiological investigation depended heavily upon the techniques of ablation and transection (Galen, 131-201 A.D.; Robert Whytt, 1714–1766; Charles Bell, 1774–1842; Magendie, 1783–1855; Flourens, 1794–1867; and Marshall Hall, 1790–1857). Electrical stimulation was made possible when an anatomist, Luigi Galvani (1737–1798), performed his fundamental experiments on the excitability of nerve and muscle, including stimulation by contact with "dissimilar metals," and when Volta developed the voltaic pile in 1800. Electrical stimulation played a small part in differentiating the functions of the posterior and anterior roots of the spinal cord. But the effective use of electrical stimulation in research on the central nervous system dates from the last decades of the nineteenth century (Fritsch and Hitzig, 1871; Ferrier, 1876; Bubnoff and Heidenhain, 1881) and the early decades of this century (Sherrington, Cushing, and many others).

To these methods of ablation and stimulation has been added the recording of evoked and spontaneous potentials from the central nervous system. Galvani's experiment (1794) on "contraction without metals," in which the injury potential of a muscle stimulates a second nerve-muscle preparation, is counted the first demonstration of animal electricity. The action potential, because of its fleeting nature, was not demonstrated until nearly half a century later (Matteucci's experiment with the "rheoscopic frog," and DuBois-Reymond's demonstration with physical instruments).

The early application of this technique to the central nervous system by Gotch and Horsley in 1891 was beset with technical difficulties; effective electrical recording from the central nervous system, and from nerve and muscle, awaited the introduction of vacuum-tube amplification which permitted the use of low-sensitivity, rapid, linear recording devices such as the iron-spring oscillograph (Adrian, Matthews) and the cathode-ray oscillograph (Gasser and Erlanger in 1923). Apart from Hans Berger's pioneer work in establishing the technique of electro-encephalography, the study of the electrical manifestations of central nervous system activity has been prosecuted for barely two decades. In fact it has been recognized only recently that action potentials recorded from nerve tracts are not of the same configuration as those in nerve trunks suspended in a dielectric (air) because a mass of nervous tissue constitutes a volume conductor (Lorente de Nó, 1939; O'Leary, 1941).

Ancillary to these physiological techniques for the study of the brain are the operative procedures by which the brain is made available for stimulation, ablation, or recording *in a normal physiological condition*. The modern technique for surgical exposure and manipulation of the brain owes much to Halsted and Cushing, and to the adaptation of that technique to the animal brain by Fulton and Keller (1932), the Johns Hopkins group, and others. Postoperative infection and epilepsy are no longer seen in experimental laboratories. Barbiturate anesthesia has

simplified the surgical procedures. Accurately controlled stimulation and electrolytic destruction of focal regions deep within the substance of the brain became possible with the development of the stereotaxic instrument (Fig. 1). This instrument is essentially

FIG. 1. Horsley-Clarke stereotaxic instrument applied to the head of a monkey. The horizontal bar seen against the shoulder is the ear bar, inserted into the external auditory meatus; the other fixed points, the inferior margins of the orbits, are concealed by the instrument.

a frame that can be fixed to the skull at the external auditory meatus and the inferior margin of the orbits. The frame carries racks and pinions with suitable millimeter scales by which a stimulating or an electrolytic electrode can be maneuvered to any point in the horizontal plane and introduced to any desired depth. Developed by Clarke and Horsley in 1905, this technique was lost sight of during World War I only to be revived and brought to a high perfection by Ranson and his school since 1928. Its use is described by Ranson (1934).

The experimental animal is an inescapable variable that must be reckoned with in interpreting results. The neurophysiology, neuroanatomy, and behavior of living organisms at all stages of ontogeny and phylogeny are traditionally and properly the legitimate objects of investigation by the comparative psychologist. However, the human physiolo-

mate physiology, which has been formally expressed by Fulton (1937–39), was manifested by 1925–1930 and has steadily increased (Ruch and Fulton, 1942). Guides to the literature on nonhuman primate anatomy, physiology, and behavior, and to primate colony management, taxonomy, etc., are available (Kennard, Ruch, and Fulton,

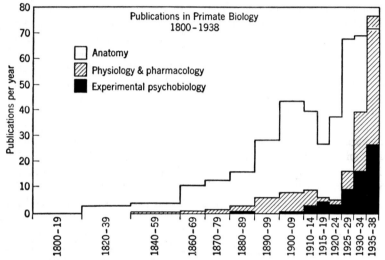

Fig. 2. A graph showing the growth of primate literature since 1800. Note the shift in emphasis from morphological to functional studies, and the acceleration of the tempo in the use of the primates for functional studies. The analysis was based on Ruch (1941) and described by Ruch and Fulton (1942).

gist and psychologist are properly interested in man and are sometimes actually misled by experimentation on the lower animals. The higher primates, the monkeys and apes, alone of the phylogenetic series have a cerebral cortex morphologically comparable to that of man. Encephalization and corticalization of function have progressed steadily throughout the mammalian series. The use of primates in experiments has, therefore, been considerably stressed. The value of the primate in neurophysiological research was early recognized by the English neurologists, Ferrier, Sherrington, and Horsley, but, like the stereotaxic technique, it was lost sight of during and for a time following World War I (Fig. 2). However, renewed interest in pri-

1946; Ruch, 1941; Yerkes, 1943; and Zuckerman and Fulton, 1934).

A further trend in experimental neurology is the development of methods for objective and quantitative observation of sensory, motor, and other types of behavior, and the use of these methods in studying the localization of function in the brain. The clinical neurological examination used by the pioneers of cerebral physiology, when supported by detailed protocols, continues to be fruitful, especially when the investigator is trained in the neurological clinic. Pavlov, the physiologist, early applied the conditioned-reflex method to problems of cortical localization; and Franz and Lashley worked with the objective techniques developed by the early comparative psychologists (Yerkes, Thorndike, and Watson *).

The growth of physiological knowledge is bound up with the growth of anatomical knowledge of the nervous system. Histology provides not only the control which determines the extent and locus of an experimental lesion, but also the guide for experimentation. The histology of the cortex (cytoarchitecture, the study of the cellular pattern; and myeloarchitecture, the study of the fiber stratification) guides the physiologist in placing lesions and provides a topographical frame and a language for the description of experimental lesions. Most commonly used for this purpose are Brodmann's demarcation and numeration of cytoarchitectural areas (Brodmann, 1909; and Fig. 3) and the modification of them by Vogt and Vogt (1919) and others (e.g. McCulloch, 1944b). Many find Brodmann unsatisfactory, and von Bonin and Bailey (1947) have published a monographic revision of the cortical cytoarchitecture of the macaque and have presented a new terminology based upon that of von Economo. Functional cyto- and myeloarchitecture in which the connections of neuron to neuron are studied by silver impregnation (Lorente de Nó, 1943) may

* Sherrington (1906) closes his chapter on the excitability of the motor cortex with the following prescient remark:

. . . The results before you must appear a meagre contribution toward the greater problems of the working of the brain; their very poverty may help to emphasize the necessity for resorting to new methods of experimental inquiry in order to advance in this field. New methods of promise seem to me those lately followed by Franz, Thorndyke, Yerkes, and others; for instance, the influence of experimental lesions of the cortex on skilled actions recently and individually, *i.e.* experientially, acquired. Despite a protest ably voiced by v. Uexküll, comparative psychology seems not only a possible experimental science but an existent one. By combining methods of comparative psychology (*e.g.* the labyrinth test) with the methods of experimental physiology, investigation may be expected ere long to furnish new data of importance toward the knowledge of movement as an outcome of the working of the brain. [P. 307.]

be contrasted with the cartography of Brodmann. Correlation of such information with electrical events is attempted (O'Leary, 1940, 1941). Silver impregnation, which shows the ramifications and interconnections of neurons, was first used by Golgi and Cajal. For some unknown but fortunate reasons, only an occasional cell precipitates the silver salts, which simplifies enormously our ability to follow the complex neuronal pattern of the cerebral cortex. Contemporary studies by Polyak on the retina (1941), and by Lorente de Nó (1934, 1943) and by O'Leary (1940, 1944) on the spinal cord, thalamus, and cerebral cortex determine the course of experimentation on synaptic and cortical physiology.

The tracts of the spinal cord and brain present a bewildering complexity under the microscope. To simplify this picture, Flechsig (1883) took advantage of the fact that various systems of tracts myelinate at different periods during pre- and postnatal development. A more critical means of accomplishing the same end is the method of experimental degeneration. Ablation and transection cause a degenerative fragmentation process in the myelin sheaths in those portions of axons separated from the cell body, so-called "secondary" or Wallerian degeneration. Such changes in the myelin sheaths are accompanied by chemical changes, altering the affinity to various dyes. Weigert's stain (hematoxylin, 1882) reveals the degeneration by failure to stain, i.e. affords a picture in negative. In Marchi's method (1886) mordanting with a chromic salt, followed by osmic acid, selectively stains degenerating myelin sheaths and gives a positive picture of black granules or dots against a yellowish-brown field. This method suffers from artifacts, stains only myelinated fibers, and must be carefully applied and critically interpreted.

Degenerative changes occur in the cell bodies of certain neurons if their axons are sectioned — "retrograde degeneration." These are revealed by toluidine blue and other anil:ne dyes, as Nissl originally showed in 1892. This method has been successfully employed by Le Gros Clark and Boggon (1935) and retrograde degeneration establishes which thalamic nucleus projects to the particular area ablated.

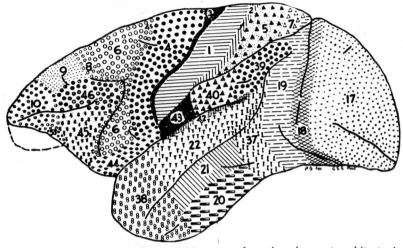

FIG. 3. Areas of the cerebral cortex of *Macaca mulatta*, based on cytoarchitectonics and physiological neuronography. The cerebral hemisphere is shown in side view, and the names of some of the principal fissures are given in the legend of Fig. 7. Apart from the use of Brodmann numbers and the inclusion of areas 8, 4s, and 2, the parcelation of the sensory motor cortex and the posterior parietal region is similar to that of von Bonin and Bailey (1947). Areas 8, 4s, and 2 are functionally distinct but not cytoarchitecturally recognizable.

The following list will aid in identifying some of the cortical regions referred to in the text by name. Identification is necessarily only approximate.

4	motor area, precentral gyrus
4s	strip area of Marion Hines
6	premotor area
8	"eye fields"
4, 6, 8	motor areas
9, 10, 45, 46	prefrontal area, lobe or lobule, frontal association area, orbitofrontal area
3, 1, ?2	primary sensory area, postcentral gyrus
5, 7, 40, 39	posterior parietal lobule. Note that areas 40 and 39 are included in Brodmann areas 5 and 7
17	striate area
18	parastriate area located on the simian or lunate sulcus
19	paristriate area
18, 19, 5, 7, 39, 40, 37	parieto-occipitotemporal region

The upper end of the superior temporal sulcus is just below the number 39, the intraparietal sulcus just above, and the simian sulcus is centered in area 18.

by Walker (1938) in studying the connections of the thalamus and cortex. The ablation of a cortical area truncates the axons running to it, and the locus of the resulting These two types of degeneration (secondary and retrograde) stop, in accordance with Waldeyer's neuronal doctrine, at the boundaries of the neuron injured. In the third type of degenerative reaction — "transneuronal degeneration," first observed by von Gudden — the cell body on which the injured neuron terminates is affected. The pathological changes are atrophic in character and are sufficiently pronounced for study in only a few neuron systems, notably the lateral geniculate body.

With the exception of the work of Cajal and of those he has taught or influenced, neuroanatomy has, until recently, been largely the study of myelinated fibers organized into tracts and the organized nuclei giving rise to them, i.e. the cities and arterial highways of the nervous system. The reticular substance of the brain which often fills the spaces between the tracts and nuclei is little known. It consists of small clumps of cell bodies embedded in a dense pile of fibers with no easily detectable pattern. However, important motor functions of the reticular substance have been demonstrated (Magoun and Rhines; A. A. Ward). Another gap in our knowledge has come about through excessive dependence on the myelin sheath stains, which are incapable of demonstrating bare axons. The axon cylinder, being an extension of the cell body, is, like the dendrites, stained only by silver stains. Greater use is now being made of silver stains. Unmyelinated axons in peripheral nerves have been extensively studied by Ranson, and systematic study of the unmyelinated fibers of the central nervous system has been undertaken, notably by Lassek and by Glees. The central and peripheral nervous systems are exceedingly rich in such fibers, and their physiological significance remains to be worked out.

Because the terminations of myelinated fibers are bare axon buttons or loops, the exact termination of tracts cannot be studied by myelin sheath stains; again silver impregnation is required. Unfortunately, differentiation of normal from degenerating terminal buttons cannot as yet be made with certainty.

Finally, the phase and the electron microscopes, and the youthful science of histochemistry, including the use of tracer elements, are contributing to an understanding of the basic structure and metabolism of nervous tissue.

THALAMUS AND CORTEX

The study of these structures since 1935 has reached a stage of synthesis in which a variety of functional and structural information can be correlated. The purely morphological definition and ticketing of the thalamic nuclei has given way to a parcelation based not only upon cellular and fiber characteristics but upon the origin and termination of the thalamofugal fiber systems. This knowledge of thalamocortical projections has profoundly affected the division of the cerebral cortex into functional regions. The topographical arrangement within systems of fibers passing to and from the thalamus has been intensively investigated. This work has provided a structural framework that has led to physiological deductions and experiments.

A second point of view considers the thalamus and somatosensory cortex as a unit, and further developments in this direction are clearly to be expected. Only a small part of the primate thalamus has purely subcortical connections. The activities of the remainder are expressed via thalamocortical projections. Therefore the thalamic contribution to sensation and perception obviously cannot be deduced from decortication experiments; the thalamus and cortex are a functional unit. A second reason for this belief is that the thalamus receives an extensive projection from the cerebral cortex. Whereas these fibers were once thought to be inhibitory, later developments in neurophysiology have directed attention to reverberating circuits, i.e. an interplay between thalamus and cortex, and cortex and thalamus. This interaction can be studied only by electrical methods. The participation of the thalamus in such reverberating circuits has also been demonstrated in connection with cortically initiated movements (see Chapter 5).

Another trend receives impetus from the fact that the thalamus projects not merely to the postcentral gyrus but to a wide expanse of the cerebral cortex, including the morphological language is necessary for description, and it can be gained by a study of Fig. 4. The thalamus, a part of the diencephalon or " 'tween-brain," consists of two egg-shaped gray masses separated by the third ventricle. Each half is divided by a vertical plate of fibers, the internal medullary lamina, which bifurcates anteriorly to form a Y. In this fashion the nuclei are

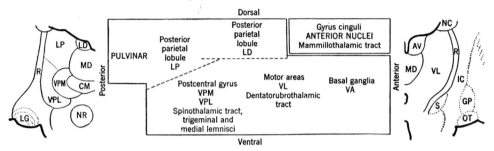

FIG. 4. Center diagram shows a schematic longitudinal view through the lateral nuclear mass of the thalamus. The abbreviations represent the principal thalamic nuclei. Projections *to* the thalamus are shown below the abbreviation; projections *from* the thalamus are shown above. Diagrams to the left and right are cross sections through the posterior (left) and anterior (right) thalamus.

Abbreviations: AV, n. anteroventralis; CM, n. centrum medianum; GP, globus pallidus; IC, internal capsule; LD, n. lateralis dorsalis; LG, lateral geniculate body; LP, n. lateralis posterior; MD, n. medialis dorsalis; MG, medial geniculate body; NC, n. caudatus; NR, n. ruber; OT, optic tract; VA, n. ventralis anterior; VL, n. ventralis lateralis; VPM, n. ventralis posteromedialis; VPL, n. ventralis posterolateralis.

motor areas and the parietal and frontal association areas. Conversely, the postcentral gyrus of the cerebral cortex gives origin to some fibers in the pyramidal tract. As a consequence, the distinction between the motor and sensory cortical areas is lessened, and the concept of association areas is broadened. A further example of the broadening concept of the sensory mechanisms is that the cerebellum, once considered "motor" in function, is perhaps implicated in sensory processes.

Anatomico-physiological classification of the thalamic nuclei. The connections of the thalamus far outweigh in importance the details of its cytoarchitecture and nuclear constitution to the understanding of thalamocortical function. However, a minimum divided into anterior, lateral, and medial nuclear groups. The medial portion of the medial group is separately distinguished as the midline nuclei. The posterior extension of the lateral mass constitutes the posterior nuclei. The lateral mass itself is divided, in turn, into a ventral and lateral group. Thus the nucleus ventralis posteromedialis (arcuate nucleus) is the most caudal and medial part of the ventral portion of the lateral mass.

A classification of the thalamic nuclei, which is proving meaningful from a functional point of view, is given below. It is based on the connections of the nuclei determined by appropriate degeneration studies carried out principally by Walker (1938) and by Le Gros Clark (1935).

Nuclei with subcortical connections. This group does not undergo retrograde degeneration after complete decortication, and hence we conclude that it sends no fibers to the cerebral cortex. This group is made up of nuclei scattered along the midline and along the internal medullary lamina. One of the intralaminar nuclei, the centromedian, is large and well organized and has undergone considerable phylogenetic development. These scattered nuclei must serve whatever sensory function is left to the decorticated animal. They form a surprisingly small portion of the thalamus in the primates. The main role of the thalamus, therefore, lies not in its functioning independently of the cortex, but in its thalamocortical relations.

Cortical relay nuclei. These are defined as those nuclei that receive fibers directly from the ascending afferent systems and project to the cerebral cortex. All sensory pathways, with the exception of the olfactory, are synaptically interrupted (relayed) in the diencephalon. The relay nucleus for vision is the lateral geniculate body; for audition it is the medial geniculate body; and for somatic sensation it is the nuclei ventralis posteromedialis and ventralis posterolateralis. As shown in Fig. 5, the latter nucleus receives impulses from the spinal nerves via the spinothalamic tract and via the posterior columns–mesial fillet system. It receives impulses from the face via the trigeminal lemniscus. In turn, it projects to the postcentral gyrus of the cerebral cortex (areas 3-1-2 in Fig. 3), the classic "primary somato-sensory area." This leaves a fourth principal relay nucleus (nucleus ventralis lateralis, or the lateroventral nucleus) quite different from the other three in its connections. Numerous fibers pass from it to the precentral gyrus of the cerebral cortex (areas 4 and 6 in Fig. 3) — the classic "motor area" — and it receives fibers from the dentate nucleus of the cerebellum. By this tract the cortical motor area is in potential connection via the cerebellum with the spinocerebellar systems, mainly proprioceptive in function.

Only functional studies can decide whether or not this system of fibers is a part of the sensory mechanism.

Association nuclei. These thalamic nuclei project to the cerebral cortex but, unlike the

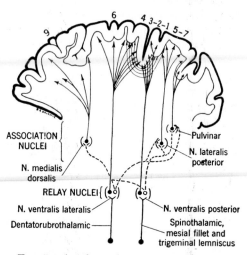

Fig. 5. A schematic representation of the thalamic nuclei and their connections, as determined by the method of retrograde degeneration. The frontal lobe is to the left, the occipital to the right. The numbers along the surface of the cerebral cortex are Brodmann cytoarchitectural areas; the deep indentation near the number 3 is the fissure of Rolando; area 3, the area of densest projection, is buried on the posterior wall of the fissure; the order is 3–1–2. The connections shown by dotted lines are not established as definitely as those indicated by solid lines or arrows. Filled and unfilled circles represent cell bodies. Only the fiber systems to the "potential sensory area" are shown; therefore, nuclei with purely subcortical connections, as well as the medial and lateral geniculate bodies, are omitted. (After Ruch, 1946.)

relay nuclei, do not receive impulses direct from the ascending sensory systems. Their afferent input appears to be from the thalamic relay nuclei. Their projection is to the so-called "association areas" of the cerebral cortex, hence the choice of name, association nuclei. The principal association nuclei and the cortical termination of their projections are as follows:

Nucleus	Cortical Projection
Dorsomedial	Frontal lobe anterior to motor areas
Dorsolateral Posterolateral	Parietal lobe posterior to primary sensory area
Pulvinar	Junction of parietal, occipital, and temporal lobes

These association nuclei form perhaps one-third of the thalamic nuclear mass. The fact of a projection to the association areas has long been known, but the extent and details of this projection have only recently been appreciated.

The newer knowledge of the thalamocortical projection systems provides several guiding principles in the design and interpretation of experiments. The existence of association nuclei suggests that the thalamus must carry out some integration of impulses, which must be expressed through the cerebral cortex. Since decortication simply blocks their "way in" to the cortex, the work of these nuclei can never be learned by that procedure. Therefore, as has been pointed out above, the thalamus and the cortex are best considered as a unit. A second prediction from the anatomical data is that the association areas of the cerebral cortex are potentially sensory areas, an assumption that has received experimental demonstration. Third, the existence of an extensive projection to association areas must alter our ideas of the function of such areas. The association areas, especially those in the frontal lobe, cannot simply elaborate information reaching the primary sensory areas and translate that information into action via the motor areas. The frontal association areas have their own "way in" and their own "way out," and it is not surprising that recent studies show that they subserve functions not implied by the term "association area."

A Functional Terminology for the Cerebral Cortex

The design and description of cortical localization experiments was first in terms of lobes, gyri, and sulci. Later cytoarchitectural studies by Brodmann provided a language of the cortex. This has proved a difficult language and has become a babel of tongues. The difficulty of establishing recognizably different types of cellular architecture and of knowing which areas are homologous in different primate brains — even the possibility of any but the simplest parcelation into cytoarchitectural areas — renders the subject highly technical. Von Bonin (1944) and McCulloch (1944b) have embodied the work of Le Gros Clark and Walker in a terminology based on *sectors*, a suggestion that promises to be of value (Fig. 6). A sector is defined by the thalamic nuclei from which it receives impulses. For example, the central sector is the cortical region receiving impulses from the lateral nuclear mass (both its lateral and ventral portions). A subsector may receive impulses from a single nucleus. Other suggestions for systematizing terminology are that "area" designate a region having similar cytoarchitecture, that "field" designate a somatotopic division, as the arm field or the leg field, and that "region" designate a group of functionally related areas.

The potential somatosensory cortex. This term was coined (Ruch, 1943, p. 359) to include all that portion of the cerebral cortex that receives projection fibers from the thalamic nuclei that are directly or indirectly connected with the trigeminal and medial lemnisci, and the spinothalamic tract. "Sensory" is used here in the broadest sense, i.e. without regard to mentalistic implications of "conscious sensation." The question, therefore, is to determine not so much *whether* the subareas of the potential sensory area are sensory, but in *what way* they are sensory. Whether these areas subserve conscious sensation may be deduced from anatomical data but must be finally decided by functional studies.

The potential somatosensory cortex has two parameters. Along the anterior-posterior axis one finds a succession of vertically running bands or zones with different cytoarchitecture and projections. By analogy with cortical motor function, zonal difference in kind of function along this parameter is

face or from strychninization of the cerebral cortex (intracortical neuronography), and (4) ablation in animals, combined with objective behavior techniques.

In the strychnine method of studying cortical localization, introduced by Dusser de Barenne (1924), a small piece of filter paper soaked in strychnine is applied to the cortical surface. The animal bites, licks, scratches,

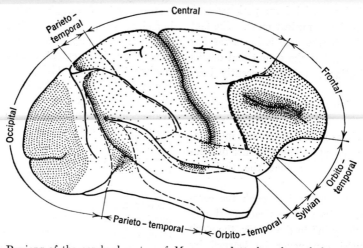

Fig. 6. Regions of the cerebral cortex of *Macaca mulatta* based on thalamocortical projections and physiological neuronography. The stippling represents the density of thalamocortical projections. (After McCulloch, 1944*b*.)

to be expected. On the inferior-superior axis, extending from the midline nearly to the sylvian fissure, is a well-documented topographical localization which is most marked in the postcentral gyrus and also quite marked in the precentral gyrus. The problem of functional localization of sensory process in the cerebral cortex thus is twofold: (1) the localization of the areas devoted to various segments of the body surface and (2) the localization of the kinds and levels of sensory and quasi-sensory functions. By and large, a given experimental approach yields some data on both points. These approaches are: (1) histological studies, (2) electrical stimulation in man and strychnine stimulation in animals, (3) evoked potentials from stimulation of the body sur-

or examines some point on its body surface. In short, it experiences a projected paresthesia. It also exhibits hyperalgesia and hyperasthesia over some specific area of the body surface. The method of evoked potentials consists in recording the pattern of electrical activity on the cortex in response to stimulation of a single point on the body surface. The technique of physiological neuronography is discussed in detail in a later section.

*The prefrontal sector.** The prefrontal sector, or lobule, despite a rich projection

* The expression "prefrontal," although established in usage, is avoided by some authors on the grounds that it implies a structure "in front of the frontal lobe." However, White gives as a specific meaning of *"prae"* in its proper usage "at the tip or extremity of," e.g. in *praecido.* (*A*

from the thalamus, has no known somato-sensory function. However, the underneath or orbital surface of this sector receives viscerosensory impulses from the lungs by way of the vagus nerve. Also, the cingular gyrus, lying in the longitudinal fissure that separates the two hemispheres, may receive some visceral impulses via the mammillotha-lamic tract and the anterior nuclei of the thalamus. Stimulation of these two regions in monkeys produces visceral or combined visceral and somatic patterns of responses, some of which are interpretable as emotional behavior. Ablation of the latter area in monkeys induces changes in the sphere of emotion, apathy, loss of fear of man, and changes in the reaction of the monkeys to one another.

The significance of the projection from the medial nucleus to the prefrontal sector is largely a matter of inference from anatomi-cal considerations. Walker (1938) suggests that "The intricate arrangement of this nucleus would appear to be a mechanism for the integration of synthesized somatosen-sory and visceral impulses from the adjoin-ing lateral nuclear mass and midline nuclei, respectively, and their relay to the cortex of the prefrontal region."

The precentral subsector. That this sec-tor of the cerebral cortex is the focus for cortically initiated movements has been proved by a variety of techniques since Fritsch and Hitzig's original demonstration of the electrical excitability of the motor cor-tex. There is a growing body of evidence that this sector is, in some manner, concerned with sensory processes, in the broadest sense of the word. Application of strychnine to the precentral gyrus of the monkey, con-taining the cortical motor areas, produces

Latin-English Dictionary. (9th Ed.) Boston: 1893.) Prefrontal has not proved confusing, whereas "frontal," by American usage, means the whole lobe lying in front of the central fissure and includes the motor areas. "Orbito-frontal" has recently been suggested as a substitute for "prefrontal," but this terms does not entirely avoid the ambiguity of "frontal."

signs of sensory activity similar to those fol-lowing application of strychnine to the post-central gyrus (Dusser de Barenne, 1924, 1934; Fig. 7). Stimulation in conscious human subjects at the time of surgical opera-tion yields sensory responses from the pre-central and postcentral gyrus alike, although the responses from the postcentral gyrus are

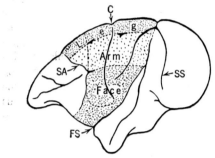

FIG. 7. A schematic view of the macaque cortex, as seen from the side, showing the po-tential somatosensory area as demarcated by strychninization. Note that this area, shown by stippling, extends anteriorly throughout the motor area and posteriorly to include the posterior parietal area. The prefrontal lobule, though in receipt of thalamic projection, does not produce sensory symptoms when strychnin-ized. FS, sylvian fissure; C, central or ro-landic fissure; SA, arcuate sulcus; SS, simian sulcus, i.e. the lateral parieto-occipital sulcus.

more numerous (Rasmussen and Penfield, 1947). Sensory responses from the pre-central gyrus persist after ablation of the adjacent portion of the postcentral gyrus, and the phenomena cannot be ascribed to any form of current spread or to spread of impulses to the postcentral gyrus. Stimula-tion of posterior spinal roots causes electrical activity in the precentral cortex (Woolsey, Chang, and Bard, 1947). Since evoked po-tentials in the precentral sector are not ob-served from stimulation of the skin, this per-haps indicates that only proprioceptive im-pulses reach the precentral sector. Ablation experiments offer suggestive evidence that hopping reactions and weight discrimination are to some degree carried out by the motor areas, since these functions persist after parietal lobectomy. Bard and Woolsey (Bard, 1938) believe that the hopping reaction is little affected by parietal lobectomy, although there is not complete agreement on this point. Considerable ability at weight discrimination survives parietal lobectomy, even in chimpanzees (Ruch, 1935; Ruch, Fulton, and German, 1938). That hopping reactions and weight discrimination are functions of the precentral sector is difficult to prove because the cortical motor apparatus is needed for the manipulations involved in the tests. However, supporting evidence has been found by approaching the problem at the subcortical level and thus avoiding motor disturbances. (Sjöqvist and Weinstein, 1942). When the sensory components destined to reach the precentral sector (dentatothalamic fibers) are included in a destruction of the main ascending somatosensory systems, the disturbances of proprioceptive functions, including weight discrimination, are rendered more severe.

Although the evidence of a sensory function on the part of the precentral sector comes from several directions, the evidence is not conclusive. However, there is a growing tendency to think, not of distinct sensory and motor areas, but of a paracentral sensorimotor area. This practice is further justified by recent evidence implicating the postcentral area in motor functions.

Sensory Representation in the Cerebellum

The thalamic projection to the precentral gyrus is derived from the cerebellum via the dentatorubrothalamic tract with a synaptic interruption in the lateroventral nucleus of the thalamus (Fig. 5). Until recently this system was considered purely proprioceptive in function because, in turn, the afferent input to the cerebellum was thought to be entirely proprioceptive. However, studies from three laboratories have clearly demonstrated that exteroceptive sensory fibers — cutaneous, auditory, and visual — pass to the cerebellum (Adrian, 1940; Dow and An-

derson, 1942; Snider and Stowell, 1944). Moreover there is evidence from studies of evoked potentials that the spinocerebellar projection is topographically organized. Stimulation of fore- and hindfoot activates different cerebellar cortical areas. Tactile impulses of the feet are doubly represented, once in the anterior lobe and again in the posteriorly situated paramedian lobe. Each half of the body surface is represented in both lateral halves of the cerebellum.

That the cerebellum receives exteroceptive impulses illustrates the necessity for scrutinizing with care the supposed facts of neurophysiology. Few "facts" were more universally accepted prior to these experiments than the proprioceptive character of the spinocerebellar projections. As a comfortless *arrière pensée* comes the thought, "How could anatomical studies, in which spinal tract fibers are on the whole nameless, ever have led to such a conclusion?"

Open to re-evaluation is the well-established clinical finding that neither disturbance of proprioceptive nor disturbance of cutaneous sensory function is detectable in human cases of cerebellar damage. That this fact excludes the cerebellum from a role in sensation is a conclusion that would be justified only if cerebellar damage were added to interference with the parietal lobe of the cerebral cortex or the main afferent pathway to it, as in the experiments of Sjöqvist and Weinstein (1942). Provisionally, the cerebellum must be included in the potential sensory mechanism. It is not improbable that the dentatothalamocortical pathway is concerned with sensory processes involved in the control of movement, which do not enter consciousness, but it is by no means proved.

The discovery of a projection of exteroceptive impulses to the cortex, via the cerebellum, may aid in explaining several facts of somatic sensation otherwise puzzling. As pointed out above, the conscious sensory responses to stimulation of the precentral gyrus are cutaneous as well as proprioceptive, as are the monkey's responses to strychninization of that area.

Posterior Parietal Sector

Ablation experiments on monkeys and chimpanzees trained to discriminate lifted weights establish the ability of the posterior parietal sector to serve sensory functions (Ruch, 1935; Ruch, Fulton, and German, 1938). The evidence is as follows: (1) Ablation of the postcentral sector, especially in monkeys, does not produce grave, enduring disturbances of weight discrimination. With retraining, the preoperative level of performance can be re-established after such lesions. This proves that the primary sensory areas of the postcentral sector are not the sole "way-in" to the cerebral cortex (assuming corticalization of somatic sensation). (2) The initial impairment of the ability to discriminate weight (following ablation of the posterior parietal sector) approximately equals that following postcentral lesions. Evans (1935) found grave disturbances of discriminative functions in man after small posterior parietal lesions. The higher level sensory functions — localization, two-point threshold, etc. — were especially affected. This suggests that the whole parietal lobe is involved in discriminatory sensory processes. At one time it was thought that impulses reached the postcentral sector and then were relayed to the posterior parietal sector for "elaboration." This is certainly not the sole pathway of sensory impulses through the cortex (Fig. 5). Because recovery virtually to preoperative level occurs after the postcentral lesions, the parietal region must be able to function independently of the postcentral region. Moreover, ablation of the two subsectors in one stage or seriatim (parietal lobectomy) produces a deeper and more persistent discriminatory defect than does ablation of either of the constituent areas separately. If the posterior region merely elaborates impulses from the postcentral subsector, ablation of it would be the equivalent of parietal lobectomy, which is

not the case. One reservation must be made, however. If, as suggested above, the precentral sector is also a "way in" to the cortex, there is the possibility that impulses are relayed from the precentral region to the posterior parietal lobe. Testing of this hypothesis was attempted but was unsuccessful because of the interference with the manipulatory abilities needed for the sensory examination.

The question naturally arises whether different modalities or groups of modalities are separately localized in the cerebral cortex. In chimpanzees the ability to discriminate roughness has been tested in observations parallel to those on weight discriminatory ability. The results were broadly similar for both tests. For the monkey, data are available on two types of sensory testing, namely, weight discrimination, and the hopping and placing reactions of Bard and Rademaker (Bard, 1938). If the foot of a blindfolded animal is brought into contact with the edge of a table, the foot is brought up and set down on the table. If the contact is light, the response is the *tactual placing reaction;* if heavy enough to bend joints, it is the *proprioceptive placing reaction.* The *hopping reaction* is elicited by blindfolding an animal and allowing only one leg to support the body. Translocating the animal in space calls forth a series of quick, neat hops which keep the leg under the body. There appears to be a real difference between the cortical management of weight discrimination, and the hopping and placing reactions. In the monkey, ablation of either the postcentral gyrus or the posterior parietal lobule, separately, is virtually without demonstrable effect upon ability at weight discrimination, given time for recovery and retraining. A complete parietal lobectomy is required to produce demonstrable discriminatory defects that persist after the initial postoperative disturbances are over. On the other hand, the tactual placing reaction is very severely disturbed by ablation of the postcentral gyrus alone (Bard, 1938), though perhaps not completely abolished unless a parietal lobectomy is performed (Kennard and Kessler, 1940). Hopping reactions appear to be less severely affected by equivalent lesions than are the placing reactions. Two explanations have been advanced. The first is based on the modality difference: hopping is a proprioceptive function like weight lifting, whereas placing is a tactual phenomenon like roughness discrimination. Bard and Woolsey (Bard, 1938) believed that hopping is less affected by parietal lesions because it is served by the sensory projections to the precentral gyrus. The interpretation is supported by the evidence from evoked potentials described above (Woolsey, Chang, and Bard, 1947).

In comparing two functions such as weight discrimination and the tactual placing reaction, we find two other ways, besides the modality difference, in which the two responses differ. In the discrimination type of experiments, recovery of function is favored by two factors: (1) the high degree of motivation elicited by a food reward and (2) the opportunity to practice the same maneuver under stable circumstances, which may lead to maximum utilization of whatever sensory cues remain to the animal. Another difference which may prove to be critical is that weight discrimination or roughness discrimination is an intensity function, whereas in placing and hopping reactions there is a definite spatial element. When the side of the foot is touched to the table top, the foot is moved laterally; when the front of the foot is touched, the foot is moved forward in order to place. In the hopping reaction the direction of the hops is determined by the direction of the translocation of the animal through space. It is possible that these reactions demand a stable, topographically organized projection system, so that there is relatively little chance for another system of somatosensory fibers to compensate for those destroyed. In contrast, weight or roughness discrimination, being intensity functions, may not depend upon any given set of thalamocortical projection fibers. Although numbers of receptors, sensory tract fibers, and cortical cells may be a factor in intensity discrimination, frequency of impulse discharge, be-

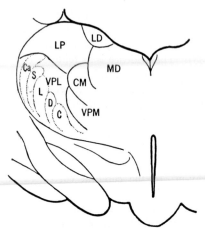

Fig. 8. A cross-sectional diagram through the left half of the thalamus, showing the areas of nucleus ventralis posterolateralis (VPL), in which the spinothalamic tract fibers from different levels of the spinal cord terminate. From Marchi degeneration studies on a monkey with a prehensile tail. The comma-shaped areas enclosed in fine dots show the termination of spinothalamic tract fibers. Order of termination from lateral to medial is: Ca, caudal; S, sacral; L, lumbar; D, thoracic; C, cervical. For abbreviation of the thalamic nuclei see legend of Fig. 4. Note that degeneration was not found in the nucleus ventralis posteromedialis (VPM), the "face" and "taste" nucleus. (After Chang and Ruch, 1947.)

cause of its enormous range, is probably a more important factor. If so, even a small part of the sensory system remaining after surgical interference may be able to serve intensity functions and, with practice and re-education, may enable the animal to approach or regain the preoperative facility.

Postcentral Subsector

This subsector contains the classic "primary somatosensory area." The anatomical justification for this is three-fold: (1) it is a highly granular koniocortex typical of primary sensory areas elsewhere in the cerebral cortex; (2) it is the area of densest thalamo-graphical organization, which feature, however, is shared by the projection to the precentral sectors. The evidence for this will be briefly outlined.

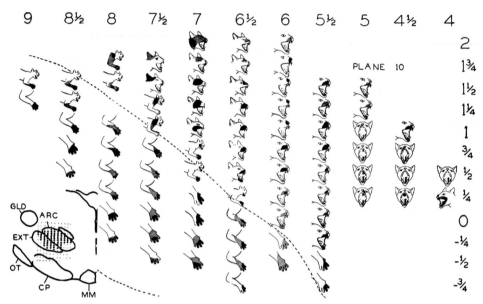

FIG. 9. An evoked-potential mapping of the representation of the body surface on the thalamus of the cat. The insert in the lower left corner is a cross section through the posterior part of the thalamus. The grid of small dots shows the points from which electrical records were made; the enlarged dots are the points from which potentials were recorded on tactual stimulation. For each of the larger points a figurine is located in the main diagram (millimeter scale), showing which area of the skin or mucosa yields a strong (black) or weak (cross-hatched) response at the given thalamic point. The line of dashes running diagonally represents the boundary between the pars externa (EXT) and pars arcuata (ARC) of the ventrolateral nucleus, which in monkey is known as the posteroventral nucleus. Other abbreviations are: OT, optic tract; CP, cerebral peduncle; MM, mammillary nucleus; GLD, lateral geniculate body. *Note that the medial portion of the pars arcuata (to the right) did not yield evoked potentials to touch stimulation and may be the area that relays taste and/or visceral impulses from the vagus nerve.* The trunk and leg appear in similar drawings made from more anterior planes. (Henneman and Mountcastle, 1948.)

cortical projection, although the number of fibers coming to it is not greatly different from the number passing to the anterior wall of the central fissure; (3) it is the area of cortex most directly connected with the ascending sensory systems via the relay thalamic nuclei (Fig. 5). It differs from other sectors of the potential somatosensory area by virtue of a high degree of topo-

Walker (1938) made lesions of the trigeminal lemniscus, the cuneate, and gracile nuclei in different animals. He traced resulting degeneration to the posteroventral nucleus. Fibers from the face (trigeminal lemniscus) ended in the medial portion (arcuate nucleus) of that nucleus. Fibers from the nucleus cuneatus (arm) ended more laterally, and those of the nucleus gracilis (leg) still more laterally (Fig. 10). Chang and Ruch (1947) have described the termination of spinothalamic fibers arising from various levels of the spinal cord, confirming in more detail the topographical projection of the body surface onto the posteroventral nucleus (Fig. 8).

The projection of the body surface upon the posteroventral nucleus of the thalamus was worked out in greater detail by Henneman and Mountcastle (1948), employing the method of evoked potentials (Fig. 9). Monopolar electrodes inserted into the thalamus by the stereotaxic instrument recorded the action potentials to punctate stimulation of the body surface. The termination of ascending sensory fibers in the posteroventral nucleus was confirmed; impulses were detected in no other nucleus of the thalamus. Cutaneous areas having a rich innervation, e.g. the lips or fingers, were represented over a wider area than relatively insentient surfaces such as the trunk. The contralateral body surface is represented in great detail, with the face posteromedial and the tail anterolateral. The axial portion of the body is represented superiorly and the extremities inferiorly in the nucleus. Thus the study of the topographical organization of the spinal and trigeminal systems is fully demonstrated both anatomically and functionally.

In other experiments Walker (1938), and Le Gros Clark and Boggon (1935) removed parts of the cortex of the postcentral gyrus and located the areas of retrograde degenerative reaction in the thalamus. In this projection the spatial arrangements are also preserved (Fig. 10). The medial "face" nucleus of the thalamus projects to the sylvian end of the postcentral gyrus. The lateral leg area of the thalamus projects to the postcentral gyrus lying near the midline. Fibers for the arm are intermediate at the thalamus and at the cortex. The evidence is clear, then, that the ascending sensory systems and thalamocortical connections project the body surface onto the postcentral gyrus of the cortex, keeping spatial rela-

tions to some degree intact. Whether this is actually a point-to-point projection cannot be learned by the relatively crude methods of experimental degeneration but can be decided only by physiological experiments.

Strychnine stimulation yielded the map of the cortex shown in Fig. 7. Here we have

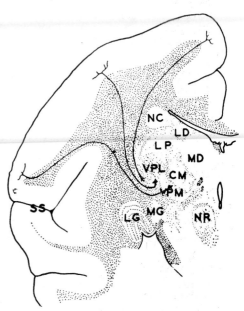

Fig. 10. A cross section through the cerebral hemispheres showing the reversal of the medial-lateral relation of the somatosensory projection between thalamus and cortex. SS is the sylvian fissure; for other abbreviations, see Fig. 4. (After Walker, 1938.)

a functional localization of the three major body regions: face, arm, and leg. No finer localization was demonstrable, yet the boundaries between arm and leg, for example, were sharp within 2 or 3 millimeters. Stimulation in conscious human subjects (Fig. 11) gives evidences of a finer topographical localization. The method of evoked potentials (Woolsey, Marshall, and Bard, 1942) shows clearly that the dermatomal segments, not simply regions or limb segments, are reflected in the topographical organization of the postcentral gyrus (Fig. 12). Woolsey, Chang, and Bard (1947) have verified this more recently by stimulating the posterior roots successively and by mapping on the cortex the points of maximal electrical activity. The method of evoked potentials does not demonstrate a strict point-to-point representation. A single point on the skin surface substrate for spatial discrimination. Examination of Figs. 11 and 12 shows that the vertical extent of the postcentral gyrus devoted to a given area of the body is out of proportion to the area of skin represented. The area for the lips or fingers is far greater

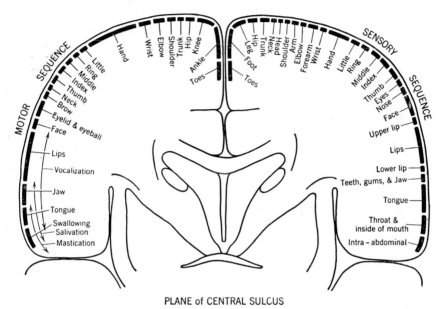

PLANE of CENTRAL SULCUS

Fig. 11. A schematic diagram combining a cross section through the postcentral gyrus (right) and the precentral gyrus (left) in the plane of the central fissure. The diagram shows the motor and sensory sequence of representation in the cerebral cortex of man, determined by electrical stimulation of conscious patients at operation. With stronger stimulation wider zones for a given part might be found, and there is considerable variation from individual to individual. Note that the sensory area devoted to the fingers and hand is greater than that devoted to the much larger skin area lying between forearm and shoulder. (From Rasmussen and Penfield, 1947.)

may activate several millimeters of the superior-inferior extent of the postcentral gyrus. What such studies do show is that for each point on the skin surface there is a point on the cortex of greatest electrical activity. Later on, in the discussion of the neural mechanism for the two-point threshold, we shall see that the requirement for spatial discrimination is the existence of "modal excitation fields," not a strict point-to-point representation.

It is believed that a topographically organized projection system constitutes the than that for the arm or for the trunk. Whether these differences simply reflect the greater density of receptors in the lips and fingers is not yet known. The situation is possibly analogous to that presented by the visual system. The fovea of the retina differs from the periphery, not so much in the concentration of receptors, but in the greater number of private paths coming from the fovea (Polyak, 1941). This is continued by a greater representation of the fovea in the lateral geniculate body and in the occipital cortex. In both systems one can regard the large cortical representation as meaning a greater number of cortical cells or "fineness of the cortical grain," by which greater ac-

ous section. As the name suggests, it forms the common ground between the three great sensory lobes of the brain. It is an asso-

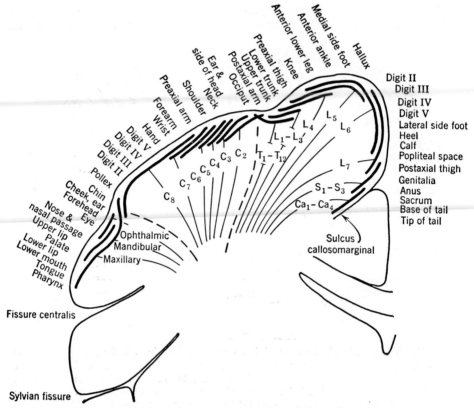

Fig. 12. A reconstruction showing the representation of the body surface upon the postcentral gyrus of the cortex, as determined by cortical potentials evoked by stimulating the body surface. The left cerebral hemisphere is shown in cross section, medial to the right and lateral to the left. The body regions are based on experimental data; the letters and subscripts are dermatomal designations deduced from known innervation: Ca, caudal; S, sacral; L, lumbar; T, thoracic; and C, cervical segments of the spinal cord, and the ophthalmic, mandibular, and maxillary divisions of the trigeminal nerve. The subscript is the number of the posterior root within the spinal cord region. Compare with Fig. 11, and note that most of the foot area is buried in the longitudinal fissure and that the cervical dermatomal representation is reversed *en bloc*. (After Woolsey, Marshall, and Bard, 1942.)

curacy of spatial discriminations is made possible.

Parieto-occipitotemporal Region

The parietal portion of this region of the cortex has been discussed in part in a previ-

ciation area that is relatively small in the monkey, and it expands progressively and becomes more complex in fissuration throughout the primate series. The sylvian and superior temporal fissures, which ascend obliquely in the monkey, become nearly parallel with the expansion of the parieto-occipito-temporal region in the higher primates. In man the posterior ends of the sylvian and superior temporal sulci are capped by the supramarginal and angular gyri, respectively, which are concerned with the receptive aspects of speech.

The projection to the parieto-occipito-temporal region is derived from the nuclei lateralis dorsalis and lateralis posterior and from the pulvinar (Fig. 5), which is a large posterior outgrowth of the nucleus lateralis posterior. The pulvinar projects to the posterior parietal lobule just posterior to the projection of the parent nucleus, nucleus lateralis posterior, and also to the anterior border of the occipital lobe and the posterior portion of the temporal lobe.* Like the parent nucleus, the pulvinar does not receive fibers directly from the great sensory systems (Fig. 5). The pulvinar, like the cortical region of its projection, has undergone conspicuous phylogenetic development. Once incorrectly supposed to receive fibers directly from the optic tract, it is now believed to receive somatic, visual, and auditory impulses from their respective relay nuclei (Walker, 1938). These connections cannot be traced by Marchi degeneration; they are probably unmyelinated. The pulvinar is in close proximity to other posterior nuclei, the geniculate bodies, and contiguous retrograde degeneration in these nuclei results from the same cortical lesion.

An analysis of this contiguous degeneration leads to the thesis that the posterior and medial parts of the pulvinar are related to the medial geniculate body; the lateral portion to the lateral geniculate body, and the anterior and medial part of the pulvinar to the nucleus ventralis posterior. This arrangement brings the somatic sensory, auditory

* It is a matter of definition whether areas 5 and 7 (Fig. 3) be considered a part of the parieto-occipitotemporal region. Von Bonin (1944) is ambiguous on this point. Areas 5 and 7 receive a projection from association nuclei, and the pulvinar is derived from these nuclei. For this reason areas 5 and 7 are here included in the parieto-occipitotemporal region.

and visual systems into close relationship, and allows integrations between these systems. Those fibers passing to the superior parietal lobule, the angular gyrus, and the lateral temporo-occipital region presumably are mainly associated with visual integrations, those to the anterior part of the supramarginal gyrus with somatic sensory, and those to the posterior part of the supramarginal gyrus with auditory. [Walker, 1938, p. 248.]

The pulvinar and the nuclei lateralis posterior and lateralis dorsalis, superimposed as they are upon the direct pathway of sensory impulses to the cortex, have no *raison d'être* unless they in some manner elaborate sensory impulses before passing them on to the cortex. Walker (1938), speaking of this group of nuclei, says:

They appear to be related to the highest and most recently developed sensory modalities.

Through these three groups of nuclei the thalamus receives incoming stimuli, integrates them to varying degrees, and then relays them to other subcortical ganglia or to the cerebral cortex. In this way the crude stimuli received by the peripheral end organs become elaborated to be presented to the highest heirarchy of the central nervous system, the cerebral cortex, as complex and at least partially synthesized impulses.

It has already been pointed out that the anterior portion of this region is able to carry out proprioceptive discriminations after ablation of the postcentral gyrus. However, the function of the parieto-occipitotemporal region is largely known from clinical cases, where the lesions are likely to be massive and unverified. Evans (1935), in a study of surgical excisions where the destruction is macroscopically known, locates an integrative center for the higher levels of somatic sensation in the region of the supramarginal and angular gyri (Fig. 13). The degree of disturbance from lesions in this region is greater in man than in chimpanzee, and greater in chimpanzee than in monkey, a clear illustration of encephalization of function and perhaps of a posterior migration of such function.

Experimental analysis of this area in animals should yield information about the kind

lesion, though visual discrimination of them was perfectly retained. The cone versus pyramid discrimination by touch was quickly and completely re-established, but protracted retraining failed to restore the pyramid versus wedge discrimination. It is not

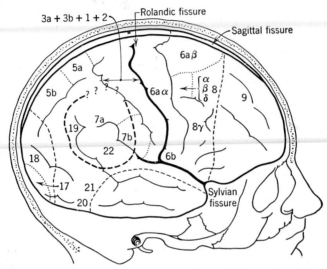

FIG. 13. Diagram showing the "common denominator" of a series of surgical excisions posterior to the postcentral gyrus that gave disturbances of somatosensory perceptions and judgments (sense of position, weight discrimination, topognosis, two-point threshold, stereognosis, etc.). The question marks completing the heavy dashed line denote uncertainty about the superior extent of the effective area. Note that the area includes the supramarginal gyrus which bends around the superior end of the sylvian fissure, and the angular gyrus at the superior end of the superior temporal fissure which is parallel and inferior to the sylvian fissure. This chart is used in the Montreal Neurological Institute for charting the location of brain operations. The numbers and letters and fine dots and dashes denote cytoarchitectural areas. (Evans, 1935.)

of function impaired and should supply the details of localization not readily obtainable in human studies. In a single experiment on a chimpanzee, Ruch, Fulton, and German (1938) demonstrated that discrimination of three-dimensional form may be disturbed by lesions in the area. Prior to operation a chimpanzee was taught to discriminate by palpation between a pyramid and a cone, and between a pyramid and a wedge. The latter was a more difficult discrimination to establish. Both discriminations were temporarily lost consequent to a posterior parietal

unlikely that the cone and pyramid problem was solved on a "sensory basis" (sharp edges versus no edges), whereas the pyramid versus the wedge presented a problem in the relation of geometrical planes and demonstrated a higher order of sensory activity. Thus what little evidence exists suggests that the posterior parietal area is concerned with the higher levels of sensory process.

In man lesions within the parieto-occipito-temporal region are accompanied by disturbances of functions characterized by intermodality elements. Pure astereognosis (inability to recognize common objects by palpation not accompanied by any marked disturbance of basic sensory modalities) is clinically associated with this region. The appreciation of three-dimensional form appears to require a synthesis of data from more than one somatic sense modality. The recognition of common objects probably involves, in addition, synthesis with visual data. Receptive aphasia, e.g. "word blindness," is traditionally associated with lesions of the angular gyrus which is located in this region. It may be concluded that the region lying between the parietal, occipital, and temporal lobes serves the higher levels of somatosensory response, especially those involving more than one modality. To what degree this is accomplished by the region correlating the sensory data from the primary sensory areas for vision and audition, and to what degree this is accomplished by the pulvinar and the association area acting as a unit, await experimental and clinical investigation.

Visual perceptual defects are also found in lesions lying between the visual and parietal lobes. Holmes (1918) and others have described, under the syndrome of *visual disorientation*, symptomatology believed characteristic of the parieto-occipitotemporal region. Although movement is not ataxic, eye-hand coordination is at fault. Visual estimation of distance is faulty; the patient will attempt to reach an object 5 or 6 feet away. The patient judges with difficulty the length of a line, or whether an object is moving away or towards him. Common objects may be clearly seen but not recognized. Disturbances of eye-hand coordination have been observed in chimpanzees with posterior parietal lesions (Ruch, unpublished). A detailed search for disturbances of high-level visual function from lesions of areas 18 and 19 in the monkey failed to confirm the clinical findings of Holmes (Ades, 1946; Lashley, 1948).

Double Sensory Representation

A duplication of sensory areas has been demonstrated for vision, audition, and somatic sensation. The evidence comes largely from the method of evoked potentials (Adrian, 1940; Woolsey and Fairman, 1946). As shown in Fig. 14, the second somatic area * is located in the upper wall of the sylvian fissure, inferior to the sensory area I. The second somatosensory area is topographically arranged, the parts of the body coming in reverse sequence to that in the postcentral gyrus, so that the face areas I and II are contiguous, and the order is face, arm, and leg in going deeper into the sylvian fissure. Sensory area II responds electrically to ipsilateral stimulation of the body surface, though not so strongly as to stimulation of the contralateral half of the body. Like the postcentral gyrus, this area is sensory-motor because stimulation of it elicits movements of the limbs and face. Rasmussen and Penfield (1947) recorded, in a few patients, sensations referred to the arm, leg, and face, when the region immediately adjacent to the sylvian fissure was stimulated. Since these responses are aberrant with respect to the ladder of sensory representation, they suggest the existence of a second sensory area in man. In many of the experiments on hopping and placing reactions and on weight discrimination, carried out prior to the discovery of the second sensory areas, the second sensory area was not included in the ablations. However, Bard and Woolsey have shown that somatic area II cannot compensate for the loss of area I in the management of tactile-placing reaction, though there was some initial slowing of the reaction from ablation of it.

* Following Woolsey and Fairman, these areas are referred to as the sensory areas I and II, or first and second sensory areas, to avoid implications of "primary" and "secondary" as applied to sensory areas. Somatic area I is the primary sensory area, but somatic area II implies nothing more than second in time of discovery. Neither in function nor in position is it a secondary sensory area, a phrase that is sometimes used to describe the posterior parietal lobule.

McCulloch (1947) integrates the second sensory areas into the general plan of the cerebral cortex as follows:

Sectors of cortex, defined by their connections with thalamic nuclei, severally exhibit a receptive area or a pair juxtaposed but

sylvian fissure, extending on to the Island of Reil, direct the carriers of their appropriate receptors, and the superior surface of the second temporal convolution pricks up the ipsilateral ear.

This close cortical coupling of each sensory input to output affecting that sensory input

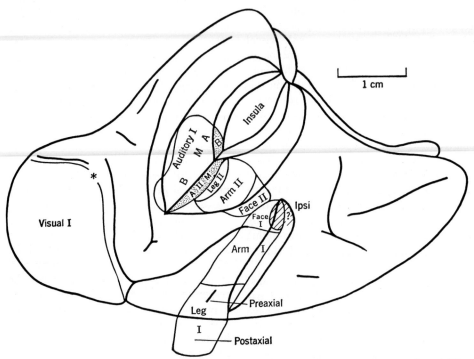

FIG. 14. Diagram showing the positions and relative sizes of somatic areas I and II, and other sensory areas in the monkey. The sylvian fissure is shown opened, revealing the insula and the normally concealed parietal and temporal walls of that fissure. The dotted portion of the auditory area is Auditory II; Auditory I is not dotted. B, M, and A refer, respectively, to base, middle, and apex of the cochlea. From the cross-hatched portion of somatic area I for the face, ipsilateral responses were obtained. (From Woolsey and Fairman, 1946.)

oriented reversely, each surrounded by a zone to which it gives many extrinsic axons. From each of these composite fields arises a projection whose activity affects that part of the body in which its organs of sense are situated. Thus the *area striata* and its surrounding zones move the eyes toward the place in the visual field corresponding to the position of excitation. The first and second somesthetic areas and the zone anterior to the former and deep to the latter in the

by moving the organ of sense is a mode of functional organization whose circuit leaves and returns to the body. [P. 450.]

Ipsilateral Representation

Up to this point, the potential sensory area for a given side of the body has been considered to be that portion of the *contralateral* hemisphere that receives cortico-thalamic projections from nuclei connected with the ascending sensory systems. It must be remembered that the potential sensory area for a given half of the body may include the ipsilateral cerebral cortex as well. A variety of evidence can be accounted for only on the supposition that in some degree each half of the body is bilaterally represented in the cerebral cortex, or, in other words, that there is some ipsilateral representation. This is apparently not equally true of all modalities of sensation, but is most conspicuous for pain; nor is it equally true of all areas of the body surface, but is most marked for the face. The evidence is as follows. Strychnine applied to one sensory cortex will produce paresthesia and hyperesthesia on both sides of the body (Dusser de Barenne, 1924, 1934). Proprioceptive sensations do not exhibit this ipsilateral representation. Woolsey et al. (1942, 1947) confirmed both conclusions in their studies of evoked potentials. In man bilateral or ipsilateral projection of sensory responses induced by cortical stimulation occurred only in the face and in only 13 per cent of the stimulations (Rasmussen and Penfield, 1947). Bilateral representation is not accomplished by fibers crossing from the thalamus of one side to the cerebral cortex of the opposite side through the corpus callosum. Retrograde degeneration following cortical ablation is found only in the thalamus on the side of the lesion (Walker, 1938). Any crossing that occurred at or above the level of the thalamus would have to be actually within the diencephalon, as, for example, in the massa intermedia. Nor is ipsilateral representation gained by failure of, for example, pain fibers to decussate in the spinal cord. Were they conducted on the ipsilateral sides of the cord, a unilateral section of the spinothalamic tract (anterolateral cordotomy) could not produce analgesia to cutaneous pain, as it appears to do. On the other hand, there is evidence of a *recrossing* of spinothalamic tract fibers in the brain stem, in fact, at many points in the brain stem. Chang and Ruch (1947) have re-

cently described the crossing of such fibers in the posterior commissure. The present status of the perplexing problem of ipsilateral representation may be summarized by saying that the phenomenon is most pronounced for pain, is most pronounced in the representation of the face, and is probably due to a recrossing of pain fibers within the brain stem or to cross connections between the two thalami.

THE TOPOGRAPHICAL PRIN- CIPLE AND THE TASTE PATHWAY

Of the eleven or more modalities of sensation, the pathways and cortical localization are known in considerable anatomical and physiological detail for vision, audition, and some of the somatosensory group. Until the last decade little was known of the cerebral pathways for gustatory, olfactory, labyrinthine, and visceral sensations. In varying degrees these modalities of sensation are now yielding to experimental analysis. Neither the older functional anatomy nor the random exploratory approach yielded accurate information. On the other hand, some of the newer knowledge of the thalamocortical projections, especially the details of their topographical organization, has proved of definite predictive value in the design of experiments on the lesser-known sensory pathways.

Two principles, sometimes conflicting, seem to govern the organization of neural systems. The functional principle is that two systems of fibers closely related functionally pursue similar courses. A good example of this is the collection of fibers, serving pain from cutaneous, muscular, and visceral nerves, that pass grouped together in a common tract (the spinothalamic) in the spinal cord. The topographical principle is that peripheral origins, including spatial relations, are reflected or continued in the organization of ascending sensory tracts, in the point of thalamic relay, and in the cortical termination, as has been described above.

That these principles may conflict is illustrated in our growing knowledge of the gustatory system.

The fact that taste is so closely linked psychologically and functionally with olfaction is probably the main reason for the general acceptance of the view that gustation and olfaction have an adjacent cortical localization. Actually this inference is virtually without experimental or clinical basis. In fact, there is evidence, going back to 1890, for different cortical localizations of taste and smell — evidence that has largely escaped notice because of the plausibility of the localization dictated by the functional principle. Börnstein (1940a, b) has pointed out the many dissimilarities between the gustatory and olfactory systems at all levels between the sense organs and the cerebral cortex. He proposed the alternative hypothesis that taste is an evolved somatosensory modality, and that a similarity between gustatory and *somatosensory* pathways, including their cortical termination, is to be expected. He found evidence in man that the cortical localization of taste does, in fact, lie in close proximity to the face and tongue sensory area of the postcentral gyrus, not in the hippocampal region adjacent to the olfactory area.

The locus of the thalamic relay for taste fibers, even the existence of such a relay, was for many years largely a matter of conjecture. The studies of thalamocortical projections established that the somatosensory fibers for the tongue and face relay in the most medial portion of the posteroventral nucleus (so-called arcuate nucleus). It was predicted that the taste fibers also relay in this nucleus. In monkeys tested preoperatively by the preference method (Patton and Ruch, 1944), lesions of this nucleus were made by means of the Horsley-Clarke apparatus. The expected lowering of taste sensibility resulted, and the arcuate nucleus was thereby established as the thalamic taste nucleus (Blum, Ruch, and Walker, 1943; Patton, Ruch, and Walker, 1944). The lo-

calization has not yet been confirmed by the method of evoked potentials. However, in the study by Henneman and Mountcastle (1948), in which the projection of the body surface on the thalamus was mapped, an area in the medial part of the arcuate nucleus was found that was not activated by somatic stimuli. This may well be the portion of the arcuate nucleus in which taste impulses are relayed.

According to the topographical principle, the thalamic relay for visceral sensation (exclusive of pain) from the chest and upper abdomen should be sought at the medial extremity of the posteroventral nuclei; and its cortical representation should be sought at the lateral extremity of the sensory cortex. Sensory impulses from the pelvic viscera should pass through the lateral portions of the posteroventral nucleus of the thalamus and should be projected to a region near the midline in the postcentral cortex. In Fig. 11 it will be noted that intra-abdominal sensations are elicited in man by stimulation just inferior to the throat area, i.e. on the lip of the sylvian fissure. Visceral pain from the chest and abdomen should be projected to the trunk areas, since it is largely conducted to the spinal cord over the thoracic and upper lumbar posterior roots. In turn, labyrinthine sensations should be located in close relation to the auditory cortical area, an expectation for which there is some evidence. Confirmation of these predictions can be found in the studies of Amassian (1950) and of Walzl and Mountcastle (1949).

NEURONOGRAPHY OF THE SOMATOSENSORY CORTEX

The cerebral cortex is centripetally and centrifugally linked with subcortical nuclei. The cortices of the two hemispheres are linked with one another by the corpus callosum, and the various cortical areas are interconnected by abundant short (U-fibers) and long association fibers, and the cortical gray matter itself contains laterally coursing fiber systems. The latter are termed by Sperry "intracortical" as opposed to the "intercortical" association fibers coursing through the white matter of the cerebral hemispheres. Anatomically these intracortical and intercortical fibers, being so numerous, give the impression of complete interconnectedness of cortical areas. Such is not the case. There are at least main highways, often one-way highways, between cortical areas.

Physiological analysis of the interconnection between cortical areas, and between cortex and subcortex, was given the name "physiological neuronography" by Dusser de Barenne (McCulloch, 1944a). In strychnine stimulation he hit upon a tool for charting the neuronographical relations of cortical areas. Strychnine acts only at synapses, probably on the cell body of neurons, since the impulses are propagated only in the direction of conduction from cell body to axon. Strychnine appears to discharge a group of neurons synchronously, and, with the aid of an oscillograph, the synchronously propagated action potential — the strychnine spike — can be detected and distinguished from spontaneous activity wherever the axons of the stimulated cell bodies are distributed. The requisite synchronicity for the strychnine spike is apparently lost whenever the volley crosses synapses. The method, therefore, plots the first-order connections between one region and another.

Intracortical association through the gray matter was demonstrated by Rosenblueth and Cannon (1942) in the highly reactive cortex of animals under chloralose anesthesia. This propagation of activity is slower than that produced by strychnine, and it does not respect cytoarchitectural boundaries. The strychnine spike persists even when the cortex is more heavily depressed under Dial anesthesia and is not blocked by circumcoagulation of the strychninized area. Physiological neuronography, carried out by means of strychnine, apparently plots unisynaptic

connections by way of association fibers of the white matter, whereas the Rosenblueth-Cannon phenomenon is a multisynaptic spread through horizontal fibers of the cortex itself.

Intra-areal and interareal effects are to be distinguished. Strychninization of, for example, the arm area of the postcentral gyrus will "fire," i.e. cause strychnine spikes to appear, throughout the whole arm area but will not spread to adjacent somatotopic areas. Interareal effects in the macaque cortex further document the close interrelation of the pre- and postcentral subsectors. Area 4, exclusive of its anterior border (4s), fires all areas of the parietal lobe, as does area 6. Conversely, with the exception of area 2, the zones of the parietal lobe available to stimulation (areas 1, 5, and 7) activate all other areas in the parietal lobe and area 4 of the frontal lobe. (Area 3 is buried in the central fissure.) Whether these interconnections pertain to sensory function or to the motor function of the sensory-motor areas is not yet known. They will be discussed in more detail, along with the "suppressor areas," in Chapter 5.

CORTICOTHALAMIC CONNECTIONS

The significance of corticothalamic projection has been a puzzle since its first description by von Monakow more than half a century ago. The details of the projection show that thalamus and cortex are reciprocally related. Thus a given sensory area of the cerebral cortex projects back to that thalamic nucleus from which the given cortical area receives an ascending projection. Head and Holmes believed that this system of fibers is inhibitory to the thalamus and, when damaged, causes the hyperpathia of the thalamic syndrome that was ascribed to overactivity of a hypothetical thalamic mechanism for affect. Dusser de Barenne (1934) demonstrated by the strychnine method that cortical stimulation induces strychnine spikes in the thalamic nuclei. The effect of these impulses reaching the thalamus appears to be excitatory and not inhibitory. Ablation or novocainization of all except an island of cortex of sensory-motor area for the arm, which is strychninized, is followed by projected paresthesias over the entire arm (Dusser de Barenne, 1924, 1934). Since it is unlikely that the whole arm is re-

Experiments of this type outline the neural substrate for long reverberating circuits between the thalamus and the cortex, as a part of the sensory mechanism. The clearest demonstration that such reverberation occurs when the cerebral sensory mechanism is activated through sense organs was made by Chang (1950). The electrical activity from the cortical auditory area in response to

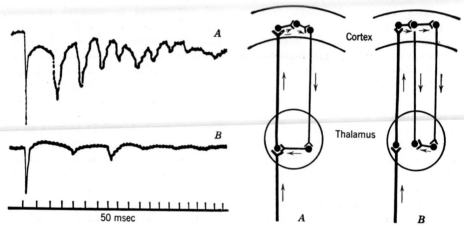

Fig. 15. Left: Cortical potentials from the somatosensory area evoked by posterior root stimulation. *A:* Under light Nembutal (barbiturate) anesthesia. *B:* Under very deep Nembutal anesthesia. The cortical potential is a downward (surface positive) spike-like excursion. Note the regularity of the rhythm and the decreasing amplitude.

Right: Highly schematic diagram to illustrate two possible mechanisms of thalamocortical interaction. *A:* The reverberation employs the main projection. *B:* The different projections are involved for the reverberation and for the initial volley. (Chang, 1950.)

represented many times in the cortex, this experiment constitutes evidence that the sensory cortex activates rather than inhibits the thalamus by way of corticothalamic fibers. Ablation or undercutting the sensory cortex causes a diminution in the spontaneous electrical activity of the appropriate thalamic nucleus (1941). Conversely, integrity of the posteroventral nucleus of the thalamus is essential for a normal electroencephalograph pattern in the somatosensory cortex, a fact indicative of a thalamocortical linkage.*

* Interaction of cortex and thalamus is not solely responsible for the maintenance of spontaneous electrical rhythms of the cortex. Fibers

click stimuli was recorded with a very slow sweep of the oscillograph. Following the initial burst of activity on the cortex were three or four smaller, broader waves of activity, coming at regular intervals but with gradually decreasing amplitude (Fig. 15). The first wave of the repetitive discharge occurs in about 220 milliseconds, a time lag

and nuclei along the internal medullary lamina, and especially the "medial intralaminar region" — the massa intermedia and related structures — are clearly pacemakers for widespread and synchronous bilateral rhythmic activities of the cortex (Dempsey and Morison, 1943; Jasper and Droogleever-Fortuyn, 1946; Morison and Dempsey, 1942). Also, the thalamus can engender spontaneous rhythmical discharge after decortication (Morison and Bassett, 1945).

indicative of conduction over multineuron pathways. Various features of the repetitive electrical response suggest that it is due to a circuit from the cortex to the medial geniculate body and back to the cortex. Similar phenomena were demonstrated for the visual and somatosensory systems with minor differences, such as a greater frequency of the repetitive discharge.

The delayed repetitive potentials following the initial burst elicited by a click stimulus were also detected in the record from the medial geniculate body. The clinching observation was that removal of the auditory cortical area abolished all but the initial response to the click stimulus in the medial geniculate body. Presumably a thalamocortical reverberatory circuit was broken by the cortical intervention.

As pointed out above, experiments of this type suggest a close interplay between the thalamus and the cerebral cortex. In the simple reception of a sensory stimulus, the cortex and the thalamus appear to function as a unit. Beyond this generalization little more can be said of the physiological significance of thalamocortical reverberation.

NEUROPHYSIOLOGY OF PERCEPTION

The method of evoked potentials, as applied to the cerebral cortex, has so far been used mainly in functional anatomical studies. Several pioneering studies encourage the belief that the study of cortical potentials can throw light on the problems of perception, judgment, conception, and other cognitive processes. The minimum separable and the two-point threshold seem to present the most convenient points of attack experimentally (Marshall and Talbot, 1942), though analysis of concept formation has been attempted biomathematically (Pitts and McCulloch, 1947). The neural basis of two-point discrimination will be discussed here as an example of a basic discriminatory process — one that may be considered the prototype of sensory discrimination in all sense modalities.

The two-point threshold of the skin was popularized as a clinical test of sensation by Sir Henry Head. He considered it a valuable indication of cortical defect. To a limited degree clinical neurology employs this test, though rarely in the quantitative fashion familiar in psychological laboratories. Although Head is to be credited with strengthening neurology by borrowing psychological methods, he and the others who followed him have not always been sensitive to the concepts developed by psychologists. They leave the impression that there exist sensory systems or sensory impulses that specifically serve the function of two-point discrimination, whereas each of the cutaneous senses has its own two-point threshold. Touch happens to be served by a system capable of making finer discriminations than those made by other forms of somatic sensation. As yet, no systematic comparison of the various sensory modalities with respect to the two-point threshold has been made, though such a study would seem feasible.

The two-point threshold is widely different in different regions of the body surface (see Fig. 16). Weber sought to explain these differences on the basis of the size of the skin area to which the terminals of a single sensory neuron are distributed. This area was called a "sensory circle." The thought was that compass points resting on adjacent areas would be appreciated as one stimulus, but, if an unexcited fiber was interposed, two points would be appreciated. Similar explanations of the mechanisms underlying visual acuity have been advanced. In audition, the resonance theory of pitch, based on sharp tuning of the basilar membrane, is somewhat comparable. In these cases the concept of an excited receptor and an adjacent unexcited receptor, each with a private path to the cortex, has been proved a gross oversimplification. The same appears to be true of somatic sensation. A variety of facts dictate a more dynamic concept, involving a statistical process on the part of the cerebral cortex in which a spatial discrimination involves an intensity of discrimination.

The static concept of two-point discrimination would predict an anatomical organi-

S' represent the points of a compass esthesiometer applied to the finger tip. The line above this represents skin deformation, so that physically the stimulus spreads beyond the points of the compass. Neurohistological studies (Weddell, 1941*a*, *b*; Woollard, Wed-

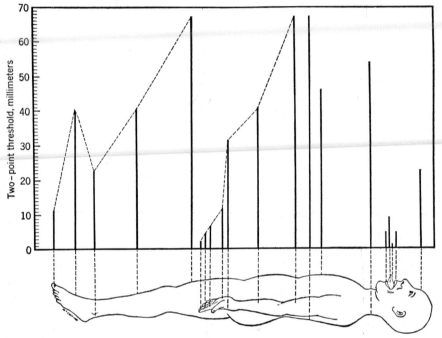

Fig. 16. A mnemonic diagram showing the magnitude of the two-point threshold in various regions of the body. The length of the vertical line closely approximates the actual separation of compass points just perceptible as "two" when applied to the point from which the line is erected. (From Ruch, 1946.)

zation consisting of parallel, insulated chains of fibers ("private lines") from skin surface to cerebral cortex. A variety of evidence fails to support this prediction and in fact has disclosed a degree of intermingling of axon terminations within the skin and opportunities for cross-talk at synaptic junctions which suggests, paradoxically, that such an arrangement is more efficient than parallel fiber chains.

As shown in Fig. 17, opportunities for overlapping or spreading excitation in topographically adjacent systems occur at several levels of the sensory pathway. *S* and

dell, and Harpman, 1940) have given us the picture of a single sensory fiber ramifying within the skin, overlapping and interlocking, but not fusing protoplasmically, with the terminations of other fibers. Meissner's corpuscles occur in groups and are innervated by fibers approaching the group from different directions. Tower (1940) discovered that a single parent pain fiber is distributed to roughly one quadrant of the cornea and the adjacent conjunctiva, an area varying in size between 50 and 200 square millimeters. Within this region are silent areas, presumably innervated by interlocking axons. In short, there is a wide topographical distribution of the "sensory unit," a term by which she designates a parent

In Fig. 17 the gradient of excitation (in terms of frequency of discharge b, b') between what may be termed the core fiber

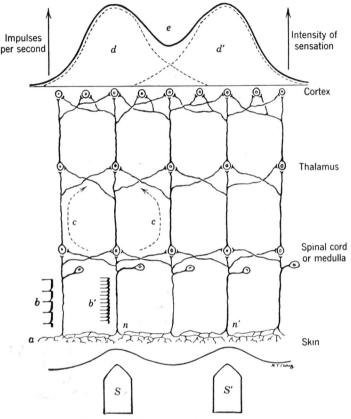

FIG. 17. A theoretical diagram of the neural factors involved in the discrimination of two points applied to the skin. S and S' are the points of the esthesiometer or compass used in determining the two-point threshold. Note that the deformation of the skin extends beyond the compass points. a is a plexus of interlocking terminals, so that more than one afferent fiber is stimulated, but the rate of discharge (b and b') is higher in the "core" neuron stimulated where the terminals converge on the parent axon. The dotted arrows, c, show how a divergence at the synapses of the spinal cord results in convergence and summation at the thalamus, contributing to the peaking of curve d or d' (modal excitation fields). The summed effect of the activity pattern is represented by e. So long as the distance between the volley intensity difference and the peak is discriminable, the points are perceived as two. For further explanation see text. (Ruch, 1946.)

sensory axon and all its terminal branches. Interlocking to the degree disclosed by these studies precludes the possibility of an excited neuron and an adjacent unexcited neuron limiting the two-point threshold.

(n) and an adjacent fiber interlocking with it is not due merely to the degree of deformation of the two fibers. Tower stimulated with equal intensity the periphery and the center of an area served by a single neuron, while recording from the parent axon. This is quite possible in the cornea where the sensory unit area is large. A higher rate of discharge was obtained from the center than from the periphery of the area served by a single axon. The frequency of discharge (b') in the core neuron is therefore shown to be high, relative to that in an adjacent neuron (b). From this discussion two reasons emerge for plotting the frequency of excitation at the cortical level as a bell-shaped curve: (1) the physical conformation of the skin deformation and (2) the more rapid rate of discharge from the core neurons stimulated in the center of their fields than from the adjacent neurons stimulated in the periphery of their fields.

At each of the synaptic relays — medulla, thalamus, and cerebral cortex — there are cross-connections between neuron chains. Such cross-connections have been demonstrated histologically, and they are much more abundant than the diagram in Fig. 17 suggests. This arrangement is variously termed "partially shifted overlap" (Lorente de Nó, 1934) and "reciprocal overlap" (Marshall and Talbot, 1942). Such connections obviously would spread the excitation horizontally to a degree determined by the number of such connections multiplied by the number of synaptic levels. However, as Lorente de Nó has pointed out, such collaterals, which are, at the first synaptic layer, divergent in effect, would concentrate rather than spread the excitation at the second synaptic relay. This is indicated by the dotted arrows, c, showing that the collateral system would tend to facilitate the core neuron, causing it to maintain a differential rate of discharge, with a consequent peaking of the pattern of cortical stimulation.

The *raison d'être* for this type of arrangement, rather than parallel chains of fibers, is probably as follows: The frequency of discharge is unquestionably one correlate of intensity of stimulation, in so far as the sense organ is concerned. The problem is how frequency of discharge becomes an intensity signal at the cortex. Parallel "insulated" chains of fibers could, at best, merely translate that frequency to the cerebral cortex.* Such chains are relatively inefficient in summating their effects for the following reasons. According to one well-founded theory of synaptic excitation, temporal summation at the synapse is hindered by the briefness of the excitatory effects on the neuron soma from a discharge of impinging axonal terminations which, at some synapses (Lorente de Nó, 1938, 1939), does not last at peak value beyond the refractory period of the axon.† Spatial summation at the synapse, the additive effect of two adjacent axon terminals firing, occurs at peak intensity and is more effective in discharging the postsynaptic neuron. Dichotomizing and multiple terminations of single axons, typical of synaptic terminations, favor excitation by increasing the statistical probability of spatial summation between terminations of the same axon. The collateral systems in Fig. 17, through the pathway indicated by the dotted arrows, may be regarded as a further provision for multiple termination. For example, instead of one stream of impulses, at the thalamic level, there are three streams converging from different fibers upon the third-order neuron. Because the fibers are different, refractory periods do not prevent the close timing of impulses favorable for summation. The net effect may, therefore, be to sharpen rather than spread the excitatory field.

The dotted lines at the top of Fig. 17 represent the cortical excitation from each

---

* This ability to follow frequency varies in different sensory systems. In the visual system flicker is paralleled by a cortical activity up to 53 per second. Synchronous volleys tend to become asynchronous in crossing synapses. The low following rate points away from simple chain transmission.

† Even if excitatory effects outlast the refractory period, the latter offers a considerable barrier to temporal summation. If the soma change effected by an arriving impulse decreases exponentially, a very considerable portion of its peak level will be lost during the refractory period.

compass point separately, as it distributes over the layers of cortical neurons. The curves are purely hypothetical, and, since no shape is critical, they have been termed "modal excitation fields" (implying only that they are "peaked") (Ruch, 1943). The cortical excitation is plotted in terms of impulses per second. The number of cortical cells active would be another possible correlate of intensity, which would derive directly from frequency of impulses. At the periphery, intensity of stimulation is translated into number of receptors firing and frequency of discharge of each. Number of receptors firing can be translated at each synapse into frequency of discharge of the postsynaptic neuron, because number of receptors firing governs the probability that spatial summation will be sufficient to discharge the next neuron. However, at the final cortical level, frequency may possibly be translated into number of cells responding within a system of divergents-convergents, as diagrammed. A population of cortical cells having different thresholds, probably normally distributed, is a reasonable assumption. A high frequency of impinging impulses from converging terminals would have a greater probability of discharging two adjacent boutons within the critical time interval for summation. Since a low-threshold neuron is probably simply a neuron receiving a sparse bouton innervation from the fibers in question, the importance of frequency is apparent. The type of record of electrical activity of the cortex obtained by stimulation of a single point on the skin surface provides evidence for a curve approximately of the character shown in Fig. 17 (Woolsey, Marshall, and Bard, 1942). The electrical activity has a maximum point and quite a large lateral distribution. The point of maximal activity shifts with shifts in the position of the stimulation over the body surface. Such experiments do not tell us whether it is frequency or number of neurons active that correlates with intensity at the cortical level. About all that can be said is that the number of units active strongly affects the recording instrument, especially when these units are synchronously involved. Frequency in the presence of asynchronicity tends not to be effectively recorded electrically.

What is the limitation on the two-point threshold? Theoretically, two points are perceived as such, provided the valley between the two peaks is sufficient to permit an intensity discrimination between them. Closer together, the bimodal pattern becomes unimodal, and the intensity discrimination is no longer possible. According to this view, then, spatial discrimination has an element of intensity discrimination.

This interpretation is supported by analogy with Hecht and Mintz' (1939) quantitative analysis of visual minimum separable. A shadow of a fine wire thrown on the retina is visualized as producing a valley in the illumination greater than the width of the geometrical projection of the wire. Hecht and Mintz (1939) calculated that, for a wire subtending 0.05 second of visual angle, the minimum visible would cause the core cone to be illuminated at 98.83 per cent of the general retinal illumination, and the two adjacent cones by 99.73 per cent. The difference of 0.95 per cent agrees closely with the difference threshold for intensity.

REFERENCES

Ades, H. W. Effect of extirpation of parastriate cortex on learned visual discriminations in monkeys. *J. Neuropathol. exp. Neurol.*, 1946, **5**, 60–65.

Adrian, E. D. Double representation of the feet in the sensory cortex of the cat. *J. Physiol.*, 1940, **98**, P16–18.

Adrian, E. D. Afferent areas in the cerebellum connected with the limbs. *Brain*, 1943, **66**, 289–315.

Amassian, V. E. Cortical representation and spinal pathways of visceral afferents. *Fed. Proc. Amer. Soc. exp. Biol.*, 1950, **9**, 5.

Bard, P. Studies on the cortical representation of somatic sensibility. *Harvey Lect.*, 1938, 143–169.

Blum, M., T. C. Ruch, and A. E. Walker. Localization of taste in the thalamus of *Macaca mulatta*. *Yale J. Biol. Med.*, 1943, **16**, 175–191.

Börnstein, W. S. Cortical representation of taste in man and monkey. I. Functional and anatomical relations of taste, olfaction and somatic sensibility. *Yale J. Biol. Med.*, 1940a, **12**, 719–736. II. The localization of the cortical taste area in man and a method of measuring impairment of taste in man. *Ibid.*, 1940b, **13**, 133–156.

Bonin, G. von. Architecture of the precentral motor cortex and some adjacent areas. Chapter 2 in *The precentral motor cortex*. *Illinois Monogr. med. sci.* (1st Ed.), 1944, **4**, Nos. 1–4. (2nd Ed., 1949.)

Bonin, G. von, and P. Bailey. The neocortex of *Macaca mulatta*. *Illinois Monogr. med. Sci.*, 1947, **5**, No. 4.

Brodmann, K. *Vergleichende Lokalisationslehre der Grosshirnrinde in ihren Prinzipien dargestellt auf Grund des Zellenbaues*. Leipzig: J. A. Barth, 1909 (reprinted 1925). (For greater detail consult Brodmann's series of papers in the early years of the *J. Psychol. Neurol., Lpz.*)

Chang, H.-T. The repetitive discharges of corticothalamic reverberating circuit. *J. Neurophysiol.*, 1950, **13**, 235–257.

Chang, H.-T., and T. C. Ruch. Topographical distribution of spinothalamic fibres in the thalamus of the spider monkey. *J. Anat. Lond.*, 1947, **81**, 150–164.

Clark, W. E. Le Gros, and R. H. Boggon. The thalamic connections of the parietal and frontal lobes of the brain in the monkey. *Philos. Trans.*, 1935, **B224**, 313–359.

Dempsey, E. W., and R. S. Morison. The electrical activity of a thalamocortical relay system. *Amer. J. Physiol.*, 1943, **138**, 283–296.

Dow, R. S., and R. Anderson. Cerebellar action potentials in response to stimulation of proprioceptors and exteroceptors in the rat. *J. Neurophysiol.*, 1942, **5**, 363–372.

Dusser de Barenne, J. G. Experimental researches on sensory localization in the cerebral cortex of the monkey (Macacus). *Proc. roy. Soc.*, 1924, **B96**, 272–291.

Dusser de Barenne, J. G. Central levels of sensory integration. *Res. Publ. Ass. nerv. ment. Dis.*, 1934, **15**, 274–286.

Dusser de Barenne, J. G., and W. S. McCulloch. Functional interdependence of sensory cortex and thalamus. *J. Neurophysiol.*, 1941, **4**, 304–310.

Evans, J. P. A study of the sensory defects resulting from gross excision of cerebral substance in humans. *Res. Publ. Ass. nerv. ment. Dis.*, 1935, **15**, 331–370.

Fulton, J. F. The chimpanzee in experimental medicine. *Trans. Kans. City Acad. Med.*, 1937–39, 1–11.

Fulton, J. F., and A. D. Keller. *The Sign of Babinski. A study of the evolution of cortical dominance*. Springfield, Ill.: Thomas, 1932.

Gotch, F., and V. Horsley. On the mammalian nervous system, its functions, and their localization determined by an electrical method

(Croonian Lecture). *Philos. Trans.*, 1891, **B182**, 267–526.

Hecht, S., and E. U. Mintz. The visibility of single lines at various illuminations and the retinal basis of visual resolution. *J. gen. Physiol.*, 1939, **22**, 593–612.

Henneman, E., and V. Mountcastle. Tactile localization in the thalamus of cat and monkey. *Fed. Proc. Amer. Soc. exp. Biol.*, 1948, **7**, 53.

Holmes, G. Disturbances of visual orientation. *Brit. J. Ophthal.*, 1918, **2**, 449–468; 506–520.

Jasper, H. H., and J. Droogleever-Fortuyn. Experimental studies on the functional anatomy of petit mal epilepsy. *Res. Publ. Ass. nerv. ment. Dis.*, 1946, **26**, 272–298.

Kennard, M. A., and M. M. Kessler. Studies of motor performance after parietal ablations in monkeys. *J. Neurophysiol.*, 1940, **3**, 248–257.

Kennard, M. A., T. C. Ruch, and J. F. Fulton. The housing, care, and surgical handling of laboratory primates. *Yale J. Biol. Med.*, 1946, **18**, 443–471.

Lashley, K. S. The mechanism of vision: XVIII. Effects of destroying the visual "associative areas" of the monkey. *Genet. Psychol. Monogr.*, 1948, **37**, 107–166.

Lorente de Nó, R. Studies on the structure of the cerebral cortex. II. Continuation of the study of the ammonic system. *J. Psychol. Neurol., Lpz.*, 1934, **46**, 133–177.

Lorente de Nó, R. Synaptic stimulation of motoneurones as a local process. *J. Neurophysiol.*, 1938, **1**, 195–206.

Lorente de Nó, R. Transmission of impulses through cranial motor nuclei. *J. Neurophysiol.*, 1939, **2**, 402–464.

Lorente de Nó, R. Cerebral cortex: Architecture, intracortical connections, motor projections. In Fulton, J. F. (Ed.) *Physiology of the nervous system* (2nd Ed.). New York: Oxford University Press, 1943. Pp. 274–300. (3rd Ed., 1949.)

Marshall, W. H., and S. A. Talbot. Recent evidence for neural mechanisms in vision leading to a general theory of sensory acuity. In H. Klüver (Ed.) *Visual mechanisms*. Lancaster, Pa.: Cattell, 1942. Pp. 117–164.

McCulloch, W. S. Cortico-cortical connections. Chapter 8 in *The precentral motor cortex*. *Illinois Monogr. med. Sci.* (1st Ed.), 1944a, **4**, Nos. 1–4. (2nd Ed., 1949.)

McCulloch, W. S. The functional organization of the cerebral cortex. *Physiol. Rev.*, 1944b, **24**, 390–407.

McCulloch, W. S. Modes of functional organization of the cerebral cortex. *Fed. Proc. Amer. Soc. exp. Biol.*, 1947, **6**, 448–452.

Morison, R. S., and E. W. Dempsey. A study of thalamocortical relations. *Amer. J. Physiol.*, 1942, **135**, 281–292.

Morison, R. S., and D. L. Bassett. Electrical activity of the thalamus and basal ganglia in decorticate cats. *J. Neurophysiol.*, 1945, **8**, 309–314.

O'Leary, J. L. A structural analysis of the lateral geniculate nucleus of the cat. *J. comp. Neurol.*, 1940, **73**, 405–430.

O'Leary, J. L., Structure of the area striata of the cat. *J. comp. Neurol.*, 1941, **75**, 131–164.

O'Leary, J. L. The role of architectonics in deciphering the electrical activity of the cortex. Chapter 3 in *The precentral motor cortex. Illinois Monogr. med. Sci.* (1st Ed.), 1944, **4**, Nos. 1–4. (2nd Ed., 1949.)

Patton, H. D., and T. C. Ruch. Preference thresholds for quinine hydrochloride in chimpanzee, monkey and rat. *J. comp. Psychol.*, 1944, **37**, 35–49.

Patton, H. D., T. C. Ruch, and A. E. Walker. Experimental hypogeusia from Horsley-Clarke lesions of the thalamus in *Macaca mulatta. J. Neurophysiol.*, 1944, **7**, 171–184.

Pitts, W., and W. S. McCulloch. How we know universals: The perception of auditory and visual forms. *Bull. math. Biophysics*, 1947, **9**, 127–147.

Polyak, S. L. *The retina.* Chicago: University of Chicago Press, 1941.

Ranson, S. W. On the use of the Horsley-Clarke stereotaxic instrument. *Psychiat. neurol. Bl., Amst.*, 1934, **38**, 534–543.

Rasmussen, T., and W. Penfield. Further studies of the sensory and motor cerebral cortex in man. *Fed. Proc. Amer. Soc. exp. Biol.*, 1947, **6**, 452–560.

Riddoch, G. Visual disorientation in homonymous half fields. *Brain*, 1935, **58**, 376–382.

Rosenblueth, A., and W. B. Cannon. Cortical responses to electrical stimulation. *Amer. J. Physiol.*, 1942, **135**, 690–741.

Rosenblueth, A., N. Wiener, and J. H. Bigelow. Behavior, purpose and teleology. *Phil. Sci.*, 1943, **10**, 18–24.

Ruch, T. C. Cortical localization of somatic sensibility. The effect of precentral, postcentral and posterior parietal lesions upon the performance of monkeys trained to discriminate weights. *Res. Publ. Ass. nerv. ment. Dis.*, 1935, **15**, 289–330.

Ruch, T. C. *Bibliographia primatologica. A classified bibliography of primates other than man. Part I. Anatomy, embryology, and quantitative morphology; physiology, pharmacology and psychology; primate phylogeny & miscellanea.* Springfield, Ill.: Thomas, 1941.

Ruch, T. C. Cerebral cortex: The parietal lobes and somatic sensation. Chapter 19 in J. F. Fulton (Ed.) *Physiology of the nervous system.* (2nd Ed.) New York: Oxford University Press, 1943. (3rd Ed., 1949.)

Ruch, T. C. The nervous system: Sensory functions. In J. F. Fulton (Ed.) *Howell's textbook of physiology.* (15th Ed.) Philadelphia: Saunders, 1946. (16th Ed., 1949.)

Ruch, T. C., and J. F. Fulton. Growth of primate literature since 1800. *Science*, 1942, **95**, 47–48.

Ruch, T. C., J. F. Fulton, and W. J. German. Sensory discrimination in monkey, chimpanzee and man after lesions of the parietal lobe. *Arch. Neurol. Psychiat., Chicago*, 1938, **39**, 919–937.

Sherrington, C. S. *The integrative action of the nervous system.* New York: Scribner, 1906.

Sjöqvist, O., and E. A. Weinstein. The effect of section of the medial lemniscus on proprioceptive functions in chimpanzees and monkeys. *J. Neurophysiol.*, 1942, **5**, 69–74.

Snider, R. S., and A. Stowell. Receiving areas of the tactile, auditory, and visual systems in the cerebellum. *J. Neurophysiol.*, 1944, **7**, 331–357.

Talbot, S. A., and W. H. Marshall. Physiological studies on neural mechanisms of visual localization and discrimination. *Amer. J. Ophthal.*, 1941, **24**, 1255–1264.

Tower, S. S. Unit for sensory reception in cornea, with notes on nerve impulses from sclera, iris and lens. *J. Neurophysiol.*, 1940, **3**, 486–500.

Vogt, O., and Cécile Vogt. Ergebnisse unserer Hirnforschung. *J. Psychol. Neurol., Lpz.*, 1919, **25**, 277–462.

Walker, A. E. *The primate thalamus.* Chicago: University of Chicago Press, 1938.

Walzl, E. M., and V. Mountcastle. Projection of vestibular nerve to cerebral cortex of the cat. *Amer. J. Physiol.*, 1949, **159**, 595.

Weddell, G. The pattern of cutaneous innervation in relation to cutaneous sensibility. *J. Anat. Lond.*, 1941, **75**, 346–367.

Weddell, G. The multiple innervation of sensory spots in the skin. *J. Anat. Lond.*, 1941, **75**, 441–446.

Woollard, H. H., G. Weddell, and J. A. Harpman. Observations on the neurohistological basis of cutaneous pain. *J. Anat. Lond.*, 1940, **74**, 413–440.

Woolsey, C. N., H.-T. Chang, and P. Bard. Distribution of cortical potentials evoked by electrical stimulation of dorsal roots in *Macaca mulatta. Fed. Proc. Amer. Soc. exp. Biol.*, 1947, **6**, 230.

Woolsey, C. N., and D. Fairman. Contralateral, ipsilateral and bilateral representation of cutaneous receptors in somatic areas I and II of the cerebral cortex of pig, sheep and other mammals. *Surgery*, 1946, **19**, 684–702.

Woolsey, C. N., W. H. Marshall, and P. Bard. Representation of cutaneous tactile sensibility in the cerebral cortex of the monkey as indicated by evoked potentials. *Johns Hopk. Hosp. Bull.*, 1942, **70**, 399–441.

Yerkes, R. M. *Chimpanzees. A laboratory colony.* New Haven: Yale University Press, 1943.

Zuckerman, S., and J. F. Fulton. *The nomenclature of primates commonly used in laboratory work.* New Haven: Tuttle, Morehouse and Taylor, 1934.

5.

Motor Systems

T. C. RUCH

University of Washington

Apart from a few forward-looking observations the motor systems originating in the cerebral cortex were until about 1930 treated in an oversimplified fashion. Thus as recently as 1945 an influential textbook of physiology described the "pathways for voluntary motor impulses" as follows:

> The pathway taken by an impulse in passing from the cerebral cortex to a muscle innervated by a spinal nerve consists of two sections: (*a*) a fiber of the corticospinal tract and (*b*) a peripheral motor neuron, i.e. a cell of the anterior horn of the spinal cord and its axon which, of course, reaches the muscle via a ventral root and a motor nerve. The corticospinal fibers pass from their cells of origin (Betz cells of the motor area of the cortex) through the white matter of the hemisphere . . .

As a result of two decades of research this concept has been modified in many respects. For example, the corticospinal tract does not end primarily upon anterior horn cells but connects with them through an elaborate system of internuncials. The corticospinal tract does not originate exclusively from Betz cells, nor does it originate exclusively from the motor area; many fibers are contributed by the postcentral gyrus and other cortical areas. Moreover voluntary activity initiated from the cerebral cortex involves many fiber systems besides the corticospinal tract. Anatomical and physiological studies show that the cerebral cortex is strongly connected with the final common path by the so-called "extrapyramidal system." This consists of all descending chains of fibers that do not pass through the medullary pyramids. Thus impulses originating in the cerebral cortex are transmitted through complex chains of fibers, interrupted synaptically in the nuclei of the basal ganglia and the brain stem, to reach the spinal cord. The cerebellum is also involved. The extrapyramidal system is so arranged that the basal ganglia and the cerebellum may influence cortical activity by reverberating or "feedback" circuits. Finally, it is now known that a large share of the pyramidal tract fibers are unmyelinated, but whether they differ in function from the myelinated ones is yet to be learned.

Thus the large fibers originating in the Betz cells, confined to a small locus in the motor area, appear to be only one component of the neural apparatus for voluntary activity. At each level of the nervous system the mechanisms of voluntary motion have proved considerably more complex than previously expected. Other cells besides those of Betz and other areas besides the motor area give origin to the pyramidal tract. Other fibers besides the large myelinated ones are found in the pyramidal tract. Other tracts besides the pyramidal tracts are involved in voluntary activity. Other than a simple relation of the pyramidal tract to anterior horn cells is definitely proved. Even the organized nuclei interposed in the extrapyramidal system, as numerous and complexly interconnected as they are, are not the whole story. The unorganized material of the brain stem, consisting of clusters of cells interwoven with fibers — the reticular substance — is probably involved in voluntary activity. At present little more than the discovery of these systems can be claimed; new methods and many years of painstaking research are clearly necessary before the neural mechanism of voluntary behavior will be known in detail.

Stimulation Experiments

Functional localization* in the cerebral cortex was first demonstrated experimentally in 1870 when Fritsch and Hitzig demarcated zones in the canine cortex from which movements of single members — face, arm, and leg — are elicitable by electrical stimulation. In primates the area of greatest excitability, and the area that is most productive of discrete movement, is area 4 which lies in the precentral gyrus of the cerebral cortex and the anterior wall of the central fissure. In man area 4 is largely concealed in this fissure. Concerning the experiments on the excitability of the motor cortex the following can be said: (1) This area has been repeatedly mapped in many mammalian forms, including man, from the point of view of the topographical representation of the musculature. (2) Its response has been compared with what results from stimulation in other zones or sectors of the brain, or after sectioning the pyramidal component of its projections. (3) The area's excitability characteristics (facilitation, extinction, after-discharge, etc.) have been repeatedly investigated and to some degree correlated with its electrical activity.

The representation of the body is, in a sense, reversed in the precentral gyrus. The face is located at the bottom of the gyrus

* Dusser de Barenne has pointed out that our conventional expression, "localization of function in the cerebral cortex," is manifestly incorrect, since the function is equally localized in the corticospinal tracts, nerves, and muscles that execute the action.

(i.e. laterally), and the leg and sacral segments are located at the top of the gyrus (medially) (Fig. 1). The area of the cortical field for a given body segment varies with the discreteness and variety of movement of that segment, not with the muscular mass involved. The tongue and finger areas, for example, are absolutely greater than the

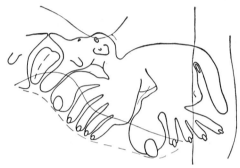

FIG. 1. Simiusculus showing the size and order of the representation of the musculature in the motor areas of the left cerebral cortex of the monkey. The area between the dashed line and the solid line above it is the anterior buried wall of the central fissure of Rolando. The area between the two vertical lines at the right is buried in the medial longitudinal fissure. The V-shaped line running through the eye of the figurine is the arcuate sulcus. The superior precentral sulcus crosses the anterior abdominal wall. (After Woolsey and Settlage.)

trunk area, and the distal segments of a limb have a more extensive cortical representation than the proximal segments (Fig. 1). These distal segments of the limb are activated by weaker cortical stimulation than are the proximal limb segments. In turn, the strength, variety, and discreteness of movements elicitable by electrical stimulation are greater for the apical musculature, as are its voluntary activities. The degree and duration of paresis from ablations of area 4 are likewise greater for the apical musculature.

These facts are based upon many observations of clinical and animal subjects and have been confirmed by an objective and quantitative technique (Chang, Ruch, and Ward, 1947). Simultaneous myographic records were made of the contraction in eight muscles, activating the toes and ankle, in response to cortical stimulation. The maximal contraction elicited in each muscle in a series was tabulated and related to muscle weight. Only the portion of the leg area appearing on the free surface of the brain was stimulated. Within this area the muscles moving the toes are more available to activation by cortical stimulation than are the larger muscles of the same class which move the ankle. Extensor hallucis longus, which dorsiflexes the great toe, although weighing only 1.42 grams, gave rise to a contraction of 310 grams of tension. Tibialis anticus, which everts and dorsiflexes the foot, weighed 8.50 grams, and gave rise to 320 grams of tension. Using grams of muscle weight as a rough index of the number of motor units contained in the muscle, the tension per gram of muscle weight from cortical stimulation gives the ratio of cortically activated motor units to total motor units. This ratio was 37.0 for the ankle muscle, and 218.3 for the toe muscle, approximately six times greater. This may mean that the cortical representation is more concentrated for the toe dorsiflexor, since the number of points that will give a preponderate tibialis response is greater than the number that will give a toe dorsiflexion. However, the toe dorsiflexor is represented as the preponderate muscle throughout several square millimeters of cortex, a large area relative to the size of the muscle. As in sensory systems multiplicity of units is one way in which finely graded responses are obtained, a conclusion consistent with Sherrington's motor-unit analysis of reflex activity.

Fundamental Plan of the Motor Cortex

How the motor cortex functions in voluntary activity cannot be directly learned from electrical stimulation, which is not its natural mode of activation. Therefore much of the research on the motor cortex has been directed towards questions of localization rather than towards the elucidation of its functions. However, if localization studies are carried far enough, the boundary between structure and function is passed.

What is the basic plan of organization of the motor cortex? Since the time of Hughlings Jackson (1834–1911), it has been taught that the motor cortex is organized to yield movements. This is sometimes picturesquely stated by saying that the motor cortex "thinks in terms of movements, not muscles." It is manifest that movements are not "localized" in the cerebral cortex. What is meant is that the Betz cells, synaptically connected with muscles via their motoneurons which produce a given movement, are collected within one area of the cerebral cortex. A muscle, or a fraction of a muscle, must be re-represented as many times as there are movements employing that muscle. This idea is well expressed by the phrase "multiplicity of representation," or simply "re-representation" of muscles. Following Hughlings Jackson's original formulation, this theory is that the ingredients of a movement (Betz cells) exist in each movement focus in various combinations.

> Then it may be said that one convolution will represent only the movements of the arm, another only those of speech, another only those of the leg, and so on. The facts above stated show that this is not the plan of structure of the nervous system. Thus, to take an illustration, the external parts, x, y, and z [segments or limbs], are each represented by units of the corpus striatum [motor cortex]. But the plan of representation is not that some units contain x largely only, as x_3,* others y largely only, as y_3, but that *each* unit contains x, y, and z — some, let us say, as x_3, y_2, z, others as x_2, y_3, z, etc. [Jackson, 1931, p. 27.]

It is undisputed that the first answer received by applying electrodes to the cerebral cortex is that muscle groups or the whole

---

* The subscript represents the number of x, y, or z units in a given area.

limb can be activated from a single cortical point. Moreover, when stimulation conditions are arranged to produce maximal excitation, even the traditional arm, face, and leg areas are not inviolate, as Murphy and Gellhorn (1945) have shown. The degree of overlap between somatotopic areas so displayed decreases as we ascend the mam-

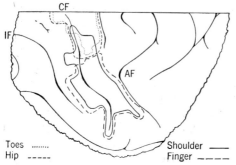

Toes ....   Shoulder ____
Hip _ _ _ _   Finger _ _ _ _

Fig. 2. A diagram of the right cerebral hemisphere of the macaque monkey on which is mapped the areas from which responses of the upper and lower limb were obtained by electrical stimulation selected to produce maximal responses. Note the zone of overlap giving responses in both upper and lower extremities, and that stimulation posterior to the central fissure produces movement. CF, central fissure; IF, intraparietal fissure; AF, arcuate fissure. (Murphy and Gellhorn, 1945.)

malian series, but nevertheless overlap exists to some degree in the monkey (Fig. 2). With such maximal stimulations the areas from which toes and hip can be excited greatly overlap and are, in fact, almost identical; the same is true of the areas for fingers and shoulder. Other workers (Chang, Ruch, and Ward, 1947; Hines, 1944; Woolsey, 1938), who have selected stimulus conditions to activate a restricted cortical focus and to avoid facilitation, have obtained a different result.

Boynton and Hines (1933) observed that reduction of the stimulus strength may restrict the response to a single muscle of a group that responds to stronger stimulation a phenomenon they termed "centripetal individuation." In 1938 Woolsey described

a pattern of cortical organization, based on detailed stimulation of the leg area, consisting of rays running obliquely across the precentral gyrus. Beginning on the mesial surface, the extensor muscles (derivatives of the dorsal muscle sheet) are represented in order from hips to toes, followed by the flexor muscles (derivatives of the ventral muscle sheet) in order from toes to hips. This arrangement would make the organization of the precentral gyrus parallel that of the postcentral gyrus (see Chapter 4).* In still another approach to the problem (Chang, Ruch, and Ward, 1947) the contraction of eight distal muscles of the leg were recorded polygraphically while the leg area of the cerebral cortex was stimulated systematically, millimeter by millimeter, in order to map the cerebral cortex in terms of muscle representation. It was hoped thereby to test the hypothesis of multiple representation of muscles and to provide data from which the plan of organization of the motor cortex could be deduced. The extent of cortex stimulated was not sufficient to permit attainment of the latter objective, but evidence for a concentration of the cortical representation of individual muscles was obtained.

The conclusion reached by previous workers that single muscles can be made to contract by cortical stimulation was confirmed. When such "solitary responses" were pro-

* Woolsey and Settlage (1950) have extended this analysis of the monkey's motor cortex. "In essence, fingers, toes and lower face are represented within and adjacent to the central sulcus. The axes of arm and leg run rostrocaudally so that proximal parts of limbs are better represented rostrally, as are also upper face, eyelids and pinna. Binding together face, arm and leg representations is an area for axial musculature, which forms the rostral border of the pattern." This may be termed a "unitary theory of the motor areas" since it draws the classic eye fields and adversive band (see below) into the ladder of motor representation and raises the question whether differences in the latency and character of movements from areas 4, 6, and 8 may not in part reflect the type of musculature represented rather than levels of motor function. This chapter should be read with this in mind.

jected onto a cortical map according to the point eliciting them, a meaningful pattern resulted (Fig. 3). The solitary response

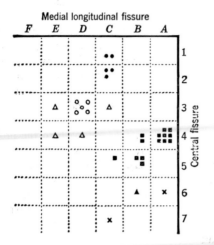

Medial longitudinal fissure

- • M. extensor digitorum longus (EDL)
- ■ M. extensor hallucis longus (EHL)
- ▲ M. tibialis anticus (TA)
- ✕ M. abductor hallucis longus (AHL)
- ○ M. flexor digitorum longus (FDL)
- ▵ M. tibialis posticus (TP)

FIG. 3. A plot of the leg area of the left cerebral cortex in the macaque monkey, showing the points at which electrical stimulation caused single muscles to respond. The ordinate (numbers) is approximately parallel to the central fissure, and the abscissa (letters) to the medial longitudinal fissure that separates the two hemispheres. Each square represents slightly more than 1 millimeter. Note that the points yielding solitary responses in a given muscle are grouped into a few contiguous squares, sometimes within a single square. TA and AHL appear only a few times because they usually respond together. The data from two monkeys are combined, indicating a high degree of reliability. (Chang, Ruch, and Ward, 1947.)

points for a given muscle are not scattered at random, but fall into groups. The area so found can be considered the focus of the cortical field for this muscle. On this map, tibialis anticus and abductor hallucis longus

appear only a few times because they tended to react together, which correlates with the fact that they are slips of the same muscle, differing only in insertion. When several muscles respond together, analysis based upon strength of contraction (tension) reveals further evidence of a topical representation for different muscles. Many factors affect the absolute magnitude of the cortically evoked contraction — the size of the muscle, electrode contact, and fluctuations in the physiological state of the cortex. To cancel these out, tension developed in two given muscles is plotted for each point stimulated as in Fig. 4. For each of the parallel or approximately parallel lines sloping upward to the extensor hallucis longus ordinate, a large filled circle is entered on a graph representing the motor cortex at the point stimulated. Similarly, lines sloping in the reverse direction are represented by a large open circle, and the intermediate slopes are represented by small circles, filled or unfilled, depending on the slope of the line. The important fact is that the points so graphed form a meaningful pattern, with the large filled circles forming a cluster surrounded by small filled circles. From such distributions it is concluded that the cortical representations of the two muscles, though overlapping, are changing topographically in respect of concentration of Betz cells, or some other determinant of cortical excitability.

Latency analysis also reveals a topographical dissociation of cortical points. The latencies for responses of a given muscle are graded and suitably entered on a cortical graph. The points for short-latency responses again tend to form a cluster, surrounded by points for responses of intermediate latency. Since absolute rather than relative latencies are graphed, this type of analysis is more subject to variations depending on the state of the cortex, etc.

In evaluating the degree of topographical dissociation so demonstrated, it is important

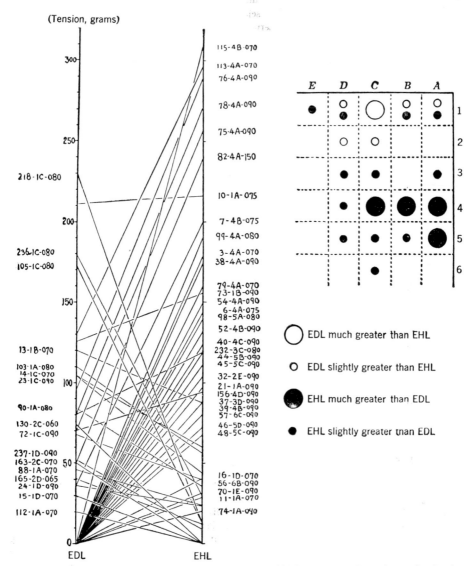

FIG. 4. An analysis of data indicating a topographical representation of muscles in the cerebral motor cortex. In the graph at the left each line shows the contraction tensions of the extensor of the toes (EDL) and the extensor of the great toe (EHL) from stimulation of various cortical points, as noted on either side of the plot. [112-1*A*-070 means 112th stimulation which was at point 1*A* (see Fig. 3) and with an intensity of 070 on the Goodwin stimulator.] The plot to the right is similar to Fig. 3, except that tension ratios are plotted in four categories determined by the slope of the lines in the graph. (Chang, Ruch, and Ward, 1947.)

to remember that the muscles that are sufficiently active to permit analysis all belong
to the same class, i.e. anatomical extensors

calculated to minimize the sharpness of
muscle localization. Assuming that the pattern of representation lies in the mosaic of

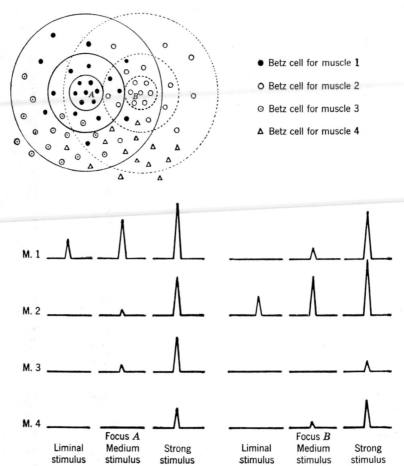

Betz cell for muscle 1

Betz cell for muscle 2

Betz cell for muscle 3

Betz cell for muscle 4

| | Liminal stimulus | Focus A Medium stimulus | Strong stimulus | Liminal stimulus | Focus B Medium stimulus | Strong stimulus |

FIG. 5. A hypothetical distribution of Betz cells in the motor area that accounts for the data shown in the previous figures. Each muscle is represented by a field of Betz cells with a fringe that overlaps the fields of other muscles and a focus that does not overlap the focus for other muscles. Each symbol stands for a Betz cell, and the concentric circles stand for the spheres of excitation with three intensities of stimulation. Below is the expected contraction in four different muscles from stimulation of the two foci, each with three intensities. (Chang, Ruch, and Ward, 1947.)

(physiological flexors), and that the toe
muscles also dorsiflex the ankle. According
to Woolsey's analysis (1938) these distal
muscles should be contiguously represented.
Chang, Ruch, and Ward (1947) point out
that the procedure of cortical stimulation is

Betz cells and in the other cells giving rise
to corticospinal fibers, the following factors
stand in the way of our seeing this pattern
of organization: (1) Each Betz cell is potentially connected with many ventral horn
cells through the internuncial neurons of the

spinal cord.* (2) Some extrapyramidal fibers arise in area 4; and, since the extrapyramidal system is diffuse, such fibers would spread excitation to a wide range of musculature. (3) Betz cells are stimulated by current passing through a dense pile of transcortical fibers, stimulation of which would spread the excitation to neighboring cortical points. Intracortical U-fibers may also be involved. By circumcision of the area stimulated, as in Murphy and Gellhorn's experiments (1945), the third factor can be controlled, though not the first or second. However, the whole area explored by Chang, Ruch, and Ward would be nearly enclosed in the small area isolated by Murphy and Gellhorn.

Figure 5 illustrates the concept that arises from these experiments, expressed in terms of Betz cell concentrations. (Other factors in cortical excitability are no doubt also involved.) The diagram indicates that the Betz cells that activate a given muscle are not uniformly spread throughout the leg area of the motor cortex, or throughout any subregion devoted to a muscle group. They are concentrated into fields that overlap those of other muscles. Within the field devoted to a given muscle is a focus of representation that is peculiar to that muscle. Thus it is believed that the pattern of the Betz layer is topographically rather than functionally organized in the sense of multiplicity of representation. Superimposed on this stable topographical pattern is an enormously complex pile of transcortical fibers by which movements may be organized. As Woolsey (1947, p. 537) has expressed it, "the whole nervous system acting dynamically makes use of stable anatomical relationships."

PHYSIOLOGY OF THE MOTOR CORTEX

The topographical features of cortical excitability were briefly outlined in the previous section. The temporal features of cortical stimulation have likewise been investigated, beginning with the pioneer researches of Bubnoff and Heidenhain (1881). The same questions are asked about the cortex as about axon and synaptic excitability. What is the time course of the response to stimulation as exhibited in latency, duration of response, after-discharge, etc.? Are there changes in excitability from a stimulus (conditioning stimulus) that reveal themselves by an altered response to a second or "testing" stimulus? The conditioning-testing procedure is the fundamental maneuver by which axon, muscle, and synapse studies have yielded information on facilitation, inhibition, refractory period, supernormal and subnormal states, etc.* The same procedure is applied to the study of the motor cortex, except that the stimuli are usually repetitive, not single shocks as with axons.

Whereas in the previous section the motor cortex was considered as a relatively stable mosaic of excitable points, in the following sections the cortex will be considered from a more dynamic point of view. Responses to stimulation of the same locus vary in degree and even in type, depending on the previous activity of this or neighboring points in the cortex. It will be shown that similar variability of response occurs from stimulation of morphological structures, such as afferent nerves, which are functionally heterogeneous in the units they contain.

---

* This may seem quibbling. However, if internuncial spread rather than multiplicity of Betz cell representation is involved, it would be better to speak of the internuncials rather than the cortex as "thinking in terms of movements, not muscles." On the other hand, expressions such as a "flexor Betz cell" or a "tibialis anticus Betz cell" should be understood to mean a Betz cell more strongly connected with the given motoneuron pool than with the motoneuron pools of other muscles.

* Concerning many neural processes, about all that is known is their time course, which has been learned by varying the interval between the conditioning and testing stimulations.

Latency

The period elapsing between the onset of a repetitive cortical stimulation and the onset of muscular response is often quite prolonged, as long as 5 or 10 seconds. This period, however, is not a true latent period but is more properly termed a *"summation period."* It is briefer, the more rapid the rate of stimulation, and fewer shocks are required to elicit the response when, for example, the rate is increased from 6 to 13 per second (Cooper and Denny-Brown, 1927). The summation period of a cortically evoked response can be shortened by facilitation from previous stimulation (see below), or by strychnine, which lowers the threshold of neurons to synaptic stimulation.

After contraction commences, summation continues and is manifested by an increased muscular response to successive members of a slow series of stimuli. Since the muscle action potentials are simple at this point in the response and therefore not indicative of repetitive firing of motoneurons, the phenomenon is one of "recruitment," in which additional motoneurons are successively brought above neuron threshold and made to discharge (Cooper and Denny-Brown, 1927).

During the actual response of a muscle to cortical stimulation, the time elapsing between the occurrence of a break shock and the occurrence of the action potential of the resulting contraction can be made out, provided the stimulus rate is low. This latency averages 14 to 16 milliseconds and is compounded of conduction times, a period of summation and true synaptic delay. It can be reduced to 8.8 milliseconds by strychnine. Less dramatically, the latent period shortens progressively as the contraction proceeds, a further evidence of summation. It is unlikely that summation times of several seconds represent solely the inertia of internuncials linking corticospinal fibers and motoneurons. Prolonged latency and a slow tension rise, characteristic of certain spinal reflexes, are due not simply to the necessity for summation to reach the threshold of

motoneurons, but to an intermixture of inhibitory and excitatory effects arising from the fact that spinal nerves contain the afferent limbs of antagonistic reflex arcs. Thus an increase in the stimulus may prolong rather than shorten the latency and the period of recruitment of the crossed extensor reflex (Matthes and Ruch, 1932). Certain features of the response to cortical stimulation are suggestive of inhibition intermixed with excitation, e.g. the rapid decline of contraction when stimulation is stopped.* In fact, little or no contraction may occur during a 10-second stimulation of the motor cortex, only to set in as a "rebound" phenomenon at the end of stimulation. In spinal reflexes rebound is interpreted to mean an admixture of excitation and inhibition. It will be shown later that cortical stimulation must be viewed as stimulation of a mixed population of units, some ultimately excitatory and some inhibitory to the motoneurons of the muscle observed. This, in turn, means that electrical stimulation is an unphysiological method, and data resulting from it must not be accepted at face value but must be subjected to careful analysis.

Another question is whether the motor cortex itself is the site of inertia and summation and is contributory to the summation

---

* ". . . The whole form of the response to stimulation of the motor cortex, and the clonic after-discharge characteristic of that response, are the outward signs of a conflict of summated excitation and inhibition. This conflict, which is not obviously a feature of normal voluntary movement, is not unlikely the result of artificial provocation to concurrent activity of two naturally opposed groups of minute cells in the mosaic of the motor area. One of these groups produces excitation at the final motor neurone and the other inhibition. The inhibition so rapidly developed is not merely the expression of activity of the antagonist, indeed our double records show the resulting impedance in both antagonists at the same time. The inference from this we think is clear, that for a given movement the excitatory units and the inhibitory units lie microscopically intermingled in the cortex, and, further, that representatives of movements in opposite directions are often closely enough related anatomically to be excited by the same stimulus." (Cooper and Denny-Brown, 1927, p. 233.)

period and true latency of the responses to cortical stimulation.

Adrian and Moruzzi (1939), taking advantage of the fact that the pyramidal tract breaks up into fine bundles prior to decussation, were able to record series of action potentials, alike in size and resembling single unit discharges or the synchronous discharges of a group of fibers. During the first few

effective in activating the spinal internuncials and, in turn, the motoneurons. As brought out in the previous chapter, the briefness of the excitatory effect at individual synapses makes a high-frequency input favorable for summation.

The experiments of Adrian and Moruzzi indicate that latency, summation, and recruitment are in part determined at the

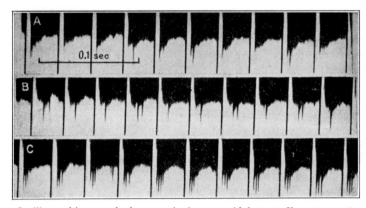

FIG. 6. Oscillographic records from a single pyramidal tract fiber at varying intervals during continuous repetitive stimulation (30 per second) of the motor cortex. The large downward excursions which appear to cut the record into segments are the shock artifacts; the smaller downward excursions are the action potentials.

A. 4 seconds after beginning of stimulation—occasional impulses.

B. 1 second later—single or double impulses to each shock.

C. 3 seconds later—three to four impulses to each shock, and movement begins. (Adrian and Moruzzi, 1939.)

seconds of stimulation of the motor cortex at 30 per second, a discharge does not occur in response to each shock (Fig. 6). Later, each shock is followed by an impulse in the pyramidal tract, and, finally, each shock produces a group of three or four impulses spaced at 1.75 milliseconds. When such groups appear, limb movement is first observed. In one experiment strengthening the stimulus reduced the interval between the shock and the pyramidal impulse from 4.5 to 2.3 milliseconds and caused a double discharge in place of a single one. Thus, by summation or increase in stimulus strength, corticospinal fibers are forced into a very high rate of discharge. A high-frequency discharge, in turn, appears to be especially

cortical level. Much remains to be learned about the excitable properties of cortical tissue in response to electrical stimulation. For example, does the summation between shocks of a series represent activities of the intracortical fibers or of the Betz cells? Does the Betz cell, because it is a cell body, or because it is large, have properties different from axons, or the same properties in exaggerated degree? The multitude of questions that arise will probably be answered when single unit techniques, analogous to those of Adrian and Moruzzi, are applied in detail.

Discovery of Facilitation

Bubnoff and Heidenhain in 1881 carried out the first systematic experiments demonstrating the facilitation phenomena of the motor cortex. They recorded myographically and kymographically the latency of limb-muscle responses to a variety of cortical stimulations. Increase in the strength of stimulations increases the size of the contraction and decreases the latency. Even strong single shocks (except those of long duration) applied to the motor cortex do not evoke muscular contraction. Subliminal stimuli, those producing no visible motor response when delivered singly, do so on repetition. The shorter the interval between stimuli, the more easily summation occurs. With repetition of a minimal current, unchanged in intensity, the height of the contraction gradually increases to a maximum. In all these cases it is clear that "each preceding stimulus therefore leaves an after-effect which increases the effect of the following one" (Bubnoff and Heindenhain, 1881). Such continued stimulation of a given point also results in a spreading of the response to include a wider range of musculature. This is called "irradiation," but the underlying mechanism is facilitation. Even a cutaneous stimulation of the limb, not in itself sufficient to evoke a visible reflex, will augment the response to a subsequent cortical stimulation.

For one stimulus to facilitate another, it is not necessary that the testing stimulus fall on the same cortical point. Such facilitation is termed "secondary." Secondary facilitation may be defined as the augmentative effect of an antecedent stimulation of a cortical focus upon the response to subsequent stimulation at a different point yielding a different but not antagonistic response. The interaction between two cortical points is strongest when they lie within the same somatotopic area, but the two points need not lie in the motor area. For example, stimulation of the postcentral gyrus will facilitate the response from a point in the motor area, and vice versa. The facilitation phenomena of the motor cortex present at least a superficial analogy to activation of reflexes by afferent

nerve stimulation. When the same nerve is stimulated successively, the resulting interaction is termed "temporal summation" and is analogous to primary facilitation. When two nerves or nerve branches are stimulated, the summation is termed "spatial" and is analogous to the stimulation of two cortical points (secondary facilitation).

McCulloch (1944) has formalized the two types of behavior that are grouped under secondary facilitation as follows:

> . . . if two points are selected such that excitation of the first point, a, evokes a motor response, A; and excitation of the second point, b, evokes B: and if a and b belong to the same [somatotopic] subdivision and if A and B are not antagonistic, then appropriately timed successive stimulation of a and b will cause either (1) a repetition of A when b is stimulated [$ab \rightarrow A$], or (2) an exaggeration of the response B [$ab \rightarrow B$]." [P. 216.]

The response $ab \rightarrow B$ means that the discharge from the a point intensifies the response typical of the second point. The B response tends to occur when a is undergoing extinction (see below). According to the analysis carried out by McCulloch and Dusser de Barenne, the $ab \rightarrow B$ sequence is associated with an electrical change in the cortex at point b and fails when the cortico-cortical connections between the two points are sectioned or when such connections do not exist. Their analysis has shown that area 6 is strongly connected by fibers running to area 4, and, when point a is in area 6 and point b in area 4, the sequence is $ab \rightarrow B$, never $a_6 b_4 \rightarrow A$. Since the two areas are not connected by fibers running from area 4 to area 6, the sequence $a_4 b_6$ always results in response A. This is perhaps further evidence that $ab \rightarrow B$ is dependent on cortico-cortical connections, although the fact that the response is that of the more excitable area might be a factor.

The second type of secondary facilitation $ab \rightarrow A$ is a repetition of the a response when b is stimulated. This sequence can occur and, in fact, tends to occur when *b* is located in the postcentral gyrus or in area 6, and *a* is a point in area 4. Dusser de Barenne and McCulloch's analysis, based on section of corticocortical fibers connecting the two points, indicates that such connections are not necessary to the response, though some transcortical facilitation may be involved. It is believed to depend "chiefly upon excitation persisting in the subcortical structures affected by the first stimulation." The sequence $ab \rightarrow A$ is more easily elicited if both points lie on the same somatotopic division, for these must project to the same or closely related portions of the spinal cord. The detailed organization of the motor cortex bears upon this question. In addition to overlap between spinal terminations of the pyramidal tract fibers arising from the two points stimulated, there is probably some overlap between the Betz cells giving the two movements (Fig. 5). In any case the excitatory residuum of the first stimulus apparently is reinforced by the discharge from the second, so that in total it preponderates over the response typical of the second volley.

The second type of facilitation ($ab \rightarrow A$) differs from the first type because the response typical of the second volley is changed from *B* to *A*. This was observed by Leyton and Sherrington (1917) and described under the term "deviation of response." They state, "a cortical point can also influence the motor response of another whose response is neither diametrically opposed to nor identical with or very closely similar to its own."

Deviation of response is a change that alters the character of the response, so that some other movement — e.g. of another joint or part — appears in place of the original. Beginning in the arm area, stimulation of a descending series of points, i.e. extending towards the sylvian fissure, gave elbow flexion to a boundary beyond which facial movements abruptly appeared. After an ascending series of stimulations of the face area, the lower points which had yielded elbow flexion

in the descending series now yielded thumb and index movements. The response of the points within an area of overlap between face and arm area were, therefore, altered on the basis of antecedent stimulation. Similarly, within somatotopic areas an ascending or descending series of closely spaced stimulations will cause a movement to appear from an area not yielding that movement in the absence of facilitation.

The mechanism of facilitation will be discussed in a later section in conjunction with the phenomena of extinction and suppression.

Instability of the Motor Point

Facilitation is a factor in the functional plasticity of the cerebral cortex, a concept expressed by Graham Brown and Sherrington (1912) as the "functional instability of a cortical motor point." The instability of the motor cortical mosaic was overemphasized in the early literature, partly because of the inadequate stimulation devices then available. Modern use of thyratron or other electronic stimulators, the employment of fixed rather than hand-held electrodes, etc., minimize the variability of responses to cortical stimulation. Yet, when all known precautions are taken, there remains a definite functional instability of the cortical point. This instability is manifested, according to Sherrington, in (1) facilitation of the type $ab \rightarrow B$, (2) deviation of response $ab \rightarrow A$, and (3) reversal of response. The last is a change in the direction of a movement of a joint, so that extension may be replaced by flexion, i.e. the sense or direction of the movement is reversed. Like the first two phenomena, reversal is temporary, and the result of antecedent stimulation. Since reversal of response is perhaps the most dramatic instance of the functional plasticity of the motor cortex, it will be examined in detail after we consider the phenomenon of reciprocal innervation as manifested in cortically initiated movements.

RECIPROCAL INNERVATION AND REVERSAL OF RESPONSE

Soon after his discovery of reciprocal innervation as a principle governing the behavior of spinal reflexes, Sherrington [and Hering] (1897) described reciprocal excitation and inhibition of limb antagonists under cortical stimulation. When a monkey or a cat was in the stage of ether anesthesia at which the legs maintain a position of flexion at the elbow or hip, a cortical point previously determined to produce extension of the elbow joint or hip joint was stimulated. Concurrent with the resulting extension, the antagonistic flexor muscle became suddenly flabby to palpation, while the extensor muscle became tense in contraction. In a stage of narcosis when an extensor posture of the limbs obtained, relaxation of the extensor muscle resulted from stimulation of the cortical point yielding contraction of the antagonistic flexor muscle. In order to determine whether the interaction was between cortical neurons, the cortex was removed, and the fibers of the internal capsule were stimulated. Reciprocal innervation was maintained.

Several years earlier Sherrington (1893) demonstrated reciprocal innervation of the eye muscles. By nerve section, all the external muscles of one eye were paralyzed except the external rectus which moves the eye to the side. The area of the ipsilateral hemisphere, which prior to nerve section yielded conjugate movement to the opposite side, was then stimulated. The eye moved in the lateral direction. The movement of the ipsilateral eye could only be due to inhibition of the tonus in the innervated lateral rectus.

Reciprocal innervation from cortical stimulation, like that from afferent nerve stimulation, has been challenged from time to time on the basis of evidence of co-contraction of antagonistic muscles. The latter without question does occur, and it was observed by Sherrington himself. The issue is how the fact of co-contraction is to be interpreted.

As with the problem of latency, much is to be gained by approaching the pyramidal system with the experience gained in the study of spinal reflexes. It is profitable, therefore, to examine briefly how the same problem was met and solved in the study of these reflexes. The experiments are detailed and technical and can only be briefly sketched. In the sphere of spinal reflexes, departures from reciprocal innervation are usually accompanied by poststimulatory inhibitory and excitatory rebound phenomena, and adequate explanation is found in the unphysiological character of nerve trunk stimulation. Mixed nerves contain the afferent limbs of many reflexes. Their collective stimulation yields a dominant and a concealed reflex, often antagonistic. By manipulating the intensity, the frequency, and the duration of the stimulation, the concealed reflex can often be made dominant. Evidence adduced in a later section indicates that the territory stimulated directly and by intracortical facilitation contains intermingled "flexor Betz cells" and "extensor Betz cells." This circumstance is adequate to explain co-contraction, especially when it follows a period of reciprocal relationship, is favored by strong and prolonged stimulation, and is followed by poststimulatory rebound, as in the observations of Bosma and Gellhorn (1946). It is often not appreciated that Sherrington's generalizations are the result of analysis, not mere observations; that he thought in terms of single units before enunciating that concept; and that he was well aware of, and often discarded, those situations in which complexity of anatomical arrangement and the bluntness of experimental tools obscure simple and fundamental relationships. The stimulating electrode applied to the cortex stimulates many units *en bloc* and without regard to their function, i.e. the synaptic connections in the spinal cord of the Betz cells lying beneath the electrodes. These same elements, grouped together morphologically, are unquestionably activated selectively by synaptic excitation in normal voluntary action.

The electrode is an unnatural mode of stimulation, and the responses mirror nature only when the stimulus can be confined to a functionally homogeneous group of neurons or when the response of a single unit can be studied.

In 1912 Graham Brown and Sherrington described, as exceptions to the usual stability of the cortical mosaic, instances in which the responses from a given cortical point differed on successive stimulations. Specifically they were concerned with "reversal of a response," i.e. instances in which a point regularly yielding flexion can be made to yield extension, and vice versa. This phenomenon differs from "deviation of response," which is a change to a different but not antagonistic muscle group. Reversal of a response is restricted to a change to response of the antagonist. Although serial stimulation usually augments the response (so-called "intensification of response") because of facilitation, it sometimes results in a reversal of the response.

Interpolating a stimulation of a flexion point in a series of stimulations delivered to an extension point will often temporarily "convert it" to a flexion point, i.e. reverse its response.

One of the factors for reversal is stimulus intensity. In exploring the motor cortex during polymyographic recording from muscles acting over the ankle joint, excitation of flexor muscles (physiological extensors) was rarely obtained (Chang, Ruch, and Ward, 1947). Figure 7 shows a series of responses from a flexion point for the toes, obtained by careful adjustment of the stimulus intensity. A moderately weak stimulus produced contractions of the toe flexor and the toe extensor, larger in the latter (obs. 110 and 111). Reducing the strength of the stimulus *increased* the contraction of the flexor and decreased the contraction of the extensor (obs. 112). Strengthening the stimulus strengthened the extensor contraction and weakened or inhibited completely the flexor response (obs. 116 and 118). A

response confined to the flexor was produced when the stimulus was again reduced to near threshold strength (obs. 119). Thus the stimulus strength determined whether flexor or extensor contractions would result from stimulation of the same point on the cortex.

Perhaps the simplest explanation of such phenomena is gained by viewing a cortical point * as a mixed population of Betz cells, as indicated in Fig. 5. A flexion point is one containing a preponderance of the Betz cells that activate flexor motoneurons. A second assumption is that there is an average threshold difference between the two categories of cells, in this case that those activating the extensor have the lower threshold. Further it is assumed that flexor-connected cells are more numerous in the cortex at the point stimulated or are preponderant in spinal synaptic connections. Finally, if the pyramidal tract fibers from the flexor and extensor Betz cells act reciprocally on the spinal motoneurons, we have a model that would adequately account for reversal of response through change in stimulus intensity.

Frequency is also a factor in the reversal and deviation of response to stimulation of a single cortical point (Boynton and Hines, 1933). Many instances can be cited in which frequency-determined reversal follows stimulation of peripheral and central neural structures. The mechanisms for frequency and for intensity reversal may not be the same. Whereas intensity determines, on the basis of threshold, which cells of the cortex are stimulated, frequency can be selective at subcortical levels if the internuncial bombardments set up by "flexor" and "extensor" pyramidal tract fibers have different time characteristics. Assume that the internuncial system interpolated between the pyramidal tract and the extensor motoneurons produces an internuncial bombardment briefer than that of the

---

* A cortical point is that area beneath the stimulating electrode, or within the electrical influence of the electrode. A flexion point is one from which a flexion of some joint is the usual response.

internuncials of the pyramidal flexor moto-neurons. A faster rate of cortical stimulation would then be required to obtain sufficient summation to discharge the extensor motoneurons and might reciprocally inhibit

can determine the response when a heterogeneous population of cells is excited.

Where there is no reason to assume a reciprocal inhibitory relationship between the two responses, it is more difficult to explain

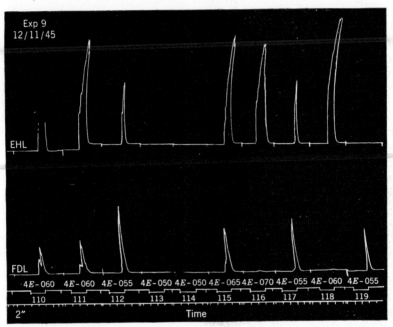

Fig. 7. A record showing reversal of response from a *single* cortical point, obtained by varying the stimulus strength. The upper two lines are kymographic tracings of two muscles whose tendons were attached to two semi-isometric myographs. The stimulus was repetitive and lasted 4 seconds. Observations Nos. 110 to 119, inclusive, are shown. The notation 4E-060 means that point 4E was stimulated with an intensity of 060 (cf. Fig. 4). EHL is extensor hallucis longus, which dorsiflexes the great toe and is a physiological flexor. FDL is flexor digitorum longus, which plantar flexes the toes and is a physiological extensor. Note that strong stimulation increases EHL response (obs. 110, 111, 116), whereas weakening the stimulation increases FDL and decreases EHL. (Chang, Ruch, and Ward, 1947.)

the flexor motoneurons. Another adequate assumption is that physiological flexors, which execute relatively active and fine movements, have a lower motoneuron threshold, a richer internuncial system, or, for that matter, simply receive more pyramidal tract fibers. Any of these conditions would result in less necessity for summation and in a greater ability to respond to slow rates of stimuli. Therefore frequency, like intensity,

deviation of response produced by changes in frequency. Bailey and von Bonin (personal communication) have given a clear-cut example of a frequency-induced change in the somatotopic distribution of response. At low frequencies (below 10 per second) stimulation of the face area of the motor cortex yielded movements of the tongue and vocal cords; at higher frequencies of stimulation facial movements *alone* were obtained. Mc-

Culloch (1947), in explaining this phenomenon, speaks of lower structures acting as "filters," accomplishing "diversion" of cortically initiated impulses from the 7th to the 12th nerve at low rates of stimulation.

A model of an internuncial filter might be as follows: Suppose the internuncial pools contain closed chains of fibers or reverberating circuits. The simplest model would be a pyramidal tract fiber and an interneuron, the axon of which gives off a collateral that returns to the interneuron cell body. With such a single loop, the moment that the recurrent impulse, initiated by the first pyramidal volley, returns to the interneuron cell body is the optimal time for the arrival of a second pyramidal volley, if summation is to occur. The pyramidal system is not so critically timed, since summation is obtained throughout a wide band of frequency, and neither were the circuits in Bailey and von Bonin's experiment. However, their results can be explained by assuming multiple loops, each with a different circuit time, the statistical distribution of which determines the optimum frequency for summation and hence the optimum frequency of cortical stimulation. If the statistical distribution of circuit times is different for facial and hypoglossal interneurons, a result like Bailey and von Bonin's can be expected.

The phenomenon of the instability of the cortical point should be viewed conservatively. When we stimulate a morphological unit (cortical point, afferent nerve, gray ramus), we are stimulating a functionally heterogeneous structure. Only when such structures are reduced to single units, or to groups of functionally homogeneous units, are we on safe ground. Nor should instability of total response be taken to support a concept of field theory until instability, reversal, etc., have been demonstrated for the individual units.

Extinction

The same technical maneuver that demonstrates facilitation — conditioning-testing sequence — demonstrates the phenomenon that Dusser de Barenne and McCulloch described in 1934 under the term "extinction." In fact, facilitation and extinction are intermingled and must be separated by analysis. Extinction is defined as *a diminution or absence of response to stimulation of a cortical motor focus following antecedent stimulation of that same focus* (1939). The phenomenon of extinction is cortical, not spinal, in origin, since it is not seen after thermal destruction of the cortex; neither is it due to the physical spread of current as opposed to the excitatory results of stimulation. The time course and other features of the response show that facilitation and extinction are dissimilar in other ways than the sign of the effect of the precedent stimulation on the testing stimulation.

1. *Time course.* Whereas facilitation is strongest immediately after the testing shock, extinction is maximal about 13 seconds after this stimulation (Fig. 8). Its point of maximum and its duration depend on the depth and type of anesthesia and upon other factors affecting the physiological state of the cortex.

2. *Extensity.* Although not strictly local, in the sense of being confined to the area immediately subjacent to the stimulating electrode, extinction is much more a local phenomenon than is facilitation. When the conditioning and testing shocks are delivered through electrodes 1.5, 3.0, and 4.5 millimeters apart, there is a sharp spatial decrement in the degree of extinction.

3. *Stimulus parameters.* Extinction is favored over facilitation by prolonged stimulation, high frequency, long pulse duration, and high voltage of the conditioning stimulation. The fundamental difference between the two phenomena is that facilitation appears to be the consequence of neuron impulses, set up locally and at a distance by the stimulus, which render nerve cells more responsive, whereas extinction appears to be a consequence of the fact that nerve cells

have fired and are thereby rendered less excitable. The duration of extinction precludes its being identified with refractory period, which, by analogy with motoneurons, is a matter of milliseconds. Nor is fatigue or exhaustion an attractive explanation, since extinction follows stimulations that do not cause overt responses.* Further differences between extinction and facilitation will be presented when the correlates of extinction and facilitation are discussed.

nition alone. This formulation overlooks the possibility that a cortical focus may represent a mixed population of cells, one class of which preponderates, as shown in Fig. 5. One group of cells may be antagonistic in its action on motoneurons to the preponderate group of cells that gives the point its name. The inhibition resulting from stimulation of a heterogeneous population of cells might, by analogy with spinal reflexes, be termed a "concealed inhibitory component." The dis-

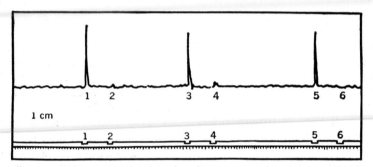

Fig. 8. Kymographic records showing the phenomenon of extinction. Wrist extension induced by repetitive stimulation of the motor area of a macaque monkey was recorded under Dial anesthesia. Lower lines show stimulus and time in 2-second intervals. Responses 2, 4, and 6 suffer extinction because of the short interval (13 seconds) following the antecedent stimuli (1, 3, and 5). The latter are fully effective because of the long preceding interval for recovery. (After Dusser de Barenne and McCulloch, 1934.)

Extinction versus Inhibition

Both extinction and inhibition result in a diminution of response, but there the parallel ends. Dusser de Barenne and McCulloch (1939a) state the distinction succinctly:

> Inhibition in the physiology of the cortex is, as far as it is known at present, the disappearance of an existing muscular contraction on stimulation of a cortical focus from which an antagonistic response may be elicited. Extinction is the diminution or absence of response to stimulation of a motor focus following antecedent stimulation of that same focus.

The dichotomy between inhibition and extinction cannot be made on the basis of defi-

tinction between a point yielding the same and a point yielding a different and antagonistic response is, therefore, a matter of degree.

Assume that the reciprocal inhibitory aspect of a cortical stimulation has a more prolonged time course than the excitatory aspect. This assumption would account in part for the different time relations of extinction and facilitation. Such delayed inhibitory components in spinal reflexes are well documented where there are latency differences between various reflexes, but the same assumption may not be justified for the pyramidal systems. Furthermore, reciprocal inhibition is not necessarily the only type of cortically initiated inhibition of the motoneurons. Perhaps the slow-conducting, unmyelinated fibers of the pyramidal tract

---

* However, Adrian and Moruzzi (1939) have shown that the pyramidal tract is conducting impulses prior to overt response.

and/or the extrapyramidal system, arising from area 4, supply a delayed inhibitory component. If the extrapyramidal system is involved, no time limitation need be placed not suggested, for reasons given above, that delayed inhibitory components are the explanation of extinction, but they might be confused with true extinction phenomena.

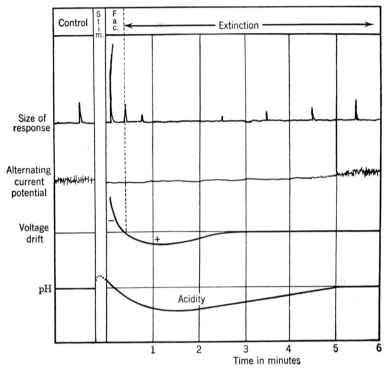

FIG. 9. Diagram showing facilitation (Fac.) and extinction of limb response due to stimulation of the motor cortex (upper record), together with electrical activity (second record), voltage drift, i.e. sustained surface positivity and negativity (third record), and the pH of the cortex (bottom record). All determinations were made at the site of stimulation. The stimulus was a 60-cycle current lasting 5 seconds. Note coincidence of the return of the response to normal with the return of spontaneous electrical activity, labeled alternating-current potential. Note also that the voltage drift (direct-current potential) ends while extinction still persists. Voltage drift and acidity, when summated, correlate well with the first and second records. (After Dusser de Barenne and McCulloch, 1939a.)

upon the delayed inhibitory component because multisynaptic arcs are involved, and there arises the possibility of reverberating circuits within or between subcortical nuclei.

An effect of a delayed inhibitory component, arising from an intermixture of diverse functional units in a cortical point, would be to reduce the response to a subsequent stimulation of the same point. It is

These considerations are, however, urged as a criticism of the definition of extinction.

Correlates of Extinction and Facilitation

By correlates of extinction are meant changes in spontaneous electrical activity and changes in potential and pH in the neighborhood of the stimulated neurons. These are summarized graphically in Fig. 9.

Electrical activity. Resulting from an electrical stimulation that causes extinction, even one producing no overt response, there is a diminution, or stilling, of the "spontaneous" electrical activity at or in the immediate neighborhood of the point stimulated. With certain stimuli the period of electrical silence may be preceded by a period of increased electrical activity coinciding with the period of facilitation and interpreted as cortical after-discharge. This discharge also occurs in neighboring foci after a delay of 10 milliseconds or more, depending on the distance. This suggests a slow spread of excitation through the cortex. During the state of facilitation and electrical after-discharge, electrical activity is observed in the spinal cord, even when the cortical stimulation is subliminal. This is evidence of a spinal component in facilitation.

Voltage drifts. These are demonstrated with an apparatus that amplifies slow potential changes as opposed to the relatively rapid "spontaneous" electrical activity of the cortex. The region at or close to the point stimulated is first surface negative, then slowly shifts to surface positive, and finally returns in a few seconds to zero potential, as shown in Fig. 9. At the point of the shift from negativity to positivity the excitability of the cortex shifts from facilitation to extinction. Since the positivity does not persist throughout the entire period of extinction, some other correlate of extinction must be sought.

Cortical pH. A glass electrode applied to the cortex detects a wave of acidity (low pH) that outlasts the positive voltage drift and terminates at about the time spontaneous electrical activity resumes. Preceded by a brief alkaline shift, this acid shift is regarded as the result of intense cortical activity, however caused. The direction of the pH changes are consistent with their being factors in the cortical excitability represented by facilitation and extinction. The association of negativity with increased responsiveness, and of positivity with decreased excitability, is also found in peripheral nerve.

Dusser de Barenne and McCulloch (1939a) believe that both factors, voltage drift and pH, combine to determine the phenomenon of extinction.

Suppression

Like facilitation and extinction, this phenomenon is demonstrated by the conditioning-testing stimulation technique. Suppression exists in two forms. The first is termed "suppression of motor activity" (Fig. 10), and the second form is "suppression of electrical activity" (Fig. 11). The latter is seen as a depression of spontaneous electrical activity throughout the cerebral cortex.[*] Suppression of motor and suppression of electrical activity must be carefully distinguished because they have quite different subcortical mechanisms. Suppression of electrical activity was first observed in 1938 by Dusser de Barenne and McCulloch (1938a, b) when strychninizing the anterior border of area 4, the "strip area" which Marion Hines (1937) had earlier shown to exert an inhibitory action on movements and reflexes. Later Dusser de Barenne and McCulloch studied the suppression of motor activity from this region (1941). Other "suppressor" areas or strips have since been discovered and will be described later.

Antecedent stimulation of area 4s will suppress the responses to stimulation of area 4. This suppression of motor activity is differentiated from extinction for several reasons.

[*] Since this chapter was written, several workers have questioned the suppression phenomena. Sloan and Jasper (1950) found many similarities between the suppression of electrical activity and the spreading depression described by Leão (1944a, b, 1947) which, according to Marshall (1950), is fundamentally non-neural in origin and caused by dehydration. Clark and Ward (1948) failed to observe suppression of motor activity in monkeys stimulated with the cranium closed and without anesthesia. Other workers have verified the phenomena of suppression but have found a latency, duration, and refractoriness that are shorter, and hence more consistent with other known neural phenomena. The degree to which spreading depression has confused observations on the suppression of electrical and motor activity has not yet been fully determined.

Time course. In the record shown in Fig. 10, the cortical responses were abolished 4 minutes after delivery of the stimulus to area 4s. Latencies as long as 10 or 12 minutes have been observed. The suppression

suppression is demonstrable only for those within a narrow band of the motor area (4s) and other similar suppressor bands.

Extensity. Suppression of motor response is not confined to the neighborhood of the

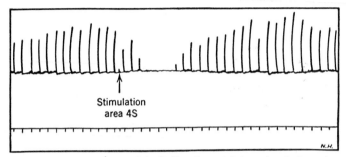

Stimulation area 4S

Fig. 10. "Suppression of motor activity" (for the arm) by stimulation of area 4s in the macaque monkey under Dial anesthesia. The upper tracing is the extension of the wrist in response to brief stimulation of the arm area at 1-minute intervals. At the arrow area 4s was stimulated for 5 seconds. Note that suppression is not fully developed until 4 minutes later and is evident for at least 10 minutes. The time line marks 1-minute intervals. (After Dusser de Barenne and McCulloch, 1941.)

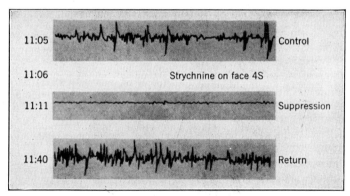

11:05   Control

11:06   Strychnine on face 4S

11:11   Suppression

11:40   Return

Fig. 11. Electrocorticograms of the motor area (arm), showing "suppression of electrical activity" from strychnine stimulation of area 4s (face). Observations on a macaque monkey under Dial anesthesia. Note that suppression is complete in 5 minutes after the application of strychnine; electrical stimulation gives a shorter latency of effect. (McCulloch, 1944.)

lasted for 4 minutes on this record, but it may be shorter or it may endure as long as 20 to 30 minutes, depending on stimulus strength and depth of narcosis. Once elicited, suppression cannot be reinduced immediately, but only after a pause of 15 to 45 minutes.

Specificity. Whereas extinction is a property of all neurons within the motor area,

point stimulated, nor is it limited to the corresponding somatotopic area of area 4.

Site of suppressor action. The interaction between areas 4s and 4 is not by intracortical or intercortical connections, because a deep incision between the two areas does not prevent either form of suppression. The suppressor impulses pursue a descending course, because suppression is ended by undercutting area 4s. The caudate nucleus is not a link in the chain for suppression of motor response, wherein it differs from the simultaneously developed suppression of electrical activity, which employs corticocaudate connections. The putamen, the globus pallidus, the thalamus, the substantia nigra, and the cerebellum are also excluded as a part of the pathway for suppression of motor activity. Subsequent to the discovery of a bulbo-inhibitory area by Magoun and Rhines (1946), evidence was adduced that area 4s projects to this region (McCulloch, Graf, and Magoun, 1946). Through the bulbo-inhibitory center, a part of the reticular substance, the impulses are presumably relayed to the spinal cord where they inhibit the motoneurons or the internuncial neurons. Employment of multisynaptic pathways is consistent with the long latency and duration that are characteristic of the two suppressor phenomena.

Distribution of suppressor areas. Systematic exploration of the cerebral cortex by topical application of strychnine (to avoid spread of current) has demarcated those areas in monkey (Dusser de Barenne, Garol, and McCulloch, 1941*b*) and chimpanzee (1941*a*) from which suppression of motor and cortical electrical activity is elicited. The location of these bands is shown in Fig. 12, with the exception of one on the mesial surface of the hemisphere at the anterior end of the cingular gyrus, area 24 of Brodmann (Ward, 1947). It is characteristic of these areas that stimulation of them suppresses the excitability of the motor cortex and suppresses electrical activity over the whole of the cerebral cortex, beginning in areas adjacent to those stimulated and spreading slowly across the cortex (15 to 20 minutes).

Significance of suppressor areas. The accumulation of detailed information on cortical physiology within the past decade has outstripped our ability to evaluate its functional significance. The suppressor areas are a case in point. The data on which an hypothesis of suppressor function can be based

are still limited and, in brief, consist of (1) what can be deduced from the position of the bands in relation to the other areas of known function, and (2) the nature of the descending pathways responsible for the suppression. The distribution of the suppressor areas is such that three of the major thala-

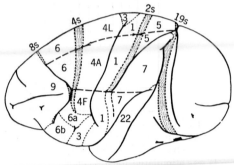

FIG. 12. Suppressor bands (areas 8s, 4s, 2s, and 19s) on the cerebral hemispheres in the macaque monkey. The numbers are Brodmann-Vogt cytoarchitectural areas. L, A, and F are leg, arm, and face areas of the sensorimotor cortex, and the dashed lines mark the boundaries between these areas. Area 24, a suppressor area of the cingular gyrus, is not visible on this view of the cortex. The mapping is based on suppression of electrical activity. Area 8s, largely buried in the arcuate fissure, is wider than the figure suggests. Later studies have shown that area 2s extends throughout the face area as well. (Dusser de Barenne, Garol, and McCulloch, 1941.)

mocortical projection areas are bounded by them; the auditory projection area is not so bounded, nor does the strong suppressor of the cingular gyrus form the boundary of a projection area. The occipital projection area of the lateral geniculate body, being polar, is bounded by area 19s; the frontal projection area of the dorsomedial nucleus, being similarly polar, is bounded by area 8s and perhaps by area 24. The central sector, the projection area of the posteroventral and lateroventral thalamic nuclei, is bounded by area 2s, area 8, and, in a sense, area 4s. This relation has suggested to some (Ward, 1949) that the suppressor areas act as dikes or barriers, preventing the spread of activity set up by impulses arriving by the thalamocortical projection systems. However, the auditory area is not so bounded, nor is there a barrier between the postcentral sensory area and the motor cortex. For area 4s a possible significance will be indicated in the discussion of the extrapyramidal system.

Marion Hines (1947) has made the interesting point that three of the major divisions of the cerebral cortex have an adversive * as well as a suppressor area. The posterior adversive zone, lying at the junction of the parietal and occipital lobes and including a portion of the superior temporal gyrus, is more concerned with movements of the eyes, and less with those of the head and body. Conjugate eye movements are elicited from the posterior part of the parietal lobe and the anterior part of the occipital lobe and throughout the striate area. This is a unique situation in that motor effects ensue from stimulation of a primary sensory area for vision. The direction of the conjugate eye movement elicited from a given point in the striate area, relative to the portion of the retina represented at that point, is such that the movements can be interpreted as visual fixation. Weak and inconstant pupillary constriction and lid movements also occur. From occipital and parietal stimulations limb movements are elicited that can be interpreted as reaching and grasping.

The frontal lobe also possesses an adversive area in close conjunction with a suppressor band, area 8s. Stimulation of area 8 and of the immediately adjacent areas causes lateral deviation of the eyes and a turning of the head and trunk on the long axis of the body away from the side stimulated. Pupillary dilatation and lid opening also occur from stimulation within area 8. Epileptic seizures beginning from a focus in this area start with lateral rotation (adversion) of

the eyes, head, and trunk. This region is therefore termed "frontal eye fields" and was termed the "frontal adversive field" by Foerster.

Considerable controversy exists about the effects of ablation of area 8, probably because much of it is buried in a deep sulcus which presents the hazards of subtotal lesion on the one hand and of invasion of underlying projections to the prefrontal lobe on the other. Ablation of this area on one side, according to Kennard (1944c), induces a disturbance consistent with the results of stimulation experiments. The head is turned toward the side of the lesion ("the animal looks at the lesion"), and, in moving about, the animal tends to circle to the side of the lesion. There is initially some paralysis of conjugate lateral deviation of the eyes to the opposite side. That something more than a pure motor phenomenon is involved is suggested by the curious observation that the animal is pseudohemianopic, tending to neglect or failing to recognize objects on the side opposite the lesion.

If we assume that the left side of the cerebral cortex is at the command of sensory impulses from the right side of the body, the adversive movements due to stimulation of the left cortex are actually an *orientation* to the side of a sensory stimulation. Therefore some such term as an *orientational field* would better denote the probable significance of this area. Furthermore, the adjective "adversive," meaning turning towards, does not specify the point of reference and is often understood to mean turning away from.

Despite the dangers of mentalistic interpretations, it is tempting to speculate that we are dealing here with a neural substrate of attention. The so-called "adversive movements," whereby the sense organs and the body as a whole are directed towards a stimulus object, may constitute a motor aspect of attention. Assuming that the adversive field is normally activated by sensory stimulation, a positive feed-back mechanism can be envisaged. A sensory stimulus on one

---

* An adversive movement is one that causes a rotation of the eyes, head, or trunk about the long axis of the body.

side causes the sense organs of the head and hands to be brought into a position for more effective stimulation and for effective manipulation of the stimulating object.

The relation between orientation (adversion) and suppressor activity is topographically close, and an equally close functional relation may be hypothesized. Hines (1947, p. 442), in describing the effect of stimulation of these regions, said: "The quieting effect, causing cessation of spontaneous movement, conferring upon the animal a curious appearance of attentive repose, was a generalized effect. This effect was most easily obtained from the anterior field on the lateral surface of Brodmann's area 9 and from the three posterior fields." These functions are presumably subserved by the extrapyramidal system.

The linkage of generalized suppression of motor activity with movements that orient the eyes and body towards a stimulus object seems best explained as a mechanism of attention. In addition to the generalized suppression of motor activity exercised through projections from area 4s to the reticular substance, the suppressor areas exert their action upon cortical areas via the corpus striatum and the thalamus, as shown by a reduction of spontaneous electrical activity of the cerebral cortex. Several indications prompt the speculation that suppression of cortical electrical activity is the third member of a triad, along with orientation and suppression of motor activity.

In the electroencephalogram of the resting cerebral cortex, a regular ten-per-second alpha rhythm is preponderant. Sensory stimulation replaces this rhythm with a faster one of smaller amplitude. Analysis has shown that attention to the stimulus is a requisite for this effect. Various explanations for this phenomenon have been given. But it is suggested here that suppression of cortical electrical activity is in some manner a device by which the reverberating thalamocortical circuits are brought under control

and prepared for the singleness of activity represented by attention.

Several difficulties present themselves in this as well as in the barrier theory. One is the extraordinary latency and long duration of the phenomenon, which would seem inappropriate to a mechanism having a quick play over environmental stimuli. But suppression, as elicited by electrical or strychnine stimulation under anesthesia, may be a poor indication of how the suppressor areas actually function in the intact animal. The latency is known to be less under light than under deep anesthesia. Another difficulty common to both hypotheses is that suppression falls first and most heavily upon the cortical fields with which the suppressor area is associated. One can conclude only that further research is needed to discover the role of suppression in the cortical processes of the intact animal.

In summary, the so-called "adversive" movements to electrical stimulation can be interpreted as *orientational* movements in the intact animal, and, therefore, as a motor component of attention. Suppression of motor activity and suppression of electrical activity may also prove to be, in some manner, concerned with attention. Another hypothesis is that the suppressor areas act as barriers to the spread of corticopetal impulses throughout the cortex.

PYRAMIDAL TRACT

Historically the pyramidal tract was defined as those fibers passing through the medullary pyramids (Türck, 1851).* Because degeneration of the large axons of injured Betz cells can easily be traced through the

---

* Excluded by this definition are those fibers that have the same relation to the motor cranial nerve nuclei that the pyramidal tract bears to the motoneurons. By usage these are sometimes called "pyramidal," though they terminate rostral to the pyramids and therefore do not pass through the pyramids. There is no harm in this convention, since it does not obscure the vital distinction between the pyramidal and the extrapyramidal systems.

pyramids and because section of the pyramids causes retrograde degeneration in the pyramid-shaped Betz cells, the term "pyramidal tract" gradually became synonymous with corticospinal fibers arising in the Betz cells of the motor area. Later studies have emphasized the necessity for adhering to the historical definition. The medullary pyramids are the only point at which pyramidal tract fibers are not intermingled with fibers of the extrapyramidal system, and here they can be separately sectioned for physiological study. Moreover, it is indisputably proved that the pyramidal tract fibers originate in many cortical areas besides area 4, and within area 4 many fibers originate in other than Betz cells.

That the oversimplified view of the origin and composition of the pyramidal tract was universally accepted illustrates the fact, pointed out in Chapter 4, that neuroanatomy has been largely the study of large, myelinated fibers, collected into well-defined tracts. In 1932 McKibben and Wheelis pointed out that the medullary pyramids are largely composed of unmyelinated fibers. In 1939 Lassek and Rasmussen inaugurated a series of painstaking quantitative studies that have considerably revised the conception of the pyramidal tract. Application of the silver technique enabled them to count roughly one million axis cylinders, myelinated and unmyelinated, in the human pyramid of one side. Two-fifths of the total are unmyelinated, and the remaining three-fifths, though myelinated, are mostly of small diameter.

By actual measurement and counts of a population of 30,000 *myelinated* pyramidal tract fibers, over half were found to be exceedingly fine, about 1 micron in diameter (Lassek, 1942a). Ninety per cent of the myelinated fibers of man are below 4 microns in diameter; about 8 per cent are 5 to 10 microns; and less than 2 per cent are fibers of large diameter, 10 to 20 microns (see Fig. 13). The large-diameter fibers contribute only some 30,000 of the total of one million

fibers. A later study (Lassek, 1940) showed that the number of cells larger than 900 to 4100 square microns in area,* situated in the intragranular layer of area 4, is about the same (34,000). Since cell body and fiber size are roughly correlated, the large Betz cells are sufficient to account for only the largest myelinated fibers (>10 microns). In any case the figures prove conclusively that the myelinated pyramidal tract fibers must arise in other than giant Betz cells. This conclusion is further supported by experiments on monkeys and chimpanzees (Lassek, 1941).†

By the method of experimental degeneration many observers have traced fibers into the pyramids from cortical areas other than area 4. Lassek's statistical method of fiber counts also proves that the pyramidal tract does not arise only from area 4. Ablation of area 4 eliminates all but a few of the large fibers in the pyramids and reduces the total number of fibers by 27 to 40 per cent (Lassek, 1942b; Mettler, 1944). That 60 per cent of the pyramidal tract fibers originate outside area 4 is in agreement with a large number of studies by other techniques. The parietal area contributes to the pyramidal tract some large fibers, presumably from the occasional giant pyramidal cells, and many smaller fibers. However, according to Lassek, large, though not complete, ablations of the pre- and postcentral regions leave intact, and hence unaccounted for, some 50 per cent

* Since there is no way to define accurately what constitutes a Betz cell, this figure will vary, depending on the size chosen as demarcating Betz cells. A smaller figure is used for the monkey because the size of Betz cells bears some relation to the size of the animal.

† The corresponding figures for the monkey are 554,000 pyramidal tract fibers and 18,845 Betz cells larger than 600 square microns, in each case about half the figure for man. The chimpanzee takes an intermediate position with 28,045 cells larger than 800 square microns and 750,000 myelinated pyramidal tract fibers. The minimum figure varies because the Betz cells are largest in man, next largest in chimpanzee, etc. These figures are an interesting quantitative demonstration of the increased encephalization of motor functions in the primate series.

of the fibers in the pyramids. This would make the postcentral contribution small but definite.

Many observers have reported degeneration in the pyramids due to ablation of the premotor area, though some dispute this finding. The possibility that some of the tine fibers, before terminating on the pontine nuclei, give rise to a long, descending, unmyelinated fiber which may traverse the pyramids. Should this suggestion be confirmed, it would constitute further evidence of the close linkage of pyramidal and extrapyramidal systems.

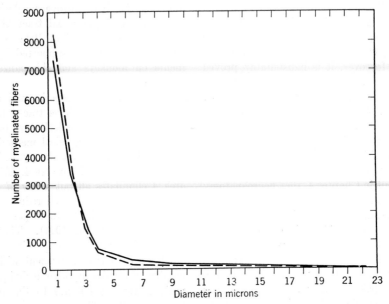

Fig. 13. A graph showing the size distribution of the myelinated fibers of the pyramidal tract in two adult human brains (solid and broken lines). It is evident that the bulk of these fibers are of small diameter (less than 0.004 millimeter). (Lassek, 1942.)

pyramidal tract fibers are of subcortical origin seems ruled out since in man (Mettler, 1944) and in monkey (Lassek and Evans, 1946) all fibers of the pyramid degenerate after hemidecortication. Therefore, allowing for the possibility of a contribution from the premotor area and a greater contribution from the postcentral gyrus than Lassek's present figures indicate, there still remains a considerable fraction of pyramidal fibers that originates elsewhere than in the sensorimotor area. Tower (1944) suggests that fibers of the corticopontine system from the frontal, parietal, and temporal lobes may contribute fibers to the pyramids. According to an observation by Cajal, corticopon-

Tower summarizes as follows the present and future problem presented by the newer work on the components of the pyramidal tract.

... it is clear that a new outlook is required on the nature of the pyramidal tract. Certainly it is not the simple motor pathway from the large cells of the precentral gyrus to the cord that it was so long considered. Nor may "pyramidal" continue to be synonymous with "corticospinal." It is even possible that the tract may not be entirely motor. With the probability looming that a considerable proportion of the corticospinal fibers arise outside the main motor area, and some from parts of the cortex which exercise little or no known motor function, Peele's suggestion that the component of cortico-spinal fibers from the parietal lobe might be considered, as others have considered the corticothalamic fibers, as a sensitization mechanism for cord sensory neurons, merits experimental investigation and serious consideration. In the end it may be necessary to redefine the pyramidal tract. [1944, pp. 155–156.]

Termination

The manner in which the pyramidal tract terminates in the spinal cord is a matter of fundamental importance. Throughout the following pages it will be repeatedly necessary to distinguish between events within the cortex and events at the spinal level. Cortical excitation presents all the complexity of reflex action of the spinal cord, plus the added complexity of stimulating, not a peripheral nerve, but an intricately organized neuronal structure, the cerebral cortex. The relation of the pyramidal tract to the final common path represented by the motoneurons, a vital link in the neural mechanism of cortically induced movement, has proved singularly difficult to investigate both anatomically and physiologically. Because the pyramidal tract fibers lose their myelin sheaths shortly before terminating synaptically, their exact termination cannot be learned from myelin sheath stains (e.g. Marchi's method). Obviously, the better method is one that differentially stains normal and degenerating synaptic terminals. Although several attempts have been made to discover the exact termination of pyramidal tract fibers by using silver methods, whether degenerating boutons can be critically differentiated from normal ones is in dispute.

With the Marchi technique, degenerating fibers of the pyramidal tracts can be traced into the external intermediate zone of the gray matter of the spinal cord close to the pyramidal tract. E. C. Hoff (1932), using Cajal's silver method to study the distribution of degenerating boutons after cortical ablation, concluded that the corticospinal tract terminates mainly at the base of the posterior horn and in the intermediate gray region, but that some degenerating boutons are found on the cells of the anterior horns.

The relation of the pyramidal tract to the spinal mechanism, internuncials, and motoneurons of the spinal cord has been studied by Lloyd (1941). To do this it was necessary to stimulate the medullary pyramids, since cortical stimulation inevitably involves extrapyramidal fibers and its own facilitation phenomena. To insure that no other descending fibers were stimulated, the medulla was transected, sparing the pyramids; and, to prevent the spread of impulses to the cortex by way of ascending systems, the brain stem was completely transected at the mesencephalon. Microelectrodes were then inserted into various regions of the spinal cord to dissect the electrical activity of the spinal mechanism.

The main result of Lloyd's analysis was to establish that the pyramidal tract does not discharge the motoneurons directly but instead activates a complex system of internuncials. The earliest response to a pyramidal volley is seen in the gray matter adjacent to the pyramidal tract (the external basilar region of Cajal, Fig. 14). This region sometimes responds to a single volley, but its response is greatly augmented by repeated volleys. With repeated pyramidal volleys activity is seen in the penultimate or premotoneurons (1) in the solitary cells of the dorsal horn (latency, 9 to 10 milliseconds) and (2) in the intermediate region between the dorsal and ventral horns (latency, 12 to 20 milliseconds). In both instances several shocks are required to activate these internuncial neurons; and the rate of discharge does not follow the rate of pyramidal tract stimulation, suggesting that these interneurons are largely activated from those in the external basilar region. Figure 15 shows electrical responses from single cells in the intermediate region of the gray matter of the spinal cord. Three volleys are necessary to obtain the first response of the unit. With four, five, and six shocks more responses are obtained; and there is little tendency to after-discharge.

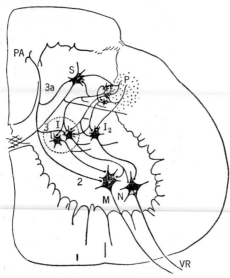

leys are instituted. The latency of such facilitation is 12 to 20 milliseconds. The time course of the facilitation parallels the electrical signs of internuncial activity in the intermediate region, suggesting a causal relationship.

By recording from ventral roots, it was determined that the latency of discharge due to pyramidal tract stimulation was 20 to 30

FIG. 14. A cross section through one-half of the spinal cord, showing the connections of the pyramidal tract fibers, of collaterals from the posterior root fibers with cell groups in the gray matter, and the interconnections between the latter. The drawing is based upon microelectrode recordings of electrical activity during pyramid stimulation. The dotted area P is the area of the pyramidal tract in the white matter from which fibers make direct connection with E, the "external basilar region" (Cajal). S is a "solitary cell" of the dorsal horn; I_2, the intermediate cells of the gray matter; I, the intermediate gray nucleus of Cajal; and MN, the motoneurons, the axons of which pass into the ventral root (VR) and ultimately reach the muscles. PA is a collateral of a posterior root fiber with terminal collaterals 2, 3, and 3a. Note that the collateral connections of the neurons in E make a closed circuit. (From Lloyd, 1941.)

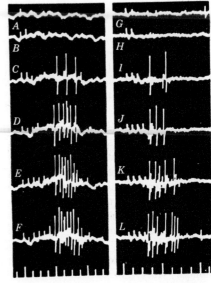

FIG. 15. Electrical activity recorded by microelectrodes in the intermediate region of the gray matter (see Fig. 14) of the spinal cord. In records *A* to *F* (lumbar region) and *G* to *L* (cervical region) the pyramids were stimulated with one to six shocks, as is seen by the small shock artifacts to the left of each tracing. Note that one and two pyramidal tract volleys were without effect (*A*, *B*; and *G*, *H*), and that the discharge increases in number and frequency, and decreases in latency, with more pyramidal volleys (*C*, *F*; and *I*, *L*). Time: 5-millisecond intervals. (Lloyd, 1941.)

Further evidence of interneuron play is that the excitability of motoneurons is not increased by pyramidal facilitation (as tested by the excitability of two-neuron reflex arcs) unless more than two pyramidal vol-

milliseconds, with an after-discharge of several hundred milliseconds. This again is consistent with activation through summation in interneuron pools and establishes that some of the latency of pyramidal tract stimulation is due to the inertia of the spinal mechanism.

The fact that the pyramidal tract fibers act predominantly upon internuncial neurons has implications with respect to the supposed inhibitory actions of that tract. "Direct inhibition" exerted upon the motoneurons was not seen. In several instances pyramidal tract volleys suspended spontaneous activity in the internuncials under observation. Reciprocal innervation by the pyramidal tract, as described by Sherrington, probably is gained by the tract's dealing reciprocally with interneuron systems, or, in other words, by its working through the spinal mechanism for the reciprocal activation of motoneurons.

It should come as no surprise that the higher levels of motor activity have proved anatomically and functionally more complex than the pyramidal fiber–motoneuron chain of the diagram makers. It is a complex system even when the pyramidal tract is excited electrically, thus short circuiting the rich interneuronal system of the cerebral cortex, as described by Lorente de Nó, through which corticopetal impulses must pass to gain access to the pyramidal tract neurons. The complexity has two dimensions: the nexus between cortex and muscle is multisynaptic, and the tract itself is heterogenous with respect to fiber composition and cortical origin. Finally, it is but one of many potential pathways between the cortex and the motoneurons. The extrapyramidal systems originating in the motor cortex will be discussed in the next section.

Functions of the Pyramidal Tract and Cortical Motor Areas

Until 1932 the functions attributed to the pyramidal tract (and to the motor area) included many that subsequent analysis has proved are those of the extrapyramidal systems. Since the degree to which the extrapyramidal system takes origin in the cerebral cortex was not appreciated, disturbances now known to be due to extrapyramidal damage were ascribed to the pyramidal sys-

tem. Injury to the pyramidal system was (and still is in many textbooks of neurology) described as producing, in addition to paralysis (or paresis) of voluntary activity, spasticity and exaggeration of tendon reflexes. Fulton and his co-workers (Fulton, Jacobsen, and Kennard, 1932; Fulton and Kennard, 1934; Kennard, 1944c) demonstrated that lesions of area 4, exclusive of its anterior border, produce not a spastic paralysis, but a flaccid paralysis; whereas lesions farther anterior (area 6 and the anterior border of area 4) produce spasticity and the grasp reflex.* In these early experiments the anterior border of area 4 was probably included in the lesions of area 6. Damage to this region, termed the strip area or area 4s, was shown by Marion Hines (1937) to be largely responsible for the spasticity, clonus, and brisk irradiating tendon reflexes previously ascribed to area 6. Later it became clear that this region gives rise to extrapyramidal fibers and is one of a series of so-called "suppressor areas" discussed above. It was gradually learned that the activities of area 4, exclusive of 4s, are predominantly, though not exclusively, executed through the pyramidal tract, whereas those of the more anterior areas are predominantly concerned with extrapyramidal function. Because the dichotomy is not complete, analysis at the cortical level is difficult. Concurrently, Tower (1935, 1936, 1940, 1944) attacked the same problem by the technically difficult maneuver of sectioning the medullary pyramids. As pointed out above, only at this point does a section interrupt only pyramidal tract fibers, because at all levels above and below the pyramids the two systems are inextricably mingled.

Tower performed two fundamental experiments to display the respective roles of the

---

* Spasticity consists of a heightened resistance to passive flexion or extension of a joint. Flaccidity is less than normal resistance. Spasticity is an exaggerated proprioceptive reflex to muscle stretch, due to changes in the play of facilitatory and inhibitory impulses from the brain on the motoneurons.

pyramidal and extrapyramidal systems: (1) section of the medullary pyramids, and observation of the resulting defects of movement and changes in reflexes; and (2) stimulation of the motor areas subsequent to pyramidal section. Certain types of responses to cortical stimulation are lost when the stimulation is applied subsequent to pyramidal section, and these responses correlate with the defects in voluntary movement from pyramidal section. The responses retained are similarly correlated with the type of voluntary activity retained after ablations in the posterior portion of the motor areas.

Traditionally, spastic paralysis was considered the consequence of "pyramidal tract damage," but Tower has conclusively demonstrated by pyramidal section in cat, monkey, and chimpanzee that "hypotonic paresis," i.e. flaccidity and partial paralysis, is the actual result. After pyramidal section there is a loss of fine, discrete movements such as the opposition of thumb and index finger in picking up small objects. Isolated movements tend to default. Grosser movements involving a wide range of musculature persist but lack "all the finer qualities which make for aim, precision and modifiability in the course of execution." These movements, though defective in quality, are clearly "purposive" and are executed with an appearance of great attentiveness and effort. It is, therefore, erroneous to associate voluntary movement exclusively with the pyramidal system.

Wanting after experimental pyramidal section are the spasticity, exaggerated deep reflexes, and clonus previously ascribed to pyramidal tract damage. Diminished resistance to passive flexion or extension of a joint obtains. The hypotonia was relatively greater in monkey, and the loss of fine movement relatively greater in the chimpanzee. Atrophy of muscle, rather than contracture (which accompanies fixed spastic position of limbs), follows pyramidal section. The up-going toe resulting from plantar stimulation (the positive Babinski reflex)

seen in the chimpanzee survives as a sign of pyramidal tract damage. The hopping and placing reactions are abolished.

The intermingling of the cortical representation of the pyramidal and extrapyramidal systems is well illustrated by the fact that section of the medullary pyramids does not abolish cortically induced movements to electrical stimulation of the motor areas. Such movements resulting from stimulation of area 4 are to some degree "somatotopically organized," i.e. movements are confined to the arm, trunk, or leg. They differ from movements induced prior to pyramidal section by involving a wider range of musculature. Discrete responses confined to a muscle or a muscle group are no longer seen when the pyramids are sectioned.

With the pyramids sectioned, stimulation of the motor cortex has another conspicuous result — chalasis, or the inhibition of posture and movement. In the anterior region of area 4 this tends to be an inhibition of tonic extensor posture, whereas, more forward, in area 6, the response tends to be a relaxation of tonic flexion, including inhibition of grasp. The latter is consistent with the observation of Fulton, Jacobsen, and Kennard (1932) and Richter and Hines (1934) that ablation of this area induces forced grasping.

Section of the pyramids intercepts many corticospinal fibers besides those originating in area 4. The portion that arises in the postcentral gyrus is also concerned with voluntary activity. Welch and Kennard (1944) have shown that postcentral lesions increase the paresis consequent to a lesion of the motor areas and increase the severity of spasticity. The postcentral area, even to a greater degree than the precentral area, exhibits an intermingling of pyramidal and extrapyramidal functions.

In summary, the function of the pyramidal tract projections from the classic motor area (area 4, exclusive of area 4s) and elsewhere in the cerebral cortex is the execution of discrete, fine, voluntary movement and the execution of the so-called "cortical" reflexes (hopping and placing reactions). Grosser movements and the inhibition of movements are served by the extrapyramidal fibers originating in the motor and other areas of the cortex. Spasticity, exaggerated reflexes, the Babinski reflex, and forced grasping are not related to pyramidal tract section. Voluntary movement, therefore, appears to be a conjoint action of pyramidal and extrapyramidal systems and also involves corticopetal systems and cerebello-cortical interaction. The extrapyramidal system and the cerebellum will be discussed in the next sections.

Recovery of Function after Lesions of the Motor Cortex

Perhaps the most ubiquitous and the least understood phenomenon in neurology is the recovery of function that follows all but a few experimental lesions of the nervous system. The problem of recovery, because of its gross similarity to the problem of learning, falls in the border zone between neurology and psychology, and perhaps for that reason the mechanism of recovery is still not analyzed. Where multiplicity of pathways exists, recovery is conspicuous; only where a bottleneck exists and all the fibers in a functional category can be sectioned is recovery wanting. Thus lesions of the motoneuron are definitive (apart from regeneration). So is section of all the posterior root supply of a limb (though vision can compensate to some degree). Section of the spinal cord ends all activities that depend on conduction through long spinal pathways connecting the brain with segments below the level of the lesion, and no recovery is possible (nor does regeneration occur).

The situation is different for reflex action, since spinal transection severs not the segmental reflex arcs but only the descending facilitatory and inhibitory tracts, and the long-circuits through the brain. After a period of abolition or severe depression certain reflexes of the spinal cord, especially flexion, return and some become exaggerated. Similarly, after lesions of the cerebral motor

systems the period of spasticity and exaggerated reflexes is preceded by a period of flaccidity and depressed reflexes. These two periods are termed the phase of "shock" and the phase of "release of function." Shock is, of course, a complete misnomer, because the depression of reflexes arises solely from interruption of descending fibers, not from any stimulation due to the trauma of the section. In lesions of the cerebral cortex trauma is a factor. Thus some of the immediate effects of cortical extirpations — so-called "neighborhood" symptoms — are artifacts due to damage of surrounding areas by trauma, interference with blood supply, edema, exposure, etc.

Such factors, being evanescent under carefully executed neurosurgical procedures, do not explain the severity of deficits in the early postoperative period. Although the intimate mechanism of recovery is not known, the factors affecting it have been worked out in some detail for voluntary motion (Kennard, 1940; Kennard, 1944a, c; Welch and Kennard, 1944). The first factor follows from facts presented in the previous section, namely that cortical areas other than area 4 give rise to pyramidal tract fibers and to extrapyramidal fibers and therefore can support some degree of recovery when the principal motor area is removed. Some of the other factors are the following:

Size of lesion. Ablation of the arm area alone has less effect on arm functions than if the arm and leg areas are both removed. This may well be due to some intermingling of arm and leg representation. Ablation of areas 4 and 6 limits voluntary movement more than ablation of only area 4. Bilateral lesions of areas 4 and 6 have a greater effect than unilateral lesions, which correlates with the observation that some ipsilateral movements are elicited by electrical stimulation of the motor areas.

Kind of lesion. Sperry (1947) has shown that crisscrossing the cerebral cortex with the scalpel has surprisingly little enduring effect on voluntary movement. This suggests that movements are integrated by an interplay between the subcortex and the cortex through the circular mechanisms described above.

Time elapsing between lesions. If areas 4 and 6 of both hemispheres are removed in four stages with time for full recovery between, the final paresis is very much less than if the same amount of cortex is removed at one time.

Age. Young animals suffer slighter defects after the removal of a given cortical area than do mature animals. Similarly the effects of spinal transection are less severe in embryos or young animals.

Phylogenetic position. In general, the higher the animal is in the evolutionary scale, the greater the degree of functional impairment from equivalent cortical lesions or decortication. This is one of several evidences of the corticalization of function.

Use. Use promotes recovery of function and is one of the main resources in the treatment of spastic paralysis and other organic disorders of the nervous system. This factor is especially important in experimental lesions of the motor cortex which cause the animal to "neglect" the limb. When binding the normal arm forces the animal to use the affected arm, an unsuspected variety of movements are seen, and recovery of function is promoted.

Motivation. During excitement an animal displays greater voluntary power and skill than it does during cage life.

Drugs. Ward and Kennard have shown that the administration of a stable cholenergic drug, i.e. one resembling acetylcholine in action, increases voluntary capacity in monkeys with cortical lesions, and with daily administration the effects outlast the presence of the drug in the blood stream. On the other hand, recovery is retarded by phenobarbital which depresses cortical function.

The necessity for making a complete lesion of a given cortical area in order to display its functions is well recognized. A small fragment of the arm area 4 will support a surprising degree of recovery of voluntary capacity. A quantitative issue is involved. We have seen that variety and delicacy of finger movements are gained by the evolution of a large cortical representation, i.e. multiplicity of units. Should the law of diminishing returns apply so that the curve relating neural units to performance is negatively accelerated, certain recovery phenomena can be explained. For example, if a large amount of cortical tissue is required to gain the highest levels of motor skill, a severe cortical insult would appear to produce little permanent deficit unless the examination methods actually test the highest levels of motor skills, which they rarely do. Added to this factor is the presumed ability of remnants of the total neural mechanism to increase their level of activity. Whether this involves any true "reorganization" in the sense of establishing new connections is an open question. But it is worth noting that "reorganization" is closely akin to "vicariation of function." There is a reluctance to believe that a cortical area can acquire a new function after the main area of representation for that function is ablated. Rather, the tendency is to believe that a small component area can increase the level of its activity, i.e. reorganization rather than vicariation.

Finally, quite a different view of recovery is held by those who accept von Monakow's doctrine of *diaschisis.** How one views re-

---

* Diaschisis literally means splitting, the thought being that the sudden withdrawal of impulses normally received from the extirpated tissue adversely affects synaptic conduction in functionally related structures, temporarily reducing their activity. Thus, temporary underactivity will be felt throughout the whole of a system of functionally related fibers. The anatomically fractional extirpation amounts to a total functional ablation. The postulated synaptic change has not been proved, but neither has the mechanism of the postulated reorganization process. The diaschisis theory avoids some of the quasi-vitalistic connotation of reorganization or vicariation.

covery depends on how one views the original deficit. The diaschisis theory is that a fractional loss of the neural apparatus for a given function temporarily puts the total neural apparatus for the function out of action by an unknown mechanism. Recovery then becomes, not the attainment of new levels of activity through reorganization of the surviving neural components, but their return to normal levels of activity. Actually, diaschisis and reorganization are not mutually exclusive, and both may be involved in sequence. Certainly no critical experiment has been devised that discriminates between the two hypotheses.

EXTRAPYRAMIDAL SYSTEM

The extrapyramidal system consists of a series of complexly interconnected nuclear masses lodged in the cerebral hemispheres and brain stem. It is sometimes convenient to include the cerebellum in a discussion of this system. The neuroanatomy of the extrapyramidal system is too large a subject to describe in this chapter. Figures 16 and 18 and a neuroanatomy text should be studied. Injury to the extrapyramidal system produces widely varied disturbances of movement and posture, but clinical studies have done little to solve the localization problem because of the diffuse character of

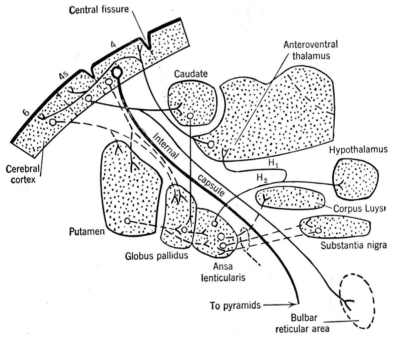

Fig. 16. A highly schematic diagram, showing cortical and other connections of the basal ganglia of the left hemisphere (left is lateral, right is medial). Cell bodies are represented by circles, and the terminations of axons by a fork. Conduction between neurons is from termination to cell body. The large fiber represents the pyramidal tract. The pathway for motor and electrical suppression from 4s is marked by fine solid axons and is 4s → caudate → globus pallidus → thalamus → areas 4, 4s, and 6. Other connections are indicated by dashed lines, and some have been omitted. H₁ and H₂ are the fields of Forel. For simplicity collateral fibers have been used where separate fibers probably exist. (Modified from Kennard, 1944.)

the lesions seen at autopsy. However, some insight into the extrapyramidal system has been gained from laboratory and neurosurgical studies of the past two decades. Progress in three directions is notable: (1) discovery that the extrapyramidal system is anatomically and functionally connected with the cerebral cortex, (2) isolation of a cerebrocerebellar circuit, and (3) discovery in the reticulum of the brain stem of links belonging to the extrapyramidal system.

Much of our knowledge of the extrapyramidal system pertains to the abnormalities that follow disease of it; little is known of what it contributes to normal voluntary and postural activities. The disorders of the extrapyramidal system are best considered from the point of view of signs rather than the syndromes into which the signs are grouped. Disturbances of the extrapyramidal system, including the cerebellum, fall into three broad categories: (1) posture, (2) movement, and (3) emotional expression; and in each category the alteration may be either one of excess or one of deficit.

I. Disturbances of posture.
   A. Spasticity and rigidity.
   B. Hypotonia.
II. Disturbances of movements.
   A. Hypokinesis (poverty of movement).
   B. Hyperkinesis.
     1. Tremors.
      a. Of rest.
      b. Of intention.
      c. Of posture, i.e. static tremors.
     2. Athetosis (sinuous, slow, twisting or writhing movements of the arms and legs, grimacing of the face).
     3. Choreo-athetosis (involuntary jerking of the limbs).
     4. Hemiballismus (repeated, sudden excursions of the arm as though flipped away from the body).
III. Disturbances of emotional expression.
   A. Overactivity of emotional expression (involuntary laughing or crying not accompanied by appropriate emotional feelings).

B. Diminution of emotional expression (e.g. masked facies in paralysis agitans).

A cursory examination of this list or of the neuroanatomy of the extrapyramidal system suffices to show that "extrapyramidal system" is a term of convenience not unlike the terra incognita of the early Renaissance map makers. It is obviously not a unitary or homogeneous system that does some one thing. Yet there is reason to hope that recent researches have established some of the main routes and continents of this terra incognita.

It has already been pointed out that spasticity results from destruction of certain of the cortical origins of the extrapyramidal system, and that posture as well as movement can be inhibited by stimulation of them. One of the extrapyramidal components concerned with posture arising from area 4s has been traced to the recticular formation of the medulla oblongata. It will be considered in detail.

Brain Stem Reticular Inhibitory and Facilitatory Areas

The ubiquitous reticular substance of the brain stem * has come into prominence with the discovery by Magoun and Rhines (1946) that its bulbar portion, specifically the ventromedial area superior to the inferior olivary nucleus, has widespread inhibitory actions (Fig. 17). Tested against sample reflexes — the ipsilateral flexor reflex of the forelimb (forelimb and nocioceptive), the knee jerk (hind limb and proprioceptive), and the blink reflex (cranial and tactile) — stimulation of the reticular area was found to inhibit them all. Such stimulation also

* "The formatio reticularis fills the interspaces among the longer tracts and their nuclei. It is composed of small islands of gray matter, separated by fine bundles of nerve tracts which run in every direction, but which are for the most part either longitudinal or transverse . . . The nerve-cells of the reticular formation are scattered through the mesh of interlacing fibers. In certain localities they are mostly grouped and form fairly well defined nuclei." (Ranson, 1943.)

inhibits the responses to stimulation of the motor cortex, and the interaction is at a spinal level. The latter effects are usually bilateral, and stimulation of a single point in the reticular area inhibits decerebrate rigidity in all four limbs. The inhibition is therefore widespread with respect to topo-

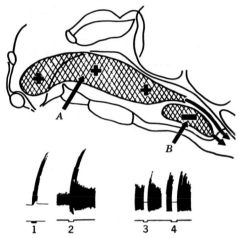

FIG. 17. A mid-sagittal plane of the cat's brain stem, showing by crosshatching the facilitatory (+) and inhibitory (−) areas of Magoun and Rhines. Below are typical records showing facilitation (A) and inhibition (B) of the patellar reflex (1 and 3) and of cortical motor response (2 and 4). The lowest line is a stimulus signal. (Niemer and Magoun, 1947.)

graphical distribution and to the type of reflex affected, and the conduction pathways must be correspondingly diffuse.

Discovery of a bulbar inhibitory area has further illuminated the suppression of cortical motor response elicited by stimulation of area 4s. Unlike suppression of electrical activity, suppression of cortical motor excitability does not depend upon a circuit through the corpus striatum and the thalamus but is exerted by a pathway descending into the brain stem. That the bulbar inhibitory area is a link in the suppression of motor activity was shown by McCulloch, Graf, and Magoun (1946) by strychninization in the neighbor-

hood of area 4s. Action potentials synchronous with the strychnine spike from the cerebral cortex were recorded from two sites, the pyramidal tract and the bulbar inhibitory area. At the latter site the potentials were triphasic — positive, negative, positive — indicating, according to volume conductor theory, electrical activity at the site of the electrodes. Electrical activity from the pyramids consisted of diphasic waves, positive-negative, indicative of activity at a distance from the electrodes. Thus it was concluded that area 4s projects to the bulbar inhibitory area. Activation of the bulbar inhibitory area by stimulation of 4s was prevented by a section through the basis pedunculi of the midbrain, which contains both pyramidal and extrapyramidal fibers, but it was not prevented by section of the pyramidal tract more caudally, just above the bulbar inhibitory area. This indicates that the fibers from 4s to the bulbar inhibitory area diverge from the corticospinal tract at a pontile level. The suppressor area of the cingular gyrus (area 24) also discharges into the bulbar reticular area. Whether other suppressor areas do likewise remains to be learned. From the bulbar reticular inhibitory area, the reticulospinal tracts descend the spinal cord, mainly in the ventral columns (Niemer and Magoun, 1947). Lesions of the spinal cord, designed to interrupt the reticulospinal tracts and spare the pyramidal tract, produce spasticity without impairing voluntary movement. Thus the reticulospinal tracts complete a pathway from the cerebral cortex to the motoneurons. The links in this pathway have been worked out by several independent groups of workers, starting at different points and using different techniques. The piecing together of the chain constitutes one of the major achievements in neurophysiology in recent years.

Hughlings Jackson laid down as a heuristic principle in neurological thinking that positive symptoms, e.g. spasticity, cannot result from a negative event represented by cortical or other lesions. The cortical lesion can "release" but cannot produce the over-activity. As Magoun (1947) picturesquely puts it, if the cerebral cortex is the lid on the jack-in-the-box, where is the spring that makes Jack jump when the lid is raised? The spring is not the segmental reflex arcs of the spinal cord. Those serving postural reflexes in animals higher than cat and dog have become so dependent on facilitation from, or long-circuiting through, the brain stem that they cannot even support normal postural activity, much less spasticity, when acting in isolation following complete transection of the spinal cord.

The spring of the jack-in-the-box is then to be sought in the brain stem. Since a transection passing through the lower part of the midbrain of a cat or a monkey results in hyperactivity of stretch reflexes (decerebrate rigidity), an upper limit is established. It has long been known that destruction of the vestibular nuclei in the cat abolishes or greatly reduces decerebrate rigidity, as does severance of the anterior columns of the spinal cord which contain the vestibulospinal and the ventral reticulospinal tracts. However, there has been considerable doubt whether the vestibulospinal system plays the same role in man that it does in lower animals. Therefore it has been a welcome disclosure that the reticular substance also appears to act as a facilitatory mechanism.

This was shown by experiments similar to those that disclosed the existence of the bulbar reticular inhibitory area (Rhines and Magoun, 1946). Stimulation of the brain stem with the Horsley-Clarke apparatus was played against the patellar reflex, or against stimulation of the pyramids or of the motor cortex. In some cases the sensory motor cortex was removed to insure that the interaction was not at a cortical level. The facilitatory area is not so circumscribed as the reticular inhibitory area (Fig. 17). The former extends from the ventral diencephalon (subthalamus and hypothalamus) caudally through the central gray matter and the tegmentum of the midbrain and the reticulum of the brain stem. The facilitation is not exerted through the vestibular nuclei, for it persists after their destruction (Bach and Magoun, 1947).

Slowness and poverty of movement are conspicuous elements of one extrapyramidal syndrome, paralysis agitans or Parkinsonianism. Since the brain stem facilitatory area acts strongly on movements induced by stimulation of the pyramid or cortex, Rhines (1947) and Rhines and Magoun (1946) suggest that clinical hypokinesis may be the result of interference with the brain stem facilitatory system. Stated positively, this means that a component of the extrapyramidal system acts to reinforce the discharge of the pyramidal system in executing voluntary acts.

In the lower vertebrates, where the cerebral cortex is poorly developed, the basal ganglia and brain stem carry on many of the functions performed by the cerebral cortex in mammals. For this reason the hyperkinesis of extrapyramidal disease is often regarded as primitive behavior patterns released from cortical control. A more recent point of view is just the reverse of this and holds that certain of the hyperkinetic phenomena are cortically initiated activities uninfluenced by the extrapyramidal system.

The results of electrical stimulation of the basal ganglia favor the second hypothesis, since few movements result from such stimulation. However, given a background of posture or of movement induced by cortical stimulation, stimulation of the basal ganglia results in prompt inhibition of pre-existing activity. Nor do large bilateral lesions of the basal ganglia cause default of any type of movement, though abnormal involuntary movements appear. On the whole the evidence of stimulation and ablation indicates little independent activity of the basal ganglia. Rather, the basal ganglia and cerebral cortex appear to act as a unit. The close interaction between them appears to be accomplished by the projection of the suppressor areas on the caudate nucleus from which impulses are returned to the motor cortex by way of the pallidum and thalamus. Because activation of this sys-

activities from control by the cerebral cortex, are abolished if the precentral gyrus is damaged incidentally by disease or intentionally by neurosurgery (Bucy, 1944). These abnormal movements are, therefore,

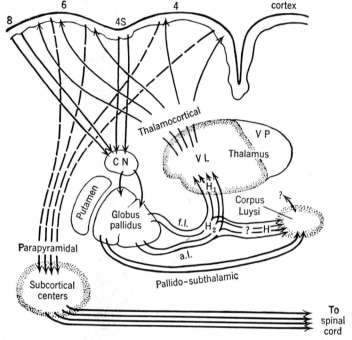

FIG. 18. Schematic diagram illustrating Bucy's view of the neural mechanism of choreo-athetosis, utilizing a suppressor circuit 4s to caudate nucleus (CN) to globus pallidus to the ventrolateral nucleus of the thalamus VL by way of the fasciculus lenticularis (f.l.) and ansa lenticularis (a.l.) and H_2 and H_1, the fields of Forel. Thalamocortical fibers return the impulses to areas 4 and 6. Parapyramidal is a synonym for extrapyramidal fibers originating in the areas 4 and 6 and are thought to be released to abnormal activity which results in the involuntary movements of choreo-athetosis. (Bucy, 1944.)

tem leads to suppression of cortical electrical activity, this circuit is believed to modulate cortical discharges. In the absence of such modulation hyperkinetic movements appear. In the next section an explanation of clinical choreo-athetosis in terms of circular systems will be presented.

Choreo-Athetosis

These hyperkinetic movements, far from being induced by the release of subcortical

cortically initiated. They might represent discharge of the pyramidal system when unaided by the damaged extrapyramidal system, or they might represent a discharge of the motor cortex through its extrapyramidal connections. The latter appears to be the case, because such involuntary movements are also abolished by section of the anterior column of the spinal cord (Putnam, 1940). Therefore, the impulses producing abnormal movements must reach the motoneurons not by the corticospinal tract, undamaged because it is situated in the lateral columns, but by one of the more ventrally lying tracts originating in the brain stem. Whether the discharges are purely extrapyramidal is still open to question. That hyperkinetic movements are initiated cortically rather than subcortically was deduced by Kinnier Wilson, a deduction that forms the rationale for an effective neurosurgical attack on athetosis suggested by Bucy. He has shown that removal of the precentral gyrus (areas 4 and 6) effectively ends or ameliorates the distressing athetoid movements. Bucy integrates his views on the origin and conduction of impulses giving rise to athetoid movements in Fig. 18 and in the following paragraph:

Choreo-athetosis is usually associated with destructive lesions of the caudate nucleus and putamen (Alexander), less commonly with destruction of the ventrolateral nucleus of the thalamus (Schuster), and still more rarely with lesions of the globus pallidus (Papez, Hertzman, and Rundles). It appears most likely that these various destructive lesions remove a "governor," thereby releasing the precentral cortex to an abnormal state of hyperactivity which finds expression via impulses travelling to the anterior horn cells through the parapyramidal fibers in the anterior fasciculus of the spinal cord. Anatomically these various subcortical nuclei are connected in a neural circuit which passes from the caudate nucleus and putamen to the globus pallidus and thence . . . into the ventrolateral nucleus of the thalamus, and from there by thalamocortical fibers to the precentral motor cortex. [1944, p. 405.]

Tremor of Rest

This form of hyperkinesis, seen in the Parkinsonian syndrome, differs in several respects from choreo-athetoid movements. It is a regularly recurring, alternating activation of antagonistic muscle groups as opposed to the irregular, jerky movements of choreo-athetosis. The tremor of rest is not

ended by section of the anterior columns of the spinal cord, but it is abolished or greatly ameliorated by section of the lateral columns of the spinal cord containing the pyramidal tract fibers, or by extirpation of the posterior part of the cortical motor area (Bucy, 1944; Putnam, 1940). These observations suggest that the pyramidal tract conducts the impulses underlying the tremor. The undamaged extrapyramidal system, either through subcortical circuits or by interaction at the spinal level, supposedly modifies the pyramidal discharge, rendering it more continuous.

An alternating tremor of rest, believed similar to that of the Parkinsonian syndrome (paralysis agitans) has been produced by lesions, not in the basal ganglia, but in the mesencephalic and the pontine tegmentum (Ward, McCulloch, and Magoun, 1948). The tremor of rest was accompanied by hypokinesis and poverty of emotional expression (masked facies) which are characteristic of paralysis agitans. The tremor was temporarily abolished by lesions of areas 4 and 6 and returned with the recovery of motor power. Interruption of the circular system from cortex to cortex through the basal ganglia did not affect the tremor, nor could the rhythm of cortical activity be correlated with the rhythm of motoneuron discharge. The latter observations raise the possibility that the source of the tremor lies in the brain stem below the destructive lesions and is an oscillatory phenomenon of the inhibitory and facilitatory mechanisms of the reticular substance. It has long been known that the upper brain stem is prone to produce rhythmic activity, whereas the lower levels subserve sustained movement or posture. The lesion may have released some upper brain stem mechanism. In any case the experimental production of a syndrome exposes it to analysis and often marks the turning point in our understanding of the disease.

CEREBELLUM

The cerebellum and the cerebral hemispheres show many features in common. Each consists of a convoluted mantle or cortex of gray (cellular) substance and a central core of white matter (centrifugal and centripetal fibers) in which are lodged gray nuclear masses. Both are suprasegmental structures. This means that they do not give rise to sensory and motor roots, as the spinal cord and brain stem do. The cerebellum, like the cerebral hemispheres, receives a large afferent input from the sensory roots of the spinal cord and the brain stem. The cerebellum is strongly connected with the motor areas of the cerebral cortex which, in turn, are strongly connected with the cerebellum. Finally, the cerebellum projects to certain brain stem nuclei. These four classes of fibers enter and leave the cerebellum by three peduncles — inferior, middle, and superior — which form three legs attaching the cerebellum to the brain stem.

The cerebellar cortex contains a large cell with profusely branching dendrites, the Purkinje cell. These cells, like the Betz cells of the cerebral cortex, are mainly reached by incoming systems only through an internuncial system. The Purkinje fibers constitute the only known exit for impulses from the cerebellar cortex. The axons of Purkinje fibers terminate within the cerebellum on the deep masses of gray matter: the large, laterally placed dentate nucleus; the smaller fastigial nucleus, lying near the midline; and two nuclei interposed between them — the globosus and emboliform nuclei. All these nuclei give rise to the efferent cerebellar systems.

Another point of similarity between cerebellar and cerebral cortex was mentioned in the previous chapter, namely, that the cerebellum receives other than proprioceptive and vestibular impulses. Oscillographic studies (Snider and Stowell, 1944) have revealed that the cerebellum receives tactile, visual, and auditory impulses, and the cerebellar cortical areas for each have been mapped. In fact, for tactile impulses there is a double representation of the body surface — one in the anterior lobe and one in the paramedian lobule — just as there are two sensory areas in the cerebral cortex. Cerebrocerebellar connections link sensory area I (postcentral gyrus) with the anterior lobe somatosensory area, and somatic area II is linked with the paramedian lobe (Hampson, 1949). The auditory and visual areas of the cerebral cortex are connected with the auditory and visual areas of the cerebellar cortex.

A further similarity between the cerebellar and cerebral cortex is that both exert a control over visceral as well as skeletal musculature. It is clear from this newer investigation that the old concept that the cerebellum is a proprioceptive center controlling skeletal musculature must be considerably revised. Like the cerebral cortex, the cerebellum must play a part in a wide array of activities. This does not mean, however, that the two structures play the same role. The cerebellum lacks, for example, the direct connection with the final common pathway that the pyramidal tract provides.

Unlike the Betz cells, the Purkinje cells do not send fibers to the spinal cord or motor nuclei of the cranial nerves. Consistent with this lack of a direct connection with the final common pathway, the cerebellum is not believed to execute voluntary or any other type of movement. No type of movement is lost through extirpation of the cerebellum, though movement is altered in character. The role of the cerebellum appears to be regulatory rather than executory. The effect projections of the cerebellum are presumed, on an anatomical basis, to be most nearly like those of the extrapyramidal system of the cerebral cortex.

Lobulation, Projections, and Nuclei

The cerebellar cortex, though highly convoluted and divided into a number of lobes.

shows none of the fractionation into cyto-architectural areas so characteristic of the cerebral cortex. Nevertheless the various areas of the cerebellum show a diversity of function. There are definite areal differences in the afferent projections, and these differences have functional significance. In fact the guiding principles in the investigation of the cerebellum have come from the study of the afferent projections by the technique of evoked potentials which, in turn, was inspired by a disentanglement of the lobulation of the cerebellum based on phylogenetic and ontogenetic studies (Larsell, 1937; Dow, 1942a). The complex morphological terminology applied to the various lobules of the cerebellum has proved largely meaningless and is now used only when necessary for descriptive purposes.

Morphologically the cerebellum consists of the cerebellar hemispheres between which lies a distinct longitudinal fold called the vermis because of its resemblance to a worm (Fig. 19). The lateral expansions, or cerebellar hemispheres, are virtually nonexistent at the anterior end and expand greatly in passing posteriorly. At one time thought to be of functional significance, this dichotomy into vermis and cerebellar hemispheres is no longer stressed. Several tranverse fissures mark off the traditional morphological lobes of the cerebellum. The comparative anatomical studies of Larsell and Dow show that only one major fissure and two minor ones demarcate functional areas and hence are significant. The earliest fissure to develop phylogenetically and ontogenetically, and hence the most fundamental one, is the fissura posterolateralis which divides the cerebellum into the flocculonodular lobe and the corpus cerebelli. The fissura prima, so named when it was considered the fundamental fissure of the cerebellum, divides the corpus cerebelli into an anterior and a posterior lobe. The posterior lobe is further divided into two areas by the fissura prepyramidalis. This results in four areas.

For reasons that will be given below, the anterior lobe and the portion of the corpus cerebelli that lies behind the prepyramidal fissure are collectively known as the paleocerebellum.* The portion of the corpus cerebelli lying between the prepyramidal fissure and the fissura prima is known as the neocerebellum because it has undergone the greatest expansion throughout the phylogenetic series. The neocerebellum has developed *pari passu* with the development of the cerebral cortex with which it is reciprocally connected. It should be noted that the neocerebellum is not synonymous with the cerebellar hemispheres, since the neocerebellum includes a portion of the vermis, namely, the folium and the tuber vermis. Note also that the "posterior lobe" is the posterior portion of the corpus cerebelli and is not the most posterior part of the cerebellum, being anterior to the flocculonodular lobe.

The justification for this division of the cerebellum is that the resultant areas have different afferent and efferent projections, a fact that has proved to have functional significance. Thus the neocerebellum receives its main afferent input from the pontine nuclei via the middle cerebral peduncle, and ultimately from the corticopontine tracts which originate in the frontal and other lobes of the cerebral cortex (see Fig. 18). It also receives impulses from the visceral and auditory receptors. The tranverse sectors just rostral and caudal to the neocerebellum have preponderately spinocerebellar connections by which they are placed in contact with the somatic sense organs of the body, especially the proprioceptors of the musculature. Still more rostral (lingula) and caudal (flocculonodular lobe) are two zones having connections, by way of the vestibular nerve, with the apparatus for equilibrium in the internal ear. The flocculonodular lobe is far

* The flocculonodular lobe is sometimes included in the paleocerebellum, a poor practice because it includes two unrelated areas of the cerebellum under the same designation. The flocculonodular lobe is better termed the archicerebellum.

larger than the lingula and, unlike the lingula, receives only vestibular connections. As pointed out above, the fissures that divide the lobe areas morphologically do not sharply delimit the areas established on the basis of afferent connections. The field in which corticopontocerebellar pathways terminate overlaps that in which the spinocerebellar fibers terminate, and this overlap is especially marked in the lateral portions of the cerebellar hemispheres. The zone with spinocerebellar connections, in turn, overlaps to some degree the vestibular fields, since some vestibular fibers are found anterior to the fissura posterolateralis in the uvula and in the lingula.

Several studies have indicated that the division of the corpus cerebelli into a pontocerebellar and a spinocerebellar field is overly schematic. Thus, a study of the pontocerebellar projections suggests that they reach all parts of the cerebellar cortex except the flocculonodular lobes (Brodal and Jensen, 1946). The absence of spinocerebellar fibers to the neocerebellum may mean only that this region, especially its vermal portion, is concerned with head functions and receives impulses not from the spinal nerves but from cranial nerves (Hampson, 1949). Thus Woolsey (1947) says: "It seems likely then that the neo- and paleocerebellum no longer define in mammals separable portions of the cerebellum unless an exception exists in the flocculonodular lobe."

The details of the projection of the cerebellar cortex upon the cerebellar nuclei and the projection of these nuclei upon those of the brain stem and thalamus have not been completely worked out. However, the broad outlines are known. The fastigial nucleus, located in the midline, is apparently the oldest nuclear mass, though it does contain a small-celled component of more recent phylogenetic origin. Consistent with its being the oldest of the cerebellar nuclei, it receives fibers from the Purkinje cells of the paleocerebellum. The fastigial nucleus, in turn, projects mainly onto the nuclear and

reticular substances of the medulla, known to be concerned with postural reflexes. The next most lateral nucleus, nucleus globosus, also receives fibers from the paleocerebellum, but it projects to the nuclear and reticular substances of the midbrain, especially the older, large-celled portions of the red nucleus. The emboliform nucleus lies between the globosus and dentate nuclei and is also intermediate with respect to afferent input, since it receives fibers from both the neocerebellum and the paleocerebellum but not from the flocculonodular lobe. The efferent projections of the emboliform nucleus are like those of the globose nucleus. The most lateral nucleus, nucleus dentatus, receives its main afferent input from the neocerebellum and projects to the lateroventral nucleus of the thalamus both directly and after a synaptic interruption in the phylogenetically recent, small-celled portion of the red nucleus. From the lateroventral nucleus, fibers pass to the motor areas of the cerebral cortex. The dentate nucleus receives some fibers from the paleocerebellum, but, since it is divided into a small- and a large-celled component, it is quite possible that it consists of phylogenetically old and new portions, with the older portion receiving the paleocerebellar connections.

The functions of the cerebellum are at present interpreted in the light of a tripartite division presented in Fig. 19, and of the phylogenetic change in the relative importance of these three divisions. Evidence drawn from lower vertebrates cannot be translated directly to man. However, there is sufficient data for plotting the cerebellar functions throughout the subprimate and primate series. When this is done, man is seen to carry further the phylogenetic development noted in passing from the dog or cat to the monkey. The symptomatology following cerebellar injury also varies considerably with the time lapsing after operation, especially in the cat and dog. Any set of observations of cerebellar symptoms must, therefore, be located on a system of three variables: (1) the area destroyed, (2) the species, and (3) the time elapsing after operation.

the limbs are not marked by tremor or hypotonicity. In the initial state the monkey documents his unsteadiness by clinging

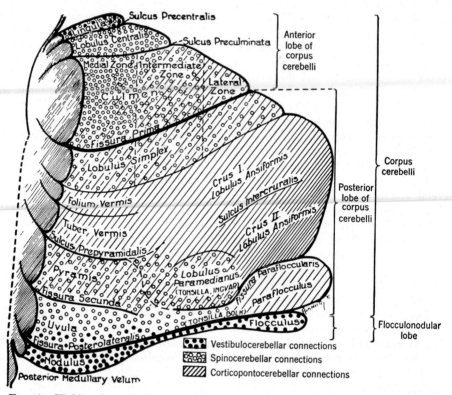

Fig. 19. Highly schematic diagram of the mammalian cerebellum, showing the cerebellopetal connections and the lobulation and terminology of the cerebellum, according to Larsell and Dow. The shaded area at the left represents a cut through the middle of the vermis to show the depth of the fissures. The diagram shows the cerebellar cortex stretched out laterally, so that the fold between vermis and hemispheres is obliterated. Note that the lobulation, based on comparative anatomical studies, delimits, with some overlapping, fields of cerebellopetal connections. (Dow, 1942.)

Flocculonodular Lobe

One of the immediate results of the Larsell-Dow analysis of the phylogenetic development of the cerebellum was the prediction that ablation of the flocculonodular lobe would produce disturbances of equilibrium. Dow confirmed this deduction by showing that isolated removal of the nodulus and flocculus causes unsteadiness of stance and gait, and swaying and oscillations of the head and trunk, even though movements of

firmly to the cage to gain support. Woolsey and Bard have recently shown that flocculonodular ablation will protect an animal from motion sickness.

The flocculonodular syndrome is quite faithfully produced in man, especially young children, by a tumor (medullablastoma) that destroys the posterior midline structures. There are few signs of cerebellar damage so long as the patient is lying down, but it becomes manifest by unsteadiness, etc., when he is placed upon his feet. It is apparent that in both monkey and man the sphere of activities affected by flocculonodular damage reflects the connections of this area with the vestibular nerve.

Anterior Lobe

The anterior lobe and the adjacent lobulus simplex are electrically excitable and are apparently topographically organized as follows: lobulus simplex — neck, masticatory, and facial movements; culmen — fore-limb movements; and centralis and lingula — hind-limb and tail movements (Woolsey, 1947). There is also mediolateral organization, with the muscles of the axis or proximal segments of the limbs most influenced from points near the midline. Hampson's (1949) results indicate that the projections from the face, arm, and leg areas of the postcentral gyrus to the cerebellum have the same pattern of localization, and that the spinocerebellar projections are probably similarly arranged.

As would be expected from neuroanatomical considerations, the effects of stimulating the anterior lobe are exerted upon the postural motor mechanisms of the brain stem. For instance, Sherrington, in his original analysis of decerebrate rigidity, showed that it could be inhibited from the anterior lobe. Actually the effects are compounded of both inhibition and facilitation. Which is obtained depends on strength and frequency of stimulation; and rebound contractions are not uncommon. Stimulation of the anterior lobe also affects pyramidal tract activities. The point of interaction between stimulations of the cerebellum and of the motor cortex appears to be in the brain stem, not in the cerebral cortex. It is not unlikely that facilitatory and inhibitory effects are exerted through two different efferent cerebellar outflows which end in the facilitatory and inhibitory areas of the brain stem. There is some evidence that the inhibitory influence may be exerted by way of the fastigiobulbar tract and the bulboreticular inhibitory area (Snider, Magoun, and McCulloch, 1947).

There is also evidence of a second electrically excitable area within the overlap between the posterior part of the neocerebellum and the paleocerebellum. Movements of the face, limbs, and tail are obtained from stimulation of the paramedian lobule and pyramis, and movements of the head and eyes from stimulation of the folium and tuber vermis. The paramedian lobule possesses spinal afferent connections and shows electrical excitability from stimulation of somatic receptors (Snider and Stowell, 1944) or the somatosensory cerebral cortex (Hampson, 1949). This area is topographically organized and projects into the bulboreticular area by way of the fastigiobulbar tract (Snider, Magoun, and McCulloch, 1947).

It will be recalled that the anterior lobe is mainly under the influence of proprioceptive and vestibular impulses through its spinocerebellar and vestibulocerebellar connections. It is related to the control of proprioceptive reflexes and of certain labyrinthine influences playing upon them. Ablation of the anterior lobe, as first emphasized by Bremer and later by Connor and German (1941), induces "an abnormal responsiveness in the antigravity muscles to all postural influences, whether local, segmental or general static in nature." There ensues a strong opisthotonos (retraction of head and concave bowing of the back), increased positive supporting reactions, and hyperactive and spreading deep reflexes. The labyrinthine tonic reflexes also appear to be directly released since they are manifest in deafferented limbs. In the dog, the overactive antigravity reflexes of the forelimbs may cause the animal to topple over backwards in attempting to walk. This relation of the anterior cerebellum to the postural reflexes is especially marked in the pigeon, and it is striking in the cat and dog; however, it is little in evidence in the monkey and chimpanzee and has not been identified in man. But in the monkey such lesions do intensify the spasticity, etc., induced by lesions of areas 4 and 6 (Soriano and Fulton). It is quite probable that, throughout phylogeny, this system has undergone a retrogression that is correlated with the greater control of postural reflexes by the cerebral cortex in the higher primates. Postural reflexes are released by motor area lesions to a much greater degree in monkeys than in cats, suggesting that such controls have passed from the cerebellum to the cerebral cortex.

In addition to being concerned with postural brain stem mechanisms, it is not improbable that the paleocerebellum is responsible for the coordination of the activities of the brain stem, such as walking. Thus the paleocerebellum may regulate both the postural and phasic activities of the brain stem and perhaps brings them under restraint during voluntary activity. This would mean that the paleocerebellum bears the same relation to phasic brain stem mechanisms that the neocerebellum does to corticospinal processes.

Neocerebellum

In the higher primates injury or abalation of the cerebellum is largely manifested in the sphere of voluntary activity, though there are striking changes in reflexes as well. Most of the disturbances of motion can be ascribed to injury of the neocerebellum which in man far overshadows the paleocerebellum and archicerebellum in size and functional importance.

In man, and to a lesser degree in the chimpanzee and the monkey, the cerebellar cortex, especially the neocerebellar cortex, is a part of the neural apparatus that effects coordinated voluntary movement. The cardinal signs of cerebellar disorder are (1) hypotonia, (2) disorders in the direction, rate, range, and force of movement, and (3) tremor.

Hypotonia is manifested on a reflex level by the characteristic "pendular knee jerk." The leg, on returning to its original position, is not stopped "dead beat" by proprioceptive reflexes but swings forth and back

like an inert body. If a limb is manipulated, it offers little resistance; if shaken, it flaps about loosely.

The influence of the cerebellum on muscle tone may be exercised through one of two known anatomical pathways. First, the cerebellum discharges via its nuclei upon brain stem mechanisms for posture. Second, the neocerebellum discharges by way of the thalamus to the motor areas, increasing their electrical activity (Walker, 1938). This might result in augmenting the continuous or tonic discharge of the corticospinal tract described by Adrian and Moruzzi (1939) and increase a facilitatory background of spinal internuncial neurons. On phylogenetic grounds the second would appear to be the more important mechanism in the higher primates.

Disturbances of the direction, rate, range, and force of movements are manifested in a variety of ways (Holmes, 1922). Eye-hand coordinations may overshoot, undershoot, or deviate laterally (errors of direction). Movements may be initiated with delay and executed slowly, or they may be executed with abnormal speed (errors of rate). Negative disturbances of force (asthenia) are manifested by a weakness and ready fatigability and are revealed by inability to maintain a sustained voluntary effort such as holding the arms outstretched. Figure 20 illustrates some of these disturbances.

Tremor consists of gross oscillations of the limb, obvious during movement (intention tremor) and especially obvious at the end of a movement (terminal tremor). In reaching towards an object, the hand follows a zigzag course, and the amplitude of the tremor increases as the object is approached (Fig. 21). Tremor almost certainly represents cortical motor activity unmodulated by the cerebellum (see below).

Paradoxically, when rapid oscillatory movements are intended, e.g. handshaking, great difficulty is encountered (adiadochokinesis). Another disturbance of voluntary movement is *asynergia* or bad timing of the components of a movement. In clenching the hand, the muscles at the back of the forearm normally contract and prevent the wrist from being palmar flexed along with the fingers. The wrist extensor may come in too early or too late in cerebellar patients.

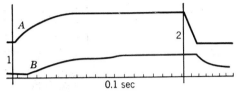

FIG. 20. Myograms of voluntary contractions from the normal (A) and affected (B) arms in a case of unilateral cerebellar lesion. At the vertical line labeled "1" the order to contract was given, and at "2" the order to relax. Note in the lower myogram the long latency, the slowly rising and weak contraction, and the pronounced delay in relaxation. (After Holmes, 1922.)

So-called *decomposition of movement* causes movements to resemble the military "manual of arms." Thus, when a patient lying in bed with arms held upwards is asked to touch his nose with a finger, the arm may be

fundamental activity of the cerebellum. This would be consistent with the lack of cyto-architectural specialization in the cerebellar cortex. Fulton (1943), for example, suggests that a combination of overshooting and undershooting may result in an oscillating tremor. A slight, fortuitous deviation of a movement is not so quickly checked by the defective cerebellum as it would be in a normal patient. Once checked, it is over-corrected (hypermetria), resulting in an opposite deviation which is, in turn, checked only after a lag and then overcorrected, thus leading to ever-increasing oscillations as the movement progresses.

Inability to perform rapid, voluntary oscillatory movements is perhaps a similar difficulty in bringing a movement to an end and initiating the opposite one. In an effort to find a unitary explanation of cerebellar symptomatology, Ectors (1942) and Bailey (1944) have suggested a "braking action." This braking action may also be the primary fault in the paleocerebellar and flocculonodular syndromes, though mani-

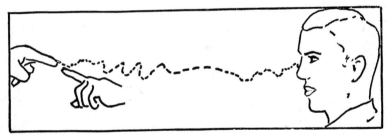

FIG. 21. A diagram showing tremulous movement in a cerebellar patient, as revealed in the nose-to-finger test. The hand of the patient is shown as it reaches the examiner's finger, pictured at the left. The figure is modified from a photograph of a patient obtained by Dr. R. S. Lyman by attaching a light to the patient's finger. Note that the tremor is more marked towards the end than in the middle or beginning of the maneuver. (After Pullen, 1944.)

first lowered to the side and then translocated to the nose, a two-stage maneuver.

Unitary Theory of Cerebellar Function

It is tempting to ascribe the protean symptomatology of cerebellar disease to some common mechanism that represents the

fested in a different category of motor activity. Thus, falling may represent a failure of the vestibular mechanisms to check one of the many small movements that make up body sway. The inhibition of postural reflexes by anterior lobe stimulation is suggestive of a braking action.

Cerebellocerebral Relation

The cerebral and cerebellar cortices are reciprocally interconnected; i.e. fiber systems pass from cerebral cortex to cerebellar cortex and from cerebellar cortex to cerebral cortex. The two components of the systems accomplishing this are as follows:

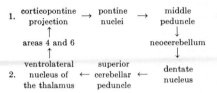

From the coincidence of origin and terminus in both the cerebellar and cerebral cortex, it is assumed that the two systems form a closed circuit. This singular arrangement must heavily influence any hypothesis of neocerebellar function. That the circuit is closed does not imply that it operates in a vacuum. Corticopontine fibers arise also in the parietal, the occipital, and probably the temporal lobes of the cerebral cortex. Furthermore the histology of the cerebellar cortex suggests ready transmission of impulses to the neocerebellum from the paleocerebellar region, and some projection of this region to the cerebral cortex is not ruled out. The various links in this circuit have been demonstrated physiologically as well as anatomically. Thus Dow (1942*b*), in applying single shock stimuli to the cerebral cortex, evoked potentials in the cerebellar cortex. The pontine nuclei have been similarly stimulated. In both cases the evoked activity was confined to the neocerebellum and closely adjoining areas. The reverse connection was demonstrated by Walker (1938). Stimulation of the cerebellar cortex increased the electrical activity in the motor areas of cats. Rossi in earlier experiments (1912) had demonstrated a lowering of the threshold to electrical stimulation of the cortical motor areas upon stimulation of the cerebellar cortex. An aspect of these experiments often overlooked is that the changes in cortical activity were in the direction of increased activity, a point inconvenient to current theories of neocerebellar function which emphasize a braking action of the cerebellum.

Further evidence that the cerebellum interacts with the cerebral cortex in the control of movements comes from hemidecerebellation followed by lesions of the cerebral cortex. The movements remaining to the cat after this sequence, decerebellation-decortication, are by no means normal, but they are free from tremor (Fulton, Liddell, and Rioch), and comparable results obtain for the monkey. In the monkey lesions in area 4 reduce tremor, which reappears when voluntary activity returns. Lesions in area 6 have a mixed effect. Added to lesions in area 4, they further restrict voluntary movement and tremor. However, a primary lesion in area 6 may exaggerate tremor (Aring and Fulton). This probably represents the loss of a controlling influence of the extrapyramidal projections of area 6 upon voluntary movement.

Feedback Circuits and the Control of Movement

So little is known of the mechanism by which the cerebellum regulates voluntary movements that speculation is permissible. Account must be taken of two principal facts — that the cerebellum receives impulses from both (1) the cerebral cortex where voluntary movements originate, and (2) the muscles that execute these movements.

Cortically initiated movements are apparently not *preformed* in the sense that a spatial and temporal pattern of impulses requisite for the movement is automatically and blindly "reeled off." This would be analogous to a military headquarters issuing detailed orders for a complicated military maneuver without the possibility of modifying them on the basis of intelligence reports of progress or of difficulties encountered. A report back to the cortical motor areas can be made by way of the posterior columns, the medial lemniscus, and the thalamus, or by way of the spinocerebellar tracts, the cerebellum, and the thalamus. Thus there are two closed loops by which voluntary activity can be modulated: one is a long loop which includes the muscle; the other is a shorter loop between the cerebral cortex and the cerebellum into which information from the muscles may or may not be fed.

Since Charles Bell discovered the "circle of nerves" * in 1826, it has been appreciated that proprioceptive impulses from muscles are a factor in the control of voluntary and even of reflex activity. On the one hand, the cerebellum receives a heavy (though not exclusively) proprioceptive input, and, on the other, it is involved in the control of movements. Because of these two facts, one view of cerebellar function places the control of movement on a proprioceptive basis. This view has been denied by some; moreover, its proponents have been unable to envisage the precise manner in which proprioceptive information is utilized in the control of movement. Considerations arising outside the field of neurology, to be discussed below, are currently arousing interest in this connection.

The development of the science and mathematics of control (servomechanisms), and of the related field of communications, provides analogies that promise further steps in the analysis of cerebellar control of movements (Brown and Campbell, 1948; Frank et al, 1948; McCulloch, 1947; Wiener, 1948).

* "In standing, walking, and running, every effort of the voluntary power, which gives motion to the body, is directed by a sense of the condition of the muscles, and without this sense we could not regulate their actions." (Bell, 1826, p. 167.)

"Between the brain and the muscles, there is a circle of nerves; one nerve conveys the influence from the brain to the muscle; and another gives the sense of the condition of the muscle to the brain. If this circle be broken by the division of the motive nerve, motion ceases; if it be broken by the division of the other nerve there is no longer a sense of the condition of the muscle, and therefore no regulation of it actively." (Bell, 1826, p. 170.)

It is an interesting coincidence that since 1935 the neurophysiologists have established the existence of numerous circular pathways within the nervous system, and that the science of control has learned the properties of closed-loop control, or feedbacks, in ampli-

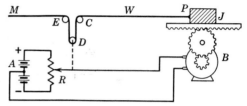

FIG. 22. A simple positioning follow-up system. M-P, a string attached to a weight J, passes through a movable pulley D and two fixed pulleys E and C. B is a servomotor. Moving pulley D shifts R and applies a potential that rotates the motor. ECD is thus an error-detecting device responsive to a change in position of either M or J. Being a continuous, as opposed to an on-off, system, the weight J follows the changing position of M. The amount of displacement of D during this translocation reflects the steady-state error. If a two-way switch is substituted for R, the system is still automatic but discontinuous. If the error-reporting device is replaced by a hand switch in the motor circuit, the device is an open-circuit control. (Lauer, Lesnick, and Matson, 1947.)

fiers and servomechanisms (see also Chapter 35).

It is convenient to distinguish as servomechanisms those regulators that employ a closed-loop control, as opposed to regulators employing an open-ended control. The components and characteristics of servomechanisms vary considerably, but the common feature in all but the simplest varieties is that they react continuously to the discrepancy (error) between the desired condition ordered from the command element, or input, and the state of the thing controlled. The servomechanism system is given this property by a closed-loop construction or feedback. The components generally found in such a system, an example of which is given in Fig. 23, are as follows:

1. A command or input station, often remote from the controlled member. Note that this is not the power input for the system.

Figure 22, showing a simple position control system, illustrates some of the principles of servomechanisms that are sensitive to magnitude of error, though not to rate of error change. Figure 23 shows an idealized

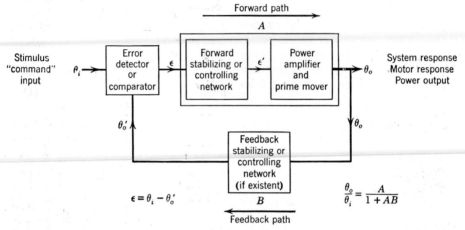

FIG. 23. A feedback system showing the basic elements of a servo system and certain analogies with biological systems as depicted by Frank (1948). A and B are the amplification in the forward and feedback paths, respectively. θ_i = input, θ_o = output. ϵ is the difference between the command and the perceived response and can be called the "error" in a system in which the activity ends when the goal is reached.

1. $\epsilon A = \theta_o$, i.e. the error amplified by A determines the output, and $\epsilon = \theta_o/A$.
2. $\epsilon = \theta_i - \theta_o B$, i.e. the error signal is the input less the θ_o as amplified in the feedback circuit.
3. Combining 1 and 2 in an equation and solving gives the formula

$$\frac{\theta_o}{\theta_i} = \frac{A}{1 + AB} \quad \text{and} \quad \epsilon = \theta_i - \theta_o B = \frac{\theta_i}{1 + AB}$$

Inspection of this formula shows that, if AB is large relative to 1, ϵ becomes inversely proportional to AB, the overall gain in the system. The importance of the amount of feedback (AB) is thus apparent. (From Frank, et al., 1948, after Donald Herr.)

2. A controlled output member.
3. An error-measuring device, or comparator, which measures the difference between the input command and output. The input and the feedback circuit lead to the comparator.
4. A device, often contained with the comparator, that orders a correction as some function of the magnitude of the error. Amplification is often needed at this stage.
5. A servomotor which exerts control directly or by regulating the flow of power into a motor. In the latter case this member is often combined with number 3 or eliminated entirely.

servomechanism with electronic components and their hypothetical biological equivalents.

A servomechanism has been described as a continuously error-sensitive follow-up amplifying system, permitting a wide range of the input command remotely located from the element being controlled (Brown and Campbell, 1948).

The analogy between the neural mechanism for voluntary movements and the servomechanism is close, though not complete. The common feature of importance is the closed-loop or feedback arrangement.

The energy released as corticofugal impulses (input) * from a point remotely located from the muscles is infinitesimal, but it controls a large force represented by the muscles (output). The input command from the motor cortex must have a wide range of freedom to order weak or strong, and fast or slow, movements. The motor cortex must also be allowed random

Since the error is continuously assayed, the output is adjusted until the error is reduced to zero. This process, being continuous, contrasts with a simple on-off step regulator. The error-detecting device not only orders the change of output required to reduce the error but does so in such a manner that the rate of error correction is dependent upon the magnitude of the error.

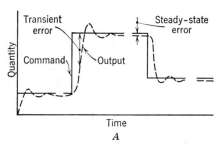

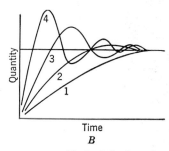

FIG. 24A. Diagram showing transient error between response (dashed line) and command (solid line) during a sudden change in command. The transient oscillatory behavior is illustrated but not labeled. Steady-state error during the period of unchanging command is also indicated.

B. Diagram illustrating transient stability of a system with varying degrees of damping. Curves 2, 3, and 4 are progressively underdamped and show increasing degrees of oscillatory behavior. Curve 1 is overdamped and shows great stability at the expense of a long response time. (Brown and Campbell, 1948.)

variation, since no mechanism is perfect and there is noise arising from spontaneous fluctuations.

The mechanisms of voluntary contractions have in common with servomechanisms the ability to perform movements accurately despite an unexpected load or a deflection of the member moved by external forces. Servo systems accomplish this by means of an error-sensitive device which assays the difference between the command and the output existing at each moment. This implies a "report back" of the condition attained at each moment, a comparison of this with the input, and an order for a change in output based upon the difference or error.

Servomechanisms accomplish continuous error correction by employing closed-loop or feedback circuits. The feedback element of a closed-loop servo system is so arranged that some of the output energy or, in positioning devices, a position signal passes to a comparator. Because some of the output energy returns to the command side of the system, it is called a "feedback." The feedback is called "negative" because the signal correcting the discrepancy between the command and the output is always such that it reduces the discrepancy.

Servomechanisms are subject to the three kinds of error defined in Fig. 24, i.e. transient errors, steady-state errors, and transient oscillatory behavior. Unless a small error induces a large change in the servomotor controlling the output, the first two are large. The steady-state error will be large when output friction is involved, and transient errors will be large where inertia is to be overcome. A small output friction and a sensitive error-correcting device reduce these errors but may introduce oscillation upon starting or stopping. A sudden shift in the input signal results in a correcting movement that may overshoot unless damped, and this error itself may even cause the reverse command to be issued with consequent oscillations that gradually die out. One means of preventing oscillation is to have the rate of error correction dependent upon the magnitude of error. Abrupt transients are, of course, involved in starting and stopping rapid voluntary movements.

In thinking of the nervous system in terms of servomechanisms, it is a mistake to seek too close an analogy and especially to identify various neural structures with the components of those particular servomachines developed in industry. Several differences between the nervous system and servomechanisms must be reckoned with. In servomechanisms the transmission of the report back is usually accomplished at high speed, whereas in the nervous system the maximal rate of conduction is slow enough to introduce critical time factors (see above). Another control problem arises from the fact that the muscular force exerted in many voluntary movements is minute in relation to the tremendous force that the muscles can develop in maximal contraction. Also, the speed with which a muscle develops its tension is a matter of milliseconds. As a limiting case suppose that a maximal motor cortex discharge reached the muscles of the arm as a synchronous volley. The result would be a tension of more than a ton developed in 20 milliseconds on the short arm of a lever, which would cause a jerky start of the movement. The arm would have a terrific kinetic energy which would result in overfling unless restrained. These factors suggest that perhaps the main problem confronting the brain is to avoid an abrupt starting and stopping of voluntary movement because of

the dangers of oscillation in any system sufficiently sensitive to control such transients. There is evidence that transient errors are deliberately incurred in the slow development of cortical discharge (Adrian and Moruzzi, 1939) and by the slow and successive activation of the spinal interneuronal pool by pyramidal tract discharge (Lloyd, 1941). In the design of a servo system there is usually a compromise between transient error and oscillatory behavior (Fig. 24). It is as though the nervous system had chosen large transient errors in order to avoid the hazard of oscillation.

The nervous system resembles complex servomechanisms by involving several closed-loop systems. At the spinal level the proprioceptive reflex arcs constitute closed loops which function not only for error reporting but also for damping. Servo systems often include a damping component, sometimes a simple viscous one, to counter oscilatory tendencies. Since viscous damping introduces a steady-state error, oscillations are better avoided by making the comparator react to the rate of change of error.

Feedback circuits control certain reflex as well as voluntary actions. This can be illustrated by considering the crossed extensor reflex, a reflex contraction of an extensor muscle of the limb elicited by repetitive stimulation of the central end of a nerve of the opposite limb. It consists of a slow rising phase, when more and more motor units are being brought into action (recruitment); a plateau of steadily maintained tension; and a long continued after-discharge following cessation of the stimulus. Part of this "inertia and momentum" is inherent in the internuncial system of the reflex arc, but part is contributed by the secondary proprioceptive reflexes, instituted by contraction of the muscles, which are superimposed on the crossed extensor reflex. Thus, if the posterior roots that conduct the impulses from the reacting muscle are sectioned, the reflex myogram changes appearance in three ways. It rises more abruptly, describing a curve that is convex upwards; it reaches a slightly higher plateau; and the contraction subsides more abruptly. This last effect is ascribed to loss of a stretch reflex normally appended to the contraction, and due to the stretching of the relaxing muscle by the myograph spring. The first and second effects are ascribed to a lack of "autogenous inhibition" from a different proprioceptive ending. The net result of these inhibitory and facilitatory feedback circuits is to make the transition from relaxation to contraction, and the return to relaxation, a smoother process. The crossed extensor reflex in a deafferented muscle is, in a sense, "ataxic."

In passing, it may be noted that the myotatic reflex bears a certain resemblance to servomechanisms of the type designed to position an object. These reflexes, according to Sherrington's analysis, enable an animal to maintain constancy of posture in the face of varying environmental forces that tend to displace the body from that posture. A load thrown on a horse's back is a good example of a sudden change in gravitational force acting on the leg muscle. The slight stretch of the muscles, resulting from the extra weight on the back, elicits a prompt reflex contraction of the muscle stretched, which neatly counteracts the gravitational force of the extra weight. The horse's posture remains virtually unchanged, although the load is now different. The stretch afferent (the muscle spindle) acts as an error-detecting device, continuously measuring the displacement from the normal posture (the error), and ordering a correcting contraction through spinal reflex connections. The stretch afferent is extraordinarily sensitive to slight stretches, and, like sensitive servomechanisms designed to reduce transient and steady-state errors, the stretch reflex arc is prone to oscillations. When, in certain diseases of the extrapyramidal system, the stretch reflex arc is made hypersensitive by abnormal facilitation from the brain, stretch is likely to throw the muscle into the oscillatory contractions and relaxations known as

"clonus." When the spinal reflex arcs receive less than the normal facilitatory impulses from the brain, an oscillatory phenomenon of quite a different significance supervenes. The knee jerk tends to be "flail-like" and pendulous in the spinal animal. The leg rises abruptly (fling), falls like an inert body, and swings about the position of rest like a pendulum damped only by the viscous properties of the relaxed muscles and ligaments. In the decerebrate cat, the knee jerk is typically dead-beat; i.e. the limb is lowered to the resting position without overshooting.

These facts may be summarized by saying that the spinal proprioceptive reflex arcs function in posture as a time-continuous, error-detecting device that positions the body in space by varying the output of the muscles to counter changes in gravitational force. When rendered oversensitive it is subject to the oscillatory errors of oversensitive feedback mechanisms. The spinal proprioceptive reflex arcs, which consist of excitatory and inhibitory feedback circuits, serve the same function as the damping elements in certain servomechanisms. When these circuits are interrupted or underfacilitated, passive oscillatory phenomena supervene (pendular knee jerk). For certain reflexes, and possibly for voluntary movement, they curb momentum in relaxation and prevent a too abrupt initiation of the movement of the limb, thus overcoming inertia slowly.

Cerebellum as a Feedback Mechanism

Potentially the spinocerebellar tracts → cerebellar cortex → dentate nucleus → thalamus → motor cortex make up a system that could correct, modulate, or intensify a movement during its course on the basis of proprioceptive sensations from the executant muscle.

The question arises whether the report back from the muscles during voluntary movement occurs with sufficient rapidity to permit effective control throughout the course of the movement. It is significant that the spinocerebellar tract is the largest-fibered and the most rapidly conducting (140 meters per second) ascending tract in the spinal cord. Twelve milliseconds would not be too long for spinocortical and corticospinal conduction in man. On the other hand, the myoneural junction and a minimum of seven synapses (not counting internuncial systems of the cerebrum and cerebellum) must be crossed in the complete circuit. Taking synaptic delay at 0.5 to 2.0 milliseconds, we must allow 3.0 to 12 milliseconds for this factor. The total time for central conduction is 15 to 24 milliseconds. The average latency of the knee jerk in man gives a rough estimate of the time consumed in the peripheral portion of the circuit, i.e. 4 to 10 milliseconds, with allowance for time lost at the synapse. The total time for the complete circuit is then 19 to 34 milliseconds.

One may pose the question: "At what rate could a single motor unit contract in voluntary contraction and yet have each contraction modulated on the basis of its previous contraction?" To 19 to 34 milliseconds for the circuit from muscle to muscle through the cerebellar and motor cortex would be added the contraction time of perhaps another 20 to 40 milliseconds, since contraction directly or indirectly stimulates the proprioceptive end organs. Taking the larger figure for circuit conduction time, discharges at slightly more than ten per second could be so modulated. Electromyographic studies show discharges at about this rate in voluntary movements of moderate strength. Slowness of voluntary movement is characteristic of cerebellar patients and of normal individuals executing unpracticed movements. In both cases this may be a device to utilize the proprioceptive return to greater advantage.

Input Informed Feedback Circuits

The essential feature of a servomechanism is an error-sensitive device that continuously measures and reacts to the discrepancy between the ordered state and the realized state. Such feedback circuits are, therefore, output informed. The question arises in respect of the nervous system whether some of the shorter loops that do not include the muscles constitute, not output-informed, but what may be called input-informed, feedbacks, and hence constitute a class apart from servomechanisms. One reason for raising this question is that cerebellar ataxia is different in some aspects from locomotor ataxia in which the fault is clearly the absence of information from the muscles due to posterior root damage. For example, in locomotor ataxia vision can partly compensate for the missing proprioceptive return, whereas cerebellar ataxia is not greatly aggravated when the eyes are closed.

We have seen that the motor cortex, in addition to firing into the spinal motoneuron pools, fires into the neocerebellum by way of the frontopontine and pontocerebellar fibers. From the neocerebellum a stream of impulses returns to the motor areas via the thalamus. Although the neocerebellum is concerned with the control of limb movements, it receives few spinocerebellar fibers, so that it is not *directly* informed of error in movements. If it is so informed, the neural data must be transmitted from the spinocerebellar projection fields, located anteriorly and posteriorly. If experimentation fails to demonstrate this connection, what function could be ascribed to such a massive uninformed fiber system?

It was pointed out above that starting a movement without jerkiness presents a problem. A movement starting abruptly would endow the limb with kinetic energy which would tax the informed negative feedback in controlling the movement. The alternative is to start movements slowly. This could be accomplished by cascading or, in neural terms, avalanche conduction in which dichotomizing neurons synapse with several neurons, the axons of which in turn dichotomize. However, positive feedback circuits that add to or "amplify" the input energy would accomplish the same purpose. Thus a recurrent pathway 180 degrees out of phase with the original discharge would double the frequency of discharge in the centrifugal pathway. The possibility that the reciprocal cerebellar cerebral circuits act in this fashion must be considered. The known effects of this circuit are in the direction of increasing excitability or electrical activity of the motor cortex. If this system is a negative feedback, the effect should be to increase or decrease the cortical discharge, depending on the sign of the error. The movements of the cerebellar patient depart from normal in their sluggishness of inception, as well as in sluggishness of termination (Fig. 20). The former may represent impairment of a positive feedback circuit.

The problem faced by the motor cortex in executing a voluntary eye-hand coordination, such as picking up an object, hinges on time considerations. It can be argued that, at the moment an act is launched, a time-tension pattern of muscle contraction is instituted, projecting into the future, with the object being the goal of this reaction. The end of the movement, removed in time, is implicit in the patterning of the discharge. It seems unlikely that the initial stage of the movement is ordered blindly, then the second stage, and so on, with the goal direction appearing only at the last moment.

The nervous system would be handicapped in "planning movements" in this fashion because there are no known methods for storing impulses in a neuron to be discharged after a fixed delay. Significant delay can be obtained by making use of conduction time. Thus the problem of delay has apparently been solved by circular chains of neurons or reverberating circuits: the nerve impulses circulate within such circuits and give off one or more impulses per circuit. The decay characteristics give a temporal patterning of the cortical discharge.

The cerebral-cerebellar circuit may represent not so much an error-correcting device as a part of a mechanism by which an instantaneous order can be extended forward in time. Such a circuit, though uninformed as to consequences, could, so to speak, "rough-in" a movement and thus reduce the troublesome transients involved in the correction of movement by output-informed feedbacks. Especially could such a circuit be effective in the termination of movement. To terminate a movement without jerkiness requires terminal deceleration. This might be accomplished by a negative feedback proportional to the velocity of the movement; and corticocerebellar circuits may represent such a feedback. Cerebellar tremor may be comparable to the oscillations of an undamped servomechanism system in which the feedback is removed or is responsive only to the extent of movement, not to its rate. It is perhaps significant that cerebellar intention tremor is also a terminal tremor.

On the other hand, if simple analogies are sought, the cerebellum could be likened to the comparator of a servomechanism. It may receive from the cerebral cortex some representation of the command and from the muscles a representation of the resulting movement. These, compared, may result in a signal that is transmitted to the motor cortex, altering its signal to the muscles so as to diminish the error. In this capacity the cerebellum is acting as a feedback to stabilize one unit of the whole system of neural reaction. However, the cerebellum receives impulses from the distance receptors, and from the cortical areas for vision and audition. These pass to the neocerebellum, which is especially concerned with voluntary movement. Such an arrangement may mean that the cerebellum can compare the true input, the auditory or visual representation of the goal, and the proprioceptive indication of the limb's position.

Finally, one may question the value of likening neural systems to servo systems. Such analogies, devoid of mathematical treatment, are essentially allegorical, somewhat akin to Freudian psychology. Whether a mathematical treatment will lead to predictions capable of experimental verification remains to be seen. Otherwise, we have added little since 1826 to Bell's "circle of nerves."

REFERENCES

Adrian, E. D., and G. Moruzzi. Impulses in the pyramidal tract. *J. Physiol.*, 1939, **97**, 153–199.

Bach, L. M. N., and H. W. Magoun. The vestibular nuclei as an excitatory mechanism for the cord. *J. Neurophysiol.*, 1947, **10**, 331–337.

Bailey, P. Relationship to the cerebellum. Chapter 10 in *The precentral motor cortex. Illinois Monogr. med. Sci.* (1st Ed.), 1944, **4**, Nos. 1–4. (2nd Ed., 1949.)

Bell, C. On the nervous circle which connects the voluntary muscles with the brain. *Philos. Trans.*, 1826, Pt. 2, 163–173; also *Abstr. Papers Philos. Trans.*, 1826, **2**, 266–267.

Bosma, J. F., and E. Gellhorn. Electromyographic studies of muscular coordination on stimulation of motor cortex. *J. Neurophysiol.*, 1946, **9**, 263–274.

Boynton, E. P., and M. Hines. On the question of threshold in stimulation of the motor cortex. *Amer. J. Physiol.*, 1933, **106**, 175–182.

Brodal, A., and J. Jensen. The ponto-cerebellar projection in the rabbit and cat. Experimental investigations. *J. comp. Neurol.*, 1946, **84**, 31–118.

Brown, G. S., and D. P. Campbell. *Principles of servomechanisms; Dynamics and synthesis of closed-loop control systems.* New York: Wiley, 1948.

Brown, T. Graham. Studies in the physiology of the nervous system. XXIV: On the phenomenon of facilitation. 3: "Secondary facilitation" and its location in the cortical mechanism itself in monkeys. *Quart. J. exp. Physiol.*, 1915, **9**, 117–130.

Brown, T. G., and C. S. Sherrington. On the instability of a cortical point. *Proc. roy. Soc.*, 1912, **B85**, 250–277.

Bubnoff, N., and R. Heidenhain. Ueber Erregungs- und Hemmungsvorgänge innerhalb der motorischen Hirncentren. *Arch. f.d. ges. Physiol.*, 1881, **26**, 137–200. English translation: *Illinois Monogr. med. Sci.*, 1944, **4**, 173–210. (2nd Ed., 1949.)

Bucy, P. C. Relation to abnormal involuntary movements. Chapter 15 in *The precentral motor cortex. Illinois Monogr. med. Sci.* (1st Ed.), 1944, **4**, 395–408. (2nd Ed., 1949.)

Chang, H.-T., T. C. Ruch, and A. A. Ward, Jr. Topographical representation of muscles in motor cortex of monkeys. *J. Neurophysiol.*, 1947, **10**, 39–56.

Clark, G., and J. W. Ward. Responses elicited from the cortex of monkeys by electrical stimulation through fixed electrodes. *Brain*, 1948, **71**, 332–342.

Connor, G. J., and W. J. German. Functional localization within the anterior cerebellar lobe. *Trans. Amer. neurol. Ass.*, 1941, **67**, 181–186.

Cooper, S., and D. Denny-Brown. Responses to stimulation of the motor area of the cerebral cortex. *Proc. roy. Soc.*, 1927, **B102**, 222–236.

Dow, R. S. The evolution and anatomy of the cerebellum. *Biol. Rev.*, 1942a, **17**, 179–220.

Dow, R. S. Cerebellar action potentials in response to stimulation of the cerebral cortex in monkeys and cats. *J. Neurophysiol.*, 1942b, **5**, 121–136.

Dusser de Barenne, J. G., H. W. Garol, and W. S. McCulloch. The "motor" cortex of the chimpanzee. *J. Neurophysiol.*, 1941a, **4**, 287–303.

Dusser de Barenne, J. G., H. W. Garol, and W. S. McCulloch. The functional organization of sensory and adjacent cortex of the monkey. *J. Neurophysiol.*, 1941b, **4**, 324–330.

Dusser de Barenne, J. G., and W. S. McCulloch. An "extinction" phenomenon on stimulation of the cerebral cortex. *Proc. Soc. exp. Biol., N. Y.*, 1934, **32**, 524–527.

Dusser de Barenne, J. G., and W. S. McCulloch. Functional organization in the sensory cortex of the monkey (*Macaca mulatta*). *J. Neurophysiol.*, 1938, **1**, 69–85.

Dusser de Barenne, J. G., and W. S. McCulloch. Sensorimotor cortex, nucleus caudatus and thalamus opticus. *J. Neurophysiol.*, 1938, **1**, 364–377.

Dusser de Barenne, J. G., and W. S. McCulloch. Factors for facilitation and extinction in the central nervous system. *J. Neurophysiol.*, 1939a, **2**, 319–355.

Dusser de Barenne, J. G., and W. S. McCulloch. Suppression of motor response obtained from area 4 by stimulation of area 4-S. *J. Neurophysiol.*, 1941, **4**, 311–323. See also *Amer. J. Physiol.*, 1939b, **126**, 482.

Ectors, L. La fonction du cervelet. *Conf. neurol.*, 1942, **4**, 181–212.

Frank, L. K., G. E. Hutchinson, W. K. Livingston, W. S. McCulloch, and N. Wiener. Teleological mechanisms. *Ann. N. Y. Acad. Sci.*, 1948, **50**, 187–277.

Fritsch, G., and E. Hitzig. Über die elektrische Erregbarkeit des Grosshirns. *Arch. Anat. Physiol. wiss. Med.*, 1870, **37**, 300–332.

Fulton, J. F. *Physiology of the nervous system.* (2nd Ed.) New York: Oxford University Press, 1943. (3rd Ed., 1949.)

Fulton, J. F., C. F. Jacobsen, and M. Kennard. A note concerning the relation of the frontal lobes to posture and forced grasping in monkeys. *Brain*, 1932, **55**, 524–536.

Fulton, J. F., and M. Kennard. A study of flaccid and spastic paralyses produced by lesions of the cerebral cortex in primates. *Res. Publ. Ass. nerv. ment. Dis.*, 1934, **13**, 158–210.

Hampson, J. L. Relationship between cat cerebral and cerebellar cortices. *J. Neurophysiol.*, 1949, **12**, 37–50.

Hines, M. The "motor cortex." *Johns Hopk. Hosp. Bull.*, 1937, **60**, 313–366.

Hines, M. Significance of the precentral motor cortex. Chapter 18 in *The precentral motor* cortex. *Illinois Monogr. med. Sci.* (1st Ed.), 1944, **4**, Nos. 1–4. (2nd Ed., 1949.)

Hines, M. The motor areas. *Fed. Proc. Amer. Soc. exp. Biol.*, 1947, **6**, 441–447.

Hoff, E. C. The distribution of spinal terminals (boutons) of the pyramidal tract determined by experimental degeneration. *Proc. roy. Soc.*, 1932, **B111**, 226–237.

Holmes, G. The Croonian Lectures on the clinical symptoms of cerebellar disease and their interpretation. *Lancet*, 1922, **202**, 1177–1182; 1231–1237; **203**, 59–65; 111–115.

Jackson, J. H. *Selected writings of John Hughlings Jackson.* (J. Taylor, Ed.) London: Hodder and Stoughton, 1931. Volume 1.

Kennard, M. A. Relation of age to motor impairment in man and in subhuman primates. *Arch. Neurol. Psychiat., Chicago*, 1940, **44**, 377–397; 1942, **48**, 227–240.

Kennard, M. A. Reactions of monkeys of various ages to partial and complete decortication. *J. Neuropathol. exp. Neurol.*, 1944a, **3**, 289–310.

Kennard, M. A. Experimental analysis of the functions of the basal ganglia in monkeys and chimpanzees. *J. Neurophysiol.*, 1944b, **7**, 127–148.

Kennard, M. A. Somatic functions. Chapter 9 in *The precentral motor cortex. Illinois Monogr. med. Sci.* (1st Ed.), 1944c, **4**, Nos. 1–4. (2nd Ed., 1949.)

Larsell, O. The cerebellum. A review and interpretation. *Arch. Neurol. Psychiat., Chicago*, 1937, **38**, 580–607.

Lassek, A. M. The human pyramidal tract. II. A numerical investigation of the Betz cells of the motor area. *Arch. Neurol. Psychiat., Chicago*, 1940, **44**, 718–724.

Lassek, A. M. The pyramidal tract of the monkey. Betz cell and pyramidal tract enumeration. *J. comp. Neurol.*, 1941, **74**, 193–202.

Lassek, A. M. The human pyramidal tract. IV. A study of the mature, myelinated fibers of the pyramid. *J. comp. Neurol.*, 1942a, **76**, 217–225.

Lassek, A. M. The pyramidal tract. The effect of pre- and post-central cortical lesions on the fiber components of the pyramids in monkey. *J. nerv. ment. Dis.*, 1942b, **95**, 721–729.

Lassek, A. M., and J. P. Evans. The human pyramidal tract. XIV. A study of the representation of the cortico-spinal components in the spinal cord. *J. comp. Neurol.*, 1946, **84**, 11–16.

Lassek, A. M., and G. L. Rasmussen. The human pyramidal tract. A fiber and numerical analysis. *Arch. Neurol. Psychiat., Chicago*, 1939, **42**, 872–876.

Lassek, A. M., and M. D. Wheatley. The pyramidal tract. An enumeration of the large motor cells of area 4 and the axons in the pyramids of the chimpanzee. *J. comp. Neurol.*, 1945, **82**, 299–302.

Lauer, H., R. Lesnick, and L. E. Matson. *Servomechanism fundamentals.* New York: McGraw-Hill. 1947.

Leão, A. A. P. Spreading depression of cortical activity in the cerebral cortex. *J. Neurophysiol.*, 1944a, **7**, 359–390.

Leão, A. A. P. Pial circulation and spreading depression of activity in the cerebral cortex. *J. Neurophysiol.*, 1944b, **7**, 391–396.

Leão, A. A. P. Further observations on the spreading depression of activity in the cerebral cortex. *J. Neurophysiol.*, 1947, **10**, 409–414.

Leão, A. A. P., and R. S. Morison. Propagation of spreading cortical depression. *J. Neurophysiol.*, 1945, **8**, 33–46.

Leyton, A. S. F., and C. S. Sherrington. Observations on the excitable cortex of the chimpanzee, orang-utan, and gorilla. *Quart. J. exp. Physiol.*, 1917, **11**, 135–222.

Lloyd, D. P. C. The spinal mechanism of the pyramidal system in cats. *J. Neurophysiol.*, 1941, **4**, 525–546.

Lorente de Nó. R. Cerebral cortex: architecture, intracortical connections, motor projections. Chapter 15 in *Physiology of the nervous system* by J. F. Fulton. (2nd Ed.) New York: Oxford University Press, 1943. (3rd Ed., 1949.)

MacColl, LeR. A. *Fundamental theory of servomechanisms.* New York: Van Nostrand, 1945.

McCulloch, W. S. Cortico-cortical connections. Chapter 8 in *The precentral motor cortex. Illinois Monogr. med. Sci.* (1st Ed.), 1944, **4**, Nos. 1–4. (2nd Ed., 1949.)

McCulloch, W. S. Modes of functional organization of the cerebral cortex. *Fed. Proc. Amer. Soc. exp. Biol.*, 1947, **6**, 448–452.

McCulloch, W. S., G. Graf, and H. W. Magoun. A cortico-bulbo-reticular pathway from area 4-s. *J. Neurophysiol.*, 1946, **9**, 127–132.

McKibben, P. S., and D. R. Wheelis. Experiments on the motor cortex of the cat. *J. comp. Neurol.*, 1932, **56**, 373–390.

Magoun, H. W. *Spasticity, the stretch reflex and extrapyramidal systems.* Springfield, Ill.: Thomas, 1947.

Magoun, H. W., and R. Rhines. An inhibitory mechanism in the bulbar reticular formation. *J. Neurophysiol.*, 1946, **9**, 165–171.

Marshall, W. H. The relation of dehydration of the brain to the spreading depression of Leão. *EEG clin. Neurophysiol.*, 1950, **2**, 177–185.

Matthes, K., and T. C. Ruch. Extensor reflexes of the chronic spinal cat. *Quart. J. exp. Physiol.*, 1932, **22**, 221–231.

Mettler, F. A. On the origin of the fibers in the pyramid of the primate brain. *Proc. Soc. exp. Biol. N. Y.*, 1944, **57**, 111–113.

Murphy, J. P., and E. Gellhorn. Multiplicity of representation versus punctate localization in the motor cortex: On experimental investigation. *Arch. Neurol. Psychiat., Chicago*, 1945, **54**, 256–273.

Nielsen, F. E., S. P. W. Black, and G. G. Drake. Inhibition and facilitation of motor activity by the anterior cerebellum. *Fed. Proc. Amer. Soc. exp. Biol.*, 1948, **7**, 86.

Niemer, W. T., and H. W. Magoun. Reticulospinal tracts influencing motor activity. *J. comp. Neurol.*, 1947, **87**, 367–379.

Penfield, W. G., and E. Boldrey. Somatic motor and sensory representation in the cerebral cortex of man as studied by electrical stimulation. *Brain*, 1937, **60**, 389–443.

Pullen, R. L. (Ed.). *Medical diagnosis.* Philadelphia : Saunders, 1944.

Putnam, T. J. Operative treatment of diseases characterized by involuntary movements (tremor, athetosis). *Res. Publ. Ass. nerv. ment. Dis.*, 1940, **21**, 666–696.

Ranson, S. W. *The anatomy of the nervous system.* (7th Ed.) Philadelphia : Saunders, 1943.

Rasmussen, T., and W. Penfield. Further studies of the sensory and motor cerebral cortex of man. *Fed. Proc. Amer. Soc. exp. Biol.*, 1947, **6**, 452–460.

Rhines, R., and H. W. Magoun. Brain stem facilitation of cortical motor responses. *J. Neurophysiol.*, 1946, **9**, 219–229.

Richter, C. P., and M. Hines. The production of the "grasp reflex" in adult macaques by experimental frontal lobe lesions. *Res. Publ. Ass. nerv. ment. Dis.*, 1934, **13**, 211–224.

Rosenblueth, A., N. Wiener, and J. Bigelow. Behavior, purpose and teleology. *Phil. Sci.*, 1943, **10**, 18–24.

Sherrington, C. S. Further experimental note on the correlation of action of antagonistic muscles. *Proc. roy. Soc.*, 1893, **B53**, 407–420.

Sherrington, C. S. Quantitative management of contraction in lowest level co-ordination. Hughlings Jackson Lecture. *Brain*, 1931, **54**, 1–28.

Sherrington, C. S., and H. E. Hering. Antagonistic muscles and reciprocal innervation. *Proc. roy. Soc.*, 1897, **B62**, 183–187.

Sloan, N., and H. Jasper. The identity of spreading depression and "suppression." *EEG clin. Neurophysiol.*, 1950, **2**, 59–78.

Snider, R. S., H. W. Magoun, and W. S. McCulloch. A suppressor cerebello-bulbo-recticular pathway from anterior and paramedian lobules. *Fed. Proc. Amer. Soc. exp. Biol.*, 1947, **6**, 207.

Snider, R. S., and A. Stowell. Receiving areas of tactile, auditory and visual systems in the cerebellum. *J. Neurophysiol.*, 1944, **7**, 331–358.

Sperry, R. W. Cerebral regulation of motor coordination in monkeys following multiple transection of sensorimotor cortex. *J. Neurophysiol.*, 1947, **10**, 275–294.

Tower, S. S. The dissociation of cortical excitation from cortical inhibition by pyramid section and the syndrome of that lesion in the cat. *Brain*, 1935, **58**, 238–255.

Tower, S. S. Extrapyramidal action from the cat's cerebral cortex : motor and inhibitory. *Brain*, 1936, **59**, 408–444.

Tower, S. S. Pyramidal lesion in the monkey. *Brain*, 1940, **63**, 36–90.

Tower, S. S. The pyramidal tract. Chapter 6 in *The precentral motor cortex. Illinois Monogr. med. Sci.* (1st Ed.), 1944, **4**, Nos. 1–4. (2nd Ed., 1949.)

Walker, A. E. An oscillographic study of the cerebello-cerebral relationships. *J. Neurophysiol.*, 1938, **1**, 16–23.

Ward, A. A., Jr. Anterior cingulate gyrus and personality. *Res. Publ. Ass. nerv. ment. Dis.*, 1947, **27**, 438–445.

Ward, A. A., Jr. 1949 (personal communication).

Ward, A. A., W. S. McCulloch, and H. W. Magoun. Production of an alternating tremor at rest in monkeys. *J. Neurophysiol.*, 1948, **11**, 317–330.

Welch, W. K., and M. A. Kennard. Relation of cerebral cortex to spasticity and flaccidity. *J. Neurophysiol.*, 1944, **7**, 255–268.

Wiener, N. *Cybernetics.* New York : Wiley, 1948.

Woolsey, C. N. Representation in the motor cortex of flexor and extensor muscles of the leg. *Amer. J. Physiol.*, 1938, **123**, 221–222.

Woolsey, C. N. The somatic functions of the central nervous system. *Ann. Rev. Physiol.*, 1947, **9**, 525–552.

Woolsey, C. N., and P. H. Settlage. Pattern of localization in the precentral motor cortex of *Macaca mulatta. Fed. Proc. Amer. Soc. exp. Biol.*, 1950, **9**, 140.

6.

Homeostasis

EDWARD W. DEMPSEY

Harvard Medical School

Viewed empirically, the physiological reactions of mammalian organisms present an array of contradictory and paradoxical phenomena. The heart rate and cardiac output may increase while the blood flow in a given region increases, decreases, or remains static. An accelerated respiratory rate may accompany muscular activity (exercise) or inactivity (panting). The glucose concentration of the blood may rise during depletion of the glycogen stores of the body, or, conversely, while the carbohydrate reserves are being augmented. Taken without reference to the total needs of the individual, these reactions can but bewilder the systematist. It is understandable, therefore, that a generalization rationalizing these and many other observations would be received gratefully by physiological investigators. Such a generalization was formulated by Claude Bernard (1859) and extensively documented by Walter B. Cannon (1932). Bernard was greatly impressed by the regulatory mechanisms that maintain the concentration of glucose in the blood at a nearly constant level. In a flash of intuitive insight he perceived this to be one example of a general law of constancy of the internal environment. Cannon, aware of many more examples in which a constant state is maintained and having investigated some of the regulatory mechanisms, applied a special name, homeostasis, to designate these steady states.

A few examples will make clear the nature of the steady states. The internal body temperature of mammals remains fixed, although the temperature of the external environment may fluctuate widely. Consequently the thermolabile reactions of cells are protected from external changes. Animals are therefore released from the limitations otherwise imposed by winter's cold and summer's heat. The acidity of the blood remains remarkably constant. A slight shift toward acidity would result in coma and death; a shift toward greater alkalinity would produce convulsions. The sugar concentration of the blood, already mentioned, is nicely regulated by storage and release of glycogen in the liver. If the regulatory mechanism is overwhelmed by excess sugar, it is wasted by excretion through the kidneys. If the concentration were allowed to fall to a low level, abnormal behavior, convulsions, and coma would ensue.

The vertebrate animals of today are the products of millions of years of evolution along widely divergent paths, and yet in many respects their internal environments are remarkably similar. The temperature at which life as we know it is possible permits but slight variation. The bloods of the various animals are closely similar in their ionic compositions, pH, and glucose concentrations. These facts suggest that the conditions under which life is possible are very restricted indeed and have not changed substantially since life first began. Consequently the evolution of different forms of life has necessarily involved the development of mechanisms for maintaining within the animal an internal environment with the properties required for the continued life of its cells (Baldwin, 1940). The essential truth is contained in Claude Bernard's dictum, "La fixité du milieu intérieur est la condition de la vie libre."

So important for the welfare of the organism are these steady states that many diverse mechanisms have been utilized for their maintenance. The pH of the blood is partly regulated by the presence of buffer systems. Thus the circulating fluid contains chemical substances in an equilibrium between ionized and nonionized forms. Adding acid or alkali to such a system shifts the equilibrium so that the free acidity remains constant, because the added substance is rendered inert in an undissociated form. This is an example of a purely physicochemical system adapted to homeostatic control. However, such mechanisms are effective only within definite limits; if too much acid or alkali is added, the equilibrium breaks down. In the mammalian organism such a contingency is guarded against by physiological mechanisms which excrete the excess through the kidneys or lungs. Too much acid, too much salt, or too much sugar are not allowed to accumulate but are eliminated from the blood by the storage or excretory organs.

The mechanisms cited above are simple and autonomous ones which can function somewhat independently of the activities of other organs and systems. The liver, even after removal from the body, can take up glucose from the surrounding medium and store it as glycogen. Nevertheless, these automatic activities may be adjusted in rate to conform with other procedures occurring elsewhere in the body. For correlating the various processes, two special regulatory systems have evolved: the autonomic nervous system and the endocrine glands. The mechanisms that maintain the steady state can therefore be classified into a hierarchy of three levels: (1) physicochemical buffer systems, (2) automatic physiological excretory and storage systems which supply and support the chemical processes, and (3) coordinating endocrine and neural systems through which the component steady states are integrated.

Two other aspects of the steady state need be considered. When stability is threatened even mildly, delicate indicators give the alarm and activate the appropriate corrective agencies, so that oscillations to either side of the homeostatic norm are slight. The effector organs react as if they were directed toward nullifying a disturbing condition. The second factor concerns the emergency nature of many of the adaptive changes. When bodily security or survival is seriously threatened, the internal fluid matrix is altered. If noxious stimuli occur, such as bacteria, toxic drugs, or physical damage, the organism responds by altering the proportions of the protective white blood corpuscles, by augmenting the protective antibodies, and by elevating the body temperature. If perceptible foes arouse fear or rage, a number of internal readjustments unify and integrate the activities of the body for its maximal physical effort — flight or combat: blood sugar is increased, the circulation to special regions is greatly augmented, respiration is accelerated, extra red blood cells are mobilized to carry the extra oxygen, and adrenalin is produced to reinforce the adaptive nerve impulses. These reactions profoundly disturb the internal environment, but they disturb it in such a way as to render the organism temporarily more effective in a contest that may end in life or death. The ultimate total stability of the organism is therefore defended even at the cost of temporary disturbance to the welfare of its component parts.

Although the endocrine and nervous systems undoubtedly play some part in maintaining the homeostatic norm, their functions are most strikingly revealed in emergency situations. The nervous reflexes which accelerate the heart and constrict the vascular bed operate more forcefully during strong emotional states than in placid situations.

The hormones which increase the metabolic rate and facilitate the utilization of sugar are secreted in larger quantity upon exposure to cold. The deficiency resulting from impairment or destruction of these systems is more pronounced in some situations than in others. In many instances it is possible to adjust the environment so that deficits of the regulatory systems are not noticeable. Nevertheless such impairment renders the organism at least potentially deficient in the myriad adjustments normally available to it.

THE ENDOCRINE GLANDS

A number of glandular structures, plentifully supplied with blood vessels but lacking ducts, secrete their products directly into the blood stream. Hence these organs are collectively called the ductless or endocrine glands. Their secretions are chemical substances called hormones, which are elaborated in one place and transported through the blood vascular system to another location at which they exert their action.

Strictly defined, there are many substances qualifying as hormones which are usually omitted from endocrinological discussions. Thus glucose is produced from the liver's glycogen stores and carried by the blood to other parts of the body. Similarly secretin and cholecystokinin are formed in the intestine and cause, respectively, pancreatic secretion and contraction of the gall bladder. However, the subject matter of endocrinology is usually restricted arbitrarily to the hormonal aspects of the gonads, the adrenal glands, the pancreatic islets, and the parathyroid, thyroid, and pituitary glands.

Hormones may be grouped into three categories, each characterized by the type of regulation exhibited. The first category comprises the hormones of the parathyroid glands, the pancreatic islands of Langerhans and, as we shall see later, probably the glomerulosal zone of the adrenal cortex. These glands continue to function adequately after denervation or hypophysectomy. They appear to be regulated in some direct way by the processes they control. Thus parathormone, when injected into an animal, causes its serum calcium to rise, and, conversely, loss of calcium such as occurs in renal diseases entails hypertrophy and overactivity of the parathyroid glands. Similarly the injection of insulin lowers the blood sugar, whereas hyperglycemia stimulates such an excessive production of insulin that, if long continued, exhaustion and death of the islet cells may occur.

The second category contains the hormones of the posterior pituitary body and the adrenal medulla. These glands develop from neural tissue and maintain throughout life extensive functional connections with the autonomic nervous system. The endocrine and neural factors are so closely related that we can profitably consider them in a later section devoted to the autonomic nervous system.

The third category of hormones comprises a group of endocrine factors centering around the anterior lobe of the pituitary gland. The pituitary has sometimes been called the "master" gland because it produces a number of factors (thyrotropin, adrenotropin, and gonadotropin) necessary for maintaining the structure and function of the thyroid, adrenal, and sex glands. In turn the hormones produced by these so-called target organs react upon the pituitary and control its production of the tropic hormones. This group of endocrine factors thus constitutes a self-regulating system.

The hormones of the first category apparently respond in a "dead-beat" fashion to their respective stimuli. That is to say, the rate of secretion is accelerated or depressed directly by the fluctuations of the end process. On the other hand, the type of regulation involved in the second and third categories is indirect. Stimulation of the adrenal medulla is accomplished only by activity in the intermediary nervous system, and alterations in the rate of secretion of thyroid hormone imply similar fluctuations in the activity of the anterior pituitary gland. With this indirect type of regulation manifold stimuli may compete for or interact in the intermediary center that discharges as the final common path to the secretory gland. In consequence of this intermediation the adrenal medulla may respond in rage, in hypotension, or in hypoglycemia, and, in seasonal animals, light or temperature may serve as the exciting agent for stimulation of the gonads. Moreover inhibition may occur in such systems, as is exemplified by the cessation of gonadotropic activity in malnutrition. The "dead-beat" character of the first category adjusts the secretory process directly to the end process, whereas the second and third categories permit the integration of stimuli so that the end process may be adjusted to a point appropriate for the activity of the whole organism.

For demonstrating hormonal effects, formalized procedures somewhat akin to Koch's postulates have been evolved. These may be described in the following manner. Removal of the organ suspected of producing a hormone must lead to a detectable deficit in the animal. This deficit, once recognized, must be remedied by replacing the secretion of the organ into the operated animal. The procedures utilized in this replacement therapy may vary widely, from transplanting the organ to a different region (thereby presumably eliminating neural effects) to the injection of the active principle prepared by extracting the organ. Once an effective replacement therapy has been found, the hormonal function of the organ may be regarded as proved. Further investigation is then directed toward the isolation, chemical identification, and synthesis of the active principle, and toward an elucidation of the physiological mechanisms that regulate the rate of secretion of the newly demonstrated hormone. These procedures, varied according to the needs of the particular situation, have been applied to all the hormones considered in the following sections.

The Testis

The testis, or male gonad, is a double organ containing tubules in which spermatozoa are generated, and intertubular or interstitial cells that elaborate the steroid substances constituting the male sex hormone. Castration, or removal of the testes, provokes in adults a prompt regression of the ducts and glands associated with the reproductive system. If castration precedes puberty, these structures never attain their adult size, and, in addition, various other events normally heralding maturity, such as change in timbre of the voice, growth of beard, and attainment of adult muscular proportions, do not occur. These defects in castrated animals and man can be repaired by the administration of an androgenic hormone from the testes, now chemically identified and named testosterone.

In addition to regulating the structures and functions mentioned above, testosterone exerts other effects upon the male animal. It regulates growth to some degree, causing a more rapid formation of protoplasm than occurs in its absence. Skeletal growth also is affected by the male hormone. The epiphyses of long bones remain open after castration and close rapidly after the administration of massive doses of testosterone. Thus testosterone will stimulate eunuchoid individuals to grow for a time, but the final stature will be limited by closure of the epiphyses, and, if the hormone is given in too large amounts at an early age, the final stature may be stunted. Androgenic hormone has also been implicated in the control of some of the skin glands and appendages. Aristotle recorded that eunuchs do not grow bald. It is now established that baldness results from an interplay of genetic and endocrine factors and that testosterone is a precipitating factor (Hamilton, 1942).

Various behavioral phenomena are related to the male sex hormone. Although copulatory ability is not destroyed completely by castration, it seems clear that sex drive and aggressiveness are partly regulated by the amount of circulating male hormone. These masculine attributes are precociously developed in boys who have secreting tumors of the testis. Similarly melancholia, frequently encountered late in life and associated with involution of the reproductive system, is alleviated by testosterone therapy. Indeed one of the major effects of androgens may be the feeling of well-being they induce. It is noteworthy in this connection that patients with interstitial cell tumors secreting fabulous amounts of hormone are usually detected by accident and have no complaint referable to their abnormal hormone conditions.

The testis is regulated by hormones arising in the anterior lobe of the pituitary gland. Hypophysectomy (removal of the pituitary gland) causes the testis to shrink. Furthermore the secondary sex characters and organs also atrophy unless testosterone or some other androgenic hormone is administered. Moore and Price (1932) described a reciprocal relation between the hormones of the testis and the pituitary gland. Injection of androgens into normal animals causes atrophy of the testis, but this atrophy can be prevented by simultaneous administration of pituitary extracts. There is thus a mutual balance between the testis and the pituitary gland. Pituitary extracts stimulate the testis, causing it to secrete testosterone, which in turn inhibits the further production of pituitary hormone.

This scheme of the endocrine interrelation of the testis and the pituitary gland is important historically because it provided a model for other interrelations. However, control of the testis is now known to be more complex. At least two pituitary hormones influence the testis. One stimulates the interstitial tissue to produce androgenic hormone, whereas the other causes activation of spermatogenesis.

The testis is constantly active in some species such as the rat and man, whereas in others it undergoes a seasonal cycle. Thus the ferret, the ground squirrel, and the deer have active spermatogenesis and enlarged accessory organs of reproduction only during the seasonal period of breeding. In these species the pituitary is responsive to some external influence, becoming activated at the appropriate time. The exciting stimulus seems to be light in the case of the ferret (Bissonnette, 1933), and heat in the ground squirrel; it has not been determined with certainty in deer.

The Ovary

Like the testis the ovary has the double function of producing female gametes and of secreting hormones that regulate the secondary sex apparatus such as the uterus, the vagina, and the mammary glands. However, whereas the testis produces only one known hormone, the ovary secretes at least two. Ovariectomy in adults causes prompt regression of the secondary sex structures; in young animals, these structures never attain their mature condition. Restoration of size and function can be partially accomplished by substances extracted from the Graafian follicle. There are many individual substances that exert this reparative effect upon the sex organs of ovariectomized rats; collectively they are called estrogens. Several such compounds have been isolated from ovaries, and some doubt exists as to whether the natural female sex hormone is a single substance or a group of steroids. These naturally occurring estrogens have been synthesized in chemical laboratories, and, in addition, several other compounds are known which are powerfully estrogenic but which do not exist normally in the mammalian body.

Administration of estrogen causes growth and proliferation of the uterus, the vagina, and other accessory sex organs, but its restorative effect is at best only partial. For the complete repair of the deficiencies induced by ovariectomy, a second ovarian hormone, progesterone, must also be administered. This second principle is produced by the corpus luteum and is peculiarly effective in producing the conditions in the genital apparatus characteristic of pregnancy. Indeed progesterone seems essential for pregnancy, since without it the normal segmentation of the egg and its subsequent implantation do not occur. Furthermore it is believed but not certainly established that deficiencies in progesterone arising after implantation cause abortion. The uncertainty on this point stems from the fact that the placenta produces progesterone, at least in some species, with the result that the ovary may be removed without interrupting the established pregnancy or destroying all sources of progesterone.

The principal events of the reproductive cycle can be adequately explained in terms of the ovarian hormones. In most animals the ovarian follicle containing the egg grows for a period during which the uterus, the vagina, and the mammary gland proliferate. The degree of stimulation of these organs corresponds closely to those obtained by the injection of estrogenic hormones into ovariectomized animals. At the end of this period the ovarian follicle ruptures, the egg is released into the uterine tubes, and the collapsed follicle becomes organized into a solid corpus luteum. This corpus luteum persists for a period during which the secondary sex apparatus undergoes further development similar to that induced experimentally by injections of estrogen and progesterone. The cycle is ordinarily divided, therefore, into two periods — a follicular phase corresponding to estrogenic stimulation, and a luteal phase characterized by the additional activity of progesterone. These phases can be greatly modified in different animals. In the rat, the mouse, and the hamster, the luteal phase is normally so short as to be practically nonexistent; a follicular phase and ovulation are succeeded without pause by another follicular phase. However, copulation induces the corpus luteum to persist so that a luteal phase is then interposed. In the rabbit the follicular phase occurs spontaneously, but ovulation does not

occur until stimulated by copulation. Once ovulation has been induced, the luteal phase follows spontaneously. The luteal phase is a period during which the uterus is prepared for implantation of the fertilized egg. If pregnancy ensues, the luteal phase is prolonged until the end of gestation; if not, a shorter pseudopregnant phase is succeeded by another follicular phase, and the cycle repeats itself. These basic phases of the cycle occur in all mammals. In the higher primates, including man, the stimulated uterine endometrium desquamates and bleeds in the menstrual process at the end of the luteal phase. In the lower mammals the endometrium atrophies at this time, but overt bleeding does not occur (cf. Allen, Danforth, and Doisy, 1939).

The reproductive cycle, basically controlled by the ovary, is subject to some influence by exterior factors. Exposure to continuous light induces a curious modification of the rat's cycle; follicles grow normally, but ovulation does not occur. Thus a condition similar to that normally occurring in the rabbit can be produced. Also, as in the rabbit, ovulation in such continuous-estrous rats can be induced by copulation (Dempsey and Searles, 1943). Other environmental effects are manifest in the seasonal reproductive rhythms of many wild animals. The ferret normally remains anestrous until spring, but it can be stimulated to estrus earlier if exposed to light. The ground squirrel also is inactive reproductively during the winter, but in this species the stimulating external factor appears to be the warmer temperature of spring.

The ovarian hormones profoundly modify female sex behavior. In rodents estrual activity does not occur after ovariectomy. Mating behavior can be induced in many species by massive dosages of estrogen, but the estrus so invoked is not entirely normal, nor is the treatment invariably successful. A course of treatment involving small amounts of estrogen followed by progesterone is much more efficacious in rodents such as the rat and guinea pig, leading, in all the animals treated, to estrus indistinguishable from that of normal animals. In the higher primates, including man, sexual behavior is more complex and is not abolished by deprivation of the sex hormones. However, even in man the nervous system is not entirely unaffected by hormones, as is attested by the fact that involutional melancholia frequently is associated with the menopause and is alleviated by the administration of estrogens.

The Adrenal Cortex

The outer portion of the adrenal gland, like the gonads, develops from the embryonic genital ridge and secretes hormones that are steroidal in nature. For many years little was known concerning these hormones other than that they were essential for life, since adrenalectomized animals invariably succumbed. With the development of potent extracts of the adrenal cortex, great progress has been made in understanding the functions of these glands. However, the topic is far from exhausted and represents one of the most active fields in endocrinology today.

As mentioned above, adrenalectomy is invariably fatal. Different species vary in the rapidity with which death ensues. The operation is rapidly fatal in the guinea pig, but the rat and dog survive for considerable periods. Gradually they lose appetite, become listless and weak, the circulation becomes sluggish, and the animal eventually succumbs. These symptoms seem to reflect profound changes that overtake the metabolism of two groups of substances, electrolytes and carbohydrates. The adrenalectomized animal is unable to conserve sodium; this element is lost in great quantity through the kidney, taking with it chloride and water, with the result that the animal becomes excessively dehydrated and has thick, viscous blood, the potassium concentration of which is abnormally high. The disturbed sodium-potassium balance accounts for the extreme lassitude and lack of irritability, and the hemal concentration accounts for the final circulatory failure. These deficiencies can be cured rapidly and dramatically by administering an extract of the gland — a dog in complete collapse will recover and evince an interest in food, water, and his surroundings within minutes following an injection of a potent extract. Moreover, to indicate that these deficiencies are caused primarily by a loss of sodium chloride, the life of adrenalectomized dogs and rats can be prolonged almost indefinitely by feeding them large quantities of salt. This added salt substitutes for that lost, and, although the ability of the kidney to conserve sodium is not restored, the concentration of the element in the tissue fluids is maintained above disastrous levels.

In addition to the effect on electrolyte balance, adrenalectomy also disturbs the metabolic machinery that regulates carbohydrates. After adrenalectomy the blood sugar falls and the glycogen stores in liver and muscle are depleted. The ability of the animal to convert protein to carbohydrate is impaired. This conversion, called gluconeogenesis, may be restored to normal or supernormal values by injections of adrenal cortical extract. However, the effect is separate from the electrolyte phenomenon, for the carbohydrate metabolism is not repaired in animals fed excess salt. Moreover it will be shown below that two different hormones from the adrenal cortex control these two phenomena.

Clinical observations provide evidence of the adrenal origin of a third group of factors, the male and female sex hormones. The so-called 17-ketosteroid substances can be isolated from the urine of both men and women. After gonadectomy, the quantity of excreted 17-ketosteroids declines, but only by about one-third. Moreover, after destruction of the adrenal cortex, as in Addison's disease, the 17-ketosteroids are reduced more severely than by gonadectomy. The current interpretation, therefore, is that about one-third of the urinary 17-ketosteroids is gonadal in origin and that the remainder arises in the adrenal cortex. This interpretation fits well with the facts that adrenal hyperplasia in women is frequently attended by masculinizing symptoms and by increased excretion of urinary ketosteroids, and that the sexual potency of men is depressed more severely by destruction of the adrenal than by castration. Similarly there are rare instances in which adrenal tumors in men have been associated with symptoms of feminization and with increased urinary excretion of estrogens.

The steroids that can be isolated from the adrenal cortex have received exhaustive chemical study. More than a score of separate compounds have been extracted and purified, and their formulas determined. Many of these have no known biological activity. The remainder fall into three general groups. The members of the first group contain oxygen attached to the eleventh carbon atom of the steroid nucleus. These compounds are therefore called 11-oxygenated steroids. The type compound of this group is named corticosterone (or 11-hydroxycorticosterone). The substances of this group regulate carbohydrate metabolism. The second group consists of several substances that lack an oxygen atom at the eleventh carbon; the type compound is therefore called desoxycorticosterone. These are the substances that influence sodium retention. The third group consists of steroids, the individual members of which have biological activity identical with those of the androgenic and estrogenic hormones of the testis and ovary.

The first two factors, the salt-conserving and the carbohydrate-regulating, apparently are elaborated in separate regions of the adrenal gland and are secreted in response to physiologically distinct stimuli. Recent work has suggested that the desoxycorticosterone-like compounds are manufactured in the outermost layer of the adrenal cortex, the glomerulosa, and that the corticosterone-like or carbohydrate-regulating factors occur in an intermediate region, the fasciculata. Moreover hypophysectomy destroys the ability of the adrenal gland to manufacture the

sugar-regulating principles but does not abolish the salt-conserving power of the kidney. Conversely injections of pituitary adrenotrophic hormone greatly stimulate the production of the sugar-regulating factor but do not markedly alter the electrolyte balance. It appears from these facts that the fasciculata, which secretes corticosterone, does so only under the stimulus of the pituitary gland, whereas the glomerulosa secretes desoxycorticosterone but is regulated by nonpituitary factors. The nature of these nonpituitary mechanisms regulating the secretion of desoxycorticosterone can only be conjectured at present. It seems likely that the adrenal glomerulosa responds to changes in the electrolytic balance of the body fluids, but the details of this mechanism are unknown. Little or nothing is known about the site of origin or the physiological regulation of the androgenic and estrogenic steroids of the adrenal cortex.

More is known about the control of the sugar-regulating factors. When animals are subjected to noxious stimuli of many different kinds, the adrenal cortex hypertrophies, and the lipids of the zona fasciculata undergo changes. Exposure to cold, traumatic injury, the administration of toxic drugs, and many other stimuli are equally effective. Such stimuli act through the anterior pituitary gland, because the adrenal changes do not occur in hypophysectomized animals. The details of the homeostatic mechanism that activates the adrenal have not been satisfactorily worked out, but, since adrenal stimulation occurs in animals in which all known nervous pathways to the pituitary have been severed, it seems likely that the noxious stimulus is transmitted to the pituitary by a humoral mechanism. A similar activation of the adrenal cortex occurs in dietary deficiencies of various vitamins, particularly in some of the B group.

The adrenal stimulation invoked in these several conditions has far-reaching physiological consequences. Glycogenesis is accelerated, thus providing a readily available supply of energy. Marked and rapid changes occur in the lymphatic tissues; the lymphocytes normally contained in the blood, the lymph nodes, and the thymus gland are rapidly destroyed, and their contents are poured into the blood stream. It has recently been shown that the cytoplasm of lymphocytes contains globulins identical with those bearing the immune bodies in the blood plasma. Consequently this lysis of lymphocytes increases the concentration of the blood globulins and provides large amounts of free antibodies. The homeostatic purpose of this reaction is obviously directed against the antigenic materials that may accompany or follow noxious situations.

The Pancreas (Islands of Langerhans)

The story of the discovery of insulin is now one of the classics of the modern era of medicine. After removal of the pancreas the blood sugar rises in concentration and glucose appears in the urine in a fashion characteristic of the human disease, diabetes mellitus. This effect on carbohydrate metabolism is independent of the digestive functions of the pancreas, because ligation of the pancreatic duct, which prevents the pancreatic secretions from reaching the digestive tract, does not affect the blood sugar concentration. On the other hand, extracts of the islet tissue of the pancreas contain a principle, named insulin, which rapidly lowers the blood sugar in diabetes, whether the disease is induced experimentally in animals or occurs adventitiously in man.

Deprivation of insulin does not seem to interfere with the formation of sugar from dietary sources. That is to say, gluconeogenesis, which is impaired after adrenalectomy, proceeds without hindrance after pancreatectomy. On the other hand, some of the pathways by which sugar is ordinarily metabolized are blocked in diabetes. Normally an excess of sugar is removed from the blood and stored in the liver. This does not occur in diabetes: the blood sugar rises because it cannot be reduced by the normal storage mechanism. However, some of the mechanisms utilizing sugar proceed apace after pancreatectomy. The brain continues to metabolize carbohydrate, and so do other organs. Despite these unaffected avenues, there is evidence that the overall utilization of carbohydrate suffers from an embarrassment of riches because combustion is incomplete, ending in acetone and other products rather than proceeding all the way to carbon dioxide and water.

The biochemical stages and intermediary products of carbohydrate metabolism have been studied intensively since 1930. The combustion of hexose sugars is now thought to proceed stepwise, each step being regulated by an enzymatic mechanism. Among these steps a process by which the sugar or intermediary product reacts with phosphoric acid under the influence of a phosphorylating enzyme is now regarded as an important mechanism for the ultimate liberation of free energy in the metabolic process. Hexokinase, one of the phosphorylating enzymes, causes hexose sugar and phosphoric acid to react, forming a hexose phosphate. This enzyme is inhibited by an anterior pituitary extract and reactivated by insulin, according to Price, Cori, and Colowick (1945). The net effect of insulin deprivation, therefore, is to block phosphorylation of glucose and to prevent any metabolism, such as glycogenesis, in which this process is a necessary antecedent. These considerations accord well with the failure of glycogen storage in diabetes. If verifiable, these results are a milestone in endocrinology, for they represent the first instance in which an enzymatic process has been found to be regulated by hormones.

Recently an experimental observation has opened an avenue into the problem of the mode of formation of insulin. Injections of alloxan cause a transient hypoglycemia, followed by a permanent hyperglycemia and glycosuria characteristic of diabetes. In animals in which diabetes has been so induced, some of the cells of the islands of Langerhans become necrotic and disappear. It appears, therefore, that alloxan has a marked and selective toxicity for the cells that manufacture insulin. Further work is necessary, but it is reasonable to assume that the selectivity of alloxan's action upon these cells has some relation to the metabolic machinery for elaborating the hormone. It may be possible to study the cellular processes involved in insulin synthesis.

The Parathyroid Glands

Parathyroidectomy causes a state of hyperirritability characterized by spasms of contraction of the skeletal muscles, or tetany. Concomitantly, the blood calcium concentration is decreased. Since calcium is required in vitro for normal contractility, the tetany of parathyroidectomy has an adequate explanation. This tetany may be alleviated or prevented by measures designed to raise the concentration of circulating calcium, e.g. by injection of calcium lactate, by administration of vitamin D, or by a replacement therapy utilizing an extract of the parathyroid gland. The active principle in such extracts has been named parathormone. The glands seem independent of the anterior pituitary, since no remarkable changes occur after either hypophysectomy or pituitary replacement therapy. The only clue as to the control of the glands comes from situations involving serious loss of calcium from the body. Thus, in pregnancy and lactation, when calcium is rapidly withdrawn from the maternal circulation, the parathyroid glands hypertrophy. Similarly diets deficient in vitamin D cause parathyroid enlargement, because in rickets calcium is not absorbed properly through the intestine, and consequently the blood level of this ion is low. A similarly depressed blood calcium occurs in some kinds of kidney disease, caused in this instance by an excessive excretion of calcium. In such diseases, sometimes called renal rickets, the parathyroid enlarges. It appears, therefore, that the parathyroid is regulated by a homeostatic

mechanism, but the details of this process are obscure.

The Thyroid Gland

The basic facts of thyroid physiology were derived from clinical observations before physiological methods for animal experiments were available. In 1874 Gull described a clinical syndrome consisting of loss of hair, thickening and dryness of the skin, and loss of physical and mental vigor. He associated these symptoms with atrophy of the thyroid gland. In 1882 the Reverdin brothers observed that these symptoms followed a total thyroidectomy undertaken for the cure of goiter, and in 1883 this was repeated and confirmed by Theodore Kocher. During the years 1891 to 1893 a number of clinicians showed that thyroid substance, whether fresh, dried, cooked, or extracted, was remarkably effective in curing the symptoms of Gull's disease. It was not until 1895 that Magnus-Levy's calorimeter was applied to the study of the thyroid. Following his demonstration that in Gull's disease the heat production was depressed by as much as 40 per cent, the instrument was used to study thyroidectomized animals. It was found that a decrease in metabolic rate was characteristic of thyroid deprivation and that administration of thyroid substance raised the metabolic rate to normal or above. These observations provided a method for detecting and understanding another clinical syndrome, hyperthyroidism or Graves' disease (cf. Marine, 1935).

The effectiveness of thyroid substance in alleviating hypothyroidism prompted an intensive search for the active principle. Baumann showed that iodine in organic combination was a normal constituent of the gland, and Ostwald identified this element in the globulin fraction of the thyroid colloid. Subsequently Kendall isolated a crystalline substance, thyroxine, which exhibited the pharmacologic effects of dried thyroid, and in 1926 Harrington announced its structural formula. Thyroxine may be synthesized by iodination and oxidation of tyrosine. In the thyroid it apparently exists as part of a larger globulin molecule, and in the blood stream it is associated with one of the fractions of the plasma proteins. For these reasons thyroxine is now regarded as the active prosthetic part of the larger protein molecule comprising the natural hormone.

The mechanism regulating the rate of secretion of the thyroid hormone has received a considerable amount of attention, since it is evident that regulatory factors are disturbed in the principal thyroid diseases, hypo- and hyperthyroidism. After hypophysectomy the thyroid atrophies and the cells appear histologically to be inactive; conversely after injection of pituitary extracts the gland enlarges and the tissue becomes active. Thyrotropin, a specific fraction from the pituitary, exhibits this stimulating effect upon the thyroid. Thyroid atrophy can also be produced by the administration of large quantities of thyroid hormone, which produces an experimental state of hyperthyroidism. From these facts it can be stated that thyroid activity is poised at a point determined by the balance between opposing forces. Pituitary thyrotropin stimulates the thyroid gland, and the thyroid hormone inhibits the further production of thyrotropin. The normal rate of secretion represents the point at which these opposing actions balance.

For a long time there has been a body of clinical impressions that this balance point might be shifted by various ecological forces. Hyperthyroidism tends to occur in excitable individuals and frequently occurs soon after an emotional crisis. The geographical distribution of hyperthyroidism strongly suggests an influence of climate, since it is a rare disease in the tropics, is more frequent in the cooler northern latitudes, and is especially prevalent in areas that have great variations in temperature. Europeans and Americans who emigrate into tropical countries frequently become lethargic and experience a mild depression of the basal metabolic rate. A speculative interpretation of these facts is that the thyroid gland becomes inactive. It has also been suggested that breeds of animals may differ in the rate of activity of the thyroid gland — the Boston terrier, for example, is regarded as a hyperthyroid breed, whereas in the St. Bernard the thyroid seems inactive.

Some of these speculative impressions have been put to physiological test. Employing a method designed to determine the rate of secretion of the thyroid hormone, Dempsey and Astwood (1943) found that rats maintained in cold temperatures secreted about twice as much hormone as did those kept at normal room temperatures. Correspondingly, maintenance in hot rooms more than halved the rate of secretion. Using a similar technique, Mixner, Reinecke, and Turner (1944) found the rate of secretion much higher in the breeds of chickens used for meat production than in the lighter strains bred for a high rate of egg production.

The discovery of the so-called "antithyroid" compounds has opened a new era in thyroid physiology. Richter and Clisby (1941) noted that thiourea caused hypertrophy of the thyroid gland. Soon thereafter MacKenzie and MacKenzie (1943) and Astwood et al. (1943) published their now classical reports in which were established the following facts: (1) several substances related to thiourea, including sulfaguanidine and thiouracil, induced rapid and extreme hyperplasia of the thyroid gland; (2) the administration of these compounds caused a decreased metabolic rate, despite the hyperactive appearance of the gland; (3) the antithyroid drugs did not interfere with the calorigenic effect of thyroid hormone when administered experimentally; (4) thyroid hormone administered together with the antithyroid drug prevented or abolished the hyperplasia of the thyroid; and (5) the drugs did not cause thyroid hyperplasia in hypophysectomized animals. From these facts it can be concluded that the antithyroid drugs prevent the synthesis of thyroid hormone in the gland and thus cause a pharmacological thyroidectomy. This conclusion was subsequently verified by demonstrating that the iodine content of the thyroid fell almost to the vanishing point during antithyroid medication. Further evidence comes also from the clinical demonstration that thiouracil and other antithyroid drugs lower the metabolic rate in man. The high rates characteristic of hyperthyroidism may be reduced to normal by appropriate dosage, or normal values may be reduced to myxedamatous levels.

The discovery that synthesis of thyroid hormone can be blocked led to an intensive search for the mode of action of the antithyroid compounds. That the blocked synthetic mechanism somehow involves the metabolism of iodine seems evident from the fact that the iodine stores of the gland are depleted by administering the drugs. Further evidence comes from experiments in which radioactive iodine is used as a tracer substance. Normally the thyroid gland takes up nearly all of a tracer dose of iodine and rapidly converts it into an organically bound compound. After thiouracil, however, any iodine taken up by the thyroid remains there as inorganic iodide. It would seem, therefore, that the antithyroid compounds prevent the iodination of organic compounds.

A word is necessary at this point about the uptake and storage of inorganic iodide. The thyroid gland can accumulate iodide so that its concentration within the gland is many times that of the blood plasma. This function is analogous to the well-known distribution of potassium, which is much more highly concentrated inside cells than in the extracellular fluids. This concentration of inorganic iodide in an "iodide compartment" is not abolished by antithyroid drugs; indeed, the iodide compartment seems to be enlarged during the hyperplastic increase in size of the thyroid brought about by thiouracil. On the other hand, the ability of the thyroid to concentrate iodide can be abolished by other means. The thiocyanate ion abolishes the iodide compartment and destroys the thyroid's ability to maintain a concentration higher than that in the blood stream. Thus the uptake of iodine into the thyroid gland is accomplished by two mechanisms. The first concentrates the available iodide ion and is destroyed by thiocyanate. The second converts the inorganic iodide to an organically bound compound and is destroyed by thiouracil and other antithyroid compounds (cf. Astwood, 1945).

The question next arises as to how the antithyroid drugs prevent the iodination of organic compounds. It was pointed out earlier that thyroxine, the active prosthetic part of the thyroid hormone, is a derivative of the amino acid tyrosine. Proteins containing tyrosine residues are easily iodinated merely by adding iodine in alkaline solution. Consequently, if the iodide normally taken into the thyroid were reduced, the iodine so formed would iodinate the tyrosine radicles of the thyroid proteins. Of the possible mechanisms to bring about this reduction of iodide, the enzyme peroxidase is a prominent contender. Peroxidase is known to catalyze the reduction of iodide to iodine, and peroxidase is inhibited by antithyroid drugs (Sumner and Somers, 1947). Furthermore peroxidase has been demonstrated histochemically in the thyroid cells (Dempsey, 1944; De Robertis and Grasso, 1946). At the present writing, therefore, the most likely mode of action of the antithyroid drugs is that they inhibit peroxidase or some similar enzyme that catalyzes the iodination reaction in the thyroid gland.

The Anterior Pituitary Gland

The anterior pituitary gland produces several principles which act upon the so-called "target glands" discussed above. A close relation between the pituitary body and these other endocrine glands has been suspected for many years by clinicians and pathologists, since tumors and other lesions of the anterior pituitary gland are followed by disturbances of the gonads and of the thyroid and adrenal glands. However, accurate and detailed knowledge of the pituitary relations dates from 1930 when Smith devised a procedure for surgically removing the pituitary body in a small experimental animal, the rat.

Hypophysectomy in growing animals causes a sudden and complete cessation of growth. The animal does not gain further weight, nor does its skeleton enlarge. If the operation is performed before puberty, the gonads remain infantile in size, and, since the accessory sex structures do not enlarge, the endocrine functions of the gonads also are impaired. If adult animals are hypophysectomized, the gonads and secondary sex apparatus promptly atrophy to a condition closely resembling that before puberty. Lactation, if occurring, stops immediately after the operation. The thyroid shrinks in size, the follicular cells become flattened, and the basal metabolic rate falls. The adrenal cortex atrophies, particularly in the zona fasciculata. The carbohydrate regulation of hypophysectomized animals is impaired to approximately the same degree as after adrenalectomy, but the electrolyte balance is relatively unimpaired.

The deficiencies in hypophysectomized animals are repaired by replacement therapy. Smith and Engle (1927) showed that subcutaneous implantation of pituitary material restored the size and function of the target glands. Following this classical study, an enormous amount of work has been devoted to isolating and purifying the hormones from the anterior pituitary gland. At the present writing at least six fractions have been isolated from the gland. These are the growth hormone, the thyrotropic hormone, and two gonadotropic hormones, comprising the follicle-stimulating hormone and the luteinizing hormone. The latter is sometimes called the interstitial-cell stimulating hormone because of its effect on the testis (cf. van Dyke et al., 1943). The last two of these six fractions are the lactogenic hormone and adrenotropin.

Several criteria of purity have been applied to these fractions. All have been shown to be biologically pure; that is to say, when injected into hypophysectomized test animals they stimulate the appropriate end response and do not affect detectably the other end effects. For example, growth hormone causes an increase in weight of hypophysectomized rats, but it does not affect the thyroid, adrenal, gonad, or mammary glands. Three physicochemical criteria of purity have also been applied to the protein hormones of the pituitary gland. These are the rate of sedimentation in the ultracentrifuge, the rate of migration in the electrophoretic field, and the solubility properties. Five of the six fractions mentioned above have been prepared in a chemically pure form as tested by one or all of these procedures; one, the follicle-stimulating hormone, satisfies the biological criterion but has not yet been purified chemically.

The physiological regulation of the pituitary hormones is complex. The injection of adrenal cortical extract causes the adrenal cortex to shrink, and this atrophy may be prevented by simultaneously administering pituitary adrenotropin. Apparently, therefore, adrenotropin stimulates the production of adrenal cortical hormone, which in turn inhibits further adrenotropin secretion, and the two hormones constitute a balanced, self-regulating system. A similar balance characterizes thyrotropin and the thyroid hormone. Likewise estrogen injections cause atresia of growing ovarian follicles, progesterone inhibits the production of luteinizing hormone, and testosterone causes testicular atrophy. These facts indicate a series of mechanisms whereby the pituitary secretions are regulated at values just adequate to provide the normal amount of activity on the part of the gonads and of the thyroid and adrenal glands. Such regulation is unknown, however, for the growth and lactogenic hormones. Moreover the situation is further complicated by the effects of varied environmental situations, a topic discussed further in the following section on endocrine balance.

Endocrine Balance

The data in the preceding sections have been presented for the most part in terms of the simple end-organ responses to the various hormones. A multiplicity of such responses has been described, together with a few words discussing the physiological mechanisms regulating the active concentrations of the various factors. The question arises as to whether each of these endocrine factors is a physiologically independent unit capable of variations without affecting the activity of the other factors, or whether some or all exhibit physiological linkages such that the varying of one item leads to a corresponding readjustment of others until the entire constellation achieves a new quantitative interrelation.

At this point a related topic should be introduced. For many years endocrinologists have debated the question of the "master" hormone of the pituitary gland. Cytologically, the pituitary contains two principal types of secreting cells, the acidophiles and basophiles. It has been suggested, therefore, that only two hormones, one from each type of cell, should be elaborated by the gland. This point of view has received some support from clinical observations, since in acromegaly, a type of pituitary disease involving the acidophiles, symptoms are present that involve the growth and thyrotropic hormones, whereas in Cushing's disease, a type of disorder associated with adenomas of the basophiles, there is another symptom complex involving chiefly adrenotropin. Nevertheless the two types are not clearly divided, because sexual failures presumably caused by gonadotropin deficiencies are common in both.

The principal evidence refuting the argument for the "master" hormone of the pituitary has been the demonstration that the individual pituitary fractions can be obtained in chemically pure form. Neverthe-

less such chemical data do not conclusively prove the point, because, conceivably, a large molecule with several prosthetic parts could be disintegrated and separated into several active fractions by chemical treatment. However, Dempsey and Searles (1943), using environmental stimuli as a means of altering the rate of secretion of the various pituitary factors, showed that luteinizing hormone, adrenotropin, and thyrotropin could vary independently, each from the others. The discovery that thiouracil, by suppressing the inhibition normally exerted by thyroid hormone, caused a great increase in the production of thyrotropin also allows observations on the physiological independence of hormones. Since in rats the reproductive cycle, pregnancy, and lactation continue normally after antithyroid treatment, it seems unlikely that the gonadotropic hormones or lactogen are seriously affected. Furthermore the adrenal may be atrophic, normal, or hypertrophic in rats treated with thiouracil, depending upon the concurrent stimuli to which the animals are exposed. These experiments indicate that the pituitary can secrete several qualitatively different factors at quantitatively independent rates.

Although considerable autonomy is possible for the individual factors, the above considerations do not imply the absence of linked readjustments of multiple endocrine factors. In preceding sections the responses to environmental and nutritional stimuli, such as light, cold, heat, and vitamin deficiencies, have been noted. As an example, after exposure to cold the adrenal cortex enlarges and the thyroid becomes more active. These hyperactive glands are still subject to their normal regulatory mechanisms, for injection of adrenal cortical extract or thyroid hormone reduces the responses of the respective glands. Similar reasoning applies to the effect of heat on the thyroid gland. In this case the new setting is achieved at a point corresponding to lessened activity. It appears, therefore, that environmental stimuli set the regulatory mechanisms of one or several of the factors at new points, corresponding individually to increased or decreased activity of the individual glands.

From the point of view of homeostasis these responses to exteroceptive stimuli represent changes in endocrine balance directed toward nullifying the external forces. Thus thyroid and adrenal activity induced by cold results in an increased metabolic rate and increased utilization of carbohydrate. This augmented metabolism provides more heat and allows the animal's body temperature to be held constant despite the cold. These environmentally induced fluctuations in endocrine activity indicate that endocrine balance is not a static, specific endocrine interrelation but that it is a flexible, dynamic state, changing and shifting constantly according to the particular constellation of stimuli operative at any instant.

For a fuller understanding of the homeostatic adjustments of the endocrine glands, there is great need of information about the concentration of the various hormones in the blood stream. It seems clear that some environmental stimuli cause increased secretion and that other stimuli suppress the production of hormones. It is not clear, however, whether the increased or decreased rate of secretion corresponds to an elevated or depressed concentration of hormones in the blood stream. Conceivably an increased secretion would be necessary to hold a constant blood concentration if the hormone were fixed and inactivated by the end organ. It is also conceivable that the metabolic process regulated by the hormone might respond to an altered concentration without the hormone's being used up in the process. In the latter type of system the secretory rate might well be proportional to the blood concentration. New and sensitive analytical methods need to be developed to answer these questions about the nature of the homeostatic mechanisms.

THE AUTONOMIC NERVOUS SYSTEM

That the motor activities of the nervous system might be divided into a voluntary and an involuntary part was appreciated many years ago by Bichat (1801), who also used as alternate terms the "animal" and "vegetative" divisions of the nervous system. During the nineteenth century came gradual clarification of the anatomical relations of what now is described as the paravertebral chain of ganglia and their connections. Toward the end of the century it was appreciated that the thoracolumbar outflow from the spinal cord was gathered into a great system of ganglia and fibers supplying smooth and cardiac muscle and glands. Langley recognized that this system formed one part of the involuntary or autonomic system and designated it the sympathetic. He also recognized a second part, which he called the parasympathetic, as composed of a craniobulbar and a sacral division. His usage has been widely adopted. (For a schematic diagram of the autonomic system, see Chapter 14.)

Langley defined the autonomic nervous system as the "nerve cells and nerve fibers, by means of which efferent impulses pass to tissues other than multi-nuclear striated muscle." This definition restricts the autonomic to a peripheral motor system, no reference being made to its ramifications in the brain and spinal cord nor to the afferent connections of these ramifications. This restriction seems untenable today, since stimulation and ablation experiments have shown that autonomic regulations are carried on within the central nervous system at all levels, including the cerebral cortex itself. Moreover the central ramifications of the somatic and autonomic functions are inextricably intermingled, both anatomically and physiologically. It seems necessary, therefore, to extend the definition to include the central ramifications and their afferent connections as well (Fulton, 1938).

With these definitions in mind it is possible to consider the autonomic system in the following ways. The efferent fibers extend to and regulate the activities of smooth and cardiac muscle and glands. The activities of these elements, which make up components of major physiological systems of the body, are coordinated in synaptic regions lying either in peripheral ganglia or in the central nervous system. The autonomic system may be activated or inhibited through its afferent supply from receptor organs (e.g. from painful stimuli) or from the higher centers of the brain (e.g. during rage). Since the efferent fibers establish connections with individual or local effector organs, and since many of these effector organs respond collectively in constellations of activity, the problem arises as to the kind and degree of integration exhibited in the various regions of the system.

The Sympathetic System

The sympathetic division of the autonomic system seems admirably designed to discharge as a unit. Stimulation of any of the rami communicantes, which constitute the spinal outflow, results in activity widely distributed in the system. In other words it appears that the preganglionic fibers of the rami synapse extensively at the paravertebral ganglia so that many of the postganglionic fibers are activated by a relatively small number of preganglionic afferents. The physiological consequences of this arrangement are that activity does not remain localized within the sympathetic system but spreads to all parts of it. In consequence, activity in the sympathetic system results simultaneously in dilatation of the pupil, increase in heart rate and rise in blood pressure, rerouting of the circulating blood by dilatation of the vessels in striated muscle and constriction of those in the skin and elsewhere, inhibition of peristaltic movements in the gastrointestinal tract, and so forth.

Inspection of this list of effects of sympathetic activity immediately brings to mind the fact that adrenalin, the hormone secreted by the adrenal medulla, exerts similar actions. Furthermore the adrenal medulla receives sympathetic fibers and is activated by sympathetic stimulation. Consequently the effector organs of the sympathetic system may be acted upon either by the nerve impulses delivered by the sympathetic fibers, or by circulating adrenalin, or by both. In other words the adaptive nerve impulses are reinforced by adrenalin.

Not only are the sympathetic activities reinforced by the secretion of adrenalin, but the effector impulses of many of the sympathetic fibers are mediated by the local production of an adrenalinlike compound. Upon stimulation of a sympathetic nerve this adrenergic substance is produced by the nerve's terminal ramifications and diffuses into the effector organ where it exerts its stimulating or inhibiting effect. Thus a chemical stage is interposed between the nerve impulse and the effector action, and the activity induced by nervous stimulation is said to be mediated by the chemical agent. Such agents are collectively known as neurohumors. Sympathetic activity, therefore, is mediated by an adrenalinlike chemical compound produced locally at the nerve endings or secreted by the adrenal medulla and carried to the effector organ by the circulation. Most of the sympathetic postganglionic fibers are adrenergic; a few, notably those supplying the sweat glands, produce acetylcholine as their neurohumor and are therefore cholinergic. The preganglionic fibers also secrete acetylcholine at their synapses in the ganglia.

The constellation of effects called forth by sympathetic stimulation or by adrenalin injection also brings to mind another correlation. The physiological effects of such stimulation are similar to those brought about during strong emotional states such as fear or rage (see Chapter 14). This similarity was recognized by Cannon, who demonstrated the essential identity between the physiological responses of strong emotional states and those of sympathetic stimulation. It appears that the autonomic nervous system is the mechanism by which many of the bodily manifestations of emotion are effected. Cannon regarded these physiological effects as preparatory for flight or combat and described them collectively as emergency functions.

The Parasympathetic System

The parasympathetic division of the autonomic nervous system is sharply contrasted with the sympathetic division in a number of ways. The parasympathetic outflow is restricted to the cranial and sacral regions of the neuraxis, whereas the sympathetic outflow is located in the thoracic and lumbar segments. The peripheral ganglia are located near the end organ so that the preganglionic fibers are long and the postganglionic fibers are short. The opposite arrangement characterizes the sympathetic system. Moreover the extensive interconnections of the paravertebral ganglia have no counterpart in the parasympathetic division, so that activation of one parasympathetic end organ does not necessitate simultaneous activation of others, as is the case with sympathetic activity.

In general, parasympathetic fibers reach the same end organs that are innervated by the sympathetic. Thus with few exceptions the involuntary muscle and glands of the body have a double innervation. The effects of activity of these two nerve supplies are opposite in direction, so that the organs are described as receiving reciprocal innervations. For example, stimulation of the sympathetic nerves accelerates the heart, whereas stimulation of the vagus (parasympathetic) slows it. Similarly the intestine is stimulated by the parasympathetic and inhibited by the sympathetic. Many other examples are known in which two divisions of the autonomic system act in opposite directions.

The reciprocal control of the involuntary activities introduces a new factor into the homeostatic mechanisms. This factor concerns the rapidity and accuracy with which the homeostatic adjustments follow disturbing stimuli. A mechanical analogy springs to mind to illustrate the nature of this mechanism. A stone resting on the ground is immobile, yet it may easily be moved by an applied force. If this stone is now anchored between two fixed posts by springs that are stretched equally in opposite directions, the stone will still be motionless; but it will now require a stronger force to move it, and it will return to its original place when the force is removed. Similarly autonomic activities are disturbed less drastically and recover to their original level more quickly when innervated by the "push-pull" reciprocal mechanism than when receiving a single nerve supply or none at all.

Another aspect of the reciprocal innervation displayed by the autonomic system is that some measure of local autonomy is achieved. The sympathetic effects are collectively mobilized as a unit, whereas the parasympathetic functions may be activated selectively. A means is thereby provided to permit local readjustments. For example, strong emotion increases sympathetic tone and therefore leads to all the sympathetic responses — increased blood pressure and heart rate, piloerection, sweating, inhibition of peristalsis, dilation of the iris, etc. Nevertheless, if a strong light is shown to an enraged man, the previously dilated pupil will constrict because of the parasympathetic light reflex. The selective nature of the parasympathetic elements, when coupled reciprocally with the sympathetic activities, permits a certain amount of individual correction and readjustment of the various components of autonomic responses.

The discrete nature of the parasympathetic activities is further exemplified by the nature of the principal neurohumor of this system. Acetylcholine is produced at the endings of both the pre- and postganglionic parasympathetic neurons. This agent is rapidly destroyed in the blood and tissues by an enzyme, cholinesterase. In consequence the neurohumor is destroyed before reaching points distant from its origin and cannot normally reinforce nervous activity at distant regions, as can adrenalin.

The relation of the posterior lobe of the pituitary gland to the autonomic nervous system requires special consideration. Embryologically the posterior lobe is derived from neural tissue. It remains attached to the brain by the pituitary stalk throughout life. A considerable number of nerve fibers arise in the supraoptic, periventricular and other hypothalamic nuclei and course through the stalk to end in the posterior lobe of the pituitary gland. The neural supply to the gland comes, therefore, from an autonomic center. There is an increasing tendency to classify this hypothalamico-hypophyseal system as part of the parasympathetic system and to regard it as part of the cranial outflow. Regardless of this question, substances are formed in the posterior lobe that inhibit the production of urine (antidiuretic substance), cause uterine contraction (oxytocic principle), and raise the blood pressure (vasopressor principle). Since these fractions act upon smooth muscle and the kidney tubules, they appear to be autonomic neurohumors analagous to adrenalin and acetylcholine.

The physiological mechanisms involved in the maintenance of water balance by the antidiuretic hormone of the pituitary gland have been investigated extensively by Fisher, Ingram, and Ranson (1938). Destruction of the hypothalamic nuclei, of the nerve tract anywhere along its course, or of the posterior lobe of the hypophysis causes a condition known as diabetes insipidus, characterized by the production of excessive amounts of dilute urine. This condition may be corrected by extracts of the posterior lobe. Furthermore destruction of the pituitary stalk leads to a profound loss of antidiuretic substance from the neural lobe of

the hypophysis. These observations are in accord with Verney's hypothesis which states that the excretion of water is regulated by a mechanism that is partly neural and partly endocrine. The neural portion resides in the hypothalamus and is activated by excessive concentration of some element of the blood, and the endocrine factor arises in the posterior pituitary gland and acts upon the kidney tubules to increase the reabsorption of water from the glomerular filtrate.

Little is known concerning the physiological regulation of the other neural lobe principles. Some observations indicate that parturition is difficult or abnormal after destruction of the hypothalamico-hypophyseal system, but the data are fragmentary and insufficient for final conclusions.

Central Representation of the Autonomic System

The autonomic outflow from the spinal cord arises in a column of nuclei lying intermediate in position between the anterior and posterior horns. Rostrally, in the brain stem, this column continues forward as the gray substance surrounding the central canal and ventricles to end finally in an enlargement, the hypothalamus. Degeneration and ablation experiments show that an extensive system of short neurons interconnect to form pathways up and down this column. Thus, although no long ascending or descending fiber tracts serve the autonomic system, its activities are mediated by multiple relays of elements. The location of this autonomic column has been determined largely from neuroanatomical studies, but significant information has also been obtained from autopsies of patients who exhibited autonomic disturbances and from physiological observations during localized stimulation of the brain stem (cf. Chapter 14).

Although the hypothalamus has been extensively studied for many years, its small size, anatomical location, and relation to the pituitary gland on the one hand, and to the higher neural centers on the other, have rendered understanding difficult. Although considerable progress has been achieved, many uncertainties and mysteries still surround the subject, and only a partial account of hypothalamic physiology can yet be attempted.

Stimulation and ablation experiments have been undertaken systematically in the cat's hypothalamus by Ranson and his collaborators (Ranson and Magoun, 1939). By means of the stereotaxic instrument designed by Clarke and Horsley, it has been possible to place small electrodes into predetermined regions of the hypothalamus. Through these electrodes electrical stimuli can be applied and the results therefrom noted. Small electrolytic lesions may also be produced in particular regions. Such experiments have drawbacks, arising from the fact that anesthetics that depress hypothalamic responsiveness must be used, and that fibers passing through or near the hypothalamus may be inadvertently stimulated. Nevertheless, when compared with the results of other kinds of observations, useful information has been obtained. It has been possible to subdivide the hypothalamus on the basis of responses to its stimulation and ablation.

The posterior and lateral hypothalamic nuclei appear to form a homogenous system that, when stimulated, evokes activity in the sympathetic system. The heart rate is accelerated, the pupils are dilated, gastrointestinal movements are inhibited, and piloerection occurs. These responses occur in chronically decorticate cats and presumably are not caused by inadvertent stimulation of descending cortical tracts, which degenerate after operation. Moreover the gastrointestinal effects still occur in vagotomized animals and must therefore be mediated by the sympathetic nerves. Ablation of these areas by electrolytic lesions leads to the opposite results; relaxation of the nictitating membrane, enophthalmos, and ptosis have been observed. Lesions in the neighborhood of the mammillary bodies frequently cause

excessive somnolence and lethargy, a condition similar to that observed in encephalitis lethargica in which degeneration of the nuclei along the floor of the third ventricle has been found.

Stimulation of the tuberal nuclei (those in the middle portion of the hypothalamus adjacent to the pituitary stalk) evokes responses quite different from those described above. In general the reactions are parasympathetic in type. The heart rate is slowed, and conduction time in the heart is increased. Intragastric pressure, intestinal peristalsis, and contraction of the bladder are increased. The gastrointestinal effects are abolished by section of the vagus, and the bladder effects are destroyed by sectioning the caudal parasympathetic nerves (cf. Fulton, 1938).

Heat regulation in warm-blooded animals has been shown to require an intact hypothalamus. After decerebration a virtually poikilothermic preparation results. On the other hand, the decorticate cat maintains its body temperature at fairly constant levels. Small lesions, located in the various hypothalamic regions, have further clarified the problem. After destruction of the posterior hypothalamus animals are unable to activate their heat-conserving mechanisms and their body temperature falls. It is noteworthy that the heat-conserving mechanisms such as piloerection, increase in heart rate, and vasoconstriction are produced by stimulating the posterior hypothalamus. On the other hand, the heat-dissipating mechanisms appear to be located in the anterior hypothalamus. Cats with anterior hypothalamic lesions are unable to hold down their body temperature when exposed to heat, but the capacity to regulate against cold is unimpaired. It appears, therefore, that separate mechanisms, one integrating the heat-conserving actions, and the other regulating the heat-dissipating functions, reside in the posterior and anterior hypothalamic regions, respectively.

The foregoing discussion indicates that both sympathetic and parasympathetic activities are integrated into patterns in the hypothalamus. Since the various autonomic responses characteristically occur in strong emotional states, it would appear that the hypothalamus must also be involved in the regulation of the bodily processes accompanying these emotions. That this is so is attested by a wealth of experimental and clinical facts (cf. Chapter 14). Decorticate animals (cf. Bard, 1934) exhibit the bodily changes associated with fear and rage in integrated patterns practically indistinguishable from those displayed by normal individuals. In order to avoid controversy over the question of the animal's perception of these conditions, they have been called pseudaffective states. At any rate the integration of the motor patterns of emotions — rage, fear, and sex — are unimpaired if the hypothalamus is intact, but they are disorganized after its destruction. Component reflexes of the emotional pattern may still be evoked after destruction of the hypothalamus, but the full-blown constellation does not appear. Similar conclusions may be drawn from clinical information. Destruction of parts or the whole of the hypothalamus, although not destroying the responsiveness of the unit end effects, leads to a deterioration of the total emotional pattern.

The hypothalamus not only integrates the activities of the autonomic nervous system but also regulates various metabolic activities. Since the anterior pituitary gland is in close proximity to the hypothalamus, and since the endocrine organs also have important metabolic functions, the separation and identification of the pituitary from the hypothalamic effects has proved difficult, and our understanding of these phenomena is still far from perfect. Nevertheless it appears that carbohydrate metabolism is somehow influenced by hypothalamic centers. Hyperglycemia can be induced by direct stimulation of the hypothalamus, and

ablation of the anterior hypothalamus causes hypoglycemia (Barris and Ingram, 1936). After such lesions animals are abnormally sensitive to insulin; with lesions elsewhere in the hypothalamus no such insulin sensitivity develops. It has also been reported that destruction of the tuberal region of the hypothalamus reduces the severity of pancreatic diabetes in a fashion similar to that occurring after hypophysectomy. This evidence indicates that carbohydrate reserves are mobilized by the posterior hypothalamus and the sympathetic-adrenal system and that insulin tolerance is somehow modified by the anterior hypothalamus.

The hypothalamus has also been implicated in fat metabolism. Although it was originally thought that cachexia was a primary result of hypophysectomy, it now appears that both animals and man can remain in states of good nourishment after destruction of the hypophysis, provided the caloric intake remains adequate. In other words so-called pituitary cachexia is now regarded primarily as a failure of appetite rather than as a metabolic deficiency. Similarly it was originally thought that pituitary abnormalities led to obesity, but the experiments of P. E. Smith and of Hetherington and Ranson (1942) have shown that obesity results from damage to the tuber cinerum and that obesity can occur in the complete absence of the pituitary gland. Although extensive search has been made, no metabolic abnormalities have been found in obesity, and it again appears that the primary difficulty is a matter of appetite, coupled perhaps with predisposing constitutional factors. Since hyperphagia can be produced routinely by lesions in the tuberal nuclei of rats, and since obesity is a common finding in all kinds of expanding tumors lying above the sella turcica in man, it seems likely that the hypothalamus presides over appetite and regulates the food intake according to the energy requirements. Disturbances of this mechanism lead to failure of appetite on the one hand and abnormally increased appetite on the other.

The metabolic functions of the hypothalamus almost surely have endocrine repercussions, since the hypophysis and its satellite glands also influence the pathways through which foodstuffs are metabolized. In addition, there is more than a suspicion that the external factors such as light and heat which modify endocrine activity are at least transmitted through the hypothalamus. Brooks (1938) reported that ovulation in rabbits, normally occurring after copulation, was abolished by transection of the pituitary stalk. However, in other species, including the rat, the guinea pig, the monkey, and man, ovulation proceeds without hindrance after transection of the stalk. Similarly the thyroid hypertrophy following exposure to cold does not occur in stalk-transected rats (Uotila, 1939), although responses to exteroceptive stimuli, enlargement of the adrenal cortex, and the ovarian response to continuous light, are unaffected by the operation (Dempsey and Searles, 1943). It has been suggested that a neurohumor links the hypothalamus to the pituitary, but the experimental facts are so meager that this is entirely speculative. In any event the mechanism through which exteroceptive stimuli are transmitted to the anterior pituitary gland is one of the important unsolved problems of neuroendocrine physiology.

Although the hypothalamus has sometimes been called the head ganglion of the autonomic nervous system, this is true only in the sense that the hypothalamus is the lowest center capable of a considerable amount of autonomic integration. Indeed the hypothalamus is extensively connected with forebrain structures, and perhaps its principal function is to integrate the autonomic activities with the somatic ones. The medial forebrain bundle is an extensive tract carrying impulses to and from the hypothalamus and the olfactory centers. The frontal cortex and the hypothalamus are interconnected both by the fronto-septo-hypothalamic tract and by interconnections through the medial thalamic nuclei. Similarly the anterior thalamic nuclei are way stations between the hypothalamus and the cingular gyrus of the cortex. These connections provide ample opportunity for cortical activity to modify autonomic responses, and vice versa. Experimentally stimulation and ablation of cortical areas have been shown to modify sympathetic reflexes (Morison and Rioch, 1937). These considerations indicate that ramifications of the autonomic nervous system extend to the very highest neural levels and provide an ample physiological and anatomical basis for the well-known influences of the higher mental functions upon autonomic responses.

Homeostatic Aspects of Somatic Behavior

The concept of homeostasis originally was applied to the automatic activities comprising the internal housekeeping affairs of the body. Once enunciated, however, the concept has gradually expanded until it now cannot be restricted to any single mechanism or activity. Rather the physiological steady states, by whatever means they are regulated, may properly be regarded as examples of homeostasis. In other words Bernard's formulation of the physiological maintenance of the *milieu interne*, originally conceived as applying to the regulation of blood sugar, has gradually evolved to include many other examples and the specific mechanisms by which the individual phenomena are controlled. Thus a generation ago the principal examples of homeostatic adjustments concerned the activities of the autonomic nervous system. The detailed knowledge of the workings of the endocrine system were later shown to constitute another comparable system. By a similar expansion of the concept many kinds of somatic activity may be recognized to have homeostatic aspects, since the end result of the activity contributes to the maintenance of steady states of the internal environment.

Perhaps the clearest example of the interweaving of somatic and automatic responses is to be found in respiration. The concentration of oxygen and of carbon dioxide in the blood are important examples of homeostasis. When carbon dioxide accumulates, respiration is quickened until normal values are again attained. Yet respiratory movements are made by somatic muscles, and the respiratory muscles may be contracted or relaxed at will.

Another example involves the restlessness and general motor activity accompanying hunger. When hungry an animal becomes active and searches for food. After feeding, the restlessness and interest in food cease. Stated in homeostatic terms, hunger calls forth a behavior pattern that leads to abatement of the hunger. The behavior pattern, therefore, counteracts the depletion of the food reserves and maintains their constancy.

A similar formula applies to many other behavioral patterns. Thirst, like hunger, calls forth motor searching activity. Postural hypotension can be alleviated by tensing the muscles of the legs and abdomen, a fact known to all soldiers compelled to stand at rigid attention. The impulse to seek shade and reduce activity to a minimum on hot summer days is irresistible to all animals, including man. Conversely, shivering and voluntary activity are well-known responses to cold. Many other examples could be cited, but enough has been said to indicate that reflexes, actions, and behavior patterns involving somatic musculature are frequently involved in activity, the purpose of which is to maintain or restore the *status quo ante* of the internal environment.

Evolutionary Aspects of Homeostasis

The principle of homeostasis has been developed as a generalization covering all activities serving to maintain constant the physiological milieu of animals. Since this constancy of the internal environment is necessary for life, it is clear that homeostasis has considerable evolutionary significance. Indeed the phylogenetic ascent may be regarded as an increasingly successful effort by animals to free themselves from the limitations of their environments. The ancestral habitats were ones in which reasonably constant conditions favorable to life were maintained. Thus temperature regulation was unnecessary for the life of tropical oceans, since wide fluctuations in the water temperature did not occur. Similarly mechanisms for regulating water and electrolytes were not essential in the dwellers of the Archean seas where the ionic concentration of salts were remarkably like those of the blood sera. In order to free themselves from the confines of their marine habitat, they had to devise mechanisms for maintaining the fluid concentrations of the body. Once this was done, the marine forms invaded fresh water and, as the mechanisms became more perfect and lungs for gaseous exchanges put in their appearance, they marched out upon the land. Conquest of the terrestrial environment was limited to diurnal or seasonal forays until temperature regulation was established, because until then the external variation was so great that a body temperature compatible with life could not be maintained. With the development of heat-conserving mechanisms, cold environments could be withstood, and migration into the temperate and arctic zones became possible; similarly, heat-dissipating mechanisms permitted the conquest of tropical regions.

From the foregoing account it seems that homeostatic regulation did not spring up full-fledged at its first appearance, but that a few simple devices were gradually succeeded by many complex mechanisms, the increasing effectiveness of which accounted for evolutionary advances. Moreover, in the course of evolutionary progress animals have adopted diverse sorts of processes to homeostatic control. Mention has already been made of the use of physicochemical buffer systems and excretory and storage mechanisms, and of the integration of these functions by the endocrine and autonomic nervous systems. Muscles have been adapted to the control of the blood vascular system and to heat regulation. The skin subserves heat regulation and protection against desiccation in addition to its other manifold functions. The skeletal supporting tissues may be regarded as devices to suspend the soft parenchyma so as to facilitate the circulation of blood and lymph. In short the principal functions of the major tissues and organs are supplemented by homeostatic functions to which the principal activities have been adapted.

Not only are diverse processes adapted to homeostatic functions, but homeostatic problems admit multiple solutions. Temperature regulation may be taken as an illustrative example. Increased metabolism may be caused by thyroid hormone and its attendant increase in metabolic rate, by adrenalin and its consequent mobilization of sugar, or by increased activity, either of a voluntary or an involuntary variety. Moreover some arctic animals protect themselves against cold by growing an extensive insulating pelt; others, notably the aquatic mammals, achieve the same result with a thick fatty pad of blubber. Evasive action may be taken against the enemy, cold. The migratory birds flee the approach of cold, and the hibernating mammals find protected places where they lapse into a poorly understood state of suspended animation by which they conserve their energies for combating a future, less rigorous climate. Lastly, the higher mammals, including man, exhibit increasing ingenuity for finding or building protective devices that mitigate the rigors of the climatic excesses. Man's activity in this direction involves highly intellectualized functions and will be examined more carefully in a later section.

It is not surprising, then, that the central nervous system is no exception to the general rule that all tissues contribute according to kind to the maintenance of the internal milieu. The examples involving nervous activity cited in the foregoing sections have involved chiefly automatic or semiautomatic activity of a reflex character. However, voluntary activity, instinctive reactions, and even intellectual behavior of a high order cannot be excluded from consideration. Indeed the homeostatic aspects of the higher neural activities are so diversified and so important that they will be considered in separate sections.

Homeostatic Aspects of the Instincts

In a thoughtful article Kubie (1948) has pointed out that the concept of instinct has led a stormy life. Since it stands at the border between the realms of the body and the mind, it has aroused many prejudices and has been regarded as all-powerful by some and as powerless by others. The concept has been restricted to patterns of behavior inherited *in toto* and unmodifiable by growth, development, or experience. On the other hand, it has sometimes been used so broadly as to include every possible form of behavior and even integrations so complex as to be almost superbiological.

By avoiding extremist definitions and assuming that instincts are based upon a biochemical milieu, an inherited but modifiable nervous system, and a complex psychic superstructure of phantasies and phobias, Kubie suggested a classification of the instincts. The primary or vital instincts comprise the behavior related to the intake of raw material and the elimination of waste. Thus the behavioral aspects of respiration, hunger, thirst, urination, and defecation come under this heading. The homeostatic relations of these are obvious. Each produces a change in the biochemical machine that is the body; each sets up a stimulus which is transmitted through the nervous system and which evokes behavior designed to nullify the biochemical change comprising the stimulus. The secondary instincts are the sexual or procreative ones. In them the biochemical basis is at best obscure. They are related to the preservation of the species rather than to the preservation of the indi-

vidual. Nevertheless they evoke behavior
that, temporarily at least, displaces other
homeostatic processes. Thus the spawning
migration of salmon and eels takes precedence over every other activity including
those preserving life itself. The tertiary instincts are designated as executive by Kubie;
they consist of the elaborate patterns of behavior through which the primary instincts
are executed. Examples of such behavior
patterns are those that involve the respiratory muscles in breathing, the execution of
the muscular activities of eating, and the
characteristic poses and muscular coordinations of excretion. These neuromuscular
synergies are directly related to the primary
instincts and through them to the underlying biochemical disequilibrium. However,
unlike the primary instincts they are played
upon by psychological forces which determine the effectiveness with which the primary and secondary instinctual needs are
served.

Homeostatic Aspects of the Intellectual Functions

Many intellectual activities are directed
toward aiding homeostatic functions. Clothing and housing, for example, are directly
related to the heat-regulating systems.
Heavy clothing permits man to withstand
temperatures that otherwise would over-
whelm his capacity for conserving heat.
Tropical clothing, on the other hand, not
only aids in heat dissipation but also protects against the excessive tropical sunlight.
Similarly houses are designed to mitigate the
natural environments in many ways; roofs
and walls insulate against heat loss in winter
and provide shade in summer; heating devices nullify cold external temperatures, and
air conditioning neutralizes excessive heat.
In other words man's solution to the problem of external climates, so severe as to over-
power his physiological mechanisms for heat
regulation, is to construct an artificial intermediate environment in which his homeo-

static capacity is adequate. Thus, just as
the appearance of salt-conserving mechanisms allowed marine animals to invade
fresh water, so has the ability to manufacture clothing and to build houses permitted man to live in climates otherwise
inimical to his existence. The intellectual
process by which this problem was solved
must therefore be regarded as a homeostatic
mechanism.

Man's use of his intellect to solve the problem of heat regulation is by no means a
unique example of this evolutionary new
homeostatic mechanism. Devices for regulating pressure, coupled with other mechanical inventions, have freed man from the
limitations of gravity. Pressure cabins in
airplanes permit life at altitudes otherwise
incompatible with life, and similar devices
worked in reverse allow man to exist in sub-
marines at depths otherwise fatal. Irrigation and water-supply projects may be regarded as adjuncts to the homeostatic controls for water balance, since in their absence reclaimed desert regions would not
support life, and the population density of
cities would prove too great for the natural
resources. Sanitary measures and public
health procedures — indeed, all of preventive
and therapeutic medicine — are designed
to aid the bodily defenses against invasion
by pathological agents. Just as appetite is a
psysiological device for balancing the intake
of food against the capacities of the body to
metabolize and store it, so is the agricultural
industry and the transportation, processing,
packaging, storage, and distribution of its
products designed to make available food
when the bodily needs require it. Thus, regardless of its primary function, the intellect
subserves homeostasis in almost every field
of human endeavor.

The adaption of the intellectual functions
introduces a new factor into homeostasis, in
that they are capable of regulating the internal environment not only of one but of
many individuals. This quality is peculiar

to the intellect alone, among all other homeostatic mechanisms. If two individuals are exposed unprotected to cold, the one with the most efficient temperature regulation will survive longer. Given access to suitable materials, however, the one with adequate intellect will contrive a shelter which can protect both. Thus the fruits of the greatest intellects can be made available widely to the lesser ones. It is possible, therefore, for a moron who is incapable of conceiving or building a house to be protected by a house conceived and built by another individual. Homeostasis, by adapting the intellectual functions to its use, has transcended the bounds of the individual and has become operative in interpersonal relationships. In other words homeostasis is a generalization applicable in the field of sociology as well as in physiology.

The suggestion that homeostatic principles govern sociological as well as physiological forces implies that parallel or analogous mechanisms should be demonstrable in both fields. We have seen that homeostasis maintains the constancy of the physiological internal environment, that "telltale" mechanisms respond to forces tending to disturb this equilibrium and activate other mechanisms directed toward nullifying the disturbances, and that the successful operation of these homeostatic forces is necessary if life is to persist. We have also seen that states of extreme emergency cause essential organs and functions to be favored at the expense of others. These statements apply equally well to social organizations. Cannon (1941) has pointed out the analogies between the body physiologic and the body politic and has presented numerous examples of the similarities between the two. Commercial storage of perishable foods by sterilization or freezing has practically made obsolete the former seasonal glut or dearth in the markets. Great strides have been made in industry toward abolishing seasonal unemployment. Agricultural and commodity

credit policies that permit the withholding of surpluses in fat years for sale in lean periods were inaugurated by Joseph in Egypt, and within recent years there has been increasing governmental recognition of the importance of uniform distribution for both producers and consumers. "Telltale" devices in social organization are so frequent as to require no more than mention. The press and radio are well adapted to discover trouble and to call for the corrective measures. Fire-alarm systems, meteorological stations, and periodic routine inspections also fulfill these functions. In the normal course of events the recognition of danger signals calls forth the appropriate protective device — pestilence reported by press or radio calls forth public health measures; the fire alarm mobilizes fire engines and teams; excessive rainfall reported through the weather bureau causes flood control procedures to go into operation in the water sheds. The failure of the physiological homeostatic mechanisms leads to disease or death of the individual, and the failure of the social homeostatic mechanisms leads to depression, pestilence, or war. Moreover, during national emergencies activities are given priorities in direct ratio to their utility for prosecuting the war or combating the pestilence.

It is perhaps not surprising, in view of the recent evolutionary emergence of the mind as a homeostatic instrument, that in some respects its functions should be less efficient than the older physiological ones. That the social homeostatic mechanisms are only partially effective is indicated by the facts that booms alternate with depressions, hunger with abundance, periods of overtime work with forced idleness, and war with peace. Adequate defense against attack by disease is often neglected, and maximum efficiency is demanded with little regard for the welfare of the units of the functioning groups. In such respects the body physiologic has evolved methods of operation better than those thus far prevailing in the body politic.

The idea of a constant internal environment and of physiological mechanisms designed to preserve it has often been paraphrased by the statement that homeostasis preserves the physiological *status quo*. This is true only in the very limited sense that the *status quo* is the only condition compatible with life, and to preserve it is a necessary condition if the individual is to be released from the limitations of his external status. Thus the homeostatic ideal is not an external environment of placid serenity but an instrument for regulating the internal environment so perfectly that external fluctuations are a matter of indifference. Similarly, in social terms homeostasis is a guiding principle directing the evolution of a social organization that will sail on an even keel in the face of buffetings by disruptive forces.

REFERENCES

Allen, E., C. H. Danforth, and E. A. Doisy. *Sex and internal secretions.* (2nd Ed.) Baltimore: Williams and Wilkins, 1939.

Astwood, E. B. Chemotherapy of hyperthyroidism. *Harvey Lect.*, 1945, **40**, 195–235.

Astwood, E. B., J. Sullivan, A. Bissell, and R. Tyslowitz. Action of certain sulfonamides and of thiourea upon the function of the thyroid gland of the rat. *Endocrinology*, 1943, **32**, 210–225.

Baldwin, E. *An introduction to comparative biochemistry.* Cambridge: Cambridge University Press, 1940.

Bard, P. On emotional expression after decortication with some remarks on certain theoretical views. *Psychol. Rev.*, 1934, **41**, 309–329, 424–449.

Barris, R. W., and W. R. Ingram. The effect of experimental hypothalamic lesions upon blood sugar. *Amer. J. Physiol.*, 1936, **114**, 551–561.

Bernard, C. *Leçons sur les propriétés physiologiques et les alterations pathologiques des liquides de l'organisme.* Paris: Ballière, 1859. Volumes I and II.

Bichat, M. *General anatomy, applied to physiology and medicine.* 1801. (Translated by George Hayward.) Boston: Richardson and Lord, 1822.

Bissonnette, T. H. Light and sexual cycles in starlings and ferrets. *Quart. Rev. Biol.*, 1933, **8**, 201–208.

Brooks, C. M. A study of the mechanism whereby coitus excites the ovulation-producing activity of the rabbit's pituitary. *Amer. J. Physiol.*, 1938, **121**, 157–177.

Cannon, W. B. *The wisdom of the body.* New York: Norton, 1932.

Cannon, W. B. The body physiologic and the body politic. *Science*, 1941, **93**, 1–10.

Dempsey, E. W. Fluorescent and histochemical reactions in the rat thyroid gland at different states of physiological activity. *Endocrinology*, 1944, **34**, 27–38.

Dempsey, E. W., and E. B. Astwood. Determination of the rate of thyroid hormone secretion at various environmental temperatures. *Endocrinology*, 1943, **32**, 509–518.

Dempsey, E. W., and H. F. Searles. Environmental modification of certain endocrine phenomena. *Endocrinology*, 1943, **32**, 119–128.

De Robertis, E., and R. Grasso. Peroxidase activity of the thyroid gland under normal and experimental conditions. *Endocrinology*, 1946, **38**, 137–146.

Fisher, C., W. R. Ingram, and S. W. Ranson. *Diabetes insipidus.* Ann Arbor: Edwards, 1938.

Fulton, J. F. *Physiology of the nervous system.* Oxford: Oxford University Press, 1938.

Hamilton, J. B. Male hormone stimulation is prerequisite and an incitant in common baldness. *Amer. J. Anat.*, 1942, **71**, 451–480.

Hetherington, A. W., and S. W. Ranson. The relation of various hypothalamic lesions to adiposity in the rat. *J. comp. Neurol.*, 1942, **76**, 475–499.

Kubie, L. S. Instincts and homeostasis. *Psychosom. Med.*, 1948, **10**, 15–30.

MacKenzie, C. G., and J. B. MacKenzie. Effect of sulfonamides and thioureas on the thyroid gland and basal metabolism. *Endocrinology*, 1943, **32**, 185–209.

Marine, D. The physiology and principal interrelations of the thyroid. In *Glandular physiology and therapy.* Chicago: American Medical Association, 1935, pp. 315–333.

Mixner, J. P., E. P. Reinecke, and C. W. Turner. Effect of thiouracil and thiourea on the thyroid gland of the chick. *Endocrinology*, 1944, **34**, 168–174.

Moore, C. R., and D. Price. Gonad hormone functions and the reciprocal influence between gonads and hypophysis, with its bearing on the problem of sex hormone antagonism. *Amer. J. Anat.*, 1932, **50**, 13–71.

Morison, R. S., and D. McK. Rioch. The influence of the forebrain on an autonomic reflex. *Amer. J. Physiol.*, 1937, **120**, 257–276.

Price, W. H., C. F. Cori, and S. P. Colowick. Effect of anterior pituitary extract and of insulin on hexokinase reaction. *J. biol. Chem.*, 1945, **160**, 633–634.

Ranson, S. W., and H. W. Magoun. The hypothalamus. *Ergebn. Physiol.*, 1939, **41**, 56–163.

Richter, C. P., and K. H. Clisby. Graying of hair

produced by ingestion of phenylthiocarbamide. *Proc. Soc. exp. Biol., N. Y.,* 1941, **48,** 681–687.

Smith, P. E. Hypophysectomy and a replacement therapy in a rat. *Amer. J. Anat.,* 1930, **45,** 205–273.

Smith, P. E., and E. T. Engle. Experimental evidence regrading the role of the anterior pituitary in the development and regulation of the genital system. *Amer. J. Anat.,* 1927, **40,** 159–215.

Sumner, J. B., and G. F. Somers. *Chemistry and methods of enzymes.* New York : Academic, 1947.

Uotila, U. U. On the role of the pituitary stalk in the regulation of the anterior pituitary, with special reference to the thyrotropic hormone. *Endocrinology,* 1939, **25,** 605–614.

van Dyke, H. B., et al. Protein hormones of the pituitary body. *Ann. N. Y. Acad. Sci.,* 1943, **43,** 253–426.

7.

Mechanisms of Neural Maturation

R. W. SPERRY

University of Chicago

The development of behavior is directly dependent upon an orderly assembling of the neurons of the nervous system into appropriate patterns of interconnections. Although neural maturation involves certain other factors, such as the adjustment of excitation thresholds, the present chapter is concerned almost entirely with what appears to constitute its principal and most problematic feature, namely, the developmental organization of those elaborate and intricate patterns of neuronal linkages necessary to adaptive function. Knowledge of this phase of neurogenesis is at present still little beyond the theoretical stage, and it extends only to relatively simple aspects of the integrative structure, such as the connections between center and periphery and the central synaptic associations of the more direct reflex circuits. However, study of the developmental organization of these elementary integrative relations may be expected to yield general principles of maturation applicable as well to the more complex behavior patterns.

When the problem is reduced for the purpose of analysis into its most simplified form, it may be stated as follows: *how do the outgrowing axons and dendrites of the developing nerve cells manage to form and to maintain proper end-organ terminations in the periphery and proper synaptic associations within the centers?* The problem requires particular regard to the differential specificity with which the neuronal connections are established. It demands answers, for example, to such questions as the following: How do motoneurons innervating a flexor muscle acquire central reflex relations different from those acquired by neighboring motoneurons innervating an extensor muscle? How are optic fibers from different retinal areas able to establish their synaptic relations in the visual centers so that the retinal field becomes projected onto the brain in an orderly manner, permitting objects in space to be seen discretely and localized accurately? Why, again, should the sensory fibers of the horizontal semicircular canal of the labyrinth, on growing into the medulla, form reflex associations different from those formed by accompanying sensory fibers entering the same vestibular centers by the same route, but associated peripherally with the vertical canals? How are the secondary central neurons, which link the different types of sensory fibers with the various motor systems, enabled to form their intracentral associations in the particular patterns necessary for adaptive reflex function? In the course of growth, sensori-neuro-motor associations are somehow laid down in a consistent, orderly manner. How are such patterns organized in development? What is the nature of the regulative processes involved?

The preparation of this chapter was aided by a grant from the Dr. Wallace C. and Clara A. Abbott Memorial Fund of the University of Chicago. Figures 1, 2, 3, 4, 7, and 8 were drawn by E. Bohlman.

"Maturation" versus Learning

A first problem to be considered is the extent to which the neuronal associations are (1) preformed directly by processes of growth and cell differentiation and (2) patterned by functional regulation through experience and training. Where adaptation by function is indicated, we are led into the problems of the physiological basis of conditioned reflexes and learning. On the other hand, where inherent predetermination is indicated, further analysis must deal with the embryological, cytological, and physicochemical phenomena involved in the growth, migration, and differentiation of nerve cells, and in the formation of contact relations with other neurons and with their respective end organs.

The maturation-learning problem has long been a subject of controversy. In 1931 Holt, among others, was arguing that none of the patterning of synaptic connections between sensory, central, and motor neurons is inherently predetermined. He maintained that developmental forces leave the nervous system an unorganized, equipotential network capable of nothing but diffuse, random reaction. Out of initially random movements, neural organization is gradually achieved, according to this view, through the supposed neurobiotactic outgrowth of dendrites toward axons excited in the course of activity. The most primitive reflexes and even the primary synaptic connections of the peripheral nerves, as well as all higher integrative relations, were presumed to be patterned functionally in this manner.

Since the proposal of this extreme hypothesis, however, contradictory data have been accumulating until now the pendulum of opinion is swinging sharply in the opposite direction toward increasing recognition of the forces of inheritance (Hunter, 1947). A survey of the evidence as it now stands leads to the conclusion that the basic patterns of synaptic association throughout the vertebrate nervous system are organized for the most part by intrinsic forces of development without the aid of learning. This would include most of the integrative structure of the spinal cord and brain stem. At higher levels of the brain, even in the primates, all the intricate interrelations known to neuroanatomy, such as the various projection systems to and from the cerebral and cerebellar cortices and the interconnecting systems between cortical areas — in so far as they are constant within a species — must likewise be included among the relations of the nervous apparatus subject to inherent organization. By process of elimination the interneuronal relations patterned by learning would seem to be relegated to those circuits farthest removed from the direct conduction pathways which, in the mammal, would be confined mainly to the cerebral cortex. Regarding the limits and overlap of the respective influences of learning and maturation, the evidence remains vague and incomplete.

For present purposes it is sufficient to recognize that the basic integrative architecture of the nervous system is organized directly in the growth process itself. Although the building of integrative circuits presents a fascinating embryological problem in its own right, it is considered here primarily with regard to its implications for the structure and function of the adult nervous system. Knowledge of how inherent behavior is installed may give some clues to the neural basis of learned behavior. The nature of central nervous integration and of the structural framework subserving it should become clearer in the light of such information.

GROSS MORPHOGENESIS

The precise patterning of neuronal interconnections constitutes the ultimate and most refined step in the development of the nervous system. A proper final adjustment of the synaptic associations, however, is dependent upon preceding grosser phases of development in which are attained the gen-

eral form, size, and location of the major
parts of the nervous system.

The manner in which the embryonic
neural tube becomes transformed into the
adult brain and spinal cord is depicted in
many standard texts. The histological picture has also been described in considerable
detail, particularly for the earlier stages of
development, including the proliferation,
polarization, differentiation, and migration
of the neuroblasts, the outgrowth of the
axons and dendrites, the appearance and enlargement of the various nuclear fields, the
laying down in successive steps of many of
the main fiber tracts, and their progressive
enlargement and myelinization (see papers
and references of Barron, Coghill, Herrick,
Langworthy, and Windle).

At first the nerve fibers are few in number, span very short distances, and interconnect only a few nuclear masses. In the
course of growth many more fibers are added
to the original "pathfinder" lines, and the
short fibers become lengthened and drawn
into circuitous courses. Additional nuclear
fields appear, and new connecting links are
laid down to form a structure of ever-increasing complexity. There are successive
shifts in topographical relations and a nicely
geared timing of the developmental events.

Further insight into these phases of development has been added by the methods
of experimental embryology, which have
begun to unravel some of the regulative
forces involved (see reviews of Detwiler,
1936; Harrison, 1935; Herrick, 1925, 1933,
1948; Piatt, 1948; Weiss, 1939, 1941c). It
has been found, for example, that fibers of
the sensory nerve roots, on entering the
brain, tend to be deflected into those nuclear
centers that happen, at the time, to be
undergoing cellular proliferation. Similarly,
outgrowing fibers of the peripheral nerves
verge toward rapidly growing peripheral
organs. Likewise intracentral fiber tracts
tend to form connections with those nuclei
undergoing accelerated proliferation at the
time of the fibers' outgrowth. As successive

constellations of proliferative foci make their
appearance, new patterns of connecting links
are established. In all these instances the
influence of proliferative centers on the direction of nerve outgrowth appears to depend upon the formation of lines of force in
the interstitial medium which converge on
the given growth centers and which in turn
cause a converging alignment of the ultramicroscopic particles along which the tips
of the nerve fibers are mechanically guided
(Weiss, 1941c). That specific chemical factors may also be involved is suggested in the
studies of Hooker (1930) who rotated a
piece of the spinal cord and found a tendency for the fiber bundles to reconnect with
their corresponding fascicles in the rotated
segment.

The ingrowth of fibers into a given nuclear
field tends to stimulate the growth of the invaded center and to enhance the development of its dendritic ramifications. A correlation has been demonstrated between the
size of peripheral structures and the quantitative development of their associated spinal
ganglia and central nuclei. The ultimate
basis of such effects is still in doubt, but the
evidence (Barron, 1945; Hamburger, 1946;
Levi and Levi, 1942) suggests that these
phenomena are correlated entirely with the
growth phase of the nerve and end-organ tissues, and not with their functional phase.

The gross architecture of the nervous system, including the locations of nuclear centers and the patterns of fiber tracts, is the
result of a manifold interaction of numerous
growth factors. Mechanical and spatial relations, and the mechanisms of cell proliferation, migration, and differentiation, along
with embryonic induction, are all involved.
The whole process depends upon a neat timing of the developmental steps. Clearly this
grosser patterning is determined independently of activity, in a manner characteristic
of the species. Even individual variations,
almost as characteristic of brain structure as
of the face (Lashley, 1947), seem to be genetically determined.

REFINED PATTERNING OF INTEGRATIVE CIRCUITS

It is not enough, of course, that fiber tracts terminate in particular nuclei. The fibers of each tract must, in addition, form the proper synapses within each nucleus of termination. For example, the optic tract in the amphibian must not only make its connection with the optic tectum instead of with other regions of the brain, but the separate fibers composing the tract must terminate in a selective, individuated fashion within the optic tectum itself. The sensory fibers of each spinal nerve must likewise form associations appropriate to the modality of their end organs and to the particular ligament, tendon, muscle, joint, or region of skin, periosteum, or fascia, etc., in which the end organs are located. And within most nuclei localized circuits must be formed. These refined aspects of neurogenesis hold most interest from the functional point of view. It is the most difficult feature to analyze, and until lately our only explanatory concepts, such as "neurobiotaxis," "chemotaxis," "electrodynamic fields," etc., have been vague and speculative.

During recent years a series of experiments dealing with the establishment of synaptic associations in the amphibian central nervous system has given rise to a more definite "chemoaffinity" theory. This scheme attempts to account for the development of neural patterns in terms of cell differentiation and embryonic "induction" processes closely akin to those known to be involved in other organ systems. This aspect of neurogenesis has thereby been brought into line with better-understood phases of development, the main difference being that in the nervous system the final product is far more specific in design and more highly differentiated.

Because it is often easier to study the secondary growth of neuronal connections than to work with the initial embryonic growth, much of the available data is derived from experiments on nerve regeneration. All evidence indicates that the patterning in regeneration is regulated by essentially the same forces as in development.

End-Organ Connections

In the periphery, where the specific termination of neurons is open to observation, the problem of linkages is more accessible to experimental analysis than it is when central connections are involved. It is not usually maintained, even in theory, that learning influences the formation of end-organ connections. Indeed the peripheral relations are generally laid down well before the onset of reflex function. The fact that a precise patterning can be achieved in the periphery without the aid of learning lends credence to the idea that associations within the centers may likewise be adjusted by the forces of growth alone.

Electrical, mechanical, and chemical influences have each been thought at various times to play the predominant role in guiding nerve fibers to their destinations. Except for a slight directive effect of strong currents under special conditions of tissue culture (Marsh and Beams, 1946), the electrical theories have found little experimental support. On the other hand, the universal importance of mechanical factors has been clearly demonstrated. It was noted by Harrison (1914) that nerve fibers grow only in contact with a supporting surface, never in a homogeneous fluid medium. The later studies of Harrison (1935) and particularly of Weiss (1941c) have further emphasized the profound influence of the mechanical substrate on the guidance of growing nerve fibers. Even the ultramicroscopic particles of the interstitial fluid and the most delicate of interfacial films, as well as all larger structures, serve to deflect and to channel the fine filamentous pseudopodia of the advancing fiber tips.

Many aspects of the growth and termination of nerve fibers, however, cannot be accounted for purely in terms of contact guidance. This is particularly true of the patterning of refined synaptic connections in the centers. From here on it will be taken for granted that mechanical factors are ubiquitous in nervous development and our attention will be concentrated on certain additional factors of more selective action which seem to be largely chemical in nature.

From observations of nerve development and regeneration it has been inferred (Cajal, 1928, 1929; Harrison, 1910; Tello, 1923; and others) that the different end organs must possess some kind of selective chemical affinity for the various types of outgrowing nerve fibers. In the development of the tongue, for example, the fibers of nerve XII establish connections selectively with the striated muscle cells; those of VII and IX connect with the cells of the taste endings; those of V form touch, pain, and thermal endings; and those of the autonomic system connect with the smooth muscle cells of the blood vessels. This selective termination seems to call for differential responses on the part of the outgrowing nerve fibers to specific chemical properties of the end organs. It need not be assumed that the advancing fiber tips are attracted from any great distance by chemicals diffusing from their prospective terminations. Presumably the interstitial pathways to terminal tissues are chemically conditioned by the types of cells surrounding them, and different nerve fiber types are prone to grow preferentially along certain of these diversely flavored pathways. This is suggested in the predisposition of sensory and motor fibers to form separate distal branches in the developing limb bud. (Hamburger, 1929; Taylor, 1944).

Piatt (1942) contributed further evidence that the role played by peripheral nerve fibers in attaining their goal is not so passive and mechanically controlled as had previously been thought. Limbs reared on parabiotic salamander twins to an advanced stage of development in complete absence of innervation were grafted in place of the cor-responding limb on animals otherwise normal. The resultant nerve pattern formed by the invasion of the host nerves into the developed "aneurogenic" limbs proved to be remarkably normal. Many features of the process, such as the penetration of cartilage masses by the nerves, the tunneling of the ulnar nerve through the belly of the ulno-carpal muscle instead of coursing around it, and the entrance of nerves into their muscles at the customary motor points, suggests a significant influence of chemical factors. The course of some of the cranial nerves is even more difficult to account for unless we assume chemical influences.

Once the fibers have reached their general region of termination, local chemical effects supposedly come into play to determine the specific type of end-organ cells with which the fibers will make connection (Cajal, 1929). In regenerating nerves in the tadpole tail, Speidel (1946) found that aberrant lateral-line fibers show a marked tendency to arrive at and innervate displaced lateral-line organ tissue, whereas no such tendency is ever displayed by spinal nerve sprouts nearby. Nerve regeneration studies, in general, reveal considerable latitude in the extent to which nerve fibers can be forced to form atypical terminations. On the other hand, some examples of strict incompatibility have been observed such as the inability of adrenergic fibers to form functional connections with cholinergic endings, and vice versa (Langley and Anderson, 1904), and the inability of sensory fibers to form transmissive junctions with muscle fibers (Langley and Anderson, 1904; Weiss and Edds, 1945).

Sometimes, instead of growing to their appropriate end organs, the nerve fibers may themselves induce the formation of the appropriate endings from indifferent tissue. In the catfish, for example, the taste buds as well as lateral-line organs are induced to develop at the tips of invading nerve fibers (Bailey, 1937; Olivo, 1928; Olmsted, 1931). On the other hand, the nerve fibers of the general cutaneous system pervade the integument in the same regions, but these do not induce formation either of taste buds or of lateral-line organs (cf. also Speidel, 1948). Thus, within a given area of the skin, fibers from the gustatory nerve induce gustatory endings, fibers from the lateral-line nerve induce lateral-line endings (these two types of receptors being quite different histologically), but fibers from the general cutaneous nerves terminate freely without inducing any specialized endings.

The type of end organ that is formed may also be conditioned by the type of tissue into which the nerve grows (Bailey, 1937; Dijkstra, 1933). Still another type of terminal relation, discussed more fully below, has been found (Weiss, 1936) where the outgrowing nerves terminate indifferently on their end organs, after which the end organs induce biochemical specificity in the nerve fibers.

The early idea that peripheral nerve fibers differ from each other in their chemical make-up (Cajal, 1928; Hering, 1913; Langley, 1898) has thus been confirmed in studies of peripheral innervation. Neuron specificity influences end-organ connections in different ways in different regions. Nevertheless it is only one factor operating in conjunction with many others. Since connections in the periphery must be made with reference to the central connections, it is difficult to deal with the one apart from the other. Accordingly more detailed discussion of neuron specificity is postponed until it can be taken up in relation to central patterning.

Synapses of Sympathetic Ganglia

A relatively simple type of synaptic relation exists within the sympathetic ganglia of the autonomic system located outside the neuraxis. Preganglionic fibers emerge from the spinal cord via the ventral roots and make synaptic terminations upon the neurons of the sympathetic ganglia. These neurons in turn send their axons to visceral end organs. The neurons within a single gan-

glion may innervate a variety of end organs which function separately and which therefore require separate control from the centers. If the preganglionic fibers were to establish their synapses in a haphazard manner within a ganglion, excitation from the centers could lead only to massive, undifferentiated response. Excluding the possibility of specific nerve energies (see p. 272), selective activation must depend upon orderly synapsis within the ganglia, which, like the end-organ linkages, can hardly be ascribed to learning.

The early studies of Langley (1898, 1900) on nerve regeneration in the sympathetic system of the cat suggest that the synaptic patterning is determined by biochemical differences among the classes of neurons involved. The superior cervical ganglion in the cat innervates the smooth muscles of the auricular blood vessels, the nictitating membrane, the eyelids, the iris, the facial hairs, and the salivary glands. The preganglionic fibers reach the ganglion through the main sympathetic trunk, which they join after emerging from the spinal cord through different thoracic nerves from T1 to T7. Preganglionic fibers associated with different classes of ganglionic neurons tend to exit from the cord at different segmental levels.

Following severance of the sympathetic trunk, the preganglionic fibers regenerate to reestablish connections within the superior cervical ganglion. Despite the mix-up and disarrangement of the original fiber pattern in the nerve scar, inevitable under the conditions of the experiments, Langley found a remarkable tendency for the preganglionic fibers to restore their original type of linkages among the various classes of ganglionic neurons. After regeneration separate stimulation of the preganglionic fibers of the different thoracic nerves, T1–T7, evoked their typical selective action in the periphery. Langley stated that he could see no feasible means, except chemiotaxis, by which the preganglionic fibers could pick and choose the particular ganglionic neurons with which they become associated. Hypoglossal fibers will also regenerate readily into the superior cervical ganglion and arborize profusely among the cell bodies, but unlike the preganglionic fibers they fail to form the proper synaptic structures necessary for impulse transmission (Hillarp, 1946).

As pointed out by Langley, chemical specificity of neurons may in many instances have only a preferential rather than an all-or-none effect on termination. In regenera-

The functional relations between retina and brain centers must be patterned with orderly precision for visual perception. Each retinal locus must possess its unique "spatial sign." Anatomically it has been shown that the retinal quadrants have an orderly projection upon the brain centers throughout the vertebrate series from fish to man (Stroer, 1939). The problem therefore is to account for the selectivity with which the ingrowing optic fibers form their central associations.

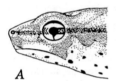 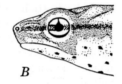  

A   B   C   D

FIG. 1. Surgical rotation and inversion of the eye. It is possible to invert the eye completely by rotating it through 180 degrees, or the eye can be inverted on any one axis by transplanting it to the contralateral orbit. *A:* Normal orientation. *B:* 180-degree rotation. *C:* Dorsoventral inversion. *D:* Nasotemporal inversion.

tion, for example, a given neuron may terminate more readily on the class of cells with which it was originally connected, but when the fibers cannot reach their favored terminals atypical connections may be formed. It is well substantiated that nerves can be forced by surgical measures, such as nerve crossing, to form atypical linkages under a wide variety of conditions. The readiness with which different types of neurons form terminal endings on other cells appears to vary from complete indifference to highly exclusive selectivity.

Central Synapses of the Retina

Much of the experimental work on the patterning of central synapses has been performed on amphibians, partly because of the oft-cited advantages of this group for embryological study and partly because the amphibian central nervous system in larval stages, and even in the adult, retains a capacity for regeneration far greater than that of higher vertebrates. In amphibians, furthermore, adjustment by learning is not so much a complicating factor.

It was shown by Matthey (1926*a, b, c*) that the optic nerve of the grafted adult urodele eye is capable of reestablishing functional connections in the brain. It was already known that most of the retina of such eyes disintegrates and is then regenerated from the surviving ciliary margin. In his microscopic examinations Matthey also observed an atypical meandering and intermixing of fibers in the regenerated optic nerves. Nevertheless his descriptions of the recovered visual reactions indicated accurate spatial localization and movement perception. Similar findings were later reported from Stone's laboratory (Stone and Ussher, 1927; Beers, 1929; Stone and Cole, 1943). Inclusion, among these earlier reports, of good visual recoveries following 90- and 180-degree rotation of the eye and following atypical connection of the optic fibers with the wrong brain center suggested that some sort of functional adaptation might be involved. Further analysis, as outlined below, however, contradicts this possibility in favor of organizational forces, strictly developmental in character.

It is possible in amphibians to rotate the eyeball on its optic axis through 180 degrees, leaving the optic nerve intact. The eye (Sperry, 1942a, 1943b). For example, the optokinetic reactions to movement of the visual field around the dorsoventral and

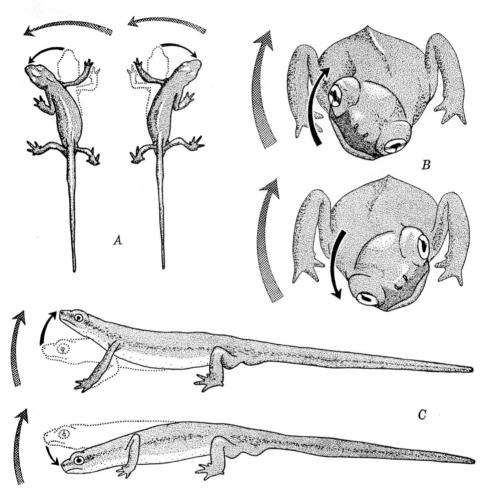

FIG. 2. Reversal of optokinetic responses following surgical rearrangement of retino-central relations. The normal pursuit phase of the response is shown, along with the reversed pursuit reactions for the three primary planes, as caused by (1) 180-degree rotation of eyes, (2) dorsoventral inversion, (3) nasotemporal inversion, and (4) cross union of the optic nerves. Large arrows indicate the actual direction of movement of the visual field. Reversal in A caused by 1, 3, and 4; in B by 1, 2 and 4; and in C by 2 and 3. More complicated correlations are obtained by 90-degree rotation and by combinations of eye rotation, inversion, and optic-nerve cross union.

heals in this new position, with the dorsal quadrant of the retina placed ventrally in the orbit and with the temporal quadrant turned to the nasal side (see Fig. 1B). The visual responses then become reversed rostrocaudal axes of the body are made in the direction opposite from normal, as illustrated in Fig. 2. The predatory reactions involving approach, pursuit, and striking at small moving objects are directed toward

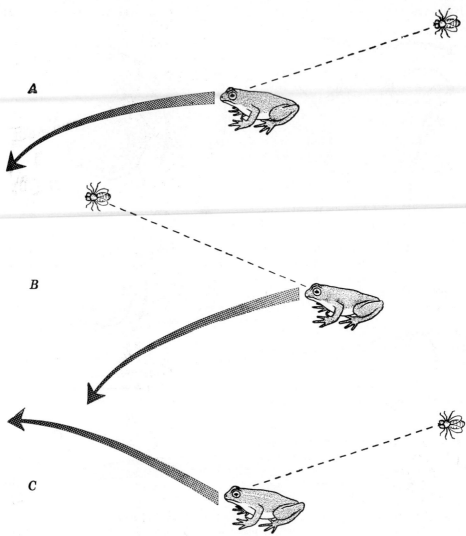

FIG. 3. Sample types of error in spatial localization of small objects following rotation and inversion of the eye. A: With eye rotated 180 degrees, frog strikes at a point in the visual field diametrically opposite that at which the lure is actually located. B: After dorsoventral inversion of the eye, frog strikes correctly with reference to the nasotemporal dimensions of the visual field, but inversely with reference to the dorsoventral dimensions. C: After nasotemporal inversion of the eye, frog strikes correctly with reference to the dorsoventral dimensions of the visual field, but inversely with reference to the nasotemporal dimensions.

corresponding points in the opposite sector of the visual field from that in which the bait is located (Fig. 3A). The animals also exhibit persistent circus movements. The maladaptive responses persist indefinitely without correction. This refractoriness to reeducation suggests, in itself, that the structure mediating these reactions is not organized by the learning process.

Surgical rotation of the eye can be combined with severance of the optic nerve (Sperry, 1942a, 1943c, 1944). This results in blindness for a period of approximately 4 weeks, during which time the fibers regenerate from the retinal stump and eventually reestablish central synaptic connections in the brain. Histological examination has shown that the optic axons, in the course of regeneration, commonly become intertangled with one another in the scar region, with a thorough disarrangement of the original fiber pattern (see Fig. 5A and B). Nevertheless the formation of synaptic relations in the centers does not follow a confused or random pattern. Instead an orderly restoration of the original functional relations between retinal fields and brain centers is achieved. This is evident in the recovery of systematically reversed visuomotor reactions directly correlated with the rotated position of the retina. Inasmuch as recovery leads to maladaptive reactions, which persist without correction, the patterning of the synaptic relations can hardly be ascribed to functional adaptation.

If the blood supply to the retina is sufficiently impaired in this operation, the retina degenerates and in the urodeles a new retina is regenerated. In the course of about 2½ months, new optic axons grow centrally from the ganglion cell layer of the regenerated retina (Fig. 5D). These new optic fibers form central reflex relations within the optic lobe in the same orderly way as do those of cases in which the original axons regenerate directly from the point of severance.

The amphibian eye can also be transplanted to the orbit on the opposite side of the head with only one of the primary retinal axes inverted instead of both, as diagrammed in Fig. 1C and D. In an eye transplanted to the contralateral orbit, the optic fibers of the original retina (or of the newly regenerated retina if the original retina degenerates) establish central synaptic connections in the same systematic manner as described in the previous experiments (Sperry, 1945a). Following recovery of vision by the transplanted eye, the animals behave as if the visual field were inverted in one dimension, corresponding to the actual inversion of the retina. Responses are properly directed with reference to the axis of the eye correctly oriented, but they are reversed with reference to the inverted axis (see Fig. 3B and C). When the eye is inverted on intermediate axes or rotated through intermediate angles, the visuomotor coordinations become misdirected accordingly. Similar results have been obtained with salamander embryos prior to the initial ingrowth of the optic axons (Stone, 1944).

The optic nerves can be cut and crossunited to the nerve stumps of the opposite eye in such a way that, after nerve regeneration, the retina becomes projected onto the opposite side of the brain from that with which it is normally connected (see Fig. 4). The consequent visual responses indicate that the part of the visual field viewed through either eye appears to the animal as if it were being seen through the contralateral eye (Sperry, 1945a). There is reversal of optokinetic reactions around the dorsoventral and rostrocaudal axes of the body, forced circus movements on these same axes, and errors of spatial localization with reference to the left-right aspect of the visual field. These visuomotor responses remain uncorrected by experience.

Following each of these surgical rearrangements, the neuronal connections are laid down in the same prefixed manner. The optic axons may be growing into the brain for the first time in embryonic development, they may arise from newly proliferated neuroblasts in a regenerated retina in the adult, or they may be old fibers regenerating directly after transection. Regardless of whether the retina is upright or upside down or whether the optic tracts are connected to the proper optic lobe or to the opposite lobe, the central reflex associations formed by the ingrowing optic fibers are established in the same systematic pattern. These functional relations are formed in a predetermined fashion without regard for the adaptiveness of the functional effect.

nections with the same areas of the optic lobe with which they were originally connected.

These experiments all indicate that fibers arising from a given locus of the retina are predestined to form their central synapses with neurons located in a specific locus. Each retinal point has its corresponding point in the optic lobe. The formation of

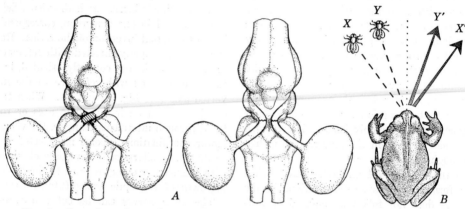

Fig. 4. Contralateral transfer of retinal projection on the brain. *A:* By excising the optic chiasma and cross-uniting the four optic nerve stumps as diagrammed, the central projection of the two retinas can be interchanged. *B:* After optic-nerve regeneration the animals respond as if everything viewed through either eye were being seen through the opposite eye. For example, when a lure is presented at *X* or at *Y,* the animal strikes at *X'* or at *Y',* respectively (see also Fig. 2).

mined fashion without regard for the adaptiveness of the functional effect. Extension of the experiments to teleost fishes (Sperry, 1948b, 1949) has yielded similar results.

A lesion made in a given quadrant of the optic lobe of the midbrain of a normal frog produces a "blind" area in the corresponding quadrant of the visual field (Sperry, 1944). The animal then makes no response when the lure is presented in the "blind" area. This fact, bolstered by the anatomical studies of Stroer, indicates that the retina normally has an orderly projection upon the optic lobe. If, in addition, the eye has been surgically rotated, the "blind" area shifts correspondingly. The regenerated optic fibers, despite their mix-up in the scar region, apparently manage to restore functional connection

associations is governed strictly by anatomical relations, not by the adequacy of the functional effects.

Although the mechanisms involved in the establishment of these central reflex relations remain somewhat obscure, several inferences may be drawn from the evidence now available. The general direction of growth of the optic tract as a whole might be due largely to mechanical guidance. On the other hand, it is clear that the arrangement of terminations within the optic lobe itself could hardly be explained in this way. The frayed and disoriented condition of the nerve stumps, the erratic and tortuously intertwined course of the optic axons through the nerve scar, the absence of preconstructed pathways both in the embryo and in animals with newly regenerated retinas, all indicate that mechanical guidance could not possibly be responsible for the patterning of synaptic relations. Nor does the assumption of a precise timing chanical alignment in the substrate of the optic pathway is lacking.

It is obviously necessary that optic fibers arising from different retinal loci be distin-

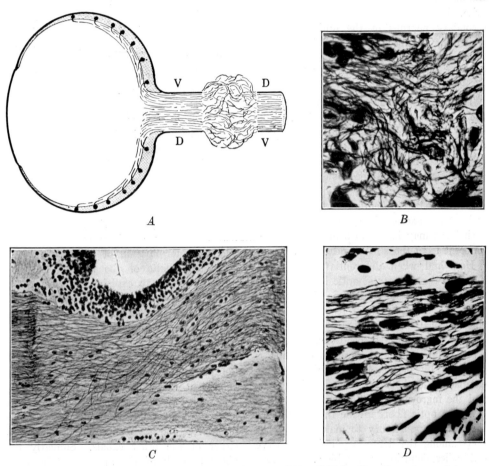

A

B

C

D

Fig. 5. Optic nerve regeneration (from Sperry, 1943c, 1945a). Despite extreme intermixing of the regenerating fibers in the scar region and despite rotation or inversion of the opposing nerve stumps as diagrammed in *A*, the fibers reestablish their functional associations in the brain in an orderly manner. The photomicrographs show the interwoven, nonparallel course of the regenerated optic fibers in animals that had shown orderly functional recovery. *B:* Optic-nerve regeneration scar in a newt. *C:* Regenerated optic chiasma in a frog, following contralateral transplantation of the eye. *D:* Regenerated optic nerve of a newt, following retinal degeneration and regeneration.

of axon outgrowth help the situation. All the fibers start their outgrowth at approximately the same time from the cut surface of the nerve stump, and the required mechanical guished from one another in the centers. Were the optic axons all alike in character, there would be no basis — with mechanical guidance, timing, and functional adaptation all ruled out — for a selective arrangement of synaptic relations. Consequently there must be some kind of qualitative specificity among the ingrowing axons determined by the loci of the retinal field from which they arise. Not only the optic axons but also the secondary neurons of the optic lobe with which they connect must each have a distinctive character. If the secondary central neurons were all alike, there would again be no way of attaining order.

The qualitative specificity must parallel the topography of the retinal field. This means a true "field" distribution of qualitative properties among the retinal ganglion cells from which the optic fibers originate and among the tectal neurons on which they terminate. It means, furthermore, that the retina must be differentiated with respect to at least two axes of the eyeball in order that each locus may have biochemical properties different from those of all other loci.

How and when differentiation is established in the retina and optic lobe are questions proper to embryology and cytochemistry. Of more direct interest to us is how this neuronal differentiation affects the patterning of synaptic associations. The simplest assumption is that this patterning is governed by biochemical affinities and incompatibilities between the central neurons and the ingrowing optic axons.

As the optic fibers invade the optic lobes, they have opportunity to make many contacts among the dense population of nerve cell bodies, dendrites, axons, blood capillaries, glial cells, and other optic fibers that have preceded them into the area. Of these many contacts only a few result in the formation of synaptic endings. The fiber tips grow around and past glial cells, capillaries, axons, and the majority of dendrites and nerve cell bodies they happen to encounter. But, when they reach the appropriate part of the optic lobe, they meet neurons whose physicochemical nature is right for the formation of synaptic end feet. It is likely that a single optic axon terminates on a large number of sec-

ondary neurons whose dendrites may spread over a considerable portion of the optic tectum but whose cell bodies occupy only a small area. The cells in the center of such an area would receive the greatest number of terminals from that particular axon. The terminations of neighboring cells would presumably overlap considerably, but the projection of each retinal locus would still be centered about a unique focal point in the field of tectal neurons. The relative degree of overlap has apparently decreased along with a decrease in the spread of the axonal and dendritic arborizations during evolutionary development.

Similar developmental phenomena could account for the orderly projection of the retinal field upon the striate cortex in mammals, although further complications arise from the overlap of the visual fields and the partial crossing of fibers at the chiasma. The close termination of optic fibers from congruent points of the two retinas is a difficult feature to explain. In this regard it is noteworthy that the geniculate cells on which the fibers from the two eyes terminate, tend to migrate into separate layers.

Central Synapses of the Vestibular Nerve

From the nature of vestibular reflexes it is evident that the fibers that supply the crista of any one semicircular canal must have different reflex relations in the hindbrain from the fibers supplying the crista of either of the other canals. Similarly the fibers to each of the approximately seven separate end organs of the amphibian labyrinth must have their own special linkages. There exists a certain overlap, undoubtedly, in the central relations of the fibers of some of these separate end organs. At the same time, however, fibers supplying different parts of a single end organ, such as those to the utricular macula, must have differential central associations to match their functional diversity.

Complete bilateral severance of the VIII cranial nerve root along with the root fibers of VII was performed in the adult frog, *Hyla squirella* (Sperry, 1945b). The root fibers were able to regenerate centripetally experimental cases but not in control cases in which regeneration was prevented. Regeneration restored the various reflex re-

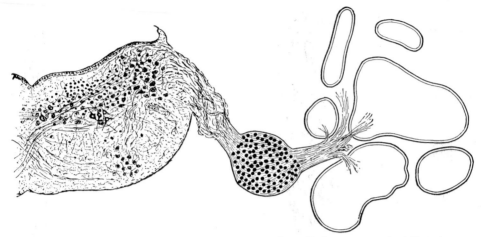

FIG. 6. Diagrammatic section through regenerated vestibular nerve root at its entrance into the medulla. Fibers connected to the various sensory endings in the semicircular canals, the utriculus, the sacculus, and the lagena become intertangled at the point of nerve section, but they nevertheless reestablish central reflex relations in a systematic pattern.

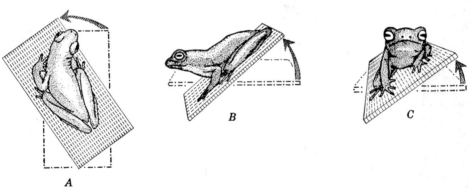

FIG. 7. Vestibular reflexes. Different patterns of labyrinthine stimulation produced by rotating and tilting animals in the three primary planes of the body elicit specific reflex responses and postures which, along with other vestibular responses, furnish good criteria of the orderliness of functional recovery following regeneration of the vestibular nerve root.

into their nuclei in the medulla, as indicated by recovery of function and by histological examination (see Fig. 6). The profound disturbance of equilibration caused by section of the vestibular nerves was repaired in the sponses to angular acceleration and tilting of the animals in the three primary planes of the body (Fig. 7). Evidently the different neuron types among the heterogeneous collection of divided sensory root fibers were able to reestablish functional relations with the secondary central cells in a discriminative manner. Judging from the number of different kinds of sensory end organs supplied by nerves VII and VIII, one would estimate that at least eleven distinct classes of fibers regenerated from the point of transection with ample opportunity for a chaotic

less. The normal development of the vestibulo-ocular reflexes in blinded animals, including amphibians (Sperry, 1946), pigeons (Mowrer, 1936), chickens (Kuo, 1932), and rabbits (Nasiell, 1924), is further evidence that learning is not important in patterning the synaptic associations of the vestibular nerve.

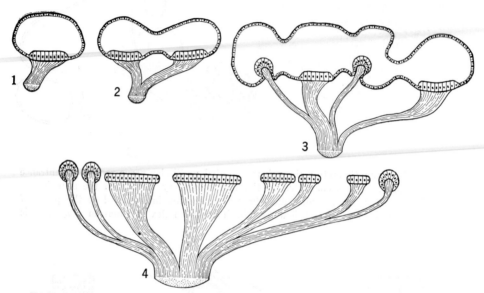

Fig. 8. Differentiation of the vestibular sense organs (schematic, after de Burlet, 1929). As the simple otic vesicle enlarges and transforms into the complicated adult labyrinth, the single patch of sensory epithelium, with nerve fibers attached, becomes subdivided into many parts which undergo independent differentiation to form the various adult sense organs.

interspersion into abnormal pathways, and with very little chance for particular fiber types to be directed to their proper central terminations by mechanical factors alone. Nevertheless reflex relations were restored in an orderly fashion.

There was no indication of learning during the period of recovery. Nor were the recovered reactions impaired by decerebration. Regeneration of the VIII root in tadpoles was also found to restore the compensatory vestibulo-ocular reflexes, even though the optic nerves in these animals had been previously excised so that the formation of proper reflex relations was functionally use-

The strict correlation between the behavior of the vestibular fibers and their peripheral connections suggests a causal relation. From descriptions of the development of the vestibular apparatus and its nerve supply (Harrison, 1936; de Burlet, 1929), it appears that here, as in the visual system, the end organs probably lead the way in the matter of differentiation and induce specificity in their associated nerve fibers. Early in development the vestibular fibers are all connected to a single patch of sensory epithelium. From this single patch of cells are pinched off approximately seven separate parts that become the various end organs of the labyrinth (see Fig. 8). Presumably, as the parts undergo differentiation, they induce a parallel differentiation in the neurons connected to them.

Unlike the situation in the retina, the sensory cell bodies and dendrites are not embedded within the end-organ tissue. It must be supposed, therefore, that specification is imposed on the neurons through their terminal connections. Specification of this kind is well authenticated in the case of the nerves to the limb muscles (Weiss, 1941*d*). The chemical or physical basis of the "induction" effects of one tissue upon the differentiation of neighboring tissue has long been a matter of conjecture. It would appear to involve some type of contact or chain-reaction process. For further discussion of the general problem, see Weiss (1947).

In order that the vestibular fibers may form proper synaptic relations among the central neurons, it is necessary that the secondary neurons also be heterogeneous in character. This could be achieved through self-differentiation or possibly, in part, through induction effects from axon connections with the motor system. It is a general rule of early development (Coghill, 1929, 1930*b*; Herrick, 1939; Windle, 1944, etc.) that the association neurons join with the motor neurons before synapses are established with the sensory fibers. Hence it is possible that axon connections with the already differentiated cells of the motor system influence the refined stages of specification among the association cells.

Genesis of Cutaneous Local Sign

Most vertebrates including man are able without visual aid to localize a tactile stimulus applied to the skin anywhere on the body. Even the frog localizes with considerable accuracy. Mild cutaneous stimuli applied at different points about the back, thorax, hip, thigh, knee, shank, and foot will evoke responses well aimed at the points stimulated. The false localization that follows misregeneration of nerves into foreign regions of the skin shows that the local sign quality depends upon the central relations of the cutaneous fibers. For normal localization the central connections of each fiber must suit the particular peripheral area that the fiber innervates. In a sense the map of the body surface must be reflected in the central circuits.

It has been widely assumed that cutaneous local sign is acquired by experience. Holt (1931) presented a scheme, based on the

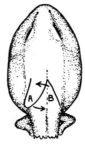

FIG. 9. Contralateral translocation of skin flaps. Skin translocation across the midline of the back in frog tadpoles results in contralateral misdirection of localizing reactions after metamorphosis.

theory of neurobiotaxis, by which this "education of the sensory surfaces" might conceivably take place (see pp. 237 and 263). A later study on the cross union of sensory nerves in the rat (Sperry, 1943*a*), however, has furnished strong evidence of an inherent organization in these animals. Inherent organization is also the rule in the development of cutaneous local sign in amphibians.

In the frog the hind-limb localizing reactions survive cord transection, indicating that they are organized mainly at the spinal level. Skin flaps with their original innervation largely intact can be transplanted across the midline of the back (Fig. 9) of the metamorphosing tadpole, prior to any experience with localizing responses. After metamorphosis is complete, the frogs display localizing reactions that are misdirected to the contralateral side. Stimuli applied to the translocated skin elicit wiping reactions on the opposite side falsely aimed at the original site of the skin flap.

It is also possible by surgery to cross-connect the dorsal roots of the hind-limb nerves to the opposite side of the cord (Fig. 10). When the operations are performed in tadpole stages, the root fibers regenerate to

responses in the urodele amphibians. In frog tadpoles the ophthalmic branch of the trigeminal nerve on one side can be crossed peripherally to the contralateral ophthalmic nerve (Fig. 11). After metamorphosis the wiping responses are misdirected to the wrong side of the head; e.g., stimulation of

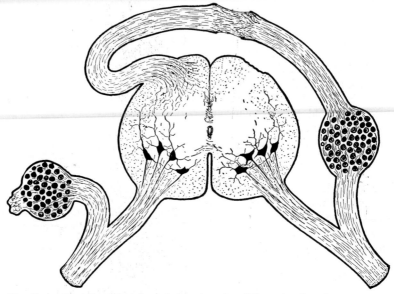

Fig. 10. Contralateral cross union of dorsal roots. When the dorsal roots of the hind-limb nerves are crossed in the manner indicated, the regenerating sensory root fibers establish functional relations with the spinal centers of the contralateral limb similar to those that they establish with the ipsilateral limb centers. This selective formation of the central reflex connections cannot be attributed either to mechanical guidance or to functional adjustment.

form reflex relations with the motor centers of the contralateral limb. After metamorphosis cutaneous stimuli applied to the foot result in characteristic reflex reactions of the opposite leg, while the foot stimulated remains motionless (Sperry, 1947b). Cutaneous local sign in the spinal hind-limb area can hardly be ascribed, therefore, to functional adjustment.

Stimulation of different points about the head and face within the area innervated by the large trigeminal nerve will elicit specific wiping reactions of the ipsilateral forelimb in frogs and toads and specific withdrawal

the left ophthalmic area elicits wiping reactions of the opposite forelimb aimed at the right ophthalmic area (Sperry and Miner, 1949). When the ophthalmic nerve is crossed into the contralateral mandibular nerve, stimulation of the ophthalmic-innervated mandibular region evokes reactions of the opposite forelimb misdirected not only to the opposite side but toward the ophthalmic instead of the mandibular area (Miner, 1949). The ophthalmic branch of V has also been crossed in efts to the ipsilateral mandibular branch of V, the central root of which was then cut and allowed to regenerate into the brain (Fig. 12). The regenerating root fibers reestablished orderly relations, but, because of the peripheral nerve cross, the resultant responses were functionally maladaptive. Pricking the underside of the jaw caused the head to be depressed more strongly against the point of the needle (Sperry and Miner, 1949). Thus, in regeneration as well as in

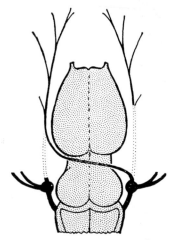

Fig. 11. Contralateral cross union of ophthalmic nerves (from Sperry and Miner, 1949). The left side of head and snout become reinnervated by the crossed right ophthalmic nerve in larval stages. After metamorphosis localizing responses are misdirected to the wrong side of the head.

development, the central circuits became patterned in an orderly manner with reference to certain anatomical relations but without regard for functional adaptiveness.

Good functional recovery of the transected root V following haphazard intertangling of fibers in the scar (Fig. 13) shows that the central patterning is not merely the product of an orderly spacing and timing of fiber ingrowth. Even when the cut root of V is made to regenerate into the brain over the central pathways of nerve VII (Fig. 14) the local sign properties of the trigeminal cutaneous field are correctly restored. It is apparent that in the latter case there is no opportunity for the individual fibers to

follow their old channels to the original central terminals. The dorsal roots of the hindlimb nerves are exceptional in this regard, in that full recovery of functional specificity is not obtained, save in a small percentage of cases. After recovery the foot reactions are less differentiated than normal, with the more refined wiping responses usually lacking. Possibly in this instance the timing of fiber ingrowth may be involved in the adjustment of central linkages.

The conclusion is evident that the sensory neurons supplying different cutaneous areas must differ in character. Fibers from different loci must somehow be distinguishable in the centers. A correlated specificity among the second-order neurons is also indicated.

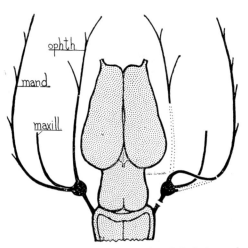

Fig. 12. Cross union of ophthalmic and mandibular nerves with section of root V (from Sperry and Miner, 1949). After recovery, the eft's withdrawal responses to stimulation of the mandible are reversed.

The central neurons must be distinguished in accordance with their various efferent relations. The orderly patterning of central reflex relations then becomes explicable, as in the visual and vestibular systems, on the basis of differential chemoaffinities between the sensory and central neurons.

Furthermore the specificity of the sensory fibers must correspond to the topography of the cutaneous field, reflecting the spatial interrelations of all cutaneous points. Finally the experiments indicate a highly refined, fieldlike differentiation of the entire integument, itself. Without this it would not be possible to obtain the neat adjustment of central-peripheral linkages.

and termination of the sensory fibers, followed later by induction of specificity in the fibers as a consequence of their connections with the cutaneous field.

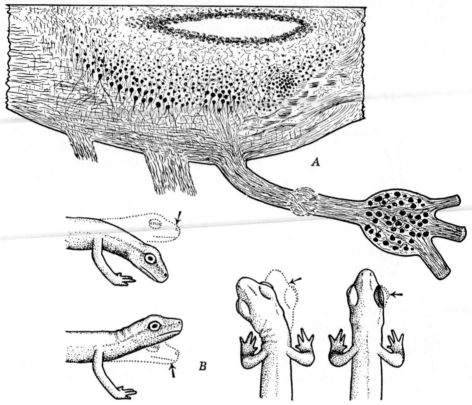

FIG. 13. Centripetal regeneration of trigeminal nerve root. *A:* Diagrammatic frontal section through the regenerated Vth nerve root at its entrance into the medulla. *B:* Different kinds of avoidance or withdrawal reflexes mediated by regenerated fibers of V are consistently restored in an orderly manner.

ment, itself. Without this it would not be possible to obtain the neat adjustment of central-peripheral linkages.

Conceivably the parallel specification of the sensory neurons and the integument might be achieved by independent self-differentiation. In this case the attainment of proper peripheral connections would call for a selective outgrowth of the sensory fibers, each to its correct cutaneous locus. The required linkages could also be established through a relatively indifferent outgrowth

The evidence at present tends to favor the latter possibility. Fibers of the thoracic nerves can be made to connect atypically with limb instead of thoracic skin by extirpating the sensory ganglia of the limb, or by transplanting limbs into the midthoracic region of the back. The sensory fibers then develop central linkages suited to the particular part of the limb integument in which they happen to terminate (Miner, 1949). A similar specification of sensory fibers mediating the corneal reflex has been inferred from the results of transplanting extra eyes to atypical locations about the head (Weiss, 1942; Kollros, 1943). Evidence of this specification failed to appear in the ophthalmic to mandibular nerve crosses cited above, but the fiber specificity may already have become irreversibly determined. Even in mid-larval stages in the frog tadpole the ophthalmic and mandibular divisions of nerve V have been found to retain their original cen-

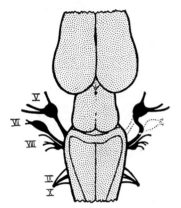

Fig. 14. Cross union of V and VII (from Sperry and Miner, 1949). The trigeminal fibers regenerate into the brain via pathways of VII.

tral associations after connecting with foreign integument (Miner, 1949).

The evidence thus far does not preclude the probability that the sensory ganglia of the various cranial and spinal nerves undergo some degree of differentiation independently of contact with the integument. But the refined specification necessary for localizing different points within a given dermal segment is apparently dependent upon inductive effects imposed upon the nerve fibers by the differentiating skin. An extensive overlap in the terminations of neighboring cutaneous fibers both in the periphery and in the centers must be assumed.

An additional dimension of differentiation among the cutaneous fibers is required for the different modalities of pain, touch, and temperature. Presumably the "local sign" specificity is superimposed upon this more general modal differentiation. How the modal differentiation is controlled and how the different classes of fibers become distributed in proper proportions to the cutaneous field are problems thus far untouched.

Central Reflex Connections of the Proprioceptive Fibers

The sensory neurons supplying the proprioceptors of the musculature develop specific reflex relations in the centers suited to the particular muscles that the neurons innervate. This is necessary to the regulation of posture and of motor coordination. Functional specificity is manifest in stretch reflexes like the knee jerk or ankle jerk, in which sudden stretching of the muscle calls forth a reflex contraction selectively centered in the same muscle (Lloyd, 1946).

It has been shown (Verzár and Weiss, 1930; Weiss, 1937a) that the reflex properties acquired by the proprioceptive fibers of different limb muscles depend upon specification of the fibers by their muscles. When divided fibers of a limb nerve regenerate into the muscles of an extra limb transplanted in the vicinity of the normal limb, their reflex relations become adjusted to suit the particular muscles with which they happen to connect. After recovery passive stretching of different muscles in the extra limb elicits a contraction of the stretched muscles, and also of the homologous muscles of the normal limb. The functional relations thus automatically become adjusted to the pattern of the peripheral connections.

This cannot be ascribed to learning, because the movements of the extra limb serve no purpose. In some cases they are positively detrimental to the animals. The assumption that fibers connect selectively with particular muscles has also been ruled out. The only remaining possibility is that the character of the proprioceptive neurons is determined by inductive effects from the muscles.

In regeneration of the dorsal roots of the hind limb, proprioceptive fibers reestablish

connections along with the exteroceptive
cutaneous fibers. The proprioceptive reflex
relations are restored in a selective manner.
If the dorsal roots of the right leg are crossed
into the spinal centers of the left leg, the
reactions of the left leg in response to

The central patterning of the proprioceptive reflexes following centripetal regeneration of the root fibers can be readily
interpreted in terms of chemoaffinity. We
need only assume that the ingrowing fibers
from different muscles form synapses with

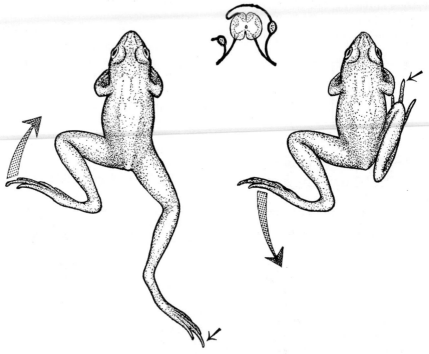

FIG. 15. Systematic reestablishment of proprioception. After crossed regeneration of
the dorsal roots, the posture of the right limb comes to condition the type of reflex
responses made by the contralateral limb in the way it usually conditions its own responses. Stimulation of the right foot (small arrows) causes flexion or extension of the
left leg, respectively, depending on whether the right leg is extended or flexed.

stimuli applied to the right leg are conditioned by the posture of the right leg. For
example, as illustrated in Fig. 15, a tactile
stimulus to the toes of the right foot may
evoke either an extensor kick or, conversely,
a flexor withdrawal of the opposite left foot,
depending on whether the right leg happens
to be flexed or extended. Similar influence
of the leg's posture upon its own responses
is observed after ipsilateral regeneration of
the divided dorsal roots.

different classes of central neurons in a discriminative manner.

The interpretation is not so easy, however,
in the earlier limb-transplant experiments of
Weiss in which the original central connections were left intact. On the assumption
that the central connections remained fixed,
the orderly establishment of the myotatic
responses after disarrangement of the peripheral connections was taken to mean that
specific connections are not basic to central

nervous integration. It was inferred that the central-peripheral selectivity must be based instead upon physiological "resonance" phenomena (see p. 273) and that the muscular specification of the proprioceptive fibers modulates the quality of the impulses the fibers transmit. In order to bring these results into harmony with our present connectionist interpretation it is necessary to postulate that the existing central synapses undergo some kind of trophic breakdown and rearrangement in response to the new peripheral relations.

The foregoing evidence on the development of sensori-central connections reveals a recurring pattern throughout. In the visual, vestibular, cutaneous, and muscular proprioceptive systems, the end-organ tissue apparently undergoes the primary differentiation and then induces local specificity in whatever sensory fibers are in contact with it. The induced fiber specificity then determines in turn the pattern of synaptic associations to be formed in the centers. It seems likely that this same type of "peripheral regulation of central synapsis" may occur also with other tissues such as the cochlea, the tendons, the joints, the ligaments, the facias, the periosteum, etc., the sensory innervation of which possesses local functional specificity. On the foregoing scheme neuronal connections neatly designed for adaptive function can be laid down between the sense organs and the centers by purely developmental forces.

Motor Neuron Associations

The central relations of the primary motor cells must be adjusted to suit their peripheral connections in the musculature. The experiments of Weiss (1922–1937) dealing with the factors controlling selectivity between musculature and nerve centers in amphibians antedate most of the investigations already cited. Much of the more recent work has been stimulated directly by these pioneer investigations and the challenging conclusions to which they led. Their consideration has been delayed to this point because the results on the motor system involve relations and interpretations somewhat more complicated than those dealing with the sensory systems.

It is conceivable that the motor neurons might attain their proper peripheral connections by means of selective axon outgrowth. A given neuron might seek its appropriate muscle. This would require a previous specification of the motor cells into as many different types as there are muscles to be innervated. Actually, however, the outgrowth and termination of the spinal motor axons in amphibians has been reported (Piatt, 1940; Weiss, 1937b) to be entirely nonselective, both in regeneration and in development. Under normal conditions some selectivity of axon termination would seem to be assured by the proximodistal order in which the limb segments develop (Saunders, 1947) and by the chronological order in which the neurons differentiate and send forth their axons. Nevertheless considerable freedom remains within any limb segment, and, since proper muscular coordination is achieved even with highly random outgrowth and termination in the periphery, it follows that the central relations must be adjusted secondarily to suit the peripheral innervation. Even when divided motor axons are forced to regenerate into entirely foreign muscles, the timing of the central discharge becomes adapted to the new terminals (Weiss, 1928, 1936, 1941d).

This adaptation in the timing of the central discharge is not achieved by the learning process. If limbs are transplanted to dorsal positions such that their movements are of no value to the animal, the central-peripheral adjustments occur in the usual systematic manner. This is true even when the limbs are transplanted to the contralateral side and reversed in such a way that the movement of the limbs tends to push the animal backward when it attempts to go forward and vice versa, as indicated in Fig. 16 (Weiss, 1941d). Similar effects are obtained when the limb transplantations are made in prefunctional stages (Brandt, 1925, 1940; Detwiler, 1925; Weiss, 1941d), showing that these relations are patterned initially through developmental forces and not through any kind of functional adjustment. Furthermore it has been shown that these motor patterns develop in the same systematic way in the absence of sensory innervation (Weiss, 1937c) and that they persist after decerebration and cord transection

turbed. The recovery of typical muscle function with atypical end-organ connections might be accounted for by assuming either (1) that central-peripheral selectivity is independent of specific connections and is achieved instead on a physiological "resonance principle" (Weiss, 1928, 1936, 1941), or (2) that the rearrangement of muscular connections produces a compensating readjustment among the central connections (Sperry, 1941, 1943c). Decisive proof re-

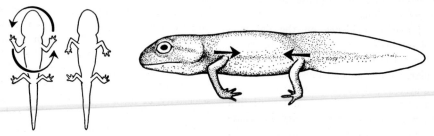

FIG. 16. Reversed locomotion after interchange of right and left forelimbs (after Weiss, 1941d). After prefunctional reversal of the anteroposterior axes of the forelimbs, the central coordination patterns develop in the usual way, with the result that the transplanted forelimbs oppose the normal action of the hind limbs.

down to levels of the cord just rostral to the limb segments (Weiss, 1936). The possibility that learning or any type of functional adaptation might be responsible has thus been excluded.

The motor neurons must somehow be distinguished from one another in the centers according to the muscles they innervate, because the timing of their central discharge is always adjusted on this basis. Weiss concluded that the motor neurons possess some constitutional (presumably biochemical) specificity induced in them by their muscles. This apparently was the first suggestion that nerves may be specified or "modulated" by their end organs. The corollary follows that each muscle of the limb must have biochemical properties all its own. Indeed it would be difficult to account for the morphogenesis of the limb musculature itself in the absence of such a differentiation.

In these experiments of Weiss it was only the end-organ connections that were dis-

garding these two alternatives is lacking. However, the latter fits in with our general chemoaffinity theory of synaptic patterning and is also favored at present because it does not necessitate any significant revision of our current views of central nervous integration. Accordingly the biochemical specification of the motor neurons may be tentatively considered to influence the type of synaptic linkages the cells will tolerate. It is presumed that the sensory and association neurons form their synapses among the motor cells originally in a selective manner, depending upon the biochemical specificity of the motor neurons. When axons regenerate into foreign muscles, the change in biochemical properties induced by the new muscles is thought to cause a trophic degeneration of the synaptic endfeet upon the motor cells. New synapses are then established according to the revised pattern of chemical affinities (see Fig. 17).

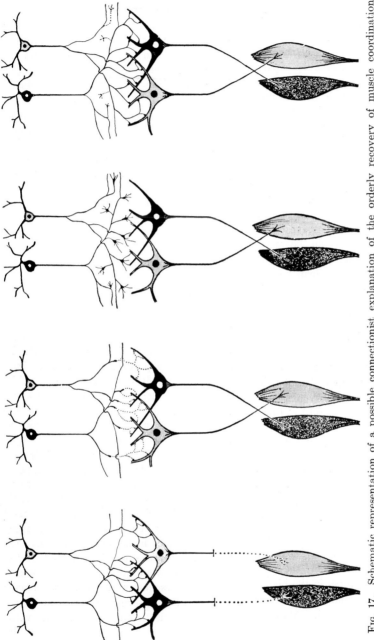

FIG. 17. Schematic representation of a possible connectionist explanation of the orderly recovery of muscle coordination that follows peripheral cross-up of nerve-muscle connections in amphibian larvae. The central synaptic associations are assumed to be established originally on a selective chemoaffinity basis. The specificity of the primary motor neurons is imposed by the musculature, and it changes when the nerves regenerate into foreign muscles, as shown by Weiss. This shift of chemical specificity is presumed to cause a breakdown of the original synaptic endings on the motor cells, followed by reestablishment of a new pattern of synaptic terminals determined by the new interneuronal affinities.

Motor reorganization of this kind occurs readily in the limbs of amphibian larvae. It goes more slowly during and shortly after metamorphosis (Weiss, 1936) and evidently does not occur at all in full-grown anurans. In the phylogenetically more ancient oculomotor system of amphibians the capacity for reorganization seems to be lost at a very early larval stage in both anurans and urodeles. Regeneration of the oculomotor nerve yields undifferentiated mass contraction similar to that obtained in mammals (Sperry, 1947a). Also cross innervation of the inferior oblique muscle by the nerve of the superior oblique muscle yields a reversal of wheel movements of the eye. The function of congenital supernumerary fingers in man (Weiss and Ruch, 1936) suggests that, if nerve rearrangements could be performed sufficiently early in mammals, results similar to those obtained in amphibian limbs might be demonstrated. In the rat the relations of the limb motor neurons has been found to be already irreversible at, or shortly after, birth (Sperry, 1941). The newborn opossum has yet to be investigated in this respect. Where adjustment fails to occur, it may be attributed to the fact that either the motor neurons in postembryonic and postlarval stages are no longer subject to respecification, or else that such respecification no longer causes a breakdown in the existing synapses.

Apparently the cranial motor nuclei III, IV, and VI undergo self-specification prior to the formation of peripheral connections, and the outgrowing axons, unlike those in the amphibian spinal system, take special courses to terminate in specific premuscle masses. Evolutionary refinement in the developmental process may verge in the higher vertebrates toward a similar arrangement in the spinal system as well. Motor axons added after establishment of the pioneer connections might follow previously specified fibers to specific muscles. These, however, remain matters for further investigation.

Tectobulbar and Tectospinal Linkages

The foregoing has not ruled out the possibility that the adjustment of synaptic relations deeper within the centers, i.e. among the second- and higher-order neurons, might be subject to a rather different sort of regulation. Independence of the learning factor, at least, is indicated in data mentioned above on the development of visual reflexes following prefunctional rotation of the eyes, development of vestibulo-ocular responses in the absence of the optic nerve, development of limb coordination following prefunctional transplantation of the limb buds, and also in studies on the development of the swimming pattern under anesthesia (Carmichael, 1926; Harrison, 1904; Matthews and Detwiler, 1926). This kind of evidence, however, fails to eliminate the possibility that mechanical relations, along with a scheduled timing of neuron proliferation, differentiation, fiber outgrowth, and related phenomena, might be sufficient in themselves for the development of central organization, with no need for neuronal specification.

That the second-order neurons are, in fact, biochemically differentiated has been inferred already from the manner in which the primary sensory and motor synapses are formed. More direct evidence of the existence of qualitative specification among the association cells, and of its regulative role in the establishment of their synaptic associations, has been found in experiments dealing with regeneration of the secondary neurons of the visual system (Sperry, 1948a). From the primary visual centers of the brain into which the optic fibers discharge, second- and higher-order neurons running mainly in the tectobulbar and tectospinal tracts transmit the impulses of vision to the motor systems of the bulb and spinal cord. The efferent synaptic relations that these higher-order neurons maintain with the bulbar and spinal systems must be selectively adjusted to suit the differential afferent relations of the cell bodies and dendrites in thalamus and midbrain. For the attainment of proper function in development or in regeneration, the efferent synapses have to be established in a discriminative manner. Otherwise distortion and confusion would appear in the visuomotor coordinations.

When the brain of the adult water newt, *Triturus viridescens,* is transected posterior to the optic lobes, somewhat rostral to the

turns during the following weeks. At the end of approximately two months all the lost functions seem to have been restored in good order.

More than a dozen main fiber tracts are recognizable histologically at the level of transection (Herrick, 1936), and each of these has its own intrafascicular fiber differentiation. With conditions favoring an

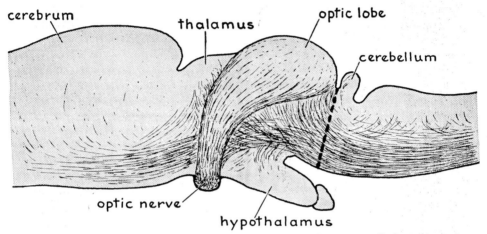

Fig. 18. Level of transection of the secondary central tracts mediating visuomotor coordination (from Sperry, 1948a). After transection of all the ascending and descending tracts that link the higher centers with spinal cord and medulla, regeneration leads to a systematic recovery of visuomotor and other coordinations, even though the eyes meanwhile have been rotated 180 degrees.

entrance of cranial nerve V and close to the level of the trochlear nuclei (Fig. 18), the tectobulbar and tectospinal tracts, plus the many other descending and ascending tracts passing through this level, are interrupted, with consequent functional defects including abolishment of all visual responses. In addition to being blind and anosmic, the animals are weak and deficient in purposeful direction of activity, and they also show abnormalities of posture, equilibrium, and coordination. Animals that manage to survive begin to show functional improvement during the third week. Optokinetic responses begin to reappear at approximately the end of the third week, and the ability to locate accurately small moving objects in space re-

extreme jumbling and intermixing of fiber types in regeneration, the fact that the functional relations are nevertheless restored in orderly fashion points to the presence of specific regulative agents.

That the orderliness of recovery is not due to functional adaptation was shown by rotating the eyes on the optic axis 180 degrees in some of the animals during the period when the central tracts were regenerating. In such animals the visual responses upon recovery showed a systematic reversal in direction just like that produced by rotation of the eyes in animals otherwise normal.

With other possibilities eliminated we are forced to conclude that these higher-order neurons, like the primary neurons, differ in character and form their synaptic associations selectively on the basis of constitutional specificities. Functional adaptation was not eliminated as a regulative factor in recovery of functions other than vision, but there is no reason for supposing that the other central fiber tracts that were transected re-established their synaptic associations in a manner entirely different from those subserving vision. Good functional recovery has also been reported to follow regeneration of the transected spinal cord in amphibian larvae (Lorente de Nó, 1921; and others) and in certain teleosts (Hooker, 1932; Tuge and Hanzawa, 1937). Although adaptation through function has not been ruled out in these cases, it appears likely that here also the adaptation mechanisms are developmental, not functional, in character.

Patterning of Complete Reflex Circuits

From the data relating to the separate systems of sensory, motor, and central neurons, it is possible to assemble a tentative working picture of the developmental organization of the entire sensori-neuro-motor pathway of a few reflex circuits. The myotatic reflexes are mediated by a "two-neuron arc" consisting of the proprioceptive and the primary motor neurons (Lloyd, 1946). Evidence regarding the acquisition of specificity and central connections has been presented for both these sets of neurons, and we need add only the temporal order of events. The motor cells first form their peripheral connections and then develop wide-spreading dendrites. The afferent neurons meanwhile attain their end-organ relations and send their central root fibers into the cord to form ascending and descending branches. Later these send off numerous collaterals into the neuropil, some of which contact directly the dendrites and cell bodies of the motor neurons. In forming synapses the afferent fibers of each muscle apparently exhibit a special predilection for those motor

neurons specified by the same muscle, and to a lesser extent for those of the most closely related muscles. This would seem to involve a simple affinity of like for like. Such simplicity in interneuron affinity is exceptional, however, and even in this case the same proprioceptive root fibers probably form connections on a different basis at other levels of the cord. Inhibitory associations also must be formed with antagonist motor neurons. Little can be said about the latter, however, in the absence of more information regarding the neural basis of reciprocal inhibition.

The cutaneous reflexes for withdrawal from irritating objects are more complicated, requiring at least one set of intracentral neurons (Lloyd, 1946). The number of distinct motor patterns employed in the localizing reflexes of the frog hind limb, for example, would require several specific classes of association neurons, each tending to activate a distinct combination of motor neurons. Specification of these association neurons must occur principally by self-differentiation. According to the usual order of development, the various classes of association cells probably form their selective relations with the motor neurons before the sensory connections are established. Neurons connected with different cutaneous regions presumably show a preference for specific types of association cells. The extent of functional variability would indicate that the neuronal affinities are not very strict and permit extensive overlap among the afferent terminations. Additional inhibitory associations must also be established among the internuncial cells so that the ascendency of one excitation pattern automatically inhibits all others.

The vestibulo-ocular reflexes for compensatory eye movements are mediated by a "three-neuron arc." Specification and synapsis of the sensory and motor neurons have already been discussed, and the existence of specificity among the association neurons located in the vestibular nuclei has been inferred. The latter could be achieved by self-differentiation or, in part, through inductive effects from contact with the already differentiated motor ocular nuclei. In the former case the outgrowing axons from the vestibular nuclei would have to find their appropriate neurons in nuclei III, IV, and VI. Alternatively the association neurons might first establish their efferent relations in a more random fashion, with the final specification being induced by the motor nuclei.

Studies on the optic nerve, the secondary visual tracts, and the primary motor cells cover the main orders of neurons involved in optokinetic and other visual reflexes. Here also the developmental steps involve specification of the motor and sensory fibers under the influence of their end organs, plus a correlated but largely independent specification of the intracentral neurons. Connections are formed in the usual order first with the motor periphery, then between the central and motor cells, and finally the circuits are closed by ingrowth of the optic fibers. Without repetition of details, the evidence indicates that the synaptic junctions are formed in each case in a selective manner on the basis of interneuronal affinities. With regard to these as well as to the foregoing reflexes, only the most direct pathways have been considered. Alternative reflex routes often exist, and, according to Lorente de Nó (1933), the main reflex pathways have superimposed upon them local open and closed circuits. It is not difficult to visualize in a general way the serial organization of such accessory circuits through the subsequent spread of inductive effects after the main lines of differentiation have been laid down.

Not only the structural linkages but also the excitatory thresholds of the nerve cells must be properly adjusted. Little is known about the mechanisms controlling the latter. Apparently the different types of neurons and neuron groups acquire a characteristic resting threshold in the course of their differentiation. Shock phenomena suggest that the excitatory thresholds must be adjusted in development to the number and type of synaptic endings present. Cutting off some of the afferent connections of a neuron raises its excitatory threshold. In the course of time the neuron then tends to regain its characteristic threshold in new equilibrium with whatever afferent influences remain. Extrinsic trophic as well as nerve-discharge effects from the connecting cells thus seem to be involved, along with intrinsic metabolic processes, in determining the neuron's basal excitatory state.

It is evident that the central organization even of the relatively simple reflex patterns can be discussed as yet only in a simplified and speculative manner. The few inquiries we have thus far made into the complex picture of the organization of central synaptic relations reveal something of the possible nature of the mechanisms involved, but they only begin to suggest the complications of actual detail.

OTHER PATTERNING FACTORS AND CERTAIN THEORETICAL CONCEPTS

Neurobiotaxis

The theory most widely supported as an explanation of the structuring of integrative patterns is Kappers' (1932) law of "neurobiotaxis." Electrical currents are presumed in this theory to play a dominant role in determining neuron relations. It is maintained (1) that the neuron is electrically polarized, (2) that axons grow out from the cell body along the direction of an electric current and dendrites against the current, (3) that the nerve cell bodies tend to migrate along with dendritic growth against the current, (4) that dendrites and axons tend to grow perpendicularly toward and away from a neighboring fiber tract, owing to the electrical field set up around the tract by the passage of impulses, and (5) that the collection of similar fibers into bundles and the selective linkage of particular neurons are due to the timing of electrical discharges in the developing nervous system. A related hypothesis proposed by Bok (1915) under the term "stimulogenous fibrillation" likewise assumed that outgrowing nerve fibers are directed by electrical irradiation from stimulated fiber tracts and also from sensory surfaces and muscles. The present discussion concerns only those aspects related to fiber outgrowth and synaptic formation.

The cogent criticisms of Weiss (1941c) cast strong doubt on the whole idea that electrical fields can play any major role in patterning the neuronal relations of the developing embryo. There are numerous phenomena in nervous development and regeneration, as, for example, the simultaneous growth of fibers in the same locality in different directions (Speidel, 1933), that are incompatible with the contention that the direction of fiber growth is electrically determined. Even some of the original observations on which the electrical theories were largely based have now been discredited (Hamburger, 1946; Windle, 1933). The report of a weak influence of electric current on nerve growth in vitro (Marsh and Beams, 1946) leaves open the possibility that certain aspects of the theory of neurobiotaxis may yet find verification. These, however, seem to have very limited explanatory value with reference to the patterning of functional interconnections.

Kappers himself was well aware that the postulated stimulo-concurrent character of axons and stimulopetal character of dendrites was not sufficient, per se, even in theory to account for the selective formation of interneuronal connections. To explain selective synapses he had to invoke the additional factor of timing. It is the differential timing of discharges in the developing nervous system that is supposed to cause selective linkage of particular neuron combinations. Connections form between neurons that happen to be excited simultaneously or in immediate succession. Thus the selective timing of neuron discharge is reasoned in circular fashion to cause the growth of selective structural relations on which is supposed to depend the selective timing of neuron discharge.

Any attempt to apply such a scheme to concrete cases leads to obvious and insurmountable difficulties. In the case of the retino-central connections it would be necessary to suppose that every animal of a species encounters exactly the same temporal and spatial pattern of retinal stimulation in the course of its development. Furthermore the light stimuli in each individual would have to be met in a schedule adjusted to the growth of the central dendrites with a precision utterly beyond the bounds of probability. Finally there is good evidence that the orderly projection of the retina upon the brain centers will develop even in complete darkness (Goodman, 1932; Hebb, 1937).

Recourse at this point to spontaneous retinal discharge is of no help, because the equally precise and systematic timing of the implicit discharges would then have to be accounted for. Assuming either implicit or overt discharges to be formative factors in the foregoing manner, it becomes necessary to suppose further that, once the various neurons have established their connections, they cease to discharge thereafter; otherwise they would continue to attract the growing fiber tips of all neurons developing subsequently, the terminals of which should be formed elsewhere. These and other difficulties discourage any attempt to make the concept of neurobiotaxis a primary formative factor in the ontogenetic patterning of synaptic associations. That something akin to neurobiotaxis may be involved in the learning process of the developed nervous system cannot be denied at this time in the face of our ignorance of the neural basis of learning. The speculative nature of any such contention should, however, be recognized.

Disuse Atrophy and Trophic Interdependence

The outgrowth of an excessive number of nerve fibers in development and in regeneration followed by atrophy and degeneration of those that fail to acquire terminal connections has been described by Cajal (1928, 1929) and others. The destruction of unconnected neurons and fiber branches is much slower in peripheral nerves than in the centers and is said to require months and perhaps years in the adult mammal. In the centers the process may occur within a few days. This phenomenon has been referred to by Cajal as the "law of utilitarian atrophy" or "atrophy of disuse."

That it is the "use" or discharge of the fibers that determines their survival, as might be inferred from the name, appears unlikely. In the first place the impulses of an axon, so far as is known, are conducted over those collaterals that are not terminally connected, as well as over those that are. Furthermore there are a number of instances in which the survival of neurons and end organs is known to depend upon the existence of adequate connections under conditions where the passage of excitations is clearly not the essential factor. For example, the degeneration of taste buds and of other sensory endings after severance of their nerve supply, the retrograde degeneration of motor horn cells in young mammals after destruction of their peripheral connections, and the retrograde degeneration of thalamic neurons after cortical lesions can hardly be attributed to lack of excitation, because ample sources of excitation under these conditions remain undisturbed. The functional relations are reversed in so-called "transneuronal" effects such as degeneration of the lateral geniculate nucleus after section of the optic nerve, degeneration in the red nucleus after section of the brachium conjunctivum, and degeneration of striated muscles after section of their somatic motor nerves. With regard to such phenomena also, however, there is evidence that the primary cause of degeneration is not the lack of excitation.

The responsible factor seems to be some kind of trophic, metabolic, chemical, or physical influence of these connections upon the nerve cells and their end organs. Apparently there is a general tendency for the elements of the sensori-neuro-motor system to become dependent in varying degree upon the linkages that they normally acquire. Accordingly some term such as "trophic degeneration" or "isolation atrophy" would seem more suitable for this class of phenomena.

To some extent the trophic interdependencies of neurons and end organs may be selective in character, as where motor fibers (Arey, 1941) or the sensory fibers of general sensibility fail to maintain taste buds in the tongue of mammals, or to maintain either taste buds or lateral-line organs in the skin of the catfish (Bailey, 1937). In other situations, however, there is considerable leeway in this respect, as where the same sensory fibers in the duck have been shown by skin transplantation to be capable of maintaining either the corpuscles of Gandry or the corpuscles of Herbst (Dijkstra, 1933).

In addition to the various phenomena of retrograde and of transneuronal chromatolysis, atrophy, and degeneration, there are certain other indications that linkages have a profound influence upon the general status of the neuron. The formation of terminal connections appears to act as an impetus to the differentiation of the embryonic neurons (Hamburger and Keefe, 1944). Terminal connections are also important in a selective manner for the attainment of normal fiber diameter (Aitken, Sharman, and Young, 1947; Weiss, Edds, and Cavanaugh, 1945). Acquisition of connections tends to bring about a state of equilibrium in the neuron, with cessation of further growth. Growing fibers are inclined to adhere to and to follow in a preferential manner other fibers that have succeeded in forming connections (Weiss, 1941c) as if there occurred a change in the surface of the connected fibers that distinguishes them from fibers still unconnected. Perhaps most important from the point of view of the present discussion is the evidence already elaborated that the terminal cells and tissues may induce specification of neurons and thereby influence their central synapsis.

The fact that any fiber branches at all should remain unconnected in the organism deserves comment because, no matter where excess fibers may stray, there are always cells of some sort in the vicinity with which connections might be established as far as mechanical accessibility is concerned. That connections are, nevertheless, not always made indicates in itself a degree of chemical selectivity in neuron termination. The saturation and denervation effects discussed below are closely related phenomena.

It is conceivable that some kind of elimination of excess and maladaptive fiber connections is achieved on an essentially functional rather than on a trophic basis in the learning process in the developed nervous system. Unlike the foregoing growth and trophic phenomena, however, this has no direct observational foundation.

"Individuation versus Integration"

Influenced by certain Gestalt concepts in vogue at the time, Coghill (1929, 1930a) emphasized features of the development of behavior patterns that seemed to illustrate the application of Gestalt principles in this field. From his classical studies on the development of the nervous system and behavior in urodele larvae Coghill inferred that discrete responses always emerge out of larger patterns by a process of individuation. The organization of the larger, "total" behavior patterns he considered to be primary, not a secondary effect arising through integration of partial patterns. In studies of embryonic and fetal behavior much concern has been given ever since to the confirmation or refutation of this idea. Windle (1944) accepts Coghill's conclusions for salamanders but not for mammals, in which he has found discrete reflex responses appear-

ing very early, with no prior mass movement or total pattern stage.

Coghill's conclusions in this regard were drawn primarily from behavioral evidence, although he was able to support the concept by certain anatomical correlations. The latter, however, were based largely on the diffuse outgrowth of the peculiar primary motor system of *Amblystoma*, which can hardly be considered typical of the organization of behavior patterns for higher vertebrates or even for succeeding developmental stages of *Amblystoma*. Precise anatomical correlates are not so easy to observe in higher vertebrates or in the later stages of urodele development, and accordingly most of the evidence from these sources is behavioral. What behavioral observations may mean regarding the nature of the underlying mechanisms is often difficult to infer. Individuation of behavior might conceivably be achieved in a variety of ways, as, for example, by the selective elimination or the addition of fiber collaterals, by the elimination or addition of entire neurons, by the selective reinforcement or the weakening of synapses already present, by the selective adjustment of excitatory thresholds, by the selective sensitization of neurons to each other, etc. On the other hand, the specificity of initial reactions need not necessarily imply absence of individuation from a "total pattern." It could mean merely that neural individuation is completed before the onset of function rather than after. Correlations between behavior and the developmental processes that produce the structure that mediates the behavior must frequently be rather remote.

When we consider the complicated developmental mechanisms involved in the patterning of interneuronal relations, "individuation versus integration" tends to fade as a crucial issue. As far as the evidence goes, there is nothing intrinsic to the nature of the developmental processes that would prevent the initial establishment of specialized, discrete functional relations. Also it is clear that the development of "total" behavior patterns, particularly in the higher vertebrates, is dependent upon an array of developmental events occurring at all levels of the nervous system as well as in the periphery, many of which are widely separated and regulated quite independently of one another.

Myelinization and Function

The addition of myelin to nerve fibers probably has little or no direct influence upon the formation of proper reflex connections. It deserves mention, however, as a conspicuous feature in the development and maturation of the nervous system and as an indicator of the order in which various systems become functional. The central nervous tracts tend to become myelinated in a definite sequence that shows considerable constancy in all mammals and follows roughly the order in which the tracts were developed phylogenetically (Langworthy, 1933). A general correlation between the order of the appearance of stainable myelin and the order in which the nerves become functional has suggested a causal relation. The relation, however, is not simple, and it appears to be reciprocal in nature.

It has been shown by Langworthy that fairly complex activity can be carried out prior to myelinization. On the other hand, functions in general show considerable improvement in speed, strength, steadiness, and precision coincident with the laying down of myelin. However, it is not entirely a matter of myelinization acting to improve function, because, conversely, the laying down of myelin is stimulated and accelerated by function. At the same time absence of normal function does not prevent or decrease the ultimate degree of myelinization (Romanes, 1947). Myelinization and the order of its occurrence would seem thus to be an inherently predetermined process capable of proceeding in the absence of function in the usual sense. Function when present, however, stimulates and accelerates myelinization, which in turn appears to act reciprocally to improve function. It cannot be said to what extent the apparent myelinization-function interrelation is directly dependent upon these factors, per se, and to what extent upon other maturational processes that may be going on simultaneously.

Flux in Neuronal Associations

Studies of the details of nerve termination in the tail of the frog tadpole (Speidel, 1940–41), in the cutaneous plexus of the ear of the rabbit, and in human skin, particularly where it is subject to frequent stretching and abrasion (Weddell and Glees, 1942), support earlier contentions that the peripheral connections are not stable but are in a continuous state of flux with degenerative and regenerative changes commonly taking place among the terminal arborizations.

Speidel suggests that a similar state of flux probably characterizes the synaptic terminals in the centers.

With constant readjustment of this sort taking place, there must exist continuous opportunity for the establishment of atypical connections. In the skin, for example, there should be ample opportunity for temperature fibers to terminate in tactile "spots," and vice versa. There should be even greater chance for the formation of abnormal terminations in the closely packed central nuclei. That the general pattern of neuronal termination does not become severely disarranged by these changes means that there must be persistent influences acting to maintain the proper relations.

It is not just a matter of the regenerating fibers' being guided back along their previous pathways to the former terminals. Speidel (1940–41) states that the regenerated pattern distal to the neurilemma sheaths bears no specific resemblance to the original pattern. Weddell and Glees (1942) describe dichotomy in regenerating fibers indicative of new collaterals, and the sprouting of new collaterals into neighboring denervated areas is well authenticated (Weddell, Guttmann, and Gutmann, 1941). Apparently the same type of selective force that determines the original pattern of connections in development continues to be effective in maintaining the general pattern after it is formed. The range of possible terminations of each neuron may be restricted by its constitution and by its affinities for the various cell types within its terminal area. This would permit some variability to occur in the terminations of individual fibers but would keep constant the overall pattern of termination.

Selective Fasciculation

During the outgrowth of fibers from spinal cord grafts into nearby grafted limbs (Weiss, 1941c) those pioneer fibers that first become attached to the limb acquire thereby some property that converts them into a preferential contact pathway for later fibers. Subsequent fibers adhere to earlier fibers that have made terminations in preference to fibers that have not. Axon fibers of supernumerary Mauthner's cells, the giant neuron of the fish brain, exhibit a marked tendency to follow the original Mauthner's fibers (Oppenheimer, 1942). Also, grafted ectopic cranial nerve roots tend to enter the brain at the same level as the corresponding host nerves to which they become adherent (Piatt, 1947). Experimental observations of this sort, plus the fact that nerve fibers of similar type tend normally to collect together in separate fascicles in the neuraxis and to some extent in the peripheral nerves, indicate that outgrowing nerve fibers adhere selectively to other fibers of their own kind, for which Weiss (1941c) has suggested the term "selective fasciculation."

As new fibers are added to the spinal nerves during growth, the outgrowing motor fibers apparently turn into muscular branches at each bifurcation, whereas cutaneous fibers avoid muscular branches and turn into cutaneous pathways (Taylor, 1944). Something must prevent the motor fibers from following cutaneous branches,

and vice versa. Moreover both motor and sensory fibers distribute themselves in proper proportions to their respective peripheries. Something, therefore, must prevent the motor fibers from all turning into the same motor channels, leaving other branches undersized. A tendency for fibers to stick selectively to preceding pioneer fibers of their own kind would conceivably help to account for this proportionate distribution of new fibers.

Saturation and Denervation Effects on Fiber Termination

Under normal conditions nerve endings tend to be limited to a characteristic density, even in situations where it is clear that many more terminations could be established were it merely a matter of space and numbers of available fibers. In muscle, for example, the nerve terminations are distributed in a strictly limited manner to the individual muscle fibers and spindles. One may well ask why some muscle fibers do not get several dozen axon terminals, others half that many, and some none. Similarly in the skin the nerve endings tend to be scattered evenly. The same is true of some of the central nuclei. In the lateral geniculate nucleus, for example, the telodendria of the optic axons are distributed evenly, with a characteristic number of endings on each geniculate cell.

One of the reasons advanced to explain the fact that neurons and end organs do not become smothered with nerve terminals beyond a characteristic limit is that nerve connections cause a reaction in the cells of termination that makes these cells impervious to the advances of additional fibers (Harrison, 1910; Weiss, 1941c). When the saturation point, which varies for different cells and tissues, is reached, conditions become unfavorable for further fiber growth and termination. The situation has been compared to that of the fertilization of eggs in which the penetration of the first spermatozoon causes a reaction in the egg cell, preventing the entrance of more sperm. Some experimental evidence for this has been found in the innervation of muscles and of whole limbs (Fort, 1940; Litwiller, 1938). The fact that some fibers in central tracts terminate abruptly in nearby centers while others push on to much more distant regions might be due in part to the successive saturation of the various areas. The additional possibility must be considered that, in the centers, neurons may reach a saturation point for certain types of synapses while still accepting others.

The opposite phenomenon has also been observed, namely, a stimulative effect of denervated areas on nerve fiber outgrowth (Speidel, 1940–41; Weddell, Guttmann, and Gutmann, 1941). Fort (1940) found that motor nerve fibers grow out faster in denervated muscle than in innervated muscle, and that, the longer the muscle is denervated, the faster the outgrowth within the time limits he investigated. Geohegan and Aidar (1942) report experiments suggesting that partial denervation of the sympathetic ganglia causes the growth within the ganglia of collaterals from the remaining intact fibers to supply the denervated cells. However, in this case it is difficult to be sure how much the effect may be due merely to hypersensitivity of the denervated neurons.

Central Self-Differentiation of Coordination Patterns

The central patterns of coordination develop with considerable independence of connections with the sensory periphery. In the early stages of differentiation the motor system, as a rule, achieves a precocious organization of its own so that spontaneous or central excitations lead to coordinated motor responses before any sensory connections have been established (Coghill, 1929; Herrick, 1939; Windle, 1944; and others). It has also been shown that coordinated limb movement develops after prefunctional excision of the sensory nerve supply of the limb itself (Weiss, 1941d; Taylor, 1944).

To this extent and to the degree that developmental organization does not depend on experience, central patterning seems to be independent of peripheral influences.

The foregoing, along with data on the autonomous nature of functional organization in the centers has led in some instances to special emphasis on the extent to which the basic patterns of coordination undergo an autonomous central self-differentiation. However, the synaptic relations of the primary sensory and motor neurons form an important part of the central pattern. If formation of these primary synaptic associations is governed by inductive effects from the periphery, then our conception of the extent to which coordination patterns undergo central self-differentiation must be adjusted accordingly. It has not yet been possible to demonstrate the development of functional organization in the nerve centers in the absence of connections on the motor side. Thus the possibility that inductive effects from the motor endings play a role in regulating the formation of neuronal interconnections in the centers has not been excluded. Nor can it be said that the present evidence completely eliminates the possibility that the ingrowth of sensory root fibers into their various central nuclei has some influence on the differentiation therein of functional relations. It has been found, for instance, that aberrant VIII and lateral-line root fibers will induce the differentiation of supernumerary Mauthner's cells in atypical sites where they enter the brain (Piatt, 1947).

Even with such allowances, however, the role of central self-differentiation in the development of coordination patterns still deserves emphasis. The differentiation or specification of the secondary and especially of the higher-order neurons and the consequent patterns of interrelations that they form must depend principally on formative agents within the centers. Differences in the inherent behavior patterns of different vertebrate species from the level of complex instincts down to that of polysynaptic reflex responses must for the most part be attributed to central and not to peripheral influences. In earlier discussions of the chemoaffinity hypothesis (Sperry, 1943c) the induction of central organization starting from the periphery and working inward has certainly been overemphasized.

In nuclear fields like the optic tectum or the striate cortex in which the functional differentiation is correlated with anatomical dimensions in a gradient, field fashion, a basic self-differentiation of the nucleus is indicated. There are many nuclei of this type that may, along with the peripheral structures, be looked upon as foci of primary self-differentiation. On the other hand, there are central nuclei, such as the spinal association centers and the reticular areas of the brain stem, in which neurons of similar functional type appear to be scattered in a more diffuse manner among other neurons of diverse functions. In such regions it is possible that specification is more dependent upon terminal contacts, as with the limb motor neurons. Neuron specification may thus arise from intrinsic self-differentiation or from extrinsic inductive actions. The latter may sometimes be effected over considerable distances through axon and dendrite contacts. Both types of specification are probably involved in varying degree in many nuclei.

Functional Reinforcement of Adaptive Patterns

It has been a common conception that synaptic linkages are adjusted in development on the basis of functional adaptiveness. Usually it has been supposed that synaptic associations are laid down initially in a diffuse, excessive, and fortuitous fashion, after which there occurs a selective reinforcement of the adaptive linkages with atrophy and degeneration of the maladaptive linkages. In the learning process in the mature animal, some kind of selective retention on the basis of functional effects does take place, of course, and it has been an easy step to infer its occurrence in development also.

In most vertebrates, however, up to and including the lower mammals (Sperry, 1945c), the learning capacity, after it has reached its peak in the adult, is still unable to effect any rearrangement of the basic integrative structure of the nervous system. Even in the primates learning appears to be largely cerebral. It effects no changes in the interneuronal relations of cord and brain stem (Sperry, 1947c). To assume that the elementary integrative relations are organized in the first place through function is thus to assume that the nervous system in its imperfect, immature condition, and under circumstances unfavorable in many respects for functional adjustment, is able to handle a type of learning of which it is incapable later on.

It is conceivable, in this regard, that neural tissue might be more plastic in the developmental stages. Learning and growth together might, through a series of irreversible steps, produce integrative structures that, when completed, would no longer be subject to functional reorganization. However, the learning capacity of the nervous system is much more than a mere passive plasticity of a highly impressionable tissue. It is more comparable to the active functional ability of a complex machine. The self-regulative, operational organization of the nervous system, not just the character of its protoplasm, is what enables it to utilize its experience selectively to improve upon its own structure. Complex self-regulative mechanisms must first be constructed in ontogeny before adaptation by learning can begin to take place.

The selectivity of learning is difficult to account for in early development. The fact that not all excitation patterns, but only the adaptive ones, reinforce themselves must be explained. Some background of organization must be present for different excitation patterns to have different reinforcement value. Otherwise all reactions would tend to reinforce themselves indiscriminately. The establishment of a central organization capable of distinguishing adaptive from nonadaptive excitation patterns must therefore logically precede any selective adjustment on the basis of functional effects.

The point in nervous development at which sufficient organization is attained to permit selective reinforcement on the basis of functional adequacy might conceivably be an early one, but the evidence indicates not. In mammals it is doubtful if any appreciable patterning of synaptic associations is achieved by function before the cerebral cortex has become differentiated and has established its subcortical connections. As this is one of the last steps of nervous development, it may be concluded that the bulk of the nervous system must be patterned without the aid of functional adjustment. From the developmental and anatomical point of view, the synaptic modifications that are later imposed by the learning process constitute a rather minute refinement in the nervous structure, so inconspicuous, in fact, that the exact location and even the nature of these learned adjustments still await demonstration.

The foregoing concerns function as a patterning factor in the organization of neuronal connections and does not apply to function as a general condition necessary to healthy growth. Development in many instances, however, is remarkably independent of function, even in this latter sense. The experiments of Harrison (1904) and others demonstrate the orderly formation of the amphibian nervous system well through the swimming stage under deep anesthesia. It is the positive toxic effects of the anesthesia, presumably, rather than the absence of function per se that prevents development from proceeding much farther under these conditions. Rabbits reared to the age of six months in complete darkness have been found to have neither gross nor histological defects detectable anywhere in the visual system, including the cortical projection area

(Goodman, 1932). A general tendency is evident in other organ systems, as well as in the nervous system, for development to be independent of function and to anticipate the needs of function. But function sometimes becomes a necessary element later on, after it has once started.

The stage at which function becomes a formative factor and its relative importance in neurogenesis obviously varies greatly in different species. Function plays its paramount role in the postnatal development of man. Where for a long period both function and maturation are operative together, the contributions of each to the final structure become interrelated in complex manner. In attempting to interpret the defective development of vision in chimpanzees reared in the dark from birth (Riesen, 1947), for example, it is extremely difficult to untangle the relative roles played by the three different factors: inherent maturation, function as a specific organizing agent, and function as a nonformative but necessary condition. One would hardly expect the lack of light in these cases to cause disorderly development of the cortical projection of the retinal field. However, retinal degeneration and inability to respond normally to light for almost a month have been observed in fish kept in the dark for more than two years (Breder and Rasquin, 1947; Ogneff, 1911). In certain cave salamanders, the larval eyes of which normally undergo regression at metamorphosis, the eyes will become quite normal if the larvae grow to adulthood in the light (Walls, 1942).

Finally it is usually impossible to assess the relative importance of maturation and of learning with reference to behavior, because most behavior depends upon a combination of neural structures, of which some may be inherently organized and others organized by experience. The issues are considerably clarified by restricting the problem to the organization of the neural structure itself. In this case the patterning of certain parts can be ascribed entirely to inherent growth forces, whereas in others the learning factor may be involved in varying degree.

Hormones and Maturation

In infraprimate mammals and especially in lower vertebrates it is evident that many of the reactions associated with reproduction, such as nest building, mating, and giving birth to, feeding, and caring for the young are largely inherent in character. The maturation of these particular reaction patterns, some of them extremely elaborate, is of especial interest because they appear so late in life and because their appearance is correlated with the perfusion of the nervous system with specific chemical agents. Similarly in the metamorphosis of anuran amphibians there occurs a relatively late maturation of a whole series of new behavior patterns dependent in part, at least, upon hormonal action.

A precocious localized maturation of the lid-closure reflex has been induced in frog tadpoles (Kollros, 1942) by implanting thyroid pellets into the hindbrain. Other lines of evidence suggest that the reproductive hormones likewise may act directly and selectively upon the nerve centers (Beach, 1947). There is also considerable specificity in the behavioral effects of the male and female hormones. This selective response of particular neural mechanisms to biochemical agents represents another indication of chemical differentiation within the centers. To it may be added a host of related phenomena involving selective susceptibility of different neuron types to the action of various drugs, toxins, histological stains, metals, viruses, bacteria, etc.

The exact manner in which hormones act on the centers is not known. It is fairly certain with regard to the sex reactions of many mammals, at least, that the patterns of nerve cells involved are well differentiated and their functional relations basically arranged early in development, long before the increased concentration of hormone brings the mechanism into functional maturity (Beach, 1947). It is usually assumed that the hormone influences the excitation threshold of specific patterns of neurons, the structural relations of which remain fixed. However, in view of Speidel's (1940–41) suggestions regarding the lability of central associations, and in view of the duration of the latent period between the onset of hormone administration and its effect on behavior, it is possible that growth and readjustment of synaptic relations may also be involved.

Neurogenesis and Specific Nerve Energies

The experiments on synaptic development and regeneration have here been interpreted entirely on a connectionist basis. This discussion has been presented in terms of the classical assumption that the integrative action of the nervous system is dependent upon refined selectivity among neuronal linkages. However, there has arisen of late a good deal of skepticism concerning this traditional connectionist theory (Bethe, 1931; Gerard, 1941; Goldstein, 1939; Koffka, 1935; Köhler, 1940; Lashley, 1942; Weiss, 1936, 1941d, etc.). Accordingly it should be stressed that there is as yet no final proof that neuron specificities determine the growth of anatomical relations. In regeneration of the optic nerve, for example, it has not been directly observed that fibers from different retinal quadrants form different central connections. This is still inferential, and at least one other interpretation is theoretically possible; i.e. it is conceivable that the central connections are laid down in a profuse and random fashion and that the subsequent specificity of response derives from some sort of specificity in the nature of the impulses carried by the different fiber types.

At the turn of the century Hering (1913) argued in favor of the existence of qualitative specificity among the excitatory energies conducted by different types of nerve fibers. It was his contention that the pattern of the central pathways excited was determined not merely by the existing anatomical connections and their threshold phenomena but also by selective sensitivity of central neurons to specific types of afferent energies. He believed that the individual nerve impulses differed intrinsically in their physicochemical properties. As an alternative he mentioned that the specificity might also reside in frequency differences, in which case the specific energies of the nerve fibers would appear as special resonance capacities and the central patterns would be determined by selective attunement of the various neuron types to different frequencies (see also Head, 1920). Later, similar concepts were invoked (Weiss, 1928, 1936, 1941d) as a possible explanation of homologous response in supernumerary amphibian limbs. The "homologous" or "myotypic" action of muscles atypically innervated seemed to rule out specific anatomical connections on the part of the motor neurons and to indicate instead a selective physiological sensitivity to specific excitatory agents, one for each muscle, within the limb centers.

All our experiments on the formation of synaptic associations could be interpreted on a similar physiological basis rather than in terms of the growth of specific anatomical connections. Discussion of this alternative possibility has been purposely postponed until now in order to avoid confusion and repetition. Once the connectionist explanation is clear, it becomes a relatively easy step — should future findings necessitate it — to translate the results and conclusions into terms of specific nerve energy or resonance phenomena. The connectionist interpretation is emphasized at present only because the great mass of neurological data fall more readily into this traditional scheme. Furthermore, with a connectionist explanation of homologous response now available, the original reasons for resorting to a resonance hypothesis have been largely removed.

For the sake of completeness mention should be made of another possible basis of interpretation. It is conceivable (Sperry, 1943c) that neurons might regularly form and maintain an excess of connections, but that only a selective minority of the synapses ever become functional. The interneuronal affinities might affect the structure of the synapses to make certain ones capable of transmitting excitations and others not. Functional specificity would still depend on selective anatomical associations rather than on resonance phenomena or specific nerve energies, but only minute differences in synaptic structure would be involved instead of complete presence or absence of synapses.

SUMMARY

A survey of the evidence supports the thesis that the inherent patterning of neuronal linkages is achieved by embryonic processes similar to those responsible for the grosser phases of neurogenesis and for the development of other organ systems. Among these developmental processes those of embryonic differentiation, determination, and induction deserve special mention. In the genetic structuring of the integrative circuits developmental forces reach their peak of refinement and complexity.

Just as the cells of the early embryo differentiate into a variety of strains to form the diverse tissues of the adult body, so the cells of the nervous system undergo a similar, though more subtle, differentiation among themselves into a multitude of neuron types. Not only the nervous system but the associated peripheral tissues as well, the musculature and its tendons, the dermis, the fascias, the ligaments, the periosteum, the retina, the cochlea, etc., are subject to a refined qualitative differentiation or specification far beyond what is visibly manifest.

After the prospective nervous tissue has become differentiated from other tissues and has formed the neural tube, the basal or motor portion of the tube differentiates from the sensory or alar portion and the gross cephalic regions become distinct — this and the following by way of illustration and without regard for the exact order of these events. An eye field emerges in the dien-cephalic region, and in the spinal cord a brachial and a hind-limb field are differentiated. The main subdivisions of the brain begin to take form, and more localized foci of differentiation subdivide these into their major nuclear fields. By transplantation methods it can be demonstrated that these various local fields differ from each other in their constitutional properties.

Differentiation continues until in many nuclei it approaches the level of the individual nerve cell. For example, in the optic field of the midbrain the cells in any given locus differ from those in all other loci. The nearer together the neurons, the more alike they remain in constitution, but even neighboring cells may differ to some extent, depending upon the steepness of the differentiation gradient across the nucleus. The development of Mauthner's neuron in the medulla illustrates an extreme example in which a single nerve cell consistently differentiates in visible manner from among its fellows to acquire specific structural and functional characteristics.

This refined specification of the neurons makes possible the formation of selective synaptic linkages on the basis of a chemoaffinity. By virtue of their specification the advancing tips of growing nerve fibers form synapses only with particular ones of the various kinds of neurons they encounter in their outgrowth. The formation of precisely designed integrative circuits thus becomes possible without the aid of functional adjustment. Synapses may be neatly arranged even in regions that appear under the microscope to be only disorderly tangles of axons, dendrites, and cell bodies. The chemical interrelations of the nerve cells must be extremely complicated. This is doubly true where axons maintain inhibitory linkages in addition to their excitatory synapses. According to the chemoaffinity principle a neuron could not maintain dissimilar axon linkages on the two sides of the midsagittal plane, in the absence of a left-right specification of

corresponding cells on each side. In the few examples studied, including neurons of the optic tract, the tectobulbar tract, and the dorsal roots, the fibers seem to form with equal readiness the same pattern of synaptic associations on either side of the midline. A left-right selectivity, especially among the commissural neurons, however, has not been excluded and is not inconceivable.

The induction of cell differentiation through contact with other cells and tissues, common throughout development, takes on a special aspect in the nervous system. Owing to the tremendous elongation of the neuron processes, induction effects may occur over long distances between widely separated cells. It becomes possible for a group of neurons to be similarly specified through similar termination even though their cell bodies are scattered diffusely among other neurons of diverse character. Neuronal differentiation thus tends to be released from some of the limitations of topography that apply to the development of other organs. Much greater diversity and refinement is possible than where induction depends upon immediate contact of the cell bodies themselves.

It has been emphasized that these qualitative specificities operate in conjunction with many other factors, and the combined action of all of them determines the final pattern. The unquestioned importance of stereotropism and of topographic and chronological relations must be taken for granted throughout. Certain other formative factors such as trophic dependencies, saturation and denervation effects, excitatory threshold adjustment, etc., are also involved, but as yet they are little understood.

Some of the salient features in the patterning of certain elementary integrative circuits are considered as far as the experimental evidence permits. These concrete examples illustrate the manner in which developmental mechanisms may operate without the aid of function to insure precise neuronal connections. Proper peripheral-central linkages, for example, are assured in many instances by having the central connections dependent upon specificity induced in the nerve fibers by their end organs.

Judging from the variation in other aspects of development among different species of vertebrates, we would hardly expect the details of these processes, as observed in the amphibians, to be maintained throughout the vertebrate series. The general plan of development and the general nature of the maturational mechanisms involved, however, presumably are not subject to any abrupt or radical modification in phylogeny.

The foregoing has been concerned almost exclusively with the development and maturation of the integrative *structure* of the nervous system. The broader problem of the maturation of *behavior* with its corollary problems regarding the relation between neural structure and function have been avoided.

Our repeated reference to the role of anatomical connections in shaping response patterns need not lead to an exaggeration of the importance of this factor relative to others. Dependence of orderly function upon the neural architecture by no means excludes dependence upon other factors. The fluctuating patterns of facilitation and inhibition, which are continually playing through the anatomical structure, constantly condition in varying degree the character of the response. Particularly with respect to the temporal organization of behavior over increasing periods of time, the regulative role of these dynamic factors rapidly increases in interest and importance. Caution is also necessary with regard to implications concerning the nature and specificity of synaptic connections. For the most part it is possible merely to infer that the qualitative specification of neurons is closely correlated with differences in their synaptic associations. Little can be said concerning the exact nature of these synaptic differences.

REFERENCES

Aitken, J. T., M. Sharman, and J. Z. Young. Maturation of regenerating nerve fibres with various peripheral connexions. *J. Anat. Lond.,* 1947, **81,** 1–22.

Arey, L. B. Can hypoglossal nerve fibers induce the formation of taste buds? *Anat. Rec.,* 1941, **81,** Suppl. 118.

Bailey, S. W. An experimental study of the origin of lateral-line structures in embryonic and adult teleosts. *J. exp. Zool.,* 1937, **76,** 187–234.

Barron, D. H. The functional development of some mammalian neuromuscular mechanisms. *Biol. Rev.,* 1941, **16,** 1–33.

Barron, D. H. The early development of the sensory and internuncial cells in the spinal cord of the sheep. *J. comp. Neurol.,* 1944, **81,** 193–226.

Barron, D. H. The role of the sensory fibers in the differentiation of the spinal cord in sheep. *J. exp. Zool.,* 1945, **100,** 431–443.

Beach, F. A. A review of physiological and psychological studies of sexual behavior in mammals. *Physiol. Rev.,* 1947, **27,** 240–307.

Beers, D. Return of vision and other observations in transplanted amphibian eyes. *Proc. Soc. exp. Biol., N. Y.,* 1929, **26,** 477–479.

Bethe, A. Plastizität und Zentrenlehre. *Handb. norm. pathol. Physiol.,* 1931, **15,** 1175–1220.

Bok, S. T. Die Entwicklung der Hirnnerven und ihrer zentralen Bahnen. Die stimulogene Fibrillation. *Folia neuro-biol.,* 1915, **9,** 475.

Bok, S. T. The development of reflexes and reflex tracts. *Psychiat. neurol. Bl. Amst.,* 1917, **21,** 281–303.

Brandt, W. Experimentell erzeugte Gliedmassenverdoppelungen bei Triton. Versuch einer allgemein biologischen Deutung. *Arch. Entw-Mech. Org.,* 1925, **106,** 193–248.

Brandt, W. Experimental production of functioning reduplications — a triple and a functioning quintuple hindlimb in the frog. *J. exp. Biol.,* 1940, **17,** 396–401.

Breder, C., and P. Rasquin. Comparative studies in the light sensitivity of blind Characins from a series of Mexican caves. *Bull. Amer. Mus. nat. Hist.,* 1947, **89,** 325–351.

de Burlet, H. M. Zur vergleichenden Anatomie der Labyrinthinnervation. *J. comp. Neurol.,* 1929, **47,** 155–169.

Burr, H. S. An electro-dynamic theory of development suggested by studies of proliferation rates in the brain of *Amblystoma. J. comp. Neurol.,* 1932, **56,** 347–371.

Cajal, R. S. *Degeneration and regeneration of the nervous system.* (Translated and edited by R. M. May.) London: Oxford University Press, 1928. Volumes I and II.

Cajal, R. S. *Études sur la neurogenèse de quelque vertébrés.* Madrid, 1929.

Campbell, B. The effects of retrograde degeneration upon reflex activity of ventral horn neurons. *Anat. Rec.,* 1944, **88,** 25–37.

Carmichael, L. The development of behavior in vertebrates experimentally removed from the influence of external stimulation. *Psychol. Rev.*, 1926, **33**, 51–58.

Carmichael, L. The experimental embryology of mind. *Psychol. Bull.*, 1941, **38**, 1–28.

Carmichael, L. The onset and early development of behavior. In L. Carmichael (Ed.), *Manual of child psychology.* New York: Wiley, 1946. Pp. 43–166.

Child, C. M. *The origin and development of the nervous system.* Chicago: University of Chicago Press, 1921.

Coghill, G. E. *Anatomy and the problem of behavior.* Cambridge: Cambridge University Press, 1929.

Coghill, G. E. Individuation versus integration in the development of behavior. *J. gen. Psychol.*, 1930a, **3**, 431–435.

Coghill, G. E. Correlated anatomical and physiological studies of the growth of the nervous system of Amphibia. IX. The mechanism of association of *Amblystoma punctatum*. *J. comp. Neurol.*, 1930b, **51**, 311–375. X. Corollaries of the anatomical and physiological study of *Amblystoma* from the age of earliest movement to swimming. *J. comp. Neurol.*, 1931, **53**, 147–168.

Detwiler, S. R. Coordinated movements in supernumerary transplanted limbs. *J. comp. Neurol.*, 1925, **38**, 461–493.

Detwiler, S. R. *Neuroembryology.* New York: Macmillan, 1936.

Dijkstra, C. Die De- und Regeneration der sensiblen Endkörperchen des Entenschnabels (Gandry- und Herbst-Körperchen) nach Durchschneidung des Nerven, nach Fortnahme der ganzen Haut und nach Transplantation des Hautstückchens. *Z. mikr.-anat. Forsch.*, 1933, **34**, 75–158.

Douglas, B., and L. Lanier. Changes in cutaneous localization in a pedicle flap. *Arch. Neurol. Psychiat. Chicago*, 1934, **32**, 756–762.

Fort, W. B. An experimental study of the factors involved in the establishment of neuromuscular connections. Dissertation, University of Chicago, 1940.

Geohegan, W. A., and O. J. Aidar. Functional reorganization following preganglionectomy. *Proc. Soc. exp. Biol., N. Y.*, 1942, **50**, 365–369.

Gerard, R. W. The interaction of neurones. *Ohio J. Sci.*, 1941, **41**, 160–172.

Gesell, A. The ontogenesis of infant behavior. In L. Carmichael (Ed.), *Manual of child psychology.* New York: Wiley, 1946. Pp. 295–331.

Goldstein, K. *The organism.* New York: American Book, 1939.

González, A. W. The differentiation of the motor cell columns in the cervical cord of albino rat fetuses. *J. comp. Neurol.*, 1940, **73**, 469–488.

Goodman, L. Effect of total absence of function on the optic system of rabbits. *Amer. J. Physiol.*, 1932, **100**, 46–63.

Hamburger, V. Experimentelle Beiträge zur Entwicklungsphysiologie der Nervenbahnen in der Froschextremität. *Arch. EntwMech. Org.*, 1929, **119**, 47–99.

Hamburger, V. Isolation of the brachial segments of the spinal cord of the chick embryo by means of tantalum foil blocks. *J. exp. Zool.*, 1946, **103**, 113–142.

Hamburger, V., and E. L. Keefe. The effects of peripheral factors on the proliferation and differentiation in the spinal cord of chick embryos. *J. exp. Zool.*, 1944, **96**, 223–242.

Harrison, R. G. An experimental study of the relation of the nervous system to the developing musculature in the embryo of the frog. *Amer. J. Anat.*, 1904, **3**, 197–220.

Harrison, R. G. The outgrowth of the nerve fiber as a mode of protoplasmic movement. *J. exp. Zool.*, 1910, **9**, 787.

Harrison, R. G. The reaction of embryonic cells to solid surfaces. *J. exp. Zool.*, 1914, **17**, 521–544.

Harrison, R. G. On relations of symmetry in transplanted limbs. *J. exp. Zool.*, 1921, **32**, 1–136.

Harrison, R. G. On the origin and development of the nervous system studied by the methods of experimental embryology. *Proc. roy. Soc.*, 1935, **B118**, 155–196.

Harrison, R. G. Relations of symmetry in the developing ear of *Amblystoma punctatum*. *Proc. nat. Acad. Sci., Wash.*, 1936, **22**, 238–247.

Head, Henry. *Studies in neurology.* London: Oxford University Press, 1920. Vol. II.

Hebb, D. O. The innate organization of visual activity. II. Transfer of response in the discrimination of brightness and size by rats reared in total darkness. *J. comp. Psychol.*, 1937, **24**, 277–299.

Hering, E. *Memory: Lectures on the specific energies of the nervous system.* Chicago: Open Court, 1913.

Herrick, C. J. Morphogenetic factors in the differentiation of the nervous system. *Physiol. Rev.*, 1925, **5**, 112–130.

Herrick, C. J. Morphogenesis of the brain. *J. Morph.*, 1933, **54** 233–258.

Herrick, C. J. Conduction pathways in the cerebral peduncle of *Amblystoma*. *J. comp. Neurol.*, 1936, **63**, 293–352.

Herrick, C. J. Cerebral fiber tracts of *Amblystoma tigrinum* in midlarval stages. *J. comp. Neurol.*, 1939, **71**, 511–612.

Herrick, C. J. *The brain of the tiger salamander.* Chicago: University of Chicago Press, 1948.

Hillarp, N. Structure of the synapse and the peripheral innervation apparatus of the autonomic nervous system. *Acta Anat.*, 1946, **2**, Suppl. 4, 1–152.

Holt, E. B. *Animal drive and the learning process.* New York: Holt, 1931.

Hooker, D. Studies on regeneration of the spinal cord. IV. Rotation about its longitudinal axis of a portion of the cord in *Amblystoma punctatum* embryos. *J. exp. Zool.*, 1930, **55**, 23–41.

Hooker, D. Spinal cord regeneration in the young rainbow fish, *Lebistes reticulatus*. *J. comp. Neurol.*, 1932, **56**, 277–297.

Hunter, W. S. Summary comments on the heredity-environment symposium. *Psychol. Rev.*, 1947, **54**, 348–352.

Kappers, C. U. A. Principles of development of the nervous system (neurobiotaxis. In W. Penfield (Ed.), *Cytology and cellular pathology of the nervous system*. New York: Hoeber, 1932. Pp. 45–89.

Koffka, K. *Principles of Gestalt psychology*. New York: Harcourt, Brace, 1935.

Köhler, W. *Dynamics in psychology*. New York: Liveright, 1940.

Kollros, J. J. Localized maturation of lid-closure reflex mechanism by thyroid implants into tadpole hindbrain. *Proc. Soc. exp. Biol., N. Y.*, 1942, **49**, 204–206.

Kollros, J. J. Experimental studies on the development of the corneal reflex in amphibia. III. The influence of the periphery upon the reflex center. *J. exp. Zool.*, 1943, **92**, 121–142.

Kuo, Z. Y. Ontogeny of embryonic behavior in Aves. I. The chronology and general nature of the behavior of the chick embryo. *J. exp. Zool.*, 1932, **61**, 395–430.

Langley, J. N. On the regeneration of pre-ganglionic and of post-ganglionic visceral nerve fibres. *J. Physiol.*, 1898, **22**, 215–230.

Langley, J. N. Notes on the regeneration of the pre-ganglionic fibers in the sympathetic system. *J. Physiol.*, 1900, **25**, 417–426.

Langley, J., and H. Anderson. The union of different kinds of nerve fibers. *J. Physiol.*, 1904, **31**, 365–391.

Langworthy, O. R. Development of behavior patterns and myelinization of the nervous system in the human fetus and infant. *Contr. Embryol. Carn. Instn.*, 1933, **24**, 1–57.

Larsell, O., E. McCrady, and A. Zimmerman. Morphological and functional development of the membranous labyrinth in the opossum. *J. comp. Neurol.*, 1935, **63**, 95–118.

Lashley, K. S. The problem of cerebral organization in vision. *Biol. Symp.*, 1942, **7**, 301–322.

Lashley, K. S. Structural variation in the nervous system in relation to behavior. *Psychol. Rev.*, 1947, **54**, 325-334.

Levi-Montalcini, R., and G. Levi. Les consequences de la destruction d'un territoire d'innervation périphérique sur le développement des centres nerveux correspondants dans l'embryon de poulet. *Arch. Biol. Paris*, 1942, **53**, 537–545.

Litwiller, R. Quantitative studies on nerve regeneration in Amphibia. I. Factors controlling nerve regeneration in adult limbs. *J. comp. Neurol.*, 1938, **69**, 427–447.

Lloyd, D. P. C. Principles of spinal reflex activity. In J. F. Fulton (Ed.), *Howell's textbook of physiology*. Philadelphia: Saunders, 1946. Pp. 146–176.

Lorente de Nó, R. La regeneracion de la medula espinal en las larves de batracio. *Trab. Lab. Invest. biol. Univ. Madrid*, 1921, **19**, 1–38.

Lorente de Nó, R. Vestibulo-ocular reflex arc. *Arch. Neurol. Psychiat., Chicago*, 1933, **30**, 244–291.

Marsh, G., and H. Beams. In vitro control of growing chick nerve fibers by applied electric currents. *J. cell. comp. Physiol.*, 1946, **27**, 139–157.

Matthews, S., and S. Detwiler. The reactions of *Amblystoma* embryos following prolonged treatment with chloretone. *J. exp. Zool.*, 1926, **45**, 279–292.

Matthey, R. Récupération de la vue après greffe de l'oeil chez le triton adulte. *C. R. Soc. biol. Paris*, 1926a, **94**, 4–5.

Matthey, R. La greffe de l'oeil. Étude exérimentale de la greffe de l'oeil chez le triton (*Triton cristatus*). *Arch. EntwMech. Org.*, 1926b, **109**, 326–341.

Matthey, R. La greffe de l'oeil. I. Étude histologique sur la greffe de l'oeil chez la larve de salamandre (*Salamandre maculosa*). *Rev. suisse zool.*, 1926c, **33**, 317–334.

Miner, N. Studies in the development of cutaneous local sign. Ph.D. thesis, University of Chicago, 1949.

Mowrer, O. H. "Maturation" vs. "learning" in the development of vestibular and optokinetic nystagmus. *J. genet. Psychol.*, 1936, **48**, 383–404.

Nasiell, V. Zur Frage des Dunkelnystagmus und über postrotatorischen Nystagmus und Deviation der Augen bei Lageveränderungen des Kopfes und des Körpers gegen den Kopfe beim Dunkelkaninchen. *Acta oto-laryng., Stockh.*, 1924, **6**, 175–177.

Ogneff, J. Ueber die Aenderungen in den Organen der Goldfische nach dreijährigem Verbleibein in Finsternis. *Anat. Anz.*, 1911, **40**, 81–87.

Olivo, O. M. Rigenerazione di organi sensitivi in "*Ameiurus nebulosus*." *Soc. Ital. di Biol. Sper. Boll.*, 1928, **3**, 1019.

Olmsted, J. M. D. The nerve as a formative influence in the development of taste-buds. *J. comp. Neurol.*, 1931, **31**, 465–468.

Oppenheimer, J. M. The decussation of Mauthner's fibers in *Fundulus* embryos. *J. comp. Neurol.*, 1942, **77**, 577–587.

Piatt, J. A study of nerve-muscle specificity in the forelimb of *Triturus pyrrhogaster*. *J. Morph.*, 1939, **65**, 155–185.

Piatt, J. Nerve-muscle specificity in *Amblystoma*, studied by means of heterotopic cord grafts. *J. exp. Zool.*, 1940, **85**, 211–237.

Piatt, J. Transplantation of aneurogenic forelimbs in *Amblystoma punctatum*. *J. exp. Zool.*, 1942, **91**, 79–101.

Piatt, J. Experiments on the decussation and course of Mauthner's fibers in *Amblystoma punctatum*. *J. comp. Neurol.*, 1944, **80**, 335–353.

Piatt, J. A study of the factors controlling the differentiation of Mauthner's cell in *Amblystoma*. *J. comp. Neurol.*, 1947, **86**, 199–236.

Piatt, J. Form and causality in neurogenesis. *Biol. Rev.*, 1948, **23**, 1–45.

Rhines, R., and W. F. Windle. The early development of the fasciculus longitudinalis medialis and associated secondary neurons in the rat, cat, and man. *J. comp. Neurol.*, 1941, **75**, 165–189.

Riesen, A. H. The development of visual perception in man and chimpanzee. *Science,* 1947, **106**, 107-108.

Rogers, W. Heterotopic spinal cord grafts in salamander embryos. *Proc. nat. Acad. Sci., Wash.*, 1934, **20**, 247.

Romanes, G. J. The development and significance of the cell columns in the ventral horn of the cervical and upper thoracic spinal cord of the rabbit. *J. Anat. Lond.*, 1942, **76**, 112–130.

Romanes, G. J. Motor localization and the effects of nerve injury on the ventral horn cells of the spinal cord. *J. Anat. Lond.*, 1946, **80**, 117–131.

Romanes, G. J. The prenatal medullation of the sheep's nervous system. *J. Anat. Lond.*, 1947, **81**, 64–81.

Sanders, F. K., and J. Z. Young. The influence of peripheral connexion on the diameter of regenerating nerve fibers. *J. exp. Biol.*, 1946, **22**, 203–212.

Saunders, J. W., Jr. The proximo-distal sequence of origin of wing parts and the role of the ectoderm. *Anat. Rec.*, 1947, **99**, 11.

Scharpenberg, L., and W. Windle. A study of spinal cord development in silver–stained sheep embryos correlated with early somatic movements. *J. Anat. Lond.*, 1937, **72**, 344–351.

Speidel, C. C. Studies of living nerves. II. Activities of amoeboid growth cones, sheath cells, and myelin segments, as revealed by prolonged observation of individual nerve fibers in frog tadpoles. *Amer. J. Anat.*, 1933, **52**, 1–79.

Speidel, C. C. Studies of living nerves. III. Phenomena of nerve irritation and recovery, degeneration and repair. *J. comp. Neurol.*, 1935, **61**, 1–79.

Speidel, C. C. Adjustments of nerve endings. *Harvey Lect.*, 1940–41, Ser. 36, 126–158.

Speidel, C. C. Studies of living nerves. VIII. Histories of nerve endings in frog tadpoles subjected to various injurious treatments. *Proc. Amer. phil. Soc.*, 1942, **85**, 168–182.

Speidel, C. C. Prolonged histories of vagus nerve regeneration patterns, sterile distal stumps and sheath cell outgrowths. *Anat. Rec.*, 1946, **94**, 55.

Speidel, C. C. Correlated studies of sense organs and nerves of the lateral-line in living frog tadpoles. II. The trophic influence of specific nerve supply as revealed by prolonged observations of denervated and reinnervated organs. *Amer. J. Anat.*, 1948, **82**, 277–320.

Sperry, R. W. The functional results of muscle transposition in the hind limb of the rat. *J. comp. Neurol.*, 1940, **73**, 379–404.

Sperry, R. W. The effect of crossing nerves to antagonistic muscles in the hind limb of the rat. *J. comp. Neurol.*, 1941, **75**, 1–19.

Sperry, R. W. Reestablishment of visuomotor coordinations by optic nerve regeneration. *Anat. Rec.*, 1942a, **84**, 470.

Sperry, R. W. Transplantation of motor nerves and muscles in the forelimb of the rat. *J. comp. Neurol.*, 1942b, **76**, 283–321.

Sperry, R. W. Functional results of crossing sensory nerves in the rat. *J. comp. Neurol.*, 1943a, **78**, 59–90.

Sperry, R. W. Effect of 180 degree rotation of the retinal field on visuomotor coordination. *J. exp. Zool.*, 1943b, **92**, 263–279.

Sperry, R. W. Visuomotor coordination in the newt (*Triturus viridescens*) after regeneration of the optic nerve. *J. comp. Neurol.*, 1943c, **79**, 33–55.

Sperry, R. W. Optic nerve regeneration with return of vision in anurans. *J. Neurophysiol.*, 1944, **7**, 57–69.

Sperry, R. W. Restoration of vision after crossing of optic nerves and after contralateral transplantation of eye. *J. Neurophysiol*, 1945a, **8**, 15–28.

Sperry, R. W. Centripetal regeneration of the 8th cranial nerve root with systematic restoration of vestibular reflexes. *Amer. J. Physiol.*, 1945b, **144**, 735, 741.

Sperry, R. W. The problem of central nervous reorganization after nerve regeneration and muscle transposition. *Quart. Rev. Biol.*, 1945c, **20**, 311–369.

Sperry, R. W. Ontogenetic development and maintenance of compensatory eye movements in complete absence of the optic nerve. *J. comp. Psychol.*, 1946, **39**, 321–330.

Sperry, R. W. Nature of functional recovery following regeneration of the oculomotor nerve in amphibians. *Anat. Rec.*, 1947a, **97**, 293–316.

Sperry, R. W. Unpublished studies on the development of cutaneous local sign, 1947b.

Sperry, R. W. Effect of crossing nerves to antagonistic limb muscles in the monkey. *Arch. Neurol. Psychiat., Chicago*, 1947c, **58**, 452–473.

Sperry, R. W. Orderly patterning of synaptic associations in regeneration of intracentral fiber tracts mediating visuomotor coordination. *Anat. Rec.*, 1948a, **102**, 63–76.

Sperry, R. W. Patterning of central synapses in regeneration of the optic nerve in teleosts. *Physiol. Zoöl.*, 1948b, **21**, 351–361.

Sperry, R. W. Reimplantation of eyes in fishes (*Bathygobius soporator*) with recovery of vision. *Proc. Soc. exp. Biol., N. Y.*, 1949, **71**, 80–81.

Sperry, R., and N. Miner. Formation within sensory nucleus V of synaptic associations mediating cutaneous localization. *J. comp. Neurol.*, 1949, **90**, 403–424.

Stone, L. S. Functional polarization in retinal development and its reestablishment in regenerating retinae of rotated grafted eyes. *Proc. Soc. exp. Biol., N. Y.*, 1944, **57**, 13–14.

Stone, L. S., and C. H. Cole. Grafted eyes of young and old adult salamanders (*Amblystoma punctatum*) showing return of vision. *Yale J. Biol. Med.*, 1943, **15**, 735–754.

Stone, L. S., and N. T. Ussher. Return of vision and other observations in replanted amphibian eyes. *Proc. Soc. exp. Biol., N. Y.*, 1927, **25**, 213–215.

Stopford, J. *Sensation and the sensory pathway.* New York : Longmans, Green, 1930.

Straus, W. L. The concept of nerve-muscle specificity. *Biol. Rev.*, 1946, **21**, 75–91.

Stroer, W. F. Zur vergleichenden Anatomie des primären optischen Systems bei Wirbeltieren. *Z. Anat. u. Entwcklngsgesch.*, 1939, **110**, 301–321.

Szepsenwol, J. Causalité de la différenciation de la cellule nerveuse et détermination de la croissance de ses prolongements. *Arch. Anat. micr.*, 1936, **32**, 1–104.

Taylor, A. C. Development of the innervation pattern in the limb bud of the frog. *Anat. Rec.*, 1943, **87**, 379–413.

Taylor, A. C. Selectivity of nerve fibers from the dorsal and ventral roots in the development of the frog limb. *J. exp. Zool.*, 1944, **96**, 159–185.

Tello, J. F. Genesis de las terminaciones nerviosas motrices y sensitivas. *Trab. Lab. Invest biol. Univ. Madrid*, 1915, **15**, 101–199.

Tello, J. F. Gegenwärtige Auschauungen über den Neurotropismus. *Arch. EntwMech. Org.*, 1923, **33**, 1–73.

Tuge, H., and S. Hanzawa. Physiological and morphological regeneration of the sectioned spinal cord in adult teleosts. *J. comp. Neurol.*, 1937, **67**, 343–365.

Verzár, F., and P. Weiss. Untersuchungen über das Phänomen der identischen Bewegungsfunktion mehrfacher benachbarter Extremitäten. Zugleich : Directe Vorführung von Eigenreflexen. *Pflüg. Arch. ges. Physiol.*, 1930, **223**, 671–684.

Walls, G. *The vertebrate eye.* Bloomfield Hills, Mich. : Cranbrook, 1942.

Weddell, G. Axonal regeneration in the cutaneous nerve plexuses. *J. Anat. Lond.*, 1942, **77**, 49–62.

Weddell, G., and P. Glees. The early stages in the degeneration of cutaneous nerve fibres. *J. Anat. Lond.*, 1942, **76**, 65–93.

Weddell, G., L. Guttmann, and E. Gutmann. The local extension of nerve fibers into denervated areas of skin. *J. Neurol. Psychiat.*, 1941, **4**, 206–225.

Weiss, P. A. Die Funktion transplantierter Amphibienextremitaten. *Anz. Akad. Wiss. Wien*, 1922, **59**, 22.

Weiss, P. A. Erregungspecifität und Erregungsresonanz. *Ergebn. Biol.*, 1928, **3**, 1–151.

Weiss, P. A. Experimental innervation of muscles by the central ends of afferent nerves (establishment of a one-neurone connection between receptor and effector organ), with functional tests. *J. comp. Neurol.*, 1935, **61**, 135–174.

Weiss, P. A. Selectivity controlling the central-peripheral relations in the nervous system. *Biol. Rev.*, 1936, **11**, 494–531.

Weiss, P. A. Further experimental investigations on the phenomenon of homologous response in transplanted amphibian limbs. I. Functional observations. *J. comp. Neurol.*, 1937a, **66**, 181–209.

Weiss, P. A. Further experimental investigations on the phenomenon of homologous response in transplanted amphibian limbs. II. Nerve regeneration and the innervation of transplanted limbs. *J. comp. Neurol.*, 1937b, **66**, 481–535.

Weiss, P. A. Further experimental investigations on the phenomenon of homologous response in transplanted amphibian limbs. III. Homologous response in the absence of sensory innervation. *J. comp. Neurol.*, 1937c, **66**, 537–548.

Weiss, P. A. Further experimental investigations on the phenomenon of homologous response in transplanted amphibian limbs. IV. Reverse locomotion after the interchange of right and left limbs. *J. comp. Neurol.*, 1937d, **7**, 269–315.

Weiss, P. A. *Principles of development.* Part IV. The development of the nervous system (neurogenesis). New York : Holt, 1939. Pp. 490–573.

Weiss, P. A. Autonomous versus reflexogenous activity of the central nervous system. *Proc. Amer. phil. Soc.*, 1941a, **84**, 53–64.

Weiss, P. A. Further experiments with deplanted and deranged nerve centers in amphibians. *Proc. Soc. exp. Biol., N. Y.*, 1941b, **46**, 14–15.

Weiss, P. A. Nerve patterns : The mechanics of nerve growth. *Third Growth Symposium*, 1941c, **5**, 163–203.

Weiss, P. A. Self-differentiation of the basic patterns of coordination. *Comp. Psychol. Monogr.*, 1941d, **17**, 1–96.

Weiss, P. A. Lid-closure reflex from eyes transplanted to atypical locations in *Triturus torosus:* Evidence of a peripheral origin of sensory specificity. *J. comp. Neurol.*, 1942, **77**, 131–169.

Weiss, P. A. The problem of specificity in growth and development. *Yale J. Biol. Med.*, 1947, **19**, 235–278.

Weiss, P., and M. Edds. Sensory-motor nerve crosses in the rat. *J. Neurophysiol.*, 1945, **8**, 173–194.

Weiss, P., M. Edds, and M. Cavanaugh. The effect of terminal connections on the caliber of nerve fibers. *Anat. Rec.*, 1945, **92**, 215–233.

Weiss, P., and A. Hoag. Competitive reinnervation of rat muscles by their own and foreign nerves. *J. Neurophysiol.*, 1946, **9**, 413–418.

Weiss, P., and A. C. Taylor. Further experimental evidence against "neurotropism" in nerve regeneration. *J. exp. Zool.*, 1944, **95** 233–257.

Weiss, P., and T. C. Ruch. Further observations on the function of supernumerary fingers in man. *Proc. Soc. exp. Biol., N. Y.*, 1936, **34**, 569–570.

Windle, W. F. Neurofibrillar development in the central nervous system of cat embryos between 8 and 12 mm. long. *J. comp. Neurol.*, 1933, **58**, 643–723.

Windle, W. F. Neurofibrillar development of cat embryos: extent of development in the telencephalon and diencephalon up to 15 mm. *J. comp. Neurol.*, 1935, **63**, 139–171.

Windle, W. F. Genesis of somatic motor function in mammalian embryos: A synthesizing article. *Physiol. Zoöl.*, 1944, **17**, 247–260.

Windle, W. F., and M. F. Austin. Neurofibrillar development in the central nervous system of chick embryos up to 5 days' incubation. *J. comp. Neurol.*, 1936, **63**, 431–463.

Windle, W. F., and R. E. Baxter. The first neurofibrillar development in albino rat embryos. *J. comp. Neurol.*, 1936, **63**, 173–187.

Windle, W. F., and R. E. Baxter. Development of reflex mechanisms in the spinal cord of albino rat embryos. Correlations between structure and function, and comparisons with the cat and the chick. *J. comp. Neurol.*, 1936, **63**, 189–209.

8·

Ontogenetic Development

LEONARD CARMICHAEL
Tufts College

In this chapter we shall consider the changes in behavior that take place during the early growth of the individual.

Maturation Affects Behavior

Emphasis is given here to "maturation" — to the growth changes in those aspects of activity that involve the adjustment of the living organism to its environment. Howells (1945) has said: " 'Maturation' is simply development in which commonly observed differences between individuals are correlated with previous differences in the inner organism rather than in the environment."

It should be remembered that maturation is a name for many different growth processes. Maturation does not *cause* the changes that take place as organisms grow older. Rather the term properly designates the varied growth processes that produce the observed changes in organisms as time passes. The question then arises: what criteria can be used to distinguish the changes in behavior attributable to *maturation* from the changes attributable to learning?

If a given type of behavior develops universally in all or nearly all apparently normal organisms of similar physiological make-up, it may usually be thought of as due to growth rather than to individual learning. But exceptions to this criterion will at once occur to the reader. For example, certain habits of response, such as the behavior of the arm in carrying food to the mouth, are in part learned. They are learned alike by a child in New York City and by a child in the jungles of New Guinea. Some parts of many reactions may be made up of acquired habits, even though the reactions may be universal in all normal members of a species. Some years ago Smith and Guthrie (1921) coined the word "coenotropes" for such common habits.

Some responses occur through maturation without ever becoming universal, for there are inborn or "inherited" neural mechanisms, basic to certain acts, that may never be activated during the life of a given individual. For example, certain aspects of the mating responses of female guinea pigs may never occur if the animals are reared in isolation, where the specific stimuli necessary to elicit such responses are absent.

A second criterion distinguishing maturation from learning may be described as follows: an observed change in the behavior of an organism that has not yet matured to the point at which habit formation can take place may be attributed to maturation. Like the first criterion, universality, this second criterion is not always applicable.

A third basis for the separation of maturation and learning is the fact that organized behavior sometimes appears for the first time in an organism that has not yet had an opportunity to learn the act in question. Such behavior is clearly due to maturation. An interesting example of such a response is the fact that newly hatched loggerhead turtles escape 3 to 5 days after hatching and without social guidance crawl directly to the sea and swim immediately for the open ocean. This response is probably visually determined by light reflected from the surf (Daniel and Smith, 1947).

To apply these criteria requires a definition of what constitutes environmentally determined *learning*. Although an identification of this basic psychological process is not easy, it may be suggested that all true learning involves a change in the organism such that specific stimulus conditions call out a response that would not have been called out by these same stimuli in the absence of previous activity by the individual. Although learned responses are of central interest to many psychologists, the study of behavior originating through maturational processes is necessary to complete the picture of the developing organism. One reason that the growth of behavior in early fetal life is so important for psychology is that these changes are typical of the alterations of behavior that are almost certainly independent of learning (Carmichael, 1938).

For the sake of convenience, all changes that take place before birth are usually regarded as resulting from maturation. But changes resulting from maturation must not be thought of as stopping at birth. Changes in behavior that result from maturation may continue long after the onset of changes resulting from learning. It may be that a newly learned response will in certain instances give novel expression to otherwise inborn patterns of response. Examples may make this clear. Some mammals, apparently by maturation, develop a preference for low levels of illumination. A purely learned habit, such as the manipulation of a lever, may, however, be used by these organisms to express this essentially inborn light-avoiding response. Thus the particular expression of this behavior in a given organism may require that the "lever habit" be learned. We may force the individual in question to learn a skill in order to display its still apparently unlearned brightness-avoidance reactions.

An example of the relation of learned and unlearned behavior is given in an experiment by Howells and Vine (1940). Bantam and leghorn chicks hatched in the same incubator later learned more easily to go to like than to unlike chicks. Howells and Vine interpreted this to mean: "The nature and amount of learning is not wholly the product of experience, but learning is accelerated or retarded for different types of individuals in different situations because of the directive influence of innate factors" (p. 547). (See also Keeler, 1948.)

Another experiment emphasizes that there are innately different behavior characteristics in ducks and chicks. In their first response to water, ducks enter readily; chicks show a strong disinclination to enter. Since environmental factors were constant, the observed behavior was apparently a result of innate constitution of the "nature" of chicks and ducks. Schoolland, who conducted these experiments, remarked:

> This difference in initial response to water, and in the relative "ease of learning" to enter, in the face of equivalent environmental experience from birth, affords striking evidence for viewing structure, function, predisposition, and discriminative or cognitive ability as integral aspects of innate organization differentiating animal behavior. [1942, p. 280.]

Individually learned language and other forms of behavior employing symbolic responses may be linked with inborn emotional responses. Under certain conditions an essentially inborn emotional pattern may be enriched, as it were, but not necessarily fundamentally "caused" by the individual's newly learned skills of language and other motor expressions. The thwarted motorist who loudly calls out to another driver and then presses his throttle to the floor in order to pass the offending car is using many learned responses. But inborn neural mechanisms, developed by maturation, almost certainly act in releasing his emotional behavior.

At every stage of ontogenetic development organisms are, of course, total, behaving entities, exhibiting many psychological and behavioral capacities. Many names have been given to special groupings of these capacities. The adaptive behavior of higher animals in certain situations is called *intelligent*. Other types of behavior are called *instinctive*. Similarly, organisms sometimes display reactions that are named *emotional* and others that are said to demonstrate the presence of basic *drives*. All such classes of behavioral acts must be seen for a first time in the continuum of development. Such acts are also observed to change after their initial appearance. This may be better put by saying that, as growth continues, acts once observed are supplanted by other acts exhibiting some novel and some old aspects.

In this chapter, therefore, an effort will be made to suggest the zero point and the subsequent developmental changes of some typical segments of human behavior. We may hope in this study to enrich our understanding of what may be called the embryology of mind (Carmichael, 1941). It is in the period before birth that the onset and development of maturational behavior can be seen in its clearest form. The large number of studies devoted to the growth of behavior after birth are not reviewed here. This literature has been summarized elsewhere (see Pratt, 1946; Gesell, 1946; McGraw, 1946). It should be noted, however, that the further toward adult life the organism progresses, the more difficult it is to assert with assurance that a given behavior change is the result of maturation rather than of learning.

Stages in the Development of Behavior

Ideally, at each level of development there could be presented a complete behavioral psychology of the organism. Actually, such completeness is seldom possible. In the early phases of development many of the experimental tools appropriate to the study of complex behavior cannot be used. Conditioned reflex and other learning methods can seldom be applied to fetal organisms. Hence, the only experimental method that has been applied extensively in early stages of behavioral growth is the determination under controlled conditions of whether or not given stimuli can release a response.

Students of the development of behavior in fetal life have typically selected a series of more or less arbitrarily chosen developmental stages for consideration. The total capacity of the organism at each of these chosen stages is then described. In this chapter general observations on the growth of human behavior will be given first, and later the part played by the senses in the release and control of these responses will be singled out for special consideration.

Difficulty of Comparing Organisms

Comparisons of the developmental stages of different mammals, including man, are important. Such comparisons, however, may easily be misleading. For example, the young of the opossum are born after a gestation period of about 14 days. The young of the guinea pig are born after a gestation period of about 64 days. In some few respects the life processes of the newborn opossum are similar to those of a 14-day-old guinea pig fetus operatively removed. In most respects, however, the two organisms at this age are very different. And at normal birth time the newborn guinea pig and the newborn opossum are also very different. At birth the 14-day opossum can perform only a few essential acts; the 64-day guinea pig, when first exposed to independent life, is almost as competent behaviorally as it will ever be. How then can these two fetal types be compared except by giving the total life history of each?

In testing the intelligence of different species of adult animals, it is difficult for the comparative psychologist to set problems that are equally "meaningful" for both groups of animals. Almost every test seems to favor the particular motor or sensory capacity of one species rather than the other. Cats and spider monkeys are born to be interested in different things and to respond in distinctive ways to their environments. To compare the problem-solving ability of cats and spider monkeys requires many safeguards and some arbitrary conclusions. In the same way the comparison of fetal animals of different species is subject to many pitfalls.

A cautious approach must be observed even in comparing early developmental stages of a given organism by methods known to be appropriate in eliciting behavior in later fetal stages of the same organism. A fetal organism in which the inhibiting effect of the cerebral cortex of the brain has hardly developed at all is a very different organism from the same individual at a later developmental stage when such cortical control is well established.

The First Human Behavior Act

With these warnings in mind let us turn to a consideration of the onset and early growth of behavior in man. The various procedures employed in determining the age of human fetal organisms have been discussed elsewhere (Carmichael, 1946, pp. 96–102). Streeter (1920) and others compiled tables showing the relation of various measurements of the human fetus and menstruation age. By menstruation age is meant age calculated from the first day of the last period of menstruation prior to the onset of pregnancy. In general, insemination age is probably about 10 days shorter than menstruation age. Such tables help in determining the presumed age of the fetus relative to fertilization. For but few of the human fetal organisms studied are there reliable indices of insemination, let alone actual fertilization age. Consequently age will here be given in weeks from assumed time of fertilization as estimated from measured height and the use of appropriate tables. In his extensive studies of early human fetuses Hooker (1944) concluded that the

sequence of ages established by tables relating measurement to age checks well with observed behavioral development.

The period comprising the first two weeks of human growth is often called *germinal*. The next stage, called *embryonic*, lasts until about the sixth week. The final stage of about 33 weeks is described as *fetal*. Infants born before full term are called *premature*. Children born before they are about 26 weeks old ordinarily do not live. Babies not born by the end of the normal term are called *postmature*. It has been accepted by legal opinion that a child may remain in the mother's body for more than 47 weeks (Carmichael, 1946, p. 100).

Heart Beat

The first reported movement in the embryonic mammal is the rhythmic beating of the primitive heart. This heart response is at first purely muscular. The mechanism of nervous control of the heart cells does not develop until later. The rhythmic contractions of human heart cells begin during the third week in what will later be the ventricular region (Williams, 1931, p. 163). The intrinsic rhythm is determined by the metabolic processes of these muscle cells (Goss, 1940). In older fetal organisms heart rate may be used as an indicator of sensitivity prior to the emergence of fetal reflex movements (Sontag and Richards, 1938; Rose, 1947).

The striated or body muscles of the human fetus also develop to the point at which they can be directly stimulated before they are controlled by nerve impulses (Coghill, 1929; Minkowski, 1928; Bolaffio and Artom, 1924). This direct response to external stimuli by muscles before neural control is established is spoken of as the "independent effector" stage of the response mechanism (cf. Parker, 1919).

The Ontogenetic Zero of Mental Life

If we do not consider heart beat or the independent action of muscles as the initial stage of *behavioral* development, what shall we consider as its onset? The answer commonly given is that this first activity, above what may be called the zero point of response, is established when receptor stimulation first elicits a definite muscular reaction that can be shown to involve activity of the central and peripheral nervous systems. At this stage certain muscles must be ready to respond; there must be functional maturity of at least some connecting mechanisms of the central nervous system; and sensory and motor peripheral neural elements and receptors must be functional.

In some organisms so-called spontaneous behavior may appear before this full mechanism is functional. This means that the central nervous system and the peripheral motor nervous system may be functional before the receptor mechanism is ready to respond to stimulation. There appears to be no evidence that such spontaneous behavior typically appears in the human fetus before at least some receptor mechanisms are functional.

In a fetus of about 7½ weeks, Hooker (1944) and Fitzgerald and Windle (1942) observed true receptor-released response. It is possible, but not clearly demonstrated, that fetuses supposed to be as young as 6 weeks old have been observed to move (see Yanase, 1907; Strassmann, 1903).

Using a quantified pressure stimulus, Hooker showed that touching the region about the mouth results in a contralateral flexion of the neck. This seemingly occurs without participation of the upper extremities. Fitzgerald and Windle (1942) described the first response of a comparable fetus in very similar terms. Soon after this first response, the zone of receptors that can elicit behavior expands.

The primitive responses that have just been described constitute the first stimulus-released behavior of which the human organism is capable. These reactions are thus the first reactions above the absolute onto-genetic zero (the state prior to that in which stimulation releases behavior).

The Problem of Fetal Condition

Human fetal specimens are usually available for study only when it has been necessary to interrupt pregnancy. This means that many observations are recorded in the presence of general anesthesia given to the mother. Since many general anesthetics pass readily through the placenta, they may to some extent narcotize the fetus before it is removed. On the other hand, Hooker (1944) found that novocain, in its various forms, appears not to affect fetal movements when used either as a spinal or as a local anesthetic. Some of the fetuses he studied had been removed during operations in which anesthetics of this type only were used.

Fitzgerald and Windle (1942) studied human fetal material that was not anesthetized or narcotized. Some of their observations were made while the fetus continued to receive oxygenated blood from the intact placenta. Under these conditions, in three fetuses of approximately 8 weeks' post-insemination age, excitability was high. Quick arm, leg, and trunk movements were called out by tapping or pressing on the amniotic sac. These reactions occurred individually and in various combinations. They did not involve a total reaction of the organism unless the stimulus was very strong.

These investigators hold that, by the eighth week of development, if the fetus has an adequate supply of oxygen, if it is un-narcotized, unanesthetized, and in other ways undamaged, its neuromuscular apparatus is capable of active functioning. They also believe that some receptors or synapses are more easily rendered nonfunctional by anoxia than others. Arm and leg responses are abolished in asphyxiated specimens after the time when stimulation applied to the skin of the face still calls out trunk flexion. In this stage of asphyxiation, strong stimulation calls out mass movements involving trunk, arms, and legs. This observation suggests, along with other evidence (Barcroft and Barron, 1937, 1939), that much early mass movement of the fetus is a function of decrease in oxygen in the blood and concomitant overstrong stimulation.

Fetal Behavior of Infrahuman Mammals

Observations on the fetuses of infrahuman mammals are important as a basis of comparison for human fetal responses. Especially in early fetal life there is a greater similarity in structure and function between human and other mammalian fetuses than appears after birth (Corner, 1944).

Typical of the procedure used to study fetal behavior in lower animals is that used by Bridgman and Carmichael (1935) who studied 47 litters of guinea pig fetuses. These litters developed in maternal animals that had been mated in the laboratory. Insemination age of these fetuses was therefore known exactly. In preparation for an experiment the mature female was given deep ether anesthesia at the appropriate number of days and hours after insemination. The spinal cord of the mother was then severed in the cervical region. A preliminary incision was made in the skin and tissues of the abdomen. This incision was clipped together. The maternal animal was then allowed to recover fully from the anesthetic before being tied upon a frame and lowered partly into a bath of physiological saline solution held at the constant temperature of the blood of the organism. The fetuses were then exposed, stimulated, observed, and photographed by a moving picture camera. Stimuli of various sorts were used, such as calibrated hairs that exerted known pressures.

In the experiments intended to determine the nature of the very first responses, 146 fetuses from the 47 litters were studied. This study made it clear that insemination age is not an absolutely accurate basis on which to predict behavioral capacity. Certain older fetuses remained nonmotile and exhibited less advanced behavior than did some of the younger ones. Length and weight seemed to provide a better index of behavioral development than age. Hooker (1944) suggested that this is also true of human fetal material. Presumably this would not be true of healthy individuals of genetically pure stock, but the guinea pigs used were from an ordinary mixed laboratory colony.

The youngest of the guinea pig fetuses studied (621 hours) were nonmotile; they made no active responses with their body muscles. When they were observed under a binocular microscope it was possible to note that passive body vibrations were brought about by the jarring of the fetal body by the beat of its own heart.

In some nonmotile guinea pig fetuses appropriate electrical stimulation led to direct muscle response. This occurred at a time when stroking, flipping of the limb, or patting did not elicit responses. Fetal muscles that showed brief active movements could later be brought to respond to faradic stimulation when active receptor-initiated movement ceased to be elicitable.

First Responses of Animal Fetuses

The very first movement in the large series under consideration occurred in an organism of 622 postinsemination hours. This first response and others like it had special characteristics. Typically, in the youngest fetuses the response could be made once or twice only. Stimulation of such young fetuses was best accomplished, before the amniotic sac was opened, by pressing the sac walls with a hair so as to touch the fetus lightly.

When several responses could be elicited in young motile fetuses, there was a long refractory or "fatigue" period between the times when stimuli could effectively call out response.

The earliest responses observed were neck flexions. The very first was a slight ventral flexion of the neck which produced head bowing. In a fetus only 1 hour older a dorsal neck bending and a slight but active flexion of one forelimb took place. The articulation of this limb movement was at the shoulder. In fetuses 1 hour older still, dorsal, ventral, and lateral neck flexions were observed, as well as additional forelimb flexions. The similarity of these responses and the early responses of the human fetus should be noted.

It is hard to overemphasize the small magnitude and the transitory nature of these earliest reactions in the guinea pig. The earliest observed responses seemed to be discrete. The head and limb responses apparently were not part of any general primitive pattern of behavior. The early limb and neck reactions did not take place at the same time. As fetal age increased, however, some responses occurred which may be called "patterned." These reactions seemed to be organized in a regular and predictable sequence both in time and in locus. At later ages very strong or long-continued stimulation seemed to call out more generalized behavior in the total organism.

Human Responses in Older Fetuses

At about 8 weeks the reflexogenous zone of the cutaneous surface of the human infant spreads from part of the upper lip and the wings of the nose to the whole upper lip, the chin, and a short distance down the neck (Hooker, 1944, p. 22). The characteristic response of the human fetus at this time is still stereotyped and mechanical in nature. Windle and Fitzgerald (1937) have shown that the elements of the reflex arc in the central nervous system are laid down during the sixth week, but spinal cord arcs are not complete before the eighth week. Hooker says, in commenting on this stage, "each stimulation in the reflexogenous area evokes a response which, within the limits of ordinary biological variation, is identical with every other one secured" (Hooker, 1944, p. 25).

Carmichael (1934) showed that in the fetal guinea pig there is a definite and almost fixed relation between the place stimulated and the response elicited. The repertory of stimulus-released behavior of each organism is limited by the stage of growth of the receptor and neuromuscular mechanisms. The nature of the response elicited during much of fetal life seems to be determined by what may be called the pushbutton action of specific areas of the receptor surfaces. This generalization applies best to cutaneous areas, but it is also suggestive in understanding the specific responses released in unborn mammals by the activation of other receptor mechanisms.

In the fetal guinea pig it appears that almost every receptor area can be thought of as having some particular response associated with it. In 60 fetal litters of known insemination age over 90 reflexogenous areas were stimulated, whenever possible, by stimuli of known intensity, and the behavior released by each point stimulated was listed. A remarkable generalization then appeared: a distinctive pattern of behavior is related to almost every point stimulated. Although it is true that these patterns changed somewhat with the age of the fetus and were at times masked by other concomitant responses, the *specificity of response to locus stimulated* is one of the principal generalities issuing from the developmental study of behavior.

In later stages of development these specific responses can be seen in new temporal patterns. One who has studied the whole course of the development of any unit of such responses cannot fail to see a relation between the old and familiar specific stimulus-released reactions of the organism in the now more-complex behavior patterns. This is tantamount to saying that in the intricate and adaptive behavior patterns of late fetal and postnatal life there is an organization of reactions which have previously been seen as specific responses to stimulation.

Now, turning again to the human fetus we may note that the first responses clearly determined by receptors other than those in the skin are reactions to stimulation of sensory end organs in the muscles, joints, or tendons. Such proprioceptive stimulation seems to follow the stretch of the limb muscles at about 9½ weeks (Hooker, 1944), and this type of stimulation is effective before the whole cutaneous area has become sensitive. In this connection it should be noted that Hogg (1941) showed that the cutaneous nerves and nerve endings are immature when they are first capable of eliciting response. No encapsulated endings are present when cutaneous receptors are first able to release behavior.

By 11 weeks stimulable cutaneous reflexogenous zones have spread over the whole upper extremity, and responses are often complex. At this age the sole of the foot first becomes sensitive to stimulation. Trunk extension is noted. When the palm of the hand is stimulated, a quick finger closure occurs (see Hooker, 1944, pp. 26ff). Other important observations on the responses of very early human fetuses have been made by Minkowski (1922), Woyciechowski (1928), Bolaffio and Artom (1924), and Hooker (1936, 1939). These observations have been summarized by Carmichael (1946).

During fetal life the same stimuli applied to the same areas may call out differing but still quite specific responses as the various connecting levels of the central nervous system mature. Thus Minkowski (1926) showed that the first response to stimulation of the sole of the foot is probably an independent effector response that follows the direct stimulation of the muscles through the thin skin (see Dewey, 1935). This reaction does not involve neural elements. The next level of reaction in a fetus of 3 to 4 months is believed to involve connections in the spinal cord. This response shows a dorsal flexion of the toes. As the central nervous system continues to mature in the midfetal period, connections in the midbrain become effective, and the pattern of response of the toes changes again: the big toe is often extended while the other toes flex. As still higher centers become functional in late

fetal life, the response becomes variable, sometimes showing a spreading of the toes. With the development, ordinarily after birth, of cortical dominance, the typical Babinski reflex (big-toe extension and flexion of other toes) disappears and is replaced by the adult plantar reflex (the contraction of all toes). In adults the presence of the Babinski reflex is sometimes indicative of a lesion of the pyramidal tracts of the brain and spinal cord (Pratt, 1946). This illustrates a view proposed by Jackson (1884) that in behavioral phenomena the dissolution of a function is often in reverse order to its evolution.

At about 12 weeks the eyelids, although still tightly closed as in the newborn kitten, have begun to respond to stimulation by what will later be a wink. Eye movements underneath these closed lids can be detected at this period also.

Preliminary experiments on guinea pig fetuses (Carmichael, 1946) suggest that at first eye movements are not related to stimulation by light but rather to activities initiated in the nonauditory labyrinth. In these experiments very fine silver wire electrodes, hooked into the skin about the eyes, made it possible to observe shifts in the so-called corneo-retinal potential caused by eye movements (see Carmichael and Dearborn, 1947).

These observations suggest that the eyes first move as part of general postural reactions to movements of the body in space. Vestibular nystagmus appears to be primary in the mammalian organism and to precede optokinetic nystagmus. More work is called for in this field.

Behavior Becomes More Complex at 13 Weeks

By 13 weeks almost the whole skin area of the human fetus is sensitive to stimulation. The top and the back of the head alone remain insensitive (Hooker, 1944). At this time almost every joint of the body that is ever to move has gained mobility, and when stimulation is strong the student may well think that he is observing what some writers have called a "generalized matrix of behavior" from which will later develop differentiated and specific responses. This impression would be strengthened if later he saw very specific responses elicited by weak stimuli applied to certain receptor areas. But here appears a basic problem of scientific method. The new patterns of response are unique in their temporal and other characteristics, and from one point of view they are not composed of previous responses. On the other hand, the practiced observer can see that there is nothing new in them when he considers them as units. In considering total patterns of response, we must not forget the importance of vestibular and proprioceptive stimuli in establishing the postural tonus of the body. The muscles mediating a movement of the shoulder joint of a fetus respond to activities resulting from the cutaneous stimulation of the palm. When the head is turned to one side, this response may not be the same as when the head is turned to the other side. Sherman and Sherman (1925) demonstrated that when the sole of the foot is stimulated the posture of the toes may determine whether the reaction of the toes themselves will be extension or flexion.

At about 13 weeks stimulation of receptor fields of one side of the body regularly leads to the response of a member on the other side of the body (Hooker, 1944). Such contralateral responses can sometimes be observed in a more limited way by the ninth week (Fitzgerald and Windle, 1942).

Development at 14 Weeks

Hooker (1944) has said that 14 weeks is an important point in development. Reflexes and movements are at this age more "graceful and fluid." Except for respiration movements, voice, the true grasping reflex, and a few others, the fetus shows most of the specific patterns of response that can be elicited in the neonate. In fact, at this time the fetus may show a subtlety and variety of responses that are quite impossible in the newborn child. It should not be forgotten that before birth the fetus lives in a liquid medium of almost the same specific gravity as its own body. There, like a man under water, it can carry out responses that it cannot duplicate after birth.

After 14 weeks there are still many subtle changes in the capacity for response. At 15 weeks a hair stimulus carefully applied to the palm of the hand will lead to a closing of the fingers, which remain, as it were, closed upon the stimulus. This means that the grasping reflex in a form similar to that seen in the newborn child is in operation.

By the fourteenth week, or even by the twelfth week, the first rhythmic movements of the chest begin. These movements, sometimes named for the German obstetrician Ahlfeld, are almost certainly related to the responses that will later be necessary in breathing. But how are they caused, and do they have utility in fetal life except as a preparation for later breathing? Ahlfeld (1890) found that these responses varied from 38 to 76 per minute, showing that the breathing mechanism is essentially in working order long before it is needed. It has been suggested that these movements form a sort of auxiliary pump to help the heart (Brown, 1915; Walz, 1922), and it is considered likely that a decrease in the oxygen available in the fetal blood is one of their causes. These movements do not normally lead to the aspiration of amniotic fluid (Windle, 1941). During the last 20 weeks of pregnancy, continuous observations for 5 or 6 hours show a relation between chest movement and the metabolic rate of the mother, a correlation of 0.6 with the increase in metabolic rate over measurements taken 52 to 197 days earlier (Richards, Newbery, and Fallgatter, 1938).

Air Breathing and the Premature Infant

By 22 weeks some prematurely delivered fetuses are capable of briefly sustaining respiration when stimulated in the air. Much study has been given to the factors that lead to the onset of air breathing at birth. It seems certain that the increase of metabolites and carbon dioxide and the lack of oxygen in the blood are important in causing the first gasps. These gasps ordinarily occur after placental circulation is interrupted (Corey, 1931). External stimuli such as the drying of the skin and its cooling are also important in initiating the first breath. If a baby on delivery does not start breathing a slap is sometimes effective (Huggett, 1930). Movements of the respiratory type seem to arise from the release of an inhibiting center in the forebrain (Barcroft et al., 1940).

Abel and Windle (1939) found circulation of blood in the lungs during late fetal life. This circulation is enough to take care of oxygenation on the assumption of respiration. There is thus no sudden increase in pulmonary circulation at birth. In the fetal guinea pig the lungs are solid, glandlike organs in which the alveolar spaces constitute only about 2 per cent of the total mass. By the end of the first hour after birth the lungs have expanded and the alveolar spaces then occupy 40 per cent of the lungs (Whitehead, Windle, and Becker, 1942). For the implications of intra-uterine respiration in the development of the fetal lung, see Potter and Bohlander (1941) and Zettleman (1946). A detailed study of breathing rhythms in fetal and newborn animals has been made by Barcroft (1947). Using the sheep, an animal with a gestation period of 5 months, he has been able to show a continuum in breathing movements from the first spasm seen on the 34th day, through the onset of rhythm on the 40th day. Segregation of chest movements began on the 45th day and the onset of inhibition of this movement in the period between 50 and 60 days. Here again we see the development of the basic mechanism of a great action system before the system can function in the economy of the organism.

If for any reason respiration is not properly established at birth, asphyxiation results.

Experiments on guinea pigs show that, even if breathing is later established, a delay in establishing breathing may result in so-called *asphyxia neonatorum*, which can produce permanent degenerative changes in the brain (Windle and Becker, 1943). The extreme susceptibility of nervous tissue to oxygen lack is well known. In one experiment pups were born of mothers deprived of normal oxygen supply before delivery. One of the pups developed convulsions 5 weeks after delivery, and another 6 weeks after delivery. It has been suggested (Fender, Neff, and Binger, 1946) that this asphyxia neonatorum may play a part in the development of some cases of epilepsy in human beings.

Now, to return to the general behavior of the human fetus, we may note that by 22 weeks the eyelids separate. It is rare, even after the eyelids have separated, however, to have the eyes open spontaneously or as a result of any stimulation by light that has so far been applied.

Endocrines in Fetal Development

The function of the endocrines in fetal life is still imperfectly understood. In general it may be said that the endocrine functions are concerned with growth and metabolism rather than directly with overt behavior as such. But, as previously emphasized in this chapter, it is not easy to separate the development of a structure and a function in fetal life.

The principal endocrine function of the pancreas is found in the secretion of the cells of the *islets of Langerhans*. There has been much consideration of the role of this secretion — fetal insulin, as it is called — in prenatal life. One difficulty met in such studies is the determination of when the effects of insulin on the fetus are a result of the secretion developed in the fetus itself and when they are a result of the insulin provided by the mother. In the study of responses related to the growth of the fetal nervous system an investigator fortunately need not fear that the specific nerve impulses he is considering may have started in the maternal rather than in the fetal central nervous system. But in the study of the endocrines no such assurance can be taken for granted. There has therefore been much study of the problem of the passage through the placenta of the various products of different endocrine glands. In the case of insulin it has been shown that the administration of this substance to pregnant cats near the normal period of birth failed to reduce the blood sugar level of the fetuses. At earlier periods of fetal life this result was not secured. Other complex relations between insulin and fetal metabolism have been worked out in mammals. It is apparently true (Windle, 1940) that the relations found in one mammal are not necessarily also true of other mammals.

The suprarenals exhibit a special function in fetal life. At the time of birth they are 0.02 per cent of the total weight of the body. In the adult they are only about 0.01 per cent. In the first week after birth this gland loses one-third of its birth weight. The full significance of this change is not known. It may well be related to the presence in fetal life of maternal sex hormones transmitted through the placental barrier. The medulla of the suprarenals is embryologically as well as functionally distinct from the cortex of the suprarenals.

Pankratz (1930) suggested that the onset of behavior may be related to the beginning of functional activity in the secretion of the suprarenal medulla. In a later study this same investigator (1931) emphasized the fact that this condition may be important in man as well as in the rodent, on which his first studies were made.

Willier (1939) has well summarized the development of sex-related hormones in the fetus. Male gonads produce male sex hormones in fetal life. This secretion probably begins about the seventh week in man. In the female the ovary is histologically recognizable by about the eighth week. This slight difference in time in the growth of sex

hormone-secreting structures suggests that possibly the internal secretions of the male sex glands begin before those of the female. This observation is reminiscent of a very ancient belief. In the canon law of the medieval church it was considered that the time of quickening of the male fetus was 40 days and that of the female 80 days (Goeckel, 1911).

The extent to which the mother's own sex hormones and her other endocrine secretions influence the growing fetus and the difference in such influence on the development of male and female fetuses has been the subject of much study and some speculation. The mammary glands of both boys and girls may secrete milk — so-called witch's milk — for a short time after birth. It seems almost certain that this lactation is stimulated by the same endocrine mechanism that leads to the maternal lactation (Pratt, 1931).

Studies have been made of iodine in fetal and maternal blood streams. It seems clear that the thyroid, which is essential in making available so-called hormone iodine to the organism, is functional in man by the sixth month. In some mammals it seems that the fetus must manufacture all its own iodine. In the human organism the mother's iodine seems able to pass through the placental barrier and become available to the fetus. It has been shown that the maturation of typical behavior patterns in the fetal rat may be delayed if the maternal organism is in a hyperthyroid state during part of pregnancy (Rose, 1947).

The fetal hypophysis elaborates several active principles, but their exact function in growth is in some doubt. The growth-promoting factor of the anterior lobe of the hypophysis appears rather late in fetal life. (For a bibliography and fuller treatment of fetal endocrine glands, see Windle, 1940).

There has been some study of the relation between the development of acetylcholine and the onset of behavior. It is believed that acetylcholine plays an important part in the chemical relation between different neurons and in the relations between neurons and muscle cells. Kuo (1939) showed that the first neurally determined responses in the chick embryo do not appear until after acetylcholine has been developed by the organism. This suggests that the first reflex-like response of the chick may be dependent upon this so-called chemical mediation. Youngstrom (1941) also found a relation between acetylcholine and related chemical substances and the development of motility.

"Anticipatory Function" and the Quickening of the Fetus

We may propose a generalization concerning fetal development: the *law of anticipatory function*. It may be stated as follows: *functional capacity may be demonstrated experimentally in many action systems of the growing organism well before the time when the function in question is normally called upon to play an active and significant part in the vital economy of the organism.*

We have seen above that cutaneous stimulation can release responses in a human fetus at about 8 weeks of age. In contrast it may be noted that there is no sure evidence that human fetal movement can be detected in the course of normal development in the mother's body before the fourteenth week, when movements have been detected by the stethoscope. At about the seventeenth week movement can usually be felt by the mother (Windle, 1940, p. 165; Feldman, 1920). Many observations on the "quickening of the fetus" were made before modern scientific techniques were available. Even the great physiologist Harvey noted that a mother can feel the kick of her unborn child (Needham, 1931).

Lindsley (1942) not only recorded electrically the beat of the fetal heart but also took fetal electroencephalograms. These latter records were made by placing electrodes on the abdomen immediately over the fetal head when the head was found in a convenient place. There have been a number of other studies of the electrocardiograms of

fetuses (see Geiger, Monroe, and Goodyer, 1941). Newbery (1941) measured the principal types of fetal activity as noted by the mother. Frequencies for hiccoughing, kicking, and squirming during the 5 months previous to birth were determined in this study. Kicking showed the most continuous increase in the 5 months preceding birth.

Sir Joseph Barcroft (1938) pointed out that a definite change takes place in the sheep fetus during the late prenatal period. The gestation period of the sheep is approximately 144 days. Barcroft says:

It seems to me a very remarkable thing that, while as yet the foetus has only passed one third of its intra-uterine life, it should possess a nervous system capable of dictating not only movement, but the specific movements which the animal will undertake shortly after birth, capable of dictating the movements of respiration which, though they will not be required for another hundred days, must at once come into play when the sheep is born and on which its survival depends, capable of coupling the locomotor and respiratory functions in harmonious activity, and capable of sense insofar as it can appreciate its relation to gravity and react to tactile stimuli. [1938, p. 26.]

Barcroft says further, however, that by the 50th day all this activity is beginning to change in the fetus of the sheep. The organisms from this time on become more quiescent. Their responses become limited. Spontaneous movements are much less in evidence. This change, Barcroft suggested, is due to the fact that by the 50th day the fetal circulation has begun to provide a less adequate supply of oxygen for the use of the fetal brain. It may be said indeed that the latter part of the fetal life in the sheep is one of growth of receptors, nervous system, and muscles, as well as of all other organ systems, but it is not a period when the special receptors release much general bodily activity. In cat fetuses it has been shown that in a deficiency of oxygen there is at first an increased responsiveness to light tactile stimuli, but this and other functions are lost with further anoxemia (Windle and Becker, 1940).

Hooker noted that at a comparable period there is also relative quiescence in the activity of the human fetus. This change begins at about the 16th week. After this time the fetus shows a marked decrease in spontaneous activity as well as in the responses that can be released by appropriate stimulation. Reactions become, in Hooker's term, sluggish (Hooker, 1944, p. 30). This sluggishness is almost certainly due in part to a decrease in the oxygen available in the blood. The growing dominance of the inhibiting function of the cerebral cortex during this period should also not be forgotten.

The facts just described show that, in the study of the control of behavior by the fetal senses, positive evidence is more important than negative evidence. The observation of a specific response at a particular age is an observation of importance. When stimulation elicits no response, however, it is not safe to conclude that in the same fetus under other conditions, or at an earlier time, responses could not have been elicited. Least of all is it appropriate to assume that, because a response cannot be elicited, the basic neural mechanism for the response is not yet mature.

As previously noted, behavior is called "spontaneous" when it is not easily traceable to specific stimulation. Thus it is a name for ignorance. So-called spontaneous behavior may result from a number of antecedent conditions, such as an alteration in the internal environment of the organism. It may also result from hidden or unobserved stimulation of receptor mechanisms such as those in the muscles, tendons, joints, or in the nonauditory labyrinth of the inner ear.

Modification of Behavior by Learning

In the normal fetus learned behavior is seen only in a very modest way, if at all. Ray (1932) presented a preliminary report on fetal conditioning, but his results were not fully conclusive. This is also true of the study of Sontag and Wallace (1934). Spelt (1938) seems to have established conditioned responses in the intact human fetus (ages 6½ to 8½ months) by the use of auditory stimuli as the unconditioned stimulus and *tactile* vibration of the maternal abdomen as the conditioned stimulus. The position of the fetus was determined by X-ray examination, and movement was observed by tambours placed on the abdomen of the mother. Stimulus presentations consisted of vibration followed 5 seconds later by the loud sound. After 100 paired presentations, responses to tactile vibration were elicited. Conditioning of this sort is not easy to accomplish. It may be said that the stimulus release of learned behavior is not typical of fetal life.

The present writer, in some unpublished studies, attempted to produce conditioned responses in prematurely delivered fetal guinea pigs. No positive results were secured. Marquis (1931) was able to establish conditioned sucking reactions to the sound of a buzzer in 8 of 10 newborn infants in 5 days of training, and Wenger (1936) also established conditioned withdrawings in the first few days of life. But these reactions were not stable. Wickens and Wickens (1939) question whether neonatal conditioning is not essentially what has been called pseudoconditioning. In their experiment 24 infants under 10 days of age were studied. A control group received twelve stimulations with shock to the sole of the foot alone for 3 consecutive days. The experimental group was given the sound of a buzzer and shock. *Both* groups gave similar positive reactions to the buzzer alone after training, but none of them had responded before training. "Extinction" and "spontaneous recovery" were the same for both groups.

There is a good deal of evidence pointing to individual differences of capacity of fetal organisms. Studies tend to show that there is a positive relation between fetal activity as reported by the mother and performance at 6 months on the normative items of the Gesell scale (Richards and Newbery, 1938). This fact may well be considered in evaluating so-called fetal learning.

Other Modifications of Fetal Behavior

Another modification of the organism by previous activity is seen in the establishment, after response to a stimulus, of a state of temporary inactivity or a "refractory period" during which subsequent stimulation is ineffective (Carmichael, 1934)

The phenomenon of "summation of stimuli" is also demonstrable in some fetal organisms. One application of a just supraliminal stimulus may not call out a response, whereas repeated stimuli of the same sort may cause a breakover into overt activity (Carmichael and Smith, 1939).

Notwithstanding the fancies of a few writers, we may dismiss the idea that complex, voluntary, centrally initiated behavior of the so-called "voluntary" type is ever seen in fetal life. Rather, responses that are observed in the fetus, and that may be considered to be on a continuum with later voluntary activity, may in actuality be related to other antecedent conditions, such as oxygen change, or to actual but concealed stimulation.

Influence of the Internal Environment

Tracy (1926), in a series of experiments on fish embryos, made observations that are relevant to the question of the nature of stimulation and of spontaneous behavior. Toadfish larvae, after hatching, typically lie quiescent at the bottom of the tank. Closer observation shows, however, that at different times these embryos make sudden movements. Tracy concluded that these spontaneous reactions are related to cumulative changes in the blood of the organism. He suggested that at certain times the nervous system of the small larva is directly stimulated by a change in the amount of oxygen in the blood, or by the concentration of metabolites — the waste products of previous

cell activity. The consequent reactions may be a result of direct stimulation of the nerve centers or of the stimulation of specialized receptors in the blood vessel system. It may also be that these responses involve a modification of existing thresholds of excitation in the central nervous system. This threshold change may render effective what were previously ineffective peripheral stimuli.

Tracy himself drew some interesting conclusions from his studies. He suggested that, if external conditions were held constant, the activity of organisms might be largely determined by their own life processes. The whole organism would then "beat" in its environment, much as the primitive heart cells beat in the environment of the fluids and tissues in which they are developing. This suggests that, were it not for changes in the external environment, behavior would be rhythmic, as it is in an excised muscle maintained under certain conditions in a balanced salt solution. It is interesting to note that in Tracy's studies the internally determined movements sufficiently changed the relations between the organism and its environment so that more effective oxygen supplies became available to it. Tracy concluded by saying: "From the beginning, and more or less continuously during its whole existence, the animal is driven through its environment as a result of stimuli which arise periodically in connection with its metabolic processes" (1926, p. 345).

As the external receptors become functional, they are utilized by the internally driven organism to initiate actions that, temporarily at least, alter the internal environment. This in turn leads to a change in the drive, or need state, of the organism. In these observations we see a parallel between early behavior, determined in part by oxygen need, and the later responses initiated by the various need states in the neonatal and in the adult organism.

No such clear, rhythmic behavior as that noted by Tracy in the toadfish has been observed in the mammalian fetus. It must be emphasized, however, that the mammalian fetus is never just a passive system of external receptors, nervous system connectors, and muscles. When an external stimulus is brought to bear on a functional receptor in a living fetus, there are inevitably many cells and systems of the organism already in activity. For example, as noted above, mechanically initiated movements of the whole body are brought about by the beating of the heart cells. In the bird's egg, at certain stages of development, the active beating of the wholly extraembryonic amnion keeps the embryo in constant activity. The embryo is like an organism being tossed in a living blanket (Kuo, 1932).

Other Internal Activities

The central nervous system is also of course in a state of continuous activity. Jasper, Bridgman, and Carmichael (1937) were able to show that some electrical rhythms of the brain of the fetal guinea pig are abolished by tying off the umbilical cord. This fact indicates that the brain in the normal fetus is rhythmically active in late fetal life. There is also some evidence that long-term physiological rhythms, such as those of sleep and wakefulness, are present during fetal life and in early infancy (Pratt, 1946). Becker et al. (1940) demonstrated that the guinea pig fetus begins to swallow amniotic fluid at about the 42nd day of gestation, and that peristalsis begins at about the 16th day. Swallowing and gastrointestinal activity have also been noted in the fetal monkey. The rate of swallowing of amniotic fluid increases and the emptying time of the fetal stomach decreases as pregnancy progresses (Speert, 1943). Yanase (1907) has studied peristaltic intestinal movements in fetal guinea pigs, cats, rabbits, and men.

Blinking movements are sometimes seen in premature human fetuses. Carmichael (1934) has seen a series of blinks following a single stimulus applied to a late fetal guinea pig. These reactions are probably in part centrally determined. The frequency and other characteristics of blinking movements in the adult cannot be fully accounted for, it is now generally believed, by peripheral factors. It seems probable that the rhythm of blinking is in part the result of a rhythmicity in a specific brain center that results in a periodic discharge of impulses through the seventh nerve (Carmichael and Dearborn, 1947, p. 96).

What are thought to be rhythmic fetal hiccoughs have been identified by various students. Norman (1942) identified what he believed to be hiccoughing in one out of seven of his records of fetal activity. Such reactions vary in rate from 10 to 45 per minute.

The existence of intrinsic rhythms in the fetus shows that the release of behavior by external stimulation may be a function of complex determiners, including the phase of the body rhythms of the fetus. Consequently it seems the more remarkable that the responses called out by stimulation are as specific as they are and as closely related to the character and intensity of the external stimulus as they have been observed to be.

Because of the great variability of internal conditions, the rhythmicity of the fetus, the possibility of interference with the oxygen supply of the fetus, and the possible persistence of the effect of an anesthetic given to the maternal organism, one definite conclusion is justified. Valid statements about any type of fetal response as typical of a given period must be based upon a statistical treatment of many observations. Because of the scarcity of human fetal material, a real statistical approach has so far been almost impossible. Better statistical controls have been possible in the study of cats and guinea pigs, but even here our procedures are far from perfect. Fully adequate studies are most laborious. They require the sacrifice of many fetal litters. The experimental animals must be mated in the laboratory at known times and in known phases of female receptivity. Stocks of genetic purity are desirable. The process quickly assumes the aspect of a long-range quest in which patience is a required virtue.

The Sense of Touch

In reviewing the activity of the cutaneous senses in fetal life, we will find it convenient to treat separately pressure, temperature, and pain.

In the preceding pages cutaneous stimulation has frequently been discussed. Reference has already been made to the fact that the first stimulus-released activity of the fetus follows tactual stimulation of the region near the lips. With individual variations, this skin sensitivity develops by spreading over the face and progresses toward the rump. An exception to this so-called cephalocaudal progression is the fact that the top of the human head remains insensitive almost until birth (Hooker, 1944).

After the cutaneous areas have become sensitive, self-stimulation is possible. Whether such self-stimulation is necessary to the development of coordinated movements is an interesting question. Holt (1931, pp. 37–43) developed a theory that this sort of stimulation is of basic importance in development, but the present writer knows of little empirical evidence to support this view.

The character of the cutaneous stimuli is significant in determining the type of behavior elicited. Many investigators have noted that punctiform stimulation produces different responses than does areal stimulation. Minkowski (1922), Coronios (1933), Windle and Griffin (1931), Carmichael (1934), and Hooker (1936) all observed that stroking often leads to a specific response when a single touch by a stimulus hair is completely ineffective. Raney and Carmichael (1934) showed that stimulation of a point on the skin by a single hair often does not elicit response, but that stimulating the same area by a small brush made up of about 10 hairs will frequently bring about response.

As previously noted, the phenomenon of temporal summation of stimuli may be seen in fetal life. A single touch with a light hair may fail to bring out a response, whereas several touches of the same intensity at the same point may be effective (Carmichael, 1934).

The pressure exerted on the cutaneous receptors is of basic importance. Hooker elaborated this point (1944, p. 20). As long ago as 1882 Genzmer noted that different responses were elicited in premature infants by weak and strong cutaneous stimulation. Carmichael and Smith (1939) attempted a quantitative study of the relation between pressure and the specificity and generality of response in fetal guinea pigs. A series of calibrated esthesiometers of the von Frey type were constructed by taking hairs of various diameters and fastening them to handles. The areas located on a chart prepared in advance were first stimulated with the lightest esthesiometer that would elicit response. After a suitable rest period these areas were stimulated again with heavier pressure. The results may be summarized by saying that in each age group studied the more intense stimuli elicited more active and more general responses than did the lighter stimuli.

Reference has already been made to the remarkable consistency in the responses elicited by weak stimuli applied to particular reflexogenous zones. This fundamental fact is nowhere more clearly demonstrated than in the constancy of response resulting from the stimulation of cutaneous receptors in the exposed mucous membrane surfaces of the body. Touching of the lips, of the internal lining of the nostrils, or of the anus leads to quite specific and consistent responses. These responses change very little as the fetus becomes older, except that in the late fetus more complex and adaptive responses may occur following the primary response. For example, sucking responses several times repeated may follow a slight lip twitch in the late fetus on stimulation of the lip, whereas in a younger fetus such a stimulus might elicit only the twitch of the lip muscle.

Temperature Sensitivity

Almost a century ago Kussmaul (1859) and Genzmer (1882) felt that they had demonstrated that prematurely born infants responded differentially to warm and cool. Preyer (1885), Canestrini (1913), Blanton (1917), and Peiper (1928) made similar observations. Pratt, Nelson, and Sun (1930) made more controlled experimental observations in this field. These collaborators report that in newborn infants reaction is much more intense to stimuli that are cooler than the body surface than to stimuli that are warmer.

Carmichael and Lehner (1937) studied the role of warmth and cold in releasing behavior in a series of 40 guinea pig fetuses ranging in age from 28 to 62 postinsemination days. An apparatus was prepared that provided six stimulus temperatures. Three (47, 67, and 85 degrees C) were above the physiological zero of the organism, which was taken to be 37.5 degrees C. Three (27, 17, and 5 degrees C) were below the physiological zero. After the fetus had been exposed and observed in a preliminary manner, six spots were stimulated in random order by liquids of the temperatures just noted. These areas were (1) the vibrissae area, (2) the ear, (3) the shoulder, (4) the rump, (5) the forepaw, and (6) the hindpaw. After each stimulation the fetus was again immersed in the saline bath, which was held essentially constant at 37.5 degrees C.

In summary, it may be concluded that temperature stimulation is effective in releasing responses during most of the motile fetal period of the guinea pig. Furthermore, the greater the difference between the temperature of the stimulus and the physiological zero of the organism, the greater the relative number of responses released by the stimulus. This seems to hold, whether the stimuli are above or below the physiological zero. At the youngest ages studied there appeared to be a slight tendency for cold stimuli to be relatively more effective than warm stimuli. No comparable study of temperature sensitivity in the human fetus appears to have been made.

Cutaneous Pain

Ever since the writings of the philosopher John Locke (1690) the capacity of experiencing pain has been attributed to the fetus. A number of observations show, however, that even the application of stimuli that cause gross destruction of the skin and of underlying tissue do not call out pronounced movements. On the basis of this evidence Genzmer (1882) held that the pain sense is poorly developed in the fetus. On the first day after a premature infant's birth, he stimulated it until blood came, but he got no response. The present writer has found that pricking a guinea pig fetus with a needle so as to bring a drop of blood may not be so effective in eliciting a response as would be a fine hair applied to a corresponding point. Similar observations have been made on the cat fetus (Windle and Griffin, 1931). There can be little doubt, however, that the destruction of protoplasm does sometimes bring about violent responses in the late fetus. It has been suggested, moreover, that the general delay in the development of the pain sense may serve a biological purpose If the pain sense developed early, the pressures and tensions incident to birth would almost certainly result in traumatic pain and shock. There are reports of infants remaining anesthetic to pain stimuli long after birth.

Pratt's (1946) careful summary of the pain sense in the normal neonate led him to the conclusion that, although the sensitivity of the neonate to pain stimuli has been demonstrated, there is lack of agreement regarding the degree of pain sensitivity in the just-born infant as compared with the older infant.

The Proprioceptive Senses

The proprioceptive senses are generally taken to include the receptor mechanisms associated with the muscles, the tendons, the joints, and the nonauditory part of the inner ear. By the fourth month of fetal life, neuromuscular spindles, which are typical proprioceptors, have been found anatomically (Elwyn, 1929, p. 248). Some psychologists have speculated that the activity of the muscles and the consequent proprioceptive stimulation is important in early life in laying a foundation for the organism's later ability to maintain equilibrium and to judge certain types of spatial relations (Peterson and Rainey, 1910). Coghill (1929) came to the conclusion that proprioceptive control is necessary in bringing about the precise response to stimulation seen in the adaptive behavior of the *Amblystoma*.

A number of investigators of fetal mammals, including Swenson (1926), Angulo y González (1932), and Coronios (1933) noted responses that seemed to them to be dependent upon proprioceptive stimulation. It has been noted above that, in the fetal opossum, sucking, breathing, and crawling are three of the earliest responses evident in this mammal, which is born in an immature condition. These are all responses of the sort that might involve proprioceptive stimulation and control. Tendon reflexes and stretch reflexes and stimuli related to receptors in the joints have been studied by such investigators as Minkowski (1922, p. 723) and Bolaffio and Artom (1924, p. 472).

It seems that much of the so-called generalized behavior of the fetus is in reality made up of responses to proprioceptive stimulation. Stimulation of this sort is brought into being as a result of the activity elicited by some relatively specific muscular responses that may follow cutaneous or other types of exteroceptive stimulation.

The receptors in the nonauditory part of the inner ear, important in the maintenance of bodily posture, also play a part in the righting responses of animals dropped from an inverted position (Warkentin and Carmichael, 1939). Lane (1917) believed that there is a correlation between the development of the semicircular canals, as deter-

mined by histological studies, and the ability of the fetal rat to regain an upright posture when placed on its side. By about the tenth week the nonauditory labyrinth is well differentiated in the human fetus. Minkowski (1922) pointed out, as noted above, that in the fetus supported in the amniotic fluid vestibular stimulation elicits many responses that would not be possible in the newborn organism. This same author was careful, however, not to disregard the possibility that some of these responses may be the result of stimulation of proprioceptors in the neck and related regions. Magnus (1924) emphasized the part of neck-initiated responses in these activities (see also Camis, 1930, pp. 262–268).

Actually it is difficult to say what part the nonauditory division of the inner ear plays in fetal life. That these complexes of receptors are important, however, seems to be generally conceded. In a matter of minutes after normal birth the newborn guinea pig can stand upright. There can be no doubt that this highly coordinated and adaptive behavior is a function of proprioceptive as well as exteroceptive mechanisms. There is also good reason to conclude from the study of the air-righting reflexes of various mammals that the sensory control of posture continues to develop for some time after normal birth.

The Organic Senses

The activating responses associated with hunger and thirst apparently develop during fetal life. Hess (1922) pointed out, however, that early premature fetuses are less able than late infants to show the somatic signs of needing to be fed. The sucking reflex basic to ingestion of food in the newborn child is also developed long before birth. Food-ingesting activities are associated with many apparently random movements until in postnatal life they become patterned into more useful responses. The organic receptors associated with the cardiovascular system are also ready for activation during fetal life and are presumably vigorously activated immediately after birth.

Taste

According to Parker (1922) taste buds develop in the human fetus during the third month. Taste receptors are actually found to be more widely distributed in the early fetus than in the adult. Parker found evidence of a retraction of the sensory field of taste during development. There seems to be evidence that salt, sour, and bitter, as against sweet, can be discriminated at birth (Carmichael, 1946; see also Pfaffmann, 1936).

Smell

Experimental work on the sense of smell in newborn infants has been summarized by Canestrini (1913), Peiper (1928), and Pratt, Nelson, and Sun (1930). It is fairly clear that during fetal life itself the receptors for the olfactory tract may be stimulated by amniotic fluid. On the other hand, they are probably not brought into differential activity for lack of a differentiated stimulus.

The so-called common chemical sense is often confused with smell. This sense is seen typically in the activation of the trigeminal nerve, and it is not olfactory in the ordinary meaning of the term. Stimulation of common chemical receptors in the nasal tract in the newborn child may bring about relatively violent reactions, such as sneezing. Ammonia is a typical irritant to this sense (Carmichael, 1946).

Hearing

Anatomical works on the structure of the ear of the late fetus (Hess, 1922) make it clear that there is no reason why the ear is not sufficiently developed to allow stimulation before birth (see summary by Pratt, Nelson, and Sun, 1930). In fact there is growing evidence that the human auditory receptors can be stimulated under certain circumstances during normal prenatal life. The auditory stimulus must then pass through the body wall of the mother, and through the liquids and membranes surrounding the fetus. Forbes and Forbes (1927) reported a definite response by an unborn child to the sound produced by striking the bathtub in which the pregnant mother was bathing. And, as already noted, a similar response has been used as a basis for the study of conditioning in human fetal organisms. Preliminary studies seem to indicate that the human fetus can be stimulated by a wide range of tones from 20 to 5000 cycles per second while in utero (Bernard and Sontag, 1947).

Rawdon-Smith, Carmichael, and Wellman (1938) studied the electrical responses from the cochlea of the fetal guinea pig. After the ear was exposed, a suitably insulated electrode in a flexible holder was placed in contact with the external surface of the bone at the base of the exposed cochlea. The youngest fetus in which a cochlear response was secured had an age of 52 postinsemination days, but this is probably not the earliest age at which the response can be elicited. In the 52-day fetus a small response (2 microvolts) was obtained for a stimulus of 600 cycles per second and an intensity of approximately 100 decibels above the human threshold. Declining responses were obtained to tones below this and above 2000 cycles per second. Later fetal organisms gave electrical responses amounting to as much as 100 microvolts.

McCrady, Wever, and Bray (1937) also studied the electrical responses from the cochlea of the postnatal opossum while the organism was still living in the pouch. By studying sound-initiated reflex startle patterns and by electrical tests they demonstrated a development of the auditory sense. The first startle responses to sound stimuli were seen at about 50 days. When the electrical activity of the ear was studied at 59 days, it was found that sensitivity was greatest in the middle range, with a maximum at about 2000 cycles per second. By 82 days the maximum had shifted to 7000 cycles per second. At all ages studied in the pouch-young opossum, the relation between the electrical response and the intensity of the stimulus is essentially linear, which suggests that these young organisms have a surprisingly efficient acoustical apparatus.

Vision

Embryologists point out that, by the second or third week of the embryonic period, changes have begun in the human fetus that are antecedent to the development of the eye (Keibel and Mall, 1910). Although it is unlikely that the fetal eye is ever strongly stimulated before birth, it may well be that, when the head of the late fetus is in just the right position, very strong light applied to the abdomen of the mother might lead to a visual response. Kussmaul long ago (1859) discovered that in a 2-months premature infant the difference between light and dark could be determined by specific reaction. Peterson and Rainey (1910) have confirmed this observation. This does not mean that the visual mechanism is structurally mature at birth, for there is evidence (Pratt, Nelson, and Sun, 1930) that the optic nerve and related structures are not fully developed even at normal birth.

Visual responses in fetal organisms can best be detected by electrical means and by observing reflex behavior, particularly the pupillary reflex (Hess, 1922). Care must be exercised (Parker, 1919) in interpreting such studies, however, not to confuse true neurally determined iris reflexes with the independent stimulation of the muscles of the iris by light. Other techniques, such as stimulation by moving striations of light and dark, have been used to study vision in developing animals (Warkentin and Smith, 1937; and Warkentin, 1938).

By way of summary it may be said that the anatomical development of the visual sense begins very early and continues throughout normal human fetal life and into postnatal life as well. It is unquestionably true that this sense has developed to a point at which some responses can be elicited long before there is any reason to believe that in the normal environment such responses have biological utility. The development of this receptor mechanism is thus a notable example of the law of anticipatory function.

REFERENCES

Abel, S., and W. F. Windle. Relation of the volume of pulmonary circulation to respiration at birth. *Anat. Rec.*, 1939, **75**, 451–464.

Ahlfeld, J. F. Beiträge zur Lehre vom Uebergange der intrauterinen Athmung zur extrauterinen. In *Beiträge zur Psysiologie, Festschrift zu Carl Ludwig zu seinem 70. Geburtstage gewidmet von seinen Schülern.* Leipzig: Vogel, 1890. Pp. 1–32.

Angulo y González, A. W. The prenatal development of behavior in the albino rat. *J. comp. Neurol.*, 1932, **55**, 395–442.

Barcroft, J. *The brain and its environment.* New Haven: Yale University Press, 1938.

Barcroft, J. *Researches on pre-natal life.* Springfield, Ill.: Thomas, 1947.

Barcroft, J., and D. H. Barron. The establishment of certain reflex arcs in foetal sheep. *Proc. Soc. exp. Biol., N. Y.*, 1937, **36**, 86–87.

Barcroft, J., and D. H. Barron. The development of behavior in foetal sheep. *J. comp. Neurol.*, 1939, **70**, 477–502.

Barcroft, J., D. H. Barron, A. T. Cowie, and P. H. Forsham. The oxygen supply of the foetal brain of the sheep and the effect of asphyxia on foetal respiratory movement. *J. Physiol.*, 1940, **97**, 338–346.

Becker, R. F., W. F. Windle, E. E. Barth, and M. D. Schulz. Fetal swallowing, gastro-intestinal activity and defecation in amnio. *Surg. Gynec. Obstet.*, 1940, **70**, 603–614.

Bernard, J., and L. W. Sontag. Fetal reactivity to tonal stimulation: a preliminary report. *J. genet. Psychol.*, 1947, **70**, 205–210.

Blanton, M. G. The behavior of the human infant during the first thirty days of life. *Psychol. Rev.*, 1917, **24**, 456–483.

Bolaffio, M., and G. Artom. Ricerche sulla fisiologia del sistema nervosa del feto umano. *Arch. Sci. biol. Napoli*, 1924, **5**, 457–487.

Bridgman, C. S., and L. Carmichael. An experimental study of the onset of behavior in the fetal guinea-pig. *J. genet. Psychol.*, 1935, **47**, 247–267.

Brown, T. G. On the activities of the central nervous system of the unborn foetus of the cat; with a discussion of the question whether progression (walking, etc.) is a "learnt" complex. *J. Physiol.*, 1915, **49**, 208–215.

Camis, M. *The physiology of the vestibular apparatus.* (Translated by R. S. Creed.) Oxford: Clarendon Press, 1930.

Canestrini, S. Über das Sinnesleben des Neugeborenen. *Monog. Neurol. Psychiat.*, No. 5. Berlin: Springer, 1913.

Carmichael, L. An experimental study in the prenatal guinea-pig of the origin and development of reflexes and patterns of behavior in relation to the stimulation of specific receptor areas during the period of active fetal life. *Genet. Psychol. Monogr.*, 1934, **16**, 337–491.

Carmichael, L. Fetal behavior and developmental psychology. *Rapp. et C. R. onzième Congr. int. psychol.*, Paris, 1938, 108–123.

Carmichael, L. The experimental embryology of mind. *Psychol. Bull.*, 1941, **38**, 1–28.

Carmichael, L. The onset and early development of behavior. In L. Carmichael (Ed.), *Manual of child psychology*. New York: Wiley, 1946.

Carmichael, L., and W. F. Dearborn. *Reading and visual fatigue*. Boston: Houghton Mifflin, 1947.

Carmichael, L., and G. F. J. Lehner. The development of temperature sensitivity during the fetal period. *J. genet. Psychol.*, 1937, **50**, 217–227.

Carmichael, L., and M. F. Smith. Quantified pressure stimulation and the specificity and generality of response in fetal life. *J. genet. Psychol.*, 1939, **54**, 425–434.

Coghill, G. E. *Anatomy and the problem of behaviour*. Cambridge: Cambridge University Press. New York: Macmillan, 1929.

Corey, E. L. Causative factors of the initial inspiration of the mammalian fetus. (Abstract.) *Anat. Rec., Suppl.*, 1931, **48**, 41.

Corner, G. W. *Ourselves unborn*. New Haven: Yale University Press, 1944.

Coronios, J. D. The development of behavior in the fetal cat. *Genet. Psychol. Monogr.*, 1933, **14**, 283–386.

Daniel, R. S., and K. U. Smith. The sea-approach behavior of the neonate loggerhead turtle (*Caretta caretta*). *J. comp. physiol. Psychol.*, 1947, **40**, 413–420.

Dewey, E. *Behavior development in infants: a survey of the literature on prenatal and post-natal activity, 1920–1934*. New York: Columbia University Press, 1935.

Elwyn, A. The structure and development of the proprioceptors. In F. Tilney et al. (Eds.), *The cerebellum*. Baltimore: Williams and Wilkins, 1929.

Feldman, W. M. *Principles of ante-natal and post-natal child physiology, pure and applied*. London and New York: Longmans, Green, 1920.

Fender, F. A., W. B. Neff, and G. Binger. Convulsions produced by fetal anoxia: experimental study. *Anesthesiol.*, 1946, **7**, 10–13.

Fitzgerald, J. E., and W. F. Windle. Some observations on early human fetal movements. *J. comp. Neurol.*, 1942, **76**, 159–167.

Forbes, H. S., and H. B. Forbes. Fetal sense reaction: hearing. *J. comp. Psychol.*, 1927, **7**, 353–355.

Geiger, A. J., W. M. Monroe, and A. V. N. Goodyer. Clinical fetal electrocardiography: Its practical accomplishment. *Proc. Soc. exp. Biol., N. Y.*, 1941, **48**, 646–648.

Genzmer, A. *Untersuchungen über die Sinneswahrnehmungen des neugeborenen Menschen.* (Dissertation, 1873.) Halle: Niemeyer, 1882.

Gesell, A. The ontogenesis of infant behavior. In L. Carmichael (Ed.), *Manual of child psychology*. New York: Wiley, 1946.

Goeckel, H. Die Wandlungen in der Bewertung des ungeborenen Kindes. Dissertation, University of Heidelberg, 1911.

Goss, C. M. First contractions of the heart without cytological differentiation. *Anat. Rec.*, 1940, **76**, 19–27.

Hess, J. H. *Premature and congenitally diseased infants*. Philadelphia: Lea and Febiger, 1922.

Hogg, I. D. Sensory nerves and associated structures in the skin of human fetuses of 8 to 14 weeks of menstrual age correlated with functional capability. *J. comp. Neurol.*, 1941, **75**, 371–410.

Holt, E. B. *Animal drive and the learning process*. New York: Holt, 1931. Volume I.

Hooker, D. Early fetal activity in mammals. *Yale J. Biol. Med.*, 1936, **8**, 579–602.

Hooker, D. Fetal behavior. *Res. Publ. Ass. nerv. ment. Dis.*, 1939, **19**, 237–243.

Hooker, D. *The origin of overt behavior.* Ann Arbor: University of Michigan, 1944.

Howells, T. H. Heredity as a differential element in behavior. *Univ. Colo. Stud.*, 1933, **20**, 173–193.

Howells, T. H. The obsolete dogmas of heredity. *Psychol. Rev.*, 1945, **52**, 23–34.

Howells, T. H., and D. O. Vine. The innate differential in social learning. *J. abnorm. soc. Psychol.*, 1940, **35**, 537–548.

Huggett, A. St. G. Foetal respiratory reflexes. *J. Physiol.*, 1930, **69**, 144–152.

Jackson, H. Evolution and dissolution of the nervous system. *Lancet*, 1884, **1**, 555–558; 649–652; 739–744.

Jasper, H. H., C. S. Bridgman, and L. Carmichael. An ontogenetic study of cerebral electrical potentials in the guinea pig. *J. exp. Psychol.*, 1937, **21**, 63–71.

Keeler, C. E. Materials for the synthesis of hereditary behavior trends in mammals. *J. comp. physiol. Psychol.*, 1948, **41**, 75–81.

Keibel, F., and F. P. Mall. *Manual of human embryology*. Philadelphia: Lippincott, 1910. Volume II.

Kuo, Z. Y. Ontogeny of embryonic behavior in Aves: I. The chronology and general nature of the behavior of the chick embryo. *J. exp. Zool.*, 1932, **61**, 395–430.

Kuo, Z. Y. Development of acetylcholine in the chick embryo. *J. Neurophysiol.*, 1939, **2**, 488–493.

Kussmaul, A. *Untersuchungen über das Seelenleben des neugeborenen Menschen.* Leipzig: Winter, 1859.

Lane, H. H. The correlation between structure and function in the development of the special senses of the white rat. *Univ. Okla. Bull.* (N. S. No. 140) (Univ. Stud., No. 8), 1917, 1–88.

Lindsley, D. B. Heart and brain potentials of human fetuses in utero. *Amer. J. Psychol.,* 1942, **55,** 412–416.

Locke, J. *Essay concerning human understanding* (1690). Philadelphia: Kay and Troutman, 1849.

Maekawa, M., and J. Toyoshima. The fetal electro-cardiogram of the human subject. *Acta Sch. med. Univ. Kioto,* 1930, **12,** 519–520.

Magnus, R. *Körperstellung.* Berlin: Springer, 1924.

Mann, H., and P. Bernstein. Fetal electrocardiography. *Amer. Heart J.,* 1941, **22,** 390–400.

Marquis, D. P. Can conditioned responses be established in the newborn infant? *J. genet. Psychol.,* 1931, **39,** 479–492.

McCrady, E., E. G. Wever, and C. W. Bray. The development of hearing in the opossum. *J. exp. Zool.,* 1937, **75,** 503–517.

McGraw, M. B. Maturation of behavior. In L. Carmichael (Ed.), *Manual of child psychology.* New York: Wiley, 1946.

Minkowski, M. Ueber frühzeitige Bewegungen. Reflexe und muskuläre Reaktionen beim menschlichen Fötus und ihre Beziehungen zum fötalen Nerven- und Muskelsystem. *Schweiz. med. Wschr.,* 1922, **52,** 721–724; 751–755.

Minkowski, M. Sur les modalités et la localisation du réflexe plantaire au cours de son évolution du foetus à l'adulte. *C. R. Cong. Méd. Alién. Neurol. Genève,* 1926, **30,** 301–308.

Minkowski, M. Ueber die elektrische Erregbarkeit der fötalen Muskulatur. *Schweiz. Arch. Neurol. Psychiat.,* 1928, **22,** 64–71.

Needham, J. *Chemical embryology.* Cambridge: Cambridge University Press, 1931. 3 vols.

Neu, M. Die Diagnose der Schwangerschaft. In A. Döderlein (Ed.), *Handbuch der Geburtschilfe.* Wiesbaden: Bergman, 1915. Pp. 246–328.

Newbery, H. Measurement of three types of fetal activity. *J. comp. Psychol.,* 1941, **32,** 521–530.

Norman, H. N. Fetal hiccups. *J. comp. Psychol.,* 1942, **34,** 65–73.

Pankratz, D. S. The possible relations of the development of the suprarenal gland to the origin of foetal movements in the albino rat. *Anat. Rec.,* 1930, **45,** 235.

Pankratz, D. S. The development of the suprarenal gland in the albino rat, with a consideration of its possible relation to the origin of foetal movements. *Anat. Rec.,* 1931, **49,** 31–49.

Parker, G. H. *The elementary nervous system.* Philadelphia: Lippincott, 1919.

Parker, G. H. *Smell, taste, and allied senses in the vertebrates.* Philadelphia: Lippincott, 1922.

Peiper, A. *Die Hirnätigkeit des Säuglings.* Berlin: Springer, 1928.

Peterson, F., and L. H. Rainey. The beginnings of mind in the newborn. *Bull. Lying-in Hosp. N. Y.,* 1910, **7,** 99–122.

Pfaffmann, C. Differential responses of the newborn cat to gustatory stimuli. *J. genet. Psychol.,* 1936, **49,** 61–67.

Potter, E. L., and G. P. Bohlander. Intrauterine respiration in relation to development of fetal lung, with report of two unusual anomalies of respiratory system. *Amer. J. Obstet. Gynaec.,* 1941, **42,** 14–22.

Pratt, J. P. Sex functions in man. In E. Allen (Ed.), *Sex and internal secretions.* Baltimore: Williams and Wilkins, 1931.

Pratt, K. C. The neonate. In L. Carmichael (Ed.), *Manual of child psychology.* New York: Wiley, 1946.

Pratt, K. C., A. K. Nelson, and K. H. Sun. The behavior of the newborn infant. *Ohio State Univ. Stud., Contr. Psychol.,* 1930, No. 10.

Preyer, W. *Die seele des Kindes.* Leipzig: Fernau, 1882 (5th Ed., 1900). *The mind of the child;* Part 1. *The senses and the will;* Part 2. *The development of the intellect.* (Translated by H. W. Brown.) New York: Appleton-Century-Crofts, 1888, 1889.

Preyer, W. *Specielle Physiologie des Embryo. Untersuchungen über die Lebenserscheinungen vor der Geburt.* Leipzig: Grieben, 1885.

Raney, E. T., and L. Carmichael. Localizing responses to tactual stimuli in the fetal rat in relation to the psychological problem of space perception. *J. genet. Psychol.,* 1934, **45,** 3–21.

Rawdon-Smith, A. F., L. Carmichael, and B. Wellman. Electrical responses from the cochlea of the fetal guinea pig. *J. exp. Psychol.,* 1938, **23,** 531–535.

Ray, W. S. A preliminary report on a study of fetal conditioning. *Child Develpm.,* 1932, **3,** 175–177.

Richards, T. W., and H. Newbery. Studies in fetal behavior. III. Can performance on test items at six months postnatally be predicted on the basis of fetal activity? *Child Develpm.,* 1938, **9,** 79–86.

Richards, T. W., H. Newbery, and R. Fallgatter. Studies in fetal behavior. II. Activity of the human fetus *in utero* and its relation to other prenatal conditions, particularly the mother's basal metabolic rate. *Child Develpm.,* 1938, **9,** 69–78.

Rose, D. Comparison of fetal development in normal and hyperthyroid rats. *J. comp. physiol. Psychol.,* 1947, **40,** 87–105.

Rose, D. Heart rate as a behavioral indicator in the fetal rat. *J. comp. physiol. Psychol.,* 1947, **40,** 157–164.

Schoolland, J. B. Are there any innate behavior tendencies? *Genet. Psychol. Monogr.,* 1942, **25,** 219–287.

Sherman, M., and I. C. Sherman. Sensorimotor responses in infants. *J. comp. Psychol.,* 1925, **5,** 53–68.

Smith, S., and E. R. Guthrie. *General psychology in terms of behavior.* New York: Appleton-Century-Crofts, 1921.

Sontag, L. W., and T. W. Richards. Studies in fetal behaviour. I. Fetal heart rate as a behavioural indicator. *Monogr. Soc. Res. Child Develpm.*, 1938, **3**, No. 4.

Sontag, L. W., and R. F. Wallace. A study of fetal activity: Preliminary report of the Fels Fund. *Amer. J. Dis. Child.*, 1934, **48**, 1050–1057.

Speert, H. Swallowing and gastrointestinal activity in the fetal monkey. *Amer. J. Obstet. Gynaec.*, 1943, **45**, 69–82.

Spelt, D. K. Conditioned responses in the human fetus *in utero*. *Psychol. Bull.*, 1938, **35**, 712–713.

Strassmann, P. Das Leben vor der Geburt. *Samml. klin. Vortr., N. F., Gynäk.*, 1903, No. 353, 947–968.

Streeter, G. L. Weight, sitting height, head size, foot length, and menstrual age of the human embryo. *Contr. Embryol. Carn. Instn.*, 1920, **11**, 143–170.

Swenson, E. A. The development of movement of the albino rat before birth. Unpublished Ph.D. thesis, University of Kansas, 1926.

Tracy, H. C. The development of motility and behavior reactions in the toadfish (*Opsanus tau*). *J. comp. Neurol.*, 1926, **40**, 253–369.

Walz, W. Ueber die Bedeutung der intrauterinen Atembewegungen. *Mschr. Geburtsh. Gynäk.*, 1922, **60**, 331–341.

Warkentin, J. A genetic study of vision in animals. Unpublished Ph.D. thesis, University of Rochester, 1938.

Warkentin, J., and L. Carmichael. A study of the development of the air-righting reflex in cats and rabbits. *J. genet. Psychol.*, 1939, **55**, 67–80.

Warkentin, J., and K. U. Smith. The development of visual acuity in the cat. *J. genet. Psychol.*, 1937, **50**, 371–399.

Wenger, M. An investigation of conditioned responses in human infants. *Univ. Ia. Stud. Child Welf.*, 1936, **12**, 7–90.

Whitehead, W. H., W. F. Windle, and R. F. Becker. Changes in lung structure during aspiration of amniotic fluid and during air-breathing at birth. *Anat. Rec.*, 1942, **83**, 255–265.

Wickens, D. D., and C. Wickens. A study of conditioning in the neonate. *Psychol. Bull.*, 1939, **36**, 599.

Williams, J. W. *Obstetrics.* New York: Appleton-Century-Crofts, 1931.

Willier, B. H. The embryonic development of sex. In E. Allen (Ed.), *Sex and internal secretions.* Baltimore: Williams and Wilkins, 1939.

Windle, W. F. *Physiology of the fetus: Origin and extent of function in prenatal life.* Philadelphia: Saunders, 1940.

Windle, W. F. Physiology and anatomy of the respiratory system in the fetus and newborn infant. *J. Pediat.*, 1941, **19**, 437–444.

Windle, W. F., and R. F. Becker. Relation of anoxemia to early activity in the fetal nervous system. *Arch. Neurol. Psychiat., Chicago*, 1940, **43**, 90–101.

Windle, W. F., and R. F. Becker. Asphyxia neonatorum, an experimental study in the guinea pig. *Amer. J. Obstet. Gynaec.*, 1943, **45**, 183–200.

Windle, W. F., and J. E. Fitzgerald. Development of the spinal reflex mechanism in human embryos. *J. comp. Neurol.*, 1937, **67**, 493–509.

Windle, W. F., and A. M. Griffin. Observations on embryonic and fetal movements of the cat. *J. comp. Neurol.*, 1931, **52**, 149–188.

Woyciechowski, B. Richy zarodka ludzkiego 42 mm. *Polsk. Gazeta Lekarska*, 1928, **7**, 409–411.

Yanase, J. Beiträge zur Physiologie der peristaltischen Bewegungen des embryonalen Darmes: I. Mitteilung. *Pflüg. Arch. ges. Physiol.*, 1907, **117**, 345–383. II. Mitteilung. *ibid.*, **119**, 451–464.

Youngstrom, K. A. Acetylcholine esterase concentration during the development of the human fetus. *J. Neurophysiol.*, 1941, **4**, 473–477.

Zettleman, H. J. Initial fetal atelectasis. *Amer. J. Obstet. Gynaec.*, 1946, **51**, 241–245.

9.

The Genetics of Behavior

CALVIN S. HALL

Western Reserve University

Six years after the inauguration of modern experimental psychology by Gustav Theodor Fechner, Gregor Johann Mendel founded the science of genetics by executing a brilliantly designed series of studies on the garden pea. It is a curious fact that these two life sciences which grew up in the same period of history have rarely worked closely together. Genetics has concerned itself almost exclusively with morphology; it has paid scant attention to behavior. Psychology, on the other hand, although it has taken a lively interest in heredity, has too often attempted to investigate the relation of behavior to genetic constitution by methods of pre-Mendelian vintage.

A real genetics of behavior promises to emerge, however, as psychologists continue to adopt the procedures of modern genetics, and as geneticists turn their attention more systematically to behavior. This encouraging trend will ultimately give status and stature to an interdisciplinary science of *psychogenetics*. The psychogeneticist of the future will presumably be trained in the methods and techniques of both genetics and psychology.

A survey of the present accomplishments of this hybrid discipline is the task of this chapter. It reviews the methods of genetics and their application to the investigation of the genetic basis for psychological traits, and it recounts some of the initial attempts to establish a genetics of behavior. It is not primarily concerned with the nature-nurture argument, nor does it attempt to evaluate investigations of human heredity. In the writer's opinion, the genetics of behavior must be worked out on species that can be subjected to controlled breeding. At the present time this precludes human subjects.

The main objectives of psychogenetics are four in number: (1) to discover whether a given behavior pattern is transmitted from generation to generation, (2) to determine the number and nature of the genetic factors involved in the trait, (3) to locate the gene or genes on the chromosomes, and (4) to determine the manner in which the genes act to produce the trait.

HEREDITY AND BEHAVIOR

The first objective, to find out whether heredity plays a part in the determination of a psychological characteristic, may be realized best by the method of selective breeding and by the method of comparison of different strains, breeds, or species. The method of selective breeding is the more arduous of the two. The comparison of strains already established, e.g. wild versus tame strains of rodents, is relatively simple.

Selective Breeding

Selective breeding consists of mating animals that display the desired trait and of selecting for breeding from among their offspring those that express the trait. If the trait is regulated by heredity, continued selection for a number of generations in a uniform environment will result in a strain that breeds more or less true for the character under study. Selection for more than one value of the trait may be made. In a trait that expresses itself alternately, e.g. susceptible or not susceptible to audiogenic seizures, two strains, susceptible and resistant, may be established concurrently by selective breeding. If the trait is one that expresses itself in degree on a continuum, e.g. maze learning, selection of a number of different values of the trait may be made. In practice, selection for a "quantitative" trait is usually limited to the extremes of the distribution, e.g. fast and slow maze learners.

Maze learning. Tryon (1940, 1942) was able to prove, by selective breeding, that maze-learning ability in the rat is inherited. Tryon describes his experiment as follows:

An experiment was begun in 1927 that had as its purpose the establishment by selective breeding of a pure line of maze-bright and a pure line of maze-dull rats. Each animal was run nineteen trials through a seventeen-blind T maze. His score was the total number of

entrances into blind alleys. The breeding schedule consisted in mating together the brightest rat within each of the brightest litters, the dullest within each of the dullest. Rigorous environmental controls were effected (1) by instituting standard procedure of animal care and of breeding, (2) by using an automatic mechanical device for delivering the animals into the maze without handling, and (3) by employing an electric recorder for the scoring of each rat's maze run. These controls have remained constant for eleven years. Selective breeding has continued for eighteen generations. [1940, p. 112.]

Tryon's parental generation consisted of an unselected, heterogeneous population of 142 rats. The distribution of their scores appears on the top line of Fig. 1. As Tryon states, "the breeding schedule consisted in mating together the brightest rats within each of the brightest litters, the dullest within each of the dullest." These F_1 rats were run on the maze, and the resultant distribution of scores appears on the next line of Fig. 1. The same breeding procedure was followed for each successive generation.

TABLE 1

A Statistical Summary of Twelve Generations of Two Strains of Rats Selectively Bred for Activity and Inactivity (Rundquist)

(Revolutions in thousands for 15 days)

Parental Generation

		Males								Females			
		No. 24	Mean 21	S.D. 10						No. 24	Mean 28	S.D. 22	
	Active Strain Males			Inactive Strain Males				Active Strain Females			Inactive Strain Females		
Generation	No.	Mean	S.D.	No.	Mean	S.D.	C.R.*	No.	Mean	S.D.	No.	Mean	S.D.	C.R.*
F_1	17	141	78	14	72	89	2.27	10	115	65	9	104	83	0.33
F_2	10	138	72	15	84	65	1.89	9	142	39	18	90	48	3.02
F_3	7	153	92	13	65	66	2.24	7	200	67	7	129	65	2.01
F_4	24	143	96	25	129	104	0.49	31	181	122	20	173	89	0.27
F_5	19	141	96	16	31	27	4.77	22	198	61	20	60	52	7.90
F_6	30	178	90	23	22	25	9.04	23	255	69	25	68	55	10.28
F_7	28	131	80	18	10	17	7.77	27	205	97	28	50	45	7.55
F_8	29	136	70	11	15	19	8.57	29	234	70	19	39	49	11.30
F_9	32	168	41	21	22	45	11.38	20	237	53	25	46	47	12.62
F_{10}	26	150	75	25	4	5	10.12	26	257	77	23	24	34	14.02
F_{11}	26	151	66	21	6	9	11.02	25	267	104	29	23	28	11.45
F_{12}	26	123	53	29	6	5	11.23	23	172	66	23	20	24	10.29

* Critical ratio.

Gradually the two groups, maze-bright and maze-dull, pulled apart, and in F_7 there was practically no overlapping between them.

Tryon's experiment has been repeated by Heron (1935) with similar results.

Voluntary activity. Rundquist (1933)

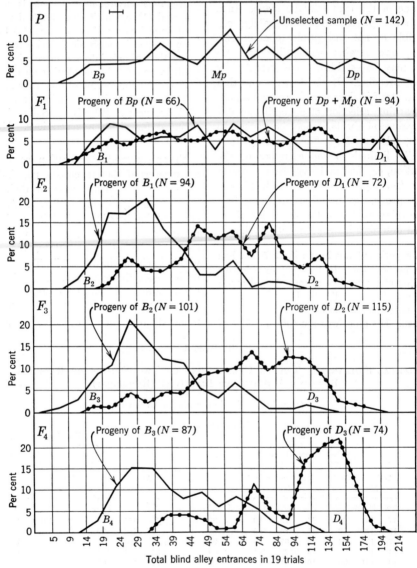

Fɪɢ. 1. Selective breeding for maze-learning ability in rats. (Tryon, 1942.)

Tryon writes, "There appears to be a law of diminishing returns, for after the F_7 negligible effects of selective breeding are noted" (1940, p. 114).

used the method of selective breeding to investigate the role of heredity in voluntary activity of the rat. Voluntary activity is defined as the number of revolutions turned by the rat in a revolving drum. Rundquist selected for high activity and for low activity and was able to establish two strains that displayed some consistency, from generation to generation, in the two extreme manifestations of the trait (Table 1). It is interesting to note that during the first four generations selection within each strain was not practiced. Instead Rundquist mated together the most active rats even though

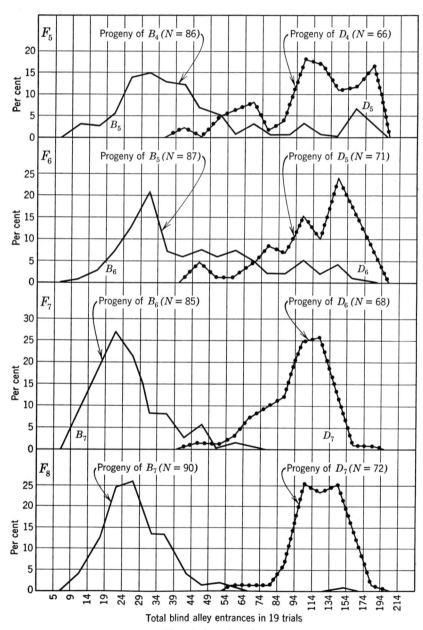

FIG. 1 (continued).

they might have had inactive parents, and the most inactive rats even though they might have had active parents. As a consequence of selection regardless of ancestry, no differentiation between the groups occurred from F_1 through F_4. If selection is to be effective in producing strains that breed true, it is necessary to continue breeding within the family lines that have been initially selected from the parental population.

Emotionality. A third example of selective breeding for a psychological trait is the investigation of emotionality in the rat by Hall (1938). Hall established that defecation and urination in a strange situation are valid measures of emotionality (1934). The procedure consists of placing a single animal in a brightly lighted circular enclosure 7 feet in diameter, for 2 minutes a day for 12 days. A record of urination and defecation on each trial is kept. The range of scores varies from 0 (no instance of either urination or defecation) to 12 (the rat defecates or urinates during every trial in the field). The parental generation, consisting of 145 rats, was a heterogeneous group. The high-scoring rats were mated together to start the emotional strain, and the low-scoring animals were bred *inter se* to initiate a nonemotional strain. In succeeding generations the highest scoring animals of the emotional strain were interbred and the lowest scoring animals of the nonemotional strain were interbred. The results appear in Table 2. The emotional strain becomes, on the average, more emotional until the ninth generation, when the mean becomes stabilized at approximately 10 and the standard deviation at a little over 2. Selection for nonemotionality yields less systematic results. The averages and variabilities fluctuate in a random fashion within rather narrow limits. It is significant that the maximum effects of selection for nonemotionality are realized in the first generation, whereas it takes nine generations for the emotional strain to become stabilized.

TABLE 2

A STATISTICAL SUMMARY OF TWELVE GENERATIONS OF TWO STRAINS OF RATS SELECTIVELY BRED FOR EMOTIONALITY AND NONEMOTIONALITY (HALL, UNPUBLISHED MATERIAL)

No. of Days of Defecation or Urination

Parental Generation

No.	Mean	S.D.
145	3.86	3.54

	Emotional Strain			Nonemotional Strain			
	No. of Days of Defecation or Urination			No. of Days of Defecation or Urination			
	No.	Mean	S.D.	No.	Mean	S.D.	C.R.
F_1	40	3.07	3.36	35	0.46	0.77	4.74
F_2	18	4.72	4.12	18	1.94	2.28	2.50
F_3	65	3.92	3.64	50	1.02	1.30	6.00
F_4	84	4.69	3.89	52	1.40	1.43	7.00
F_5	75	4.96	3.85	59	0.41	1.18	8.44
F_6	48	6.87	3.28	51	0.51	1.13	12.72
F_7	72	7.82	3.18	53	0.17	0.47	20.40
F_8	77	8.37	2.94	40	1.07	2.46	14.29
F_9	85	10.31	2.09	32	1.68	3.25	14.15
F_{10}	66	10.41	2.08	22	1.45	3.13	12.45
F_{11}	57	10.11	2.39	42	1.05	2.01	20.11
F_{12}	47	10.40	2.18	31	1.65	2.53	15.91

Further comment upon this point will be reserved for a later section.

The consistency within some litters of the emotional and nonemotional strains may be illustrated by two examples of parent-child resemblances. Two F_9 rats with scores of 10 and 12 had a litter of nine whose scores were 12, 12, 12, 12, 12, 12, 11, 11, and 10. Two nonemotional F_9 rats with scores of 0 and 0 had a litter of six whose scores were 0, 0, 0, 0, 1, and 1.

To the investigator planning a selective breeding experiment the following suggestions and cautions may prove useful. (1) Since an experiment of this nature usually requires many years and many dollars, the investigation of psychological traits of primary importance should be given priority. (2) The investigator should make certain that the measure or measures employed are reliable and valid. Tryon (1942) has discussed this point thoroughly. (3) Uniform procedures for raising, handling, and testing the animals are essential, since variations in procedure may distort conclusions. Temperature, feeding schedules, the type of food, the amount and kind of handling, litter, size, the type of living cages, the age at which the animals are tested, and numerous other details must remain constant from generation to generation. The animals should also be kept free of parasites, for, as Russell (1941) reminds us,

. . . some differences that have been attributed to genetic causes may be due to parasites. Because of the limited number of parents, there is a relatively high probability that an inbred line will become uniformly infected, particularly with parasitic organisms that are transmitted from mother to offspring. [P. 347.]

(4) The health and vigor of the strains should be maintained at a constant level. Selection for uniform vigor as well as for the trait under study will help to insure the maintenance of the strains. (5) Fertility is another important requisite. Obviously the loss of a strain through sterility must be avoided. Fertility must be maintained even at the risk of the confusion that would be introduced into the genetic picture if the trait investigated should turn out to be correlated closely with fertility. However, the danger of such confusion is probably not great, for Wright (1922) has shown that variations in fertility and vigor are determined largely by environment. In practice only fertile animals should be selected for breeding. (6) The transmission of a trait from generation to generation may appear to be genetic, whereas in reality it is due to an extragenetic factor. The mode of transmission may be some prenatal or postnatal influence of the mother on the young. The prenatal influence can be determined by transplanting the fertilized egg to a host mother of a different strain. The postnatal influence can be investigated by placing the neonates with a foster mother.

In sum, the psychogeneticist must always remember that in studying trait inheritance he puts himself in the difficult position of trying to prove a negative: that the trait in question is *not* due to extragenetic factors. He adds to the plausibility of his conclusions in direct measure as he controls the effects of all extraneous influences.

Strain Differences

A strain is defined as a group of individuals of a species that have a common lineage resulting from either natural or artificial selection and inbreeding. The extent of common ancestry determines the degree to which the strain is inbred. Close inbreeding, viz., brother-sister matings, for a number of generations eventually produces a pure strain. The animals of a pure strain are genetically identical except for the segregation of sex chromosomes. A pure strain will breed true for genetically determined traits, unless mutations occur. The animals of a strain that is not homozygous (pure), but in which some inbreeding has occurred, will tend to possess certain common characteristics that differentiate them from animals of other strains. Hence, by comparing the behavior of different strains, whether pure or not, we gain some information regarding the influence of heredity on behavior.

Wild and tame strains. Wild and tame strains of certain species, such as the dog, have been in existence since the Stone Age. The domesticated type differs markedly from the wild form in temperament. In rodents the viciousness of the wild animal stands out in sharp contrast to the docility of the tame form. Yerkes (1913), Coburn (1922), Stone (1932), and Dawson (1932) have made quantitative measurements of the difference in wildness and savageness of wild and tame rats and mice, and their results corroborate those evident to casual observation. Since the two strains breed true for wildness and tameness, it is evident that this difference has a hereditary basis.

Audiogenic seizures. Differential susceptibility of various strains of rats and mice to convulsions produced by auditory stimulation has been noted by a number of investigators. Farris and Yeakel (1943) found that wild gray Norway rats, descendants of a captive wild strain maintained by King, reacted with greater frequency and severity to an air blast than did a sample of the inbred Wistar albino strain. Griffiths (1944), however, reports that not one animal out of 141 trapped wild Norway and Alexandrine

of these two investigations are in need of further elucidation.*

Maier (1943) found a difference between two strains of rats in his colony. In one strain 79 per cent of 116 animals tested reacted to the jingling of keys, whereas in the other only 29 per cent of 130 rats were susceptible. Martin and Hall (1941) obtained differences in susceptibility to audiogenic seizures between two strains of rats,

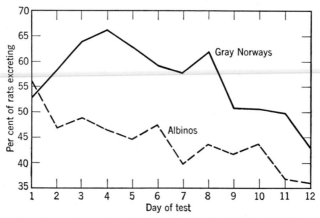

FIG. 2. A comparison of emotional defecation and urination in Norway and albino strains of rats. (Farris and Yeakel, 1945.)

rats displayed either hyperactivity or convulsions when stimulated by an air blast, key jingling, or a Galton whistle. Most of the rats were tested within a few days after they were trapped. Instead of displaying fear, they attacked the metal nozzle of the air hose. Griffiths suggests that the difference between his newly trapped nonsusceptible wild rats and the highly susceptible King wild strain which had bred in captivity for from 46 to 49 generations may be due to conditions peculiar to domestication; for example, dietary deficiencies produced by laboratory stock diets, confinement in small cages, lack of practice in meeting new situations, and endocrine changes occurring during captivity. He also suggests that the King strain may have been selectively bred for sensitivity to sounds of high frequency. The contradictory findings

one that had been selectively bred for emotionality, the other for nonemotionality. More frequent and more serious seizures were displayed by the rats of the nonemotional strain.

In the foregoing investigations it is not at all clear just how inbred were the strains compared. One study (Hall, 1947) has been reported comparing two *pure* strains of mice maintained at the Jackson Memorial Laboratory. Mice of the Little *dba* strain (line 1) manifested many more audiogenic seizures and with greater severity than did mice of the Little *C57* black strain (line 6).

Emotionality. Gray Norway rats, descendants of the forty-third generation of the

* Another hypothesis (Patton, 1947) is that a necessary, though perhaps not sufficient, condition for audiogenic seizures in rats is middle-ear infection (Editor).

King captive wild strain, proved to be more emotional than Wistar albino rats (Farris and Yeakel, 1945). The test of emotionality used was defecation or urination during a 2-minute period on each of 12 days in a circular enclosed field (Fig. 2).

Tryon has reported briefly (1942) that there are personality differences between his two strains of rats. The rats of the maze-bright strain are more emotionally disturbed in nonmaze situations than are the maze-dull animals, whereas just the opposite is true in the maze proper, where the dull animals display more emotional upset.

These two studies confirm the finding that emotionality (or nonemotionality) is an inheritable trait in the rat.

Aggressiveness. It is fashionable to reject an instinct of pugnacity in favor of a frustration-aggression hypothesis. Social scientists are prone to assert that men fight for economic or political or social reasons or because they were taught to fight as children, not because there is anything inherent in man's nature that makes him aggressive. The Freudian theory that aggressiveness has its roots in the constitutional impulse has not been widely accepted outside psychoanalytic circles.

That aggressiveness (fighting) has a genetic basis is supported by three studies. Hall and Klein (1942) compared two strains of rats for aggressiveness. One strain had been selectively bred for emotionality (fearfulness), the other for nonemotionality (fearlessness). Two rats were placed together in a cage for 5 minutes, and they were rated for aggressiveness according to the following scale:

THE KLEIN-HALL SCALE OF AGGRESSIVENESS

0 No interest in each other except occasional slight nosing.

1 Frequent vigorous nosing. No blocking, shoving, crowding, or any other display of hostility.

2 Occasional blocking, shoving, or crowding.

3 Frequent blocking, shoving, or crowding of opponent. The aggressor keeps after the other animal throughout the period.

4 Slight wrestling and/or assuming a dancing position in which the rats clasp each other while standing nose to nose.

5 Fierce wrestling. They jump, roll, and turn all over the cage very rapidly.

6 Fierce wrestling. A rat bites the other hard enough to draw blood.

Three groups of male rats, 10 in a group, were tested. Each rat was paired with every rat in its group *twice*, once in its own living cage and once as a visitor to the other rat's home cage. The 15 nonemotional rats initiated 326 attacks as against 68 initiated by the 15 emotional rats. The severity of the attacks by the nonemotional rats was, on the average, twice that of the emotional animals. The investigators concluded that the basic determiner of fighting is a genetic one.

Scott (1942) observed differences in aggressiveness among three *pure* strains of mice maintained at the Jackson Memorial Laboratory. Observations were made under the following conditions: A strange male mouse was introduced into the home cage of the mouse to be tested, and behavior was recorded for a 10-minute period. As soon as a fight started, the visitor was removed in order to avoid fatal injuries. The visiting mouse was selected from a pure stock (Bagg albino), and a new mouse was used for each observation.

Scott, in lieu of quantitative data, presents the following impressionistic descriptions of the behavior of the three strains selected for study.

The *C57* blacks (subline 10) always showed immediate interest in the intruding male and made many contacts, at times apparently licking and cleaning him. There was no evidence of aggressive behavior, although they fought back when attacked. The *A* albino males made very little preliminary contact with the intruders and usually attacked them within a couple of minutes. Finally, the *C3H* agouti males tended to sniff briefly at the intruder and then to keep to the opposite side of the pen for several minutes. During this time the fur fluffed up and the animals breathed in a labored fashion. If the intruder had not attacked in the meantime the *C3H* males eventually

after birth, so that each dam reared both black and albino offspring together. This did not produce a difference in fighting ability; the black mice reared by an albino foster mother were still superior, and the albino mice reared by a black foster mother were still inferior.

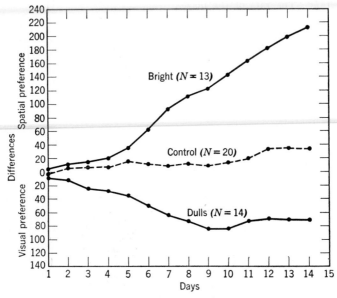

Fig. 3. A comparison of the types of "hypotheses" displayed in a multiple discrimination box by strains of rats selectively bred for brightness and dullness in maze-learning ability. (Krechevsky, 1933.)

started a fight, usually preceded by a series of feints and withdrawals. [Pp. 12–13.]

A quantified study of the aggressiveness of three of the Jackson Laboratory inbred strains of house mice was performed by Ginsburg and Allee (1942). Each mouse was paired with every other experimental mouse, and the winner of each bout was recorded. The *C57* black mice won the greatest number of fights, followed by the *C3H* agoutis, and the *C* albinos proved to be the most inferior in fighting ability. In order to control for the possible influence of the mother on the aggressiveness of her offspring, litters born by black and by albino females on the same day were split shortly

In the light of these findings, continued insistence upon the acquired nature of aggressiveness and the exclusion of the genetic contribution is unwarranted.

"*Hypotheses.*" Krechevsky (1932) has conclusively proved that during the pre-solution period in discrimination learning the rat displays systematic rather than random choices among the alternatives offered it. He has termed this systematic behavior an "hypothesis." In order to discover whether genetic factors play a part in the type of hypothesis selected, Krechevsky (1933) ran groups of Tryon's F_7 maze-bright and maze-dull strains in a multiple-discrimination box. He also tested a group of heterogeneous animals. The problem set the animal had no solution, since the correct pathway through the box was varied at random from trial to trial. It was possible for the animal to have eight different "hypotheses," four of which were visual and four spatial. The results are depicted graphically in Fig. 3. Krechevsky concludes,

... there is a definite indication that the "bright" strain of animals, when placed in a

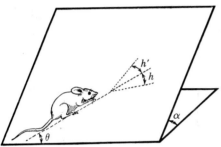

FIG. 4. Illustrating the definition of the angles θ and α in geotropic orientation in young rats. (Crozier and Hoagland, 1934.)

difficult (non-solvable) situation, attempt spatial "hypotheses" in trying to solve the problem, the "dull" animals attempt non-spatial (visual) "hypotheses," and a non-selected group try about as many spatial as visual "hypotheses." In other words the kind of "hypotheses" which an animal can bring with him to a problem situation is to some extent hereditarily determined. [Pp. 108–109.]

Geotropism. Young rats are negatively geotropic; i.e. they will crawl up an inclined plane (Crozier and Hoagland, 1934). The rat's path up the plane forms an angle with the horizontal which is a function of the angle of inclination (Fig. 4) and is described by the formula,

$$\cos \theta = a - b \sin \alpha$$

where a and b are constants. Three different strains of rats, A, B, and K, each of genetic uniformity, were tested for the form of the functional relations. The form of the function is the same in the three strains, but the

numerical values of the constants are characteristic for each strain. Figure 5 shows that the intercept constants and the slope factor are clearly different for the two races, A and K, although the form of the function is the same. The slope factor is the same for strains A and B, but the threshold intercept is higher. The three strains differ in two respects, namely, slope and intercept constants.

Temperature preferences. If a mouse is presented with a wide range of cage floor temperatures from which to choose, he will select after some trials a particular temperature in which to rest and sleep. This temperature is referred to as his "thermotactic optimum." Herter (1936) found dif-

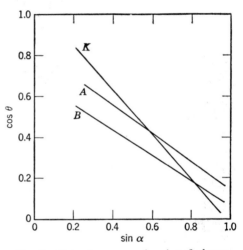

FIG. 5. Data from several series of observations with young rats of three strains, K, A, and B, which illustrate strain differences in geotropism. (Crozier and Hoagland, 1934.)

ferences between the temperatures preferred by wild and albino strains of mice. The thermotactic optimum of the albino strain is 34.36 ± 0.12, and that of the wild strain is 37.36 ± 0.12 degrees C.

Speed of reaction. Utsurikawa (1917) invented a simple device for measuring the rat's speed of reaction. One end of a small box rests on legs; the other is suspended from a spring. Movements of the rat in the box move the spring, and these vertical displacements are recorded on a kymograph. A bell was used as the stimulus, and the speed and intensity of reaction were measured. Utsurikawa tested two strains of rats, one inbred and the other outbred, and found that the inbred rats reacted more quickly and with greater intensity than the outbred animals. Vicari (1929) measures speed of running in a simple two-unit maze. Different strains of mice differed in the average speed with which they traversed the pathway.

This summary of experiments involving selective breeding and strain comparisons is intended to be illustrative rather than complete. Heredity is pervasive. The major dimensions of temperament, viz. emotionality, activity, aggressiveness, reactivity, have their source in the germ plasm. Intelligence as measured by maze learning and by the use of "hypotheses" has a genetic basis. The fact that temperature preference is inherited suggests that 'interests' and 'values' may be originally determined by genetic constitution.

It is likely, on theoretical grounds, that heredity is a factor in all psychological traits. The justification for this broad generalization rests upon the organismic or holistic viewpoint which has gained prominence in recent years. According to this doctrine, as applied to behavior, any act is an expression of the whole organism. Since the chromosomes are constituents of the organism — indeed, they are the principal differentiated structures of the primary organism, the fertilized egg, as well as of each cell in the multicellular individual — they must be of extensive organismic significance. Genetics has proved this to be true for morphology and some physiological functions. It has yet to be fully documented for psychological characteristics.

It needs to be reiterated that the building of a science of psychogenetics does not deny the role of modifiability, which is itself an inborn property of living organisms. Is there anyone who doubts that profound alterations can be made in the structure, function, and behavior of living organisms? With each addition to his knowledge, man gains an increment of power to change the world and himself. The genes themselves are subject to alteration by external forces, e.g. X-rays, radium rays, ultraviolet light, and heat rays. It should be emphasized, however, that, if a change is to be instituted through education, therapy, or stimulation by various forms of energy, the effectiveness and precision of the alteration will depend primarily upon our knowing the nature of the raw material that is to be altered. Psychogenetics is the study of this raw material.

GENETIC ANALYSIS OF BEHAVIOR

In order to have a genetics of behavior it is not sufficient merely to show that psychological traits, like morphological features, have a genetic foundation. Genetic analysis is also required. The number of gene pairs that contribute to the expression of the trait and the presence or absence of dominance in each pair should be identified. A slight beginning in this direction has been made; more rapid strides will follow as investigators make increased use of highly inbred strains — strains that have reached maximum homozygosity. Calvin Stone (1947) has observed,

> To many of us who have worked for a long time in the field of comparative psychology it is a matter of shame and regret that only an amateurish beginning has yet been made by psychologists in the utilization of pure lines of animals in fundamental research in the nature-nurture area. [P. 344.]

Geneticists assert that in order to work out the genetics of quantitative traits, such as maze learning, highly purified and genetically homogeneous strains are essential. Since quantitative traits are the ones that most interest the psychologist, let us consider more at length the method of obtaining these essential pure strains (see also the excellent account by Russell, 1941).

Inbreeding

The objective of inbreeding is to produce a homozygous strain, one in which all the animals are identical genotypes except for the segregation of the X and Y chromosomes.

there are only two parents for each generation and these parents are always brother and sister. When a pure line has been established, complete relaxation of inbreeding should be avoided: it will tend to perpetuate any heterozygosis that may be introduced by mutation. However, in order to make available a large number of homozygous

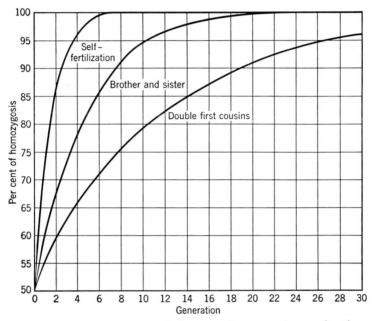

Fig. 6. The percentage of homozygosis in successive generations under three systems of inbreeding. (Russell, 1941.)

The rate at which homozygosity is reached varies with the closeness of inbreeding. Self-fertilization, which is possible only in certain plants, results in virtual homozygosity after eight generations. Brother-sister matings produce approximate homozygosity in about thirty generations, and double first cousins in about forty-five generations (Fig. 6). When the inbreeding is as far removed as second cousins, the percentage of homozygotes does not materially increase from generation to generation.

Inbred strains of laboratory mammals have been produced almost exclusively by brother-sister mating. Under this system

animals, inbreeding in an isogenic line may be temporarily halted; but it is always advisable occasionally to bring the inbred line back to a single pair of parents by discarding for breeding purposes all but a single brother-sister pair.

Russell (1941) has issued a warning regarding the risk of an accidental outcross of an inbred line.

Since a high degree of homozygosis is obtained only after many generations of inbreeding, a single unfortunate outcross may undo years of work. In a mouse colony in which different lines are maintained, an accidental outcross may occur as a result of faulty pens, into which stray animals can enter, or the returning of animals to the wrong pen after removal for any purpose. Risk of the latter can be reduced to a minimum by handling different lines and sublines at different times and by keeping them in separate parts of the laboratory or cage rack, certainly not in adjacent sections of wooden boxes. When several inbred lines are to be started it is desirable to mark them with different coat colors or other genetic characteristics, contamination of which will be readily recognized. [Pp. 344–345.]

Selection for a particular characteristic is often combined with inbreeding. In selective inbreeding it is desirable to start with a parental generation of maximum heterogeneity in order that all the alleles (genes occupying corresponding loci on homologous chromosomes) of all factors that influence the trait may be represented. Furthermore it is a wise practice to start a number of sublines from the parental generation, since the expression of the trait in some animals may be nongenetically controlled. If two animals, i.e. a brother and sister, in which the trait is nongenetic should be selected, the desired genetic factors would be lost, and the investigator would have to begin all over again with a heterozygous population. If he starts with a number of sublines, he can discard those that do not produce offspring like themselves. Selection and brother-sister matings within each subline should be rigorously followed and crosses between sublines studiously avoided if complete homozygosity is desired. One subline may not be genetically identical with another subline, since it is probable that different genetic patterns become fixed within each subline. Starting a number of sublines from the original parental generation helps also to insure against the strain's dying out. When genetic uniformity has been attained in the several sublines, it is then possible to retain one line and discard the others.

In order to work out the genetics of a psychological trait it is necessary to obtain two or more pure strains that differ in their expression of the trait. These strains may be secured by selective breeding, or they may be obtained by finding differences in a trait between strains that have been inbred for other purposes or in which there has been natural inbreeding. Since many inbred strains of mice have been developed and are now available, particularly from the Jackson Laboratory at Bar Harbor, Maine, it would be fruitful to investigate other psychological traits in these strains already at hand.

Another advantage of employing pure lines is that the occurrence of a mutation that might influence a behavior trait is more easily noticed. If the mutant form differs in behavior from the pure strain, we are informed of the additional fact that the trait is controlled by a single pair of genes.

Unit Characters

A trait conditioned by a single pair of alleles is called a unit character. It is sometimes assumed that, because psychological characteristics are predominantly quantitative in their expression and are distributed normally, they must be determined by many genetic factors rather than by one or two pairs. On the other hand, several unit characters of distinct psychological significance have been discovered. Other unit characters will doubtless be identified as progress is made in psychogenetics.

A unit character is identified by making various types of crosses and comparing the results with those that would be theoretically expected if a single pair of genes were operating. If two pure strains, A and B, display a dichotomy in behavior, M and N, the first step is to hybridize the two strains. If the trait is a unit character, the hybrids can behave in only one of three possible ways: M, N, or intermediate between M and N. If they all manifest behavior M, resembling thereby the parent strain A, the allele conditioning M is dominant over the allele conditioning N. If the F_1's resemble the other parent strain B, the allele for N is dominant over the one for M. Finally, if the hybrids are intermediate in behavior between M and N, the pair of genes are said to blend; that is to say, they contribute equally to the trait and no dominance exists.

The second step is to mate the F_1's *inter se* to obtain the F_2's. If dominance exists, a ratio of three animals resembling the dominant strain to one animal resembling the recessive strain is expected among the F_2's. Two backcross matings, F_1 with the dominant strain and F_1 with the recessive strain, will yield ratios of 1:0 and 1:1 respectively, for a unit character.

Russell (1941) observes that even when these ratios are obtained they are not critical criteria for the presence of a single pair of genes.

There is a common belief that a character occurring only in alternate categories (as opposed to the other extreme: a continuous distribution) must be due to alternate genes in the same way that agouti and black coat color are. This has sometimes led to a hunt for a single major gene difference as the cause of a character difference that shows no, or little, overlap in two inbred strains. . . . Such a hunt is all right if it is critical. It can only be critical if cognizance is paid to the fact that, owing to the common occurrence of biological thresholds, of all-or-none processes in development, many characters are necessarily alternate in expression. Many genes may be involved, the effects of some combinations falling below the threshold, while the effects of the others fall above. If this fact is realized it will be appreciated that apparent dominance in the F_1 of a cross between strains, a 3:1 ratio in the F_2, and a 1:1 ratio in the backcross, are not critical criteria of the presence of a single major pair of genes. Many genes may be involved and the above generations happen to be cut by a threshold of effect into approximately the above proportions. . . . *The critical experiment is to test the genetic nature of the types apparently segregating in the backcross or F_2 by breeding them with the "recessive" stock.* [P. 346, italics Hall's.]

Several examples of unit behavior characters will be presented.

Audiogenic seizures. Two pure strains of house mice which differed greatly in the number and severity of audiogenic seizures were crossbred according to the steps outlined above, including the crucial test suggested by Russell (Witt and Hall, 1949). The results of the several types of matings are summarized in Table 3. The observed percentages conform closely, except for the critical backcross (the last cross in Table 3), to those that would be expected if audiogenic seizures are a unit character. The divergence of the critical backcross suggests that there may be some modifying factors. If there are such modifying factors, they are of minor importance since the other crosses yield progeny who react as though audiogenic seizures were inherited as a *single dominant gene.*

The genetics of audiogenic seizures has been investigated in the genus *Peromyscus,* which includes the deer mouse and other white-footed mice of North America. The genetic analysis differs from that found by Witt and Hall for the common house mouse of the genus *Mus musculus.* Dice (1935) and Watson (1939) conclude from their investigations that epilepsy, as they label the behavior that is conventionally called "audiogenic seizure," is a recessive character. Dice's conclusion is based upon meager data. Epileptic males mated with normal females yielded 15 offspring, all of whom behaved normally when they were exposed to jingling keys. The backcross of the F_1's to epileptic males produced 48 offspring, 12 epileptic and 36 normal. This obtained ratio of 1:3 diverges greatly from the expected ratio of 1:1, were the trait a recessive one.

Watson used many more mice in her investigation. A summary of the most pertinent results appear in Table 4. The 12 mice of the Palouse River stock who should have reacted, but did not, Watson terms "normal overlaps." A normal overlap is a mouse who is genotypically epileptic but pheno-

TABLE 3

GENETIC ANALYSIS OF AUDIOGENIC (*As*) * SEIZURES IN HOUSE MICE (*Mus musculus*)
(WITT AND HALL, 1949)

	No.	Percentage	Percentage Expected	Genetic Formula
Inbred *C57* strain				
Susceptible	2	5 ± 3.5	0	
Resistant	36	95 ± 3.5	100	*as as*
Inbred *dba* strain				
Susceptible	31	94 ± 4.1	100	*As As*
Resistant	2	6 ± 4.1	0	
F_1 (*C57* × *dba*)				
Susceptible	72	91 ± 3.2	100	*As as*
Resistant	7	9 ± 3.2	0	
F_2 (F_1 × F_1)				
Susceptible	54	76 ± 5.1	75	*As As* + *As as*
Resistant	17	24 ± 5.1	25	*as as*
Backcross (*F1* × *C57*)				
Susceptible	38	54 ± 5.9	50	*As as*
Resistant	32	46 ± 5.9	50	*as as*
Backcross (F_1 × *dba*)				
Susceptible	20	91 ± 6.1	100	*As As* + *As as*
Resistant	2	9 ± 6.1	0	
Backcross [resistant (F_1 × *C57*) × *C57*]				
Susceptible	12	25 ± 6.2	0	
Resistant	36	75 ± 6.2	100	*as as*

* The symbol *As* has been chosen to designate the dominant gene for audiogenic seizures; *as* represents the recessive gene.

TABLE 4

INHERITANCE OF EPILEPSY (*p*) IN *Peromyscus maniculatus artemisiae* COLLECTED FROM PALOUSE
RIVER, WASHINGTON (AFTER WATSON, 1939)

	No.	Percentage	Percentage Expected	Percentage Expected, Corrected for Normal Overlap	Genetic Formula
Palouse River stock (*PRS*)					
Susceptible	184	93.9 ± 1.7	100	93.9	*pp*
Resistant	12	6.1 ± 1.7	0	6.1	
Backcross (F_1 × *PRS*)					
Susceptible	97	41.6 ± 3.2	50	43.9	*pp*
Resistant	136	58.4 ± 3.2	50	56.1	*Pp*
F_2 (F_1 × F_1)					
Susceptible	86	20.6 ± 2.0	25	18.9	*pp*
Resistant	331	79.4 ± 2.0	75	81.1	*PP* + *Pp*

typically resistant to auditory stimulation. By correcting the backcross and F_2 progeny for the percentage of normal overlaps (6.1), the obtained percentages conform very closely to those that would be expected on the assumption that audiogenic seizure (epilepsy) is inherited as a *single recessive gene* in *Peromyscus maniculatus artemisiae.*

	No.	PERCENTAGE SUSCEPTIBLE
Susceptible × susceptible	58	66
Susceptible × resistant	63	73
Resistant × resistant	22	68

The contrasting results obtained for *Mus musculus* and *Peromyscus maniculatus artemisiae* demonstrate that for two genera the genetic constitution underlying the same type of behavior may be different. In the former genus the gene for audiogenic seizures is a dominant; in the latter it is a recessive. Modifying factors may, of course, be present in both.

Investigations of the genetics of audiogenic seizures in rats have yielded contradictory results. Maier and Glaser (1940) found that their data, obtained from crossing (1) susceptible with susceptible, (2) susceptible with resistant, and (3) resistant with resistant, fitted the assumption that the trait was a dominant one. The percentages of offspring reacting with seizures from the three types of crosses were 74, 52 and 0, respectively. However, Maier (1943), in a later investigation, did not confirm the Maier and Glaser findings. He concluded that the genetics of audiogenic seizures is complex rather than simple. However, since in neither study were uniform strains used, the results are necessarily ambiguous. The same criticism applies to Griffith's (1942) attempt to unravel the genetics of audiogenic seizures in rats. He divided his animals into an *H* group which reacted on 50 per cent or more of their 60 standard preliminary trials and an *L* group which reacted on less than 50 per cent of the trails. The results of $H \times H$, $H \times L$, and $L \times L$ crosses suggests, according to Griffiths, two pairs of genetic factors.

Finger's (1943) experiment does not help to elucidate the genetics of audiogenic seizures in the rat. He made various crosses and obtained the results shown. He observes

that "it appears very doubtful that the tendency (to react with a seizure) is inherited as a simple Mendelian dominant."

As a result of using impure strains of rats, three different types of genetic constitution have been postulated for audiogenic seizures: a simple dominant (Maier and Glaser), two pairs of genes (Griffiths, 1942), and multiple factors (Maier, Finger). It should be clear, from this example, that a genetics of behavior cannot be developed by utilizing strains of unknown genetic constitution.

Thermotactic optimum. As previously mentioned, different strains of mice may prefer different temperatures. A cross between a wild strain whose average thermotactic optimum was 37.36 degrees C and an albino strain whose preferred temperature averaged 34.36 degrees C resulted in an F_1 whose preference, 34.76 degrees C, resembled that of the albino strain. Other crosses were made. A summary of all the results is presented in Table 5.

These findings, according to Herter (1936, 1938a, b), indicate that the thermotactic optimum is dependent upon a single pair of genes, the gene causing the lower optimum being dominant over its allelomorph causing the higher optimum. The small number of animals observed is a weakness of this study. However, should this finding be corroborated, it would suggest that other preferential or choice behavior might have a simple genetic basis.

Mutations in Inbred Strains

The value of maintaining and systematically observing inbred strains is enhanced by the fact that any mutation that occurs will be more readily noticed in a uniform stock than in a heterogeneous one. In support of this statement, the important findings of King and Donaldson (1929), King (1939),

TABLE 5

CROSSES BETWEEN STRAINS OF MICE WITH DIFFERENT TEMPERATURE PREFERENCES (AFTER GRÜNEBERG)

	No. of Individuals		No. of Determinations	Average Thermotactic Optimum in Degrees C	Range of Averages for Individual Mice
	Obtained	Expected			
Wild strain	19	19	1048	37.36 ± 0.12	36.34–37.92
Albino strain	16	16	1300	34.63 ± 0.12	33.88–35.60
Wild × Albino (F_1)	17	17	850	34.76 ± 0.12	34.20–35.78
$F_1 \times F_1$ (F_2)					
Type 1 (dominant)	12	14.25	600	34.62 ± 0.11	34.06–34.96
Type 2 (recessive)	7	4.75	350	37.16 ± 0.15	36.94–37.54
$F_1 \times$ albino	28	28	1400	34.93 ± 0.10	34.24–35.76
$F_1 \times$ wild					
Type 1 (dominant)	16	14	800	34.80 ± 0.19	34.28–35.42
Type 2 (recessive)	12	14	600	37.32 ± 0.12	36.74–37.80

and Keeler and King (1942) of the Wistar Institute may be cited. Wild gray Norway rats were trapped, and they constituted the parental generation from which numerous filial generations were bred. Many mutations, expressed in coat colors, occurred during the maintenance of this uniform, although not entirely purified, strain. In 1942 Keeler and King published an account of the differences in behavior of these mutant strains. The following character sketches were formulated from independent descriptions made by five observers who were familiar with the strains.

Mutant albino. When not tamed they are as wild and vicious as the original gray Norway rats. When tamed they resemble the tamed Norway in their tendency to bite when handled.

Cinnamon (brown pigment). They are easier to tame than grays, but they may revert to their original wildness. They are ordinarily more peaceful than grays, but, when they do fight, they fight as well as the grays.

Curly. They are difficult to catch even after they are tamed. They ordinarily do not bite when held, but they can never be entirely trusted.

Stub. These animals are always fighting one another. They do not mind their own business as do the gray rats, but throw themselves against the cage when anyone approaches.

Albino waltzers. They are easier to tame than mutant albinos from which they were derived. When tamed they rarely bite their handler.

Black. The black strain does not have to be tamed, since they are tame by nature. If very excited they may click their teeth, but they are not apt to bite.

Although these descriptions are impressionistic, one of these mutant strains, the black, is unique in comparison with the others. This difference in behavior of the wild and savage gray Norway rat and the tame and docile black rat is ascribed by Keeler and King to the mutation of a single gene in the original Norway strain. They write:

A survey of eighteen stocks shows that most of the naturally tame strains of albino rats now employed in American scientific laboratories were tamed principally by the black gene or by the black and piebald genes combined, the coat color effects of which genes are masked by albinism as we have stated above. Most of the stocks not bearing the black gene are probably tamed principally by other mendelian genes such as pink-eyed yellow, red-eyed yellow, hairless, and ruby-eyed dilute, because strains containing these genes singly are, in our experience, invariably tame. [1942, p. 249.]

This is a dramatic finding. The popular theory of domestication asserts that tame strains of animals came into existence as a consequence of the accumulation of a host of gene mutations, each mutation contributing an almost imperceptible amount to the final result of the domesticated strain. According to Keeler and King, a single mutation transforms a wild form into a domesticated one. A major evolutionary step is mediated by a minor gene-change. They state, "*It is also clear that the basis of temperament and behavior is inherited in gene controlled patterns, the effects of a single gene being distributed irregularly throughout the whole field of response, like dabs of a particular color in a polychrome print*" (1942, p. 246).

It should be borne in mind that this discovery was made possible by having available for observation over a number of generations a relatively homozygous line.

A number of mutations that express themselves in bizarre neuromuscular disorders have been found in inbred strains of house mice. The mutant forms, all of which are recessive, the genetic symbol, and a brief description of the behavior of each form follow.

Waltzing: (*v* for *valse*, French). As described by Yerkes in 1907, the behavior consists of "(1) movement in circles with all the feet close together under the body, (2) movement in circles, which vary in diameter from 5 to 30 cm., with the feet spread widely, and (3) movements now to the right, now to the left, in figure eights." Exclusive circling in one direction does not occur, although preference for right or left turning does appear.

Shaker 1: (*sh*-1). The salient feature is a nervous head movement which consists of rapid, successive, upward jerks of the head.

Shaker 2: (*sh*-2). This form is phenotypically indistinguishable from shaker 1.

That the genes for shakers 1 and 2 are different has been established by crossing *sh*-1 with *sh*-2. If they were the same recessive gene, all F_1's should express choreic head movements. Actually, all F_1's are quite normal.

Jerker: (*je*). This mutant is also indistinguishable from both shakers, but that it is a different gene has been confirmed by appropriate crosses.

Pirouetting: (*pi*). As first described by Woolley and Dickie (1945), the behavior is that of rapid whirling in circles of small diameter.

The mouse swings its head sharply to one side, places the inner forefoot back toward the rear foot, toes turned out, and seems to place the opposite forefoot in such a position that it aids in pushing the mouse into a small diameter rotation. The mice whirl incessantly for long periods of time. [Pp. 282–283.]

It is regrettable that comparative psychologists have not had or availed themselves of the opportunity to make routine behavior measurements of inbred strains of rodents. Such strains have been in existence in this country and in Europe for some years and have provided the biogeneticist with some of his best material. Numerous gene mutations, affecting principally such morphological characters as coat color, hair texture, size and body form, and diverse skeletal features, have been described by Grüneberg for the mouse. In his 412-page book, fewer than four pages are devoted to behavior.

Multiple Factors

When several sets of genes contribute to the determination of the same character, they are called multiple factors. Formerly it was assumed that multiple factors have equal and cumulative effects on the character, but it is now well established that dominance may also be present. The existence of multiple factors is indicated when the F_1's are uniform and intermediate between the two parental strains in behavior and the F_2's are extremely variable.

Tryon (1942) believes that a theory of multiple factors explains the fact that a continuous unimodal distribution is usually found when a population is measured for a psychological trait. He writes:

We shall describe this theory by showing how it may account for individual differences in maze-learning ability. It is assumed that there is a large number, k, of genes determining this ability. First, consider one of these genes, A, which exists in two degrees of expression, A and a. An individual of homozygous constitution, AA, is brighter than one of aa constitution, and a heterozygous individual, Aa, lies between the two. No dominance is assumed. But there are k such genes, A, B, C, D, $\cdots$, each possessing the same properties as those described for A. Thus an individual of constitution $AABBCCDD \cdots$ would be the brightest possible in maze ability; $aabbccdd \cdots$ the dullest; and $AaBbCcDd \cdots$ would be average. All degrees of ability would be possible: $aABBCCDD \cdots$ next to brightest, $aaBBCCDD \cdots$ next, $aabBCCDD \cdots$ next, and so on. Thus the continuity of individual differences is adequately explained. Under random mating, the types of individual that could exist and the frequency of each can be found from the product of $(A + a)^2$ $(B + b)^2$ $(C + c)^2$ $(D + d)^2 \cdots$. In the resulting series the terms show the various genotypes, and their coefficients the frequency of their occurrence. The result is a *normal distribution curve*, if k is large enough. Hence, the wide, continuous, and unimodal dispersion of individuals in the P generation . . . [see Fig. 1] whose parents were randomly mated is adequately accounted for.

According to this theory, the effects of selective breeding result simply from the gradual sorting into one race of all the large-lettered genes for brightness, and into the other, all the small-lettered genes for dullness. In a final bright pure line, *all* individuals would be $AABBCCDD \cdots$, and their progeny would be exactly like them; analogously, in the dull pure line, all would be

$aabbccdd \cdots$ and would breed true for dullness. [P. 349.]

Although Tryon has made a plausible case for the importance of multiple factors in the genetics of behavior, as yet his view can be supported by very little concrete evidence. To date, more unit characters than multiple factor traits have been isolated. Tryon's own investigation of the inheritance of maze-learning ability has produced equivocal results. Those of Brody (1942) and of Hall (unpublished material) are equally inconclusive. These three studies contain inherent weaknesses which will be brought out in the following discussion.

Maze learning. Tryon crossed his 'bright' and 'dull' strains to produce an F_1 and intermated the F_1's to secure an F_2. If the lines were pure at the time of hybridizing, the F_1 generation would show uniform maze performance and the F_2 generation would display wide variability in maze learning. The F_1 progeny were not uniform; they were just as variable as the F_2 rats (Fig. 7). These results mean that the strains were not pure at the time they were crossed. This is to be expected because of the type of inbreeding Tryon followed. Instead of a single line of brother-sister matings, each strain actually consists of a number of sublines. It is not likely that different sublines will be genetically identical; different hereditary patterns will ordinarily become fixed within each subline. Accordingly, if a heterogeneous sample of rats from several bright sublines are mated with an equally heterogeneous sample from various dull sublines, the F_1 progeny obviously will vary widely in maze performance. Moreover, if Tryon had permitted a certain amount of crossbreeding between sublines while he was developing the two strains, genetic homozygosity within each strain would not have been achieved. Close inbreeding within a single line is essential for the establishment of pure lines.

Voluntary activity. The ambiguity that results from crossing strains that are not homozygous for the trait being studied is revealed by Brody's study (1942) using Rundquist's active and inactive strains of rats. Brody crossed active F_{21} females with inactive F_{21} males and inactive F_{21} females with active F_{21} males. Since the offspring of these reciprocal crosses did not differ significantly in their activity, they may be lumped together. The F_1 progeny were bred together to obtain an F_2. The F_1 rats were also backcrossed to (1) rats of the active strain and (2) rats of the inactive strain. The same breeding program was carried out with a sample of the F_{22} generation. The results of these several crosses for the two

generations are presented in Table 6. Only one systematic trend appears in the results for both generations. F_1 backcrossed to the active strain produces offspring that resemble the active parent strain, whereas the progeny of $F_1 \times$ inactive strain resemble the inactive parent strain. This suggests that more of the contributing genes are dominant for higher activity level. Other than this, the data are inconclusive. By some legerdemain I am unable to follow, Brody concludes that ". . . the two strains differ with respect to a single gene rather than with respect to multiple factors . . . . The gene apparently behaves as a dominant

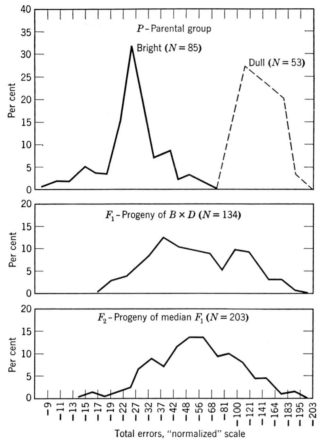

FIG. 7. The results of crossing two strains of rats selectively bred for brightness and dullness in maze-learning ability. (Tryon, 1940.)

TABLE 6

A Summary of Results Obtained from Crosses between Active and Inactive Strains of Rats (after Brody, 1942)

(Revolutions in thousands for 15 days)

	Mean	S.D.		Mean	S.D.
F_{21}	Active females		$\times$	Inactive males	
	125	37		10	14
F_{21}	Inactive females		$\times$	Active males	
	14	20		140	54
	Females			Males	
F_1	116	56		75	43
F_2	69	66		33	44
$F_1 \times$ active	129	69		55	57
$F_1 \times$ inactive	41	67		2	4
F_{22}	Active females		$\times$	Inactive males	
	169	54		11	19
F_{22}	Inactive females		$\times$	Active males	
	17	24		110	51
	Females			Males	
F_1	81	60		22	28
F_2	143	80		42	47
$F_1 \times$ active	182	43		95	61
$F_1 \times$ inactive	53	52		11	13

in the males and as a recessive in the females" (1942, p. 23). This type of gene, which is dominant in males and recessive in females, is called a *sex-influenced* factor.* An example of sex-influenced characters, which are quite uncommon, is baldness in man. Brody's findings do not seem to justify the conclusion that the difference between the Rundquist strains results from a single sex-influenced gene pair. That there is a genetics of activity cannot be questioned, but until strains homozygous for activity and inactivity are available the genetics of this important trait will remain unknown.

Emotionality. Hall (unpublished data) made three crosses for the F_{10}, F_{11}, and F_{12} generations of his emotional and nonemotional strains of rats. The results are presented in Table 7. Had the two strains been pure, the variability of the hybrids would

* A sex-influenced factor should not be confused with either a *sex-linked* or a *sex-limited* factor. A sex-linked factor is one that is carried in the sex chromosomes and may be either dominant or recessive. A sex-limited factor is one that is capable of expression in one sex but not in the other.

TABLE 7

A Summary of the Results Obtained from Crosses between Emotional and Nonemotional Strains

Generation Emotional $\times$ nonemotional	No. of Offspring	Defecation-Urination Scores Mean	S.D.
$F_{10} \times F_{10}$	32	4.53	3.84
$F_{11} \times F_{11}$	22	2.81	2.15
$F_{12} \times F_{12}$	27	3.00	2.55

have been smaller than that found. These results duplicate those of Tryon, since the means and standard deviations closely resemble the heterogeneous parental population, whose mean and standard deviation was 3.86 and 3.54, respectively. It was deemed unfruitful to make further crosses with impure strains. The most that can be inferred is that the alleles for nonemotionality are dominant over those for emotionality. The dominance of the nonemotional factors would explain (1) the skewness of the distribution of scores for the parental generation; i.e. there was an overbalance of low-scoring animals; (2) the rapid effects of selection in the nonemotional strain (Table 2); (3) the slower effects of selection for emotionality (Table 2); and (4) the greater resemblance of the scores of the hybrids to the nonemotional animals than to the emotional rats.

In view of the negative results obtained by Tryon, Brody, and Hall, the multiple-factor theory as applied to the genetics of behavior traits remains unproved. Since the negative results were obtained by faulty methods, it is probably only a matter of time before evidence for the theory will be provided. It is certainly the most plausible theory by which to explain the genetics of traits that conform to the normal probability curve.

THE MAPPING OF CHROMOSOMES

In view of the embryonic state of psychogenetics any extensive discussion of this topic at this time would appear to be premature. With the exception of some of the neuromuscular disorders, e.g. waltzing, shaker, and pirouetting, there is no information regarding the location of the genes on the chromosomes for behavior characters. Consequently this objective of psychogenetics will be discussed only in general terms.

When two or more factors are located on the same chromosome, they are said to be *linked*. The evidence for linkage is provided by the way in which characters hang together. Thus in the house mouse, the two characters, waltzing and jittery, appear together, whereas waltzing and shaker 1 do not. The factors for waltzing and jittery are assigned to the same chromosome (No. 10) whereas waltzing and shaker 1 are assigned to different chromosomes (Nos. 10 and 1, respectively). However, linked factors do not invariably stay together, and because of this it is assumed that there is an exchange of homologous parts between the chromosome pairs early in the maturation of germ cells. This is called *crossing over*. The amount of crossing over provides the basis for locating the genes more or less accurately on the chromosomes. A large amount of crossing over implies that the two genes are far apart on the chromosome; a small amount implies that they are close together on the chromosome.

Snell (1945), for example, found that there was 26 per cent crossing over in an F_2 population bred from an F_1 generation heterozygous for waltzing and jittery. This is a high value for crossing over and suggests that the two genes are widely separated on the same chromosome. Their location as given on a chromosome map of the mouse is at the two ends of chromosome 10 (Staff, Jackson Laboratory, 1945).

Aside from shaker 1, shaker 2, waltzing, and jittery, no other genes for behavior characteristics in the mouse have been mapped.

HOW GENES PRODUCE BEHAVIOR TRAITS

"Between the presence of the genes in the chromosomes and the appearance of the developed characters in the individual organism there exists a gap which is not yet thoroughly understood" (Snyder, 1940, p. 356). This is Snyder's opening sentence in his chapter on *How Genes Act*. In the same chapter he summarizes the known genetic effects in development:

> . . . a complete complement of chromosomes as well as a normal environment is necessary for development; early differentiation is probably effected primarily by gradients imposed from without upon a cytoplasm already under the control of genes; later differentiation takes place through interactions of genic substances in differential gradients, the whole process being a continuous one of reciprocal reactions between genes and cytoplasm in progressively differing gradient fields; and finally the action of the genes may take the form of enzyme production, elaboration of reactive chemical substances, or modification of the plane or frequency of cell division in localized areas. [Pp. 364–365.]

It is not within the scope of the present chapter to weigh and evaluate the conflicting hypotheses regarding the action of the genes. The exact nature of gene action will be worked out by the cooperative efforts of geneticists, cytologists, and embryologists.

It is within the province of psychogenetics to inquire about the bodily structures and functions which regulate behavior and which are in turn regulated by the genes. For it should be apparent that the genes cannot control directly a psychological trait, e.g. maze-learning ability; they can only exert an influence through the mediation of physical structures.

Few clear-cut studies correlating genetic constitution, bodily structures, and behavior have been reported. Herter's (1938) investigation of the thermotactic optimum is a model in this respect. Having discovered that the temperature preference of the mouse is dependent upon a single pair of genes, he then sought an answer to the question: upon what physical feature does this preference rest? He found that body temperature as taken rectally was not the factor, since the wild strain, which preferred the higher temperature, had approximately the same body temperature (37.39 degrees C) as the albino strain (37.68 degrees C), which chose the lower temperature. Also, the temperature of the belly differed only slightly: 32.93 degrees C for the wild mice and 31.14 degrees C for the albino mice. Herter then examined the skin and fur of the belly and ascertained that the density of the fur and the thickness of the epidermis differed in the two strains. The wild mice had about 70 hairs per unit square as compared with about 46 hairs for the albino mice. The skin of the wild mice was markedly thinner than that of the albino animals. The F_1 progeny obtained from crossing wild × albino resembled the albinos in thermotactic optimum, hair density (51.66 hairs per unit square), and thickness of epidermis. In a backcross of F_1 mice to the wild strain, 12 mice with a preferred temperature of 34.56 degrees C had an average hair density of 52.75, and 8 mice with a thermotactic optimum of 37.10 degrees C had a density of fur of 70.94. Undoubtedly the preferred temperature is controlled by the density of the belly fur and the thickness of the belly skin, and it is these features that are determined by the genes.

Many differences in behavior are probably mediated principally by neurohumeral mechanisms. Yeakel and Rhoades compared the weights of several endocrine glands, viz. adrenal, thyroid, and pituitary, of the emotional and nonemotional strains of rats selectively bred by Hall. Significant differences both for absolute weight of the glands and relative weight, i.e. gland weight divided by body weight, were obtained. The emotional males had heavier adrenals and thyroids than the nonemotional males. There was no appreciable difference in the weight of the pituitary for the males of the two strains. The emotional females had heavier thyroids and pituitaries than the nonemotional females, but the difference for the adrenals did not

reach the criterion of significance. If it is assumed that heavy glands produce more hormones than light glands, then it may be surmised that the emotional rats are emotional because they are primed by their blood chemistry to react emotionally. Their chemique produces a lower threshold for the evocation of fear as compared with the threshold of the nonemotional rats. Such speculations are interesting, but only a more intensive and critical search for the precise *modus operandi* of the genes upon emotionality, similar to that performed by Herter on thermotactic preference, will provide exact knowledge.

Rundquist and Bellis (1933) compared the respiratory metabolism of the F_{15} generation of active and inactive strains of rats using the Ebeling-Corey method for determining metabolism. The average number of calories per gram body weight per hour for the two strains by sex are given in the table. The

	No.	ACTIVE STRAIN	No.	INACTIVE STRAIN
Males	29	8.25	16	6.28
Females	20	8.70	22	6.45

differences between the means are statistically significant. The higher metabolic rate of the active strain is to be expected and suggests that the inherited structural feature upon which voluntary activity is based is the thyroid.

No difference in the brain weights of maze-bright and maze-dull rats was found by Silverman, Shapiro, and Heron (1940).

Lashley (1947) has recently surveyed the available knowledge of the inheritance of structure in the nervous system in relation to behavior. Actually very little is known about this subject. It has been established that "the brain is extremely variable in every character that has been subjected to measurement" and "some of the more conspicuous structural differences have been shown to be hereditary" (p. 333). These inherited differences include brain size, fissurization, absence of corpus callosum, and the irregular twisted fibers of the corpus striatum in athetosis. Although the relation of these macroscopic features either to behavior or to genetic constitution has not been clearly revealed, Lashley feels that the structural variations must have functional significance.

It is not conceivable that the inferior frontal convolutions of two brains would function in the same way or with equal effectiveness when one contains only half as many cells as the other; that two parietal association areas should be identical in function when the cells of one are mostly minute granules and of the other large pyramids; that the presence of Betz cells in the prefrontal region is without influence on behavior. [P. 333.]

CONCLUDING REMARKS

The foregoing sections have presented a brief review of the nature and potentialities of the interdisciplinary science of *psychogenetics*. As an organized and dependable body of knowledge of the inheritance of psychological traits, psychogenetics is as yet more a promise than an actuality. The experimental work in this area is fragmentary, and what has been done has sometimes failed to utilize the proper methods of genetic analysis. Specifically, psychologists have not always realized the importance of employing pure strains of animals in their investigations of quantitatively expressed traits. This is an oversight that can easily be rectified since pure strains of some mammals, notably mice, are available.

As the science matures we may confidently expect it to free itself of distracting excursions into pseudo-problems, chief of which has been the heredity-environment issue. This issue is one of the legacies inherited by psychology from philosophy, and it has plagued experimental psychology for nearly a hundred years. Nativism versus empiricism, McDougall's instinct psychology, Watson's adoption of a strict Lockean viewpoint,

the anti-instinct polemics of the 1920's, the nature-nurture controversy of the 1930's, culminating in the publication of *The Thirty-Ninth Yearbook* of the National Society for the Study of Education (1940), are but a few manifestations of this age-old debate. Although hindsight is always easy, it now appears that if the energy, not to mention the money, that has been expended in casuistry and the collection of amphibolous data had been devoted to carefully designed psychogenetic investigations, we might now have a substantial body of knowledge about the genetics of behavior. If such knowledge were in existence, it would then be possible to evaluate by experimental methods the role of modifiability in altering innate constitution.

The writer has attempted, in this chapter, to avoid speculation and argument from analogy. For instance, the whole question of sex differences has been omitted because its discussion would have to be largely inferential. There is no doubt that innate sex differences in psychological traits exist: the aggressiveness of the male rat versus the pacificism of the female, contrasting courtship and copulatory patterns, and maternal behavior, to mention a few. These disparities have been traced to the action of gonadal hormones: androgen, estrogen, and progesterone. It is now well established that the male secretes some female sex hormone and the female secretes some male sex hormone, which fact precludes a sharp dichotomy between the sexes. All this information is extremely valuable, but it does not belong in a chapter on the genetics of behavior. One might infer that these established sex differences were controlled, primordially, by the sex chromosomes, but this inference has yet to be confirmed.

In order to have a science of psychogenetics it is not sufficient to determine merely that certain behavior traits are genetically transmitted. This is the first step. Genetic analysis, the mapping of chromosomes, and the specification of the *modus operandi* of the genes are also necessary functions of the psychogeneticist. In short, psychogenetics must imitate biogenetics.

One might ask, what will psychogenetics contribute to our understanding of the individual? The answer is that it may well be of tremendous value in clarifying the dynamics of behavior. The individual is a purposive, striving, selective, adjusting, animated organism. He does not spring to life just because stimuli from the outside world fall upon him. Nor does he lapse back into passivity and desuetude at their termination. There are inner forces that regulate, control, and precipitate his responses to the world. Psychologically these forces are called motives, intentions, values, interests, attitudes, and sentiments. Physiologically they are hormones, neural impulses, and chemical states. Genetically they are forces residing within the chromosomes. These genetic forces must be extremely important in shaping the psychological destiny of the individual. Any structures that can produce such varied forms as the flea and the elephant, the starfish and the kangaroo, the shark and the rabbit, must be potent causes of individuality within a species. Accordingly, an understanding of psychogenetics is a prerequisite for the development of a dynamic psychology.

REFERENCES

Brody, E. G. Genetic basis of spontaneous activity in the albino rat. *Comp. Psychol. Monogr.*, 1942, **17**, No. 5.

Coburn, C. A. Heredity of wildness and savageness in mice. *Behav. Monogr.*, 1922, **4**, No. 5.

Crozier, W. J., and H. Hoagland. The study of living organisms. In C. Murchison (Ed.), *Handbook of general experimental psychology.* Worcester: Clark University Press, 1934.

Dawson, W. M. Inheritance of wildness and tameness in mice. *Genetics*, 1932, **17**, 296–326.

Dice, L. R. Inheritance of waltzing and of epilepsy in mice of the genus *Peromyscus.* *J. Mammal.*, 1935, **16**, 25–35.

Farris, E. J., and E. H. Yeakel. The susceptibility of albino and gray Norway rats to audiogenic seizures. *J. comp. Psychol.*, 1943, **35**, 73–80.

Farris, E. J., and E. H. Yeakel. Emotional behavior of gray Norway and Wistar albino rats. *J. comp. Psychol.*, 1945, **38**, 109–118.

Finger, F. W. Factors influencing audiogenic seizures in the rat. II. Heredity and age. *J. comp. Psychol.*, 1943, **35**, 227–232.

Ginsburg, B., and W. C. Allee. Some effects of conditioning on social dominance and subordination in inbred strains of mice. *Physiol. Zoöl.*, 1942, **15**, 485–506.

Griffiths, W. J. Transmission of convulsions in the white rat. *J. comp. Psychol.*, 1942, **34**, 263–277.

Griffiths, W. J. Absence of audiogenic seizures in wild Norway and Alexandrine rats. *Science*, 1944, **99**, 62–63.

Grüneberg, H. *The genetics of the mouse.* Cambridge: Cambridge University Press, 1943.

Hall, C. S. Emotional behavior in the rat. I. Defecation and urination as measures of individual differences in emotionality. *J. comp. Psychol.*, 1934, **18**, 385–403.

Hall, C. S. The inheritance of emotionality. *Sigma Xi Quart.*, 1938, **26**, No. 1, 17–27.

Hall, C. S. Genetic differences in fatal audiogenic seizures between two inbred strains of house mice. *J. Heredity*, 1947, **38**, 2–6.

Hall, C. S., and S. J. Klein. Individual differences in aggressiveness in rats. *J. comp. Psychol.*, 1942, **33**, 371–383.

Heron, W. T. The inheritance of maze learning ability in rats. *J. comp. Psychol.*, 1935, **19**, 77–89.

Herter, K. Das thermotaktische Optimum bei Nagetieren, ein mendelndes Art- und Rassenmerkmal. *Z. vergl. Physiol.*, 1936, **23**, 605–650.

Herter, K. Die Beziehugen zwischen Vorzugstemperatur und Hautbeschaffenheit bie Mäusen. *Zool. Anz. Suppl.* 1938, **11**, 48–55.

Herter, K., and K. Sgonina. Vorzugstemperatur und Hautbeschaffenheit_ bei Mäusen. *Z. vergl. Physiol.*, 1938, **26**, 366–415.

Keeler, C. E., and H. D. King. Multiple effects of coat color genes in the Norway rat, with special reference to temperament and domestication. *J. comp. Psychol.*, 1942, **34**, 241–250.

King, H. D. Life processes in gray Norway rats during fourteen years in captivity. *Amer. anat. Mem.*, 1939, **17**, 1–72.

King, H. D., and H. H. Donaldson. Life processes and size of body and organs of the Gray Norway rat during ten generations in captivity. *Amer. Anat. Mem.*, 1929, No. 14.

Krechevsky, I. "Hypotheses" vs. "chance" in the pre-solution period in sensory discrimination-learning. *Univ. Calif. Publ. Psychol.*, 1932, **6**, 27–44.

Krechevsky, I. Hereditary nature of "hypotheses." *J. comp. Psychol.*, 1933, **16**, 99–116.

Lashley, K. S. Structural variation in the nervous system in relation to behavior. *Psychol. Rev.*, 1947, **54**, 325–334.

Maier, N. R. F. Studies of abnormal behavior in the rat. XIV. Strain differences in the inheritance of susceptibility to convulsions. *J. comp. Psychol.,* 1943, **35,** 327–335.

Maier, N. R. F., and N. M. Glaser. Studies of abnormal behavior in the rat. V. The inheritance of the "neurotic pattern." *J. comp. Psychol.,* 1940, **30,** 413–418.

Martin, R. F., and C. S. Hall. Emotional behavior in the rat. V. The incidence of behavior derangements resulting from air-blast stimulation in emotional and non-emotional strains of rats. *J. comp. Psychol.,* 1941, **32,** 191–204.

National Society for the Study of Education. *The thirty-ninth yearbook. Intelligence: its nature and nurture.* Parts I and II. Bloomington, Ill.: Public School Publishing, 1940.

Patton, R. A. Purulent otitis media in albino rats susceptible to sound-induced seizures. *J. Psychol.,* 1947, **24,** 313–317.

Rundquist, E. A. The inheritance of spontaneous activity in rats. *J. comp. Psychol.,* 1933, **16,** 415–438.

Rundquist, E. A., and C. J. Bellis. Respiratory metabolism of active and inactive rats. *Amer. J. Physiol.,* 1933, **106,** 670–675.

Russell, W. L. Inbred and hybrid animals and their value in research. In G. D. Snell (Ed.), *Biology of the laboratory mouse.* Philadelphia: Blakiston, 1941.

Scott, J. P. Genetic differences in the social behavior of inbred strains of mice. *J. Hered.,* 1942, **33,** 11–15.

Silverman, W., F. Shapiro, and W. T. Heron. Brain weight and maze learning in the rat. *J. comp. Psychol.,* 1940, **30,** 279–282.

Snell, G. D. Linkage of jittery and waltzing in the mouse. *J. Hered.,* 1945, **36,** 279–280.

Snyder, L. H. *The principles of heredity.* (2nd Ed.). New York: Heath, 1940.

Staff, Roscoe B. Jackson Memorial Laboratory. A chromosome map of the mouse. *J. Hered.,* 1945, **36,** 271–273.

Stone, C. P. Wildness and savageness in rats of different strains. In K. S. Lashley (Ed.), *Studies in the dynamics of behavior.* Chicago: Univ. Chicago Press, 1932.

Stone, C. P. Methodological resources for the experimental study of innate behavior as related to environmental factors. *Psychol. Rev.,* 1947, **54,** 342–347.

Tryon, R. C. Genetic differences in maze learning in rats. In National Society for the Study of Education, *The thirty-ninth yearbook.* Bloomington, Ill.: Public School Publishing, 1940.

Tryon, R. C. Individual differences. In F. A. Moss (Ed.), *Comparative psychology.* New York: Prentice-Hall, 1942.

Utsurikawa, N. Temperamental differences between outbred and inbred strains of the albino rat. *J. Anim. Behav.,* 1917, **7,** 111–129.

Vicari, E. M. Mode of inheritance of reaction time and degrees of learning in mice. *J. exp. Zool.,* 1929, **54,** 31–88.

Watson, M. L. The inheritance of epilepsy and of waltzing in *Peromyscus. Contr. Lab. Vertebr. Genet., Univ. Mich.,* 1939, No. 11.

Witt, G. M., and C. S. Hall. The genetics of audiogenic seizures in the house mouse. *J. comp. physiol. Psychol.,* 1949, **42,** 58–63.

Woolley, G. W., and M. M. Dickie. Pirouetting mice. *J. Hered.,* 1945, **36,** 281–284.

Wright, S. The effects of inbreeding and crossbreeding on guinea pigs. I. Decline in vigor. II. Differentiation among inbred families. *Bull. U. S. Dept. Agric.,* 1922, No. 1090.

Yeakel, E. H., and R. P. Rhoades. A comparison of the body and endocrine gland (adrenal, thyroid and pituitary) weights of emotional and non-emotional rats. *Endocrinology,* 1941, **28,** 337–340.

Yerkes, R. M. *The dancing mouse.* The Animal Behavior Series. No. 1. New York: Macmillan, 1907.

Yerkes, R. M. The heredity of savageness and wildness in rats. *J. Anim. Behav.,* 1913, **3,** 286–296.

10·

Growth Curves

NATHAN W. SHOCK

National Institutes of Health and Baltimore City Hospitals

Growth is one of the fundamental properties of living things. Broadly defined it represents the irreversible changes in size or function that occur with time. Although most of these changes represent increments in substance or in function, this is not always the case, as will be shown later in the discussion of certain physiological characteristics.

Although, according to this definition, any plot of size or function against time constitutes a growth curve, it is customary to regard as growth only that portion of the curve concerned with changes taking place prior to the attainment of a protracted plateau. Learning curves are usually excluded from discussions of growth because they are concerned with only a restricted portion of the total life span of the organism. Furthermore the primary parameter in a learning curve is number of trials, which may be related to time in an arbitrary manner, depending on the design of the experiment.

Basically growth refers to increments in the number of cells or elements in the organism. In multicellular organisms, such as man, however, it is impossible to count the individual cells, so that growth phenomena are usually related to increases in mass, volume, or surface area. Psychologists have broadened the concept of growth to include increments in functional capacities as well. Thus one may speak of mental growth as well as physical growth. Growth has both static and dynamic aspects. One may be interested in the amount of a substance or in the state of a function at a given time, or one may consider the rate of change in substance or function.

Growth Curves

A growth curve is a graph or plot of size or function against time. It usually includes a major portion of the life span of the organism or cellular colony. This chapter will consider questions that can be answered by growth-curve analysis. It is important to recognize that many questions about the growth process cannot be answered by a study of growth curves alone: it is clear that a human adult cannot be described simply as a child of increased dimensions. Many developmental changes take place with growth: changes in functions, proportions, interactions, etc., which cannot be adequately described by simple growth curves. There are other questions, however, to which a study of growth curves can provide significant answers.

First of all, it is possible to determine the amount of growth in size or function at a given time either for individuals or for groups of individuals. Further analysis of growth curves makes it possible to determine the rate of change of growth over a finite time interval. Using mathematical procedures, it is possible to estimate instantaneous rates as well. Comparison of growth curves can also be used to measure the effects of various environmental factors on the growth process.

For example, much of the experimental work on the effects of diet, vitamins, and hormones depends upon the use of growth curves. Growth curves may also be of value in testing hypotheses about the underlying processes involved (Morales and Kreutzer, 1945; Hutchens, Podolsky, and Morales, 1948). Other practical uses of growth curves are presented in a later section.

THEORY OF GROWTH CURVES *

Rational Equations

The rational description of how a multicellular organism changes in time t requires the choice of a parameter of description ψ (t) with the following characteristics: (1) ψ must depend only upon the activity of living cells, and (2) ψ must be such that all other parameters can be unambiguously expressed in terms of it (Shock and Morales, 1942). The one parameter that can best satisfy these conditions is total cell number (N).

Living cells always exhibit the phenomena of metabolism and irritability, although not all the substance of the cell contributes to or takes part in these essential processes. Yolk stores, fat stores, or water stores within the cell are no more "living" than the same substances outside the cell; but as the amounts of these substances in a cell change with time, the parameters of mass, surface, and volume may also change. It is, therefore, clear that such parameters as mass and surface area can express in only an indirect sense the phenomena of growth or life. Furthermore, indices of metabolism and irritability vary in time as a result of physiological processes not associated with growth itself, such as exercise and temperature. The process of cell division, on the other hand, is unquestionably associated with living protoplasm in a direct way, and it must there-

fore be concluded that the measure of cell division, namely, the number of cells (N), is a basic parameter for a theoretical analysis of growth.

Let us postulate that two factors are responsible for changes in N as t increases: (1) a factor ϕ, which resides within the cells and is present even if the cells are infinitely removed from one another, and (2) a factor θ, which is the interaction between cells. Assuming that these two effects are additive, we may write

$$\frac{dN}{dt} = \phi + \theta \qquad (1)$$

If there is no interaction between cells, it is reasonable to suppose that at any one time the increase in cell number is proportional to the number of cells present. However, the constant of proportionality generally changes with time and should be a function of it. Thus

$$\frac{dN}{dt} = f_1(x_1, x_2, \cdots, x_n, t)$$

where the x's are physical parameters and t is time.† Since the coefficient of N may depend upon N as well as upon t, we may write

$$\phi = A(N, t) \cdot N \qquad (2)$$

Although the interaction effect θ must somehow depend upon the number of cells present, the dependence need not be linear. Hence we may write

$$\theta = B(N, t) \cdot N^k \qquad (3)$$

† The reasoning whereby t is introduced into the right-hand member of the equation is as follows: physical functions are determined at any instant by the values of physical variables and depend on time only insofar as the latter depend on time. Thus it may be that a parameter, x_i, changes in time,

$$\frac{dx_i}{dt} = f_2(r_1, r_2, \cdots, r_m)$$

whence

$$x_i = f_3(x_{i_0}, t)$$

where x_{i_0} is the value of x_i at the zero point of time. Substituting in the equation for N, x_i is replaced by x_{i_0}, t, and similarly for other parameters. The right-hand member thus becomes rigorously meaningful with the zero point of time operationally defined and can be evaluated for any given t.

* The assistance of Dr. Manuel F. Morales in the preparation of this section is gratefully acknowledged.

where in the simplest case the exponent k is some constant. Assembling equations 1, 2, and 3, we may write

$$\frac{dN}{dt} = A(N, t) \cdot N + B(N, t) \cdot N^k \qquad (4)$$

This represents the fundamental equation of growth. The effect of many of the phenomena that affect growth can be estimated by this form of equation simply by making reasonable assumptions about the functions A and B. It may be shown that all the important rational growth equations, and two of the equations heretofore regarded as empirical, can be derived by making logical assumptions with regard to the functions A and B. These functions A and B represent the intrinsic growth factor and effects of interaction between cells, respectively.

Case I. Linear proliferation: universally deleterious metabolite produced by all cells at a uniform rate. Assuming that cells infinitely removed from each other have equal and constant division times, it may be shown that

$$\phi = AN \qquad (5)$$

where A is a true constant (without transient or lag effects). If the cells are brought together and if each cell produces a substance that is harmful to every cell in the community including itself, and the proportionality constant is B, then the sum of the harmful effects is BN^2. This follows because the total number of effects of N cells upon themselves is BN. Furthermore, each cell acts upon $N - 1$ others, so that the number of effects of cells upon their fellows is $BN(N - 1)$. The total number of harmful effects is therefore $BN + BN(N - 1) = BN^2$. Thus

$$\theta = -BN^2 \qquad (6)$$

Combining equations 1, 5, and 6, we obtain

$$\frac{dN}{dt} = AN - BN^2 = BN\left(\frac{A}{B} - N\right) \qquad (7)$$

Equation 7 integrates directly into

$$N = \frac{\dfrac{A}{B}}{1 + \left(\dfrac{A}{B} - 1\right)e^{-At}} \qquad (8)$$

where e is the base of the natural logarithms.

Case II. Linear proliferation: universally deleterious metabolite produced by all cells at a variable rate. In addition to the postulates of case I, let us postulate that the proportionality constant B changes in time as discussed in an earlier paragraph. This variation may be expressed by a power function of t:

$$B = \sum_{s=0}^{s=n} K_s t^s \qquad (9)$$

Substituting into equation 1 we obtain

$$\frac{dN}{dt} = AN - N^2 \sum_{s=0}^{s=n} K_s t^s \qquad (10)$$

This equation integrates to

$$N = \frac{1}{Ke^{-At} + e^{-At} \int B(t)e^{At}\, dt} \qquad (11)$$

where K is a constant of integration.*

Case III. Constant rate of proliferation: foodstuffs as limiting factor. If we assume a constant rate of proliferation, we may write

$$\phi = \alpha k$$

where α and k are constants separated into two factors for algebraic convenience. Assuming that retardation is due to a shortage of foodstuffs, the retarding interaction factor θ will be proportional to the number of cells present; that is,

$$\theta = -kN$$

The rate equation

$$\frac{dN}{dt} = \alpha k - kN \qquad (12)$$

integrates to

$$N = \alpha(1 - e^{-kt}) \qquad (13)$$

---

* The integration given in the original reference (Shock and Morales, 1942) was in error. Thanks are due Dr. John Z. Heason for calling this to our attention.

Case IV. All cells produce a stimulating substance which takes effect according to pharmacological laws: foodstuffs as limiting factor. If all cells produce a growth stimulant, the amount of this substance present at any time is proportional to the number of cells. The effect, however, may be proportional to the per cent increase in the stimulating substance. This relation between dosage and effect occurs frequently in pharmacology and physiology. A parallel effect in psychological phenomena was formulated by Weber and Fechner. According to this principle, the effect of a unit amount of substance is proportional to the logarithm of the amount present, which in turn is proportional to the number of cells. The total effect is then proportional to the effect of unit amount and to the amount present; in other words,

$$\phi = (-C \log A)N$$

As before,

$$\theta = CN \log N$$

Combining according to equation 1,

$$\frac{dN}{dt} = (\log N - \log A)CN \qquad (14)$$

which integrates to

$$N = Ae^{Be^{Ct}} \qquad (15)$$

where B is a constant of integration.

Transformation to Units of Size

Thus it has been shown that, if we make reasonable hypotheses about the intrinsic and extrinsic factors affecting growth, as outlined in equation 1, we may derive rational equations for growth in terms of cell number. Since the number of cells in multicellular animals is not an experimentally determinable quantity, it is necessary to make certain transformations in these equations in order to apply them to experimental data. The assumptions involved in this transformation will be made explicit. For example, we may consider the relation between the differential and integrated functions derived above and their analogues, using mass M as the essential parameter. We may assume that for the kth cell the average density is $\bar{p}_k$ and the volume v_k, so that the mass is

$$m_k = \bar{p}_k v_k \qquad (16)$$

and obviously

$$M = \sum_{k=1}^{k=N} \bar{p}_k v_k \qquad (17)$$

Since $M = f(N, t, \bar{p}_k, v_k)$ we may also write:

$$\frac{dM}{dt} = \frac{\partial M}{\partial N}\frac{dN}{dt} + \sum_{k=1}^{k=N} \frac{\partial M}{\partial \bar{p}_k}\frac{d\bar{p}_k}{dt} + \sum_{k=1}^{k=N} \frac{\partial M}{\partial v_k}\frac{dv_k}{dt} \qquad (18)$$

Equations 17 and 18 thus give the desired relations. In practice it must be assumed that the cells are homogeneous with respect to mass, density, and volume. Under this assumption we may express equation 18 as:

$$M = Npv \qquad (19)$$

Substituting into equation 18, we have

$$\frac{dM}{dt} = \frac{M}{N}\frac{dN}{dt} + \frac{M}{p}\frac{dp}{dt} + \frac{M}{v}\frac{dv}{dt} \qquad (20)$$

If, in addition, p and v are constant in time, equation 20 becomes simply $dM/dt = c\, dN/dt$, where c is a constant, and the four cases we have derived above can be written with the constants referred to mass and time. The mass analogues of equations 8, 11, 13, and 15 are thus

$$M = \frac{\dfrac{A}{B}}{1 + \left(\dfrac{A}{B} - 1\right)e^{-At}} \qquad (21)$$

$$M = \frac{1}{Ke^{-At} + e^{-At}\int B(t)e^{At}\,dt} \qquad (22)$$

$$M = \alpha(1 - e^{-kt}) \qquad (23)$$

and

$$M = Ae^{Be^{ct}} \qquad (24)$$

These equations are those presented by other authors in various connections: equation 21 by Robertson (1907–08, 1926–28); equation 22 by Pearl (1925); equation 23 by Brody (1945), Schmalhausen (1928, 1929, 1930), and Jenss and Bayley (1937); equation 24 by Gompertz (1925) and Courtis (1929, 1932).*

The first two of these equations have heretofore been derived on the basis of chemical analogues that were admittedly fictitious; the last two have up to now been regarded as purely empirical.

between an integral form and a differential equation, the interpretation of the constants in equations 21 to 24 is not unique, although the meanings ascribed to them in the foregoing derivations are certainly one possible set. Because of this inherent lack of uniqueness in the mathematical approach, the

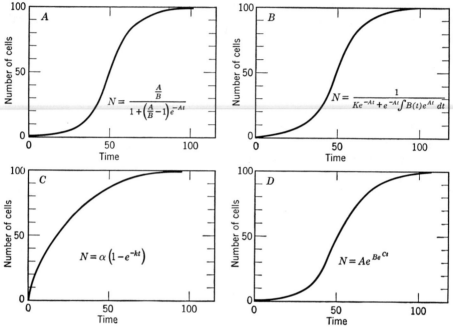

$$N = \frac{\frac{A}{B}}{1 + \left(\frac{A}{B} - 1\right)e^{-At}}$$

$$N = \frac{1}{Ke^{-At} + e^{-At}\int B(t)e^{At}\,dt}$$

$$N = \alpha\left(1 - e^{-kt}\right)$$

$$N = Ae^{Be^{Ct}}$$

Fig. 1.   Theoretical growth functions derived rationally.

Limitations of Interpretations of Rational Growth Curves

It should be pointed out that an infinite number of growth equations could be developed from the fundamental equation above. It would be necessary simply to alter the hypotheses and the functional relations proposed for the intrinsic and extrinsic factors. Since there is a many-to-one correspondence

nature of the growth process cannot be determined by this method alone. Furthermore, the unreliability of measurements, or the heterogeneity of the sample in an experimental situation, may be so great that a precise statement of whether the observations do or do not fit a given formulation cannot be made. For example, J. Gray (1929) presents two curves fitted to the same set of observations; in one the inflection point is at $x = \frac{1}{2}a$, and in the other $x = \frac{1}{3}a$. Both curves fit the data within the limits set by the errors of observation.

The characteristics of form and shape of the theoretical curves derived from equations 21 to 24, respectively, are illustrated in Fig. 1.

* Details of statistical methods for fitting experimental observations to each of these curves may be found in the references cited. See also Cowden (1947).

Of the four theoretical curves, three are in general S-shaped (Fig. 1*A*, *B*, *D*), and the fourth is logistic (Fig. 1*C*). The first of these (Fig. 1*A*) is symmetrical about the point of inflection, whereas the second (Fig. 1*B*) is not. These four types of curves have proved most useful in the analysis of growth data, and many examples may be found in publications of Brody (1945), Courtis (1929, 1932), Crozier (1926), Davenport (1926–27), Kavanaugh and Richards (1942), Merrill (1931), Robertson (1907–08, 1926–28), Schmalhausen (1928, 1929, 1930), and von Bertalanffy (1934, 1938), etc. Although close fits to growth data for various animals may be cited (Brody, 1945), no single curve has been found that completely describes the entire growth period of the human. For this reason, human growth has been regarded as progressing in two (Davenport, 1926–27) or three (Robertson, 1926–28) cycles, each of which must be described by its own equation.

We may now turn to a consideration of the uses of various types of growth curves in experimental investigations.

AMOUNT OF GROWTH AT A GIVEN TIME

Anthropometric Measurements

Numerous references to studies of anthropometric measurements of growing children and animals may be found in the literature (Krogman, 1941; Meredith, 1936a, 1943). Measurements range from those of height and weight to segmental measurements of practically every part of the body (Dearborn, Rothney, and Shuttleworth, 1938; Gray and Ayres, 1931; Meredith, 1936a, 1943; Shuttleworth, 1937, 1938a, 1938b, 1939; Simmons, 1944; Stuart, 1939, 1942, 1946; Thompson, 1946). Growth curves have been constructed showing the average value of such measurements for groups of individuals at various ages. Figure 2 showing the average weight of American school children is an example of this type of curve. Similar curves exist for such anthropometric measurements as stem length, sitting height, leg length, arm length, shoulder width, hip width, chest circumference, arm circumference, leg circum-

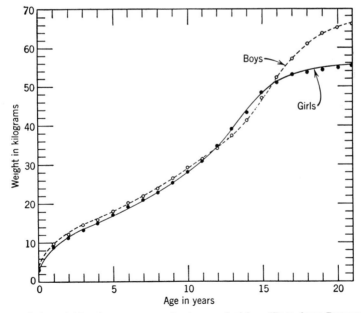

FIG. 2. Growth in weight. Average curves for boys and girls. (Data from Davenport, 1926.)

ference, and many others. There was a time
when curves like those in Fig. 2 were used
as a standard of comparison to assess the
growth status of individual children. It soon
became apparent, however, that factors other
than age alone are important in determining
the growth of an individual child. Consequently this method of assessment was augmented by setting up so-called standards of
weight in terms not only of age but of other
characteristics such as height or body widths
(Baldwin, 1925; Pryor and Stolz, 1933; Wetzel, 1944, 1946) and physiological maturation
(Shuttleworth, 1937, 1938a). The chief usefulness of this type of curve lies in the
evaluation of the effects of various dietary
and endocrine substances on the growth process, as will be discussed in a subsequent section.

It has been found experimentally that the
standard deviation of measurements of any
particular body characteristic changes systematically with age (Davenport, 1931).
This is particularly true of measurements on
human subjects: the standard deviations of
measurements made during the adolescent
period are significantly greater than those
of measurements made either in early childhood or in early adulthood. Such a finding
could result only from individual differences
in the chronological age at which the adolescent growth spurt occurs (Shuttleworth,
1937, 1938a). Let us turn then to a consideration of individual growth curves.

Individual Growth Curves

The accumulation of serial measurements
on the same child from birth to maturity is
extremely laborious. Although data of this
kind may be found in the literature covering
certain age periods, such as birth to three
years (Davenport, 1937; Davenport and
Drager, 1936; Jenss and Bayley, 1937) or
during the adolescent period (Dearborn,
Rothney, and Shuttleworth, 1938), measurements of individuals over the entire growth
period are extremely rare (Gray and Faber,
1940; Guttman, 1915; Scammon, 1927).

Figure 3 illustrates growth in height and
weight from two studies (Scammon, 1927;
Gray, 1941). Examination of these curves
reveals significant differences between the
growth of individual children as compared
to the average curve. It has been shown
that the prediction of the expected growth
or the ultimate adult size of the individual
can be made with much greater accuracy
from the individual growth curve than from
average curves alone (Bayley, 1943; Jenss
and Bayley, 1937). The chief limitation on
the value of the individual growth curve
lies in the experimental error attached to
the serial measurements, and unfortunately
for certain measurements, such as circum-
ferences, the error may be relatively large
(Meredith, 1936b).

Psychological Functions

For the most part psychologists have considered mental growth in terms of the average test performance of children at increasing ages. In some instances, raw scores have
been converted to mental age scores, and
curves have been constructed showing the
relation between average mental age and
chronological age (Ebert and Simmons, 1943;
Freeman and Flory, 1937). Although such
curves are useful in determining the performance of an individual child with respect
to others of the same chronological age, they
may not represent a growth function that
can be compared with growth in other
characteristics since they do not meet two
essential criteria of "ratio scale" measurement: namely, a zero point and units of
uniform size. This is particularly true when
we attempt to characterize the growth of an
abstract phenomenon such as intelligence.
It is clear that raw scores in performance
tests do not determine an absolute zero of
the function measured, since the zero test
score does not necessarily indicate the complete absence of the ability tested. Furthermore, we have no direct means of knowing
that the difference in ability represented by
the raw scores of 10 or 20, for example, is

the same as that between the raw scores of 90 and 100. Thus, although raw scores make it possible to place individuals in rank order on "ordinal scales," they cannot be used for more sophisticated analysis involving the calculation of product moment correlation or coefficients of variation (Stevens, 1946; also, see Chapter 1).

cessive age groups made it possible to plot absolute mean test performance against absolute variability and to determine by extrapolation the absolute zero of the scale (Thurstone, 1928). This is possible because the absolute variability of test intelligence

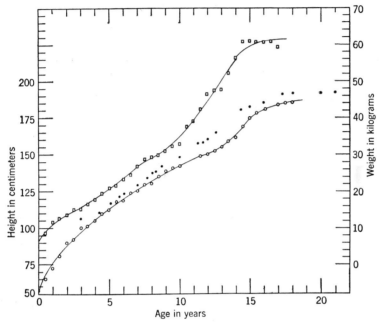

Fig. 3. Individual growth curves of height and weight. Squares: weight of girl (data from Gray and Farber, 1940). Dots: height of boy (data from Gray, 1941). Open circles: height of boy (data of Buffon, 1827, from Scammon, 1927).

Intelligence

These problems of mental measurement have been attacked by Thurstone (1925, 1928), who sought to obtain a uniform unit of measurement by a method of "absolute scaling." Details of the statistical procedure cannot be presented here, but the essence of the technique is the use of the standard deviation of the performance of one age group as a unit of measurement (Thurstone, 1925). The discovery that, with uniform conditions of selection, there is a linear relation between the absolute variability and the mean test performance of suc-

must be zero when the mean test performance is zero; that is, the variability cannot be negative. Armed thus with an absolute zero and a uniform unit of scale measurement, it was possible for Thurstone and Ackerson (1929) to construct the mental growth curve shown in Fig. 4. These investigators derive several fundamental facts concerning the laws of mental growth: (1) The mental growth curve has a positive acceleration up to the age level of about 10 years. (2) The mental growth curve is asymptotic to an adult level. (3) The mental growth curve has an inflection point somewhere in the age range of 9 to 12. (4) The inflection point comes earlier for bright children than for dull children. (5) The mental growth curve is asymptotic to absolute zero. (6) The absolute variability of test intelligence increases with age until adult intelligence is attained.

These findings contradict the hypothetical growth curve of mental age or raw scores, which is usually shown to have a negative acceleration from birth onward and no inflection point. It is unfortunate that the

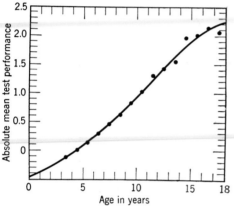

technique used in this study has not been applied to tests of performance in other mental functions. The generality of the absolute scaling method devised by Thurstone makes it possible to apply the same technique to other performance tests. Many of the inferences about the relation between mental and physical growth may be subject to question, since raw scores, sigma scores, or mental age scores have been used in most studies (Simmons, 1944; Bayley, 1940). For comparisons between mental or performance test data and other growth characteristics, it is obvious that methods leading to comparable scales must be utilized for both kinds of data. This represents a major field for future development by psychologists.

Intellectual Achievement

Growth curves of physical performance, such as strength (Jones, 1944), motor skills

(Jones and Seashore, 1944), etc., may be drawn to describe changes with age, since the criteria for measurement are satisfactorily met. However, growth curves of mental performance, such as reading skill, spelling ability, etc., are usually based on raw score values that have not been scaled. For this reason many of the studies of growth in different types of mental performance are subject to question.

If, however, sigma or standard scores are calculated for each type of mental performance, comparisons of growth curves can be made, provided the mean of a single age group is used as a reference point and the standard deviation of that group is used as the unit of measurement. If sigma scores are calculated in terms of deviation from the mean value of each age group, the trend due to age is of course eliminated. Therefore it is necessary to use one age group as the standard to which others are referred. The validity of results obtained by this method depends in large measure on the size and random character of the standardizing group, since the assignment of scale units is based on the assumption that the *form* of the distribution of scores is *known*.

Physiological Functions

Growth changes in physiological functions such as pulse rate, blood pressure, basal oxygen consumption, etc., have in general been presented as average growth curves by age groups. Such curves have been used chiefly to assess the deviations of individuals from the average values for a given age group (Shock, 1944, 1946a, b; Greulich et al., 1942; Henry, 1944). It is important to note when dealing with physiological variables that the changes with age may include negative as well as positive increments. For example, Fig. 5 shows the average values of oxygen consumption per unit of surface area as a function of chronological age. These values attain a maximum at the age of 3 to 4 years, followed by decreases through

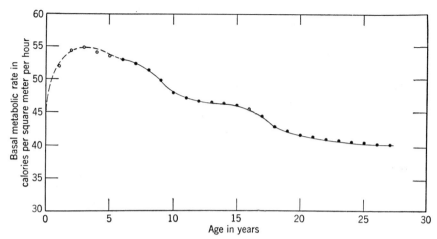

FIG. 5. Physiological growth curve. Average basal metabolic rate (calories per square meter per hour) as a function of chronological age. (Dots: data from Boothby, Berkson, and Dunn, 1938. Open circles: adjusted values of Lewis, Duval and Iliff, 1943.)

maturity (Du Bois, 1936; Boothby, Berkson, and Dunn, 1936; Lewis, Duval, and Iliff, 1943).

It may be pointed out that physiological functions are not fixed or static but vary from time to time. Consequently, the measurements include not only variability in technique but biological variation of the organism from moment to moment. The standard deviation of physiological measurements is commonly greater than that of anthropometric measurements. It may be found that other physiological variables alter the values of the physiological measurement and that these other variables are not highly correlated with chronological age. Thus the use of individual curves of development may bring to light findings that are not apparent from average curves (Davenport, 1931). This may be illustrated by a comparison of the average change in metabolic rate with that of an individual over the adolescent period. Figure 6 shows that for an individual the change in metabolic rate with age may be quite different from that shown by the average curve. In this instance, a rapid fall in metabolic rate occurred within the 6 to 12 months following the beginning of menstruation (Shock, 1944).

Weinbach (1937, 1938a, b, 1940) fitted growth curves to certain physiological observations such as the duration of the Moro

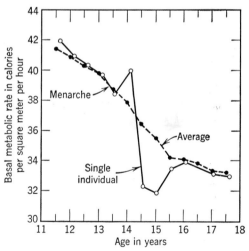

FIG. 6. Average growth curve of basal metabolic rate compared with curve for an individual female. (Data from Shock, 1944.)

reflex in infants, brain potentials, and time of climbing slopes of varying degrees of inclination. The variability of the observations is so great that the curves fitted can be regarded only as a rough gradation technique.

In a later publication Weinbach (1941) fitted the same equation ($M = M_m - M_m e^{-kt}$) to both alpha-rhythm observations and brain weight. The fact that the calculated growth rates for both phenomena (brain weight and alpha rhythm) are the same is not proof that the two phenomena are dependent on each other or in any way connected.

ESTIMATES OF GROWTH RATE

Since growth is a dynamic process, one of the important questions for study is the rate at which this process occurs. The rate of growth is expressed in terms of the increment per unit of time. If one knows the functional relation between the amount of growth or the size and time, the rate at a given instant is obtained by differentiating the equation with respect to time, that is to say, by solving the equation $W = F(t)$ for dW/dt. Since this functional relation, $W = f(t)$, is usually unknown, certain other estimates have been proposed by students of the problem.

Raw Increments

One solution to the problem of estimating the growth rate is to compute the increment between two successive measurements. This calculation may be expressed as $(W_2 - W_1)/(t_2 - t_1)$, where W_2 and W_1 are the larger and smaller measurements, respectively, and t_2 and t_1 the respective ages. This expression of the rate of growth suffers from certain disadvantages; for example, the arbitrariness of the unit of time taken for the measurement. Thus, if measurements are made at monthly rather than at yearly intervals and the rates expressed as increments per month, a set of rates will be obtained entirely different from that calculated on the basis of annual increments (Scammon, 1930). Similarly a unit increment in weight, for instance, does not have the same significance when added to individuals of different orig-

inal weights. Thus the addition of 1 pound of weight to the 6-pound infant is not equivalent to an increment of 1 pound in a child weighing 50 pounds. In order to meet this difficulty, increments may be expressed in terms of the per cent of the weight at the beginning of the interval.

Percentage Increments

The procedure of reporting growth rates by computing the ratio of the gain in weight

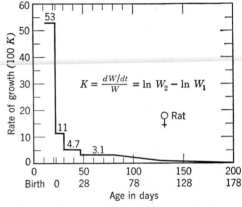

FIG. 7. Instantaneous growth rates for the female rat. (Data from Schmalhausen, 1928.)

to the weight at the beginning of the time interval, $100 \times (W_2 - W_1)/W_1$, as originally introduced by Minot (1908), is obviously influenced to a large extent by the time interval over which measurements are made. Brody (1945) has shown that by shortening the time interval and by using the mean weight for this time interval as the denominator, a closer approximation of the growth rate may be obtained. A further refinement in the calculation of growth rates has been introduced by Schmalhausen (1929), who has calculated the instantaneous relative growth rate as follows:

$$K = \frac{\ln W_2 - \ln W_1}{t_2 - t_1}$$

where ln signifies the natural logarithm. This so-called instantaneous growth rate has been computed for the rat as shown in Fig.

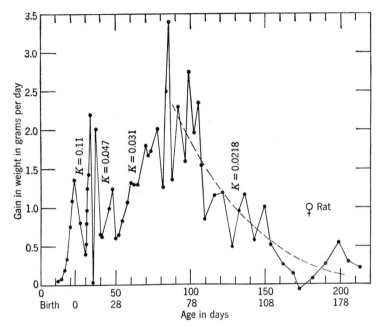

Fɪɢ. 8. Growth rates for the female rat. (Data from Brody, 1945.)

7. In reality this process is one of fitting a series of logarithmic curves to the growth data and obtaining the slope of the logarithmic curve over finite time intervals. As indicated in Fig. 8, growth is represented as a discontinuous process with changing growth constants.

Instantaneous Rates

The Schmalhausen technique gives a different rate constant for various parts of the growth curve. On the other hand, it is clear that, if a rational equation for the growth process is derived as outlined in the theoretical part of this chapter, the estimation of the growth rate at any time (t_i) is simply a matter of differentiating the appropriate equation and substituting the value of t_i into the differential form. However, the growth of human beings does not lend itself to a simple formulation, and consequently no rational equation has yet been developed that can be fitted to the complete growth curve of the human organism, even though a number of equations have been found satisfactory for various parts of the growth curve (Davenport, 1926–27; Jenss and Bayley, 1937). It should be pointed out, however, that, even though a rational equation cannot be developed, a true instantaneous rate can be derived from an empirical equation that has been fitted to experimental data. This possibility constitutes an argument for the fitting of functional relationships, even though they be empirical, to experimental data. Methods used in fitting empirical curves to experimental observations may be found in Brody (1945), Courtis (1932), Cowden (1947), Davenport (1926–27), Guilford (1936), Jenss and Bayley (1937), Merrill (1931), Pearl (1925), Robertson (1907–08), and Schmalhausen (1929).

OTHER USES OF GROWTH CURVES

The primary uses of growth curves, namely, the estimation of the amount and rate of growth, have been presented in previous sections. Space does not permit a detailed discussion of the many specific uses of growth curves in experimental and clinical studies. However, brief mention may be made of some additional problems in which growth curves have been of value.

the diet. Figure 9 illustrates the use of growth curves to demonstrate the effect of changes of diet on growth curves (Brody, 1945). By means of a decreased food supply the rat whose growth curve is shown at the right was kept at a constant body weight

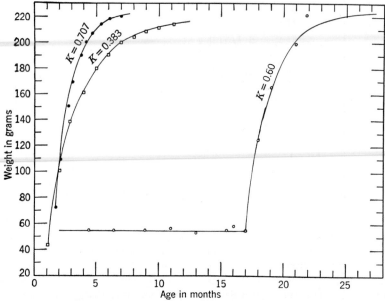

FIG. 9. Effect of undernutrition on growth of the rat. Dots: growth of well-nourished female rat. Squares: growth of inbred female rats. Open circles: growth curve of female rat maintained at constant body weight from age 1.3 months to 17.1 months by undernutrition. At 17.1 months an adequate food supply was provided. The rat began to grow at a rate characteristic of its weight and not of its age. (Data from Brody, 1928.)

Effects of Diet

Growth curves have proved a useful tool in the evaluation of various dietary factors. For these studies the white rat has commonly been used. Average growth curves for groups of animals deprived of specific nutritional elements have been compared with growth curves of animals that have received an optimal diet. The efficacy of the specific nutritional element has furthermore been demonstrated by showing that the growth curves of groups of animals are significantly depressed during periods of deprivation and that a marked change in the slope and direction of the growth curves occurs when the missing element is added to

of 55 grams from the age of 1.3 months to the age of 17.1 months. When an adequate food supply was made available, the rat began to grow at a rate characteristic of its weight and not of its age, indicating that within limits the growth rate of rats is independent of age.

Effects of Hormones

The effects of hormones on growth have been demonstrated by comparing growth curves of animals from which a given endocrine organ has been surgically removed with the growth curve of a litter mate. The restoration of growth rates following the administration of purified hormones has served as a useful tool in estimating the purity of the endocrine product as well as its importance in regulating growth. Examples of curves showing the effect of the growth hormone of the anterior pituitary gland are presented in the publication of Selye (1947, p. 239).

Seasonal Variations

Figure 10 illustrates a method of evaluating seasonal variations in growth by plot-

for a variety of species, except man (Brody, 1945). Figure 11 shows how such curves for the rat and cow may be superimposed. The extremely long juvenile period of man shows a striking species difference.

Problems of Relative Growth

The changes in the form of animals during growth and development are usually included under the general term morphogenesis. For the most part, studies of

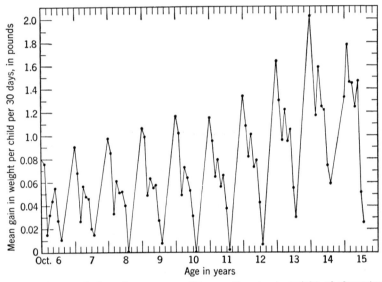

Fig. 10. Seasonal variation of average monthly growth rates in weight of elementary school boys. (Data from Palmer, 1933.)

ting serial measurements on groups of children (Palmer, 1933). It may be pointed out that such fluctuations in growth are more apparent in curves showing increments over fixed time periods and that some evaluation of the results can be made even though the functional relation between growth and age is not known.

Equivalence of Growth among Different Species

Growth curves have proved of value in equating growth rates for animals of widely different mature size and growth rates. Thus, by appropriate alterations of the time scale, it is possible to superimpose growth curves

changes in form have been descriptive in nature. However, certain aspects of changes in form have been quantified in terms of growth curves. In higher organisms these studies have plotted the growth of various parts of the animal in terms of the growth of the entire organism. For a detailed treatment of this problem the reader is referred to the publications of Huxley (1932), Jackson (1928), Scammon (1930), and Thompson (1942).

SUMMARY

In summary it may be pointed out that answers to certain questions may be ob-

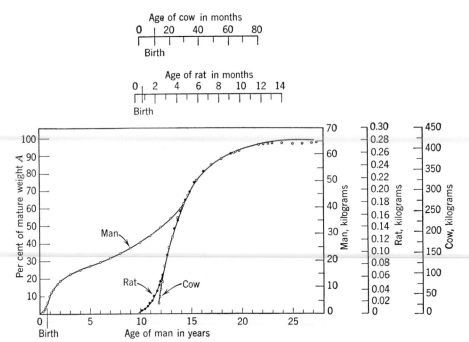

FIG. 11.   Comparison of growth curves for man, rat, and cow.   Time scales adjusted for equivalence.   (Data from Brody, 1945.)

tained by plotting growth curves. Among these questions is the use of growth curves to study the effects of various dietary and endocrine factors in the growth process. Such curves represent an experimental technique that has proved most useful in physiology and medicine. Growth curves are also of value in determining the relative status of progress of an individual with respect to a group. Answers to this question may be obtained even though the functional relation between size and age is unknown. The estimation of instantaneous growth rates can be made only where a rational formulation of the functional relation between growth and age has been fitted to the experimental observations. However, a close approximation to instantaneous growth rates may be obtained when only an empirical equation has been fitted to the observations. Further research lies in the direction of formulating hypotheses for which rational equations can be developed

and the testing of these hypotheses by fitting the equations to observational data.

REFERENCES

Baldwin, B. T.   Weight-height-age standards in metric units for American-born children.   Amer. J. phys. Anthrop., 1925, 8, 1–11.

Bayley, N.   Mental growth in young children.   In National Society for the Study of Education, The thirty-ninth yearbook.   Part II.   Bloomington, Ill.: Public School Publishing, 1940.   Pp. 11–47.

Bayley, N.   Skeletal maturing in adolescence as a basis for determining percentage of completed growth.   Child Develpm., 1943, 14, 1–46.

von Bertalanffy, L.   A quantitative theory of organic growth; inquiries on growth laws. Hum. Biol., 1938, 10, 181–213.

von Bertalanffy, L.   Untersuchungen über die Gesetzlichkeit des Wachstums.   Arch. Entw-Mech. Org., 1934, 131, 613–652.

Boothby, W. M., J. Berkson, and H. L. Dunn. Studies of the energy metabolism of normal individuals.   Amer. J. Physiol., 1936, 116, 468–484.

Brody, S.   An analysis of growth and senescence. Chapter II in Growth.   New Haven: Yale University Press, 1928.   Pp. 31–64.

Brody, S. *Bioenergetics and growth.* New York : Reinhold, 1945.

Courtis, S. A. Maturation units for the measurement of growth. *Sch. and Soc.,* 1929, **30,** 683–690.

Courtis, S. A. *The measurement of growth.* Ann Arbor : Brumfield and Brumfield, 1932.

Cowden, D. J. Simplified methods of fitting certain types of growth curves. *J. Amer. statist. Ass.,* 1947, **42,** 585–590.

Crozier, W. J. On curves of growth, especially in relation to temperature. *J. gen. Physiol.,* 1926, **10,** 53–73.

Davenport, C. B. Human metamorphosis. *Amer. J. phys. Anthrop.,* 1926, **9,** 205–232.

Davenport, C. B. Human growth curve. *J. gen. Physiol.,* 1926–27, **10,** 205–215.

Davenport, C. B. Individual versus mass studies in child growth. *Proc. Amer. phil. Soc.,* 1931, **60,** 381–389.

Davenport, C. B. Interpretation of certain infantile growth curves. *Growth,* 1937, **1,** 279–283.

Davenport, C. B., and W. Drager. Growth curves of infants. *Proc. nat. Acad. Sci., Wash.,* 1936, **22,** 639–645.

Dearborn, W. F., J. Rothney, and F. K. Shuttleworth. Data on the growth of public school children. *Monogr. Soc. Res. Child Develpm.,* 1938, **3,** 136.

Du Bois, E. F. *Basal metabolism in health and disease.* Philadelphia : Lea and Febiger, 1936.

Ebert, E., and K. Simmons. The Brush Foundation study of child growth and development. I. Psychometric tests. *Monogr. Soc. Res. Child Develpm.,* 1943, **8,** 1–113.

Freeman, F. N., and C. D. Flory. Growth in intellectual ability as measured by repeated tests. *Monogr. Soc. Res. Child Develpm.,* 1937, **2,** 1–116.

Gompertz, B. *On the nature of the function expressive of the law of human mortality, and on a new mode of determining the value of life contingencies.* London : *Philos. Trans. roy. Soc.,* 1925.

Gray, H. Individual growth rates. *Hum. Biol.,* 1941, **13,** 306–333.

Gray, H., and J. G. Ayres. *Growth in private school children.* Chicago : University of Chicago Press, 1931.

Gray, H., and H. K. Faber. Individual growth records of two healthy girls from birth to maturity. *Amer. J. Dis. Child.,* 1940, **59,** 255–280.

Gray, J. The kinetics of growth. *Brit. J. exp. Biol.,* 1929, **6,** 245–274.

Greulich, W. W., R. I. Dorfman, H. R. Catchpole, C. I. Solomon, and C. S. Culotta. Somatic and endocrine studies of puberal and adolescent boys. *Monogr. Soc. Res. Child Develpm.,* 1942, **8,** 1–86.

Guilford, J. P. *Psychometric methods.* New York : McGraw-Hill, 1936.

Guttmann, M. Einige Beispiel individueller körperlichen Entwicklung. *Z. Kinderhlk.,* 1915, **13,** 248–256.

Henry, C. E. Electroencephalograms of normal children. *Monogr. Soc. Res. Child Develpm.,* 1944, **9,** 1–71.

Hogan, A. G. *Some relations between growth and nutrition.* Chapter III in *Growth.* New Haven : Yale University Press, 1928.

Hutchens, J. O., Betty Podolsky, and M. F. Morales. Studies on the kinetics and energetics of carbon and nitrogen metabolism of chelomonas paramecium. *J. cell. comp. Physiol.,* 1948, **32,** 117–142.

Huxley, J. S. *Problems of relative growth.* London : Methuen, 1932.

Jackson, C. M. *Some aspects of form and growth.* Chapter IV in *Growth.* New Haven : Yale University Press, 1928.

Jenss, R. M., and N. Bayley. A mathematical method for studying the growth of a child. *Hum. Biol.,* 1937, **9,** 556–563.

Jones, H. E. The development of physical abilities. In National Society for the Study of Education, *The forty-third yearbook.* Part I. Bloomington, Ill. : 1944. Pp. 100–122.

Jones, H. E., and R. H. Seashore. The development of fine motor and mechanical abilities. In National Society for the Study of Education, *The forty-second yearbook.* Part I. Bloomington, Ill. : 1944. Pp. 123–145.

Kavanaugh, A. J., and O. W. Richards. Mathematical analysis of the relative growth of organisms. *Proc. Rochester Acad. Sci.,* 1942, **8,** 150–174.

Krogman, W. M. *A bibliography of human morphology, 1914–1939.* Chicago : University of Chicago Press, 1941.

Lewis, R. C., A. M. Duval, and A. Iliff. Basal metabolism of normal boys and girls from two to twelve years old, inclusive. *Amer. J. Dis. Child.,* 1943, **65,** 834–844.

Meredith, H. V. *Physical growth of white children: A review of American research prior to 1900.* Washington : Monogr. Soc. for Res. Child Develpm., 1936a.

Meredith, H. V. The reliability of anthropometric measurements taken on eight- and nine-year-old white males. *Child Develpm.,* 1936b, **7,** 262–272.

Meredith, H. V. *Physical growth from birth to two years: I. Stature, a review and synthesis of North American research for the period 1850–1941.* Iowa : Univ. Ia. Stud. in Child Welf., 1943.

Merrill, M. The relationship of individual growth to average growth. *Hum. Biol.,* 1931, **3,** 37–70.

Minot, C. S. *The problem of age, growth, and death.* New York : Putnam, 1908.

Morales, M. F., and F. L. Kreutzer. Some nutritional and excretional interactions and the growth of an organ or colony. *Bull. of math. Biophysics,* 1945, **7,** 15–24.

Palmer, C. E. Seasonal variation of average growth in weight of elementary school children. *U. S. publ. Hlth. Reports,* 1933, **48,** 211–242.

Pearl, R. *The biology of population growth.* New York: Knopf, 1925.

Pryor, H., and H. Stolz. Determining appropriate weight for body build. *J. Pediat.,* 1933, **3,** 608–624.

Robertson, T. B. On the normal rate of growth of an individual and its biochemical significance. *Arch. EntwMech. Org.,* 1907–08, **25,** 581–614.

Robertson, T. B. The analysis of the growth of the normal white mouse into its constituent processes. *J. gen. Physiol.,* 1926–28, **8,** 463–507.

Scammon, R. E. First seriatim study of human growth. *Amer. J. phys. Anthrop.,* 1927, **10,** 329–336.

Scammon, R. E. The measurement of the body in childhood. In *The Measurement of Man.* Minneapolis: University of Minnesota Press, 1930.

Schmalhausen, I. Das Wachstumsgesetz und die Methode der Bestimmung der Wachstumskonstante. *Arch. EntwMech. Org.,* 1928, **113,** 462–518.

Schmalhausen, I. Die Bestimmung des spezifischen Wachstumsertrages als vergleichende Untersuchungsmethode. *Arch. EntwMech. Org.,* 1929, **115,** 678–692.

Schmalhausen, I. Über Wachstumsformeln und Wachstumstheorien. *Biol. Zbl.,* 1930, **50,** 292–307.

Selye, H. *Textbook of endocrinology.* Montreal: Acta Endocrinologia, University de Montreal, 1947.

Shock, N. W. Physiological changes in adolescence. In National Society for the Study of Education, *The forty-third yearbook.* Part I. Bloomington, Ill.: 1944. Pp. 56–79.

Shock, N. W. Physiological responses of adolescents to exercise. *Texas Reports on Biol. Med.,* 1946a, **4,** 368–386.

Shock, N. W. Some physiological aspects of adolescence. *Texas Reports on Biol. Med.,* 1946b, **4,** 289–310.

Shock, N. W., and M. F. Morales. A fundamental form for the differential equation of colonial and organism growth. *Bull. math. Biophysics,* 1942, **4,** 63–71.

Shuttleworth, F. K. Sexual maturation and the physical growth of girls age six to nineteen. *Monogr. Soc. Res. Child Develpm.,* 1937, **2,** 1–253.

Shuttleworth, F. K. Sexual maturation and the skeletal growth of girls age six to nineteen. *Monogr. Soc. Res. Child Develpm.,* 1938a, **3,** 1–56.

Shuttleworth, F. K. The adolescent period: A graphic and pictorial atlas. *Monogr. Soc. Res. Child Develpm.,* 1938b, **3,** 1–246.

Shuttleworth, F. K. The physical and mental growth of girls and boys age six to nineteen in relation to age at maximum growth. *Monogr. Soc. Res. Child Develpm.,* 1939, **4,** 291.

Simmons, K. The Brush Foundation study of child growth and development: II. Physical growth and development. *Monogr. Soc. Res. Child Develpm.,* 1944, **9,** 1–87.

Stevens, S. S. On the theory of scales of measurement. *Science,* 1946, **103,** 677–680.

Stuart, H. C. Studies from the Center for Research in Child Health and Development. I. The Center, the group under observation, sources of information, and studies in progress. *Monogr. Soc. Res. Child Develpm.,* 1939, **4,** 1–261.

Stuart, H. C., and P. H. Dwinell. The growth of bone, muscle and overlying tissues in children six to ten years of age as revealed by studies of roentgenograms of the leg area. *Child Develpm.,* 1942, **13,** 195–213.

Stuart, H. C., and E. H. Sobel. The thickness of the skin and subcutaneous tissue by age and sex in childhood. *J. Pediat.,* 1946, **28,** 637–647.

Thompson, D. W. *On growth and form.* New York: Macmillan, 1942.

Thompson, H. *Physical growth.* Chapter 5 in L. Carmichael (Ed.), *Manual of Child Psychology.* New York: Wiley, 1946.

Thurstone, L. L. A method of scaling psychological and educational tests. *J. educ. Psychol.,* 1925, **16,** 433–451.

Thurstone, L. L. The absolute zero in intelligence measurement. *Psychol. Rev.,* 1928, **35,** 175–197.

Thurstone. L. L., and L. Ackerson. The mental growth curve for the Binet tests. *J. Educ. Psychol.,* 1929, **20,** 569–583.

Weinbach, A. P. Some physiological phenomena fitted to growth equations: I. Moro reflex. *Hum. Biol.,* 1937, **9,** 549–555.

Weinbach, A. P. Some physiological phenomena fitted to growth equations: II. Brain potentials. *Hum. Biol.,* 1938a, **10,** 145–150.

Weinbach, A. P. Some physiological phenomena fitted to growth equations: II. Rate of growth of brain potentials (alpha frequency) compared with rate of growth of the brain. *Growth,* 1938b, **2,** 247–251.

Weinbach, A. P. Some physiological phenomena fitted to growth equations: IV. Time and power relations for a human infant climbing inclines of various slopes. *Growth,* 1940, **4,** 123–134.

Weinbach, A. P. The human growth curve. *Growth,* 1941, **5,** 230.

Wetzel, N. C. On the motion of growth: XVII. Theoretical foundations. *Growth,* 1937, **1,** 6–59.

Wetzel, N. C. Growth. In O. Glasser (Ed.), *Medical Physics.* Chicago: Yearbook Publishers, 1944.

Wetzel, N. C. The baby grid: An application of the grid technique to growth and development in infants. *J. Pediat.,* 1946, **29,** 439–454.

Phylogenetic Comparison

HENRY W. NISSEN

Yerkes Laboratories of Primate Biology and Yale University

In this chapter we shall examine the role of comparative psychology in general biology, and its contribution towards the solution of basic problems of experimental and theoretical psychology. A search will be made for concepts or behavioral mechanisms in terms of which the behaviors of different animals may be compared. This treatment does not promote one or another of the currently active schools; it tries rather to synthesize a systematic, theoretical approach with the naturalistic point of view which looks at behavior in its wider setting and which refuses to exclude from consideration phenomena lying outside an arbitrarily circumscribed area of interest.

FUNCTIONS AND METHODS

Comparative psychology may be defined broadly as the science concerned with similarities and differences of behavior at various phylogenetic levels. Its aims and functions (1) as a branch of biology and (2) as part of experimental and theoretical psychology are closely interrelated.

Comparative Psychology and Evolution

As a biological science, comparative psychology supplements morphological and physiological evidence concerning phylogenetic development and the interrelations of species and phyla. The fragmentary story of evolution is interrupted most conspicuously and exasperatingly at the critical points of transition from one main grouping to another. One reason for this may be, as Lecomte du Noüy (1947, p. 79) suggests, that the transitional forms evolved quickly and survived only briefly. "Each group, order, or family," he says, "seems to be born suddenly and we hardly ever find the forms which link them to the preceding strain. When we discover them they are already completely differentiated." The present status of our knowledge about phylogenetic origins is admirably summarized by Thompson:

We have long known, in more or less satisfactory detail, the pedigree of horses, elephants, turtles, crocodiles and some few more; and our conclusions tally as to these, again more or less to our satisfaction, with the direct evidence of paleontological succession. But the larger and at first sight simpler questions remain unanswered; for eighty years' study of Darwinian evolution has not taught us how birds descend from reptiles, mammals from earlier quadrupeds, quadrupeds from fishes, nor vertebrates from the invertebrate stock. . . . We may fail to find the actual links between the vertebrate groups, but yet their resemblance and their relationship, real though indefinable, are plain to see; there are gaps between the groups, but we can see, so to speak, across the gap. On the other hand, the breach between vertebrate and invertebrate, worm and coelenterate, coelenterate and protozoan, is in each case of another order, and is so wide that we cannot see across the intervening gap at all. [1942, p. 1093.]

The conclusion is already implicit in these words that evolution, as manifested in structural characteristics, has been a discontinuous affair rather than the continuous process envisaged by Darwin. Thompson proceeds to draw an analogy with mathematics and phenomena of the inorganic world:

> An algebraic curve has its fundamental formula, which defines the family to which it belongs; and its parameters, whose quantitative variation admits of infinite variety within the limits which the formula prescribes. With some extension of the meaning of parameters, we may say the same of the families, or genera, or other classificatory groups of plants and animals. . . . We never think of "transforming" a helicoid into an ellipsoid, or a circle into a frequency curve. So it is with the forms of animals. We *cannot* transform an invertebrate into a vertebrate, nor a coelenterate into a worm, by any simple and legitimate deformation, nor by anything short of reduction to elementary principles. . . . A "principle of discontinuity," then, is inherent in all our classifications, whether mathematical, physical or biological. . . . This is no argument against the theory of evolutionary descent. . . . Our argument indicates, if it does not prove, that such mutations, occurring on a comparatively few definite lines, or plain alternatives, of physico-mathematical possibility, are likely to repeat themselves; that the "higher" protozoa, for instance, may have sprung not from or through one another, but severally from the simpler forms; or that the worm-type, to take another example, may have come into being again and again. [1942, pp. 1094–95.] *

This emphasis on large and abrupt variations in evolution is representative of most modern biological thinking. Its implication for comparative psychology is that in behavior also we may expect to find discon-

tinuity — qualitative rather than merely quantitative changes — as we pass from the lower to the higher animal forms. Unlike the early post-Darwinians, who looked for a gradual development of behavioral capacity in the animal kingdom, the comparative psychologist is now relatively free to postulate new capacities or new behavioral mechanisms at various points along the phylogenetic scale, without doing violence to general biological theory. It would be expected, however, that such major psychological emergents would coincide with the major and abrupt changes in structural characteristics differentiating the larger taxonomic groups, especially the phyla. This expectation, we may say now, is not substantiated by the considerations that follow.†

Taxonomy and evolutionary theory in general have been based almost entirely on "formal resemblance" among structural criteria, which often are of a most superficial character. Now there is no a priori reason, and certainly no compulsion, to make the study of mental (i.e. behavioral) evolution subsidiary to the known or inferred facts of structural evolution. A comparative evolutionary psychology could be developed *in vacuo*, strictly and completely "on the behavioral level," *à la* Skinner (1938). This, however, would be unnecessarily restrictive and would repeat in principle the error of the taxonomists who confine themselves entirely to the structural aspects of evolution.

As Zuckerman (1933) suggested, behavioral data should contribute to an understanding of the historical relations among animals and to a more rational basis for their classification. Zuckerman has already demonstrated how the inclusion of func-

---

* Relevant in this connection is the possibility of reversals in the evolutionary succession; D. M. S. Watson (1929, p. 976) expresses the opinion that "it is far from improbable that some Protozoa are the degenerate descendants of multicellular animals."

† Thompson's "principle of discontinuity" would suggest also that, in a systematic treatment such as Hull's (1943), species differences could be accounted for merely by changing the "empirical constants" of the equations (Hull, 1945) only within limits; at other points the forms of the equations would need to be changed, or new equations would have to be added.

tional (i.e. physiological and behavioral) data can help to disentangle the confused relations within the order of primates. Lorenz (1937) points out that, although the family of pigeons, Columbidae, form a definite taxonomic group, there is no one distinctive morphological character that is common to all species and that distinguishes them all from other groups. All pigeons, however, are distinguished from other birds by a behavioral criterion, namely, the manner of drinking. Pigeons pump water, whereas all other birds scoop it up. Petrunkevitsch (1926) has pointed out "the value of instinct as a taxonomic character in spiders," and other examples are given by Heinroth (1910), Plath (1934), Lorenz (1941), and Adriaanse (1947).

The contribution that comparative psychology can make to the problems of phylogeny is a function of (1) the scope and precision of its data, (2) the adequacy of the behavioral categories under which the data are organized, and (3) the comparability of the data. The second of these problems is especially crucial. What are the "dimensions of behavioral evolution," the behavioral units, mechanisms, processes, or capacities that differentiate, quantitatively or qualitatively, among different levels on the phylogenetic scale? Some of the simpler ones, such as sensory acuity, are relatively easy to identify. But it is the more involved patterning of behavior that is most significant in differentiating the behavior of various animal groups, and it is here that the problem of identification is most difficult.

Given that the aspect of behavior in terms of which two species are to be compared has been satisfactorily defined, problems of technique remain to tax the ingenuity of the experimenter. If an intellective function is to be tested, all those factors that affect the expression of the function, but that are not part of it, must be experimentally controlled. Conditions of motivation, past experience, and sensory and motor char-

acteristics are among the determinants of any performance, and, unless this entire "assisting cast" is rendered functionally equivalent, the differences in performance in the testing situation cannot be interpreted as reflecting a difference in the function under investigation. In addition, the possibility that a given problem may be solved in different ways by different species is a source of difficulty.

Animal Psychology

Psychological studies using animal subjects * may be grouped according to the purpose of the investigator. Those experiments in which interest is focused on a special *problem*, or on a particular *animal form*, are here considered under the heading "animal psychology."

Animal experimentation. In a large proportion of animal experiments the use of this or that species is incidental or even accidental; a particular animal is chosen because it happens to be convenient. The fact that insects, fish, and birds have been used more than other forms for studies of instinct is attributable to the fact that these animals display instinctive behavior with particular clarity, not because it is absent in other animals. All such animal experimentation is simply an extension of general (human) experimental psychology; the phylogenetic status of the species used is more or less irrelevant.

For certain types of investigation animals have definite advantages over human subjects. Their life span is usually shorter, their entire life history prior to experimentation can be known and controlled, and they may be subjected to operative and other procedures that could not otherwise be used. Most important of all, basic mechanisms that in man are obscured by the complexity of his behavior, as well as by cultural (especially language) factors, may often be

---

* Except where otherwise indicated, the term "animal" will be used in this chapter to refer to infrahuman organisms.

clearly discernible in simpler organisms. These points have been elaborated by Washburn (1936), Katz (1937), Thorndike (1942), Harlow (1942), and others.

Studies of the animal-as-a-whole. A second class of studies is concerned more with a rounded-out delineation of a given kind of animal than with a specific problem in behavior analysis. The method is more often observational than experimental. Such studies are in the tradition of the older naturalists who set about to give complete accounts of every form of animal life. The early emphasis was on morphological characteristics, but ecological and behavioral features are being given increasing attention.*

Most contributions of the so-called anecdotal school (roughly 1852 to 1890) belong to this category, although the anecdotalists were motivated largely by the desire to produce "evidence of reasoning and other characteristically human mental life in the higher animals" (Warden, 1927, p. 147). Field studies by trained observers, casual or incidental observations by ecologists, hunters, and explorers, the reports of animal trainers, zoo caretakers, and veterinarians, and the books written about pets of various kinds also belong here. Some of these are valuable contributions to our knowledge; others are useless or worse. Many of them are guilty of anthropomorphism — or of its opposite extreme (a delinquency for which there seems to be no good term: "brutalization" and "mechanomorphism" say too much).

The importance of *good* descriptive studies of animal behavior must not be minimized. The value of careful observation under natural conditions is indicated by Tinbergen (1942). He points out that the controversy between von Hess and von Frisch regarding color vision in the honeybee is resolved by "knowledge of the whole behavior-pattern" of the species: in its food-gathering activities

the honeybee responds to the colors of flowers, whereas in other situations its visual behavior is guided entirely by relative brightness, as if it were color-blind. In the case of the chimpanzee, Nissen (1931) has suggested that intellectual capacities will be revealed more clearly in the laboratory, where artificially imposed obstacles may be used to encourage the exploitation of those capacities, than in their natural habitat, where the necessities of life are obtained with little effort. The emotional and social aspects of anthropoid behavior, on the other hand, are greatly distorted in captivity and are more validly observed in the field.

Comparative Psychology

We wish to consider now the bearing of all animal behavior work on the central problems of psychology. How may phylogenetic differences and similarities of behavior be used to clarify the important principles of behavior? This, as I see it, is the *raison d'être* of what is called comparative psychology.

The genetic method. The genetic or historical method attempts to find explanations in origins. With the aid of temporal and causal continuity the present is explained in terms of the past. Ontogeny, phylogeny, and culture are the three areas within which behavioral development may occur. The three areas of development are, of course, interdependent: the accomplishments of ontogeny and culture depend, in the first place, on phylogenetic heritage. What the individual contributes to the culture is a function of complex interactions between phylogenetic status, ontogenetic development, and prior cultural accumulation. And some writers such as Hooton (1940) are perturbed about the debilitating effects of cultural influences on the future biological status of the human race.

The credo of the comparative psychologist is well stated by Tolman (1945):

> . . . whereas man's successes, persistences and socially unacceptable divagations—that is,

---

* For brief histories of comparative psychology the reader may consult Warden (1927), Warden, Jenkins, and Warner (1935), or Waters, (1942).

his intelligences, his motivations and his instabilities—are all ultimately shaped and materialized by specific cultures, it is still true that most of the formal underlying laws of intelligence, motivation and instability can still be studied in rats as well as, and more easily than, in men.

Unless there is a continuity or homology of behavioral mechanisms from the lower to the higher animals (including man), there would be no rationale for the comparative method. This does not mean, necessarily, that the higher (later) is *merely* an extension or elaboration of the lower (earlier), although this is and has been a most provocative and fruitful working hypothesis. Quantitative complication may become so great that it produces, in effect, qualitative differences with new, "emergent" properties.

> Each level of organization possesses unique properties of structure and behavior which, though dependent on the properties of the constituent elements, appear only when these elements are combined in the new system. Knowledge of the laws of the lower level is necessary for a full understanding of the higher level; yet the unique properties of the phenomena at the higher level cannot be predicted, *a priori,* from the laws of the lower level. [Novikoff, 1945.]

One further point deserves mention: Although the laws that hold on one level may not be adequate to explain all phenomena on the next higher level, the former are never contradicted, reversed, or negated by the latter "No physical law, any more than gravity itself, not even among the puzzles of stereochemistry or of physiological surface-action and osmosis, is known to be transgressed by the bodily mechanism" (Thompson, 1942, p. 13).

When interest is focused on individual differences within the higher group, it *may* be that these later emergent properties have primary significance in distinguishing between this and that individual or class. In this sense and to this extent only, we may agree with Allport (1947) in his objection to the "phylogenetic model" and "the animal paradigm for personality and for social psychology." We can agree that differences of intention among people are of great practical significance. But these intentions are superstructures erected on a phylogenetically inherited foundation. Would the superstructure remain the same, or ever have become what it is, without the foundation? Can anyone conceive of what our "intentional morality" would be like in the absence of food, water, and sex hungers, without competition, without frustration or conflict? Intentions will never be understood without reference to the phylogenetic matrix from which they have arisen. They are the product of a long and tortuous development.

Structure-function correlations and homologies. There is a school of thought in psychology that holds that a psychological (behavioral) event is explained when, and only when, its underlying physiological-morphological basis has been identified. Whether or not we concur with this extreme position, it is undeniable that the demonstrated correlation between "physical" and behavioral phenomena is a long step towards explanation. A psychological theory that is at variance with established principles of physiological (e.g. neurological) action is thereby summarily ruled out, whereas one that does mesh with such principles is *ipso facto* given increased probability.

Within any one species the expression of a given mechanism or process is almost certain to be obscured by other mechanisms, the problem of isolation (experimental or otherwise) being often insuperably difficult. Within that one species it is often impossible to abstract what is essential from what is incidental. But, when the process is observed in various contexts (i.e. species), the irreducible minimum, the essence of the process under consideration, gradually becomes clear. Zuckerman has stated it as follows: "What is obscure in a functional activity of one species, for example man, may be clarified by some peculiarity in the working of the homologous process in a related species, and problems whose existence had not previously been realized might be revealed by this method of approach" (1933, p. xvi).

The comparison of the behavior of species and of phyla is one of the more important ways in which we may exploit naturally given, ready-made variations. Nature has provided us with well over half a million species that vary, greatly or minutely, in structure *and* behavior. Also, they show greater or lesser similarities, resemblances, homologies, in both aspects. This wealth of materials is ready to be used (1) to help in the definition of fundamental mechanisms or principles of behavior, and (2) in explaining behavior in terms of its underlying physical bases.

Dimensions of behavioral evolution. The literature contains an amazingly small number of studies in comparative psychology — investigations in which two or more species have been compared *directly*. Comparisons are mostly attempts to relate the findings of different workers, using various organisms in more or less similar experimental or naturalistic situations.*

Whether we are impressed more by the similarities or by the differences of behavior within the animal kingdom depends on the scale of observation used. The broader the category, the more do the similarities stand out, and vice versa. All animals reproduce and maintain a relatively constant internal environment, but the specific behaviors associated with reproduction and with homeostasis differ greatly among species. All animals are sensitive to stimuli, and almost all move from place to place, but the mechanisms of receptivity and of locomotion vary widely. In general the similarities are expressed in terms of function or "purpose"; the differences in terms of mechanisms or efficient causes.

Many criteria for differentiation among the behaviors exhibited at various stages of the phyletic scale have been suggested. Some of these are proposed as continua of quantitative variation from the most primitive to the highest forms. Others refer to emergent characteristics, absent at one level, present full-blown at the next. The following listing of modes, areas, or axes of phylogenetic differences is by no means inclusive but gives a sampling of those that have been suggested.

Anatomical-Physiological Foundations

1. Increasing differentiation of parts and specialization of function. In protista all life functions are incorporated within one cell. Amebas show little permanent differentiation, whereas paramecia have a permanent body axis and a high degree of structural-functional specialization.

In metazoans there is a steadily increasing specialization of cells and tissues, with partial or complete loss of other functions and consequent interdependence of body parts. Complexity and variety of motor patterns increase; locomotion is supplemented by manipulation and vocalization. The relative importance of vision and audition in-

---

* Among the major American contributions which cover the entire range of the animal kingdom are the books of Washburn (1936) and of Maier and Schneirla (1935). The three-volume work of Warden, Jenkins, and Warner (1935, 1936, 1940) is an invaluable handbook for the field of animal behavior; these volumes contain also comprehensive bibliographies of the literature. Among briefer or more specialized treatments that have appeared since 1930 may be mentioned Lashley (1934), Warden, Jenkins, and Warner (1934), Russell (1934), Moss (1934, 1942), Katz (1937), Munn (1938), Fischel (1938), Bierens de Haan (1940), Werner (1940), Moore (1941), C. T. Morgan (1943). Earlier classics in the field include Romanes (1881), C. L. Morgan (1894, 1900, 1927), Loeb (1900, 1918), Hobhouse (1901), Jennings (1906), Yerkes (1907), Thorndike (1911), Watson (1914), Kafka (1914, 1922), Holmes (1916), Uexküll (1921, 1926), Child (1924), Herrick (1924), Köhler (1925), Hemplemann (1926), Hingston (1928), Pavlov (1927), and Coghill (1929). The present chapter owes much to these earlier compilations; as a rule, studies already described in them will be treated as "general knowledge," and specific reference to those studies and their authors will usually be omitted in our subsequent discussions.

creases at the expense of the contact receptors; special sensory cells and accessory apparatus are developed. The transmissive-integrative system changes from radial symmetry (sponges, coelenterates, adult echinoderms) to bilateral symmetry (worms, most mollusks, arthropods, vertebrates). The neuroid conduction found in sponges is replaced by the nerve net or syncytium of nerve cells (giving diffuse, nonpolarized conduction with decrement) which is characteristic of coelenterates, echinoderms, and flat worms. Synaptic polarized conduction of neurones is predominant in annelids, crustaceans, insects, and vertebrates.

The nervous elements become increasingly concentrated, and these concentrations become localized at the head end. The linear system (nerve ring of the jellyfish) is replaced by paired chains of segmental ganglia in the annelids. In insects the ganglia coalesce, the main one being dorsal and anterior. Vertebrates have the dorsal tubular system, and within this phylum encephalization and corticalization increase.

2. Decreasing autonomy of parts, and of regenerative capacity. There is, however, an increase in the capacity for one sense modality or one effector to substitute for another.

3. Poikilothermism of lower animals replaced by homoiothermism in birds and mammals.

4. Increasing proportion of immaturity and dependence in the life span.

Cognitive Functions

1. Sensory discrimination. Irregularly increasing sensitivity to environmental energies. "One cannot seek, therefore, in the sense organs themselves for the differences known to exist between human and animal intelligence" (Moore, 1941, p. 100).

2. Perception. Irregular increase in variety of stimulus patternings to which organisms respond differentially. Perception of change in stimulus intensity is universal. Visual distance, size, form perception in arthropods. More highly developed in many birds than in some mammals.

3. Learning. Generally assumed that relative importance of learning increases from lower to higher animals. "The behavior of lower animals depends largely upon their structural characteristics and the immediate stimulating conditions, but that of mammals is largely conditioned by previous responses" (Maier and Schneirla, 1935, p. 265). Rate of simple learning does not increase phylogenetically, but "there is a fairly consistent rise in the limits of training and in the formation of complex habits with ascent in the phylogenetic scale" (Lashley, 1934, p. 468).

4. Abstraction, generalization, transfer, transposition. Transfer or transposition, as in brightness discriminations, "is present in all birds and mammals that have been studied," but "higher levels of generalization are limited to higher vertebrates" (Morgan, 1943, p. 110). Brightness transposition has been demonstrated also in fish (Perkins, 1931) and in bees (Hörmann, 1934).

5. Concepts and symbolic behavior. "What does undergo phylogenetic development, however, is the kind of capacity encompassed by the terms concept formation and symbolization. Most of the development, it may be noted, takes place in the mammalian scale between rats and man" (Morgan, 1943, p. 114). "Between the receptor system and the effector system, which are to be found in all animal species, we find in man a third link which we may describe as the *symbolic system*. This new acquisition transforms the whole of human life. . . . There is an unmistakable difference between organic reactions and human responses. In the first case a direct and immediate answer is given to an outward stimulus; in the second case the answer is delayed" (Cassirer, 1944, p. 24). In referring to experimental studies of monkeys and apes, Moore (1941) says, "But when we attempt to measure their power of abstract thought and their ability to see and form general principles in the logical order,

we obtain zero scores, for such abilities are simply not present."

6. Language. "The difference between *propositional language* and *emotional language* is the real landmark between the human and the animal world" (Cassirer, 1944, p. 30). "It is this faculty of language which seems to be the overt expression of a mental ability which is uniquely human" (Hooton, 1942, p. xxxvii). On the other hand, in referring to birds and fishes, Tinbergen (1942, p. 86) says that "many objective and experimental studies have revealed numerous relations between individuals worthy to be called 'language.'"

Motivational Aspects

1. Genetic and environmental determinism. The notion that the behavior of man is "free" whereas that of animals is strictly determined by inherited structures that react automatically and in set ways to the forces of the environment was given its most extreme expression by Descartes. The reaction against this position has taken two forms, emphasizing (1) the indeterminism of animal behavior, or (2) the determinism of human behavior. The question has been formulated frequently in terms of instinct versus intelligence. The current trend is towards a breakdown of the dichotomy; many writers suggest that the *relative* importance of structurally determined behavior decreases phylogenetically, whereas that of individual experience increases.

2. Viscerogenic (biogenic) versus psychogenic motivation. Behavior of the lower organisms is said to be motivated entirely by nutritional, eliminative, and reproductive "needs" or drives. Among the mammals independent or derived motives of curiosity or exploration and of play are sometimes admitted. Altruistic, ethical, esthetic, and religious motives are usually ascribed only to man, although their beginnings are sometimes reported as manifest in the behavior of infrahuman primates and even lower animals.

3. Purpose. A controversial concept in comparative psychology, owing in part to its mentalistic implications. The recent trend is to ascribe some degree or kind of purpose, at least to the higher animals, as indicated by the use of such terms as anticipation, expectancy, and goal orientation.

4. Scope of needs. Needs of the organism increase in number and complexity. There is greater temporal persistence of emotions, attitudes, sentiments, greater complexity of goal and subgoal hierarchies, and increasing indication of conflict, frustration, conscience, or guilt.

General Adaptive Characteristics

1. Increasing diversity, richness, and complexity of behavior. Adaptivity to variable and complex environmental conditions versus uniform and simple ones.

2. Increasing plasticity or docility versus rigidly fixed, stereotyped response. Adaptation of the environment by the organism to its uses versus adaptation of the organism to the environment. Action versus reaction.

3. Increasing socialization, specialization and division of labor, and cooperation. Genetic versus psychological basis of social organization (e.g. Schneirla, 1946).

4. Cultural accretions (almost exclusively human).

5. Increasing degrees of awareness or consciousness. Self-consciousness is usually ascribed only to man (e.g. Verworn, 1889; Yerkes, 1905; Washburn, 1936).

6. Increasing incidence and complexity of behavioral aberrations: neuroses, psychoses, perversions (cf. Hebb, 1947).

7. Increasing value and importance of the individual as opposed to the race. Greater proportion of individuals born survive. (But intraspecies mass conflict is most prominent in ants and man.)

This fragmentary résumé indicates, if nothing else, how vaguely phylogenetic differences of behavior are formulated. The terms overlap, refer indiscriminately to physiological processes, end products, or postulated intervening variables. They are often mentalistic and lack analytic precision, this being especially true for the so-called higher mental processes. The dimensions or axes of behavioral evolution along which phylogenetic differences may be measured quantitatively, or even in terms of more or less, have not been identified; we have, at best, approximations to usable definitions.

The recurring theme in the outline above is increasing *complexity*. In this or that detail, complexity may actually decrease with ascent in the phyletic scale, but in general it certainly increases. The term is, of course, too broad to be useful, unless the complexity is further specified: phylogenetically, behavior determination involves an increasingly larger number of factors. In the lowest organisms the most intense stimulus of the moment tends to govern the reaction. Later the reaction is increasingly determined by a number of concomitant stimuli that influence each other by summation, inhibition, or otherwise. The effects of previous experience become major factors in governing response to present stimulation, and this influence extends to more remote time.

As regards temporal integration, we are here considering the individual rather than the race. Man's designation as "the space- and time-binding animal" probably derived more from a recognition of his cultural achievements than from an analysis of his capacities as an individual. The cultural realm of development, perhaps even more than his individual capacities, sets man apart from the rest of the animal kingdom. Culture itself is the cumulative effect of individual capacity; it accelerates the biological advantage of man as an individual.

MOTIVATIONAL ASPECTS OF BEHAVIOR

One of the more obvious distinctions between animate and inanimate structures is that the former contain within themselves

mechanisms for maintaining the integrity of their organization under diverse environmental conditions. In our present state of ignorance about the physicochemical-neural mechanisms involved, the student of animal behavior is justified in accepting the capacity of organisms for self-regulation or homeostasis as an ultimate concept or principle. This does not mean, however, that it may be exploited as an overall explanation of behavior, as was done in the post-Darwinian treatment of instinct.

Homeostasis and the Biogenic Drives

Homeostasis depends on the preservation of an organism-environment balance within certain limits, and behavior serves to hold that relation close to the optimum. The life processes are continuous; nutrients are used up, wastes accumulate, internal secretions build up to threshold concentrations. The bodily mechanisms are such that these alterations of intraorganic states often lead to periodic or rhythmic outbursts of activity rather than to a gradually increasing intensity of motor expression. Variations in the temporal span of such rhythms are illustrated by respiration, feeding, and sex behavior.

The effectiveness of internal disequilibria in arousing activity in an organism may be designated the *sensitizing component* in behavior determination. It corresponds, roughly, to what Morgan (1943) has termed "the central motive state." When the situation is such that internal equilibrium is not restored promptly, the sensitizing factor persists over a period of time as a drive. The *directive components* * of behavior determination specify the precise nature of the behavior and include that object or environmental condition — the goal or incentive —

* This use of the term "directive" should not be confused with that of Lorenz (1937). For Lorenz (following Heinroth and Uexküll), the sensitizing factor is the *Stimmung*, and our directive components are subdivided by him into "releasive" and "directive" factors in the external stimulating situation.

that elicits the final (consummatory) response leading to restoration of physiological balance.

When the consummatory response can occur without delay, the behavior is spoken of as a reflex or taxis. In such cases the directive factor is immediately present or is, in effect, unessential. When carbon dioxide is added to the water of their aquarium, *Daphnia* ordinarily rise to the surface. But, if the aquarium is lighted from below, the addition of carbon dioxide results in movement to the bottom of the tank. Without the added carbon dioxide there is no orientation with respect to light. Carbon dioxide supplies the sensitizing factor, light the directive component. Extreme intensities of any sensory modality may disturb homeostasis and thus may both initiate and direct behavior.

The behavior manifested when a drive is operative depends on the directive elements in the external situation. If the situation is a restricted and confining one, it will consist of whatever activity is possible: "general" or "spontaneous" activity. If the situation is a relatively open one and provides opportunity for varied activities, the behavior may be called "random" or "trial-and-error." It is, of course, never truly random, since the environmental features, and the animal's perceptions of them, delimit the possibilities. Finally, the animal may find itself in a situation providing a series of specifically directive elements, in which case the behavior will be termed "habit" or "instinct," depending on whether the directiveness is a function of experience or of inherited structure. In either case there is a fairly definite sequence of acts, which is repeated on subsequent occurrences of like circumstances. The final directive element, the goal or incentive, may be the same, whether the preceding behavior sequence has been trial-and-error, instinctive, or habitual.

Most of the situations provided by the natural habitats of animals are mixtures of the extreme types suggested above. The hungry bird stays in the trees, soars high up in the air, goes to the ground, or wades along the shore, in accordance with characteristics of its species. The particular direction it takes may be quite haphazard, a matter of trial and error, or it may be determined by the individual's previous success or failure in obtaining food in a certain area. In either case the details of its progress are guided by the exigencies of the moment: air currents, spatial arrangement of trees and their parts, nature of the terrain.

Although details of the bodily mechanisms involved are mostly unknown, the relation between homeostasis and the sensitizing components of behavior determination dealt with thus far is reasonably direct and obvious. There are other cases in which the relation is not nearly so clear. The bee constructs a hive and fills it with honey; the spider weaves an elaborate web; the beaver fells trees and builds a dam. All three activities serve the nutritional needs of the animal in question. But the bee is presumably not hungry all the time that it is storing honey (and, if it is, this particular activity does not satisfy the present hunger). Furthermore many activities do not even indirectly serve the present or future needs of the individual in the ordinary sense of the term. At the proper season the bird builds a nest, mates, lays its eggs, broods, for weeks brings food to the young. The carnivore goes through an elaborate and stereotyped ritual in selecting a site for evacuation and in covering over its excrements.

The relevance of homeostasis in connection with such behavior is not obvious and certainly not direct. Much behavior must be ascribed to built-in sensitizing mechanisms that have either an extremely indirect and devious bearing, or possibly none at all, on the maintenance of *general* physiological equilibrium. However, homeostasis presumably applies to the nervous system, as a part of the organism, and the "normal" functioning of nerve tissue may be thought of as a *specific* requirement of its physiological equilibrium. The inherited nervous structure contains within itself the "need" for functional expression, just as the inherited muscular structure requires exercise. The unique status of the nervous system in this respect is that it mediates its own sensitization as well as that of the other bodily tissues.

The Motivation of Perception and Play

A form of behavior seen so often that it has been taken for granted is the almost constant activity concerned with keeping informed about the environment. Much of the daily activity of the rodent, the dog, the monkey, or the chimpanzee consists in movements of the body and of the sense organs designed to keep the animal in touch with what is going on. Even in a familiar environment, and at times when there seems to be no external stimulation, the animal takes a look around, pricks up its ears, or sniffs the air.

When the motivational aspect of the behavior becomes too obvious to be ignored, we speak of an exploratory drive or instinct of curiosity. McDougall (1923, pp. 59–61) includes curiosity as one of the principal instincts of man and believes that it is "displayed by many of the higher animals, although its impulse remains relatively feeble in most of them. . . . In the animals nearest to ourselves, namely, the monkeys, curiosity is notoriously strong, and then it impels not merely to approach its object and to direct the senses attentively upon it, but also to active manipulation of it." Exploratory behavior may also be thought of (1) as reflecting a primary tendency of all tissues, including the sense organs and their central nervous connections, towards functional expression, or (2) as a secondary tendency derived ontogenetically from the primary drives. The latter interpretation is the more widely accepted one. Tolman (1932), for instance, classifies curiosity with gregariousness, self-assertion, and imitativeness as sec-

ond-order drives. Pavlov (1927), on the other hand, speaks of the "investigatory reflex."

Always accompanying gross exploratory behavior and often occurring independently of locomotion are adjustments of the sense organs and their accessory apparatus. The eyes (and/or the head) are turned and focused; the tongue, the lips or the fingers explore the object tactually; other activities are suspended. Gross exploration has no meaning except as it "exposes" the environment to the sense organs, making perception possible.

The fact that perceptual activity begins very early in life suggests that its motivation is primary rather than derived. Locomotor and manipulative exploration, being extensions of perception, would then be counted among the primary drives. The sensitizing component determining this behavior, it would appear, is almost constantly active; its directing incentive comprises all incoming sensory data, and its consummatory response is to make sense of those data — to identify them with inborn or previously established patterns, to relate their parts into an organized whole, and to analyze the whole into its constituent parts. The subheading of Woodworth's (1921) chapter on perception reads: "Mental life consists largely in the discovery of facts new to the individual, and in the re-discovery of facts previously observed." Woodworth (1947) has since elaborated this notion:

> The present thesis . . . is that perception is always driven by a direct, inherent motive which might be called the will to perceive. . . . To see, to hear—to see clearly, to hear distinctly—to make out what it is one is seeing or hearing—moment by moment, such concrete, immediate motives dominate the life of relation with the environment.

In those animals whose repertory of perceptions is more or less limited to the relatively small number determined by innate organization, we find correspondingly little perceptual investigation of the environment. In those animals, on the other hand, whose perceptual organizations are primarily acquired, the potential number of perceptual organizations provided by environmental stimulation is enormously increased, and to realize them all requires incessant perceptual investigation. The process of forming *new* perceptions is continuous, never finished.

Birds are, on the whole, very active creatures, and in them (as well as in the lower vertebrates and insects) an appreciable share of activity evidently goes into informing themselves about the environment. Most of their behavior, however, is a matter of executing, repetitiously and energetically, certain motor coordinations in accordance with environmental stimulus patterns corresponding to inborn perceptual organizations. In the mammal, and especially in the primate, the level of activity may be lower, but a proportionately greater share goes into keeping track of what's what in the world about. Almost nothing is thrown into the discard as irrelevant, and this appears to be especially true of younger individuals. The lesser distractability of the adult primate (including man) as compared to young individuals is probably in part a function of (1) quicker, more efficient perception in experienced individuals and (2) a decrease in the number of new and unfamiliar stimulus patterns that motivate the animal to perceptual exploration and organization.

The motivational aspect of play behavior has been interpreted in various ways, none of which, as Beach (1945) points out, are very satisfactory. Schlosberg (1947) concludes that "the category 'playful activity' is so loose that it is almost useless for modern psychology." His criteria of uselessness and incompleteness, however, are not discriminative, since they would admit all instances of unsuccessful behavior, no matter how serious the situation. A second objection is that these criteria suggest that play behavior is essentially a "mistake" — the distortion, the thwarting, or the miscarriage of a more adequate course of events. Play behavior seems objectively and introspectively neither incomplete nor useless; the game has as much a beginning, a middle, and an end as most activities and seems to have its own motivating force. It is not merely an aberration of some other activity.

A theory of play must account for both its motivational and its formal aspects. This twofold requirement is met by the theory of Groos (1915), namely, that play represents a ripening and activation of the instincts before they are needed for serious use. The concept of "instinct," as used by Groos and many other writers, comprehends both the motivational factor and the specific, innately determined patterning of behavior. The similarity of youthful play behavior to serious adult activities is thereby accounted for. The "surplus energy" theory of play accounts for certain facts about play, such as that it occurs mostly in the young whose energies are not yet needed for serious activities, but it leaves the formal side of play behavior unexplained.

Whether or not it is a matter of using surplus energy, it does seem that a certain amount of muscular exercise is a primary need of the organism. If to this muscular activity drive we add the "direct, inherent motive" of perception, the dynamic aspect of play behavior, independent of other drives, would be adequately accounted for. Human play behavior is typically of a kind that gives much opportunity for perceptual activity. The same predilection for play involving perceptual factors may be seen also in chimpanzees, although here there is already a lesser variety, a greater tendency to repeat the same actions over and over again. In lower animals (with certain notable exceptions among the birds) play tends to duplicate serious, "biologically adequate" behavior. In animals whose inherited structure makes possible the acquisition of perceptions through experience, play behavior is correspondingly more variable, and there is more of it because the environment provides these animals with more stimulation to perceptual activity.* In biological-teleological terms, play serves the purpose of developing an equipment of perceptual and motor patterns in the higher mammals, whereas animals with an inherited repertory of perceptions and motor coordinations do not need this opportunity, being already provided with such neural organizations.

Innate Determination of Directive Factors

The sensitizing component of behavior determination, it has been suggested above, is provided by the functioning of inherited structures. With respect to most sensitizing components, individuals and species are rather alike, although they may differ considerably in the relative importance of one or another kind of sensitization. It is with respect to the *directive* components of behavior that animals may be classified as being guided primarily either by instinct or by experience. The final, consummatory response is almost always structurally determined. But the stimulus-response sequence that precedes the final act may be primarily a function of experience in man and primarily a function of structurally determined responses to environmental stimuli in the insect or bird.

Much of our progress in the observation and analysis of instinctive behavior has been made by European investigators: Uexküll, Heinroth, Lorenz, Tinbergen, Brock, and others, together with their students and colleagues. Uexküll's (1921) concept of the *Umwelt*, the circumscribed portion of the environment that is meaningful and effective for a given species and that changes its significance in accordance with the *Stimmung* (Heinroth) or mood operative at a given moment, is of fundamental importance. The sequential chaining of stimuli and responses

subserving a given biological function, regardless of their innate or experiential determination, he designates as a *Funktionskreis* or functional cycle. Lorenz (1935) points out that in many "instinctive acts" the motor coordination involved may be completely determined by inherited structure (*Erbkoordination*), whereas the "releasing pattern," the stimulus concatenation that elicits it, may be innate or acquired. The chaining of behavior elements of diverse etiology he terms an "instinct-training interlacement." If the external releasing pattern is not forthcoming, the threshold of the reaction decreases until the latter may occur in the absence of the usual precipitating stimulus: a *Leerlaufreaktion* or "reaction in a vacuum." Thus, if it is sufficiently hungry, the very young bird may hold open its beak even when the usually necessary stimuli are not present.

The directive components of behavior determination are analyzed further by Lorenz and Tinbergen (1938) into externally "releasive" and "directive" factors. When an egg of the gray lag goose has rolled outside the nest, the goose stretches its neck out towards it, brings the bill behind the egg, and then rolls the egg towards the nest. During this maneuver the coordination is constantly adjusted to the tendency of the egg to roll sidewards. These variable movements depend on the present stimulating situation, but the retraction of the bill and neck is invariable, an *Erbkoordination*. Once released, the latter is carried through in typical, stereotyped fashion even if the egg is removed as soon as the reaction has started. Tinbergen and Kuenen (1939) have shown that the "gaping reaction" of young thrushes is released by jarring of the nest and is directed or oriented (upwards) by gravitational stimuli.

The releasing pattern for an instinctive act, Lorenz (1935) points out, is usually a simple one, composed of only a few elements, but those elements are in a combination that is unusual or improbable in nature. Improb-

---

* In laying stress on the role of perception, I do not intend to deny the possible importance of other primary or second-order drives, such as rivalry, mastery, or submission in play behavior.

ability of the pattern is a safeguard against release of the act at the biologically wrong time or place. Particularly in social behavior, the releasing pattern may be the form and/or color of a structure (an ornament) or a certain act (movement pattern) of another animal. The simplicity of the releasing pattern is a "biological economy" and also insures that its effectiveness is not restricted to highly specific, possibly irrelevant details. Thus the inborn pattern of "child" or "parent" includes enough characteristics to designate the species, but not so many that only a particular individual of the species elicits the response.

Lorenz lays great stress on the phenomenon, apparently first described by Heinroth (1910), of *Prägung* or "imprinting." In autophagous birds, which are able to run about and obtain their own food right after hatching, only the adult of the species is effective in eliciting responses directed to the parent, such as trailing, food begging, and food acceptance. In many other birds the "object" of the parent-directed activities is not determined innately but is fixed, permanently and irreversibly, during a short period (often a matter of minutes or a few hours) following hatching. Goslings of the gray goose, hatched in an incubator, attach themselves permanently to whatever kind of animal, including man, the gosling sees during the first few hours after hatching. The object of possible imprinting is delimited, more or less in various species, by schematic inborn patterns to which the object must correspond, and the period in the life cycle during which imprinting may occur varies with different functional cycles in the same species.

Bierens de Haan (1937) expresses doubt that imprinting is basically different from conditioning or learning. Lorenz (1935) emphasizes the facts that (1) unlike learned behavior, which is subject to forgetting and relearning, the effects of imprinting are permanent and irreversible; (2) imprinting can occur only during a narrowly delimited period of the life span, whereas the process of learning is not similarly restricted.

Furthermore, in all animals there are innate predispositions for particular motor coordinations, perceptions, and sensory or perceptual motor sequences. Certain neural organizations are more likely to occur as a result of experience than others. To a certain extent this readiness may be attributed to the effector equipment of the organism, but to a large extent it is a matter of inherited neural organization. The higher up we go in the animal scale, the fewer instances of purely instinctive behavior do we find. Even the eye-muscle coordinations of pecking in the chick are improved by practice, as well as by maturation (Cruze, 1935). Here we have a core of structural patterning that is refined or improved through learning. This seems to be the rule for *motor skills* in all animals, although even here the relative importance of the learning factor increases phylogenetically. The phenomenon of imprinting, as contrasted to the inborn releasing pattern, is one rather special instance of the increasing importance of experience in perception.

It is important to distinguish between the effects of variability and of experience. One source of *apparent* variability may be the simplicity of the inborn schema, which means that a large class of objects or stimulus patterns may release a given response. Another source of behavioral plasticity is a multiplicity of inborn stimulus-response connections, which may be activated by different stimulus patterns. The righting reaction of the sea star shows more plasticity than the combbuilding reactions of a bee. Uexküll has said that the horse is more of a machine than is an ameba, the behavior of the former being more predictable.

Modification of Motivation by Experience

For purposes of description and comparison we shall discuss instances of behavior modification under the six categories indicated by the encircled numbers in Fig. 1. The first three categories represent modifications traditionally referred to in connection with motivation, whereas the last three are usually included in the discussion of learning one, perhaps, conforming fully to the criteria of an unconditioned reflex. (3) The dotted line from C_f to S.C.S. and P.E.R., the vertical alignment of P.E.R. and S.C.S., and the two impartial arrows are in recognition of our ignorance concerning the mechanism of

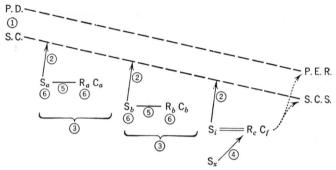

Fɪɢ. 1. Schema of drive behavior, indicating six proposed categories or types of behavior modification.

Left to right: temporal succession of events.
Horizontal levels: arbitrary units of description.
P.D.: physiological disequilibrium, persisting (dashed line) until
P.E.R.: physiological equilibrium is restored (in whole or in part).
S.C.: neural representation of sensitizing component, persisting until
S.C.S.: the sensitizing component of behavior determination subsides.
S_a and S_b: external directive components or stimuli.
S_i: external directive component; the incentive or goal-object.
S_x: a conditioned stimulus.
R_a and R_b: innate or acquired responses to (S_a, S.C.) and (S_b, S.C.).
R_c: innate consummatory response to (Si, S.C.).
C_a and C_b: consequents (on environment-organism relations) of
    R_a and R_b, and "leading to" the occurrence of S_b and S_i, respectively.
C_f: final consequent of R_c, and (dotted line) resulting in P.E.R. and S.C.S.
Encircled figures: proposed categories of behavior modification:
    1. Modification of the sensitizing component.
    2. Externalization of drive.
    3. "Transformation of mechanisms into drives" (Woodworth).
    4. Classical or respondent conditioning.
    5. Instrumental learning.
    6. Experiential organization of perceptions and motor coordinations.

and the higher mental processes. In the present section we shall be concerned only with Nos. 1, 2, 3, and 4; Nos. 5 and 6 will be taken up in later sections on learning and on the genesis and scope of perceptions.

Supplementing the legend of the diagram, several further points should be noted. (1) S_a—R_aC_a and S_b—R_bC_b are intended as representative of a *much* longer series of such units usually comprising a drive sequence. (2) S_i—R_c may be considered representative of several "goal responses," only the final reinforcement. The effect may occur before physiological equilibrium has been restored and perhaps even without any restoration of such balance. (4) Each S and each R in the diagram (e.g. S_a and R_a) may be conceived of as representing an organization of subordinate s-r's, such a patterning constituting the higher-unit S or R in which the psychologist dealing with molar behavior happens to be interested. (5) The numbering of the following paragraphs corresponds to the numbering in the diagram.

1. *Sensitizing component of behavior determination.*[*] It seems doubtful that primary sensitizing factors, not provided by inherited structure, are ever developed through experience. The *details* of physiological need are determined to some extent by previous environment. Similar to this phenomenon, known as acclimation, are the specific needs associated with disease, pregnancy, and other special physiological conditions; drug "habits" and addictions are extreme examples of need specificity determined by earlier organism-environment relations. Spragg (1940) has presented convincing evidence of morphine addiction in chimpanzees, and other workers have shown somewhat similar phenomena in monkeys and dogs. (As Lindesmith, 1946, points out, the addiction syndrome is more elaborate in man than in chimpanzee, and this difference may be ascribed to man's linguistic symbols and/or the thought processes associated with them.)

The innate sensitizing component may be altered by interference or control of the relevant physiological mechanisms. Beach (1947), in his review of the work on endocrine and nervous control of mating behavior in mammals, concludes that "susceptibility to sexual arousal . . . in lower mammals depends heavily upon hormones from the re-

productive glands, and that in higher species, particularly apes and humans, the rigidity of such hormonal control is relaxed sufficiently to permit a considerable amount of sexual responsiveness and potency in the complete absence of sexual secretions." That is to say, in the higher primates the central nervous system mediates the sensitizing component somewhat independently of the gonadal secretions. The directive factors, as Beach points out, are often experientially modified and cortically controlled even in lower mammals. There is some indication that the sensitizing component of hoarding behavior in rats (Wolfe, 1939; Hunt, 1941; Morgan, 1947) is affected by food deprivation during early life; whether this is a result of physiological acclimation or of behavioral experience still needs to be worked out.

2. *Externalization of drive.* There are some drives (e.g. for rest, or for exercise) that can express themselves under most environmental conditions. Other drives, such as hunger and sex, require a highly specific external object for the consummatory response. Sometimes there are almost no behavioral indications of the presence of such a drive in the absence of the goal object. Even "general activity" may be absent. An adult male chimpanzee may be resting quietly, even sleeping, when food, or a receptive female, is introduced into the cage. At once there are unmistakable signs of the hunger or sex drive, and eating or copulation occurs, if the situation permits. This phenomenon Anderson (1941) has termed "the externalization of drive." Two interpretations seem possible: (*a*) Stimulation from the goal object is an essential part of the *sensitizing component;* the neural pattern is ineffective unless the external stimulation is added to the internal physiological condition. (*b*) The sensitizing component has become associated with the incentive, so that the latter sets off the former; the central nervous mechanisms originally activated only by certain hormones, for instance, may later be

---

[*] Just how a physiological need affects behavior is not known. That it does so is obvious. The hungry animal "looks for" food, makes an "effort" to obtain it, eats when food is available. The satiated animal does none of this. Somewhere the nutritive deficit acts upon the nervous system. This action is describable as a selective sensitization: the organism becomes sensitive and responsive to stimuli that innately or through experience are related to need-reduction activities. Whether responsiveness to stimuli not so related becomes inhibited, or merely relatively less, we do not know. Nor need we ask here *how* the physiological disequilibrium "works on" the central nervous system. The objective fact is a change in relative threshold of response to stimuli that do and do not have meaning for the need — for instance, whether food will be approached or disregarded. The directive components of behavior determination specify details of the response — whether the milk is lapped up or the meat is chewed.

aroused by other stimuli previously associated with the functioning of those mechanisms. This second interpretation does not preclude the need for specific internal conditions that permit the conditioned response to occur. Summation may be necessary. Anderson (1941), however, believes that when externalization has gone far enough "the drive becomes aroused in the absence of the original internal conditions." Obviously there are limits to this process, since the sight of the drinking fountain is less likely to arouse the behavior associated with thirst in the water-satiated than in the water-deprived animal. The implications of the theory of externalization have not been consistently verified in experiment (e.g. Koch and Daniel, 1945; Siegel, 1943).*

There has been no systematic work on drive externalization in animals below the mammals. Various observations suggest that it is more frequent among the higher than among the lower mammals and, as regards

the sex drive in particular, more so in the male than in the female.

3. *"Transformation of mechanisms into drives" (Woodworth), or "functional autonomy of motives" (Allport).* In discussions of these phenomena it is usually assumed that some portion of a drive behavior sequence becomes detached, motivationally, from the usual end unit (consummatory response) of the chain. Whether this part becomes completely divorced also from the original sensitizing component is not always so explicitly stated. The concept of functional autonomy derives particularly from the observation of human subjects; its applicability to lower organisms is rarely unambiguous. First, it is necessary to rule out the possibility that the behavior in question, which may resemble an intermediate portion of a longer sequence, is not motivated independently by its own drive mechanism, such as that of muscular exercise, perception, or play. The hoarding behavior of rodents would readily fit the interpretation of an autonomous motive derived from the nutritional drive, but Morgan (1947) champions the independent status of a hoarding instinct. Second, the various part behaviors of a prolonged drive sequence involve subgoals — approaches, avoidances, manipulations — that may temporarily manifest a quasi-independence, but that disintegrate (extinguish) if their relation to the sensitizing component or to the final response of the drive is lost. The acquisition of money by the human miser *may* represent a functionally autonomous motive, but the accumulation of tokens by the chimpanzee (Wolfe, 1936; Cowles, 1937) continues only as long as the tokens remain a means for satisfying a primary drive — i.e. as long as they operate as a secondary reinforcement. Williams (1924) showed that an unbaited white-black discrimination box (in which correct choice previously had been rewarded with food), placed at the end of a maze, was, for some time, about as effective in promoting maze learning as was a food reward.

---

* Inactivity or sleep during the absence of the incentive may have biological utility; in the case of hunger, for instance, it would conserve energy and so keep the animal from getting even hungrier. The conception of sleep as an instinct (Claparède, 1928) or independent drive, providing escape from other motives (Willey and Rice, 1924), is a possible substitute for "externalization" in accounting for the observed behavior.

It should be noted that the theory (see Chapter 13) that an acquired fear drive motivates avoidance learning implies a rather special form of drive externalization. Two sensitizing factors are involved. An external stimulus, occurring in association with a noxious situation (e.g. electric shock), becomes conditioned (1) to the adequate (shock-reducing) overt response to shock, and (2) to the emotional response that is innately elicited by shock. The emotional response has physiological effects or sensory consequences that provide a second sensitizing component, namely fear. Any response that removes the external fear-arousing stimulus reduces the fear, and therefore becomes conditioned to that stimulus. According to this explanation the original drive, whose sensitizing component derives from the electric shock, is not externalized. The fear drive, on the other hand, is usually if not always externalized, fear being typically aroused by a danger signal rather than by actual injury or other physiological disequilibrium.

4. *Classical or respondent conditioning.* In any reflex or taxis, where the sensitizing and directive components occur together, or where the latter is absent, the S-R connection is rigidly fixed by inherited structure. This is usually true also of the S_i—R_c sequence (see diagram) of drive behavior. Any stimulus concurrent with S_i or the unconditioned stimulus will, after a number of pairings, independently elicit the response. Such substitution may be carried along for several steps (higher order conditioning). Summarizing the experimental literature on classical conditioning in animals from the protozoa to the primates, Razran (1933) concluded that there was no convincing evidence for consistent phylogenetic trends in any of the investigated aspects of conditioning.

The specificity of the stimulus eliciting R_c in accordance with the particular need of the organism has been demonstrated especially by the work of Richter (1942–43, 1947) and Young (1941) with rats. When the requirement for a given type of food, mineral, or vitamin was raised by inanition or gland extirpation, the animal's preference for that item greatly increased. After sectioning of the gustatory nerves, adrenalectomized rats lost their selective preference for salt and died of salt deficiency.

COGNITIVE ASPECTS OF BEHAVIOR

Most problem-solving situations are extremely complex, in the sense that many behavior mechanisms are involved. Although the situation may be psychologically uncomplicated for the animal, the particular mechanisms functional in this or that individual or species and the specific sources of difficulty for the subject may be quite obscure. We are baffled, for instance, when the difficulty of discrimination learning by chimpanzees is enormously increased by moving the cue object just a few centimeters back from the place against which the animal must push

in making its choice response (Jenkins, 1942).

The present discussion proceeds from the convictions (1) that the process of connecting perceptions to overt responses—probably seen in its purest form in simple "conditioning" experiments—differentiates the lower from the higher invertebrates but is not highly discriminative among the several vertebrate levels; (2) that animals differ greatly with respect to the innate versus experiential basis of their perceptions and that this difference constitutes the most important axis of behavioral evolution within the vertebrate series from fish to the anthropoid apes; (3) that, in so far as perception is organized by experience, variations among individuals and species in perceptual and conceptual development are functions of several behavior mechanisms that must be postulated as determinants of perceptual-conceptual organization; (4) that a sudden increase in the efficacy of one of these mechanisms, symbolization, has made possible the great range of concepts used by man.

The repertory of inborn perceptions, plus the functioning of organizing mechanisms, determines the perceptual-conceptual scope of the organism. Perceptual-conceptual scope represents the organism's information about (cognition of) its environment. The gamut of innate and learned connections between its percepts-concepts and its various overt responses constitutes the organism's adjustment to the environment.

Before proceeding to a discussion of this formulation of the principal axes of behavioral evolution in the higher animals, we may consider briefly some basic integrative processes to be seen in the behavior of the most primitive forms of animal life.*

* This division of the chapter, being organized around supposedly primary or fundamental cognitive mechanisms and their evolutionary development, does *not* present a comparative survey of adaptive or intelligent behavior. Only the main trends of development are illustrated by representative instances from the appropriate phyla. Examples of basic integrative processes are taken exclusively from the behavior of

Integrative Processes in Protista

No unambiguous instances of learning among protista are reported in the literature. The behavior of these one-celled organisms does manifest alteration with continued stimulation, however, and such alterations are often analogous to the modifications seen in higher animals. The effects of continued or repeated stimulation in protista are most conveniently described in terms that apply also to certain aspects of metazoan behavior, especially the behavior observed in artificially simplified situations (see, for instance, Skinner, 1938).

Variability. Some degree of response variability is obviously a prerequisite for learning, although most learning experiments make very limited use of the animal's motor versatility. The direction of locomotor responses in amebas is notably variable. Strong stimulation usually results in withdrawal of all pseudopods and temporary immobility; resumed locomotion tends to be in the direction opposite to the original one. With weaker and nonlocalized stimulation locomotion may be changed to almost any direction. The response of paramecia is relatively stereotyped, varying in magnitude with intensity of the stimulus.* The nature of the locomotor response is such, however, that change of direction increases automatically with increasing intensity of the response. The ciliate *Stentor*, by contrast, has a variety of distinct responses that may be given to the same stimulus.

Spatial and temporal summation. When two or more stimuli, each of subthreshold intensity, are applied simultaneously or within a short interval, a response may be elicited. The stimuli whose effects are thus combined need not belong to the same modality. Often it is not known whether the two modalities are differentiable by the organism or whether both are mediated by the same sensory surface. It seems probable that in some instances, at least, distinct receptor mechanisms are involved and that the summation or facilitation is intersensory. Folger (1927) demonstrated with amebas that a mechanical stimulus and a light stimulus, each of intensity insufficient to elicit a response by itself, would produce responses in a high percentage of cases when one of these stimuli followed the other (in either order) within about three seconds. If "summation" is defined as an algebraic process, we may include here those cases in which a second stimulus minimizes response to the first. General activity, as well as responsiveness to light, mechanical jarring, and other stimuli, may be greatly reduced in paramecia by contact with a solid.

Acclimation and adaptation. There are many observations of the intensification, reversal, inhibition, or other alteration of response to one stimulus by the action of a second stimulus modality (particularly chemical and thermal) which probably are not instances of summation in the usual sense. At one temperature the organism may react strongly to light, whereas at a lower temperature it remains indifferent to light changes; orientation to an electric current may be reversed by changing the chemical composition of the medium. In these cases the environmental agent is more important in its effect on the physiological state of the organism (compare the role of anoxia, nutrition, drugs) than as a stimulus in the usual sense of the word.

Adaptation to continuous (versus repeated) stimulation is usually termed acclimation (or acclimatization) and, with respect to thermal and chemical modalities at least, often involves alterations in the organism's

---

protista; those of learning, from the behavior of invertebrates and lower vertebrates. The section on the genesis of perception gives specific illustrations for only the more common perceptions that are found even among the lower animals. In the section dealing with factors of perceptual-conceptual organization few specific illustrations are presented, but the discussion concerns itself increasingly with the determinants of behavior seen only in the mammals and especially in the primates.

* The beating of cilia of the oral groove, however, may be quite independent of that of the body cilia (Mast and Lashley, 1916).

physiological processes as well as in its response to the stimulus. The range of environmental conditions to which many protista can adjust themselves is quite remarkable, provided the changes are gradual rather than sudden. Several species of flagellates successfully acclimated themselves, over a period of seven years, from an initial temperature of 16 degrees C to a final temperature of 70 degrees C.

The effects of continued stimulation on behavior are often obscured by concurrent influences on the organism's physiological condition. When exposed to continuing illumination, dark-adapted colonies of *Volvox* are at first indifferent, then positive, then negative, and finally positive again. In general it is the onset of external stimulation that elicits response (onset being defined as including the total period necessary to bring the product of intensity × time to threshold value), whereas continuation of the environmental energy merely provides a new base line for determining the direction and amount — and thus the stimulating value — of further changes in the stimulus. Increase of illumination produces temporary immobility in an ameba, the duration of which varies with stimulus intensity; subsequently the organism sends out pseudopods and moves about as before.

Cessation of response, when a stimulus of mild intensity is repeated frequently, has been observed in all protistan forms studied. *Stentor*, for instance, contracts on its stalk when stimulated by a weak mechanical stimulus, but it omits this response after the stimulation has been repeated a few times at intervals of a minute or so. If the stimulus is of sufficiently high intensity or is applied at widely spaced intervals, adaptation does not occur. A strong mechanical shock still elicited contraction in *Vorticella* after a series of 420 stimulations.

Refractory phase. It is often difficult to distinguish between the effects of sensory and motor fatigue, adaptation, and acclimation in the behavior of protista. A distinction may be made, however, between the effects of stimuli repeated at very short intervals and those more widely spaced. In the former case the second stimulus may fail to elicit a response at all, or the response may have a longer latency and be of reduced magnitude. As Warden, Jenkins, and Warner (1940, p. 72) have pointed out, this phenomenon bears a marked resemblance to that of refractory phase as seen in vertebrate nerves.

Sensitization. Repetition of a stimulus-response sequence sometimes results in increased sensitivity — an effect exactly the opposite of that just considered. A *Nostoc hormogonium*, which at first stimulation failed to react to illumination lasting 340 seconds, on the nineteenth trial responded to a stimulus duration of only 45 seconds. Amebas, moving into a lighted area, continue to send out pseudopods in the same general direction until, after a number of repetitions of the stimulus, they reverse the direction of locomotion. On subsequent trials the number of repetitive responses in the original direction decreased to zero (in 6 to 27 trials). Effects such as these, which are concerned with successive stimulus-response sequences, are not to be confused with the summation of stimuli to produce a single response.

Interactions. The several processes outlined above, some producing effects opposite to those of others, interact in complex ways. The following tabulation may be helpful in organizing the main factors under consideration:

I. Algebraic summation of total effective stimulation eliciting one response. Time span relatively short.
   A. Positive (additive).
      1. Intrasensory temporal summation.
      2. Intersensory spatial (simultaneous) and/or temporal summation.
   B. Negative (subtractive).
      1. Intrasensory. "Refractory phase" phenomenon.
      2. Intersensory. Interference or inhibitory effects by stimuli of one mo-

dality on response to those of a different modality.

    a. "Sensory" or "central" inhibition.

    b. Interference by prepotency of secondary, incompatible response.

II. Effects of previous stimulation or S-R experience on subsequent behavior. Time span relatively longer.

    A. Positive. Intrasensory or intersensory.

      1. Acclimation.

      2. Sensitization; increased sensitivity, augmented speed, and/or magnitude of response.

    B. Negative.

      1. Acclimation.

      2. Sensory or motor fatigue.

      3. Adaptation. A gradient of decreasing responsiveness to the intensity or quality of continued or repeated stimulation.

Stimulated by particles of carmine dropped from above, *Stentor roeselii* exhibits a sequence of responses (described by Jennings, 1906) conforming closely to the usual picture of trial-and-error learning: (1) The head end bends towards the aboral side; (2) the oral cilia reverse the direction of their beat, so that the water stream is carried away from the body cavity; (3) the stalk contracts into its tube of mucus; (4) the organism breaks off its attachment to the substratum and swims away. If the stimulation is then repeated sufficiently soon and often, the earlier phases of the sequence may be omitted in accordance with what Jennings has called the "readier resolution of physiological states." These various events may involve (1) the anterior-posterior physiological gradient, making the anterior parts more sensitive and responsive; (2) fatigue and/or adaptation of the anterior sensory-motor elements; (3) temporal (and spatial) summation of stimuli until thresholds of the later responses are reached; (4) sensitization of the later phases of the sequence.

Learning

The term learning refers to a relatively enduring change in the response to a constant external stimulating situation under fairly constant physiological conditions — a change that is a function primarily of intervening experience, i.e. of stimulus-response sequences and their consequences. Variability of response as such, and changes produced by growth or maturation, by variations in drive, state of health, drugs, hormones, fatigue, sensory adaptation, and so on, are not instances of learning. By specifying "a constant, external stimulating situation" the definition seeks to avoid confusion between learning and other phenomena, such as transfer or abstraction generalization.

Most learning experiments produce evidence falling into one of two classes: a uniform response is given to a constant stimulating situation that previously elicited either a different response or variable, and generally unpredictable, responses. Thus the two-object discrimination situation may elicit, initially, chance response to white (positive) and to black (negative), or consistent response, by pre-established preference, to black. Later the animal responds consistently to white.* Sometimes the original behavior, prior to experience, is not observed, but the improbability of the observed response occurring by chance, i.e. without experience, may be acceptable evidence for learning. This would be the case, for instance, when the wasp returns to its nest on its initial excursion into new territory, or when the monkey responds consistently to the "correct" container (which changes from trial to trial) in a series of delayed response trials.

* In classical conditioning the S_c often precedes the S_u, so that development of conditioning may be followed by noting the onset of the conditioned response before S_u occurs; in that case the recurring external stimulating situation is constant in the same way as it is in instrumental conditioning. Where the S_c and S_u are actually simultaneous, the stimulating situation during training includes S_c and S_u, whereas the initial and final testing situations include only S_c. Since the external stimulating situation eliciting the critical response is not constant, simultaneous conditioning does not conform to our operational definition of learning; within the framework of the present

The total training time required by an animal for mastery of a given problem *may* include (1) a period devoted to organizing the critical perception; (2) time consumed in discovering the critical stimulus pattern in the context of the present situation, in discarding possibly prepotent but here irrelevant perceptions, and in responding to the less obtrusive but differential pattern; (3) time used in the S-R connecting process itself (including, often, the formation of wrong connections before or in addition to the right connection). Usually it is impossible to determine the relative importance of these three phases, although in any given case extraneous evidence may indicate the presence or absence of the first one listed.

Given the effectiveness of the S, there are certain factors that influence formation of the S-R connection and that presumably are common to all learning situations; they include the strength of the principal drive, the kind and amount of incentive, the time relations in the stimulus-response-consequence succession, the effectiveness of subsidiary facilitating and interfering drives, the spacing of trials, and so on. As far as the writer is aware, there is no evidence indicating consistent phylogenetic differences with respect to the direct effectiveness of these factors,

formulation, failure of conditioning could be ascribed either (1) to a failure of S_c to elicit an independent perception during training, or (2) to a failure of the connecting process (S_c—R) itself. Positive results, on the other hand, would indicate that there was a perceptual response to S_c during training *and* that this became connected to R.

The status of backward conditioning is, in this connection, somewhat ambiguous. If the stimulating situation were described as starting with and including only S_c, backward conditioning would be an instance of learning as here defined. Exclusion of the brief aftereffects of S_u or of S_u—R_u, however, seems arbitrary and unjustifiable; these aftereffects would be part of the stimulating situation during training but not in the critical test of behavior modification. It may be noted in this connection that Spooner and Kellogg (1947) concluded, on the basis of an experiment with human subjects, that "backward conditioning is apparently an entirely different phenomenon from forward conditioning."

with the possible exception of an increasing time limit, in the higher animals, on the maximum interval between successive trials.

There is a second group of determining factors that are specific to the particular learning situation and to the phylogenetic position and ontogenetic history of the subject. As may be seen in the following incomplete listing of such factors, they are responsible for many of the most important differences in the relative difficulty of various learning situations, and they refer, not to the S-R connecting process, but rather to conditions relating to the prerequisite of that process: perceptual responsiveness to "the stimulus" (i.e. phases 1 and 2 as given above).

1. Stimulus and response option. Difficulty increases with the number of stimuli to which the subject may respond and with the number of overt responses that can be made to each. The objective details contributing to the enhancement or attenuation of stimulus obtrusiveness are, of course, not the same for all animals.

2. Stimulus and response prepotency. Difficulty decreases as the critical stimulus and the correct response become increasingly prepotent over other stimuli and responses.

3. Differential reinforcement of irrelevant cues. In almost all learning situations numerous irrelevant stimuli impinge on the animal's sensorium at the moment of reinforcement or nonreinforcement. The differential rewarding of an irrelevant stimulus, especially if it is a prepotent one, retards the learning.

4. Perceptual-conceptual repertory and span. Species differ radically in their capacity to organize sensory complexes into stable recognized patterns or perceptions. Some perceptions are ubiquitous; others, as of number, middleness, or triangularity, are rare. Some are already fully organized when the learning experiment begins; others are formed in the course of training.

Recognition of the primary role of perception in behavior determination serves to focus attention on a pervasive difficulty in the analysis of learning. The usual learning experiment yields a single, overall score. If behavior modification may be a function of two or three processes (i.e. phases 1, 2, and 3, as postulated above), to which of these, or in what proportion to each, shall the single index of change be ascribed? An experimental design that would yield separate, independent indices for the several variables would be the ideal solution.*

Before discussing perception and its determinants, we may briefly examine some instances of learning among those animal groups whose perceptual organization is relatively simple and, to a major extent, innately determined.

All the modes of integration observed in protista are seen even more clearly in coelenterates, echinoderms, worms, and mollusks. (The sessile sponges are behaviorally more primitive, and therefore psychologically less interesting, than are many unicellular organisms.) Instances of adaptation and sensitization are especially numerous, and in these metazoan forms the mechanisms involved are more often attributable to "central" than to peripheral factors.

Echinoderms. Although in certain structural features the Echinodermata most

---

* One type of solution, by Hull (1943), may be stated in three parts: (1) Phases 1 and 2 are minimized by the assumption that any "sensory aggregate" impinging on the sensorium when a reinforced response occurs becomes connected to that response. (2) It is assumed that the performance indices deriving from learning experiments pertain to the connecting process, and that therefore the laws of this process are quite accurately known. (3) Any differences between performance scores and the results predicted from the laws of connection are attributed to primary stimulus generalization and/or the principle of afferent interaction. This conceptualization has the advantage of including the facts of perception within a highly integrated, formalized, and partly quantified system of psychology. Against this must be weighed the danger of treating perception as a subsidiary adjunct of the total learning process rather than as its most important component.

---

closely resemble the vertebrates, they are not far advanced behaviorally and there is no convincing evidence of learning capacity in this phylum. Much experimental work on the righting reaction of the starfish leaves unanswered the question whether local tissue change or learning is to be credited for the shift, produced in the course of training, from the use of the preferred to use of the nonpreferred arms in the reaction.

Coelenterates. Pieces of filter paper were placed on certain tentacles of sea anemones at 24-hour intervals. At first the tentacles grasped the paper and brought it to the mouth where it was swallowed, later to be rejected. After several experiences the paper was not swallowed. Finally the particular tentacles being trained failed to grasp the paper at all. At this time the untrained tentacles still accepted the paper, but they reached the stage of rejection in many fewer trails than had been required initially. Apparently the learning involved central as well as local modification.

Worms. Flatworms, which are stimulated to locomotion by light, were repeatedly exposed to cycles of 5 minutes of illumination, followed by 30 minutes of darkness. Each time they started creeping forward, a tactual stimulus was applied to the head end, which stopped the movement. By the end of twenty-five such cycles no movements were occurring during the periods of illumination. Extirpation of the cephalic ganglion abolished this suppression (conditioned inhibition) of the crawling response to light. The annelid, *Nereis virens,* was conditioned in a few trials to come out of an open glass tube in response to sudden changes in light intensity when this light stimulus was regularly followed, after about 20 seconds, by chemical stimulation from a piece of clam placed at the entrance of the tube.

Earthworms have been trained successfully to make consistent left or right turns in T- and Y-shaped mazes. Peculiarly enough, reversal of the habit required fewer trials than had the original habit; one possible interpretation of this result is that mastery of the maze involved both (1) development of prepotent responsiveness to the effective cue, and (2) the association of that perception with a particular overt motor response.

Mollusks. Somewhat faster learning of a T-maze has been reported for land snails. In a conditioning experiment the pond snail *Physa* was given double stimulations with (1) lettuce touching the mouth region (eliciting mouth opening) and (2) pressure on the foot (inhibiting mouth opening). Originally (2) was prepotent over (1). After some 250 double stimulations however, the mechanical stimulus on the foot resulted in mouth opening even when the unconditioned stimulus (lettuce) was omitted. In this experiment the conditioned stimulus, instead of being neutral in regard to the required response, was one that originally inhibited the response. Retention of the habit for 96 hours was demonstrated. Experimental extinction occurred within about twelve trials, but reconditioning required fewer trials than had the original training. Differential conditioning has been observed in the mollusk, *Eledones moschatae.* The unconditioned stimulus was tactile, and the conditioned stimuli were flashing lights of various wavelengths (which probably varied also in brightness value).

Arthropods and lower vertebrates. Some of the insecta, ants in particular, are capable of learning the shortest path through long mazes with many culs. Their performances in this situation are in most respects not inferior to those of mammals and are superior to those of the lower vertebrates. Among the latter, reptiles appear to be somewhat better than fishes and amphibians. Instances of response substitution have been observed in representatives of the arthropods and lower vertebrates. Cockroaches, which are strongly negative to light, were trained to stay in the lighted part of a long box by giving them electric shocks in the darkened end of the box. A glass partition in an aquarium separated specimens of pike or perch from their natural prey, small minnows. After numerous experiences of bumping against the partition, the larger fish learned to suppress their attacks on the minnows even after the glass partition was removed. Electric shock or other noxious stimulation, concomitant with the response of snapping at food, effectively inhibited eating behavior in amphibians and reptiles. Differential conditioning, and mastery of visual discrimination problems involving approach-avoidance responses, have been demonstrated in arthropods, fish, amphibians, and reptiles.

The Genesis of Perception

The lower organisms begin life as more or less finished products, then or soon thereafter possessing all the behavioral tools that they will ever have. By contrast the higher animals and especially the primates go through a long period of maturation and growth. Bones grow, bodily proportions change, muscles get stronger, motor skills develop. This rather spectacular emancipation from physical inferiority has tended to obscure the more important cumulative development of permanent acquisitions that serve as instruments of behavioral adjustment in all later life. The most striking example of this is the child's acquisition of language — a stupendously complicated symbolic system, not even approximately achieved by any other organism. (Consideration of the magnitude of this achievement makes questionable the notion that "intelligence," in the sense of capacity or power, increases from birth to maturity; exactly the opposite seems at least as probable.)

The importance of experience in the development of perception among the higher primates is suggested by the work of Riesen (1947) with chimpanzees raised in darkness. These animals were first brought out into the light when about 18 months old. With respect to visual perceptive abilities they were then roughly equivalent to newborn animals. Even after 6 months in a normal environment visual perception was still greatly retarded in comparison with other animals of like age. The importance of experience in the development of human vision is indicated in the data from cases of congenital blindness compiled by Senden (1932): children and adults required months and years to attain or approximate normal visual perception after the operation that first brought them vision.

Data on the course of ontogenetic perceptual development in lower animals is fragmentary (see Cruikshank, 1946; Munn, 1938). The general trend, however, is clear: the difference between initial and ultimate perceptual ability increases as we go from the earlier to the more recent stages of phylogeny; the time, both absolute and relative to life span, during which perception is improved becomes progressively longer. It is less in carnivores and rodents than in primates, still less in birds. The butterfly, having emerged from its cocoon and dried its wings, is then about as well equipped to respond to the significant objects and energies of its environment as it ever will be.

In the following paragraphs a brief comparative survey is made of some of the more common or universal perceptions. Where the inherited structure provides a capacity for organizing sensory elements into these fundamental patterns, the potential number of perceptions is much greater than where the structure provides those basic organizations ready-made. It is very much like being supplied with a large stock of raw materials and tools or, instead, with a fixed number of finished products.

Locus of stimulation. Responses that depend on the particular point of the body being stimulated are seen in the lowest animals. The spatial relations of the pseudopods forming the food cup of the ameba are adjusted precisely to the position of the food particle. With increasing intensity of a noxious stimulus, the altered direction of locomotion approaches a deviation of 180 degrees from the point of stimulation. In the paramecium, on the other hand, the stereotyped "shock reaction" — a reversal of ciliary beat which sends the organism backwards in a spiral path — is variable in magnitude according to the intensity of the stimulus but apparently bears no relation to the locus of stimulation. A strong chemical diffusing from the rear of the organism may produce a shock reaction that brings the animal into higher concentrations of the poisonous substance. This maladaptive reaction may be in part a function of the paramecium's sensitivity gradient, the chemical stimulus being relatively ineffective on the posterior parts. A mechanical stimulus applied to the posterior end, on the other hand, results in forward movement, whereas a similar stimulus applied to the anterior part produces the shock reaction. The differential reactions of coelenterates to locus of stimulation are clearly a function of the "conduction with decrement" characteristic of their nerve-net system. Localized mechanical stimulation of the jellyfish produces strongest contraction of those parts of the bell nearest the point of stimulation, and the result is locomotion away from that point. In feeding, the tip of the stimulated tentacle contracts so as to grasp the food, then bends as a whole towards the center; the manubrium, in the meantime, bends quite precisely towards the stimulated tentacle. Similar locus-determined responses are seen in the echinoderms.

The relative importance in the adaptive behavior of the lower organisms of reactions based on body locus of stimulation is largely replaced, in higher animals, by perceptions based on the distance receptors (which depend in part on location within the sense organ). Among mammals, however, response to body locus is still seen in such activities as scratching, cleaning, grooming, and in many manipulations. It is clear that in the lower organisms the effect of locus of stimulation is structurally determined;

the question of nativism-empiricism as regards "local sign" becomes a problem only in the higher forms.

Movement. Although a few exceptions have been reported, it is generally true that animals are more responsive to a moving stimulus than to a still one (see reviews by Kennedy, 1936, and Schiller, 1937). A moving stimulus avoids sensory adaptation and multiplies the on-off effects of stimulation many times. Reaction to *apparent movement* has been demonstrated in fish, but it was not found in crabs, dragonfly larvae, and houseflies (Gaffron, 1934; Schiller, 1934).

Direction, distance, depth. Ample evidence is available to show that most animals, including many unicellular forms, adjust their responses (particularly of locomotion) in accordance with the direction of the stimulating source relative to the body. Concerning the mechanisms mediating such adjustment, interpretations have varied widely. The highly mechanical and rigid determination postulated by Loeb (1918) has proved to be inadequate in many cases, especially where bilateral symmetry has been artificially destroyed; the more "psychological" trial-and-error theory of Jennings (1906), involving comparison or temporal integration of moment-to-moment differences in stimulation, also fails to account for all the facts. The problem of orientation in the lower animals has been reviewed by Crozier and Hoagland (1934) and by Fraenkel and Gunn (1940). Light, thermal, vibrational, static (gravity), and chemical stimuli may provide the cues for directional perception in lower organisms; in higher animals these are augmented by the development of special sense organs such as the lateral-line system and auditory apparatus. The greatest advance in this direction arises from improvements in the organ of vision.

The most primitive basis of distance perception is intensity of stimulation, and in some modalities (e.g. olfaction, audition) it remains the principal cue. In animals like the bat, having a "radar apparatus" (Hartridge, 1945), the intensity and temporal lag of the reflected vibration are presumably responsible for distance perception. In general, however, the principal improvements in distance and depth perception are again associated with the visual mechanism (Walls, 1942).

Size and form. Tactual size perception is manifested in the feeding behavior of many unicellular organisms, coelenterates, mollusks, and higher forms: acceptance or rejection depends on size as well as on chemical composition. There is evidence of crude visual size perception among mollusks, but that for visual form perception, even in the octopods which have a well-developed camera eye, is not convincing (Ten Cate and Ten Cate-Kazeewa, 1938). Among arthropods the evidence seems to indicate visual size and form perception in those groups having eidoscopic eyes. Warden, Jenkins, and Warner (1940, p. 698), however, consider it likely "that insects, such as the honeybee, *distinguish patterns, not on the basis of form but primarily through the relative stimulating efficiency of intermittent illumination.*" Hertz (1934) has presented evidence in support of her interpretation that form perception in bees is not (in all cases, at least) merely a matter of flicker rate produced by the degree of articulation of the figure, as suggested by Zerrahn (1933) and later writers. Even spiders, having the ocellar type of euthoscopic eye, have been reported to be able to detect and capture prey visually. Forel (1904) suggested that insects that can move their antennae, bearing the organs of smell, over objects, may have olfactory size and form perceptions. Among fish, amphibians, and reptiles, visual size and form perception varies considerably, according to the habitat and mode of life of different species within each class. All three groups are excelled in this respect by the birds, whose visual acuity is probably equaled only by the higher primates.

Perceptual and Conceptual Scope

A given stimulus patterning may, in one animal, correspond to an innate perceptual organization and elicit a definite, species-constant reaction. In another animal this pattern may gradually be organized into a perception that comes to elicit one or another overt response. In a third species this particular concatenation never, under any circumstances, becomes integrated and cannot, therefore, serve to evoke a response. There are innate differences in the potentiality of certain patternings to be organized into perceptions. If the potentiality is not there, no amount of training will be effective in bringing about a response to the pattern.

The following four sections will be concerned with the factors that determine what is a "stimulus" for a given animal. The basic factors determining stimulus organizations will be discussed under the headings of *pattern specificity* (identification of specific stimulating patterns or concatenations in successive experiences); *the selective process of attention* (the separation or abstraction of an identified pattern from other elements in the total stimulating situation); *concept formation* (the interaction and *balance* of pattern specificity and the selective process); and *symbolization* (an instrumental aid to the integration of temporally separated experiences).*

A preliminary question pertaining to the definition of what may constitute a stimulus

---

* The theoretical and experimental significance of these terms in reference to the behavior of organisms with innately determined perceptions is quite different from their significance for the behavior of animals whose perceptual organization is developed in and by experience. In the former the concepts are of value in describing certain constancies of relations manifested in the limited repertory of species-uniform behavior; they may therefore help in classifying the observed phenomena. In the latter, on the other hand, these concepts are postulated as mechanisms or functional principles and so imply the possibility of predicting and experimentally controlling behavior; the mechanisms provide a basis for explaining behavior but must themselves be accounted for in terms of the inherited structure.

concerns perceptual responsiveness to relations — the problem of whether such responsiveness is elementary and "primitive," or whether it is instead a later development, deriving perhaps from the mechanism of symbolization. To this question we now turn our attention.

Perception of relations. The bearing of stimulus intensity on response, as seen in the behavior of the lower organisms and often in the unconditioned reflexes of higher animals, has been noted above: with increasing intensity the response increases in magnitude (decreases in latency, etc.) or may change to a different kind of response. In conditioned or learned behavior a different relation seems to obtain, at least in some cases: the specific intensity used in conditioning evokes the maximum response, whereas greater and lesser intensities elicit responses of a magnitude that decreases with the "distance," in either direction, of the test intensity from the original conditioning intensity. This relation has been reported also for "distance" on continua of wavelength of sound and (within limits) of light, as well as for spatial distance of a tactual stimulus on the skin. The phenomenon has been termed irradiation (Pavlov), primary stimulus generalization (Hull), and induction (Skinner); the evidence has been reviewed by Hull (1947).

Lashley and Wade (1946) deny that the available data support the concept of a primary stimulus gradient. The phenomenon of so-called stimulus generalization, they say, represents "a failure of association." Generalization indicates that the perception that determines the response (e.g. approach) includes in its pattern only those elements that are common to both the training and test stimulus; elements representing, for instance, "a tone" or "a white surface." The specificity of the pattern is not such as to represent "a tone of this pitch and of that intensity," or "a white square of such and such a size." In differential conditioning the perception comes to include these specifying elements.

Perhaps the strongest argument in favor of the "absolute" theory is that it postulates a single mechanism to account for both absolute and relational response (Spence, 1937, 1941). Its most serious drawback is that as yet no one has been able to suggest a plausible neurological basis for the assumed process of irradiation (e.g. Hovland, 1937). The neurological speculations advanced by Lashley (1929 and 1942), Köhler (1940), and Householder (1947) in explanation of relational response are, in various respects, inadequate, but they are at least a beginning. The relational theory does not deny that absolute properties become effective under proper training conditions; it holds only that animals often respond to ratios of excitation and that in many cases the perception of a relation is more primitive or elementary than, and prepotent over, the perception of specific magnitudes.

If the assumption is accepted that when an animal is responding "relationally" its behavior is in fact determined by the perception of a relation (and not by the net effect of excitatory and inhibitory strengths of the specific magnitudes of the stimuli presented), the available comparative data indicate that relational response appears earlier, phylogenetically, than does response to absolute properties. Moreover there is no indication of any reduction in the prepotency of the perception of relations with ascent in the animal scale.

Pattern Specificity

When we say that an organism is responding to a "stimulus," what is usually meant is that the response has been elicited by a simple change in the environmental energies impinging on the sensorium — an increase of light intensity, for instance, or a change of tonal pitch. Being a *change*, a stimulus involves a spatial and/or temporal *pattern* of stimulation; the nature of the stimulus depends as much on the preceding or adjacent light intensity as on the intensity of the so-called stimulus. When the patterning becomes more obvious or more complicated, as in a melodic sequence or in the spatial light distribution of a picture, the term, perception, is commonly used. Insofar as it is determined by external stimulation of the moment, every response is elicited by a perception. And every perception depends on a certain minimum of sensory patterning.

Visual size perception, as mediated by the primate eye, illustrates the need for a high degree of pattern *specificity*. A given combination of sensory data deriving from retinal-image size, accommodation, and convergence (disregarding other, supplementary cues) gives a certain size perception; the same perception is given by proper concomitant variation of all three constituents, whereas variation of the first one alone gives a different size perception. To this fundamental process of perception — the response to unique concatenations of interdependent sensory elements — we apply here the behaviorally descriptive phrase: *identification of specific patterns*.

The pattern may consist of just a few determining elements. In other cases it involves a large number of necessary elements, and any deficit or deviation from this complex pattern means that the perceptual response will not be elicited. Such instances are the basis of the Gestaltist argument (e.g. Volkelt, 1914; Buytendijk, 1924) that animals react to the total situation and are unable to analyze the whole into its component parts.

The Selective Process of Attention

Since pattern specificity usually pertains to only a part of the total environmental situation, perception involves not only an associative synthesizing process but also an analysis or dissociation whereby the essential pertinent elements are separated out from the rest of the concomitant stimulation. It will be convenient to discuss this separative insulating process under three subheadings for which we use the arbitrary designations: (1) contextual isolation, (2) cue reduction or redintegration (Hollingworth, 1928), and (3) abstraction-generalization.

1. One may imagine an experiment in which an animal, say a chimpanzee, is raised under controlled conditions such that every rectilinear form it ever sees is green, whereas no curvilinear figure is ever green. That animal's perception of a rectangle would presumably include green as one of the necessary items constituting the perceptual pattern. Under the more usual conditions such aspects as color, size, and so on, are quite irrelevant to rectangles; they, together with features of the background and perhaps some visceral distress of the moment, are context. Normally the essential elements, $A_1B_1C_1$ are more or less independent of the items $D_1E_1F_1 \cdots$ in forming the perception. If $A_1B_1C_1$ are the necessary components of the pattern X_1 for "rectangle," and D represents color, then $A_1B_1C_1D_1 = A_1B_1C_1D_2 = X_1$. For our hypothetical chimpanzee, on the other hand, $A_1B_1C_1D_1 = X_1$, but $A_1B_1C_1D_2 \neq X_1$ (where D_1 represents green, and D_2 any other color). To the degree that a perception is independent of irrelevant elements in the total situation we may say that it has been isolated from its context.

2. In learned perceptions involving many sensory elements, the presence of just a few of these elements elicits the response appropriate to the much larger pattern. A particular individual is perceived in darkness by his voice, or by his odor. Schematically, in the perception $A_1B_1C_1 = X_1$, the discrimination of A_1 from A_2, A_3, $\cdots$, plus the previously established association of A_1 with B_1 and C_1 results in $A_1 —— = X_1$. The phenomenon is presumably a function of the frequency and invariability of the concomitant occurrences of A_1, B_1, and C_1, and of other A's (A_2, A_3, $\cdots$) with other B's and C's. On the other hand, inborn perceptual organizations appear to require always the full complement of sensory elements constituting the pattern.

All available evidence is consistent in indicating that the perceptual response is a central rather than a peripheral process. The structural basis of a perceptual response being at least one step removed from the primary sensory fibers, it is possible for one or a few of the latter to activate the response as a whole, thereby providing a conceivable mechanism for cue reduction.*

3. Two or more total stimulating situations may have one or several elements in common. When an acquired response evoked by one situation is elicited also by others, we say that the common elements have been abstracted; it is the perception of the pattern appearing within each of these complexes that determines the response. Any nonspatial, two-choice discrimination problem calls for some degree of abstraction. The second part of the hyphenated term, abstraction-generalization, has been included in order to emphasize that in infrahuman animals abstraction (as also "contextual isolation" and "cue reduction") can be inferred only from generalization tests. That is, whether the animal has been responding to the perception $A_1B_1C_1$ in the training context $D_1E_1F_1$ may be tested by determining whether the response is generalized to $A_1B_1C_1D_2E_2F_2$, and so on. And conversely, generalization (or transfer) from one situation to another means that something has been abstracted from the context of the first and is now operative in that of the second. In animal behavior, abstraction and generalization are inseparable, each implying the other.†

The three divisions of the separative process serve mainly to locate an approximate region within a broad range of behavioral phenomena. These regions may be schematically illustrated in terms of a simple discrimination situation. Assuming that the

* For an excellent discussion and fertile theory of the neurological correlates of perception and thinking, see D. O. Hebb (1949). I am indebted to Dr. Hebb for the privilege of reading the manuscript of his book and also for many stimulating discussions related to various problems considered in this chapter.

† The inseparability of abstraction, generalization, and classification in human perception and thinking was recognized on rational and introspective grounds by the English associationists. For a particularly lucid discussion, see Charles A. Mercier's *Psychology, normal and morbid.* New York: Macmillan, 1901.

subject has learned to choose a plaque bearing a green square and to avoid a similar plaque bearing an erect red triangle of similar size, (1) continued response to the former when a new experimenter presents the plaques in a different room indicates contextual isolation; (2) differential response to plaques on which the figures were both yellow or were represented only by black dots at the corners illustrates cue reduction; (3) response to a plaque bearing many small red squares versus one bearing a very large inverted red triangle indicates abstraction of squareness from triangularity. The choice of terms is arbitrary. Finally it should be pointed out that the separative process involved in innate perceptions reduces to a question of pattern specificity and the potency of that pattern in relation to the total stimulating situation.

Concept Formation

Smoke (1946) defines concept formation as "the process whereby an organism develops a symbolic response — usually, but not necessarily, linguistic — which is made to the members of a class of stimulus patterns, or to an aspect of such a class, but not to other stimuli." A common (symbolic) response to the members of a class is termed a "class concept"; to an aspect of a class, an "abstract concept." A third type of concept might be called a "thing concept" (often termed "perception of things"). It is the sum total of the subject's knowledge or perceptions of a discrete object. In the present section we consider whether there is any evidence for concept formation below the human level, regardless of whether it is necessary to postulate a mediating symbolic process.

One implication of these definitions is that a high degree of abstraction and prepotency of a specific pattern is involved. Thus if the animal gives a consistent response to red, regardless of its shade or the variety of contexts in which red appears (Weinstein, 1945), it may be said to have an abstract concept of redness. Or, if a variety of suitable objects are used interchangeably to reach a suspended lure, the animal may be said to have a concept of the class of objects that may serve as a platform.

A second characteristic implied in discussions of concept formation is that it requires the integration of multiple, temporally discrete events. Diverse experiences must be brought together in order that the concept may emerge or be educed. (In this respect the difference between concepts and percepts is one of degree.) In Hamilton's quadruple choice, Yerkes' multiple choice, and Hunter's single or double alternation problems, the effective cue cannot be discovered in a single trial, but only on the basis of repeated experience. Sometimes the animal is said to be responding on the basis of a principle of alternation, of oddity, of matching, and so on. In each case a temporal integration of experiences is involved. It seems reasonable, therefore, that this conceptual organizing may take up most of the time used in "learning" a problem involving the concept, and that its connection to a given overt response may then occur very rapidly, as Guthrie (1935), Lashley (1929), Krechevsky (1932), and others have suggested for relatively simpler learning situations.

A third characteristic of concept formation is implied in its definition as "response to an aspect of a class." Response to "a class" involves specificity of a larger pattern; response to "an aspect" involves a separative abstracting process. Responsiveness to both identities and differences, and a necessary balance between the two, is implied.* Consistent response to red (versus other colors) requires identification (of red) and differ-

* The importance of this balance for "intelligent" behavior was recognized by William James (1890, Chapter 22) under the term, "sagacity," but the problem has received almost no experimental attention. Hollingworth (1928, p. 412) describes the sagacious individual as occupying a position between the extremes represented by the "obsessed" and the "scatterbrained."

entiation (from yellow, green, blue); but in the consistent response to color (versus visual form, size, texture) the identification itself requires an abstraction or differentiation (e.g. of what is common to various colors) and the differentiation involves identification (of that common element). "Color" qualifies without much question as a concept; "red" is more often considered a percept.

The conditional matching problem furnishes one of the best illustrations of the balanced responsiveness to identity and difference involved in conceptual behavior. The subject must choose that one of two objects that matches a third object (sample) in either color *or* form, in accordance with an independent (background) cue. This problem has been mastered by monkeys (Harlow, 1943*a*) and by a chimpanzee (Nissen, Blum, and Blum, 1949). In further tests with monkeys generalization of the response to *new* colors and forms was demonstrated (Harlow, 1943*b*; Young and Harlow, 1943). This achievement of infrahuman primates approximates conceptualization as it is known in man.

The thing concept (or perception) also involves a balance of the specifying and separative processes, as well as an integration of temporally discrete experiences. In animal behavior, a thing concept is indicated when the response is based not on one or another of the constituent perceptions, but on an integration of all of them. Behavior completely dominated by one *or* another aspect of a larger situation is characteristic of the lower animals but is labeled regressive or disintegrated when it occurs in man. The behavior of the mother bird that responds to the genus-constant distress call of the young and rescues it, only later to kill the young bird because it does not show the species-characteristic markings or behavior (Lorenz, 1935), illustrates an almost complete absence of thing perception. The male chimpanzee who defers to a physically weaker but sexually receptive female in a food situation (Yerkes, 1943) is perhaps responding to the female not only as a competitor for food, but also, simultaneously, as a partner in the sexual relation.

Symbolization and Language

The necessity of postulating a symbolizing process to explain human thinking has long been recognized, and the process has been investigated by introspective and objective techniques. The anecdotal school of comparative psychology was uncritically generous in postulating ideational and imaginal processes to explain the behavior of animals, especially of the higher forms. Since Lloyd Morgan (1894) first formulated his famous canon regarding parsimony, the pendulum has swung from one extreme to the other. Most writers now invoke symbolic processes only when simpler mechanisms, such as conditioning, seem inadequate, or when their faith in a reduction to these principles breaks down under the fantastic complexity of animal behavior. It is not easy to decide whether it is more parsimonious to make the established principles do by elaborating their interrelations, or instead to bring in a new concept that, at one stroke, "solves" a whole array of perplexing problems.

A criterion for the justified invocation of symbolism is expressed by C. T. Morgan as follows: "Only when the response of an organism must be determined by conditions not present at the time of adjustment can it be supposed that a symbolic process is operating. . . . a symbolic process is indicated when the signal or cue for adjustment made is not present at the time of response" (1943, p. 543). Among the infrahuman animals there are two types of behavior that have persistently demanded a symbolic process for their interpretation: (1) trace conditioning, double alternation, delayed-reaction learning, and delayed-reward learning, and (2) the prompt solution of novel problem situations apparently involving reflection, implicit trial-and-error, insight, foresight, or inferential reasoning.

Delayed reaction to spatial cues appears to be a relatively simple task for primates. With sufficiently favorable motivating conditions, the complexity of the problem (number of alternatives) and the length of the delay interval may be extended almost indefinitely. The capacity for delayed response has been demonstrated also in lower mammals, in birds, and (with 4-second delays) in fish (Schiller, 1948). The performances of insects in returning to the nest after the initial excursion into new territory, and the relocation of a food source, seem often to involve this same ability. Nonspatial delayed reaction is apparently much more difficult, although only monkeys and apes have been adequately tested in this problem. Various observations such as those of Baerends (1941) suggest that, when certain biologically vital cues are involved, nonspatial delayed response may occur in lower animals, even in insects. (In these cases it is of course necessary to rule out the possibility that the performance reflects merely the activation of a particular motivation plus innately determined response to immediate external stimulation.) Finally, it has been shown that even rats can learn spatial discriminations if the reward or punishment is delayed for some time after the critical response (Wolfe, 1934), whereas differentiation of nonpositional cues with delayed reward is very difficult even for chimpanzees (Riesen, 1940).

The facts lend themselves to the interpretation (Nissen, Riesen, and Nowlis, 1938) that the learning of delayed-reaction and delayed-reward discrimination requires the mediation of ready-made differential responses to the cues involved. (The operation of a symbolic process or "representative factor" in delayed reaction was originally suggested by Hunter, 1913.) Because of the ubiquitousness of spatial relations, symbolic responses (whether in the form of implicit iconic movements or purely "central responses") to spatial factors were developed earlier, phylogenetically, than those representing other stimulus characteristics. Several lines of evidence accord with this interpretation: (1) Rats can learn a nonspatial discrimination with delayed reward when forced to make differential movements at the time of choice (Grice, 1948). (2) Nonpositional delayed response is aided by a "forced" movement to the correct stimulus (Forster, 1934; Finan, 1942; Cowles, 1940). (3) Chimpanzees improve their performance in nonspatial delayed response (Riesen and Nissen, 1942) and delayed-reward learning (Riesen, 1940) after being trained to make certain arbitrary movements that are differential with respect to the pertinent visual cues.

The second type of problem for which it has often been considered necessary to postulate a symbolic process is that in which the animal effects a prompt solution without having had experience with all elements of the situation in their present concatenation. Many such apparently insightful solutions may be ascribed to the prepotency of a perception, abstracted from the new context, to which a response (appropriate in the new context) has previously been learned. The immediate use of a string to draw in food may be a direct transfer from experiences in the wild where branches or twigs were grasped at their tips to bring fruit within reach. In some instances the seemingly insightful solution may even be ascribed to the prepotency of a perception for which there is an innately determined response.

The prompt solution of detour problems is frequently interpreted as evidence of insight or reasoning ability. Tolman and Honzik (1930), for instance, gave rats opportunity to become acquainted with three routes, A, B, and C, of progressively increasing lengths, from the starting place to the goal. Given free choice, the rats chose the shortest route, A, or, if this was prevented, the next-to-shortest route, B. If, now, a block was placed in that final part of the pathway common to both A and B, the rats, finding their favorite route blocked, tended to take the longest but unblocked route, C, rather than B. (When the block was placed in the nearer portion of A, which did *not* form a part of route B, the rats tended to choose B rather C.) Such insight *may* involve a spatial perception elicited by a reduced cue: the initial parts of B evoke a perception of the complete route B, and this now includes the block that was experienced on that part of B common to A and B. This interpretation assumes (1) the abstraction (from the total perceptions of A and B) and identification of the element that is common to A and B, (2) a prompt (one-trial) learning similar to that displayed in the delayed reaction, and (3) a temporal integration of successive events into a perception. The latter assumption, as Woodworth points out, may be used also in explaining the elimination of blind alleys in ordinary maze learning: the stimuli received at the end of the cul are not the same as those received at its entrance. How, then, is response to the entrance stimuli modified by the temporally distinct stimuli of the end of the alley? "If the rat first perceives an alley as an alley and proceeds to explore it, the alley remains the same for him and the dead end, when discovered, is registered as pertaining to the same alley that was perceived at the entrance. . . . The conditioning experiment is really concerned with the establishing of a new perception" (Woodworth, 1947). Experiments similar in principle to that of Tolman and Honzik have been performed by Maier (1929) with rats and by Bingham (1929) with chimpanzees.

In the multiple-stick test (e.g. Köhler, 1925; Jackson, 1942; Birch, 1945) the monkey or ape uses a short stick to rake in a long stick. The long stick is then used to rake in the food. The short stick and the food (which cannot be reached with it) may be together on one platform, the long stick on a second platform. The animal takes the short stick to the second platform, uses the short stick to get the long one, returns to the first platform and rakes in the food.

Let us now assume that the second platform is moved farther and farther away from the first one until, finally, one platform cannot be seen from the position of the other. The subject is brought to the first platform. The available short stick does not suffice to reach the food. But the present situation redintegrates a perception of the long stick and of the route to the second platform on which it previously has appeared. Let us suppose, further, that *this* subject has had experience only with one stick, on the same platform with the food, and that a week earlier it had merely seen a long stick, out of reach behind bars, in another room. Now (a week later) our hypothetical subject is confronted with the platform on which there is food and a stick too short to reach the food. The subject looks at the situation, goes to the other room, taking along the short stick, rakes in the long stick, returns to the first platform, and rakes in the food.

The question now is whether we must assume the mediation of symbolic processes, of memory images, or something of the sort, in order to explain this hypothetical behavior. The series of detour situations outlined above was chosen deliberately to indicate (1) the impossibility of defining with any precision the kind of animal behavior that does or does not require the postulation of symbolic processes, and (2) a basic continuity in the transition from perceptually to symbolically mediated behavior. Specificity of identifiable patterns and abstraction, i.e. association, are always involved, but in varying degree. To what extent we describe the behavior of our subject in the two-stick experiment as being ideational or symbolic depends on such factors as how much stick experience he has had, how far apart the platforms are, how long ago he saw the second stick, how well he knows the pathway from the food platform to the other room — all subject to quantitative variation. The more attenuated the basis of association, the more compelled do we feel to postulate a symbolizing process, an instrumental aid to problem solving, such as language.

Brief consideration of certain characteristics and uses of linguistic responses (words) may give some clues to the function of symbolic processes in concept formation and problem solving: (1) A word response is a concise and discrete central representation of a thing, a class, or an aspect of a class; it isolates what is pertinent, excludes what is irrelevant. (2) In itself (i.e. in its problem-solving noncommunicative function) it has no effect on the organism-environment relation; it does not commit or implicate the organism as does, for instance, an overt response of locomotion. (3) Word responses are not mutually incompatible, interfering, inhibiting; many words can occur together or in rapid sequence. Words, therefore, may effect temporal integration; they summarize many past experiences into a manageable unit. Concepts that derive from a diversity of experience can occur — can be organized or educed — only when symbol or word units are available to assemble and incorporate a large body of experience. Many relational concepts (e.g. causality) are a function of diverse experiences, and these concepts could hardly be formed without the aid of words (or other symbols) to compress those experiences into the compass of a functional moment. Now, in the narrower sense, at least, linguistic responses are unknown among animals other than man. However, if we think of language as a symptom or indicator of symbolism, rather than as its necessary condition, the possibility of symbolic processes occurring in animals is not excluded. But our conclusion that occasional instances of infrahuman behavior reflect early and fragmentary stages in the phylogenetic development of symbolization must be considered quite tentative.

RECAPITULATION

The present section, being, so to speak, a summary of summaries, must be presented in condensed and dogmatic form, without the development of implications or the consideration of alternative points of view.

Motivational versus Cognitive Differences in Evolution

For psychology, differences among animals with respect to what they want are trifling by comparison with differences in the means by which they satisfy their wants. The fact that one organism feeds itself by ingesting algae, others by eating crabs, insects, grass, or eggs, is of only incidental interest in contrast to the various behaviors by which algae or crabs, insects, grass, or eggs are obtained. It is in the cognitive rather than in the motivational aspects of behavior that we find the significant axes of behavioral evolution. Differences in motivation consist largely in an increasing complexity or degree of indirection of drive sequences terminating in goal attainment. These motivational differences are derivative, depending on the cognitive equipment of the animal. Differences in forms of social interaction, including those aspects we call culture, also derive from cognitive factors. In an earlier section we found only one type of behavior modification, namely, "transformation of mechanisms into drives," for which there is any convincing evidence of phylogenetic difference, and this distinction applies mainly to man as contrasted with other animals. This emphasis on cognitive factors does *not* mean, of course, that the student of comparative behavior may disregard its motivational aspects. Such neglect would be as inexcusable as disregarding the animal's sensory equipment or mode of locomotion, as if its receptor capacities and whether it walks, crawls, flies, or swims were irrelevant to the problem.

Axes of Cognitive Development

Sensory elements and response units may be thought of as the raw materials of behavior. The range and differentiation of environmental energies to which the organism is sensitive depend on the sense organs and their central connections. With increasing sensory differentiation, the possibilities of central (perceptual) organization into unique patterns are rapidly multiplied. Sensory differentiation is, therefore, a necessary, but not a sufficient, condition for breadth of perceptual scope. Behavioral complexity is likewise increased as the organism is able to make discrete and independent movements of all parts of its body. Phylogenetically the locomotor coordinations develop earlier than those involved in manipulation. Variety and precision of motor patterning culminates in the manual dexterities and speech of man.

Perceptual organization (sensory correlation) in evolutionary development proceeds along two axes: (1) inherited perceptual patterns and (2) individual acquisition of perceptions. Acquired perceptions are organized in the course of experience by the postulated mechanisms of pattern identification, the selective process, and symbolization. As regards (1), an initial peak, phylogenetically, is seen in the insects, and a second one in the birds. In the higher primates this trend takes a pronounced drop. Experiential perceptual organization (2), on the other hand, seems to play only a minor part until we come to some of the birds and especially the mammals. Among the monkeys and apes (2) rapidly displaces (1) and leads to a wider perceptual scope than is found among any of the lower organisms. Somewhere among the higher mammals, perhaps not before the primate level, there emerges a new instrumentality for perceptual and conceptual organization, namely, symbolization. Although we have suggested a gradual development of the symbolic process, the evidence is overwhelming that the curve representing this dimension of behavioral evolution rises sharply upwards with the appearance of man.

The effectiveness of the S-R connecting process rises from the lower to the higher invertebrates; and no further rise is apparent until we come to the higher primates. It is probable that symbolization helps not only in perceptual organization but also in making possible prompt and efficient connection of percepts and concepts to specific responses. One-trial learning becomes the rule rather than the exception among the highest primates. There the connecting of the central symbolic processes with one another, and with overt responses, seems to occur with unique facility.

A Phylogenetic Comparison of Intelligence

Behavioral evolution is characterized by increasing complexity. With ascent in the phyletic scale, the effective environment expands spatially and temporally and provides an ever-wider range of behavior determinants. This expansion follows upon the organism's ability to integrate and organize. It is only with the advent of "culture" that the effective environment itself expands rapidly from generation to generation.

We have now discussed and summarized what appear to be important axes along which phylogenetic changes in behavioral complexity may be traced. We have also seen, usually rather vaguely, the points of the phyletic scale at which inflections or origins of the curves representing these several axes occur. The accompanying figure is a rash venture, presenting a tentative estimate of the composite of those curves.

The ordinate of Fig. 2, it will be noted, is labeled "Intelligence level." It could as well have been called "Behavioral complexity" or "Spatio-temporal span of behavior determination." Or it may be taken to represent the sum total of the organism's cognitions and adjustments.*

---

* By thus including those behavior integrations strictly determined by the inherited structure, as well as those whose development is contingent upon individual interaction with the environment, we depart from the traditional instinct-intelligence dichotomy. The distinction between the innate and the acquired is certainly an important one. But the usual connotation of "intelligence" is a measurable, or at least describable, performance. Intelligence that does not express itself in behavior is a contradiction of terms. Performance reflects neural organization, and this comprises structurally determined pat-

The particular divisions of the animal kingdom indicated in Fig. 2, where one division contains a single species and another includes several phyla, represent a compromise between conventional classification and present behavioral evidence. (A single continuous curve could have been drawn by reordering the usual taxonomic sequence.) Within the division of protista the Rhizo-

sion of lower mammals behavioral data are inadequate to permit an estimate of the relative positions of the various orders.

It is quite possible that the continuous curves drawn for each division should be broken up into numerous discrete curves, each representing a subgroup. Further refinements in behavioral measurement might indicate, for instance, that the higher am-

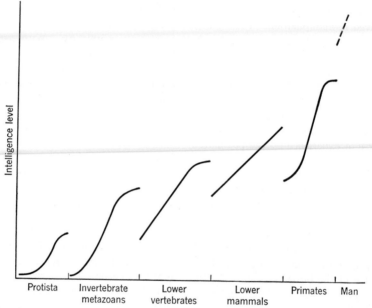

Fig. 2. A tentative estimate of comparative intelligence in the animal kingdom.

poda, Mastigophora, and Infusoria are represented by the upper (right-hand) portion of the curve; among the lower invertebrates the Echinodermata are displaced to the left of their usual taxonomic position; within the lower vertebrates and the primates the conventional order is maintained; for the divi-

terns as well as patterns formed in the course of experience. The fact that there *will be* organizing activity is determined structurally as much as is the fact that there *are* certain species-constant organizations. The variability of environmental factors that enter into individually acquired organizations provides for a greater degree of plasticity in behavior. There is little indication in the final test of survival, however, that nature is prejudiced in favor of one or the other mode of intelligence.

phibians are more advanced than the most primitive reptiles. Needless to say, distance along the abscissa is *not* proportional to the number of species or individuals included. The fact that the curve represents an average, a pooling of attainments along each of several dimensions, means that, with respect to one or another of these, a given species may stand considerably higher or lower than its position on the curve indicates. There are, obviously, no absolute units of measurement for the ordinate; a given distance on one curve cannot be presumed to be equal to the same distance on another curve or at another level of the same curve. The vertical axis thus represents only order, or direction of difference. The top of the final curve suggests the debatable position of modern natural man. Because we know so little about the behavior of earlier forms of *Homo sapiens,* this curve is dotted.

REFERENCES

Adriaanse, A. Ammophila campestris Latr. und Ammophila adriaansei Wilcke ; ein Beiträge zur vergleichenden Verhaltensforschung. *Behaviour,* 1947, **1,** 1–34.

Allport, G. W. Scientific models and human morals. *Psychol. Rev.,* 1947, **54,** 182–192.

Anderson, E. E. The externalization of drive. I. Theoretical considerations. *Psychol. Rev.,* 1941, **48,** 204–224.

Baerends, G. P. Fortpflanzungsverhalten und Orientierung der Grabwespe *Ammophila campestris* Jur. *Tijdschr. Ent.,* 1941, **84,** 68–275.

Beach, F. A. Current concepts of play in animals. *Amer. Nat.,* 1945, **79,** 523–541.

Beach, F. A. Evolutionary changes in the physiological control of mating behavior in mammals. *Psychol. Rev.,* 1947, **54,** 297–315.

Bierens de Haan, J. A. Ueber den Begriff des Instinktes in der Tierpsychologie. *Folia biotheor.,* 1937, **2,** 1–16.

Bierens de Haan, J. A. *Die tierischen Instinkte und ihr Umbau durch Erfahrung.* Leiden : Brill, 1940.

Bingham, H. C. Selective transportation by chimpanzees. *Comp. Psychol. Monogr.,* 1929, **5.**

Birch, H. G. The relation of previous experience to insightful problem-solving. *J. comp. Psychol.,* 1945, **38,** 367–383.

Buytendijk, F. J. Über die Formwahrnehmung beim Hund. *Pflüg. Arch. ges. Physiol.,* 1924, **205,** 4–14.

Cassirer, E. *An essay on man.* New Haven : Yale University Press, 1944.

Child, C. M. *Physiological foundations of behavior.* New York : Holt, 1924.

Claparède, E. Opinions et travaux divers relatifs à la théorie biologique du sommeil et de l'hystérie. *Arch. Psychol., Genève,* 1928, **21,** 113.

Coghill, G. E. *Anatomy and the problem of behaviour.* Cambridge : Cambridge University Press, 1929.

Cowles, J. T. Food-tokens as incentives for learning by chimpanzees. *Comp. Psychol. Monogr.,* 1937, **14,** 1–96.

Cowles, J. T. "Delayed response" as tested by three methods and its relation to other learning situations. *J. Psychol.,* 1940, **9,** 103–130.

Cowles, J. T., and H. W. Nissen. Reward-expectancy in delayed responses of chimpanzees. *J. comp. Psychol.,* 1937, **24,** 345–358.

Crozier, W. J., and H. Hoagland. The study of living organisms. Chapter I in C. Murchison (Ed.), *A handbook of general experimental psychology.* Worcester : Clark University Press, 1934.

Cruikshank, R. M. Animal infancy. Chapter 3 in L. Carmichael (Ed.), *Manual of child psychology.* New York : Wiley, 1946.

Cruze, W. W. Maturation and learning in chicks. *J. comp. Psychol.,* 1935, **19,** 371–409.

Finan, J. L. Delayed response with pre-delay re-enforcement in monkeys after the removal of the frontal lobes. *Amer. J. Psychol.,* 1942, **55,** 202–214.

Fischel, W. *Psyche und Leistung der Tiere.* Berlin : De Gruyter, 1938.

Folger, H. T. The relation between the responses by *Amoeba* to shock and to sudden illumination. *Biol. Bull. Woods Hole,* 1927, **53,** 405–412.

Forel, A. *Ants and some other insects.* Chicago : Open Court, 1904.

Forster, M. C. Unpublished work. Yale University, Laboratories of Comparative Psychobiology, 1934.

Fraenkel, G. S., and D. L. Gunn. *The orientation of animals. Kineses, taxes, and compass reactions.* Oxford : Clarendon, 1940.

Frisch, K. von. Der Farbensinn und Formensinn der Biene. *Zool. Jb. (Physiol.),* 1914, **35,** 1–188.

Gaffron, M. Untersuchungen ueber das Bewegungssehen bei Libellenlarven, Fliegen und Fischen. *Z. vergl. Physiol.,* 1934, **20,** 299–337.

Grice, Robert G. The relation of secondary reinforcement to delayed reward in visual discrimination learning. *J. exp. Psychol.,* 1948, **38,** 1–16.

Groos, K. *The play of animals.* New York : Appleton-Century-Crofts, 1915. (1st German Ed., 1896).

Guthrie, E. R. *The psychology of learning.* New York : Harper, 1935.

Harlow, H. F. Animal behavior. Chapter 12 in R. H. Seashore (Ed.), *Fields of psychology.* New York : Holt, 1942.

Harlow, H. F. Solution by rhesus monkeys of a problem involving the Weigl principle using the matching-from-sample method. *J. comp. Psychol.,* 1943a, **36,** 217–227.

Harlow, H. F. Generalization by rhesus monkeys of a problem involving the Weigl principle using the matching-from-sample method. Unpublished manuscript, 1943b.

Hartridge, H. Acoustic control in the flight of bats. *Nature, Lond.,* 1945, **156,** 490–494.

Hebb, D. O. Spontaneous neurosis in chimpanzees. *Psychosom. Med.,* 1947, **9,** 3–19.

Hebb, D. O. *The organization of behavior. A neuropsychological theory.* New York : Wiley, 1949.

Heinroth, O. Beiträge zur Biologie, namentlich Ethologie und Psychologie der Anatiden. *Int. Orn. Congr. 5.* Berlin, 1910.

Hemplemann, F. *Tierpsychologie vom Standpunkte des Biologen.* Leipzig : Akademische Verlagsgesellschaft, 1926.

Herrick, C. J. *Neurological foundations of animal behavior.* New York : Holt, 1924.

Hertz, M. Zur Physiologie des Formen- und Bewegungssehens. III. Figurale Unterscheidung und reziproke Dressuren bei der Biene. *Z. vergl. Physiol.*, 1934, **21**, 604–615.

Hilgard, E. R., and D. G. Marquis. *Conditioning and learning.* New York: Appleton Century-Crofts, 1940.

Hingston, R. W. G. *Problems of instinct and intelligence.* New York: Macmillan, 1928.

Hobhouse, L. T. *Mind in evolution.* New York: Macmillan, 1901. (2nd Ed., 1915; 3rd Ed., 1926).

Hollingworth, H. L. *Psychology: its facts and principles.* New York: Appleton-Century-Crofts, 1928.

Holmes, S. J. *Studies in animal behavior.* Boston: Badger, 1916.

Hooton, E. A. *Why men behave like apes and vice versa.* Princeton: Princeton University Press, 1940.

Hooton, E. A. *Man's poor relations.* New York: Doubleday, Doran, 1942.

Hörmann, M. Über den Helligkeitssin der Bienen. *Z. vergl. Physiol.*, 1934, **21**, 188–249.

Householder, A. S. Neural structure in perception and response. *Psychol. Rev.*, 1947, **54**, 169–176.

Hovland, C. I. The generalization of conditioned responses: II. The sensory generalization of conditioned responses with varying intensities of tone. *J. genet. Psychol.*, 1937, **51**, 279–291.

Hull, C. L. *Principles of behavior. An introduction to behavior theory.* New York: Appleton-Century-Crofts, 1943.

Hull, C. L. The place of innate individual and species differences in a natural-science theory of behavior. *Psychol. Rev.*, 1945, **52**, 55–60.

Hull, C. L. The problem of primary stimulus generalization. *Psychol. Rev.*, 1947, **54**, 120–134.

Hunt, J. McV. The effects of infant feeding-frustration upon adult hoarding in the albino rat. *J. abnorm. soc. Psychol.*, 1941, **36**, 338–360.

Hunter, W. S. The delayed reaction in animals and children. *Behav. Monogr.*, 1913, **2**.

Jackson, T. A. Use of the stick as a tool by young chimpanzees. *J. comp. Psychol.*, 1942, **34**, 223–235.

James, W. *The principles of psychology.* New York: Holt, 1890. Volume II.

Jenkins, W. O. A spatial factor in chimpanzee learning. *J. comp. Psychol.*, 1942, **35**, 81–84.

Jennings, H. S. *Behavior of the lower organisms.* New York: Columbia University Press, 1906.

Kafka, G. *Einführung in die Tierpsychologie.* Volume I. *Die Sinne der Wirbellosen.* Leipzig: Barth, 1914.

Kafka, G. (Ed.). *Handbuch der vergleichenden Psychologie.* Munich: Reinhardt, 1922.

Katz, David. *Animals and men. Studies in comparative psychology.* New York: Longmans, Green, 1937.

Kennedy, J. L. The nature and physiological basis of visual movement discrimination in animals. *Psychol. Rev.*, 1936, **43**, 494–521.

Klüver, H. *Behavior mechanisms in monkeys.* Chicago: University of Chicago, 1933.

Koch, Sigmund, and William J. Daniel. The effect of satiation on the behavior mediated by a habit of maximum strength. *J. exp. Psychol.*, 1945, **35**, 167–187.

Köhler, W. *The mentality of apes.* New York: Harcourt, Brace, 1925.

Köhler, W. *Dynamics in psychology.* New York: Liveright, 1940.

Krechevsky, I. "Hypotheses" in rats. *Psychol. Rev.*, 1932, **39**, 516–532.

Lashley, K. S. *Brain mechanisms and intelligence.* Chicago: University of Chicago, 1929.

Lashley, K. S. Learning: III. Nervous mechanisms in learning. Chapter 10 in C. Murchison (Ed.), *A handbook of general experimental psychology.* Worcester: Clark University Press, 1934.

Lashley, K. S. Experimental analysis of instinctive behavior. *Psychol. Rev.*, 1938, **45**, 445–471.

Lashley, K. S. The problem of cerebral organization in vision. *Biol. Symp.*, 1942, **8**, 301–322.

Lashley, K. S., and M. Wade. The Pavlovian theory of generalization. *Psychol. Rev.*, 1946, **53**, 72–87.

Lecomte du Noüy, P. *Human destiny.* New York: Longmans, Green, 1947.

Lindesmith, A. F. Can chimpanzees become morphine addicts? *J. comp. Psychol.*, 1946, **39**, 109–117.

Loeb, J. *Comparative physiology of the brain and comparative psychology.* New York: Putnam, 1900.

Loeb, J. *Forced movements, tropisms and animal conduct.* Philadelphia: Lippincott, 1918.

Lorenz, K. Der Kumpan in der Umwelt des Vogels. Der Artgenosse als ausloesendes Moment sozialer Verhaltungsweisen. *J. Orn., Lpz,.* 1935, **83**, 137–213, 289–413. (See also The companion in the bird's world. *Auk*, 1937, **54**, 245–273.)

Lorenz, K. Über die Bildung des Instinktbegriffs. *Naturwissenschaften*, 1937, **25**, 289–300, 307–318, 324–331.

Lorenz, K. Vergleichende Bewegungsstudien an Anatinen. *J. Orn. Leipzig*, 1941, **89**, 194–294.

Lorenz, K., and N. Tinbergen. Taxis und Instinkthandlung in der Eirollbewegung der Graugans I. *Z. Tierpsychol.*, 1938, **2**, 1–29.

Maier, N. R. F. Reasoning in white rats. *Comp. Psychol. Monogr.*, 1929, **6**.

Maier, N. R. F., and T. C. Schneirla. *Principles of animal psychology.* New York: McGraw-Hill, 1935.

Mast, S. O,. and K. S. Lashley. Observations on ciliary current in free-swimming paramecia. *J. exp. Zool.*, 1916, **21**, 281–293.

McDougall, W. *An introduction to social psychology.* (16th Ed.) Boston: Luce, 1923.

Moore, T. V. Human and animal intelligence. In H. S. Jennings et al., *Scientific aspects of the race problem.* New York: Longmans, Green, 1941. Pp. 93–108.

Morgan, C. L. *An introduction to comparative psychology.* London: Scott, 1894.

Morgan, C. L. *Animal behavior.* London: Arnold, 1900.

Morgan, C. L. *Emergent evolution.* New York: Holt, 1927.

Morgan, C. T. *Physiological psychology.* New York: McGraw-Hill, 1943.

Morgan, C. T. The hoarding instinct. *Psychol. Rev.,* 1947, **54**, 335–341.

Moss, F. A. (Ed.). *Comparative Psychology.* New York: Prentice-Hall, 1934. (Revised Ed., 1942.)

Munn, N. L. *An introduction to animal psychology.* New York: Houghton Mifflin, 1933.

Munn, N. L. *Psychological development.* New York: Houghton Mifflin, 1938.

Nissen, H. W. A field study of the chimpanzee. *Comp. Psychol. Monogr.,* 1931, **8.**

Nissen, H. W., J. S. Blum, and R. A. Blum. Conditional matching behavior of chimpanzees. *J. comp. physiol. Psychol.,* 1949, **42.,** 339–356.

Nissen, H. W., A. H. Riesen, and V. Nowlis. Delayed response and discrimination learning by chimpanzees. *J. comp. Psychol.,* 1938, **26,** 361–386.

Novikoff, A. B. The concept of integrative levels and biology. *Science,* 1945, **101,** 209–215.

Pavlov, I. P. *Conditioned reflexes.* Oxford: Oxford University Press, 1927.

Perkins, F. T. Study of configurational learning in the goldfish. *J. exp. Psychol.,* 1931, **14,** 508–538.

Petrunkevitsch, A. The value of instinct as a taxonomic character in spiders. *Biol. Bull. Woods Hole,* 1926, **50,** 427–432.

Plath, O. E. *Bumblebees and their ways.* New York: Macmillan, 1934.

Razran, G. H. S. Conditioned responses in animals other than dogs. *Psychol. Bull.,* 1933, **30,** 261–324.

Richter, C. P. Total self regulatory functions in animals and human beings. *Harvey Lect.,* 1942–43, **38,** 63–103.

Richter, C. P. Biology of drives. *J. comp. physiol. Psychol.,* 1947, **40,** 129–134.

Riesen, A. H. Delayed reward in discrimination learning by chimpanzees. *Comp. Psychol. Monogr.,* 1940, **15,** 1–54.

Riesen, A. H. The development of visual perception in man and chimpanzee. *Science,* 1947, **106,** 107–108.

Riesen, A. H., and H. W. Nissen. Non-spatial delayed response by the matching technique. *J. comp. Psychol.,* 1942, **34,** 307–313.

Romanes, G. J. *Animal intelligence.* London: Keegan Paul, 1881.

Russell, E. S. *The behaviour of animals. An introduction to its study.* London: Arnold, 1934. (2nd Ed., 1938.)

Schiller, P. H. Kinematoskopisches Sehen der Fische. *Z. vergl. Physiol.,* 1934, **20,** 454–462.

Schiller, P. H. Vergleichende Untersuchungen über Bewegungssehen. *Biol. Rev.,* 1937, **12,** 116–153.

Schiller, P. H. Delayed response in the minnow. *J. comp. physiol. Psychol.,* 1948, **41,** 233–238.

Schlosberg, H. The concept of play. *Psychol. Rev.,* 1947, **54,** 229–231.

Schneirla, T. C. Problems in the biopsychology of social organization. *J. abnorm. soc. Psychol.,* 1946, **41,** 385–402.

Senden, M. von. *Raum- und Gestaltauffassung bei operierten Blindgeborenen vor und nach der Operation.* Leipzig: Barth, 1932.

Siegel, P. S. Drive shift, a conceptual and experimental analysis. *J. comp. Psychol.,* 1943, **35,** 139–148.

Skinner, B. F. *The behavior of organisms. An experimental analysis.* New York: Appleton-Century-Crofts, 1938.

Smoke, K. L. Concept formation. In *Encyclopaedia of psychology.* New York: Philosophical Library, 1946.

Spence, K. W. The differential response in animals to stimuli varying within a single dimension. *Psychol. Rev.,* 1937, **44,** 430–444.

Spence, K. W. Failure of transposition in size-discrimination of chimpanzees. *Amer. J. Psychol.,* 1941, **54,** 223–229.

Spence, K. W. The role of secondary reinforcement in delayed reward learning. *Psychol. Rev.,* 1947, **54,** 1–8.

Spooner, Alice, and W. N. Kellogg. The backward conditioning curve. *Amer. J. Psychol.,* 1947, **60,** 321–334.

Spragg, S. D. S. Morphine addiction in chimpanzees. *Comp. Psychol. Monogr.,* 1940, **15,** 1–132.

Ten Cate, J., and B. Ten Cate-Kazeewa. Les *Octopus vulgaris* peuvent-ils discerner les formes? *Arch. néerl. Physiol.,* 1938, **23,** 541–551.

Thompson, D. W. *On growth and form.* Cambridge: Cambridge University Press, 1942.

Thorndike, E. L. *Animal intelligence.* New York: Macmillan, 1911.

Thorndike, E. L. Why study animal psychology? Chapter 1 in F. A. Moss (Ed.), *Comparative psychology.* New York: Prentice-Hall, 1942.

Tinbergen, N. An objectivistic study of the innate behaviour of animals. *Bibl. Biotheor.,* 1942, **1,** Series D, 39–98.

Tinbergen, N., and D. J. Kuenen. Über die auslösenden und die richtunggebenden Reizsituationen der Sperrbewegung von jungen Drosseln (*Turdus m. merula* L. und *T. E. ericetorum* Turton). *Z. Tierpsychol.,* 1939, **3,** 37–60.

Tolman, E. C. *Purposive behavior in animals and man.* New York: Appleton-Century-Crofts, 1932.

Tolman, E. C. A stimulus-expectancy need-cathexis psychology. *Science,* 1945, **101,** 160–166.

Tolman, E. C., and C. H. Honzik. "Insight" in rats. *Univ. Calif. Publ. Psychol.,* 1930, **4,** 215–232.

Uexküll, J. von. *Umwelt und Innenwelt der Tiere.* (2nd Ed.) Berlin: Springer, 1921.

Uexküll, J. von. *Theoretical biology.* New York: Harcourt, Brace, 1926.

Verworn, M. *Psycho-physiologische Protisten-studien.* Jena: Fischer, 1889.

Volkelt, H. Über die Vorstellungen der Tiere. *Arb. EntwPsychol.,* 1914, No. 2.

Walls, G. L. *The vertebrate eye and its adaptive radiation.* Bloomfield Hills, Mich.: Cranbrook, 1942.

Warden, C. J. The historical development of comparative psychology. *Psychol. Rev.,* 1927, **34,** 57–85, 135–168.

Warden, C. J., T. N. Jenkins, and L. H. Warner. *Introduction to comparative psychology.* New York: Ronald, 1934.

Warden, C. J., T. N. Jenkins, and L. H. Warner. *Comparative psychology.* Volume I. *Principles and Methods.* New York: Ronald, 1935.

Warden, C. J., T. N. Jenkins, and L. H. Warner. *Comparative psychology.* Volume III. *Vertebrates.* New York: Ronald, 1936.

Warden, C. J., T. N. Jenkins, and L. H. Warner. *Comparative psychology.* Volume II. *Plants and invertebrates.* New York: Ronald, 1940.

Washburn, M. F. *The animal mind.* (4th Ed.) New York: Macmillan, 1936.

Waters, R. H. The historical background of comparative psychology. Chapter 2 in F. A. Moss (Ed.), *Comparative psychology.* New York: Prentice-Hall, 1942.

Watson, D. M. S. Zoology, in *Encycl. Brit.* (14th Ed.), 1929, **23,** 974–986.

Watson, J. B. *Behavior: An introduction to comparative psychology.* New York: Holt, 1914.

Weinstein, B. The evolution of intelligent behavior in rhesus monkeys. *Genet. Psychol. Monogr.,* 1945, **31,** 3–48.

Werner, H. *Comparative psychology of mental development.* New York: Harper, 1940.

Willey, M. M., and S. A. Rice. The psychic utility of sleep. *J. abnorm. Psychol.,* 1924, **19,** 174–178.

Williams, K. A. The reward value of a conditioned stimulus. *Univ. Calif. Publ. Psychol.,* 1924, **4,** 31–55.

Wolfe, J. B. The effect of delayed reward upon learning in the white rat. *J. comp. Psychol.,* 1934, **17,** 1–21.

Wolfe, J. B. Effectiveness of token-rewards for chimpanzees. *Comp. Psychol. Monogr.,* 1936, **12,** 1–72.

Wolfe, J. B. An exploratory study in food-storing in rats. *J. comp. Psychol.,* 1939, **28,** 97–108.

Woodworth, R. S. *Psychology. A study of mental life.* New York: Holt, 1921.

Woodworth, R. S. Reënforcement of perception. *Amer. J. Psychol.,* 1947, **60,** 119–124.

Yerkes, R. M. Animal psychology and criteria of the psychic. *J. Phil. Psychol. sci. Meth.,* 1905, **2,** 141–149.

Yerkes, R. M. *The dancing mouse.* New York: Macmillan, 1907.

Yerkes, R. M. *Chimpanzees.* New Haven: Yale University Press, 1943.

Young, M. L., and H. F. Harlow. Solution by rhesus monkeys of a problem involving the Weigl principle using the oddity method. *J. comp. Psychol.,* 1943, **35,** 205–217.

Young, P. T. The experimental analysis of appetite. *Psychol. Bull.,* 1941, **38,** 129–164.

Zerrahn, G. Formdressur und Formunterscheidung bei der Honigbiene. *Z. wiss. Biol., Abt. C, Z. vergl. Physiol.,* 1933, **20,** 117–150.

Zuckerman, S. *Functional affinities of man, monkeys, and apes.* New York: Harcourt, Brace, 1933.

12·

Instinctive Behavior:
Reproductive Activities

FRANK A. BEACH
Yale University

Certain patterns of behavior are commonly referred to as "instinctive." They are thought to differ in various ways from other reactions that are called "learned." We shall not be concerned with the validity of this distinction. As Stone (1942a) has stated, the experimentalist is less interested in classifying behavior than in determining the factors that control its development and organization.

The experimental analysis of instinctive activities does not differ significantly from one response pattern to another. In fact methods of investigating the dynamics of an instinctive reaction are equally applicable to the study of learned behavior. The same questions have to be answered, and very often the same techniques can be applied.

Very few of the responses relegated to the instinct category have been experimentally analyzed. It is conceivable that this is why they are regarded as qualitatively different from other forms of behavior that have been systematically examined in the psychological laboratory. Only after a bit of behavior has been studied exhaustively can it be meaningfully compared and contrasted with other reactions.

The following material has been selected to illustrate the methods that have proved useful, the kinds of information currently available, and the types of interpretation customarily advanced in connection with the experimental analysis of instinctive activities. Reproductive behavior has been studied more intensively than most instinctive patterns. This chapter deals therefore with observations and experiments on sexual, parental, and filial behavior.

SEXUAL BEHAVIOR

The central features of reproductive behavior are the responses involved in courtship and mating. Analysis of these reactions includes identification of their external correlates — the environmental factors responsible for their occurrence, or, in a narrower sense, the stimuli that elicit them.

Functions of Sensory Stimulation

The environmental stimuli that influence sexual behavior can be divided arbitrarily into three categories.

Stimuli affecting physiological readiness. These are the external conditions that produce within the organism a physiological state necessary for the occurrence of sexual reactions. These may include general climatological factors such as length of day, temperature cycles, or seasonal rainfall. Or they may be more directly associated with the presence and activity of other animals of the same species. The distinguishing characteristic of the events, processes, and objects placed in this category is that they do not elicit behavioral responses, but instead they prepare the organism for reaction to more specific types of sensory cues.

ILLUMINATION. Annual and diurnal cycles of illumination affect sexual activity in many vertebrate species. Seasonal occurrence of courtship and mating in some fishes, birds, and mammals is closely related to the progressive increase or decrease in the amount of daylight per 24 hours. The correlation is dependent upon functional changes in the anterior pituitary gland and in several other endocrine organs controlled by the pituitary. Marshall (1942) and Beach (1948) have summarized the evidence.

Brook trout ordinarily spawn during December when the days are growing shorter, but Hoover and Hubbard (1937) induced fertile reproduction in this species during August by artificially decreasing the duration of light per 24-hour period. Rowan's (1932) early work on the American crow and other studies by Bissonnette (1932a), Cole (1933), Witschi (1935), and Wolfson (1940) prove that a gradual increase in the amount of daily illumination induces recrudescence of the sex glands and concomitant appearance of mating behavior in several avian species. Burger (1943) found that the starling testis is activated by wavelengths falling between 580 and 680 millimicrons. Longer or shorter wavelengths that are plainly visible to the bird do not influence reproductive condition.

Some seasonally breeding mammals are affected by changes in the length of day. Sheep, goats, deer, cats, and ferrets can be brought into full breeding condition during months in which this would not normally occur, provided the lighting conditions are appropriately manipulated (Hammond, 1944; Dawson, 1941; Bissonnette, 1932b, 1941; Rice, 1942). Marshall and Bowden (1934) showed that the sexual cycle of the ferret is influenced by all wavelengths from 365 to 650 millimicrons.

Some animals that breed throughout most of the year display cycles of reproductive activity that are correlated with the diurnal rhythm of illumination. The Japanese medaka fish ovulates just before dawn; but artificial reversal of the day-night cycle is accompanied by egg laying at the time of the artificial dawn (Robinson and Rugh, 1943). Norway rats are most active during the night, and females come into heat in late evening or early morning (Ball, 1937). Females maintained under reversed light-dark rhythm display a 12-hour shift in their mating behavior and are sexually active during the solar day (Beach, 1938). Beach and Levinson (1949) found that the sexual responses of male rats are more intense and frequent during the night than in daytime.

TEMPERATURE. Environmental temperature influences sexual behavior in many invertebrates. Fertile mating awaits the attainment of reproductive maturity, and this is affected by temperature in some cases. Hogben (1940) described two species of moths, the larvae of which feed upon plants that bloom at different seasons. If larvae of the earlier emerging species are artificially cooled, their metamorphosis is delayed and they reach maturity simultaneously with the second species. Under such conditions males and females of the two types can be crossed and fertile hybrids are produced. The continued separation of the two species is thus dependent upon differential reactivity to environmental temperatures.

The seasonal occurrence of breeding behavior in several vertebrate species is a function of changes in external temperature. The testes of the killifish involute at the end of the spring spawning season when the weather is growing warmer; but gonadal regression can be markedly retarded by artificially reducing the water temperature (Burger, 1939). Kendeigh (1934) believes that seasonal temperature cycles are as important in controlling avian reproduction as are changes in the amount of daily illumination.

The thirteen-lined ground squirrel breeds in April and May, before and after which time the sex glands are relatively inactive. Wells (1935) analyzed the anterior pituitary glands of these animals and found a seasonal increase in the concentration of gonadotrophic hormones which stimulate the testis and ovary. The rise in hormone level just before breeding season cannot be attributed to changes in illumination, for it begins while the animals are hibernating in subterranean burrows. Temperature may play a role in the gonadal cycle. Wells (1936) showed that testicular regression at the close of the season can be delayed for as long as 5 months if the males are kept in temperatures of 4 degrees C.

Daily cycles of environmental temperature also influence sexual activity. Browman (1943) noted that female rats maintained in constant light or constant dark tended to excavate nests and lay infertile eggs. Control tests showed that chemical and tactile stimuli have little or no effect upon the female's performance.

Matthews (1939) observed that visually isolated hen pigeons do not lay eggs. Installation of mirrors in the cage induces occasional egg laying; and the frequency of ovulation is further increased if the females can see other pigeons. Field observations show that the presence of other individuals is biologically important to the reproduction of wild birds that form large breeding colonies. Comparison of the reproductive success of four colonies of herring gulls as recorded by Darling (1938) gave the results summarized in Table 1.

TABLE 1

REPRODUCTIVE SUCCESS IN HERRING GULLS AS A FUNCTION OF THE SIZE OF THE BREEDING COLONY

Number of Birds in Colony	Date of First Egg	Total Days of Egg Laying	Nests Built and Occupied	Eggs Laid	Fledg-lings	Repro-ductive Success *
84–90	May 7	17	40	84	35	42%
30–34	May 12	23	12	26	8	31%
20	May 18	26	7	16	3	19%
4	....	..	0 †	0	0	0%

* Percentage of eggs incubated and hatched.

† Some nest building began 19 days after egg laying started in the largest colony (May 26), but since no nests were occupied and no eggs laid the structures were classified as "nonfunctional."

come into heat during the cooler portion of the 24-hour period.

PRESENCE OF OTHER ANIMALS. Stimulation afforded by other individuals of their own species contributes to the attainment of reproductive condition in some fishes, birds, and mammals. Ripening of eggs in the ovary, secretion of sex hormones, and the resultant execution of mating reactions may be partly or completely dependent upon the presence and behavior of associates.

The female African mouthbreeder fish rarely digs a nest, lays eggs, or exhibits any other sexual activity if she is visually isolated from others of her kind. But Aronson (1945) demonstrated that when females can see another mouthbreeder they periodically

The large colonies were more effective reproductive units. In them oviposition began earlier, was better synchronized within the colony, and resulted in a higher proportion of mated pairs. More birds laid eggs and a larger percentage of eggs was hatched in the large than in the small colonies. Smith's (1943) studies of the Eastern redwing indicate that reproductive success in the second brood is greater for large than for small colonies.

R. K. Enders (personal communication) has shown that seasonal ovarian development and the accompanying behavioral changes in some mammals are influenced by association with other individuals. Female minks were isolated at some distance from others of their species, and other females were subjected to daily vaginal smears and kept in individual wire cages near the rest of the herd. Examination of the gonads early in the breeding season showed that ovarian follicles were significantly smaller in visually isolated individuals than in minks that lived near others of their kind.

Ovarian function in the human female can be altered by so-called "psychic" factors. Menstruation is appreciably delayed in some women suffering from homesickness, fear of pregnancy, or chronic anxiety (Dunbar, 1938; Gill, 1943; Klinefelter, Albright, and Griswold, 1943; Loeser, 1943; Fuerstner, 1944).

Critical features of the immediate surroundings. The second type of stimulation involved in sexual performance is derived from external factors that do not directly evoke behavioral reactions but predispose the sexually ready individual to respond appropriately and completely to stimuli afforded by the potential mate. Fertile males and females of some species are capable of sexual behavior only in a particular environmental setting.

ESSENTIAL CHARACTERISTICS OF THE HABITAT. Many adult amphibians that live a terrestrial existence can mate only in the water. Various species of toads come into full breeding condition in the spring or summer but show no sexual activity if the weather has been exceptionally dry. A sudden rainfall that creates temporary ponds and puddles is followed by the prompt appearance of courtship and mating (Noble, 1931).

Aquatic birds usually mate and nest near a body of water, and Schoolland (1942) observed that proximity to water stimulates sexual behavior in domestic ducks. Ducklings were hatched and reared under conditions in which the only water encountered was contained in a small drinking saucer. When the birds were 5 months old they were permitted to approach but not to enter a large washtub sunk in the ground and

filled with water. Mating behavior appeared while the ducks walked around the tub, although it had never been observed before.

Failure of wild animals to reproduce in captivity is sometimes due to the absence of one critical environmental condition. The common catfish rarely spawns in aquaria, but Breder (1935) induced fertile mating by placing rocks and plants in the aquarium to pro-

FIG. 1. Mating in the Siamese fighting fish. The male "embraces" the female and fertilizes the eggs as she extrudes them. Mating takes place directly beneath the bubble nest that the male has built on the surface of the water. When mating is completed, the male retrieves the fertilized eggs and puts them in the bubble nest where they remain until hatching. (Reproduced through the courtesy of the American Museum of Natural History.)

vide a natural shelter where courtship and nesting could occur. An appropriate spawning site proved to be an essential prerequisite to sexual behavior.

The presence of a nest or some other structur created by one or both partners is necessary for successful courtship and mating in some species. Some male fish and birds prepare a nest before engaging a female in courtship. The Siamese fighting fish that is ready to spawn builds a "bubble nest" on the surface of the water. The passing female is lured beneath the nest by the male's courtship behavior, and there mating takes place (Fig. 1). A closely related species of fish (*Betta picta*) has a mating pattern that is very much like that of the fighting fish, save for the fact that the male builds no nest.

Female fighting fish will enter into preliminary courtship with males of the second species, but the pattern is broken off before copulation can occur, apparently because the presence of a nest is essential to complete receptivity on the part of the female (C. M. Breder, personal communication).

TERRITORY POSSESSION. Males or females of some species establish a breeding territory and restrict their mating behavior to this geographical area. Potential mates evoke a sexual response only when they are encountered within the territory of the reacting individual.

Nice (1941) has assembled numerous examples of sexual territory in birds. Males of some species gather together in "leks" where they perform their courtship displays and are visited by females. Each male has a small territory that he defends against other males. Once a female has entered the territory of one individual she is no longer courted by other males. Fertilized females depart, and each male serves a number of females in succession. Birds that form more permanent mateships may show sexual behavior only within the boundaries of the male's territory, although they go elsewhere to feed.

Comparable behavior is characteristic of mammals (Burt, 1943). Some of the most dramatic examples are seen in the sexual behavior of the fur seal and elephant seal (Osgood, Preble, and Parker, 1914; Matthews, 1929). Bulls arrive at the rookery several weeks in advance of the cows, and with a great deal of fighting each male chooses and protects his particular area on the beach. Old and large individuals claim locations near the water's edge, and younger bulls are forced to settle down in less desirable regions. When a cow arrives and climbs out on the beach, she enters the territory of some male and he forcefully prevents her departure.

By permitting females to join his harem and then holding them there, the bull accumulates from three or four to as many as 50 or 75 cows. Pups conceived the previous year are born shortly after the female's arrival, and then copulation takes place. Cows are not allowed to leave the territory of their mate until they have been impregnated. Thereafter they are free to enter the ocean and feed, later returning to suckle the pups. In these cetaceans sexual and territorial behavior are interdependent.

Stimuli afforded by the sexual partner. The third class of stimuli involved in courtship and mating comprises the sensory qualities of the male or female that influence the reactions of the opposite sex. The majority of studies on sensory functions in sexual behavior have dealt exclusively with stimuli belonging in this category. Different conclusions have been reached according to the species observed, the methods of investigation, and the general point of view held by the experimenter (Lashley, 1938; Tinbergen, 1942).

INSECTS. Courtship and mating in insects involve a sequence of reactions, each of which may occur in response to a different sensory cue. In some species, for example, the male's approach to a female depends exclusively upon chemical stimuli.

Male June beetles fly from distances of 15 yards to join a female whose genitalia and adjacent scent glands are extruded. The same orientation response is made to a freshly killed and crushed female, but a crushed male is not approached. The chemical compound isoamyline attracts males as effectively as does a receptive female (Travis, 1939). Male wireworm beetles exposed to the odor of lactic, butyric, or caproic acid crawl upon other males in the vicinity, extrude their genitalia, and execute abortive copulatory responses (Lehman, 1932).

Collins and Potts (1932) observed individually marked gypsy moths in the field and found that the male's approach to the female consists of a zigzag, upwind flight over distances up to half a mile. The effective stimulus is a glandular secretion that can be extracted with benzene. Concentrated extracts of this material are species-specific. They have no stimulative value for other kinds of moths (Haller, Acree, and Potts, 1944) but will attract male gypsy moths from distances of more than 2 miles (Collins and Potts, 1932).

Grosch (1947, 1948) found that male wasps display characteristic signs of sexual excitement when exposed to paper upon which females have been crushed but from which all body fragments have been removed. Males attempt to mate with amputated female abdomens but not with the severed thorax and head. A chemical substance produced by the abdominal glands of the female attracts males over a distance of 15 centimeters. Blind males readily approach and mate with females, but wasps deprived of the antennae that bear the chemoreceptors show no excitement in the presence of females and no tendency to approach them.

In some insects auditory stimulation is responsible for preliminary orientation to a sexual partner. Sexually active male field crickets produce a chirping sound by rubbing the wing covers together, and females that are ready to mate tend to move toward the source of this sound. Baier (1930) placed a number of females in one cage and males in another. The two cages were connected by a sound system, and the females clustered around the loudspeaker from which the males' chirping issued. Males in glass containers were placed in the females' cage, but the visual stimulus did not produce orientation responses on the part of the females.

Although a single sensory cue may suffice to bring males and females together, other stimuli influence subsequent phases of the mating pattern. Kellogg (1907) found that the male silkworm moth is attracted to the female exclusively by chemical stimuli. Males approach and attempt to copulate with scent glands that have been dissected out of the female, but they pay no attention to females from which these glands have been removed. When a female is touched by the male, her scent glands are drawn into the body and the source of chemical stimulation is removed. The subsequent copulatory activities of the male are guided entirely by tactile cues.

It has been stated that male wasps deprived of the antennal chemoreceptors show no sexual excitement in the presence of females and do not approach them. However, Grosch (1947) observed that when antennaless males accidentally bump into a female they sometimes mount in sexual fashion. This suggests that tactile stimuli evoke the mounting reaction in normal mating.

FISHES. Vision contributes to piscian courtship and mating. In certain species visual perception of form and movement is important. Breder and Coates (1935) showed that male guppies attempt to mate with the projected shadow of a swimming female, approaching the silhouette with normal orientation and moving the gonapodium (male sex organ) directly toward the location of the female's genital opening. Noble (1934) examined the response of male sunfish to models moved through the water on a wire. Crude cardboard replicas elicited courting behavior when they were made to move in the manner of a female sunfish. The same stimulus object evoked aggressive responses when a different motion was imparted to it.

Morphological differences between males and females provide visual cues that affect sexual behavior in the three-spined stickleback. Males that have built their nests drive other males away and court any gravid females. The ventral body surface of the male stickleback is red. Females lack this characteristic, but those that contain eggs have a markedly swollen abdomen. Tinbergen (1942) discovered that nest-guarding males display courtship reactions when confronted with a rough model in which the abdominal region is enlarged. Very accurate models of the female stickleback do not evoke sexual responses if the abdominal area is slim (Fig. 2). Models painted red on the underside elicit an attack by the experimental males; but when the same model is inverted it calls forth a much less intense response.

According to Noble and Curtis (1939) the female jewel fish in spawning condition discriminates between males and females on the basis of visual cues. The essential masculine characteristics include bright-red body colors

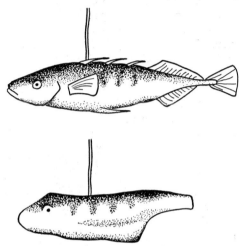

FIG. 2. Models of the three-spined stickleback presented as stimulus objects to the male. The crude model with a swollen abdomen evokes courtship, whereas the more accurate model lacking this essential characteristic is not sexually stimulating to the male. (Redrawn from Tinbergen, 1942.)

and special swimming movements. Gravid females were placed in large aquaria with smaller tanks on each of three sides. Stimulus animals in the small aquaria were clearly visible to the experimental female through two panes of glass and an air space of 1 centimeter. Two of the small tanks contained female jewel fish, and one contained a male. All experimental females with previous spawning experience laid their eggs as close as possible to the male's tank.

In the same testing situation two males were offered as stimulus animals. One was injected with yohimbine hydrochloride, and one with adrenalin chloride. Yohimbine expands the melanophores, intensifying the fish's coloration, whereas adrenalin contracts

these structures and renders the animal pale. By spawning at a point adjacent to the tank containing the yohimbine-treated male, the female indicated her preference for a brightly colored mate. Both males were then transferred to the female's tank, and she drove the adrenalin-treated fish away from her eggs but permitted the other male to assist in caring for them.

Internal fertilization occurs in several fishes, and it is probable that tactile stimuli control certain phases of the copulatory act. Descriptions of mating in the Mexican swordtail and the platyfish (Schlosberg, Duncan, and Daitch, 1949) strongly suggest that insertion of the male's sexual organ and maintenance of body contact between the pair during sperm transfer involves considerable cutaneous stimulation.

AMPHIBIANS. Male frogs and toads that are ready to breed utter a characteristic "sex call," and in some tree frogs this auditory stimulus is known to attract gravid females (Noble and Noble, 1923). Calling male toads attract others of their own sex and large breeding congresses are built up as a result (Bragg, 1940). Male cricket frogs are sexually excited by the calling of other males and respond by clasping and attempting to mate with the nearest individual, regardless of its sex (Greenberg, 1942).

The experiments of Noble and Aronson (1942) revealed that several different kinds of stimuli are involved in the mating behavior of male and female leopard frogs. Males approach and try to clasp any other frog, regardless of its sex or reproductive condition. The initial orientation depends upon vision. Blinded males do not approach a second individual although they mate normally with the female once contact has been established. Auditory and tactile stimuli control the male's tendency to retain his hold or to release the clasped object. Males, and females that have laid their eggs, utter a "warning croak" when clasped by another frog. In addition they are much slimmer than the female containing eggs. Males promptly release any frog that is not fat and that emits the "warning croak," and maintain their hold on any fat and silent partner.

The gravid female leopard frog clasped by a male releases several batches of eggs at fairly regular intervals. Synchronized with the female's spawning movements are the "ejaculatory pumps" of the male. These consist in sliding forward and then backward on the female's back and are accompanied by the emission of sperm. The ejaculatory pumps depend upon tactile sensations arising as a result of the female's muscular contractions when she expels each cluster of eggs.

The female's spawning reactions depend upon tactile stimuli derived from the male's clasp. Throughout the mating the male's forelimbs are locked tightly about the female's chest just behind the axilla. Normal egg-laying behavior is shown by isolated females if a rubber band is stretched tightly around the body at this point.

Many salamanders mate on land, and Noble (1929) showed that in some of these species chemical stimulation contributes to effective reproduction. The male two-lined salamander bears special scent glands in the skin of the head and at the base of the tail. During courtship the male first presses his temporal region against the female's snout and then walks away. The female follows the male closely, keeping her chin pressed against his tailbase. Spermatophores deposited by the male are promptly taken into the cloaca of the female, and fertilization is thereby achieved.

REPTILES. The courtship and mating of lizards depends heavily upon vision. The male American chameleon extends his dewlap and bobs his head up and down when another lizard comes in sight. Other males respond to this display by withdrawing or by executing the same behavior, and in the latter case the two animals usually fight. Female chameleons approach the challenging male and show a characteristic flexing of the neck, which indicates sexual receptivity (Fig. 3). This visual stimulus evokes courtship on the part of the male (Greenberg and Noble, 1944).

Male fence lizards react to the approach of a second individual by rising high on all four legs, displaying the brilliant colors of the lateral and ventral body surfaces. If the newcomer is a male he adopts the same posture. An aggressive encounter follows and one or the other male is driven from the scene. Females are dull in color and respond to the male's display with the execution of receptive behavior. Noble and Bradley (1933) painted female fence lizards with colors like those of the male and found that these individuals were treated as rivals rather than as potential mates. The receptive behavioral reactions of experimentally altered females were not sufficient to evoke courtship when combined with masculine coloration. Male lizards attempted to mate with other males whose legs were tied together to prevent the assumption of the fully erect posture and the display of masculine body colors.

Contact stimuli are important in the copulation of all lizards. At the beginning of mating the male holds the female's neck in his jaws, and later he may bite other portions of her body. Breeding males of some species bear hypertrophied "combs" on the inner surfaces of the thighs. During courtship these are rubbed against the female's flank and the resulting stimulation induces her to cooperate in copulation (Noble and Bradley, 1933).

The gecko and a few other lizards react sexually to certain auditory stimuli. Receptive females utter a sex call or chirp that attracts the male (Evans, 1935a). Greenberg (1943) found that male geckos are able to discriminate between the sexes on the basis of a chemical stimulus emanating from the skin of the female's tail. Bodily adjustments of the pair during coition consist in reflexive responses to stimulation of specialized tactile receptors. In this species, therefore, auditory, chemical, and touch sensations are all involved in sexual performance.

Male brown snakes and garter snakes are attracted by moving objects during the breeding season, and vision thus contributes

BIRDS. The importance of visual and auditory cues to sexual behavior in birds is attested by numerous experiments. Peripherally blinded male pigeons court the female, but their behavior is so poorly oriented that copulation does not occur (Schrader, 1889).

FIG. 3. Sexual display by the American chameleon. Males react to the sight of another lizard by extending the fan or dewlap and by bobbing the head up and down. Other males retreat or respond by performing the same actions. In the latter instance a fight may occur. Estrous females, such as the one shown in front of and below the male, remain quiet, flex the neck laterally in a receptive gesture, and as a result are courted and fertilized. (Reproduced through the courtesy of the American Museum of Natural History.)

to encounters between potential mates. The subsequent discrimination between males and females depends to a large extent upon chemical sensitivity. Skin from a receptive female exerts a stimulating effect upon breeding males. During coition bodily movements of the partner provide essential tactile cues, and males do not attempt to copulate with anesthetized estrous females. Tactile receptors in the male's chin mediate cues that assist in orientation; covering this region of the head prevents successful mating (Noble, 1937).

Noble (1936) showed that female flickers invite the male to copulate by uttering a specific call and assuming the coital position. Under normal conditions male flickers court any other individual of their species that shows these reactions. They attack a second male, apparently recognizing sex on the basis of the black "moustache" that is worn by all males but not by females. Females to which an artificial "moustache" is attached are attacked by their mates in spite of uttering the sex call and adopting the copulatory pose.

Male golden pheasants make copulatory responses to the stuffed skin of a female pheasant, but male skins are promptly attacked (Noble and Vogt, 1935). The stimulus object need not be posed in the coital position, because the male's discrimination is based upon differences in color pattern. Male robins rely heavily upon color vision in discriminating between the sexes. Mounted birds with a red breast are attacked, and those lacking this characteristic are often courted (Lack, 1939).

MAMMALS. It is often assumed that olfactory stimuli play a primary role in the sexual activity of lower animals. Under laboratory conditions, however, anosmic male rats and rabbits will mate with receptive females (Stone, 1923; Brooks, 1937; Beach, 1942a). Several sources of tactile stimulation can be eliminated without abolishing copulation. Anesthetizing the skin of the ventral body surfaces does not prevent such activity (Stone, 1923), and clipping the vibrissae or desensitizing the skin of the snout and lips permits the survival of effective sexual performance (Beach, 1942a). Partial deafening is without apparent effect (Stone, 1923). The combination of blindness and anosmia, or the elimination of olfaction and touch in the snout and lips, lowers the probability of copulation but does not insure its elimination (Beach, 1942a). Removal of the eyes and olfactory bulbs and destruction of the cochlea do not prevent the female rabbit from receiving the buck (Brooks, 1937).

It can be concluded that sexual arousal and coital reactions in rats and rabbits do not depend exclusively upon vision, olfaction, audition, or touch. However, survival of mating behavior after interference with one afferent pathway does not prove that the same system made no contribution when it was functional. Furthermore the methods of testing behavior have not been designed to measure the animal's capacity to court and mate under natural conditions. Males and females confined in small observation cages are forced into physical proximity.

Bodily contact occurs frequently, and the possible role of distance receptors is not revealed. Finally, desensitized animals have always been tested with normal mates, and under these conditions a deficiency in the responsiveness of the operated individual is frequently compensated when the intact partner intensifies its sexual behavior.

The normal mating performance of male and female rodents almost certainly is facilitated by several kinds of sensory stimulation, including those eliminated in the experiments described above. Olfaction undoubtedly contributes to sexual arousal in some male carnivores. Beach and Gilmore (1949) showed that urine from the estrous bitch has a stimulative value for sexually active male dogs. Urine collected from females in heat was compared with that of nonestrous bitches. Males spent a significantly greater amount of time investigating the urine collected from receptive females.

Female cats that are blind, deaf, and anosmic will mate with the male (Bard, 1939), but a normal male will approach and grip the female and she need only respond appropriately to touch and pressure sensations arising from contact initiated by the partner. The importance of vision in feline reproduction is indicated by the fact that cortically blind male cats do not approach or follow the receptive queen although they copulate normally if the female rubs against them in the course of her spontaneous courtship (Beach, 1949).

Observational evidence indicates that sexual arousal and orientation to the potential mate in male and female primates rests upon visual and auditory cues. When the pair comes together, chemical and contact stimuli also contribute to mating (Yerkes and Elder, 1936).

In mammals, as in all animals that reproduce by copulation, the behavior of males and females just prior to and during coitus appears to be governed primarily by tactile and pressure stimuli. The estrous rat sometimes displays mating responses when the experimenter strokes or palpates her back and sides with his fingers (Ball, 1937). Stroking the rump of the receptive guinea pig evokes assumption of the copulatory posture (Young et al., 1938), and comparable reactions can be elicited in the golden hamster (Beach, 1950). By pressing heavily on the back and sides of the sow in heat and moving the tail to one side, it is possible to induce the female to present the genitalia and grunt as in copulation (Altmann, 1941). Estrous female cats adopt the mating position if the experimenter grips the loose skin of the animal's neck in his fingers and presses upon its back (Bard, 1939). In each case the stimuli described mimic those normally provided by the sexually active male.

Genital sensation contributes heavily to effective mating in male and female mammals. Female hamsters, skunks, porcupines, and dogs adopt the mating position when the male licks, nibbles, or scratches at the vaginal region (Beach, 1947). The blood pressure of the estrous bitch rises abruptly in response to this form of contact (Pussep, 1922), and females that resist the male's initial attempts to mount often become fully receptive after a period of genital stimulation. Male primates stimulate the feminine genitalia manually and orally prior to coition, and the reactions of the female plainly indicate the sexually exciting quality of the resulting sensations (Bingham, 1928).

Females in which genital sensations are lacking may nevertheless show some mating behavior. This is the case in rats (Beach, 1945) and mice (Raynaud, 1938) with congenital absence of uterus and vagina. De-afferentation of the genitalia does not eliminate copulatory reactions in female rabbits (Brooks, 1937) or cats (Bard, 1935). Under normal conditions sensations from the genitals contribute to sexual behavior in female mammals, but it is evident that in at least some species this source of stimulation is not essential to mating.

Sexual arousal and the execution of copulatory responses occur in male cats after surgical anesthetization of the genitals and surrounding regions (Root and Bard, 1947). However, ejaculation has not been demonstrated in these animals, and other findings prove the importance of penile sensitivity to normal copulatory performance in several mammalian species. Male dogs show erection, ejaculation, and coital movements in response to manual stimulation of the phallus (Bard, 1939). Male rats rendered incapable of intromission by transection of the os penis continue to pursue and mount females. But intromission is rarely achieved, and the ejaculatory response is lacking. The results suggest that the attainment of the sexual climax is prevented by the absence of normal genital stimulation (Beach and Holz, 1946).

Sexual arousal and mating behavior in all or nearly all animals appear to involve the activation of several different afferent systems. Orientation to and movement toward a potential mate may occur in response to visual, auditory, or chemical cues. Any or all of these modalities may continue to influence the degree of excitement and to guide the bodily reactions of male and female during precoital courtship. The final stages of the copulatory relation are almost universally dependent upon somatic sensations of touch and pressure.

As far as the sensory basis for sexual arousal is concerned, there is no clear evidence of any progressive evolutionary change from invertebrates to mammals. Some classes include species that rely heavily if not exclusively on visual or chemical or auditory cues for the initiation of erotic excitement. But other species in the same classes depend upon multisensory stimulation for the same effect. The specificity of the adequate stimulus varies from species to species, and intra-class variability is as great as that between major phyletic divisions.

Studies of the Nervous System

A complete analysis of any type of behavior includes examination of its internal correlates. It is necessary to understand the contributions of the nervous system, the muscles, and the various chemical factors in the blood to the occurrence of the responses under examination. Some evidence concerning internal correlates of sexual behavior has been presented in the discussion of sensory functions. Studies of external and internal correlates are often complementary. Investigation of the role of various receptor systems frequently helps the experimentalist to delimit the range of external factors that might be essential.

Insects. Male wasps and silkworm moths do not approach the receptive female after removal of the antennae on which the olfactory organs are located. But these operated males mount a female if they come into contact with her, and in such circumstances fertile mating is possible. Grosch (1947) amputated the posterior body segments containing the reproductive organs. Male wasps prepared in this fashion displayed typical courtship reactions and repeatedly tried to mount the female. The sensory and motor mechanisms of the anterior body parts are, therefore, capable of carrying out their part of the sexual pattern even though large segments of the total response system are missing.

Kellogg (1907) found that, although antennaless male silkworm moths mate when placed in contact with the female, this behavior cannot be induced after the entire head has been removed. In the absence of the dominant cephalic ganglia the segmental nervous centers lose their excitability and are incapable of mediating even fragments of the total sexual pattern. The same operation does not eliminate sexual responses in the female of this species. Males mate with headless females and the latter display normal oviposition reflexes and lay eggs. Female bodies deprived of the head, thorax, and part of the abdomen continue to attract the male. This fractional part of the female lays a few eggs during mating and some of the eggs develop.

Fishes. The primary importance of the visual system to sexual behavior in some fishes is revealed by descriptions of courtship and mating in peripherally blinded jewel fish (Noble and Curtis, 1939). Eyeless females of this species will lay eggs in the presence of a normal mate. But the eggs are scattered over an area about three times as large as usual, and the female does not synchronize her behavior with that of the male. Blind males may fertilize a small portion of the eggs laid by their normal partners, but they are unable to time the spawning responses appropriately, and they fail to integrate their behavior with that of the female.

Unilateral destruction of the cerebrum, or the placement of small bilateral lesions in this area, does not prevent normal reproduction in the jewel fish, according to the preliminary findings of Noble and Borne (1941). But more extensive forebrain loss disorganizes courtship and spawning. There is no indication of localized function in any part of the forebrain. Different elements in the pattern drop out as a result of large brain lesions, but the same reaction may disappear after destruction of different portions of the forebrain, and the number of elements eliminated appears to be a function of the extent of the lesion. Complete decerebration abolishes sexual activity.

Aronson (1948) studied the effects of partial and total removal of the forebrain upon sexual behavior in the male African mouthbreeder fish. He found that subtotal decerebration has little or no effect upon courtship and mating. Completely decerebrate males display no change in the early phases of courtship, but the reactions immediately before and during spawning are seriously affected.

Nest building, which usually precedes spawning, is appreciably reduced by this operation. Normal males always fertilize the eggs promptly after the female has laid them, but decerebrate fishes did so in only 8 per cent of the cases. Forebrainless males rarely carry the fertilized eggs in the mouth in the manner of normal individuals. Control lesions in the cerebellum had no effect upon sexual activities, and Aronson concluded that changes noted in decerebrate males could be referred specifically to disturbance of forebrain function rather than general shock following injury to any part of the nervous system.

Amphibians. We have seen that the visual system contributes to effective mating in

lesions do not orient themselves normally on the female after the clasp has been achieved.

The "warning croak" which the male emits when clasped by another frog depends upon the presence of the inferior colliculi and is independent of higher centers. Males that are ready to breed produce a characteristic sex call which is mediated primarily by the midbrain although it may survive extensive invasion of this area. The spawning move-

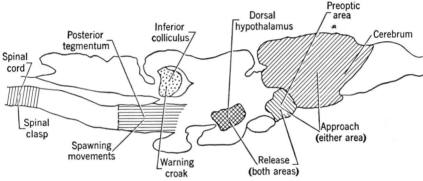

Fig. 4. Diagrammatic sagittal section through the brain of the leopard frog, showing some of the regions that mediate different elements in the male's mating pattern. (Redrawn from Aronson and Noble, 1945.)

some amphibians. Peripherally blinded male leopard frogs fail to swim toward the waiting female, although they are capable of fertile spawning if they come into physical contact with a mate. The South African clawed toad is less dependent upon visual cues, according to the report of Berk, Cheetham, and Shapiro (1936). Blind males of this species approach and clasp females, and, although the clasping position is often abnormal, it is usually corrected without delay.

Aronson and Noble's (1945) careful studies of mating in brain-operated leopard frogs show that different parts of the nervous system exert special control over particular elements in the total pattern (Fig. 4). The male's tendency to clasp a second frog in sexual fashion depends in large measure upon spinal mechanisms. Clasping occurs despite complete transection through the caudal end of the medulla, although animals with such

ments shown by the clasping male each time the female expels a cluster of eggs are not affected by removal of the forebrain. They survive as long as the posterior tegmentum is intact.

After spawning is completed, the normal male relaxes his mating clasp. Frogs with large lesions in the preoptic region of the forebrain and the pars dorsalis of the hypothalamus fail to release the female, but injury to more anterior brain parts does not produce this effect. The male's tendency to swim toward another frog survives removal of most of the forebrain, provided the preoptic area is spared. It is not eliminated by operations that destroy only the preoptic region. Apparently both the preoptic nucleus and the remainder of the forebrain normally contribute to this response although either area is capable of mediating it independently.

Reptiles. There is very little evidence concerning neural correlates of sexual behavior in reptiles. Diebschlag (1938) reported that unilateral decerebration does not prevent mating in the male emerald lizard, but bilateral removal of the forebrain abolishes courtship and copulation.

Birds. It was stated above that peripherally blind male pigeons are incapable of coordinated courtship and mating. Schrader's (1889) observations on brain-operated pigeons showed that total decerebration eliminates mating. Forebrainless males may display some courtship responses, but they do not orient their behavior to the receptive female. Rogers (1922) also noted the absence of effective reproductive behavior in pigeons deprived of the hyperstriatum, which constitutes a large part of the complex avian forebrain. He concluded that the hyperstriatum "ties together" the discrete responses involved in courtship and copulation.

Unpublished studies conducted in the writer's laboratory indicate that the partial destruction of the forebrain reduces the probability that male pigeons will copulate with females, but it does not always affect preliminary courtship behavior. Total decerebration (confirmed by examination of the sectioned brains) eliminates courtship as well as copulation. Different elements in the sexual pattern do not appear to be controlled by separate parts of the corpus striatum. Forebrain injury reduces the male's responsiveness to the female without rendering him physically incapable of sexual performance. Some males sustaining extensive brain injury resume copulating after the injection of androgen.

Mammals. The neural correlates of sexual behavior have been studied more extensively in mammals than in lower vertebrates. Progressive encephalization of nervous function in the course of mammalian evolution has been accompanied by several changes in the control of courtship and mating, but there are many basic similarities between mammals and other animals.

SPINAL MECHANISMS. Erection and ejaculation occur in male rodents (Bacq and Brouha, 1933), rabbits (Durfee, Lerner, and Kaplan, 1940), and dogs (Schafer, 1900) in response to electrical stimulation of the sacral cord. These genital reflexes survive in male mammals despite complete transection of the spinal cord in the lumbar region.

Abdominal sympathectomy eliminates ejaculation but does not prevent erection or active copulatory responses in male rats, rabbits, guinea pigs, or cats (Bacq, 1931; Bacq and Brouha, 1933; Root and Bard, 1947).

Male cats (Dusser de Barenne and Koskoff, 1934) and dogs (Schafer, 1900) in which the cord is sectioned above the lumbar region react to stimulation of the penis by executing gross movements suggestive of intercourse. Riddoch (1917) described the "coital reflex" which occurs in spinal man in response to genital stimulation. More recent observations by Munro, Horne, and Paull (1948) and Rosenquist (1949) reveal that complete spinal section does not necessarily prevent fertile copulation in the human male.

Certain elements of the female mammal's sexual pattern survive transection of the spinal cord. Some estrous reactions continue in the bitch after lumbar section (Golz, 1874), and female cats with the cord cut at the cervical level react to stimulation of the perineum by treading and moving the tail to one side as in copulation (Maes, 1939).

Description of the fragmentary sexual responses shown by the spinal animal should not obscure the fact that these are isolated segments of a pattern. In intact individuals the spinal mechanisms are subject to control by higher nervous centers. Nevertheless, in mammals as in insects and lower vertebrates the neural correlates of sexual behavior include segmental reflex mechanisms capable of a considerable degree of autonomous function.

BRAIN MECHANISMS. Coital behavior of female mammals depends in part upon certain diencephalic mechanisms. Guinea pigs, rats, and cats show marked reduction or complete elimination of sexual responsiveness following destruction of the anterior hypothalamus (Fisher, Magoun, and Ranson, 1938; Dempsey and Rioch, 1939; Bard, 1940). Male rats with hypothalamic lesions are reported to display less sexual behavior postoperatively, although no description of the changes has been published (Clark, 1942).

The importance of higher brain regions varies according to the sex of the individual and the species to which it belongs. Complete removal of the cerebral cortex, hippocampus, and corpus striatum does not abolish copulatory activity in female guinea pigs, rabbits, rats, or cats (Dempsey and Rioch, 1939; Brooks, 1937; Davis, 1939; Bard, 1936). Beach reported (1944) that decorticated female rats show increased sexual excitability accompanied by certain behavioral deficiencies. The tendency to direct the receptive reactions toward the male is lost; and separate elements in the sexual pattern are not normally synchronized.

Male rabbits deprived of all neocortical tissue continue to display grossly normal sexual reactions (Brooks, 1937). Davis (1939) found that extensive cortical injury did not always eliminate mating behavior in male rats, but investigations by the present writer (Beach, 1940, 1941) showed that sexual activity in males of this species is definitely affected by cortical lesions involving more than 20 per cent of the total neopallium. Destruction of 20 to 50 per cent of the cortex eliminates mating in some individuals but not in others, and the number of rats copulating after operation is inversely related to the amount of tissue removed (Fig. 5). Male rats with bilateral lesions exceeding 60 per cent of the cortex do not copulate postoperatively.

Smaller lesions that do not abolish coition may render it more difficult to elicit. The proportion of tests in which the male shows mating reactions is reduced after operation. However, when the copulation does occur, the pattern of the response is normal. Some animals that fail to mate after relatively small lesions can be induced to do so when injected with large amounts of male hormone.

These findings suggest that the cortex is not directly involved in the organization of sexual

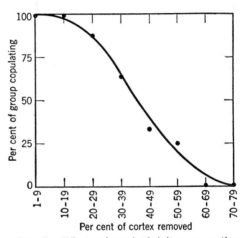

FIG. 5. Effects of cerebral injury on mating behavior in male rats. The proportion of different groups continuing to copulate after operation varies according to the amount of cortex removed. (Redrawn from Beach, 1940.)

responses in the male rat but serves to maintain the excitability of lower centers that are essential to the integration of mating behavior. In the absence of facilitative support from the cortex, these hypothetical executive mechanisms become relatively unresponsive to exteroceptive stimuli.

It has been pointed out that female rats continue to mate despite total decortication. Presumably this indicates that the neural circuits essential to feminine sexual performance are not so dependent upon cortical facilitation as are those for masculine reactions. Convincing proof of this assumption is provided by the results of another experiment (Beach, 1943). Many normal female rats display masculine mating responses when placed with a second female that is in heat. Male behavior is eliminated in these females by large cortical lesions, but their feminine mating responses survive.

Unlike females of their species, male cats do not mate after extensive forebrain injury (Bard, 1940). This difference is due in part to the fact that the female's coital adjustments do not involve precise sensory-motor coordinations mediated at the cortical level. But, in addition, the decerebrate female displays spontaneous courtship, and no comparable behavior is seen in decorticate males. Sexual excitability in female carnivores, as in female rodents, appears to be much less dependent upon cortical facilitation than it does in males.

Removal of critical cortical areas produces specific deficiencies in the male cat's mating performance. Animals lacking the visual cortex have difficulty locating and following the female, but their coital behavior is normal if they are placed in contact with her. Removal of the frontal lobes renders the male incapable of coordinated sexual activity. Cats with such lesions show no reduction in sexual excitability, but they experience great difficulty in achieving intromission because their bodily adjustments to the female are awkward and uncoordinated (Langworthy, 1943). The completely decorticated male shows no signs of excitement in the presence of an estrous female and does not attempt to copulate when placed in the proper position (Beach, 1949).

Differences between male rats and male cats reflect the increased corticalization of sensory-motor functions in carnivores. Cats retain their sexual excitability but fail to copulate after the removal of particular cortical areas because these areas are essential for the integration and timing of successive stages in the coital pattern. Absense of responsiveness in complete decorticates suggests that the entire neopallium contributes to the male's capacity for sexual arousal in carnivores as well as in rodents.

The neurological evidence shows that the sexual behavior of all animals includes a number of reflexes controlled by primitive neural circuits. From frog to man we find proof that certain elements in the normal mating pattern can be mediated by spinal mechanisms lacking any connection with the brain. At the same time it is clear that the integration of the individual reactions into a biologically effective sequence becomes increasingly dependent upon the forebrain as encephalization of sensory-motor functions progresses. Finally, there are several indications that susceptibility to sexual arousal, and the ability to engage in fertile copulation, are less dependent upon the cerebrum in the female than in the male.

Studies of Blood Chemistry

Sexual behavior in vertebrates and invertebrates may be strongly affected by various alterations in blood chemistry such as those produced by drugs, special diets, or hormonal secretions.

Drugs. Several commercially available aphrodisiacs, widely used by animal husbandrymen, have been tested on laboratory animals. Cantharides, which is prepared from the dried body of a species of beetle, stimulates the mucous membranes of the urogenital tract and is given to domestic animals as a sex stimulant. However, the present writer administered different concentrations of this substance to castrated male rats without producing any change in mating behavior.

Another drug commonly used as an aphrodisiac is yohimbine, an alkaloid derived from the bark of the West African yohimbehe tree. Fugo and Gross (1942) reported that female rats injected with yohimbine-HCl displayed abnormally long estrous cycles and exhibited masculine mating responses. Hypophysectomized animals were not affected by the drug, and the authors concluded that the drug affects the ovaries indirectly as a result of its influence upon the anterior pituitary. In contradiction to this report, Sulman and

Black (1945) state that they were unable to demonstrate any effect of yohimbine on the sex glands, the sexual organs, or the behavior of mice or rats of either sex. And we have already noted that masculine sexual behavior frequently occurs in untreated female rats.

Alcohol depresses genital reflexes in male dogs (Gantt, 1940).

Sexual activity decreases in monkeys addicted to heroin and reappears in exaggerated form when the drug is withdrawn (Seevers, 1936). Dogs maintained on a schedule of morphine injections become sexually hyperactive during periods of withdrawal (Tatum, Seevers, and Collins, 1929), and monkeys masturbate frequently under similar conditions (Kolb and DuMez, 1931). Morphine decreases sexual desire and potency in human beings, and prolonged withdrawal of the drug is accompanied by increased sexual reactions. Continued erections and frequent emissions occur in the deprived male addict, and "spontaneous" orgasms are reported by females (Terry and Pellens, 1928). Spragg (1940) found that morphine acts as a sex stimulant in male chimpanzees. Shortly after the daily shot of the drug males display frequent erections, masturbation, and eagerness to copulate with females. Sexual excitability and potency decrease progressively during the 24-hour period following an injection. No explanation is available for these species differences in the effects of morphine.

Diet. Stone (1924) showed that the onset of adult sexual behavior is delayed in rats maintained on a quantitatively reduced diet. The results cannot be referred to retardation in secretion of testicular hormone, for prolonged inanition does not affect the histological condition of the secretory cells (Siperstein, 1920–21). However, male rats raised on a quantitatively insufficient diet copulate as early as or earlier than control animals, provided they are treated with androgen (Stone, 1942a). The most likely explanation is that the hypernormal concentration of male hormone compensates for the detrimental effects of semistarvation.

Miles (1919) described decreased interest in sexual matters on the part of young men whose normal caloric intake was reduced by one-third to one-half. Specific dietary deficiencies sometimes affect sexual reactions. Wiesner and Bacharach (1937) maintained rats on a diet lacking vitamin E but adequate with respect to A and D and containing yeast. After several months, mating responses disappeared in many animals and became less frequent and less complete in the remaining individuals.

Hormones. Much of the evidence concerning the effects of hormones upon behavior has been summarized elsewhere (Beach, 1948). The mating reactions of some insects appear to be independent of sex hormones, for removal of the reproductive glands in larvae or adults does not prevent copulatory behavior in the gypsy moth (Oudemanns, 1899), the silkworm moth (Kellogg, 1904), or the cricket (Regen, 1909). In most vertebrates, however, sexual activities are strongly affected by glandular products. All endocrine secretions that contribute to metabolic processes of the organism are indirectly involved in sexual behavior. Sexual functions are likely to be depressed or eliminated by acute hypothyroidism, by deficiency of adrenocortical hormone, or by any other glandular disturbance having an adverse influence upon general health. More immediate and direct effects are exerted by the gonadal hormones.

FISHES. Sexual behavior can be induced before the normal breeding season by stimulating the gonads to produce sex hormones. This effect has been produced in goldfish by injections of pituitary hormones (Hasler and Meyer, 1942). Immature male guppies show adult mating reactions if treated with androgen (Eversole, 1941). Noble and Kumpf (1936–37) found that removal of the ovaries eliminated mating activity in female jewel fish and Siamese fighting fish, but adult castration did not influence the male's sexual responses. Administration of ovarian hormones to spayed females was followed by the reappearance of breeding behavior.

AMPHIBIANS. Sexual behavior in amphibians occurs seasonally, and the sex glands are maximally active during the breeding period. The male leopard frog utters the sex call only when the secretory cells of the testis are functional. Administration of androgen to immature male toads elicits a precocious appearance of the adult mating call (Blair, 1946). Male and female frogs and toads become sexually active out of season if they are injected with a pituitary substance that brings the gonads into functional condition (Noble and Aronson, 1942). Castration of male amphibians before the beginning of the mating season prevents breeding behavior (Noble and Aronson, 1942), but gonadectomized frogs display normal sexual behavior following implantation of testicular tissue or injection of appropriate extracts (Edinger, 1913).

REPTILES. The seasonal appearance of sexual behavior in snakes and lizards is closely correlated with recrudescence of the sex glands and secretion of gonadal hormones (Blanchard and Blanchard, 1942; Reynolds, 1943; Cieslak, 1945). Administration of gonadotrophic hormones is followed by out-of-season mating in lizards (Evans, 1935b; Greenberg and Noble, 1944). Evans (1935c) treated immature female chameleons with pituitary hormones and obtained precocious sexual responses; and similar effects have been produced in males by the administration of androgen (Noble and Greenberg, 1941). Removal of the reproductive glands during the breeding season is followed by a rapid loss of sex responses in male and female lizards, and the injection of androgen into castrated males or of estrogen into spayed females restores copulatory behavior (Reynolds, 1943; Greenberg and Noble, 1944).

BIRDS. Annual breeding cycles in some birds are closely and positively related to the functional development of the sex glands (Bullough, 1942a). Premature sexual responses appear in male and female domestic fowl treated with androgen and estrogen, respectively (Noble and Zitrin, 1942). Castration eliminates copulatory behavior in male pigeons, although some courtship responses survive indefinitely. The loss is gradual, extending over several months (Carpenter, 1933). Ovariectomized adult domestic and wild birds show no breeding behavior. But gonadectomized females are capable of normal sexual behavior under the influence of injected ovarian hormones, and the same is true of castrated males treated with androgen (Noble and Wurm, 1940; Davis and Domm, 1943).

SUBPRIMATE MAMMALS. A great many mammalian species are seasonal breeders, and the yearly occurrence of sexual activity depends upon the development of the secretory function in the gonads (Rice, 1942). Out-of-season breeding has been induced by the administration of pituitary hormones that stimulate the reproductive glands (Gaunt and Hays, 1938; Nelsen and Maxwell, 1941). Some domesticated mammals are fertile at all seasons, and the female comes into heat at regular intervals. The rhythms of sexual receptivity are closely associated with parallel cycles of hormone secretion by the ovaries (Hammond, 1944; Blandau, Boling, and Young, 1941). Immature female rats display no mating behavior, but they can be induced to do so by precocious stimulation of the ovaries (Smith and Engle, 1927), and males and females show adult behavior 2 to 4 weeks earlier than usual after treatment with the appropriate sex hormone (Beach, 1942b). Castration of either sex in infancy prevents the appearance of adult mating reactions at the time of puberty (Beach, 1942c, d; Hertz, Meyer, and Spielman, 1937). However, males and females gonadectomized in infancy show normal coital behavior if treated with gonadal hormones in adulthood (Moore and Price, 1938; Boling, Young, and Dempsey, 1938).

Female rodents and carnivores promptly cease to show sexual responsiveness and possess little stimulative value for the male after ovariectomy in adulthood, but normal mating occurs in these animals in response to the appropriate hormone treatment (Wiesner and Mirskaia, 1930; Ring, 1944). Male rats, rabbits, and hamsters react to adult castra-

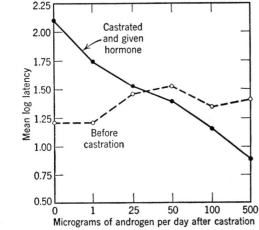

FIG. 6. One effect of androgen administration upon mating behavior in castrated male rats. "Latency" refers to the interval between the introduction of a receptive female and the occurrence of the first copulation. The speed with which coitus is initiated by castrated animals is seen to depend upon the amount of male hormone they are given. Other aspects of the coital pattern are similarly affected. (Redrawn from Beach and Holz-Tucker, 1949.)

tion with a gradual loss of sexual activity (Stone, 1927, 1932; Beach and Pauker, 1949). Ejaculatory responses disappear a week or two after the operation. The capacity for erection and intromission survives somewhat longer but is lost within approximately 1 month. Incomplete mating reactions tend to persist indefinitely. These postoperative changes can be prevented or reversed by supplying the castrated male with androgen, and the behavioral effect is quantitatively related to the amount of hormone administered (Fig. 6).

The behavioral consequences of castration in larger domestic mammals have not been studied systematically. Casual observation suggests that male sheep, pigs, horses, and cattle exhibit some sexual activity for long periods after castration in adulthood, but no details are available (Steinach, 1894; Rice, 1942). Experiments now being conducted in the writer's laboratory prove that some male dogs show normal sexual behavior at least as long as 2 years after castration in adulthood.

PRIMATES. The sexual behavior of lower primates is less dependent upon gonadal hormones than is that of some lower mammals. Monkeys have a clear-cut menstrual cycle which depends upon the periodic increase and decrease in the concentration of ovarian hormones, but the female's willingness to copulate is not entirely restricted to the estrous period (Carpenter, 1942). Captive and free-living females occasionally receive the male when they are not physiologically in heat. Furthermore, ovariectomized females are capable of some sexual activity without the support of exogenous hormones (Kluver and Bucy, 1939).

Yerkes and Elder (1936) observed that female chimpanzees often encourage copulation despite low levels of estrogen. Mating may continue after removal of the ovaries, although it occurs rarely and perhaps only in rather unusual situations (G. Clark, personal communication). It should be understood that reduction in dependence upon gonadal hormones is relative rather than complete. Monkeys and apes are most receptive and eager for intercourse at times when the estrogen level is high.

Many women experience cycles of sexual responsiveness that correlate with the menstrual rhythm (Davis, 1929; Stopes, 1931; Dickinson, 1931). In most instances, however, maximal desire occurs just before or just after menstruation. These are not fertile periods and do not correspond with the peak of estrogen secretion. The additional fact that erotic excitability survives ovariectomy or menopause, often without reduction (Filler and Drezner, 1944), suggests that the trend observed in subhuman primates has been extended even further in our own species with the result that ovarian hormones are not necessary to full sexual behavior.

Very little is known concerning the sexual capacity of castrated monkeys or apes. One adult chimpanzee gonadectomized in infancy is reported to copulate readily and vigorously with receptive females. The ejaculatory response is lacking, but it appears under androgen therapy (Clark, 1945). Prepuberally castrated men are rarely if ever capable of complete sexual response. Removal of the testes in adult males sometimes causes marked reduction in sex drive and capacity for satisfactory intercourse. In other cases, however, no change is experienced for as long as 10 to 20 years after the operation (Feiner and Rothman, 1939; Tauber, 1940). Men whose sexual ability declines as a result of castration can sometimes be restored to normal by androgen therapy (Moehlig, 1940). Until more data are collected we can only point out the range of individual differences and observe that in some men testicular hormone is not necessary for normal sexual activity.

This review of the endocrine basis for sexual behavior indicates that ovarian hormones are essential to mating in females of many if not all vertebrate classes and orders with the specific exception of primates. Considering successively monkeys, apes, and human beings, we see evidence of a progressive relaxation of this hormonal control over sexual responsiveness. In male animals it is clear that testicular hormone is necessary to normal development of mating behavior, for prepuberal castration usually reduces the frequency of sexual reactions in adulthood, and the responses that occur are never complete. However, the effects of castration in adulthood may vary with the species and even with the individual involved. Some male fish, dogs, horses, cattle, and human beings are capable of normal sexual performance years after removal of the sex glands. It is possible that differ-

ences in the importance of gonadal hormones for masculine and feminine sexual behavior are related to differences in the extent to which the forebrain influences these two types of reaction.

Development in the Individual and Modification by Experience

Sexual behavior appears in many animals before they are reproductively mature, and a few elements in the adult mating pattern are present in infancy.

Behavior of immature individuals. Basic sexual reflexes mediated by spinal centers may be fully developed at the time of birth. Erection of the penis occurs in newborn boys and in neonatal primates of other species (Halverson, 1940; Hines, 1942). For a few hours after birth infant guinea pigs respond to tactile stimulation of the perineal region by adopting the mating posture of the adult female (Boling et al., 1939).

The play of juvenile mammals often includes portions of the adult mating pattern. Rats of most domestic strains become fertile at approximately 50 days of age, but young animals pursue, mount, and clasp other individuals as early as 21 days after birth. Pelvic thrusts sometimes occur, and the only element lacking is the ejaculatory reflex (Beach, 1942b). Comparable prepuberal sex play is common in guinea pigs, hamsters, and other rodents (Louttit, 1929; Bond, 1945). Scott (1945) noted that male lambs mount other sheep in sexual fashion as early as 3 days after birth though they do not become mature until the following year. According to Hooker (1944) copulatory behavior appears in male calves 3 months before fertile mating is possible. Male lion cubs exhibit incomplete mating reactions at 3 months of age and attain reproductive maturity at the end of the second year (Cooper, 1942).

Subprimate mammals rarely display any part of the female mating pattern before puberty. Absence of prepuberal feminine behavior in lower mammals is due to the rigid dependence of such reactions upon gonadal hormones. The complete adult response can be elicited precociously if the appropriate ovarian hormones are administered, and this shows that the essential neuromuscular mechanisms are mature before they are normally called into play. In some species the testis secretes small amounts of hormone soon after birth (Oesting and Webster, 1938; Hooker, 1944), but the sex play of immature males is unchanged by castration at birth (Beach, 1942d). The difference in prepuberal behavior reflects differences in the extent to which the male and female patterns are controlled by gonadal secretions, and perhaps the unequal contribution of the forebrain to the two types of response.

Infantile sex play is more frequent and complete in primates than in lower mammals. Furthermore it appears in females as well as in males, and this probably reflects the partial independence of feminine sexual activity from strict hormonal control. Male macaque monkeys rub the erect penis against objects in the environment as early as 3 weeks after birth, and during the first year they exhibit rhythmic motions of the pelvis in response to stimulation of the penis. Use of rubber playthings and other small objects in sexual fashion is common (Hines, 1942). Male chimpanzees masturbate themselves and mount other individuals in sexual play several years before adolescence (Bingham, 1928).

Female rhesus monkeys display the sexual presentation pattern as early as 6 months after birth (Carpenter, 1942). Several years before puberty female chimpanzees engage in sexual play with young males, exhibiting invitational responses and permitting mounting with partial intromission (Bingham, 1928).

Behavior of inexperienced adults. Observations by naturalists and animal husbandrymen suggest that mature males without mating experience frequently attempt to copulate with biologically inadequate partners.

Cichlid fishes reared in isolation attempt to mate with other fish of either sex, but after some experience they restrict their courtship to females (Noble and Curtis, 1935). Young red-winged blackbirds attempt coition with the stuffed skins of either males, or females; but older males mount only the dummy females (Noble and Vogt, 1935). Craig (1914) found that doves reared in isolation do not respond normally to receptive females but often try to mount the hand of the experimenter. Inexperienced bulls try to mount heifers that are in proestrus and are not yet receptive, whereas the experienced breeder mounts only those cows that are fully in heat. De Alba and Asdell (1946) state that adult males lose this discriminatory ability if they are isolated from females for a long time. According to Macirone and Walton (1938) sexually inexperienced male rabbits mount the doe in abnormal positions more frequently than do older bucks.

Heterosexual experience is not essential to effective mating in adult rats (Stone, 1922), and unpublished observations by the writer indicate that the same is true of dogs. Male and female rats reared in individual cages from the age of weaning display normal mating reactions when placed together after they mature. Inexperienced males given the opportunity to mate with young female guinea pigs, infant rabbits, male rats, nonestrous female rats, and female rats in heat rarely mount any animal save the receptive female (Beach, 1942a). This disagreement with impressions based upon field and farmyard observations may reflect species differences, but the observational evidence will have to be validated by systematic studies before any final conclusion can be reached.

Several observers have reported that inexperienced male primates are incapable of complete copulation (Bingham, 1928; Yerkes and Elder, 1936). Mature monkeys and apes that have never mated give evidence of sexual arousal in the presence of receptive partners, but their coital responses are fragmentary and disorganized. Attempts to cover the female are poorly oriented, and intromission is not achieved. The capacity for prompt and effective copulation is developed gradually through practice.

Female primates are less dependent upon learning, and the naive monkey or ape usually responds adequately to an experienced male. When an inexperienced male and female are placed together, the sexual behavior of the latter is much more appropriate and effective than that of her partner. Female monkeys that have never copulated sometimes attempt to assist the consort in the performance of his role. It is possible that sex differences in the mating behavior of inexperienced primates is indicative of a parallel difference in the contribution of the cerebral cortex to masculine and feminine performance.

Alterations produced by experience. Practice is not essential for effective coitus in many animals, but susceptibility to sexual arousal and the kinds of behavior shown by the sexually excited individual can be altered by experience.

ELIMINATION OF INHIBITION. Male mammals often fail to respond to receptive females encountered in new and strange environments. In general the absence of arousal seems due to the distracting effects of nonsexual stimuli (Beach, 1947). Females are much less susceptible to this form of inhibition, and commercial animal breeders usually take receptive females to the male to be bred in surroundings with which he is familiar (Kokolsky, 1945). The sex difference may be due in part to the relative independence of feminine behavior from cerebral functions.

The sexually inhibiting effects of a strange environment may be dissipated gradually as the male becomes accustomed to his new surroundings, and some individuals that fail to mate at first contact succeed in doing so after they have been put with a receptive female in the same pen or cage several days in succession. The proportion of male rats

showing copulatory reactions increases in the course of the first three or four sex tests, and this presumably reflects individual variation in the readiness with which different males adapt to the testing situation (Beach, 1940).

Environmental interference may be suddenly and completely eliminated as the result of a successful copulation. Regardless of their term of residence in the laboratory very few male cats copulate the first time they are taken to the observation room and placed with a receptive female. The absence of sexual responsiveness may continue for months, but after one completed mating the male displays spontaneous courtship and copulation in all subsequent tests (Zitrin and Beach, 1945).

PRODUCTION OF INHIBITION. Male mammals often fail to copulate in an environmental setting previously associated with punishment. Dogs that have become "neurotic" as a result of experimental treatment are slow to respond to estrous females presented in the room where the experiments were conducted, but the same males mate readily in the kennel (Gantt, 1944). Male rats subjected to electric shock during or immediately after copulation with the receptive female usually fail to mate in subsequent tests (Wheeler, 1933).

Painful or frustrating experiences associated with initial heterosexual contacts often depress responsiveness to receptive females. Young male foxes that have been attacked or frightened by the female often avoid contact with other vixens in later tests, and consequently males are trained for breeding by placing them with gentle females that are fully receptive (Enders, 1945). If a severe fight occurs during initial matings, young male mink fail to develop the sexual aggressiveness necessary for effective breeding. But males that have copulated successfully several times are not repelled by temporary resistance on the part of the female and can be depended upon to fertilize any animal that is in estrus (Kokolsky, 1945).

A male's readiness to mate may be conditioned by the presence and behavior of other males. In one experiment four roosters kept in a small pen with several hens developed a dominance hierarchy. One male was completely subordinate to the other three, and his attempts to mate with females were a signal for prompt attack by all other males. Eventually the sexual activity of this individual was completely suppressed. Even when the three dominant cocks were removed from the pen, the subordinate rooster made no attempt to court or tread the females (Guhl, Collias, and Allee, 1945).

Schneirla (1946) has called attention to the fact that the behavior of confined animals may bear little resemblance to what would appear in a natural environment. However, the importance of social dominance to sexual activities has been revealed by field studies of free-living birds. J. W. Scott (1944) noted that dominant male sage grouse have free access to receptive females whereas socially subordinate cocks rarely have an opportunity to mate.

POSITIVE RESPONSES TO NONSEXUAL STIMULI. Sexual arousal and mating behavior are most likely to occur in a setting that offers few distracting stimuli. Furthermore a specific environment previously associated with sexual activity tends to acquire a stimulating value that increases the probability of mating. Male rats that have copulated with receptive females in a particular cage often attempt to mate with males or nonreceptive females encountered in the original testing situation (Beach, 1942a). Male rabbits accustomed to receiving estrous does in the living cage will mount small animals of several species or even inanimate objects that are offered in similar fashion (Brooks, 1937).

Breder and Coates (1935) established in male guppies conditioned sexual responses to a glass beaker. In preliminary tests the empty beaker was investigated by the male fish but no mating behavior occurred. Next a receptive female was placed in the beaker, and some of the males became sexually active, attempting to copulate with the female through the glass. Successive presentations of the beaker containing a female were made at hourly intervals and produced an increase in the percentage of males responding. After this the empty beaker was lowered into the males' tank and evoked sexual attempts on the part of many individuals. The empty beaker introduced 24 hours after it had been paired with the visual stimulus of a female called forth mating responses in 16 per cent of the tests. One hour later the female was offered inside the beaker, and 83 per cent of the tests were positive. A single presentation of the empty beaker extinguished the response.

Certain behavioral characteristics of the estrous female appear to become sexually exciting to the male as a result of experience. Female howler monkeys display a sporadic arm reflex when they are approaching or copulating with a male. Carpenter's (1942) field observations of this species led him to suggest that through associative learning the female's arm movements come to exert a stimulating effect upon the male before physical contact is established.

CONDITIONING TO SPECIFIC PARTNERS. Experience is responsible for the specific preferences shown by some animals in their selection of sexual partners. Guhl, Collias, and Allee (1945) found that in chicken flocks roosters court and mate with hens of low social rank more frequently than with those whose dominance status in the flock is high. High-ranking females are less likely to show the sex invitation and less likely to respond receptively when approached by the male. Guhl and Warren (1946) reported that individual hens show a preference for mating with particular roosters, and a female that is entirely receptive to one cock may avoid copulation by another male.

Male mammals of several species do not attempt to mate with strange females even though they are fully receptive. Comparable discrimination is not always shown by females. The estrous porcupine accepts any sexually aggressive male without delay, but males do not copulate with a female until the two animals have inhabited adjacent cages for several days (Shadle, 1946). Domesticated male ungulates sometimes refuse to serve a particular type of female. A stallion bred exclusively to dark mares may show no inclination to mount a white one; and jacks that have been allowed to mate with jennets often fail to copulate with mares (Marshall and Hammond, 1945).

Tinklepaugh's (1928) description of sexual behavior in a male rhesus monkey reveals a very complex sort of conditioning. After two years of cohabitation with one female monkey of a different species, the male was caged with a mate of his own kind. Although she was sexually receptive, the male's reactions consisted solely of violent aggression. Eventually his aversion was reduced to the point of permitting coition, but immediately after copulating the male inflicted severe wounds on his own body. Self-mutilation occurred whenever the original mate came into sight.

This brief survey of the development of sexual behavior in the individual indicates the dangers of broad generalizations concerning the role of learning in courtship and mating. Although, under laboratory conditions, some animals are capable of mating without previous heterosexual experience, there are many species for which this is not true. And even within the same species the two sexes may differ in the completeness of their initial coital performance. Finally, although fertile copulation is possible in some inexperienced animals, it is abundantly clear that the individual's subsequent sexual reactions may be profoundly modified by experience.

PARENTAL AND FILIAL BEHAVIOR

In the following discussion all responses involved in care of the eggs and young are classified as parental behavior. Preparation for egg laying and provision for the welfare of the offspring are arbitrarily treated as parental activities even if the eggs or young are subsequently left to develop without incubation, protection, or feeding. All responses of young animals to the parents or to other adults acting in a parental capacity are listed as filial behavior. Methods of analyzing parental and filial reactions are the same as those employed in the study of courtship and mating. In fact it is worth repeating that this general type of analysis is applicable to any form of behavior.

Functions of Sensory Stimulation

In parental as in sexual behavior we find that certain forms of stimulation lead to relatively long-term physiological changes that in turn make possible adaptive reactions to more specific external correlates.

Stimuli affecting physiological readiness. The crop sacs of pigeons and doves are thin membraneous structures at all stages of the life cycle except during the last 8 to 10 days of the incubation period. At this time the two lateral pouches of the crop in both sexes increase as much as twenty times in thickness; and during the succeeding 3 weeks, while the young are being fed, the thickened mucosa is desquamated intermittently in thick layers of caseous "crop milk." Formation of "crop milk" is influenced by exteroceptive stimuli. The cock pigeon with no squabs to feed produces "milk" if he is able to see other adults caring for their young (Witschi, 1935).

In a number of birds and mammals parental reactions appear after a period of exposure to young animals of the same species. It is not unlikely that stimuli afforded by the young evoke physiological changes in the adult that predispose the latter to behave in a parental manner. It should be understood, however, that this interpretation is speculative and alternative ones are not lacking. Exteroceptive stimulation may create the physiological conditions necessary to parental behavior in colonial nesting birds that have no young of their own. Newly hatched Adelie penguins are herded into groups and guarded by one or two "nurses" while the rest of the adults search for food which is brought back to the young. Adults that have no offspring of their own are nonetheless stimulated to participate in the communal feeding of fledglings (Bullough, 1942*b*). The eggs of the emperor penguin are laid on the sea ice in the depth of the antarctic winter. Owing to the rigorous climate many eggs fail to hatch, and incubation and care of the surviving eggs and chicks are shared by all adults. A dozen or more birds stand about each egg, taking turns at incubation, and later all adults cooperate in feeding the young (Wilson, 1907).

Virgin rats or mice rarely display parental reactions toward newborn young of their species. However, Leblond and Nelson (1937) found that retrieving and hovering over young can be induced in animals of either sex by exposing the inexperienced individuals to fresh litters for 3 or 4 days. The maternal responsiveness of laboratory rats ordinarily is coextensive with lactation. Milk is produced for approximately 3 weeks, and nest building, retrieving, and protection of young rats tend to die out at the end of this period. Wiesner and Sheard (1933) showed that the female rat's tendency to care for young can be extended long after lactation ceases if she is regularly provided with newborn foster litters. Some rats subjected to this treatment remained "maternal" for 5 months. Apparently an underlying physiological state favorable to maternality can be maintained by appropriate exteroceptive stimulation.

Stimuli controlling oviposition. Females of some species lay their eggs while mating is in progress, and this type of oviposition has

been discussed in connection with sexual behavior. In other oviparous species fertilization is internal, and the eggs are not deposited for some time after copulation. Oviposition reactions of this sort are here classified as parental responses. The distinction is merely one of convenience.

The gravid female's choice of a site for egg laying is obviously influenced by exteroceptive cues. In some cases the stimulus involves only one sensory modality, but more often the behavior pattern is controlled by a series of stimuli mediated by several receptor systems. Flies that normally deposit their eggs in overripe fruit exhibit oviposition movements in response to the chemical stimulus provided by 20 per cent alcohol mixed with 5 per cent acetic acid (Barrows, 1907). These are the concentrations of the two compounds in fermented apple juice.

Some parasitic wasps inject their eggs into the caterpillar of the flour moth, and the first phases of the pattern appear to be evoked exclusively by chemical stimuli. Living caterpillars sealed in glass capsules are not approached, but wasps placed upon a glass plate that has been rubbed with the skin of the caterpillar flex the abdomen and extend the ovipositor in preparation for egg extrusion. Caterpillar models made of clay or wood are disregarded unless smeared with the juice of the normal host, in which case they stimulate preliminary oviposition responses. Larvae of beetles that differ in shape and color from the flour moth caterpillar evoke the same behavior when they have been covered with body fluids from caterpillars. Neither the models nor the beetle larvae are actually parasitized, however, and it is probable that the final act of inserting the ovipositor depends upon tactile cues (Murr, 1930).

Other wasps lay their eggs in the larva of the sawfly while it is still enclosed in a compact cocoon. Chemical stimuli associated with the larva induce orientation responses in the gravid wasp; but after contact is established the female mounts the cocoon and explores it with her antennae, and tactile stimuli assume primary importance (Russell, 1941). Artificial cocoons with rough edges are rejected in favor of others with more rounded contours. Models that are texturally similar to the sawfly cocoon are selected in preference to others lacking this resemblance. Still another type of stimulus is involved in the first stage of the normal oviposition pattern of this insect. Although it is chemically attractive and possesses appropriate tactile characteristics, a cocoon is not parasitized if it contains advanced wasp grubs from a previous parasitization.

These few examples show that oviposition in insects is not controlled by one simple stimulus or by a single receptor system. Instead it resembles sexual behavior in being a concatenated sequence of reactions, each depending upon different external cues.

The parental reactions of some vertebrates are restricted to depositing the eggs in an appropriate environment. Loggerhead turtles leave their eggs in deep sand nests several yards above the high-tide line. Daniel and Smith (1947) observed that females always select nest sites from which the ocean is clearly visible, even though the choice of a location involves extended detours and wanderings from the point of approach to the beach. Visual stimuli are particularly important at one stage in the life history of the species. Newly hatched turtles emerge from the nest at night and proceed directly to the ocean and out to the deep sea which is their natural habitat. The going to sea depends exclusively upon movement toward the most brightly illuminated region of the horizon. Because the water reflects light from the sky, the seaward segment of the horizon is brighter than any other. But the young turtle's positively phototropistic tendencies are brought into play only if the nest site offers a direct view of the ocean.

Effects of the immediate surroundings upon response to the eggs or young. The parental reactions of animals are influenced by many factors in addition to the stimulus pattern afforded by the eggs or young. The behavior elicited by a given stimulus often depends upon the setting in which it is encountered. The male three-spined stickleback fish builds a nest in which the female deposits her eggs. The spawn is guarded by the male, and if eggs fall out of the nest he replaces them. However, any eggs that the female may deposit outside the nest are not retrieved (Russell, 1944).

Black-headed gulls will retrieve eggs that roll out of the nest. The normal clutch in this species consists of two, but birds roll as many as seven additional eggs into the nest if they are placed only an inch or so away. The strength of the retrieving tendency is inversely related to the distance involved and the number of eggs left in the nest (Kirkman, 1937). Eggs placed 9 to 12 inches away usually are not retrieved as long as some eggs remain in the nest. But if the nest is empty all birds will roll in at least one egg from this distance. Eggs offered at distances of 3 to 4 feet are never retrieved; but if the nest is empty some gulls build a new nest around the displaced eggs. Noble and Lehrman's (1940) field experiments with laughing gulls showed that in this species also the tendency to retrieve displaced eggs is a function of the distance from the nest, the number of eggs displaced, and the number remaining in the nest.

If the nest and eggs of the sooty tern are moved as much as a yard during the bird's absence, the returning parent usually spends some time hovering over the original nest site. It may even alight at the place where the nest was built and execute the customary movements of rearranging the clutch. Appropriate responses eventually are made to the nest and eggs in the new position, but the adjustment takes some time (Watson, 1908).

For the broody laughing gull the eggs, the nest, and the nest site all have stimulus value. Normally these three factors occupy the same position in space, but it is possible to separate them experimentally. According to Noble and Lehrman (1940) gulls that are given a choice settle upon the eggs in preference to the old nest site or to the empty nest in a new position. When offered the empty nest versus the original nest site, the birds react positively to the site and ignore the displaced nest. Simple field tests of this sort make it clear that under normal circumstances the bird's parental responses are conditioned not only by the sensory qualities of the eggs but by a complex combination of cues associated with the nest and its immediate surroundings. This generalization also applies to reactions toward the young after hatching.

Young cuckoos that are hatched by birds of another species frequently eject the normal young of their foster parents from the nest. The adults do not protect or feed the displaced nestlings even though they fall only an inch or so away from the nest's edge (Russell, 1944). Many songbirds continue to feed their offspring as long as they remain in the nest, and spontaneous departure from the nest does not occur until the young bird is capable of an independent existence. Occasionally, however, an immature fledgling may topple out of the nest, and under such conditions the youngster is ignored and left to die. Only in the nest setting does the young bird possess stimulus value as an object to be fed.

Birds of colonial breeding species such as the arctic tern establish a small territory around the nest, and for several days after the young have hatched the parents will protect and feed them only within the territorial boundaries. Later the parents are able to recognize their own offspring and will feed them wherever they are encountered (Bullough, 1942b). Some birds including the sooty tern viciously attack one of their own young that has wandered out of the nest territory and attempts to return (Watson, 1908).

In all species of doves and pigeons the male and female share responsibility for incubating the clutch. The female sits on the eggs from late afternoon until the following morning and the male takes her place during the day. If the female dies or disappears the male incubates through the day and spends the night near the eggs, but does not sit on them (Lorenz, 1935). The stimulus value of the nest and eggs varies with time of day and is not simply a function of their sensory qualities. The male will feed his young despite the loss of the female, and in such circumstances the behavior of the nestlings presumably affords a more intense and compelling stimulus to parental behavior.

Stimuli afforded by the eggs, the young, or the parent. The parental responses of animals that feed and protect their offspring depends heavily upon the behavior of the young themselves. It is, therefore, appropriate to examine simultaneously the sensory bases for filial and parental reactions.

FISHES. Mated pairs of jewel fish cooperate in protecting and "fanning" the eggs, and both parents continue to guard the fry after hatching. The young remain close to the adults for a week or more, and Noble and Curtis (1939) showed that this tendency is dependent upon the reddish color and general movement of the parents.

Young jewel fish were placed in the central tank of the apparatus illustrated in Fig. 7. Circular metal disks in the adjacent aquaria could be moved back and forth mechanically. Colored disks 1 inch in diameter had no effect upon behavior. A bright-red 2-inch disk was promptly approached by the young fish, whereas black or blue disks of the same size were avoided or ignored. Regardless of its shape any moving red object within a certain size range served as a posive stimulus. Motionless disks and those without red coloration were ineffective.

Recently hatched young of some species of African mouthbreeders swim into the mouth of the parent in response to sudden and intense stimulation. Peters (1937) found that this reaction is guided by relatively simple visual cues. Young mouthbreeders readily approach crude models of an adult, orienting to the position of the dummy's eyes and attempting to swim into it at the normal location of the mouth.

REPTILES. Female lizards of some species incubate their eggs and retrieve any that are

The female's initial response to a displaced egg is to touch it lightly with the tip of the tongue. Lizards and some other reptiles possess a chemoreceptor known as Jacobsen's organ. It is situated in the roof of the mouth, and odoriferous particles are depos-

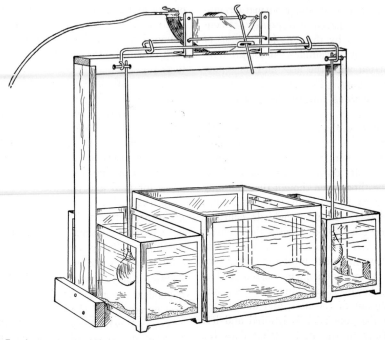

FIG. 7. Apparatus used to test responses of young jewel fish to moving objects of different colors. The experimental animals are placed in the center tank, and metal disks suspended in the smaller aquaria move back and forth mechanically. The offspring of red parents swim toward moving red disks and avoid blue or black ones. Young of black species approach black or dark blue disks but not those painted red. The strength of these tendencies is altered in young fish that are reared by foster parents of a foreign species. (Redrawn from Noble and Curtis, 1939.)

displaced from the nest. The blue-tailed skink reacts differentially toward her own eggs as compared with similar stimulus objects. She does not retrieve or incubate eggs of closely related genera that closely resemble her own in size and shape (Noble and Mason, 1933). Paraffin models of eggs are rejected as are the female's own eggs that have been covered with shellac. Egg identification does not depend upon vision, for blindfolded lizards readily retrieve their own eggs and discriminate against models or eggs of other species.

ited upon this organ by the tip of the tongue as it flicks in and out of the mouth. The lizard's reaction to different kinds of eggs apparently depends upon chemical stimulation of Jacobsen's organ, for removal of the tip of the tongue eliminates retrieving.

BIRDS. In most avian species the retrieving and brooding of eggs depend primarily upon visual and tactile stimuli. Some birds are influenced chiefly by one form of stimulation, and some by another. Kirkman (1937) observed that black-headed gulls continued to sit upon their own eggs painted a variety of bright colors. Eggs of other species, wooden models, or balls were incubated as readily as normal eggs. Artificial eggs with sharp contours were not brooded. The effective stimulus to incubation in this species can be of any color, or any material, and can possess any odor. The shape is immaterial as long as the contours are rounded. Any suitably shaped object will be brooded if it is small enough to sit on and large enough so that it does not sink into the material of the nest. Other birds such as the graylag goose are so sensitive to irregularities in the shape of the egg that they will not roll into the nest their own eggs that have a small lump of putty on one side (Lorenz and Tinbergen, 1938).

Certain visual characteristics of the eggs may be especially important in controlling parental reactions. Ringed plovers will accept and brood spotted eggs of a variety of colors, but unspotted ones are deserted or ejected from the nest (Koehler and Zagarus, 1937). Color rather than pattern is the essential visual stimulus in other species. Marples and Marples (1934) noted that sea swallows were slow to brood their own eggs that had been painted red or blue. Some females eventually sat on the eggs, but many never resumed incubation.

Broody female laughing gulls will sit upon their own eggs that have been dotted with spots of blue, red, or yellow, but there is usually a long delay before the bird accepts the altered eggs (Noble and Lehrman, 1940). Blue and yellow are less disturbing than red, and some females push red-spotted eggs out of the nest. These negative responses are not due to alteration in the visual pattern of the egg, for females readily incubate eggs of another gull even though the spatial distribution of chromatic material on the shell is highly variable from one clutch to another. Eggs that are entirely covered with paint are not accepted by the gull even if the painted pattern is identical to the normal one. Chemical cues may be involved in this discrimination.

According to Noble and Lehrman (1940), when the eggs of the laughing gull are colored artificially it interferes with retrieving more than with brooding, and displaced eggs marked with spots of color are frequently left outside the nest. This observation agrees with our earlier conclusion that the bird's parental responses are conditioned in part by the immediate surroundings of the stimulus object. Colored eggs outside the nest are inadequate stimuli, whereas the same eggs in the nest may evoke parental behavior. The general setting of the nest adds to the stimulus value of the abnormal eggs and renders them acceptable as objects to be brooded.

The importance of tactile stimuli in the gull's brooding behavior is revealed by the fact that eggs to which bits of grass are attached by rubber cement are incubated briefly and then deserted.

Interaction between parent birds and recently hatched young usually consists of a sequence in which a particular activity on the part of the adult calls forth a specific response by the young which in turn elicits the next reaction by the parent. Young birds that remain in the nest after hatching exhibit a gaping response which stimulates the parent to place food in the nestling's mouth. Very young blackbirds gape in response to tactile stimulation produced by jarring the nest. Normally this stimulus occurs when the returning parent alights on a nearby branch or on the edge of the nest. About 10 days after hatching, the blackbird's eyes open, and thenceforth the gaping response is elicited by visual rather than tactile stimuli. Crude silhouettes of a bird head evoke gaping when they are raised above the edge of the nest (Tinbergen and Kuenen, 1939).

Flickers nest in holes in trees or posts, and in the young of this species gaping is stimulated by a sudden darkening of the nest, which normally occurs when the adult blocks the opening of the nest hole. Artificial closure of the opening evokes gaping even though no vibratory or auditory stimuli accompany the visual change (Lehrman and Stephenson, 1940).

Feeding behavior shown by the parent in response to gaping and begging young is controlled in some instances by visual stimuli. In nestlings of many species the roof of the mouth is marked with special structures or bright colors, and Tinbergen (1942) has suggested that these visual signs elicit the adult's feeding reaction. In other cases auditory cues provided by the vocalizations of the young birds are important. Young flickers utter a special note while they are gaping, and it seems probable that this facilitates the parent's attempts to deliver food in the relatively dim surroundings of the nest hole.

Precocial birds like the duck or chicken are not fed by the mother, but they often find edible objects by following her or coming when she utters the special calls associated with the discovery of food. Females of the same species respond to young ones on the basis of visual or auditory stimulation. Audition is of major importance for chickens. Katz (1937) tied chicks to stakes in locations outside the hen's visual field. When the little birds uttered the "fright chirp," the female became very active and continued to run about until she located the young ones. The hens frequently attacked the string and the stake as they would a living enemy. Chicks confined in glass containers struggled against the vessels but were ignored by hens that could see but not hear them.

Audition and vision are jointly involved in the maternal behavior of some precocial birds. Muscovy and mallard ducklings are quite different in physical appearance, but they utter similar "fright calls" when attacked. The muscovy female with a brood of her own will run toward any mallard duckling that gives this call, but when she comes close enough to see the typical mallard head markings the female attacks the strange individual (Lorenz, 1935).

MAMMALS. Naturalistic observations suggest that the parental and filial behavior of mammals is controlled by a combination of sensory cues, that various modalities may be dominant in different species, and that different kinds of stimulation influence separate elements in the total pattern. Experimental investigations of this problem are meager and incomplete.

It is clear that lactating females of many mammalian species discriminate between their own offspring and other young ones of the same age, but the sensory basis for this selective responsiveness is known in only a few instances. Just before parturition the ewe tends to react in maternal fashion to any newborn lamb in her vicinity, but after giving birth she restricts her attentions to the individual she has delivered and rejects others of the same age group (Fraser, 1937). Auditory stimulation is one of the factors involved in this discrimination, for the lactating sheep reacts specifically to the bleating of her own offspring and disregards the vocalizations of other lambs (Scott, 1945).

Comparable maternal behavior is displayed by fur seals and elephant seals according to the reports of Preble (1923), Bonnot (1929), and Hamilton (1934). Cows leave the rookery to enter the ocean and feed, and upon returning the female hesitates on the periphery of the herd and bellows loudly. After a short delay she rushes directly to her own young one, paying no attention to the hundreds or thousands of pups belonging to other cows. If any pup except her own attempts to suckle the female, she vigorously repels it and may toss the strange young one several feet away. Not all species of seals are equally discriminating, for lactating African cape seals readily nurse an orphan pup (Shortridge, 1934).

Young mammals of many species are able to identify their own mothers. Scott (1945) believes that the necessary learning occurs very rapidly in domestic sheep, since the lamb's discriminatory reactions appear within a few days after birth. The wild lamb remains very close to its mother for 2 weeks after birth. Later it may wander about, but it runs to the ewe when she utters a special call. Among the Dall sheep of Alaska, lambs are herded into groups and guarded by one or two ewes while the remainder of the adults graze. Murie (1944) noted that returning ewes begin to bleat when they are within 100 yards of the lamb flock. Hungry lambs respond to this stimulus by leaving the flock and running directly to their mothers. Each young one reacts exclusively to the voice of its own parent.

The responses of female rodents to their young involve several types of stimulation. Audition contributes to parental behavior in meadow mice and rice rats. Bailey (1924) and Svihal (1931) noted that young of these species that have fallen out of the nest utter a series of shrill squeaks. In response to this stimulus the female becomes highly active and continues to search until the pup is found and returned to the nest. Young Norway rats squeal in response to painful stimulation, and this sound elicits marked agitation and hyperactivity in the lactating female.

Female cotton rats bred in the laboratory can be induced to adopt and rear offspring of the Norway rat (Meyer and Meyer, 1944). This indicates that the stimuli to maternal behavior are not always species-specific. Lactating albino rats will sometimes nurse young mice (Shadle, 1945), and under certain conditions they may retrieve young rabbits to their nests (Wiesner and Sheard, 1933).

However, the writer has noted marked differences between female rats of the same strain. Some parturient individuals do retrieve baby rabbits, but other nursing rats invariably attack and kill them. A few domestic rats retrieve their young that have been sprinkled with oil of lavender, but others reject a pup that has this pungent and foreign odor. Some females display a consistent tendency to retrieve their own young and to ignore foster pups of the same age, but other females persistently steal the litters of other mothers inhabiting the same cage.

It is obvious that the sensory cues responsible for parental and filial behavior are poorly understood and that systematic studies of the problem are needed. Present evidence makes it clear that species and individual differences are often pronounced, that several forms of stimulation are usually involved, and that the entire situation is further complicated by the fact that learning enters the picture at a very early stage.

Some slight insight into the sensory basis for parental reactions is afforded by studies of the nervous mechanisms mediating such behavior.

Studies of the Nervous System

There have been very few experimental studies of the neural correlates of parental behavior and no investigations of the nervous basis for filial responses.

Fishes. Noble (1939) states that the removal of all the forebrain in the male jewel fish eliminates any tendency to care for the eggs or young. Partial decerebration is followed by disruption of the pattern and usually by loss of one or more of the separate responses constituting it. The number of behavioral elements eliminated depends principally upon the amount of brain tissue removed and is independent of the locus of injury within the forebrain. Female jewel fish with small bilateral forebrain lesions court and mate normally, but instead of permitting their mate to help care for the eggs and the young the brain-operated females drive the male away as they would any stranger. The survival of sexual responses in these individuals is important. The tendency for the female's parental performance to deteriorate as a result of cerebral lesions that do not interfere with mating is found in several vertebrate classes.

It was noted earlier that decerebrate male African mouthbreeder fish do not pick up the fertilized eggs and incubate them in the mouth as do normal individuals of this species (Aronson, 1948).

Birds. Decerebrate hen pigeons may mate and lay fertile eggs but will not brood them (Schrader, 1889), another illustration of the relative importance of forebrain mechanisms in sexual and maternal reactions. Ceni's (1938) experiments with several species of birds convinced him that the "frontal pole" of the brain contains a center essential to maternal behavior. According to Rogers (1922) male and female pigeons with lesions in the corpus striatum show various deficiencies in the care of squabs. The details of the deficit are not described, but Rogers states that certain reactions are dependent upon localized mechanisms within the forebrain.

Mammals. Golz (1874) described a bitch that showed normal gestation and maternal care of the litter despite complete section of the lumbar cord. And Ranson (1934) found that female cats with "large bilaterally symmetrical lesions in the tuber, lateral to or behind the infundibulum," give birth to normal litters and suckle their young.

The only systematic studies of nervous functions in mammalian maternal behavior have dealt with the laboratory rat. Wiesner and Sheard (1933) reported that anosmic and deaf female rats continue to retrieve young to the nest. Unpublished experiments by the present writer showed that nest building, cleaning of the newborn young, and retrieving responses survive in primiparous females despite enucleation of the eyes, removal of the olfactory bulbs, or section of the sensory nerves to the snout and lips. The combination of any two of these operations greatly interfered with the female's maternal behavior without eliminating any essential reactions, but rats suffering interruption of all three afferent pathways were unable to retrieve or care for their pups.

Furthermore animals deprived of any one sensory receptor were slower and less accurate than normal females in their maternal responses. A few females that consistently discriminated between their own young and the offspring of other mothers lost this ability after destruction of the olfactory bulbs. It appears that several sensory modalities contribute to maternal efficiency in the rat, although no one receptor system is essential.

Davis (1939) found that female rats deprived of the cerebral cortex were unable to rear their litters. Unilateral hemidecortication did not have this effect, but no special tests were conducted, and the operated animals were permitted to raise their offspring under conditions that demanded a minimum of adaptability. Stone's (1938) studies of maternal reactions in partially decorticated rats indicate that large lesions may produce quantitative reduction in the female's performance without preventing the survival of the litter.

Beach (1937) reported that several elements in the rat's maternal pattern are affected by cerebral injury. Normal females start to build a nest several days before parturition, but animals with cortical lesions tend to delay until just before the litter is born, and if the brain injury is sufficiently extensive there is no nest building at any time. Removal of more than 30 per cent of the cortex decreases the female's tendency to collect her young into the nest and to clean them as they are born. When the litter is scattered about the cage, the normal mother begins at once to return her pups to the nest and completes this task in a relatively short time. Cortically operated rats are slower to begin retrieving, wait longer between trips from the nest, and tend to stop before all the young have been gathered (Fig. 8).

Females with cortical lesions are less efficient than unoperated animals in moving their nests from under an air blast or electric heater. The type and severity of behavioral loss bear little relation to the site of the lesion within the cortex, but in general there is a positive relation between the amount of brain tissue removed and the extent of deterioration of the maternal pattern.

All three studies of maternal behavior in rats sustaining cerebral injury show that extensive brain loss seriously interferes with the female's ability to care for her young, although it does not prevent her from mating and becoming pregnant. Male rats with similar lesions do not mate. The maternal reactions of female rats and the sexual responses of males are comparable in several ways. First, maternal females and sexually

Studies of Blood Chemistry

The parental and filial responses of some invertebrate and many vertebrate species are modified by certain changes in the chemical constitution of the blood.

Diet and drugs. The need for nourishment tends to intensify the young animal's positive reactions to its parents. Gaping re-

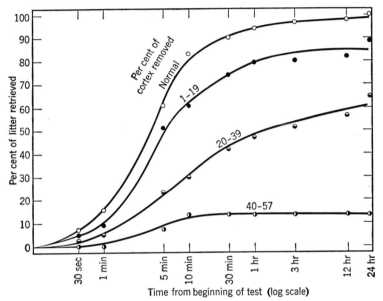

FIG. 8. Records of retrieving behavior in normal and cortically operated female rats. The numbers on the curves show the per cent of cortex removed. The litter is scattered by the experimenter, and the female retrieves the pups to the nest, one at a time. Speed and completeness of retrieving behavior decrease with increasing size of cortical lesion. (Redrawn from Beach, 1937.)

active males are required to take the initiative in responding to another animal. This is not true of the female's estrous behavior. Second, their performance depends upon a combination of sensory cues involving several modalities. The female's coital pattern depends primarily upon sensations of touch and pressure. Third, maternal responses and masculine mating reactions are less dependent upon specific hormonal secretions than is the feminine sexual pattern. Finally, both types of behavior are dependent upon cortical mechanisms, whereas estrous reactions are not.

sponses of nestling birds depend upon the time elapsed since the last feeding. Recently fed fledglings do not gape; but when the preceding meal has been digested the response reappears and grows increasingly vigorous until the young one is fed again. Seward (1940) found that satiated infant guinea pigs will cross a barrier that separates them from the mother, but unfed babies surmount the barrier more rapidly than nonhungry ones.

Special physiological demands of pregnancy often produce spontaneous changes in the diet selected by female mammals. Martins (cited by Riess, 1948) found that pregnant guinea pigs display a preference for meat, although nonpregnant females choose vegetable foods. Domestic and wild ungulates are herbivorous, but pregnant females frequently masticate old, dry bones which presumably augment the calcium content of the diet. Richter (1938) maintained female rats on a self-selection diet from 1 month before pregnancy until lactation was completed. The daily caloric intake rose from 45.3 to 59.8 in the course of gestation, and to 118.3 at the end of the lactation period. Protein consumption increased during gestation, and the amount of fat ingested rose during pregnancy and lactation. The appetite for sodium chloride, calcium lactate, and dibasic sodium phosphate increased. There was no significant change in the intake of wheat germ oil, cod-liver oil, potassium chloride, or carbohydrates.

Manganese deficiency in the diet of parturient rats interferes with lactation, interrupts nursing, and sometimes causes females to eat their litters. Diets containing excessive amounts of vitamin B have the same effect. An oversupply of vitamin B combined with excessive manganese does not affect lactation or maternal behavior. Perla and Sandberg (1939) who reported these results suggest that under normal conditions manganese acts as an oxydative catalyst in the utilization of the vitamin. The toxic effects of too much vitamin B are neutralized by increasing the amount of manganese, and in the absence of manganese normal amounts of the vitamin are not neutralized and therefore exert their harmful effects on behavior.

Poisons introduced into the mother may affect her reaction to the young. Rats given a diet containing lead tend to destroy their litters toward the end of the lactation period (Dalldorf and Williams, 1945).

Hormones. We noted earlier that the sexual responses of insects do not depend upon gonadal hormones. There is no direct proof that the female's maternal behavior depends upon hormones, but the response to certain stimuli is a function of conditions in the reproductive organs, and this suggests some form of hormonal control.

INSECTS AND SPIDERS. The cabbage butterfly lays its eggs on the green leaves or stems of plants, and gravid females will alight upon objects that are emerald green to greenish blue and execute the characteristic "drumming reaction" associated with oviposition. Infertile females show no response to green but readily approach red, yellow, blue, and violet stimuli. The latter hues are normally associated with flowers on which the insect feeds, and they evoke no reactions on the part of females that are ready to lay eggs (Isle, 1937). Just before oviposition the female hawk moth responds positively to green and to the odor of etheric oil of Galium. This combination of visual and chemical stimuli occurs normally in the plants on which the species deposits its eggs. The same combination does not attract males or nongravid females (Bodenheimer, 1938).

Savory (1936) noted that the behavior of the wolf spider toward its cocoon is a function of the presence or absence of ripe eggs in the ovaries. For approximately 5 weeks the female carries her cocoon with its embedded eggs; then the young emerge and are carried upon the mother's back for another week. Two weeks later a second cocoon is produced, and the cycle recurs. The readiness with which a female will seize and carry a cotton pledget or her own cocoon after it has been taken away from her varies inversely with the time elapsed since the last eggs were produced. The implied relation between ovarian condition and parental responsiveness is similar to the gradual waning of the retrieving behavior in mammals, which is discussed below.

FISHES. Noble, Kumpf, and Billings (1938) found that female jewel fish that have not mated or spawned will care for foster eggs after treatment with progesterone (from the ovaries) or prolactin (from the anterior pituitary). Thyroid extract and phenol produce similar results, but the behavior is less complete and intense. The pre-oviposition nest building of some fishes depends upon a gonadal hormone that transforms part of the kidney into a mucous-producing organ that aids in nidification (Cohen, 1942).

AMPHIBIANS AND REPTILES. Female salamanders treated with fresh pituitary substance at times other than the normal breeding season extrude their eggs and attach them to the underside of stones in the characteristic manner (Noble and Richards, 1932). Comparable results have been obtained by Barden and Kezer (1944) with other salamandrian species.

The spiny swift lizard normally lays its eggs during the spring and early summer, but Evans (1946) induced this behavior in the winter by the administration of sheep or frog pituitaries.

BIRDS. Prolactin from the anterior pituitary stimulates parental responses in various avian species, and gonadal hormones tend to inhibit such behavior. The ovaries of the broody hen are relatively inactive, and she does not produce eggs. Conversely, the active secretion of ovarian hormones reduces or eliminates the tendency to care for chicks. Ceni (1927) observed the persistence of parental reactions in ovariectomized fowl and was able to inhibit this behavior by implanting a functional ovary. Actively laying hens injected with prolactin cease producing eggs and begin to show maternal responses (Riddle, Bates, and Lahr, 1935). Virgin pigeons treated with this substance produce crop milk and incubate foster eggs (Riddle, 1935). The effect is not specific, however, for unmated pigeons of either sex will incubate eggs and feed squabs after treatment with progesterone or adrenocortical hormone (Riddle et al., 1942–43).

Androgen inhibits parental responses in male birds of some species and facilitates the same reactions in others. Castration is followed by the appearance of broodiness and care of the chicks in brown leghorn males (Goodale, 1918). Roosters implanted with ovarian tissue (Ceni, 1927) or injected with prolactin (Nalvandov, 1945) display parental responses toward young chicks. These results may be due to a depession of androgen production by the testis or to some more direct effect of the implanted or injected material.

Males of many avian species normally care for the brood, and in such cases testicular hormone can scarcely be classified as "antiparental." Male pigeons are as active as females in the incubation and feeding of the young. Rowan (1931) has noted that the male bobolink helps the female build a nest and care for the nestlings when the testes are maximally developed. Later in the season the gonads regress and the bird shows no interest in nesting material, eggs, or fledglings. Additional evidence that testicular hormone facilitates paternal behavior in some birds is found in the report of Noble and Wurm (1940) to the effect that blackcrowned night herons become broody after treatment with testosterone propionate.

MAMMALS. There is a clear-cut relation between rhythms of glandular activity and cycles of parental behavior in many mammals. Furthermore it is possible in some cases to produce maternal responses in males and virgin females by the administration of hormones. However, the effects of exteroceptive stimulation are so powerful that in certain instances they appear to elicit parental behavior without any demonstrable hormonal change.

Shortly before parturition the lion pulls out the fur surrounding the nipples, and the same reaction is seen in pseudopregnant females whose hormonal condition resembles that of the pregnant individual (Cooper, 1942). Rabbits that are about to give birth exhibit similar behavior, and Tietz (1933) induced it in nonpregnant females by injecting gonadotrophic hormone. Under normal conditions these reactions probably depend upon estrogen, which is present in large amounts during pregnancy, or upon gonadotrophins secreted by the placenta. Tietz's results do not permit a choice between these alternatives, since injections of gonadotrophin evoke an increase in estrogen secretion by the ovaries.

Kunde et al. (1930) produced copious lactation and maternal behavior in nonpregnant bitches by the administration of estrin. One experimental female suckled and reared a foster litter. These results are difficult to reconcile with other findings.

In the first place, the secretion of estrogen decreases abruptly after parturition and remains minimal throughout lactation. Maternal responses, which are maximal at this time, would not be expected to depend upon estrogen. Second, although estrogen stimulates the growth of the mammary glands, the actual production of milk depends upon hormones from the pituitary, the adrenal cortex, the thyroid, and probably other glands as well. Finally, estrogen evokes complete heat behavior in spayed or intact dogs, and under normal conditions sexual and maternal patterns of behavior do not occur concurrently. The estrous bitch is not maternal, and the lactating one is not receptive. The most likely explanation for the appearance of parental responses in estrin-treated dogs is that the extract contained impurities that stimulated the pituitary to secrete hormones capable of supporting lactation and the associated behavior.

It is known that estrogen depresses maternal behavior in some mammals. Hain (1942) injected this hormone into lactating rats and found that, although lactation continued, nursing and retrieving disappeared after 5 days of treatment, and the litters died. Confirmatory results have been reported by Weichert and Kerrigan (1942).

Experiments dealing with the role of pituitary hormones in maternal behavior of mammals have yielded conflicting results. According to Wiesner and Sheard (1933), virgin rats display retrieving responses after receiving injections of anterior pituitary extracts; and Riddle, Bates, and Lahr (1935) found that the administration of prolactin

from the pituitary induced nest building, retrieving, and "cuddling" of newborn young in approximately 60 per cent of the virgin rats in their colony. However, Leblond and Nelson (1937) removed the pituitary from lactating mice and found that maternal behavior survived although lactation ceased. And hypophysectomy is reported to induce maternal reactions in some virgin rats (Riddle et al., 1941–42). It is probable that prolactin normally contributes but is not essential to maternal behavior. Estrogen exerts an inhibiting effect in most species. Progesterone probably is involved in prepartum activities but not in parental behavior after the arrival of the young.

Maternal behavior changes as the lactation period progresses. Seward and Seward (1940) tested the female guinea pig's willingness to climb over a barrier that separated her from her young, and found that the strength of the tendency declines progressively in the first 3 weeks after parturition. Control experiments showed that the behavior does not depend upon decreasing amounts of milk in the mammary glands, nor upon increasing size of the young. It was concluded that a gradual change in hormonal activity is responsible for the decline in maternal responsiveness. Wiesner and Sheard (1933) described a comparable reduction in the tendency of female rats to retreive young ones. They also showed that during the latter stages of the lactation period the stimulus value of a rat pup depends upon its age. Shortly after parturition females will retrieve young ones of any age; but toward the end of the lactation they carry to the nest only the small, hairless pups and disregard older animals that would have been retrieved earlier in the nursing period. The essential characteristics of the adequate stimulus for retrieving behavior are thus seen to vary according to the physiological condition of the responding individual.

During the final stages of lactation the bitch disgorges before her litter part of the food she has eaten. This behavior continues for several days after lactation has ceased and helps the puppies make the transition to a solid diet. Females usually disgorge within 15 minutes after returning to the nest, but if the pups are removed the bitch will retain the ingested food for three-quarters of an hour and then promptly disgorge it when allowed access to her litter. The reaction is not given in response to toy dogs or to kittens. Martins (1949), who recorded these findings, considers the behavior to be hormonally controlled.

Endocrine secretions characteristic of late pregnancy and the period of lactation undoubtedly contribute to maternal responsiveness in many mammals; but they cannot be regarded as indispensable in every instance. In some species parental behavior is normally exhibited by individuals that are neither pregnant nor lactating. It is possible that these reactions are hormonally conditioned, but there is as yet no support for any such interpretation. Male mice of several species regularly assist the female in cleaning and protecting the litter (Blair, 1941; Horner, 1947), and field studies of chimpanzees suggest that adults other than the parents sometimes protect and care for immature members of the band (Nissen, 1931). Murie's (1944) careful observations of feral wolves show that care of the pups may be shared by several adults. Unmated females are particularly solicitous of another's litter and often remain with the young when the mother joins in the pack's nocturnal hunt. After the pups are weaned they eat food brought to the den by all members of the pack.

Development in the Individual and Modification by Experience

Parental behavior involves many responses, some of which also occur in conjunction with other patterns of reaction. A few elements in the parental complex, such as the delivery and cleaning of young, do not appear in any other context. The development and modification of both types of response have been studied by several investigators. The ontogenesis of filial reactions has been described in some fishes, birds, and mammals.

Parental behavior. Egg-laying behavior that does not occur during mating has been arbitrarily classified as a parental response, and the initial step in this pattern is the selection of the oviposition site. Some insects invariably leave their eggs on certain kinds of plants or insert them into the bodies of living hosts of a particular species. The gravid female's positive response to a given type of plant or animal depends in part upon previous events in her own life history.

In England there are two races of the moth, *Hyponomenta padella*, which lay their eggs upon different hosts. One oviposits upon hackberry hedges, and the other upon apple trees. Thorpe (cited in Imms, 1931) showed that females of the apple race, given a choice of oviposition sites, laid 90.2 per cent of their eggs upon apple and only 9.8 per cent on hackberry. Larvae of the apple race were then transferred to hackberry upon which they grew and developed normally. When the experimental larvae became adult females their preference for oviposition sites was measured, and they laid 30.8 per cent of their eggs on hackberry. In comparison with the behavior of the parent generation this represents a 21 per cent decrease in the strength of the original preference.

Summarizing a large number of similar studies upon different insect species, Imms (1931) offered the following tentative interpretation:

The repetition of the habit of specific host-preference appears to be explainable as the result of a chemical influence, derived from the food-plant, acting upon each successive generation. Specific host-preference and its repetition in each generation seems to afford an analogy with what Pavlov has termed a conditioned reflex. The conditioning takes place during the developmental cycle of the insect and influences the chemotropic responses of the female during oviposition.

The analogy to Pavlovian conditioning is questionable, but the effect of environmental conditions during development upon parental responses in adulthood is well established.

Parental behavior normally appears in some birds before the attainment of reproductive maturity. Watson (1908) described the carrying of nesting material by noddy terns 16 days after hatching, and Craig (1909) observed a 21-day-old ringdove that became broody and incubated eggs laid by its parents. According to White (1941) it is common for young swallows of the season's first brood to help feed those of the second.

The maternal behavior of some mammals includes nest building, but this type of activity is not confined to the pregnant or lactating female. Under appropriate environmental conditions it occurs in males and in immature animals. Wood rats bred in captivity begin random transportation of small objects at about 30 days of age, long before they are sexually mature. Bits of nesting material are collected and nests are begun although they are rarely completed (Richardson, 1943). Juvenile domestic rats of both sexes display some nest building shortly after they are weaned (Kinder, 1927).

It might be supposed that the primiparous female's ability to build an adequate nest depends upon practice gained earlier in life. Against this conclusion is the observation that inexperienced rats build serviceable nests even though they have been reared in cages containing no nesting material (Beach, 1937). However, these animals have been able to carry food pellets and wood shavings about the cage, and this sort of experience might conceivably contribute to nest building at a later date. In an exploratory experiment Riess (1948) reared female rats in an environment containing nothing that could be picked up or transported. When these animals delivered their first litters they failed to build nests although appropriate material was available. This study was repeated with a second group of animals (Riess, personal communication) reared in complete isolation from other rats and under conditions that prevented carrying responses. They showed some nesting behavior at parturition, but the paper strips were heaped loosely over the litter, and afforded relatively little protection for the young. More significantly, the females made no attempt to suckle their offspring but treated them as though they were strips of paper or inanimate objects to be carried and manipulated. This type of behavior is typical of the male rat, and indeed the experimentally isolated females were no more "maternal" than the normal male. Confirmation of these preliminary findings is needed, but the results emphasize the necessity for rigorous control in any study of the effects of experience upon a given behavior pattern.

Wiesner and Sheard (1933) were unable to detect any difference between the parturitional behavior of primiparous and multiparous rats. Beach (1937) also noted that female rats clean their first litter effectively and care for the young throughout lactation. Birch (cited in Riess, 1948) reared rats under conditions that prevented self-grooming. Each animal was fitted with a large shield that encircled the neck and made it impossible for the rat to reach any part of the body with its mouth. The shields were removed during the last stages of pregnancy, but when the young were born the females failed to clean them. Additional data are desirable on this point, but the potential value of the method is evident.

The female's tendency to clean and suckle her young appears in some cases to improve after the first parturition. Freud and Uyldert (1948) induced lactation in nonpregnant rats by hormonal treatment. They found that females that had previously delivered and cared for litters would adopt and nurse foster young, whereas lactating rats without any maternal experience would not permit young ones to suckle. Cooper (1942) reports that infanticide is more common in primiparous than multiparous lionesses.

Inexperienced chimpanzees often show marked deficiencies in their maternal responses. The multiparous ape supports the head of the baby during birth and picks the infant up immediately after delivery. A great deal of time is spent licking up the fetal fluids and chewing the afterbirth. If the baby cries, the experienced mother attempts to quiet it. Some primiparous chimpanzees appear puzzled by the presence of the infant and treat it as they would any unfamiliar object. Curiosity is evinced, but the resultant behavior is not appropriate. A few inexperienced chimpanzees observed in captivity have shown intense emotional disturbance during parturition and have immediately and permanently rejected their offspring (Yerkes and Elder, 1936; Budd, Smith, and Shelley, 1943). Total avoidance or completely inadequate care occurs as far as is known only in the case of the first delivery. And it remains to be discovered whether similar deficiencies ever appear under natural life conditions.

The female animal's tendency to suckle and protect her young may be inhibited by emotionally disturbing experiences. Pallen (1944) has described the cessation of lactation and the killing of kits that occurred when female minks were frightened by aircraft flying close to their pens. According to Petersen (1944) dairy cattle with well-filled udders display inhibition of milk release in response to noxious stimulation. The inhibition can be conditioned to a variety of normally innocuous stimuli.

Naturalistic descriptions of maternal responses in sheep and seals that react discriminatively to their own offspring indicate the importance of learning in parental behavior although the process has not yet been analyzed.

Filial behavior. The tendency of young birds and mammals of many species to react selectively to their own parents rests in part upon the effects of early experience. We have described the findings of Noble and Curtis (1939) to the effect that recently hatched jewel fish respond positively to their parents and that this behavior depends to a large extent upon the red coloration of the broody adult.

Young jewel fish hatched and reared without parental contact were tested in the apparatus illustrated in Fig. 7. They displayed a clear-cut discrimination in favor of red as compared with black stimulus disks; but the preference was less marked than in young reared by adults, and it was concluded that the fry inherit a tendency to approach moving red objects which under normal conditions is strengthened by association with the parents.

A related species of fish assumes bluish-black body colors when brooding young, and offspring of this species placed in the experimental tank moved to a dark blue disk and away from a red one. Eggs laid by black-colored adults were given to broody pairs of the red-colored species, and the foster parents accepted and reared the young. When the fry were tested for color preference they were found to move toward a red disk and to avoid the dark-blue one. Apparently the coloration of the adults with whom these young fish associate during the first week after hatching influences their color preference and determines the type of adult to which they will respond. Species differences were apparent in the results of this study. Young born of red-colored parents and reared by the black species did not develop a positive response to black or dark blue although the strength of the reaction to red was materially reduced.

Young birds of some precocial species are able within a few days after hatching to discriminate between their own mothers and other adult females. Learning is undoubtedly involved, but the process has never been analyzed. Bruckner (1933) artificially altered the physical appearance of the hen and discovered that this interfered with the chick's ability to recognize its mother. Vision is not essential, however, for, when two broods of chicks were mixed and placed in total darkness with the hens, all young birds were found grouped under the proper female 2 hours later.

To account for the reactions of young animals to the parents and others of the same species Lorenz (1935) advanced the concept of "imprinting." The process is described as depending upon experience but differing from what is ordinarily called learning in that it occurs very rapidly and is "irreversible." To support his theory Lorenz cites many simple experiments, most of which he conducted.

Jackdaws reared by hand responded to human beings as they would to their own parents, and in adulthood these birds oriented their sexual display to men rather than to other jackdaws. Geese hatched in an incubator and reared by Lorenz followed him about as goslings normally follow the goose, reacted to his call, and were unresponsive to adult geese. A muscovy duckling reared by a gray goose was removed from the foster family at the age of 7 weeks and placed with birds of its own kind. The following year when mating reactions appeared they were directed toward the species of the foster parents. Many psychologists would classify such behavior as a product of learning, but regardless of interpretation the evidence suggests that early filial associations may exert lasting effects upon animal conduct.

Experimenters and naturalists who do not belong to the Lorenzian school have reported data that harmonize with its major tenets. Hudson (1892) recorded the fact that young rhea birds will adopt a man as a foster parent, and when the human being imitates the loud warning call of the adult rhea the young bird rushes to him and squats at his feet. The infancy of many ungulates affords excellent opportunity for conditioning to the mother. When she is about to drop her calf the caribou cow leaves the main herd, and mother and offspring remain in se-

clusion for several days (Murie, 1944). The calf is able to walk within an hour after birth, and it maintains close contact with the female at all times. Under these conditions the calf can form associations with one female before it comes in contact with other adults, and when the pair rejoins the herd the young one responds only to its mother.

Scott (1945) concluded that the domestic lamb's tendency to remain close to its mother depends upon early reinforcement in the form of food and protection. After weaning, the response is generalized to include other sheep, and strong habits of gregariousness are thereby built up. Lambs isolated from other sheep during infancy and reared on a bottle develop a tendency to follow human beings, and when they are returned to the flock these individuals are less gregarious than animals reared by the ewe. Lambs of mountain sheep captured shortly after birth and reared by men do not join their wild relatives when the opportunity is presented, but instead they show a preference for following human beings (Murie, 1944).

Mammals that are less gregarious than sheep may show atypical behavior if deprived of normal species associations in infancy. According to Cooper (1942) lion cubs raised by hand are tamer than those suckled by the female. They do not snarl so often as normal cubs; they fail to exhibit nursing reactions directed toward the bodies of other cubs; and they tend to play with inanimate objects in their pens instead of with littermates. Levy (1934) found that when puppies reared on a bottle were returned to the bitch they were not so expert as their normal siblings in finding the teat.

Descriptions of mother-infant relations in monkeys (Tinklepaugh and Hartman, 1940) and chimpanzees (Yerkes and Tomlin, 1935) leave no doubt as to the importance of learning in the filial responses of immature primates. The infant learns to obey gestures and vocal communications given by the mother and derives considerable advantage from her tuition and guidance.

CONCLUSIONS

In restricting our attention to studies of reproductive behavior we have been compelled to neglect many other types of activity that are usually classified as instinctive. But the fact is that very few instinctive patterns have been subjected to experimental analysis. Most of the literature in this field consists of simple description combined with speculative interpretation.

Evidence marshaled in this chapter raises some question concerning the legitimacy of classifying reproductive reactions under the heading of instinct. As a matter of fact the widespread practice of postulating a general category of instincts, as discriminable from other types of behavior, is of dubious validity. We have seen that sexual behavior develops in various ways in different animals and may be controlled by different external and internal correlates in males and females of the same species. Parental behavior appears to be affected by a variety of factors ranging from the female's diet during immaturity to her previous experience in rearing young. Species differences are pronounced, and in any one species the behavior is governed by a complex combination of processes. This kind of evidence contraindicates categorization of mating and maternal behavior as unlearned or instinctive.

The category is artificial and bears little relation to the observed facts precisely because it was not originally derived from these facts. A wide variety of responses are grouped together under the heading of instinct, not because they share any positive characteristics, but because they have been arbitrarily excluded from a rather narrowly conceived category called learned behavior. It is certain that the so-called instincts do not all belong together, even in the same "wastebasket," and the term might profitably

be dropped from the scientific vocabulary. To discard the concept of instincts does not force us to classify all behavior as "learned." Such a procedure would jump us from the frying pan into the fire. Current concepts of learning are too confused and contradictory to be useful in interpreting much of the complex behavior that occurs under natural conditions.

The most fruitful approach would seem to involve further study of a greater number of responses so that they can profitably be compared and contrasted. Once we have analyzed several kinds of reactions in a number of different species, it becomes possible to compare the same pattern in different species or different patterns in the same species. Only by this means can we hope to understand how an animal's "instinctive" behavior resembles and differs from its performance in a maze or puzzle box. Only after such an analysis will interspecies differences and similarities in any given type of activity become intelligible.

REFERENCES

Altmann, M. Interrelations of the sex cycle and the behavior of the sow. *J. comp. Psychol.*, 1941, **31**, 481–498.

Aronson, L. R. Influence of the stimuli provided by the male cichlid fish, *Tilapia macrocephala,* on the spawning frequency of the female. *Physiol. Zool.*, 1945, **18**, 403–415.

Aronson, L. R. Problems in the behavior and physiology of a species of African mouthbreeding fish. *Trans. N. Y. Acad. Sci.*, 1948, **2**, 33–42.

Aronson, L. R., and G. K. Noble. The sexual behavior of Anura. 2. Neural mechanisms controlling mating in the male leopard frog, *Rana pipiens. Bull. Amer. Mus. nat. Hist.*, 1945, **86**, 87–139.

Bacq, Z. M. Impotence of the male rodent after sympathetic denervation of the genital organs. *Amer. J. Physiol.*, 1931, **96**, 321.

Bacq, Z. M., and L. Brouha. Recherches sur la physiologie du système nerveux autonome. II. Le comportement des organs génitaux après énervation sympathetique. *Arch. int. Physiol.*, 1933, **35**, 250.

Baier, L. J. Role of auditory stimulation in the sexual behavior of insects. *Zool. Jb.* (*allg.*), 1930, **47**, 151–248.

Bailey, V. Breeding, feeding and other life habits of meadow mice (*Microtus*). *J. agric. Res.*, 1924, **27**, 523–536.

Ball, J. A test for measuring sexual excitability in the female rat. *Comp. Psychol. Monogr.*, 1937, **14**, 1-37.

Bard, P. The effects of denervation of the genitalia on the oestrual behavior of cats. *Amer. J. Physiol.*, 1935, **113**, 5.

Bard, P. Oestrual behavior in surviving decorticate cats. *Amer. J. Physiol.*, 1936, **116**, 4–5.

Bard, P. Central nervous mechanisms for emotional behavior patterns in animals. *Res. Publ. Ass. nerv. ment. Dis.*, 1939, **19**, 190–218.

Bard, P. *The hypothalamus and central levels of autonomic function.* Baltimore: Williams and Wilkins, 1940.

Barden, R. B., and L. J. Kezer. The eggs of certain *Plethodontid* salamanders obtained by pituitary gland implantation. *Copeia*, 1944, 115–118.

Barrows, W. M. The reactions of the pomace fly, *Drosophila ampelophila* Loew, to odorous substances. *J. exp. Zool.*, 1907, **4**, 515–537.

Beach, F. A. The neural basis of innate behavior. I. Effects of cortical lesions upon the maternal behavior pattern in the rat. *J. comp. Psychol.*, 1937, **24**, 393–436.

Beach, F. A. Techniques useful in studying the sex behavior of the rat. *J. comp. Psychol.*, 1938, **26**, 355–359.

Beach, F. A. Effects of cortical lesions upon the copulatory behavior of male rats. *J. comp. Psychol.*, 1940, **29**, 193–239.

Beach, F. A. Copulatory behavior of male rats raised in isolation and subjected to partial decortication prior to the acquisition of sexual experience. *J. comp. Psychol.*, 1941, **31**, 457–470.

Beach, F. A. Analysis of the stimuli adequate to elicit mating behavior in the sexually inexperienced male rat. *J. comp. Psychol.*, 1942a, **33**, 163–207.

Beach, F. A. Sexual behavior of prepuberal male and female rats treated with gonadal hormones. *J. comp. Psychol.*, 1942b, **34**, 285–292.

Beach, F. A. Male and female mating behavior in prepuberally castrated female rats treated with androgens. *Endocrinology*, 1942c, **31**, 673–678.

Beach, F. A. Copulatory behavior in prepuberally castrated male rats and its modification by estrogen administration. *Endocrinology*, 1942d, **31**, 679–683.

Beach, F. A. Effects of injury to the cerebral cortex upon the display of masculine and feminine mating behavior by female rats. *J. comp. Psychol.*, 1943, **36**, 169–198.

Beach, F. A. Effects of injury to the cerebral cortex upon sexually-receptive behavior in the female rat. *Psychosom. Med.*, 1944, **6**, 40–55.

Beach, F. A. Hormonal induction of mating responses in a rat with congenital absence of gonadal tissue. *Anat. Rec.*, 1945, **92**, 289–292.

Beach, F. A. A review of physiological and psychological studies of sexual behavior in mammals. *Physiol. Rev.*, 1947, **27**, 240–307.

Beach, F. A. *Hormones and behavior.* New York: Hoeber, 1948.

Beach, F. A. Sexual behavior in animals and men. *The Harvey Lectures 1947–48.* Springfield, Ill.: Thomas, 1950. Pp. 254–280.

Beach, F. A., and R. Gilmore. Response of male dogs to urine from females in heat. *J. Mammal.*, 1949, **30**, 391–392.

Beach, F. A., and A. M. Holz. Mating behavior in male rats castrated at various ages and injected with androgen. *J. exp. Zool.*, 1946, **101**, 91–142.

Beach, F. A., and A. M. Holz-Tucker. Effects of different concentrations of androgen upon sexual behavior in castrated male rats. *J. comp. physiol. Psychol.*, 1949, **42**, 433–453.

Beach, F. A., and G. Levinson. Diurnal variations in the mating behavior of male rats. *Proc. Soc. exp. Biol., N. Y.*, 1949, **72**, 78–80.

Beach, F. A., and R. S. Pauker. Effects of castration and subsequent androgen administration upon mating behavior in the male hamster (*Cricetus auratus*). *Endocrinology*, 1949, **45**, 211–221.

Berk, L., R. W. S. Cheetham, and H. W. Shapiro. The biological basis of sexual behavior in amphibia. III. The role of distance receptors in the establishment of the mating reflex (coupling) in *Xenopus laevis* (South African clawed toad): The eyes. *J. exp. Biol.*, 1936, **13**, 60–63.

Bingham, H. C. Sex development in apes. *Comp. Psychol. Monogr.*, 1928, **5**, 1–165.

Bissonnette, T. H. Studies on the sexual cycle in birds. VI. Effects of white, green, and red lights of equal luminous intensity on the testis activity of the European starling (*Sturnus vulgaris*). *Physiol. Zool.*, 1932a, **5**, 92–123.

Bissonnette, T. H. Modification of mammalian sexual cycles: Reactions of ferrets (*Putorius vulgaris*) of both sexes to electric light added after dark in November and December. *Proc. roy. Soc.*, 1932b, **B110**, 322–334.

Bissonnette, T. H. Experimental modifications of breeding cycles in goats. *Physiol. Zool.*, 1941, **14**, 379–383.

Blair, A. P. The effects of various hormones on primary and secondary sex characters of juvenile *Bufo fowleri*. *J. exp. Zool.*, 1946, **103**, 365–400.

Blair, W. F. Observations on the life history of *Baiomys taylori subater*. *J. Mammal.*, 1941, **22**, 378–383.

Blanchard, F. N., and F. C. Blanchard. Mating of the garter snake, *Thamnophis sirtalis*. *Pap. Mich. Acad. Sci.*, 1942, **27**, 215–234.

Blandau, R. J., J. L. Boling, and W. C. Young. The length of heat in the albino rat as determined by the copulatory response. *Anat. Rec.*, 1941, **79**, 453–463.

Bodenheimer, F. S. *Problems of animal ecology.* London: Oxford University Press, 1938.

Boling, J. L., R. J. Blandau, J. G. Wilson, and W. C. Young. Post-parturitional heat responses of newborn and adult guinea pigs. Data on parturition. *Proc. Soc. exp. Biol., N. Y.*, 1939, **42**, 128–132.

Boling, J. L., W. C. Young, and E. W. Dempsey. Miscellaneous experiments on the estrogen-progesterone induced heat in the spayed guinea-pig. *Endocrinology*, 1938, **23**, 182–187.

Bond, C. R. The golden hamster (*Cricetus auratus*): care, breeding, and growth. *Physiol. Zoöl.*, 1945, **18**, 52–59.

Bonnot, P. Report on the seals and the sea lions of California. *Calif. Div. Fish Game, Fisheries Bull.*, 1929, **14**, 1–62.

Bragg, A. N. Observations on the ecology and natural history of Anura. I. Habits, habitat and breeding of *Bufo cognatus* Say. *Amer. Nat.*, 1940, **74**, 424–438.

Breder, C. M. The reproductive habits of the common catfish, *Ameiurus nebulosus* (Le Seuer), with a discussion of their significance in ontogeny and phylogeny. *Zoologica*, 1935, **19**, 143–185.

Breder, C. M., and C. W. Coates. Sex recognition in the guppy, *Lebistes reticulatus* Peters. *Zoologica*, 1935, **19**, 187–207.

Brooks, C. McC. The role of the cerebral cortex and of various sense organs in the excitation and execution of mating activity in the rabbit. *Amer. J. Physiol.*, 1937, **120**, 544–553.

Browman, L. G. The effect of controlled temperatures upon the spontaneous activity rhythms of the albino rat. *J. exp. Zool.*, 1943, **94**, 477–489.

Bruckner, G. H. Untersuchungen zur Tiersoziologie, insbesonbere zur Auflonug der Familie. *Z. Psychol.*, 1933, **128**, 1–110.

Budd, A., L. G. Smith and F. W. Shelley. On the birth and upbringing of the female chimpanzee "Jacqueline." *Proc. zool. Soc. Lond.*, 1943, **113**, 1–20.

Bullough, W. S. The reproductive cycles of the British and Continental races of the starling (*Sturmus vulgaris* L.). *Philos. Trans.*, 1942a, **231**, 165.

Bullough, W. S. Observations on the colonies of the Arctic tern (*Sterna macrura* Naumann) on the Farne Islands. *Proc. zool. Soc., Lond.*, 1942b, **112**, 1–12.

Burger, J. W. Some further experiments on the relation of the external environment to the spermatogenetic cycle of *Fundulus heteroclitus*. *Anat. Rec.*, 1939, **75** Suppl., 138.

Burger, J. W. Some effects of colored illumination on the sexual activation of the male starling. *J. exp. Zool.*, 1943, **94**, 161–168.

Burt, W. H. Territoriality and home range concepts as applied to mammals. *J. Mammal.*, 1943, **24**, 346–352.

Carpenter, C. R. Psychobiological studies of social behavior in Aves. I. The effect of complete and incomplete gonadectomy on the primary sexual activity of the male pigeon. *J. comp. Psychol.*, 1933, **16**, 25–94.

Carpenter, C. R. Sexual behavior of free ranging Rhesus monkeys (*Macaca mulatta*). I. Specimens, procedures and behavioral characteristics of estrus. II. Periodicity of estrus, homosexual, autoerotic and nonconformist behavior. *J. comp. Psychol.*, 1942, **33**, 113–162.

Ceni, C. Die endokrinen Faktoren der Mutterliebe und die psychische Feminierung von Mannschen. *Schweiz. Arch. Neurol. Psychiat.*, 1927, **21**, 131–142.

Ceni, C. Die Psyche im Lichte der Biologie des Mutterinstinktes. *Schweiz. Arch. Neurol. Psychiat.*, 1938, **42**.

Cieslak, E. S. Relations between the reproductive cycle and the pituitary gland in the snake *Thamnophis radix*. *Physiol. Zool.*, 1945, **18**, 299–329.

Clark, G. Sexual behavior in rats with lesions in the interior hypothalamus. *Amer. J. Physiol.*, 1942, **137**, 746.

Clark, G. Prepubertal castration in the male chimpanzee, with some effects of replacement therapy. *Growth*, 1945, **9**, 327–339.

Cohen, H. Effects of androgens and estrogens on *Platypoecilus maculatus*. Master's thesis in Washington Square College Library, New York University, 1942.

Cole, L. J. The relation of light periodicity to the reproductive cycle, migration and distribution of the mourning dove (*Zenaidura macroura carolinensis*). *Auk*, 1933, **50**, 284–296.

Collins, C. W., and S. F. Potts. Attractants for the flying gypsy moths as an aid in locating new infestations. *U. S. Dept. Agric. Tech. Bull.*, 1932, No. 336, 1–43.

Cooper, J. B. An exploratory study on African lions. *Comp. Psychol. Monogr.*, 1942, **17**, 1–48.

Craig, W. The expression of emotions in the pigeons. I. The blond ringdove (*Turtur risorius*). *J. comp. Neurol.* 1909, **19**, 29–40.

Craig, W. Male doves reared in isolation. *J. Anim. Behav.*, 1914, **4**, 121–133.

Dalldorf, G., and R. R. Williams. Impairment of reproduction in rats by ingestion of lead. *Science*, 1945, **102**, 668-670.

Daniel, R. S., and K. U. Smith. The sea-approach behavior of the neonate loggerhead turtle (*Caretta caretta*). *J. comp. physiol. Psychol.*, 1947, **40**, 413–420.

Darling, F. F. *Bird flocks and the breeding cycle*. Cambridge: Cambridge University Press, 1938.

Davis, C. D. The effect of ablations of neocortex on mating, maternal behavior and the production of pseudopregnancy in the female rat and on copulatory activity in the male. *Amer. J. Physiol.*, 1939, **127**, 374–380.

Davis, D. E., and L. V. Domm. The influence of hormones on the sexual behavior of domestic fowl. *Essays in Biology*, 1943, 171–181.

Davis, K. B. *Factors in the sex life of twenty-two hundred women*. New York: Harpers, 1929.

Dawson, A. B. Early estrus in the cat following increased illumination. *Endocrinology*, 1941, **28**, 907–910.

DeAlba, J., and S. A. Asdell. Estrus behavior and hormones in the cow. *J. comp. Psychol.*, 1946, **39**, 119–121.

Dempsey, E. W., and D. McK. Rioch. The localization in the brain stem of the oestrous responses of the female guinea pig. *J. Neurophysiol.*, 1939, **11**, 9–18.

Dickinson, R. L. *A thousand marriages: A medical study of sex adjustment.* Baltimore : Williams and Wilkins, 1931.

Diebschlag, E. Beobachtungen und Versuche an intakten und grosshirnlosen Eidechsen und Ringlenattern. *Zool. Anz.*, 1938, **124**, 30.

Dunbar, H. F. *Emotions and bodily changes.* New York : Columbia University Press, 1938.

Durfee, Th., M. W. Lerner, and N. Kaplan. The artificial production of seminal ejaculation. *Anat. Rec.*, 1940, **76** Suppl., 65–68.

Dusser de Barenne, J. G., and V. D. Koskoff. Further observations on the flexor rigidity in the hind legs of the spinal cat. *Amer. J. Physiol.*, 1934, **107**, 441–446.

Edinger, F. Die Leistungen des Zentralnervensystems beim Frosch dargestellt mit Ruecksicht auf die Lebensweise des Tiers. *Z. allg. Physiol.*, 1913, **15**, 15–64.

Enders, R. K. Training the polygamous male. *Fur Trade J. Canada*, 1945, **23**, 16.

Evans, L. T. The development of the cochlea in the gecko, with special reference to the cochlealagena ratio and its bearing on vocality and social behavior. *Anat. Rec.*, 1935a, **64**, 187–201.

Evans, L. T. Winter mating and fighting behavior of *Anolis carolinensis* as induced by pituitary injections. *Copeia*, 1935b, **1**, 3–6.

Evans, L. T. The effect of Antuitrin S on the male lizard, *Anolis carolinensis*. *Anat. Rec.*, 1935c, **62**, 213–218.

Evans, L. T. Behavior of *Sceloporus grammicus microlepidotus* as modified by certain endocrines. *Anat. Rec.*, 1946, **94**, 63.

Eversole, W. J. The effects of pregneninolone and related steroids on sexual development in fish (*Lebistes reticulatus*). *Endocrinology*, 1941, **28**, 603–610.

Feiner, L., and T. Rothman. Study of a male castrate. *J. Amer. med. Ass.*, 1939, **113**, 2144–2146.

Filler, W., and N. Drezner. Results of surgical castration in women over forty. *Amer. J. Obstet. Gynaec.*, 1944, **47**, 122–124.

Fisher, C., H. W. Magoun, and S. W. Ranson. Dystocia in diabetes insipidus. The relation of pituitary oxytocin to parturition. *Amer. J. Obstet. Gynaec.*, 1938, **36**, 1–9.

Fraser, A. *Sheep farming.* London : Crosby Lockwood, 1937.

Freud, J., and I. E. Uyldert. Mamma and lactation in rats and other species. *Arch. int. Pharmacodyn.*, 1948, **76**, 74–94.

Fuerstner, P. G. Some neurophysiological aspects of the menstrual cycle and its disturbances. *J. nerv. ment. Dis.*, 1944, **99**, 588–594.

Fugo, N. W., and E. G. Gross. Anterior pituitary-stimulating action of yohimbine. *Endocrinology*, 1942, **31**, 529–534.

Gantt, W. H. Effect of alcohol on sexual reflexes in dogs. *Amer. J. Physiol.*, 1940, **129**, 360.

Gantt, W. H. *Experimental basis for neurotic behavior.* New York : Hoeber, 1944.

Gaunt, R., and H. Hays. Role of progesterone and other hormones in survival of pseudopregnant adrenalectomized ferrets. *Amer. J. Physiol.*, 1938, **124**, 767–773.

Gill, M. M. Functional disturbances of menstruation. *Bull. Menninger Clin.*, 1943, **7**, 6–15.

Golz, F. Über den Einfluss des Nervensystems auf die Vorgange wahrend der Schwangerschaft und des Gebarakts. *Arch. ges. Physiol.*, 1874, **9**, 552.

Goodale, H. D. Feminized male birds. *Genetics*, 1918, **3**, 276–299.

Greenberg, B. Some effects of testosterone on the sexual pigmentation and other sex characters of the cricket frog (*Acris gryllus*). *J. exp. Zool.*, 1942, **91**, 435–451.

Greenberg, B. Social behavior of the western banded gecko, *Coleonyx variegatus* Baird. *Physiol. Zool.*, 1943, **16**, 110–122.

Greenberg, B., and G. K. Noble. Social behavior of the American chameleon (*Anolis carolinensis voigt*). *Physiol. Zool.*, 1944, **17**, 392–439.

Grosch, D. S. The importance of antennae in mating reaction of male *Habrobracon*. *J. comp. physiol. Psychol.*, 1947, **40**, 23–39.

Grosch, D. S. Experimental studies of the mating reaction of male *Habrobracon*. *J. comp. physiol. Psychol.*, 1948, **41**, 188–195.

Guhl, A. M., N. E. Collias, and W. C. Allee. Mating behavior and the social hierarchy in small flocks of white leghorns. *Physiol. Zool.*, 1945, **18**, 365–390.

Guhl, A. M., and D. C. Warren. Number of offspring sired by cockerels related to social dominance in chickens. *Poultry Sci.*, 1946, **25**, 460–472.

Hain, A. M. The effect (a) of litter-size on growth and (b) of oestrone administered during lactation (rat). *Quart. J. exp. Physiol.*, 1942, **25**, 303–313.

Haller, H. L., F. Acree, and S. F. Potts. The nature of the sex attractant of the female gypsy moth. *J. Amer. chem. Soc.*, 1944, **66**, 1659–1662.

Halverson, H. M. Genital and sphincter behavior of the male infant. *J. genet. Psychol.*, 1940, **56**, 95.

Hamilton, J. E. The southern sea lion (*Otharia byronia DeBlainville*). *Discovery reports*, Cambridge University Press, 1934, **8**, 268–318.

Hammond, J. Control of ovulation in farm animals. *Nature, Lond.*, 1944, **153**, 702–705.

Hasler, A. D., and R. K. Meyer. Respiratory responses of normal and castrated goldfish to teleost and mammalian hormones. *J. exp. Zool.*, 1942, **91**, 391–404.

Hertz, R., R. K. Meyer, and M. A. Spielman. The specificity of progesterone in inducing receptivity in the ovariectomized guinea pig. *Endocrinology*, 1937, **21**, 533–535.

Hines, M. The development and regression of reflexes, postures, and progression in the young macaque. *Pub., Carnegie Inst.*, 1942, No. 541, 153–209.

Hogben, L. T. Problems of the origin of species. in J. S. Huxley (Ed.), *The new systematics*, London : Oxford University Press, 1940.

Hooker, C. W. The postnatal history and function of the interstitial cells of the testis of the bull. *Amer. J. Anat.*, 1944, **74**, 1–28.

Hoover, E. E., and H. F. Hubbard. Modification of the sexual cycle of trout by control of light. *Copeia*, 1937, **4**, 206–210.

Horner, B. E. Paternal care of young mice of the genus *Peromyscus*. *J. Mammal.*, 1947, **28**, 31–36.

Hudson, W. H. *The naturalist in La Plata.* London : Chapman and Hall, 1892.

Imms, A. D. *Recent advances in entomology.* Philadelphia : Blakiston, 1931.

Isle, D. New observations on responses to colors in egg laying butterflies. *Nature, Lond.*, 1937, **140**, 544–545.

Katz, D. *Animals and men.* London : Longmans, Green, 1937.

Kellogg, V. Influence of the primary reproductive organs on the secondary sexual characters. *J. exp. Zool.*, 1904, **1**, 601–605.

Kellogg, V. Some silkworm moth reflexes. *Biol. Bull. Woods Hole*, 1907, **12**, 152–154.

Kendeigh, S. C. The role of environment in the life of birds. *Ecol. Monogr.*, 1934, **4**, 299–417.

Kinder, E. F. A study of the nest building activity of the albino rat. *J. exp. Zool.*, 1927, **47**, 117.

Kirkman, F. B. Egg retrieving experiments. *Summary Reports of Researches*, 1936–37, 6–9.

Kirkman, F. B. *Bird behavior.* London and Edinburgh : Nelson, 1937.

Klinefelter, H. F., F. Albright, and G. C. Griswold. Experience with a quantitative test for normal or decreased amounts of follicle stimulating hormone in the urine in endocrinological diagnosis. *J. clin. Endocrinology*, 1943, **3**, 529–544.

Kluver, H., and P. C. Bucy. Preliminary analysis of functions of the temporal lobe in monkeys. *Arch. Neurol. Psychiat., Chicago*, 1939, **42**, 979–1000.

Koehler, O., and A. Zagarus. Beiträge zum Brutverhalten des Halsbandregenpfeifers (*Charadrius hiaticula* L.). *Beitr. Fortpflanzungsbiol. Vogel*, 1937, **13**, 1–9.

Kokolsky, C. Practical mink breeding methods. *Fur Trade J. Canada*, 1945, **22**, 12–13, 28.

Kolb, L., and A. G. DuMez. Experimental addiction of animals to opiates. *Publ. Hlth. Rep., Wash.*, 1931, **46**, No. 13.

Kunde, M., F. D'Amour, A. Carlson, and R. Gustafson. The effect of estrin injections on the basal metabolism, uterine endometrium, lactation, mating, and maternal instincts of the adult dog. *Amer. J. Physiol.*, 1930, **95**, 630.

Lack, D. The behaviour of the robin. I. and II. *Proc. zool. Soc. Lond.*, 1939, **109**, 169–219.

Langworthy, O. R. Behavior disturbances related to decomposition of reflex activity caused by cerebral injury. An experimental study of the cat. *J. Neuropath. exp. Neurol.*, 1943, **3**, 87–100.

Lashley, K. S. Experimental analysis of instinctive behavior. *Psychol. Rev.*, 1938, **45**, 445–471.

Leblond, C. P., and W. O. Nelson. Maternal behavior in hypophysectomized male and female mice. *Amer. J. Physiol.*, 1937, **120**, 167–172.

Lehman, R. S. Experiments to determine the attractiveness of various aromatic compounds to adults of the wireworms. *J. econ. Ent.*, 1932, **25**, 949–958.

Lehrman, D. S., and O. K. Stephenson. A note on the "begging" of nestling flickers. *Proc. Linn. Soc. N. Y.*, 1940, Nos. 50–51, 36–37.

Levy, D. M. Experiments on the sucking reflex and social behavior of dogs. *Amer. J. Orthopsychiat.*, 1934, **4**, 203–224.

Loeser, A. A. Emotional shock and endometrium. *Lancet*, 1943, **244**, 518–519.

Lorenz, K. Der Kumpan in der Umwelt des Vogels. *J. Orn. Lpz.*, 1935, **83**, 137–213.

Lorenz, K., and N. Tinbergen. Taxis und Instinkthandlung in der Eirollbewegung der Graugans I. *Z. Tierpsychol.*, 1938, **2**, 1–29.

Loutitt, C. M. Reproductive behavior of the guinea pig. II. The ontogenesis of the reproductive behavior pattern. *J. comp. Psychol.*, 1929, **9**, 293–304.

Macirone, C., and A. Walton. Fecundity of male rabbits as determined by "dummy matings." *J. agric. Sci.*, 1938, **28**, 122–134.

Maes, J. P. Neural mechanism of sexual behavior in the female cat. *Nature, Lond.*, 1939, **144**, 598–599.

Marples, G., and A. Marples. *Sea terns or sea swallows. Their habits, language, arrival and departure.* London : Copp Clark, 1934.

Marshall, F. H. A. Exteroceptive factors in sexual periodicity. *Biol. Rev.*, 1942, **17**, 68–90.

Marshall, F. H. A., and F. P. Bowden. The effect of irradiation with different wavelengths on the oestrous cycle of the ferret, with remarks on the factors controlling sexual periodicity. *J. exp. Biol.*, 1934, **11**, 409–422.

Marshall, F. H. A., and J. Hammond. Fertility and animal breeding. *Min. Agric. and Fish. Bull.*, 1945, No. 39, 1–44.

Martins, T. Disgorging of food to the puppies by the lactating dog. *Physiol. Zool.*, 1949, **22**, 169–172.

Matthews, H. L. Visual stimulation and ovulation in pigeons. *Proc. roy. Soc.*, 1939, **B126**, 557–560.

Matthews, L. H. The natural history of the elephant seal. *Discovery report gov. dependencies*, 1929, Faulkland Islands, **1**, 235–249.

Meyer, B. J., and R. K. Meyer. Growth and reproduction of the cotton rat, *Sigmodon hispidus*

hispidus, under laboratory conditions. *J. Mammal.*, 1944, **25**, 107–129.

Miles, W. R. The sex expression of men living on a lowered nutritional level. *J. nerv. ment. Dis.*, 1919, **49**, 208–224.

Moehlig, R. C. Castration in the male. Notes on the hypothalamicopituitary-gonadal system. *Endocrinology*, 1940, **27**, 743–748.

Moore, C. R., and D. Price. Some effects of testosterone and testosterone propionate in the rat. *Anat. Rec.*, 1938, **71**, 59–78.

Munro, D., H. W. Horne, Jr., and D. P. Paull. Effect of injury to spinal cord and cauda equina on sexual potency of men. *New Engl. J. Med.*, 1948, **239**, 903–911.

Murie, A. The wolves of Mt. McKinley. *Nat. Park Ser., U. S. Dept. Int.*, 1944, Fauna Series No. 5.

Murr, L. Ueber den Geruchsinn der Mehlmottenschlupfwespe *Habrobracon juglandis*. *Z. vergl. Physiol.*, 1930, **11**, 210–217.

Nalvandov, A. V. A study of the effect of prolactin on broodiness and on cock testes. *Endocrinology*, 1945, **36**, 251–258.

Nelsen, O. E., and N. Maxwell. Induced oestrus and mating in the opossum, *Didelphys virginiana*. *Anat. Rec.*, 1941, **81**, 105.

Nice, M. M. The role of territory in bird life. *Amer. Midl. Nat.*, 1941, **26**, 441–487.

Nissen, H. W. A field study of the chimpanzee. Observations of chimpanzee behavior and environment in Western French Guinea. *Comp. Psychol. Monogr.*, 1931, **8**, 1–122.

Noble, G. K. The relation of courtship to the secondary sexual characters of the two-lined salamander, *Eurycea bislineata* (Green). *Amer. Mus. Novit.*, 1929, No. 362, 1–5.

Noble, G. K. *The biology of the amphibia*. New York: McGraw-Hill, 1931.

Noble, G. K. Sex recognition in the sunfish (*Eupomotis gibbosus* Linne). *Copeia*, 1934, No. 4, 151–154.

Noble, G. K. Courtship and sexual selection of the flicker (*Colaptes auratus luteus*). *Auk*, 1936, **53**, 269–282.

Noble, G. K. The sense organs involved in the courtship of *Storeria*, *Thamnophis* and other snakes. *Nat. Hist.*, 1937, **128**, 673–725.

Noble, G. K. Neural basis of social behavior in vertebrates. *The Collecting Net*, 1939, **14**, 121–124.

Noble, G. K., and L. R. Aronson. The sexual behavior of anura. I. The normal mating pattern of *Rana pipiens*. *Bull. Amer. Mus. nat. Hist.*, 1942, **80**, 127–142.

Noble, G. K., and R. Borne. The effect of forebrain lesions on the sexual and fighting behavior in *Betta splendens* and other fishes. *Anat. Rec.*, 1941, **79** Suppl., 49.

Noble, G. K., and H. T. Bradley. The mating behavior of lizards; its bearing on the theory of sexual selection. *Ann. N. Y. Acad. Sci.*, 1933, **35**, 25–100.

Noble, G. K., and B. Curtis. Sexual selection in fishes. *Anat. Rec.*, 1935–36, **64**, 84–85.

Noble, G. K., and B. Curtis. The social behavior of the jewel fish, *Hemichromis bimaculatus* Gill. *Bull. Amer. Mus. nat. Hist.*, 1939, **76**, 1–46.

Noble, G. K., and B. Greenberg. Effects of seasons, castration and crystalline sex hormones upon the urogenital system and sexual behavior of the lizard (*Anolis carolinensis*). I. The adult female. *J. exp. Zool.*, 1941, **88**, 451–478.

Noble, G. K., and K. F. Kumpf. The sexual behavior and secondary sexual characters of gonadectomized fish. *Anat. Rec.*, 1936–37, **67**, 113.

Noble, G. K., K. F. Kumpf, and V. N. Billings. The induction of brooding behavior in the jewel fish. *Endocrinology*, 1938, **23**, 353–359.

Noble, G. K., and D. S. Lehrman. Egg recognition by the laughing gull. *Auk*, 1940, **57**, 22–43.

Noble, G. K., and E. R. Mason. Experiments on the brooding habits of the lizards *Eumeces* and *Ophisaurus*. *Amer. Mus. Novit.*, 1933, No. 619, 1–29.

Noble, G. K., and R. C. Noble. The Anderson tree frog (*Hyla andersonii* Baird); observations on its habits and life history. *Zoologica*, 1923, **2**, 416–455.

Noble, G. K., and L. B. Richards. Experiments on the egg-laying of salamanders. *Amer. Mus. Novit.*, 1932, No. 513, 1–25.

Noble, G. K., and W. Vogt. An experimental study of sex recognition in birds. *Auk*, 1935, **52**, 278–286.

Noble, G. K., and M. Wurm. The effect of testosterone propionate on the black-crowned night heron. *Endocrinology*, 1940, **26**, 837–850.

Noble, G. K., and A. Zitrin. Induction of mating behavior in male and female chicks following injection of sex hormones. Including notations on body weight and comb growth. *Endocrinology*, 1942, **30**, 327–334.

Oesting, R. B., and B. Webster. The sex hormone secretion of children. *Endocrinology*, 1938, **22**, 307.

Osgood, W. H., E. A. Preble, and G. H. Parker. The fur seals and other life of the Pribilof Islands, Alaska. *U. S. Bur. Fish. Bull.*, 1914, **34**, Document 820.

Oudemanns, J. Th. Falter aus castrirten Raupen vie sie auschen und wie sie sich benehmen. *Zool. Jb. (Abt. f. Syst.)*, 1899, **12**, 71–88.

Pallen, D. Practical mink breeding methods. *Fur Trade J. Canada*, 1944, **22**, 8–9, 24.

Perla, D., and M. Sandberg. Metabolic interdependence of vitamin B and manganese. Reciprocal neutralization of their toxic effects. *Proc. Soc. exp. Biol., N. Y.*, 1939, **41**, 522–527.

Peters, H. Experimentelle untersuchung über die Brutpflege von Haplochromis multicolor. *Z. Tierpsychol.*, 1937, **1**, 201–218.

Petersen, W. E. Lactation. *Physiol. Rev.*, 1944, **24**, 340–371.

Preble, E. A. Mammals of the Pribilof Islands. *N. Amer. Fauna*, 1923, **46**, 107.

Pussep, L. M. The blood circulation in the brain during coitus. In A. Weil (Ed.), *Pro-*

ceedings of the first international conference of the congress for sexual reform on the basis of sexual science, 1922. (Translated by A. C. Kinsey.)

Ranson, S. W. The hypothalamus: Its significance for visceral innervation and emotional expression. (The Weir Mitchell oration.) *Trans. Coll. Phys. Philad.*, 1934, **2**, 222–242.

Raynaud, A. Comportement sexual des souris femelles intersexuées. *C. R. Soc. Biol. Paris*, 1938, **127**, 903–995.

Regen, J. Kastration und ihre Folgerscheinungen bei *Gryllus campestris* I. *Mitt. Zool. Anz.*, 1909, **34**, 477–478.

Reynolds, A. E. The normal seasonal reproductive cycle in the male *Eumeces fasciatus* together with some observations on the effects of castration and hormone administration. *J. Morph.*, 1943, **72**, 331–377.

Rice, V. A. *Breeding and improvement of farm animals*. New York: McGraw-Hill, 1942.

Richardson, W. B. Wood rats (*Neotama albigula*): Their growth and development. *J. Mammal.*, 1943, **24**, 130–143.

Richter, C. P. Nutritional requirements of pregnant and lactating rats studied by the self-selection method. *Amer. J. Physiol.*, 1938, **123**, 170.

Riddle, O. Aspects and implications of the hormonal control of the maternal instinct. *Proc. Amer. phil. Soc.*, 1935, **75**, 521–525.

Riddle, O., R. W. Bates, and E. L. Lahr. Prolactin induces broodiness in fowl. *Amer. J. Physiol.*, 1935, **111**, 352–360.

Riddle, O., W. F. Hollander, R. A. Miller, E. L. Lahr, G. C. Smith, and H. N. Marvin. Endocrine studies. *Yearb. Carnegie Instn.*, 1941–42, No. 41, 203–211.

Riddle, O., W. F. Hollander, R. A. Miller, F. E. Visscher, E. L. Lahr, G. C. Smith, and V. M. Rauch. Endocrine studies. *Yearb. Carnegie Instn.*, 1942–43, 129–139.

Riddoch, G. The reflex functions of the completely divided spinal cord in man, compared with those associated with less severe lesions. *Brain*, 1917, **40**, 264–402.

Riess, B. F. The isolation of factors of learning and native behavior in field and laboratory studies. 1948 (unpublished manuscript).

Ring, J. R. The estrogen-progesterone induction of sexual receptivity in the spayed female mouse. *Endocrinology*, 1944, **34**, 269–275.

Robinson, E. J., and R. Rugh. The reproductive processes of the fish, *Oryzias latipes*. *Biol. Bull. Woods Hole*, 1943, **84**, 115–125.

Rogers, F. T. Studies of the brain stem. VI. An experimental study of the corpus striatum of the pigeon as related to various instinctive types of behavior. *J. comp. Neurol.*, 1922, **35**, 21–60.

Root, W. S., and P. Bard. The mediation of feline erection through sympathetic pathways with some remarks on sexual behavior after deafferentation of the genitalia. *Amer. J. Physiol.*, 1947, **151**, 80–90.

Rosenquist, R. C. Fertility studies and sex behavior in paraplegic patients. A preliminary report. 1949 (unpublished manuscript).

Rowan, W. *The riddle of migration*. Baltimore: Williams and Wilkins, 1931.

Rowan, W. Experiments in bird migration. III. The effects of artificial light, castration and certain extracts on the autumn movements of the American crow (*Corvus brachyrhynchos*). *Proc. nat. Acad. Sci., Wash.*, 1932, **18**, 639–654.

Russell, E. S. Biological adaptedness and specialization of instinctive behaviour. *Proc. Linn. Soc. Lond.*, 1941, Sess. 153, Pt. 2, 250–268.

Russell, E. S. The stereotypy of instinctive behaviour. *Proc. Linn. Soc. Lond.*, 1944, 186–208.

Savory, T. H. *Mechanistic biology and animal behavior*. London: Watts, 1936.

Schafer, E. A. *Textbook of physiology*. New York: Macmillan, 1900. Volume II.

Schlosberg, H., M. C. Duncan, and B. H. Daitch. Mating behavior of two live-bearing fish *Xiphophorus hellerii* and *Plattypoecilus maculatus*. *Physiol. Zool.*, 1949, **22**, 149–161.

Schneirla, T. C. Problems in the biopsychology of social organization. *J. abnorm. soc. Psychol.*, 1946, **41**, 385–402.

Schoolland, J. B. Are there any innate behavior tendencies? *Genet. Psychol. Monogr.*, 1942, **25**, 219–287.

Schrader, M. E. G. Zur Physiologie des Vogelhirns. *Arch. ges. Physiol.*, 1889, **44**, 175–238.

Scott, J. P. Social behavior, organization and leadership in a small flock of domestic sheep. *Comp. Psychol. Monogr.*, 1945, **18**, 1–29.

Scott, J. W. Additional observations on mating behavior of the sage grouse. *Anat. Rec.*, 1944, **89**, 552.

Seevers, M. H. Opiate addiction in the monkey. II. Dilaudid in comparison with morphine, heroin and codeine. *J. Pharmacol.*, 1936, **56**, 157–165.

Seward, G. H. Studies on the reproductive activities of the guinea pig. II. The role of hunger in filial behavior. *J. comp. Psychol.*, 1940, **29**, 25–41.

Seward, J. P., and G. H. Seward. Studies on the reproductive activities of the guinea pig. I. Factors in maternal behavior. *J. comp. Psychol.*, 1940, **29**, 1–24.

Shadle, A. R. Rat foster mother of mice. *J. Mammal.*, 1945, **26**, 193–194.

Shadle, A. R. Copulation in the porcupine. *J. Wildlife Manage.*, 1946, **10**, 159–162.

Shortridge, G. C. *The mammals of southwest Africa*. London: Heinemann, 1934.

Siperstein, D. M. The effects of acute and chronic inanition upon the development and structure of the testis in the albino rat. *Anat. Rec.*, 1920–21, **20**, 355–381.

Smith, H. M. Size of breeding populations in relation to egg-laying and reproductive success in the eastern red-wing (*Agelaius p. phoeniceus*). *Ecology*, 1943, **24**, 183–207.

Smith, P. E., and E. T. Engle. Experimental evidence regarding the role of the anterior pituitary in the development and regulation of the genital system. *Amer. J. Anat.*, 1927, **40**, 159.

Spragg, S. D. S. Morphine addiction in chimpanzees. *Comp. Psychol. Monogr.*, 1940, **15**, 1–132.

Steinach, E. Untersuchungen zur vergleichenden Physiologie der Mannlichen Geschlechtsorgane. III. Über den Geschlechtsrieb der vor und nach der Pubertat Kastrierten Ratten und über das Schicksal der akzessorischen Geschlechtsdrusen in Folge der Kastration. *Arch. ges. Physiol.*, 1894, **56**, 304.

Stone, C. P. The congenital sexual behavior of the young male albino rat. *J. comp. Psychol.*, 1922, **2**, 95–153.

Stone, C. P. Further study of sensory functions in the activation of sexual behavior in the young male albino rat. *J. comp. Psychol.*, 1923, **3**, 469–473.

Stone, C. P. Delay in the awakening of copulatory ability in the male albino rat incurred by defective diets. I. Quantitative deficiency. *J. comp. Psychol.*, 1924, **4**, 195–210.

Stone, C. P. The retention of copulatory ability in male rats following castration. *J. comp. Psychol.*, 1927, **7**, 369–387.

Stone, C. P. The retention of copulatory activity in male rabbits following castration. *J. genet. Psychol.*, 1932, **40**, 296–305.

Stone, C. P. Effects of cortical destruction on reproductive behavior and maze learning in albino rats. *J. comp. Psychol.*, 1938, **26**, 217–236.

Stone, C. P. Maturation and instinctive functions. Chapter 2 in F. A. Moss (Ed.), *Comparative psychology.* New York: Prentice-Hall, 1942a.

Stone, C. P. Counteracting the retarding effects of inanition on the awakening of copulatory ability in male rats by testosterone propionate. *J. comp. Psychol.*, 1942b, **33**, 97–105.

Stopes, M. C. *Married love.* New York: Putnam, 1931.

Sulman, F., and B. Black. The alleged endocrine effect of yohimbine. *Endocrinology*, 1945, **36**, 70–72.

Svihal, A. Life history of the Texas rice rat (*Oryzomys palustris texensis*). *J. Mammal.*, 1931, **12**, 238–242.

Tatum, A. L., M. H. Seevers, and K. H. Collins. Morphine addiction and its physiological interpretation based on experimental evidences. *J. Pharmacol.*, 1929, **36**, 447–475.

Tauber, E. S. Effects of castration upon the sexuality of the adult male. *Psychosom. Med.*, 1940, **2**, 74–87.

Terry, C. E., and M. Pellens. *The opium problem.* New York: Haddon Craftsmen, 1928.

Tietz, E. G. The humoral excitation of the nesting intincts in rabbits. *Science*, 1933, **78**, 316.

Tinbergen, N. An objectivistic study of the innate behaviour of animals. *Bibliotheca Biotheoretica*, 1942, **1**, Pt. 2, 39–98.

Tinbergen, N., and D. J. Kuenen. Über die auslosenden und die rechlunggebenden Reizsituationen der Sperrbewegung von jungen Drosseln. (*Turdus m. merula* L. und *T. e. ericetorum* Turton). *Z. Tierpsychol.*, 1939, **3**, 37–60.

Tinklepaugh, O. L. The self-mutilation of a male Macacus rhesus monkey. *J. Mammal.*, 1928, **9**, 293–300.

Tinklepaugh, O. L., and C. G. Hartman. Behavior and maternal care of the newborn monkey (*Macaca mulatta* — "M. rhesus"). *J. genet. Psychol.*, 1940, **40**, 257–286.

Travis, B. B. Habits of the june beetle *Phyllophaga lanceolata* (Say) in Iowa. *J. econ. Ent.*, 1939, **32**, 690–693.

Watson, J. B. The behavior of noddy and sooty terns. *Pub. Carnegie Instn.*, 1908, **103**, 189–255.

Weichert, C. K., and S. Kerrigan. Effects of estrogens upon the young injected lactating rats. *Endocrinology*, 1942, **30**, 741–752.

Wells, L. J. Seasonal sexual rhythm and its experimental modification in the male of the thirteen-lined ground squirrel (*Citellus tridecemlineatus*). *Anat. Rec.*, 1935, **62**, 409–444.

Wells, L. J. Prolongation of breeding capacity in males of an annual breeding wild rodent (*Citellus tridecemlineatus*) by constant low temperature. *Anat. Rec.*, 1936, **64**, 138.

Wheeler, D. R. The inhibitory effects of punishment: An experimental study of the white rat. Ph.D. thesis, Harvard University, 1933.

White, W. W. Bird of first brood of swallow assisting to feed second brood. *Brit. Birds*, 1941, **34**, 179–184.

Wiesner, B. P., and A. L. Bacharach. Effect upon sex behavior of a diet deficient in vitamin E. *Nature, Lond.*, 1937, **140**, 972–973.

Wiesner, B. P., and L. Mirskaia. On the endocrine basis of mating in the mouse. *Quart. J. exp. Physiol.*, 1930, **20**, 274–279.

Wiesner, B. P., and N. M. Sheard. *Maternal behavior in the rat.* Edinburgh: Oliver and Boyd, 1933.

Wilson, E. A. Aves. *Nat. Antarctic Exped.*, 1907, **2**.

Witschi, E. Seasonal sex characters in birds and their hormonal control. *Wilson Bull.*, 1935, **47**, 177–188.

Wolfson, A. A preliminary report on some experiments on bird migration. *Condor*, 1940, **42**, 93–99.

Yerkes, R. M., and J. H. Elder. The sexual and reproductive cycles of chimpanzees. *Proc. nat. Acad. Sci., Wash.*, 1936, **22**, 276–283.

Yerkes, R. M., and M. I. Tomlin. Mother-infant relations in chimpanzees. *J. comp. Psychol.*, 1935, **20**, 321–358.

Young, W. C., E. W. Dempsey, H. I. Myers, and C. W. Hagquist. The ovarian condition and sexual behavior in the female guinea pig. *Amer. J. Anat.*, 1938, **63**, 457–487.

Zitrin, A., and F. A. Beach. Induction of mating activity in male cats. *Ann. N. Y. Acad. Sci.*, 1945, **46**, 42–44.

13

Learnable Drives and Rewards

NEAL E. MILLER

Yale University

People are not born with a tendency to strive for money, for the discovery of scientific truths, or for symbols of social status and security. Such motives are learned during socialization. Many of them (such as jealousy when another man makes love to one's wife) vary greatly in different societies and even among the social classes in our society (cf. Ford, 1949). Even the primary drives themselves may be modified by learning, so that hunger becomes a desire for a particular type of food appetizingly prepared. Many Frenchmen abhor sweet corn and like snails.

Many writers have used the concept of secondary or learned drives and rewards.* Woodworth (1918) advanced the thesis that habits can become drives and used it to attack McDougall's doctrine of instinct. Davis (1948) indicated that the scholastic inferiority of lower-class children is due partly to a failure to acquire interests that provide motivation and reward for school work. Roethlisberger and Dickson (1941) described the importance of social motivations in in-

Work on this chapter was supported by the Institute of Human Relations, Yale University. The ideas in it have been materially extended and sharpened by collaboration with John Dollard on problems of psychotherapy. Robert F. Grose and Martin Kohn helped to assemble and check the references. The colleagues who read a preliminary mimeographed version are warmly thanked for their helpful suggestions.

* As used in this chapter the following words are roughly equivalent: drive and motivation; reward and reinforcement; cue and distinctive stimulus; learned, acquired, and secondary.

dustry. They showed that the direct effects of improved illumination or added rest periods may be completely overshadowed by motivational changes, depending on whether the workers feel that management is taking an interest in their welfare. Miller and Dollard (1941) discussed the social conditions apparently responsible for the learning of certain drives, such as a tendency to copy people with prestige. Allport (1937) emphasized the crucial role of learned drives in his book on personality, and Shaffer (1936) used them in his discussion of abnormality and adjustment. Dollard and Miller (1950) assigned great importance to learned drives and learned reinforcements in the higher mental processes, personality, and psychotherapy.

Freudian theory contains many assumptions about how drives are changed by experience and how these changes affect the personality. Mowrer (1939) translated Freud's (1936) assumptions about one of these drives, anxiety, into stimulus-response terms. He postulated that anxiety can motivate trial-and-error behavior and anxiety reduction can reinforce the learning of new habits. He used this hypothesis to interpret phenomena ranging from conditioning experiments to rituals and superstitions. Dollard (1945) used the same hypothesis to explain how certain symptoms of war neuroses are learned.

The experimental work on learned drives and rewards is limited almost exclusively to

(1) fear as a learnable drive and fear reduction as a reward or (2) learned rewards and drives based on hunger and food. This work will be discussed first and will constitute most of the chapter. It will be followed by a brief discussion of other drives as sources of learned motivation, some general problems, and studies of complex social motives.

We shall try to integrate the facts around a theory of learning built on drive-stimulus-response-reward, which Hull (1943) has described mathematically, and Miller and Dollard (1941) more simply. Different theoretical approaches have been made by Allport (1937), Tolman (1943), and Lewin (1942, 1946).

Criteria of Learnable Drives and Rewards

A learnable drive or reward is one that can be acquired by a previously ineffective cue as a result of learning. Thus, if a child that has not previously feared dogs learns to fear them after having been bitten, it shows that fear is learnable. Similarly, if appropriate training causes a previously ineffective token or coin to serve as a reward, we may call it a learned reward. This criterion rules out drives or rewards that are produced by changes other than learning, for example, those cases of drug addiction that are primarily caused by severe withdrawal symptoms.

The fact that a drive is learnable as a reaction to new cues does not rule out the possibility that it may also be an innate response to certain stimuli. Thus, although fear may be an innate response to pain, it may also be learned as a reaction to many other stimuli.

The ultimate test of drive and reward is their ability to produce the learning and performance of new responses. When, as a result of learning, previously neutral cues gain the capacity to play the same functional role in the learning and performance of new responses as do other drives, such as hunger and thirst, these cues may be said to have a learned drive value; when they gain the capacity to function in the same way as other rewards, such as food and water, they may be said to have a learned reward value.

FEAR AS A LEARNABLE DRIVE, AND FEAR REDUCTION AS A REWARD

Fear, or anxiety as it often is called when its source is vague, has been studied most thoroughly, and it provides the clearest examples of the basic concepts we are concerned with here.

Basic Principles

Fear is an important drive because it can be learned so readily and can become so strong. Fear is called *learnable* because it can be learned as a response to previously neutral cues; it is called a *drive* because it can motivate the learning and performance of new responses in the same way as hunger, thirst, or other drives. These attributes are demonstrated by the following experiment.*

The apparatus, illustrated in Fig. 1, consisted of two compartments: one white with a grid as a floor, the other black with a smooth solid floor. These compartments were separated by a door which could be opened in any one of three ways: by the experimenter's pressing a button, by the rat's moving a wheel above the right-hand half of the door, or by the rat's pressing a bar near the upper left-hand corner of the door.

Albino rats tested before training in this apparatus showed no marked preference for either compartment. In order to teach them to fear the white compartment, they were given an electric shock from the grid, and allowed to escape into the black compartment. They received ten such trials.

After this they were given five test trials *without shock*. They continued to run rapidly, but this might possibly be explained

* For a preliminary report, see Miller (1941); for a more complete one, see Miller (1948a).

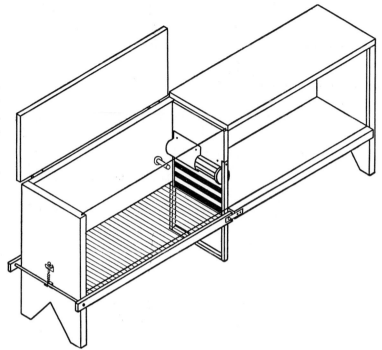

FIG. 1. Learned-drive apparatus. The left compartment is painted white, the right one black. Electric shocks are given through the grid which is the floor of the white compartment. Under different conditions the door (painted with horizontal black and white stripes) drops out of the way when the experimenter presses a button, the rat turns the wheel, or the rat presses the bar. Automatic records are made of the time from the rat's contact with the grid to his performance of the correct response, and of each quarter rotation of the wheel. (From Miller 1948a, p. 90.)

as the mere persistence of the habit of running.

The most rigorous test for a learned drive was made by determining whether or not the cues in the white compartment could lead the animals to learn a *new* response without further electric shocks. The conditions were changed: the door was left closed, but the rat could open it by moving the wheel a fraction of a turn. On the first of these nonshock trials the animals showed symptoms of fear, such as urination, defecation, tenseness, and crouching. They also performed a variety of other responses, and eventually most of them moved the wheel, caused the door to drop, and ran through into the black compartment. As shown in Fig. 2 the speed of operating the wheel increased on subsequent trials. In other

words, previously neutral cues in the white compartment were able to motivate the learning of a new response in the same way as do hunger, thirst, and other drives.* Similarly escape from the white into the black compartment had acquired the functional properties of a reward.

If running from the white into the black compartment served as a reward, we should expect that preventing it would extinguish the habit of moving the wheel. This prediction was tested by giving the rats additional nonshock trials with the control of the door changed from the wheel to the bar. At first the rats responded vigorously to the

* For evidence that these cues cannot produce such learning unless they have been associated with moderately strong shocks, see the 90-volt group in Fig. 6.

wheel. Eventually these responses were extinguished, and other responses emerged. As would be expected, the one response (pressing the bar) that caused the door to

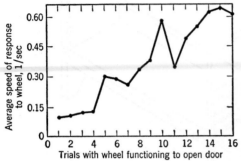

FIG. 2. Learning the first new habit (turning the wheel) during nonshock trials with fear as a learned drive. Rats received electric shocks in the white compartment (see Fig. 1). They escaped by running through the already open door. Then they received trials without shock, during which the door was closed but could be opened by turning the wheel. (From Miller 1948a, p. 94.)

drop and permitted escape was learned, and wheel turning was displaced. This is shown in Figs. 3 and 4. From this it can be seen

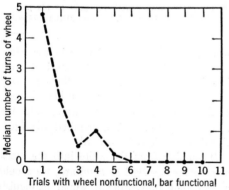

FIG. 3. The response of turning the wheel extinguishes when it fails to open the door that prevents escape from the frightening white compartment. During this extinction the rat was also learning the competing response of pressing the bar, shown in Fig. 4. (From Miller 1948a, p. 95.)

that escape from the white compartment played a crucial role, similar to that of a primary reward, in the learning and the maintenance of new habits.

Control on the possible effects of tension created by conflict. Brown and Jacobs (1949) pointed out that the drive attributed to fear in the foregoing experiment might have been caused by tension created by the conflict and frustration produced when the door prevented the animals from running. Similarly the effect of fear reduction cannot clearly be separated from the disappearance of this conflict when the door opens.

In order to avoid this difficulty they locked albino rats in one of two identical

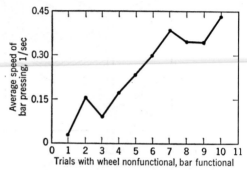

FIG. 4. Learning a second new habit (pressing the bar) during nonshock trials with fear as a learned drive. (From Miller, 1948a, p. 96.)

compartments and gave them trials during which a rapidly interrupted light and tone were paired with an electric shock. Then they gave nonshock trials with the two compartments separated by only a small hurdle. On each trial the light and tone were turned on and kept on until the rat crossed the hurdle into the other compartment; then they were immediately turned off. The speed of shuttling across the hurdle increased in a typical learning curve. Control rats, who had not had the preliminary pairing of the light and tone with shock, did not learn. Since no interruption of a running response was involved, it could not have produced the learning.

Higher-order conditioning. Experiments on higher-order conditioning also show that cues previously associated with pain can motivate the learning of new habits. Instead of learning a new response, however, the subject learns to perform the same response to a new stimulus. Foursikof (Pavlov, 1927) first used electric shock to condition a dog to lift his front foot to a previously neutral mechanical stimulus on the hind foot. After this he used the mechanical stimulus without the primary drive of shock to condition the dog to lift his foot to the sound of bubbling water. Eventually he used the sound of bubbling water (without the mechanical stimulus or shock) to condition withdrawal to a tone. By primary reinforcement to the mechanical stimulus, secondary to the bubbling water, and tertiary to the tone, he maintained these responses for over a year.

Hypothesis that learnable drives are strong stimuli produced by responses. External sources of stimulation and overt responses can be observed directly, and we know many of their properties. At present learnable drives, such as fear, cannot be observed directly and have not been studied thoroughly. On the basis of what we do know, two related hypotheses are advanced: (1) that learned drives, such as fear, obey the same laws as do overt responses; and (2) that they have the same drive and cue properties as strong external stimuli.

These hypotheses are purely functional and do not say anything about the anatomical location of the inferred process. As a short way of expressing the first hypothesis, learnable drives will be called responses; to express the second hypothesis, they will be called stimulus-producing responses. This is a somewhat unorthodox expansion of the use of these two words.

If fear is a strong response-produced stimulus, anything that produces a sudden decrease in the fear response should have a rewarding effect. The same factors that reduce other responses should reduce the fear response, namely: (1) removal of the cues eliciting the response (for example, getting out of the white compartment); or (2) introduction of cues eliciting incompatible responses (for example, cues that have been associated with the extinction of fear or with other responses, such as eating when hungry, that are more or less incompatible with fear). In dealing with these other responses we are handicapped by not knowing exactly which ones are incompatible with fear or their different degrees of incompatibility. Furthermore, with many if not all such responses, other primary and secondary rewards occur in addition to those produced by the reduction in the strength of the fear.

According to the drive-reduction hypothesis, a primary drive (e.g. pain) is necessary before a response producing a learnable drive (e.g. fear) can be acquired. But, once it is learned, the fear is observed to persist on nonshock trials without pain. This raises three possibilities:

1. Some other drive is present to motivate the onset of the fear during these trials.

2. There are two kinds of responses: (*a*) those producing learnable drives, such as fear, which can be elicited without a drive to motivate them, and (*b*) those involved in instrumental behavior, such as bar pressing, which cannot be elicited without a drive.

3. Once any response is learned, its strength varies with the strength of drive, but some strength may remain at zero drive.

According to the third possibility, a drive is necessary for learning and also to prevent eventual extinction, since rewarding drive reduction cannot occur without a drive to be reduced. A well-established response, however, might persist without drive for many trials before extinction. Some evidence for and against this assumption is presented in Miller (1948*b*). Further work is needed to determine which possibility is correct.

The foregoing hypotheses may be summarized as follows: Learned drives depend on responses that produce strong stimuli. (Fear is a strong stimulus in the same sense that pain is.) Furthermore fear may be an innate reponse to certain stimuli, such as pain, and the fear response innately produces the fear stimulus, just as electric shock produces pain. The only difference is that it is easy to attach the fear response to new cues. Similarly, learned rewards are pro-

sign and theoretical expectations are summarized in the following diagram, in which the dotted arrows represent learned connections:

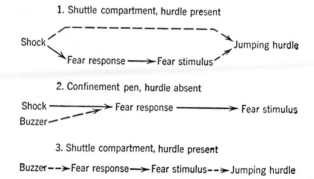

1. Shuttle compartment, hurdle present

Shock — — — — — — — — — — — → Jumping hurdle
Fear response ——→ Fear stimulus

2. Confinement pen, hurdle absent

Shock ————→ Fear response ————→ Fear stimulus
Buzzer —

3. Shuttle compartment, hurdle present

Buzzer— —→Fear response—→Fear stimulus— —→Jumping hurdle

duced by responses that remove sources of strong stimulation. Thus the basic mechanism of motivation (strong stimulation) is the same for primary and learned drives, and the basic mechanism of reinforcement (a reduction in strong stimulation) is the same for primary and learned rewards.

Secondary generalization mediated by fear. If fear is a strong response-produced stimulus, it should function not only as a drive but also as a cue mediating secondary generalization. May (1948) first trained rats to jump over a low hurdle that separated two identical compartments, in order to escape an electric shock from the floor of the compartment. He assumed that the shock elicited fear and that the rats learned hurdle jumping to the fear stimulus as well as to shock. His second step was to train the animals to fear a buzzer. He paired the buzzer with shock while the animals were penned in the center of the apparatus (with the hurdle removed) so that they could not perform an escape response. His third step was to put the animals in the apparatus with the hurdle present and to test their response to the buzzer without shock. During these trials he expected the stimulus produced by the fear response to mediate transfer of the hurdle-jumping habit from the shock to the buzzer. His experimental de-

Control animals were trained in exactly the same way except that in the confinement pen they got the buzzer and shock in random order, not paired. Thus they learned the same hurdle-jumping habits but did not have any specific training to fear the buzzer.

On the first test trial the experimental animals gave more hurdle-jumping responses to the buzzer than did the controls. This was in line with the deduction that the response-produced stimulus of fear should serve as a cue to mediate secondary generalization of the hurdle-jumping response from the shock to the buzzer.*

The experiments described earlier show that fear has the functional properties of a response-produced drive; the present experiment suggests that it has the functional properties of a response-produced cue. These results agree with the everyday observation

* It is possible that the buzzer produced quicker hurdle jumping by an increase in random activity without any transfer of that specific response. But untrained rats usually respond to fear of this sort by crouching. An additional group trained to fear the buzzer but not to jump the hurdle would have clinched the matter. The fact that the difference between the experimental and control groups appeared on the first trial was learned through personal discussion with Mark May; the appearance of this difference on the first trial rules out the effects of learning to jump the hurdle in order to escape the buzzer.

that fear can motivate people to learn a great variety of responses, and that it is sufficiently distinctive so that people can be taught to respond to it with a verbal label that transfers to a variety of new frightening situations.

Characteristic responses to fear. The preceding experiment indicates that when fear is learned as a response to a new situation it tends to bring with it responses that have been learned in other situations. It should also bring with it responses that are either a part of the fear pattern itself or are high in the innate hierarchy of responses to the fear stimulus. These responses will influence the course of subsequent learning.

Two of the most obvious behavioral effects of fear present a striking contrast. One is the tendency to remain motionless and mute, which reaches its extreme form in the death-feigning of certain animals, and sometimes produces results suggestive of the waxy flexibility of catatonics.* The other is the pattern of startle, withdrawal, running, and vocalization. Both of these incompatible patterns seem to be activated by fear, and behavior may shift rapidly from one to the other, as when a frightened animal first freezes, then suddenly scurries to shelter.

Other reactions are described in studies of the strong fears produced in military combat (Dollard, 1943, p. 19; Wickert, 1947, p. 128; Hastings, 1944). In these studies it is difficult to differentiate between the symptoms produced directly by fear and those produced indirectly by the conflict between fear and loyalty. Whatever the causal sequence, the studies agree that the most frequent reactions to strong fear in combat are a pounding heart and rapid pulse, a strong feeling of muscular tenseness, trembling, exaggerated startle, dryness of the throat and mouth, a sinking feeling in the stomach,

---

* It seems probable that this tendency is involved in the temporary inhibition of the bar-pressing activity that Estes and Skinner (1941) have used as a measure of anxiety.

perspiration, a frequent need to urinate, irritability and aggression, an overpowering urge to cry, run, or hide, feelings of unreality, confusion, faintness, nausea, and sometimes subsequent amnesia. Common chronic effects of fear between air missions are fatigue, a feeling of depression and a slowing down of movements and mental processes, restlessness, aggression, loss of appetite, trembling, being easily startled, not wanting to go on any more missions, insomnia, nightmares, interference with speech, making meaningless gestures, and maintaining peculiar postures. Grinker and Spiegel (1945) give a vivid picture of severe states of combat anxiety and report that the symptoms can resemble closely those of schizophrenia.

On the other hand, we must remember that fear, like any other drive, can motivate the learning and performance of socially useful responses such as driving carefully or having a medical examination. Even in aerial combat, 37 per cent of the men reported that they performed their duties better when they were very afraid, and 50 per cent reported that mild fear had a beneficial effect (Wickert, 1947, p. 131).

A study by Mahl (1949) suggests that it may be necessary to differentiate between the effects of acute and chronic fear. According to Cannon (1929) acute fear decreases the secretion of hydrochloric acid by the stomach, whereas Mahl found that chronic fear greatly increases the stomach acidity of dogs. Since there are other differences between the two situations, one cannot certainly attribute the results to the chronic-acute variable.

Summary of ways in which fear can influence behavior. Fear can influence behavior in the following three ways:

1. It can be learned and bring with it the innate responses to fear, such as an increase in stomach acidity, immobility, or exaggerated startle responses.

2. It can be learned and serve as a cue to mediate the transfer of responses previously learned in other situations.*

3. It can be learned and serve as a drive to motivate (whereas fear reduction serves as a reward to reinforce) the learning of new responses. This learning will be influenced by the preceding two factors through their role in determining which responses are likely to occur.

Applications of Basic Concepts

After Mowrer (1939) put forward the hypothesis that fear (or anxiety, as he called it) operates as a drive, and fear reduction as a reward, he applied it in a series of experiments. Although, as he pointed out, most of these experiments may yield to alternative interpretations, taken as a group they support his hypothesis.

In one experiment Mowrer and Lamoreaux (1942) conditioned rats to avoid shock by running to the cue of a buzzer. The experimenters found that better learning was produced when the buzzer was turned off as soon as the animals made the response than when it was turned off either before or 5 seconds after. They had expected this on the grounds (1) that fear should become conditioned to the buzzer with the result that turning the buzzer off would produce a rewarding reduction in the strength of the fear, and (2) that this reward should be more effective when given immediately after the response than either before or 5 seconds after it.

Another experiment by Mowrer and Lamoreaux (1946) used a change in the pattern of illumination as the conditioned stimulus in shock-avoidance training. For half of the rats this change consisted in turning off two lights above them and turn-

* One will expect fear to be able to become a part of a pattern in the same way as do other cues (Hull, 1943, pp. 349–380). Thus a subject can learn to respond to fear by crouching in one situation and by running in another. In such cases transfer will depend on the external situation as well as on the fear.

ing on a nearer one below; for the other half it was the opposite. In this way any possible influence of a change in the overall intensity of light was ingeniously controlled. One part of this experiment demonstrated that rats would learn to jump if, whenever they performed this response within 5 seconds after the onset of the conditioned stimulus, it was turned off (i.e. changed back to the normal pattern) and not followed by shock. By a similar procedure a control group was taught the different response of running to the conditioned stimulus. In both cases the shock, given whenever the animal failed to respond properly to the conditioned stimulus, lasted for exactly 2 seconds, irrespective of what the animal did.

Another part of this experiment indicated that the animals could learn to make one response to turn off the fear-producing conditioned stimulus and a different response to turn off the unconditioned stimulus of electric shock.

The results of both parts of this experiment are what would be expected from the hypothesis that the animals learn to fear the conditioned stimulus and that turning it off serves to reward whatever response is occuring at that time. Two variables, however, are involved: (1) turning off the conditioned stimulus when the selected response (running or jumping) occurs, and (2) having all responses other than the selected one followed by shock. It is simplest to assume that the sole effect of the second variable is to allow fear to be reduced, but it may have had other effects, such as a tendency to eliminate all responses except the correct one.

Whenever an electric shock is used to train animals to make a specific response, such as bar pressing, the animals tend to make this response "spontaneously" between trials during the first part of learning. Coppock and Mowrer (1947) reasoned that the making of such responses between trials was probably motivated by the learned drive of fear, and that it was rewarded by the reduction of the strength of this fear. If this were so, the making of such responses between trials should help learning. To test this deduction they trained rats to avoid shock by touching a bar whenever a light changed. For the experimental animals the bar was present between trials so that they could "rehearse." For the controls it was absent so that they were prevented from making "spontaneous" responses between trials. As expected, the experimental group learned reliably faster than the controls.

Fear reduction as an explanation for fixation. When animals that have learned a specific habit (such as turning right in a T-maze to secure food) are given a few electric shocks at the choice point, it "fixates" their behavior. In other words, if the food is shifted to the left, they will keep going to the right much longer than will animals that have not been shocked. Farber (1948) deduced such fixation from the assumption that the animal is being reinforced by a reduction in the strength of fear every time it turns to the right and escapes the cues at the choice point. He supported this deduction by showing that reducing the fear of the cues at the choice point (by confining the animal and feeding him there) greatly reduces the tendency for the "fixated" habit to persist after the location of the food has been changed.

The response that occurs can differ from the one that is reinforced. If an animal runs down an alley, receives a shock at a distinctive place, *and runs ahead* to escape it, on the next trial he may not run ahead but stop and crouch near the place where he was shocked. Such differences between the response that was reinforced by escape from shock and the response that subsequently occurs have been used by exponents of an expectancy theory of learning (Hilgard, 1948, p. 108; Tolman, 1932, p. 325) as an argument against the principle of reinforcement. This behavior can be deduced, however, from the cue function of fear that was shown in May's (1948) experiment.

On the first trial the shock elicits running ahead and also fear, and both responses are reinforced at the distinctive place. On the next trial, therefore, the cues at this place tend to elicit both running ahead and fear. But since crouching (and perhaps turning around and withdrawing) are either innate or learned reactions to the fear stimulus, it will tend to elicit these responses.* Thus the animal may stop, and, if he does this and turns away, the reduction in the strength of fear will reinforce this new response.

Which of the two opposing tendencies (running ahead or crouching) will be dominant is a quantitative matter. The author has secured evidence for the existence of both tendencies. He gave hungry rats a brief shock at a distinctive place halfway down an alley to the goal of food. When he increased the shock rapidly on successive trials, rats that had escaped the last shock by running forward tended to stop as they approached the shock area. When he increased the shock slowly and alternated shock and nonshock trials, some of the rats dashed ahead into the shock area faster than they had ever run for food and continued doing this after they were too excited to eat.

Reinforcement theory leads one to expect this difference. When shock is given on alternate trials and gradually increased in strength, there is more chance for running to be reinforced and crouching eliminated as a response to ever greater amounts of fear. Further evidence for the two opposing tendencies, the conflict between them, and the way this varies with different conditions was secured in a series of experiments by Gwinn (1949). In interpreting these experiments Gwinn had to assume that an in-

---

* It is also possible that the animals come into the situation with a hierarchy of functionally equivalent avoidance habits somewhat analogous to Hull's (1934*a*) habit-family hierarchy, or that fear produced by a stimulus ahead of the animal elicits crouching or withdrawal, whereas fear produced by a stimulus behind him elicits running.

crease in fear, not just its absolute value, serves as a cue.

Somewhat similar dynamics appear to be involved in the differences between conditioned and unconditioned responses found by Wever (1930) with cats, and by Upton (1929) with guinea pigs.

Fear and alcoholism. An experiment by Masserman and Yum (1946) suggested that fear, or a conflict induced by it, may motivate cats to learn to choose an alcohol solution instead of avoiding it. First they trained cats to perform a complex series of manipulations to secure food. Next they put two dishes in the same apparatus and found that the cats regularly preferred plain milk to milk containing 5 per cent alcohol. Then, returning to the complex series of manipulations, they established a conflict between hunger and fear by giving the animals a blast of air or an electric shock just as they were taking the food. After several trials the animals showed a marked fear of the food box and other parts of the apparatus.

Then they forced the cats to take mild doses of alcohol and found that intoxication tended to restore the original behavior of operating the apparatus to secure food. After the cats had experienced this relief from fear and conflict, they developed a progressively increasing preference for the 5 per cent solution of alcohol. Finally, after a series of trials in which the animals manipulated the apparatus without punishment, all signs of fear were extinguished and the preference for alcohol disappeared.

It is clear that fear was involved in producing the preference for alcohol. Whether its effects were direct or indirect is not so clear. It seems possible that the preference for alcohol was reinforced in one or more of the following ways: by a reduction in the strength of the fear, by a reduction in the strength of stimulation from the conflict produced by the fear, and by the food itself when the fear was reduced enough to allow the hungry cat to reach it.

Acquisition of Fear

The main psychological functions of fear have been described. The next step will be to investigate the factors determining the acquisition of fear and, after that, those involved in its elimination.

Stimuli innately arousing fear. In all the preceding experiments the fear was originally elicited by pain produced by an electric shock. Studies of children and young animals suggest that sudden and intense enough stimulation through any sense modality may have an innate tendency to produce fear (Jersild, 1946; Cruikshank, 1946). Clinicians and anthropologists observe that even a slowly mounting drive, such as hunger, can be a source of strong fear (Freud, 1936; Holmberg, 1950), but so much of the subject's complex life history is unknown that it is impossible to be sure that such fears are not learned.

Certain weak but distinctive cues may also have an innate capacity to elicit fear. For example, Tinbergen (1948) summarized studies of the reactions of several species of birds raised in isolation to the silhouette illustrated in Fig. 5. When this figure was moved on an overhead wire in one direction so that it resembled a hawk with a short neck and long tail, it was an adequate stimulus for flight and other responses of fear. When it was moved in the opposite direction so that it resembled a harmless long-necked goose, it did not elicit any fear.

The subjects had never had experience with hawks or adult geese. Hence the response must have been innate. Since fear appeared only when the stimulus was moved in one direction, it must have depended on the pattern rather than the suddenness or strength of the stimulus.

Sometimes innate fears are not present at birth but appear only at later stages of maturation. For example, in geese raised in isolation, fear of the silhouette described above did not appear until they were about 4 weeks old. The fact that a fear is absent at first and appears later does not necessarily mean that it has been learned.

On the other hand, the fact that an animal fears a stimulus that it has never before experienced does not necessarily mean that this fear is innate; the fear may have generalized along some continuum of similarity with another situation in which it was learned. For example, Watson and Rayner (1920) conditioned a child to fear a rabbit and found generalized fear of dogs, fur coats, and Santa Claus masks.

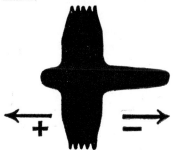

Fig. 5. Silhouette that frightened inexperienced birds raised in captivity when it was moved overhead to the left but did not when moved to the right. (From Tinbergen, 1948, p. 34.)

Both children and animals tend to fear the unexpected, the sudden, and the strange. It is possible that such fears are spontaneous, as Hebb (1946) concluded from studies of chimpanzees born and raised in captivity. He advanced the provocative hypothesis that the disruption of an established neural pattern of response is the physiological basis of fear. Sometimes learning may be indirectly necessary to establish the pattern and to define strangeness, but the fear produced by strangeness itself is not supposed to be learned.

On the other hand, it is possible that such fears are the product of generalization. Different forms of strangeness, suddenness, or unexpectedness (i.e. conflict with an established habit of responding) may produce similar cues. It seems possible that children and chimpanzees learn to fear a large number of different situations of this type when they unexpectedly trip and fall, or have a strange feeling in the stomach followed by sharp pains of colic, or are unexpectedly burnt or cut after reaching for a shiny object. After such fears are learned, they could generalize to other situations with similar elements of strangeness or unexpectedness.

Between the two extremes of completely innate and completely learned there is another possibility. Certain cues that do not spontaneously arouse fear may have a latent tendency to elicit it, with the result that (1) the subject will learn to fear these cues much more quickly than others, and (2) if he is already mildly afraid these cues can intensify the fear. In other words, fear may be high in the innate hierarchy of responses to a stimulus without being the dominant response.

Such latent fears may be involved in sensitization or pseudoconditioning. Sometimes a stimulus seems neutral at first, but after the subject has received a few electric shocks he shows strong fear of the stimulus in spite of the fact that it has never been paired with the shock (May, 1949). It is necessary to control for this pseudoconditioning in designing experiments on the learning of fear.

Thorndike (1935) criticized the classic experiment of Watson and Rayner (1920) on the grounds that the rabbit used as a conditioned stimulus may have had some inherent capacity to frighten the child so that learning was exceptionally easy. Thorndike believed that the rapid learning in this experiment did not agree with the extreme difficulty of teaching children to avoid many dangerous objects. One of his students, Bregman (1934), failed to reproduce Watson's results when she used stimuli believed to be more nearly neutral.

Finally, it is known that general susceptibility to fear varies widely from species to species and even among different strains of the same species (Hall, 1941).

Nature of reinforcement in learning fear. We can teach an animal to fear a neutral stimulus by pairing it with some other stimulus that already elicits fear. Thus rats were made to fear the white compartment of the apparatus shown in Fig. 1 by receiving electric shocks there. Theories of learning differ in their interpretation of this fact. Such differences may yield a crucial test of some of these theories. Some of the main possibilities follow:

1. Drive reduction for all learning. One hypothesis is that all reinforcement is produced by a reduction in the strength of a drive (Hull, 1943; Miller and Dollard, 1941). According to this hypothesis, running out of the white compartment is reinforced by the reduction in pain when the animal escapes. In order to apply it consistently, we must also assume that fear is reinforced by a reduction in the strength of the pain rather than by its onset. According to this hypothesis it does not matter whether or not a response, such as fear, causes the drive reduction as long as it is contiguous with it.

At first glance this hypothesis might seem inadequate to explain the obvious fact that people learn to fear an experience, such as a severe burn, that produces prolonged pain. Electrical recording from afferent nerves, however, shows that the sudden onset of a new stimulus produces at first a strong burst of impulses, followed by a rapid reduction until a plateau is reached (Adrian, 1928, pp. 67, 116). This is called adaptation. Thus, when a person is subjected to a strong stimulus such as a burn, it is possible that this reduction in stimulation after the sudden onset, plus the other temporary reductions occurring during throbbing changes in intensity, could reinforce the fear even though the peaks of pain might continue to increase for some time.

2. A separate mechanism for emotions. A different hypothesis, advanced by Skinner (1938) and elaborated by Mowrer (1947), states that there are two different mechanisms of reinforcement: (a) drive reduction, which is the sole principle for the skeletal muscles under the somatic nervous system, and (b) conditioning by contiguity, which is the sole mechanism for the smooth muscles, glands, and emotions controlled by the autonomic nervous system. Fear falls into the second category.

In order to obtain evidence on this problem, Mowrer and Suter (1950) gave rats a conditioned stimulus followed by an electric shock lasting 10 seconds. The conditioned stimulus always preceded the shock by 5 seconds, but in one group it ended with the onset of the shock and in another it lasted until the end of the shock. The authors reasoned that, if the end of the shock constituted the reinforcement, the second group should fear the conditioned stimulus more because it persisted until the shock was turned off. No such difference occurred. They interpreted this to mean that reinforcement occurred with the beginning of the shock, not with its end.*

Though it poses an important problem, this experiment is open to the following criticisms:

(a) The animals probably escaped shock several times by jumping, so that drive reduction was not limited to the end of the 10-second shock period.

(b) The crucial thing that had to be reinforced by drive reduction may have been the response of starting to be afraid at the onset of the conditioned stimulus, and this response may be different from the one of maintaining an already elicited fear while the conditioned stimulus persists.

* Cognition or expectancy theories would also lead one to think that the association of a stimulus with the beginning of shock would cause the stimulus to elicit fear, and that association of a motor response with the end of the shock would cause the response to be selected. The author makes this statement, however, on the basis of what he feels would be reasonable, i.e. what he would do. Thus it is circularly based on the type of behavior it is trying to explain rather than on certain explicitly stated principles. This of course does not deny the possibility that expectancy or cognitive postulates could be specifically formulated so that one could make this a rigorous deduction.

3. Conditioning by contiguity for all learning. The third possibility is to assume, as Guthrie (1935) did, that all learning occurs through conditioning by contiguity and that drive reduction acts only by removing the opportunity to learn conflicting responses to the drive. Thus, if the animal makes a number of different motor responses while the shock persists, the strongest association will be with the last response to the shock, because the conditioning of each response tends to uncondition all preceding ones. Turning off the shock will have a selective influence by determining which response will be the last one. But, if fear is a response that always persists throughout the shock, there will be no chance for it to be unlearned during the shock. Since it will always be a last response, its selection will not depend on when the shock is turned off.

It can be seen that the first and third of these hypotheses are alike in stating that a single mechanism is involved in all learning; the second one assumes that there are two different kinds of learning.

Factors influencing strength of fear. Only a few studies have used the most rigorous test for fear as a drive, namely, the use of fear to motivate the learning of new responses. This survey will therefore include studies that used pain or other intense stimuli as the primary drive, and that measured responses such as withdrawal. It is assumed (but by no means certain) that fear is involved in the persistence of these responses on test trials without the primary drive of pain. It will be noted that the variables influencing the strength of the learned drive of fear seem to be the same as those governing the learning of other responses.

1. Strength of primary drive. Miller and Lawrence (1950) studied the effect of the strength of the shock used during original training upon the strength of the acquired drive produced. The apparatus was like the one shown in Fig. 1, and the procedure was similar to the one used in that experiment. The stronger shock produced a stronger learned drive, presumably fear. During the subsequent nonshock trials there was a higher level of performance of the new response, as is shown in Fig. 6, and also a greater resistance of this new response to experimental extinction. These results confirm those of other studies (Estes, 1944; Miller, 1944) which almost certainly involved fear, although its effects were not unequivocally isolated by forcing the animals to learn a new habit.

2. Number of trials with primary drive. In their classic experiment on the child, Watson and Rayner (1920) observed only mild fear of the rabbit after the first trial on which it was paired with the sudden loud sound. On subsequent trials they observed signs of stronger fear. Similar results have been secured in experiments on conditioned galvanic and other responses (Hovland, 1937b). In another part of their experiment on strength of shock, however, Miller and Lawrence (1950) failed to find any reliable difference between animals that had received 4 and those that had received 24 trials of original training with electric shock. It is possible that this anomalous result occurred because the animals received a large and variable number of shocks while they were jumping around and learning to escape from the white compartment on the first trials. It is also possible that when the cues are distinctive fear is learned to maximum strength in very few trials.

3. Time interval. Delayed electric shocks are less effective than immediate ones in preventing albino rats from performing the punished response (Miller, 1944; Mowrer and Ullman, 1945). Furthermore the conditioning of avoidance responses is less effective when the conditioned stimulus deviates from a position slightly in front of the unconditioned one. From this it may be inferred that the fear of a stimulus will decrease when the interval between it and the punishment is lengthened.

4. Generalization. Conditioned responses established to one stimulus tend to generalize

to other similar stimuli, and the generalized response is stronger, the more similar the stimuli. In the experiment by Watson and Rayner (1920) the conditioned fear of the rabbit spread to fur muffs, fur coats, Santa Claus masks, and a variety of other objects. change in the rate of breathing, both of which are presumably correlated with the amount of fear elicited by electric shock. Temporal summation, which occurs when a stimulus is repeated a number of times in rapid succession, is presumably involved in

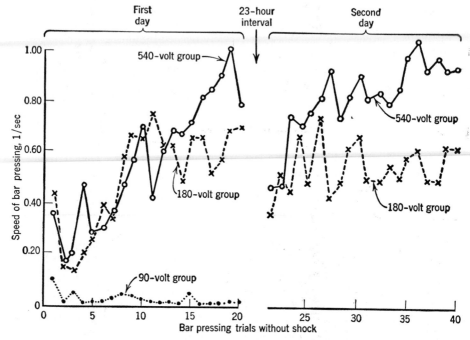

FIG. 6. The effect of the strength of electric shock as a primary drive on the strength of fear as a learned drive. This was measured by the learning and performance of a new habit during trials without shock. Different strengths of shock were used to establish fear in different groups of rats. Then, during trials without shock the rats were tested for their motivation to learn a new habit (bar pressing) in order to get out of the place where they had been shocked. (Miller and Lawrence, 1950.)

Hovland (1937a) plotted curves for the generalization of conditioned galvanic responses based on shock from tones of one pitch to those of different pitches. Both May (1948) and Miller (1941) observed generalization in their experiments on fear as a learned drive.

5. Summation. If two stimuli such as a buzzer and a vibrator have been separately associated with electric shock, the responses elicited when both of them are given simultaneously will be greater than when either is given separately (Hull, 1934b). This has been shown for finger retraction and for warming up and pseudoconditioning as summarized by May (1949).

6. Primary versus secondary reinforcement. In general, conditioned responses seem to be weaker than unconditioned ones (Hull, 1934b). Similarly higher-order conditioned responses (secondary, tertiary, etc.) seem to be weaker than those of lower order (Pavlov, 1927), although it is just possible that a finding by Eccher and Culler (1941) is an exception to this principle. In these experiments the higher-order responses were established without primary reinforcement.

Experiments in which thoracic shock is used to maintain fear (Brogden and Culler, 1935) are not relevant to this particular problem since the thoracic shock is a primary reinforcement.

Elimination of Fear

Experimental extinction. If a learned response is repeated without reinforcement, it tends to become weaker. This is called experimental extinction. It occurs with a wide variety of overt responses. It also occurs with the covert, drive-producing response of fear, although this response may sometimes extinguish very slowly.

In the apparatus shown in Fig. 1, turning the wheel should continue to be reinforced as long as the subject fears the white compartment and as long as this response allows him to escape and reduce that fear. Two kinds of extinction are possible:

1. The turning of the wheel can be extinguished by preventing escape. In Fig. 3 we have already seen rapid extinction of this kind. The fear remained, as is shown by the rapid learning of the new response of pressing the bar (Fig. 4).

2. The fear can be extinguished by means of repeated trials without shock. The subject is no longer motivated to turn the wheel, and this response cannot be reinforced because there is no drive to be reduced.

The second type of extinction is shown in Fig. 7. Each rat received 20 shock trials in the white compartment. These were mixed with a larger number of nonshock trials to increase resistance to extinction. The new habit of pressing the bar to escape from the white compartment was then learned during trials without shock. This new habit persisted at a high level for many trials without shock. One animal continued to improve for almost 200 trials. Observing only this many trials, one might think that the fear motivating this habit was not subject to extinction, that it was, in other words, functionally autonomous (Allport, 1937). But additional trials produced a definite curve of extinction.

A large number of other animals trained in this apparatus have shown similar curves of extinction. Furthermore, experimental extinction during nonreinforced trials seems to be a characteristic of the conditioned psychogalvanic response, as well as of conditioned

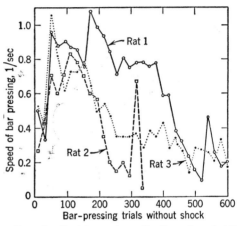

Fig. 7. Resistance to extinction of a habit motivated by fear. Each rat received 20 shocks, mixed with a larger number of nonshock trials, in the white compartment of the apparatus shown in Fig. 1. During these trials they learned to escape through the already open door. Then, during trials without shock they learned the new habit of pressing the bar to open the closed door so that they could escape. Each point on each curve is the average of 20 trials given to a rat on 1 day. (From Miller, unpublished data.)

defense reactions and various forms of escape and avoidance behavior that are presumed to indicate fear.*

In the study of any given instance, the following related questions may be raised: (1) Does any extinction occur? (2) Does the curve of extinction reach zero, or does it become flat at some point above zero? (3) How permanent is extinction, and what factors determine its permanence? (4) What factors determine resistance to extinction? The difficulty of answering these questions

* Sheffield (1948) showed the fallacy of interpreting Brogden, Lipman, and Culler's (1938) results to mean that successful avoidance strengthens fear.

is increased by the possibility of exceedingly slow extinction, cyclic fluctuations in its course, generalization from other sources, and extreme variability. Fluctuations will introduce a constant error if subjects are discarded upon reaching a criterion of failure to perform.

Factors influencing resistance to extinction. The factors listed below are known to influence the resistance of fear to extinction. The search for additional ones should have theoretical and practical importance.

1. Strength of fear. Other things being equal, stronger fears should be more resistant to extinction than weaker ones. Each of the variables that increase the strength of fear should increase its resistance to extinction, but only a few of them have been experimentally tested. Miller and Lawrence (1950) found that a stronger primary drive of pain during the original training increased the resistance of fear to extinction. Hovland (1937a) found that generalized conditioned galvanic responses are extinguished more rapidly than nongeneralized ones.

2. Escape or avoidance training (partial reinforcement). Sheffield and Temmer (1950) found that rats that were shocked only when they failed to run within a given time resisted extinction much better than those shocked on every training trial. This was to be expected because the former procedure, called avoidance training, specifically trains the subject to remain fearful and run under conditions similar to those he will encounter in extinction. To illustrate, it is just when the subject relaxes, stops, and sits down that he exceeds the time limit and is shocked. Thus the responses of fear and running get attached to the cues produced by relaxing and sitting down. During extinction, therefore, whenever the response to the cues in the alley is so weakened that the animal starts to relax and sit down, he gives himself new cues eliciting more fear and running. Conversely, the animals given an immediate shock on every trial (a procedure called escape training) are not specifically

trained to remain fearful and to run under the conditions of extinction. As a result their responses extinguish much more quickly.

Similarly Estes (1944) increased the resistance of punishment to extinction by interspersing nonpunished trials among punished ones. He called this partial reinforcement.

3. Interval between extinction trials. Using an apparatus similar to the one in Fig. 1, Burros (1949) found that massed extinction trials reduced fear more than did daily trials. This would be expected on the basis of spontaneous recovery. It is also possible that other effects, such as perseveration or summation of fear, might reverse the curve somewhere between the two extremes Burros used. Furthermore, although extinction should be faster with massed nonreinforced trials, it probably will be more permanent with distributed trials.

4. Habit learned with pain versus habit learned with fear. In the same apparatus Burros (1949) used the primary drive of shock to train one group of rats to press a bar that opened a door and permitted them to escape. For a second group the door opened as soon as they touched it. Then he gave nonshock trials to both groups. The first group continued the old habit of pressing the bar, but the second group had to learn this as a new habit. In short, bar pressing was learned with shock plus fear for the first group and with fear alone for the second group.

As nonshock trials were continued, Burros found that both groups extinguished at approximately the same rate. This suggests that the extinction of fear was the crucial factor determining when the subjects would stop pressing the bar.*

In Burros' experiment the fear remained attached to the same cues, those in the white compartment. This is different from higher-order conditioning where the fear is trans-

* It should be noted that the two groups were compared on the type of extinction produced by trials without shock rather than by trials without the door dropping.

ferred from one cue, the original conditioned stimulus, to another, the higher-order conditioned stimulus. From the fact that higher-order conditioned responses seem to be weaker than those based directly on primary reinforcement (Pavlov, 1927), we would expect them to be less resistant to extinction. An experiment by Brogden and Culler (1935) seems to confirm this expectation in spite of the fact that it was complicated by some primary reinforcement from thoracic shock during the "higher-order" conditioning.

Forgetting. Experimental extinction, which occurs when a response is elicited without reinforcement, must be distinguished from forgetting, which occurs during the time when a response is not elicited. Masserman (1943) found that fears are not easily forgotten. After as much as 5 months of rest, his animals showed little if any permanent reduction in their fears of the food device in which they had received air blasts or electric shock. On the first trial after a long rest the animals tended to show a temporary great reduction in fear, but on additional trials without air blasts or shock strong avoidance reappeared.

Role of anticipatory relaxation. If a reduction in the strength of fear reinforces the response of bar pressing, we may ask, why doesn't it reinforce the fear response enough to prevent its extinction? A possible answer follows. According to the gradient of reinforcement the responses most closely associated with the reduction in the strength of fear should be those most strongly reinforced. If fear stimuli require a moment to die out, the responses most closely associated with their reduction must inevitably be those involved in ceasing to be afraid. These responses will be those most strongly reinforced. Thus they should tend to become anticipatory and should eventually crowd out the fear.

This is exactly what seems to happen during extinction trials in the apparatus shown in Fig. 1. At first the rats dash to the far end of the black compartment. Gradually

they begin to stop sooner. Finally they fail to go through the door after pressing the bar. Although there is considerable variability, it appears that the tendency to stop becomes progressively more anticipatory until the animals stop before they get started.

Similarly, although it is harder to observe in detail, general relaxation seems to move forward in the series. At first the animals do not relax until they have been sitting in the black compartment for some time; eventually they go through the whole sequence nonchalantly and seemingly without drive. That fear has not been completely lost as a potential drive, however, can often be shown by disrupting the patterned sequence that elicits the anticipatory relaxation. For example, if the switch is disconnected so that the door does not open, the rats often become tense again, press the bar vigorously, urinate, defecate, and show other signs of strong fear.

We may venture the hypothesis that learned anticipatory drive-reducing responses often obscure the true role of drive in smoothly functioning human behavior. Similarly interruptions of well-established habits may release motivation by removing the cues that elicit the anticipatory relaxation and also by creating new sources of strong stimulation such as conflict and anger. For example, in driving to class the author often seems to be proceeding mechanically from sheer force of habit without any drive. But, if he is sufficiently delayed by one bad snarl of traffic after another, obvious signs of strong drive begin to appear so that he blows his horn, tries detours, and fervently resolves to allow more time the next day. It can be seen that having motivation reappear just when a sequence is threatened with failure is a highly adaptive mechanism worthy of further experimental analysis.

An experiment by Mowrer and Viek (1948) further illustrates how anticipatory relaxation, or conditioned inhibition, may reduce fear. On each trial hungry rats were offered food on a stick for 10 seconds. If the rat ate, he was given an electric shock 10 seconds later. For one group the shock was left on until the rat performed a specific response, i.e. jumping. Each rat had a control partner who upon eating was shocked for exactly the same length of time. The animals in the first group could perform a definite response to stop the shock; their controls received an equally long shock that was out of their control. The authors reasoned that, for the first group, the anticipatory tendency to jump should bring with it some of the relaxation that ordinarily follows the end of shock. Therefore these rats should be less frightened and more likely to eat. This is exactly what happened. It is possible, however, that more of the rats in the first group sat on their haunches in an anticipatory jumping position so that their more sensitive front feet were off the grid. If this was true, their shocks may have been less painful than those of the rats in the second group.

However this experiment is interpreted, evidence from the studies of military combat, cited above, shows that a feeling of helplessness intensifies fear, and that having something to do tends to reduce it. At present it is not known how much of this effect is due to the distraction of attention from the fear-producing cues and how much is due to cues similar to those previously associated with escape from pain or danger.

Specific reinforcement of responses antagonistic to fear. According to the hypothesis just discussed, experimental extinction reinforces the responses involved in ceasing to be afraid. In certain other techniques of eliminating fear the reinforcement of antagonistic responses is more obvious. In one such procedure a hungry subject is fed in the fear-arousing situation. Eating and the emotional responses that accompany it are apparently incompatible with fear, and the attaching of these responses to the stimuli that arouse the fear suppresses it. Thus, in order to eliminate a child's fear of a rabbit, Jones (1924) first showed the rabbit at a distance while the child was eating, and then gradually brought it nearer until the child ate with one hand and petted the rabbit with the other.

Sometimes this method can eliminate even the presumably innate fear of painful stimuli. Thus Pavlov (1927, p. 30) used electric shocks, cauterization, and pricking of the skin as conditioned stimuli for feeding. Starting with mildly painful stimuli and working up to strongly painful ones, he observed that the original defense responses of very hungry dogs disappeared. To quote him:

> Subjected to the very closest scrutiny, not even the tiniest and most subtle objective phenomenon usually exhibited by animals under the influence of strong injurious stimuli can be observed in these dogs. No appreciable changes in the pulse or in the respiration occur in these animals, whereas such changes are always most prominent when the nocuous stimulus has not been converted into an alimentary conditioned stimulus.

The results depended on the relative strengths of the two drives. With extremely strong pain it was impossible to eliminate the fear.

We do not know yet exactly which responses are antagonistic to fear or the degree of incompatibility of each. Pavlov's results show that, for the hungry animal, eating is at least partially antagonistic to fear. Tinklepaugh and Hartman (Cruikshank, 1946) found that small monkeys are much less likely to be frightened if they are clinging to some object. Watson and Rayner (1920) reported that Albert had a strong tendency to put his thumb in his mouth as soon as they presented frightening stimuli. They also reported that they could not elicit any conditioned fear responses as long as he had his thumb in his mouth.

Method of exposing subject to fear-producing stimuli. Avoidance responses reinforced by escape from fear often keep the subject out of the frightening situation, with the result that extinction does not occur and responses antagonistic to fear cannot be reinforced. Even when it is easy to expose the subject to the frightening stimuli, there is still the problem of which procedure is best.

One technique emphasized by Guthrie (1935) is to start with stimuli exceedingly weak, distant, or only remotely similar to the ones feared, and to approach the strongly feared stimuli so gradually that no fear is elicited. One often has to use this procedure in order to get the responses antagonistic to fear to occur so that they can be reinforced.

The opposite technique — that of physically forcing the hungry animal toward the frightening food box — was used with some success by Masserman (1943). According to the conflict theory (Miller, 1944, p. 441), this technique should be especially effective when the original punishment coincides with stimuli that precede the food box. At least two other possibilities should be considered: (1) Shoving the animal toward the food with a movable barrier changes the stimulus situation and weakens the avoidance more than the approach, because the generalization of avoidance based on fear falls off more rapidly than does the generalization of approach based on hunger (Miller, 1948b). (2) Experimental extinction is more effective when the animal is in the original punished situation that evokes the most intense fear.

In general, extreme coercion does not seem to produce good results with children (Jersild, 1946).

Masserman (1943) also gave hungry cats a chance to press a pedal they had been trained to use. They could thereby produce the feeding signals they had learned to fear. Given this "control over the situation" some of the cats produced the phobic stimuli until they lost all fear of them. Jersild (1946) described the successful use of somewhat similar techniques with children.

Social factors. In various studies summarized by Jersild (1946) social example and imitation sometimes helped children to eliminate their fears. Similarly Masserman (1943) reported that watching another cat eat without getting punished had some effect on a frightened cat. Sometimes gentle stroking by the hand of an experimenter who customarily fed and cared for the cat also had a reassuring effect. Children's fears are often greatly reduced by the presence of a parent or other person whom they love and trust.

Drugs. As has been mentioned, Masserman and Yum (1946) found that alcohol can cause frightened cats to resume manipulating an apparatus to secure food. The same effect is produced by morphine (Masserman, 1943). Similarly Conger (1949) trained hungry rats to approach the distinctively lighted end of an alley to secure food and then threw them into an approach-avoidance conflict by giving them electric shocks at the goal. Five minutes after a control injection of water the rats would not approach the food-shock end of the alley; 5 minutes after an alcohol injection (1.5 parts of alcohol to 1000 of body weight) they ran up to get the food.

The results of the preceding experiments could have been produced in a number of different ways: for example, the alcohol might have either strengthened the approach habits based on hunger or weakened the avoidance ones based on fear. In order to analyze the results, Conger (1949) trained one group of rats to approach the lighted end of the alley for food and a different group to avoid the lighted end of the alley to escape shock. The rats wore a harness, and on test trials the strength of approach or avoidance was measured by the strength of pull they exerted against a temporary restraint. These tests showed that the alcohol produced a slight reduction in the strength of the approach response motivated by hunger and a much greater reduction in the avoidance response motivated by fear. This result fits in nicely with the hypothesis, previously mentioned, that the habit of drinking alcohol in a conflict situation is reinforced by a fear-reducing effect of the alcohol. On the other hand, it is possible that the greater effect of alcohol on the avoidance group was due not to any effect specific to fear but to some other factor, such as the fact that the avoidance habit was established in fewer trials and hence was more recent than the approach habit.

Sympathectomy. Solomon and Wynne (1949) trained dogs to jump out of a darkened compartment into a lighted one in order to avoid electric shock. Normal dogs learned the avoidance habit quickly and showed overt signs of fear during the early stages of learning and whenever the experimenters introduced a block that delayed their jumping out of the darkened compartment. When the shock was turned off, the normal dogs continued jumping for more than 500 trials with no signs of stopping. Dogs that were completely sympathectomized learned the avoidance but showed no overt signs of fear. When the shock was turned off, their jumping extinguished in less than 100 trials. These results suggest that sympathectomy removed (or greatly reduced) the fear so that avoidance was not reinforced by fear reduction on shockless trials.

LEARNED REWARDS AND DRIVES BASED ON FOOD AND HUNGER

Experiments in which pain is used to establish fear have illustrated the functions of learnable drive; those in which hunger and food are the primary drive and reward point up the role of learned reward, or, as it is often called, secondary reinforcement. Early experiments of this kind were reported by Pavlov (1927) and Williams (1929). Since certain later experiments bring out the principles more clearly, they will be used as the models. These are the experiments in which Wolfe (1936) and Cowles (1937) trained chimpanzees to value poker chips somewhat as human beings value money.

Learning reinforced by token reward. In order to give reward value to the tokens (poker chips) Cowles (1937) first trained hungry chimpanzees to insert them into a vending machine which delivered a raisin for each token inserted. As a preliminary test, and as a further means of establishing the reward value, he repeated Wolfe's (1936) procedure of requiring the chimpanzee to work for the chip by pulling a handle against a weight. First the animals were allowed to exchange the chip immediately for a raisin; then by stages they were forced to accumulate 20 chips before they could spend them.

In order to determine whether or not the poker chips could serve as a learned reward, he took the animals into another room where they were confronted with two boxes. If they opened the one to the left they found a token, and if they opened the one to the right they found nothing. They quickly learned to open the box on the left in spite of the fact that they were not allowed to exchange the tokens for food until the end of the day's session. The next day they were taught to select the box on the right.

In later experiments they were taught a variety of more complicated habits. In some of these experiments the possible innate reward value of the token was controlled by giving the animal a token that had been associated with food if he performed the correct response, and a different colored token, that the animal had learned could not be exchanged for food, if he performed the incorrect response. The learning of the correct response under these circumstances showed that the reward value of the token depended on its previous association with the primary reward of receiving food when hungry.

Additional experiments. Table 1 summarizes other experiments on learned reward. It can be seen that successful results have been secured with subjects ranging from rats to people. Lower animals, however, seem to have a tendency to respond to the position of the token object. Thus it is much harder for them than for chimpanzees or children to establish a generalized response to the object as such, irrespective of its position.

Other stimuli, ranging from the click of a food-delivery apparatus to the cues in the food box of a maze, have been given learned

TABLE 1

SUMMARY OF STUDIES OF LEARNED REWARD BASED ON HUNGER AND FOOD

Investigator	Subjects	Acquisition of Learned Reward (Under Hunger Drive) by	Learned Reward	Performance (P) or Learning and Performance (L) Based on Learned Reward	Chief Principles Demonstrated *
Wolfe (1936)	Chimpanzees	Use of vending machines yielding grapes and peanuts, etc. (also used water with primary drive of thirst).	Token reward: white, blue, black, and brass poker chips exchangeable in vender for one grape, two grapes, peanuts, and nothing, respectively.	Work task (P); begging for tokens (P).	2. Incentive. 4. Bridge delay. 5. Pri. sup. to learned (D). 7. Subj. ext. 9. Generalization. 10. Discrimination. 11. Strength pri. drive.
Cowles (1937)	Chimpanzees	Use of vending machine yielding raisins.	Token reward: various colored poker chips exchangeable in vender for food.	Simple position habit (L); 5-choice position habit (L); visual size discrimination (L); color discrimination (L); work-task performance (P); delayed response (P).	1. Prod. learn. 2. Incentive. 3. Prolong perform. 4. Bridge delay. 5. Pri. sup. to learned (D). 7. Subj. ext. 9. Generalization. 10. Discrimination.
Ellson (1937)	Dogs	Use of vending machine yielding food.	Token reward: rubber balls exchangeable for food.	Retrieving balls (P).	2. Incentive. 3. Prolong perform.
Smith (1939)	Cats	Use of vending machine yielding food.	Token reward: ball which yielded food when dropped down chute.	Pulling string to get balls (L).	1. Prod. learn. 2. Incentive. 6. Little diff. pri. vs learned (I). 7. Subj. ext.
Mitrano (1939)	Mentally defective children	Use of vending machine yielding candy.	Token reward: poker chip yielding candy in vending machine.	Insertion of marble in vending machine to get poker chip (P); getting marbles from chair (P).	3. Prolong perform. 7. Subj. ext. (greater effects when interruption was nearer goal). 8. Spontan. recovery 11. Strength pri. drive.
Lambert et al. (1949)	Normal children	Use of vending machine yielding candy.	Token reward: poker chip yielding candy in vender.	Turning crank to get poker chip (P).	7. Subj. ext. (greater effects when interruption was nearer goal).
Williams (1929)	Rats	Feeding in discrimination box.	Stimuli from discrimination box.	Running down alley (P).	3. Prolong perform. 6. Little diff. pri. vs learned (D).
Grindley (1929)	Chicks	Previous association of sight of rice with eating.	Sight of rice under glass; sight of food tray.	Running down alley (L).	1. Prod. learn. 2. Incentive. 7. Subj. ext.

* See end of table for key.

TABLE 1 *(Continued)*

SUMMARY OF STUDIES OF LEARNED REWARD BASED ON HUNGER AND FOOD

Investigator	Subjects	Acquisition of Learned Reward (Under Hunger Drive) by	Learned Reward	Performance (P) or Learning and Performance (L) Based on Learned Reward	Chief Principles Demonstrated *
Bruce (1932)	Rats	Previous association of sight and smell of food with eating of it.	Sight and smell of food.	Running square maze most directly (P).	3. Prolong perform. 11. Strength pri. drive.
Anderson (1941)	Rats	Running maze with food reward.	Stimuli in maze and goal box.	Different 6 and 14 unit mazes (L).	1. Prod. learn. 9. Generalization.
Mote and Finger (1942)	Rats	Food in goal box.	Stimuli in goal box.	Running down elevated strip (L).	1. Prod. learn. 3. Prolong perform. 7. Subj. ext. 8. Spontan. recovery.
Denny (1946)	Rats	Food in goal box.	Stimuli in goal box.	T-maze (L).	12. Reduced the difference between 50% and 100% reinforcement.
Denny (1948)	Rats	Food in goal box.	Stimuli in distinctive goal boxes.	T-maze (L).	9. Generalization.
Perkins (1947)	Rats	Association of stimuli in delay box with food.	Stimuli in delay boxes.	T-maze with delay (L).	4. Bridge delay. 9. Generalization.
Saltzman (1949)	Rats	Food in goal box.	Stimuli in goal box.	U-maze (L).	1. Prod. learn. 3. Prolong perform. 7. Subj. ext. 9. Generalization.
Ehrenfreund (1948)	Rats	Food in goal box.	Stimuli in goal box.	T-maze (L).	1. Prod. learn. 12. 100% primary reinf. better than 50% in establishing sec. reinf.
Ehrenfreund (1949)	Rats	Food in food cup.	Empty food cup.	Black-white discrimination (L).	12. Generalized sec. reinf. affects rate of learning.
Skinner (1938)	Rats	Food after click of food-delivery apparatus.	Sound of click.	Bar pressing (L).	1. Prod. learn. 7. Subj. ext.
Bugelski (1938)	Rats	Food after click of food-delivery apparatus.	Sound of click.	Bar pressing (P).	3. Prolong perform. 7. Subj. ext.
Estes (1949)	Rats	Water (with thirst instead of hunger) after click of water-delivery apparatus.	Sound of click.	Bar pressing (L).	1. Prod. learn. 11. Strength pri. drive. 12. Effect of irrelevant drive.

* See end of table for key.

TABLE 1 (*Continued*)

SUMMARY OF STUDIES OF LEARNED REWARD BASED ON HUNGER AND FOOD

Investigator	Subjects	Acquisition of Learned Reward (Under Hunger Drive) by	Learned Reward	Performance (P) or Learning and Performance (L) Based on Learned Reward	Chief Principles Demonstrated *
Pavlov (1927)	Dogs	Sounding metronome and then blowing meat powder into mouth.	Conditioned stimulus of metronome.	Higher-order conditioning of salivation to stimulus of black square (L).	1. Prod. learn. 5. Pri.sup.to learned.

* Key to principles demonstrated.
1. Prod. learn. Learned (i.e. secondary) rewards can be used to produce new learning.
2. Incentive. The sight of a learned reward can be used as an incentive to induce striving.
3. Prolong perform. Learned rewards can be used to induce or prolong the performance of a learned response in the absence of primary reward (i.e. stave off experimental extinction).
4. Bridge delay. Learned rewards can be used to lessen the decrement produced by a delay in the primary reward.
5. Pri. sup. to learned. Primary rewards are more effective than learned rewards. (I = learned reward followed quickly by primary one; D = delay between receiving learned reward stimulus and its reinforcement by primary reward.)
6. Little diff. pri. vs learned. No great difference was found between the effectiveness of primary and learned rewards (I and D, see 5 above).
7. Subj. ext. The learned reward value of stimuli is subject to experimental extinction.
8. Spontan. recovery. Extinguished learned rewards are subject to spontaneous recovery.
9. Generalization. Learned reward value of stimuli generalizes to other similar stimuli.
10. Discrimination. A discrimination can be established so that an object associated with primary reward has greater learned reward value than a similar one not associated with primary reward.
11. Strength pri. drive. The effectiveness of learned reward is dependent on the strength of the primary drive at the time of the test.
12. Other.

reward value. This reward value has been used to reinforce the learning of a variety of habits, ranging from running a maze to higher-order conditioning. Until evidence to the contrary is forthcoming, we may assume that any response the subject can learn can be reinforced by learned reward, and that any stimulus to which he can respond can acquire reward value.

It should be noted, however, that Pavlov (1927) found that higher-order conditioning was successful only if the new stimulus was withdrawn before the already conditioned one was given. This poses the problem of determining whether some stimulus conditions are much more favorable than others for the learning of reward, and, if so, why.*

* Cowles (1937) believed that it is important for the chimpanzee to have the token with him during the interval between earning and spending

Relative effectiveness of primary and learned reward. In judging the effectiveness of tokens and other learned rewards, we must differentiate between experiments that allow the subject to exchange the token quickly for a primary reward and those in which the exchange is delayed. In the former the effects of the almost immediate primary re-

it. Intuitively this seems correct, but from the present formulation of reinforcement theory one might make the opposite prediction, since having the token during this time when it cannot be spent should tend to extinguish its reward value. Similarly intuition suggests that the reward value of the token would be reduced greatly if there were no relation between the number earned in the first part of a session and the number that could be spent at the end of the session, even though the discrepancy in one session counteracted that of the next so that no change was made in the total amount of primary reinforcement received for the tokens during the whole experiment.

ward are added to those of the token and may cause its effectiveness to be overestimated. Table 1 shows that, when the effects of learned reward are clearly separated from those of primary reward, they tend to be weaker. None of these experiments have produced a learned reward that is stronger than the primary one used to establish it.

Extinction of learned reward value. Experiments cited in Table 1 show that the learned-reward effect of a stimulus is weakened if it is used for many trials without reinforcement by a primary reward. An experiment by Saltzman (1949) suggests that the interspersing of a number of nonrewarded trials during training with primary drive and reward (i.e. partial reinforcement) may increase the resistance of a learned reward to experimental extinction.* Virginia Sheffield's (1949) experiment indicated, however, that this effect should be weakened or eliminated if the intervals between the original training trials were long enough to allow the cues produced by nonreward to die out. Then the subjects are not rewarded for continuing to respond in the presence of these cues. Finally, Mitrano (1939) and Lambert and Solomon (1950) found that, when children perform a task to get a token they can spend for candy, interruption of this sequence near the goal (token yields no candy) produces more rapid extinction than interruption near the start (task yields no token).

Generalization and discrimination of learned reward value. Both Wolfe (1936) and Cowles (1937) found that chimpanzees trained to use tokens of one color would work to secure similar tokens of other colors, thereby demonstrating generalization from one type of token to another. When food was given consistently in exchange for tokens of one color but never for tokens of another

---

* Ehrenfreund (1948) found that partial reinforcement seemed to produce a weaker learned reward as measured by the rate of learning of a new habit reinforced by the learned reward. This would not necessarily be incompatible, however, with a greater resistance of the learned reward to experimental extinction.

color, the responses to the nonfood token gradually extinguished. A discrimination was established.

That the discrimination was not quite complete and thus left the nonfood token with a small amount of generalized reward value is suggested by Cowles' (1937) experiment. He found that learning to make a correct choice was somewhat slower if the animals received the nonfood token when they made an incorrect response than if they received nothing. This result indicates that receipt of the nonfood token tends to reward the incorrect response.

Similarly Denny (1948) found that rats learn a T-maze more rapidly if the end box on the incorrect side is different from the correct one, and Ehrenfreund (1949) found that they learn a visual discrimination faster if both the food and food dish are absent on the negative side than if the food is absent but the food dish present.

When learned reward generalizes to the cues that follow the incorrect response, learning is hindered. Similarly, when it generalizes to the cues that follow the correct response, learning should be helped. Thus Saltzman (1949) trained rats to learn a simple maze in order to get to a distinctive box that had been associated with food but no longer contained it. He found that learning was improved if the rats ran down an alley and received food in the same box on alternate trials. The learned-reward value of the box was maintained by generalization from the situation where it appeared at the end of the alley to the one where it appeared at the end of the maze. As we shall see, generalization of learned reward can also help to offset the effects of a delay in the primary reward.

Learned reward and the gradient of reinforcement. Wolfe (1936) studied the effects of the following two conditions upon the length of time the primary reward of food at the vending machine could be delayed without causing the animal to stop his performance of the task: (1) the chimpanzee received a token immediately after performing the task but was not permitted to use it for food until the end of a period of delay; and (2) the chimpanzee learned to execute the task and wait (without receiving any token) until the food reward was given at the vender. As a control, two additional conditions were tested: (3) the subjects did not receive food tokens for work but had nonfood tokens in their cage during the delay; and (4) immediately after the work task the subjects received a token which they promptly deposited in the vender, after which they had to wait until the food appeared. After the animals had been thoroughly trained in a given condition, the period of delay was gradually increased to determine the limit beyond which the animal would stop working.

Wolfe found that the first condition was far superior to all others. In other words, when the animals received a token and were allowed to keep it during the delay, the degree to which the primary reward could be postponed was greatly increased. Presumably the token had this function because (1) it appeared as a learned reward immediately after the performance of the work task, and (2) it had its learned reward value maintained by immediate association with food. That the token was only partly effective in neutralizing the effects of the delay in the primary reward was demonstrated by the fact that the animals would work harder when the exchange was immediate than when it was delayed, and they tended to stop work altogether if the delay was too long.

Hull (1943) pointed out that the effects of the gradient of reinforcement may be extended by the progressive higher-order conditioning of secondary reinforcement. Spence (1947) advanced the hypothesis that all the effects of reward upon preceding responses are due either to this mechanism or to what he believes is probably more important in most situations, the generalization of learned reward. In Wolfe's (1936) experiment the token was present as a stimulus element to mediate this generalization of learned reward; in other experiments positional and other external cues, and the proprioceptive stimulus traces of different responses, are presumed to mediate similar generalization. After analyzing experiments on delayed reward, Spence concluded that the more such opportunities for the generalization of learned reward are excluded, the steeper is the temporal gradient of reinforcement. When both the external and proprioceptive cues that mediate such generalization are made as alike as possible after the correct and incorrect responses, delays in the primary reward as short as 5 seconds will prevent learning from occurring in either rats or chimpanzees.

Satiation on food tokens. In one test, chimpanzees were permitted to work for 10 minutes and to secure as many tokens as they wanted, and at the end of that time to exchange them all for food. In this situation Wolfe (1936) found that he could decrease the number they were willing to work for by giving them tokens at the beginning of the session. One animal worked for an average of 21 tokens when he began the session without any, and for only 2.6 tokens when he began with 30.

Effect of amount of primary reward. Wolfe (1936) found that his chimpanzees could learn to select a token that yielded two grapes in preference to a different colored token that yielded only one grape. He did not test the effect of these two types of tokens on the amount of work performed or on the speed of learning.

Effect of immediacy of primary reward. Jenkins (1950) gave rats 80 training trials during which a buzzer was followed by food. For different experimental groups the intervals between the buzzer and food were, respectively, 1, 3, 9, 27, and 81 seconds. For a control group the buzzer was sounded without food. On test trials 30 minutes long, a lever was available for the first time. Pressing the lever produced the buzz but no food. During these test trials the animals in the experimental groups pressed the lever more frequently than those in the control group, and the amount of lever pressing was greater, the shorter the interval had been between buzzer and food. Apparently the buzzer became a stronger learned reward when the interval between it and the food was shorter.

Effect of strength of primary drive on reward value of token. The strength of the primary drive can be varied at two different places: (1) when the reward value of the token is being reinforced by exchange for food, and (2) when the tokens are being used to reinforce the learning or performance of a new habit. The effects of changes of the first kind have not been investigated separately; there is some evidence on the second. Wolfe (1936) reported that an animal satiated on bananas will not beg for tokens and does not seem interested in them. When hungry, the same animal is very much interested in getting tokens. Similarly Bruce's (1932) experiment suggested that an increase in the hunger drive raises the reward value of the sight and the smell of food that rats are prevented from eating by the presence of a screen. Wolfe (1936) also found that chimpanzees can be trained to discriminate among drives so that they use one kind of token to secure water, another for food, and still another for certain activity privileges.

Estes (1949) showed that, if the relevant primary drive is satiated, the effects of learned reward will vary with the strength of an irrelevant primary drive. First a click was associated with the delivery of water to thirsty rats. When they had been satiated on water, the click was found to be more effective as a learned reward when the rats were 23 hours hungry than when they were only 6 hours hungry.

Learned Drive Based on Hunger and Food

Incentive value of token. In the foregoing experiments the chimpanzees worked in order to receive a token they could see and did not work when they saw that the apparatus was empty. In other words, the sight of the token served as an incentive. Wolfe (1936) also observed that after the token had acquired reward value the sight of it caused the animal to perform without further training habits previously established on the basis of food.

Food preferences. Harris et al. (1933) showed that if a vitamin B_1 concentrate is added to a distinctively flavored food rats deficient in vitamin B_1 will learn to prefer food of that flavor. Those without a vitamin deficiency do not learn to prefer this mixture. Rats are unable to develop any preference for the vitamin-containing food in the absence of the distinctive flavor, and the preference for a given flavor lasts for a time after the vitamin has been removed and put into a differently flavored food. Thus the preference is not due to the taste of the vitamin itself; it is a learned response to the distinctive flavor serving as a cue. This learning seems to depend on the fast action of the vitamin, since similar results are not produced by slower acting vitamins such as A or D, or by proteins.

Perhaps other specific hungers are learned in a similar way. Additional work showing that food preferences can be learned is summarized in the *Manual for the Study of Food Habits* (1945) and by Young (1948). Lewin's (1947) studies of group decision will be mentioned later.

Learning by satiated animals. In Wolfe's (1936) experiments the chimpanzees' motivation to secure tokens seemed to disappear, or at least it was not clearly demonstrated, when the hunger drive was satiated. In Anderson's (1941) experiments animals learned a new habit when apparently they were not hungry. First he gave hungry rats 73 trials on one maze with food as a reward. Then he fed them to satiety and found that they would learn a different maze with food at the goal, or even without food. A satiated group without the previous training with primary drive and reward in the first maze failed to learn the second one.

Brogden (1942) trained hungry dogs to lift their paws to get food. When the dogs were satiated he found that they continued to respond longer if he kept giving them food (which they did not eat) than if he disconnected the food-delivery mechanism. Presumably some learned drive must have been present to make the sight of food effective as a learned reward in the absence of hunger.

A different experiment by Myers (1949) showed a similar effect. In order to get rats that were satiated on food to run on a T-maze he used social lures, other rats, in the goal boxes at the ends of *both* arms of the T. On the way to the goal box, one arm also contained food. The satiated rats learned to prefer this arm, and when the food was shifted to the opposite arm they learned to reverse their preference in spite of the fact that they did not eat. Thus the mere sight of the food must have had some reward value, a result obviously relevant to the interpretation of experiments on latent learning.

Gregariousness in sheep. Scott (1945) observed that adult sheep usually follow their mothers in the flock. When he fed two orphan lambs from bottles, he found that they grew up to be much less gregarious than other sheep. Furthermore they had a greater tendency to follow people.

Hoarding behavior in rats. Under some conditions, described in Morgan's (1947) review, rats have a strong tendency to hoard food. Although hoarding seems to be partly instinctive, it can be modified by conditions that seem to involve learning. A period of food deprivation increases hoarding, and this increase is greater if the animals have been severely deprived during infancy. Rats will store pellets in a familiar cage but not in a strange one. The increased hoarding produced by lighting the alley that contains the food persists for a considerable time after the alley is darkened again.

It would seem profitable to determine (1) whether these changes in the strength of the urge to hoard actually follow the laws of learning and experimental extinction, (2) whether this urge can be used to establish new learning if conditions are arranged so that the animals get no immediate primary reward by eating the food, and (3) to what extent the "value" of the object hoarded is determined by previous experience in which the hunger drive was reduced by a similar object. Studies aimed at these points might elucidate the relation between learned and instinctive motivations.

Sucking and oral activity. On the basis of Levy's (1934) experiment it has been assumed that there is an innate drive to suck and that the frustration of this drive during early infancy produces an abnormal amount of sucking later on. A recent experiment by Davis et al. (1948) throws doubt on this hypothesis applied at the human level. They gave a standard sucking test and also sampled incidental oral movements and crying in three different groups: breast-fed, bottle-fed, and cup-fed babies. If sucking is an innate drive that requires a certain amount of satisfaction, the cup-fed babies should show more nonnutritional sucking, more mouth-movements, and perhaps more crying than the breast-fed babies. This did not occur. In fact, toward the end of the 10-day observation period the breast-fed babies showed the most nonnutritional sucking, though the difference was not highly reliable.

Another study by Sears and Wise (1950) compared groups of children that were weaned at different ages: before 2 weeks, between 2 weeks and 3 months, and after 4 months. On the basis of evidence that the vigor of frustration reactions is directly related to the strength of the frustrated drive, they assumed that, if the strength of the sucking drive increases with practice, the expression of rebellion and resentment at weaning should be greater, the older the child is at the time of weaning. Their data confirmed this expectation; the average strength of frustration reaction was reliably greater in the groups that were weaned later. The children that were weaned later also showed somewhat more thumb sucking, but the difference was of a size that would be expected to occur by chance 15 times in 100.

These studies suggest that the drive to suck (which can cause children to learn a variety of new ways to outwit their parents) may be acquired by reward in the feeding situation. Furthermore it was much harder for Watson and Rayner (1920) to frighten the child Albert when he had his thumb in his mouth. If thumb-sucking should reduce fear, this reduction should strongly reinforce that habit.

OTHER DRIVES AS SOURCES OF LEARNED MOTIVATION

Practically all the experimental studies of learned drive and reward have used either pain or hunger as the primary drive. Since the evidence for other drives is so scanty and indirect, only a few samples will be given.

Thirst. Wolfe (1936) showed that chimpanzees can learn to use tokens of the appropriate color to get water when thirsty, and Estes (1949) that the click of a Skinner bar-pressing apparatus can acquire reward value by association with the giving of water to a thirsty rat.

Aggression. Miller and Dollard (1941) described conditions that are likely to reward aggression as a response to frustration. They advanced the hypothesis that the pattern of aggression can be modified at the following three points:

come exceedingly pugnacious and dominant. Children (Whiting, 1941) and goats (Scott, 1948) respond to frustration by aggression against a submissive competitor and by withdrawal from a dominant one. It is not known, however, whether these changes in overt behavior involve similar learned changes in the strength of anger.

Drug addiction. Spragg (1940) showed that morphine-addicted chimpanzees will strive to get the syringe and other objects they have learned to associate with an injection. Sometimes the use of morphine may be reinforced by a reduction in fear like that described for alcohol, but in this experiment it seems probable that the motivation was produced by physiological withdrawal symptoms and hence was not a learned drive. Furthermore, the animals worked for the syringe only when they had withdrawal symptoms. Later in the experiment, however, incidental observations suggested that temporary relief from withdrawal symptoms could be produced by injections of physiological saline. Such relief must have been the product of learning and would be expected to give reward value to the cues involved in the injection.

Sex. Sexual behavior should be a good source of learnable drive and reward. Since some of the preparatory acts, such as tumescence, increase stimulation and may be learned as responses to environmental stimuli, they should be sources of learned drive. Since the orgasm, which is a goal response

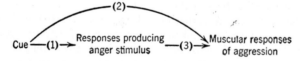

There is considerable evidence that the tendency to respond with aggression can be modified by training. Goodenough (1931) reported a relation between the frequency of outbursts of anger and the proportion of instances in which the issue is yielded to the child. Allee (1942) and his collaborators trained meek and submissive mice to be-

followed by a decrease in total stimulation, seems to be capable of being conditioned to a variety of external cues, it should be a basis of learned reward.* (See also Chapter 12).

* With certain aspects of sexual behavior, an attempt to formulate a consistent drive-reduction theory of learning appears to run counter to

Relative learnableness of different drives and rewards. Using an apparatus similar to the one illustrated in Fig. 1, Miller (1947) found that the moderately strong pain from an electric shock produces a much stronger learned drive than the hunger from a 22-hour period of food deprivation superimposed on a diet that held the animals considerably underweight. Was this difference produced by the greater strength of the pain, or by the suddenness of its beginning and end, in contrast to the slow changes in hunger? The pattern of cue without hunger cannot be quickly followed by reinforcement based on hunger and food; the pattern of cue without pain can be quickly followed by reinforcement based on pain. When such factors are controlled, will both these primary drives produce learned drives that are equally strong?

The verbal reports of human subjects indicate that, when a learned drive is acquired on the basis of pain, the cues do not elicit an hallucination of pain but, rather, only a part of the original pain-fear reaction, the part that is called fear. It is clear that fear is much more learnable than pain. Clinical evidence on hallucinations of pain suggests, however, that sometimes even the primary drive of pain may be learnable. This raises the question of whether the difference between the drives and rewards that are learn-

able and those that do not seem to be is one of kind or degree.

Lorenz's imprinting of releasers. Lorenz (1937) described instances in which complex behavior patterns involving strong motivations seem to be innately organized with the exception of one crucial link, namely, the determination of the stimulus pattern that will release them. The behavior pattern is innate, but the cue depends upon experience. For example, he reported that newly hatched ducks will follow the first moving object they see, be it a mother duck or a human being. He claims that this tendency is very quickly established, can occur only during a specific brief period of development, and, once set up, is irreversible. Furthermore it may determine the objects toward which later patterns, such as courting behavior, are exhibited.

Having observed ducks following Lorenz in typical formation, the author believes that they would probably learn a new response in order to get out of a cage that prevented them from following. Further work is necessary to determine (1) whether this type of behavior follows the same laws as other learnable drives, or (2) whether its mode of acquisition, its alleged irreversibility, and its limitation to a particular period of development are enough to set it apart as a new type of learning or as a phenomenon (imprinting) entirely different from learning.

Some General Problems

Learnable drives versus learnable rewards. According to the drive-reduction hypothesis, stimulus situations acquire drive value if responses that increase stimulation are reinforced by a subsequent reduction in the total strength of drive. They acquire reward value if responses that reduce stimulation are reinforced. It is impossible for the same situation to be a drive and reward simultaneously, but these two effects could be produced in rapid succession or in slightly different contexts. For example, entering a food box could first serve as a

introspective experience. The overall picture of the mounting tension from sexual motivation, the orgasm, and the consequent sharp decrease in tension seem to be the pattern, but many of the subgoals are experienced as pleasant and striven for in spite of the fact that they appear to involve increases rather than decreases in the total amount of stimulation. These, however, often may be observed to lose their goal value and be avoided rather than sought if they consistently fail to be associated with eventual drive reduction, either directly or through the mediation of fantasies associated with masturbation or nocturnal emission. On closer examination these subgoals may be found to involve rapid fluctuations between increases and decreases in total stimulation, or they may turn out to be genuine and instructive exceptions to the generality of the drive-reduction principle.

learned reward, and then, if food were not forthcoming, it could arouse learned drive. Furthermore an increase in external stimulation may produce a reduction in total stimulation, as when a fairly strong light seen by a person lost at night reduces a very strong fear.

Other theories of reinforcement (contiguity, confirming reactions, pleasure, or expectancy) might allow the same stimulus to act simultaneously as drive and reward. To date there are no experiments that indicate whether a given stimulus can act simultaneously as a learned drive and reward or that show the conditions that determine whether it will act as one or the other.

Mediated learned drives or rewards. An experiment by Miller (1935b) illustrates a

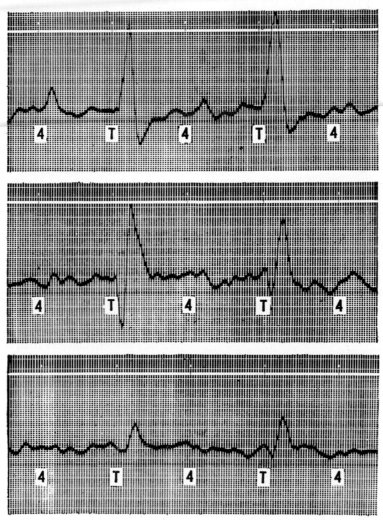

Fig. 8. Conditioned galvanic skin responses mediated by thoughts. The subject was presented with *T* followed by an electric shock, and *4* not followed by shock, in an unpredictable order. He named each symbol when he saw it. After a discrimination had been established, the subject was presented with a series of dots and instructed to think *4* when he saw the first dot, *T* when he saw the second, *4* when he saw the third, etc. The figure shows his galvanic responses to presentations 1 to 5, 11 to 15, and 21 to 25. (From Miller, 1935b, p. 65.)

mediated response, presumably fear. To human subjects he presented in unpredictable order the symbols T (followed by electric shock) and 4 (not followed by shock). The subjects soon reported that T always preceded shock and 4 never did, but it took them much longer to learn the emotional discrimination of giving a large conditioned galvanic response to the T and a small one to the 4. During this training the subjects read each symbol aloud. From this we should expect the galvanic responses to be conditioned not only to the sight of the symbols but also to the cues produced by pronouncing them. If this is true, any other stimulus causing the subject to say the same words should also elicit the same conditioned galvanic responses. In order to test this the subjects were presented with a series of dots and told to say 4 to the first one, T to the second, 4 to the third, etc. When they did this, the small and large galvanic responses were immediately transferred to the alternate dots. As a further test subjects were instructed to think 4 and T instead of saying them aloud. As Fig. 8 shows, the thinking of T in response to one dot elicited a large galvanic response, and the thinking of 4 a small one. This apparent functional equivalence between saying a word aloud and thinking it is the justification for tentatively calling them both "cue-producing" responses. It shows that the cues produced by these two responses are similar enough for generalization to occur from one to the other.

In another experiment Miller (1935a) predicted that rats should behave "foresightfully" because fear and avoidance would be mediated by cues from a distinctive anticipatory goal response. This prediction was confirmed.

A simplified social example of a mediated fear is shown in the accompanying theoretical diagram. (1) By actual punishment a child is taught to fear the thought of punishment. (2) By purely verbal threats he is taught to respond to the sight of a new forbidden object with the thought of punishment. After this the sight of the forbidden object elicits the thought of punishment, which evokes fear. If the child withdraws, the sight of the object and the thought of punishment are removed and the fear subsides. This reinforces withdrawal. (3) Eventually the sight of the forbidden object directly elicits fear and withdrawal.

Presumably, learned rewards can be mediated in a similar manner. For example, once the phrase, "this is good," has acquired the capacity to elicit relaxing, rewarding responses, these responses should be transferred to any new situation the subject learns to label as "good." Many of the techniques of advertising and propaganda seem to involve this mechanism. An attempt is made to change a subject's motivational responses to a given stimulus situation by getting him to label it with phrases such as "in style," "out of style," or "aggressor nation" that already have drive or reward value.

When a person is convinced that something he has not yet experienced is a means to an end he already desires, that thing tends to become a subgoal. Presumably this behavior is produced by mediated learned drives and rewards.

An important feature of mediated learned drives and rewards is that by the simple expedient of the learning of a new label (i.e. cue-producing response) complex motivational habits built up over a period of many years can be quickly elicited. Thus, labeling an idea as "the Chief's" or getting the subject to label it as his own may immediately elicit motivations that have been slowly learned during the subject's previous life. Similarly, making a decision or labeling one course of action as the one that is accepted and others as rejected may produce an immediate shift in the balance of

Sight of forbidden object —(2)→ Thought of punishment —(1)→ Fear
— — (3) — —

motivations, as Lewin (1947) has pointed out.

Removal of inhibition from responses that produce learned drive or reward. One of the properties of responses is that they can be inhibited by conflicting responses. Thus response-produced drives and rewards should be subject to inhibition, and the removal of the inhibition should produce an increase in the net strength of the drive or reward. For example, a young man might be motivated by fear to suppress all the responses that would normally produce sexual excitement in the presence of a girl. The fear that produces the inhibition might be removed directly by experimental extinction in that situation, indirectly by the generalization of extinction from other situations involving girls, or by the introduction into the situation of reassuring stimuli. If the fear was aroused indirectly via some cue-producing response, such as the thought that she was married, it might be reduced by eliminating that response, as would occur if the young man heard that the girl was divorced. However produced, the effect of any reduction in the inhibiting fear would be to increase the net sexual drives and rewards.

Goal-directed learned drives. Miller and Dollard (1941) made a stimulus-response analysis of the learning of one goal-directed drive, copying. In one example a subject who could not sing on key was trying to copy the notes sung by a teacher who also served as a critic. In this case the goal was to sing the same note as the teacher. They analyzed the process of learning to copy into the following factors which are roughly sequential but overlap considerably.

1. In the beginning the subject's trial and error was almost entirely random and completely dependent on the corrections of the critic.

2. Eventually the subject learned to respond with mild tension and anxiety to the cue of a difference between his own response and that of the teacher. As he learned to discriminate smaller differences, he was moti-

vated to try to correct his own mistakes without the need for criticism from the critic. The reduction in tension whenever he approached a perfect match rewarded the correct response.

3. The subject learned to respond to the direction of the difference by singing higher when he was flat and lower when he was sharp. Thus trial and error was restricted to the direction of the goal.

4. The subject learned to respond to the size of the difference by making a larger correction when he was farther off and a smaller one when he was nearer.

5. The subject learned to respond immediately with the proper note. This eliminated the need for random behavior and for approximation and correction.

It can be seen that having the drive attached to the cues produced by a difference and the corrective responses attached to the direction and size of that difference is what gives the goal-directed quality to the behavior in this example.

This type of analysis could probably be extended to situations in which the subject learns to attach responses producing a drive to cues produced by the conflict between an anticipatory goal response and the direct responses to the features of the immediate environment that prevent the complete goal response from occurring. In human behavior the cue for the learned drive may be a discrepancy between a verbal statement of a goal and the current stimulus situation. For example, a subject may learn to feel anxious in a situation that arouses the two thoughts: "I must get to this class on time," and "I am late." It is obvious that the rigorous analysis of complex examples of this kind will pose many problems of perception and language.

Whiting (1949) observed that many of the drives children learn during socialization are directed toward definite goals. He advanced the hypothesis that the conflict between an anticipatory goal response and the direct responses to the immediate environment produces a stimulus that is strong enough to serve as a drive, instead of merely as a cue. Some evidence suggesting that conflict can produce stimuli strong enough to function as a drive was presented by Miller (1944, p. 462).

Combinations of a number of drives and rewards. If learnable drives are produced by responses, it should be possible to attach a number of them to the same cue. In our society the desire for money is the focus of many drives, and possession of it is reinforced by many rewards. To date none of the experiments on learnable drives or rewards has shown how the effects of a number of different primary drives or rewards summate when they are all attached to the same stimulus.

Differentiation. If learnable drives and rewards obey the same laws as responses, discrimination training should narrow the range of cues that elicit them. General observation suggests that learning can make drives and rewards more specific, but this has not been experimentally analyzed.

When, as a result of differentiation, the same drive-producing response is attached to two quite different sets of socially defined cues, it may seem like two different motives. To take an extremely simple example, one animal might be motivated to escape from white compartments, and another to turn off buzzers. The observer who did not know that both responses were based on fear might be tempted to describe these motives by different names, white avoidance and buzzer drive, and from a practical point of view these two motives would be quite different. Similarly one might speculate that many socially acquired drives, such as guilt, pride, the desire for power, and the need for approval, are composed of a considerable element of fear. This fear might be blended with different mixtures of other motives, but according to this hypothesis the main distinctiveness of these drives lies in the conditions of social training that cause specific categories of cues to arouse the fear, and

other specific categories of cues to serve as goals because they reduce it. It is interesting to note that we speak of the fear of disapproval, the fear of failure, and the fear of losing status, money, or love.

Differences between innate and learned drives. If a drive is innate, it should follow the principles of physiology; if learned, it should be governed by the principles and conditions of learning. Thus learned drives should exist in a baffling variety of combinations that vary with the specific conditions of learning. It seems impossible to make a definitive list of them. A number of apparently different learned drives (such as claustrophobia, ambition, and conscience) all may involve the same physiological mechanism (such as fear), and they may be distinctive only because the social conditions of learning have caused different classes of stimuli to elicit the drive in each of the different cases. The situation is further confused by the fact that some learnable drives, like nausea, are named by the internal mechanism involved, and others, like avarice, by their external goal objects. Finally, as Miller and Dollard (1941) noted, learned drives may extinguish when innate ones would persist, and they may be reinforced instead of satiated by success in achieving a goal.

STUDIES AT A COMPLEX HUMAN LEVEL

Thorndike's studies. Thorndike (1940) has illustrated the great diversity of human wants. He studied what people spend their time and money on and attempted to measure the strength of various motivations by equating them with different sums of money in a questionnaire technique, the generality of which has not been tested against other criteria. He also reported (1935) a lengthy series of experiments that demonstrate that changes in the subject's ratings of his liking or disliking of objects, such as poetry, Christmas cards, and colored papers, can be produced by the rewarding of certain responses and not of others. He believed that these experiments indicated that mere contiguity is not effective in producing such changes, but, as he himself pointed out, they are not completely controlled in this respect. Furthermore his ratings have not been validated against other indices, such as the amount the subjects actually would pay for the objects.

Subjects who were hired to repeat unpleasant acts, such as handling a snake or drinking cod-liver oil, rated them as being less unpleasant after many repetitions. Thorndike noted, however, that repetition is not always effective (some people never lose their distaste of cod-liver oil or alarm clocks, or their love of turtle soup or golf). He concluded that it is safer to look for specific causes than to attribute decreases to a general tendency for negative adaptation. He pointed out that one of the difficulties in the teaching of new motivations is in being able to elicit and identify them so that they can be immediately rewarded. In general Thorndike's (1935, 1940) two books are full of important observations on human motivation. His experiments raise many interesting questions without giving definitive answers.

Level of aspiration. Studies of the level of aspiration, summarized by Lewin et al. (1944), yield insights into human motivation. Some workers have focused their attention on contemporary factors in the field; others (e.g. Sears, 1940) have tried to include the social conditions and principles of learning. A systematic development of the latter approach should throw additional light on learned drives and rewards. Davis (1948) and Ford (1949) showed how much cultural conditions of learning, such as social class, influence the tendency to strive for specific goals.

Effect of barriers. Studies of the effects of barriers illustrate the advantage of taking learning into account. From his ingenious experiments Wright (1937) concluded that a barrier usually enhances a positive valence. But Child (1946) showed that this preference for the more difficult goal is not present with young children. It increases with age and thus presumably with social training. Furthermore, when children are asked about it, their answers reveal a great variety of motives, many of which are obviously products of social learning.

Experiments on "group decision." Lewin (1947) summarized a series of studies that compared the effectiveness of different techniques in motivating people to change their behavior. In a typical study the problem was to get housewives to try serving a non-preferred kind of meat during World War II. The investigators found that a group of housewives who participated in a discussion, made a public decision by raising their hands, and were told that there would be a follow-up study to check on what they did were much more likely to serve the non-preferred meat than another group who listened to a lecture without making a public decision and without being told to expect a follow-up study. In this pioneer stage these investigators have tended to lump together a number of factors, such as hearing the views of other group members, having a chance to express one's objections, being required to make some immediate public or private decision, etc. Their emphasis upon the contemporary factors in the field has tended to make them relatively less interested in determining how the various motivational effects, such as copying other members of the group (Miller and Dollard, 1941), were learned.

Other studies of changes in human needs and goals are summarized in Lewin (1946).

Human personality. If many of the important adult human motivations are learned or are greatly modified by learning, they should exist in a baffling array of combinations and blends that are difficult to decode without a detailed knowledge of the great variety of learning conditions to which the different individuals have been exposed. As

Allport (1937) pointed out, this is exactly what seems to occur; there is a great variety of human motives and goals, and these are an important aspect of what is commonly referred to as differences in the ego, or personality.

Allport also maintained that once these drives are learned they may become functionally autonomous so that they do not extinguish. This position has been criticized by McClelland (1942) and Rethlingshaefer (1943). In Fig. 7 we saw that a strong learned drive might seem to be unaffected for many trials and still eventually extinguish. When generalization, higher-order reinforcement, and shifts from one reinforcing agent to another are added to this possibility, it can be seen how difficult it is in complex human situations to determine whether or not a habit actually is functionally autonomous.

Although the answer may be difficult, the general problem is exceedingly important. Some learned drives are amazingly resistant to change; others change easily. Great differences may be observed in this respect between different motives in the same person and between the same motive in different people. Sometimes a motivation can be changed with relatively little effect upon the rest of the personality; at other times its removal produces a profound effect upon the whole personality. What are the exact principles (including constitutional factors) determining such differences? How are hierarchies of learned drives and rewards built up, and how do they interact?

It can be seen that the theoretical and experimental work has a long way to go before it bridges completely the gap between the fundamental biological drives and the wonderfully complex web of socially learned motives that determine adult human behavior.

REFERENCES

Adrian, E. D. *The basis of sensation, the action of the sense organs.* New York: Norton, 1928.

Allee, W. C. Group organization among vertebrates. *Science*, 1942, **95**, 289–293.

Allport, G. W. *Personality: A psychological interpretation.* New York: Holt, 1937.

Anderson, E. The externalization of drive: III. Maze learning by non-rewarded and satiated rats. *J. genet. Psychol.*, 1941, **59**, 397–426.

Bregman, E. O. An attempt to modify the emotional attitudes of infants by the conditioned response technique. *J. genet. Psychol.*, 1934, **45**, 169–198.

Brogden, W. J. Non-alimentary components in the food-reinforcement of conditioned forelimb-flexion in food-satiated dogs. *J. exp. Psychol.*, 1942, **30**, 326–335.

Brogden, W. J., and E. Culler. Experimental extinction of higher-order responses. *Amer. J. Psychol.*, 1935, **47**, 663–669.

Brogden, W. J., E. A. Lipman, and E. Culler. The role of incentive in conditioning and extinction. *Amer. J. Psychol.*, 1938, **51**, 109–117.

Brown, J. S. Gradients of approach and avoidance responses and their relation to level of motivation. *J. comp. physiol. Psychol.*, 1948, **41**, 450–465.

Brown, J. S., and A. Jacobs. The role of fear in the motivation and acquisition of responses. *J. exp. Psychol.*, 1949, **39**, 747–759.

Bruce, R. H. The effect of removal of reward on the maze performance of rats. III. *Univ. Calif. Publ. Psychol.*, 1932, **6**, 75–82.

Bugelski, R. Extinction with and without subgoal reinforcement. *J. comp. Psychol.*, 1938, **26**, 121–134.

Burros, R. H. Quantitative studies in secondary drive. Ph.D. dissertation, Yale University, 1949.

Cannon, W. B. *Bodily changes in pain, hunger, fear, and rage.* New York: Appleton-Century-Crofts, 1929.

Child, I. L. Children's preference for goals easy or difficult to attain. *Psychol. Monogr.*, 1946, **60**, No. 4.

Conger, J. J. An analysis of the effect of alcohol on conflict behavior in the albino rat. Ph.D. dissertation, Yale University, 1949.

Coppock, H., and O. H. Mowrer. Inter-trial responses as "rehearsal"; a study of "overt thinking" in animals. *Amer. J. Psychol.*, 1947, **60**, 608–616.

Cowles, J. T. Food tokens as incentives for learning by chimpanzees. *Comp. Psychol. Monogr.*, 1937, **14**, No. 5.

Cruikshank, R. M. Animal infancy. In L. Carmichael (Ed.), *Manual of child psychology.* New York: Wiley, 1946. Pp. 167–189.

Davis, A. *Social class influences upon learning.* Cambridge: Harvard University Press, 1948.

Davis, H. C., et al. Effects of cup, bottle, and breast feeding on oral activities of newborn infants. *Pediatrics*, 1948, **3**, 549–558.

Denny, M. R. The role of secondary reinforcement in a partial reinforcement learning situation. *J. exp. Psychol.*, 1946, **36**, 373–389.

Denny, M. R. The effect of using differential end boxes in a simple T-maze learning situation. *J. exp. Psychol.*, 1948, **38**, 245–249.

Dollard, J. *Fear in battle.* New Haven: Yale University Press, 1943.

Dollard, J. *Exploration of morale factors among combat air crewmen.* Memorandum to Experimental Section, Research Branch, Information and Education Division, War Department, 9 March 1945.

Dollard, J., and N. E. Miller. *Personality and psychotherapy: An analysis in terms of learning, thinking and culture.* New York: McGraw-Hill, 1950.

Eccher, W., and E. Culler. Reciprocal facilitation of the conditioned and conditioning mechanisms. *J. comp. Psychol.,* 1941, **31,** 223–231.

Ectors, L., N. L. Brookens, and R. W. Gerard. Autonomic and motor localization in the hypothalamus. *Arch. Neurol. Psychiat., Chicago,* 1938, **39,** 789–798.

Ehrenfreund, D. The effect of partial reinforcement on the strength of secondary reinforcing cues. *Amer. Psychologist,* 1948, **37,** 241.

Ehrenfreund, D. Effect of a secondary reinforcing agent in black-white discrimination. *J. comp. physiol. Psychol.,* 1949, **42,** 1–5.

Ellson, D. G. The acquisition of a token reward habit in dogs. *J. comp. Psychol.,* 1937, **24,** 504–522.

Estes, W. K. An experimental study of punishment. *Psychol. Monogr.,* 1944, **57,** No. 3.

Estes, W. K. A study of motivating conditions necessary for secondary reinforcement. *J. exp. Psychol.,* 1949, **39,** 306–310.

Estes, W. K., and B. F. Skinner. Some quantitative properties of anxiety. *J. exp. Psychol.,* 1941, **29,** 390–400.

Farber, I. E. Response fixation under anxiety and non-anxiety conditions. *J. exp. Psychol.,* 1948, **38,** 111–131.

Ford, C. S. The arbitrary values of mankind. *Amer. Merc.,* 1949, **68,** No. 306, 746–751.

Freud, S. *The problem of anxiety.* New York: Norton, 1936.

Goodenough, F. L. *Anger in young children.* Minneapolis: University of Minnesota Press, 1931.

Grindley, G. C. Experiments on the influence of the amount of reward in learning of young chickens. *Brit. J. Psychol.,* 1929, **20,** 173–180.

Grinker, R. R., and J. P. Spiegel. *War neuroses.* Philadelphia: Blakiston, 1945.

Guthrie, E. R. *The psychology of learning.* New York: Harper, 1935.

Gwinn, G. T. The effects of punishment on acts motivated by fear. *J. exp. Psychol.,* 1949, **39,** 260–269.

Hall, C. S. Temperament: A survey of animal studies. *Psychol. Bull.,* 1941, **38,** 909–943.

Harris, L. J., J. Clay, F. J. Hargreaves, and A. Ward. Appetite and choice of diet. The ability of the vitamin B deficient rat to discriminate between diets containing and lacking the vitamin. *Proc. roy. Soc.,* 1933, **B113,** 161–190.

Hastings, D. W. *Psychiatric experiences of the 8th Air Force.* New York: Josiah Macy, Jr., Foundation, 1944.

Hebb, D. O. On the nature of fear. *Psychol. Rev.,* 1946, **53,** 259–276.

Hilgard, E. R. *Theories of learning.* New York: Appleton-Century-Crofts, 1948.

Hilgard, E. R., and D. G. Marquis. *Conditioning and learning.* New York: Appleton-Century-Crofts, 1940.

Holmberg, A. H. *Nomads of the long bow.* Washington, D. C.: Institute of Social Anthropology, Smithsonian Institution, 1950 (in press).

Hovland, C. I. The generalization of conditioned responses. III. Extinction, spontaneous recovery, and disinhibition of conditioned and of generalized responses. *J. exp. Psychol.,* 1937*a,* **21,** 47–62.

Hovland, C. I. The generalization of conditioned responses. IV. The effects of varying amounts of reinforcement upon the degree of generalization of conditioned responses. *J. exp. Psychol.,* 1937*b,* **21,** 261–276.

Hull, C. L. The concept of the habit family hierarchy and maze learning. Parts I and II. *Psychol. Rev.,* 1934*a,* **41,** 33–54, 134–152.

Hull, C. L. Learning: II. The factor of the conditioned reflex. In C. Murchison (Ed.), *Handbook of general experimental psychology.* Worcester: Clark University Press, 1934*b.* Pp. 382–455.

Hull, C. L. *Principles of behavior.* New York: Appleton-Century-Crofts, 1943.

Jenkins, W. O. A temporal gradient of derived reinforcement. *Amer. J. Psychol.,* 1950, **63,** 237–243.

Jersild, A. T. Emotional development. In L. Carmichael (Ed.), *Manual of child psychology.* New York: Wiley, 1946. Pp. 752–790.

Jones, M. C. Elimination of children's fears. *J. exp. Psychol.,* 1924, **7,** 382–390.

Lambert, W. W., and R. L. Solomon. The extinction of a token reward behavior sequence. *J. exp. Psychol.,* 1950 (in preparation).

Levy, D. M. Experiments on the sucking reflex and social behavior of dogs. *Amer. J. Orthopsychiat.,* 1934, **4,** 203–224.

Lewin, K. Field theory of learning. In National Society for the Study of Education, *The forty-first yearbook.* Bloomington, Ill.: Public School Publishing, 1942. Part 2, pp. 215–242.

Lewin, K. Behavior and development as a function of the total situation. In L. Carmichael (Ed.), *Manual of child psychology.* New York: Wiley, 1946. Pp. 791–844.

Lewin, K. Group decision and social change. In T. M. Newcomb, E. L. Hartley, et al., *Readings in social psychology.* New York: Holt, 1947. Pp. 330–344.

Lewin, K., T. Dembo, L. Festinger, and P. S. Sears. Level of aspiration. In J. McV. Hunt (Ed.), *Personality and the behavior disorders.* New York: Ronald, 1944. Pp. 333–378.

Lorenz, K. S. The companion in the birds' world. *Auk,* 1937, **54,** 245–273.

McClelland, D. C. Functional autonomy of motives as an extinction phenomenon. *Psychol. Rev.,* 1942, **49,** 272–283.

Mahl, G. F. The effect of chronic fear on the gastric secretion of HCl in dogs. *Psychosom. Med.*, 1949, **11**, 30–44.

Mahl, G. F. Anxiety, HCl secretion, and peptic ulcer etiology. *Psychosom. Med.*, 1950, **12**, 140–169.

Manual for the study of food habits. Committee on Food Habits, National Research Council Bulletin, No. 111. Washington, D. C., 1945.

Masserman, J. H. *Behavior and neurosis.* Chicago : University of Chicago Press, 1943.

Masserman, J. H., M. G. Jacques, and M. R. Nicholson. Alcohol as a preventive of experimental neurosis. *Quart. J. Stud. Alcohol*, 1945, **6**, 281–299.

Masserman, J. H., and K. S. Yum. An analysis of the influence of alcohol on experimental neurosis in cats. *Psychosom. Med.*, 1946, **8**, 36–52.

May, M. A. Experimentally acquired drives. *J. exp. Psychol.*, 1948, **38**, 66–77.

May, M. A. An interpretation of pseudoconditioning. *Psychol. Rev.*, 1949, **56**, 177–183.

Miller, N. E. A reply to "sign-Gestalt or conditioned reflex?" *Psychol. Rev.*, 1935a, **42**, 280–292.

Miller, N. E. The influence of past experience upon the transfer of subsequent training. Ph.D. dissertation, Yale University, 1935b.

Miller, N. E. An experimental investigation of acquired drives. *Psychol. Bull.*, 1941, **38**, 534–535.

Miller, N. E. Experimental studies of conflict. In J. McV. Hunt (Ed.), *Personality and the behavior disorders.* New York : Ronald, 1944. Pp. 431–465.

Miller, N. E. Experiments on the strength of acquired drives based on hunger. *Amer. Psychologist*, 1947, **2**, 303.

Miller, N. E. Studies of fear as an acquirable drive : I. Fear as motivation and fear-reduction as reinforcement in the learning of new responses. *J. exp. Psychol.*, 1948a, **38**, 89–101.

Miller, N. E. Theory and experiment relating psychoanalytic displacement to stimulus-response generalization. *J. abnorm. soc. Psychol.*, 1948b, **43**, 155–178.

Miller, N. E., and J. Dollard. *Social learning and imitation.* New Haven : Yale University Press, 1941.

Miller, N. E., and D. H. Lawrence. Studies of fear as an acquirable drive : III. Effect of strength of electric shock as a primary drive and of number of trials with the primary drive on the strength of fear. 1950 (in preparation).

Mitrano, A. J. Principles of conditioning in human goal behavior. *Psychol. Monogr.*, 1939, **51**, No. 4.

Morgan, C. T. The hoarding instinct. *Psychol. Rev.*, 1947, **54**, 335–341.

Mote, F. A., Jr., and F. W. Finger. Exploratory drive and secondary reinforcement in the acquisition and extinction of a simple running response. *J. exp. Psychol.*, 1942, **31**, 57–69.

Mowrer, O. H. A stimulus-response analysis of anxiety and its role as a reinforcing agent. *Psychol. Rev.*, 1939, **46**, 553–566.

Mowrer, O. H. On the dual nature of learning— a reinterpretation of "conditioning" and "problem solving." *Harv. educ. Rev.*, 1947, **17**, 102–148.

Mowrer, O. H., and R. R. Lamoreaux. Avoidance conditioning and signal duration — a study of secondary motivation and reward. *Psychol. Monogr.*, 1942, **54**, No. 5.

Mowrer, O. H., and R. R. Lamoreaux. Fear as an intervening variable in avoidance conditioning. *J. comp. Psychol.*, 1946, **39**, 29–50.

Mowrer, O. H., and J. W. Suter. Further evidence for a two-factor theory of learning. Chapter 10 in *Learning theory and personality dynamics.* New York : Ronald, 1950 (in press).

Mowrer, O. H., and A. D. Ullman. Time as a determinant in integrative learning. *Psychol. Rev.*, 1945, **52**, 61–90.

Mowrer, O. H., and P. Viek. An experimental analogue of fear from a sense of helplessness. *J. abnorm. soc. Psychol.*, 1948, **43**, 193–200.

Myers, J. A. An experimental study of the reinforcing value of food for non-hungry rats. M. A. thesis, University of Iowa Library, 1949.

Pavlov, I. P. *Conditioned reflexes.* (Translated by G. V. Anrep.) London : Oxford University Press, 1927.

Perkins, C. C. The relation of secondary reward to gradients of reinforcement. *J. exp. Psychol.*, 1947, **37**, 377–392.

Rethlingshaefer, D. Experimental evidence for functional autonomy of motives. *Psychol. Rev.*, 1943, **50**, 397–407.

Roethlisberger, F. J., and W. J. Dickson. *Management and the worker.* Cambridge : Harvard University Press, 1941.

Saltzman, I. J. Maze learning in the absence of primary reinforcement : A study of secondary reinforcement. *J. comp. physiol. Psychol.*, 1949, **42**, 161–173.

Scott, J. P. Social behavior, organization and leadership in a small flock of domestic sheep. *Comp. Psychol. Monogr.*, 1945, **18**, No. 4.

Scott, J. P. Dominance and the frustration-aggression hypothesis. *Physiol. Zool.*, 1948, **21**, 31–39.

Sears, P. S. Levels of aspiration in academically successful and unsuccessful children. *J. abnorm. soc. Psychol.*, 1940, **35**, 498–536.

Sears, R. R., and G. M. Wise. Relation of cup-feeding in infancy to thumbsucking and the oral drive. *Amer. J. Orthopsychiat.*, 1950, **20**, 123–138.

Shaffer, L. F. *The psychology of adjustment.* Boston : Houghton Mifflin, 1936.

Sheffield, F. D. Avoidance training and the contiguity principle. *J. comp. physiol. Psychol.*, 1948, **41**, 165–177.

Sheffield, F. D., and H. W. Temmer. Relative resistance to extinction of escape training and avoidance training. *J. exp. Psychol.*, 1950, **40**, 287–297.

Sheffield, V. F. Extinction as a function of partial reinforcement and distribution of practice. *J. exp. Psychol.*, 1949, **39**, 511–526.

Skinner, B. F. *The behavior of organisms.* New York: Appleton-Century-Crofts, 1938.

Smith, M. F. The establishment and extinction of the token-reward habit in the cat. *J. gen. Psychol.*, 1939, **20**, 475–486.

Solomon, R. L., and L. C. Wynne. 1949 (personal communication). See also: Avoidance conditioning in normal dogs and in dogs deprived of normal autonomic functioning. *Amer. Psychologist*, 1950, **5**, 264.

Spence, K. W. The role of secondary reinforcement in delayed reward learning. *Psychol. Rev.*, 1947, **54**, 1–8.

Spragg, S. D. S. Morphine addiction in chimpanzees. *Comp. Psychol. Monogr.*, 1940, **15**, No. 7.

Thorndike, E. L. *Psychology of wants, interests, and attitudes.* New York: Appleton-Century-Crofts, 1935.

Thorndike, E. L. *Human nature and the social order.* New York: Macmillan, 1940.

Tinbergen, N. Social releasers and the experimental method required for their study. *Wilson Bull.*, 1948, **60**, 6–51. (Supplemented by personal correspondence.)

Tolman, E. C. *Purposive behavior in animals and men.* New York: Appleton-Century-Crofts, 1932.

Tolman, E. C. A drive-conversion diagram. *Psychol. Rev.*, 1943, **50**, 503–513.

Upton, M. The auditory sensitivity of guinea pigs. *Amer. J. Psychol.*, 1929, **41**, 412–421.

Watson, J. B., and R. Rayner. Conditioned emotional reactions. *J. exp. Psychol.*, 1920, **3**, 1–14.

Wever, E. G. Upper limit of hearing in the cat. *J. comp. Psychol.*, 1930, **10**, 221–233.

Whiting, J. W. M. *Becoming a Kwoma.* New Haven: Yale University Press, 1941.

Whiting, J. W. M. A brief theory of purposive acquired drives. 1949 (unpublished manuscript).

Wickert, F. (Ed.). *Psychological research on problems of redistribution.* Army Air Forces Aviation Psychology Program, Research Report No. 14. Washington, D. C.: U. S. Govt. Printing Office, 1947.

Williams, K. A. The reward value of a conditioned stimulus. *Univ. Calif. Publ. Psychol.*, 1929, **4**, 31–55.

Wolfe, J. B. Effectiveness of token rewards for chimpanzees. *Comp. Psychol. Monogr.*, 1936, **12**, No. 60.

Woodworth, R. S. *Dynamic psychology.* New York: Columbia University Press, 1918.

Wright, H. F. The influence of barriers upon strength of motivation. *Contr. psychol. Theor.*, 1937, **1**, No. 3.

Young, P. T. Appetite, palatability and feeding habit: A critical review. *Psychol. Bull.*, 1948, **45**, 289–320.

14

Emotion

DONALD B. LINDSLEY

Northwestern University

Emotion is one of the most complex phenomena known to psychology. It is complex because it involves so much of the organism at so many levels of neural and chemical integration. Both subjectively and objectively its ramifications are diffuse and intermingled with other processes. Perhaps therein lies the uniqueness, and possibly the major significance, of emotion.

It appears that any final description of emotion must be in terms of a reacting mechanism; furthermore it appears that the scientific study of emotion must be confined to emotional behavior, broadly interpreted, and to its underlying mechanisms. Nevertheless the problem is not simple, even when we approach it in this objective manner, because in emotional behavior many bodily changes occur within the organism that are not directly observable. Postural orientations, facial expressions, gestures, and vocalizations provide some external indications, but even these, because of their dynamic qualities and their relation to other bodily processes, require more detailed examination than casual observation can provide. These external indications are not universally acceptable criteria of emotion, because they are highly susceptible to cultural and social modification and they are admixtures of voluntary and involuntary modes of response. Skin reactions such as blanching, blushing, and sweating provide external signs of a reflexive character in some of the more intense emotions, but only sweating (galvanic skin response) can be used very adequately as an index of mild emotional responsiveness. Although the overt signs of emotion are utilized daily in social adjustments and personal evaluations, it is difficult to be sure just what aspects of the various expressive changes constitute the basis of prediction. It is hard to know how adequately behavior can be interpreted on the basis of these clues alone, independent of the stimulus situation and the projection of one's own feelings into the interpretation of the emotional expression of another.

In general the topic of emotion has been approached via two principal aspects: the experiential or feeling aspect, and the expressive or behavioral aspect. The former has been studied by introspective methods; the latter by way of inferences based upon observed behavior. Both procedures are notably unreliable and both have led to highly speculative theories of emotion.* Nevertheless such basic data as there are on emotion have come largely through the study of its expressive aspects and objectively recorded bodily changes.

BODILY CHANGES AND THEIR MEASUREMENT

Emotion is characterized by many combinations of bodily change. There are overt

* For an excellent historical account, see *Feeling and Emotion: A History of Theories* by Gardiner, Metcalf, and Beebe-Center (1937). Another source of historical reference is *The Psychology of Feeling and Emotion* by Ruckmick (1936).

manifestations that are readily observable, and there are organic and physiological changes that are revealed only by special procedures and recording devices. All bodily changes during emotion are dependent on complex underlying processes that become integrated by the autonomic nervous system, the cerebrospinal system, and the endocrine glands. The complexity of these interactions makes it clear that the measurement of bodily change in emotion can never be definitive or exhaustive. We can only hope, by judicious choice, to make our procedures reasonably representative of the activity of the organism as a whole. A single measure may be useful under certain conditions, but two or more well-chosen measures will usually facilitate the interpretation of results.

Some of the measurable bodily changes in emotion and the techniques for recording them have been described by Landis (1934), Ruckmick (1936), Darrow (1943), Wenger and Ellington (1943), Young (1943, 1948), and Davis (1948). Therefore it will suffice to describe briefly each process or bodily change and to indicate one or more methods of measurement. Reference will be made to only a few selected studies, usually those that have a particular bearing upon the technique of measurement. A complete bibliography of all the studies employing one or more of the methods of measurement would be prohibitive.

The development of polygraphs, multichannel amplifiers, and associated inkwriting and optical oscillographs has greatly facilitated the simultaneous recording of autonomic and somatic responses that occur in emotion. Electrical recorders make possible the study of phenomena whose processes are accompanied by electrical activity, or whose movements or pressures may be transduced to electrical form. Among those having an electrical basis are brain waves, muscle action potentials, galvanic skin responses, electrocardiograms, and eye blinks. Skin temperature measurements are transduced electrically by means of a thermocouple. Respiration and blood pressure, usually recorded by a pneumatic system, can be recorded electrically by means of suitable mechanical-electrical transducers such as microphones and strain gauges. It has even become possible to record remotely, without encumbering wires, the electrical phenomena originating in a subject at a distance. This is accomplished by a miniature transmitting system worn by the subject as he moves about, and a suitable receiving system at the recording station (Prast and Blinn, 1949; Breakell, Parker, and Christopherson, 1949).

Electrical Phenomena of the Skin

One of the most popular measures of autonomic activity associated with affective and emotional states is the *galvanic skin response* (GSR). This phenomenon is known by various other terms such as psychogalvanic reflex, skin resistance, palmar resistance, palmar conductance, electrodermal response, and skin potential. They are all related to *sweating*, the effector mechanism for which is the sweat gland membranes, activated by the sympathetic nervous system.

Féré introduced the method of measuring resistance of the skin to a current externally applied. Consequently this method of measuring sweat gland activity is known as the *Féré method*, or the *exosomatic method*, since an external source of current is utilized in the measurement. The resistance of the skin is believed to be due to a polarization-capacity effect that varies as a function of the sweat gland activity (Gildemeister, 1915; McClendon and Hemingway, 1930). Tarchanoff discovered the skin potential change known as the *Tarchanoff method*. Since this potential difference arises from currents in the skin, it is said to be an *endosomatic method*. It may be that the skin potential, like the resistance of the skin, arises as a function of the polarization-capacity effect due to secretion of sweat. Another explanation is that it is associated with the contraction of the smooth muscles in the sweat glands. Favoring this latter view is the fact that the form and time characteristics of the potential wave are similar to those of smooth muscle potentials recorded elsewhere in the body.

The exosomatic method has the advantage that it provides a measure of skin resistance level and a measure of the transitory changes in resistance that accompany sensory or emotional stimulation. An unfavorable aspect is that the resistance level frequently increases steadily as a subject relaxes, and rises to still higher levels during sleep. When discrete responses are recorded they are accordingly superimposed on a shifting resistance level. This means that two responses of the same magnitude, but superimposed on different resistance levels, will not be recorded as equal. To avoid this confusion Darrow (1934, 1937) adopted a method of expressing the resistance change in terms of log conductance multiplied by a factor of 100. Conductance, or the reciprocal of resistance, is expressed in micromhos. Such a measure is similar to a percentage resistance change, which has been employed by others to compensate for the variation in resistance level. The unit of measurement of the GSR has been discussed by Hunt and Hunt (1935), Haggard (1945), Lacey (1947), and Lacey and Siegel (1949).

The neural and effector mechanisms of the sweat glands underlying the GSR have been the subject of study and discussion by Richter (1930), O'Leary (1932), Greenwald (1935), Solomon (1935), Schwartz (1937), Darrow (1937), and Richter and Levine (1937). The evidence indicates that the nerve supply is exclusively sympathetic, but the neurohumoral agent at the effector is acetylcholine rather than an adrenergic substance. In this connection Darrow (1943) points out that electrical response may therefore be complicated by factors other than sympathetic nerve discharge. Skin resistance increases under light anesthesia and during sleep, and it is high in newborn infants; in all these instances the level of diencephalic and forebrain excitation or activation is reduced, probably owing to decreased sensory influx. In line with this explanation is the fact that the GSR is particularly sensitive to sensory and ideational stimuli, especially those associated with alertness, attention, apprehension, and arousal. The resistance level is lower, and the magnitude of response (drop in resistance) is greater to specific sensory stimuli. The GSR, perhaps more than any other indicator of bodily change (with the possible exception of blood pressure and heart rate), is a sensitive index of cortical and higher-level mental functions. Its use in lie detection and deception studies attests this fact.

Circuits and recording methods in use prior to 1935 have been critically evaluated by Greenwald (1935); others who have published details of circuits and recording methods are Floyd (1935, 1936), Forbes (1936), Jeffress (1937), Lauer and Anderson (1938), Hoelandt and Stovkis (1939), Stoddard and Fisk (1940), Grant (1946), Haggard and Gerbrands (1947), and Lacey and Siegel (1948). Although most investigators have used the resistance method, there are certain advantages to the endosomatic or potential method. With amplifiers of high input impedance it is relatively free of influence from the changing resistance level, although the resistance level as a measurement per se may well be an important factor. Furthermore the potential method is less complicated to handle experimentally and in all probability is actually a less complex response. Ordinary resistance-capacity coupled amplifiers, such as those employed in recording brain potentials, are applicable to the study of latency and magnitude of the response, but they do not provide a true picture of waveform. The ideal would be a d-c amplifier, but stable d-c amplifiers of adequate sensitivity unfortunately have not yet become available. An example of the GSR recorded as an electrical potential from two small electrodes in the palm of the hand is shown below (see Fig. 5).

Blood Pressure and Volume

Of the various measures of bodily change in emotion, Darrow (1936) argues that blood pressure and galvanic skin reflex (sweating) are probably the best indicators of facilitative, preparatory, or emergency functions mediated predominantly by the sympathetic system. In animals under anesthesia, or with cord or brain stem transected, blood pressure may be measured by a direct method with a cannula inserted in an artery so that pressure effects may be transmitted directly to a pressure capsule and a recording instrument. However, with intact animals or human subjects one must resort to an indirect method such as balancing an external pressure against an artery. This is usually accomplished by inflating a pneumatic cuff around one of the limbs and connecting it to a pressure recorder. The device for measuring blood pressure is called a *sphygmomanometer*.

There are two measures of blood pressure, *systolic* and *diastolic,* and the difference between them is known as *pulse pressure.* Systolic pressure is the maximal pressure reached during the contraction of the heart; diastolic pressure is the least pressure during expansion. In measuring these by the auscultatory method of Korotkow, a stethoscope is applied over an artery below the blood-pressure cuff. The pressure in the cuff is raised to a point where circulation in the artery is occluded and the heart sounds can no longer be heard in the stethoscope. The pressure is immediately but gradually released, and the first pulse sounds heard indicate the point at which the systolic pressure is to be read from the mercury manometer. As the pressure in the cuff decreases further, a point is reached where the pulse sounds disappear or only muffled sounds are heard. A reading at this point gives the diastolic pressure. There are also devices that give visual indications of the beginning of pulse oscillations at the systolic level and their cessation at the diastolic level.

For experimental purposes a continuous method of recording is usually desirable. It is extremely difficult to measure systolic pressure continuously, although several methods have been developed (Darrow, 1937; Stovkis, 1938; Doupe, Newman, and Wilkins, 1939). Many experimenters have accepted a compromise and record what is known as *relative blood pressure.* The cuff is inflated to a level above diastolic pressure, but where it is not uncomfortable and does not occlude circulation. Variations in pressure from this level are recorded continuously. The significance of these changes is not always apparent in terms of absolute pressures, but the relative pressures can be correlated with other happenings during the course of an experiment.

The effect of vasomotor changes, vasoconstriction and vasodilatation, are reflected in the size or volume of a particular part of the body. Usually a finger, hand, or foot is used for this purpose, the particular part being enclosed in a *plethysmograph.* Variations in volume increase or decrease the pressure in the closed system and reflect vasomotor changes. Unfortunately what occurs in peripheral parts is not always correlated with vasomotor changes elsewhere, especially those in cerebral vessels. Nevertheless this measure of the changes in peripheral vessels has been used in a number of studies (see Lhamon, 1949). In animals such as the rabbit, light shone through the thin ear tissues permits photometric measures of vasomotor changes.

Electrocardiogram and Heart Rate

The electrocardiogram (EKG) may be recorded from electrodes attached to the two arms or to either arm and the left leg. These are the standard EKG leads, but electrodes attached to the body wall in the neighborhood of the heart will also pick up the spreading electrical potential that accompanies the cycle of the heart beat. The pattern has a typical recurring form that enables a cardiologist to analyze the performance of the heart, but in general the pattern has not proved very useful as a measure of emotional change. The heart rate, which can be measured from the recurring pattern (see Fig. 5), reflects both sympathetic and parasympathetic effects, but, as Darrow (1943) pointed out, it should be used with caution as an index of balance between these two systems since it is subject to subsidiary reflexes via the carotid sinus and other moderator nerves. Another consideration is the fact that the slightest movement of a part of the body may produce a temporary change in rate. Heart rate may be measured by plotting the duration between individual beats or by counting the number of beats during an interval of time.

The *cardiotachometer* is a useful device for counting the number of heart beats. Another device is the Fleisch *Zeitschreiber*, also known as a *cardiochronograph*. It draws successive lines whose height is proportional to the duration of each heart cycle, so that heart rate per minute is immediately apparent. The use and description of cardiochronographs is given by Whitehorn, Kaufman, and Thomas (1935), Whitehorn and Richter (1937), and Henry (1938).

Respiration

The usual method of measuring respiration is by thoracic and/or abdominal pneumograph — a flexible air-filled tube connected to a sensitive rubber or metal diaphragm that moves a pen or stylus (see Higley and Renshaw, 1937). A strain gauge or carbon microphone button may be adapted for use as a mechanical-electrical transducer for the electrical recording of respiration. Another method of recording is by spirogram (see Finesinger, 1944). The principal respiration variables are rate, depth, pattern, and inspiration/expiration ratio. Although respiration is a complex indicator subject to voluntary control, it is mainly regulated reflexly through the respiratory center in the medulla, which responds to changes in blood chemistry, especially carbon dioxide and oxygen levels. Respiration is also subject to interference by various other reflexes such as coughing, sneezing, sighing, and yawning. Despite these complications respiration is frequently a sensitive indicator in certain emotional situations, especially startle, conscious attempts at deception, and conflict (Brower, 1946). The respiratory pattern is frequently disturbed in anxiety states.

Skin Temperature

The measurement of skin temperature in emotion has not been used extensively, apparently because of technical difficulties. The usual method is to apply a thermocouple to the skin area concerned. Variations in temperature produce a change in the electrical current in the thermocouple. Skin temperature is mainly a function of local vasoconstriction, although the temperature of the blood, and of the body generally, is regulated by a variety of factors. Emotional stress is reported to produce a fall in skin temperature when the sympathetic supply to the part is intact, but it does not vary with emotional state when the sympathetic is interfered with, as in Raynaud's disease (Mittelmann and Wolff, 1939, 1943). Conflict is associated with vasoconstriction and a fall in temperature, whereas uninhibited action and emotional security are said to result in vasodilatation and a rising skin temperature.

Pupillary Response

The antagonistic action of the sympathetic and parasympathetic systems is manifest in the action of the pupil. Dilatation is mediated through the sympathetic system; the preganglionic fibers originate in the upper thoracic region of the cord, and the postganglionic fibers in the superior cervical ganglion (see Fig. 1). Constriction is mediated by the parasympathetic system with preganglionic fibers originating in the midbrain and traversing the oculomotor nerve (III cranial) to the ciliary ganglion, whence impulses are transmitted via postganglionic neurons. However, the pupillary response is complicated by synergic action of the sphincter and dilator muscles whereby inhibition of tone in one may facilitate the action of the other. Midbrain, diencephalic, and even cortical points have been found where stimulation will produce changes in pupillary diameter.

Pupillary response to pain and to emotional stimuli has been studied by Bender (1933), who made motion pictures of the pupil. A similar procedure was used by Lindsley and Sassaman (1938) in studying the latency and size of the pupillary response associated with a generalized sympathetic reaction. A pioneer in the study of the pupil in a variety of clinical conditions, including emotional reactions, was Löwenstein, who also reviewed progress in pupillography (Löwenstein and Friedman, 1942). A recent development in pupillography is the use of infrared illumination and infrared sensitive film. This eliminates the constriction induced by the light reflex when the illumination necessary for ordinary photography is used.

Salivary Secretion

The secretion of the salivary glands has not been used extensively in the study of emotion, although the secretion of the parotid gland in particular has been studied in connection with conditioning procedures. Wenger and Ellington (1943) described a method of measuring salivary output as an index of autonomic activity. Finesinger, Sutherland, and McGuire (1942) studied the output of the parotid gland in psychoneurotic patients in response to an auditory stimulus. Winsor and Korchin (1938, 1940) studied parotid outflow during different kinds of stimulation and mental activity.

The salivary glands are supplied by both sympathetic and parasympathetic nerves, if not directly, at least to the blood vessels. The secretion resulting from parasympathetic stimulation is usually thin and watery, whereas that after sympathetic stimulation tends to be thick and mucouslike. This corresponds to the general observation that emotional excitement, anticipation, fear, and anger often seem to produce a dryness of the mouth due to predominance of sympathetic activity. It would appear that greater use might be made of parotid secretion in studies of emotion.

Pilomotor Response

The small smooth muscles that lie at the base of hairs and cause them to stand up when one is afraid or chilly are innervated solely by sympathetic fibers. Therefore this response should constitute a good measure of sympathetic activity. It is evoked by a wider variety of stimuli than is generally recognized and seems particularly subject to conditioning. In some persons it accompanies a sneeze, probably as a conditioned element to the reflex elevation of hairs and the production of "goose flesh" when chilly. The scraping of a piece of chalk on a blackboard will also often produce a shivering response and pilomotor activity. Lindsley and Sassaman (1938) studied a subject who had gained voluntary control over the ability to erect the hairs on the surface of the body and who could put them up or down at will. They studied the pilomotor response by two methods. Motion pictures of the hairs were studied in order to determine latency and magnitude of the response. A hypodermic needle electrode system inserted at the base of the hair permitted the electrical recording of smooth muscle potentials from the arrectores pilorum muscles responsible for the elevation of the hairs. A number of associated sympathetic effects were also studied. This voluntary phenomenon is believed to be a type of conditioned response. A movie made of this case is listed with the Psychological Cinema Register.

Dermographia

A reaction that has been utilized by Wenger and Ellington (1943) is that of red dermographia. It is produced by a firm, constant pressure stroke, with a rounded instrument, on the arm of a subject. The immediate appearance of the stroked area is one of blanching or whiteness, followed in a few seconds by redness. Latency is measured to the beginning of redness, and total duration of the response until the redness disappears, which may require from 3 to 30 minutes or more. Such a reaction is probably a better measure of autonomic balance or stability than of emotional response or susceptibility per se.

Skin Sweating

In addition to the galvanic skin response as an index of palmar sweating and sympathetic activity, there have been several types of chemical applications that reveal the distribution of sweating on the surface of the body. A colorimetric method was described by Silverman and Powell (1944). Wenger and Gilchrist (1948) tested this method against the galvanic skin response in the case of palmar sweating and found it to be less reliable than the GSR. Since it reveals areas of differential sweating, the method is probably mainly useful for diagnosing clinical cases where lesions affecting the sympathetic system are suspected. It seems possible that it might also be applied to problems involving differential autonomic activity in certain emotional states.

Analysis of Blood, Saliva, and Urine

A number of chemical constituents of the blood have been shown to be affected by emotional stimulation (Gellhorn, 1943). Among them are blood sugar level (Gildea, Mailhouse, and Morris, 1935), adrenin content (Diethelm, Doty, and Milhorat, 1945), pH or acid-base balance, red blood cells, blood platelets, and numerous other factors. The taking of blood samples can be accomplished at intervals, but it is a somewhat complicated procedure if many samples are to be taken during the course of an experiment. Tests of reaction to the injection of glucose and insulin are made by taking blood samples at specified intervals, and these tests frequently reveal activity of both the sympathico-adrenal and vago-insulin systems (Diethelm, 1936). Urine may be analyzed for excess sugar excretion from samples taken at intervals before, during, and after emotional stimulation. A significant factor revealed by urine analysis appears to be the output of ketosteroids, a metabolic product resulting from steroids secreted by the adrenal cortex during stressful activities, especially those involving emotion (Pincus and Hoagland, 1943; Hoagland, 1947). Salivary samples can be taken continuously. A factor of interest in connection with salivary secretion is the pH or acid-base balance (Gaskill, 1933; Winsor and Korchin, 1938), which has been shown to vary with stimulation, mental activity, fatigue, etc.

Gastrointestinal Motility

A good deal of work has been done on the motility of the stomach and intestine in animals under emotional, electrical, and chemical stimulation. Cannon (1915, 1929) demonstrated that emotions of fear or anger inhibit activities in the gastrointestinal tract. Todd and Rowlands (1930) demonstrated similar reactions in man by X-ray and fluoroscopic examination after barium milk and buttermilk meals. The action of the stomach has also been studied by means of an inflated stomach-balloon, connected to a recording device.

Metabolic Rate

The rate of oxygen consumption or basal metabolic rate (BMR) is generally increased in emotions involving excitement and general bodily mobilization. It is likewise increased following a meal, even though action of the parasympathetic system may at such a time predominate, and excitement and activity may be minimal. Metabolism is usually recorded on a fasting stomach after a period of relaxation and rest. A standard BMR machine is used for this purpose. Metabolism is markedly affected by the activity of the thyroid gland, which in turn is under the influence of the pituitary gland.

Muscle Tension

A common symptom of anxiety is somatic tension. Many emotional reactions of more sporadic nature involve varying degrees of generalized muscular tension. It seems particularly important in the study of bodily changes in emotion to secure measures of visceral change and also of somatic activity. Muscle tension can be recorded by means of mechanical tension recorders, but a more convenient and perhaps more adequate sampling of muscular activity can be obtained from the recording of muscle action potentials.

With electrodes placed over the active muscle group, Travis and Lindsley (1931) showed that with increasing intensity of contraction the frequency and voltage of the recorded waves increase. This can also be demonstrated by means of needle electrodes inserted in the muscle mass (Lindsley, 1935), where the response of a group of muscle fibers innervated by a single nerve fiber, known as a motor unit, will show increased frequency with increasing tension, but the magnitude of the unit response remains constant.

For purposes of recording the muscle tension associated with emotional reactions, surface leads are preferable since more of the muscle activity can be surveyed.

The relation of muscular tension to frustration and performance has been studied by Davis (1938). Courts (1942) has reviewed the literature in this field. Jacobsen (1938) has summarized his results of studies of muscle tension in relation to therapeutic measures for inducing relaxation. In general, insufficient use has been made of electromyography or muscle action potentials as indicators of muscle tension in emotional states. More than one muscle group should be sampled in recording muscular tension since postural factors and shifting body movements can produce differential degrees of contraction in the various muscle groups.

A method of recording muscular tension in psychiatric patients mechanically has been described by Ruesch and Finesinger (1943) who used handwriting pressures as an index.

Tremor

The tremor of emotional excitement, anger, fear and even grief is well known. Tremor is found in conditions of tension where antagonistic muscle groups are pitted against one another, but it is also found under some conditions in relative relaxation and rest. The extended fingers of any normal individual will manifest a fine, rhythmic tremor of about 10 to 12 oscillations per second (Travis and Hunter, 1931). Jasper and Andrews (1938a) attempted to determine the relation between tremor rhythms of the fingers and the cortical alpha rhythm, which typically has a frequency about like the tremor frequency. Although they concluded that there was some relation between cortical rhythms and peripheral tremors, the evidence does not seem to be unequivocal, and it appears that the correspondence in the frequency may be partly fortuitous.

Luria (1932) recorded tremor mechanically by means of a pneumatic system. He found that emotional conflict externalized in motor performance led to tremor and disorganization of motor response. An improved form of the Luria tremorgraph has been described by Langer (1936). Others who have used or discussed this technique are Runkel (1936) and Reymert and Speer (1939). Berrien (1939) has used finger tremors as indices of emotion.

Eye Blink and Eye Movement

The significance of the eye blink as a measure of emotion or emotional tension is not known. Excessive eye blinking, like other facial tics, seems to suggest a kind of "nervousness." There are evidences that it may be increased with emotional arousal and excitement. The electrical potentials associated with eye blink may be recorded by attaching small electrodes to the skin at the corner of the eye and above the eyebrow, or for that matter anywhere in the neighborhood of the eye. Records of eye blink show that there are different patterns of blinking in different people; in some there may be continuous blinking; in others, sporadic groups of rapid blinks; and in still others blinks may occur singly or doubly at irregular intervals. The eye blink needs further study in relation to emotional tension and anxiety.

Eye movement can be recorded by appropriately placed electrodes in the region of the eye. With one electrode on the edge of the nose and another above the eyebrow, movements of the eyeball either laterally or horizontally will be recorded (Lindsley and Hunter, 1939). The effect is due to the static polarity potential of the eyeball, which when rotated produces an electrical change relative to the two electrodes. The significance of eye movements for emotion is little understood. Nevertheless, it is a motor outlet that seems to participate in excitement, embarrassment, and other emotional reactions.

The foregoing bodily changes are all possible indicators of emotional response. However, it should be strongly emphasized that in order to use them intelligently, we need a thorough knowledge of the underlying processes they signal or indicate. Furthermore it should be recognized that each of these possible measures represents a dynamic process integrated in various ways with other processes. This is especially true of the autonomic and endocrine systems, and of the central nervous system as well. The following section attempts to provide an overview of some of the basic factors underlying emotional mechanisms.

NEURAL AND HORMONAL MECHANISMS

The importance of emotion and the nature of its widespread influence have been emphasized by Sherrington (1948) in the foreword of a new edition of a book first published in 1906. He says, "The process by which a reaction of merely 'quantum' order is biologically raised to molar dimensions is called by some biologists 'amplification.' A means to 'amplification' is emotion. As physical stimulus a ghost may be of barely threshold power; but given emotion, and it can convulse the whole individual."

Elsewhere in the same book he states:

Of points where physiology and psychology touch, the place of one lies at 'emotion.' . . . It has a special physiological interest in that certain visceral reactions are peculiarly colligate with it. Heart, blood-vessels, respiratory muscles, and secretory glands take special and characteristic part in the various emotions. These viscera, though otherwise remote from the general play of psychical process, are affected vividly by the emotional. . . . To the ordinary day's consciousness in the healthy individual the life of the viscera contributes little at all, except under emotion. The perceptions of the normal consciousness are rather those of outlook upon the circumambient universe than inlook into the microcosm of the 'material me.' Yet heightened beating of the heart, blanching or flushing of the blood-vessels, the pallor of fear, the blush of shame, the Rabelaisian effect of fright upon the bowel, the secretion by the lachrymal gland in grief, all these are prominent characters in the pantomime of natural emotion. Visceral disturbance is evidently a part of the corporeal expression of emotion. [P. 257.]

Since emotional response may involve somatic and visceral activities, both the autonomic nervous system and the central and peripheral parts of the cerebrospinal nervous system enter the act. We need, therefore, to understand both the autonomic system and the phylogenetically newer cerebrospinal system. We need to understand the neuro-humoral factors concerned with the transmission of impulses at synapses as well as with the final disposition of impulses at neuro-effector junctions. And we need also to appreciate the role played by the hormonal factors secreted by the endocrine glands. A general description of these systems and functions is given in Chapter 6. Here we shall review those aspects of them that are of particular significance in emotion.

The Autonomic Nervous System

For much of our basic knowledge of the peripheral autonomic system we are indebted to Gaskell (1916) and Langley (1921). It was Langley who distinguished its two principal parts, the *sympathetic* and *parasympathetic* divisions.

Figure 1 shows the widespread ramifications of the autonomic nervous system. For the sake of simplicity, only the *efferent* outflow of the autonomic is shown on the left, and only the *afferent* pathways are shown on the right. Actually it is debatable whether there are any true autonomic afferent pathways at all, since most of the incoming sensory pathways from the viscera have their cell bodies in spinal or cranial dorsal root ganglia rather than in the ganglia of the sympathetic or parasympathetic systems. However, there is a sensory influx from the various receptors and nerve endings of the viscera, blood vessels, etc., but these incoming pathways may be more properly called *visceral afferents*. Furthermore these pathways pass through the sympathetic ganglia, although they do not have their cell bodies in the ganglia, nor do they synapse there; instead they enter the cord with the dorsal roots of the somatic sensory nerves (see Fig. 2).

These visceral afferent pathways may synapse in the lateral horn of the gray matter of the spinal cord upon visceral efferents, thereby forming *viscerovisceral reflexes;* they may synapse upon internuncial neurons in

the gray matter which connect with somatic efferents, thereby forming *viscerosomatic reflexes;* or they may synapse in other spinal segments or proceed to the region of the nucleus solitarius in the medulla, where they may participate in brain stem reflexes or be relayed to the thalamus. Buchanan (1948) states that visceral sensations, like somatic pain sensations, reach the conscious level in the thalamus. However, there does not yet appear to be any clear evidence of this. Although localization and intensity differentiation for somatic pain are thought to be functions of the cerebral cortex, it is doubtful that such differentiations are made for visceral sensations. This is an important point, and whether visceral afferent impulses reach the thalamus (for which there is at present no conclusive evidence) and the cortex (for which there is also apparently none) are crucial factors for the James-Lange theory and perhaps also for other theories.

Let us now return to the efferent autonomic pathways. There are three principal groups of efferent outlets for autonomic impulses, but two of them may be combined because of structural and functional similarities. These are the *cranial* and *sacral* divisions of the *parasympathetic system*. In Fig. 1 it will be noted that the efferent neurons of the cranial division of the parasympathetic system issue from the III, VII, IX, and X cranial nerves, whereas those of the sacral division originate in the I, II, III, and possibly IV sacral segments of the lower cord. In this figure all parasympathetic efferent cells of origin (preganglionic neurons) in the brain stem or cord are symbolized by an open circle. Likewise the postganglionic neurons of the parasympathetic, which are always in or near the structures they innervate, have their cell bodies represented by open circles. Note that the parasympathetic components of the III, VII, and IX cranial nerves send their preganglionic processes to special ganglia where, after synapse, a postganglionic neuron then conducts the impulses to a nearby effector.

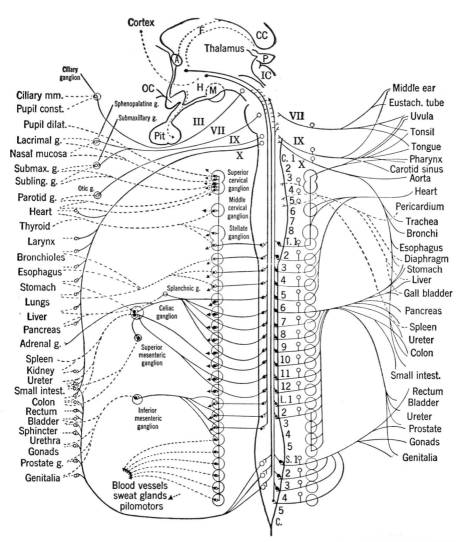

FIG. 1. Schematic representation of the autonomic nervous system, showing the central origin and the peripheral termination of *sympathetic* and *parasympathetic efferent pathways* on the *left* and the origin of *visceral afferent pathways* on the *right*. Cell bodies of pre- and postganglionic neurons of the parasympathetic system are symbolized by open circles; those of the sympathetic system, by solid circles. Arrows projecting from sympathetic chain ganglia symbolize postganglionic fibers to blood vessels, sweat glands, and pilomotors. Dotted lines on left of figure represent efferent postganglionic fibers; those on right are nonautonomic fibers of the phrenic nerve. Key: A—anterior commissure; CC—corpus callosum; F—fornix; H—hypothalamus; IC—inferior colliculus; M—mammillary bodies; OC—optic chiasma; P—pineal body; Pit—pituitary or hypophysis. (After Mettler, 1948; Buchanan, 1948; Strong and Elwyn, 1943; with modifications.)

Note also that each of these effectors has counterbalancing innervation by the sympathetic system, shown by the dotted lines emanating from the superior cervical ganglion of the sympathetic chain.

We may now turn to the sympathetic division, whose preganglionic efferents (cell bodies shown by solid black circles) have their cells of origin in the lateral horn of the gray matter of the spinal cord. These preganglionic neurons either terminate in a chain of ganglia lying alongside the cord, where they make synapse with postganglionic fibers, or they proceed through these ganglia without synapse to special ganglia, where postganglionic neurons transmit the impulses to the effectors. There is one exception to this arrangement for sympathetic pathways, namely, the adrenal glands. The schema shows the preganglionic neuron issuing from the fifth thoracic segment and giving off a branch, which without synapse extends to the adrenal medulla, where it may synapse with a local postganglionic neuron, although there is a possibility that it has direct access to the adrenal medulla by means of a chemical mediator (acetylcholine). In either case, in contrast to most other sympathetic innervation of autonomic effectors, which are said to be *adrenergic* and liberate sympathin, an adreninlike substance, the chemical mediator at the adrenal gland is acetylcholine, and therefore the innervation is classed as *cholinergic*. Other exceptions to the general rule that parasympathetic nerve endings liberate acetylocholine as a chemical mediator, whereas sympathetic endings liberate an adreninlike substance, will be mentioned later.

The manner in which the trunks and ganglia connect with the spinal cord is shown in Fig. 2. The autonomic or visceral efferent preganglionic neurons have their origin in the lateral horn of the gray matter of the cord and exit through the ventral root of the spinal nerve, from which they proceed via the white rami to the particular ganglion of the chain in which they are to synapse. When synapse occurs between pre- and postganglionic neurons, the latter rejoin the spinal nerve via the gray ramus. In some cases the preganglionic neuron passes through the trunk ganglion and synapses at a special ganglion nearer the organ innervated. This is also illustrated in the diagram.

These arrangements, it will be recognized, permit a diffuse and widespread interconnection of the effects of sympathetic discharge. Another condition favoring diffuse discharge, especially in the sympathetic system, is the fact that for each preganglionic neuron entering a sympathetic ganglion there are as many as thirty-two postganglionic neurons represented. Since it is conceivable that a whole pool of postganglionic neurons is activated by the discharge of a single preganglionic neuron, the possibilities for summation and diffusion of peripheral response are great. In essence, this diffusion and reinforcement of sympathetic discharge is what Cannon and others have demonstrated: the sympathetic system is primarily one for meeting emergency situations by rapid mobilization of the bodily resources. Furthermore the adrenal medulla is at least partly innervated by preganglionic fibers, and medulliadrenal secretion or adrenin in the blood stream reinforces the effects of sympathetic nerve impulses.

As Cannon and Rosenblueth (1937) point out, however, there are exceptions to the diffuse discharge of the sympathetic system. For example, impulses from sympathetic nerves are continuously discharging into certain smooth muscles of the blood vessels and the nictitating membrane (a covering of the eye of the cat).

Despite its usefulness in emergencies the sympathetic system is not absolutely essential for existence. The complete ganglionic chains and special sympathetic ganglia may be removed from animals such as cats without serious detriment to their existence in the well-regulated environment of the laboratory. Cannon et al. (1927, 1929) did this as a test of the James-Lange theory and found it made no difference in the animal's emotional response. However, when such an animal is exposed to marked changes in temperature, loss of blood, or lowering of blood

eral sympathetic control, Cannon and Rosenblueth (1937) describe a substance thought to be liberated at sympathetically controlled effectors. This substance, called *sympathin,*

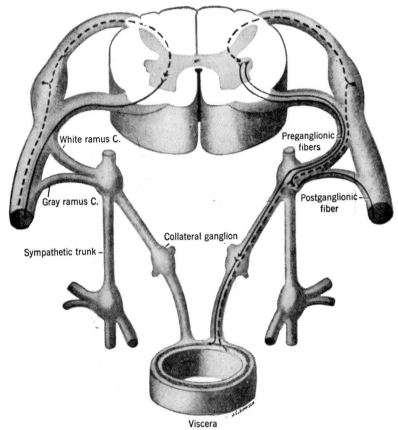

Viscera

FIG. 2. Schematic diagram illustrating relation of sympathetic ganglia and pathways to spinal nerves and the spinal cord. Somatic afferent and efferent paths are shown on the left; visceral afferent and efferent paths are shown on the right. Afferent neurons are shown by broken lines; efferent neurons by continuous lines. [After Cunningham's *Textbook of Anatomy* (J. C. Brash and E. B. Jamieson, Eds., 7th Ed., 1937), London: Oxford University Press; with two modifications.]

sugar level, the deficiencies in the homeostatic or regulating mechanism become apparent. Cannon (1935) provided numerous examples of the way in which the autonomic system tends to preserve steady states in the internal milieu of the organism.

In addition to the potentiation effects of adrenin liberated into the blood stream and circulated to responsive structures under gen-

has been shown to have many features in common with adrenin, although the two are probably not identical. Sympathin has a less strong and less widespread effect than adrenin. The excitatory substance, *sympathin E,* has effects similar to those of adrenin; another type known as *sympathin I* has an inhibitory action. Both substances are thought to be liberated by some combination of chemical processes at sympathetic nerve effectors. Because of this adreninlike substance liberated by sympathetic nerve impulses, sympathetic innervation is frequently referred to as *adrenergic*, meaning adreninlike in its action. However, as Dale (1934, 1935) has pointed out, there are some obvious exceptions to the adrenergic nature of sympathetic action. First and foremost is the fact that at the synaptic junction of pre- and postganglionic neurons in the sympathetic system a *parasympathomimetic substance, acetylcholine*, is liberated, rather than a *sympathomimetic substance* such as *adrenin* or *sympathin*. The cholinergic nature of sympathetic innervation of the adrenal medulla has already been mentioned. Another example is the sweat gland which is not aroused to secretion by adrenin (or by injections of adrenaline, a synthetic commercial product) and yet is stimulated to profuse activity by pilocarpine and acetylcholine and is paralyzed by atropine, an anticholinergic drug. Obviously this is another case of a sympathetic nerve having cholinergic action. Still another example is vasodilatation of the mucosa of the dog's mouth by sympathetic discharge, but absence of this response to injection of adrenaline. Finally, it should be pointed out that the somatic innervation to skeletal muscles is also accompanied by cholinergic action. This fact, were it not for the rapid manner in which acetylcholine is destroyed by blood esterase, might lead to severe contractures, if the effects of parasympathetic activity were potentiated by circulation of acetylcholine.

Dual innervation. Figure 1 shows that most of the structures under the control of the autonomic system have a double innervation shared by sympathetic and parasympathetic divisions. In general these two systems have opposing effects that facilitate regulation of visceral activities and assist in the maintenance of homeostasis. According to Cannon (1930) the diffuse arrangement of the sympathetic tends to make it work as a unit, whereas the action of the parasympa-

thetic may be specific for individual structures. Hence, by *diffuse* action of the sympathetic division and the opposite *particular* action of the nerves composing the sacral and cranial portions of the parasympathetic division, various gradations in the activity of any structure may be provided for both locally and temporally.

It is at this point that we can see the complexity that must characterize emotional reactions and their manifestations in the various structures influenced by the autonomic nervous system. What any given indicator or measure of activity in a particular structure reveals in the way of increased or decreased activity must be evaluated in terms of what other autonomic indicators are doing, not only by way of specific adjustment to the particular stimulating situation but in relation to the total function of the autonomic system.

Cannon (1930) summarized the actions of the various divisions of the autonomic. The *sacral division* functions mainly as a group of reflexes for emptying hollow organs that are periodically filled. The pressure created by the contents in such a viscus as the rectum, the colon, or the bladder sets up visceral impulses that reflexly initiate emptying action through sacral efferent nerves. Similar reactions may occur in connection with the seminal vesicles and the uterus, although here the picture is more complex. In addition to reflex response produced by local distention, emotions may produce discharges over the sacral nerves, as evidenced by involuntary voiding of bowel and bladder at times of great fear and stress. Hall (1934) and others have made use of this fact to measure emotional behavior in the rat. Similarly the various stimulations by sight, touch, smell, etc., give rise to sexual excitement involving not only sacral discharge and activation of the sexual apparatus but endocrine and somatic activity as well (Beach, 1942a, b).

The functions of the *cranial division* are characterized by Cannon as a group of reflexes that serve protective and conservative functions. Examples are the protective function of pupillary constriction, the secretion of salivary and digestive juices and the maintenance of tone in the alimentary tract, and vagal control of insulin secretion for regulating glycogen storage in the liver. Like the sacral division it may be involved in emotional reactions and affective states. For example, pleasurable tastes and smells facilitate gastric functions, whereas nausea and vomiting may be induced by the sight and smell of unsavory objects.

A significant fact about the sacral and cranial divisions is that their activities are much more subject to interference by voluntary control than are the activities initiated by the sympathetic system. The striated muscle of the sphincters of the bowel and bladder under voluntary or cerebral control can oppose the actions of the sacral division. In speech and respiratory functions the voluntary control of striated muscle often interferes with, although it does not always override, activities of the cranial division.

The *sympathetic division* is concerned with the maintenance of stability in the internal fluid matrix of the organism despite disturbing external influences. In case of hemorrhage the sympathetic acts to constrict vessels and prevent further loss of blood and facilitates coagulation or clotting. In sudden extremes of temperature the sympathico-adrenal system comes into operation to regulate heat loss. Oxygen lack produces compensating heart and circulatory reactions. Under the influence of strong and prolonged muscular exercise, accumulation of metabolites and development of acidity in the blood is accompanied by compensating increases in respiratory and circulatory functions initiated by the sympathetic division.

Central connections. It appears that, upon entering the cord through the dorsal spinal roots, some of the visceral afferent axons terminate upon cell bodies in the dorsal gray columns, giving off axons that pass upward a few segments. By successive relays these may eventually reach the medulla and possibly the thalamus. Neurosurgical evidence suggests that some of the visceral pathways, especially those conducting visceral pain, pass upward to the thalamus in the lateral spinothalamic tract, since bilateral cordotomy by Hyndman and Wolkin (1943) was found to relieve renal pelvic pain. However, anatomical evidence seems not to have traced the pathways for visceral afferents beyond the medulla. If visceral afferents reach the thalamus it is uncertain to what particular nucleus they go, and there is as yet no evidence that they reach cortical levels unless one insists that to be conscious of such pains implies cortical reception. Conscious awareness of visceral pain, but without localization and discrimination, is attributed by some to a thalamic level.

However that may be, we are concerned for the moment with higher-order reflex connections of visceral afferent pathways at the level of the medulla. Since centers for the regulation of respiration, blood pressure, and other vital functions have been demonstrated in the medulla, it is evident that the incoming visceral afferents have a good deal to do with these regulatory functions. The evidence for such reflex connections and their effects is dealt with in detail by Kuntz (1945).

There is accumulating evidence (Moruzzi and Magoun, 1949; Lindsley, Bowden, and Magoun, 1949) that exteroceptive and proprioceptive pathways in passing through the lower brain stem give off collaterals into the reticular formation which extends from the lower brain stem through the tegmentum of the midbrain and into the hypothalamus and thalamus (see Figs. 3 and 9). This system is believed to be part of a diffuse projection pathway to the cortex. That the visceral afferents also contribute collaterals to the reticular formation is a possibility, but it has not been demonstrated. Thus it may be seen that exteroceptive and proprioceptive impulses have two means of influencing cortical activities: a direct projection via relay in the thalamus (Fig. 9; paths 1 and 1′), and a diffuse projection via the reticular formation and the intralaminar and reticular nuclei of the thalamus (Fig. 9; paths 3 and 4). The evidence for the latter is not complete, although some evidence for it will be

these statements is based upon localized lesions in the hypothalamus and more specifically upon electrical stimulation, which in general has produced sympathetic responses over a major portion of the hypothalamus. It is still uncertain whether a distinct center

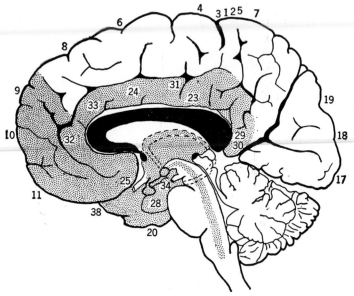

FIG. 3. Sagittal section of the brain. Stippled areas represent the principal structures involved in the central integration and control of emotional behavior. These include the frontal pole and orbital surfaces of the frontal lobes, gyrus cinguli, inner surface of temporal lobes, piriform area, hippocampal formation, uncus, and amygdala. Among subcortical structures are: thalamus, subthalamus, hypothalamus, fornix, pituitary, and the reticular formation extending to the lower brain stem. Although other cortical and subcortical areas are undoubtedly involved, these probably constitute the principal centers. (See Fig. 4 for an expanded view of the diencephalic region.) The numbers indicate Brodmann's differentiation of cortical areas.

described below. If interoceptive or visceral afferent pathways may be assumed to follow a similar course, at least as far as the thalamus, it will be significant for the central integration of autonomic effects in emotional behavior as well as in homeostatic adjustments of the organism.

Turning now to the efferent autonomic pathways we find that the principal center of origin for parasympathetic discharge seems to reside in the anterior portion of the hypothalamus and in the preoptic region rostral to it, whereas the principal focus for sympathetic discharge lies in the middle and posterior regions (see Fig. 1). The evidence for

for parasympathetic discharge is present in the hypothalamus. The wider distribution of sympathetic effects by electrical stimulation in the hypothalamus is in keeping with the unitary and diffuse nature of sympathetic discharge.

The Hypothalamus

The hypothalamus, although a comparatively small structure, is an extremely important one. It is concerned with the regulation of homeostasis, reproduction, and emotional behavior (cf. Chapter 6). In addition it plays a significant part in the control of the pituitary gland. It is part of the diencephalon lying below the thalamus and sub-thalamus at the base of the brain in a rela-tively inaccessible position. Portions of it form the wall and floor of the third ventricle. As may be seen in Fig. 4, it lies immediately behind the optic chiasma. For purposes of

and Ranson and Magoun (1939), and an entire volume edited by Fulton, Ranson, and Frantz (1940) is devoted to clinical and ex-perimental aspects. It will suffice here to mention only briefly the principal functions, the connections of the hypothalamus with

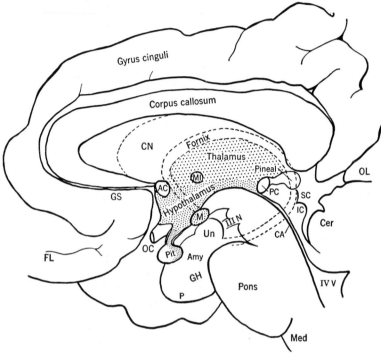

Fig. 4. Expanded view of structures important in autonomic regulation and in the control of emotional behavior. Diencephalic structures are stippled. Key: AC—anterior commissure; Amy—amygdala; CA—cerebral aqueduct; Cer—cerebellum; CN—caudate nucleus; FL—frontal lobe; GH—gyrus hippocampus; GS—subcallosal gyrus; IC—inferior colliculus; M—mammillary body; Med—medulla oblongata; MI—massa intermedia; OC—optic chiasma; OL—occipital lobe; P—piriform area; PC—posterior commissure; Pit—pituitary; SC—superior colliculus; Un—uncus. III N—third nerve; IV V—4th ventricle.

gross reference it may be divided into supra-optic, tuberal, and mammillary portions. On its base the tuberal region (tuber cinereum) gives rise to the infundibular stalk to which is attached the hypophysis or pituitary gland. The latter nestles in a small bony cavity in the floor of the skull known as the sella turcica.

The principal experimental findings related to the functions of the hypothalamus have been surveyed in detail by Ranson (1937)

other parts of the brain, and its relation to the pituitary, since these all have a bearing either directly or indirectly upon the prob-lem of emotion.

Afferent fibers to hypothalamus from cor-tex, thalamus, and elsewhere. The hypo-thalamus receives fibers from the olfactory region, from the hippocampus, and from the frontal pole of the cerebral hemispheres, pos-sibly via the septum and medial forebrain bundle. Furthermore fibers from the frontal cortex relay via the dorsomedial nucleus of the thalamus to the posterior region of the hypothalamus. Numerous connections have also been found between the thalamus and hypothalamus. Papez (1937a, b, 1939) and Vonderahe (1935, 1943) discussed these and other connections of the hypothalamus in considerable detail and especially in relation to emotion.

Visceral afferent pathways have been mentioned previously. The anatomical evidence that they reach the thalamus or hypothalamus is not clear, yet some visceral sensation, especially visceral pain, occurs. Furthermore the sham rage response described by Bard (1928, 1934) was induced in decorticate dogs, with most of the thalamus removed, by pinching or otherwise stimulating peripheral receptors. This suggests that somatic sensory pathways reach the hypothalamus, either directly or through thalamic relays. Whether the same is true for visceral sensory pathways is not known, except that Bronk, Pitts, and Larrabee (1940) have shown that vagal impulses reach the hypothalamus.

The cortical connections with the hypothalamus have predominantly an inhibitory function, and it is the release of this inhibitory control by decortication that presumably produced sham rage in Bard's cats and dogs.

Efferent pathways. There are in all probability efferent pathways from the hypothalamus to the subthalamus and corpus striatum. The motor activity of Bard's decorticate cats both in and out of sham rage would suggest this. Other efferent pathways about which there is greater assurance are those that go to the thalamus, from whence they apparently relay to the cortex. Papez (1937a, b) traced a path from the gyrus cinguli through the hippocampus and fornix to the mammillary body and thence via the mammillothalamic tract to the anterior nuclei of the thalamus and back to the starting point in the gyrus cinguli. He believed this

a very significant series of interconnections in the neural mechanism of the emotions.

Descending pathways, arising from the region adjacent to the third ventricle, pass through the tegmental region of midbrain and pons and end eventually in the spinal cord where they synapse with sympathetic preganglionic neurons. All these descending pathways apparently give off collaterals to the reticular formation in the brain stem, but many of the fibers from the lateral nuclei seem to end there, perhaps synapsing with visceral efferents in the lower brain stem to participate in the vital regulatory functions of this area. Pathways representing parasympathetic functions and influencing the bladder, respiration, and blood pressure are said to originate in the preoptic region and the anterior hypothalamus, although not all evidence is in agreement that there is such a parasympathetic center.

The Endocrine and Neurohumoral Systems

Since a survey of the endocrine glands and their function has been given in Chapter 6, only a brief listing will be given here.

The pituitary is often known as the master gland because of its controlling influence upon so many of the other endocrines by means of *tropic* hormones of the anterior pituitary. Attention has already been drawn to the regulation of water metabolism by the hypothalamo-pituitary complex. In addition, the anterior lobe liberates growth and sex development hormones. Some of the regulatory functions of other endocrines are: *thyroid* — metabolism and temperature regulation; *parathyroid* — blood calcium level, which along with potassium has a marked effect upon excitability of receptors and effectors; *pancreas* — digestive juices and insulin secretion, the latter influencing sugar utilization and therefore blood sugar level, which in turn affects nervous function; *adrenal medulla* — potentiation of sympathetic effects, and also influence upon blood sugar level and blood oxygen through its effects on the liver and spleen, respectively; *adrenal cortex* — a variety of functions through its various steroids, but especially mineral, water, and sugar metabolism.

The posterior pituitary is believed to antagonize the action of insulin and to heighten sympathetic irritability, whereas insulin is believed to increase parasympathetic irritability. As previously mentioned, the neurohumors, acetylcholine and adrenin, plus the adreninlike sympathin E and sympathin I, sensitize their respective autonomic effectors. Whereas somatic effectors deteriorate with nerve section, autonomic effectors do not, and they continue to remain sensitive to their appropriate neurohumors (see Cannon and Rosenblueth, 1949; Gellhorn, 1943).

Thus we see that not only are the sympathetic and parasympathetic divisions of the autonomic generally antagonistic to one another, but the antagonism extends to their neurohumors and to some of the secretions of the endocrine glands they innervate. An example of the latter is seen in the sympathetic innervation of the adrenal medulla and its hormone adrenin, and in the parasympathetic (vagal) innervation of the islands of Langerhans and the hormone insulin. Furthermore the autonomic nervous system and the endocrine glands are seen to have mutual interactions of both inhibitory and facilitatory character. As Gellhorn (1943) put it:

> Not only do autonomic centers regulate the rate of hormonal secretions, but alterations in the secretion of various hormones alter the endocrine balance in the organism and lead to disturbances in the composition of the blood with regard to organic substances and ions, thereby profoundly changing the function of the autonomic centers and the central nervous system as a whole.

We shall turn now to some of the studies that shed light on the nature of central organization and control of emotional behavior.

Central Neural Organization in Emotion

Experimental lesions. Goltz (1892) observed growling, barking, and other forms of anger and rage responses in a decerebrate dog. These responses arose from mere handling of the dog, which prior to the lesion showed no such reactions. After the operation the dog gave no evidence of joy or satisfaction and showed no sex behavior. Woodworth and Sherrington (1904), investigating the spinal pathways for pain in the decerebrate cat, observed similar behavior which they called "pseudaffective." The responses to nociceptive stimulation of the skin were said to simulate mimetic expressions of anger and defense, such as opening of the mouth, retraction of lips and tongue, snapping of jaws, snarling, lowering of head as if to attack, and increase in blood pressure. They observed that all responses were brief and did not outlast stimulation, in which respect they were unlike anger and rage in a normal cat.

Other observations on decerebrate preparations have been made by Bazett and Penfield (1922), Rothmann (1923), Schaltenbrand and Cobb (1930), and Keller (1932). In general these have shown, in addition to a poorly organized rage response of brief duration, a number of associated sympathetic reactions. In not all cases was there a complete absence of pleasurable reaction, for the cats studied by Bazett and Penfield and by Schaltenbrand and Cobb were said to purr on occasion.

Acute decortications in cats were performed by Dusser de Barenne (1920) and Cannon and Britton (1925) with the observation that a form of organized rage response could be elicited by the stimulation of ordinary handling and care. Cannon called this sham rage. It was characterized by a better organized and more intense display than in the decerebrate preparations and in general was set off more easily. Bard (1928) followed up this work with a special effort to localize the region critical for sham rage. He utilized acute and chronic preparations (1934a, b) and was able to localize the sham rage mechanism in the caudal half of the hypothalamus. Later Bard and Rioch (1937) described four cats with neocortex and varying portions of forebrain destroyed. These were chronic animals and survived for several months of observation and study. The authors looked for what, in a normal cat, would constitute emotional excitement and found evidence in these chronically decorticate animals of fear, rage, and sexual excitement. Fear was induced by loud high-pitched noises. In an animal lacking the medial geniculate bodies these auditory stimuli produced only erection of hair and twitching of the skin on the back. The behavior of decorticate animals has been further discussed by Rioch (1938) and by Bard (1939).

Their description of sham rage of chronic decorticate animals, usually with only the caudal portion of the hypothalamus intact but with varying amounts of brain stem structures remaining, is as follows: lowering head and body in crouch, raising back, drawing back ears, loud angry growling, hissing, biting, striking with claws unsheathed, erection of hair, pupillodilatation, retraction of nictitating membrane, and widening of palpebral fissures. The response was prompt and strong, but poorly directed; it involved both somatic and visceral components. They concluded that the response was made possible by release of cortical inhibitory control of the hypothalamus.

Bromiley (1948), in the course of establishing discriminative conditioned responses to light and sound in a decorticate dog that survived for 33 months, made note of the fact that sham rage behavior could be elicited throughout this time. Barking, growling, snarling, and snapping characterized its rage behavior when its cage was manipulated, or in some cases when it was handled gently. Continued progressive movements against obstacles is said to occur in this and other decorticate animals, to the extent of producing sores on scalp and feet.

Bard and Mountcastle (1947) have pointed out that the responses of decorticate animals suggest *hyperexcitability* and that the low threshold for the rage response is a *release phenomenon*. Since Bard had pre-

viously located the mechanism for this response in the caudal hypothalamus, it seemed evident that some cortical region must normally suppress the sham rage response. Spiegel, Miller, and Oppenheimer (1940) have shown in acute experiments with cats that lesions involving the olfactory tubercles, the amygdala, or the hippocampal-fornix tracts are capable of producing rage reactions, although lesions of the frontal pole and elsewhere in the neocortex, or of the piriform region of the rhinencephalon, did not have this effect.

Klüver and Bucy (1938, 1939) found that bilateral temporal lobectomy in the monkey provided a marked contrast to the preceding results so far as emotional behavior is concerned. The monkeys were expressionless, and despite their curiosity about their surroundings, nothing seemed to produce anger, fear, resentment, or pleasure. Things that preoperatively would have produced marked emotional reactions did not do so after temporal lobectomy. For example, one monkey licked the fangs of a bull snake and was entirely casual about a severe bite on the hand from another monkey. The anatomic changes in these cases were later reported by Bucy and Klüver (1940) and involved among other things the hippocampus and fornix. According to Papez (1937) the hypothalamus, the anterior thalamic nuclei, the gyrus cinguli, and the hippocampus and interconnections, including the fornix, constitute a mechanism capable of emotional experience and expression.

In their later experiments Bard and Mountcastle (1947) removed the neocortex in cats, leaving the rhinencephalon and the gyrus cinguli (midline or transitional cortex) intact. Placidity was the result, with marked refractoriness to rage-producing stimuli. When the amygdala, the pyriform area, and the hippocampus were then removed in addition, the animal showed marked sensitivity to rage induction. The authors propose that inhibitory influences from the neocortex, the gyrus cinguli, and the other midline cortex, as well as from the amygdala, all funnel through the amygdala. They also believe that a separate facilitatory or excitatory pathway by-passing the amygdala exists. The fact that Klüver and Bucy (1939), having destroyed essentially the same structures in the monkey, found their animals almost emotionless seems contradictory. However, the difference may lie in the addition of the lateral portions of the temporal lobes, or it may be that the inhibitory and excitatory functions that in the cat lie in the rhinencephalic region have migrated farther rostrally in the monkey.

Lesions of the hypothalamus in cats and monkeys were studied by Ingram, Barris, and Ranson (1936) and Ranson (1939). This region, when intact and stimulated electrically, gave rise to emotional excitement and fear and rage responses with multiple sympathetic reactions, and the opposite tendency appeared when the region was destroyed electrolytically. The animals lost all sign of emotional responsiveness, faces were masklike, and they developed a marked stolidity. In addition somnolence or a form of sleep was characteristic after lesions in the caudal part of the thalamus. Furthermore the cats with hypothalamic lesions manifested a form of catalepsy in which they could be molded to some extent and would hold the position. Although such animals are sometimes able to stand and walk, they seldom do so; they sink rapidly into sleep but can be awakened from it fairly readily.

Alert, active monkeys, Ranson (1939) found, were good subjects for hypothalamic lesions since the contrast in their postoperative behavior was so marked. Their faces became masklike, and they failed to show the characteristic amount of activity and vocalization. They slept much of the time but could be awakened by handling. In some animals the sleep took the form of drowsiness, apparently depending upon the location of the lesion. Lesions producing somnolence and sleep were generally in the region of the posterior hypothalamus and mammil-

lary bodies, sometimes toward the rostral midbrain. This general region has for some time been recognized as a sleep or waking center, depending upon one's point of view. As we have seen, stimulation of this region produces excitement and activity; lesions in it tend to produce somnolence, sleep, stolidity, and general inactivity. That sleep and its opposite, waking and emotion, may ultimately prove to have a number of features in common appears likely and will be touched upon in later discussion.

Electrical stimulation. Summaries of the results of a number of studies on electrical stimulation of the hypothalamus have been presented by Hess (1936), Karplus (1937), and Ranson and Magoun (1939). In general the results confirm the fact that the hypothalamus is a center for the excitation and integration of sympathetic effects such as are found in fear and rage reactions. For cats lightly anesthetized with nembutal, Ranson and Magoun (1939) reported that hypothalamic stimulation produced a rise in blood pressure, increased rate and depth of respiration, pupillary dilatation, and contraction of the bladder. Pilomotor and sweating reactions did not occur under light anesthesia. If stimulation is continued it will often produce somatic motor activities such as running and struggling movements. Some experimenters locate the principal focus of sympathetic activity in the posterior half of the hypothalamus, but others have observed sympathetic responses from a major portion of it. Parasympathetic responses are less definite but may be elicited from the anterior hypothalamus and preoptic region. They consist mainly of lowered blood pressure, decreased respiration, and bladder contraction.

Electrical stimulation in a waking cat with electrodes implanted in the hypothalamus produces rage reactions very much like those seen in the decorticate animals. These reactions show a sympathetic predominance with dilatation of pupils, piloerection, retraction of nictitating membrane, increased respiration, and restless behavior, with spitting, biting, and struggling. Inhibition of gastrointestinal activities also occurs.

The results of electrical stimulation of the hypothalamus in animals have been partially confirmed by White (1940) in the electrical stimulation of the hypothalamus of conscious human patients under local anesthesia. He observed diffuse efferent discharge over the sympathetic system from stimulation of the wall of the third ventricle, in the region of the paraventricular nucleus. Stimulation in the anterior region of the hypothalamus near the preoptic nucleus produced some evidence of slowing of the heart and decreased blood pressure, suggesting parasympathetic activation. Of significance here are the observations that patients did not report any unusual sensation resulting from the electrical stimulation of the hypothalamus, and neither emotional changes nor alterations in the level of consciousness were noted. Mechanical manipulation in the region of the optic chiasma and anterior hypothalamus produced marked slowing of the heart, peristalsis, nausea, and vomiting, all parasympathetic reactions — which supports the belief that there is a parasympathetic center in the region of the anterior hypothalamus. Contrary to the results in animal experiments where electrical stimulation of lateral hypothalamic nuclei produced alertness and excitement together with sympathetic discharge, and where lesions produced drowsiness and somnolence, White found that electrical stimulation in human patients did not produce any alteration in the level of alertness. Manipulation near the anterior hypothalamus did tend to produce drowsiness, which he interprets as an effect of increased tone in the parasympathetic center depressing or inhibiting the "waking center" in the posterior hypothalamus.

On the basis of electrical stimulation of the hypothalamus and subthalamus in cats, Hinsey (1940) concluded that not only are sympathetic discharges produced but somatic movements as well. Apparently there are levels of integration in the hypothalamus for somatic as well as autonomic activity.

Masserman (1941) reported a series of experiments designed to answer the questions: What are an animal's affective reactions to external situations during hypothalamic stimulation? How persistent is the response induced by stimulation of the hypothalamus? Does the induced activity modify or displace behavior occasioned by spontaneous effects? Do extensive lesions of the hypothalamus permanently change the emotional reactivity? And, finally, can the animal be trained to adapt to direct hypothalamic stimulation (hypothalamic conditioning)? Here and elsewhere (1943) he concluded that the fear and rage and other aspects of the pseudoaffective reactions induced by electrical stimulation of the hypothalamus differ significantly from true emotional states. The reaction, in addition to being undirected and brief, is described as mechanical, diffuse, stereotyped, and stimulus-bound, without apparent emotional connotation for the animal. In these respects it differs from normal expression of emotion in cats. He found further support for this conclusion in cats stimulated through electrodes implanted in the hypothalamus while they were engaged in normal behavior such as eating, purring, and cleaning. These activities were not interfered with by hypothalamic stimulation until vigorous motor components of the total pseudoaffective pattern disrupted them. He reported that an animal will continue to lap milk or respond to petting while being stimulated hypothalamically and while various sympathetic responses are in evidence.

With regard to hypothalamic lesions Masserman felt that the effects of large bilateral lesions in producing, as Ranson (1939) has shown, stuporous, somnolent, cataleptic, and emotionally apathetic states must be considered in the light of changes in metabolic and homeostatic functions. On the basis of his own experiments (1938), he concluded that if the animal recovers sufficiently to restore bodily economy the emotional behavior of the animal will return nearly to normal.

In an effort to determine whether the emotional reactions of electrical stimulation of the hypothalamus are accompanied by "meaningful subjective experience" Masserman attempted to condition various sensory stimuli to the response produced by electrical stimulation of the hypothalamus. The assumption underlying this procedure was that if hypothalamically induced behavior is accompanied by subjective meaning the various sensory conditional stimuli may then come to represent this experience and make possible the conditioning. He was unable to establish a conditioned response to lights, sounds, tactual stimuli, etc. He concluded that the hypothalamus does not behave as "an afferent, experience-mediating organ but as a way-station on efferent sympathetic and motor pathways." Another possible explanation of the failure of Masserman and others to condition electrically induced behavior is that the effect of an electrical field created in the region where the neural connection must be made follows so soon after the spreading of impulses from the conditioned stimulus to the effector circuit of the unconditioned response that any functional relation between the afferent and efferent circuits may well be obliterated. The effect of electroshock in obliterating or reducing previously learned habits might be a possible analogy.

Clinical and neurosurgical observations. The effect of manipulation of the hypothalamus during surgical operations on adjacent structures has been reported by several neurosurgeons and summarized by Gagel (1936) and Dott (1938). Mechanical manipulation of the hypothalamus by the neurosurgeon has been reported to produce maniacal excitement. The effects of tumors and other pathological disturbances in the general region of the hypothalamus are difficult to appraise because of pressure effects, interruption of pathways to and from other structures, etc. However, the clinical reports give

evidence of many of the symptoms that characterize patients who have frontal lobe pathology or have undergone frontal lobotomy. There is release from inhibition resulting in euphoria, accentuated flow of speech and ideas, restlessness, and lack of social inhibitions.

Alpers (1940), in summarizing the effects upon the personality of pathological lesions in the hypothalamus, emphasized four principal kinds of clinical features: emotional changes, intellectual deficits, personality disorders, and psychotic manifestations. Among the emotional changes are excitement, manic-like reactions with push of speech and ideas, swings of mood alternating between depression and excitement, emotional lability with a low threshold for uncontrolled laughter, and sometimes apathy and negativism. Since these kinds of emotional response may appear with lesions in other regions of the brain, Alpers looked upon the hypothalamus as one of a series of stations concerned with emotional expression. Similarly symptoms often referred to the cortex, such as memory loss and inability to concentrate, have been reported in connection with hypothalamic lesions. Alpers listed other personality changes such as carelessness, indifference, antisocial tendencies, lack of social restraint, and loss of appreciation of personality change. The psychotic manifestations included confusion, hallucinations, disorientation, manic excitements, and in some cases Korsakoff psychosis. Alpers claimed that the physical manifestations of excitement or mania, depression, or anxiety often are accompanied by subjective experiences characteristic of true emotional responses.

In discussing hypothalamic syndromes Kennedy (1940) stressed the fact that the hypothalamus is concerned with the control of numerous rhythmic processes. Among these he mentioned the regularity of the rhythm of breathing, constancy of the pulse, the cycle of sleep, balance of intake and output of fluid, menstrual periodicity, and exact maintenance of body temperature. Not all of these are controlled solely by the hypo-thalamus-hypophysis complex, but, as he pointed out, lesions frequently bring out paradoxical and complex symptoms for which the diffusely acting sympathetic and the discretely acting parasympathetic, in combination with pituitary activation from the hypothalamus, are apparently respon-sible. Lesions in this area following epi-demic encephalitis provide examples. He believed that the hypothalamus is concerned not only with *emotional expression* but also with *mood*.

Electroencephalographic studies. With the discovery by Berger (1929) that the brain has a recordable electrical beat, and with the further discovery by Adrian (1931) and Adrian and Buytendijk (1931) that isolated ganglia and parts of the brain give rhythmic potential oscillations independent of sensory influx, a new approach to brain function was evolved. The autonomous or self-maintained rhythmicity of various parts of the nervous system has led to new concepts of brain function and integration, but perhaps more important it has provided by its presence or absence or variations a new index of cor-tical activity. Reviews covering most of the early literature in this field have been presented by Jasper (1937) and Lindsley (1944). One of the earliest findings by Berger, many times confirmed by others, is the fact that in a relaxed state in the ab-sence of special stimulation the dominant activity is a fairly rhythmic 10-per-second potential oscillation called the *alpha rhythm*. When light, sound, or other types of sensory stimulation are introduced, the alpha rhythm is blocked or markedly reduced. This has been variously explained as inhibition by a specific active area of the wider, spontane-ously active region, interference by sensory influx and its irradiations with resting rhythms tending to produce desynchroniza-tion of the multicellular rhythmic beat, dis-ruption at thalamic levels of presumed pace-makers for the several cortical rhythms, etc. However this may be, an interesting aspect

of sensory stimulation and its effect upon the alpha rhythm is that it seems to depend more upon attention or set under conditions of anticipation, or upon suddenness and un-expectedness, as in arousal by startle, than upon sensory stimulation per se.

Figure 5 illustrates the effect of a brief flash of light or a brief buzzer sound in blocking the alpha rhythm while the subject was sitting in the dark, relaxed, with eyes open. The blocking of the alpha rhythm by such sensory stimuli typically occurs about ⅔ second after the onset of the stimulus; the alpha rhythm often returns 1 to 2 seconds after the cessation of the stimulus, unless the startle aspect of the stimulus has produced marked surprise, tension, and apprehension. This latter seems to be illustrated in Fig. 5 by the response to the buzzer.

Shown on the same records is a tracing of the galvanic skin response (GSR), here recorded as a change of electrical potential (Tarchanoff effect) from the palm of the hand, rather than as a resistance change (Féré effect). It will be noted that in asso-ciation with both light and sound stimuli there is a GSR of moderate potential change with a latency of about 1.5 seconds. Also shown on the records is a tracing of the electrocardiogram (EKG) which provides a measure of change in heart rate, as well as other characteristics of heart action. We shall be concerned here, however, only with the changes in the EEG (electroencephalo-gram) and the GSR.

Since the GSR reflects the activity of the sweat glands, which are activated by sym-pathetic nerve impulses, it is apparent that a somatic sensory stimulation, light or sound, has activated the sympathetic branch of the autonomic system. At what level this comes about is not immediately apparent; it might be at the level of the lower brain stem, diencephalon, or cortex. The significant thing here is that any sensory stimulus that initially invokes a galvanic skin response tends, after repetition a number of times, to produce either no response or a very small one. This is certainly true of the same auditory stimulus, although a change to a new and even weaker one may reinstate the response. Here then is a kind of adaptation or adjustment to repeated stimulation. The same is characteristic of the blocking of the alpha rhythm by auditory stimuli; visual stimuli are more resistant to this type of

perhaps suffice to show that the flux and flow of the ordinary daily environment, with its shifting sensory impressions, tends to produce continual changes in the level of autonomic activity and in the state of the brain's activity insofar as this is revealed by the electroencephalogram. This might be considered one of the lower levels of emo-

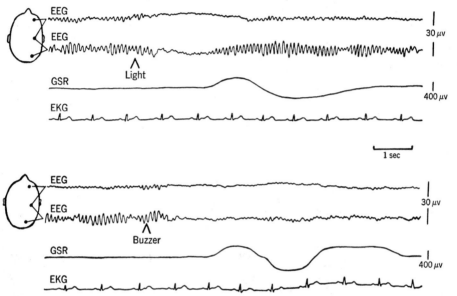

FIG. 5. Effect of unexpected light and sound stimuli upon the electroencephalogram (EEG), the galvanic skin response (GSR), and the electrocardiogram (EKG). Note that both light and sound stimuli block the alpha rhythm of the electroencephalogram after a latency of about 0.4 second; the galvanic skin response occurs after a latency of approximately 1 to 1.5 seconds. (From Lindsley, 1950.)

adaptation, although the instructions or anticipatory set may be a significant factor.

The initial effectiveness of a stimulus in blocking the alpha rhythm and in causing a galvanic skin response appears to be the "arousal aspect" of a new or unexpected stimulus. This seems to be like the situation involved in startle reactions, except that the intensity of the stimulus and the magnitude and diffuseness of the response may not be so great.

We seem to have here, in the effect of the sensory stimulus on the brain and autonomic system, an example of both central and peripheral influence. These examples will

tional responsiveness, and, if so, the organism might be described as being in a more or less continual state of emotional flux. That such activation does not have to be conscious has been suggested by the fact that subjectively subthreshold visual stimuli have been found to produce blocking of cortical alpha waves (Lindsley and J. R. Smith, unpublished observations). Likewise in records of GSR activity during auditory stimulation it appears likely that responses may be obtained to subjectively subthreshold stimuli.

To turn now to another phenomenon of the electroencephalogram, Fig. 6 illustrates in the records from a normal subject the effect of apprehension and tension as opposed to a relaxed, nonapprehensive state. This phenomenon is familiar to all electroencephalographers, who frequently find that a normal subject or a patient brought in for an EEG is tense, worried, and generally apprehensive about the procedure. The initial ("apprehensive") record in Fig. 6

pulses, both peripheral and central, to play upon an activation mechanism, which appears to have its principal focus in the hypothalamus. This mechanism, apparently the reticular formation, extends into the thalamus and downward into the lower brain stem and permits discharge of impulses both centripetally and centrifugally. The conse-

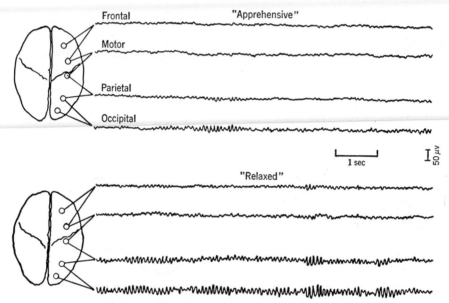

Fig. 6. Electroencephalograms from a normal subject during initial "apprehensive" period and later "relaxed" period. Note reduction or suppression of alpha rhythm during apprehension. (From Lindsley, 1950.)

shows low-amplitude poorly developed alpha waves, and sometimes faster rhythms of low amplitude. After a few minutes of recording, the subject usually quiets down and assumes a relaxed state, with the result shown in the lower record of the figure. Here the alpha waves are well developed and of considerably greater magnitude than in the initial record. As will be shown later, this is probably an effect of "activation" or "arousal" and may be considered akin to the effects of discrete sensory stimuli in producing arousal with consequent blocking of the alpha rhythm and GSR activity. Physical tension and apprehension provide a persistent source of im-

quence of this action is to further somatic and autonomic activity peripherally, reduce alpha waves in the electroencephalogram, and substitute an activation pattern.

Cohn (1946) reports two general types of EEG patterns among patients with anxiety states characterized by excitement, depression, or general irritability. Type I shows reduced alpha-wave activity and low-amplitude beta waves; type II shows predominantly high-voltage beta waves mixed with alpha waves. In the first type the patient is generally tense, and presumably the resulting sensory influx tends to obliterate the alpha rhythm. Such a patient is said to show a more normal picture when distracted and relaxed, especially after a period of hyperventilation. The EEG of the second type is associated with increased emotionality and marked autonomic response.

The "anxiety" record shown in Fig. 7 appears to be similar to Cohn's type I EEG. It is the record of a man who broke under severe emotional strain during a wartime encounter with the enemy. The record

the effect of specific emotional arousals on the EEG seem to have confirmed these EEG changes (Williams, 1939; Thiesen, 1943; Harrison, 1946; Darrow, Pathman, and Kronenberg, 1946).

Effects of subcortical lesions and stimulation on the EEG. Some recent experiments by Lindsley, Bowden, and Magoun (1949) and by Moruzzi and Magoun (1949) con-

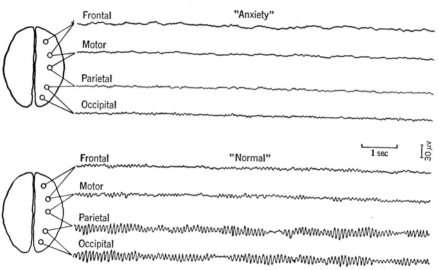

FIG. 7. Electroencephalograms illustrating absence of alpha waves in the records of a patient in an "anxiety" state and the well-regulated alpha rhythms of a "normal" subject. The former should not be considered pathognomonic of anxiety; furthermore the electroencephalograms of normal subjects and those of patients with anxiety cannot always be so readily differentiated. (From Lindsley, 1950.)

was taken sometime later when he had recovered, at least to the extent of appearing superficially "normal." The normal record, shown for contrast, was from a man who had shared the same battle experiences. The "anxiety" record was flat throughout and showed almost no evidence of alpha rhythm; hyperventilation did not change the picture.

The foregoing accounts of the effects on the EEG of unexpected sensory stimulation, apprehension, and anxiety all indicate some degree of emotional arousal or activation effect that tends to suppress the alpha rhythm and to increase the rapid, apparently desynchronized activity. Others who have studied

tribute to a better understanding of the electroencephalogram and seem to have explanatory value with respect to the effects of emotional arousal upon the EEG. The latter study demonstrated, among other things, that electrical stimulation of the reticular formation in the lower brain stem of the cat abolishes the large rhythmic potentials of the cortex under nembutal and replaces them with an "activation" pattern consisting of rapid low-amplitude waves. The activation pattern is not unlike the EEG pattern described above for emotional arousal and tension in human subjects. One is impressed by the fact that the increased sensory influx in these latter conditions may feed into the reticular formation of the lower brain stem via collaterals from spinothalamic tracts and, like the effects of electrical stimulation, produce the activation pattern described.

The study by Lindsley, Bowden, and Magoun (1949) dealt with the simultaneous recording of electrical potentials from the cortex and thalamus in unanesthetized cats after transection of the spinal cord at the first cervical level, or after transection at higher brain stem levels. Transection at progressively higher levels in the brain stem permitted greater delimitation of the effects of the reticular formation on higher centers. Bilateral lesions in the hypothalamus toward the head end of the reticular system completely eliminated influx through the reticular formation. As more and more of the reticular formation was eliminated by higher transections at the level of the pons and the midbrain, the electrocortical pattern changed from one of activation with the initial cord transection to one of increased synchronization. Bilateral lesions in the hypothalamus eliminated all fast activity composing the activation pattern and introduced rhythmic synchronized large waves that occurred in "bursts" or spindlelike formations similar to those of normal sleep. Thus the removal of sensory influx via the reticular formation, which normally imposes its influence upon the hypothalamus, thalamus, and even the cortex via the diffuse projection system, permits the thalamus and cortex to beat with their own spontaneous rhythms in a waxing and waning pattern. Simultaneous recording from certain nuclei in the thalamus and from the cortex demonstrated that these rhythms occur in unison, thereby indicating that there is some form of thalamocortical linkage. The similarity of these bursts of rhythmic activity to the normal sleep spindles is of special interest, since the "waking center" appears to be in the posterior region of the hypothalamus, and, as previous experiments have shown, lesions in this area produce somnolence and drowsiness. According to Kleitman's (1939) theory of sleep, the influx of sensory discharge into the waking center must be markedly reduced for sleep to occur. The preceding experiments suggest that this influx is via the reticular formation; lesions of the hypothalamus either destroy this center or markedly reduce the sensory influx to it.

With regard to emotion it appears that the sensory influx via the reticular formation in the intact organism may initiate autonomic reflex effects in the hypothalamus — for example, the galvanic skin response to sound stimulation, or the startle response and other visceral changes — but at the same time the cortical activation effect may induce cortical inhibition (or facilitation) of hypothalamic mechanisms. Some of these possibilities have been schematically diagrammed in Fig. 9 and will be mentioned later.

Hypothalamic recording and emotional probing. Grinker (1938) described a method presumed to make possible the recording of electrical potentials from the hypothalamus in human subjects. It consisted in inserting a special long needlelike electrode through the nasal passages to the proximity of the base of the brain and the hypothalamus. Grinker (1939), Grinker and Serota (1938, 1941), and Hoagland et al. (1938b) recorded what they thought were hypothalamic potentials simultaneously with those from cortical regions. In general the electrical activity in the two regions was similar: electrical stimulation of the hypothalamic region gave rise to concurrent cortical changes, and emotional probing of the patients produced changes in both the hypothalamus and the cortex. Masserman (1941) criticized the "hypothalamic" lead, pointing out that in man it is probably 3 to 6 centimeters removed from the hypothalamus and is in all probability closer to the pons and the medulla. Accordingly he felt that electrical activity recorded between this point and other reference leads on the ear lobe or head should not necessarily be interpreted as hypothalamic in origin.

Hoagland, Cameron, and Rubin (1938a) recorded standard electroencephalograms in psychotic patients and normal subjects during probing of emotional details in the life history. Using a measure of slow waves called the "delta index," they reported that both normals and psychotics showed an increase in heart rate and delta index during strong emotional excitation. Discussion of significant emotional factors or conflicts brought out an increase in the slow waves, which was reduced with repetition of the emotionally charged questions. Since Thiesen (1943) found no increase in the delta index during emotional excitement and since other studies have not revealed evidence of slow waves during emotional states, it seems likely that the delta waves might have been artifactual or the results of skin potential changes arising from sympathetic discharges.

THEORETICAL CONSIDERATIONS

Despite the long history of emotion, going back to the Greek philosophers, there has been little discussion of emotion as theory. The modern interest and discussion have centered chiefly around the writings of James and Cannon. James' stimulating writings at the turn of the century were responsible for an increased interest in emotion, and the earlier formulated theories of James (1884) and Lange (1885) came to be a dominating influence in subsequent psychological thinking. James' position is perhaps best summarized in his *Principles of Psychology* (1890) where he states:

Our natural way of thinking about these coarser emotions [e.g. grief, fear, rage, love] is that the mental perception of some fact excites the mental affection called the emotion, and that this latter state of mind gives rise to the bodily expression. My theory, on the contrary, is that *the bodily changes follow directly the perception of the exciting fact, and that our feeling of the same changes as they occur IS the emotion. . . . every one of the bodily changes, whatsoever it be, is FELT acutely or obscurely, the moment it occurs.*

Lange's theory, put forth independently, held that a stimulus object or situation gives rise immediately to vasomotor changes wherever blood vessels are found. The secondary changes occurring in the tissues were believed to give rise to the sensations that constitute the emotion. More recent interpretations of Lange's theory have recognized that the sensory impulses may arise from receptors in the blood vessels themselves.

Cannon (1931) schematized the neural basis for the James-Lange theory (see Fig. 8). Briefly this may be described as follows: an object stimulates one or more receptors (R); afferent impulses proceed to the cortex (path 1), and the object is perceived; efferent impulses immediately activate muscles and viscera (path 2); the activity of these organs stimulates receptors, causing afferent impulses to reach the cortex via paths 3 and 4. The perception of these changes in muscles and viscera, following upon the original perception of the external stimulus object, transforms the object-simply-apprehended into the object-emotionally-felt. According to James, "the feeling of the bodily changes as they occur is the emotion."

James and Lange did not attempt to portray the neural mechanisms of emotion, for the intricacies of neuroanatomy and neurophysiology were largely unknown in 1884 or 1885.

Cannon (1927) cited the following objections to the James-Lange theory: (1) Total separation of the viscera from the central nervous system does not alter emotional behavior. (2) The same visceral changes occur in very different emotional states and in nonemotional states. (3) The viscera are relatively insensitive structures. (4) Visceral changes are too slow to be a source of emotional feeling. (5) Artificial induction of the visceral changes typical of strong emotions does not produce them.

Although the experiments supporting these criticisms were ingenious and apparently sound, the question remains whether they proved anything about the James-Lange theory. Rather it appears that the James-

nomic system, since efferent fibers issue from cranial nerves III, VII, and IX, and afferent fibers enter the brain stem via VII and IX; likewise sensory response of skin and proprioceptors was possible in the neck, the head, and the shoulder of Sherrington's dogs. However, much of the sensory influx from the viscera was cut off (and all of it

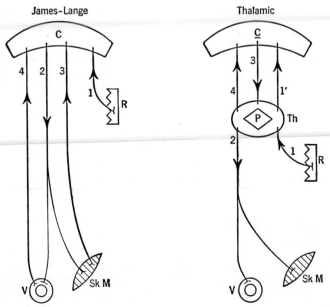

FIG. 8. Diagrammatic representation of the James-Lange and of the thalamic theories of emotion. Key: R—receptor; C—cerebral cortex; V—viscus; Sk M—skeletal muscle; Th—thalamus; P—pattern. The connecting lines represent nerve paths; direction of impulses is indicated by arrows. Corticothalamic path 3, on the right, is inhibitory in function. (From Cannon, 1931.)

Lange theory, by its very nature and formulation, is not a theory but an untestable hypothesis. By way of illustration, some of the evidence supporting point 1 above will be cited. Sherrington (1900) destroyed connections between brain and viscera completely, and isolated most of the skin and musculature of the body as well, by transecting the spinal cord and vagus nerves in dogs. Cannon, Lewis, and Britton (1927) removed the ganglia of the sympathetic chain in cats. As reference to Fig. 1 will show, neither procedure removed completely the possibilities of response or sensory influx from structures innervated by the auto-

from the circulatory system), and it was the perception of visceral changes upon which James had heavily relied for the object-emotionally-felt. Both Sherrington and Cannon report no diminution in the dogs' ability to express signs of various emotions such as anger, joy, fear, disgust, and rage except in the parts of the body where autonomic and somatic efferents had been eliminated.

Hebb (1946, 1949) objects to the logic of the interpretation of these experiments, pointing out that James did not say that the expression of emotional behavior would be lost by interfering with the viscera, but rather that the awareness or consciousness of the emotional feeling would be lost. It is true that one cannot, except by unwarranted inference, assume that, because an animal responds as if angry or afraid, it has actually *felt* that way, but the same is true of a human being, despite the fact that he may have reported that he *felt* that way. An objective method cannot be expected to prove or disprove an immaterial consequence or epiphenomenon, as consciousness is often regarded. The two levels of discourse do not mix. Until the phenomena of consciousness are identified objectively the scientific study of emotion will have to be confined to emotional behavior, broadly interpreted to include all measurable organic changes. Some of these organic changes, especially the electrophysiological, already appear to be useful substitutes for the phenomenology of consciousness. They measure excitation level which seems to be, more than anything else, related to the phenomena that have been called consciousness.

Let us turn now to the Cannon-Bard thalamic theory of emotion. The thalamic theory is sometimes associated with the names of Head and Cannon, for on the basis of clinical material in neurology Head (1920) made notable contributions, some of which Cannon (1927, 1931) applied in the formulation of the *thalamic theory*. Much of the subsequent support for the theory has come from the work of Bard.

Cannon's formulation of the thalamic theory may be best understood by reference to Fig. 8. An external emotion-provoking stimulus excites receptors (R) and starts impulses toward the thalamus (path 1); at this point they may activate thalamic processes or go on to the cortex (path 1') where they may arouse conditioned responses that in turn excite thalamic processes (by release of inhibition in path 3). Thus efferent discharges are set up in path 2, either through direct activation of the thalamus over path 1 or after impulses have passed to cortex (path 1'), where they inactivate inhibition over path 3, which allows patterned motor

responses in the diencephalon to find expression in effectors via path 2. At the same time an upward discharge in path 4 carries to the cortex an appreciation of the pattern just released. Thus this *quale* combined with the original sensory experience permits the impulses over path 4 to transform in the cortex the object-simply-apprehended to the object-emotionally-felt. The difference between this view and that of James and Lange is that for Cannon (1927) "the peculiar quality of the emotion is added to simple sensation when the thalamic processes are aroused." Bard (1934) makes it clear that this involves reactivation of the cortex via path 4. For James and Lange the object-emotionally-felt occurs only when sensory impulses from reacting effectors have reached the cortex.

In reply to a critique of his theory by Newman, Perkins, and Wheeler (1930), Cannon (1931) countered with additional evidence and made his position more explicit. Subsequent critiques by Harlow and Stagner (1932, 1933) were answered in two articles by Bard (1934). A final shot in this particular battle of critiques was the scholarly contribution of Lashley (1938), who questioned some of the thalamocortical mechanisms postulated by Dana (1921), Wilson (1924, 1929), and Head (1920), which were accepted in partial support of the thalamic theory by Cannon and Bard. Lashley doubted that there was sufficient evidence to endow the thalamus (diencephalon) with the ability to control patterns of emotional expression and provide, at the same time, for the wide range of affective states observed in normal and psychopathologic individuals. Lashley questioned the adequacy of thalamic mechanisms to serve as a reservoir of emotional tension and to account for the motivational aspects of emotional behavior upon which so much of modern dynamic psychology depends. However, in fairness to Cannon and Bard it should be emphasized that the thalamic theory did not pretend to account for all aspects of emotional experience, or for drive and motivation.

Arnold (1945) criticized Cannon's views on homeostatic control and his notion that fear and anger are emergency functions. She marshaled some interesting evidence to prove that neither anger nor fear has emergency functions; that, contrary to Cannon's position, anger is associated with predominantly parasympathetic excitation, fear with predominantly sympathetic activity, and excitement or elation with moderate parasympathetic activity. Later Arnold (1950) presented "An Excitatory Theory of Emotion," in which emotion is said to be an excitatory phenomenon represented in the threefold division of fear, anger, and excitement transmitted over separate cortico-hypothalamic pathways and touching off different hypothalamic effector systems. Arnold drew upon several lines of evidence to support her theory.

Although perhaps antedated by Duffy (1934, 1941), a new wave of interest and critique concerning the general status of emotion was touched off by Leeper (1948), whose penetrating article attacked not the theories per se but the implication of many writers that emotional behavior is a disrupting and disorganizing process. Leeper considered this a fallacious interpretation of the work of Cannon and others on the physiological aspects of emotional behavior, not intended by the authors of the original experimental work. On the contrary Leeper interpreted much of emotional behavior as an organizing, mobilizing process, which he attempted to fit into a motivational framework. In this he was joined in part by Duffy (1948) and Webb (1948). On the other hand, Young (1949) took issue with Leeper and defended a position previously expressed in his book, *Emotion in Man and Animal* (1943).

Hebb (1949) has presented a theory that qualifies emotion as *emotional disturbance,* which he says is neither innate nor learned but a little of both, for some nonspecific

learning must precede the expression of a pattern that is ready-made. Emotional disturbance is basically a disruption of the timing of neuronal activity in the cerebrum, produced by conflict of phase sequences or lack of sensory support for a phase sequence. A phase sequence appears to be a molar grouping of smaller units or patterns of activity in cell assemblies, but a dynamic, constantly changing sequence. Hebb attempts to reconcile a number of seemingly diverse psychological concepts based on experimental observation in terms of neurophysiological theory.

With increasing knowledge of the central and peripheral nervous systems and their functions, it becomes apparent that previous theories of emotion (James-Lange) or of emotional behavior (thalamic theory) are inadequate to account for not only the peripheral bodily changes in emotion, but the central manifestations as revealed by electrocortical activity. The basic framework of the thalamic theory may be retained, but it must be expanded to include some newly conceived mechanisms. Some of these newly discovered facts have been touched upon in a preceding section. It now remains to consider their place in a theory of emotion. As with most theories, this attempt to integrate the facts falls far short of the goal, but a useful purpose is served if new light can be brought to focus upon the problem and if a further search for facts can be stimulated.

An Activation Theory of Emotion

As far as it may be considered a theory, the conception to be described here may be labeled an "activation theory." It is based largely upon recent findings concerning the electroencephalogram and particularly the interaction of the cerebral cortex and subcortical structures. The activation theory is not solely an explanatory concept for emotional behavior but relates also to the phenomena of sleep-wakefulness, to EEG manifestations of cortical activity, and to certain types of abnormal behavior revealed in neurologic and psychiatric syndromes.

The theory rests mainly upon the following points, which are supported by experimental evidence:

1. The electroencephalogram in emotion presents an "activation pattern," characterized by reduction or abolition of synchronized (alpha) rhythms and the induction of low-amplitude fast activity.

2. The activation pattern in the EEG can be reproduced by electrical stimulation of the brain-stem reticular formation extending forward into the basal diencephalon through which its influence projects to the thalamus and cortex.

3. Destruction of the basal diencephalon, i.e. the rostral end of the brain-stem activating mechanism, abolishes activation of the EEG and permits restoration of synchronized rhythmic discharges in thalamus and cortex.

4. The behavioral picture associated with point 3 is the antithesis of emotional excitement or arousal, namely, apathy, lethargy, somnolence, catalepsy, hypokinesis, etc.

5. The mechanism of the basal diencephalon and lower brain-stem reticular formation, which discharges to motor outflows and causes the objective features of emotional expression, is either identical with or overlaps the EEG activating mechanism, described under point 2, which arouses the cortex.

Evidence for point 1 has been discussed in a preceding section of this chapter, and Figs. 5 to 7 illustrate the "activation effect" under conditions of moderate sensory stimulation causing emotional arousal, a condition of apprehension, and a state of anxiety. In addition it should be mentioned that Berger (1933) reported that fright abolishes the alpha rhythm, and that fear and anxiety tend to produce rapid waves. Jasper and Andrews (1938a) found that startle would block the alpha rhythm for a period of time (see effect of auditory stimulus in Fig. 5). Williams (1939) observed that embarrass-ment and apprehension tend to abolish alpha waves. Jost (1941) found that the reaction of an unstable group of children to frustration was accompanied by reduction of alpha activity and increased autonomic responsiveness. Rheinberger and Jasper (1937), in recording electrical activity from the cortex of an unanesthetized cat, found that when the animal was alert or emotionally aroused the pattern was characteristically one of low-amplitude fast activity with an absence of synchronized waves. As the animal became more relaxed and quiescent, slower alpha-like rhythms appeared. During sleep slower waves and spindlelike bursts dominated the picture. Under barbiturate anesthesia, thought to have its principal effect on the diencephalon, similar slow waves and spindling patterns occur. Lindsley, Bowden, and Magoun (1949) found that the alert unanesthetized cat with cord transected in the upper cervical region shows a low-amplitude fast electrocortical activity, i.e. an activation pattern.

The work of Moruzzi and Magoun (1949) supplies evidence for point 2. Direct electrical stimulation of the reticular formation in the lower brain stem in the cat abolished synchronized activity in the cortex and introduced in its place fast activity of moderate amplitude. Furthermore they found that the evoked potentials resulting from stimulation of a peripheral sensory nerve were not blocked by electrical stimulation of the reticular formation, but that the rhythmic after-discharge following each evoked potential was abolished. Likewise the recruiting potentials (Dempsey and Morison, 1942) induced by thalamic stimulation were abolished.

With regard to point 3 the evidence supplied by Lindsley, Bowden, and Magoun (1949) indicates that lesions in the diencephalon, at the rostral end of the activating system, abolish the activation effect and reinstate synchronized rhythmic discharges that may be recorded diffusely over the cortex and at the same time in a limited region of the thalamus. The simultaneity of discharges in the thalamus and the cortex suggests reverberating circuits or some form of mutual interaction of cortex and thalamus. The limited thalamic area involved seems to be a continuation of the diffuse projection system. Lesions or transections of the lower brain stem that left more and more of the reticular formation intact resulted in greater cortical activation. Lesions in the midbrain, eliminating medial and lateral lemnisci (direct sensory pathways to the thalamus and the cortex) but leaving intact the tegmentum and the reticular formation, did not abolish the activation pattern, whereas the reverse condition did abolish it and produced synchronized activity. Consequently it is evident that spinothalamic pathways projecting directly to the cortex via the thalamus do not produce the generalized activation pattern of the cortex. Rather it appears that these ascending pathways, by way of collaterals, shunt some of their impulses into the lower brain-stem reticular formation, which affects the cortex through the agency of the diffuse projection system.

Both experimental animals with hypothalamic destruction and clinical patients with pathology involving the hypothalamus (e.g. epidemic encephalitis) show symptoms that are the reverse of those due to hypothalamic stimulation (which causes emotional excitement and autonomic and motor discharge). Such animals and patients show little sign of emotion and are typically apathetic, lethargic, and somnolent. Some more limited lesions produce catalepsy, hypokinesis, and other symptoms found in neurologic and psychiatric syndromes. Additional evidence of this kind in support of point 4 has been given in a preceding section of this chapter.

The evidence reviewed by Ranson and Magoun (1939) strongly supports point 5. Electrical stimulation of the hypothalamus and of the downward extension of the reticular formation produces both somatic and visceral discharge. Emotional excitement and arousal is part of this picture. They state:

> It is probable that the active hypothalamus not only discharges downward through the brain stem, spinal cord and peripheral nervous system into the body but also upward into the thalamus and cerebral cortex. This upward discharge may well be associated with emotion as a conscious experience. This is in line with Cannon's theory (1927). But this excitation of the cerebral cortex by the hypothalamus is not essential for maintaining the waking state.

Magoun and collaborators (Sprague et al., 1948; Lindsley, Schreiner, and Magoun, 1949; Schreiner, Lindsley, and Magoun, 1949) have demonstrated that the lower brain-stem reticular formation plays a significant role in both facilitating and inhibiting spinal motor activity, depending upon the region stimulated.

Figure 9 is an attempt to represent schematically the principal structures and interconnections involved in the central regulation of emotional behavior. The diagram does not include basal ganglia of the extrapyramidal system or the cerebellum, both of which may also participate to some extent in emotional response. Reference to Figs. 4, 5, and 9 should help to make clear the extent of the hierarchical arrangement of reflex pathways involved in emotion. Most of the interconnections illustrated in Fig. 9 are supported by both anatomical and physiological evidence, although a few of them are merely inferred from suggestive data. The activation theory requires all the possible mechanisms schematized in Fig. 9, and these will be referred to in the subsequent discussion.

How is the activation theory of emotion related to sleep? Kleitman (1939) held that sleep is dependent upon a reduction in the bombardment of the waking center in the hypothalamus by afferent impulses from the various somatic and proprioceptive receptors, but particularly from the visceral receptors. It is under similar circumstances of reduction of afferent influx that the electroencephalogram shifts from a picture of activation and desynchronization (alert state) to one of increased synchrony with rhythmic

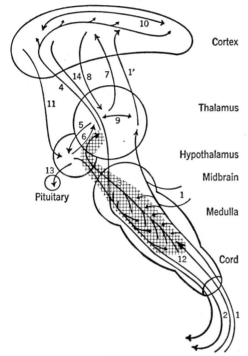

FIG. 9. Schematic representation of principal central nervous structures and probable pathways involved in emotional behavior. The diagram does not include the cerebellum and certain basal ganglia that may also participate. Key: 1—somatic and cranial afferents; 1'—direct thalamocortical projections; 2—visceral afferent pathways; 3—centripetal projections of reticular formation; 4—diffuse thalamocortical projections; 5 and 6—interconnections of hypothalamus and thalamus; 7 and 8—interconnections between thalamus and cortex; 9—intrathalamic connections; 10—intracortical connections; 11—corticohypothalamic pathways; 12—visceral efferent pathways; 13—hypothalamohypophyseal tract; 14 —corticospinal pathways. The crosshatched area represents the reticular formation.

alpha waves (relaxed state), and finally to one of large slow waves and even greater synchronization (sleep).

The more intense, unexpected, and persistent the external stimulation, the greater is the bodily tension aroused reflexly through lower levels of the spinal cord and brain-

stem. But these afferent impulses are not necessarily limited to reflex adjustments via spinal or lower brain-stem levels; some of them undoubtedly relay upward to successively higher levels. It is believed that both visceral and somatic afferent impulses feed into the reticular formation of the lower brain stem (see Fig. 9, paths 1 and 2). In this system of forward projections to the hypothalamus and the thalamus (pathway 3) the impulses activate not only the waking center (in the rostral midbrain or the basal diencephalon) but reach the cortex via the diffuse projection system (pathway 4). The activation pattern of the entire cortex seems to attest to this fact. Whether all such afferent impulses also reach the cortex via direct relay in the thalamus is not known. It appears that some of them at least do not; for example, visceral impulses in general do not give rise to awareness, and those that are appreciated provide only a vague awareness and little or no localization and discrimination.

Homeostatic adjustments preserving constancy of the internal environment are in some instances partly organized at low reflex levels (viscerovisceral reflex) but at the same time are influenced by and participate in external adjustments via somatovisceral and viscerosomatic reflexes. These reflexes probably constitute one of the lowest orders of reflex activation in the cerebrospinal system. How much of these activities is referred to higher, central levels of integration is uncertain, but no doubt some of the impulses affect the waking center and may well involve autonomic reflex adjustments in lower-brain-stem and hypothalamic levels.

A higher order of reflex adjustment, and one we commonly accept as a form of emotional response (probably a primitive and transient form of fear), is the startle pattern described by Landis and Hunt (1939). This is apparently a somato-viscero-somatic response, since both visceral and somatic reactions occur. For example, a strong, unexpected auditory stimulus produces a generalized bodily response, predominantly of flexion. Visceral manifestations are increased blood pressure, heart rate, and galvanic skin response, to mention only a few. There is no doubt that a cortical activation occurs as well (see Fig. 5), even to an auditory stimulus of moderate intensity, and the effect is generalized over the cortex, suggesting diffuse cortical projection. But the impulses from the VIII nerve, after passing through the pons and the midbrain, make final synaptic relay in the medial geniculate body of the thalamus and proceed to the auditory cortex by direct projection. It seems likely that on their way to the thalamus these pathways contribute collaterals to the reticular formation in the lower brain stem. Activation of this system makes possible the diffuse activation of the cortex as well as the waking center and the hypothalamic centers of visceral response.

Davis (1948) has shown that the muscle tension response to strong auditory stimuli reveals *a* and *b* components in the muscle action potential record. The first of these components has a latency of 0.1 second; the second component has a latency of 1 second or more. Both components, like the galvanic skin response, show adaptation effects to stimulus repetition, and Davis believes that they are both components of the startle response. Landis and Hunt (1939) found that the latency of the eye blink accompanying startle was even less than that of the *a* response, averaging about 40 milliseconds. A significant point, so far as the hierarchy of reflex adjustments is concerned, is that here we see evidence, in terms of latency, of the differential nature of the components of the startle response. The eye blink and the *a* response appear to occur at a lower brain-stem level and with more direct reflex connections (shorter latency) than the *b* response and the galvanic skin response, which probably involve at least a diencephalic level of reflex integration. A third stage of adjustment verges on the voluntary, involving the cortical level after the significance of

the stimulus is recognized. Impulses mediating this level of response apparently reach the cortex via direct projection pathways (Fig. 9, pathway 1'). However, before discrimination at the cortical level occurs, it appears that the cortex has already been alerted via the diffuse projection system, since the alpha rhythm is blocked and the EEG activated by the auditory stimulus in about 0.3 second.

Thus it may be seen that, through the mechanisms illustrated in Fig. 9, varying degrees and complexity of activation are possible as a hierarchy of reflex responses progressively involves higher levels of the neuraxis. Beyond the relatively simple startle response, involving mainly a brain-stem level in the hierarchy of response mechanisms, the nature of the more complex emotional responses is less clear. However, as Fig. 9 shows, there is reason to believe that additional complications are involved, for there are not only intrathalamic and intracortical connections (paths 9 and 10) but thalamocortical connections (paths 7 and 8) and corticohypothalamic tracts (path 11).

That cortical inhibitory and facilitatory influences upon diencephalic and other subcortical centers are possible is revealed by the influence of frontal lobectomy, lobotomy, and topectomy in human patients (Freeman and Watts, 1942, and others). These influences are also shown in cats by the effect of bilateral removal of the neocortex, sparing rhinencephalic structures, which causes *placidity*, whereas removal of rhinencephalic structures induces *anger* and *rage* reactions (Bard and Mountcastle, 1947). Other evidences of inhibitory and facilitatory effects of the cortex upon diencephalic structures come from the results of local stimulation in the premotor and other frontal areas (see Fulton, 1949). Other indications of corticohypothalamic control and the pathways involved have been discussed above.

These mechanisms make it possible to account for emotional excitement and rage responses normally held in check by cortical inhibition, but capable of release by rhinencephalic lesion and presumably also by activation through the reticular formation and the diffuse projection system. Experimental evidence for the former is clear; but for the latter the evidence is not complete, it is merely suggestive. The cortical activation is clear, but so far only alertness and moderate excitement have been demonstrated. Apparently cortical inhibitory mechanisms must be released, or greater facilitation induced, through accessory mechanisms in the cortex before rage and other strong responses can be aroused.

What of the milder emotions, the so-called pleasant and relaxed states or mildly exciting emotions? The evidence is not yet definitive, although it suggests that the degree of activation is very much less under these conditions. The cortical activity apparently remains relatively synchronized, and the ratio of sympathetic to parasympathetic activation is probably reduced to one of only moderate sympathetic dominance. White (1940) reported that stimulation of the preoptic and anterior hypothalamus in the region of the presumed parasympathetic center seemed to inhibit sympathetic discharge and the waking center, thereby producing greater relaxation and drowsiness. A differential control of parasympathetic and sympathetic centers in the hypothalamus, through inhibitory and facilitatory effects, should make it possible to provide for the different forms of emotional behavior. However, it is not profitable on the basis of present experimental evidence to attempt to account for all the varieties of emotional expression. These explanations will have to await further research. Many of the nuances of behavior undoubtedly depend upon learning and habituation, which, reinstated through memory and ideation and operating through the complex network of intracortical connections, make possible emotional responses that represent varying gradations between maximal excitement and

its opposite — relaxation and sleep. In short, the activation theory appears to account for the extremes, but leaves intermediate and mixed states relatively unexplained as yet.

REFERENCES

Adrian, E. D. Potential changes in the isolated nervous system of the *Dysticus marginalis*. *J. Physiol.*, 1931, **72**, 132–151.

Adrian, E. D., and F. J. J. Buytendijk. Potential changes in the isolated brainstem of the goldfish. *J. Physiol.*, 1931, **71**, 121–135.

Alexander, F., and T. M. French. *Studies in psychosomatic medicine*. New York: Ronald, 1948.

Alpers, B. J. Personality and emotional disorders associated with hypothalamic lesions. *Res. Publ. Ass. nerv. ment. Dis.*, 1940, **20**, 725–752.

Arnold, M. B. Physiological differentiation of emotional states. *Psychol. Rev.*, 1945, **52**, 35–48.

Arnold, M. B. An excitatory theory of emotion. In M. L. Reymert (Ed.), *The second international symposium on feelings and emotions*. New York: McGraw-Hill, 1950.

Bard, P. A diencephalic mechanism for the expression of rage with special reference to the sympathetic nervous system. *Amer. J. Physiol.*, 1928, **84**, 490–515.

Bard, P. The central representation of the sympathetic system as indicated by certain physiologic observations. *Arch. Neurol. Psychiat., Chicago*, 1929, **22**, 230–246.

Bard, P. Emotion: I. The neuro-humoral basis of emotional reactions. In C. Murchison (Ed.), *Handbook of general experimental psychology*. Worcester: Clark University Press, 1934*a*.

Bard, P. On emotional expression after decortication with some remarks on certain theoretical views. Parts I and II. *Psychol. Rev.*, 1934*b*, **41**, 309–329; 424–449.

Bard, P. Central nervous mechanisms for emotional behavior patterns in animals. *Res. Publ. Ass. nerv. ment. Dis.*, 1939, **19**, 190–218.

Bard, P. Central nervous mechanisms for the expression of anger. In M. L. Reymert (Ed.), *The second international symposium on feelings and emotions*. New York: McGraw-Hill, 1950.

Bard, P., and V. B. Mountcastle. Some forebrain mechanisms involved in expression of rage with special reference to suppression of angry behavior. *Res. Publ. Ass. nerv. ment. Dis.*, 1947, **27**, 362–404.

Bard, P., and D. McK. Rioch. A study of four cats deprived of neocortex and additional portions of the forebrain. *Johns Hopk. Hosp. Bull.*, 1937, **60**, 73–147.

Barker, R., T. Dembo, and K. Lewin. Frustration and regression: an experiment with young children. *Univ. Ia. Stud. Child Welf.*, 1941, **18**, No. 1.

Bazett, H. C., and W. G. Penfield. A study of the Sherrington decerebrate animal in the chronic as well as the acute condition. *Brain*, 1922, **45**, 185–265.

Beach, F. A. Analysis of factors involved in the arousal, maintenance and manifestation of sexual excitement in male animals. *Psychosom. Med.*, 1942a, **4**, 173–198.

Beach, F. A. Central nervous mechanisms involved in the reproductive behavior of vertebrates. *Psychol. Bull.*, 1942b, **39**, 200–226.

Beebe-Center, J. G., and S. S. Stevens. Cardiac acceleration in emotional situations. *J. exp. Psychol.*, 1937, **21**, 72–87.

Beebe-Center, J. G., and S. S. Stevens. The emotional responses: Changes of heart-rate in a gun-shy dog. *J. exp. Psychol.*, 1938, **23**, 239–257.

Bekhterev, V. M. Die Bedeutung der Sehhügel auf Grund von experimentellen und pathologischen Daten. *Virchows Arch.*, 1887, **110**, 322–365.

Bekhterev, V. M. *La psychologie objective*. Paris: Alcan, 1913.

Bekhterev, V. M. Emotions as somato-mimetic reflexes. In M. L. Reymert (Ed.), *Feelings and emotions: The Wittenberg symposium*. Worcester: Clark University Press, 1928.

Bekhterev, V. M. *General principles of human reflexology*. New York: International, 1932.

Bender, W. R. G. The effect of pain and emotional stimuli and alcohol upon pupillary reflex activity. *Psychol. Monogr.*, 1933, **44**, 1–32.

Berg, R. L., and J. G. Beebe-Center. Cardiac startle in man. *J. exp. Psychol.*, 1941, **28**, 262–279.

Berger, H. Über das Elektrenkephalogramm des Menschen. I. *Arch. Psychiat. Nervenkr.*, 1929, **87**, 527–570.

Berger, H. Über das Elektrenkephalogramm des Menschen. VI. *Arch. Psychiat. Nervenkr.*, 1933, **99**, 555–574.

Berrien, F. K. Finger oscillations as indices of emotion. I. Preliminary validation. *J. exp. Psychol.*, 1939, **24**, 485–498.

Blatz, W. E., and D. A. Millichamp. The development of emotion in the infant. *Univ. Toronto Stud. Child Develpm.*, 1935, Ser. No. 4.

Breakell, C. C., C. S. Parker, and F. Christopherson. Radio transmission of the human electroencephalogram and other electrophysiological data. *EEG clin. Neurophysiol.*, 1949, **1**, 243–244.

Bridges, K. M. B. A genetic theory of the emotions. *J. genet. Psychol.*, 1930, **37**, 514–527.

Bridges, K. M. B. Emotional development in early infancy. *Child Develpm.*, 1932, **3**, 324–341.

Bridges, K. M. B. Le development des emotions chez le jeune enfant. *J. Psychol. norm. path.*, 1936, **33**, 40–87.

Bromiley, R. B. Conditioned responses in a dog after removal of neocortex. *J. comp. physiol. Psychol.*, 1948, **41**, 102–110.

Bronk, D. W., R. F. Pitts, and M. G. Larrabee. Role of hypothalamus in cardiovascular regulation. *Res. Publ. Ass. nerv. ment. Dis.*, 1940, **20**, 323–341.

Brower, D. Respiration and blood pressure in sensory motor conflict. *J. gen. Psychol.*, 1946, **34**, 47–58.

Buchanan, A. R. *Functional neuro-anatomy*. Philadelphia: Lea and Febiger, 1948.

Bucy, P. C., and H. Klüver. Anatomic changes secondary to temporal lobectomy. *Arch. Neurol. Psychiat., Chicago.*, 1940, **44**, 1142–1146.

Cannon, W. B. *Bodily changes in pain, hunger, fear and rage: An account of recent researches into the function of emotional excitement*. New York: Appleton-Century-Crofts, 1915; 2nd Ed., 1929.

Cannon, W. B. The James-Lange theory of emotions: A critical examination and an alternative theory. *Amer. J. Psychol.*, 1927, **39**, 106–124.

Cannon, W. B. The mechanism of emotional disturbance of bodily functions. *New Engl. J. Med.*, 1928, **198**, 877–884.

Cannon, W. B. The autonomic nervous system: An interpretation. *Lancet*, 1930, **218**, 1109–1115.

Cannon, W. B. Again the James-Lange and the thalamic theories of emotion. *Psychol. Rev.*, 1931, **38**, 281–295.

Cannon, W. B. *The wisdom of the body*. New York: Norton, 1932.

Cannon, W. B. The significance of the emotional level. *J. Missouri Med. Ass.*, 1934a, **31**, 177–184.

Cannon, W. B. The story of the development of our ideas of chemical mediation of nerve impulses. *Amer. J. med. Sci.*, 1934b, **188**, 145–159.

Cannon, W. B. Stresses and strains of homeostasis. *Amer. J. med. Sci.*, 1935, **189**, 1–14.

Cannon, W. B. The role of emotion in disease. *Ann. intern. Med.*, 1936a, **9**, 1453–1465.

Cannon, W. B. Gray's objective theory of emotion. *Psychol. Rev.*, 1936b, **43**, 100–106.

Cannon, W. B., and S. W. Britton. Studies on the conditions of activity in endocrine glands. XV. Psuedaffective medulliadrenal secretion. *Amer. J. Physiol.*, 1925, **72**, 283–294.

Cannon, W. B., J. T. Lewis, and S. W. Britton. The dispensability of the sympathetic division of the autonomic nervous system. *Boston Med. Surg. J.*, 1927, **197**, 514–515.

Cannon, W. B., H. F. Newton, E. M. Bright, V. Menken, and R. M. Moore. Some aspects of the physiology of animals surviving complete exclusion of sympathetic nerve impulses. *Amer. J. Physiol.*, 1929, **89**, 84–107.

Cannon, W. B., and A. Rosenblueth. *Autonomic neuro-effector systems*. New York: Macmillan, 1937.

Cannon, W. B., and A. Rosenblueth. *The supersensitivity of denervated structures: A law of denervation*. New York: Macmillan, 1949.

Cohn, R. The influence of emotion on the human electroencephalogram. *J. nerv. ment. Dis.*, 1946, **104**, 351–357.

Courts, F. A. Relations between muscular tension and performance. *Psychol. Bull.,* 1942, **39,** 347–367.

Dale, H. H. Chemical transmission of the effects of nerve impulses. *Brit. med. J.,* 1934, **1,** 835–841.

Dale, H. H. Pharmacology and nerve-endings. *Proc. roy. soc. Med.,* 1935, **28,** 319–332.

Dana, C. L. The anatomic seat of the emotions: A discussion of the James-Lange theory. *Arch. Neurol. Psychiat., Chicago,* 1921, **6,** 634–639.

Darling, R. P. Autonomic action in relation to personality traits of children. *J. abnorm. soc. Psychol.,* 1940, **35,** 246–260.

Darrow, C. W. The significance of skin resistance in the light of its relation to the amount of perspiration. *J. gen. Psychol.,* 1934, **11,** 451–452.

Darrow, C. W. Emotion as relative functional decortication: The role of conflict. *Psychol. Rev.,* 1935, **42,** 566–578.

Darrow, C. W. The galvanic skin reflex (sweating) and blood-pressure as preparatory and facilitative functions. *Psychol. Bull.,* 1936, **33,** 73–94.

Darrow, C. W. Neural mechanisms controlling the palmar galvanic skin reflex and palmar sweating. *Arch. Neurol. Psychiat., Chicago,* 1937a, **37,** 641–663.

Darrow, C. W. Continuous records of systolic and diastolic blood pressure. *Arch. Neurol. Psychiat., Chicago,* 1937b, **38,** 365–370.

Darrow, C. W. Physiological and clinical tests of autonomic function and autonomic balance. *Physiol. Rev.,* 1943, **23,** 1–36.

Darrow, C. W. The electroencephalogram and psychophysiological regulation in the brain. *Amer. J. Psychiat.,* 1946, **102,** 791–798.

Darrow, C. W. Psychological and psychophysiological significance of the electroencephalogram. *Psychol. Rev.,* 1947, **54,** 157–168.

Darrow, C. W. A new frontier: Neurophysiological effects of emotion on the brain. In M. L. Reymert (Ed.), *The second international symposium on feelings and emotions.* New York: McGraw-Hill, 1950.

Darrow, C. W., and C. G. Graf. Relation of electroencephalogram to photometrically observed vasomotor changes in the brain. *J. Neurophysiol.,* 1945, **8,** 449–462.

Darrow, C. W., J. Pathman, and G. Kronenberg. Level of autonomic activity and electroencephalogram. *J. exp. Psychol.,* 1946, **36,** 355–365.

Davis, R. C. The relation of muscle action potentials to difficulty and frustration. *J. exp. Psychol.,* 1938, **23,** 141–158.

Davis, R. C. Motor effects of strong auditory stimuli. *J. exp. Psychol.,* 1948a, **38,** 257–275.

Davis, R. C. Methods of measuring and recording action. In T. G. Andrews (Ed.), *Methods of psychology.* New York: Wiley, 1948b.

Dempsey, E. W., and R. S. Morison. The production of rhythmically recurrent cortical potentials after localized thalamic stimulation. *Amer. J. Physiol.,* 1942, **135,** 293–300.

Dennis, W. Infant reaction to restraint: An evaluation of Watson's theory. *Trans. N. Y. Acad. Sci.,* 1940, **2,** 202–218.

Diethelm, O. Influence of emotions on dextrose tolerance. *Arch. Neurol. Psychiat., Chicago,* 1936, **36,** 342–361.

Diethelm, O., E. J. Doty, and A. T. Milhorat. Emotions and adrenergic and cholinergic changes in the blood. *Arch. Neurol. Psychiat., Chicago,* 1945, **54,** 110–115.

Dollard, J., L. W. Doob, N. E. Miller, O. H. Mowrer, and R. R. Sears. *Frustration and aggression.* New Haven: Yale University Press, 1939.

Dott, N. M. Surgical aspects of the hypothalamus. In Clark et al., *The hypothalamus.* Edinburgh: Oliver and Boyd, 1938.

Doupe, J., H. W. Newman, and R. W. Wilkins. A method for the continuous recording of systolic arterial pressure in man. *J. Physiol.,* 1939, **95,** 239–243.

Duffy, E. Emotion: An example of the need for reorientation in psychology. *Psychol. Rev.,* 1934, **41,** 184–198.

Duffy, E. An explanation of "emotional" phenomena without the use of the concept "emotion." *J. gen. Psychol.,* 1941, **25,** 283–293.

Duffy, E. Leeper's 'motivational theory of emotions.' *Psychol. Rev.,* 1948, **55,** 324–328.

Dunbar, H. F. *Emotions and bodily changes: A survey of literature on psychosomatic interrelationships, 1910–1945.* New York: Columbia University Press, 1946.

Dusser de Barenne, J. G. Recherches expérimentales sur les fonctions du système nerveux central, faites en particulier sur deux chat dont le néopallium avait été enlevé. *Arch. néerl. Physiol.,* 1920, **4,** 31–123.

Eppinger, H., and L. Hess. *Die Vagotonie.* Berlin, 1910 (Translation: Vagotonia. *Nerv. ment. Dis. Monogr.,* 1915, No. 20).

Finesinger, J. E. The effect of pleasant and unpleasant ideas on the respiratory pattern (spirogram) in psychoneurotic patients. *Amer. J. Psychiat.,* 1944, **100,** 659–667.

Finesinger, J. E., G. F. Sutherland, and F. F. McGuire. The positive conditional salivary reflex in psychoneurotic patients. *Amer. J. Psychiat.,* 1942, **99,** 61–74.

Finger, F. W. Experimental behavior disorders in the rat. In J. McV. Hunt (Ed.), *Personality and the behavior disorders.* New York: Ronald, 1944. Volume I.

Floyd, W. F. Apparatus for the continuous recording of potentials and E.M.F.'s from the skin. *J. Physiol.,* 1935, **85,** 28–30P.

Floyd, W. F. A modification of the apparatus for recording electrical phenomena from the skin. *J. Physiol.,* 1936, **87,** 24–25P.

Forbes, T. W. Skin potential and impedance responses with recurring shock stimulation. *Amer. J. Physiol.,* 1936, **117,** 189–199.

Fulton, J. F. *Physiology of the nervous system.* New York: Oxford University Press, 1949.

Fulton, J. F., S. W. Ranson, and A. M. Frantz (Eds.). *The hypothalamus and central levels of autonomic function.* Baltimore: Williams and Wilkins, 1940.

Freeman, W., and J. W. Watts. *Psychosurgery.* Springfield, Ill.: Thomas, 1942.

Freud, S. *The psychopathology of everyday life.* New York: International, 1904.

Freud, S. *Beyond the pleasure principle.* London: Hogarth, 1922.

Freud, S. *New introductory lectures on psychoanalysis.* New York: Norton, 1933.

Freud, S. *The problem of anxiety.* New York: Norton, 1936.

Gagel, O. Symptomatologie der Erkrankungen des Hypothalamus. Bumke and Foerster (Eds.), *Handb. Neurol.* Berlin: Springer, 1936. Pp. 482–522.

Gardiner, H. M., R. C. Metcalf, and J. G. Beebe-Center. *Feeling and emotion: A history of theories.* New York: American, 1937.

Gaskell, W. H. *The involuntary nervous system.* New York: Longmans, Green, 1916.

Gaskill, H. V. The objective measurement of emotional reactions. *Genet. Psychol. Monogr.,* 1933, **14,** 177–280.

Gellhorn, E. Physiological and pharmacological investigations on the nature of hypothalamic excitation. *Amer. J. Psychiat.,* 1941, **97,** 944–951.

Gellhorn, E. *Autonomic regulations: Their significance for physiology, psychology and neuropsychiatry.* New York: Interscience, 1943.

Gellhorn, E., R. Cortell, and J. Feldman. The autonomic basis of emotion. *Science,* 1940, **92,** 288–289.

Gellhorn, E., R. Cortell, and J. Feldman. The effect of emotion, sham rage and hypothalamic stimulation on the vago-insulin system. *Amer. J. Physiol.,* 1941, **133,** 532–541.

Gellhorn, E., J. Feldman, and A. Allen. The effect of emotional excitement on the insulin content of the blood. A contribution to the physiology of the psychoses. *Arch. Neurol. Psychiat., Chicago,* 1942, **47,** 234–244.

Gildea, E. F., V. L. Mailhouse, and D. F. Morris. The relationship between various emotional disturbances and the sugar content of the blood. *Amer. J. Psychiat.,* 1935, **92,** 115–130.

Gildemeister, M. Der sogennante psycho-galvanische Reflex und seine physikalischchemische Deutung. *Pflüg. Arch. ges. Physiol.,* 1915, **162,** 489–506.

Goltz, F. Der Hund ohne Grosshirn. *Arch. ges. Physiol.,* 1892, **51,** 570–614.

Goodenough, F. L. The expression of emotions in infancy. *Child Develpm.,* 1931, **2,** 96–101.

Grant, D. A. A convenient alternating current circuit for measuring GSR's. *Amer. J. Psychol.,* 1946, **59,** 149–151.

Greenwald, D. U. Circuits now available for the measurement of electrodermal responses. *Psychol. Bull.,* 1935, **32,** 779–791.

Grinker, R. R. Method for studying and influencing cortico-hypothalamic relations. *Science,* 1938, **87,** 73–74.

Grinker, R. R. Hypothalamic functions in psychosomatic interrelations. *Psychosom. Med.,* 1939, **1,** 19–47.

Grinker, R. R., and H. M. Serota. Studies on corticohypothalamic relations in cat and man. *J. Neurophysiol.,* 1938, **1,** 573–589.

Grinker, R. R., and H. M. Serota. Electroencephalographic studies of corticohypothalamic relations in schizophrenia. *Amer. J. Psychiat.,* 1941, **98,** 385–392.

Haggard, E. A. Experimental studies in affective processes: II. On the quantification and evaluation of 'measured' changes in skin resistance. *J. exp. Psychol.,* 1945, **35,** 46–56.

Haggard, E. A., and R. Gerbrands. An apparatus for the measurement of continuous changes in palmar skin resistance. *J. exp. Psychol.,* 1947, **37,** 92–98.

Hall, C. S. Emotional behavior in the rat. I. Defecation and urination as measures of individual differences in emotionality. *J. comp. Psychol.,* 1934, **18,** 385–403.

Harlow, H. F., and R. Stagner. Psychology of feelings and emotions: I. Theory of feelings. *Psychol. Rev.,* 1932, **39,** 570–589; II. Theory of emotions. *Ibid.,* 1933, **40,** 184–195.

Harrison, J. M. An examination of the varying effect of certain stimuli upon the alpha rhythm of a single normal individual. *Brit. J. Psychol.,* 1946, **37,** 20–29.

Hebb, D. O. On the nature of fear. *Psychol. Bull.,* 1946a, **53,** 259–276.

Hebb, D. O. Emotion in man and animal: An analysis of the intuitive processes of recognition. *Psychol. Bull.,* 1946b, **53,** 88–106.

Hebb, D. O. *Organization of behavior: A neuropsychological theory.* New York: Wiley, 1949.

Head, H. *Studies in neurology.* London: Oxford University Press, 1920. Volume II.

Henry, F. A direct reading cardio-chronoscope. *J. exp. Psychol.,* 1938, **22,** 598–601.

Hess, W. R. Hypothalamus und die Zentren des autonomen Nervensystems: Physiologie. *Arch. Psychiat. Nervenkr.,* 1936, **104,** 548–557.

Higley, B. R., and S. Renshaw. An improved device for the continuous pneumatic recording of respiration and changes in blood pressure. *J. Psychol.,* 1937, **4,** 281–285.

Hinsey, J. C. The hypothalamus and somatic responses. *Res. Publ. Ass. nerv. ment. Dis.,* 1940, **20,** 657–688.

Hyndman, O. R., and J. Wolkin. Anterior cordotomy: Further observations on physiologic results and optimum manner of performance. *Arch. Neurol. Psychiat., Chicago,* 1943, **50,** 129–148.

Hoagland, H., D. E. Cameron, and M. A. Rubin. Emotion in man as tested by the delta index of the electroencephalogram. *J. gen. Psychol.,* 1938a, **19,** 227–245.

Hoagland, H., D. E. Cameron, M. A. Rubin, and J. J. Tegelberg. Emotion in man as tested by the delta index of the electroencephalogram. II. Simultaneous records from the cortex and from a region near the hypothalamus. *J. gen. Psychol.,* 1938b, **19,** 247–261.

Hoagland, H. The human adrenal cortex in relation to stressful activities. *J. Aviat. Med.,* 1947, **18,** 450–468.

Hodge, F. A. The emotions in a new role. *Psychol. Rev.,* 1935, **42,** 555–565.

Hoelandt, M., and B. Stovkis. Einfache Technik für Psychogalvanographie mittels Verstärkerkardiographs. *Schweiz. med. Wschr.,* 1939, **69,** 384–386.

Hunt, J. McV. The effects of infant feeding-frustration upon adult hoarding in the albino rat. *J. abnorm. soc. Psychol.,* 1941, **36,** 338–360.

Hunt, W. A. A critical review of current approaches to affectivity. *Psychol. Bull.,* 1939, **36,** 807–828.

Hunt, W. A. Recent developments in the field of emotion. *Psychol. Bull.,* 1941, **38,** 249–276.

Hunt, W. A., and E. B. Hunt. A comparison of five methods of scoring the galvanic skin response. *J. exp. Psychol.,* 1935, **18,** 383–387.

Hunter, J., and H. H. Jasper. Effects of thalamic stimulation in unanesthetized animals. *EEG Clin. Neurophysiol.,* 1949, **1,** 305–324.

Ingram, W. R., R. W. Barris, and S. W. Ranson. Catalepsy: An experimental study. *Arch. Neurol. Psychiat., Chicago,* 1936, **35,** 1175–1197.

Jacobsen, E. *Progressive relaxation.* Chicago: University of Chicago Press, 1938.

James, W. What is an emotion? *Mind,* 1884, **9,** 188–205.

James, W. *The principles of psychology.* New York: Holt, 1890.

James, W. The physical basis of the emotions. *Psychol. Rev.,* 1894, **1,** 516–529.

James, W., and G. C. Lange. *The emotions.* Baltimore: Williams and Wilkins, 1922.

Janet, P. *The major symptoms of hysteria.* New York: Macmillan, 1920.

Janet, P. *Principles of psychotherapy.* New York: Macmillan, 1924.

Janet, P. *Psychological healing.* London: Allen and Unwin, 1926.

Janet, P. Fear of action as an essential element in the sentiment of melancholia. In C. Murchison (Ed.), *Feelings and emotions: The Wittenberg symposium.* Worcester: Clark University Press, 1928.

Jasper, H. H. Electrical signs of cortical activity. *Psychol. Bull.,* 1937, **34,** 411–481.

Jasper, H. H., and H. L. Andrews. Brain potentials and voluntary muscle activity in man. *J. Neurophysiol.,* 1938a, **1,** 87–100.

Jasper, H. H., and H. L. Andrews. Electro-encephalography. III. Normal differentiation of occipital and precentral regions in man. *Arch. Neurol. Psychiat., Chicago,* 1938b, **39,** 96–115.

Jasper, H. H., and J. Droogleever-Fortuyn. Experimental studies on the functional anatomy of petit mal epilepsy. *Res. Publ. Ass. nerv. ment. Dis.,* 1947, **26,** 272–298.

Jeffress, L. A. An ink-recording galvanic skin reaction apparatus. *J. gen. Psychol.,* 1937, **17,** 184–189.

Jost, H. Some physiological changes during frustration. *Child Develpm.,* 1941, **12,** 9–15.

Karplus, J. P. Die Physiologie der vegetativen Zentren. (Auf. Grund experimenteller Erfahrungen.) In Bumke and Foerster (Eds.), *Handb. Neurol.* Berlin: Springer, 1937.

Karplus, J. P., and A. Kreidl. Gehirn und Sympathicus. II. Ein Sympathicuszentrum im Zwischenhirn. *Pflüg. Arch. ges. Physiol.,* 1910, **135,** 401–416.

Keller, A. D. Autonomic discharges elicited by physiological stimuli in midbrain preparations. *Amer. J. Physiol.,* 1932, **100,** 576–586.

Kennedy, F. Medical syndromes of the hypothalamus. *Res. Publ. Ass. nerv. ment. Dis.,* 1940, **20,** 864–874.

Kleitman, N. *Sleep and wakefulness.* Chicago: University of Chicago Press, 1939.

Kling, C. The role of the parasympathetics in emotion. *Psychol. Rev.,* 1933, **40,** 368–380.

Klüver, H., and P. C. Bucy. An analysis of certain effects of bilateral temporal lobectomy in the rhesus monkey, with special reference to "psychic blindness." *J. Psychol.,* 1938, **5,** 33–54.

Klüver, H., and P. C. Bucy. Preliminary analysis of functions of the temporal lobes in monkeys. *Arch. Neurol. Psychiat., Chicago,* 1939, **42,** 979–1000.

Kuntz, A. *Autonomic nervous system.* Philadelphia: Lea and Febiger, 1945.

Lacey, O. L. An analysis of the appropriate unit for use in the measurement of the galvanic skin response. *J. exp. Psychol.,* 1947, **37,** 449–457.

Lacey, O. L., and P. S. Siegel. An improved potentiometric circuit for measuring the galvanic skin response. *Amer. J. Psychol.,* 1948, **61,** 272–274.

Lacey, O. L., and P. S. Siegel. An analysis of the unit of measurement of the galvanic skin response. *J. exp. Psychol.,* 1949, **39,** 122–127.

Landis, C. Studies of emotional reactions. II. General behavior and facial expression. *J. comp. Psychol.,* 1924, **4,** 447–509.

Landis, C. The interpretation of facial expression in emotion. *J. gen. Psychol.,* 1929, **2,** 59–72.

Landis, C. Emotion. II. The expressions of emotion. In C. Murchison (Ed.), *Handbook of general experimental psychology.* Worcester: Clark University Press, 1934.

Landis, C. The effect of the injection of adrenalin on complex muscular activity. *J. comp. Psychol.,* 1935, **19,** 113–117.

Landis, C., and W. A. Hunt. *The startle pattern.* New York: Farrar and Rinehart, 1939.

Lange, G. C. *Om Sindsbevägelser.* Copenhagen, 1885.

Langer, W. C. The tremorgraph: An improved and modified form of the Luria apparatus. *J. gen. Psychol.,* 1936, **15,** 459–465.

Langley, J. N. *The autonomic nervous system.* Cambridge: Heffer, 1921.

Lanier, L. H. An experimental study of "affective conflict." *J. Psychol.*, 1941*a*, **11**, 199–217.

Lanier, L. H. Incidental memory for words differing in affective value. *J. Psychol.*, 1941*b*, **11**, 219–228.

Lashley, K. S. The thalamus and emotion. *Psychol. Rev.*, 1938, **45**, 42–61.

Lauer, A. R., and D. E. Anderson. An apparatus for measuring changes in bodily resistance. *Amer. J. Psychol.*, 1938, **51**, 156–159.

Leeper, R. W. A motivational theory of emotion to replace 'emotion as disorganized response.' *Psychol. Rev.*, 1948, **55**, 5–21.

Lhamon, W. T. Relation between certain finger volume changes, electroencephalographically manifested brain activity, and psychopathologic reactions. *Psychosom. Med.*, 1949, **11**, 113–118.

Liddell, H. S. Conditioned reflex method and experimental neurosis. In J. McV. Hunt (Ed.), *Personality and the behavior disorders.* New York: Ronald, 1944. Volume I.

Lindsley, D. B. Electrical activity of human motor units during voluntary contraction. *Amer. J. Physiol.*, 1935, **114**, 90–99.

Lindsley, D. B. Electroencephalography. In J. McV. Hunt (Ed.), *Personality and the behavior disorders.* New York: Ronald, 1944.

Lindsley, D. B. Emotions and the electroencephalogram. In M. L. Reymert (Ed.), *The second international symposium on feelings and emotions.* New York: McGraw-Hill, 1950.

Lindsley, D. B., J. Bowden, and H. W. Magoun. Effect upon the EEG of acute injury to the brain stem activating system. *EEG clin. Neurophysiol.*, 1949, **1**, 475–486.

Lindsley, D. B., and W. S. Hunter. A note on polarity potentials from the human eye. *Proc. nat. Acad. Sci., Wash.*, 1939, **25**, 180–183.

Lindsley, D. B., and W. H. Sassaman. Autonomic activity and brain potentials associated with "voluntary" control of the pilomotors (*MM. arrectores pilorum*). *J. Neurophysiol.*, 1938, **1**, 342–349.

Lindsley, D. B., L. H. Schreiner, and H. W. Magoun. An electromyographic study of spasticity. *J. Neurophysiol*, 1949, **12**, 197–205.

Löwenstein, O., and E. D. Friedman. Pupillographic studies. I. Present state of pupillography ; its method and diagnostic significance. *Arch. Ophthal., Chicago*, 1942, **27**, 969–993.

Lund, F. H. *Emotions: their psychological, physiological and educative implications.* New York: Ronald, 1939.

Luria, A. R. *The nature of human conflicts.* New York: Liveright, 1932.

McClendon, J. F., and A. Hemingway. The psychogalvanic reflex as related to the polarization-capacity of the skin. *Amer. J. Physiol.*, 1930, **94**, 77–83.

McDougall, W. *Outline of psychology.* New York: Scribner, 1923.

McDougall, W. Emotion and feeling distinguished. In M. L. Reymert (Ed.), *Feelings and emotions:*

The Wittenberg symposium. Worcester: Clark University Press, 1928.

Masserman, J. H. The effects of sodium amytal and other drugs on the reactivity of the hypothalamus of the cat. *Arch. Neurol. Psychiat., Chicago*, 1937, **37**, 617–628.

Masserman, J. H. Destruction of the hypothalamus in cats. *Arch. Neurol. Psychiat., Chicago*, 1938, **39**, 1250–1271.

Masserman, J. H. Is the hypothalamus a center of emotion? *Psychosom. Med.*, 1941, **3**, 3–25.

Masserman, J. H. *Behavior and neurosis.* Chicago: University of Chicago Press, 1943.

Mettler, F. A. *Neuroanatomy.* St. Louis: Mosby, 1948.

Miller, N. E. Experimental studies of conflict. In J. McV. Hunt (Ed.), *Personality and the behavior disorders.* New York: Ronald, 1944. Volume I.

Miller, N. E. Theory and experiment relating psychoanalytic displacement to stimulus-response generalization. *J. abnorm. soc. Psychol.*, 1948, **43**, 155–178.

Mittelmann, B., and H. G. Wolff. Affective states and skin temperature : Experimental study of subjects with "cold hands" and Raynaud's syndrome. *Psychosom. Med.*, 1939, **71**, 257–266.

Mittelmann, B., and H. G. Wolff. Emotions and skin temperature: Observations on patients during psychotherapeutic (psychoanalytic) interviews. *Psychosom. Med.*, 1943, **5**, 211–231.

Morison, R. S., and E. W. Dempsey. A study of thalamocortical relations. *Amer. J. Physiol.*, 1942, **135**, 281–292.

Morison, R. S., and E. W. Dempsey. Mechanism of thalamocortical augmentation and repetition. *Amer. J. Physiol.*, 1943, **138**, 297–308.

Moruzzi, G., and H. W. Magoun. Brain stem reticular formation and activation of the EEG. *EEG clin. Neurophysiol*, 1949, **1**, 455–473.

Mowrer, O. H. An experimental analogue of "regression" with incidental observations on "reaction-formation." *J. abnorm. soc. Psychol.*, 1940, **35**, 56–87.

Munn, N. The effect of knowledge of the situation upon judgment of emotion from facial expressions. *J. abnorm. soc. Psychol.*, 1940, **35**, 324–338.

Murphy, J. P., and E. Gellhorn. The influence of hypothalamic stimulation on cortically induced movements and on action potentials of the cortex. *J. Neurophysiol.*, 1945*a*, **8**, 341–364.

Murphy, J. P., and E. Gellhorn. Further investigations on diencephalic-cortical relations and their significance for the problem of emotion. *J. Neurophysiol.*, 1945*b*, **8**, 431–447.

Newman, E. B., F. T. Perkins, and R. H. Wheeler. Cannon's theory of emotion : A critique. *Psychol. Rev.*, 1930, **37**, 305–326.

O'Leary, W. D. The autonomic nervous system as a factor in the psychogalvanic reflex. *J. exp. Psychol.*, 1932, **15**, 767–772.

Papez, J. W. The brain considered as an organ : Neural systems and central levels of organization. *Amer. J. Psychol.*, 1937*a*, **49**, 217–232.

Papez, J. W. A proposed mechanism of emotion. *Arch. Neurol. Psychiat., Chicago*, 1937*b*, **38**, 725–743.

Papez, J. W. Cerebral mechanisms. *J. nerv. ment. Dis.*, 1939, **89**, 145–159.

Pincus, G., and H. Hoagland. Steroid excretion and the stress of flying. *J. Aviat. Med.*, 1943, **14**, 173–193.

Prast, J. W., and K. A. Blinn. A system for remote electroencephalography. Quarterly Research Report, April 1949. School of Aviation Medicine, Randolph Field, Texas. Project No. 21-02-116; 8.

Pratt, K. C., A. K. Nelson, and K. H. Sun. The behavior of the newborn infant. *Ohio State Univ. Stud. Contr. Psychol.*, No. 10, 1930.

Ranson, S. W. Some functions of the hypothalamus. *Harvey Lect.*, Ser. 32. Baltimore: Williams and Wilkins, 1937.

Ranson, S. W. Somnolence caused by hypothalamic lesions in the monkey. *Arch. Neurol. Psychiat., Chicago*, 1939, **41**, 1–23.

Ranson, S. W., and H. W. Magoun. The hypothalamus. *Ergebn. Physiol.*, 1939, **41**, 56–163.

Reusch, J., and J. E. Finesinger. Muscular tension in psychiatric patients. Pressure measurements on handwriting as an indicator. *Arch. Neurol. Psychiat., Chicago*, 1943, **50**, 439–449.

Reymert, M. L., and G. S. Speer. Does the Luria technique measure emotion or merely bodily tension? *Character & Pers.*, 1939, **7**, 192–200.

Rheinberger, M., and H. H. Jasper. Electrical activity of the cerebral cortex in the unanesthetized cat. *Amer. J. Physiol.*, 1937, **119**, 186–196.

Richter, C. P. High electrical resistance of the skin of new-born infants and its significance. *Amer. J. Dis. Child.*, 1930, **40**, 18–26.

Richter, C. P., and M. Levine. Sympathectomy in man, effect on electrical resistance of skin. *Arch. Neurol. Psychiat., Chicago*, 1937, **38**, 756–760.

Rioch, D. McK. Certain aspects of the behavior of decorticate cats. *Psychiatry*, 1938, **1**, 339–345.

Rosenzweig, S. III. Need-persistive and ego-defensive reactions to frustration as demonstrated by an experiment on repression. *Psychol. Rev.*, 1941, **48**, 347–349.

Rothmann, H. Zusammenfassender Bericht über den Rothmannschen grosshirnlosen Hund nach klinischer und anatomischer Untersuchung. *Z. ges. Neurol. Psychiat.*, 1923, **87**, 247–313.

Ruckmick, C. A. *The psychology of feeling and emotion.* New York: McGraw-Hill, 1936.

Runkel, J. E. Luria's motor method and word association in the study of deception. *J. gen. Psychol.*, 1936, **15**, 23–37.

Saul, L. J. Physiological effects of emotional tension. In J. McV. Hunt (Ed.), *Personality and the behavior disorders.* New York: Ronald, 1944. Volume I.

Schaltenbrand, G., and S. Cobb. Clinical and anatomical studies on two cats without neocortex. *Brain*, 1930, **53**, 449–488.

Schreiner, L. H., D. B. Lindsley, and H. W. Magoun. Role of brain stem facilitatory systems in maintenance of spasticity. *J. Neurophysiol.*, 1949, **12**, 207–216.

Schwartz, H. G. Effect of experimental lesions of the cortex on the "psychogalvanic reflex" in the cat. *Arch. Neurol. Psychiat., Chicago*, 1937, **38**, 308–320.

Sears, R. R. Experimental studies of projection: I. Attribution of traits. *J. soc. Psychol.*, 1936, **7**, 151–163.

Sears, R. R. Experimental studies of projection: II. Ideas of reference. *J. soc. Psychol.*, 1937*a*, **8**, 389–400.

Sears, R. R. Initiation of the repression sequence by experienced failure. *J. exp. Psychol.*, 1937*b*, **20**, 570–580.

Sears, R. R. Experimental analysis of psychoanalytic phenomena. In J. McV. Hunt (Ed.), *Personality and the behavior disorders.* New York: Ronald, 1944. Volume I.

Sherman, M. The differentiation of emotional responses in infants: I. Judgments of emotional responses from motion picture views and from actual observation. *J. comp. Psychol.*, 1927, **7**, 265–284.

Sherman, M., and H. Jost. Frustration reactions of normal and neurotic persons. *J. Psychol.*, 1942, **13**, 3–19.

Sherman, M., and H. Jost. Diagnosis of juvenile psychosis. *Amer. J. Dis. Child.*, 1943, **65**, 868–872.

Sherrington, C. S. Experiments on the value of vascular and visceral factors for the genesis of emotion. *Proc. roy. Soc.*, 1900, **B66**, 390–403.

Sherrington, C. S. *The integrative action of the nervous system.* New Haven: Yale University Press, 1948.

Silverman, J. J., and V. E. Powell. Studies on palmar sweating. I. A technique for the study of palmar sweating. *Amer. J. med. Sci.*, 1944, **208**, 297–305.

Solomon, P. The psychogalvanic reflex. Applications in neurology and psychiatry. *Arch. Neurol. Psychiat., Chicago*, 1935, **34**, 818–827.

Spiegel, E. A., H. R. Miller, and M. J. Oppenheimer. Forebrain and rage reactions. *J. Neurophysiol.*, 1940, **3**, 538–548.

Sprague, J. M., L. H. Schreiner, D. B. Lindsley, and H. W. Magoun. Reticulo-spinal influences on stretch reflexes. *J. Neurophysiol.*, 1948, **11**, 501–508.

Stoddard, S. E., and C. Fisk. A new device for measuring the galvanic skin response. *Amer. J. Psychol.*, 1940, **53**, 444–445.

Stovkis, B. A method for the uninterrupted registering of blood pressure as a psychophysiological research-technique for the study of psychic stimuli on the blood pressure. *J. exp. Psychol.*, 1938, **22**, 365–376.

Strong, O. S., and A. Elwyn. *Human neuroanatomy.* Baltimore: Williams and Wilkins, 1943.

Thiesen, J. W. Effects of certain forms of emotion on the normal electroencephalogram. *Arch. Psychol., N. Y.*, 1943, No. 265.

Todd, T. W., and M. E. Rowlands. Studies in the alimentary canal of man. VI. Emotional interference in gastric behavior patterns. *J. comp. Psychol.*, 1930, **10**, 167–188.

Tolman, E. C. A behavioristic account of the emotions. *Psychol. Rev.*, 1923, **30**, 217–227.

Travis, L. E., and T. A. Hunter. Tremor frequencies. *J. gen. Psychol.*, 1931, **5**, 255–260.

Travis, L. E., and D. B. Lindsley. The relation of frequency and extent of action currents to intensity of muscular contraction. *J. exp. Psychol.*, 1931, **14**, 359–381.

Vonderahe, A. R. The representation of visceral function in the brain. *Ohio St. med. J.*, 1935, **31**, 104–108.

Vonderahe, A. R. The anatomic basis of emotion. *Ohio St. med. J.*, 1943, **39**, 325–330.

Watson, J. B. *Psychology from the standpoint of a behaviorist.* Philadelphia: Lippincott, 1919.

Watson, J. B. *Behaviorism.* New York: Norton, 1925.

Webb, W. B. A motivational theory of emotions. *Psychol. Rev.*, 1948, **55**, 329–335.

Weber, O. Homeostasis and servo-mechanisms for what? *Psychol. Rev.*, 1949, **56**, 234–239.

Weiss, E., and O. S. English. *Psychosomatic medicine.* Philadelphia: Saunders, 1943.

Wenger, M. A. The measurement of individual differences in autonomic balance. *Psychosom. Med.*, 1941, **3**, 427–434.

Wenger, M. A. A study of physiological factors: The autonomic nervous system and the skeletal musculature. *Hum. Biol.*, 1942, **14**, 69–84.

Wenger, M. A. Emotion as visceral action: An extension of Lange's theory. In M. L. Reymart (Ed.), *The second international symposium on feelings and emotions.* New York: McGraw-Hill, 1950.

Wenger, M. A., and M. Ellington. The measurement of autonomic balance in children: Method and normative data. *Psychosom. Med.*, 1943, **5**, 241–253.

Wenger, M. A., and J. C. Gilchrist. A comparison of two indices of palmar sweating. *J. exp. Psychol.*, 1948, **38**, 757–761.

White, B. V., and E. F. Gildea. "Cold pressor test" in tension and anxiety. *Arch. Neurol. Psychiat., Chicago*, 1937, **38**, 964–984.

White, J. C. Autonomic discharge from stimulation of the hypothalamus in man. *Res. Publ. Ass. nerv. ment. Dis.*, 1940, **20**, 854–863.

Whitehorn, J. C., M. R. Kaufman, and J. M. Thomas. Heart rate in relation to emotional disturbances. *Arch. Neurol. Psychiat., Chicago*, 1935, **33**, 712–731.

Whitehorn, J. C., and H. Richter. Unsteadiness of the heart rate in psychotic and neurotic states. *Arch. Neurol. Psychiat., Chicago*, 1937, **38**, 62–70.

Williams, A. C., Jr. Some psychological correlates of the electroencephalogram. *Arch. Psychol., N. Y.*, 1939, No. 240.

Wilson, S. A. K. Pathological laughing and crying. *J. Neurol. Psychopath.*, 1924, **4**, 299–333.

Wilson, S. A. K. *Modern problems in neurology.* New York: Wood, 1929.

Winkler, F. Die zerebrale Beeinflussung der Schweisssekretion. *Arch. ges. Physiol.*, 1908, **125**, 584–594.

Winsor, A. L., and B. Korchin. The effect of different types of stimulation upon the pH of human parotid secretion. *J. exp. Psychol.*, 1938, **23**, 62–79.

Winsor, A. L., and B. Korchin. Some observations on the effect of mental activity upon parotid secretion. *J. gen. Psychol.*, 1940, **22**, 25–32.

Woodworth, R. S., and C. S. Sherrington. A pseudaffective reflex and its spinal path. *J. Physiol.*, 1904, **31**, 234–243.

Young, P. T. *Emotion in man and animal.* New York: Wiley, 1943.

Young, P. T. Motivation, feeling, and emotion. In T. G. Andrews (Ed.), *Methods of psychology.* New York: Wiley, 1948.

Young, P. T. Emotion as disorganized response — A reply to Professor Leeper. *Psychol. Rev.*, 1949, **56**, 184–191.

15

Methods and Procedures in the Study of Learning

ERNEST R. HILGARD

Stanford University

In order to bring the study of learning into the laboratory, it is necessary to discover or to invent situations in which graduated improvement may occur, so that scores may be obtained. Such situations exist in familiar tasks like typing and piano playing. In these it is possible to score success according to time required, or errors made, or repetitions needed. Rote memorizing lends itself readily to this kind of study. All that is needed is the introduction of measures of progress, such as the number of promptings needed after different amounts of study. It was natural that the earliest quantitative studies of learning made use of these familiar experiences. Ebbinghaus (1885) selected rote learning for study; Bryan and Harter (1897, 1899) chose the learning of telegraphy. Students of animal learning found it simplest to score tasks that required the animal to move about, so that it could be timed or its course of action followed. The problem box (Thorndike, 1898) and the maze (Small, 1899, 1900) can be scored in these ways.

If we can score progress, that is all we need to start a learning experiment. But we have to add more to the design of the experiments if their data are to solve the problems of learning theory. The measurements must be relevant to a conceptual scheme. For one thing, variations classified as learning must not be of a kind more ap-propriately attributed to other psychological functions, such as maturation or motivation. Learning is always an inference, derived from changes in performance, and learning is not the only factor that can cause these changes. Performances change as organisms grow older, they change as organisms become fatigued, they change with the state of the organism (as when it is drugged), and they change with motivation. Only by appropriate controls can it be ascertained that the changes studied are surely to be classified as learning, or, more strictly, to be used to make inferences about learning. Even though we achieve this first step successfully and can distinguish learning from other influences, additional problems remain. It is a scientific truism that any given experiment can bear quantitatively on only a limited number of questions of theory. This is particularly evident in experiments on learning. Knowledge about memorization and retention derived from Ebbinghaus' experiments on nonsense syllables is valid scientific knowledge, but it does not cover all the features of remembering and forgetting, such as those to which Freud, Lewin, and others have later called attention. The Bryan and Harter experiments were appropriate to their interest in the form of learning curve, but their methods would not bear on problem solving and creative ability. Once we accept the fact that any one experiment can provide information about limited aspects of learning only, we see the need for an integrated plan of attack if comprehensive answers are to be obtained.

In this chapter primary attention is given to the problem of making learning situations quantifiable, and only secondary consideration is given to making them relevant to theory. The relevance of the experiments to generalizations about learning are more fully discussed in the chapters that follow.

A precise definition of learning is not necessary, so long as we agree that the inference to learning is made from changes in performance that are the result of training or experience, as distinguished from changes such as growth or fatigue and from changes attributable to the temporary state of the learner. The experiments themselves define the field ostensively.

TYPICAL EXPERIMENTS

A list of typical experiments may serve to remind us that methods and procedures vary widely with the situations studied. The problems that may be studied also differ within and among such situations. In the short statements that follow, typical experiments will be characterized, and a few references will be cited where additional information about such experiments may be found.

Situations Used with Both Lower Animals and Human Subjects

Throughout the history of the experimental study of learning there has been a strong emphasis upon the comparative method. Interest in animal learning has not usually been directed at animal training (as it might be in training homing pigeons or hunting dogs). Instead it has been directed at general principles of learning, applicable not only to the species studied but to the learning of other animals and to human learning as well. Nearly all the problems set for lower animals have been adapted in

one way or another for use with human infants or adults. In recognition of this tendency references are given in this part of the chapter to studies using both lower animals and man.

Negative adaptation or habituation. The classical experiment upon learning not to respond to a repeated stimulus is that of the spider studied by the Peckhams (1887). The spider dropped from its web when a tuning fork vibrated, but on successive trials it reacted less and less until finally it did not react at all. Other experiments on habituation are cited in the chapter by that title in Humphrey (1933). A typical parallel is provided in the experiments of Dodge (1923) on habituation to rotation.

Classical conditioning. The dog that learns to salivate to the sound of a tuning fork (Pavlov, 1927) serves as the prototype of one form of experiment widely copied and adapted to other species, including man. The experiments on both animals and human subjects are reviewed by Hilgard and Marquis (1940).

Instrumental or operant conditioning. The rat that learns to press a lever in order to deliver a pellet of food presents us with an example of instrumental or operant conditioning. The situation is defined by the responses of the organism that produce the reinforcing or rewarding goal object. It is the movements of the rat which bring the pellet of food. In classical conditioning, by contrast, the unconditioned stimulus appears even though the organism does nothing. The lever-pressing situation was most extensively studied by Skinner (1938), although it has become an integral part of the experimental program in Hull's laboratory (Hull, 1943). This experimental method has also been used with pigeons (Skinner, 1948).

The equivalent experiments with children were introduced by Ivanov-Smolensky (1927) and extended by others (Jackson et al., 1938).

The puzzle box or problem box. Thorndike's hungry cat trying to release the latch on a cage in order to obtain food outside (Thorndike, 1898) illustrates a number of experiments making use of a wide variety of latch boxes, sawdust boxes, platform boxes, and other devices (Warden, Jenkins, and Warner, 1935, pp. 244–254). Although these may also be considered instrumental conditioning, they different mechanically from the lever-pressing box in that the end state

one of which food might be found. The animal was trained to find food in the one compartment that was lighted. After this preliminary training the signal light was turned on and then off, and the animal's choice was forcibly delayed for some seconds. The aim was to find out how long the animal could delay without "forgetting" where the light had been turned on. In later experi-

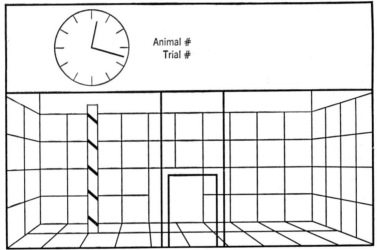

FIG. 1. Puzzle box for cats (after Guthrie and Horton, 1946, p. 14). The front is of clear sheet glass. The diagonally striped pole operates the release mechanism, opening the door at front center.

usually involves release from confinement as well as access to the lure. Among the later variations of Thorndike's method with cats are those of Adams (1929) and of Guthrie and Horton (1946). (See Fig. 1.)

The corresponding experiments with human subjects are analogous without being altogether comparable. They involve discovering an appropriate movement or combination of movements in order to resolve a problematic situation, as in the solution of wire puzzles (Ruger, 1910).

Delayed-reaction experiments. The delayed-reaction experiment was introduced by Hunter (1913). He confronted an animal with a limited number of behavior choices, such as three open compartments, in

ments (Hunter, 1917) the method was modified to what has been called the "direct" method. That is, the sight of food being placed into the compartment is substituted for the indirect signal, the light. This procedure appears to place less strain upon the animal's symbolic capacities, so that much longer delays are obtained with the direct method than with the indirect ones (e.g. Tinklepaugh, 1932; Harlow, Uehling, and Maslow, 1932). The relevant experiments are reviewed by Munn (1933), Cowles (1940), and Heron (1942).

The delayed-reaction experiment is readily adapted for use with human infants. Hunter performed some preliminary experiments himself (Hunter, 1913, 1917), and later experimenters have gone on with the method (Skalet, 1931; Bühler and Hetzer, 1935).*

The discrimination experiment. The discrimination experiment was originally devised to test the discriminatory capacities of animals. Training problems were a necessary nuisance which had to be disposed of before the animal could exhibit its sensory capabilities. Each sense modality presents its own problems. Because we are here concerned with learning rather than with sensory discrimination, our discussion will be limited to the learning of discriminations within one modality, vision. An elaborate apparatus was designed by Yerkes and Watson (1911) chiefly to control the visual stimulus. The problem required the use of visual cues for turning to the right or to the left to find food at the end of the runways. A simple form had been used successfully by Yerkes (1907) in his study of the dancing mouse. Some of the difficulties encountered in the use of the discrimination box led other experimenters to become more interested in the learning problems as such. They have found that the directness of the relation between the visual cue and the reward determines the ease with which the discrimination can be made. This is consistent with the fact that the direct method in the delayed-reaction experiment is easier than the indirect method. An important advance was achieved in the ease of teaching rats to discriminate by the invention of the jumping apparatus (Lashley, 1930), which requires the rats to jump directly at the stimuli which are used as signals for the location of food (see Fig. 2). If the rat jumps toward and strikes the correct card, the card drops down and the rat finds itself

* The delayed-reaction experiment is to be distinguished from the delayed-reward experiment, with which it may be verbally confused. In the delayed-reaction experiment the response is delayed, but the reward follows the successful response immediately; in the delayed reward experiment the correct response may be made promptly, but time elapses before the reward is delivered. As illustration of delayed reward, see Wolfe (1934).

on the feeding platform behind the open window. If it jumps to the wrong card, it finds the window locked and falls into the net below. Other methods are described in some detail by Kreezer (1942). Because the learning problems have turned out to be as

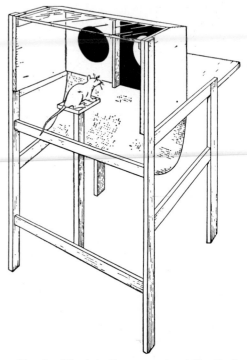

FIG. 2. Discrimination apparatus (after Lashley, 1930, as redrawn by Munn, 1946, p. 253). The positive ("correct") card falls over when the rat jumps against it, giving access to the food table. The negative card is locked, and after jumping to it the animal falls into the net.

perplexing as the problems of sensory discrimination, the discrimination method has proved useful for studying a number of problems within learning. It has been used, for example, by Muenzinger and his associates (e.g. Muenzinger, Bernstone, and Richards, 1938) to study motivation in learning.

A variation of the discrimination box consists in a series of discriminatory choices arranged along a pathway, as in a maze, with the reward obtained only at the end of a series of choices (Stone, 1928). This permits the study of serial problems not possible with a single discrimination.

Other variations of the discrimination experiment include the presentation of several stimulus patterns from among which the choice has to be made. The selection of an odd stimulus from a number of similar stimuli has been studied with chimpanzees (Nissen and McCulloch, 1937); matching from samples, originally done by Kohts (1928), has been used extensively by Harlow and his associates (e.g. Harlow, 1942).

The equivalence method, developed by Klüver (1933), requires the organism to at-

with many blind alleys. The first step of simplification made each choice that between two alternatives. With retracing prevented by valvelike doors, the animal progressed from one choice-point to another. Only fairly recently has it been realized that there are real advantages in studying single choice-point mazes (e.g. Tolman, 1938) and some things to be learned from single alley mazes with no choice-points whatever (e.g. Hull, 1934).

Mazes have been constructed in great variety. In experiments with rats the pathways are either enclosed or raised from the

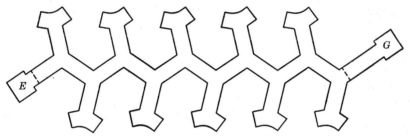

FIG. 3. Warner-Warden maze—linear pattern (after Warden, 1929). The symmetrical pathway permits an analysis of serial learning problems.

tend to the stimuli that are mounted upon platforms pulled in by the animal. A correct choice is rewarded by food on the platform.

The discrimination experiment can be applied to young children by methods quite similar to those used with animals. One method requires a choice between boxes on the basis of stimuli upon their lids. The correct choice finds the lid unlocked and the reward inside. If the wrong card is chosen, the child finds the lid locked and is deprived of the reward (Gellerman, 1933a).

The alley maze. An alley maze provides a learning situation in which the obstacle interposed between the organism and the satisfaction of an aroused appetite is a path that has to be traversed before the goal can be reached. As so often happens in the course of scientific progress, the maze has evolved from complexity to simplicity. The earlier mazes were often bewildering affairs

floor so that the maze is a trestlelike structure. Most two-dimensional mazes are built in a horizontal plane, although some are built vertically. There are also three-dimensional mazes (e.g. Hunter, 1929). In addition to the recent trends toward unit mazes, with each unit a single choice, there is also some trend toward a linear arrangement of these units (Fig. 3), so that an animal makes all choices from the mid-line between start and food box (e.g. Warden, 1929). Earlier mazes were often constructed for the convenience of the experimenter, returning the rat to a food box near its starting point. This imposed either a clockwise or counter-clockwise trend to the correct path and biased the entrances into blind alleys at different choice-points (Ballachey and Buel, 1934).

The patterns of mazes used with animals have been duplicated for human subjects, either full-scale or as stylus mazes in which the path is a slot to be followed manually (e.g. Warden, 1924). The raised wire path is another form of finger maze (Miles, 1928). The human subject is usually blindfolded when he 'runs' such mazes. Direct comparative studies between man and lower animals are complicated by verbal factors in human maze learning and by the difficulty of equating the pretraining given animals with instructions given the human subject.

Another variation of the maze is worthy of mention here: the maze with multiple paths. The choice is not between true path and blind alley, but must be made on some other basis. There may be paths of different length, to study the preference for shorter paths (Yoshioka, 1929), or one fixed path and one variable path, to study the preference for variety (Krechevsky, 1937). In the Dashiell checkerboard maze (Dashiell, 1925) the paths form a grid like the streets of a city laid out in blocks with streets at right angles. The goal is placed diagonally opposite the entrance, and all possible paths in the goal-ward direction are the same length. Hence the maze is useful for studying the degree of fixity of successive runs from start to goal.

The temporal maze. Maze relations need not be spatial only. A longer alley requires a longer running time, and the discrimination between long and short alleys could conceivably be based upon differences in time. This conjecture can be put to the test by introducing time as a variable either through interposing delays or through requiring that turns within the same alleys be made in a fixed temporal order.

Study of time discrimination through the use of delay boxes in alternative paths has been done by Sams and Tolman (1925) and by Anderson (1932).

What is more commonly referred to as a temporal maze is that used by Hunter (1928) in the study of double alternation. The animal is required to run around two adjacent squares, in the order twice around the right, then twice around the left. This requires

that the run down the common path between the two squares shall end twice in turns to the right, then twice in turns to the left. According to simple association theory, the two occasions upon which the run down the path has terminated in turning to the right should make it difficult for a subsequent run down the path to become the cue for turning to the left. Hunter believes the mediation of a symbolic process to be necessary. The problem is, indeed, a difficult one for an animal at the level of the rat, although it can be solved by the raccoon.

Linear mazes can be constructed with multiple units requiring for solution repeated double alternation in the form rr–ll–rr–ll, etc. (Buel, 1934).

The double alternation problem can readily be presented to the human subject in the form of a stylus maze.

Multiple choice. In the effort to find an instrument appropriate to the study of the differences in higher mental capacities among different species of animals, Yerkes early invented the multiple-choice experiment (Yerkes, 1917), developing an apparatus previously used by Hamilton (1916). The apparatus consists of a number of compartments entered by doors arranged fan-shaped, equidistant from the starting point. Several adjacent doors may be opened at once, in any section of the bank of doors. Food is to be found in one of the compartments, located according to a relation among the open doors. An easier sort of problem is to react to the door at the extreme left of the bank of open doors. A harder problem is to react always to the middle one of an odd number of open doors.

For the human subject an arrangement of telegraph keys is used, the exposed keys corresponding to the open doors. More complicated relations may be used with the human subjects, such as the problem: "If an odd number, the first left of the middle; if an even number, the right end." Probably no animal below man can master a problem of this order of difficulty. The many experiments with species as different as birds, rats, pigs, cats, monkeys, and chimpanzees are reviewed by Warden, Jenkins, and Warner (1936) and by Munn (1938).

Detour ("insight") problems. The detour problems have been so named by Köhler (1925) because the path toward solution of the animal's problem is not direct but calls for the circumventing of some sort of obstacle. Either the animal must literally go around an obstacle (perhaps first of all by moving away from the goal), or it must make some use of tools or their equivalents. In any case it is necessary for a time to divert attention away from the goal and toward the means by which the goal can be reached. The problems that Köhler popularized by his experiments with chimpanzees involved tool using, as in obtaining a banana from outside the cage by means of a stick, and box stacking, in which a lure suspended from the ceiling could be reached only by building some kind of structure beneath it. These experiments have been extended by others, e.g. Bingham (1929) and Jackson (1942).

Comparable insight experiments have been done with children (Alpert, 1928). In the string-pulling experiment some strings lead directly to the object to be drawn in, and others, although open to observation, are placed in misleading positions. This procedure has been used with monkeys (Harlow and Settlage, 1934), with chimpanzees (Finch, 1941), and with children (Richardson, 1932).

By an appropriate modification, mazes have been used to study behavior in rats somewhat like the detour behavior of primates. Thus Tolman and Honzik (1930) arranged a multiple-path maze with some common segments. Their problem was to determine whether or not, following a block of the common segment of two paths, the rat would follow the remaining open path, even though it was the least preferred of the three possible paths. They believed that

their results proved the rat's capacity for insight.

Reasoning problems. Closely related to the detour problems are those on reasoning. Experiments have been done with rats (Maier, 1929), with children (Maier, 1936), and with human adults (Duncker, 1926; Maier, 1930).

The method consists essentially in teaching segments of behavior in isolation, then setting a problem in which the segments have to be combined in novel ways. In the typical experiment with rats, the rat is fed briefly on one platform and then required to return to this platfrom either by a route not used before or by a route that, though familiar, has to be selected appropriately as against alternative familiar routes. In the experiments with human adults, a number of ingenious situations have been arranged in which familiar objects must be used in unfamiliar ways. Thus a pair of pliers may be used as a pendulum bob, a metal clamp as a coathanger, a Bunsen burner tube as a blowpipe. Although Maier prefers to think of the reasoning task as involving functions other than those employed in learning, it is difficult to defend a sharp distinction between learning and reasoning.

Social learning. The influence of one learner upon another has been a matter of recurrent interest, in part because of the importance of imitation as one of the possible modes of learning. It was inferred from the earlier studies (e.g. Thorndike, 1911; Haggerty, 1909) that little imitation occurred, although later studies have been more friendly to the claims of imitation (Warden and Jackson, 1935; Yerkes, 1943). One method of studying the problem is to have animals in neighboring cages subjected to similar problems. The question is whether an untrained animal can learn from one that has solved the problem. Another method is to expose several animals at once to the problem, to see whether and under what conditions copying behavior occurs (Miller and Dollard, 1941).

Other problems studied with animals include competition and cooperation, dominance and submission, and the like (e.g. Crawford, 1937; Maslow, 1940).

The field of human learning is readily extended to the learning of social attitudes, as, for example, by way of movies (Thurstone, 1931).

Situations Used Primarily or Exclusively in the Study of Human Learning

Despite the litheness and agility of lower animals, it is man who is the past master in the art of motion. His laryngeal and manual skills, under control of his superior nervous system, permit him to achieve performances unmatched by other animals. Hence there

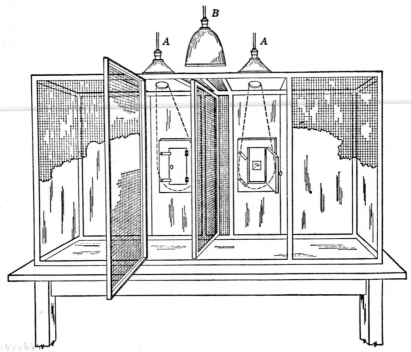

Fig. 4. Duplicate-cage imitation apparatus (after Warden, as reproduced by Warden, Jenkins, and Warner, 1935, p. 258). Other devices may be substituted for the double-latch problem shown in the panels.

Behavior in the clinical situation where symptoms are either developed or relinquished is important as learning, but clinical observations have done little to further our knowledge about learning. Some of the studies by students of Kurt Lewin on the forgetting of an intention, on the recall of interrupted tasks, on task resumption, and the like, have about them much of the flavor of the clinic, although they are strictly experimental studies. Some of the animal studies on fixation, regression, experimental neuroses, etc., are also relevant (Sears, 1943).

are skills, both verbal and nonverbal, little represented in studies of animals below man. These include studies of rote memorization and retention of verbal materials, studies of verbal reasoning and concept formation, and studies of skilled performances of the perceptual-motor type.

Rote memorization and retention. Ebbinghaus (1885) introduced the nonsense-syllable experiment which has since served as the basis for countless experiments. The literature has been well summarized by McGeoch (1942).

The pattern of the nonsense-syllable experiment can be followed with other verbal materials, such as adjectives or related discourse. With appropriate changes the methods may be used for the study of memory for objects or pictures or tasks. The study of testimony, as originated by Münsterberg (1909), is one such variation.

Verbal reasoning and concept formation. Although some reasoning experiments with children (Maier, 1936) have been designed parallel to animal experiments, and although some work has been done on concept formation in animals (Fields, 1932), studies of syllogistic reasoning and concept formation in man cannot be paralleled in any precise manner by work with animals.

The method of concept formation, named by James "the dissociation of varying concomitants," was put to test by Hull (1920) through the use of Chinese symbols identified by a concept sign that had to be discovered as the common element among symbols bearing the same name. Work along somewhat the same lines was continued by Smoke (1932). The experiments are reviewed in Woodworth (1938).

Motor skills. Motor skills, or, more accurately, perceptual-motor skills, have been studied in a variety of forms since the pioneer work of Bryan and Harter on telegraphy. Ball tossing, dart throwing, archery, typewriting, digit-symbol substitution, spool packing, mirror star tracing, and many other tasks have been made use of. One of the tasks used widely enough to justify theoretical analyses is that of rotary pursuit learning (Fig. 5). A number of devices have been used, but most extensively that introduced by Koerth (cf. Seashore, 1928). This consists of a small brass target near the edge of a revolving turntable. The subject is required to keep the point of a hinged stylus on the target, and receives a score according to the amount of time that he is able to keep the stylus in contact with the target as the turntable revolves.

There is no special reason why motor skills should not be studied among animals. They can be taught acts of balancing, tightrope walking, jumping, and running. Some studies of individual differences in motor skills have appeared, but these have not been treated primarily as studies of learning, e.g. the running abilities of horses

FIG. 5. Pursuit rotor. The subject attempts to keep the hinged stylus in contact with a small brass target which revolves with the phonograph turntable. The electric clock registers the amount of time that the stylus is in contact (photograph courtesy Stanford Psychological Laboratory).

(Stone, 1935), handedness in rats (Wentworth, 1942), and in chimpanzees (Finch, 1941).

The foregoing list gives an introductory overview of the kinds of situations that have been brought into the laboratory for study. The problems studied can in part be inferred from the situations, although their listing would require additional dimensions. There are the problems of part-whole learning, of distribution of practice, of transfer of training, of motivational control of learning, and many others — each of which can be studied in several of the situations previously listed.

CLASSICAL CONDITIONED RESPONSE EXPERIMENTS

Once we decide to do an experiment on the conditioned response, we face a number of additional decisions. Among these are:

The kind of subject, lower animal, child, or adult, to be used.

The response that is to serve as the unconditioned response.

The unconditioned stimulus to be used (including the range of intensities).

The conditioned stimulus to be used (including the range of intensities).

The duration of stimuli and intervals between them.

The number of trials per session, with the intervals between them.

Many of these decisions can be made only after some preliminary experimentation. Supplementary decisions arise concerning the experimental room (soundproofing, etc.), the animal holder or other arrangement for fitting the subject to the apparatus, the methods of producing the stimuli and of recording their occurrence, the registration of the response, etc. The most helpful reference on the Pavlov procedures is that of Podkopaev (1926). Other suggestions may be found in Hull (1934), Hilgard and Marquis (1940), and Liddell (1942). Animal holders and recording equipment are described by Wendt (1938) and Wendt and Dodge (1938).

Controls against Irrelevant Responses

The conditioned response, like any other response, is recorded as a movement or a secretion. It has to be defined by its functional relations within a total stimulus-response situation. It is often difficult to distinguish between conditioned responses and the other kinds of responses that occur.

Original responses and pseudoconditioned responses. Conditioned stimuli are seldom completely neutral. They may evoke slight reactions at the beginning of experimentation. These responses may decrease if the conditioned stimulus is repeated in isolation. Hence preliminary habituation trials commonly precede conditioning. New responses may appear, however, without the introduction of the unconditioned stimulus. These are pseudoconditioned responses (Grether, 1938), and sufficient trials need to be run with the conditioned stimulus alone, either to permit them to appear or to assure that they are unlikely to appear. In human eyelid conditioning, they have been shown to be more likely to appear in response to visual stimuli if the subject is dark adapted (Grant and Norris, 1946).

Although pseudoconditioned responses may appear when the conditioned stimulus is presented alone, they are more likely to appear if trials with the unconditioned stimulus alone are interspersed among trials with the conditioned stimulus. Presentation of the unconditioned stimulus appears to raise the excitability in some manner. Pseudoconditioning of this sort is prevalent enough to require controls. If such controls are not run, changes may be attributed to the paired stimulation when they are not actually a function of the pairing.

If conditioning is conducted in daily sessions, usually at least one daily session should be devoted to these controls, prior to the undertaking of conditioning proper.

Responses to extraneous stimuli. Within conditioning proper there are three kinds of control trials: those with the conditioned stimulus alone, those with the unconditioned stimulus alone, and those without either of the stimuli. In trials without either stimulus, as much of the background as possible remains the same as during paired stimulation, except that the stimuli do not reach the subject. Responses that are the result of time relations or noisy switches or of other cues may be detected on these control trials. The matter of extraneous cues is especially important when thresholds are being determined. The controls recommended by Pavlov are probably excessive; we can obtain quantifiable conditioned responses without building elaborate soundproof laboratories. When the intended cues are sufficiently prominent, animals do not tend to react to marginal cues. This is, of course, a relative matter, but few experimenters have found it a handicap to be without specially constructed laboratories.

Some Favorable Arrangements

Instructions. It has been shown that instructions are important in human conditioning (Miller, 1939; Hilgard and Humphreys, 1938). If the experimenter tries to avoid giving instructions, the subject becomes self-instructed. The experiment is under better control if the experimenter sets the stage through his own instructions and then reports these instructions in his account of the experiment. One finding of some interest is that the usual instructions, supposedly producing a neutral attitude toward the stimuli, tend to produce a set not to respond (Miller, 1939).

Nonreinforced trials. Some experimenters have been wary of introducing nonreinforced trials in the midst of paired stimulations, lest extinction be introduced and conditioning delayed. The alternative, if a record is to be kept of the rate of conditioning, is to measure conditioning according to the prevalence of anticipatory conditioned responses within reinforced trials. Such responses are not unusual; they are the rule in conditioning experiments done with the more favorable intervals between conditioned and unconditioned stimuli.

Intervals too short for anticipatory responses to appear within paired stimulation tend to be unfavorable for conditioning, but in order to find this out we have to do experiments with such unfavorable intervals. To test for conditioning it is then necessary to intersperse test trials to the conditioned stimulus alone. According to present evidence, we need not fear that such nonreinforced trials will delay conditioning, for in experiments with partial or intermittent reinforcement there is no slowing up of conditioning even though reinforcement is

omitted on half or more of the trials (Brogden, 1939; Humphreys, 1939).

Nonreinforced trials within paired stimulation may in fact produce resistance to extinction when nonreinforcement becomes the rule (Humphreys, 1939). It is essential that all procedures be carefully thought out and fully reported if one study is to be made

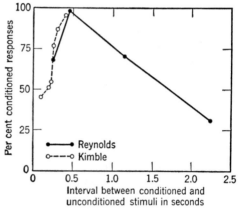

FIG. 6. Effect of stimulus separation upon simple eyelid conditioning. The interval plotted is that between the conditioned stimulus (light or sound) and the unconditioned stimulus (an air-puff to the eye) with human adult subjects. The most favorable interval appears to be at or near 0.5 second. Backward intervals, in which the conditioned stimulus follows the unconditioned, are not shown.

comparable to another, for many unexpected relations are found to hold.

Stimulus intervals. Although for phasic responses, like finger withdrawal or eyelid reactions, the most favorable stimulus interval appears to be about half a second between conditioned and unconditioned stimulus (Reynolds, 1945; Kimble, 1947), it is quite possible that smooth muscle responses may call for longer intervals. The practice in conditioning salivation, galvanic skin responses, and pupillary reactions has been to use somewhat longer intervals, but the critical experiments on time interval have not been done. It appears to be a fairly safe rule of thumb to expect the most favorable interval to be somewhat longer than the latent time of the conditioned response to the conditioned stimulus, so that this response may appear prior to the onset of the unconditioned stimulus and response. In the arrangement he called simultaneous conditioning, Pavlov had the conditioned stimulus precede the unconditioned stimulus by an interval from a fraction of a second to 5 seconds.

Trial intervals. Most experimenters have found it best to run but a few trials per day, in banks of not more than 10 trials, although several banks are sometimes run in a day. Overcrowding of trials, either through having them too close together or too many in one period, appears disadvantageous (Calvin, 1939).

Favorable arrangements for conditioned discrimination. The usual method of obtaining conditioned discrimination is the method of contrasts, in which one of a pair of stimuli is reinforced, the other not reinforced. The stimuli are presented one at a time in a random order. It is somewhat more satisfactory to establish the response to the positive stimulus first, before the discrimination is undertaken. This has the advantage that generalization or induction effects are less complicated, and discrimination proceeds more smoothly when the negative stimulus is later introduced. When both stimuli are present from the start, the situation parallels that of partial or intermittent reinforcement, and both stimuli share for a time in the reinforcement. This may delay discrimination.

Measures of Conditioning

Types of score. Provided accurate records of response are obtained, the progress of conditioning (or of extinction or discrimination) may be scored according to amplitude of responses, latency of responses, or relative frequency of responses. If all these measures are obtained, it is desirable to make frequency and amplitude as independent as possible by scoring amplitude only

for obtained responses. Then frequency will refer to the number of conditioned responses relative to the possible number, and amplitude and latency will both be descriptive of the obtained conditioned responses. Humphreys (1943a) has proposed using the term *magnitude* to refer to amplitude scores that are computed on the basis of all responses, including those of zero amplitude, reserving *amplitude* for scores derived from responses of measurable size.

It is extremely difficult to avoid some artificiality in scores because of inadequacies of recording. Thus the reliability of amplitude measures will be spuriously high if the measures are taken within a single period. Then the method of attaching the recording system to the subject may introduce a constant error. Frequency measures will depend upon the amplitude of response necessary before a response is recorded (Lumsdaine, 1941). If there is no inertia in the recording system, latency can be recorded accurately, except for the difficulty of determining when a response of small amplitude departs from its baseline.

Reliability of conditioning scores. Humphreys (1943a) has summarized data for the eyelid reaction which show what is to be expected in the scoring of conditioning according to the several movement characteristics. The reliabilities are given in Table 1. The acquisition-extinction correlations

TABLE 1

RELIABILITIES OF MEASURES OF STRENGTH OF CONDITIONED EYELID RESPONSES (AFTER HUMPHREYS, 1943a)

	Acquisition-Extinction		Segment-Segment		Odd-Even	
	N	r	N	r	N	r
Frequency	188	0.61	188	0.86	82	0.94
Amplitude	128	0.68	188	0.87	82	0.92
Magnitude	82	0.65	82	0.93	82	0.97
Latency	128	0.54	188	0.73	82	0.87

show to what extent we may use resistance to extinction as a measure of response strength during conditioning. The segment-segment correlation was used earlier by Campbell and Hilgard (1936) and Campbell (1938) in order to avoid correlated errors of measurement which make odd-even reliabilities too high. Trials were divided into fourths, and the totals of the first and last fourths are compared with the totals of the middle fourths. The odd-even correlations are presented for comparison. Humphreys believes the 'true' reliabilities to lie somewhere between the segment-segment correlations and the odd-even estimates.

Intercorrelations of measures of conditioning. In Table 2 are presented some inter-

TABLE 2

INTERCORRELATIONS OF MEASURES OF REFLEX SENSITIVITY AND OF CONDITIONED EYELID RESPONSES (AFTER HUMPHREYS, 1943a)

	Light Reflex	Crit.	Freq.	Mag.	Amp.	Lat.
Reflex to puff	0.35	−0.30	0.40	0.30	0.43	−0.09
Reflex to light		−0.42	0.45	0.35	0.30	−0.09
Criterion			−0.88	−0.63	−0.43	0.40
Frequency				0.71	0.47	−0.48
Magnitude					0.89	−0.25
Amplitude						−0.15

correlations of measures of reflex sensitivity and of conditioned eyelid responses. Reflex sensitivity to puff refers to the magnitude of eyelid responses to an air-puff on the cornea, the puff being alike for all subjects. Reflex sensitivity to light refers to the magnitude of reflex lid closure to a sudden illumination change, at a latency much shorter than that of the conditioned response. The criterion score is a special type of frequency score. It refers to the number of the trial upon which the fifth conditioned response occurred.

These tables indicate the sorts of information it would be desirable to have in relation to other responses used in conditioning experiments. Unfortunately only fragmentary additional data are available (e.g. Kellogg and Walker, 1938).

EXPERIMENTS ON OPERANT OR INSTRUMENTAL CONDITIONING

The experiments introduced by Skinner (1938) with the rat and later with the pigeon (Skinner, 1948) permit the study of a number of learning processes according to units of measurement unfamiliar in other situations. Therefore some of these arrangements will be described in detail.

The rat has usually been studied in a dark and soundproof box which contains a lever and a food receptacle. When the rat presses the lever a food pellet is dropped into the food receptacle. The rat, which has been maintained on a standard diet and rigid feeding schedule, responds and eats and responds again without leaving the box. A record is kept of its responses to the lever, plotted against time. Skinner prefers a cumulative record, so that each response raises the record line one notch. An extinction curve is obtained by disconnecting the food magazine so that food no longer is delivered when the lever is pressed.

Arrangements within Operant Conditioning

The most important arrangements besides those of regular reinforcement and extinction with nonreinforcement are those of periodic reconditioning, reinforcement at a fixed ratio, discrimination, and differentiation.

Periodic reconditioning refers to an arrangement under which food is delivered on a regular schedule, independent of the rate of lever pressing by the rat. That is, a pellet appears every 3 minutes or 6 minutes or 9 minutes, as the case may be. Under these circumstances uniform rates of responding tend to appear. The number of responses per reinforcement is described as the *extinction ratio*, e.g. 18:1. Pigeons trained under the arrangements of periodic reconditioning have been shown to develop highly stereotyped or ritualistic ("superstitious") behavior (Skinner, 1948).

Reinforcement at a fixed ratio consists of delivering food after a predetermined number of responses, e.g. every fifth or tenth response. By gradually increasing the ratio very rapid rates of responding can be obtained. Once established, the rule is that the rate will be higher, the fewer the reinforcements. After each reinforcement there is a delay followed by an accelerated increase in rate of responding.

Discrimination is set up in this situation by presenting food following the lever pressing only in the presence of a discriminatory stimulus, such as a light. The discrimination is established if the animal responds only when the light is on. The choice is between response and no response, not between alternative responses.

Differentiation of response refers to the situation in which lever pressing of a given force or producing a given excursion is rewarded. The animal then learns to restrict the range of its response to the limits set by the experimenter.

The method of approximation. Because the food appears in the same space where the animal is working, it is possible to train animals in the Skinner box to do what the experimenter wishes (within limits set by the animal's response repertory) by rewarding approach reactions. This makes possible fairly rapid teaching of responses otherwise difficult to elicit, such as visual discriminations. One of Skinner's demonstration experiments with the pigeon will be described, as illustrative of the method.*

A tame pigeon, about 1 year old, is reduced to about 80 per cent of its well-fed weight and fed once a day. On this schedule it is active as an experimental animal. A small food tray is arranged to swing into its wire cage by activation of a solenoid, and to swing out again when the current is shut

* Acknowledgment is made of a private communication from Dr. Skinner explaining his method, which was tried out successfully with the aid of Dr. Roger B. Loucks at the University of Washington during the summer of 1947.

off. The pigeon readily learns to come to the food tray at the sound of the solenoid. A pigeon thus prepared, and kept without food for 24 hours, is ready for experimentation. A white cardboard with a black spot is placed in the cage, and the pigeon is to be taught to peck at the spot. The pigeon may be activated by preliminary feeding with the mechanical tray. The hungry bird, in moving about the cage, eventually faces in the direction of the card. It is again fed. After it pecks five or six times the food is removed. Now the pigeon tends to return to the place where it was when the solenoid sounded. If it again faces the card it is again reinforced and again returns to where it was. The experimenter waits until it takes a step toward the card, then again reinforces. The fact that the behavior is disrupted by the pigeon's returning each time to the food tray does not matter. Presently it will be nearly against the card, each approach response being reinforced. Against the card it may attempt to fly up or do something else, but if always brought back by reinforcing it will eventually peck at the card. If the pecking is reinforced, it will be repeated. If the pigeon did not begin by pecking the spot, delay in reinforcement will cause it to vary its pecking somewhat, so that finally only pecks on the spot need be reinforced. The whole process requires about 3 to 5 minutes and may be demonstrated before a class, despite all the confusion of an interested audience. The same method makes possible very rapid teaching of discrimination, as between a black and white spot, or between a large and small spot, or between vertical and horizontal lines.

The method of approximation is the laboratory equivalent of what animal trainers have long done in order to achieve the remarkable performances of hunting dogs and circus animals. Although the illustrative experiment has been done with the pigeon, the method would undoubtedly work well with other animals. Some of the arrangements used by

Masserman (1943) in the development and cure of neuroses in cats are dynamically very similar.

Measures of Operant Conditioning

Because the animal remains in the apparatus, in the presence of the response mechanism, how often it responds depends upon itself rather than upon the experimenter. New types of scores are required in this situation, because a single trial does not have its conventional meaning.

Rate of response becomes a useful score. This may be defined as so many responses per unit of time, or as so many responses per reinforcement. This latter score, used by Skinner in reporting results of periodic reconditioning, is called an "extinction ratio" because it shows the number of nonreinforced responses (extinction responses) for each reinforcement.

When reinforcement ceases entirely, the total number of responses yielded before the animal ceases to respond provides a measure of resistance to extinction. This is used by Hull (1943) as one measure of strength. Skinner sometimes speaks of this total number of responses as making up a "reflex reserve."

Reliabilities of scores in the Skinner box experiment have not been reported, but there are studies of the variability of several types of extinction score (Humphreys, 1940; Walker, 1948).

MAZE AND DISCRIMINA-
TION EXPERIMENTS

The procedures and methods used in the study of animal learning have been well summarized by Warden, Jenkins, and Warner (1935), Munn (1933), Kreezer (1942), and Yerkes (1943). On the maintenance of laboratory animals, the manual by Warden, Ross, and Klein (1942) is useful. At this point only some general methodological considerations will be discussed and some precautions suggested.

Considerations Prior to Experimentation

Strains of animals. The albino rat differs in some situations from the rat with pigmented eyes. The wild rat differs from the laboratory rat. Mixed strains, because of their greater range of individual differences, may yield higher coefficients of reliability in standard learning situations than more homogeneous strains — without necessarily being more suitable than selected strains for the purposes intended. For some purposes, of course, homozygous strains are desirable. If the ideal of perfect homogeneity in both inheritance and training were obtained, reliability coefficients as ordinarily computed would reduce to zero. It is to some extent an absurd situation that we value the very coefficients that we do our best to reduce by careful inbreeding of experimental animals.

Feeding and maintenance schedule. In the course of long-continued experimentation, rats get older and larger. If they are on a reduced diet it is necessary that they be fed enough to increase in weight while growing, or their hunger motivation will be disturbed through inanition. Preferred motivational levels can be maintained by permitting young rats to gain weight and older rats to lose weight during the experimentation period (Stone, 1929a). Under these circumstances there is little change in learning ability with age over the period from 100 days to 2 years, so far as it has been studied in mazes, serial discrimination, and simple escape boxes.

For purposes of maintaining weight control it is desirable to have age-weight norms available for comparison. Although there are marked individual differences in well-fed weight, the norms are useful in showing age-weight trends for the two sexes. Representative values are given in Table 3. Because these norms are inappropriate with different stocks and different diets, it is preferable to have norms for the local colony. The Stanford colony, for example, falls below the King norm after 60 days.

TABLE 3

AGE-WEIGHT NORMS FOR ALBINO RATS
(AFTER KING, 1915)

Age in Days	Average Body Weight in Grams	
	Males	Females
13	17	16
30	49	46
60	123	107
90	185	148
120	223	173
151	245	186
182	258	197
212	268	197
243	280	210
273	281	211
304	296	219
334	301	222
365	306	223
395	314	221
425	312	216
455	324	220
485	326	235

Taming and pretraining. The handling of the animals prior to the experimentation proper undoubtedly makes a difference in their later performances. Therefore it is important to specify as precisely as possible what this prehistory has been. Animals raised in isolation may differ in some respects from animals raised in a cage with other animals. Those animals that are frightened by handling approach the experimental situation differently from those accustomed to being handled. Pretraining corresponds in animal training to instructions in human learning, and for purposes of comparative study careful controls of pretraining are essential. An animal that has been taught to run down a straight alley to receive food in a box at the end is already to some extent a "maze-wise" rat when placed at the start of an alley maze. The study by Jackson (1932) on transfer presents much relevant material. Karn and Porter (1946) have shown the influence of different kinds of pretraining on the latent learning experiment.

Natural Propensities Affecting Experimental Design

We can save time in the training of animals and obtain performances more nearly representative of the animal's capacity if we arrange the experiment in a way that is psychologically natural, that is, in accordance with behavior that is characteristic of the organism being studied. The rat has evolved as a good maze-running animal. Birds may prove to be superior to the rat in their ease of learning visual discriminations. Animal trainers do not expect the same sorts of performances from cats as from dogs, from sea lions as from monkeys. Even within performances that are readily obtainable there are types of bias that affect the design of experiments. Such natural biases have been most fully studied in the rat maze situation, although we know a good deal about other forms, such as the chimpanzee (Yerkes, 1943).

Position preferences. One of the most common tendencies found in rat learning is that of turning one way at a choice-point (either right or left) beyond chance expectancy. Because the maze is a series of such choices and because the discrimination experiment depends upon such choices, the apparatus and stimulus presentation sequences must be so arranged that an animal with a right-going or a left-going tendency will not achieve a score above chance. Since these tendencies may be strengthened by frustration, care must be taken that the problem set is not too difficult.

Stimulus preferences. In discrimination experiments there is often an initial preference for one of a pair of stimuli. If this happens to be the positive stimulus, the discrimination may appear to be easy. If this happens to be the negative stimulus, the discrimination may appear to be difficult. Seeing rats, for example, tend to prefer darker to lighter visual stimuli, whereas rats with cerebral lesions may reverse this preference (Krechevsky, 1936).

It is important to test for such initial preferences before discrimination experiments are undertaken. Half the animals should be run against their original preferences, half in accordance with their original preferences. The reason for dividing the group in this way is that the effects of frustration are not completely understood. It is not known whether training in line with original preferences is more or less satisfactory than training against original preferences. Maier, Glaser, and Klee (1940) suggest that animals that have learned in accordance with original preferences transfer more easily to new situations (including reversal of the discrimination) than animals that have learned against original preferences.

Sequence preferences. In addition to position habits, in which the same direction of turn is preferred, there are both single and double alternation habits. In simple alternation the rat tends to turn now right, now left. On a simple T-maze the commonest response on trial 2 is to choose opposite to trial 1. Double alternation, a less common sequence preference, is twice to the right followed by twice to the left. Gellerman has provided a table of stimulus sequences that prevent scores above chance from occurring by position habits, simple alternation, or double alternation. These sequences are reproduced in Table 4.

Centrifugal swing. The inertia of running produces a tendency for the rat to run off at a tangent when the choice-point is so arranged that one path (either true path or blind alley) more nearly continues the directional set already present. Ballachey and Buel (1934), extending Schneirla's earlier observations on ants (Schneirla, 1929), were able to predict which blinds in a multiple-T maze would be entered most frequently by the rat on the early runs. The tendency shows even on the first run, before any learning of the maze pattern can have taken place. This is one reason for preferring mazes of the linear type, as earlier described.

TABLE 4

TRIAL ORDERS TO AVOID SCORES DUE TO POSITION HABITS, SIMPLE ALTERNATION, AND DOUBLE ALTERNATION (AFTER GELLERMAN, 1933*b*)

1	R R R L L R L R L L	23	L R R R L L R L L R
2	R R R L L R L L R L	24	L R R L R R L L L R
3	R R L R L R R L L L	25	L R R L R L L L R R
4	R R L R L L R R L L	26	L R R L L R R L L R
5	R R L R L L L R R L	27	L R R L L R L L R R
6	R R L L R R L R L L	28	L R R L L L R R L R
7	R R L L R R L L R L	29	L R R L L L R L R R
8	R R L L R L R R L L	30	L R L R R L L L R R
9	R R L L R L L R R L	31	L R L L R R R L L R
10	R R L L L R R L R L	32	L R L L R R L L R R
11	R R L L L R L R R L	33	L R L L R L L R R R
12	R L R R L R R L L L	34	L L R R R L R L L R
13	R L R R L L R R L L	35	L L R R R L L R L R
14	R L R R L L L R R L	36	L L R R L R R L L R
15	R L R L L R R R L L	37	L L R R L R L L R R
16	R L L R R R L R L L	38	L L R R L L R R L R
17	R L L R R R L L R L	39	L L R R L L R L R R
18	R L L R R L R R L L	40	L L R L R R R L L R
19	R L L R R L L R R L	41	L L R L R R L L R R
20	R L L R L R R R L L	42	L L R L R L L R R R
21	R L L R L L R R R L	43	L L L R R L R R L R
22	R L L L R R L R R L	44	L L L R R L R L R R

Clarity of relation between reward and rewarded behavior. Experience with direct and indirect methods of delayed reaction and with the various methods of setting up discrimination experiments shows the importance of structuring carefully the relation between the behavior to be encouraged and discouraged and the rewards (or punishments) used. What such structuring means will be described differently according to one's psychological theory, but the practical consequence is the same. The situation must be clear to the learner. This means that the figure-ground structure should be adequate, that secondary reinforcements should enhance the discriminations required, that reward and punishment should be prompt. Between the experiments of Hull (1933*a*) and of Leeper (1935) there were great differences in the ease of teaching rats to go one way when hungry, the other way when thirsty. What was a relatively slight change in the experimental arrangement made an enormous change in difficulty. The difference is to be attributed to the clarity of the situation (or the differential nature of the secondary reinforcements).

A distinction hard to state satisfactorily is that between something simple for the learner and something clear to the learner. In a mechanically easy but psychologically unclear situation, a learner may achieve the correct performance promptly, but the learning may be highly stereotyped and show little transfer to new situations. This kind of learning is easy, but unclear. On the other hand, in some insight experiments the solution may be obtained with great difficulty, but once the principle is mastered it is clear and readily used in new situations. This kind of situation is difficult, but eventually clear. Improvement of experimental controls, following the warnings of the Clever Hans experiment (Pfungst, 1911), have tended to overmechanize experimental arrangements, and only in later years have we recognized the importance of making a more careful psychological analysis of the situation confronting the animal learner.

Other factors. Animal behavior in the maze situation is a very complicated affair. In his attempt to predict the precise behavior of blind alley entrance and elimination, Tryon has worked out a quantitative theory of ten components: direction sets, food pointing, short-cut, counter tendency, centrifugal swing, adaptation, lassitude, exit gradient, inertia, and conflict (Tryon, 1940a, b).

Measures of Maze and Discrimination Learning

Types of score. In the maze the most obvious scores are the amounts of time required to run the maze on successive trials, and the number of blind alleys entered per trial. More analytical scores show which blind alleys were entered on which trial and give added information such as the depth of blind alley entrance, the tendency to run along the outer or inner wall, the nature of

retracings, and so on. Some criterion of mastery is commonly chosen, usually one or more errorless runs. It is necessary to make some decision about the first run through the maze, because some animals may not complete the run in a reasonable time. In such a case an arbitrary maximum time is often allowed. Pretraining that results in a successful maze run on the first trial is more satisfactory, because arbitrary scores prevent adequate statistical treatment.

In the discrimination experiment the usually reported scores are the proportion of correct choices, or the number of trials required to reach a criterion. An important statistical characteristic of the criterion in discrimination learning has been reported by Grant (1946, 1947). Because in a choice between two things repeated choices of one of the pair are likely to occur by chance, a criterion has to be selected such that it would be unlikely to be reached in the number of trials required for the discrimination. Thus, if an animal requires 200 trials to learn a discrimination, a criterion of 5 successive correct choices would not do, for that criterion would be reached by chance too frequently in 200 trials. Merely tossing coins, in other words, would lead to this kind of evidence of discrimination. Only a longer run would be statistically improbable. Table 5 is useful in determining how long a run is needed for significance. Additional tables are provided by Grant (1947), covering other standards of significance.

Reliability of maze scores. Many studies have been made of the reliability of maze scores. Representative coefficients have been assembled by Kreezer (1942) and by Tryon (1942). The most common measure of reliability is determined by correlating the errors made on odd and even trials, then correcting the correlation by the Spearman-Brown formula. Under favorable circumstances the reliabilities of mazes such as the multiple-T maze reach 0.99. These circumstances include a large number of choice-points (17 to 20), heterogeneous rats (mixed

TABLE 5

CRITERIA FOR DETERMINING LENGTH OF RUN
REQUIRED FOR STATISTICAL SIGNIFICANCE WITH
DIFFERENT NUMBERS OF TOTAL TRIALS (AFTER
GRANT, 1947)

S (Length of Run of Successes)	Largest Number of Total Trials for Which Probability of a Run of at Least S Successes is Below 0.05			
	$p = \frac{1}{2}$	$p = \frac{1}{3}$	$p = \frac{1}{4}$	$p = \frac{1}{5}$
2				2
3			5	9
4		8	19	42
5	6	21	73	203
6	10	60	284	1006
7	17	173	1125	5014
8	31	510	4486	
9	59	1521		
10	112	4551		
11	218			
12	429			
13	850			
14	1692			
15	3374			

Note: p refers to the proportion that successful choices bear by chance to total alternatives. In the usual discrimination experiment $p = \frac{1}{2}$. The experimenter decides in advance how many trials are to be run. Suppose in a discrimination experiment the decision is to run 429 trials. The table shows that a subject may be said to have learned by the chosen criterion if it makes 12 consecutive successful responses by its 429th trial. The end of one day and the beginning of the next must be permitted to count as part of a run.

strains of pigmented and nonpigmented rats), doors to prevent retracing, automatic recording, uniformity of handling, and other conditions. Representative experiments obtaining such high reliability coefficients are those of Tryon (1930) and Brown and Ghiselli (1938). Provided similar favorable conditions hold, multiple-U and multiple-Y mazes may also yield high reliabilities.

Other methods of computing reliability fall into two general classes: first, those using data from a single learning series; second, those using data from two learning series. Within a single learning it is possible to use time scores instead of error scores, segments of learning instead of odd-even trials, odd-even blinds instead of odd-even trials, and so on. Comparisons of various methods have been made by Leeper (1932) and by Spence (1932). When repeated learnings are used there are still more possibilities. One method is that of learning another maze of a form comparable to the one first learned. Another is to relearn the same maze after an interval of time. Obviously these different measures of reliability imply different definitions, and the correlations obtained depend upon somewhat different sorts of consistencies. The only generalization that can be made is that these methods all yield lower reliability coefficients than those obtained by correlating errors on odd and even trials. Representative relearning coefficients over intervals of time up to 230 days run from 0.75 to 0.89 (Leeper, 1932; Tryon, 1931b; McNemar and Stone, 1931); alternate forms yield somewhat lower coefficients, a representative range being 0.56 to 0.81 (Commins, McNemar, and Stone, 1932; Tryon, 1931a).

Reliability of visual discrimination learning. Stone (1928) found that a relatively high coefficient (0.94) could be obtained in a five-unit multiple light-dark discrimination box, provided the first 10 of 40 trials were omitted. Brown and Ghiselli (1934) report a reliability coefficient of 0.98 for their multiple visual-discrimination apparatus. Williams (1929) found a coefficient of 0.96 for errors on 24 trials of a one-chamber box. Apparently consistent measures of individual differences may be obtained for such tasks.

Reliabilities and interrelations of other measures of animal learning. A great many measures of animal drive and learning have been reported in studies making factorial analyses of animal behavior. Among these are studies by Anderson (1938), Thorndike (1935), and Vaughn (1937). In general, even though reliabilities of the separate instruments may be high, intercorrelations between tasks using unlike apparatus are quite low.

EXPERIMENTS ON MOTOR SKILLS

A great variety of materials have been used in the study of the learning of motor skills, among them ball tossing, dart throwing, telegraphy, archery, spool packing, digit-symbol substitution, mirror star tracing, and pursuit learning. The maze is sometimes included as a skill, but its motor aspects are in fact subordinate to the serial learning of choices, often learned verbally. These tasks are commonly used as tests of motor proficiency, in which case the problem of learning is subordinated to that of individual differences. The two problems are related in that a measure of individual differences obtained in a learning situation can be truly reliable only if there is some prediction made about ultimate level of skill with practice.

Determining Effects of Conditions of Practice

Skills lend themselves well to studies of the most efficient means of practicing — by wholes or parts, with massed or distributed repetitions, with or without manual guidance, and so on. There are two chief arrangements for conducting such experiments. One makes use of a new group of subjects for each new condition studied. This is the familiar control-group method, and its logical and statistical comparisons are best understood. The second arrangement makes use of the same subjects over again under the various conditions being tested. This has the advantage of assuring that the background learning abilities are really alike throughout, so that smaller groups may be used. The disadvantage is that the different conditions are used at different stages in practice (at different stages in "learning how to learn"), and controls are necessary, which introduces statistical difficulties. The arrangement of counterbalanced practice effects is sometimes referred to as the method

of equal average order (Robinson, 1929). The methods of the control group and of equal average order both require some further comments.

Method of the control group. The main problem in establishing a control group and an experimental group is to ascertain that both groups are representative samples of a single population, so that the groups may be considered alike, within the limits of sampling errors, at the beginning of practice. Only then can differences under two or more conditions of practice be attributed to the experimental variable or variables. From a sampling point of view, the simplest procedure is to draw the two samples independently in some unbiased way. The initial scores of the two samples may then be compared to demonstrate that such matching was indeed satisfactory.

An alternative is to pair the subjects in experimental and control groups on the basis of some variable correlated with the experimental variable. Such pairing cannot assure that the groups are representative of the whole population, but it can improve the probability that they are matched for the purposes of the experimental comparison. Economy is introduced, provided the matching method results in correlated scores between the matched pairs on the experimental variable.

The correlational term that enters into computations of significance of differences is not always between the same pair of measures. The correlational term most commonly used is that between the scores whose differences are being tested. This requires that the subjects of the control and experimental groups be individually matched, and that the experimental and control groups be of the same size. Another possibility is that the correlation is between scores on the matching variable (obtained prior to practice) and the scores whose differences are being tested. In this case subjects need not be matched individually, and the two groups (experimental and control) need not be of the same size. All that is required is that experimental and control groups have the same initial mean and standard deviation in the matching variable. One control group may thus serve for several different experimental comparisons in which a correlational term enters, thereby introducing considerable saving in experimental time and subjects. The appropriate formulas to be used in the two methods, and considerations affecting their use, may be found in McNemar (1940).

The logic of the control group is somewhat modified in the experimental designs, made familiar by Fisher (1938), which are appropriate for treatment through analysis of variance. Instead of holding all background factors alike at a single value and changing one variable at a time, the one variable is studied against a background in which other variables represent different values, but in randomized fashion. The two methods lead to similar experimental arrangements when each condition of practice studied in the design for the analysis of variance makes use of a representative sample of subjects drawn from the same population. Economy is introduced by analysis of variance because all subjects of all groups enter into all comparisons. Suppose, for example, there are sixteen conditions of practice, representing different combinations of the experimental variables. Then, with but a single subject in each condition, the effect of any variable in the design is tested in relation to the performance of all sixteen subjects.

Factorial design does more than provide economy: it permits analyses otherwise impossible. For example, Grant and Schneider (1948) by means of such a design solved the baffling problem of distinguishing at once between strength of response and strength of association as functions of stimulus intensity.

Method of equal average order (counterbalanced order). When it is not feasible to use separate experimental and control groups (as in the extreme case when one subject alone is available for testing, e.g. after brain surgery), practice effects may be equalized by presenting two conditions of practice in an A–B–B–A order. That is, the first test is under condition A; then there are two tests under condition B; then another under A. Whatever initial advantage condition A has because of freshness is counterbalanced by the disadvantage of fatigue (or boredom) in the final position; whatever initial disadvantage it has because of novelty is compensated for by its final advantage after the intervening practice on B. If such changes progressed uniformly throughout learning, the A–B–B–A order would provide perfect balancing. Because the changes are not actually linear, the means obtained by averaging A-scores and B-scores are not strictly comparable. An additional objection, however, is that variability may not be controlled even though the means are. This arises because some A-scores are obtained early and others late in practice. A correction can be introduced by considering the average of a subject's scores from the first and final quarter to be a single score, representing A-scores, and the average for the second and third quarter to be a single score, representing B-scores. Such scores will make the distributions of A-scores and B-scores from a number of subjects as much alike as the experimental arrangements permit, although some distortion persists.*

More complete rotations of conditions may be used when there are several conditions, such as:

ABC–CBA
BCA–ACB
CAB–BAC

When several conditions enter, as in the arrangement above, some statistical difficulties arise because the controlled orders do not permit the use of statistical formulas

* The point is that, if there were no differences in conditions A and B, A-scores and B-scores should turn up with the same means and standard deviations. This is the ideal of the method of equal average order. This can be tested by running in the order A–A–A–A, then comparing the scores in first and fourth quarter with those in the second and third.

that assume chance variations. The problem has been discussed in some detail by Melton (1936). If chance orders replace systematic ones, a better estimate of the reliability of the means may be obtained, but the price paid is that the means are, in fact, less reliable. The statistical problems are too complex to be discussed here. When the analysis-of-variance technique is used in any situation in which the same subject is used more than once, it is necessary to adapt the usual formulas so that a distinction is made between the variables and interactions that involve correlated means and those that do not. A specimen computational procedure in learning situations is given by Humphreys (1943b).

Measures in Experiments on Motor Skills

Time scores versus work scores. Most of the tasks used in the study of skill permit an arbitrary definition of a trial, and a choice between time scores (time per unit amount) and work scores (amount per unit time) becomes necessary. When both scores produce symmetrical distributions about means representing similar performances, the scores are equally reliable and essentially interchangeable (McNemar, 1934). There are, however, conveniences of use that in many situations favor work scores. These conveniences of scores in terms of amount per unit time include: (1) scores can be obtained for the poorest learners (who receive a score of zero if they do not achieve anything measurable *); (2) improvement is shown by a rising curve, which produces divergences of scores later in practice when small differences are of greater theoretical interest; and (3) the experiment is easily conducted in groups because trials are of

* This does not solve the problem of absolute zero of performance, because an achievement not scorable is not necessarily no achievement. Scores in terms of time per unit amount are still at a disadvantage in that the score for a learner who cannot complete the assigned task must be entered either as requiring infinite time or as of some arbitrary value.

uniform length for all learners throughout the learning.

Work scores are not feasible when the nature of the material is such as to have a natural completion point, as in the assembling of an object from its parts or in the running of a maze. In general, it is desirable to present the data in the form obtained, and not to attempt conversion in any manner that will distort their meaning. Thus it is mathematically possible to convert scores in time per unit amount to scores in amount per unit time. This conversion will not always yield the same scores that would have been obtained had the experimental arrangements been altered to make the units of the converted scores directly appropriate. Thus the actual time to type exactly 100 words is different from what the average time to type 100 words is if derived from an assignment to see how many words can be typed in 15 minutes. The latter method would tend to result in longer times per 100 words.

Many other kinds of scores are possible. Direct measures closely analogous to time scores and work scores are to be preferred — scores such as errors per trial or per task. Derived scores are to be avoided, especially those that attempt to weight speed and accuracy, or those that make use of ratios computed with variable denominators. These seldom increase reliability, and they make difficult the comparison of results with those of other studies done by slightly altered methods.

Reliabilities of scores obtained in experiments on motor skills. Because individual differences in motor skills are both great and relatively persistent, high reliabilities may be obtained. Some representative reliabilities are given in Table 6. It should be emphasized that these coefficients are useful chiefly to determine how successfully the learning task can be used as a measure of relatively stable individual differences. In themselves they do not tell anything about how representative the task is of learning,

TABLE 6

SOME RELIABILITY COEFFICIENTS OBTAINED IN MOTOR SKILLS EXPERIMENTS

Type of Task	Reported by	Nature of Coefficient	N	r
Spool packing	McNemar (1934)	Work scores vs time scores	50	0.925
		Work scores vs work scores	50	0.945
Card sorting	McNemar (1934)	Work scores vs time scores	50	0.954
		Work scores vs work scores	50	0.934
	Hilgard and Sait (1941)	Odd-even time scores	50	0.99
		Odd-even discrepancy scores ("aspiration")	50	0.86
Pursuit rotor	Hilgard and Sait (1941)	Odd-even work scores	50	0.99
		Odd-even discrepancy scores ("aspiration")	50	0.95
Punchboard maze	Hall (1936)	Odd-even errors	100	0.955
		Gain, trials 1–13 vs trials 2–14	100	0.67
Stylus maze	Hall (1936)	Odd-even errors	100	0.927
		Gain, trials 1–13 vs trials 2–14	100	0.44

or how useful it is in relation to any of the special problems of learning, such as the determination of the form of the practice curve. A task may yield overall reliability of high order and yet yield unreliable gains, as in the maze tasks reported in the table. The low reliabilities for gains in this case are due chiefly to the unreliability of the first trial in a maze experiment; the coefficients would undoubtedly have been higher if the comparisons had been made, for example between trials 2 to 14 and 3 to 15.

If the primary interest is in some measure of improvement, rather than in sustained level of performance, the usual reliability coefficient should be replaced by one based upon the stability of trends. The method of trend analysis proposed by Alexander (1946) has possibilities in this direction. In any event a reliability coefficient always has to be computed in relation to the problem at hand, and a task reliable for one purpose may or may not be reliable for another.

EXPERIMENTS ON MEMORIZATION AND RETENTION

Although experiments upon skill may also become experiments upon retention, verbal

or perceptual materials have more often been used in conventional memory experiments. What materials were used reflected in part the contemporary theoretical interest in memory. When the problem of memory was that of the decay of the memory image, it was natural to use pictures or objects, which could be recalled in imagery. When the problem was that of associative strength, it was easy to see the importance of verbal materials to be committed to memory. With the shift to more dynamic problems, materials with more personal reference became important. If amnesia or repression or other forms of motivational distortion are to be studied, the materials have to be appropriate to the hypotheses being tested.

Materials for the Study of Memorization and Retention

Nonsense verbal materials. Ebbinghaus (1885) used both meaningful and relatively nonsense materials in his pioneer studies. He invented the nonsense syllable (a vowel between two consonants, not found as a word in the dictionary). The English language makes pronunciation of many such combinations difficult, so that Luh (1922), while retaining the Ebbinghaus syllable, introduced the practice of spelling out the syllables during memorization. This practice has been followed since by those trained in the Chicago tradition, under Carr, Robinson, McGeoch, and Melton. If syllables were to be spelled out, Witmer (1935) argued that more combinations would be available if three consonants were used, omitting vowels entirely, and she provided a list of consonant groups graded according to the extent to which they suggested words. Three-place numerals have also been used parallel to nonsense syllables and to consonant units. Other artificial materials have been proposed, such as four-letter nonsense syllables (more pronounceable in English than three-letter ones), and dissyllabic items, constructed of three consonants and two vowels (Woodworth, 1938).

Sets of rules for the construction of non-sense syllable lists have been proposed from time to time. The following rules are typical: *

1. A consonant appears as the first letter of a syllable only once within a list.

2. A consonant appears as the third letter of a syllable only once within a list.

3. No vowel occurs more than once within any four consecutive syllables.

4. No consonant appears more than once in any four consecutive syllables.

5. No two letters of a syllable in a list are the same as two letters of another syllable in the same list.

6. In so far as possible the list is considered as a circular series, so that the rules apply if the first syllables of the list are considered to follow the end of the list.

7. Alphabetical sequences of consonants from syllable to syllable and within a syllable are avoided as far as possible, e.g.

* These rules represent extensions of Luh's (1922) list as suggested by Melton (unpublished). The rules cannot always be followed strictly, and additional rules need to be provided concerning similarities and differences between lists to be used in retroactive and proactive inhibition experiments. See, for example, Melton and Irwin (1940).

avoiding the sequences POK-LEJ, or a syllable like *LEM*.

8. The syllables are chosen in reference to their degree of association value.

Six lists constructed according to these rules are presented in Table 7.

TABLE 7

Specimen 12-Unit Nonsense Syllable Lists of Low Association Value (Average Association Values According to Glaze) *

TAJ	YIC	HUZ	CEX	YAD	MEP
ZIN	QOM	GOK	MOQ	FEP	GAW
VEC	GEP	YIN	RUY	SUH	KOJ
YOX	DUZ	TEV	GAF	JIK	CIB
FUQ	RIJ	ZAD	LIQ	WOZ	ZUR
BIP	NAW	XUR	KOC	LEQ	TEY
DAK	XOL	QIG	QUZ	XAF	WOQ
XEW	HUQ	LOJ	DEJ	MUJ	XIG
CUG	TEF	DEH	TAH	RIY	NAH
JOF	ZIK	BUP	WOG	KEB	JEC
QID	VOB	WIX	FIK	QON	QUT
LEH	PAH	KAQ	VUS	GUW	YOF
26.7	27.3	27.3	26.2	24.5	22.7

* Prepared by Melton and Malmo (unpublished).

The calibration of nonsense syllables according to their association values, that is, according to the ease with which they suggest words, was first undertaken by Glaze (1928), whose published list of syllables was used in determining the association values of the syllables presented in Table 7. Hull (1933b) used a somewhat superior method, in that the associated items were called for in a situation more nearly approximating that of the usual memory experiment, but he did not calibrate as many syllables as Glaze. Krueger (1934) extended Glaze's list. Witmer (1935) calibrated 4,534 consonant groups by a method similar to that of Glaze.

The Glaze list, with deletion of duplications and of syllables in which "y" was used as a vowel, is reproduced in Table 8. A list of syllables of low association values, making use of information from the studies of Glaze, Hull, and Krueger, has been prepared by Melton (unpublished) and is reproduced in Table 9. A selection of Witmer consonant groups is given in Table 10.

TABLE 8

ASSOCIATION VALUE OF NONSENSE SYLLABLES (AFTER GLAZE, 1928) *

100%			93%			87%			80%		
BAL	LIK	RAC	BAC	JON	RAB	BIC	KET	ROG	BIF	JOS	SEK
BAS	LIM	TAK	BES	KAF	RAS	BIR	KIS	ROQ	BOD	JUN	SEN
BEC	LIQ	TAL	BIL	KIL	REF	BOC	KUC	SAB	BOM	KIP	SIK
BEL	LIS	TAM	BIS	LAK	REM	BOK	LAF	SAF	BUC	KOF	SOM
BER	LIV	TER	BOR	LAN	RIC	BOT	LAM	SED	BUK	KOL	SOY
BEV	LON	TES	BUZ	LAR	ROS	BUX	LAS	SID	CAV	KOM	TAS
BIZ	LOS	TIC	CIR	LAZ	RUJ	CAK	LEF	SIG	CEL	KOZ	TEC
BOL	LOV	TEX	COF	LEC	RUL	CER	LEK	SUG	CID	LAT	TIF
BUL	MAK	TIG	COS	LEV	SAK	CIG	LEN	SUL	DAL	LAV	TIK
BUR	MEX	VAC	COV	LIB	SAV	COR	LEP	TEP	DAP	LEM	TIL
CEN	MOD	VES	COZ	LIC	SEC	CUL	LES	TOK	DAW	LIZ	TOL
CIN	MON	VIC	CUF	LOB	SEV	DEB	LIN	TOR	DEL	LOD	TUC
COL	NAR	VIF	CUM	LOC	SIC	DER	LOF	TOX	DEV	LOK	TUS
CUS	NAV	VIK	DEF	LOY	SIL	DEY	LUS	TUF	DIK	LOR	TUX
DAR	NOV	VIN	DEK	LUK	SOL	DOR	MAG	TUK	DIL	LOX	VAX
DEC	PAC	VIS	DET	LUN	SOV	DUK	MER	TUL	DIT	LUM	VEW
DEP	PAS	WAK	DOM	MAL	SUD	DUR	MID	TYC	DIZ	LUR	WEN
DIC	PED	WAT	DOP	MAS	TEL	FAC	MOC	VEG	DOW	MAB	WES
DIF	PES	WEV	DOS	MED	TIR	FIC	MOS	VEL	DUT	MAC	WIC
DIS	PIL	WIL	DUS	MIL	TOS	GEN	MOV	VER	FER	MAJ	WID
DOB	PUF	WIS	FAB	MIN	TUR	GER	NAM	WAV	FIL	MAX	WUD
DOV	PUS	WOM	FAK	MIR	VAR	GES	NEG	WIM	FIS	MAZ	WUL
DOZ	QIL		FAL	MOL	VAS	GIB	NEV	WIP	FIJ	MIK	YEG
DUC	RAC		FAV	MUF	VET	GIL	NIL	WIR	FOD	MIS	YEH
DUL	RAD		FEM	MUR	VIL	GIR	NOC	WIZ	FOK	MOT	YEP
FAM	RAL		FEV	MUS	VIR	GOL	NOK	WOD	FOM	MUC	YON
FAS	RAV		FIV	NEC	VOL	HAN	PAK	WOL	FOS	NAS	
FEL	REG		FOL	NEK	YAC	HOD	PEB	WOR	FOT	NAZ	
FES	REV		FON	NIG	YAJ	HOF	PEK	XAM	FOW	NEB	
GIV	ROM		FUS	NIT	YAR	HOR	PEY		FUD	NEL	
GUL	ROP		FUT	NOM	YEL	HOV	PON		FUL	NES	
HAV	ROV		FUZ	NOS	YOK	HIG	QES		FUM	NOZ	
HAZ	RUD		GAB	NUF	YUT	HIK	QIT		GAN	PAM	
HIL	RUF		GOB	NUG		HUD	QIZ		GEL	PAX	
HOB	RUS		GON	NUL		HUF	RAJ		GID	PEL	
HOL	SAR		GOV	PAV		JAC	RAK		GOR	PIK	
HOM	SEL		HIN	PIC		JAV	RAZ		GOS	PIR	
HON	SEM		HIR	POK		JEN	REK		GUZ	POM	
HUR	SEP		HOS	POL		JIL	RES		HAW	RAF	
JAN	SER		JAS	POS		JUM	RET		HET	REC	
JEL	SOC		JAZ	PUB		JUR	RIF		HUL	REN	
JIN	SOF		JER	PUD		KAN	RIN		HUP	REY	
JUS	SUB		JES	PUL		KAS	RIS		HUV	RIL	
KEN	SUR		JOK	PUR		KEL	RIV		JEM	RON	
LIF	SUT		JOL	PUZ		KEP	ROC		JOR	SAN	

* Syllables appearing more than once have been eliminated. These were called to my attention by A. W. Melton. Syllables using "y" as a vowel have also been eliminated. The association values assume that the syllables will be spelled rather than pronounced.

TABLE 8 (*Continued*)

ASSOCIATION VALUE OF NONSENSE SYLLABLES (AFTER GLAZE, 1928)

73%			67%			60%			53%		
BAF	LIY	WIV	BAP	LIX	VOS	BAC	MES	WUN	BAJ	NUH	ZEB
BAV	LOM	WOF	BAK	LOH	VOT	BAW	MUK	XAS	BIJ	NUR	ZEP
BEF	LUV	WOV	BEQ	LUF	WAB	BEM	MUV	XEM	BOP	NUV	ZET
BOV	MAH	XES	BIK	LUT	WAC	BEZ	NAD	XER	BOQ	NUZ	ZEM
BUF	MUL	ZEK	CAS	MEG	WAM	BOH	NEM	YAS	BOZ	PAJ	ZUL
CAG	MUZ		CAY	MEK	WOK	CED	NIF	YIS	CAZ	PIV	
CIM	NEP		CIF	MEL	WUR	CEM	NIK	ZAG	CEG	POV	
COK	NER		CIP	MOK	YAL	CEW	NIS	ZIG	CUY	POY	
CUV	NEX		CIV	NEZ	YER	CIX	NOP		DAF	QAT	
CUZ	NUP		DAG	NIM	ZAR	CIY	NUS		DOJ	QIX	
DAT	PEC		DAV	NOG		CUK	PAB		DUP	QOT	
DEM	PIF		DEG	NOX		CUN	PAZ		DUY	QOZ	
DEX	PIQ		DEZ	NUD		DAS	PIM		FAP	RIK	
DOF	PUM		DUV	NUM		DES	POG		FAX	RIQ	
DOK	QAC		DUQ	PIX		DIY	POW		FIP	ROF	
DOX	QAK		FAW	POF		DUX	QAW		FOV	SIQ	
FEB	QAL		FIY	QAN		FEK	QEL		GAC	SOH	
FEN	QIC		FUG	QIK		FET	QIP		GEV	SUJ	
FID	RAQ		GAV	QIR		FEY	QOG		GOP	TEB	
FIM	REL		GIF	QIV		FOZ	RAH		HEX	TIQ	
FOC	REW		GIM	RAX		GIP	REB		HUJ	TOC	
GUR	RIZ		GIS	REQ		GOZ	SAH		JAL	TOF	
HAC	ROK		GOF	ROH		HIY	SAQ		JED	TOQ	
HAF	ROX		GOM	ROL		HIZ	SAZ		JIR	VAP	
HAR	SIV		GUP	ROZ		HUK	SEF		KAR	VAQ	
HEV	SIZ		HAB	RUP		HUX	SIB		KAW	VAY	
HIB	SOK		HAK	SEG		JIB	SIY		KER	VIP	
HOK	SOG		HED	SEQ		JOH	SUK		KIB	VOK	
HOX	SUC		JAG	SEY		JUK	TAV		KIQ	VOM	
HUS	TEM		JAQ	SEZ		KAY	TAY		KOB	WEM	
JAD	TIB		JIF	SIM		KES	TIY		KON	WEP	
JAK	TIX		JIT	SUW		KIC	VEZ		KUB	WEX	
JEF	TOB		JOP	SUZ		KIM	VOX		KUD	WOB	
JOC	TOG		JOV	TAF		KOV	VUB		KUF	WUZ	
JOW	TUM		JUB	TAQ		KOW	VUL		KUM	XAN	
JUP	TUN		KOP	TAZ		KUS	WAQ		LER	XEL	
JUV	VAG		KUM	TUP		KUT	WEC		LOQ	XIR	
KAC	VAM		KUP	VEM		LIR	WEK		LOZ	XUN	
KAD	VEY		KUR	VEN		LUZ	WUF		LUQ	YAK	
KAV	VUG		LEY	VIT		MAV	WUM		MIC	YAX	
KEW	VOY								MIQ	YEZ	
KIR	WAF								NAJ	YUL	
KOT	WER								NEY	YUR	
LAQ	WEY								NOH	ZAK	
LIG	WIF								NOK	ZAM	

TABLE 8 (*Continued*)

ASSOCIATION VALUE OF NONSENSE SYLLABLES (AFTER GLAZE, 1928)

47%			40%			33%			27%		
BEK	LEH	VAW	BIQ	MOQ	WEJ	BIW	NAF	XEN	BIX	NIZ	XOL
BEW	LUB	VEB	BAZ	NIY	WIJ	BIY	NID	XIB	BOJ	NUW	XOR
BIH	LUJ	VOD	BIV	NOF	WIK	CEV	NIV	XIK	BUH	NUJ	XOT
BUP	LUW	VIW	BUV	PAH	WOH	CEQ	NIH	XOM	BUJ	PAQ	XOY
BUW	MAQ	VOZ	CAJ	PEF	XAC	CIK	PEJ	YEQ	CEB	PEH	YAH
CES	MEP	VUT	CAQ	PEX	XAK	CIQ	PEM	YEX	CIB	QAH	YAG
CEZ	MIH	WAH	CAX	PUH	XEP	CIZ	PEZ	YOD	COH	QAJ	YEB
COQ	MIJ	WAZ	CEK	PUQ	XIC	DAH	PIB	YUM	COJ	QAX	YEC
DAK	MUB	WEH	CEY	PUV	XIP	DAJ	PID	ZAB	DEH	QEG	YED
DUF	MUN	WIH	CIH	PUX	XIS	DIH	POQ	ZAP	DIQ	QEN	YEF
DUZ	NAC	WIQ	CUG	PUY	XOD	DOQ	PUW	ZAY	DUH	QOK	YEJ
FAH	NAW	WUS	CUQ	QAB	YAN	DUJ	QEJ	ZAV	FEQ	QOL	YIZ
FAZ	NEF	WUY	CUW	QAD	YAP	FAJ	QIN	ZEL	FIW	QOP	YOC
FEC	NIR	XOW	DAC	QAV	YID	FAQ	QUX	ZIT	FUQ	QUV	YOL
FEG	NIW	YAD	DEQ	QAY	YIR	FOH	QUY	ZOD	GAF	RIH	YUC
FEJ	NOL	YAF	DIB	QEH	YOG	FOY	REZ	ZON	GAK	RIJ	YUH
FEX	NOQ	YAT	DIJ	QEK	YOS	FUX	RUC		GAW	RIY	YUP
FIQ	NOY	YIT	DUW	QEZ	YUK	FUY	RUX		GEK	ROJ	ZAC
FUW	NUY	YOB	FIH	QOF	ZAH	GEP	SEH		GOJ	RUZ	ZAF
GEY	PEQ	YOR	FIK	QUH	ZAN	GOC	SEJ		GOX	SUQ	ZAL
GEZ	PIJ	YUG	FUJ	QUR	ZES	GAJ	SOJ		GUB	TEG	ZAQ
GIJ	POB	ZAD	GEQ	QUT	ZEW	HEZ	SUY		GUF	TEW	ZED
GIZ	PUK	ZEN	GEW	REH	ZUN	HOZ	TEH		GUX	TIW	ZIJ
GOH	PUJ	ZIM	GUD	RIW		JEB	TEY		HEJ	TUW	ZOC
GOW	QAF	ZUG	HAJ	SIF		JEY	TOH		HEQ	VAD	ZOL
HAQ	QAR		HIX	SUH		JOD	TUJ		HES	VEF	ZOQ
HAX	QET		HUY	SUX		JOF	TUQ		JIV	VIG	ZOX
HEB	QIB		JEK	TAW		JOM	TUZ		JIY	VOB	ZUC
HEF	QIG		KOG	TEJ		JOZ	VAZ		JIZ	VOC	ZUD
HUZ	QOR		KUG	TEK		KAH	VED		JOQ	VOF	
JAX	QUC		KUV	TIH		KAL	VOR		JUX	VOP	
JEP	QUD		KUW	TIJ		KEC	VOQ		KAG	VUD	
JEV	QUN		LIX	TOJ		KIW	VUC		KAX	VUJ	
JIS	RUH		LUD	TOZ		KOQ	VUN		KIF	VUW	
JUW	RUK		LUH	VAH		KOY	VUP		KIY	VUY	
JUY	RUV		MEB	VAJ		KUJ	VUR		LEJ	WIX	
KAB	SOQ		MEH	VEH		KUX	WAP		LIH	WIY	
KAM	SOZ		MIW	VEK		LEX	WIB		LIJ	WOZ	
KED	TAJ		MOF	VID		MIG	WOQ		LOJ	XEV	
KEM	TEZ		MOG	VIJ		MIP	WOY		MAF	XET	
KIX	TIS		MUP	VIQ		MIY	WUK		MEV	XIM	
KIV	TIZ		MUY	VIX		MOJ	WUV		MUX	XIN	
KOC	TUD		NAL	VOG		MUH	XAG		NAQ	XIZ	
KOR	TUY		NEQ	VUS		MUJ	XEC		NEH	XOG	
LAH	VAB		MOH	WEG		MUQ	XED		NIQ	XOP	

TABLE 8 (*Continued*)

ASSOCIATION VALUE OF NONSENSE SYLLABLES (AFTER GLAZE, 1928)

20%			13%			7%			0%		
BEJ	QED	YIC	BEP	RIX	ZIS	BOF	XAJ	ZUF	CEF	XAT	ZUK
BEH	QEY	YOJ	CEH	RUQ	ZIY	CEJ	XAH	ZUH	CIJ	XEF	ZUM
BIP	QEP	YOW	CEX	SEB	ZOB	DAQ	XAL	ZUV	DAX	XEH	
BUQ	QID	YUN	CUH	TEV	ZOK	FUH	XAQ	ZUP	FEH	XEJ	
CIW	QOH	YUS	CUX	TUV	ZOG	GEC	XAV	ZUY	GAH	XEQ	
CUJ	QON	YUW	FOQ	VEJ	ZOM	GID	XEB		GAX	XIH	
DEJ	QOX	YUX	FUB	VEQ	ZOV	GUK	XEZ		GEX	XIP	
DIW	QUK	ZEC	GED	VIB	ZOY	GIX	XIF		GIW	XIV	
FEP	QUN	ZEF	GEF	VOH	ZUJ	HUC	XIJ		GOQ	XIW	
FOJ	QUP	ZER	GIC	WUG	ZUT	JEQ	XIQ		GUQ	XUC	
FUP	QUS	ZEV	GIK	WUP		JIQ	XIY		JEX	XUH	
GEB	QUZ	ZEY	GUC	XAR		JUH	XOJ		JIC	XUK	
GEJ	RUW	ZIC	HUW	XAW		JUQ	XUL		JID	XUM	
GIH	RUY	ZIB	JEC	XAZ		KEB	XUQ		LAJ	XUR	
GIY	SAJ	ZID	JEH	XEG		KEZ	XUB		MEF	XUV	
GOK	SIH	ZIX	JIK	XES		KOJ	XUD		MEQ	XUY	
GUH	SIW	ZOR	JIW	XEY		MEC	YAV		QAP	XUW	
GUW	TAH	ZUR	JUC	XOB		MIB	YAZ		QIF	YEM	
HEG	TEF	ZOP	KAJ	XIG		MIF	YEK		QIH	YIL	
HIF	TIV	ZUS	KAQ	XID		NUX	YIF		QIJ	YIM	
HUQ	TUH	ZUW	KEX	XON		PIW	YIG		QOB	YOF	
JAT	VAK	ZUX	KIH	XOV		QAS	YIW		QOC	YOP	
JEG	VEP		KUQ	XUF		QEM	YIX		QOV	YOV	
JEZ	VIH		KUY	XUJ		QEW	YOM		QUG	YUD	
JIH	VOJ		MEJ	YAB		QIM	YOQ		QUJ	YUF	
JUF	VUM		MIV	YIB		QIW	YOX		SIJ	YUV	
JUZ	VUZ		MUW	YIK		QOJ	YOZ		TOV	YUZ	
KAZ	WAJ		NAH	YIJ		QOS	YUJ		VAF	ZEJ	
KEF	WEF		NAX	YIN		QOW	YUQ		VEC	ZEQ	
KEH	WEQ		NOJ	YIQ		QUB	ZAJ		VUK	ZEX	
KEJ	WUC		NUB	YOH		QUW	ZEG		VUQ	ZIF	
KEV	WUT		PAF	YOT		VEH	ZIH		WUB	ZIL	
KIG	WUX		PIY	YUB		VUF	ZIK		WUH	ZIQ	
KIZ	XAF		QEB	ZAS		VUH	ZIV		WUQ	ZIW	
KUH	XAP		QEF	ZAT		VUX	ZOF		XAD	ZOJ	
LEB	XAY		QEX	ZAW		WEZ	ZOH				
LEQ	XEW		QIY	ZEH		WOG	ZOS				
LIW	XOC		QOD	ZAX		WOJ	ZOT				
LUY	XOF		QOM	ZIN		WUJ	ZOW				
MEZ	XOH		QOY	ZIR		XAB	ZUB				
NEJ	XOK										
NIJ	XOQ										
NUK	XUG										
POH	XUS										
QAM	XUT										

TABLE 9

NONSENSE SYLLABLES OF LOW ASSOCIATION VALUE †

BEH	FIW	JEQ	MAF*	QAZ	QUW	VEQ	WUX*	XIY	YEJ	YUX*	ZUB
BEJ*	FOH	JEV	MAQ	QEB	QUX	VID	XAB	XIZ	YEK*	ZAB	ZUC
BEP*	FOJ	JEX*	MEF*	QEF	QUY	VIH	XAD	XOB	YEM*	ZAF	ZUD*
BEW*	FOQ	JEY	MEH	QEG	RIH	VIJ	XAF	XOC	YEQ	ZAH*	ZUF
BEX	FUB*	JIC	MEJ*	QEH	RIW	VOB	XAG	XOD	YEX	ZAJ	ZUG
BIH	FUP*	JID*	MEP*	QEJ	RIX*	VOF*	XAH	XOF	YIB*	ZAL*	ZUH
BIP*	GAH	JIH*	MEQ	QEK	RUC	VOH	XAJ	XOG	YIC	ZAN*	ZUJ
BIW*	GAK	JIK*	MEV*	QEM	RUQ	VOJ	XAK	XOH	YIF	ZAQ	ZUK*
BIX	GAQ	JIQ	MIB*	QEN	RUV*	VOP	XAL	XOJ	YIG	ZAS	ZUR*
BOF*	GAW	JIV	MIF	QEP	RUX	VOQ	XAP	XOK	YIJ	ZAV	ZUS
BUH	GAX	JIZ	MIJ	QEW	RUY*	VOR	XAQ	XOL	YIK*	ZEC	ZUT*
BUP*	GEB	JOM*	MIP*	QEX	RUZ	VOX	XAR	XOM	YIL*	ZEF	ZUW
BUV	GEC	JUC	MIV*	QIF	SEB	VOZ	XAT	XON	YIM	ZEG	ZUX*
BUW*	GED	JUF*	MIW	QIG	SIJ	VUC	XAW	XOP	YIN*	ZEH	ZUY
CAQ	GEJ	JUQ	MOJ*	QIH	SOZ	VUD*	XAY	XOQ	YIQ	ZEJ	
CEF	GEK	JUX	MUB*	QIJ	SUY	VUF	XAZ	XOR	YIR	ZEQ	
CEH	GEP	KAJ	NAF*	QIM	TAH*	VUH	XEB	XOV	YIW	ZER*	
CEJ	GEQ	KAQ	NEJ*	QIW	TEF*	VUJ	XEC	XOW	YIX	ZEV	
CEK	GEX	KAX	NID	QIY	TEJ	VUK*	XED	XOY	YIZ	ZEW	
CEQ	GIC	KAZ	NIJ*	QOB	TEV*	VUM*	XEF	XUB	YOB*	ZEY	
CEX	GIH	KEB*	NIW	QOC	TEZ	VUP*	XEG	XUC	YOC	ZIB*	
CIB	GIJ	KEC	NIY	QOF	TIH	VUQ	XEH	XUD	YOD*	ZIC	
CIH	GIK	KEF*	NIZ	QOH	TIJ*	VUR*	XEJ	XUF	YOF	ZID*	
CIJ	GIW	KEH	NOJ*	QOJ	TIV*	VUT*	XEN	XUG	YOG	ZIF	
CIW	GIX	KEJ*	NUY*	QOL	TIW	VUW	XEP	XUH	YOH	ZIH*	
CIZ	GIY	KEV	PAF*	QOM	TIZ	VUX	XEQ	XUJ	YOJ*	ZIJ	
COJ	GIZ	KEX*	PEF*	QON	TOJ*	VUY	XES	XUK	YOL*	ZIK*	
CUG	GOC	KEZ	PEH	QOP	TOV*	VUZ	XET	XUL	YOP	ZIM	
CUH	GOJ	KIF*	PEJ*	QOR	TOZ	WAJ	XEV	XUM	YOQ	ZIN	
CUJ	GOQ	KIG	PEZ	QOS	TUD*	WEF*	XEW	XUQ	YOT	ZIQ	
CUQ	GOX	KIH*	PIB*	QOV	TUJ*	WEQ	XEY	XUR	YOV	ZIR*	
CUW	GUB	KIV*	PID	QOW	TUV	WIB*	XEZ	XUS	YOX	ZIV*	
CUX	GUH	KIW	PIY	QOX	TUZ	WIH	XIB	XUT	YOZ	ZIW	
DAJ*	GUK	KOJ*	POB*	QUB	VAB*	WIJ	XIC	XUV	YUB	ZIY	
DAQ	GUQ	KOQ	PUV*	QUC	VAF	WOG	XID	XUW	YUC	ZOB	
DAX*	GUW	KUG	PUX	QUD	VAH*	WOJ*	XIF	XUY	YUD	ZOC	
DEJ*	GUX	KUH	PUY*	QUG	VAJ	WOQ	XIG	YAB	YUF*	ZOF*	
DIJ*	HAJ*	KUJ*	QAB	QUH	VAW*	WOY	XIH	YAD*	YUG	ZOG	
DUH	HIF*	KUQ	QAD	QUJ	VEB	WUB*	XIJ	YAF*	YUJ	ZOH	
FAJ*	HUW	KUW	QAH	QUK	VEC	WUC	XIK	YAG	YUK*	ZOJ*	
FEG	JAT*	KUY	QAJ	QUN	VEF*	WUG	XIM	YAV	YUN*	ZOM*	
FEH	JEB*	LEQ	QAM	QUP	VEH	WUH	XIQ	YEB	YUP	ZOQ	
FEJ	JEC	LIJ*	QAP	QUR	VEJ	WUJ	XIS	YEC	YUQ	ZOS	
FEP*	JEG	LIW	QAS	QUS	VEK*	WUQ	XIV	YED*	YUV	ZOT*	
FEQ	JEH	LUJ*	QAV	QUV	VEP*	WUV	XIW	YEF	YUW	ZOV	

† Syllables with less than 50 per-cent-association value for Glaze's subjects, less than 70 per cent for Krueger's subjects. Those starred are less than 20 per cent for Hull's subjects. (After Melton, unpublished.)

TABLE 10

ASSOCIATION VALUES OF SELECTED CONSONANT UNITS (AFTER WITMER, 1935) *

0%	4%	8%	13%		17%		21%		25%		29%	
QJF	BQJ	BJH	CGJ	QXH	BFM	NPB	BJS	NQK	BJG	MKR	BXK	LRH
QJH	CXJ	CQH	DJZ	QZM	CSF	PJZ	CFP	PXJ	CKM	NQG	CTJ	NFP
XFQ	DJX	DJQ	FQJ	TFJ	DJH	QHX	DXK	QGZ	DKQ	QCN	DZH	PFH
XJQ	FHJ	FJH	GXJ	XBN	FJC	RBM	FBM	RCJ	FNX	QMX	FMJ	QBM
XZF	GQC	GXC	JCF	XFZ	GZK	SGJ	GKN	SFM	GJZ	SBG	FXM	QMG
ZGJ	HFC	HFK	JZH	XKB	HFM	TZX	HZC	TJH	GXT	SZQ	HJZ	RXT
ZJF	JFH	JHQ	KXZ	XQD	JSB	XCZ	JGP	XMG	HNQ	XDB	JLZ	TKF
ZJQ	KXB	KQZ	LCF	XZL	KHF	XJS	KMH	XZB	JQX	XMH	JTH	XGD
ZQJ	XJF	MZB	MQJ	ZGQ	LJX	XZG	LJS	ZDG	KSF	ZCG	KCM	XTN
ZXJ	ZBJ	TZH	QFZ	ZKG	MGQ	ZMF	MZC	ZHL	LJD	ZMK	LBJ	ZQM

33%		38%		42%		45%		50%		54%	
BFH	LDP	BPM	MPB	BGK	NCJ	BNJ	NSD	BKX	NDL	BPS	LPT
CMZ	LXH	CQK	NRZ	CJP	NPX	CMF	PDB	CMG	NJR	CMK	MJG
DFX	MBK	DSZ	PXT	DKM	PGZ	DKB	PTL	DBM	PSC	DHP	NHD
DXL	MQX	FSB	QSN	FDM	QKG	FHN	RCF	FCR	QHS	DSG	NXC
FNQ	NLR	GSX	SBF	GJP	RJH	GLQ	RNC	GMB	RKX	FDN	PLR
GPZ	QSG	HBK	THL	HCT	SHX	HSD	SDJ	HLR	SHQ	FQT	RDZ
HZT	RPB	JCP	XFR	JDP	TDM	KCP	SQG	JBR	SLH	GDK	SLX
JNB	SZP	JXC	XRF	KGD	TJN	LCN	THJ	KPG	TBX	HPL	TNZ
JZT	TQH	KPB	ZLD	LHS	XGT	LXG	TXF	LSD	XCL	JGM	XSP
KMX	ZBK	LHZ	ZSN	MBS	ZFT	NDK	ZGR	MKB	ZNH	JXS	ZMT

58%		63%		71%	75%	79%	83%	88%	92%	96%	100%
BFD	MSZ	BGL	SQD	BGN	BKS	BLN	BRK	BRT	BNK	BLD	DNT
BTN	NCT	BPD	TRZ	CPT	CRG	CRP	CLS	CRN	CHL	BND	DPT
DLR	NPD	CMS	BLH	DRJ	FLN	DKS	FLR	DRG	DRT	BRD	DRK
FDJ	PCL	FSN	BZD	FTB	GNS	GMP	HTL	FNT	FND	DSH	HRD
GCL	PRH	JFR	DMS	HRK	HSB	HNK	JNT	GRB	GRL	FLP	PNK
HPT	QMD	LPC	HDR	KPT	LTR	LPS	MRK	HZL	HLT	FRM	SNK
JRM	RFZ	NBK	LPR	MDR	NKS	NBS	PLN	MCH	JMP	GLD	
KRD	SBL	PFD	PGM	NXT	RBN	PRZ	RPD	PLT	KNG	GRN	
LXN	THZ	PMB	RGT	RFT	SMD	SPK	SCH	RTZ	LRD	HLD	
MKG	ZMD	RDT	TPF	TNR	TRH	TRM	TGR	SNG	RNK	LFT	

* Units containing "V" and "W" have been eliminated. The others represent a selection from Witmer's published lists.

That degree of association value affects the ease with which nonsense syllables can be learned and retained has been shown by McGeoch (1930). When 10-item lists were studied for 2 minutes, the immediate recall varied directly with the associative value. Recall was highest for three-letter words (9.1), next for 100 per cent syllables (7.4), next for 53 per cent syllables (6.4), lowest for the 0 per cent syllables (5.1). It is of interest that the gap between the 100 per cent syllables and meaningful words is greater than that between adjacent steps of associative value for nonsense syllables.

Meaningful verbal materials. The discovery that nonsense syllables can be classified according to association value both justifies their use (because they are not so remote as might be supposed from the kinds of materials more practically important) and denies some of the unique value attributed to them. There is, in fact, some trend away from the use of nonsense materials in memorization experiments. This is in part because the motivational value of meaningful materials is much higher, and some of the supposed advantages of nonsense syllables do not exist (Davis, 1930; Sauer, 1930). In addition, there are problems, such as the effects of meaningful similarity, for which the nonsense syllable is inappropriate. Three-letter words have been used in experiments designed like those with nonsense syllables, and two-syllable adjectives have become increasingly popular. Melton and Safier (unpublished study) have rated 300 adjectives for degree of similarity (Table 11). Other meaningful materials include those with patterns of

stimuli, all have been the subject of study in experiments concerned with memorization, recognition, and recall. Such materials, like the verbal ones, vary from meaningless items (e.g. asymmetrical line patterns) to items rich in personal association, as in testimony experiments. Often the cue item is nonverbal and the response item verbal, so that the distinction between a verbal and a nonverbal task is not a sharp one. Satisfactory attempts to standardize nonverbal materials are lacking.

Methods for the Study of Memorization

Immediate memory span. Related to what has sometimes been called the span of at-

FIG. 7. Memory drum (University of Missouri model). The material to be memorized appears in the small aperture as the drum revolves. A number of lists may be mounted on the drum at once, the list to be exposed being selected by the position of the aperture (photograph courtesy Stanford Psychological Laboratory).

meaning, as in prose or poetry. Standardization has seldom been attempted. There is usually an assumption that the author of a long poem or treatise maintains about the same difficulty throughout. This assumption is subject to test, through the use of word counts or difficulty scores on the pattern suggested by Flesch (1945).

Nonverbal materials. Objects, pictures, observed activities, assigned tasks, sensory

tention or the span of apprehension is the immediate memory span — the number of items that can be learned in one trial when they are presented serially at a controlled rate. Digits, words, pictures, or objects may be used, although the verbal items are the more common. The method is an adaptation of threshold methods used in psychophysics. Lists of 4 to 12 items are commonly used. Several scores are possible.

TABLE 11

PAIRS OF TWO-SYLLABLE ADJECTIVES ARRANGED IN ORDER OF AVERAGE SIMILARITY RATINGS BY 96 UNIVERSITY STUDENTS (AFTER MELTON AND SAFIER, UNPUBLISHED STUDY)

Item No.	Paired Adjectives	Average Score	Item No.	Paired Adjectives	Average Score
1	Perfect — Faultless	2.85	36	Showy — Gaudy	2.49
2	Noonday — Midday	2.84	37	Evil — Wicked	2.49
3	Exact — Precise	2.80	38	Sudden — Abrupt	2.49
4	Boastful — Bragging	2.75	39	Gloomy — Dismal	2.49
5	Fatal — Deadly	2.75	40	Heavy — Weighty	2.48
6	Ready — Prepared	2.71	41	Select — Chosen	2.48
7	Foremost — Leading	2.70	42	Cursed — Damned	2.48
8	Total — Entire	2.68	43	Filthy — Dirty	2.47
9	Empty — Vacant	2.67	44	Foamy — Frothy	2.46
10	Awkward — Clumsy	2.67	45	Fearful — Afraid	2.46
11	Useless — Futile	2.67	46	Hardy — Sturdy	2.46
12	Baffling — Puzzling	2.66	47	Complex — Involved	2.46
13	Alien — Foreign	2.63	48	Modish — Stylish	2.45
14	Fated — Destined	2.63	49	Insane — Crazy	2.45
15	Crafty — Cunning	2.61	50	Sticky — Gummy	2.44
16	Absorbed — Engrossed	2.61	51	Human — Mortal	2.44
17	Lawful — Legal	2.61	52	Joyful — Merry	2.44
18	Aware — Conscious	2.61	53	Fertile — Fruitful	2.42
19	Open — Unshut	2.60	54	Sickly — Ailing	2.42
20	Famous — Noted	2.59	55	Weary — Fatigued	2.42
21	Comic — Funny	2.58	56	Complete — Thorough	2.40
22	Rocky — Stony	2.57	57	Tranquil — Serene	2.40
23	Happy — Joyous	2.57	58	Cautious — Wary	2.40
24	Tepid — Lukewarm	2.57	59	Handy — Useful	2.39
25	Valued — Prized	2.57	60	Skillful — Expert	2.38
26	Pensive — Thoughtful	2.56	61	Angry — Wrathful	2.36
27	Absent — Missing	2.55	62	Glossy — Shining	2.35
28	Urgent — Pressing	2.55	63	Ardent — Zealous	2.35
29	Drowsy — Sleepy	2.55	64	Steadfast — Loyal	2.35
30	Double — Twofold	2.54	65	Hasty — Hurried	2.34
31	Timid — Bashful	2.54	66	Honored — Revered	2.34
32	Constant — Steady	2.51	67	Ghostly — Eerie	2.34
33	Endless — Ceaseless	2.51	68	Mixed — Jumbled	2.34
34	Regal — Royal	2.51	69	Compact — Solid	2.33
35	Fitting — Proper	2.50	70	Active — Lively	2.33

TABLE 11 (*Continued*)

PAIRS OF TWO-SYLLABLE ADJECTIVES ARRANGED IN ORDER OF AVERAGE SIMILARITY RATINGS BY
96 UNIVERSITY STUDENTS (AFTER MELTON AND SAFIER, UNPUBLISHED STUDY)

Item No.	Paired Adjectives	Average Score	Item No.	Paired Adjectives	Average Score
71	Senior — Elder	2.33	106	Only — Single	2.13
72	Diverse — Varied	2.32	107	Impure — Unclean	2.13
73	Nuptial — Bridal	2.31	108	Hungry — Famished	2.11
74	Oily — Greasy	2.30	109	Windy — Breezy	2.11
75	Paltry — Meager	2.29	110	Holy — Sinless	2.11
76	Godly — Pious	2.28	111	Unsound — Faulty	2.10
77	Vocal — Oral	2.27	112	Peaceful — Quiet	2.10
78	Heathen — Pagan	2.25	113	Teeming — Swarming	2.09
79	Frantic — Frenzied	2.25	114	Frigid — Arctic	2.09
80	Sacred — Divine	2.24	115	Cleanly — Spotless	2.08
81	Wishful — Longing	2.24	116	Dreamy — Musing	2.08
82	Middle — Midmost	2.23	117	Manly — Virile	2.07
83	Paired — Mated	2.20	118	Secret — Hidden	2.07
84	Brazen — Shameless	2.20	119	Stifled — Muffled	2.06
85	Careless — Heedless	2.20	120	Savage — Brutal	2.05
86	Gallant — Knightly	2.20	121	Listless — Languid	2.05
87	Cheerful — Pleasant	2.20	122	Covered — Shielded	2.04
88	Careful — Heedful	2.18	123	Ancient — Antique	2.04
89	Partial — Biased	2.18	124	Local — Nearby	2.04
90	Marine — Naval	2.18	125	Brainless — Senseless	2.03
91	Supreme — Utmost	2.18	126	Wholesome — Healthy	2.02
92	Prior — Former	2.17	127	Honest — Sincere	2.02
93	Limber — Supple	2.17	128	Massive — Bulky	2.01
94	Upper — Higher	2.16	129	Severed — Broken	2.01
95	Sterile — Fruitless	2.16	130	Winding — Curved	2.00
96	Wrongful — Unjust	2.16	131	Even — Level	2.00
97	Witty — Clever	2.16	132	Neuter — Sexless	1.99
98	Misty — Foggy	2.15	133	Daring — Fearless	1.99
99	Mulish — Stubborn	2.15	134	Squatty — Stubby	1.99
100	Required — Needed	2.14	135	Idle — Unused	1.99
101	Dreadful — Frightful	2.14	136	Discreet — Prudent	1.99
102	Foolish — Silly	2.14	137	Bloated — Swollen	1.98
103	Spiral — Coiled	2.14	138	Equal — Alike	1.98
104	Pleasing — Charming	2.13	139	Handsome — Comely	1.98
105	Stringy — Fibrous	2.13	140	Witless — Stupid	1.97

TABLE 11 (*Continued*)

Item No.	Paired Adjectives	Average Score	Item No.	Paired Adjectives	Average Score
141	Costly — Precious	1.97	176	Torrid — Heated	1.77
142	Recent — Modern	1.96	177	Dizzy — Giddy	1.77
143	Stuffy — Stifling	1.96	178	Furtive — Stealthy	1.75
144	Dextrous — Adroit	1.95	179	Caustic — Biting	1.75
145	Feeble — Infirm	1.95	180	Pliant — Plastic	1.74
146	Warlike — Martial	1.94	181	Scornful — Mocking	1.74
147	Moldy — Musty	1.93	182	Frugal — Thrifty	1.74
148	Humdrum — Tiresome	1.92	183	Nameless — Unknown	1.74
149	Profuse — Lavish	1.92	184	Juicy — Sappy	1.73
150	Awful — Direful	1.92	185	Fickle — Flighty	1.73
151	Rainy — Drizzly	1.90	186	Rotten — Corrupt	1.72
152	Soiled — Stained	1.90	187	Vital — Living	1.72
153	Thirsty — Parched	1.89	188	Nasty — Obscene	1.72
154	Wordy — Verbose	1.89	189	Brawny — Stalwart	1.71
155	Folded — Creased	1.88	190	Noisy — Blatant	1.71
156	Pallid — Sallow	1.86	191	Rigid — Severe	1.71
157	Blotchy — Smudgy	1.86	192	Tender — Loving	1.69
158	Thorny — Barbed	1.85	193	Decayed — Crumbling	1.67
159	Civil — Polite	1.85	194	Aged — Mature	1.66
160	Jocund — Cheery	1.85	195	Cutting — Piercing	1.66
161	Restless — Nervous	1.83	196	Seething — Foaming	1.66
162	Yellow — Golden	1.83	197	Intense — Extreme	1.66
163	Hoggish — Swinish	1.82	198	Outer — Outward	1.66
164	Playful — Sportive	1.82	199	Bizarre — Grotesque	1.65
165	Jerky — Shaky	1.82	200	Unique — Matchless	1.61
166	Grumbling — Peevish	1.81	201	Hairy — Bearded	1.61
167	Counter — Adverse	1.81	202	Lusty — Robust	1.60
168	Unsought — Unasked	1.80	203	Fragile — Brittle	1.58
169	Minor — Smaller	1.79	204	Hateful — Horrid	1.58
170	Dowdy — Unkempt	1.78	205	Intact — Unhurt	1.57
171	Exempt — Immune	1.78	206	Crooked—Jagged	1.55
172	Skinny — Lanky	1.78	207	Swarthy — Dusky	1.55
173	Shopworn — Shabby	1.77	208	Servile — Slavish	1.55
174	Lovely — Pretty	1.77	209	Haughty — Austere	1.54
175	Allied — Akin	1.77	210	Garish — Flashy	1.54

TABLE 11 (*Continued*)

PAIRS OF TWO-SYLLABLE ADJECTIVES ARRANGED IN ORDER OF AVERAGE SIMILARITY RATINGS BY 96 UNIVERSITY STUDENTS (AFTER MELTON AND SAFIER, UNPUBLISHED STUDY)

Item No.	Paired Adjectives	Average Score	Item No.	Paired Adjectives	Average Score
211	Fervid — Fiery	1.53	246	Racy — Spicy	1.19
212	Certain — Special	1.52	247	Weathered — Rusty	1.18
213	Reigning — Kingly	1.52	248	Obscure — Disguised	1.17
214	Sunken — Hollow	1.51	249	Worldly — Mundane	1.17
215	Vicious — Spiteful	1.48	250	Perverse — Wayward	1.16
216	Toilsome — Irksome	1.48	251	Faithful — Upright	1.16
217	Vulgar — Boorish	1.48	252	Ribald — Shocking	1.11
218	Occult — Mystic	1.47	253	Hostile — Factious	1.11
219	Airy — Lofty	1.46	254	Hybrid — Mongrel	1.10
220	Opaque — Clouded	1.46	255	Sedate — Demure	1.08
221	Normal — Common	1.46	256	Overt — Public	1.07
222	Glowing — Flaming	1.46	257	Rural — Silvan	1.06
223	Acrid — Stinging	1.45	258	Cringing — Sneaky	1.05
224	Puny — Tiny	1.45	259	Rhythmic — Wavy	1.02
225	Guilty — Sinful	1.45	260	Sorry — Chagrined	0.97
226	Reckless — Wanton	1.45	261	August — Sublime	0.93
227	Artless — Naive	1.44	262	Strident — Raucous	0.92
228	Direct — Candid	1.44	263	Prostrate — Supine	0.90
229	Vesper — Nightly	1.41	264	Flabby — Flaccid	0.90
230	Touchy — Fretful	1.40	265	Hidebound — Prudish	0.89
231	Eager — Earnest	1.40	266	Ugly — Morbid	0.86
232	Milky — Pearly	1.39	267	Undone — Ruined	0.86
233	Crimson — Bloody	1.39	268	Trenchant — Pungent	0.86
234	Vivid — Graphic	1.38	269	Implied — Tacit	0.86
235	Anxious — Fervent	1.35	270	Homeless — Lonely	0.85
236	Profound — Learned	1.33	271	Abstract — Abstruse	0.85
237	Uphill — Rising	1.31	272	Oblong — Lengthy	0.83
238	Rabid — Raving	1.30	273	Dulcet — Tuneful	0.82
239	Formal — Solemn	1.29	274	Yeasty — Spumy	0.79
240	Dainty — Refined	1.27	275	Obese — Bulbous	0.73
241	Agape — Agog	1.26	276	Waggish — Jocose	0.69
242	Crying — Plaintive	1.24	277	Natal — Nascent	0.63
243	Sylphlike — Elfish	1.22	278	Zigzag — Forked	0.59
244	Gawky — Uncouth	1.22	279	Limpid — Lucid	0.57
245	Basic — Causal	1.21	280	Acute — Astute	0.56

TABLE 11 (*Continued*)

PAIRS OF TWO-SYLLABLE ADJECTIVES ARRANGED IN ORDER OF AVERAGE SIMILARITY RATINGS BY
96 UNIVERSITY STUDENTS (AFTER MELTON AND SAFIER, UNPUBLISHED STUDY)

Item No.	Paired Adjectives	Average Score	Item No.	Paired Adjectives	Average Score
281	Noxious — Toxic	0.55	291	Classic — Ruddy	0.11
282	Early — Pristine	0.50	292	Concave — Unseen	0.10
283	Fallow — Carnal	0.24	293	Yearly — Inverse	0.09
284	Clannish — Fishy	0.21	294	Fiendish — Mellow	0.06
285	Spongy — Transverse	0.20	295	Tardy — Absurd	0.05
286	Fiscal — Random	0.20	296	Lawless — Distinct	0.05
287	Urbane — Ample	0.15	297	Feline — Hilly	0.04
288	Verdant — Captious	0.15	298	Fleshy — Standard	0.03
289	Festive — Slender	0.11	299	Erect — Fancy	0.02
290	Crucial — Glassy	0.11	300	Western — Rounded	0.01

The longest list successfully recalled is often taken as the measure of span, although alternative scores may be used. The one recommended by Woodworth (1938) is the average of two tests, the score for each being the length of longest list recalled without error.

The serial-anticipation method. The chief laboratory method for the study of lists of items to be learned by rote memorization is that known as the serial-anticipation method, developed by Finkenbinder (1913) from Ebbinghaus' method of prompting. Items are presented one after the other, only one exposed at a time. The exposed item serves as the cue to the one that follows. It also serves to confirm or to correct the subject's anticipations. Because the subject announces his anticipation for each item, the experimenter can record the exact response and obtain not only the rate of memorization but also the nature and number of the errors made. By the use of a voice key and supplementary apparatus the latency of response may be recorded as well as the accuracy. This is probably the most used method in American laboratories during the last twenty-five years.

Among the problems of procedure that have to be settled are the following:

1. The nature of the material to be learned, and the rules to be followed in list construction.

2. The subjects to be selected for the experiment.

3. The instructions to be given the subjects.

4. The preliminary training to be given the subjects before the experimental study proper begins.

5. The interval between serially presented items, and the exposure time for the item.

6. The interval between repeated trials through the list.

7. The scores to be recorded.

8. The criterion for mastery.

It is not unreasonable to expect experimenters in different laboratories to adopt standardized procedures for many of the conventional aspects of their experiments and then to introduce such changes as are necessary in order to test whatever new hypothesis interests them. By introducing unessential novelties in procedure many experiments that ought to be brought into relation are made so different that comparative appraisal is impossible.

The subject must be told either to pronounce or to spell the syllables. McGeoch (1942), following Luh (1922), recommended spelling, because of the confusion in the pronunciation of syllables like XED and ZEQ. If pronunciation is not required, unpronounceable syllables like XOQ may be used. Most of the work in Hull's laboratory (e.g. Hovland, 1938) was done with syllables that were pronounced rather than spelled. One disadvantage of the method of spelling out syllables is its artificiality when meaningful words are used. In the comparative studies of Davis (1930) and Sauer (1930), syllables were spelled out and words were not, thereby introducing an additional variable of unknown influence.

The importance of preliminary training is emphasized in studies that show the rapidity with which subjects "learn how to learn." The results of Ward (1937) are presented in Fig. 8, showing the rapid decrease in the number of trials required for learning each of the first six lists, with gradual improvement thereafter. This is an average curve. Subjects do not all follow the same pattern, and, unless some preliminary practice lists are given before experimentation proper, there is no way of telling where the subject is in the course of his changes in speed of learning.

The most common intervals between serially presented items are 2 seconds and 3 seconds. Because different types of mechanical presentation have been used, some experiments using the same interval have had different amounts of time used in changing from one item to the next and hence different proportions of the interval during which the item was exposed. It is desirable to minimize the time used in changing the items, so that for practical purposes the stated interval is also the exposure time for each item.

The interval between trials becomes a variable in experiments on distributed prac-

tice. Occasionally the lists have been run as a circular series, with the same time between the last and the first items as between the first and second items. A common practice for base conditions has been to make the time between trials three times as long as the presentation interval.

Because each item within the list is both a stimulus and a response, the first and last items are somewhat unique. The first is not

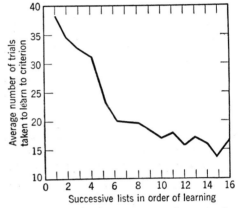

FIG. 8. Changes in rate of learning successive lists of 12 nonsense syllables (after Ward, 1937, as reproduced by McGeoch, 1942, p. 400).

a response item; the last is not a stimulus item. A decision is required about the use of the first item, because some signal is needed to inform the subject to begin recall. Two practices are used. One uses an indifferent item, such as 000, which tells the subject to attempt to recall the first nonsense syllable of the list. This makes the first syllable a response as well as a cue, which is important in some kinds of experiments, such as those on remote association. The other practice makes use of a cue item that is in all respects like other members of the list, but is not itself used as a response. In that case, if the subject is asked to learn a 10-item list, the list is actually constructed with 11 items, the first serving merely as a starting signal. The argument in favor of the latter method is that throughout the learning a nonsense syllable is used as a cue,

In the studying of such factors as serial position effect, it is desirable to have the cue conditions as like as possible for all items.

The data to be recorded depend upon the purposes of the experiment. The minimum is a score of hits and misses throughout memorization. In addition, actual responses may be recorded in order to study partial recall, place-skipping tendencies, intrusions from other lists, etc. Latency of response may also provide data of interest.

The experimenter must decide what criterion of mastery to employ. If all subjects practice memorization for a given number of trials, they will reach the end stage at different degrees of underlearning or overlearning. The more usual practice is to continue the trials until the subject has learned some standard proportion of the items (say 75-per-cent correct), or has yielded one perfect recitation, or two or three consecutive perfect recitations. What shall be considered mastery is arbitrary. Ideally the choice should be made in favor of the most reliable criterion. More severe criteria are not necessarily more reliable. There is a statistical problem with criterial scores which is sometimes overlooked. Any criterion that depends upon the first reaching of some high level of performance capitalizes on chance fluctuations in the direction of good scores. The mean of scores just after the criterion will tend to fall below the criterion trial.* Unless these artifacts are understood, misinterpretation of score values around the criterion are likely to arise. How serious these factors are may be illustrated by some data from Ward (1937). He found that on the trial following the criterion of one perfect recitation for a 12-unit list the number of syllables recalled was only 9.75. The "true" learning, which should serve as the

base for studying retention, was not the artificially high 12 units (which depended on the peaks of fluctuation in memorization) but was actually 2.25 syllables less. For partial mastery, in which the subject had learned 7 of the 12 items, the next trial yielded an average of 7 items. This might seem to negate the generalization that the trial beyond the criterion is invariably too low. If we remember that the memorization curve is rising rapidly at the point at which 7 of 12 items are being learned, we would predict that the trial beyond that on which 7 items are correct would be somewhat above 7. Hence the fact that only 7 correct responses are found shows that the principle of this following trial's being too low is not violated.

The method of paired associates. The task presented the subject in the method of paired associates is that of learning a series of discrete pairs so that the first member of the pair (stimulus member) will come to elicit the second member of the pair (response member). The learning of which pair follows which is not called for, and, in fact, the order is varied in the preferred experimental arrangement so that serial position effects are counteracted. That this makes a difference is clear, for it is easier to learn paired associates if the order remains constant than if the order is varied (McGeoch and McKinney, 1937). In order to obtain scores from the learning of paired associates similar to those from the serial-anticipation method, the memory drum is so arranged that the stimulus item appears in the aperture for a time before the response item appears. This permits the subject to announce the response item before it comes, so that the response may be recorded exactly as in the other method. The simplest way to do this with an ordinary memory drum is to have the stimulus item appear alone in the aperture and then in the next turn of the drum to have it appear again with its associated item. This uses two turns per item instead of the one turn used in

---

* In the case of more severe criteria, such as two consecutive perfect trials, the trial just preceding the criterion tends to average too low because of the exclusion of all perfect scores. Perfect scores may be made on all trials *except* that just preceding the criterial trials.

the serial-anticipation method, and the time intervals are changed to that extent. A more complex method is to use a supplementary shutter that conceals the response item when the stimulus item is first exposed, but then opens and exposes both members of the pair before the drum turns to the next pair.

Comparison of the methods. Although a number of other methods of studying acquisition have been used, the three mentioned are the best standardized. Since the memory-span method is somewhat specialized, interest centers in the similarities and differences between the serial-anticipation method and the paired-associates method. The serial method is the natural one for studying connected passages of meaningful material, like poetry or prose, and its use with artificial material provides analogies with such rote memorizing. The paired-associates method is equally natural, in that it parallels what goes on in connecting the names of objects or persons with their appearance, and in learning the equivalence between familiar and foreign words.* The processes are somewhat different, and it is appropriate to have standardized laboratory methods which may be used in studying them. A number of features such as serial-position effects and remote associations may be studied only in the serial-anticipation method, although for some purposes the paired-associates method may serve as control. The methods may complement each other in the test of certain hypotheses, as, for example, the nature of reminiscence. If reminiscence depends upon intraserial interferences, it should be found

* A variant of the paired-associates method is the word-number experiment made familiar by Thorndike in his experiments on spread of effect. The subject is required to guess the correct associate. If the guess is correct it is rewarded by being called "right" (Thorndike, 1933). Earlier experimenters working with the phenomena of spread of effect have made a number of errors in experimental design and in treatment of data, so that the principle as enunciated by Thorndike is of dubious validity. Some critical experiments are summarized by Hilgard (1948). Additional criticisms appear in Smith (1947).

with the serial method, not with the paired-associates method (Hovland, 1938).

Overlearning. The problem of the criterion of mastery has already been discussed. A related problem is that of a measure of learning beyond simple mastery.

Faced with the problem of defining overlearning, Luh (1922) assumed that the number of trials to mastery could serve as the base for 100-per-cent learning. Any additional trials could be counted as so much overlearning, expressed as a ratio to this base. Thus, if 20 trials were required to mastery, an additional 20 trials would add 100 per cent, or would be counted as 200 per cent of learning. The same definition has been used by Krueger (1929, 1930). This method is clear enough, but it exaggerates whatever chance factors led to the attainment of the original criterion of mastery, and it lacks a theoretical justification for the units of the overlearning scale.

It would be desirable to express overlearning in a manner that can be checked internally to see whether its meaning is similar from subject to subject. One method might be to describe learning according to the average number of successful responses per item. This implies that overlearning really begins when an item has been learned, and is proportional to the number of times that item has been given correctly in attempted recall. The value obtained by this method will tend to be higher for the slow learner than for the rapid learner, because the slow learner is often troubled by a few syllables while greatly overresponding to the others. In approaching some standard amount of overlearning, Luh's method would provide many more trials for this slow learner who may have already overlearned more prior to mastery than the rapid learner. If the proposed method were adopted, different stages of overlearning could be expressed by the same type of score:

Degree of learning

$$= 100 \frac{\text{Total correct anticipations}}{\text{Total opportunities to respond}}$$

Such a score would have to be given empirical standardization, for it is not known what its values would be at different criteria of mastery or at different stages of over-learning as described by Luh's method. Unfortunately such standardizing has not been done.

Methods for the Study of Retention

The problem of memorization, of committing to memory, is but the beginning of a cycle of activities in which the student of the acquisition-retention process is interested. What happens after memorization constitutes the problem of retention. Retention is measured by retesting following a lapse of time after memorization. There are a number of methods, of which the five made familiar by Luh (1922) may be taken as typical.

Recognition. All that is asked of memory in recognition is that a situation that recurs be recognized as familiar. Because the original situation is again present to the senses, cues to reinstatement are fully present and the task is relatively easy. The problem of the experimenter is to distinguish between false recognition and true recognition, because even a fully cooperative subject may be inaccurate in what is seen as familiar as well as in what is seen as unfamiliar. The usual experimental method is to present an equal number of familiar and unfamiliar items in random order. The subject is asked to select those familiar, those unfamiliar. A doubtful category may also be used. Success is scored as in a true-false examination.

$$\text{Score} = \frac{100(R - W)}{T}$$

where R = number right, correctly sorted.
W = number wrong, incorrectly sorted.
T = total number of items, including doubtful ones.

This score ranges from zero at chance level to 100 per cent at perfect recognition.

Reconstruction of series. To test retention of arrangement rather than of substance, the subject is given cards on which are printed the items that were learned in serial order. He is asked to arrange them in the correct order. This kind of test is difficult to score in a manner symmetrical with that employed in other tests of recognition and recall. One possibility is to use a rank difference correlation between the rearranged order and the original order. This score will vary between zero at chance and 100 at perfect reconstruction. The possibility of negative values exists, as indeed it does in the method of recognition described above.

Unaided reproduction. The subject attempts to write out the material without prompting of any sort. This is the test of memory with the minimum of cues. The instructions are simply: "Try to reproduce what you learned." Because partial recall aids further recall, it is often desirable to separate the recall record so that material immediately recalled can be distinguished from material subsequently recalled. In some experiments (e.g. Zeigarnik, 1927) the results depend upon this distinction.

Recall score. In the anticipation method the first relearning trial serves as a test of recall. The score is the percentage of items correctly anticipated. Because of the artificiality of mastery defined by a criterion, the base for 100-per-cent recall should be a control trial following that on which the arbitrary criterion is reached. In the paired-associates method, the score is the percentage of right associates in the first trial. In both cases there are somewhat more cues ('promptings') than in the method of unaided reproduction.

Saving score. If there is any residue whatever from an earlier learning, it should reduce the time required to remaster the material. A poem learned in childhood, apparently forgotten, might still show some residue under this relearning method. The saving score is computed as the ratio of the trials saved in relearning to the trials required in original learning, expressed as a percentage.

There is an ambiguity in saving scores that arises because of the use of criterial trials in learning and relearning. In order for scores to extend from 0 to 100 per cent, it is necessary to make allowance for the fact that even with perfect retention it is still necessary to meet the criterion in order to demonstrate this retention. The correction is to subtract the criterion trials from all the items entering into the saving score formula (Hilgard, 1934):

$$\text{Saving score} = \frac{100[(OL - C) - (RL - C)]}{(OL - C)}$$

$$= \frac{100(OL - RL)}{(OL - C)}$$

where OL = trials required for original learning.

RL = trials required for relearning.

C = trials required to meet the criterion of mastery.

The simplest test of the appropriateness of a score of this kind is to use it with artificial data for the conditions of 100-per-cent saving and 0-per-cent saving. If 100 per cent and 0 per cent are not yielded by the formula, values are being inappropriately entered.

There is a further correction needed in order to interpret saving scores (Bunch, 1941). Because "learning how to learn" is going on, a saving score should be tested against control learning of a new but equivalent set of materials. Thus if a poem learned in 30 repetitions in early childhood can be learned several years later in 20 repetitions, the difference cannot be attributed to retention unless an equivalent poem, learned at the later time, requires the original 30 repetitions. Perhaps memorization skill has gone up in the meantime.

Curves of retention. In plotting curves of retention, it is customary to have a learning session and a retention session for each interval to be studied. This avoids a progressive effect that would be encountered if after a single learning several successive retests were used.* It requires that the learning groups be matched or equated in some manner, not only in learning scores but in the amount of prior practice. This can be achieved either by using a new group of subjects for each interval studied or by a fairly elaborate rotation of conditions. In any case, precise determination of the form of the curve of retention is a laborious process.

Retroactive and proactive inhibition. One of the favorite fields of study within memory has been that of retroactive inhibition: the negative transfer whereby the learning of new material makes it increasingly difficult to retain items learned earlier. The standard arrangement is as follows:

	ORIGINAL LEARNING	INTERPO-LATED ACTIVITY	RECALL OR RE-LEARNING	POSTEXPERI-MENTAL TRAINING
Experimental group	Learn A_e	Learn B	Test A_e	Test B
Control group	Learn A_c	(Rest)	Test A_c	Learn B

If the experimental and control groups are comparable in their learning of A_e and A_c, then the amount of retroactive inhibition is the amount by which test A_e lies below test A_c.

McGeoch (1942, p. 459n) points out that it is desirable to keep all the subjects at the same level of practice, and hence to follow the test for the control group by the learning of material B. Similarly, if subjects are to be used in further cycles of the experiment, a retest for at least two relearning trials of material B is given the experimental group, lest the learning of material B (interpolated activity) be not taken as seriously as the learning of the other lists.

Proactive inhibition refers to the interference with new learning because of prior learning. The paradigm is:

	ORIGINAL LEARNING	TEST SITUATION
Experimental group	Learn A_E	Learn B_E
Control group	(Rest)	Learn B_C

* Hebb and Foord (1945) have made this objection to many of the earlier studies on changes in the reproduction of perceived forms, following Wulf (1922).

If the learning of B_E takes longer than the learning of B_C, proactive inhibition may be said to have occurred.

Motivational Factors in Forgetting

The clinical facts of amnesia, a memory loss from which there is later recovery, are supported by experimental studies in hypnosis. The facts are interpreted by the Freudian theory of repression. Problems are set for the experimental study of memory by these facts, but the results of such studies have thus far been rather meager (Rapaport, 1942; Sears, 1943).

Memory for pleasant and unpleasant items. Subjects are asked to rate items later to be used in memorization experiments for their degree of pleasantness or unpleasantness. Usual memorization and retention experiments are then conducted to determine which type of item is more rapidly committed to memory and which is more permanently retained. Summaries of the literature may be found in Gilbert (1938) and Rapaport (1942).

Memory for pleasant and unpleasant experiences. Because the personal involvement of the subject is important in experiments that stress motives, subjects have been asked to recall pleasant and unpleasant experiences, e.g. those had during a vacation period. Later recall is then used to determine whether there is a progressive forgetting of the unpleasant compared with the pleasant experiences. Although these experiments are designed to test the dynamic features of Freud's theory, their procedural difficulties are very great. Not only does the change in number of items reported occur, but changes occur in the hedonic appraisal of these same items on two different recalls (Meltzer, 1930).

A variation of the experiment, which holds some promise, was introduced by Sharp (1938), who examined the case histories of neurotic patients for items that would presumably arouse guilt or anxiety, and used these as the basis for retention studies. An attempt to repeat Sharp's experiment has unfortunately been unsuccessful (Heathers and Sears, as reported in Sears, 1943).

Hypnotically induced complexes. The method of Huston, Shakow, and Erickson (1934) can undoubtedly be extended in the study of the dynamics of memorial distortion. The problems of control in hypnotic experiments are many (e.g. Hull, 1933c), but that does not mean that the experiments are to be avoided.

Memory for completed and uncompleted tasks. An experiment first undertaken by Zeigarnik (1927), since repeated and extended by others, shows a differential effect upon retention when tasks are interrupted or completed. With some twenty tasks done in a single period, subjects recall only about half (immediate unaided recall), and, under some circumstances, many more of the unfinished tasks are recalled than of the finished ones. The differential effect appears to be quite temporary, being lost over 24 hours, but the whole matter requires further study.

Word-association experiments. Although word-association experiments are not ordinarily thought of as tests of retention, they serve in fact to exhibit the conditions under which one rather than another of possible associates is aroused. Familiar in guilt-detection studies and in personality investigations, they also hold some promise in the study of the circumstances of recall.

Word-association experiments have been used in formal memory studies chiefly in the investigation of remote associations, following Wolgemuth (1913). These studies (McGeoch, 1936; Raskin and Cook, 1937) suffice to show that the method might be adapted to other studies of the dynamics of retention.

Reliabilities of Memorization Scores

It has not been customary in memorization experiments, as it has in maze experiments, to report reliability coefficients. Much remains to be done to determine the dependability and reproducibility of such scores as reflecting individual differences.

A set of reliability coefficients is available from the study by Stroud, Lehman, and McCue (1934). These are reproduced in Table 12. Nonsense syllables were memorized by 76 college students. The serial anticipation method was used, with a 3-second presentation interval. Learning was to a

TABLE 12

TRIALS TO LEARN AND RELIABILITY COEFFICIENTS FOR LEARNING OF NONSENSE SYLLABLE LISTS BY THE ANTICIPATION METHOD (AFTER STROUD, LEHMAN, AND McCUE, 1934)

	6-Syllable List	12-Syllable List	18-Syllable List
Trials to learn			
Mean and S.D. (1)	5.90 ± 1.97	10.5 ± 3.74	14.9 ± 3.95
Mean and S.D. (2)	5.60 ± 2.06	10.1 ± 3.56	13.8 ± 4.20
Reliability coefficients			
Scores on odd-even trials	0.65	0.95	0.96
Trials to mastery, list 1 vs list 2	0.61	0.73	0.77

criterion of three consecutive perfect responses. Because the subjects learned one list per day for 6 consecutive days (two lists of each of three lengths), there were some disturbing practice effects affecting the coefficients, as pointed out by Melton (1936). In the absence of other coefficients obtained with more elegant controls, these are useful in giving some idea of what may be expected.

Studies that have attempted to deal with the common abilities in memory experiments by the methods of factor analysis have usually reported reliability coefficients (e.g. Garrett, 1928; Anastasi, 1930, 1932–33). Some representative ones from Garrett (1928) are given in Table 13.

Such reliabilities have no absolute meaning, because the tests have varied in length, in types of score, and so on. They show, however, that care is needed to ascertain that the situation used is sufficiently reliable for the purposes at hand because a range of

TABLE 13

RELIABILITY COEFFICIENTS FOR SOME MEMORY-LEARNING TASKS (AFTER GARRETT, 1928)

Paired associates (visual)	0.95
Digit-symbol substitution	0.95
Turkish-English vocabulary	0.91
Paired associates (auditory)	0.90
Code learning	0.85
Digit span (auditory)	0.80
Digit span (visual)	0.68
Logical memory	0.60

reliabilities may be found among tasks that appear to be equally serviceable.

LEARNING CURVES AS ANALYTIC DEVICES

Plotting the scores from learning experiments in the form of performance curves has proved serviceable since the earliest days of experimentation. Such curves are ordinarily plotted with the independent variable on the abscissa in units of repetitions, trials, or time; the ordinate shows the dependent variable of proficiency as measured by time, errors, amount, quality, rate, or other convenient scores.

Acceleration in Learning Curves

In the description of learning curves it has been customary to describe their course according to the rate of change in gains. Thus, if gains between later trials are greater than gains between earlier ones, the curve is said to be a curve of *increasing gains*. If gains grow less with practice, the curve is said to be one of *decreasing gains*. These terms are applied whether the units lead to a rising or falling curve, keeping the psychological meaning the same whether a "gain" is an increase or a decrease in score.* In the nature of the units there is a greater tend-

---

* The common designations of 'negative acceleration' for decreasing gains and of 'positive acceleration' for increasing gains are to be avoided because, as used in the description of learning curves, they sometimes depart from mathematical conventions.

ency for falling curves to show decreasing gains than for rising ones to depart in that direction from linearity, i.e. from a curve of uniform gains. This can be demonstrated easily by transmuting the scores from one kind of unit to scores in another kind of unit, as in Fig. 9. The two sets of curves, plotted from the same hypothetical data, dramatize the tendency for curves plotted in

learners. This is what the learning curve is intended to show.

The method runs into difficulties when learning is to a criterion of mastery, so that different subjects have had different numbers of trials. Either the average curve must be stopped when the most rapid learner reaches the criterion of mastery, or some arbitrary solution must be adopted. One

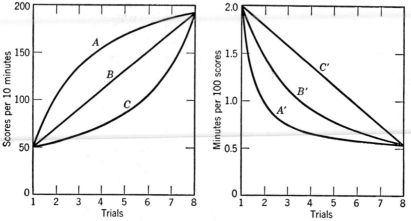

FIG. 9. Influence of type of score upon acceleration of learning curves. Curves *A, B,* and *C* represent scores plotted as amount per unit time, yielding rising curves that illustrate decreasing gains, uniform gains, and increasing gains, respectively. In curves *A', B',* and *C'* the same scores (hypothetical data) have been transmuted to time per unit amount, yielding falling curves. Now the data result in one curve that is linear and two that show decreasing gains. Curves *A', B',* and *C',* constructed from the same original scores as those of curves *A, B,* and *C,* illustrate the greater tendency toward decreasing gains in falling curves.

units such as time per unit to show decreasing gains. As an empirical finding a curve of decreasing gains is common also for data plotted in amount per unit time, but such curves reveal better than falling curves the inflection points in learning.

Combining Scores from Several Subjects

Trial-by-trial averages. The problem of combining scores from different learners into one curve has been solved in several ways. The simplest and often most satisfactory method is a trial-by-trial average for learners who have had the same number of trials. Then the mean and standard deviation of each point is contributed by the individual differences in trial-by-trial progress of the

possibility is to assume that the successful learners would have continued to score at criterial level had they been permitted to continue. This is a fallacious assumption, and in any case it restricts the variability of the later trials through the artificial maximum imposed upon those learners who have reached the criterion.

The Vincent method. Another solution, first proposed in crude form by Vincent (1912), has since been described by her name, although the details have been much modified. The problem of combining the results of subjects who have required different numbers of trials to mastery is solved by dividing the total course of learning into an equal number of fractions. The subjects' scores are then averaged according to the achievements within each such fraction of progress to mastery. The fraction includes more trials for the slow learner than for the rapid one. In effect the method shrinks and stretches the learning curves of all subjects so that they begin and end at the same points. Hence all that the final curve can reveal is something of the *form* of the function between the start of learning and the criterion of mastery. This is a very limited amount of information, and Vincent curves have occasionally been used inappropriately on the assumption that they could be used for more general purposes.

Several revisions of the Vincent method have been proposed. These have been reviewed by Hilgard (1938), their assumptions compared, and a preferred method suggested. Because the Vincent method is so limited in its applications, the details of computation will not be given here. The characteristics of the preferred method are as follows: (1) the form of the curve is expressed in the most general units (per cent of total scores given in stated per cents of learning trials); (2) all subjects are weighted equally (each subject contributes 100 per cent of his scores in 100 per cent of his trials); (3) all the scores of all the subjects enter into the computations; and (4) a serious artifact at the criterion, pointed out by Melton (1936), is eliminated.*

Equations of the Learning Curve

When the results of learning are plotted in a form that shows some regularity of curvature, it is possible to fit a mathematical function to the points. Two approaches may be

* If the criterion is met in a single trial, scores on that trial are eliminated in the computations, thus getting rid of the end spurt caused by one trial that is artificially high. If the criterion requires two or more trials (whether or not consecutive), it is necessary to eliminate not only the criterial trials but also the trial just before the criterion. The trial just before such criterial trials is artificially low, and eliminating only the criterial trials would result in an end dip in the average Vincent curve instead of an end spurt.

followed in fitting a curve to data. One is to judge by inspection what function will fit, and then to proceed to try it out mathematically. This is a purely empirical method, resulting in a formula that gives a shorthand description of the curve. If a formula with a large number of parameters is chosen, it may be made to fit a variety of empirical results (Woodrow, 1942). The other approach requires that an inference be made about the form of the function according to some rational theory. Then this function is fitted to the data. In this case the constants are still determined empirically, but they then have rational meaning according to the theory by which the curve was selected.

Among the many attempts to fit curves to learning data, several have proposed functions that have two parameters, one representing the upper limit of learning, the other representing the rate at which this limit is approached. Woodrow (1940) compared two such formulas and found a high correlation between the constants obtained when both were used on learning data. The first formula was that proposed by Robertson (1915).

$$\log \frac{(y)}{(A-y)} = k(x-x_0)$$

The second formula was that proposed by Moore (1932).

$$\log y = a + bc^x$$

Hull (1943) has made extensive use of a somewhat simpler growth function, expressed in the form:

$$H = M(1 - e^{-kt})$$

where H = habit strength.

M = upper limit of habit strength.

t = number of reinforced trials.

k = constant expressing learning rate.

The importance of such equations as analytic devices rests both in the form of the function and in the constants that they determine. If the curves are based on acceptable rational inferences, the same constants ought to reappear in different situations. These constants not only define individual differences in learning but also make possible additional inferences about the zero point in learning and about the upper limit of learning. These inferences are very important when learning data are to be scaled, as in the attempt to answer questions about the change in variability with practice (e.g. Anastasi, 1934; Woodrow, 1937).

For a recent discussion of the problem of quantifying learning data, see Hull et al. (1947).

NEXT STEPS IN THE STUDY OF LEARNING

In order for the science of learning to advance, two developments must take place together. Methods must be made increasingly precise so that more verified, reproducible relations may be known. At the same time conceptual formulations must be made increasingly appropriate to the processes investigated. Improvement in experimental methods, without the exploring of new concepts, is something of a danger and might lead to sterility. There is no real antithesis between experiments that are inventive and novel and those that are well controlled and dependable in their findings. Novelty should not be introduced as a decoration or as a mere gesture of originality, for the only consequence then is lack of comparability between experiments. Sufficient novelty can be achieved by the study of new variables or the consequences of new formulations, without departing in the control experiments from situations that have been standardized by others.

The possibility of 'miniature systems' (Hull, 1935, 1937) is not to be overlooked as one device for giving concepts careful quantitative testing within restricted domains, without arrogant claims that these concepts will solve all the problems of learning. Such systems, if they appear in number, will give alternative concepts a chance to be refined before the stage is reached when transformation equations will combine the smaller systems into more comprehensive ones.

Finally, a word needs to be said for naturalistic studies, which continue to make fresh starts in the uncovering of problems that have been neglected in the laboratory. In the end, one service of the laboratory must be to answer in precise fashion the questions that are raised by nonpsychologists confronted with the understanding and control of learning in situations outside the laboratory.

REFERENCES

Adams, D. K. Experimental studies of adaptive behavior in cats. *Comp. Psychol. Monogr.*, 1929, **6**, No. 27.

Alexander, H. W. A general test for trend. *Psychol. Bull.*, 1946, **43**, 533–557.

Alpert, A. The solving of problem-situations by preschool children. *Teach. Coll. Contr. Educ.*, 1928, No. 323.

Anastasi, A. A group factor in immediate memory. *Arch. Psychol., N. Y.*, 1930, **18**, No. 120.

Anastasi, A. Further studies of the memory factor. *Arch. Psychol., N. Y.*, 1932–33, **22**, No. 142.

Anastasi, A. Practice and variability. *Psychol. Monogr.*, 1934, **45**, No. 204.

Anderson, A. C. Time discrimination in the white rat. *J. comp. Psychol.*, 1932, **13**, 27–55.

Anderson, E. E. The interrelationship of drives of the male albino rat. II. Intercorrelations between 47 measures of drives and of learning. *Comp. Psychol. Monogr.*, 1938, **14**, No. 8.

Ballachey, E. L., and J. Buel. Centrifugal swing as a factor determining the distribution of errors in the maze running of the rat. *J. genet. Psychol.*, 1934, **45**, 358–370.

Bingham, H. C. Chimpanzee translocation by means of boxes. *Comp. Psychol. Monogr.*, 1929, **5**.

Brogden, W. J. The effect of frequency of reinforcement upon the level of conditioning. *J. exp. Psychol.*, 1939, **24**, 419–431.

Brown, C. W., and E. E. Ghiselli. A multiple-unit apparatus for measuring the rat's ability to discriminate visual patterns. *J. comp. Psychol.*, 1934, **18**, 451–454.

Bryan, W. L., and N. Harter. Studies in the physiology and psychology of the telegraphic language. *Psychol. Rev.*, 1897, **4**, 27–53.

Bryan, W. L., and N. Harter. Studies on the telegraphic language. The acquisition of a hierarchy of habits. *Psychol. Rev.*, 1899, **6**, 345–375.

Buel, J. The linear maze. I. "Choice-point expectancy," "correctness," and the goal gradient. *J. comp. Psychol.*, 1934, **17**, 185–199.

Bühler, C., and H. Hetzer. *Testing children's development from birth to school age.* New York: Farrar and Rinehart, 1935.

Bunch, M. E. The measurement of retention by the relearning method. *Psychol. Rev.*, 1941, **48**, 450–456.

Calvin, J. S. Decremental factors in conditioned response learning. Ph.D. dissertation, Yale University, 1939.

Campbell, A. A. The interrelations of two measures of conditioning in man. *J. exp. Psychol.*, 1938, **22**, 225–243.

Campbell, A. A., and E. R. Hilgard. Individual differences in ease of conditioning. *J. exp. Psychol.*, 1936, **19**, 561–571.

Commins, W. D., Q. McNemar, and C. P. Stone. Interrelations of measures of ability in the rat. *J. comp. Psychol.*, 1932, **14**, 225–235.

Cowles, J. T. "Delayed response" as tested by three methods and its relation to other learning situations. *J. Psychol.*, 1940, **9**, 103–130.

Crawford, M. P. The cooperative solving of problems by young chimpanzees. *Comp. Psychol. Monogr.*, 1937, **14**, No. 2.

Dashiell, J. F. A quantitative demonstration of animal drive. *J. comp. Psychol.*, 1925, **5**, 205–208.

Davis, F. C. The relative reliability of words and nonsense syllables as learning material. *J. exp. Psychol.*, 1930, **13**, 221–234.

Dodge, R. Habituation to rotation. *J. exp. Psychol.*, 1923, **6**, 1–35.

Duncker, K. A qualitative (experimental and theoretical) study of productive thinking (solving of comprehensible problems). *J. genet. Psychol.*, 1926, **33**, 642–708.

Ebbinghaus, H. *Memory.* (Translated by H. A. Ruger, and C. E. Bussenius, New York: Teachers College, 1913.) 1885.

Fields, P. E. Studies in concept formation: I. The development of the concept of triangularity by the white rat. *Comp. Psychol. Monogr.*, 1932, **9**, No. 2.

Finch, G. Chimpanzee handedness. *Science*, 1941a, **94**, 117–118.

Finch, G. The solution of patterned string problems by chimpanzees. *J. comp. Psychol.*, 1941b, **32**, 83–90.

Finkenbinder, E. O. The curve of forgetting. *Amer. J. Psychol.*, 1913, **24**, 8–32.

Fisher, R. A. *The design of experiments.* Edinburgh: Oliver and Boyd, 1935.

Flesch, R. *The art of plain talk.* New York: Harper, 1946.

Garrett, H. E. The relation of tests of memory and learning to each other and to general intelligence in a highly selected adult group. *J. educ. Psychol.*, 1928, **19**, 601–613.

Gellerman, L. W. Form discrimination in chimpanzees and two-year-old children. I. Discrimination of form *per se*. II. Form vs. background. *J. genet. Psychol.*, 1933a, **42**, 1–50.

Gellerman, L. W. Chance orders of alternating stimuli in visual discrimination experiments. *J. genet. Psychol.*, 1933b, **42**, 207–208.

Gilbert, G. M. The new status of experimental studies on the relationship of feeling to memory. *Psychol. Bull.*, 1938, **35**, 26–35.

Glaze, J. A. The association value of nonsense syllables. *J. genet. Psychol.*, 1928, **35**, 255–267.

Grant, D. A. New statistical criteria for learning and problem solution in experiments involving repeated trials. *Psychol. Bull.*, 1946, **43**, 272–282.

Grant, D. A. Additional tables of the probability of "runs" of correct responses in learning and problem-solving. *Psychol. Bull.*, 1947, **44**, 276–279.

Grant, D. A., and E. B. Norris. Dark adaptation as a factor in the sensitization of the Beta response of the eyelid to light. *J. exp. Psychol.*, 1946, **36**, 390–397.

Grant, D. A., and D. E. Schneider. Intensity of the conditioned stimulus and strength of conditioning: I. The conditioned eyelid response to light. *J. exp. Psychol.*, 1948, **38**, 690–696.

Grether, W. F. Pseudo-conditioning without paired stimulation encountered in attempted backward conditioning. *J. comp. Psychol.*, 1938, **25**, 91–96.

Guthrie, E. R., and G. P. Horton. *Cats in a puzzle box.* New York: Rinehart, 1946.

Haggerty, M. E. Imitation in monkeys. *J. comp. Neurol.*, 1909, **19**, 337–455.

Hall, C. S. Intercorrelations of measures of human learning. *Psychol. Rev.*, 1936, **43**, 179–196.

Hamilton, G. V. A study of perseverance reactions in primates and rodents. *Behav. Monogr.*, 1916, **3**, No. 13.

Harlow, H. F. Responses by rhesus monkeys to stimuli having multiple sign-values. In Q. McNemar and M. A. Merrill (Eds.), *Studies in personality: contributed in honor of Lewis M. Terman.* New York: McGraw-Hill, 1942. Pp. 105–123.

Harlow, H. F., and P. H. Settlage. Comparative behavior of primates. VII. Capacity of monkeys to solve patterned string tests. *J. comp. Psychol.*, 1934, **18**, 423–435.

Harlow, H. F., H. Uehling, and A. H. Maslow. Comparative behavior of primates. I. Delayed reaction tests on primates from the lemur to the orang-utan. *J. comp. Psychol.*, 1932, **13**, 313–344.

Hebb, D. O., and E. N. Foord. Errors of visual recognition and the nature of the trace. *J. exp. Psychol.*, 1945, **35**, 335–348.

Heron, W. T. Complex learning processes. In F. A. Moss (Ed.), *Comparative psychology.* New York: Prentice-Hall, 1942. Pp. 248–279.

Hilgard, E. R. The saving score as a measure of retention. *Amer. J. Psychol.*, 1934, **46**, 337–339.

Hilgard, E. R. A summary and evaluation of alternative procedures for the construction of

Vincent curves. *Psychol. Bull.*, 1938, **35**, 282–297.

Hilgard, E. R. *Theories of learning.* New York: Appleton-Century-Crofts, 1948.

Hilgard, E. R., and L. G. Humphreys. The effect of supporting and antagonistic voluntary instructions on conditioned discrimination. *J. exp. Psychol.*, 1938, **22**, 291–304.

Hilgard, E. R., and D. G. Marquis. *Conditioning and learning.* New York: Appleton-Century-Crofts, 1940.

Hilgard, E. R., and E. M. Sait. Estimates of past and of future performances as measures of aspiration. *Amer. J. Psychol.*, 1941, **54**, 102–108.

Hovland, C. I. Experimental studies in rote-learning theory. I. Reminiscence following learning by massed and by distributed practice. *J. exp. Psychol.*, 1938, **22**, 201–224.

Hull, C. L. Quantitative aspects of the evolution of concepts. *Psychol. Monogr.*, 1920, No. 123.

Hull, C. L. Differential habituation to internal stimuli in the albino rat. *J. comp. Psychol.*, 1933*a*, **16**, 255–273.

Hull, C. L. The meaningfulness of 320 selected nonsense syllables. *Amer. J. Psychol.*, 1933*b*, **45**, 730–734.

Hull, C. L. *Hypnosis and suggestibility.* New York: Appleton-Century-Crofts, 1933*c*.

Hull, C. L. Learning: II. The factor of the conditioned reflex. In C. Murchison (Ed.), *Handbook of general experimental psychology.* Worcester: Clark University Press, 1934*a*, pp. 382–455.

Hull, C. L. The rat's speed-of-locomotion gradient in the approach to food. *J. comp. Psychol.*, 1934*b*, **17**, 393–422.

Hull, C. L. The conflicting psychologies of learning — a way out. *Psychol. Rev.*, 1935, **42**, 491–516.

Hull, C. L. Mind, mechanism, and adaptive behavior. *Psychol. Rev.*, 1937, **44**, 1–32.

Hull, C. L. *Principles of behavior.* New York: Appleton-Century-Crofts, 1943.

Hull, C. L., J. M. Felsinger, A. I. Gladstone, and H. G. Yamaguchi. A proposed quantification of habit strength. *Psychol. Rev.*, 1947, **54**, 237–254.

Hull, C. L., C. I. Hovland, R. T. Ross, M. Hall, D. T. Perkins, and F. B. Fitch. *Mathematico-deductive theory of rote learning.* New Haven: Yale University Press, 1940.

Humphrey, G. *The nature of learning in its relation to the living system.* New York: Harcourt-Brace, 1933.

Humphreys, L. G. The effect of random alternation of reinforcement on the acquisition and extinction of conditioned eyelid reactions. *J. exp. Psychol.*, 1939, **25**, 141–158.

Humphreys, L. G. The variability of extinction scores in 'Skinner-box' experiments. *J. exp. Psychol.*, 1940, **26**, 614–618.

Humphreys, L. G. Measures of strength of conditioned eyelid responses. *J. gen. Psychol.*, 1943*a*, **29**, 101–111.

Humphreys, L. G. The strength of a Thorndikean response as a function of the number of practice trials. *J. comp. Psychol.*, 1943*b*, **35**, 101–110.

Hunter, W. S. The delayed reaction in animals and children. *Behav. Monogr.*, 1913, **2**, No. 6.

Hunter, W. S. The delayed reaction in a child. *Psychol. Rev.*, 1917, **24**, 75–87.

Hunter, W. S. The behavior of raccoons in a double alternation temporal maze. *J. genet. Psychol.*, 1928, **35**, 374–388.

Hunter, W. S. A tridimensional maze. *J. gen. Psychol.*, 1929, **2**, 130–134.

Hunter, W. S. Learning. IV: Experimental studies in learning. In C. Murchison (Ed.), *Handbook of general experimental psychology.* Worcester: Clark University Press, 1934, 497–570.

Huston, P. E., D. Shakow, and M. H. Erickson. A study of hypnotically induced complexes by means of the Luria technique. *J. gen. Psychol.*, 1934, **11**, 65–97.

Ivanov-Smolensky, A. G. On the methods of examining the conditioned food reflexes in children and in mental disorders. *Brain*, 1927, **50**, 138–141.

Jackson, T. A. General factors in transfer of training in the white rat. *Genet. Psychol. Monogr.*, 1932, **11**, No. 1.

Jackson, T. A. Use of the stick as a tool by young chimpanzees. *J. comp. Psychol.*, 1942, **34**, 223–235.

Jackson, T. A., E. Stonex, E. Lane, and K. Dominguez. Studies in the transposition of learning by children. I. Relative vs. absolute response as a function of the amount of training. *J. exp. Psychol.*, 1938, **23**, 578–600.

Karn, H. W., and J. M. Porter, Jr. The effects of certain pretraining procedures upon maze performance and their significance for the concept of latent learning. *J. exp. Psychol.*, 1946, **36**, 461–469.

Kellogg, W. N., and E. L. Walker. An analysis of the bilateral transfer of conditioning in dogs, in terms of frequency, amplitude, and latency of the responses. *J. gen. Psychol.*, 1938, **18**, 253–265.

Kimble, G. A. Conditioning as a function of the time between conditioned and unconditioned stimuli. *J. exp. Psychol.*, 1947, **37**, 1–15.

King, H. A. Growth and variability in the body weight of the rat. *Anat. Rec.*, 1915, **9**, 751–776.

Klüver, H. *Behavior mechanisms in monkeys.* Chicago: University of Chicago Press, 1933.

Köhler, W. *The mentality of apes.* New York: Harcourt-Brace, 1925.

Kohts, N. Recherches sur l'intelligence du chimpanzé par la méthode de "choix d'après modèle." *J. de Psychol.*, 1928, **25**, 255–275.

Krechevsky, I. Brain mechanisms and brightness discrimination learning. *J. comp. Psychol.*, 1936, **21**, 405–445.

Krechevsky, I. Brain mechanisms and variability: I. Variability within a means-end-readiness. *J. comp. Psychol.*, 1937, **23**, 121–138.

Kreezer, G. L. Technics for the investigation of psychological phenomena in the rat. In J. Q. Griffith and E. J. Farris (Eds.), *The rat in laboratory investigation*. Philadelphia: Lippincott, 1942. Pp. 199–273.

Krueger, W. C. F. The effect of overlearning on retention. *J. exp. Psychol.*, 1929, **12**, 71–78.

Krueger, W. C. F. Further studies in overlearning. *J. exp. Psychol.*, 1930, **13**, 152–163.

Lashley, K. S. The mechanism of vision. I. A method for rapid analysis of pattern vision in the rat. *J. genet. Psychol.*, 1930, **37**, 453–460.

Leeper, R. The reliability and validity of maze experiments with white rats. *Genet. Psychol. Monogr.*, 1932, **11**, 137–245.

Leeper, R. The role of motivation in learning; a study of the phenomenon of differential motivational control of the utilization of habits. *J. genet. Psychol.*, 1935, **46**, 3–40.

Luh, C. W. The conditions of retention. *Psychol. Monogr.*, 1922, **31**, No. 142.

Lumsdaine, A. A. Measures of individual differences in susceptibility to conditioning. *J. exp. Psychol.*, 1941, **28**, 428–435.

McGeoch, J. A. The influence of associative value upon the difficulty of nonsense-syllable lists. *J. genet. Psychol.*, 1930, **37**, 420–430.

McGeoch, J. A. The direction and extent of intraserial associations at recall. *Amer. J. Psychol.*, 1936, **48**, 221–245.

McGeoch, J. A. The psychology of human learning. New York: Longmans, Green, 1942.

McGeoch, J. A., and F. McKinney. Studies in retroactive inhibition: VIII. The influence of the relative order of presentation of original and interpolated paired associates. *J. exp. Psychol.*, 1937, **20**, 60–83.

McNemar, Q. Work-scores vs. time scores. *Amer. J. Psychol.*, 1934, **46**, 462–464.

McNemar, Q. Sampling in psychological research. *Psychol. Bull.*, 1940, **37**, 331–365.

McNemar, Q., and C. P. Stone. Studies in animal retention: I. Notes on the relearning of a multiple-T maze by albino rats. *J. genet. Psychol.*, 1931, **39**, 135–156.

Maier, N. R. F. Reasoning in white rats. *Comp. Psychol. Monogr.*, 1929, **6**, No. 29.

Maier, N. R. F. Reasoning in humans. I. On direction. *J. comp. Psychol.*, 1930, **10**, 115–143.

Maier, N. R. F. Reasoning in children. *J. comp. Psychol.*, 1936, **21**, 357–366.

Maier, N. R. F., N. M. Glaser, and J. B. Klee. Studies of abnormal behavior in the rat. III. The development of behavior fixations through frustration. *J. exp. Psychol.*, 1940, **26**, 521–546.

Maslow, A. H. Dominance-quality and social behavior in infra-human primates. *J. soc. Psychol.*, 1940, **11**, 313–324.

Masserman, J. H. *Behavior and neurosis*. Chicago: University of Chicago Press, 1943.

Melton, A. W. The methodology of experimental studies of human learning and retention: I. The functions of a methodology and the available criteria for evaluating different experimental methods. *Psychol. Bull.*, 1936, **33**, 305–394.

Melton, A. W., and J. McQ. Irwin. The influence of degree of interpolated learning on retroactive inhibition and the overt transfer of specific responses. *Amer. J. Psychol.*, 1940, **53**, 173–203.

Meltzer, H. Individual differences in forgetting pleasant and unpleasant experiences. *J. educ. Psychol.*, 1930, **21**, 399–409.

Miles, W. R. The high relief finger maze for human learning. *J. gen. Psychol.*, 1928, **1**, 3–14.

Miller, J. The effect of facilitatory and inhibitory attitudes on eyelid conditioning. Ph.D. dissertation, Yale University. (Abstract in *Psychol. Bull.*, 1939, **36**, 577–578.)

Miller, N. E., and J. Dollard. *Social learning and imitation*. New Haven: Yale University Press, 1947.

Muenzinger, K. F., A. H. Bernstone, and L. Richards. Motivation in learning. VIII. Equivalent amounts of electric shock for right and wrong responses in a visual discrimination habit. *J. comp. Psychol.*, 1938, **26**, 177–186.

Munn, N. L. *An introduction to animal psychology. The behavior of the rat*. Boston: Houghton Mifflin, 1933.

Munn, N. L. *Psychological development*. Boston: Houghton Mifflin, 1938.

Münsterberg, H. *On the witness stand: Essays on psychology and crime*. New York: McClure, 1908.

Nissen, H. W., and T. L. McCulloch. Equated and non-equated stimulus situations in discrimination learning by chimpanzees. III. Prepotency of response to oddity through training. *J. comp. Psychol.*, 1937, **23**, 377–381.

Pavlov, I. P. *Conditioned reflexes*. (Translated by G. V. Anrep.) London: Oxford University Press, 1927.

Peckham, G. W., and E. G. Peckham. Some observations on the mental powers of spiders. *J. Morph.*, 1887, **1**, 383–419.

Pfungst, O. *Clever Hans*. (Translated by C. L. Rahn.) New York: Holt, 1911.

Podkopaev, N. A. *Die Methodik der Erforschung der bedingten Reflexe*. München: Bergmann, 1926.

Rapaport, D. *Emotions and memory*. Baltimore: Williams and Wilkins, 1942.

Raskin, E., and S. W. Cook. The strength and direction of associations formed in the learning of nonsense syllables. *J. exp. Psychol.*, 1937, **20**, 381–395.

Reynolds, B. The acquisition of a trace conditioned response as a function of the magnitude of the stimulus trace. *J. exp. Psychol.*, 1945, **35**, 15–30.

Richardson, H. M. The growth of adaptive behavior in infants: an experimental study at seven age levels. *Genet. Psychol. Monogr.,* 1932, **12,** 195–397.

Robinson, E. S. Methods of practice equilibration. *Amer. J. Psychol.,* 1929, **41,** 153–156.

Ruger, H. A. The psychology of efficiency: An experimental study of the processes involved in the solution of mechanical puzzles and in the acquisition of skill in their manipulation. *Arch. Psychol., N. Y.,* 1910, **2,** No. 15.

Sams, C. F., and E. C. Tolman. Time discrimination in white rats. *J. comp. Psychol.,* 1925, **5,** 255–263.

Sauer, F. M. The relative variability of nonsense syllables and words. *J. exp. Psychol.,* 1930, **13,** 235–246.

Schneirla, T. C. Learning and orientation in ants. *Comp. Psychol. Monogr.,* 1929, **6,** No. 30.

Sears, R. R. *Survey of objective studies of psychoanalytic concepts.* New York: Social Science Research Council, Bull. 51, 1943.

Seashore, R. H. Stanford motor skills unit. *Psychol. Monogr.,* 1928, **39,** 51–66.

Sharp, A. A. An experimental test of Freud's doctrine of the relation of hedonic tone to memory revival. *J. exp. Psychol.,* 1938, **22,** 395–418.

Skalet, M. The significance of delayed reactions in young children. *Comp. Psychol. Monogr.,* 1931, **7,** No. 4.

Skinner, B. F. *The behavior of organisms.* New York: Appleton-Century-Crofts, 1938.

Skinner, B. F. Differential reinforcement with respect to time. (Abstract) *Amer. Psychologist,* 1946, **1,** 275–276.

Skinner, B. F. 'Superstition' in the pigeon. *J. exp. Psychol.,* 1948, **38,** 168–172.

Small, W. S. Notes on the psychic development of the young white rat. *Amer. J. Psychol.,* 1899, **11,** 80–100.

Small, W. S. An experimental study of the mental processes of the rat. *Amer. J. Psychol.,* 1900, **11,** 133–165.

Smith, M. H., Jr. Spread of effect and the probability bias hypothesis. Ph.D. dissertation, Stanford University, 1947.

Smoke, K. L. An objective study of concept formation. *Psychol. Monogr.,* 1932, **42,** No. 191.

Spence, K. W. The reliability of the maze and methods of its determination. *Comp. Psychol. Monogr.,* 1932, **8,** No. 40.

Stone, C. P. A multiple discrimination box and its use in studying learning ability of rats. I. Reliability of scores. *J. genet. Psychol.,* 1928, **35,** 557–573.

Stone, C. P. The age factor in animal learning. I. Rats in the problem box and maze. *Genet. Psychol. Monogr.,* 1929a, **5,** No. 1; II. Rats on a multiple light discrimination box. *Ibid.,* 1929b, **6,** No. 2.

Stone, C. P. Sex difference in running ability of thoroughbred horses. *J. comp. Psychol.,* 1935, **19,** 59–67.

Stroud, J. B., A. F. Lehman, and C. McCue. The reliability of nonsense-syllable scores. *J. exp. Psychol.,* 1934, **17,** 294–304.

Thorndike, E. L. Animal intelligence: an experimental study of the associative processes in animals. *Psychol. Monogr.,* 1898, **2,** No. 8.

Thorndike, E. L. *Animal intelligence.* New York: Macmillan, 1911.

Thorndike, E. L. An experimental study of rewards. *Teach. Coll. Contr. Educ.,* 1933, No. 580.

Thorndike, R. L. Organization of behavior in the albino rat. *Genet. Psychol. Monogr.,* 1935, **17,** No. 1.

Thurstone, L. L. Influence of motion pictures on children's attitudes. *J. soc. Psychol.,* 1931, **2,** 291–305.

Tinklepaugh, O. L. Multiple delayed reactions with chimpanzees and monkeys. *J. comp. Psychol.,* 1932, **13,** 207–243.

Tolman, E. C. The determiners of behavior at a choice-point. *Psychol. Rev.,* 1938, **45,** 1–41.

Tolman, E. C., and C. H. Honzik. "Insight" in rats. *Univ. Calif. Publ. Psychol.,* 1930, **4,** 215–232.

Tryon, R. C. Studies in individual differences in maze ability: III. The community of function between two maze abilities. *J. comp. Psychol.* 1931a, **12,** 95–116; IV. The constancy of individual differences: correlation between learning and relearning. *Ibid.,* 1931b, **12,** 303–345; VII. The specific components of maze ability, and a general theory of psychological components. *Ibid.,* 1940a, **30,** 283–335; VIII. Prediction validity of the psychological components of maze ability. *Ibid.,* 1940b, **30,** 535–582.

Vaughn, C. L. Factors in rat learning. An analysis of the intercorrelations between 34 variables. *Comp. Psychol. Monogr.,* 1937, **14,** 1–41.

Vincent, S. B. The function of the vibrissae in the behavior of the white rat. *Behav. Monogr.,* 1912, **1,** No. 5.

Walker, E. L. Variability in extinction scores in Skinner-box problems. *J. comp. physiol. Psychol.,* 1948, **41,** 432–437.

Ward, L. B. Reminiscence and rote learning. *Psychol. Monogr.,* 1937, **49,** No. 220.

Warden, C. J. The relative economy of various modes of attack in the mastery of a stylus maze. *J. exp. Psychol.,* 1924, **7,** 243–275.

Warden, C. J. A symmetrical linear maze for use in the analysis of animal serial learning. *J. genet. Psychol.,* 1929, **36,** 177–178.

Warden, C. J., and T. A. Jackson. Imitative behavior in the rhesus monkey. *J. genet. Psychol.,* 1935, **46,** 103–125.

Warden, C. J., T. N. Jenkins, and L. H. Warner. *Comparative psychology. Vol. I. Principles and methods.* New York: Ronald, 1935.

Warden, C. J., T. N. Jenkins, and L. H. Warner. *Comparative psychology. Vol. III. Vertebrates.* New York: Ronald, 1936.

Warden, C. J., T. N. Jenkins, and L. H. Warner. *Comparative psychology. Vol. II. Plants and invertebrates.* New York: Ronald, 1940.

Warden, C. J., S. Ross, and G. S. Klein. *Laboratory manual for experimental comparative psychology*. New York: Authors, 1942.

Wendt, G. R. Methods of recording action. *Arch. Psychol., N. Y.*, 1938, **32**, No. 228.

Wendt, G. R., and R. Dodge. Practical directions for stimulating and for photographically recording eye-movements of animals. *J. comp. Psychol.*, 1938, **25**, 9–49.

Wentworth, K. L. Some factors determining handedness in the white rat. *Genet. Psychol. Monogr.*, 1942, **26**, 55–117.

Williams, K. A. The reward value of a conditioned stimulus. *Univ. Calif. Publ. Psychol.*, 1929, **4**, 31–55.

Witmer, L. R. The association value of three-place consonant syllables. *J. genet. Psychol.*, 1935, **47**, 337–359.

Wohlgemuth, A. On memory and the direction of associations. *Brit. J. Psychol.*, 1913, **5**, 447–465.

Wolfe, J. B. The effect of delayed reward upon learning in the white rat. *J. comp. Psychol.*, 1934, **17**, 1–21.

Woodrow, H. The scaling of practice data. *Psychometrika*, 1937, **2**, 237–247.

Woodrow, H. Interrelations of measures of learning. *J. Psychol.*, 1940, **10**, 49–73

Woodrow, H. The problem of general quantitative laws in psychology. *Psychol. Bull.*, 1942, **39**, 1–37.

Woodworth, R. S. *Experimental psychology*. New York: Holt, 1938.

Wulf, F. Über die Veränderung von Vorstellungen (Gedächtnis und Gestalt). *Psychol. Forsch.*, 1922, **1**, 333–373.

Yerkes, R. M. Methods of exhibiting reactive tendencies characteristic of ontogenetic and phylogenetic stages. *J. Anim. Behav.*, 1917, **7**, 11–28.

Yerkes, R. M. The mind of a gorilla. *Genet. Psychol. Monogr.*, 1927, **2**, 1–193; 375–532.

Yerkes, R. M. *Chimpanzees. A laboratory colony*. New Haven: Yale University Press, 1943.

Yerkes, R. M., and J. B. Watson. Methods of studying vision in animals. *Behav. Monogr.*, 1911, **1**, No. 2.

Yerkes, R. M. *The dancing mouse*. New York: Macmillan, 1907.

Yoshioka, J. G. Weber's law in the discrimination of maze distance by the white rat. *Univ. Calif. Publ. Psychol.*, 1929, **4**, 155–184.

Zeigarnik, B. Das Berhalten erledigter und unerledigter Handlungen. *Psychol. Forsch.*, 1927, **9**, 1–85.

16.

Animal Studies of Learning

W. J. BROGDEN

University of Wisconsin

Although learning has been the concern of most psychological experiments with animal subjects, not all these experiments fall within the scope of this chapter. Even when learning has not been the subject of investigation, the problem has often required a specific training procedure. In other experiments a practice effect has had to be controlled or eliminated, because learning interfered with the phenomenon under investigation. Studies of this sort lie clearly outside our present concern.

Even within the field of learning itself we shall have to restrict our interests. A complete bibliography of animal studies of learning would be enormous. Consequently it is necessary to sort these studies into categories, in order to guide our selection. Rated according to the nature of their scientific contribution, animal studies of learning fall into four classes. They provide evidence to the effect that: (1) learning occurs in a given kind of organism under conditions only vaguely specified; (2) learning of a certain kind occurs to a greater or lesser extent in a given animal under given conditions than does learning in the same animal when one or more aspects of the conditions are changed; (3) learning of a given kind shows progressive variation in amount or in rate as a function of a change in a single variable; and (4) learning of a given kind shows progressive variation in amount or in rate as a function of the systematic variation of a set of variables. Experiments lead-

ing to conclusions 1 and 2 demonstrate merely that learning occurs, that it occurs under conditions that are specified vaguely, or that a particular variable influences the rate or the amount of learning. These may be important first steps in the advancement of a science, but it is only the experiments of categories 3 and 4 that approach the scientific ideal of precise quantitative relations between the phenomenon of learning and the factors governing it. Emphasis will therefore be given to these latter experiments. The present treatment of animal learning will examine the variables that influence the rate and the quantity of learning, and will forego an enumeration of the many different kinds of learning phenomena and the species in which they occur.

Even with this restriction, the facts of animal learning are difficult to organize. No matter what the efficiency of experimental design, the variation in conditions from one experiment to another is appalling. This is often true of experiments that purport to examine the effect of the same variables on the same phenomenon of learning. Even the same research worker may not maintain standard conditions in a series of experiments on similar problems. Lack of standardization makes most experiments wholly unique.

Despite these negative aspects, however, there is much to be said on the positive side. Our fund of knowledge about animal learning is great, and the ingenuity and skill of numerous workers have produced impressive results. It is possible to marshal these results in a number of ways, each of which has its special advantage. The preference of the writer is to classify the phenomena of animal learning under three categories, acquisition, transfer, and retention, and to show how they occur in three classes of animal learning — conditioning, discrimination learning, and serial learning. This approach requires the development first of adequate definitions.

Acquisition is the primary phenomenon of learning. Its definition provides the basis for defining transfer and retention, for establishing the categories of conditioning, discrimination learning, and serial learning, and for distinguishing learning from other psychological phenomena. Acquisition is a change in performance by an organism. Its course is limited by the arbitrary initiation and termination of measurement, and it comes about through the repetitive or continuous presentation of controlled conditions. The factor of change distinguishes acquisition from psychological phenomena that are relatively static. The direction of change in performance separates acquisition from other dynamic phenomena like inhibition and fatigue. These characteristics may be integrated in the following definition: *acquisition is a progressive incremental change in the proficiency of performance by an organism; the direction, rate, and extent of change in the proficiency of performance are functions of the repetitive or continuous presentation of the conditions under which measurement of the change in performance is made.*

Transfer is the effect of a previous acquisition upon its subsequent proficiency under altered conditions, or upon the proficiency of the subsequent acquisition of some other performance. The measurement of transfer requires that there be a difference in performance under at least two training conditions. The two conditions may be met either by: (1) the acquisition of a given performance and its reacquisition under an altered training procedure, or (2) the acquisition of two different performances, one after the other. These methods require the use of control groups that are given only the second training procedure of the sequence. A further step in precision can often be obtained by making initial tests of the performance under the second set of training conditions, prior to occurrence of the first set.

Transfer is thus always a difference in performance. Although it may be positive or negative, it must be demonstrated to have occurred as a result of differences between at least two training conditions. Transfer cannot be determined precisely by the difference in performance between the two training conditions. The base line of performance from which transfer is measured must come from the control procedures mentioned above. We arrive, then, at the following definition: *transfer is a change in the proficiency of a performance that is demonstrated, by appropriate control procedures, to be a function of a change in the conditions under which it was originally acquired or in the conditions under which a similar performance was previously acquired.*

Retention is the persistence of an acquired performance after a lapse of time during which the performance has not taken place. Theoretically, retention is involved in both acquisition and transfer. There could be no acquisition of a performance if there were no persistence of increments from trial to trial. Nor could there be transfer if the change involved in the acquisition of a performance did not remain to influence the subsequent acquisition of another performance. However, as with transfer, the definition of retention must be made relative to the definition of acquisition and in terms of the experimental procedures used to study retention. In animal studies, retention may be measured as the saving in the cost of reacquiring a performance after a lapse of time from the cost of the original acquisition. Or it may be measured by the proficiency of a performance in a short series of trials relative to that for an equal series of trials made earlier in the terminal stage of an original acquisition. The variables that operate within the lapse of time may either be controlled by the experimenter or they may be left to chance. In any case the lapse of time involved is relatively greater than the intervals between the trials that led to the acquisition. The following, then, is our definition: *retention is the difference in proficiency of a performance during reacquisition or retest from that during acquisition; the subsequent measure is made after a lapse of time (1) ordinarily greater than the intervals between trials during acquisition, (2) in which the performance does not occur, and (3) during which variables that are a function of it may be controlled.*

Every special kind of learning represents a subclass of acquisition. The definitions of conditioning, discrimination learning, and serial learning first must fall within our definition of acquisition, and second must be such that each is differentiated from the other two. Measurement of any performance defines its beginning and its end. The beginning and end of the performance determine its duration in time and its location and extent in space. Thus performances may be relatively long or short in time and of relatively large or small extent in space. The acquisition of performances of relatively short duration is characteristic of conditioning. The acquisition of performances of relatively long duration, where subunits of performance may be measured, is characteristic of serial learning. Either kind of performance may be involved in discrimination learning.

The acquisition of a performance occurs in a set of environmental conditions that are presented to the organism continuously or repetitively. Some one or more aspects of the environment that are controlled by the experimenter are called the stimulus. When the stimulus is manipulated as a discrete and unitary event in space and is of relatively short duration, the performance involved is ordinarily of short duration. This situation is characteristic of conditioning. Where the stimulus is of relatively long duration and is patterned in space and time, the performance is ordinarily one of long duration and capable of division into subunits. These circumstances are characteristic of serial learning. Discrimination learning requires that there be at least two different stimulus situations to which the organism is required to make different responses. The experimenter may manipulate the stimuli so that they occur simultaneously or in temporal succession.

CONDITIONING

The classification system of Hilgard and Marquis (1940) will be followed in discussing the procedures for acquisition of CR's.[*] The primary distinction is between the classical and the instrumental training procedures, with a subclassification for the training procedures of instrumental reward, instrumental escape, instrumental avoidance, and secondary reward.[†] The classical train-

[*] Abbreviations: US = unconditioned stimulus; UR = unconditioned response; CS = conditioned stimulus; CR = conditioned response; RS = reinforcing stimulus.

[†] The distinction of four varieties of instrumental training is open to question. Instrumental reward and secondary reward training may be reduced to a single variety. Once training has been given the animal to establish the token-reward habit, the training for acquisition of the CR is the same. The preliminary training on the token habit is itself instrumental reward training: the experimenter selects an RS that has been shown to be effective as an RS by other observations. The effectiveness of this stimulus is probably the result of previous training. Instrumental avoidance and instrumental escape training may be reduced to a single variety by the introduction of a CS to the escape training procedure. If a CS is introduced into reward training, as was done by Skinner (1935) to establish what he called a pseudotype CR, all varieties of instrumental CR become comparable. Although a distinction is made between instrumental CR's established with noxious and reward-type US's or RS's, this is not done for classical training. In fact, that a given instrumental CR may be

ing procedure is that originally used by Pavlov (1927, 1928). A response already within the repertory of the animal is designated the UR, and the stimulus that elicits it is called the US. The UR is preferably a conveniently measurable response readily and consistently evoked by the US. Another stimulus that has been shown by test not to elicit the UR is called the CS. The CS and the US are presented repeatedly to the organism either simultaneously or with the CS preceding but overlapping the US in time. A response that is similar to the UR develops to the CS and is called the CR. The change in response to the CS from an initial zero magnitude of CR to some terminal magnitude constitutes an acquisition that is called conditioning.

Pavlov and his many collaborators worked with the dog. Ordinarily the UR was salivation; the US was food or weak acid; the CS was a stimulus for the auditory, tactile, or visual sense modalities; and the CR was salivation.

The procedures used in instrumental conditioning differ from the classical procedures in that there are two conditions of stimulus presentation: one prevails when a CR occurs, the other when a CR fails to occur. When the condition results in an increase of the CR, it is called reinforcement; when it results in no increase of CR, it is called nonreinforcement. These terms are also applied to the classical procedure: the US paired with the CS constitutes reinforcement; presentation of the CS alone is nonreinforcement. With instrumental training, reinforcement may occur in the absence of a US. The presence or absence of an RS provides the conditions for reinforcement and nonreinforcement in the training procedures.

readily maintained when a shift is made of the RS from shock to food has been shown by Brogden (1939a). The distinction of four varieties of instrumental training is based primarily upon the lack of control exercised by the experimenter over the conditions under which acquisition takes place and the time at which responses occur.

Reinforcement may be homogeneous or heterogeneous. Homogeneous reinforcement is typical of classical conditioning. It occurs when the US determines the nature of the response to be conditioned, and the presence or absence of the US provides the conditions for reinforcement or nonreinforcement. Heterogeneous reinforcement means that the response to be conditioned is not determined by the RS, but the presence or absence of the RS constitutes reinforcement or nonreinforcement.

Instrumental reward training has the following characteristics: (1) When the animal makes a response previously selected by the experimenter (the CR), an appropriate incentive such as food or water (the RS) is immediately presented. (2) If the animal is allowed to remain in the experimental situation, reinforcement takes place again when next the CR appears; if the animal has been removed, the experimenter returns it to the experimental situation so that a second CR may occur and be reinforced by the RS; in either case, the CR is the instrument that controls the occurrence of the RS. (3) Acquisition is measured in terms of time required for the CR to occur after the last CR, or after introduction to the experimental environment (latency), or in terms of frequency or rate of CR in a fixed unit of time. (4) These training conditions are continued until the individual animals have reached a criterial performance, or until a predetermined number of trials is given or a predetermined amount of time has passed. (5) The experimenter does not exercise specific control over events similar to either a CS or a US. He merely sets the general experimental environment and introduces the animal to it.

The characteristics of instrumental escape training * parallel closely those for reward training, except that the conditions of rein-

* Although instrumental escape training has received relatively little study, it has been shown to provide an excellent means for the study of acquired drives (see Chapter 13).

forcement involve noxious stimulation by electric shock, water, or extreme deviations of environmental temperature from body temperature. (1) The animal is presented with a noxious stimulus that continues to operate until a performance already within the repertory of the animal (the CR) occurs. (2) Either the CR terminates the RS, or it is the means of escape to another locus. (3) The animal is returned to the noxious environment if the CR results in escape to another locus, or the RS is reinstated by the experimenter; the appropriate condition prevails until the CR occurs again. (4) Measurement of acquisition may be in terms of latency or amplitude or in terms of frequency or rate of CR. (5) Practice is handled in terms of trials or units of time and is terminated when a criterion is attained or a given amount of practice is completed. (6) There is no US or CS under the control of the experimenter, except in terms of the extent to which the RS may function originally as a US or come to function as a CS.

Instrumental avoidance training is very similar to classical training in which the US is a noxious stimulus such as electric shock. (1) There is a definite US under the control of the experimenter that evokes a UR. (2) The CS and US are presented initially under the same conditions as in classical training. (3) The CR selected by the experimenter is similar in character to the UR. (4) When the CR is evoked by the CS, the US is not applied — the CR is the instrument of shock avoidance. (5) The measurement of acquisition may be in terms of amplitude, latency, or frequency of response. (6) Practice is handled in trial units and is terminated when a criterion is reached or a given number of trials has occurred.

Secondary reward training is a special case of instrumental reward training.* Initial

---

* Studies of secondary reward training provide a measure of the effectiveness of an acquired drive. Since an extended discussion of such studies in relation to learnable drives is given

training must be given to establish the performance, e.g. the operation of a food vendor by the insertion of poker chips. When this performance has been acquired, instrumental reward training is applied, except that the stimulus object for the food-vending machine is used as the RS.

Acquisition of a Conditioned Response

The UR. Many responses have served as the UR in experiments on conditioning. Lists of responses that have been conditioned are presented by Hull (1934) and by Hilgard and Marquis (1940).

The UR is rarely the independent variable in an experiment on the acquisition of a CR. In most situations it is not possible to vary the UR without varying its US. However, when the US is electric shock, the locus of application may be varied without other appreciable change in the UR. With dogs, cats, and rats investigators have reported on the acquisition of flexion responses of one or the other of the four limbs, but few have compared acquisition as a function of the responding members. Brogden (1940b) was unable to demonstrate a difference in the rate of acquisition of an instrumental avoidance response in dogs for the right and left forelimbs.

The acquisition of a CR may involve at least two stages: a first step that requires development of the UR to the US alone (or response to the RS alone); and a second stage, dependent upon completion of the first, during which the CS begins to evoke the CR (or during which the RS may be applied effectively). Both Skinner (1938, p. 66) and Girden (1938) cite evidence for two stages in the acquisition of a CR.

The definition of the UR also influences the measurement of acquisition. A US may evoke many changes in the effector system of an organism, of which usually only one is measured quantitatively as the UR. Re-

---

in Chapter 13 the present chapter will give only limited treatment to experiments on secondary reward training.

striction in measuring the UR usually imposes the same restriction on measurement of the CR. Research workers have been acutely aware of this, and it has been customary for them to comment on aspects of performance during acquisition that have not been subjected to measurement. An extensive description of these performances in urination, and defecation. The measurement of any one of these aspects would provide data on the acquisition of a CR. The four curves of Fig. 1 are evidence that the results of an experiment on acquisition are in part a function of the response component to the US that has been selected for measurement as the UR and CR. This consid-

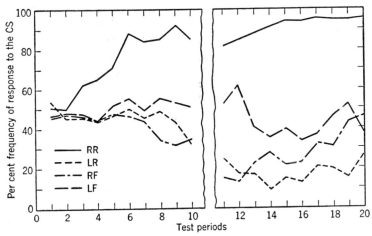

Fig. 1. Relative frequency curves of leg flexion made to the CS when the right rear foot of a dog receives the shock US during instrumental avoidance training. The break in the curves indicates a time interval of 2 to 4 months. The curves for test periods 1 to 10 are based on data for 6 dogs; test periods 11 to 20 are based on data for 5 dogs. (Wolf and Kellogg, 1940.)

the salivary conditioning of dogs has been given by Zener (1937). Moore and Marcuse (1945) have dealt with salivary, motor, and cardiac indices of conditioning in sows.

Kellogg and Wolf (1940) and Wolf and Kellogg (1940) gave this problem particular attention in the acquisition of instrumental avoidance CR's in dogs. During training for acquisition, measurements were made of the responses of each of the four limbs and of respiration to both the bell CS and the electric shock US. The shock was applied to the right rear foot, and a flexion to the bell that raised this foot 2½ inches resulted in shock avoidance. Figure 1 presents the composite relative frequency curves for CR's of each of the four feet. A still more complete picture of acquisition would include the changes in respiration made to the bell and such components of reaction as vocalization,

eration is pertinent to all studies of animal learning.

The US and RS. The US is not completely independent of the UR, but it is more readily subject to manipulation than the UR. Although a change in the US will usually produce a change in the UR, the manipulation of certain aspects of the US affects acquisition. For example, many experimenters have stated that there is an optimal intensity of the shock US. Dunlap, Gentry, and Zeigler (1931) studied the relation of intensity of electric shock to the acquisition of an instrumental escape response in rats. All animals were given training of 10 trials daily until they attained the criterion of 8 CR's for one test period. The intensity of the shock was 0.044, 0.088, and 0.176 milliampere, respectively, for each of three groups of 20 animals each. The 0.044 level was apparently close to the threshold, since only 9 of the 20 animals reached the criterion. The mean number of test periods required for the group to reach the criterion was 11.3 for the 0.088 value, and 13.5 for the 0.176 value. These results support the generalization given above and are also in agreement with the effect of shock on human learning.

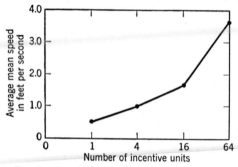

Fig. 2. Acquisition as a function of magnitude of reinforcing food stimulus. Each point on the curve represents the performance of a different group of animals and is the average of the individual mean performances for the terminal stage of acquisition of an instrumental reward running response. The RS unit is a 0.02-gram piece of Purina dog chow presented to a rat deprived of food for 22 hours. (Crespi, 1942.)

When food is the RS, its quantity might be expected to affect the rate of acquisition of a CR. Indeed, Crespi (1942) has shown that the acquisition of an instrumental reward CR by the rat is positively related to the magnitude of the food RS (see Fig. 2). In terms of the average maintenance diet of 7.5 grams, the range of 1 to 64 incentive units (0.02 to 1.28 grams) is considerable. Similar studies have used a smaller number of values of the RS and a more restricted range, but the results have agreed with those obtained by Crespi.

It is possible to vary the frequency with which the US or RS is presented within a given training procedure. Pavlov (1927, p. 384) reported that with a single animal the first salivary CR appeared on the twentieth trial when the US followed the CS on every other trial (50-per-cent reinforcement). This result does not differ from that obtained with 100-per-cent reinforcement, when the first CR also occurs by approximately the twentieth trial. No statements are made by Pavlov about the further course of acquisition under these two conditions of reinforcement.

Similar experiments have been carried out by Skinner (1938, pp. 116ff.) on an instrumental reward CR in rats. In each animal the response was first conditioned and then extinguished. Thereafter for different groups of animals the food RS was presented at intervals of 3, 6, 9, and 12 minutes. Rate of acquisition was found to be inversely related to the interval between reinforcements up to 9 minutes. The results for the 9-minute interval are little different from those for the 12-minute interval. Similar results are obtained when these conditions prevail for a single experimental session (1 hour) and for a series of experimental sessions (25 1-hour sessions). In two almost identical experiments with rats, Finger (1942a, b) found, with an instrumental reward CR (running), that acquisition was significantly greater for 100-per-cent reinforcement by the food than for 50-per-cent random reinforcement, and that extent of acquisition for the 50-per-cent reinforcement group was equivalent to that for a group of animals that was given 100-per-cent reinforcement, but only half the number of practice trials.

The CR. The CR is the dependent variable in studies of acquisition; however, the results are in part a function of its definition and measurement. Just as with the UR, the definition of the CR is arbitrary, and only certain aspects of the animal's performance to the CS are measured. There is also another factor that influences the measurement of acquisition. Data on acquisition of a CR may be in terms of frequency, latency, or amplitude. It is rare that all three measures are recorded and reported. When they are reported, the three measures are found to intercorrelate differently with one another and to vary in their reliability. The problem of standardization is perhaps more critical for the dependent variable in studies of animal learning than for any other aspect.

The CS. Many different CS's have been used in studies of conditioning. The limits appear to be determined by the sensitivity of the animal's receptor equipment and by the organism's previous training.

Investigations of the effect of the CS upon rate or quantity of acquisition might take place for many stimulus dimensions. The sense modality of the stimulus is one such dimension. A CR in some form or other has been established in some species of animal to every sense modality possessed by the human being, but the visual and auditory modalities have been used most frequently. Experimenters have often noted that acquisition is slower to a visual CS than to an auditory CS, but differences in other conditions might have been responsible for the difference in acquisition. In any case it would be necessary to equate the intensity of the visual and auditory stimuli before any difference in acquisition could be attributed to the difference in sense modality.

Within a given sense modality, it should be possible to determine the effect of the magnitude of the CS in terms of intensity, duration, and other characteristics. Intensities of CS have most often been described as being within a middle range. Pavlov (1927, pp. 383ff; 1928, pp. 89, 91) reported that for some stimuli acquisition is slowed when the CS is weak, but that for others no effect of intensity occurs. The frequent use of conditioning techniques for obtaining absolute thresholds demonstrates that, once a CR has been acquired, it may be evoked by stimuli of minimal intensity.

The factor of duration of CS is relative to the duration of the US and to the latency and duration of the UR and the expected CR. The duration of the CS is customarily greater than the latency of the CR. It may be greater or less than the duration of the US. Duration of the CS does affect acquisition, but it is not independent of the interval of time between termination of the CS and onset of the US. In general, a CS of relatively long duration results in slow acquisition.

Pavlov (1928, p. 91) reported that the combination of two or more stimuli representing different sense modalities produces a salivary CR of greater magnitude than will occur to either stimulus alone. What effect these stimulus conditions have on acquisition is not known. Other characteristics of stimuli that have served as the CS in conditioning studies, such as form, size, and frequency, have not been subjected to investigation in relation to acquisition.

Time relations of US and CS. Pavlov (1927, 1928) demonstrated that both acquisition and the characteristics of the salivary CR in dogs are affected by the relative duration of the CS and US, the degree of overlap and separation of the two, and their temporal order. He gave a classification of CR's in terms of these variables, which in general has been shown to hold for other animals and other CR's. Other investigators have presented results for other time variables. The following classification is both a modification and an extension of Pavlov's original classification of CR's in terms of procedures with temporal variables.

1. The simultaneous CR. The CS is either coextensive in time with the US, or it starts from a fraction of a second to several seconds before the US, and overlaps with it. If the US and CS are coextensive, test trials of the CS alone offer the only opportunity for measuring the CR. If the onset of the CS occurs before the onset of the US, the CR may be measured on each trial. This interval is customarily proportional to the latency of the CR. For the salivary response in dogs it varies from 5 to 30 seconds. For striate muscle responses a shorter time interval is used, from ¼ second to several seconds.

2. The delayed CR.* The CS has a greater duration than it has for the simultaneous CR. This name was given by Pavlov because here the latency of the CR is longer than the latency of CR's in the simultaneous category. The duration of the CS is therefore greater than the upper limit for duration of CS with the simultaneous CR.

3. The trace CR. The CS is presented and terminated, and there is a lapse of time before the onset of the US. With salivary conditioning of dogs, the interval of time may vary between a few seconds and several minutes. The terms short trace and long trace are applied, respectively.

4. The temporal CR. The US is presented alone at a constant rate, and the time interval between presentations of the US functions as a CS.

5. The backward CR. The onset of the CS occurs after termination of the US and after the occurrence of the UR.

6. The pseudo CR. The US is presented alone in a series of massed trials, and then, after a short interval of time, the CS is presented in a series of massed trials.

With other conditions equal, the simultaneous CR is acquired at a more rapid rate than CR's involving other time relations. Curves of acquisition for simultaneous CR's established by classical training, and by instrumental reward, avoidance, and secondary reward training are shown in Figs. 1, 3, 4, 5, 6, and 8.† Comparable curves of acquisition for other temporal relations are not available

* Pavlov refers to short-delayed and long-delayed CR's but does not distinguish between these two categories in terms of the duration of the CS (1927, p. 90).

† Acquisition curves of different forms have been obtained in conditioning studies. Since many variables have been found to influence the extent or rate of acquisition, the form of the acquisition curve is also probably influenced by these same variables. It is doubtful whether there is a form of curve common to the acquisition of all CR's. Although there has been considerable study of the form of curves of acquisition and extinction of CR's (for examples, see Hull, 1943, and Skinner, 1938), this topic will not be treated in the present chapter.

for all types of training. Pavlov's results are not presented in such form that curves of acquisition, rate of acquisition, or terminal quantity of acquisition may be obtained. However, Pavlov reports that the simultaneous CR is acquired more readily than CR's involving other time relations. The CR then is of relatively short latency and begins to occur early in the training, usually by the

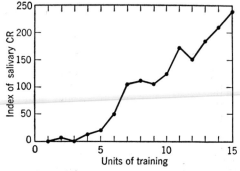

FIG. 3. Curve of acquisition for a classical salivary CR in dogs. Each point represents an equally weighted Vincent fraction for magnitude of salivary CR by 4 dogs given classical training. The Vincent curve data were derived by Hull (1934) from data of Kleitman and Crisler, *Amer. J. Physiol.*, 1927, **79**, 571–614.

twentieth trial (1927, p. 385). As training continues, the frequency and amplitude of CR increase and the latency decreases. Finally a relatively stable CR is established. Pavlov reported no studies of the effect of duration of the CS within the 0- to 30-second range. A 30-second CS is the most frequent duration of CS reported in his books, and, when greater intervals of CS occur in tables, the CR's are labeled delayed CR's. Finch (1938) reported that there is no difference in the reliability of the magnitude of the salivary CR between a CS of 30 seconds' duration and one of 10 seconds' duration. He suggested therefore that the latter duration of CS be used, since more trials may be given per test period and any possibility of the development of a delayed CR is eliminated. Although this is not direct evidence that the duration of the CS affects acquisition of the salivary CR, it does support the inference drawn from Pavlov's writings that acquisition of the salivary CR is not markedly affected by variation in the duration of the CS from a few to 30 seconds.

may be carried out in either of two ways. The duration of the CS is gradually increased at successive test periods (in steps of the order of 5 seconds). The CR is thereby

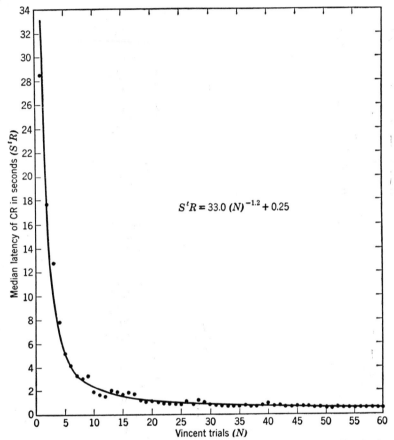

$$S^t R = 33.0\ (N)^{-1.2} + 0.25$$

FIG. 4. Curve of acquisition for an instrumental reward CR in rats. Each point is the median latency of an instrumental reward CR for 59 rats and was obtained by the justly weighted Vincent technique. Latency of CR was measured from the time of raising a shutter (CS) that exposed a lever to the time at which the rat pressed the lever (CR). The lever was made inaccessible to the animal immediately after the CR. Each CR was instrumental in producing a pellet of food (RS). One trial was given each day to each animal when the animal had been deprived of food for 22 hours. The equation is for the fitted function represented by the smooth curve. (Felsinger, Gladstone, Yamaguchi, and Hull, 1947.)

The delayed salivary CR results with extension in time of the CS beyond the 5 to 30 seconds' range. Pavlov indicated that CR's to stimuli lasting longer than 30 seconds are extremely difficult to establish, unless prior training on a simultaneous CR has been given. Training for the delayed CR

maintained, but its latency shows a progressive increase with increase in the duration of the CS. The second technique is to increase the duration of the CS to that desired in a single step. The CR then disappears, but as training continues it reappears — with a long latency. With further training, latency diminishes, magnitude increases, and a stable delayed CR is formed. The latency of a delayed CR is proportional to the duration of the CS. The rate of acquisition of a delayed CR by either of the two techniques described above varies considerably from animal to animal. In some dogs the delayed salivary CR may be produced after only a day's training; in others, more than a month's training may be required.

Studies of the effect of duration of CS upon motor conditioning cover conditions that might be expected to distinguish simultaneous, delayed, and trace CR's. Kappauf and Schlosberg (1937) conditioned limb flexion in rats to durations of CS of ⅓, ⅔, 1, 2, 4, and 7 seconds. No evidence of the development of delayed CR's was obtained. The latency of CR was brief for all animals, no matter what the duration of the CS. There was a greater frequency of CR for animals in the group with a CS of ⅔ second, but individual differences were large.

Warner (1932) gave avoidance training to rats in which the CS was a buzzer of 1-second duration and the CR involved jumping into another compartment of the apparatus. Different groups of animals were trained with intervals of 1, 10, 20, and 30 seconds between the termination of the CS and the onset of the US. Although the longer time intervals provided an opportunity for trace conditioning, no such CR's were developed; when CR's occurred, they were made to the CS and not during the interval between termination of the CS and onset of the US. All 5 animals in the 1-second delay group met the criterion of conditioning (6 consecutive CR's within one 50-trial test period). The criterion was met within 20 test periods by 4 of 5 animals in the 10-second delay group, by 6 of 10 in the 20-second delay group, and by none of the 10 animals in the 30-second delay group. For the animals that reached the conditioning criterion there was a progressive increase in the number of test periods required to reach the criterion as the delay interval was increased.

Mowrer and Lamoreaux (1942) studied the effect of duration of the CS on acquisition of instrumental avoidance by rats. For one group of animals the buzzer CS was 1 second in duration and the shock US occurred 6 seconds after the onset of the CS. For a second group the US was given 6 seconds after the onset of the CS, but the duration of the CS was determined by the latency of the CR; that is to say, the duration of the CS was made equal to the latency of the CR by having the CR terminate the CS. The relation between onset of CS and US for the animals of a third group was the same as that for the other two groups, but the duration of the CS was held constant at 5 seconds. Acquisition occurred more rapidly and to a greater extent for the group in which the CR terminated the CS than for either group with a fixed duration CS. There was no difference in acquisition between the 1-second and 5-second CS groups. Throughout training, average latency of CR was of the same order for the groups with fixed duration CS but was less for the animals that received the variable duration, i.e. response-terminated CS. The results for the 1-second group might be considered representative of that obtained by training for trace conditioning, since the CR's occurred after termination of the CS. Thus there is no difference in the acquisition or characteristics of this trace CR and the simultaneous (or delayed?) CR of the 5-second CS group. However, the most important outcome of this experiment is the identification of an independent variable — termination of the CS by occurrence of the CR — that contributes to efficiency of acquisition.

Pavlov says little about the characteristics of trace salivary CR's. If only the interval between the onset of the CS and the onset of the US is considered, there is no difference between the conditions for the delayed and the trace CR. Presumably the characteristics and mode of acquisition of delayed and trace CR's are similar if the time interval between onset of CS and onset of US is the same. Certainly there is no evidence that the duration of the CS affects either the acquisition or the characteristics of CR's independently of the interval between onset of CS and onset of US. Although for motor CR's there is evidence that acquisition is inversely related to the magnitude of the interval between onset of CS and of US, there is no evidence for either trace or delayed CR's in terms of latency or amplitude of CR.

Strictly speaking, with the usual conditions of instrumental reward training, it is not possible to generate either delayed or trace CR's. Because there is no CS under the control of the experimenter, more than one CR may occur before the delay period is completed and the RS presented. Skinner (1938, pp. 72ff.) states that an instrumental reward CR may be established with delays of RS up to 8 seconds, but his results are complicated by the occurrence of CR's during the delay period. Perin (1943a) eliminated this difficulty by removing the bar once it had been pressed by the rat. This puts the CS under the control of the experimenter, who can then control the presentation of trials and the occurrence of responses. The latency of the CR (interval of time between opening the door into the experimental compartment and pressing the bar) can then be investigated as a function of delay of reinforcement (interval between bar pressing and the presentation of food RS). Five groups of animals were trained with delays of 0, 2, 5, 10, and 30 seconds. The 30-second group failed to acquire the bar-pressing response within 50 practice trials. The acquisition curves for the other groups were similar to one another. Each approached a relatively stable latency by about the twenty-fifth practice trial, and terminal latency was positively related to the delay interval. Group mean latencies for the last 5 of the 50 training trials were 2.14, 4.20, 5.46, and 12.73 seconds for delays of 0, 2, 5, and 10 seconds, respectively. Differences between successive means are reliable

by the t test at better than the 5-per-cent level of confidence. Figure 5 shows the relation between the delay interval and the measure of terminal acquisition. Perin's results demonstrate clearly that delayed instrumental reward CR's may be acquired by rats and that latency of CR at a terminal stage of acquisition increases with the interval of delay in reinforcement. The maximum delay at which acquisition may take

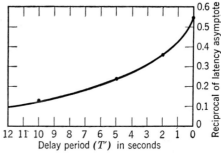

FIG. 5. Acquisition of an instrumental reward CR as a function of the period of delay in reinforcement. Each point represents the reciprocal of the latency asymptote of a function fitted to the acquisition data for a group of 25 rats given instrumental reward training of 50 trials, with a delay in reinforcement equal to that shown on the abscissa. The equation of the fitted curve is $1/L = 0.22 \cdot 10^{-215\,T'} - 0.0188T' + 0.320$. (Perin, 1943a.)

place is between 10 and 30 seconds. From theoretical curves, Perin sets these limits at 14 and 21 seconds.

The temporal CR has been little studied as such. Intervals as great as 30 minutes have been used successfully in establishing salivary CR's in dogs. Temporal motor CR's are apparently also acquired with ease. In most conditioning procedures, it is customary to vary the interval between trials at random during training in order to avoid the formation of a temporal CR.

Pavlov (1927, p. 27) stated very positively that backward conditioning is not possible. Later work apparently resulted in the statement that a backward CR could be formed but that such a CR is very unstable (1927, p. 381). Additional evidence that backward conditioning may take place has been obtained in experiments on human beings.

Pseudoconditioning has been obtained in many different animals. In general, a US of relatively high intensity appears to be a necessary condition. The pseudo CR is not so well established nor so stable as a similar CR based upon equivalent training by simultaneous forward conditioning procedures (Harris, 1943). Wickens and Wickens (1942) reported that the amount of pseudoconditioning depends on the similarity between the US and CS. In this study, rats given training with an electric shock US that increased gradually in intensity gave a greater frequency of CR when the CS was a light that increased gradually in intensity than when the onset of the light CS was abrupt. The reverse training procedure, trials with abrupt shock followed by abrupt or gradual light, gave results similar to those obtained with gradual shock followed by gradual and abrupt light. With monkeys Grether (1937) found no difference in the acquisition of a CR produced by backward and by pseudoconditioning procedures. Pseudoconditioning should probably be treated as a variant of backward conditioning. However, both varieties of training involve time relations of the US and CS that are inefficient for the acquisition of a CR.

Training procedure. The relative efficiency of classical training and of instrumental avoidance training for the acquisition of a CR has been studied by several investigators. In all these studies the US for both training procedures has been electric shock. Experiments by Schlosberg (1934, 1936) and Munn (1939) with rats, and by Brogden (1939c) and Whatmore, Morgan, and Kleitman (1946) with dogs, have failed to demonstrate any difference in rate or quantity of acquisition for the two procedures. On the other hand, instrumental avoidance training has been shown to be a more efficient condition for acquisition of a CR than classical training for running responses of guinea pigs by Brogden, Lipman, and Culler (1938) and

Sheffield (1948), and running responses of rats by Hunter (1935). No one reports the superiority of classical training over instrumental avoidance training. It may be assumed that instrumental avoidance training is superior to classical training, and that in experiments that have failed to demonstrate a difference other variables reduce the efficiency of instrumental avoidance training.*

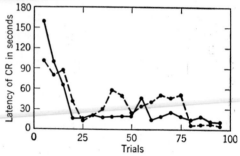

Fig. 6. Acquisition curves of a string-pulling CR in cats for instrumental reward and secondary reward training. The broken line is for instrumental reward training of one animal (string pulling produced food), and the solid line is for secondary reward training of another animal (string pulling netted a token exchangeable for food). Each point is the mean latency of CR for a block of 5 trials. Acquisition curves for some of the other animals start with shorter latency and show less change than do these sample curves. (Smith, 1939.)

It is also possible to compare the relative efficiency of instrumental reward and secondary reward training upon the acquisition of a CR. An experiment by Smith (1939) on the acquisition of a string-pulling response in cats, with instrumental reward and secondary reward training, resulted in no difference for the two procedures, provided the training trials required to establish the effectiveness of the token as a reward were ignored (see Fig. 6). It is reasonable to ignore the time required to establish the token habit. If a difference were to be found in the acquisition of a CR by instrumental

* Studies of this kind are similar to those on the frequency of application of the US or RS. Both bear on the reinforcement-nonreinforcement controversy in learning theory.

reward and secondary reward training, the lesser acquisition might be expected to occur with the latter procedure. The difference would be less a function of training than of the effectiveness of the RS. Mote and Finger (1942) report such a difference in acquisition when the RS for a running response in rats was merely the goal box in which the animals had been fed prior to training.

What Pavlov (1927, pp. 33ff.) called higher-order conditioning is an example of secondary reward involving the classical training procedure. The CR (e.g. salivation) established to a CS (e.g. bell) by classical training is called a first-order CR. When a neutral stimulus (e.g. light) is paired with the CS (bell) for a series of trials in which the US (food) is omitted, the salivary response that is evoked by the light alone is called a second-order CR. Third- and higher-order CR's would be established by pairing a neutral stimulus with the CS of the preceding order. The use of the CS in higher-order conditioning is similar to the use of the token RS in secondary reward training. By these procedures it has not been possible to produce more than a second-order salivary CR nor more than a third-order defense CR (electric shock as US for the first-order CR). The acquisition of higher-order CR's is difficult and requires much retraining at the first-order level. A higher-order CR is weaker than the CR of the next lower order.

A more efficient procedure for establishing higher-order CR's was developed by Finch and Culler (1934). The first-order flexion response was established by avoidance training. When a second-order CR had been established, its vigor was maintained by shocking the animal's thorax whenever the flexion CR failed to occur to the second-order CS. Conditioning was carried out to the fifth order by this procedure. Brogden (1939d) started first-order conditioning as did Finch and Culler, but for the higher orders he adapted their technique of reinforcement to food. A still more efficient procedure of higher-order conditioning was discovered by Eccher and Culler (1941). When a first-order CR had been established in cats by instrumental avoidance training, the second-order CS was followed by the first-order CS only when there was no CR to the second-order CS. Under these conditions it was never necessary to return to first-order training in order to set up the second-order CR. A third-order CR was readily established by the same procedure.

A CR was established by Miller and Konorski (1928a) through a variation on classical and instrumental reward training. Following presentation of the CS, the forelimb of a dog was lifted passively by means of a mechanical system. Although no CR's occurred to the CS during this procedure, conditioning took place readily when a food RS was presented on each trial after passive flexion and after each CR made to the CS. Woodbury (1942) was not able to repeat this experiment, but Wing (1947) has confirmed the results obtained by Miller and Konorski. Loucks (1935) obtained similar results by a somewhat different procedure. No CR was obtained to a CS when the UR was evoked by faradic stimulation of the motor cortex of a dog. When a food RS was presented following both the UR and any occurrence of a CR to the CS, conditioning was established readily. Loucks and Gantt (1938) obtained similar results with faradic stimulation of the motor root of the spinal column.

It is frequently impossible to compare experiments based on classical and instrumental training procedures because of differences in more than a single variable. Because of the lack of control by the experimenter of a CS and a US, the classical procedure may not be compared with varieties of instrumental training other than avoidance. This also prevents comparison of avoidance training with other varieties of instrumental training.

Distribution of practice. Some degree of distributed practice is generally more efficient for the acquisition of a CR than the massing of training trials. Practice is ordinarily distributed over a number of test periods and also within the test period. Although in some studies the training trials have all been given within a single session, the intervals between trials have been distinctly larger than the durations of the CR and the UR.

five groups of 12 rats each, the intervals between trials being 0.5, 1, 2, 3, and 5 minutes. Only 8 trials were given, and the amount of the food RS was increased progressively with the interval between trials, the amounts being 0.06, 0.18, 0.56, 0.98, and 1.32 grams. Although the absolute amount of food RS varied directly with the interval

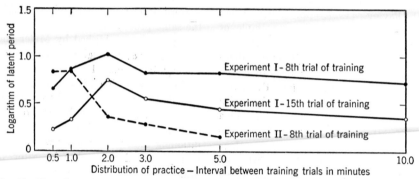

FIG. 7. The effect of distribution of practice upon the acquisition of an instrumental reward CR. Each point connected by solid lines is for the same group of 8 rats. Each trial was reinforced by a single pellet of food. The broken line represents data for five groups of 12 animals each, with amount of food reinforcement increasing proportionally to the size of the interval between trials, but with rate of eating held approximately constant. The two solid lines thus represent the relation of distribution of practice to acquisition when food reinforcement is held constant. The broken line shows the relation of distribution of practice to acquisition when rate of eating is held constant but magnitude of the reinforcing stimulus is not. The difference between the solid curve (eighth trial) and the broken curve is due to the two conditions of reinforcement. (Gagné, 1941a.)

Although the distribution of practice may vary over a wide range, for a given CR under a given set of conditions there is a distribution for which acquisition is optimal. Several studies have compared two conditions of distributed practice and found one of them to be the more efficient. This comparison was extended to more than two conditions by Gagné (1941a). Two experiments make up this study. In the first experiment, 15 trials of reward training were given rats during a single session. The intervals between trials were 0.5, 1, 2, 3, 5, and 10 minutes for the six groups. The CR was traversal of a 3-foot runway, and the RS was a pellet of dog food that weighed 0.06 gram. Acquisition was measured in terms of running time and of latency. In the second experiment, similar training was given

between trials, the rate of eating approximated a constant value.

The results for these experiments are shown in Fig. 7. With the absolute amount of the RS held constant, the optimum intervals between trials were 0.5 and 1.0 minute; with the rate of eating held approximately constant, the optimum interval was 5.0 minutes. Whatever the effect of magnitude of the RS may be, the effect of distribution of practice does not seem to be independent of it. The effect of amount of practice is also related to the effects of magnitude of RS and distribution of practice. If number of practice trials is equated for the two experiments (see Fig 7), terminal acquisition does not differ for the short intertrial intervals, in spite of differences in magnitude of RS, but it does differ markedly for the longer intervals. The curve for Crespi's data on the relation of acquisition to magnitude of the RS (see Fig. 2) suggests that the results of Gagné's second experiment are more a function of the magnitude of the RS than they are a function of the interval between trials.

Transfer of CR's

Many instances of transfer, both positive and negative, have been found in studies of conditioning. Transfer is usually positive when it is measured as the difference in performance under different conditions, each of which involves training for acquisition. Transfer is most often negative when it is measured as the difference between performance at a terminal stage of acquisition and a subsequent performance that results from alteration of some variable that was present during acquisition. In this latter case positive transfer may then be produced by the reversal of conditions or by the introduction of new or altered variables. Many phenomena of transfer were discovered in Pavlov's laboratory and were given special names. An attempt will be made to preserve these names and at the same time to classify the phenomena of transfer in terms of the variables that affect their occurrence.

Experimental extinction. The most striking phenomenon of negative transfer occurs when the US or the RS is deleted from the procedure used in acquisition. A progressive decrement then ensues, and finally a point is reached at which the CS fails to evoke the CR. This phenomenon was originally discovered and named experimental extinction by Pavlov (1927, 1928). It has been much studied for its own sake and for its importance in learning theory. Experimental extinction occurs for CR's acquired through all types of training. The CR usually drops to zero when the CS is presented repetitively with absence of the US or the RS. The zero level may be obtained in some cases only after long repetition, and in others there may be no evidence that ex-

tinction will ever take place, even with endless repetition of the CS alone.

The fact that the US or the RS is required in order to set up and maintain a CR and that its absence results in experimental extinction has led to the inference that acquisition and experimental extinction are inversely related. In fact, resistance to extinction has frequently been used as a direct measure of the strength of an acquisition. Studies of extinction have also been undertaken to help determine the role of reinforcement in conditioning. Some have found measures of resistance to extinction to be directly related to measures of acquisition, but others have not. Even though the experimental results are in conflict and no generalizations may be arrived at safely, a few of the representative studies will be discussed here because of the theoretical importance of the problem.

Hunter (1935) reported that, for instrumental running CR's in rats, there is a negative correlation between the number of trials to reach the criterion of acquisition and the number of trials for extinction. Youtz (1938a) obtained a correlation (rho) of −0.77 between the time required by rats to make 40 bar-pressing CR's and trials to an extinction criterion, when extinction occurred immediately after acquisition. In a second study (Youtz, 1938b), where there was a 24-hour interval between the last acquisition trial and the beginning of the extinction training, this same correlation turned out to be 0.69. However, in both these studies resistance to extinction was greater for animals given 40 acquisition trials than for animals given 10 acquisition trials. Ellson (1938) obtained a correlation (r) of −0.14 between the time required to make 30 instrumental reward CR's and the number of responses to the extinction criterion. Williams (1941) reported correlations (r) between measures of acquisition and resistance to extinction that are not significantly different from a zero correlation. Rohrer (1947) found correlations (rho) of 0.70 and 0.46 between the mean latency of an instrumental reward CR at the termination of acquisition training and the number of trials required to reach the extinction criterion for two groups of rats that were given similar training for acquisition but that were extinguished with massed and distributed practice, respectively. Brogden (1949) obtained a correlation (r)

and the period of food deprivation at the start of the experiment was 24 hours. The slope of the extinction curves appears to increase as the number of practice trials was increased, indicating a decrease in resistance to extinction with increase in training for acquisition. Mote and Finger (1943) gave groups of rats 4, 8, 16, and 32 acquisition

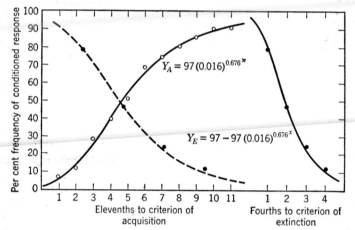

$$Y_A = 97(0.016)^{0.676^x}$$

$$Y_E = 97 - 97(0.016)^{0.676^x}$$

Elevenths to criterion of
acquisition

Fourths to criterion of
extinction

FIG. 8. Vincent curves of acquisition and extinction of an instrumental avoidance response in dogs. The open circles represent the mean per cent frequency of CR for a group of 30 dogs for the appropriate fraction of training at the rate of 20 trials per day to a conditioning criterion of 100 per cent. The mean number of test periods required for the group to reach the criterion was 11.37 ($\sigma_M = 0.41$). The filled circles represent mean per cent frequency of CR for the same animals during extinction training at the rate of 20 trials per day to the response criterion of 0 per cent. The mean number of test periods to the extinction criterion was 4.30 ($\sigma_M = 0.79$). The solid lines represent the equations shown on the graph for acquisition and extinction. The equation $Y = vg^{L^x}$ was fitted to the empirical data by Dr. Don Lewis. The broken-line extinction curve is drawn on the same extent of abscissa as that for the curve of acquisition in order to show the inverse relation between the two curves. (Brogden, 1949.)

not significantly different from zero between the number of trials to the criterion of acquisition and the number of trials to the criterion of extinction for an instrumental avoidance CR in dogs. However, in this same study, the form of the Vincent curve for acquisition showed an almost perfect inverse relation to that of the Vincent curve for extinction (see Fig. 8).

Mote (1944) found no difference in the extinction scores for groups of rats that had been given 3, 6, 12, 18, and 24 practice trials for acquisition of an instrumental reward CR (running). Acquisition and extinction were carried out in a single experimental session,

trials and measured resistance to extinction 24 hours later.* There were no reliable differences in extinction among the four groups of animals.

* The interval of time between the acquisition of a CR and the measurement of extinction may be a critical factor since it is the variable manipulated in retention studies. However, the high degree of retention of CR's after long periods of no practice makes this seem unlikely (see section on retention of CR's). Studies of resistance to extinction after relatively long periods of time offer little help in resolving the differences obtained in resistance to extinction between a brief interval and a 24-hour interval. Youtz (1938b) reported greater resistance to extinction of an instrumental reward CR in rats after 15 days than after 1 day. The difference in favor of the

In a study where there was no interval between acquisition and extinction, Finger (1942a) found resistance to extinction to be greater for 8 acquisition trials than for 16. In a second experiment, with a 24-hour interval between acquisition and extinction (1942b), he found no difference between the extinction following 8 and following 16 acquisition trials. Lawrence and Miller (1947) repeated Finger's first experiment but altered the apparatus so that the start and goal boxes were clearly distinguishable. Resistance to extinction was found to be significantly greater for the 16-trial group than for the 8-trial group. Williams (1938) gave four groups of rats 5, 10, 30, and 90 acquisition trials on a bar-pressing instrumental reward CR and then carried out extinction. Resistance to extinction was found to increase as the number of acquisition trials increased. Perin (1942) obtained similar results for groups of rats given 5, 8, 16, 30, and 70 acquisition trials. Finan (1940) gave groups of rats equal practice on acquisition of an instrumental reward CR, but different periods of food deprivation (1, 12, 24, and 48 hours) prior to the acquisition training sessions. Resistance to extinction turned out to be significantly greater for the 12-hour group than for the 1-hour group but did not differ reliably for the groups with other periods of deprivation.

Another measure of the relation of acquisition to extinction is the number of trials for reacquisition following experimental extinction. In general the greater the extinction training or decrement, the more trials are required for reacquisition (Pavlov, 1927, p. 59; Finch and Culler, 1935; Brogden, Lipman, and Culler, 1938; Hilgard and Marquis, 1935; and Skinner, 1938, pp. 85ff.).

15-day interval was greater for animals given 40 acquisition trials than for animals given 10 trials. Brogden (1940a) found a high degree of resistance to extinction of instrumental reward and instrumental avoidance CR's in dogs after an interval of 6 months. The animals with instrumental reward CR's showed significantly less resistance to extinction than animals with instrumental avoidance CR's.

On the other hand, the reliability of measures of experimental extinction is usually less than the reliability of measures of acquisition. Individual differences in extinction time and extent are large, and, as has been mentioned earlier, instances of failure to obtain experimental extinction of CR's have been reported. Because of the diversity in the results, experiments in which a measure of experimental extinction is the dependent variable are treated as experiments on extinction, even though the inference may have been made that resistance to extinction is a positive measure of the strength of a CR or the magnitude of its acquisition.

Many studies have been reported that show experimental extinction to be a function of the conditions of reinforcement during acquisition or during extinction. The relative frequency of reinforcement during trials for acquisition may influence the course of experimental extinction. Finger (1942a) found that a mean of 15.2 trials was required to reach the criterion of extinction of an instrumental reward CR by rats given 16 acquisition trials with 100-per-cent reinforcement (group I), whereas a group (II) given 16 acquisition trials with 50-per-cent random food reinforcement required 27.1 trials to reach the extinction criterion. A third group (III) which was given 8 acquisition trials with 100-per-cent reinforcement reached the criterion in 23.8 trials. The confidence levels of the differences between groups I and II, I and III, and II and III are 2 per cent, 8 per cent, and 57 per cent, respectively. It is not clear from this study to what extent the influences of relative frequency of reinforcement, absolute number of practice trials, and absolute number of reinforced trials are separate. Finger (1942b) repeated the study with a 24-hour interval between the termination of acquisition and the start of extinction. No reliable differences in experimental extinction were obtained for the three different conditions of reinforcement. Skinner (1938, pp. 118ff.), Humphreys (1943), and Mowrer and Jones (1945) reported data on the extinction of instrumental reward CR's in rats that were conditioned or reconditioned under different relative frequencies of reinforcement. These authors interpret their results as showing a greater resistance to extinction for relative frequencies of reinforcement less than 100 per cent.

Essentially the same problem was studied by Brogden (1939c) with a different technique. Conditioning of a salivary CR by classical training, of a flexion CR by classical training, and of a flexion CR by instrumental reward training was established in three groups of 4 dogs each. Frequency of CR was measured for each group, after the criterion of acquisition had been met, for 5 test periods each at 100-, 80-, 60-, 40-, and 20-per-cent reinforcement. The sequence in which the fractional levels of reinforcement were given was balanced. The results of this experiment are shown in Fig. 9. For the two food-reinforced CR's there is a progressive decrement as frequency of reinforcement decreases. For the shock-reinforced group, the CR shows a slight increment in frequency of CR as frequency of reinforcement is decreased to the 40-per-cent level, with a drop taking place at the 20-per-cent level. Even at the 20-per-cent level, frequency of CR is not less than 80 per cent for any one of the three groups. The results of other studies indicate that the extinction of any one of the three CR's might be expected to be complete or nearly so by the end of 100 trials of 0-per-cent reinforcement. Thus the critical frequency of reinforcement for experimental extinction probably lies between 20- and 0-per-cent reinforcement.

The period of food deprivation at the time the measure of extinction is made affects the rate and amount of extinction of instrumental reward CR's. Over a fairly wide range, increase in the period of food deprivation increases resistance to extinction (Finger, 1942a, b; Perin, 1942; Rohrer, 1947; Sackett, 1939; and Skinner, 1938, pp. 380ff.). Koch and Daniel (1945) showed that extinction takes place most rapidly when the animals

have been satiated with the food used for reinforcement just prior to the extinction tests. However, for dogs Brogden (1942) found no difference between the extinction of an instrumental reward CR that was extinguished immediately following satiation and the extinction of a CR extinguished after

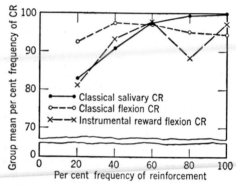

FIG. 9. The effect of relative frequency of reinforcement upon the frequency of CR. Each point is the mean frequency of CR for 5 test periods of 20 trials. The acquisition of the CR for each of the 12 animals was brought to the criterion of 100 per cent. Four additional test periods of training at 100-per-cent reinforcement were given before the relative frequency of reinforcement was altered. Only the differences in frequency of CR between 100-per-cent reinforcement and 40 and 20 per cent are statistically significant for the group with the salivary CR. None of the differences in frequency of CR for the group with the classical flexion CR are statistically significant. For the group with an instrumental reward flexion CR, only the difference between 100- and 20-per-cent reinforcement is significant. (Brogden, 1939c.)

18 to 20 hours of food deprivation. The CR of this study was developed initially by instrumental avoidance training and was then converted to instrumental reward conditioning by the substitution of a food RS for the shock US. This may account for the lack of difference in rate of extinction.

When resistance to extinction is shown to increase with an increase in the period of food deprivation, it should be least for zero deprivation (satiation). The above studies have not dealt with periods of deprivation greater than 30 hours. Finch (1938) has shown that the magnitude of both the salivary CR and UR of the dog increases with increase of the period of food deprivation up to 72 hours, but decreases again when the period is increased to 96 hours. This suggests that resistance to extinction will reach a maximum at some point beyond 30 hours and then decrease with further increase in the period of deprivation. Kendler (1945) studied resistance to extinction of an instrumental reward CR in rats under a constant food deprivation of 22 hours but with varying degrees of water deprivation. Resistance to extinction increases as the period of water deprivation increases through 0, 3, 6, and 12 hours. From the maximum resistance to extinction at 12 hours, the curve falls at 22 hours of water deprivation to a level below that for the 0-hour deprivation group.

The rate at which extinction takes place may be altered by a special condition of reinforcement. Brogden, Lipman, and Culler (1938) showed that extinction of an instrumental avoidance CR is speeded up when electric shock is given to the thorax of a dog for each flexion CR made to the CS during extinction. Extinction by this procedure takes place with only a few applications of thoracic shock and at about the same rate as that required for reconditioning with pedal shock. Skinner (1938, pp. 151ff.) reported a similar effect on extinction of the bar-pressing CR in rats when the mechanism is set so that pressure on the bar makes it jump upwards. The initial reaction of the rat to the "slapper" is an increase in the rate of CR. This is followed by a rapid extinction. Mowrer and Jones (1943) found that rate of extinction for an instrumental reward CR in rats increases as the pressure required to depress the bar is increased from 5 to 42.5 to 80 grams. All three groups of animals were trained to the same level of acquisition of CR for pressures of 5 and 80 grams. Solomon (1948) reported the rate of extinction of an instrumental jumping response in rats to be more

rapid for a jump of a long distance than for a jump of a short distance.

That stimulus components involved in reinforcement during acquisition of a CR may acquire secondary reinforcement was discovered in studies of resistance to extinction. Finch and Culler (1935) demonstrated that the presence of a buzzer during extinction training increased resistance to extinction of an instrumental avoidance CR in dogs, during the acquisition of which the buzzer sounded just after the CS. Skinner (1938, pp. 82ff.) showed that the click of the food-vending machine increases the resistance to extinction of instrumental reward CR's in the rat. There are secondary reinforcement situations that maintain the CR at full strength. Elimination of the US or RS results in no negative transfer or extinction.

Experimental extinction is affected by the distribution of the extinction trials. Pavlov (1928, p. 85) stated that the massing of trials produces a more rapid extinction than an equivalent number of distributed trials. However, Porter (1939) obtained no difference in the rate of extinction of an instrumental running CR in rats for three different intertrial intervals. No studies have been reported in which a distributed condition produced a more rapid extinction than some less distributed condition. Hilgard and Marquis (1935) found that massed practice produced more extinction of an eyelid CR in dogs than did distributed practice. Rohrer 1947) reported the extinction of an instrumental reward CR in rats to be more rapid when the interval between extinction trials was 10 seconds than when it was 90 seconds. Acquisition in both cases was based upon 90 training trials. The difference in favor of the massed group was greater when extinction was carried out after 30 hours of food deprivation than when the period of deprivation was only 6 hours. Less clear results were obtained for groups of animals given only 10 acquisition trials but with the same intervals between trials and the same periods of food deprivation. Gagné (1941a) found a more rapid extinction of a reward CR in rats as the interval between trials was decreased. These results are complicated by an increase in the amount of the food RS with increase in the interval between practice trials.

The interval of time between the end of acquisition and the beginning of extinction appears to be a critical factor in resistance to extinction of instrumental reward CR's. Comparisons of immediate extinction with extinction after 24 hours have shown no difference, greater resistance for immediate extinction, and greater resistance for extinction after 24 hours. The diverse results of the currently available studies are complicated by differences in other variables. Time interval in these studies may not be independent of period of food deprivation. The number of acquisition trials, the relative frequency of reinforcement, and the method of measuring resistance to extinction also appear to be important complicating variables.

There are other variables that affect experimental extinction. Increase in the time between the CR and the RS during instrumental reward training, after acquisition has taken place, results in some experimental extinction (Brogden, 1941; Skinner, 1938, p. 73). When a CR has been extinguished, similar CR's show decrement in response, even though there has not been specific extinction training (Pavlov, 1927, p. 54; Ellson, 1938). This is called secondary extinction. Higher-order CR's are less resistant to extinction than are first-order CR's (Brogden and Culler, 1935). Delay and trace CR's are much less resistant to extinction than simultaneous CR's (Pavlov, 1927, 1928); the pseudo CR is less resistant to extinction than the simultaneous CR (Harris, 1943); and generalized CR's extinguish more rapidly than do primary CR's (Liddell, James, and Anderson, 1934; Brown, 1942). Walker (1942) has shown that extinction of an instrumental reward CR is delayed if a tone that was the positive stimulus in a discrimination habit established after acquisition of the CR is present during extinction training. Similar results were obtained by Estes (1948).

Alterations of US or RS not producing extinction. Some circumstances involving change in the US or RS result either in no decrement of a CR, or in a temporary decrement followed by full recovery. Within limits that are not well defined, it is possible to change the food US or RS without appreciably altering the CR. Change in the magnitude of the food US has been shown by Gantt (1938) to be directly related to the magnitude of both the CR and UR, but such change did not affect frequency of CR. Brogden (1939a) found there was only a temporary decrement in an instrumental flexion CR in dogs when the shock US was replaced in the training procedure by a food RS. Once the transfer was made from shock to food reinforcement, the response level in dogs given this treatment was the same as that in dogs continued on instrumental avoidance training. Incidental observations have indicated that, once CR's based on a shock US have reached a criterial level of acquisition, the intensity of the shock may be varied considerably without affecting frequency of CR. Kellogg (1941) has shown that, once an instrumental avoidance CR has been acquired, if it is to be kept at a constant magnitude, the intensity of the shock US must be decreased within the test period, and the average intensity during the test period must be increased from test period to test period.

Reversal of experimental extinction. A terminal level of extinction represents a reference point in negative transfer of a CR by which positive transfer may be measured. Pavlov (1927, 1928) reported four procedures that are effective in reversing the decrement in CR obtained by extinction training. These procedures have been found effective for instrumental CR's as well as for CR's established by classical training. If the animal is removed from the experimental situation at the close of extinction training and returned at a later time, the CR to the CS alone will be of greater magnitude than that to the CS alone at the end of the previous extinction training period. Pavlov named this phenomenon spontaneous recovery. Spontaneous recovery occurs only to the initial trials of the test period. Continuation of extinction trials soon results in a level of zero CR. Spontaneous recovery may be complete in the case of well-established CR's. More often the extent of recovery is small. In general, the extent of spontaneous recovery is proportional to the extent of experimental extinction.

The second procedure for reversing the decrement of extinction Pavlov called disinhibition. The CR rises above the extinction level when the animal is presented with a novel stimulus. Disinhibition is a temporary positive transfer, and its magnitude is a function of the extent of extinction and the intensity of the disinhibiting stimulus.

The third method involves presentation of the US (or RS) alone for a few trials. Then, when the CS is presented alone, it evokes a CR. Recovery of the CR is temporary, for continued extinction training results in a zero level of CR. Note that this procedure is exactly the same as the training procedure used initially for elaboration of the pseudo CR.

The fourth method for reversing experimental extinction is reintroduction of the US or RS to the training procedure. This return to the conditions of original training for acquisition results in a rapid recovery of the CR to its pre-extinction level, and this level is maintained as long as the US or RS is present in the training procedure.

The reestablishment of a CR after extinction to the zero level always takes place in less time and with fewer trials than were required for the initial acquisition. Although Pavlov (1927, p. 59) reported that reacquisition is directly proportional to the extent of extinction, this problem has received little investigation. Pavlov's statement was based

in part upon the fact that the magnitude of spontaneous recovery decreases with increase in the amount of extinction training. This relation holds when extinction training is continued beyond the zero level of CR. Brogden, Lipman, and Culler (1938) showed that the number of trials required for reacquisition of an instrumental avoidance CR in dogs is greater when extinction training is carried beyond the zero level than when reacquisition training is started immediately after the zero level of CR has been reached. These workers also showed that during "silent" extinction the response of the forelimb to the CS was one of extension (the CR was flexion) and that the amplitude of the extension response to the CS increased as the extinction training increased. However, with continued training for extinction beyond zero, reacquisition was found to be more rapid than the original acquisition. When alternate extinction and reacquisition training was given and the extinction training included trials beyond the zero level, the effect of these additional extinction trials on reacquisition eventually disappeared. Brogden (1940c) demonstrated that reacquisition of an instrumental left forelimb flexion CR in dogs takes place as rapidly after extinction when shock is applied to loci other than the left forepaw as when shock is applied to the left forepaw. For any given locus of electric shock, left forelimb flexion to the CS was alone instrumental in shock avoidance. It was further shown in this study that continuation of these conditions of reinforcement maintained the frequency level of CR as effectively as did shock to the left forelimb, flexion of which was the CR. This effect of change in locus of application of US is an example of the transfer phenomenon called generalization. Brogden suggested that this particular phenomenon be called incentive generalization to distinguish it from stimulus generalization and response generalization.

Generalization. Pavlov (1927, pp. 110ff.) early found that, when a CR was elaborated to a specific CS, similar stimuli, neutral before formation of the CR, had become capable also of evoking the CR. This phenomenon he called generalization. In the present chapter, the term stimulus generalization (Hilgard and Marquis, 1940) is used for this phenomenon and also for the transfer of a CR that occurs when a similar stimulus to the CS is substituted for it in a continuation of acquisition training. In the latter situation the CR is rapidly built up to the level evoked by the previous CS. Tests of stimulus generalization therefore may be made by either acquisition or extinction training. Stimulus generalization has been studied more often by means of extinction training than by the acquisition method. Acquisition takes place so rapidly to the transfer CS that this latter method provides a relatively insensitive measure of stimulus generalization. Although measurement of stimulus generalization by extinction training is more sensitive, the results are complicated by secondary extinction. Only a small number of trials may be given for each stimulus in tests for sensory generalization. A larger number of trials results in experimental extinction of the CR, both to the generalized stimuli and to the primary CS. It is not possible after a few test trials of sensory generalization to reinforce the primary CS, since reinforcement of the primary CS and nonreinforcement of the generalized stimuli constitute the conditions for discrimination learning. In many situations generalization and discrimination are so measured that they are perfect inverse measures of each other.

Because of the inherent difficulties of the methods for studying sensory generalization, precise experimental information is difficult to obtain. Stimulus generalization occurs most readily for stimuli within a given sensory mode, but it also takes place across sense modalities. Evidence for stimulus generalization of many of the characteristics of stimuli within sensory systems, and for most sensory modes to the others, has been ob-

tained by Pavlov and his co-workers. Generalization curves based upon extinction tests have been reported by Anrep (1923) for the salivary response of dogs to tactile stimuli at varying distances from the locus of the CS; by Brown (1942) for measures of an instrumental running CR to visual stimuli of varying brightness from that of the CS; and by Blackwell and Schlosberg (1943) for an instrumental running CR to tones of different frequency from that of the CS. The curves in these studies show less response to generalized stimuli, the greater the difference between the CS and the generalized stimuli. Beritoff (1924) reported that generalization is greater early in acquisition training than later. Brogden (1939b) found cross-modal generalization to be enhanced by presenting a sound and a light together, prior to using one of these as the CS for an instrumental avoidance response. This result may be interpreted as evidence of sensory conditioning.

The term response generalization refers to transfer where there is alteration of the CR. In training for acquisition, the method of measurement may permit considerable variation in the CR. For example, in the acquisition of a bar-pressing response in the rat, any response that results in depression of the bar is recorded as a CR, whether it results from movements of the right or left forelimbs, the head, or the body. Response generalization thus occurs to some extent during the acquisition training of any CR. Arnold (1945) showed that variability in the magnitude of a bar-pressing CR in rats decreases during acquisition. When only a given magnitude of the CR is reinforced, variability in magnitude of the CR is reduced further. If, after acquisition has taken place, the CR is experimentally prevented from occurring, a similar response may be elicited by the CS. Bekhterev (1932, p. 216) reported that, when a dog's limb to which shock was applied during acquisition is tied down so that the flexion CR cannot occur, presentation of the CS elicits flexion of some other limb. Lashley (1924) found that a manipulative performance was carried out by a monkey with the other hand, when the hand used in acquisition became paralyzed following brain surgery. Kellogg and Walker (1938a, b) studied bilateral transfer of CR in the dog by first conditioning the right forelimb and then giving acquisition training for the left forelimb. Positive bilateral transfer was found; acquisition of the left-forelimb flexion CR took place more rapidly than did the original acquisition of the right-forelimb CR. During acquisition training of the left forelimb, the right-forelimb CR became extinguished in about half the animals. The other animals continued to make right-forelimb CR's as well as left-forelimb CR's to the CS. During the period of left-foot training, these animals made more right-foot CR's to the CS than left-limb CR's. Thus CR's of both forelimbs occurred at the end of training. Kellogg and Walker called this latter phenomenon ambiguous conditioning. James (1947) found that ambiguous conditioning could be resolved by adding a work factor to the response of the limb involved in the transfer conditioning. Brogden (1940c) found transfer of conditioning to the right front, right hind, and left hind limbs to take as many trials as the original acquisition of the left-forelimb CR. However, there was an interval between the acquisition of the left-forelimb CR and the acquisition of the transfer CR's during which the left-forelimb CR was extinguished, reconditioned, and maintained for 100 trials. This may account for the failure to obtain positive transfer. In the transfer training, ambiguous conditioning as described by Kellogg and Walker was found with some of the animals.

Generalization of a CR may involve both stimulus and response generalization. Youtz (1939) reported the positive transfer of an instrumental reward CR in rats from pressing a horizontal bar to pressing a vertical bar and vice versa. Williams (1941) found transfer from a horizontal to a vertical bar

to be negative in rats when 7 trials were given on the horizontal bar, and positive when 18 or 45 acquisition trials were given. Graham (1944) reported negative transfer in the acquisition of an instrumental avoidance CR in dogs that was preceded by the acquisition of another instrumental avoidance CR. However, the US of the first CR was made the CS for the second CR. This factor may be responsible for the negative transfer. After Graham's animals had been given the training just described, the CS for the first CR was presented and it evoked the second CR. This latter transfer is a chainlike reaction that was originally studied by Miller and Konorski (1928b). Transfer that involves change in the general conditions under which the CR was established has been reported by James (1941). Positive transfer was found for flexion conditioning of dogs in a laboratory room to subsequent performance of this response in the kennel enclosure.

Retention of CR's

There has been less study of the retention of CR's than of their acquisition and transfer. Experiments on this topic have dealt almost wholly with the time interval between acquisition and the measurement of retention. There are no studies comparable to the retroactive-inhibition type of experiment. Studies that involve comparison of performance at a terminal stage of acquisition with performance under altered conditions have been treated already under transfer of CR's, even though such studies might be considered as experiments on retention. Retention of CR's has been measured by the savings method and by the method of reproduction. Other experimenters have studied retention in terms of resistance to extinction. The validity of this procedure for measuring retention of a CR depends upon the assumption of a high degree of positive relation between measures of acquisition and measures of resistance to extinction. The uncertain nature of this relation has led to the discussion of such studies under the topic of experimental extinction, since this phenomenon was the dependent variable. However, the first few trials of an extinction test provide a measure of retention by the method of reproduction, and these studies can be treated under the topic of retention

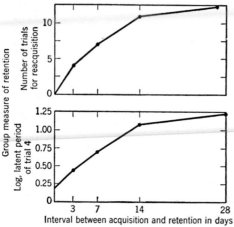

FIG. 10. Retention by rats of an instrumental reward running CR as a function of interval of time between acquisition and retention. Retention following conditioning to a criterion of three consecutive CR's with a latency of 5 seconds or less is plotted for two measures: (1) number of trials of reacquisition to attain criterion of three consecutive CR's with latency of 5 seconds or less; and (2) the logarithm of the latent period of the CR on the fourth trial of reacquisition. Each point is the mean obtained from 4 animals. (Gagné, 1941b.)

if results are presented separately for the initial extinction trials.

The degree of retention of a CR is undoubtedly related to the extent of its acquisition, but systematic study of this relation for all varieties of CR has not been made. There is ample evidence that a well-established CR will be retained for long intervals of time. Liddell, James, and Anderson (1934) reported considerable retention after an interval of 2 years of a flexion CR in sheep established by classical training. Wendt (1937) found a high degree of retention after an interval of 2½ years of a flexion CR in a dog elaborated by instrumental

avoidance training. Good retention of CR's after 30 days has been reported by Hunter (1935) for instrumental avoidance CR's in rats, by Kellogg and Wolf (1939) after 6 months for instrumental avoidance CR's in dogs, and by Hilgard and Marquis (1935) after 6 months for classical eyelid CR's in dogs. Gagné (1941b) measured retention of an instrumental reward CR in rats after intervals of 3, 7, 14, and 28 days, following acquisition of the CR to a criterion of latency of CR of less than 5 seconds on 3 consecutive trials. Prior to being brought to this criterion, all animals were given 15 acquisition trials and extinction training until they met the extinction criterion of one CR with a latent period of 3 or more minutes. The results of this experiment, given in Fig. 10, show that retention decreases as the interval of time between acquisition and the measure of retention increases.

DISCRIMINATION LEARNING

Several distinctions may be made among the different kinds of discrimination learning. It was pointed out earlier that the stimuli to be discriminated may be presented to the animal either simultaneously or successively. With simultaneous presentation, the training method for acquisition is comparable to the instrumental reward or instrumental escape training of CR's. Response to the positive stimulus is reinforced by means of an RS; response to the negative stimulus is not reinforced. When there is successive presentation of stimuli, the training method is comparable to the classical or instrumental avoidance training of CR's. By this method, training for acquisition of a CR to the positive CS is usually the first step.* Once the CR is well estab-

* The point of view may be taken that, during the acquisition of a CR, a discrimination is being established between the presence of the CS and its absence. In the early stages of acquisition of a CR, "spontaneous" CR's occur during the intervals between trials of the training stim-

lished, the negative CS is presented alternately or in random order with the positive CS. The US is present on trials of the positive CS and absent on trials of the negative CS. These two procedures result in different baselines from which the course of acquisition is measured. In terms of frequency of response to the positive and negative stimuli, the zero level for discrimination with simultaneous presentation of stimuli is 50 per cent.* With successive presentation the zero level is not known because the positive CS has been brought to the 100-per-cent level through prior training, and there is positive transfer of CR to the negative stimulus (stimulus generalization). However, the criterion for the acquisition of discrimination learning is the same for both procedures: a frequency of response near 100 per cent for the positive stimulus and near 0 per cent for the negative stimulus.

There is usually a difference in the conditions of reinforcement for acquisition involving simultaneous and successive presentation of the positive and negative stimuli. Discrimination learning based on simultaneous presentation of stimuli involves heterogeneous reinforcement of response, and successive presentation involves homogeneous reinforcement of response. Because Pavlov (1927, pp. 117ff.) gave the name differentiation to discrimination that involved successive presentation of positive and negative stimuli and also homogeneous reinforcement, the term differentiation training is used in this chapter to refer to the latter procedure.† The term discrimination training is applied to discrimination learning acquired with the simultaneous presentation of the positive and negative stimuli, and heterogeneous reinforcement.

In the prosecution of discrimination training, two alternative procedures may be used, correction and noncorrection. When the correction procedure is used, if the first response of the animal is to the negative stimulus, the experimenter permits it to continue responding until response is made to the positive stimulus. The response to the positive stimulus brings forth the RS. The trial is then terminated. If the first response is to the positive stimulus, the RS follows immediately, and the trial is terminated. With the noncorrection procedure each trial is terminated immediately after the animal responds to either the positive or negative stimulus. If the response was to the positive stimulus, the RS is presented; if to the negative stimulus, the RS is withheld.

The noncorrection procedure provides the more uniform measure of the trials involved in acquisition. All trials are equal in the sense that the animal makes a single response in each. With the correction method the nature of the trial varies, for the animal may make several responses to the negative stimulus before the trial is terminated. The number of responses is not under the control of the experimenter, and it has no definite relation to the number of stimulus presentations or to the duration of the stimulus presentations. The conditions of reinforcement and nonreinforcement from trial to trial are differential only in terms of delay of reinforcement by the RS. The definition of error and correct response is poor, and there is less control over the amount of time consumed by the animal

uli. This has been taken as support for the view stated above.

*In many discrimination training situations, the initial level of response has been found to differ from 50 per cent. Since animals frequently show an initial "preference" for one of the two stimuli, it is customary to run initial control trials to test for this phenomenon. If a proportion of response significantly different from 50 per cent is found, the group may be split in two with the positive and negative stimuli reversed and animals assigned to the subgroups so that the effect of initial bias is balanced.

† Differentiation training has been modified to provide a more efficient means of studying sensory acuity by making the positive stimulus one that changes within its duration and the negative stimulus one that does not so change (Brown, 1936; Kappauf, 1943).

during an acquisition trial. With the correction procedure, however, consistency from trial to trial is maintained in the sense that a trial always terminates with response to the positive stimulus and attainment of the RS.

Discrimination learning is usually carried out with two stimuli, one positive and one negative. From a practical standpoint it is difficult to increase the number of stimuli used in differentiation training because the stimuli must be presented successively. With discrimination training it is much easier to present more than two stimuli simultaneously. The number of positive stimuli, the number of negative stimuli, or both may be increased. Another variation of discrimination training makes use of two positive stimuli to which different responses are made. This procedure may also be used in differentiation training.

Acquisition of Discrimination Learning

The response. Any response that can be conditioned may be used in discrimination learning, since it is the degree of the absence of this response to the negative stimulus, relative to the degree of its presence to the positive stimulus, that is the measure of discrimination learning. The response itself has rarely been the independent variable. That it may be an important variable is shown by the results of Muenzinger and Newcomb (1936) and of Honzik and Tolman (1938). A black-white discrimination was acquired by rats more rapidly when the response was jumping a gap to the stimulus card than when the response was running across an elevated platform. Grice (1948) obtained a more rapid acquisition of a black-white discrimination in rats when the responses to the positive and negative stimuli were of different kinds than when a single response was used. Thompson (1944c) obtained similar results in a different discrimination training situation with rats.

The acquisition of a CR to the positive CS prior to differentiation training may re-sult in a more rapid acquisition of discrimination than if differentiation training is started when the animal is naïve to both the positive and negative stimuli. Preliminary training is sometimes given with the US or RS, and some workers have assumed that this adaptation procedure facilitates the acquisition of a discrimination. Although this assumption has not been put to an adequate experimental test, the evidence for the effect of such preliminary training on the acquisition of CR's is equally relevant to the acquisition of discrimination learning.

The definition of the response is an important variable in the acquisition of discrimination learning as well as in the acquisition of other kinds of performances. Marcuse and Moore (1946) showed the factor of response definition to be important in the measurement of discrimination learning by the pig when differentiation training is used. Another variant of definition of response has received considerable study in the acquisition of discrimination learning. Orienting responses to the positive and negative stimuli frequently take place prior to the occurrence of differential responses. This kind of responding was called vicarious trial and error by Muenzinger (1938) and was abbreviated to VTE by Tolman (1938). Many investigators have noted the occurrence of VTE during discrimination training.* Girden (1938) reported its presence in auditory differentiation training of dogs. When VTE is recorded during discrimination learning of rats, its frequency is positively correlated with the frequency of response to the positive stimulus (Muenzinger, 1938), and it increases with increase in acquisition training

---

* VTE might be expected to play a similar role in the successive discriminations that must be made by the animal in the acquisition of a maze performance. Jackson (1943) found this not to be the case. The frequency of VTE in maze learning by rats was found to be directly related to errors rather than to correct responses. Tolman and Ritchie (1943) trained Jackson's animals on a black-white discrimination and found the usual negative correlation between VTE and errors.

to a maximum at the point where discrimination begins to appear and drops out when the discrimination is well established. It is more likely to occur on those trials where response is made to the positive stimulus than where response is made to the negative stimulus (Dennis, 1930). In general, independent variables that facilitate the acquisition of discrimination learning also increase VTE (Muenzinger, 1938; Tolman, 1938).

The US and RS. Differentiation training involves appropriate application of the US to maintain a CR to the positive CS and to extinguish the generalized CR to the negative CS. Discrimination training may be considered to involve the simultaneous development of a CR to the positive CS, and the generalization and subsequent extinction of the CR to the negative CS. Therefore any effect of the US or RS on either the acquisition or extinction of a CR should influence the course of discrimination learning. The kind of RS appears to affect the rate of discrimination learning, but experiments purporting to measure such differences are hard to evaluate because of the difficulty of equating the intensity of the different RS's. However, it is clear that the acquisition of discrimination learning is affected by the magnitude of the RS.

Dodson (1917) reports that the rate of acquisition of a brightness discrimination in rats increases when the electric shock US, given for response to the negative stimulus, is increased in intensity, up to a point. Beyond this point there is a decrease in acquisition with further increase in shock intensity.

The effect of a food RS has been studied directly by varying the magnitude, and indirectly through variation of the period of food deprivation. Grindley (1929) found the acquisition by chickens of a spatial discrimination to be more rapid for a large food RS than for a small one. Wolfe and Kaplon (1941) compared the rate of acquisition of a spatial discrimination for three groups of chicks that were given, respectively, for each

correct response, 1 one-quarter grain of popcorn, 1 grain of popcorn, and 4 one-quarter grains of popcorn. The rate of acquisition increased in the order in which the conditions of reinforcement are listed. Their results show that acquisition increases with the amount of the food RS, and with the amount of the food RS coupled with the amount of consummatory activity (4 one-quarter grains require 4 pecks). Dodson (1917) found an increase in the rate of acquisition of a brightness discrimination in rats as the interval of food deprivation was increased from 24 to 41 hours. But there was a slower rate of acquisition for 48 hours than for 24 hours of deprivation. Kendler (1947) reported that a greater degree of spatial discrimination learning was attained by rats given discrimination training under 22-hour food and water deprivation than that shown by animals given equivalent training but tested under food and water satiation.

The mode of application of the RS influences discrimination learning. Muenzinger (1934) found no difference in the acquisition of a black-white discrimination in rats when electric shock was given following response to the negative stimulus for one group and to the positive stimulus for another group, and when both groups received a food RS following response to the positive stimulus. Muenzinger, Bernstone, and Richards (1938) repeated this experiment with a control for the amount of shock given in the two conditions and found acquisition to be greater for wrong-response shock than for right-response shock. Acquisition of the discrimination by animals shocked for the right response was greater than that for animals given only the food RS for right response. A study by Drew (1938) confirmed these results.

Muenzinger and Wood (1935) showed that the facilitating effect of right-response shock does not occur when shock is given prior to the choice of response to the positive stimulus. Fairlie (1937) tested shock right and shock wrong as the animal was about to enter the appropriate runway and found little acquisition of a black-white discrimination under these circumstances. However, the shock-wrong group showed significantly greater acquisition than the shock-right group. Wischner (1947) performed the shock-right, shock-wrong experiment on acquisition of discrimination learning by rats, but he used the noncorrection method of food reinforcement. The shock-wrong group was superior to both the shock-right and the no-shock (food RS only) groups. The latter two groups showed no significant difference in acquisition. Comparison of Wischner's experiment with the other experiments of this type, all of which used the correction method, is virtually impossible because of the different definitions of trial and error inherent in the correction and noncorrection procedures. A controversy between Muenzinger (1948) and Wischner (1948) centered mainly on the interpretation of trial and error when the correction and noncorrection procedures are used.

A decrease in rate or amount of discrimination learning takes place with progressive increase in the interval of time between the response to the positive stimulus and application of the RS. Seward (1943), Grice (1942), and Spence and Grice (1942) demonstrated this relation in terms of the distance the rat must travel between the point at which a distance discrimination response has been made and the goal box. Wolfe (1934) varied the interval of delay between 0 and 20 minutes and found a progressive decrease in the acquisition of a spatial discrimination and of a black-white discrimination in rats as the interval increased. Perin (1943b), Perkins (1947), Grice (1948), Riessen (1940), and Thompson (1944b) obtained similar results with smaller intervals. Cowles (1937) reported a decrease in rate of discrimination learning by chimpanzees when there was in increase in the time interval at which the token RS could be exchanged for food. Williams (1929), Perkins (1947), and

Grice (1948) showed that secondary reinforcement may play a role in delayed reward, depending upon how the delay was enforced.

The relative frequency of reinforcement to the positive stimulus might be expected to affect rate of acquisition. Denny (1946) found no difference in the acquisition of a spatial discrimination for a group of rats given the RS on 50 per cent of the correct responses from that of a group given 100-per-cent reinforcement.

However, when (1) the component parts of the discrimination apparatus were re-oriented, (2) the delay boxes were changed from day to day, and (3) a gray goal box replaced the white goal box on trials when the RS was omitted, a group of animals given 50-per-cent reinforcement acquired the discrimination at a reliably slower rate than animals given 100-per-cent reinforcement. Skinner (1938, pp. 325ff.) reported that differentiation training of rats with periodic reinforcement results in the acquisition of discrimination learning at approximately the same rate as with 100-per-cent reinforcement. Moss and Harlow (1947) gave 8 monkeys, that had received previous training on discrimination and discrimination reversal, training trials on discrimination learning in which the positive stimulus was reinforced 0, 50, and 100 per cent of the trials. The 90-per-cent level of correct responses was attained with 1 trial of 0-per-cent reinforcement, with 2 trials of 50-per-cent reinforcement, and with 10 trials of 100-per-cent reinforcement. Although the results of this latter experiment may be complicated by transfer from previous training, it shows that the effect of partial reinforcement is complex. Brunswik (1939) and Heron (1942) showed that discrimination learning occurs when both the positive and negative stimuli are reinforced but at a differential frequency.

Positive and negative stimuli. Discrimination learning may apparently take place to stimuli over a wide range. The limiting factor is the differential acuity of the animal for a given stimulus dimension. In fact, the difference threshold is measured in animals by means of discrimination-learning techniques.

Although discrimination learning may be acquired by animals to pairs of stimuli both within and across the sense modalities that they possess, the task of equating conditions makes it difficult to assess the effect of sense modality upon the acquisition of discrimination learning. Over a wide range of conditions investigators report that a spatial discrimination is much more readily acquired than are other kinds of discriminations. Training for other discriminations requires that the position of the stimuli be varied at random in order that the solution cannot be based on spatial cues.

To demonstrate that a discrimination response is based upon a stimulus difference within a single dimension requires that the stimuli differ only in this one respect. This condition is difficult to fulfill. In general it can be said that the rate of acquisition of discrimination learning decreases as the degree of difference between the positive and negative stimuli is decreased. When the degree of difference reaches the threshold value, discrimination fails.

Grether and Wolfle (1936) have shown that rate of acquisition of a brightness discrimination by rats is decreased as the number of pairs of stimuli used during training is increased. The results of their experiment are shown in Fig. 11.

Training procedure. No experiments have been found that test the relative efficiency of discrimination and differentiation training in the acquisition of discrimination learning. Such a test would contribute little to the understanding of discrimination learning, but it would have practical value for the animal psychologist who is interested in the acquisition of a discrimination response as the first step in the study of other problems.

There have been studies comparing the relative efficiency of the correction and non-

correction procedures in discrimination training, perhaps because of the prominent role reinforcement plays in some theories of learning. Since a trial by the correction method may include more than a single response, a lack of difference in acquisition

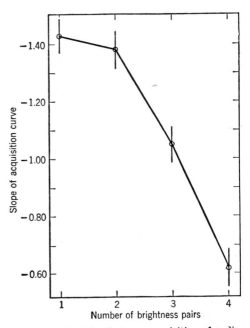

Fig. 11. Relation between acquisition of a discrimination response and variation in stimulus conditions during training. The slopes of the acquisition curves for four groups of rats are plotted against the number of brightness pairs used in discrimination training in which the brighter of the pair was always the positive stimulus. The vertical line through each point indicates the standard deviation of the slope. (Grether and Wolfle, 1936.)

would favor the noncorrection method. Comparisons of the two methods have resulted either in no difference or in a more rapid acquisition with the noncorrection method. Hull and Spence (1938) found no difference in the acquisition of a spatial discrimination response by rats, but the noncorrection method was superior in learning a reversal of the positive and negative stimuli. Seward (1943) reported the noncorrection method to be superior for the acquisition of a spatial discrimination response by rats, and Kalish

(1946) obtained similar results for the acquisition of a delayed response.

Although most studies of acquisition of discrimination learning have made use of only two stimuli, one positive and the other negative, the effect of additional stimuli has been investigated. Smith (1936) studied the effect of increase in the number of negative stimuli upon the acquisition of a visual form discrimination in cats. Three groups of animals were trained with one positive stimulus and either one, two, or three negative stimuli. In terms of trials to the criterion there was no difference between the groups given training with one and with two negative stimuli, but the group trained with three negative stimuli required fewer trials to reach the criterion. However, the correction procedure was used, and the groups did not differ from each other in terms of the number of errors made in reaching the criterial level. Nissen and McCulloch (1937a) found acquisition of discrimination learning by chimpanzees to be more efficient in terms of trials, time, and error trials (the correction technique was used) when nine negative stimuli were used than when only one negative stimulus was used. Since there were fewer total errors with the single negative stimulus, these authors carried out a second experiment (1937b) in which conditions were the same except that, when there were nine negative stimuli, the animal was permitted to make only a single response to a negative stimulus on each trial. The results of this experiment showed acquisition to be more rapid for the situation with nine negative stimuli than for that with the single negative stimulus.

Although discrimination learning to the position of stimuli is acquired readily, the introduction of more than one negative position decreases the rate of acquisition. In some cases it results in no evidence of acquisition. However, studies of this kind, spoken of as multiple-choice problems, show that the location of the positive stimulus relative to the negative stimuli is a more important variable than the absolute number of negative stimuli (Yerkes, 1916, 1934; Spence, 1939). Other arrangements of more than two stimuli have been used in discrimination learning, but not under conditions that permit comparison of rate or amount of acquisition as a function of the number or the arrangement of the stimuli.

Other variables. From studies on acquisition of CR's, variables such as distribution of practice and secondary reinforcement might be expected to influence the acquisition of discrimination learning. Verplanck (1942) found slower acquisition of a black-white discrimination by rats for a massed practice condition than for a distributed condition. Pavlov (1927) used a condition of distributed practice in presenting trials of the positive and negative CS's during differentiation training. Although Pavlov did not say so, his use of this training procedure suggests, perhaps, that massed trials during differentiation training slows acquisition.

Secondary reinforcement has been shown to increase the rate at which acquisition takes place (Perkins, 1947; Grice, 1948; Denny, 1948). Wolfe (1936) and Cowles (1937) have shown that discrimination learning by chimpanzees may take place when a food token is the RS for response to the positive stimulus. Jenkins (1943c) found a space factor to operate in discrimination learning by chimpanzees. Discrimination performance was superior when the stimuli were at a distance of 1½ inches from the restraining cage than when they were 7½ inches away.

Transfer of Discrimination Learning

Perhaps the greatest interest in discrimination learning has centered in the problem of its transfer. Both positive and negative transfer can occur under a number of conditions, many of which are complex. Furthermore the transfer of discrimination learning is similar in many respects to the transfer of CR's. Consequently the discussion of transfer of discrimination learning will be limited.

Experimental extinction. Once a discrimination response has been acquired, if the US or RS is removed from the training procedure, there is a progressive decrement in response to the positive stimulus similar to the experimental extinction of a CR (Farber,

say, by reversing the conditions of reinforcement. This training procedure may also be regarded as one of reacquisition of response to the previously negative stimulus, since at the time of initiation of discrimination training the negative stimulus elicited responses. Studies of this kind, and also those in which the reversal procedure has been changed back and forth, have resulted in

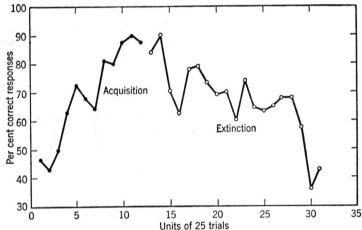

FIG. 12. Acquisition and extinction of a discrimination response. Each point is the mean for 4 animals given 25 trials each at the rate of 5 trials per day on a temporal discrimination. Training for acquisition was given by presenting the food RS following response to one side of a discrimination apparatus in which there was detention for an interval of time, and by withholding the RS when response was made to the other side, for which there was a different interval. Extinction was carried out by equalizing the detention period and by presenting the RS following response to either side. (Anderson, 1937.)

1948). The variables that affect the extinction of discrimination learning are probably similar to those that affect the extinction of CR's.

Negative transfer of a discrimination similar to experimental extinction has been shown by Anderson (1937) to take place when the positive and negative stimuli are made equal to each other, and the RS is applied when a response occurs to either of the two stimuli. The acquisition of a discrimination response and its extinction by this procedure are pictured in Fig. 12 for one group of Anderson's animals.

Experimental extinction of discrimination learning may also be studied by reversing the positive and negative stimuli, that is to

positive transfer, no transfer, and negative transfer. The many differences among these studies do not make it possible to resolve the differences in results.

Generalization. Stimulus generalization is demonstrated for discrimination learning by the same procedures that are used with CR's, and the same problems of measurement therefore hold. Both cross-modal and within-modal generalization occur. Smith (1936) obtained cross-modal generalization of discrimination learning in cats from visual to auditory stimuli. Many studies have shown stimulus generalization within a given sense modality both for single and multidimensional stimuli. Kluever (1933) and Harlow (1944) have shown that extensive generalization may take place in visual discrimination learning by monkeys. Some studies of stimulus generalization in discrimination learning have been designed to obtain curves of generalization similar to those found for conditioning procedures (Schlosberg and Solomon, 1943; Felsinger, 1944; Czehura, 1943), but others have sought to determine whether during the original discrimination learning the animal has been responding to the positive and negative stimuli in an absolute or relative manner. These experiments have come to be known as transposition experiments. Other studies of stimulus generalization and of response generalization have been directed towards investigation of complex symbolic behavior. This is also true of the generalization studies on discrimination learning that involve both stimulus and response generalization.

Retention of Discrimination Learning

The retention of discrimination learning has apparently received no systematic study. Incidental observations for short periods of time show retention to be of a fairly high degree, but retention of discrimination learning has not been reported for the long time intervals that have been found to produce little loss in proficiency of CR's. Many of the studies of transfer of discrimination learning would have provided data on retention if appropriate measures of performance in the initial discrimination training situation had been made following the transfer tests or training. However, as has been pointed out before, the majority of studies of discrimination learning have been designed for the investigation of complex symbolic behavior.

SERIAL LEARNING

Serial learning has much in common with both conditioning and discrimination learning. However, the spatial mazes in which serial learning is most often studied require the animal to respond sequentially to the different stimulating conditions in a serial space-time dimension.* It is equally possible to present conditions requiring the sequential occurrence of CR's or discrimination responses, but this technique has been little used even though it offers more precise control over the presentation of the stimulus conditions and measurement of the animal's responses to them.

Measurement of serial learning may be in terms of the overall performance as a unit, or in terms of the component parts. Time or errors per trial provide the units. The beginning of a trial is defined by the introduction of the animal to the experimental situation, and its end by the removal of the animal when the terminal response has occurred and the RS has been applied. The food RS has been used most frequently in studies of serial learning; but electric shock, escape from water, and similar RS's have been applied successfully. Since both time and errors are a function of practice trials, acquisition is expressed by the quantity of time or errors after a given number of trials, or in terms of trials, time, or errors to attain a given criterial performance.

Acquisition of Serial Learning

Maze pattern. The acquisition of serial learning has been demonstrated for many different kinds of maze pattern.† Kind of maze is undoubtedly an important factor in rate of acquisition, but data on acquisition as a function of this variable are limited in range because of the difficulty of quantifying maze pattern and because of the wide range of reliability of different maze patterns. Sectional T- and Y-shaped units are joined to form mazes that have high reliability for measuring acquisition (Tryon, 1930; Jack-

---

* Although temporal mazes have been used for the study of serial learning in animals, the acquisition of this kind of performance is considered to involve complex symbolic processes.

† Since the white rat has been used most often as the experimental subject in animal studies of serial learning, the animal will not be named unless it is other than the rat.

son, 1932). When the same maze pattern is constructed in both an alley and elevated runway form, rate of acquisition is more rapid on the elevated maze (Miles, 1930). The multiple-unit maze may be varied in length without altering the basic pattern. Warden and Hamilton (1929) reported that absolute measures of acquisition increase as the length of the maze increases for 2, 4, 6, 8, and 10 units, but that error and time scores per unit vary inversely with increase in the length of the maze. Ballachey (1934) found a similar relation between measures of acquisition per unit and length of maze; but in terms of absolute measures of acquisition the order of difficulty was 12, 4, and 8 unit lengths. Warden and Riess (1941) reported that with chicks an increase in the number of units of the maze produced a progressive increase in rate of acquisition per unit.

Maze pattern may also be varied by the presence or absence of doors to prevent retracing. The presence of doors that prevent the rat from retracing back beyond the section it is in has been shown to increase the rate of acquisition and the reliability of the maze (Tolman and Nyswander, 1927; Leeper, 1932). The length of the blinds for a given maze pattern affects the rate of acquisition. Peterson (1917) found elimination of blinds to be more rapid when the blinds were 9 inches long than when they were 22 inches long. White and Tolman (1923) studied this same variable with longer alleys that also had a right-angle elbow and found elimination to be more rapid for the long alleys than for the short ones. Although the discrepancy between these studies may be a function of other differences, White and Tolman suggested that Peterson's results were a function of differential visibility for the long and short blinds.

Analysis of the frequency of errors for the different sections of mazes has shown that unbalanced maze patterns result in characteristic performances by rats. Centrifugal swing is the tendency of the animal to go to the outer wall of an alley maze after a turn and to continue this direction of response at the next turn. The number and direction of turns in the true path of the maze determine the extent to which errors will be made as a function of this factor (Ballachey and Krechevsky, 1932; Ballachey and Buel, 1934; Witkin and Schneirla, 1937). Schneirla (1933) observed this same phenomenon in the acquisition of certain maze patterns by ants.

Goal orientation is the term given to the occurrence of a greater frequency of errors for blinds that lie in the direction of the goal box (Dashiell, 1930; Tolman and Honzik, 1930a; Spence and Shipley, 1934). W. L. Brown (1946) showed that this performance occurs in a maze for which the start and goal box are common.

The direction before the last turn of a maze may be an important factor in goal orientation, since Buell (1934) found more errors to occur on blinds in the same direction as that of the last turn when the food box of the maze was on the central axis. Jones and Taylor (1938) used a maze similar to that of Spence and Shipley, with the goal box to the left for one group of animals and to the right for the other group, but with the direction of the last turn the same for both groups. A greater frequency of errors was made by animals of both groups on the side of the last turn, irrespective of the direction of the goal box. Thompson (1944a) failed to find evidence of goal orientation in mazes that were of a different pattern from those used by the above investigators but that were designed to produce goal orientation.

Differential frequency of errors within the maze. The frequency with which blinds are entered has been found to be a function of the distance of the blind from the start and goal positions. When the frequency of entering blind alleys increases as a function of the distance from the start box, it is spoken of as an entrance gradient. A goal gradient occurs when the frequency of entrance increases with the distance of the blind from the goal box. Since blind-alley entrance is affected by both general and specific factors of maze design, by certain characteristics of the rat, and by most variables that influence the acquisition of maze habits, investigators have obtained conflicting results concerning the order of elimination of blinds.

Spence and Shipley (1934) found that during the initial acquisition trials the relative frequency of errors gives an entrance gradient, but that during the later trials a goal gradient occurs. Hill (1939) found a goal gradient for the initial 10 acquisition trials and a bidirectional gradient (error frequency greatest for middle blinds) for the next 10 acquisition trials. Other investigators have found goal, entrance, and bidirectional gradients or no gradients at all. Bidirectional gradients have also been found in mazes with the food box located in the middle of the maze (Thompson and Dove, 1943; Jenkins, 1943a). Jenkins (1943a, b) showed that both the period of food deprivation and the amount of incentive affect the bidirectional gradient.

The distribution of errors is influenced by many variables other than the goal and the entrance. There are tendencies for the animal to prefer certain sides of the maze, to repeat entrance into certain blinds, and to alternate in making certain errors. Arnold (1947a, b, 1948) studied gradients in serial learning in terms of the latency of manipulative responses. The gradients were shown to be a function of the kind and locus of the RS, the stage of acquisition, and the alteration of the manipulanda.

Stimulus conditions. The acquisition of a maze pattern depends upon the animal's responses to cues that differentiate the true pathway from the blind alley at each choice point. Each bifurcation of the maze thus presents the animal with a problem in discrimination. The problem of sensory control of the maze has a long history. It has been approached traditionally by comparing the efficiency of acquisition by animals that have been deprived of the sense organs for

different sense modalities, or by making the cues at choice-points of the maze nondifferential for a given sense modality. Visual, auditory, olfactory, kinesthetic, and tactile cues have all been shown to play a role in the acquisition of maze learning. The relative importance of these modalities is not known precisely, although many investigators have concluded that the kinesthetic-tactile cues play the dominant role.

The RS. The effect of the RS upon rate of acquisition has been the subject of a number of studies. Food, sex object, and offspring have been found to be nondifferential for rate of maze learning (Moss, 1924; Simmons, 1924; Stone and Sturman-Hulbe, 1927). Escape from water is comparable to food as an RS (Dunn, 1935; Moss, 1924; Ruch, 1930). Electric shock for errors results in more rapid acquisition than food in the goal box; however, the use of shock for errors and food in the goal box produces more efficient acquisition than either one alone (Bunch and Magdsick, 1938; Dorcus and Gray, 1932; Ni, 1934; Valentine, 1930). Arnold (1947a) found acquisition of a serial button-pressing response by rats to be more rapid with a food RS than with a shock RS.

Studies of the effect of variation in magnitude or intensity of RS upon acquisition of serial learning have been restricted largely to food. Increase in magnitude of RS, increase in period of food deprivation at the time of training, and decrease in the delay of reinforcement all produce an increase in rate of acquisition (Blodgett, 1929; Elliott, 1929; Williams, 1929; Macduff, 1946; Tolman and Honzik, 1930a, b; Hamilton, 1929; Simmons, 1924). Although the range of independent variable has been small, the results are comparable to the effect of the same variables upon the acquisition of CR's and of discrimination learning. Macduff's study showed acquisition to be directly related to degree of deprivation for both a condition of distributed practice and one of massed practice.

Distribution of practice. Some degree of distributed practice has often been found to be a more efficient condition for the acquisition of a maze performance than has a condition of massed practice (Brockbank, 1919; Lashley, 1917, 1918; Ulrich, 1915). Warden (1923) showed both for blocks of trials and for intervals between trials that distribution produces a more rapid acquisition than massing. Other experimenters have reported no difference, or a difference in favor of massed practice (Cook, 1928; Pechstein, 1921). Mayer and Stone (1931) found no difference between massed and distributed conditions of practice for young rats but found an increase in rate of acquisition with an increase in distribution of practice for adult animals. It has been suggested that difficulty of maze (Cook, 1928) and the stage of acquisition at which the massing or distribution of practice is applied (Lashley, 1917, 1918) may be critical factors.

Other variables. The whole-versus-part problem in the acquisition of serial learning has been studied by Pechstein (1917) and by Hanawalt (1931). Opposite results were obtained in the two studies. Since Hanawalt's experimental control was superior to that of Pechstein's study, her results are given greater credence. They show the whole method to be most efficient, the intermediate part method to be next, and the pure part method to be least efficient for acquisition.

A variety of pretraining treatments have been shown to facilitate the acquisition of serial learning. Preliminary handling by the experimenter (Jackson, 1932), preliminary feeding in the goal box (Anderson, 1941; Jackson, 1932), preliminary exploration of the maze without application of the food RS (Blodgett, 1929; Haney, 1931; Lashley, 1918), and general laboratory adjustment (Jackson, 1932) result in more rapid acquisition. Bunch and Lund (1932) found that guided trials in a maze facilitate its subsequent acquisition. Stone and Smith (1941) gave preliminary training on a discrimination that was to be required later in the acquisition of serial learning. Training of blind, vibrissaless rats on an inclined-plane

discrimination and training of blind rats on a rough-smooth discrimination resulted in a rapid acquisition of mazes making use of these cues. Similar results were obtained with normal animals that were given preliminary training on a black and white runway section of an elevated maze made up of such units. Negative results were obtained for normal rats trained to use visual cues in alley mazes of variable pattern and for blind rats given training on an odor trail.

Transfer of Serial Learning

Transfer of serial learning has been found to be both positive and negative. The variables that affect transfer of serial learning are similar to those that affect transfer of conditioning and discrimination learning. Stimulus generalization (alteration of maze pattern) is usually positive, but, because the nature of stimulus conditions within a maze pattern is obscure, the extent and course of generalization as a function of change in maze pattern are not known precisely. Response generalization and stimulus and response generalization have been little studied for serial learning. Transfer as a function of alteration of the RS has received much study, and both positive and negative transfer have been found. Other variables have also been shown to influence transfer.

Maze pattern. Acquisition of one maze pattern usually results in positive transfer for acquisition of other maze patterns. Webb (1917) found positive transfer to 4 mazes designed to produce negative transfer. The extent of positive transfer appeared to be a function of the degree of similarity between the first and second mazes acquired. Hunter (1922) reported positive transfer from one maze to another that differed only in reversal of the start and goal boxes, but Alm (1931) obtained negative transfer with reversal of direction of the goal box. Wiltbank (1919) reported positive transfer in the acquisition of a succession of different mazes. Amount of transfer was not cumulative from one maze to another, but the extent of transfer was found to be a positive function of the number of practice trials on the original maze. Marx (1944) found transfer to be positive and cumulative through a series of 12 mazes. Ho (1928) reported that the extent of positive transfer is a direct function of the amount of acquisition training on the

tinction is comparable to the terminal level of acquisition attained by rats given training with no food RS (Tolman and Honzik, 1930*b*). Reintroduction of the food RS would undoubtedly produce a rapid recovery of maze performance, but this appears not to have been studied. Nor have conditions

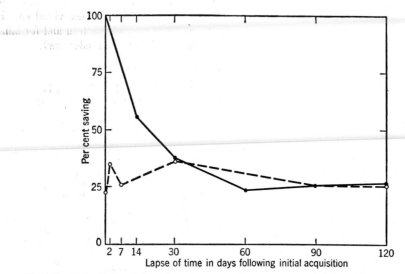

Fig. 13. Retention and transfer of maze performance measured by the saving method as a function of lapse of time following initial acquisition. Each point is the mean saving score in terms of trials for the reacquisition or initial acquisition of a multiple T-maze performance by a group of rats (*N* = 24 or greater). The filled circles are the saving scores of animals who reacquired the maze pattern after varying intervals of time. The solid line connecting them thus constitutes a retention curve. The open circles are the saving scores of animals who acquired the same maze as did the retention animals at varying intervals of time after they had acquired a different multiple T-maze pattern. The dotted line connecting these circles is therefore a curve of transfer as a function of time interval. (Bunch, 1941.)

initial maze pattern. Bunch (1941) found that the positive transfer from one maze pattern to another was of the same extent when there was a lapse of 0, 2, 7, 30, 90, or 120 days between the learning of the two mazes (see Fig. 13).

Alteration of RS. Removal of the food RS results in negative transfer of serial learning similar to the experimental extinction of a CR (Bruce, 1930; Sharp, 1929; Tolman and Honzik, 1930*b*; Warden and Lubow, 1942). Complete extinction of the maze performance was not obtained in these studies, but both time and errors show a marked increase. The terminal level of ex-

comparable to spontaneous recovery, to disinhibition, and to the application of the US alone on recovery from extinction of CR's been studied for serial learning.

Change in the nature of the RS results in a temporary decrement in maze performance from which there is rapid recovery. Elliott (1928) reported that a shift from bran mash RS to sunflower seed RS results in positive transfer. A shift in amount of RS has also been shown by Elliott to produce a temporary decrement in performance from which there is quick recovery. Bruce (1930) showed that the decrement produced by removal of a food RS is further increased by increasing the period of food deprivation from 18 to 42 hours. He also reported a decrement in response when the food RS is placed behind a screen (1932b) and a temporary decrement when the food box is altered (1932a). A shift from food to water RS with appropriate change in deprivation conditions also results in the positive transfer of maze performance (Elliott, 1929). The range of incentive generalization in serial learning is probably much greater than is demonstrated by the foregoing experiments.

Other variables. Jackson (1932) found that stimulus and response generalization takes place from acquisition of a problem box performance to the acquisition of a maze. Gengerelli (1930) found that rats trained on a maze with all right (or all left) blinds carried the acquired response pattern over to a maze of different design. The degree of acquisition and the interval of time between acquisition of the first performance and acquisition of a subsequent performance have been shown by Bunch and Lang (1939) to affect the degree of transfer. Guidance given animals on one maze increases the rate of acquisition on a second maze (Bunch and Lund, 1932).

Retention of Serial Learning

The retention of serial learning has been studied no more systematically than has the retention of conditioning and discrimination learning. It has been tested after intervals of time both with and without interpolation of acquisition training for other performances and with alteration of the conditions under which the initial acquisition took place. A number of variables have been shown to affect the extent of retention tested under these three conditions.

Passage of time. Many investigators have reported a fairly high degree of retention for an interval of time up to several months. Tsai (1924) studied retention in groups of rats after intervals of 7, 14, 21, 28, 42, 56, and 84 days and found less retention for the longer intervals. Bunch (1941) studied

retention after 14, 30, 60, 90, and 120 days and found a similar relation. Figure 13 gives the retention curve obtained by Bunch and also shows that the degree of retention after 30 days and longer is roughly comparable to the savings involved in transfer to the same maze after intervals between 0 and 120 days.

Macduff (1946) found that rats that had acquired a maze performance under different periods of food deprivation showed an amount of retention positively related to the period of deprivation during acquisition, when retention tests were made for all groups after the same interval of time and under 24-hour food deprivation. Similar results were obtained in two experiments, for one of which practice was distributed and for the other, massed.

Interpolated activity. The acquisition of another performance may impair the retention of a previous acquisition. This phenomenon is called retroactive inhibition. Evidence of retroactive inhibition for serial learning has been obtained with acquisition of another maze as the interpolated activity by Webb (1917) and by Wiltbank (1919). Brockbank (1919) found no evidence for retroactive inhibition of serial learning when the interpolated activity was training on a rope-ladder problem. Ho (1928) studied the effect on retention of the number of trials given on the interpolated maze. The results were not uniform, but there was a trend of increase in retention with increase in training on the interpolated maze. Waters and Vitale (1945) failed to obtain evidence of retroactive inhibition or of differential retention for different amounts of training on an interpolated maze in two experiments, each of which involved a different interval of time between acquisition and the measurement of retention. Marx (1944) found not only clear-cut evidence of retroactive inhibition of serial learning by interpolation of training on other mazes but also that the degree of retroactive inhibition was a function of the number of mazes on which inter-

polated training was given. Retroactive inhibition increased as the number of mazes
increased up to 8 but decreased for the group
given 12 interpolated mazes.

Alteration of stimulus conditions. The effect of this variable on the retention of maze
performance has been studied primarily in
terms of rotation of the maze within the
experimental room. Rotation alters a number of stimulus conditions whose identification and isolation are difficult. In general, rotation of the maze results in poorer retention
of serial learning (Carr, 1917; Higginson,
1930). Higginson showed that alteration of
the position of the maze within the experimental room reduces the efficiency of performance, and that retention is poorer when
tested in the dark than when tested in the
conditions of light under which the performance was acquired. Higginson found no
effect of rotation in the dark on retention
when acquisition took place in the dark.
This suggests that alteration of visual cues
accounts for most of the drop in retention
found with rotation of the maze.

REFERENCES

Alm, O. W. The effect of habit interference upon
performance in maze learning. *Genet. Psychol.
Monogr.*, 1931, **10**, 379–526.

Anderson, A. C. The effect of equalizing reward
upon the breakdown of a discrimination habit
and its bearing upon reminiscence. *J. comp.
Psychol.*, 1937, **23**, 421–437.

Anderson, E. E. The externalization of drive.
IV. The effect of pre-feeding on the maze performance of hungry non-rewarded rats. *J.
comp. Psychol.*, 1941, **31**, 349–352.

Anrep, G. V. The irradiation of conditioned reflexes. *Proc. roy. Soc.*, 1923, **B94**, 404–425.

Arnold, W. J. An exploratory investigation of
primary response generalization. *J. comp. Psychol.*, 1945, **38**, 87–102.

Arnold, W. J. Simple reaction chains and their
integration. I. Homogeneous chaining with
terminal reinforcement. *J. comp. physiol. Psychol.*, 1947a, **40**, 349–364.

Arnold, W. J. Simple reaction chains and their
integration. II. Heterogeneous chaining with
terminal reinforcement. *J. comp. physiol. Psychol.*, 1947b, **40**, 427–440.

Arnold, W. J. Simple reaction chains and their
integration. III. Heterogeneous chaining with
serial reinforcement. *J. comp. physiol. Psychol.*,
1948, **41**, 1–10.

Ballachey, E. L. Variations in maze length as a
factor influencing rate of learning in the white
rat. *J. comp. Psychol.*, 1934, **17**, 23–45.

Ballachey, E. L., and J. Buel. Centrifugal swing
as a determinant of choice-point behavior in the
maze running of the white rat. *J. comp. Psychol.*, 1934, **17**, 201–223.

Ballachey, E. L., and I. Krechevsky. "Specific"
vs. "general" orientation factors in maze running of the white rat. *Univ. Calif. Publ. Psychol.*, 1932, **6**, 83–97.

Bechterev, V. M. *General principles of human reflexology.* (Translated by E. and W. Murphy
from the Russian of the 1928 Ed.) New York:
International, 1932.

Beritoff, J. S. On the fundamental nervous processes in the cortex of the cerebral hemispheres.
I. The principle stages of the development of
the individual reflex: its generalization and
differentiation. *Brain*, 1924, **47**, 109–148.

Blackwell, H. R., and H. Schlosberg. Octave
generalization, pitch discrimination, and loudness thresholds in the white rat. *J. exp. Psychol.*, 1943, **33**, 407–419.

Blodgett, H. C. The effect of the introduction of
reward upon the maze performance of rats.
Univ. Calif. Publ. Psychol., 1929, **4**, 113–134.

Brockbank, T. W. Redintegration in the albino
rat: A study in retention. *Behav. Monogr.*,
1919, **4**, No. 2.

Brogden, W. J. Unconditioned stimulus-substitution in the conditioning process. *Amer. J.
Psychol.*, 1939a, **52**, 46–55.

Brogden, W. J. Sensory pre-conditioning. *J.
exp. Psychol.*, 1939b, **25**, 323–332.

Brogden, W. J. The effect of frequency of reinforcement upon the level of conditioning. *J.
exp. Psychol.*, 1939c, **24**, 419–431.

Brogden, W. J. Higher order conditioning. *Amer.
J. Psychol.*, 1939d, **52**, 579–591.

Brogden, W. J. Retention of conditioned responses tested by experimental extinction.
Amer. J. Psychol., 1940a, **53**, 285–288.

Brogden, W. J. Lateral cerebral dominance in
the dog tested by the conditioning and extinction of forelimb flexion. *J. gen. Psychol.*, 1940b,
23, 387–392.

Brogden, W. J. Conditioned flexion responses in
dogs re-established and maintained with change
of locus in the application of the unconditioned
stimulus. *J. exp. Psychol.*, 1940c, **27**, 583–600.

Brogden, W. J. The effect of change in time of
reinforcement in the maintenance of conditioned
flexion responses in dogs. *J. exp. Psychol.*,
1941, **29**, 49–57.

Brogden, W. J. Non-alimentary components in
the food-reinforcement of conditioned-forelimb
flexion in food-satiated dogs. *J. exp. Psychol.*,
1942, **30**, 326–335.

Brogden, W. J. Acquisition and extinction of a
conditioned avoidance response in dogs. *J.
comp. physiol. Psychol.*, 1949, **42**, 296–302.

Brogden, W. J., and E. Culler. Experimental extinction of higher-order responses. *Amer. J.
Psychol.*, 1935, **47**, 663–669.

Brogden, W. J., E. A. Lipman, and E. Culler. The role of incentive in conditioning and extinction. *Amer. J. Psychol.*, 1938, **51**, 109–117.

Brown, J. S. The generalization of approach responses as a function of stimulus intensity and strength of motivation. *J. comp. Psychol.*, 1942, **33**, 209–226.

Brown, R. H. Color vision in the rabbit. *J. gen. Psychol.*, 1936, **14**, 83–97.

Brown, W. L. The effects of a common start-finish locus on orientation and behavior in a multiple-T maze. *J. comp. Psychol.*, 1946, **39**, 331–338.

Bruce, R. H. The effect of removal of reward on the maze performance of rats. *Univ. Calif. Publ. Psychol.*, 1930, **4**, 203–214; II. *Ibid.*, 1932a, **6**, 65–73; III. *Ibid.*, 1932b, **6**, 75–82.

Brunswik, E. Probability as a determiner of rat behavior. *J. exp. Psychol.*, 1939, **25**, 175–197.

Buel, J. The linear maze. I. "Choice-point expectancy," "correctness," and the goal-gradient. *J. comp. Psychol.*, 1934, **17**, 185–199.

Bunch, M. E. A comparison of retention and transfer of training from similar material after relatively long intervals of time. *J. comp. Psychol.*, 1941, **32**, 217–231.

Bunch, M. E., and E. S. Lang. The amount of transfer of training from partial learning after varying intervals of time. *J. comp. Psychol.*, 1939, **27**, 449–459.

Bunch, M. E., and W. R. Lund. An experiment on backward association in animal learning. *J. comp. Psychol.*, 1932, **13**, 143–156.

Bunch, M. E., and W. K. Magdsick. A study of electric shock motivation in maze learning. *J. comp. Psychol.*, 1938, **25**, 497–506.

Carr, H. A. Maze studies in the white rat. III. Anosmic animals. *J. Anim. Behav.*, 1917, **7**, 295–306.

Cook, S. A. The effect of various temporal arrangements of practice on the mastery of an animal maze of moderate complexity. *Arch. Psychol. N. Y.*, 1928, **15**, Ser. 98, p. 33.

Cowles, J. T. Food-tokens as incentives for learning by chimpanzees. *Comp. Psychol. Monogr.*, 1937, **14**, No. 5.

Crespi, L. P. Quantitative variation of incentive and performance in the white rat. *Amer. J. Psychol.*, 1942, **55**, 467–517.

Czehura, W. S. The generalization of temporal stimulus patterns on the time continuum. *J. comp. Psychol.*, 1943, **36**, 79–90.

Dashiell, J. F. Direction orientation in maze running by the white rat. *Comp. Psychol. Monogr.*, 1930, **7**, No. 2.

Dennis, W. A study of learning in the white rat. *J. genet. Psychol.*, 1930, **37**, 294–308.

Denny, M. R. The role of secondary reinforcement in a partial reinforcement learning situation. *J. exp. Psychol.*, 1946, **36**, 373–389.

Denny, M. R. The effect of using differential end boxes in a simple T-maze learning situation. *J. exp. Psychol.*, 1948, **38**, 245–249.

Dodson, J. D. Relative values of reward and punishment in habit formation. *Psychobiology*, 1917, **1**, 231–276.

Dorcus, R. M., and W. L. Gray. The effectiveness of food and electric shock in learning and retention by rats when applied at critical points in the maze. *J. comp. Psychol.*, 1932, **14**, 191–218.

Drew, G. C. The function of punishment in learning. *J. genet. Psychol.*, 1938, **52**, 257–266.

Dunlap, K., E. Gentry, and T. W. Zeigler. The behavior of white rats under food and electric shock stimulation. *J. comp. Psychol.*, 1931, **12**, 371–378.

Dunn, B. M. A comparison of food reward and escape from water in motivating learning in the white rat. *J. comp. Psychol.*, 1935, **19**, 107–112.

Eccher, W., and E. Culler. Reciprocal facilitation of the conditioned and conditioning mechanisms. *J. comp. Psychol.*, 1941, **31**, 223–231.

Elliott, M. H. The effect of change of reward on the maze performance of rats. *Univ. Calif. Publ. Psychol.*, 1928, **4**, 19–30.

Elliott, M. H. The effect of change "drive" on maze performance. *Univ. Calif. Publ. Psychol.*, 1929, **4**, 185–188.

Ellson, D. G. Quantitative studies of the interaction of simple habits. I. Recovery from specific and generalized effects of extinction. *J. exp. Psychol.*, 1938, **23**, 339–358.

Estes, W. K. Discriminative conditioning. II. Effects of a Pavlovian conditioned stimulus upon a subsequently conditioned operant response. *J. exp. Psychol.*, 1948, **38**, 173–177.

Fairlie, C. W., Jr. The effect of shock at the 'moment of choice' on the formation of a visual discrimination habit. *J. exp. Psychol.*, 1937, **21**, 662–669.

Farber, I. E. Response fixation under anxiety and non-anxiety conditions. *J. exp. Psychol.*, 1948, **38**, 111–131.

Felsinger, J. M. The generalization of extinction effects within a habit pattern. *J. exp. Psychol.*, 1944, **34**, 477–485.

Felsinger, J. M., A. I. Gladstone, H. G. Yamaguchi, and C. L. Hull. Reaction latency (StR) as a function of the number of reinforcements (N). *J. exp. Psychol.*, 1947, **37**, 214–228.

Finan, J. L. Quantitative studies in motivation. I. Strength of conditioning in rats under varying degrees of hunger. *J. comp. Psychol.*, 1940, **29**, 119–134.

Finch, G. Hunger as a determinant of conditional and unconditional salivary response magnitude. *Amer. J. Physiol.*, 1938, **123**, 379–382.

Finch, G., and E. Culler. Higher order conditioning with constant motivation. *Amer. J. Psychol.*, 1934, **46**, 596–602.

Finch, G., and E. Culler. Relation of forgetting to experimental extinction. *Amer. J. Psychol.*, 1935, **47**, 656–662.

Finger, F. W. The effect of varying conditions of reinforcement upon a simple running response. *J. exp. Psychol.*, 1942a, **30**, 53–68.

Finger, F. W. Retention and subsequent extinction of a simple running response following varying conditions of reinforcement. *J. exp. Psychol.*, 1942b, **31**, 120–133.

Gagné, R. M. The effect of spacing of trials on the acquisition and extinction of a conditioned operant response. *J. exp. Psychol.*, 1941a, **29**, 201–216.

Gagné, R. M. The retention of a conditioned operant response. *J. exp. Psychol.*, 1941b, **29**, 296–305.

Gantt, W. H. The nervous secretion of saliva: The relation of the conditioned reflex to the intensity of the unconditioned stimulus. *Amer. J. Physiol.*, 1938, **123**, 74.

Gengerelli, J. A. Studies in abstraction with the white rat. *J. genet. Psychol.*, 1930, **38**, 171–202.

Girden, E. Conditioning and problem-solving behavior. *Amer. J. Psychol.*, 1938, **51**, 677–687.

Graham, D. T. Experimental transfer of conditioning in dogs. *J. exp. Psychol.*, 1944, **34**, 486–493.

Grether, W. F. Pseudo-conditioning without paired stimulation encountered in attempted backward conditioning. *J. comp. Psychol.*, 1937, **25**, 91–96.

Grether, W. F., and D. L. Wolfle. The relative efficiency of constant and varied stimulation during learning: II. White rats on a brightness discrimination problem. *J. comp. Psychol.*, 1936, **22**, 365–374.

Grice, G. R. An experimental study of the gradient of reinforcement in maze learning. *J. exp. Psychol.*, 1942, **30**, 475–489.

Grice, G. R. The relation of secondary reinforcement to delayed reward in visual discrimination learning. *J. exp. Psychol.*, 1948, **38**, 1–16.

Grindley, G. C. Experiments on the influence of the amount of reward on the learning of young chickens. *Brit. J. Psychol.*, 1929, **20**, 173–180.

Hamilton, E. L. The effect of delayed incentive on the hunger drive in the white rat. *Genet. Psychol. Monogr.*, 1929, **5**, 133–207.

Hanawalt, E. M. Whole and part methods in trial and error learning. *Comp. Psychol. Monogr.*, 1931, **7**, No. 5.

Haney, G. W. The effect of familiarity on maze performance of albino rats. *Univ. Calif. Publ. Psychol.*, 1931, **4**, 319–333.

Harlow, H. F. Studies in discrimination learning by monkeys: I. The learning of discrimination series and the reversal of discrimination series. *J. gen. Psychol.*, 1944, **30**, 3–12.

Harris, J. D. Studies on nonassociative factors inherent in conditioning. *Comp. Psychol. Monogr.*, 1943, **18**, No. 1.

Heron, W. T. The effect of a differential rate of reinforcement of responses to two levers. *J. comp. Psychol.*, 1942, **33**, 87–96.

Higginson, G. D. The performance of the white rat in a rotated maze. *J. comp. Psychol.*, 1930, **10**, 355–373.

Hilgard, E. R., and D. G. Marquis. Acquisition, extinction, and retention of conditioned lid responses to light in dogs. *J. comp. Psychol.*, 1935, **19**, 29–58.

Hilgard, E. R., and D. G. Marquis. *Conditioning and learning.* New York: Appleton-Century-Crofts, 1940.

Hill, C. H. Goal gradient, anticipation, and perseveration in compound trial-and-error learning. *J. exp. Psychol.*, 1939, **25**, 566–585.

Ho, Y. H. Transfer and degree of integration. *J. comp. Psychol.*, 1928, **8**, 87–99.

Honzik, C. H., and E. C. Tolman. The action of punishment in accelerating learning. *J. comp. Psychol.*, 1938, **26**, 187–200.

Hull, C. L. Learning: II. The factor of the conditioned reflex. In C. Murchison (Ed.), *Handbook of general experimental psychology.* Worcester: Clark University Press, 1934.

Hull, C. L. *Principles of behavior.* New York: Appleton-Century-Crofts, 1943.

Hull, C. L., and K. W. Spence. "Correction" vs. "non-correction" method of trial-and-error learning in rats. *J. comp. Psychol.*, 1938, **25**, 127–145.

Humphreys, L. G. The strength of a Thorndikian response as a function of the number of practice trials. *J. comp. Psychol.*, 1943, **35**, 101–110.

Hunter, W. S. Habit interference in white rat and human subjects. *J. comp. Psychol.*, 1922, **2**, 29–59.

Hunter, W. S. Conditioning and extinction in the rat. *Brit. J. Psychol.*, 1935, **6**, 135–148.

Jackson, L. L. VTE on an elevated maze. *J. comp. Psychol.*, 1943, **30**, 99–107.

Jackson, T. A. General factors in transfer of training in the white rat. *Genet. Psychol. Monogr.*, 1932, **11**.

James, W. T. An experiment on transfer of a conditioned avoiding reaction under laboratory conditions to a similar situation under kennel conditions. *J. comp. Psychol.*, 1941, **32**, 341–351.

James, W. T. The use of work in developing a differential conditioned reaction of antagonistic reflex systems. *J. comp. physiol. Psychol.*, 1947, **40**, 177–182.

Jenkins, W. O. Studies in spread of effect. I. The bi-directional gradient in the performance of white rats on a linear maze. *J. comp. Psychol.*, 1943a, **35**, 41–56; II. The effect of increased motivation upon the bi-directional gradient. *Ibid.*, 1943b, **35**, 57–63.

Jenkins, W. O. A spatial factor in chimpanzee learning. *J. comp. Psychol.*, 1943c, **35**, 81–84.

Jones, F. N., and F. E. Taylor. The relative effects of goal orientation and direction of the last turn on maze learning in the rat. *J. comp. Psychol.*, 1938, **26**, 19–26.

Kalish, D. The non-correction method and the delayed response problem of Blodgett and

McCutchan. *J. comp. Psychol.*, 1946, **39**, 91–107.

Kappauf, W. E. The application of conditioning methods to the study of discrimination and the measurement of differential thresholds in animals. *J. Psychol.*, 1943, **15**, 129–135.

Kappauf, W. E., and H. Schlosberg. Conditioned responses in the white rat: III. Conditioning as a function of the length of the period of delay. *J. genet. Psychol.*, 1937, **50**, 27–45.

Kellogg, W. N. Electric shock as a motivating stimulus in conditioning experiments. *J. gen. Psychol.*, 1941, **25**, 85–96.

Kellogg, W. N., and E. L. Walker. "Ambiguous conditioning," a phenomenon of bilateral transfer. *J. comp. Psychol.*, 1938a, **26**, 63–77.

Kellogg, W. N., and E. L. Walker. An analysis of bilateral transfer of conditioning in dogs in terms of frequency, amplitude, and latency of the responses. *J. gen. Psychol.*, 1938b, **18**, 253–265.

Kellogg, W. N., and I. S. Wolf. The nature of the response retained after several varieties of conditioning in the same subjects. *J. exp. Psychol.*, 1939, **24**, 366–383.

Kellogg, W. N., and I. S. Wolf. 'Hypotheses' and 'random activity' during the conditioning of dogs. *J. exp. Psychol.*, 1940, **26**, 588–601.

Kendler, H. H. Drive interaction: I. Learning as a function of the simultaneous presence of hunger and thirst drives. *J. exp. Psychol.*, 1945, **35**, 96–109.

Kendler, H. H. A comparison of learning under motivated and satiated conditions in the white rat. *J. exp. Psychol.*, 1947, **37**, 545–549.

Kluever, H. *Behavior mechanisms in monkeys.* Chicago: University of Chicago Press, 1933.

Koch, S., and W. J. Daniel. The effect of satiation on the behavior mediated by a habit of maximum strength. *J. exp. Psychol.*, 1945, **35**, 167–187.

Lashley, K. S. A causal factor in the relation of the distribution of practice to the rate of learning. *J. Anim. Behav.*, 1917, **7**, 139–142.

Lashley, K. S. A simple maze with data on the relation of the distribution of practice to the rate of learning. *Psychobiology*, 1918, **1**, 353–368.

Lashley, K. S. Studies of cerebral function in learning. V. The retention of motor habits after destruction of the so-called motor areas in primates. *Arch. Neurol. Psychiat.*, Chicago, 1924, **12**, 249–276.

Lawrence, D. H., and N. E. Miller. A positive relationship between reinforcement and resistance to extinction produced by removing a source of confusion from a technique that had produced the opposite results. *J. exp. Psychol.*, 1947, **37**, 494–509.

Leeper, R. The reliability and validity of maze experiments with white rats. *Genet. Psychol. Monogr.*, 1932, **11**, 137–245.

Liddell, H. S., W. T. James, and O. D. Anderson. The comparative physiology of the conditioned motor reflex based on experiments with the pig, dog, sheep, goat, and rabbit. *Comp. Psychol. Monogr.*, 1934, **11**, No. 1.

Loucks, R. B. The experimental delimitation of neural structures essential for learning: The attempt to condition striped muscle responses with faradization of the sigmoid gyri. *J. Psychol.*, 1935, **1**, 5–44.

Loucks, R. B., and W. H. Gantt. The conditioning of striped muscle responses based upon faradic stimulation of dorsal roots and dorsal columns of the spinal cord. *J. comp. Psychol.*, 1938, **25**, 415–426.

Macduff, M. M. The effect on retention of varying degrees of motivation during learning in rats. *J. comp. Psychol.*, 1946, **39**, 207–240.

Marcuse, F. L., and A. U. Moore. Motor criteria of discrimination. *J. comp. Psychol.*, 1946, **39**, 25–27.

Marx, M. H. The effects of cumulative training upon retroactive inhibition and transfer. *Comp. Psychol. Monogr.*, 1944, **18**, No. 2.

Mayer, B. A., and C. P. Stone. The relative efficiency of distributed and massed practice in maze learning by young and adult albino rats. *J. genet. Psychol.*, 1931, **39**, 28–49.

Miles, W. R. The comparative learning of rats on elevated and alley mazes of the same pattern. *J. comp. Psychol.*, 1930, **10**, 237–261.

Miller, S., and J. Konorski. Sur une forme particulière des réflexes conditionnels. *C. R. Soc. Biol.*, Paris, 1928a, **99**, 1155–1157.

Miller, S., and J. Konorski. Le phénomène de la généralisation motrice. *C. R. Soc. Biol.*, Paris, 1928b, **99**, 1158.

Moore, A. U., and F. L. Marcuse. Salivary and motor indices of conditioning in two sows. *J. comp. Psychol.*, 1945, **38**, 1–16.

Moss, E., and H. F. Harlow. The role of reward in discrimination learning in monkeys. *J. comp. physiol. Psychol.*, 1947, **40**, 333–342.

Moss, F. A. Study of animal drives. *J. exp. Psychol.*, 1924, **7**, 165–185.

Mote, F. A. The effect of different amounts of reinforcement upon the acquisition and extinction of a simple running response. *J. exp. Psychol.*, 1944, **34**, 216–226.

Mote, F. A., and F. W. Finger. Exploratory drive and secondary reinforcement in the acquisition and extinction of a simple running response. *J. exp. Psychol.*, 1942, **31**, 57–68.

Mote, F. A., and F. W. Finger. The retention of a simple running response after varying amounts of reinforcement. *J. exp. Psychol.*, 1943, **33**, 317–322.

Mowrer, O. H., and H. M. Jones. Extinction and behavior variability as functions of effortfulness of task. *J. exp. Psychol.*, 1943, **33**, 369–386.

Mowrer, O. H., and H. Jones. Habit strength as a function of pattern of reinforcement. *J. exp. Psychol.*, 1945, **35**, 293–311.

Mowrer, O. H., and R. R. Lamoreaux. Avoidance conditioning and signal duration. A study of secondary motivation and reward. *Psychol. Monogr.*, 1942, **54**, No. 5.

Muenzinger, K. F. Motivation in learning. I. Electric shock for correct response in the visual discrimination habit. *J. comp. Psychol.*, 1934, **17**, 267–277.

Muenzinger, K. F. Vicarious trial and error at a point of choice: I. A general survey of its relation to learning efficiency. *J. genet. Psychol.*, 1938, **53**, 75–86.

Muenzinger, K. F. Concerning the effect of shock for right responses in visual discrimination learning. *J. exp. Psychol.*, 1948, **38**, 201–203.

Muenzinger, K. F., A. H. Bernstone, and L. Richards. Motivation in learning. VIII. Equivalent amounts of electric shock for right and wrong responses in a visual discrimination habit. *J. comp. Psychol.*, 1938, **26**, 177–186.

Muenzinger, K. F., and H. Newcomb. Motivation in learning. V. The relative effectiveness of jumping a gap and crossing an electric grid in a visual discrimination habit. *J. comp. Psychol.*, 1936, **21**, 95–104.

Muenzinger, K. F., and A. Wood. Motivation in learning. IV. The function of punishment as determined by its temporal relation to act of choice in the visual discrimination habit. *J. comp. Psychol.*, 1935, **20**, 95–106.

Munn, N. L. The relative effectiveness of two conditioning procedures. *J. gen. Psychol.*, 1939, **21**, 119–136.

Ni, C. F. An experimental study of the influence of punishment for errors during learning and retention. *J. comp. Psychol.*, 1934, **17**, 279–301.

Nissen, H. W., and T. L. McCulloch. Equated and non-equated stimulus conditions in discrimination learning by chimpanzees. I. Comparison with unlimited response. *J. comp. Psychol.*, 1937a, **23**, 165–189.

Nissen, H. W., and T. L. McCulloch. Equated and non-equated stimulus situations in discrimination learning by chimpanzees. II. Comparisons with limited response. *J. comp. Psychol.*, 1937b, **23**, 365–376.

Pavlov, I. P. *Conditioned reflexes.* (Translated by G. V. Anrep) London: Oxford University Press, 1927.

Pavlov, I. P. *Lectures on conditioned reflexes.* (Translated by W. H. Gantt.) New York: International, 1928.

Pechstein, L. A. Whole vs. part methods in motor learning. A comparative study. *Psychol. Monogr.*, 1917, **23**, No. 2, p. 80.

Pechstein, L. A. Massed vs. distributed effort in learning. *J. educ. Psychol.*, 1921, **12**, 92–97.

Perin, C. T. Behavior potentiality as a joint function of the amount of training and degree of hunger at the time of extinction. *J. exp. Psychol.*, 1942, **30**, 93–113.

Perin, C. T. A quantitative investigation of the delay-of-reinforcement gradient. *J. exp. Psychol.*, 1943a, **32**, 37–51.

Perin, C. T. The effect of delayed reinforcement upon the differentiation of bar responses in white rats. *J. exp. Psychol.*, 1943b, **32**, 95–109.

Perkins, C. C., Jr. The relation of secondary reward to gradients of reinforcement. *J. exp. Psychol.*, 1947, **37**, 377–392.

Peterson, J. The effect of length of blind alleys on maze learning: An experiment on twenty-four rats. *Behav. Monogr.*, 1917, **3**, No. 4.

Porter, J. M., Jr. Experimental extinction as a function of the interval between successive non-reinforced elicitations. *J. gen. Psychol.*, 1939, **21**, 109–134.

Riesen, A. H. Delayed reward in discrimination learning by chimpanzees. *Comp. Psychol. Monogr.*, 1940, **15**, No. 5.

Rohrer, J. H. Experimental extinction as a function of the distribution of extinction trials and response strength. *J. exp. Psychol.*, 1947, **37**, 473–493.

Ruch, F. L. Food-reward vs. escape-from-water as conditions motivating learning in the white rat. *J. genet. Psychol.*, 1930, **38**, 127–145.

Sackett, R. S. The effect of strength of drive at the time of extinction upon resistance to extinction in rats. *J. comp. Psychol.*, 1939, **27**, 411–431.

Schlosberg, H. Conditioned responses in the white rat. *J. genet. Psychol.*, 1934, **45**, 303–335; II. Conditioned responses based upon shock to the foreleg. *Ibid.*, 1936, **49**, 107–138.

Schlosberg, H., and R. L. Solomon. Latency of response in a choice discrimination. *J. exp. Psychol.*, 1943, **33**, 22–39.

Schneirla, T. C. Some comparative psychology. *J. comp. Psychol.*, 1933, **16**, 307–315.

Seward, J. P. An experimental analysis of maze discrimination. *J. comp. Psychol.*, 1943, **35**, 17–27.

Sharp, W. L. Disintegrative effects of continuous running and removal of the food incentive upon a maze habit of albino rats. *J. comp. Psychol.*, 1929, **9**, 405–423.

Sheffield, F. D. Avoidance training and the contiguity principle. *J. comp. physiol. Psychol.*, 1948, **41**, 165–177.

Simmons, R. The relative effectiveness of certain incentives in animal learning. *Comp. Psychol. Monogr.*, 1924, **2**, No. 7, p. 79.

Skinner, B. F. Two types of conditioned reflex and a pseudo-type. *J. gen. Psychol.*, 1935, **12**, 66–77.

Skinner, B. F. *The behavior of organisms.* New York: Appleton-Century-Crofts, 1938.

Smith, K. U. Visual discrimination in the cat: III. The relative effect of paired and unpaired stimuli in the discriminative behavior of the cat. *J. genet. Psychol.*, 1936, **48**, 29–57.

Smith, M. F. The establishment and extinction of the token-reward habit in the cat. *J. gen. Psychol.*, 1939, **20**, 475–486.

Solomon, R. L. Effort and extinction rate: A confirmation. *J. comp. physiol. Psychol.*, 1948, **41**, 93–101.

Spence, K. W. The solution of multiple choice problems by chimpanzees. *Comp. Psychol. Monogr.*, 1939, **15**, No. 3.

Spence, K. W., and G. R. Grice. The role of final and sub-goals in distance discrimination by the white rat. *J. comp. Psychol.*, 1942, **34**, 179–184.

Spence, K. W., and W. C. Shipley. The factors determining the difficulty of blind alleys in maze learning by the white rat. *J. comp. Psychol.*, 1934, **17**, 423–436.

Stone, C. P., and M. B. Smith. Serial discrimination by rats at the choice points of elevated mazes. *J. comp. Psychol.*, 1941, **31**, 79–95.

Stone, C. P., and M. Sturman-Hulbe. Food vs. sex as incentives for male rats on the maze-learning problem. *Amer. J. Psychol.*, 1927, **38**, 403–408.

Thompson, M. E. An experimental investigation of goal orientation as a factor in maze learning by the white rat. *J. comp. Psychol.*, 1944a, **37**, 289–296.

Thompson, M. E. An experimental investigation of the gradient of reinforcement in maze learning. *J. exp. Psychol.*, 1944b, **34**, 390–403.

Thompson, M. E. Learning as a function of the absolute and relative amounts of work. *J. exp. Psychol.*, 1944c, **34**, 506–515.

Thompson, M. E., and C. C. Dove. A further study on the bi-directional goal gradient on the endless maze. *J. exp. Psychol.*, 1943, **33**, 447–456.

Tolman, E. C. The determiners of behavior at a choice point. *Psychol. Rev.*, 1938, **45**, 1–41.

Tolman, E. C., and C. H. Honzik. Degrees of hunger, reward, and non-reward and maze learning in rats. *Univ. Calif. Publ. Psychol.*, 1930a, **4**, 241–256.

Tolman, E. C., and C. H. Honzik. Introduction and removal of reward and maze performance in rats. *Univ. Calif. Publ. Psychol.*, 1930b, **4**, 257–275.

Tolman, E. C., and D. B. Nyswander. The reliability and validity of maze-measures for rats. *J. comp. Psychol.*, 1927, **7**, 425–460.

Tolman, E. C., and B. F. Ritchie. Correlation between VTE's on a maze and on a visual discrimination apparatus. *J. comp. Psychol.*, 1943, **36**, 91–98.

Tryon, R. C. Studies in individual differences in maze ability. I. The measurement of the reliability of individual differences. *J. comp. Psychol.*, 1930, **11**, 145–170.

Tsai, C. A comparative study of retention curves for motor habits. *Comp. Psychol. Monogr.*, 1924, **2**, Ser. 11, p. 29.

Ulrich, J. L. The distribution of effort in learning in the white rat. *Behav. Monogr.*, 1915, **2**, No. 5, p. 51.

Valentine, R. The effects of punishment for errors on the maze learning of rats. *J. comp. Psychol.*, 1930, **10**, 35–53.

Verplanck, W. S. The development of discrimination in a simple locomotor habit. *J. exp. Psychol.*, 1942, **31**, 441–464.

Walker, K. C. The effect of a discriminative stimulus transferred to a previously unassociated response. *J. exp. Psychol.*, 1942, **31**, 312–321.

Warden, C. J. The distribution of practice in animal learning. *Comp. Psychol. Monogr.*, 1923, **1**, No. 3, p. 64.

Warden, C. J., and E. L. Hamilton. The effect of variations in length of maze pattern upon rate of fixation in the white rat. *J. genet. Psychol.*, 1929, **36**, 229–239.

Warden, C. J., and L. Lubow. Effect of performance without reward on the retention of the maze habit in the white rat. *J. genet. Psychol.*, 1942, **60**, 321–325.

Warden, C. J., and B. F. Riess. The relative difficulty of mazes of different lengths for the chick. *J. Psychol.*, 1941, **11**, 411–419.

Warner, L. H. The association span of the white rat. *J. genet. Psychol.*, 1932, **41**, 57–90.

Waters, R. H., and A. G. Vitale. Degree of interpolated learning and retroactive inhibition in maze learning. *J. comp. Psychol.*, 1945, **38**, 119–126.

Webb, L. W. Transfer of training and retroaction. *Psychol. Monogr.*, 1917, **24**, No. 3.

Wendt, G. R. Two and one-half year retention of a conditioned response. *J. gen. Psychol.*, 1937, **17**, 178–180.

Whatmore, G. B., E. A. Morgan, and N. Kleitman. The influence of avoidance conditioning on the course of non-avoidance conditioning in dogs. *Amer. J. Physiol.*, 1946, **145**, 432–435.

White, A. E., and E. C. Tolman. A note on elimination of short and long blind alleys. *J. comp. Psychol.*, 1923, **3**, 327–331.

Wickens, D. D., and C. Wickens. Some factors related to pseudo-conditioning. *J. exp. Psychol.*, 1942, **31**, 518–526.

Williams, K. A. The reward value of a conditioned stimulus. *Univ. Calif. Publ. Psychol.*, 1929, **4**, 31–55.

Williams, S. B. Resistance to extinction as a function of number of reinforcements. *J. exp. Psychol.*, 1938, **23**, 506–522.

Williams, S. B. Transfer of reinforcement in the rat as a function of habit strength. *J. comp. Psychol.*, 1941, **31**, 281–296.

Williams, S. B. Reversal learning after two degrees of training. *J. comp. Psychol.*, 1942, **34**, 353–360.

Wiltbank, R. T. Transfer of training in white rats upon various series of mazes. *Behav. Monogr.*, 1919, **4**, No. 1, p. 65.

Wing, K. G. The role of the optic cortex of the dog in the retention of learned responses to light: Conditioning with light and food. *Amer. J. Psychol.*, 1947, **60**, 30–67.

Wischner, G. J. The effect of punishment on discrimination learning in a non-correction situation. *J. exp. Psychol.*, 1947, **37**, 271–284.

Wischner, G. J. A reply to Dr. Muenzinger on the effect of punishment on discrimination learning in a non-correction situation. *J. exp. Psychol.*, 1948, **38**, 203–204.

Witkin, H. A., and T. C. Schneirla. Initial maze behavior as a function of maze design. *J. comp. Psychol.*, 1937, **23,** 275–304.

Wolf, I. S., and W. N. Kellogg. Changes in general behavior during flexion conditioning and their importance for the learning process. *Amer. J. Psychol.*, 1940, **53,** 384–396.

Wolfe, J. B. The effect of delayed reward upon learning in the white rat. *J. comp. Psychol.*, 1934, **17,** 1–21.

Wolfe, J. B. Effectiveness of token-rewards for chimpanzees. *Comp. Psychol. Monogr.*, 1936, **12,** No. 5.

Wolfe, J. B., and M. D. Kaplon. Effect of amount of reward and consumative activity on learning in chickens. *J. comp. Psychol.*, 1941, **31,** 353–361.

Woodbury, C. B. A note on "passive" conditioning. *J. gen. Psychol.*, 1942, **27,** 359–361.

Yerkes, R. M. The mental life of monkeys and apes: A study of ideational behavior. *Behav. Monogr.*, 1916, **3,** No. 1.

Yerkes, R. M. Modes of behavioral adaptation in chimpanzee to multiple-choice problems. *Comp. Psychol. Monogr.*, 1934, **10,** No. 1.

Youtz, R. E. P. Reinforcement, extinction, and spontaneous recovery in a non-Pavlovian reaction. *J. exp. Psychol.*, 1938a, **22,** 305–318.

Youtz, R. E. P. The change with time of a Thorndikian response in the rat. *J. exp. Psychol.*, 1938b, **23,** 128–140.

Youtz, R. E. P. The weakening of one Thorndikian response following the extinction of another. *J. exp. Psychol.*, 1939, **24,** 294–304.

Zener, K. The significance of behavior accompanying conditioned salivary secretion for theories of conditioned response. *Amer. J. Psychol.*, 1937, **50.** 384–403.

17·

Human Learning and Retention

CARL I. HOVLAND

Yale University

This chapter deals with experimental studies of the acquisition and the retention of verbal, perceptual, and motor learning of human subjects. For simplicity of exposition, acquisition is stressed in one portion of the chapter, transfer of training in a second portion, and retention in a third. It is apparent, however, that these phases are highly interdependent: acquisition involves a series of trials, each of which is based on retention of the effects of previous practice, and retention is influenced by the conditions under which acquisition took place. Furthermore the acquisition of new material is greatly affected by previous learning, and retention is influenced by the intervening learning of new material between acquisition and recall.

Several arbitrary restrictions of subject matter have been necessary to avoid overlap with other chapters. For example, the content is restricted to human learning, although it will be recognized that many infrahuman studies are conducted primarily to increase our understanding of human learning. The restriction of coverage to human learning necessarily gives the treatment a strongly empirical flavor, since analytical treatment of theoretical variables often requires the type of simplification and control attainable only with animal experimentation.

The writer expresses his appreciation to Professors Arthur Melton, Arthur Lumsdaine, and Fred D. Sheffield for their helpful suggestions, and to Seymour Feshbach for aid in checking the bibliography.

More extensive coverage is given in this chapter to the research of the last decade than to earlier studies, although the intervention of the war during this period reduced greatly the amount of fundamental research on learning performed. The reader is referred to McGeoch's excellent treatment of the period up to 1940 in his *Psychology of Human Learning* (1942). It is impossible to write a chapter on the same subject without being profoundly influenced by his thoughtful and comprehensive review of the earlier work.

Definition of Learning

Although scores of definitions of learning have been proposed, none has become uniformly accepted. There is, however, considerable agreement on what phenomena are to be included and what excluded: it is desired to include the trend of improvement in performance that comes about as a result of practice and to exclude changes in performance due to fatigue, sensory adaptation, and drugs, changes due to physical development (maturation), and artifacts in measurement, such as changes in rapport between subject and experimenter. The definition used by Hunter (1934) seems to fit these specifications best and hence will be used with only minor modifications. Learning will be defined as the change in performance associated with practice and not explicable on the basis of fatigue, of artifacts of measurement, or of receptor and effector changes.

Three Major Traditions in Human Learning Experimentation

From the pioneer experiments of Pavlov, Ebbinghaus, and Bryan and Harter three main currents in research on human learning have developed. Pavlov's influence has shown itself in the contributions of Watson, Hull, Guthrie, and a long line of other students of conditioning. The Ebbinghaus tradition has continued strong to the present day through the work of Müller, Carr, McGeoch, and others who have studied verbal learning. Research on motor learning and skills springs primarily from the work of Bryan and Harter (1897) who developed the methods, but it has been greatly influenced on the theoretical side by the work of Thorndike (1911 and later) on trial-and-error learning.

A challenging task facing contemporary psychology is the integration of these three major traditions with their diverse methods and concepts. When this integration has been achieved, the chapter on human learning can be made more rigorously systematic.

Many characteristics of learning are already known to be common to the different types of experiment. Accordingly, this chapter will discuss the phenomena common to all three of these types of learning. First, however, a brief description will be given of each of the three main types of human learning experiments and of their most salient characteristics.

CONDITIONING

Much of the research on conditioning has been done with animals. Consequently the treatment here is restricted to a review of the principal phenomena of conditioning and of the relevant reference experiments performed with human subjects. The presentation is arranged in the framework of experimentally investigated phenomena rather than in terms of theoretical formulations. For a discussion of conditioning concepts, theories, and research methods, the reader is referred to the excellent review of the field in Hilgard

and Marquis' *Conditioning and Learning* (1940).

The handbook review of conditioning by Hull (1934) lists the large number of different responses that have been conditioned and the types of stimuli used. The responses most commonly used in human studies have been hand withdrawal, eyelid closure, knee jerk, and vasomotor and psychogalvanic responses. Recent experiments have employed

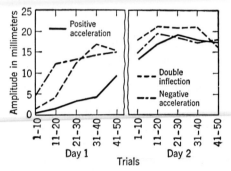

Fig. 1. Course of acquisition of conditioned eyelid response. Subjects were divided into positive acceleration, negative acceleration, and double inflection types on the basis of their individual performance, and the means of each such group were determined. (From Hilgard and Campbell, 1936.)

such esoteric responses as the occipital alpha rhythm (Jasper and Shagass, 1941) and the autokinetic phenomenon (Haggard and Rose, 1944).

Acquisition curves. The strength of connection between stimulus and response increases with the number of reinforcements. Samples of acquisition curves obtained in human eyelid conditioning by Hilgard and Campbell (1936) are illustrated in Fig. 1.*

* Here and in subsequent discussions of verbal and motor learning, acquisition curves have been plotted against trials or number of repetitions. This may suggest that repetition is the critical factor in producing increments in learning, in line with our popular expression "Practice makes perfect." This generalization has even been given the status of a law—the law of frequency. But it must be pointed out that there is a wealth of evidence that frequency per se is not a sufficient condition for learning. The principal lines of evidence, which are presented throughout the chapter, are (1) the failure to learn without motivation even if the situation is frequently re-

The authors remark, "Possibly all of the curves belong to the same family of ogival or S-curves, differing simply in the rapidity with which the positive acceleration phase is completed" (p. 232). The S-shaped type of curve is commonly obtained when frequency of response is used as an index of response strength. Amplitude of response, on the other hand, characteristically shows a nega-

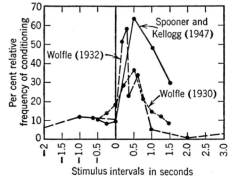

FIG. 2. Percentage of conditioned finger withdrawals with varying time intervals between the conditioned and the unconditioned stimulus in studies by Spooner and Kellogg (1947) and by Wolfle (1930, 1932). (From Spooner and Kellogg, 1947.)

tively accelerated learning curve (cf. e.g. Hovland, 1937*d*).

Temporal relations. Conditioned responses are most strongly established when the unconditioned (or "reinforcing") stimulus follows the conditioned stimulus by a short time interval. The most widely known studies of temporal factors in human conditioning are those of Wolfle (1930, 1932). She used a finger-withdrawal technique, with sound as the conditioned stimulus and electric shock as the unconditioned stimulus. The highest percentage of conditioning was found when the conditioned stimulus preceded the unconditioned by 0.5 second. Some condition-

peated, (2) the reduction in the strength of response with repetition when reinforcement does not follow (experimental extinction), and (3) negative practice, where frequent repetition may actually reduce the strength of an association. Frequency is thus seen to be a necessary, but certainly not a sufficient, condition of learning.

ing was also obtained when the unconditioned stimulus preceded the conditioned, a phenomenon called *backward conditioning.* Spooner and Kellogg (1947) confirmed the general outline of Wolfle's results (Fig. 2) but found that the forward conditioned responses are distinctly different from backward conditioned responses in frequency, latency, and threshold, suggesting that "forward and backward conditioning are fundamentally distinct processes" (p. 334).

Temporal relations for eyelid conditioning were investigated by Reynolds (1945*a*). Conditioning was best with a 450-millisecond interval between conditioned and unconditioned stimuli (Fig. 3). Within the interval from 0 to 400 milliseconds the level and rate of eyelid conditioning were shown by Kimble (1947) to be an increasing, negatively accelerated function of the length of interval between conditioned and unconditioned stimuli.

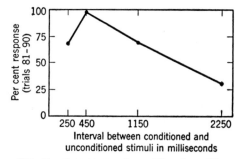

FIG. 3. Percentage of conditioned eyelid responses (on trials 81 to 90) with varying time intervals between conditioned and unconditioned stimuli, following learning by distributed practice (1 to 2 minutes between trials). (Data from Reynolds, 1945*a*.)

When the conditioned stimulus precedes the unconditioned stimulus by a considerable time interval, there is a corresponding delay in the response after the onset of the conditioned stimulus. When the conditioned stimulus continues during the delay until the unconditioned stimulus is presented, the conditioning is called *delayed* conditioning. Other conditioned responses occurring in the interval of delay show a decrement (Rodnick, 1937). When the conditioned stimulus is terminated and the unconditioned stimulus is given after an interval, the response is called a *trace* conditioned response. The study by Reynolds just cited and his subsequent article on extinction (1945*b*) both investigated this type of conditioning.

Decremental factors. Prolonged reinforcement may ultimately produce an actual decrease in the measured strength of response (Pavlov, 1927). This effect is relevant to other conditioning phenomena, particularly the initial rise in the extinction curves (Hovland, 1936) and the efficacy of distributed practice in conditioning to be discussed later. An analysis of decremental factors in conditioning, and their relation to work phenomena, is given by Solomon (1948).

Extinction. When, after learning, the conditioned stimulus is repeatedly presented without reinforcement by the unconditioned stimulus, the response decreases and eventually disappears. A sample curve of extinction is presented in Fig. 4. Extinction is more rapid when there is reinforcement on every trial during conditioning than when there is partial reinforcement, i.e. when reinforcement during acquisition is sometimes present and sometimes not (Humphreys, 1939*a*).

External inhibition. An extraneous stimulus presented just before or during the presentation of the conditioned stimulus often reduces the strength of conditioned response. The influence of such distracting stimuli upon conditioned salivary responses in human subjects was analyzed by Razran (1939*c*).

Disinhibition. When an extraneous stimulus is presented after a conditioned response has become extinguished, a temporary increase in the conditioned response occurs. This phenomenon was studied in human subjects by Razran (1939*c*) who used a buzzer as an extraneous stimulus to restore an extinguished conditioned salivary response.

Spontaneous recovery. When time is allowed to elapse after a conditioned response is extinguished, the response may increase in strength and reappear spontaneously (i.e.

without further reinforcement). Spontaneous recovery is sometimes counteracted by simultaneous "forgetting" of the conditioned response (Razran, 1939*b*).

Stimulus generalization. When a response is conditioned to a particular stimulus, the conditioned response is also made to similar stimuli without specific reinforcement. Immediately following the conditioning trials generalization may be almost complete, i.e.

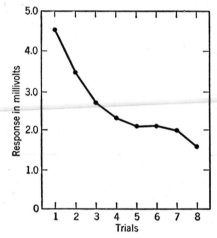

Fig. 4. Extinction curve showing galvanic skin responses on successive unreinforced trials following conditioning. (Data from Humphreys, 1940*a*.)

as large a response being made to stimuli not previously paired with the unconditioned stimulus as to the stimuli given paired presentation (Hovland, 1937*a*, *b*). With subsequent testing the generalized responses appear to extinguish more rapidly than those established to the original conditioned stimulus (Hovland, 1937*c*).

The factors affecting the *form* of the generalization gradient have not yet been adequately determined. Bass and Hull (1934) obtained a positively accelerated gradient when the conditioned and generalized tactile stimuli were spatially separated on the body. Hovland (1937*a*), using auditory stimuli separated by fixed jnd distances in frequency, found a negatively accelerated gradient of mean galvanic responses. Spence

(1939), however, contended that Hovland's median values, which showed a positively accelerated gradient, are more representative. Repetition of Hovland's experiment by Humphreys (1939b) gave a somewhat steeper curve, but a repetition by Littman (1949) gave a gradient with less slope. Results from the last three experiments are presented in Fig. 5.

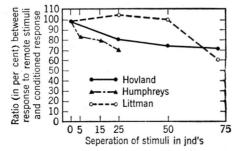

FIG. 5. Generalization curves showing relative response to stimulus used in conditioning and to other stimuli differing from conditioned stimulus by varying numbers of just noticeable differences. Average responses on first two cycles of testing. (Data from Hovland, 1937a; Humphreys, 1939b; and Littman, 1949.)

Work on the form of generalization gradients is seriously limited by the lack, at the present time, of adequate scales of stimulus similarity and of response magnitude. Studies are also needed on the factors influencing the form of the gradient. One relevant factor (Brown, 1942) is the strength of the unconditioned stimulus. The stronger the unconditioned stimulus, the wider the generalization. Another factor reported by Humphreys (1939b) is the method of reinforcement. He found a negatively accelerated gradient with 100-per-cent reinforcement but positive acceleration with 50-per-cent reinforcement (i.e. with reinforcement present on only half of the trials).

Generalization appears to increase with amount of training in the initial stages of conditioning and to become restricted with further training (Hovland, 1937d). The extent of generalization appears to increase for a much longer period with complex patterns

of stimuli than with single stimuli (Razran, 1940).*

Discrimination. If reinforcement is always present when the original conditioned stimulus occurs, but is always absent when the generalized stimulus occurs, the combination of increased strength of the conditioned response and extinction of the generalized response reduces the degree of generalization until finally the response occurs to only a very narrow range of stimuli. The accuracy of discrimination is reduced when the stimuli are presented rapidly and in irregular order (Cole, Woodbury, and Philleo, 1942).

Stimulus patterning. In real-life situations the stimuli to which conditioning occurs are seldom simple, but are complex patterns or "configurations." With practice, identical elements in different combinations can readily be discriminated. A good discussion of this phenomenon, which is referred to as "stimulus patterning," may be found in a study by Hull (1940).

Higher-order conditioning. After a conditioned response has been set up to a particular conditioned stimulus, the conditioned stimulus will sometimes function as as "unconditioned stimulus" in setting up a second conditioned response to a third stimulus. This process can sometimes be con-

* Phenomena somewhat analogous to stimulus generalization are obtained on the response side. That is to say, the stimulus used in initial conditioning may elicit a number of responses similar to the response involved in the initial training. This phenomenon has been called by some writers *response generalization.* An illustrative study is that of Wickens (1943). Human subjects learned to extend their finger to a tone signal reinforced by an electric shock. When the hand was then turned over, the subjects characteristically flexed rather than extended their finger to the conditioned stimulus. With human subjects, however, this may illustrate not a response generalization but rather a transfer to the new situation of a host of pain-avoiding responses learned in other situations, not at all specific to the anatomical relations of the responses. Language may also be involved in the mediation. Until better evidence is available on the nature of the phenomenon, it appears unwise to list response generalization as a primary phenomenon of conditioning.

tinued for several steps. The higher-order conditioned responses are more easily extinguished and presumably require some continued reinforcement of the prior conditioned responses in order to remain effective. This form of conditioning is particularly important in attempts to explain complex human learning in terms of concepts derived from conditioning experiments, because in human learning we deal primarily with secondary motives generated from primary motives on the basis of learning. Much work remains to be done if we are to understand in terms of conditioning principles the persistence of learning in human beings when so much dependence is placed on derived reinforcement that rarely receives primary reinforcement. Undoubtedly the mediating function of language is important in this connection.

Pseudoconditioning. A number of experiments have been done on the phenomenon reported by Grether (1938) that repetition of the unconditioned stimulus alone (without pairing of the conditioned and unconditioned stimuli) results in the evocation of a response to a conditioned stimulus that had previously been inadequate. These responses are retained with little loss for at least a week and do not appear to extinguish (Grant, 1943). Pseudoconditioning may be involved in backward conditioning (Harris, 1941).

Relation of human to animal conditioning. The foregoing brief review of human conditioning phenomena indicates a close parallel between the human and the animal studies of conditioning. At the same time at least two important differences have been suggested. The first relates to the importance of attitude in human conditioning. Studies by Miller (1939), Razran (1936), Grant (1939), Hilgard and Humphreys (1938), and other investigators show the extent to which conditioning phenomena are affected by verbal instructions. An extreme position on this point is held by Woodworth (1938) who described human conditioning as a "game" between the experimenter and the subject.

If given no instruction they [adults] usu. ally assume that E wishes them to take the shock and that they are beating his game if they escape the shock by hand withdrawal; whereas E regards the experiment as a success if O does withdraw. Suppose E were frank with O and instructed him as follows: "I will give you strong shocks preceded (or accompanied) by sounds. I wish to discover how soon you will learn to avoid the shock by withdrawing the hand at the sound." The experiment would lose all point. [P. 110.]

Other experimenters have taken the position that "set" is always present in conditioning and that verbal instructions are just one way of producing sets. With animals one could produce the same results by other procedural means.

The second difference between human and animal conditioning is also attributed to the role of language in human behavior. In one form this is shown in the extensive role of language in mediating other forms of behavior, exemplified in studies such as that of Foley and Cofer (1943) on gradients of response to synonyms and antonyms. Even more significant is the increase in the complexity of discrimination that is made possible by the ability of human subjects to reduce complex patterns to verbal formulae. A particularly important phase of this process is that of counting, which permits discriminations completely impossible for animals.

VERBAL LEARNING

Because of the obvious importance of the learning of verbal material in human affairs, work has been more extensive in this area than on any other phase of research on human learning. Nevertheless much remains to be known about the process, particularly at the basic level of symbolization and the functioning of language. The methods used in the field of verbal learning were well described by Woodworth (1938, pp. 6–17). The reader is also referred to the important article of Melton (1936) on methodology of experimentation in learning.

Factors Influencing Form of Acquisition Curve

Almost every study provides some evidence concerning the changes of performance with practice. Customarily the results are presented graphically with performance plotted on the ordinate and units of practice on the abscissa to provide "acquisition curves."

Length of material. Extensive investigations by Kjersted (1919), Robinson and Heron (1922), Robinson and Darrow (1924), and a number of other researchers have indicated that the form of the acquisition curve is substantially similar over a wide range of lengths of material. The generalization that the proportion of material learned during corresponding fractions of the total learning time is relatively constant for different lengths of material is often referred to as the Kjersted-Robinson law. Typical results obtained on this problem are presented in Table 1 from the study of Robinson and

TABLE 1

PERCENTAGES OF LISTS OF DIFFERENT LENGTHS LEARNED IN SUCCESSIVE SIXTHS OF THE TOTAL LEARNING TIME (FROM ROBINSON AND DARROW, 1924)

Percentages of Total Learning Time	Length of List (Numbers)			
	4	6	8	10
16.7	19.4	31.8	29.3	30.4
33.3	36.1	44.5	45.9	45.3
50.0	49.8	54.0	55.3	54.6
66.7	63.1	62.7	64.0	64.7
83.3	82.3	71.0	75.8	70.4
100.0	100.0	100.0	100.0	100.0

	Length of List (Syllables)				
	6	9	12	15	18
16.7	23.3	33.9	34.6	30.9	33.1
33.3	45.0	51.2	52.3	52.2	53.2
50.0	60.5	62.0	66.3	62.0	66.3
66.7	72.3	73.6	74.9	74.2	76.3
83.3	83.4	80.8	80.5	80.3	82.8
100.0	100.0	100.0	100.0	100.0	100.0

Darrow. Note the similarity (except for the shortest list) in proportions of material learned during successive fractions of the learning time.

Meaningfulness of material. Another factor affecting the form of the learning curve is the meaningfulness of the material to be learned. But the most extensive compilation of data on this point, that of R. A. Davis (1935), fails to provide clear-cut results. Davis concluded that improvement with

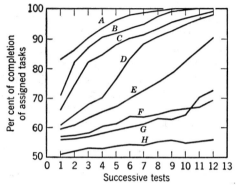

FIG. 6. Curves of learning derived from tasks of varying difficulty. *A,* 5 easy items; *B,* 15 easy items; *C,* 50 easy items; *D,* 100 easy items; *E,* 5 difficult items; *F,* 15 difficult items; *G,* 50 difficult items; *H,* 100 difficult items. (From W. C. F. Krueger, 1946.)

meaningless material is very erratic whereas that for meaningful material is more constant. But it is not clear why his procedure of averaging the curves of different investigators would not tend to smooth out "erratic" fluctuation. In any case the procedure of averaging curves employed by him is open to serious criticism.

Difficulty of material. A factor that appears significant in the few studies devoted to it is the difficulty of the material to be learned. In Fig. 6 results of W. C. F. Krueger (1946) are presented to show the change in the acquisition curve for nonsense syllable learning as the difficulty of the material is increased. With easy material the curve is negatively accelerated, but as the difficulty is increased the curves become linear, and with maximal difficulty the curves are positively accelerated. Similar results are obtained when the learning curves for the easy and for the difficult items in a list are separately plotted (G. M. Peterson, 1928).

Factors Influencing Time Required for Learning

The factors of length and meaningfulness affect not only the form of the acquisition curve, but also the overall ease or difficulty of learning.

Meaningfulness of material. Meaningfulness is an obvious factor affecting ease of learning. A typical experiment compares the number of repetitions required to learn the same number of nonsense syllables and three-letter words. Illustrative results obtained by Guilford (1934) are presented in Table 2. It is further known that, if analy-

TABLE 2

NUMBER OF TRIALS REQUIRED TO LEARN VARIOUS KINDS OF VERBAL MATERIAL (FROM GUILFORD, 1934, p. 122)

Material	Number of Trials
15 nonsense syllables	20.4
15 unrelated words	8.1
15 related words	3.5

sis is restricted to relatively meaningless material (e.g. nonsense syllables), those units that are more "meaningful" in the sense of calling forth more related associations are learned more rapidly than those evoking few associations (McGeoch, 1930).

Amount of material. The relation between quantity of material and time required for learning has been studied by a large number of investigators. When nonsense syllables are used, results generally indicate not only a general increase in length of learning time with increased length of list but also an increase in time required *per unit.* The most extensive range of lengths and materials is found in the study by Lyon (1914) although the number of subjects employed was small. His results are presented

in Fig. 7. Much more extensive data are available over the range of lengths up to 36 syllables. Results over this range by Ebbinghaus (1885), Meumann (1913), and

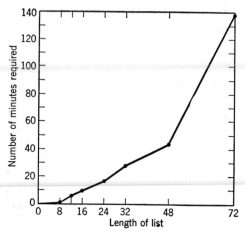

FIG. 7. Time required to learn nonsense-syllable lists of varying lengths. (Data from Lyon, 1914.)

Hovland (1940b) are presented in Fig. 8. They show a negative acceleration in difficulty with increased lengths. The same negative acceleration is obtained when various lengths of lists are scaled by the Thur-

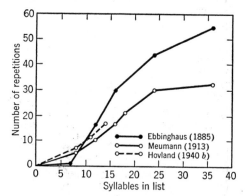

FIG. 8. Mean number of repetitions required for learning various lengths of lists. (From Hull et al., 1940.)

stone-Woodrow absolute scaling technique (Fig. 9). Repetition of Lyon's experiment with more subjects appears desirable to cover a wide range of lengths.

Raskin and Cook (1937) applied a correction to take account of the differential possibility of associations of differing remoteness. Their results are shown in Table 3.

Serial position effects. Ordinarily the items toward the beginning and end of the series are easier to learn than those in the center. This is illustrated in Fig. 12, which shows

TABLE 3

FREQUENCY OF FORWARD AND BACKWARD ASSOCIATIONS WITHIN A SINGLE REPETITION OF THE SERIES (DATA FROM RASKIN AND COOK, 1937)

Forward Associations	Raw Frequency	Correction Factor	Corrected	Backward Associations	Raw Frequency	Correction Factor	Corrected
Immediate direct	195	7/7	195	6th backward remote	11	7/1	77
1st forward remote	44	7/6	51	5th backward remote	12	7/2	42
2nd forward remote	19	7/5	27	4th backward remote	12	7/3	28
3rd forward remote	8	7/4	14	3rd backward remote	12	7/4	21
4th forward remote	9	7/3	21	2nd backward remote	11	7/5	15
5th forward remote	10	7/2	35	1st backward remote	25	7/6	29
6th forward remote	5	7/1	35	Immediate backward	45	7/7	45

A significant factor affecting strength of remote associations is the degree of learning. Ebbinghaus (1885) used three degrees of

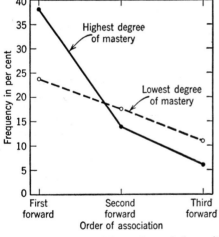

FIG. 11. Gradients of forward associations with low and high degrees of learning mastery. (Data from Hertzman and Neff, 1939.)

learning and found that the extent of remote association decreased with increased practice. The progressive gradient of forward associations with varying degrees of mastery as reported by Hertzman and Neff (1939) is shown in Fig. 11.

the number of errors made in learning a series of 12 syllables to the criterion of one perfect recitation. The relative difficulty of the various items can also be indicated by showing the acquisition curves of the individual units. Results on this point reported

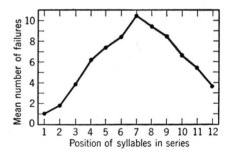

FIG. 12. Serial position curves showing mean number of failures made in learning nonsense syllables in various positions in list. (Data from Hovland, 1938c.)

by Robinson and Brown (1926) are shown in Fig. 13. Note the rapid curves of acquisition for the items toward the ends (2 and 18) and the slower rates for those nearer the center (6 and 12).

Another indication of serial position effects is found in the oscillation between the correct and incorrect response which occurs with

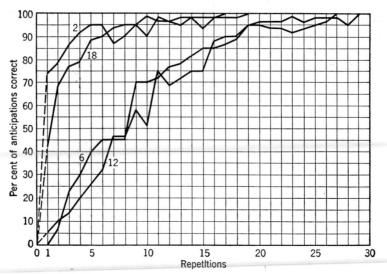

FIG. 13. Learning curves plotted for individual syllables in end positions (2 and 18) and central positions (6 and 12) of list. (From Robinson and Brown, 1926.)

partial learning. This phenomenon was first described by Hull (1935) who showed that an association may often be correctly recalled on one trial and then not be recalled on a

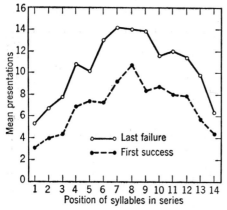

FIG. 14. Fluctuation in learning, showing mean number of repetitions preceding first success and up to and including last failure for syllables in various positions. Data from Hovland (1940b). (From Hull et al., 1940.)

subsequent trial. Finally, the association is recalled on every trial. The end units are much less apt to show such oscillation than are the middle syllables. This phenomenon is shown in Fig. 14.

Serial position effects play a prominent part in the rote-learning theory advanced by Hull et al. (1940). An important alternative theory is that of Foucault (1928) who explained serial effects as due to "proactive" and "retroactive" inhibition within the units of the list to be learned.

MOTOR LEARNING

In laboratory studies of motor learning there is usually an attempt to find a relatively simple type of activity with which the learner has had little previous experience. A good example is the task of tracing a star with a stylus when the star is seen not directly but in a mirror. Here one has to learn to reverse his response to cues, since what he sees in the mirror as up is actually down, and vice versa. In Fig. 15 there are illustrated the changes in performance on successive trials in the learning of such a task. The qualitative change with practice is noted by comparing the shaky erratic tracing on the first trial with the relatively smooth tracing on the fifteenth trial. The quantitative changes are seen when results are plotted in terms of the number of errors

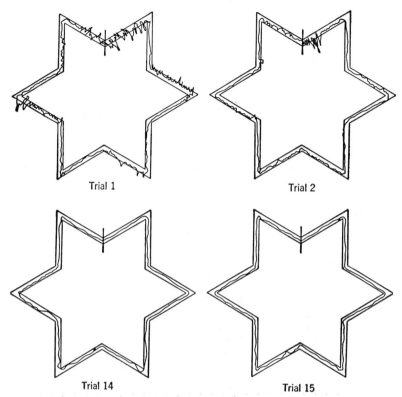

Trial 1   Trial 2

Trial 14   Trial 15

FIG. 15. Qualitative changes with practice. Tracings made on various trials in mirror drawing experiment. (From Kingsley, 1946.)

made on each trial, or in terms of the time required to trace the star on successive trials. Both measures show a gradual decrease with practice (Fig. 16).

Quantitative Changes with Practice

If acquisition is recorded in terms of speed and accuracy (rather than in terms of time and errors, as in Fig. 16), a rising curve is typically found. The curves obtained by Bryan and Harter (1899) are presented in Fig. 17 to illustrate the nature of such changes. Their records indicate a gradual but negatively accelerated improvement. The feature of their curves that has caused the most controversy is the arrest in improvement, the *plateau*, midway through the learning. Bryan and Harter believed that the plateau occurs at the region of transition

from one order to the next in a hierarchy of habits. They summarized their results on telegraphic receiving as follows:

All the facts point to the conclusion that the telegrapher must acquire, besides letter, syllable, and word habits, an array of higher language habits, associated with the combination of words in connected discourse. . . . Learning to receive the telegraphic language consists in acquiring a hierarchy of psychophysical habits. . . . A plateau in the curve means that the lower-order habits are approaching their maximum development, but are not yet sufficiently automatic to leave the attention free to attack the higher-order habits. The length of the plateau is a measure of the difficulty of making the lower-order habits sufficiently automatic. [Pp. 356–357.]

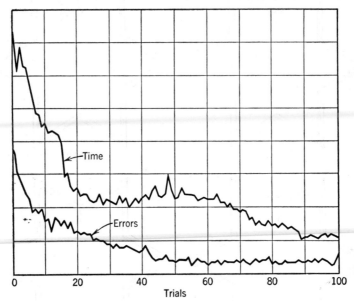

Fig. 16. Acquisition curves showing improvement in time and in errors on successive trials in learning to trace star seen in mirror. (From Starch, 1910.)

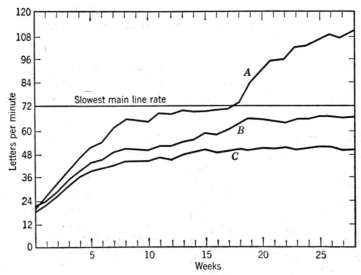

Fig. 17. Acquisition curves for learning to receive telegraphy. *A*, connected discourse; *B*, words; *C*, letters. Tests began with seventh week of practice. (From Bryan and Harter, 1899.)

Plateaus have also been found for learning ball tossing (Swift, 1903), learning a foreign language (Swift, 1906a) and learning to type (Book, 1908). Swift attributed the appearance of plateaus in large part to changes in motivation. Book added the idea that plateaus are due partly to practice on incorrect and useless responses which do not contribute to immediate improvement.

Later work on telegraphic receiving has failed to confirm the generality of plateaus in learning. Taylor (1943) reported an unpublished study of Rees Tulloss in which he failed to obtain a single plateau among his 25 subjects. Reed and Zinszer (1943) likewise reported the absence of prolonged plateaus among their 43 subjects. Studies since 1940 have shown that plateaus are sometimes absent, but we are still confronted with the task of untangling the factors of learning, motivation, and work decrement in the causation of plateaus.

Numerous other investigations have been made of the form of the learning curve for the acquisition of motor skills. For many types of skill acquisition a curve of negative acceleration is obtained; for others positive acceleration is obtained. Differences in results are due sometimes to the units of measurement (J. Peterson, 1917), sometimes to starting the new learning after varying amounts of prior practice (E. Culler, 1928; Ehrlich, 1943a), and sometimes to difference in the character of material and types of learners. From a compilation of nine studies of simple motor learning and twenty studies of complex motor processes (like typewriting or piano playing) R. A. Davis (1935) concluded that the initial rise is more rapid in simple than in complex learning, and that plateaus and fluctuations are more frequent in complex learning. Davis' compilation is given in Fig. 18. Closely related to complexity is the difficulty of a task. An interesting experiment on this factor was reported by W. C. F. Krueger (1947). The curves of each of four groups of subjects learning to toss rings from differing distances were

compared. As the task increased in difficulty, the curve of learning shifted from negative to positive acceleration.

Qualitative Changes with Practice

The pioneer studies on the qualitative changes at various stages of learning skills are those of Lashley (1915) on archery, Ruger (1910) on puzzle solving, Book (1908) on typewriting, Kline (1920) on card sorting, and Starch (1910) on mirror tracing.

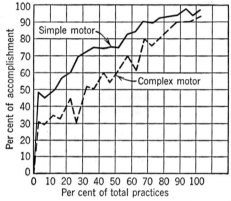

Fig. 18. Acquisition curves. Composite of 9 studies of simple motor learning and 20 studies of complex motor learning. (From Davis, 1935.)

A good review of these and other studies will be found in Woodworth (1938).

An important change with practice in motor learning is change in muscular tension. In some learning, as the task becomes highly skilled, the amount of tension declines (Stroud, 1931; Ghiselli, 1936). In other tasks the tension appears to increase. Telford and Swenson (1942), for example, found that muscular tension during mirror tracing was initially low and was increased and maintained at a high level as learning progressed. Places of increased difficulty were correlated with increased tension. Tension, however, was not diffuse; with progress in learning, there was improved localization of tension in the muscles specific to the task. The relation of tension to performance in various types of learning is an important problem needing further research.

Telford and Swenson's paper provides a good bibliography on the topic.

Some of the studies cited above, particularly those of Lashley and Ruger, stress the sudden improvements that occur with practice, often attributed to "insight" (Köhler, 1929). There has been no sizable recent contribution to our understanding of this problem to alter the summary by McGeoch (1942):

> The abrupt changes which occur are functions of transfer from prior training, of the subject's experience with the particular problem he is trying to solve, of passage from one level to another in a hierarchy of response, and of many other conditions which are continuous with such concepts as trial and error and association. The subject's trials and errors need not be overt to be trials and errors, but may take place symbolically or in some other fashion beyond the direct observation of the experimenter. Actually, many of the descriptions of insight behavior contain rich descriptions of presolution trials and errors. [P. 47.]

Intraserial Phenomena

When a motor task calls for a series of movements to be learned in sequence, serial phenomena similar to those shown earlier for verbal learning are found. The apparatus most frequently used to investigate these phenomena is the maze. The remote associations in a forward direction are called *anticipatory* errors, and those in a backward direction, *perseverative* errors. In a maze where the alternatives are the same at each choice-point it is not possible to know for sure what the degree of remoteness of a particular association is. With mazes in which different elements obtain throughout the series, however, this difficulty is obviated. Lumley's (1932) typewriter "maze" was of this type. The subjects were required to press a series of letters on the typewriter when an auditory signal was sounded until, through trial and error, they discovered the correct letter. Errors could be related to

position in the sequence. Lumley's results are given in Table 4.

TABLE 4

AVERAGE NUMBER OF ERRORS MADE, ANTICIPATING THE FIRST, SECOND, THIRD, ETC., LETTERS AHEAD (FROM LUMLEY, 1932)

	Number of Letters Ahead						
	1	2	3	4	5	6	7
Maze I	66.7	49.8	43.3	32.9	31.3	31.1	24.7
Maze II	15.1	11.4	9.8	6.8	7.1	8.4	6.4
Maze III	28.6	17.6	22.8	15.5	17.4	9.7	12.4

Other data presented by Lumley indicate that with increasing practice there is a decrease in the more remote errors. Serial

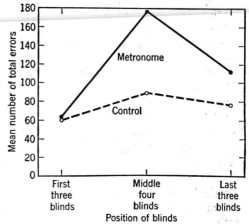

FIG. 19. Mean number of total failures per blind made in various portions of Warden maze learned either to a metronome beat of 100 per minute or with unlimited time in experiment of Husband (1929). (From Hovland, 1938c.)

position effects show that the first units and the last units in the maze * are less difficult than those in the middle, exactly as in the case of verbal material. Husband's (1929)

* For readers interested in the learning of mazes apart from their use as instruments for studying the general field of learning there is an extensive literature on the kinds of cues involved, the role of "centrifugal swing" (e.g. Bitterman and Bretz, 1946), the relative efficiency of finger versus stylus learning (Welsh and Waters, 1944), the patterns of error elimination (McGeoch and Peters, 1933), etc. A good review of early studies will be found in Woodworth (1938) in his chapter on maze learning.

results with college students learning a visual maze are shown in Fig. 19.

Role of Verbalization in Motor Learning

Human learning is seldom quite like animal learning. Language makes the difference. Even in the learning of such a highly motor task as a maze, human subjects rely heavily on language. Warden (1924), for example, reported the frequent use of a verbal formula on the part of his subjects. The subject guided himself through the maze by saying, "First a right turn, then a left turn, then another right," etc. Other subjects used visual images of the maze. Sometimes the subject followed "the lead of his hand" without consciously organizing his movements ("motor learning"). The relative efficiency of subjects using each of these methods is shown in Table 5.

TABLE 5

MAZE LEARNING WITH VARIOUS TYPES OF APPROACH (DATA FROM WARDEN, 1924)

Method of Learning	No. Using	Average No. of Trials to Learn	Range
Word reaction	25	32.2	16–62
Visual imagery	18	67.9	41–104
Motor reaction	17	123.9	72–195

The "verbal" learners showed a clear superiority over the other two groups. This outcome may be due to the superiority of this technique, or it may be that superior individuals are more apt to employ this particular method of learning.

Other evidence of the importance of verbalization is furnished by L. M. Thompson (1944). The task was the assembly of a mechanical puzzle. Six groups of children were given different amounts of aid toward verbalization of the procedure. As shown in Table 6, the greater the verbalization, the more rapid the learning.

TABLE 6

ROLE OF VERBALIZATION IN LEARNING FROM DEMONSTRATION (FROM THOMPSON, 1944)

Group	Procedure	No. of Subjects Learning	Average No. of Trials
1	Silent demonstration. Child prevented from verbalizing by being required to count.	3	25
2	Silent demonstration. Child describes proceedings orally.	22	22.00
3	Demonstrator describes partly. Child watches silently.	25	16.16
4	Demonstrator describes fully. Child watches silently.	25	14.12
5	Child describes process. Teacher watches but makes corrections when child's description is in error.	25	12.44
6	Same as group 5 except that blocks are numbered in the order in which they are to be assembled.	25	9.52

THE ROLE OF MOTIVATION IN HUMAN LEARNING

Research with human subjects has added much less than that with animals to the analysis of basic issues concerning the relation between motivation and learning. This is due in part to the fact that, whereas with animals we can subject to experimental control such basic drives as hunger, thirst, or sex, we must, in the case of human subjects, deal with complex acquired motives that are little understood.

The earliest work on the problem of motivation in human learning was the demonstration of the importance of intent to learn. The study of Myers (1913) is a good example. The task assigned the subjects was to count the number of 0's distributed among letters printed in color on colored paper. Subsequently the subjects were asked questions about what other letters were present and about the color of the paper and the letters. Their inaccurate answers indicated that they failed to learn much of the material to which they had been exposed but which they had not been instructed to learn. Many other experiments indicate the superiority of intentional learning (e.g. Bromer, 1942, and Huang, 1944).

Even without explicit instructions from the experimenter, subjects often learn under self-instruction. This is brought out in Jenkins' (1933) study. Although his subjects were not instructed to learn the material they read, ten of them reported deliberate and self-instructed attempts to learn, and no subject failed to report the presence of occasional self-instruction. Self-instruction may account for the negative results reported by Biel and Force (1943) who found that the group instructed only to observe the syllables presented to them learned as many as the group instructed to learn the syllables.

Considerable circularity is involved, however, if we contend that low memory for material learned incidentally is due to lack of motivation, but seek other possible motivating factors when sizable incidental learning is obtained. To get around this problem Postman and Senders (1946) suggested that we draw a distinction between "explicit" and "covert" instructions and avoid the distinction between "intentional" and "unintentional" learning. In their study they systematically varied the instructions to the subjects. With no instructions only general comprehension of the material was attained, whereas instructions that covered details of content, details of wording, or the sequence of individual events in the material to be tested produced highly specific learning.

Other evidence for the importance of motivation in human learning comes from the immense number of studies showing that learning was facilitated when this or that motivation was employed with adults or children. Positive evidence is valid here, but when negative results are obtained (as when Rubin-Rabson, 1941a, reported that musicians did not learn faster when they were given cash rewards) we do not know whether the incentive was inadequate or whether motivation was aroused but did not affect learning.

Since much basic work remains to be done on how complex human motives are acquired and how they affect learning, the studies mentioned here will be illustrative only. In a widely quoted study, Hurlock (1925) indicated that school children showed large and consistent improvement in the learning of arithmetic problems when publicly praised for their performance, but adverse effects when reproved or ignored. Another well-known study is that of Sims (1928) on the role of competition in learning. Sims had two subgroups compete with each other; the subjects were told the scores of each subgroup but not their own individual scores. These results were compared with those of groups in which each subject had a personal rival and the subjects were told their own scores and those of their rivals. His results indicated that both forms of rivalry are superior to those of a control group with no rivalry, and that individual rivalry is more motivating than that between groups.

An important type of motivation in many human studies is based on competing against one's own record. Experiments here have usually gone under the name "knowledge of results." The classical study on this problem is that of Thorndike (1927) who had his subjects try to draw a line 4 inches long. A group of 7 blindfolded subjects drew 400 times with no indication of whether they drew the line correctly. The errors averaged almost an inch at the beginning of the experiment and remained practically the same at the end. The subjects were then given 25 more trials, with an opportunity after each trial to open their eyes and check the line they had drawn. In only 4 trials were they able to reduce their error to $\frac{3}{16}$ inch.

Thorndike's experiment also calls attention to the importance of information as a motivating condition in human learning. The role of information was not clearly understood among early workers. For example, electric shock was assumed to be a punishment, as it frequently is in animal experimentation. But it was found that shock, if given when the correct response is made, helps bring about fixation of the response. Its informative role exceeds its function as a punishment. This was brought out clearly in the experiment of Bernard and Gilbert (1941) on human maze learning. Alleys in which shock was received were eliminated more readily than those in which no shock was received. They concluded from these and similar results:

> From the evidence available it seems reasonable to postulate that any well defined stimulus introduced consistently in connection with either right or wrong responses will tend to favor their repetition if they are right or their elimination if they are wrong, provided that the stimulus is not of such type or strength as to introduce a distracting effect. . . .
> In human subjects, knowledge of the significance of a "punishment" stimulus appears to mean much more than direct affective reactions to the stimulus. [Pp. 184–185.]

Work on this topic has assumed such proportions that a brief review of it would be completely inadequate. Fortunately, however, this topic has been thoroughly covered in a review by Postman (1947). The interested reader is also referred to the critique of Postman's article by Stone (1948).

The one area of research on motivation in which human experimentation has played a significant part has concerned Thorndike's (1933) "spread of effect" phenomenon. "Spread of effect" was obtained when subjects were asked to respond to each word in the reading of a long list of words by giving the correct associated number between 1 and 10. Arbitrarily the experimenter said "right" after some combinations and "wrong" after others. Not only was there a greater tendency for the same number to be given as an associate on subsequent trials when the experimenter had announced that the number was "right" and less tendency when he had said "wrong," but also the effect was not restricted to the rewarded or punished pairs

but showed a "spread" to words preceding and following the reference word-number pair. The type of curve obtained is illustrated in Fig. 20. Thorndike interpreted his results to mean that the after-effect of reward or punishment is not highly specific but "irradiates" to adjacent associations.

Subsequent experimenters have confirmed the empirical results of the experiment but

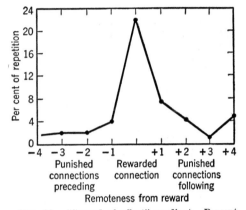

FIG. 20. "Spread of effect" gradient. Percentage of repetitions of word-number pairs when reward pair (labeled "Right" by experimenter) is preceded or followed by punished pairs (labeled "Wrong" by experimenter). (From Thorndike et al., 1933.)

have quarreled with the interpretation. Two interpretations are of especial interest. Zirkle (1946) stressed perceptual factors, finding that, the more isolated the rewarded response, the greater the repetition of correct responses and the steeper the gradient of errors. This explanation is closely related to the theory of Wallach and Henle (1941, 1942) that the avoiding of items interferes with the subject's memory for wrong responses and contributes to his tendency to repeat them.

A quite different explanation was advanced by Jenkins and Sheffield (1946). They believed the spread of effect to be due to the subject's guessing habits: his tendency to repeat the same sequences of responses from trial to trial. A repeated rewarded response thus insured that the errors following reward would frequently be preceded by the same response. Evidence is presented by the authors that the gradient failed to appear when the rewarded response itself was not repeated, but that the typical gradient was obtained when the rewarded response itself was repeated.

The interpretation proposed by Jenkins and Sheffield was extended by Smith (1949), who pointed out that people do not use numbers (or other responses) in a random fashion. These deviations from randomness can be used to predict both the before- and after-gradient in the spread-of-effect experiment. Smith set up a modified experimental situation that allowed him to assign the "correct" and the "incorrect" numbers. When the assignments were from a table of random numbers, there were no gradients; but, when the assigned numbers reflected sequential response tendencies (empirically observed), the gradients promptly appeared. These results seem to indicate that learning factors influence only the extent to which the rewarded response is repeated, and that spread of effect around the rewarded response is an artifact of the experimental situation: it is the spurious result of non-random response habits in the learner.

INDIVIDUAL DIFFERENCES

Much of the literature on human learning is presented in terms of the broadest types of generalization possible. But every worker in the field is struck by the wide variability from individual to individual in even the simplest types of learning. Greatly needed are systematic investigations of the sources of variability. The three factors that have been most extensively studied are age differences, sex differences, and differences in mental ability.

Age Differences

The available evidence on learning at various chronological ages has been summarized by Munn (1946). Learning of the conditioned response variety is found even

before birth. Findings concerning changes with age in the speed of conditioning, however, have been inconsistent, some studies showing more rapid learning with increasing age, and others obtaining diametrically opposed results. In motor learning there appears a rather consistent trend of improvement in the *performance* of learning tasks with increasing age (cf. e.g. Pyle, 1925a) but Munn concluded that there is no clear evidence that a given amount of practice causes a greater *improvement* with older than with younger individuals. Munn did not, however, stress the methodological difficulties inherent in such studies of providing a learning test in which the "gain scores" are of adequate reliability. A test may be quite reliable over a wide range of abilities and still be of practically zero reliability as a measure of gains during practice sessions. Evidence on the reliabilities of the gains is not given in the studies reported, and hence the lack of correlation may be attributable primarily to the attenuation produced by low reliability. Other questions that must be raised are whether the duration of practice was long enough to be significant and whether the range of items was great enough to permit the better learners to indicate the true extent of their learning.

Studies of verbal learning and problem solving have rather consistently shown a progressive improvement in learning with increased age (cf. Heidbreder, 1928; Stroud and Maul, 1933). Even in these studies, however, we cannot be sure that the changes in learning with age are attributable to improved learning *ability* rather than to more extensive previous experience or to greater motivation to learn.

From maturity to old age most studies show a continuous decline in speed and accuracy of learning. Typical are the results of Miles (1933) on an alphabet substitution task (Fig. 21). Again it is difficult to know how much of the decline is attributable to changes in learning ability and how much to differences in motivation. A widely quoted investigation of learning during adulthood is that of Thorndike et al. (1928). They concluded that considerable decline occurs in those of the tests designed to measure "basic modifiability," but that in school subjects the learning of older subjects shows relatively little decline. The absence of decline in the latter is explained as perhaps being due to greater motivation and increased organizing skill. Relatively few cases were involved

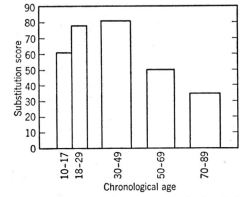

FIG. 21. Scores in learning a substitution task, for groups of various ages. (Data from Miles, 1933.)

in some of the crucial comparisons, however, and the representativeness of many of the samples was certainly not established.

The actual extent of the decline of learning ability with age is much affected by the type of learning task involved. One of the most interesting studies on this problem is that of Ruch (1934a). He chose tasks representative of different types of psychological function. Two motor tasks were used. One, a direct-vision pursuit rotor, required the use of habits previously acquired by the subject in the normal course of his activity. The other was a mirror-vision rotor that required breaking down previous habits and building up new ones. Three types of verbal learning were also employed. The first, paired associates, involved the use of old associations between logically connected words (like horse–sheep). The second, nonsense equations (like $F \times P = V$), required the learning

of completely new verbal habits. The third task required learning false products (like $2 \times 4 = 9$) where old associations had to be broken down and new ones substituted. The subjects had to learn to give the second part of the pair or equation upon seeing the first.

The motor learning task in which prior learning could be used showed less loss with age than the task in which the subjects were required to learn new habits that conflicted with those they had already acquired. Similarly with the verbal material, the tasks involving old associations were better mastered with increased age than were those in which the old associations had to be unlearned and new ones acquired. It is Ruch's (1934b) interpretation that senescence brings about lower functional plasticity of nervous tissue. As a consequence, older people should encounter greater difficulty in learning tasks whose mastery demands a greater amount of reorganization of previously formed habit patterns than in learning tasks whose mastery demands less of this reorganization.

Much work remains to be done to permit a satisfactory explanation of the changes in learning with age. A part of the initial improvement and subsequent decline may be explicable on grounds of physical maturation and degeneration, although little support for this explanation is furnished by Hunter (1934) in his review of the evidence (based mostly on animal studies). Particularly difficult to separate are the concomitant variations in motivation, transfer of past learning to new situations, and true changes in learning ability per se. The disentanglement of these factors is a genuine challenge.

Sex Differences

In many studies of the learning of school children no systematic differences between the sexes have been obtained (Munn, 1946). Some studies have found differences favoring males, and others favoring females. Any consistent differences have usually been explicable in terms of differences in interest in the material and consequent practice. The way in which such differences in content may affect differences between the sexes in learning is illustrated in a study by Pyle (1925b). Boys and girls of high school age were compared on the learning of several types of prose material: some referred to technical processes (physical, chemical, and mechanical), some to fur and fur-bearing animals, and some dealt with geography. The boys learned the technical material somewhat more rapidly than did the girls, but the girls learned the material about furs somewhat more rapidly than did the boys. Similar evidence of differences between the sexes for particular items of content in re-calling a motion picture has been reported by Conrad and Jones (1931). Experiments have not supported the common belief that girls learn more rapidly than boys during the period before adolescence (McGeoch, 1942).

Intelligence Differences

Since mental age and chronological age are highly correlated during the first fifteen or sixteen years of life, any increments with age in learning ability are concomitantly associated with increments in intelligence. Thus, when mental age is partialed out of the correlation between learning and chronological age, the correlation is markedly reduced (Roberts, 1933). But, when chronological age is partialed out, the correlation between mental age and learning scores remains quite high. Studies almost invariably show poorer learning by the mentally retarded (Werner, 1944; Gardner, 1945; Kulcinski, 1945). After maturity is reached, the correlation between learning scores and intelligence tends to be fairly high for complex ideational tasks and for verbal learning, but rather low for simple motor learning (McGeoch, 1942). A good bibliography of studies of the relation between intelligence and learning ability is provided in the paper by Thompson and Witryol (1946). They believe their own results support the contention of a sizable relation between IQ and learning ability, but their data in support of this point are not completely convincing. They report, for example, a correlation of 0.027 between IQ and trials to learn a high-relief finger maze, but they raise this to 0.731 by correcting for range!

A close relation between intelligence and learning ability is implied in most definitions of intelligence. In fact, intelligence is frequently defined as "the ability to learn." This definition has recently been challenged by a number of writers. Simrall (1947) states: "Operationally, the theory that intelligence is the ability to learn means that the sum or average of the scores made on a number of tests given once are highly related to gains due to the practice of a test or tests similar to those which compose an intelligence test" (p. 41).

Mental ability tests (Otis Group) were administered by Simrall to 95 high-school students before the experiment. Then the subjects were given intensive practice on spatial (backward writing) and perceptual (jumbled words maze) tests. An alternate form of the Otis test was given at the end of practice. Her results indicated that, although initial performance on the tests correlated 0.60 with mental age, the gains due to practice had very low correlations with intelligence test scores (−0.079 for the perceptual test and +0.277 for the spatial test). She concluded from these data that "under no circumstances do these data support the hypothesis that the ability to learn these tests is related to mental age" (p. 41). She presented no data on the reliability of the practice gains (not to be confused with the reliability of the test scores themselves). To establish the fact that correlations of the magnitude of 0.277 (reported on the spatial test) are not indicative of significant relation between intelligence and ability to learn requires extremely reliable measures of gain, since otherwise the low correlation may be due merely to attenuation. Nevertheless the most comprehensive review to date of this topic by Woodrow (1946) concludes that "the ability to learn cannot be identified with the ability known as intelligence" (p. 148).

Tilton (1949) reported that, when a test having adequate reliability and suitable difficulty is used to measure gains in learning, a correlation of about 0.50 is obtained between amount of history learned during a school year and scores on the Otis intelligence tests. This correlation is about the same as that obtained between intelligence test scores and initial score on the learning test. Tilton points out that a very high correlation is not to be expected because of the influence of other factors such as motivation and because of the specialization of learning ability.

Is There a "Learning Ability"?

Questioning the definition of intelligence as the "ability to learn" also raises the fundamental issue of whether there is a unitary "ability to learn." Research on this problem has made such a general ability appear doubtful (Woodrow, 1946). Low intercorrelations among learning tasks have been the general rule (Husband, 1939; Brace, 1941; Carlson and Carr, 1940). The methods of factor analysis have also failed to reveal any general learning factor (Woodrow, 1940; Heese, 1942). Heese was able to isolate three common factors — (1) speed of movement, (2) memory, and (3) perception — factors certainly not unique to learning scores. Woodrow (1946) concluded from his review of the evidence:

> In general, the statistically discovered high degree of specificity of practice gains may be interpreted as meaning that each particular activity can best be performed by methods which to an important degree are peculiar to that activity. Improvement with practice depends very largely upon the adoption at repeated trials, to a degree varying with the individual, of these particular methods. [P. 157.]

Changes in Variability with Practice

An early review of the problem of whether individual differences increase or decrease with practice was made by Kincaid (1925). Later studies have not served to resolve the differences in results obtained: they show that variability increases (Ryans, 1939), decreases (Ehrlich, 1943b), or stays the same (Owens, 1942) with practice. There is no obvious reason for the discrepancies among different studies. Greene (1943) believes they may be attributable to variation in the complexity of the learning task.

There are serious problems of method involved in determining the appropriate measure of variability — whether absolute or relative, whether in terms of units performed or rate of performance, etc. The problem is further complicated by the lack of true scales for the measurement of learning. Such scales must have absolute zeroes and possess units of equal size throughout the range if the questions raised are to be answered adequately. A discussion of method in experiments of this type will be found in Anastasi (1934) and Woodworth (1938). Until some of the problems of adequate scales of measurement are solved no clear-cut generalization is likely to emerge. Hunter (1934) prophesied that when adequate procedures become available it will be found that individual differences in degree of skill increase rather than diminish with training.

EFFICIENT METHODS OF LEARNING

A high percentage of the studies of human learning have sought the conditions giving greatest efficiency in learning. These studies have not usually been focused on the analytical study of principles, but in many instances they do isolate factors having relevance in a systematic theory. In the present treatment stress will be placed on those investigations that are oriented toward determining such general factors.

DISTRIBUTION OF PRACTICE

Should material be studied continuously or learned in a series of short sessions? This practical problem has theoretical importance when viewed as an analysis of the roles of learning, motivation, and work decrement in acquisition.

Ebbinghaus (1885) found it better to spread practice over 3 days than to concentrate a greater number of trials into one sitting. Most subsequent investigations favor some form of distributed practice, but there are enough studies favoring massed practice to indicate that there are certain factors that favor massing of practice and others that favor distribution of effort. Accordingly, the task is to ascertain which factors are which, and how they interact.

Two basic designs are commonly used in research on this problem. In the first design, single readings are separated by varying intervals of time. This method is illustrated in the design used in a recent study by Kientzle (1946), shown in Table 7. In the

and Hilgard, 1938). In still others the time between trials is kept constant but the time between items in the series is varied (e.g. Hovland, 1938c).

Material

The nature of the material learned does not in itself seem to affect the advantage of distributed practice. For acquisition of conditioned responses, Calvin (1939) showed that 3 trials per minute were superior to 9 or 18 per minute. A somewhat similar but less striking difference was found by Humphreys (1940b). Two blocks of 48 trials, each with an interspersed rest period, gave better results than a single block of 96 trials presented without rest period. Humphreys, Miller, and Ellson (1940) attributed this result to "decremental" rather than "expectancy" factors.

Studies of verbal learning have generally given the advantage to distributed effort. The early studies of Ebbinghaus and Jost have already been mentioned. Studies by

TABLE 7

	Practice	Rest Period	Practice	Rest Period	Practice	Rest Period	Etc.
Group 1	Trial 1	None	Trial 2	None	Trial 3	None	Trials 4 to 20 with alterna-
Group 2	Trial 1	10 seconds	Trial 2	10 seconds	Trial 3	10 seconds	tion of trials and rest
Group 3	Trial 1	60 seconds	Trial 2	60 seconds	Trial 3	60 seconds	periods as before

other design, varying numbers of trials are given at each sitting with a constant time interval between successive blocks of trials. Such a design is illustrated in Jost's (1897) study (Table 8).

In some studies both the interval between blocks and the number of trials within a block have been varied. In others the number of trials within a block is kept constant but progressively larger or smaller intervals are interpolated between blocks (e.g. Doré

Lyon (1914) and Hovland (1940b) will be discussed shortly. To these should be added the studies of Bumstead (1940, 1943) on the learning of prose and poetry. He found (1943) that, the longer the interval between

TABLE 8

	Practice	Rest Period	Practice	Rest Period	Practice	Rest Period	Etc.
Group 1	Trials 1–2	24 hours	Trials 3–4	24 hours	Trials 5–6	24 hours	7–8, Rest, 9–10, Rest...23–24
Group 2	Trials 1–4	24 hours	Trials 5–8	24 hours	Trials 9–12	24 hours	13–16, Rest, 17–20, Rest, 21–24
Group 3	Trials 1–8	24 hours	Trials 9–16	24 hours	Trials 17–24		

readings, the more rapid was the learning. His results, presented in Fig. 22, show an increase in learning time with decreased rest intervals that is even more pronounced than the increase due to greater length of material.

The majority of studies of motor learning have also shown distributed practice to be superior to massed. When equal units of learning are employed, with varying pauses between trials, the results usually show greater benefit from increasing length of pause, up to a maximum beyond which there is either no additional benefit or an actual reduction in benefit. For the pur-

Travis (1937) believed that a maximum is reached at about 20 minutes, and that longer intervals are less effective.

When the rest pauses are kept uniform it appears that there is usually an optimal length of practice period peculiar to each motor task. Pyle (1928) found that in a substitution task a 30-minute practice period was optimal, being superior to either the

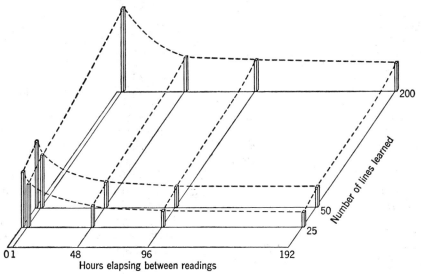

FIG. 22. Tridimensional drawing showing difficulty of learning (represented by height of bars) for various lengths of material and with varying intervals between readings. (Data from Bumstead, 1943.)

suit rotor (1-minute trials), Doré and Hilgard (1937) found that 11 minutes between trials was better than 3 minutes, which was in turn better than 1 minute. Lorge (1930), using a mirror-drawing task, found both 1-minute and 1-day intervals between trials considerably superior to massed practice, but he found little difference between the two distribution intervals. Kientzle (1946) got similar results with an inverted alphabet task: Distributed practice was more effective than massed, and the predicted upper limits of learning were a negatively accelerated function of duration of rest interval. The curves flatten out in the vicinity of 1 minute, which confirms the lack of difference in Lorge's data. For the pursuit oscillator,

shorter (15-minute) or the longer (40- and 60-minute) sessions. For the manual pursuit rotor, Travis (1939) found 2-minute practice sessions superior to 1-minute and 4-minute lengths. Snoddy (1945) reported that, in learning to trace a star pattern reflected in a mirror, the group that had only 1 trial per day performed better than the group that had 10 trials per session with 48 hours between sessions.

The short intervals between trials necessary to reach maximal advantage of distributed practice may help explain the results of Franklin and Brozek (1947) who found no difference between 3, 2, and 1 trials per day and 3 trials per week in pattern tracing and other psychomotor tasks.

Important early articles on the distribution of practice are those of Book (1908), Pyle (1914), and Lashley (1915).

Factors Favoring Massing of Trials

Massing is favored when a period of time is required to "get set" or to "warm up." As many can testify, when a writer works at his job only when he can squeeze in the time between other activities he starts each writing session "cold" and uses much of his time in warming up to the task (getting set or oriented toward what he has done and still has to do, etc.). This contrasts with his behavior as the deadline approaches and the writing is crowded into successive days. He then stays warmed up to the end. The relevance of "warm up" to distribution of practice is stressed by Bell (1942).

A second factor favoring massing of practice is the fact that with very long intervals so much is forgotten that one has to start practically from the beginning on each new trial. This factor has been stressed by Cook (1944).

A third factor is the difference in variability reported under massed and distributed practice. Ericksen (1942) has summarized the studies showing that distributed practice tends to produce a fixation of response, whereas massed practice results in greater variability of behavior. Supporting this hypothesis were his own results: a puzzle box that allowed for great variability of attack was learned more quickly with massed practice. Indirect support has also been furnished by Garrett's (1940) study showing greater variability in the complex tasks and the superiority of massed practice for these materials.

Factors Favoring Distributed Practice

In some situations the superiority of distributed practice may be due to surreptitious extra practice in the form of overt or implicit rehearsal during the rest pause. This can be prevented by filling the interval with controlled activity, provided this does not interact with the task itself. (See below for a discussion of this problem as it applies in reminiscence.) That rehearsal is not a sufficient explanation is established by the fact that distributed practice is beneficial in many situations where rehearsal is prevented.

Undoubtedly many of the results that show an advantage for distributed practice are attributable to work decrement rather than to learning factors. In some studies fatigue produces an artificial lowering of performance, which is overcome by interpolation of rest pauses. Hull (1943) sought to bridge the gap between work decrement and learning principles by the concept of "reactive inhibition." He postulated that all effortful responses, whether reinforced or not, produce a tendency to avoid the repetition of the response. Reactive inhibition is thus a negative drive state similar to what is usually called fatigue. The greater the effort involved in the response, the greater the amount of inhibition. Reactive inhibition develops more rapidly, the shorter the time interval between reactions. Reactive inhibition is believed by Hull to dissipate as a simple decay function of the amount of time allowed for rest, a relation indirectly verified by the experiment of Kimble and Horenstein (1948). An excellent formulation of the implications of this concept for distribution of practice in motor skill is given by Ammons (1947a). The reader is also referred to the comprehensive summary by Solomon (1948) of the work on the relation between work-decrement factors and learning.

In some simple types of learning, barriers to response similar to the phenomenon of "refractory phase" in nerve-muscle studies have been found. Telford (1931) showed that there is a tendency to avoid repeating responses at short time intervals and also that serial reaction time is increased with closely spaced stimuli. In a very limited number of studies this factor may be responsible for poor learning under massed practice. Another related explanation derived from physiology is that of some kind of neural after-effect, called by Müller and Pilzecker (1900) *perseveration*. Woodworth (1938) supported this type of explanation:

The muscle profits from an alteration of exercise and rest and cannot be forced into rapid increase of strength by massing the exercise. The size and internal structure of the muscle fibers improve after exercise, and this nutritive after-effect takes some hours to reach completion. The same after-effect, occurring in the nervous system, may "consolidate" the memory trace of an activity . . . and this consolidation may well be one of the factors in giving advantage to spaced learning. [P. 216.]

Prolonged practice can easily result in reduced motivation with attendant reduction in learning. An alternation of work and rest appears to increase alertness and attentiveness. This may be a factor in the alleged greater effectiveness of distribution of practice with meaningless than with meaningful material. Undoubtedly this motivational factor operates in some prolonged learning series that would, consequently, benefit by distributed practice. Data difficult to explain without resort to motivation were obtained by Gentry (1940). He found that the introduction of spaced practice after massed practice rapidly brought the group to the level of a group that had formerly had spaced practice right along, and vice versa.

Perhaps the most important factor favoring distribution of practice is the chance for interferences built up during learning to dissipate during the rest pauses. Unfortunately it is not easy to disentangle the effects of interferences from those of fatigue and motivation.

As one means of trying to isolate the interference factor, Hovland (1938c) presented nonsense syllables at two different rates — one every 4 seconds and one every 2 seconds — and compared the effectiveness of

distributed practice under these conditions. If the height of serial position curves is used as a criterion, both intraserial interference and the advantages of distributed practice were greatly reduced at the slower rate of presentation (Table 9). As would be ex-

TABLE 9

MEAN NUMBER OF TRIALS REQUIRED FOR LEARNING BY MASSED AND BY DISTRIBUTED PRACTICE AT TWO RATES OF SYLLABLE PRESENTATION (FROM HOVLAND, 1938c)

Two-Second Rate of Presentation

	Mean	σM
Trials required by massed practice	14.89	0.93
Trials required by distributed practice	11.18	0.87
Difference	3.71	
σdiff.	1.05	
C.R. σ	3.53	

Four-Second Rate of Presentation

	Mean	σM
Trials required by massed practice	6.78	0.56
Trials required by distributed practice	5.85	0.54
Difference	0.93	
σdiff.	0.77	
C.R. σ	1.21	

pected, however, the learning at the slower rate of presentation required fewer trials; hence there is not complete proof that fatigue and motivation remained unaffected. In another study Hovland (1939b) compared the effect of massed and distributed practice on serial material (where high interference is to be expected) with paired-associate material (where less interference would be predicted theoretically). The advantage of distributed practice was more marked with the serial material. When the rate for paired associates is made sufficiently rapid, however, distributed practice is more economical than massed (Hovland, 1949).

The three factors of motivation, work decrement, and interference all tend to operate in the same direction when the quantity of material to be learned is increased. Thus it is not surprising that the advantage of distributed practice appears to increase with increased length of lists. This was first shown by Lyon (1914). His results are presented in Fig. 23. They have been confirmed by Hovland (1940b) who showed that the increase in length is accompanied by increased intraserial interferences, which were reduced under conditions of distributed practice. His results are shown in Fig. 24.

WHOLE-PART LEARNING

A practical problem is whether to learn an entire sequence from beginning to end or

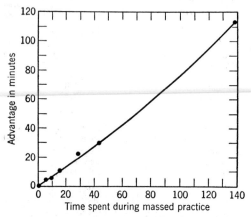

Fig. 23. Advantage of distributed practice over massed practice (in minutes saved) relative to length of time required for learning by massed practice. Data from Lyon (1914). (From Hull et al., 1940.)

to break the whole into parts and to learn each part before combining them into the total sequence. Early workers seemed to think that this problem had a universal answer. They asked, "Which is superior, whole or part learning?" Phrased in this way, the question has no answer. A number of the early studies, starting with the work of Steffens (1900), showed the whole method to be more effective than learning by parts. But other studies, beginning with those of Pechstein (1917), found the part method more effective. In the absence of a universal superiority of one or the other method we must seek the conditions determining the relative advantage of each. Some of these factors will be mentioned.

Motivation

Motivation is obviously relevant. How it might operate has been described by Kingsley (1946):

With the whole method much more time and work is required before any results of learning are manifest. One may read a long poem through a dozen times without being able to recite a single line, while with the same amount of work by the part method the learner would probably be able to recite several stanzas. For this reason a learner gets the feeling of success sooner with the part method. The recitation of parts become sub-goals, which provide a series of steps toward the main goal, the ability to

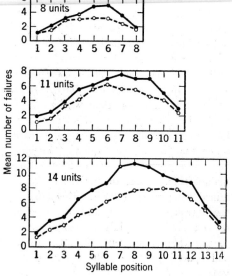

Fig. 24. Composite curves showing mean number of failures for various syllables during learning of three lengths of list by massed (solid line) and distributed (dashed line) practice. (From Hovland, 1940b.)

recite the whole. These intermediate goals and the satisfactions derived from reaching them no doubt favor the part method, particularly with children and with adults unaccustomed to rote memory work. The whole method is likely to be discouraging because the learner has to work so long before he can see any returns for his effort. He may feel that he is not making any progress or that he is wasting his time with this "new-fangled method." This attitude operates against the success of the method. The experienced and informed learner knows that the readings in the whole method are not a waste of time. He knows, as Ebbinghaus demonstrated, that every reading yields an increment of learning, which is spread over the whole, and that if he continues, he will eventually find the whole selection rising above the threshold of recall. He knows that while he must work longer before results are manifest, the final returns fully justify his patience and endurance. [Pp. 314–315.]

Material

No systematic differences in the relative advantage of the whole method for different kinds of material have been obtained. Mazes, for example, were found to be learned more rapidly by the whole method (E. M. Hanawalt, 1934), by the part method (Pechstein, 1917; Barton, 1921), and about equally rapidly by the whole and part method (Cook, 1936, 1937). Nonsense syllables were learned more rapidly by the whole method (Steffens, 1900) and by the part method (Pechstein, 1918), and without decisive difference (Pentschew, 1903). Similarly, for poetry the whole method was found superior by Steffens (1900) and by Meyer (1926), the part method by Winch (1924) and by Reed (1924), and the two methods were found to be about equal by G. O. McGeoch (1931). In the case of the complex skills required in memorization of music, both Rubin-Rabson (1940b) and O'Brien (1943) found that some subjects learn better with the whole method, others with the part.

Curiously, the amount of material in relation to the advantage of whole or part learning has not been studied very extensively. There is probably an upper limit to the amount of material that any given learner can grasp as a unit, and there is a lower limit within which subdivision into parts is probably inefficient. McGeoch (1942) stated that the part method is superior if the difference between the time required to learn by the whole method and the time required to learn the parts separately is greater than the time required to combine the parts. Orbison (1944) tested this point experimentally, using the hypothesis that increase in length of list involves disproportionate increase in interference. Lists of 8, 12, 16, and 24 paired associates presented in random order were learned by the whole and by the part methods. At no length was the whole method superior, but as the length of list increased the part method became increasingly superior to the whole method. His results are presented in Table 10.

TABLE 10

MEAN NUMBER OF PRESENTATIONS PER PAIR REQUIRED TO REACH CRITERION OF ONE PERFECT RECITATION (FROM ORBISON, 1944)

Number of Paired Associates	Whole Method	Part Method	Difference
8	18.75	18.67	0.08
12	20.58	16.96	3.62
16	28.75	23.42	5.33
24	38.50	25.21	13.29

The relation between length and the advantage of whole over part may help to explain the fact that, when distributed practice is employed in learning, the whole method is superior (Pechstein, 1917; Winch, 1924; Crafts, 1930; Davis and Meenes, 1932). It is well known that the relation between length and number of trials for learning is much more linear with distributed than with massed practice. If, for example, 50 trials are required to learn a 20-unit list by massed practice and 15 trials are required to learn a 10-unit list, the division into parts may take advantage of the relative ease of learning the shorter parts. On the other hand, if with distributed practice the 20-unit list requires 18 repetitions and a 10-unit list requires 8, the advantage of subdividing may be sufficiently small to permit other advantages of the whole method to manifest themselves.

By and large, it appears that the greater the continuity and meaningfulness, the more advantageous is the whole method. When poems are understood as a whole, the whole method was found by Northway (1937) to be best for memorization. When the parts are better integrated than the whole, the part method is superior (Seagoe, 1936a, b).

Individual Differences

Both Pechstein (1926) and G. O. Mc-Geoch (1931) showed that, the higher the level of mental development, due to age and higher IQ, the greater the superiority of the whole method. Similar results were obtained by Rubin-Rabson (1940b) for memorization of piano music. She reported that the ability to work comfortably with larger units is specific to the more capable subjects.

Stage of Learning

Practice with both methods appears to bring about a superiority of the whole method. Steffens (1900) found that the advantages of the whole method became evident only when the learner had become accustomed to using this method. Similarly Lakenan (1913) found that at first the part method was better but after practice the whole method proved superior.

Summary

Hunter in his handbook review (1934) concluded: "We cannot generalize and say without qualification that either method is superior to the other" (p. 518). The present writer will be somewhat more rash and attempt the following summary: In a practical situation, factors like fatigue, interest, etc., may play an important part in the relative advantage of whole or part learning. But, if these are held reasonably constant, the best advice seems to be to learn by using the largest units that are meaningful and within the individual's capacity. The older the individual, the higher his in-

telligence, the more practice he has had, the greater is the size of the unit he is able to handle. This generalization is in line with the results of Cook, who found that individuals differ in the size of the unit they can handle with maximum efficiency, and that the size of this "most favorable unit" increases with practice (Cook, 1936). When the size of the unit to be learned was smaller than the optimal length, learning by the whole method was most efficient, but, when the size was larger than the optimal length, the part method was superior (Cook, 1937).

RECITATION

Ebbinghaus, in his experiments, recited the words he knew and then looked up those he did not know. Witasek (1907) showed that this method requires fewer trials than does the method of reading the material over and over until it can be recited completely. Subsequent work has thoroughly confirmed these early observations. The best-known experiment on this problem is that of Gates (1917), who compared the effectiveness of various subdivisions of the total learning time between reading over the material and attempting to recall it. The results he obtained with eighth-grade school children on the learning of nonsense syllables and short biographical prose selections show a pronounced advantage for recitation (Table 11). That the learning of nonsense syllables is affected more than the learning

TABLE 11

INFLUENCE OF DIFFERENT AMOUNTS OF RECITATION UPON LEARNING (FROM GATES, 1917)

Percentage of Total Time Spent		Materials Learned	
In Reading	In Recitation	Syllables	Biographies
100	0	65.4	87.8
80	20	92.2	94.6
60	40	99.7	105.0
40	60	105.5	105.5
20	80	137.3	106.8

of prose has been confirmed by later investigators. Woodworth (1938) attributed the small advantage of recitation in prose to the fact that in rereading such material time after time one inevitably anticipates what is coming and consequently recites while reading.

The advantages of recitation probably depend upon a number of factors. First, recitation arouses a more active attitude on the part of the learner. This point was brought out clearly by Hovland, Lumsdaine, and Sheffield (1949). Soldiers were taught the phonetic alphabet, in which word equivalents are learned for letters, e.g. *Able* for *A*, *Baker* for *B*, *Charlie* for *C*. The standard method of instruction was to employ a film in which each letter was presented on the screen, followed by its word equivalent. After a number of individual letters were presented, a portion of the list was repeated by the narrator. In the "participation" method the same film was used, but, instead of the narrator's repeating the words in groups, the trainees were instructed to recite aloud the word equivalent when the letters were presented. The effectiveness of this procedure is shown in Fig. 25.

A second factor favoring rehearsal is the fact that the material is learned in the way it is going to be used. This closely relates to the problem of whole-part learning discussed above. Gates says, "In reading, the syllables are handled more as isolated terms; the learner tries to imprint each by itself. In recitation more of an attempt is made to make the material over into some sort of pattern, a more or less highly organized structure" (p. 75).

Lastly, recitation is probably effective in part because of motivational factors. Recitation guarantees that the effort will be expended where it is needed most, since the subject will be aware of what he knows and what he does not know. When he gets the material correct immediate satisfaction ensues, and when he is in error he is immediately apprised of this fact and motivated to improve.

There is not complete agreement on the optimal point at which recitation is to be introduced. Woodworth (1938) stated that "recitation, attempted too early, wastes time and may establish errors" (p. 211). He found reading to be most effective in the first or exploratory stage of learning, whereas during the organization and mechanization stages recitation favored rapid learning. Skaggs

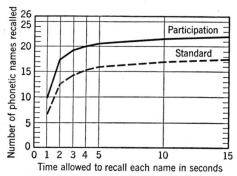

FIG. 25. Average number of phonetic names correctly recalled within designated periods of time per name, with and without participation technique. (From Hovland, Lumsdaine, and Sheffield, 1949.)

and Grossman (1930) found recall with prompting to be most effective after a small number of initial readings, whereas L. O. Krueger (1930) found introduction of a single recall without prompting to be most effective late in practice.

An experiment of H. A. Peterson (1944) supports Gates' (1917) finding that recitation is much less effective with meaningful prose. Peterson attempted to make the material and conditions as close to real-life learning as possible. He used regular assignments for college sophomores and tested learning by means of objective tests. His results for immediate recall are given in Table 12. The highest proportion of recall appears the least effective. Peterson pointed out that one must take into account the amount of time necessary to read and understand, and that, when learning time is not greatly

TABLE 12

RECALL WITH VARYING DISTRIBUTIONS OF
READING AND RECALL (FROM PETERSON, 1944)

Condition	Number of Items in Immediate Recall	Number of Items in Delayed Recall
All reading, no recall	16.03	16.26
⅔ reading, ⅓ recall	16.33	15.98
½ reading, ½ recall	13.94	14.46

in excess of the time required to read a passage once, devoting all the time to reading is substantially as effective as giving part time to recall.

With nonverbal materials the equivalent of recall is "imaginary practice." This has been found to be effective, although usually not so effective as direct practice. In Perry's (1939) study imaginary practice was found better than direct practice with a peg board, about equal for symbol-digit substitution and card sorting, and less effective in mirror tracing. Introduction of such practice appears to be most effective in the middle of learning of complex skills like piano playing, according to Rubin-Rabson (1941b). After minimal learning was reached, direct practice was more effective (Rubin-Rabson, 1941d). Perry has a good discussion of the nature of imaginary practice. In an experiment on dart throwing, Vandell, Davis, and Clugston (1943) found mental practice about as effective as direct physical practice (Table 13).

TABLE 13

EFFECTS OF "PHYSICAL" AND "MENTAL" PRACTICE IN DART THROWING (FROM VANDELL, DAVIS, AND CLUGSTON, 1943)

	Gain	
	Junior High-School Students	College Students
Control Group	−2	0
"Physical" practice	+7	+23
"Mental" practice	+4	+22

OTHER PROBLEMS

There are many other practical problems of learning that have great relevance for training. A number of these are discussed in a review by Hovland (1941) of the relation of learning principles to problems of industrial training. One of these problems is the amount and type of guidance given the learner. The most extensive work on this problem was done by Carr (1930), who also presented a good summary of the literature. Guidance given early apparently helps to establish the correct habits right from the start. Since, however, the learner will later have to perform the task without help, guidance must not continue too long, for the learner may become overdependent upon outside assistance. A recent experiment showing the role of guidance in motivating the learner was reported by Davies (1945).

Another problem is the relative efficiency of learning with the stress on accuracy or with the stress on speed. This problem was discussed by Hovland (1941) in the following terms:

> . . . the correct pattern must be practiced from the very start, if at all possible. We must, therefore, analyze the operations to determine whether the performance at slow speeds is the same as that at high speed. If it is, we should start our training with emphasis upon accuracy so that the exactly correct performance is carried out from the very beginning. This would certainly be the situation in learning typing. No fundamental change in the nature of the movement occurs as greater speed is achieved. If, on the other hand, the operation changes significantly from low to high speeds, we should strive toward the form of the finally correct performance even if some accuracy is sacrificed. This type of situation apparently exists in learning bricklaying. Gilbreth found that an entirely different method is involved when the job is done slowly, one which hardly resembles the form used when the job is done rapidly. Speed would therefore have to be stressed from the start, even if

the work done would have to be redone by an experienced laborer. [P. 12.]

In learning ballistic movements like batting a baseball one would expect that the performance would differ markedly at slow and fast speeds. Hence, on the basis of the foregoing, it is not surprising that Fulton (1942) found that stressing speed from the beginning was superior in learning to bat a baseball. An excellent analysis of the speed-accuracy problem with a review of earlier studies will be found in a monograph by Fulton (1945).

PRINCIPAL PHENOMENA OF RETENTION

In the preceding sections the principal interest has been in changes in performance *during* practice. In the present section attention shifts to the changes in performance at various time intervals *following* a given stage of practice. When retention decreases with the passage of time, the change is referred to as *forgetting;* when retention improves, the term *reminiscence* is applied.

Conditioned Responses

A great deal of anecdotal evidence points to the fact that conditioned responses once acquired are retained with little diminution over considerable periods of time (Guthrie, 1935, pp. 116ff.), but little systematic research has been done on the retention of conditioned responses. The study of Hilgard and Campbell (1936) supports the earlier informal observations in showing sizable retention over a considerable period of time. Using a conditioned eyelid response to a light stimulus, these investigators measured the magnitude of eyelid responses on 5 unreinforced trials following intervals of 1 day, 1 week, and 4, 8, and 20 weeks. Their results are shown in Fig. 26.

Verbal Learning

The classical study of the retention of verbal material is that of Ebbinghaus (1885)

for memorization of nonsense syllables. His curve of retention has become such a commonplace that it is almost invariably graphed in elementary textbooks, often labeled *the* curve of retention. Ebbinghaus' curve shows a rapid initial drop in retention followed by a gradual fall thereafter (Fig. 27).

Another widely quoted curve for retention of nonsense syllables is that of Radossawl-

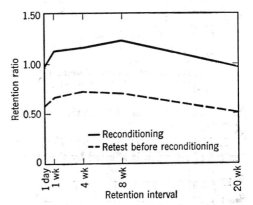

FIG. 26. Retention of conditioned responses at various intervals. Reconditioning retention ratio is performance on third day after retention interval divided by performance on second day of original conditioning. Ratio of retest before reconditioning compares 5 extinguishing trials after the interval with 5 at the end of the original conditioning. (From Hilgard and Campbell, 1936.)

jewitsch (1907). His curve showed a more gradual beginning drop than did that of Ebbinghaus. Waters (1941) believed the discrepancy here to be due to the fact that Ebbinghaus learned 8 lists at a time whereas Radossawljewitsch learned only 3 at a time. The latter arrangement might result in less interference and hence show higher retention.

In general, the *form* of retention curve for meaningful material (poetry and prose) is similar to that for nonsense syllables, but the *level* of retention is higher throughout. The difference in level as a function of meaningfulness of material is brought out clearly in the compilation of 18 studies employing meaningless material and 24 involving mean-

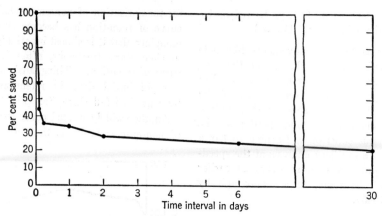

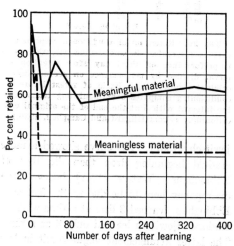

FIG. 27. Retention curve showing percentage of original learning trials saved when relearning is at various intervals following original learning. (From data of Ebbinghaus, 1885.)

ingful material prepared by Davis and Moore (1935). (See Fig. 28.)

1. *Method of measuring retention.* The extent of retention is affected by the method

FIG. 28. Retention curves. Composite of 18 studies of meaningless material and 24 studies of meaningful material. (Data from Davis and Moore, 1935; from Davis, 1935.)

of measurement. In Fig. 27 the results are based on the *savings method:* here the subject relearns, after an interval, material he has previously mastered, and the relearning is compared with the original learning in terms of time, number of trials, or number of errors. The "saving score" is often pre-

sented as a percentage referred to the original learning.

In Fig. 28 the results are based on the *recall score,* the percentage of original material that can be recalled at a later time. In a third method the individual is shown material he has learned earlier, together with items not studied earlier. He is asked to identify the items in the original material. The amount he identifies correctly is a measure of his *recognition* memory. When material has been learned in serial order, a fourth procedure is often used in which the individual is required to arrange the items in the order used in the original learning. This is called the method of *reconstruction.*

None of these measures is completely satisfactory. Recall is sometimes a rather insensitive index. Material may be entirely "forgotten" in the sense that none of it can be recalled and still it may be relearned easily and quickly, or it may be readily recognized as material once studied. The recognition method does not measure the entire sequence of events previously involved, and the deviation from the order of original learning tends to confuse some learners (Davis, 1935). The relearning method, on the other hand, encounters the objection that it is not purely a measure of retention but of learning ability as well. Using original learning as the control time neglects the possibility of positive transfer (Bunch, 1941). Woodworth (1938) pointed out: "In strictness we should compare the relearning time, not with the original learning time but with the time it now takes to learn an equivalent lesson" (p. 10).

The most systematic study of the relation between the curve of retention and the method of measuring retention is that of Luh (1922). His subjects learned lists of

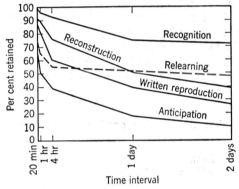

FIG. 29. Retention curves obtained by five different methods of measuring retention. (From Luh, 1922.)

12 nonsense syllables to a criterion of one perfect recitation. Retention was subsequently tested at various time intervals up to 2 days by use of recall (anticipation and written reproduction), recognition, and reconstruction. His results are presented in Fig. 29. All the curves, with the possible exception of that for recognition, show an initial rapid drop and a more gradual fall thereafter. But, whereas 72 per cent is retained after 2 days when measured by recognition, when measured by anticipation only 11 per cent is retained. Analysis of other studies on this topic will be found in Davis and Moore (1935).

Several studies have been made of the difference between exact retention of the material covered (verbatim memory) and retention of the gist of the material (substance memory). Studies by English and his collaborators (cf. e.g. English, Welborn, and Killian, 1934) showed considerable forgetting for verbatim memory, whereas either no forgetting or an actual increase ("reminiscence") was shown for substance memory. Closely related is the study by Briggs and Reed (1943) on retention of ideas, an idea being defined as a concept that cannot be derived from a single sentence in the text. The curve of retention for this material falls at a decelerating rate, but retention is at a much higher level than curves heretofore published for other verbal materials. These results may be related to those reported by Katona (1940) on the superior retention of meaningful learning as compared to senseless learning.

2. Characteristics of the material learned. Some of the effects of difference in material have already been alluded to. Meaningfulness, for example, has been shown to affect the level of retention, but how this comes about we do not fully know.

Vividness of material is another factor favoring good retention. Van Buskirk (1932) had his subjects learn a list of nine syllables in which ordinary black-on-white type was used. In the experimental list, one syllable was printed in red on a green background. This syllable was retained better than the corresponding syllable in the control list.

Closely akin is the finding of von Restorff (1933) that if a syllable is inserted in a list of numbers or a number in a series of syllables the exceptional (she calls it "isolated") item will be better recalled (22 per cent for average unit, 70 per cent for isolated). As the number of isolated items is increased, the advantage in recall is gradually reduced (Pillsbury and Raush, 1943), although there is some advantage even when half the items are of a different type (Siegel, 1943). Gibson (1940) believed that these phenomena could be explained in terms of generalization and differentiation.

AFFECT. The affective character of material has an important influence on retention. Research on this topic stems largely from Freud's conception of forgetting as an active process that protects the individual from disturbing memories. On the basis of the more frequent recall of pleasant experiences, many studies have concluded that pleasant material is better retained than unpleasant. Flügel (1925) has shown, however, that most people describe more of their experiences as "pleasant" than as "unpleasant," which may account for the higher frequency of recall of pleasant experiences. A number of studies record the subject's initial reaction to his experiences and then compare their retention. Pleasant experiences are better recalled than unpleasant (Jersild, 1931; Stagner, 1931; Meltzer, 1930; O'Kelly and Steckle, 1940). Both pleasant and unpleasant experiences are better remembered than neutral (Koch, 1930).

A second method, originally used by Gordon (1925), studied the retention of material associated with pleasant and unpleasant sensations (e.g. odors). No significant differences were found. A closely related procedure compared the learning and retention of words judged by the subjects to be pleasant, unpleasant, or neutral. With adults, Pintner and Forlano (1940) found a loss of 24 per cent for pleasant words, 29 per cent for unpleasant, and 27 per cent for neutral. Children retained unpleasant material better than pleasant. Reviews of studies using these various methods will be found in Meltzer (1930) and Gilbert (1938).

Edwards (1942) has criticized many of these studies on the grounds that it is not necessarily the affective tone that is basic, but rather the presence or absence of conflict between the experience and the individual's values or "frame of reference." Edwards (1941) and Watson and Hartmann (1939) showed that retention was significantly greater for material that was compatible with the attitudes of the subjects than for material that was incompatible. Sharp (1938) took essentially the same point of view — that the acceptability of material

in terms of the individual's values favors retention.

The majority of the results indicate that pleasant experiences are better retained than unpleasant. But, until we know that there are no differences in rehearsal (Jersild, 1931) nor in intensity of experiences (Menzies, 1935) for the two types of material, we cannot conclude that they support Freud's theory of repression.

LENGTH. Length of material bears an interesting relation to retention. At least in the case of verbal materials, when a small and a large quantity of material are learned to the same criterion, later retention is higher for the longer material (Robinson and Heron, 1922; Robinson and Darrow, 1924). Data on this point are presented in Table 14.

TABLE 14

RETENTION OF VARIOUS LENGTHS OF LIST

Length of List	Average Percentage Recalled	Average Percentage Saved
Nonsense Syllables *		
6	71.3	68.7
9	78.3	78.8
12	78.7	78.1
15	77.0	80.7
18	81.7	86.3
Three-Place Numbers †		
4	60.0	25.0
6	66.5	72.5
8	66.6	69.4
10	70.8	78.9

* From Robinson and Heron (1922).
† From Robinson and Darrow (1924).

A large part of the difference is attributable to the greater amount of practice required to learn the longer material. When paired associates were removed from learning as soon as the response had been given correctly three times, lists of 8, 10, 12, and 15 pairs were retained about equally well over a 10-minute period (Sand, 1939).

3. *Degree of learning.* An important determiner of the amount of retention is the

degree of original learning. In the study of Luh (1922) already referred to, the superior retention with higher degrees of learning is clearly shown, but the forms of the curves are similar. W. C. F. Krueger's (1929) data for serial learning (Fig. 30) show the same general results — the higher the degree of learning, the higher the retention. A subsequent study by the same author showed similar results for the retention of finger mazes

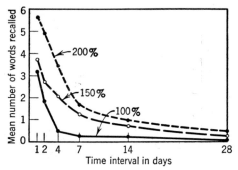

FIG. 30. Retention curves showing recall when material is learned to criterion of one perfect repetition or overlearned by being given 50 per cent more trials (150 per cent) or double the number (200 per cent). (Data from W. C. F. Krueger, 1929.)

(W. C. F. Krueger, 1930). Diminishing returns may be found with high degrees of overlearning (Rubin-Rabson, 1941c).

4. *Methods used in acquisition.* The methods used in learning a task have a significant effect on how well it is retained. If, for example, material is learned to the same criterion by massed as by distributed practice, that learned by distributed has been shown to be retained better, even though more trials were used for massed practice in the original acquisition. Hovland's (1940a) results on this point are shown in Fig. 31. Other studies have also shown superior retention of material learned by distributed practice (Cain and Willey, 1939; Robinson, 1921; Strong, 1914). Rubin-Rabson (1940a) found no significant difference in number of trials to learn piano music by massed and distributed practice, but in relearning there

was a difference in favor of distributed practice.

The advantage of material learned by distributed practice is closely related to the results of Ebbinghaus (1885), who found that, when lists are learned on successive days to the same criterion, the number of trials becomes progressively less. On the basis of Ebbinghaus' work and his own, Jost (1897) formulated what has since been known as Jost's laws:

First law: "Given two associations of the same strength, but of different ages, the older one has greater value on a new repetition."

Second law: "Given two associations of the same strength, but of different ages, the older falls off less rapidly in a given length of time" (p. 472).

A comprehensive study of Jost's laws has been made by Youtz (1941). She confirmed the fact that the older habit shows a larger

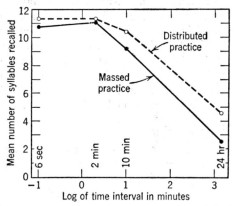

FIG. 31. Mean number of syllables recalled at various time intervals following learning to one perfect recitation by massed and distributed practice. (From Hovland, 1940a.)

learning increment after a single relearning trial. When comparable parts are initially equated, as on the first recall, the amount of increment from new repetitions tends to increase logarithmically from the time since learning:

$$y = K \log t + c$$

where y is the increment on a new repetition, t is the time since learning, and K and c are constants. Older associations required fewer trials to relearn than did younger associations.

Since younger habits display an excess of errors in the middle of rote series, the ratio of errors in the central position to those in the end positions was used as one of the indicators of age. On the basis of this fact Youtz reformulated Jost's first law in these terms: "Of two series of associations which are overtly remembered to the same degree, the one exhibiting the most extensive dissipation of intralist inhibition will profit more on a new repetition" (p. 46).

Material learned by the whole method has been reported to be better retained than that learned by parts (Larguier des Bancels, 1901; Pentschew, 1903. Hsiao (1940) reports that superiority of the whole method becomes more manifest with longer intervals for retention.

The amount of retention is also affected by whether or not recitation was used in the original learning. In the experiment by Gates (1917) cited earlier it was found that retention was greatest when a large portion of the time was spent in practice, although this type of learning may have influenced the original degree of learning directly.

Motor Learning

The classical study of the curve of retention for mazes is that of Tsai (1924) on a stylus maze. Learning was to the criterion of three perfect trials in succession. The maze was relearned to the same criterion at various intervals up to 9 weeks by different groups of subjects. His curve of retention is shown in Fig. 32.

Skills are retained with little loss over very long periods of time. Swift (1906b) reported retention of about 67 per cent of his typing speed over a 2-year period, and Hill, Rejall, and Thorndike (1913) reported little loss after 4 years. Unfortunately there are few systematic studies of retention of skills at various time intervals. One of the best studies of retention of motor learning

is that reported by Leavitt and Schlosberg (1944) for the pursuit rotor. Their retention curve for tests at 1, 7, 28, and 70 days is shown in Fig. 33.

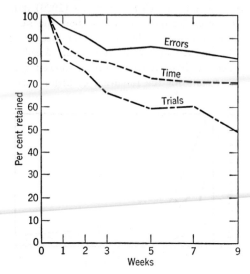

FIG. 32. Retention curves for a stylus maze habit. (From Tsai, 1924.)

The data of Leavitt and Schlosberg are also relevant to a long-standing controversy concerning the relative retention of motor

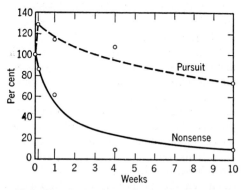

FIG. 33. Comparison of retention curves for pursuit-rotor and nonsense-syllable learning. Retention was measured at first relearning, and the last learning trial was taken as 100 per cent. (From Leavitt and Schlosberg, 1944.)

and verbal learning. Retention of pursuit-rotor learning was found by them to be superior to that of nonsense syllables. This confirmed earlier findings by Freeman and Abernethy (1930, 1932), but, in view of the fact that the majority of other studies have not found this result, they searched for specific factors within the tasks to account for the difference. The degree of integration of the tasks appeared to be one such factor. In a follow-up study Van Dusen and Schlosberg (1948) compared verbal and motor tasks that had a similar simple and clear-cut organization. The subjects learned to operate switches that had nonsense-syllable labels. One set constituted the first terms of paired associates; the other set provided the second terms of the pairs. Simultaneously the subjects learned the names of the syllables that appeared as labels on the paired switches. No significant difference was obtained in the retention of the two types of habits (Table 15). The authors did not believe that the

TABLE 15

COMPARISON OF RETENTION OF SYLLABLES (VERBAL LEARNING) AND SWITCHES (MOTOR LEARNING) (DATA FROM VAN DUSEN AND SCHLOSBERG, 1948)

	Tests			
	Immediate *	1-day	7-day	28-day
Syllables	4.68	5.42	3.00	1.39
Switches	6.45	5.67	4.00	2.48

* Unweighted mean for the three groups given delayed tests.

similarity in retention was due to the fact that learning to actuate the switches was more a verbal than a motor habit. They attributed the superior retention of many motor skills to their organization rather than to the fact that they are motor. In any case it appears that the popular belief that verbal material is readily forgotten but motor skills well retained over long periods is probably exaggerated and, when true, is probably due to differences in the organization of the tasks and the typically greater overlearning of motor skills.

Limits of Retention

Since most studies employ relatively short-time intervals to test retention, little precise information is available on the real limits of retention. The many studies furnishing incidental evidence of long-term retention are summarized in McGeoch and Melton (1929). To their summary should be added two later studies.

Burtt (1941) reports long-term retention of material presented during childhood. Each day for 3 months 3 selections in Greek were read aloud once to a 15-month-old child. Between the eighteenth and twenty-first months 3 other selections were read daily. This procedure, with a different set of selections for each successive 3-month period, was continued until the child was 3 years old, making a total of 21 selections presented. At the age of 8½ years the subject learned 7 of these selections and 3 new ones by the anticipation method. At 14 years he learned a second third of the original 21, together with 3 new selections for control; at the age of 18, the remaining 7 and 3 new ones. At age 8½ (after about 6 years) a 30-per-cent saving was found. At age 14 (after about 11 years) 8 per cent was retained. No retention was found at age 18 (after 15 years).

Another study on long-term retention is by Cofer (1943). Appreciable retention 4 years after original learning was found for only three of his six subjects, stressing the importance of individual difference in retention.

REMINISCENCE

As suggested earlier, retention curves sometimes show a period of increased retention immediately after the cessation of practice. This phenomenon of an initial rise has been labeled *reminiscence*. The literature before 1935 is reviewed by G. O. McGeoch (1935) and for the period from 1935 to 1943 by Buxton (1943b).

The first study showing reminiscence was that of Ballard (1913). He had school children learn long selections of poetry, with a time limit somewhat shorter than that required for mastery. At the end of the learning period the children were asked to recall all they had learned. Some of the children were asked to recall the material again on the following day without previous knowledge that they would be retested. Another group had its recall test after 2 days. Others were retested at 3, 4, 5, 6, and 7 days. The amounts recalled after the various periods are shown in Fig. 34. It will be observed that retention is higher after 2 or 3 days than immediately after learning. The amount of reminiscence was found to be greater for younger than for older children. Williams (1926) confirmed Ballard's observations but found that the improvement occurred only with poetry and not with short abstract words. Only the youngest group of his children showed pronounced reminiscence.

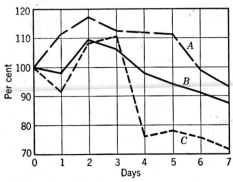

FIG. 34. "Reminiscence" curves showing ratios, in per cent, of amounts reproduced after varying numbers of days to amount reproduced immediately after learning. The three curves are for the following: A, "The Wreck of the Hesperus"; B, "The Ancient Mariner"; C, nonsense verses. (From Ballard, 1913.)

A related phenomenon is the post-learning increase in retention of "substance learning." English, Welborn, and Killian (1934) had their subjects study a long (1100-word) article. True-false tests were then administered to some subjects immediately after study, to others after intervals of 1 or 2 days. One form of the test contained items requiring specific memory; the other required only general comprehension of the material. The first test showed a conventional forgetting curve, but the second showed either no loss or an increase in retention (Fig. 35).

It is important to note that in the Ballard-Williams studies each subject was tested twice — once immediately after learning, and a second time in the delayed test of retention. This, of course, permits the recitation on the first test to improve recall on the second. Before these results can be accepted as showing real improvement in retention there must be more convincing evidence that the improvement is not due principally to the effect of prior recitation.

Ward (1937) called attention to an initial rise in retention for very short periods (2 to 10 minutes) following the learning of non-

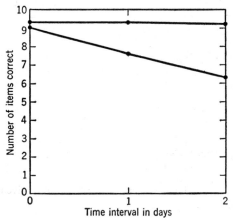

FIG. 35. Comparison of retention based on tests requiring memory for specific facts (lower curve) and for general comprehension of material learned (upper curve). (Data from English, Welborn, and Killian, 1934.)

sense syllables (Fig. 36). In his study the effect on a second recall was eliminated by using a different group for each time interval (including the zero interval). Thus one of the criticisms of the results of Ballard was eliminated. Another possible explanation bobs up however — that of unobserved implicit review during the rest interval. In his main experiment the subjects read a humor-magazine, but it might have been possible for rehearsal to take place anyhow. In order to reduce this possibility still further, Hovland (1938a, b, 1939a) had his subjects name colors presented at the rate of one every 2 seconds during the rest interval. Melton and Stone (1942) have since stepped up the rate of color naming further to reduce the factor of implicit rehearsal. In their study no reminiscence was obtained, but their materials and methods also differed in several

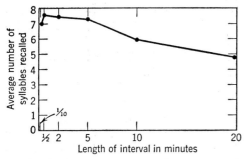

FIG. 36. "Reminiscence" curve showing initial increase in number of nonsense syllables recalled at short-time intervals following original learning. (Data from Ward, 1937.)

other respects from the methods used by Ward and by Hovland.

Reminiscence has also been reported by McClelland (1942a, b) for what he calls "serial verbal discrimination learning." Subjects learned to read aloud the "right" words and to remain silent to the "wrong" words in a list of 20 words. The learning was interrupted when a criterion of 15 out of 20 correct was reached. The half of the subjects who had a 2-minute rest pause filled with color naming performed better on subsequent trials than those who did not have the rest pause. In a later article in the series McClelland (1943a) found that reminiscence occurred only among those who had a high average score on the original learning.

Although most of the work on reminiscence had used verbal material, the appearance of reminiscence is not restricted to verbal learning. An analogous phenomenon of increased retention occurs in conditioning

(Hovland, 1936). Sizable reminiscence has also been found for pursuit rotor learning (Ammons, 1947b; Buxton, 1943a; Doré and Hilgard, 1937, 1938; Hilgard and Smith, 1942; Leavitt, 1945; Leavitt and Schlosberg, 1944), for mirror tracing (Snoddy, 1935), and for other skills (Buxton, 1942a).

There is therefore no doubt about the *fact* of reminiscence. But what is the nature of the phenomenon? Before it can be considered a fundamental *learning* phenomenon, explanation of it in terms of fatigue, motivation, and artifacts of measurement must be eliminated. For example, repeated trials may bring about fatigue and a rest interval may result in recovery from the fatigue with a resulting improvement in performance that may more than offset the forgetting that occurs in the interval. There is evidence that this cannot be the sole explanation of reminiscence, for reminiscence is sometimes found with learning periods so short that they could hardly cause fatigue. Motivational factors could operate in an analogous manner. It is possible that subjects who have become bored with the task may show renewed interest after a rest interval. On the other hand, the appearance of reminiscence after a very limited period of learning makes it unlikely that this is the sole explanation of reminiscence.

The problem of eliminating artifacts of measurement as an explanation of reminiscence requires some discussion.

1. *The effect of immediate recall.* In the studies of Ballard and of Williams the postlearning improvement may have been the result of the practice obtained on the test given immediately after learning. In this sense the recall is like another practice trial and could well cause an apparent improvement of a second trial over that of the first (cf. experiments by Bunch, 1938; Gray, 1940; Spitzer, 1939; and Spencer, 1941). In the experimental design used by Ward and Hovland the practice effect of an immediate recall is eliminated by the use of a separate

control group to assess the extent of learning at the end of practice.

2. *Rehearsal.* Williams (1926) was inclined to explain his results as due to voluntary and involuntary rehearsal of the material during the interval between test and retest. It is extremely difficult to control this factor. G. O. McGeoch (1935) found that 84 per cent of her younger subjects and 70 per cent of the older ones reported that they had rehearsed in the interval between learning and recall. But those who reported rehearsing showed no more reminiscence than those who denied reviewing during the interval. Ballard (1913), on the other hand, found that children who reported going over the material in their mind showed more reminiscence than those who did not report doing so. As noted above in the Ward-Hovland design, color naming has commonly been used during the rest interval in an attempt to reduce rehearsal. But it is difficult to be absolutely sure that this eliminates all rehearsal.

3. *Positive transfer.* In some of English's experiments (e.g. English, Welborn, and Killian, 1934) the material used dealt with general topics in psychology, and the subjects were students continuing their study of psychology during the interval. What they learned in their courses could, therefore, make it easier for them to give correct answers on the items requiring just the substance of the material. The verbatim material would presumably be less affected and hence show more forgetting.

4. *Difficulty of items.* The experiments of English have also been criticized on the grounds that the results deal with *absolute* numbers of reminiscent or forgotten items (Buxton, 1942b). This does not take into account the fact that, since the "substance" test items were more often wrong on the first test, the opportunity for reminiscence in them was much greater than for the verbatim items. When difficulty was ruled out, Buxton found no difference in the amount of reminiscence for the two types of item.

Some differential trends were, however, presented in English's (1942) reply to Buxton's criticisms.

5. *Reproductive interference.* Activities during the rest interval may affect adversely the recall after the interval. It is conceivable, for example, that the "double-quick" color naming used by Melton and Stone (1942) may have had an interference effect and reduced the chance for reminiscence to appear, although other differences between their experiment and those of Ward and of Hovland may have been responsible. Absence of reproductive interference may increase the likelihood of obtaining reminiscence when fatigue is dissipated (Leavitt and Schlosberg, 1944).

6. *Set.* Difference in practice and in instructions may affect the subjects' set to recall. Subjects may, for example, be set to recall on each trial, and this pattern may be disrupted by the introduction of a rest interval. This would depress the level obtained. This factor could be important in accounting for variations in the results of experimenters who used varying numbers of practice series to give the subjects familiarity with the interruption of learning required to test for reminiscence. This point has been made by Buxton (1943b) in these terms:

> A possibility needing exploration is that reminiscence may not be found in experiments employing interpolated activities (e.g. color naming) unless S is well-practiced at shifting from learning to naming and back again. That is, at the time of recall S may not have the appropriate set unless he is accustomed to making the rapid shifts required in such experiments, and his recall score will suffer accordingly. [Footnote, p. 316.]

Design Requirements for Reminiscence Experiments

Truly crucial experiments have still to be performed to demonstrate that reminiscence is a genuine phenomenon of learning, rather than merely of performance. It is easier to write the specifications for such experiments than to arrange the appropriate conditions. Control of the following variables is essential. First, we must be sure that an intervening practice trial is not inserted as a measure of recall. Second, rehearsal must absolutely be prevented. This, as we have seen, is an extremely difficult condition to achieve without other complications. Third, the activity during the rest interval must show neither positive nor negative transfer to the original activity. Fourth, it is necessary that the motivation be the same at each interval. Fifth, sufficient practice in the pattern of the experiment must be given to make the subject highly practiced in shifting from learning to the interpolated activities during rest. Last, conditions must be so arranged that fatigue and other work decrement factors are not produced by prolonged learning periods.

Other Factors Influencing Reminiscence

1. *Stage of learning.* It goes without saying that reminiscence occurs only with incomplete learning. If the learner can recall the material perfectly, no post-learning improvement is measurable in terms of recall. From Hovland's (1938a) data it appears that a low degree of learning (one trial) or a very high degree of learning (one perfect repetition) is less conducive to reminiscence than a moderate degree (7 out of 12 correct). Relative amount of reminiscence has also been found to decline with increased amount of pursuit-rotor learning (Buxton, 1943a).

2. *Materials.* In addition to the effects of material, discussed above, there have been a few studies on the effects of different types of learning on reminiscence. Of the studies using the Ward-Hovland design, those with nonsense-syllable materials have shown reminiscence, whereas the study of Melton and Stone (1942) in which meaningful adjectives were employed failed to show absolute reminiscence, but their retention curve

did not show the usual rapid decline. In a study using nonsense syllables Stone (1946) found some evidence of reminiscence at a 2-minute interval, but its amount was not statistically significant. Buxton (1949) found that under identical experimental conditions reminiscence occurs with nonsense syllables but not with meaningful syllables. But what factors in meaningfulness account for the difference? The difference may be related to the difficulty of learning, the effect of previous familiarity, the effect on motivation, or a host of other factors. It is to be recalled that with the Ballard-Williams procedure meaningful material showed reminiscence. Martin (1940) even suggests that, the more meaningful the material, the greater the reminiscence.

Reminiscence was found by Hovland (1939a) to be greater for serial than for paired-associate learning. This may be due to the differences in the extent of remote associations in the two situations (which might be expected to increase the amount of interference). It may also be due to the fact that to make the time per syllable constant (2 seconds per syllable in each pair or in the series) the subject gave responses once every 2 seconds with the serial lists but only once every 4 seconds with paired associates (cf. Hovland, 1949).

3. *Method of learning.* Closely related to the type of material is the method by which learning takes place:

a. MASSED-DISTRIBUTED PRACTICE. On the theory that reminiscence is due at least in part to dissipation of interferences accumulating in learning, Hovland (1938a) tested for reminiscence following learning by massed and by spaced practice (where the interferences would presumably be dissipated between trials). He found that reminiscence was greater following learning by massed practice.

b. SPEED OF PRESENTATION. Another way to reduce interference is to slow down the rate of presentation of material. Hovland (1938b) found that reducing the rate of presentation from one syllable every 2 seconds to one every 4 seconds decreased the amount of reminiscence. McClelland's (1942a) results also appear to indicate that reminiscence is more likely to obtain with more rapid presentation. Melton and Stone (1942), however, found that, with rapid rates of presentation of their syllables, numerous signs of intraserial interference occurred, but reminiscence was not obtained.

c. "CROWDING." Interference in verbal material is presumably increased when several lists are learned in a period. The effect of this factor has been studied by Newman (1939). One group of subjects learned and recalled single lists of eight nonsense syllables. The other group learned and recalled the lists in blocks of three. The retention intervals were 1, 24, and 48 hours. Newman found that the single list showed a more or less conventional forgetting curve but that lists learned together (under what he calls "crowded" conditions) showed reminiscence.

4. Individual differences. Although early investigators believed that age was an important variable in the amount of reminiscence, a careful review of the literature by G. O. McGeoch (1935) convinced her that there was no reliable evidence that reminiscence is related to age, sex, or intelligence of the learner. McClelland (1943a) suggested that the brighter and faster learners may reminisce more than those who are less able, although this may depend on the particular time interval used. Leavitt (1945) found that fast learners show greatest reminiscence with a short interval, whereas slow learners showed greater reminiscence with a longer interval.

UNLEARNING

In the preceding studies of retention the losses with time were those occurring spontaneously ("forgetting"). Much less studied is the problem of deliberately reducing the strength of habits ("unlearning").

One of the earliest studies of unlearning was carried out by Jones (1924), who attempted to eliminate children's fears of being alone or in a dark room, or of snakes, rabbits, or other animals. She tried a number of methods. Despite the common belief that fears disappear spontaneously if no further contact with the feared object occurs, she found no diminution in fear by simple "disuse." Verbal appeal, in which the experimenter talked about the feared object and connected it verbally with pleasant experiences, was likewise quite ineffective.

The method of negative adaptation was also tried, in which the child was exposed to the feared object repeatedly. In one case considerable improvement occurred under this procedure, but in other cases the child actually became more frightened. Ridicule of the fear caused the children to hide or repress their fear, but there was no real reduction in the fear itself.

Under certain conditions distraction was effective. When toys were placed near the animal the child was sometimes so eager to get the toys he would ignore the animal. But this method required the constant presence of an adult to arrange the distractions, and the effects seemed temporary.

The two most effective ways of overcoming the children's fears were: (1) reconditioning and (2) social imitation. In the first method direct conditioning was used to associate the feared object with a stimulus capable of arousing positive reactions, e.g. food. Tolerance was gradually built up until the child became indifferent to the feared object and in some cases finally responded positively to the object. This method must, however, be very carefully applied. If the object is feared intensely and introduced too rapidly, the treatment may "boomerang" so that the child becomes negatively conditioned to the eating rather than positively conditioned to the object feared.

The other method found effective was to allow the children to participate in the activity of other children who reacted to the object without fear. When the social group in which the child was placed was one of high prestige, the child behaved the way the group behaved, and, when the other children approached the object without fear, the child soon imitated them.

Another method of breaking habits is the "negative practice" method described by Dunlap (1928). He showed that a "bad" habit like typing *hte* instead of *the* could be eliminated by deliberately practicing the typing of *hte* repeatedly. A systematic study of Dunlap's hypothesis was conducted by Holsopple and Vanouse (1929) with typing students who were just learning to transcribe from shorthand notes. Eleven students who had consistently misspelled four words were given practice on two of the words in misspelled form, and on the other two words in correct form. On a later test no errors were made on the words that had been given negative practice, but 10 of the 11 students made errors on the words practiced correctly.

A repetition of this study using words misspelled in spelling tests was conducted by Peak, Brooks, and Hobson (1941). They found no superiority of one method over the other. Dunlap's (1942) criticism of this experiment and Peak's (1942) reply should be read by readers interested in the problem. A good review of experiments on negative practice and their implications in terms of theories of learning will be found in Peak (1941).

Guthrie (1938) describes three general ways in which unlearning can be brought about: (1) The stimulus is introduced at such weak strengths that it does not cause the response, and then its intensity is gradually increased but is kept below the "threshold of response." (2) The cues for the unwanted action are presented at a strength that would ordinarily cause the response, but at the same time the situation is controlled in such a way as to prevent the occurrence of the response so that it becomes inhibited. (3) Stimuli for an act are presented at a time when some of the instruments necessary for carrying out the act are not present. If the means of execution are absent, something else is done, which then becomes the associated habit. These three methods all reduce to the presentation of cues for an undesired action whose performance is prevented. These points of Guthrie are based largely upon armchair analysis and clinical judgment.

QUALITATIVE CHANGES IN RETENTION

The heavy emphasis on quantitative changes in learning has almost crowded out interest in qualitative changes. With the publication of Bartlett's book on *Remembering* (1932) there has been a renewed interest in the nature of changes taking place in retention. Bartlett used stories, pictures, and figures as material and studied the details recalled.

These and other studies have brought out the fact that considerable simplification occurs and that material not relevant to the central theme drops out. Inconsistent material tends also to be omitted, and the story takes on a simple structure. Similar phenomena are found in studies on memory for events, and on the reliability of testimony. A good survey of these experiments will be found in Lipmann (1935).

The experiment of Tresselt and Spragg (1941) uses the Bartlett approach. A verbal passage was read twice to a subject who reproduced it as accurately as possible after 15 minutes. This reproduction was in turn read to a second subject, whose reproduction was in turn passed on, etc. The changes reported by these investigators were in the direction of "simplification, cohesion, and symmetry."

A related problem of considerable interest, but one that has not yet yielded to rigorous analysis, is that of retention of visual forms. The best review to date is to be found in Woodworth's (1938) chapter on memory for form.

Much of the research on this topic was inspired by the work of Wulf (1922) who believed that memory was influenced by the Gestalt principles.

The most general law which governs all the memory changes is the law of pregnance [Prëgnanz] which says that every gestalt becomes as good as possible. In perception the 'possible' is sharply limited by the existing stimulus complex, but in memory the 'engram' or trace, freed from this limitation, can transform itself in the direction of pregnance. Therefore figures, in memory, tend toward definite outstanding forms. [P. 372; quoted from Woodworth, 1938, p. 80.]

Results of Perkins (1932) and others seem to support the theory by showing changes in the direction of balanced and symmetrical patterns, but judgments of this sort have usually been made only by the experimenter. Publications have shown only "representative samples." Sorge (1940) confirmed earlier results: his subjects improved the symmetry of abstract figures, introduced right angles and straight lines, and clarified the functional role of ambiguous parts. Other studies have shown increases in complexity and size of visually perceived forms (Burton and Tueller, 1941; Wallen, 1943).

This field presents difficult problems of procedure. In the first place, the usual method is for the subject to draw the figure. The correlation between memory and ability to draw the figure is questionable. The second difficulty is that in most studies the subject is asked to keep repeating his drawing. This has been shown by N. G. Hanawalt (1937) to operate, for both visual forms and verbal material, in the direction of increasing retention. When only a single reproduction is involved, a normal type of forgetting curve is obtained. Goldmeier (1941) has contended, however, that Hanawalt's results are attributable to the material used, finding in his own study "autonomous changes . . . directed toward outstanding or prägnant value and toward consistent structure of the whole" (p. 503). Philip (1940) showed that memory for figures is influenced by proactive and retroactive interferences in the same way as other material.

INDIVIDUAL DIFFERENCES IN RETENTION

All the factors of individual differences discussed earlier in connection with acquisition also affect retention. The close relation makes it difficult to know in many cases whether the differences in retention of different groups (analyzed by age, intelligence, or other factors) are due to real differences in retention or to superior initial acquisition.

Results on one phase of the problem of individual differences in retention are of special interest. It is popularly thought that those who learn readily forget readily, and that the individual who acquires material slowly retains it for a long time. This relation may sometimes exist owing to the fact that the "slow" learner may greatly overlearn the material, whereas the "rapid" learner is satisfied with barely reaching criterion. But if we compare the retention of individuals who reach a criterion performance rapidly with individuals who reach the same criterion slowly, we find that the retention of the fast learners is better than that of the slow learners. This is borne out by the study of Gillette (1936) whose subjects learned paired associates. As soon as a pair was repeated correctly it was removed from the series so that the pairs learned early would not be so greatly overlearned. The fast learners retained significantly more material than the slow learners. Gillette's monograph contains a bibliography and a good discussion of the problems of method involved.

The time interval at which retention is tested may affect the relation between speed of learning and amount retained. This is indicated by a recent study of Leavitt (1945) on the learning and retention of nonsense syllables and a pursuit-rotor task. The correlation was positive between speed of learning and amount of retention at short-time intervals, whereas at long-time intervals it was negative.

A fascinating aspect of individual differences, on which there has been little work, concerns the qualitative changes in memory with age. There is a great deal of speculation about this topic, with anecdotal evidence of superior retention by old people of early youthful experiences, but few systematic studies are available. It will also be recalled that we still have no satisfactory explanation for the differences in retention between various age groups found by Ballard (1913) and Williams (1926) in their studies of reminiscence.

EFFECT OF PRIOR LEARNING ON ACQUISITION (TRANSFER OF TRAINING)

Even under highly controlled conditions the learning of a new task is not independent of previous learning but is built upon previous acquisitions. In everyday life we count heavily on past learning to make it easier for us to add new material. On the other hand, we often find our old habits interfering with the formation of new ones. The fact that past learning makes it sometimes easier and at other times harder to learn new materials points up the need for systematic exploration of the problem.

How previous learning affects new learning has customarily been dealt with under the label "transfer of training." The central interest is usually in determining how the learning of one activity "transfers" to the learning of a new activity. The effect of previous learning may either *improve* or *retard* the new learning. The first result is referred to as *positive transfer;* the latter as *negative transfer.* In some cases, of course, the learning of the first material has no measurable effect on the learning of the second.

Good reviews of this topic have been provided by Orata (1928, 1935, 1941) and by Woodworth (1938). Only a brief summary of early studies will be presented here as an introduction to recent investigations.

Bilateral Transfer

The earliest reports of transfer come from observations on how habits learned with one hand can be performed without further practice by the other. Thus Weber is quoted by Woodworth (1938) as having reported that a noted surgeon of his day found it economical, in teaching certain delicate operations that must be performed sometimes with one hand and sometimes with the other, to train his students only in the use of the left hand. They were then able to perform the operation with the right hand without further training. Significant early studies of bilateral transfer (sometimes called cross-education) were those of Scripture, Smith, and Brown (1894) and of W. W. Davis (1898, 1900) on dynamometer grip, steadiness, and tapping. Their research design, however, was faulty, for it lacked a control group.

Later studies have been conducted with better controlled conditions. A good example is that of Munn (1932) who used a game involving a wooden cup on a handle, from which a wooden ball was suspended by a string. The task was to grasp the handle and flip the ball into the cup. Subjects were given 50 trials with the left hand to provide a measure of initial skill. Then one group was given 500 trials with the right hand while the other group rested. Each group was then given 50 practice trials with the left hand. The experimental group improved 61.14 per cent, whereas the control group improved only 28.5 per cent.

Bilateral transfer effects are not limited to bilaterally symmetrical members. This was shown by Bray's (1928) experiment on aiming at a target seen in a mirror, where he found that there was positive transfer not only from hand to hand but from hand to foot. Similar findings have been reported by Cook (1934): a stylus path was learned by blindfolded subjects with one hand and was subsequently positively transferred not only to the other hand but to the feet as well.

Reports by the subjects and observations by the experimenters in the Munn and Bray experiments indicate in a general way how transfer was mediated. Various "tricks of the trade" which the subjects learned could subsequently be transferred to the other side. There was also a reduction in the nervousness and self-consciousness of the subjects.

Analogous results on bilateral transfer of perceptual discrimination date back to the studies of Volkmann (1858). He found that practicing with the left hand in two-point threshold discrimination helped the right hand to make the discrimination. From introspective reports (Boring, 1920) it appears that the improvement in discrimination is the result of becoming acquainted with the difference in feel between two points and one.

Perceptual Transfer

A pioneer study by Thorndike and Woodworth (1901) showed that practice in estimating areas of figures improves the accuracy of estimation of other areas, and that, the more similar are the new areas to those on which there had been practice, the greater is the transfer. But far greater improvement was brought about through direct practice than through transfer. It was in connection with this experimental work that the authors drew the conclusion which seemed so revolutionary at the time:

> Improvement in any single mental function need not improve the ability in functions commonly called by the same name. It may injure it. Improvement in any single mental function rarely brings about equal improvement in any other function, no matter how similar, for the working of every mental function-group is conditioned by the

nature of the data in each particular case. [P. 250.]

In his later writings (cf. particularly 1913) Thorndike made more explicit his famous theory of "identical elements."

In another classical study Coover and Angell (1907) showed that practice on discriminating sound intensities improved subsequent discrimination of shades of gray, which they attributed to the knack of "divesting the essential process of the unessential factors" (p. 333).

Motor Transfer

When successive units of the same type of motor performance are learned, there is commonly a positive transfer. A good example is furnished by the experiment of Webb (1917). His results, shown in Table 16, indi-

TABLE 16

EFFECT OF PREVIOUS LEARNING ON PERFORMANCE OF NEW LEARNING TASK (FROM WEBB, 1917)

	Previous Learning	Performance in Learning Maze B	
		Trials	Errors
Experimental group	Learn maze A	10.8	32.4
Control group	Rest	33.6	285.2
Improvement (difference between experimental and control groups)		22.8	252.8

cate a sizeable improvement in the learning of a second maze as a result of the learning of the first.

When one motor task is learned and transfer is subsequently tested on other types of motor performance, both positive and negative effects have been found. Woodward (1943) investigated the effect of learning to assemble a safety switch on learning to assemble a simple loom and found some positive transfer. But Cook (1941) found marked negative transfer from mirror tracing in one position to mirror tracing in another position. Which motor tasks yield positive and which yield negative transfer is at the present time largely a matter for empirical determination.

Memory

The pioneer study of the effects of memory training is the oft-cited study of William James (1890). James first learned 158 lines of Hugo's *Satyr* and recorded his time. He then spent a month committing to memory Milton's *Paradise Lost*. When he had finished with this he returned to the *Satyr* and memorized another 158 lines. He found that this actually took longer than the first 158 lines. He concluded that there was no general improvement in memorizing ability. Later experimenters have repeated this type of study with more subjects and with the necessary controls. Sleight (1911) used a control group and three experimental groups equated on the basis of memory ability. One experimental group memorized poetry, another tables, and a third prose. No indication was found of any general improvement in memory.

On the other hand, experimenters have uniformly noted the improvement that comes from practice in learning successive lists of the same type. Ebert and Meumann (1904) attributed the improvement to better methods of memorizing, discovery of helpful aids, increased confidence, and reduction of anxiety about the learning. At least part of the discrepancy in the results of various experimenters is probably attributable to the stage of proficiency already attained in the task practiced in the experiment.

Woodrow (1927) reasoned that, if subjects were given systematic instruction in how to memorize, the improvement would be more marked. Accordingly he set up a study with two experimental groups and one control group. One group devoted itself to intensive memorizing of poetry and nonsense syllables. The second group spent the same amount of time but divided it between receiving instruction in good methods of memorizing and performing exercises using these methods. The group that spent all the time

in practice performed little better than the control group on subsequent memory tests, but the group given instruction in methods of efficient memorizing showed marked improvement: ". . . The experiment shows that in a case where one kind of training — undirected drill — produces amounts of transference which are sometimes positive and sometimes negative, but always small, another kind of training with the same drill material may result in a transference, the effects of which are uniformly large and positive" (p. 171).

Transfer of Principles

Many other experiments have supported the finding of Woodrow that transfer is facilitated when the initial learning can be formulated in terms of general principles applicable to new learning. Judd (1908) showed this in an experiment in which groups of boys practiced shooting targets under water. One group was first taught the principles of light refraction; the other was not. Both groups were then given practice in shooting at submerged targets. Both groups learned about equally well to adjust for refractive errors by trial and error. But when the depth of the target was changed the group previously taught about refraction quickly learned to correct their aim for the new conditions, whereas the other group required extensive further practice. Judd's results have since been confirmed by Hendrickson and Schroeder (1941). (Cf. also Cox, 1933.)

Without stress on principles, habits are often highly specific to the situation in which they are practiced. Bagley (1906) reported a study in which the arithmetic teacher constantly stressed neatness in the papers handed in by the students. A gradual improvement was noted in the neatness of these papers. But no transfer was found with respect to the neatness of papers turned in by these students in other subjects such as language and spelling. Ruediger (1908) repeated this experiment but had the teacher who emphasized neatness also stress the general importance of neatness in dress, business, and the home. Under these conditions improvement was obtained not only in the subject taught by the teacher but in other subjects as well. The stress on generalization has been supported recently by a study of Swenson (1942) on transfer of training in arithmetic, where she found that stressing interrelations between facts produced better results than drilling on the task itself.

Further evidence relating to this topic is furnished by the experiments of Katona (1940). Geometric puzzles and card and match tricks were used as interesting learning material. Transfer was tested with other puzzles embodying the same general principles. One group was instructed to memorize the initial solution and was given practice through repetition. The second group was taught the principles involved. A control group received no practice. The test results demonstrated the advantage of learning principles (cf. Table 17).

TABLE 17

Percentage of Perfect Solutions to New Puzzles Following Various Types of Initial Training (from Katona, 1940)

	Control Group	Memorization Group	Example Group
Task A	6	21	34
Task B	9	8	46 *
Task C	6	42 *	21

* Subjects had previous experience on these tasks.

Katona attributed the differences in the amount of transfer to the superiority of "meaningful" over "senseless" learning. He concluded that, although meaningful learning transferred to new situations, senseless did not. The extent to which Katona's results are specific to tasks like puzzles that are "derivable" (i.e. where if part of the series is known the rest of the sequence can be filled in without learning) remains a serious question.

Transfer in School Subjects

Traditionally, educators have relied upon what has been called the doctrine of "formal discipline," i.e. that training in such subject matter as classical studies and mathematics would improve understanding of other subjects. A good review of studies in this field is that of Kingsley (1946). By way of illustration the work of Thorndike (1924) may be mentioned. He studied the effect of a year's work in such high school studies as Latin, mathematics, and history. All students used in the study were first given a test of "selective and relational thinking." During the year some students took a program that included Latin, history, etc., while others took shopwork, bookkeeping, etc. At the end of the year another form of the general test was given. Only small effects attributable to the different subjects were obtained, and Thorndike concluded that no marked balance in favor of one rather than another subject was found. Many subsequent studies have confirmed his findings.

Summary

The foregoing brief review indicates the difficulty of generalizing adequately the conditions of transfer. When the conditions of cross-education obtain, positive transfer may be uniformly expected. But this form of transfer has extremely limited generality. When the material learned through practice results in discovery of a rule or theory, considerable transfer to new applications is possible. But the teaching of principles directly is more efficient than the discovery of it through trial and error. With motor learning, positive and negative transfer effects are both frequently obtained, and description of the task does not always enable us to predict which will occur. This difficulty may be due to the complex relations existing among various tasks whose transfer effects have been studied. Perhaps more precise analysis of what is being transferred to what would clarify the picture.

ANALYSIS OF TRANSFER IN TERMS OF STIMULUS AND RESPONSE FACTORS

A simple type of transfer situation exists if we have the same response in the original and new task but vary the relation between the stimuli. This pattern could be represented diagrammatically as follows:

	PRIOR LEARNING	NEW LEARNING
Experimental group	Learn $S_1 \rightarrow R_1$	Learn $S_2 \rightarrow R_1$
Control group	Rest	Learn $S_2 \rightarrow R_1$
	(Do not learn $S_1 \rightarrow R_1$)	

This situation is similar to the type of set-up that produces stimulus generalization in conditioning experiments. Response is obtained to stimuli not originally used in the conditioning, and the response is greater to stimuli similar to the stimulus originally used than to those more remote.*

The relevance of the principle of generalization to problems of verbal learning has been pointed out by a series of experiments on "semantic conditioning" (also labeled

* Here as in conditioning experiments (see above) there is an inherent difficulty in defining the dimension of similarity. On the stimulus side this has often been done in terms of judgments concerning similarity (e.g. Yum, 1931) or in terms of discriminability (e.g. Hovland, 1936, spaced his stimuli by equal numbers of just noticeable differences in pitch). Both methods have severe limitations. In the first, there is no certainty that a unitary dimension is involved: different judges may be using different factors in scaling. In the second, irregularities in the dimension are common. A well-known example is the octave effect in pitch. A large number of just noticeable differences in pitch may, for example, exist between 400 and 775 cycles, whereas 400 and 800 cycles may be very difficult to discriminate because they are exactly an octave apart. The problem of units is even more difficult on the response side where we know too little about response organization to devise appropriate units to measure response similarity. Consequently it is particularly difficult to predict transfer in motor learning.

"mediated generalization"). Russian investigators, whose work is summarized by Keller (1943), found generalization from a verbal symbol to the object denoted by the word and to phonetically and meaningfully related words. Razran (1939a) used his conditioned salivary technique to study these relations, finding antonym, synonym, and homophonic gradients. Other studies related to this problem are those of Riess (1946) and Foley and Cofer (1943).

Results analogous to those in conditioning are obtained with verbal learning. This was first shown by Yum (1931). He had his subjects learn to give a four-letter word response to hyphenated nonsense syllables. For example, the subjects were taught to respond with the word "WOLF" to the stimulus "REB-QIM." In the recall series the same syllables, or variants with one or more letters changed, were employed as stimuli. He found that many subjects gave the originally learned reseponse to stimuli that were similar but not identical to those initially used, but that the frequency of recall was less than to the original stimuli. This led him to experiment systematically with similarity of stimuli. He had raters classify words and figures used as stimuli into various degrees of similarity. After training with one set of stimuli, recall was tested to the stimuli used in training and to the stimuli rated as having varying degrees of similarity. His results are shown in Table 18 for both verbal and visual stimuli. Similar results have been obtained by Gibson (1939), who varied the similarity of tactual stimuli. The subjects were taught to respond to a vibratory stimulus with a verbal response. Other vibratory stimuli separated spatially from the one used in training evoked the verbal response, the frequency of response being progressively less, the farther apart the stimuli. See also Gulliksen (1932) and McKinney (1933).

Transfer based on the similarity of stimuli thus appears to be well established. In the field of verbal learning the generalization

TABLE 18

Transfer with Varying Degrees of Similarity between Stimuli (from Yum, 1931)

	Percentage Recalled
Verbal Stimuli	
Identical word	50.154
Close similarity	32.562
Moderate similarity	11.266
Figures	
Identical	84.616
First degree of similarity	64.530
Second degree of similarity	49.146
Third degree of similarity	45.299
Fourth degree of similarity	36.324

about the relations between similarity of stimuli and the amount of response is covered by the *law of assimilation,* which

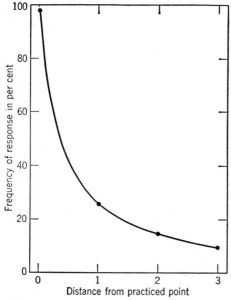

FIG. 37. Frequency of false ("generalized") verbal responses as a function of proximity of vibratory stimuli to initially practiced point. (From E. J. Gibson, 1939.)

states that "each new stimulating condition tends to elicit the response which has been connected with similar stimulating conditions in the past" (Carr, 1925).

The foregoing results are based on percentage of recall for different conditions. Bruce (1933) experimented with conditions even more closely approximating those used in conventional experiments on the transfer of training. He gave his subjects 12 training trials on paired nonsense syllables. Then, keeping the response words constant, he had his subjects learn lists in which the stimuli were either similar to or different from those used in training. His results can be expressed in terms of the per cent difference between the mean number of trials under these conditions compared with the number of trials required with no previous learning (Table 19). Greater positive transfer is

TABLE 19

Amount of Transfer as Function of Similarity of Stimuli (from Bruce, 1933)

	Percentage of Trials Saved
Similar stimulus words, identical response words	56
Different stimulus words, identical response words	37

produced by similar stimuli than by those that are different.

Let us turn now to results obtained when transfer is studied with identical stimuli but with varying response. This situation may be diagrammed as follows:

	Prior Learning	New Learning
Group 1	Learn $S_1 \rightarrow R_1$	Learn $S_1 \rightarrow R_2$
Group 2	Rest (Do not learn $S_1 \rightarrow R_1$)	Learn $S_1 \rightarrow R_2$

At first glance this may seem to represent the conditions obtaining for bilateral transfer, where we have seen that marked positive transfer occurs. But, whereas in bilateral transfer the execution of the cross-member responses is not incompatible with the originally learned responses, under most learning conditions the execution of the new responses (R_2 in the paradigm) is incompatible with the response initially learned

(R₁). Under the latter circumstances negative transfer is usually obtained.

Although anecdotal evidence was available earlier (Münsterberg, 1889), the first systematic study of this problem was by Müller and Schumann (1894). Their generalization is that "when any two items, as A and B, have been associated, it is more difficult to form an association between either and a third item, K." Subsequent studies have provided many examples where prior association makes the new association easier. When the learning of a new association is made more difficult because of a prior association, the effect may be called *associative interference;* when it is made easier, the effect may be called *associative facilitation.*

Adequate data are not available on the amount of transfer as a function of the similarity of the two responses. Bruce (1933) presented data on only two conditions relevant to this analysis, one in which the responses were similar and one in which they were different. The stimuli were identical for the training and the transfer series. With 2 and 6 repetitions of the training lists negative transfer was obtained. The extent of negative transfer was less when the responses were similar. After 12 training trials on the original series, positive transfer (20 per cent) was obtained when the responses were similar, and slight negative transfer (9 per cent) when the responses were different. I. P. Robinson (1948) obtained greater transfer with similarity in responses. On the basis of the present scanty data the generalization would be that negative transfer is obtained when stimuli in the original and transfer situation are identical; i.e. the more similar the response, the less the negative transfer.

What is the effect upon transfer of varying both stimuli and responses? Gibson's (1941) results bear upon this question. She had her subjects learn paired-associate lists with visual forms as stimuli. After 5 trials with the original lists, the subjects learned new lists made up of entirely different response syllables but with stimulus terms varying from identity to considerable dissimilarity. The results, presented in Fig. 38, show a clear tendency for the learning of new material to be increasingly difficult with greater similarity of stimuli, provided different responses are involved. I. P. Robinson (1948) stressed the fact that the effect

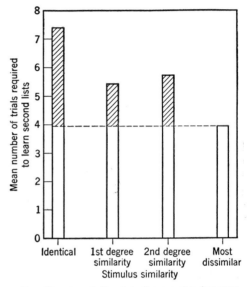

Fig. 38. Associative interference showing numbers of trials required to learn new list following initial list as a function of similarity between stimuli in initial and new lists. (Data from E. J. Gibson, 1941.)

of degree of stimulus similarity on amount of transfer is dependent on response conditions. "The amount of transfer is an increasing function of response similarity, rate of increase being a positive function of stimulus similarity" (p. 250).

In the light of these facts it is easy to see why it is so difficult to predict whether positive or negative effects will be obtained in transfer of training experiments without knowing the specific stimuli and responses involved. The generalization made by Wylie (1919) that "the transfer effect is positive when an old response can be transferred to a new stimulus, but negative when a new response is required to an old stimulus" still appears valid, but it requires supplementation to cover the effects of varying similarity between stimulus and response. Osgood (1949) showed how the empirical relations could be integrated by representing stimulus similarity, response similarity, and degree of transfer on a three-dimensional graph.

OTHER FACTORS AFFECTING TRANSFER OF TRAINING

The literature on the effects of various factors on the amount of transfer obtained is so extensive that adequate summary is impossible; only a mention of the most significant variables will be made.

Degree of Learning

In the simple type of transfer represented by stimulus generalization in conditioning there is typically an initial increase in extent of generalization with increase in amount of training. Beyond a certain point there is sometimes a decrease in generalization with further training. The experiments of Hovland (1937d) and Razran (1940) on this point have already been mentioned. Analogous results were obtained in transposition experiments by Jackson et al. (1938), and by Gibson (1942) for verbal learning.

In more typical situations, such as those represented in Bruce's (1933) experiment, corresponding results were obtained. Where the initial and transfer tasks had identical responses and similar stimuli (the situation producing positive transfer), increase in training on the initial task increased the amount of positive transfer (Table 20).

Where negative transfer is typical (identical stimuli, different responses) Bruce's results indicate a reduction in the extent of negative transfer with increasing practice. Siipola and Israel (1933) found that with increasing amounts of initial training the negative transfer may even be followed by positive transfer.

A related problem is how the amount of transfer varies with varying amounts of

TABLE 20

AMOUNT OF TRANSFER AS A FUNCTION OF AMOUNT OF TRAINING ON INITIAL TASK (FROM BRUCE, 1933)

Number of Repetitions of Initial List	Percentage of Savings on Transfer List Compared with 0 Repetition
0	0
2	16
6	36
12	56

practice on the new activity, given a constant amount of training on the initial task. Müller and Schumann (1894) found negative transfer to be evident on only the first few trials of the new learning. Their results have been confirmed in the case of the maze learning of children by Yoshioka and Jones (1945), who found the transfer effect primarily on the first trial. Similarly Melton and Von Lackum (1941) found decreasing interference through the first five trials of the new learning.

It would be expected on theoretical grounds that if negative transfer is produced through competition the amount of practice on the original and the transfer tasks would be of less importance than the relative strengths of the two habits in competition. Consequently the amount of practice on the two tasks should be studied in combination. In line with this reasoning the experiments of Siipola and Israel (1933) and Melton and Irwin (1940) indicate that negative transfer is greatest when the degrees of learning of the initial and transfer activities are close to equality. This is the situation that produces maximum conflict in motor tasks (Sears and Hovland, 1941). There is, of course, an upper limit to this relation in transfer, since two extremely well-established habits of equal strength may suffer little interference.

Time Interval between Learning and Test

It would be expected that the time interval between the initial learning and the testing for transfer would be critical, but the evidence on this point is not clear-cut. Time interval had no effect in the studies of Bunch (1936) and Bunch and McCraven (1938). Ray (1945), on the other hand, found that interference increased with moderate time intervals but then decreased with longer intervals. His time intervals were 14, 27, and 91 days. He tied his results to the theory that learning and forgetting are merely two aspects of the same phenomenon. It must again be emphasized, however, that the relative strength of the two habits, rather than the degree of learning or the time interval, may be the primary variable.

Successive Transfer

Some evidence is accumulating concerning successive transfer. So-called "practice curves" are relevant to this point. It is usually found that the rate of improvement through practice is high at first and then declines. In situations where negative transfer occurs through habit interference, successive shifts from habit to habit appear to reduce the extent of interference (A. J. Culler, 1912; Stroop, 1935). The reversals become easier, the greater the degree of original learning, according to the result of McClelland (1943b) for his "serial verbal discrimination" task.

An interesting series of studies on successive transfer conducted by Dr. Margaret Kuenne was reported by Harlow (1949) in connection with his own results on animals. Her results indicated an orderly progression in the performance of children on successive discrimination problems (Fig. 39). When a series of tasks is learned successively, the amount of transfer is affected by the number of prior tasks, although the relation is very complex, for reasons analyzed by Underwood (1944). He found that, the greater the number of prior tasks, the greater the extent of negative transfer. The amount of transfer in such successive tasks is also affected by the time interval between successive units. Bunch (1944) had one group

learn five problems consecutively; another group waited 24 hours between problems. His results indicated that the cumulative effects of transfer are more pronounced in the early stages under massed practice but that the cumulative transfer at the end of the series was approximately equal for the two conditions.

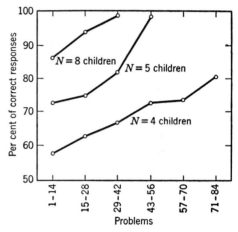

FIG. 39. Percentage of responses correct on trials 2 to 6 in successive groups of discrimination learning problems. (From Harlow, 1949.)

EFFECT OF INTERVENING LEARNING ON RETENTION (REPRODUCTIVE FACILITATION AND INTERFERENCE)

Learning activities not only influence the acquisition of new habits; they also affect the *retention* of habits learned earlier. The research design used to investigate these effects is of the following type:

Experimental group	Control group
Learn activity *A*	Learn activity *A*
Learn activity *B*	Rest (Do not learn activity *B*)
Recall activity *A*	Recall activity *A*

The experimental and control groups differ only in whether a particular learning activity *B* was interposed between the learning and recall of *A*. When the intervening learning interferes with the retention of the first learned task, the effect is called *reproductive interference* (in contrast with *associative* interference discussed earlier). When the intervening learning increases the retention of the original material, we may speak of *reproductive facilitation.*

"Proactive" and "Retroactive" Effects

In the usual experiment on reproductive interference the interpolated material is inserted between the initial learning and the test of retention of the original material, as in the diagram above. Because the interference shows up on the retention of material learned earlier, the interference has been described as "retroactive." Strictly speaking, however, this is a poor term, since the effects do not operate backwards on the prior learning, but only in a forward direction on subsequent recall. Nevertheless the term "retroactive inhibition" is very frequently applied in this connection.

Interference in retention can also be produced by learning other material prior to the primary learning. In this case the interference is said to be "proactive" and the effects are often attributed to "proactive inhibition." The type of experimental design used to study this phenomena is diagrammed below:

Experimental group	Control group
Learn activity *B*	Rest (Do not learn activity *B*)
Learn activity *A*	Learn activity *A*
Recall activity *A*	Recall activity *A*

If the learning of *B* decreases the recall of *A*, the effect is described as "proactive interference"; if the learning of *B* increases the recall of *A*, the effect is called "proactive facilitation."

The existence of proactive effects on retention was first studied by Whitely (1927). A good review is to be found in Underwood (1945, 1948). Although most studies have measured the effects in terms of recall and relearning, proactive interference is also obtained when recognition methods are used (Peixotto, 1947).

Early Studies

The pioneer work on reproductive interference is that of Müller and Pilzecker (1900), who worked with verbal material. These investigators showed that learning new material (nonsense syllables) during the rest interval made the amount of original material recalled less than the amount retained when simple rest was interpolated. Müller and Pilzecker explained the phenomenon on the basis of a post-learning perseveration. They believed that the associative process perseverates for a period following learning and that associations are strengthened and consolidated during this period. Rest immediately after learning favors perseveration and allows a full consolidation of the traces, whereas intervening activity interferes with the setting-in process and leaves the traces less strong. Their explanation thus covers not only intervening learning but any type of intervening activity.

Starting with DeCamp (1915) attention has been focused primarily on the problem of how the retention of prior learning is affected by interpolated new learning. DeCamp found that little reproductive interference in nonsense syllable learning was produced by interpolated mental work. His failure to obtain much interference with divergent materials made him believe that similarity in material was a necessary condition and that "the effect of retroactive inhibition would vary directly as the relative identity of the neurological groups involved" (p. 62). Webb (1917), on the basis of his maze experiments, reformulated the transfer theory of DeCamp to eliminate neural connotations. His statement is as follows:

> *Transfer hypothesis.* "The retroactive effect is regarded as a case of transfer. In the maze sequence A–B–A the term retroaction refers to the effect of the acquisition of the B habit upon the subsequent functioning, or relearning of the A habit. The transfer hypothesis assumes that this effect is medi-

ated by the simple transference of certain elements of the B habit to the succeeding maze A situation. Theoretically this transference may operate either in an advantageous or detrimental manner; in other words retroaction may be positive or negative."

Disruption hypothesis. "In the maze sequence of A–B–A, we know that transfer obtained in proceeding from A to B. Certain elements of the complex A habit have been transferred to and utilized in the maze B situation. The hypothesis assumes that this incorporation of certain components of the A habit into the subsequently acquired B habit must necessarily involve its partial disruption and disorganization." (P. 84.)

Webb specified how the transfer may cause disruption and disorganization of the habit under certain conditions but may result in facilitative effects under others.

Reproductive interference has been one of the most popular topics of study in learning (cf. reviews by Britt, 1935, and Swenson, 1941). There has been an increasing tendency to concentrate on the analysis of how new learning affects retention rather than on how retention is affected by non-learning activities such as physical and recreational activities, which are typically less interfering than learning activities (McGeoch, 1931; Irion, 1946). As a consequence it seems desirable to employ the terms "reproductive interference" and "reproductive facilitation" to cover the phenomena rather than the frequently used term "retroactive inhibition" (coined by Müller and Pilzecker), which usually covers intervening learning as only a special case of intervening activity. The way has been paved for this transition in terminology by the contributions of McGeoch (cf. especially McGeoch, McKinney, and Peters, 1937). If it is desired to specify whether the reproduction is interfered with by prior learning or by materials interposed between learning and retention, the terms "proactive" and "retroactive" may be applied.

Similarity between Original and Interpolated Learning

One of the most significant factors affecting the amount of interference or facilitation has been found to be the similarity between the interpolated learning and the original material. Robinson (1927) defined the problem clearly by analyzing certain a priori considerations. He reasoned that with identity of the original and interpolated materials there would have to be positive transfer. On the other hand, with no resemblance the ef-

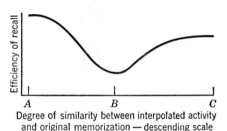

Fig. 40. Hypothetical relation between similarity of original and interpolated material and amount of reproductive interference. (From E. S. Robinson, 1927.)

fect should approach zero. In between there should be varying amounts of inhibition. "As similarity between interpolation and original memorization is reduced from near identity, retention falls away to a minimum and then rises again, but with decreasing similarity it never reaches the level obtaining with maximum similarity" (pp. 298–299). This formulation would give the accompanying hypothetical curve (Fig. 40).

This type of analysis raises the question: what aspect of the interpolated activity is to be rated in terms of similarity to the original activity, and how can it be measured? Pending an answer, we are unable to know whether obtained results are relevant to the *A–B* or *B–C* portion of the curve.

Robinson used as his definition of similarity the proportion of interpolated units that were identical to the original. He used lists of 8 consonants for learning material in a memory-span setup. He regarded the learning of the first 4 in the list as the original task and the learning of the last 4 as the interpolated task. These lists can be schematized as follows:

ELEMENTS IN COMMON	ORIGINAL	INTERPOLATED
None	a–b–c–d	e–f–g–h
One	a–b–c–d	a–f–g–h
Two	a–b–c–d	a–b–g–h
Three	a–b–c–d	a–b–c–h
Four	a–b–c–d	a–b–c–d

Sixteen different arrangements of elements were used in all. His experimental results are shown in Fig. 41. There is a continuous

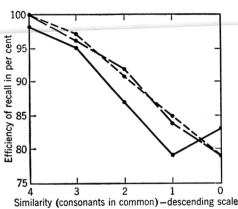

FIG. 41. Reproductive interference as a function of varying amounts of similarity between original and interpolated material. Each curve is for a different cycle of the experiment. (From E. S. Robinson, 1927.)

drop in retention as predicted. There is no suggestion, however, of a rise with maximum difference between original and interpolated learning.

Harden (1929) contended that Robinson's procedure was appropriate only for testing the initial part of the curve. She used consonants in the first positions of the list and varying proportions of letters and numerals in the second half. Her most "similar" list consisted entirely of consonants, and her most "dissimilar" list contained consonants in the first half (original material) and all digits in the second half (interpolated ma-

terial). She found a sharp end rise in the second portion of the curve.

In the writer's opinion Harden confused the issue by introducing two dimensions of similarity. If similarity is to be defined as degree of identity of elements (as Robinson defined it), the extremes would be represented on the one hand by all elements in common and on the other by no common elements. Numerous other possible definitions of similarity exist, of which her factor of proportion of the list coming from the same class of material (consonants or digits) is but one example. Accordingly the Robinson and the Harden experiments cannot well be plotted on a unitary dimension of similarity.

Boring (1941) tried to formulate the identity (or communality) dimension more rigorously and to test some of its quantitative implications. He analyzed the original and interpolated learning into n terms. He let n_1 represent the number of terms used in A repeated in B. (This would represent various numbers of consonants in common in Robinson's study.)

n_1 = number of terms from A repeated in B.

n_2 = number of new terms in B.

n = number of terms in A and in B = $n_1 + n_2$.

He then distinguished between the kinds of relations existing between various pairs of terms. These may be of three kinds: repeated relations where both terms that make the relation are repeated from A in B, unrepeated relations where both terms are changed from A in B, and altered relations where one term is changed and the other is not. He then proposed the following designations:

r_1 = number of repeated relations between n_1 terms.

r_2 = number of entirely new relations between n_2 terms in B.

r_3 = number of altered relations, where one term is repeated and the other changed.

r = number of paired relations between n terms = $r_1 + r_2 + r_3$.

If it is assumed that identical repetitions (r_1 relations) are facilitating, and those in which one term is changed and the other is not (r_3 relations) are interfering, the amount of facilitation (F) becomes

$$F = r_1 - r_3 = \frac{n_1(3n_1 - 2n - 1)}{2}$$

If we apply this formulation to Robinson's experimental design we would substitute

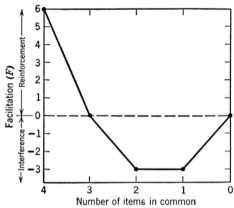

FIG. 42. Rationally derived relation between similarity and extent of reproductive facilitation or interference. (Based on formula of Boring, 1941.)

values of n_1 from 4 down to 0 (and let $n = 8$). The curve that would result is shown in Fig. 42.

The overall form of the curve is similar to that hypothesized by Robinson and has a more rigorously defined rationale. Boring doubted, however, that "the right end of the curve, $n_1 = 0$, could ever be found, since evidence from transfer and retroaction is that no two comparable organizations could be completely disparate" (p. 282). Does he at this point depart from his original operational definition of similarity?

A systematic repetition of the experiments of Robinson and of Harden has been reported by Kennelly (1941). He confirmed the results obtained by Robinson but got data that were markedly divergent from those of Harden. He then set up an experiment that conformed more closely to the procedures of the typical "retroactive inhibition" study by having the subjects learn and

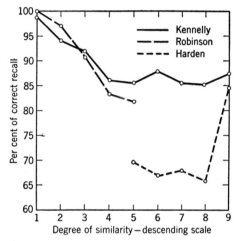

FIG. 43. Percentage of recall with varying degrees of similarity between items in original and interpolated materials. (From Kennelly, 1941.)

recall the original and interpolated materials as separate units. The subjects were given three repetitions of a list of 8 consonants or 8 numbers. After a 10-second pause the subjects were given three repetitions of interpolated material also consisting of 8 consonants and numbers with varying similarity to the original lists. His results are shown in Fig. 43. They do not confirm the results of Harden, but they look interestingly similar to the equation of Boring.

Another definition of similarity of material would be in terms of the similarity of the individual stimuli and responses. This definition leads to an analysis along lines exactly similar to those used above in analyzing transfer of training.

Using this approach, one might first analyze the effect of varying the stimulus but keeping the response constant. This can be diagrammed as follows:

	Original Learning	Interpolated Learning	Recall of Original Learning
Experimental group A	Learn $S_1 \rightarrow R_1$	Learn $S_{1a} \rightarrow R_1$	Recall $S_1 \rightarrow R_1$
Control group	Learn $S_1 \rightarrow R_1$	Rest (Do not learn $S_{1a} \rightarrow R$)	Recall $S_1 \rightarrow R_1$

S_{1a} designates a stimulus similar but not identical to that learned originally.

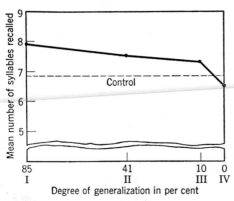

FIG. 44. Reproductive facilitation as related to degree of similarity between stimuli when responses are identical. (Index of similarity based on percentage of generalization found in prior experimentation.) (Data from Hamilton, 1943.)

Results under these conditions can also be compared with continuous practice on the same material (identity):

Experimental group B	Learn $S_1 \rightarrow R_1$	Learn $S_1 \rightarrow R_1$	Recall $S_1 \rightarrow R_1$

or with distinctly different material (where a different stimulus is designated S_2):

Experimental group C	Learn $S_1 \rightarrow R_1$	Learn $S_2 \rightarrow R_1$	Recall $S_1 \rightarrow R_1$

Hamilton (1943) showed that interpolated material having stimuli similar to the one used in the original learning have a *facilitating* effect which decreases with decreasing similarity of stimuli (Fig. 44) when identical responses are involved. This is analogous to the finding of stimulus generalization or "assimilation" in the case of transfer of training. Osgood (1946) obtained

reproductive interference rather than facilitation under these circumstances, but he did find that, the greater the similarity of stimuli, the less the interference.

If the response is varied but the stimuli are identical (analogous to the situation that produces associative interference in transfer of training), we have the following paradigm:

Learn $S_1 \rightarrow R_1$ Learn $S_1 \rightarrow R_{1a}$ Recall $S_1 \rightarrow R_1$

R_{1a} indicates a response similar to R_1.

At the extreme where responses are actually identical, the interpolated material would constitute another practice trial, and hence high facilitation is expected. When

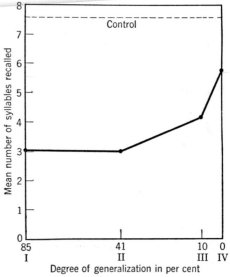

FIG. 45. Reproductive interference as related to similarity of stimuli in original and interpolated learning when responses are different. (Index of similarity based on percentage of generalization found in prior experimentation.) (From E. J. Gibson, 1941.)

R_{1a} is extremely different from R_1, interference is customarily obtained. No systematic evidence is available on how the extent of interference is affected by the degree of similarity of responses.

When variation in both stimuli and responses is studied, it is found that the more similar the stimulus in the interpolated learning is to that used in the original learning, the greater the interference. This has been shown by Gibson (1941) for forms paired with nonsense syllables. The stimuli were chosen to represent various points on the gradient of generalization. Her results are shown in Fig. 45.

From the foregoing considerations it is clear that it is necessary to specify both the stimulus and the response dimensions rather than the single one of varying degrees of identity specified by Robinson (1927). A good analysis of this problem was made by Gibson (1940).

In addition to the two methods of defining similarity presented above there are many others. They include similarity of meaning (e.g. McGeoch and McDonald, 1931; Treverton, 1941), similarity in degree of association value (Sisson, 1938), similarity of task and operation (Gibson and Gibson, 1934), similarity of spelling (Cheng, 1929) and similarity of association (McClelland and Heath, 1943).

OTHER FACTORS AFFECTING REPRODUCTIVE INTERFERENCE

Degree of Learning

The higher the degree of original learning, the less is the amount of reproductive interference. This is illustrated in the results of McGeoch (1929) in which the interpolated learning was always given 11 trials but the number of trials of the original learning varied from 6 to 26 trials. See also Shaw (1942).

When, on the other hand, original learning is held constant, there is a curvilinear relation between degree of interpolated learning and interference. Initially, increases in degree of interpolated learning are accompanied by increases in the amount of interference, but later increases in interpolated learning are accompanied by a decline in the amount of interference (Melton and Irwin,

1940; Fig. 46). Thune and Underwood (1943) reported that reproductive interference increased up to 16 repetitions of the interpolated list, beyond which an additional 10 repetitions yielded no further increase in interference.

Other data reported by Melton and Irwin (1940) support the hypothesis that maximal retroaction occurs when original and interpolated activities have been learned to approximately equal degrees. This accords with the

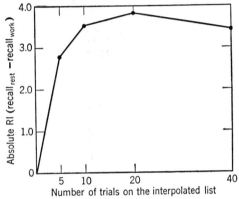

Fig. 46. Reproductive interference with varying numbers of practice trials on an interpolated list. (Data from Melton and Irwin, 1940.)

results of Siipola and Israel (1933) and Sears and Hovland (1941), cited in connection with transfer of training: in a conflict situation the probability of blocking becomes greater as the strength of the competing responses approaches equality. As in transfer of training there may be an upper limit at which there is no interference when both habits are very strong.

Temporal Relations

Results to date do not give a clear picture of the relation between the amount of interference and the time when the interpolation occurs. Early studies have given conflicting results, and later experiments do not clarify the picture. Houlahan (1941) found the amount of reproductive interference to vary directly with the proximity of interpolated learning to recall. Bunch (1946) found that, with a punchboard maze, interpolated learning of a similar maze immediately after learning produced interference, but, when the interpolated maze was learned 120 days after learning, the relearning that followed immediately showed facilitation rather than interference. Postman and Alper (1946) obtained the greatest relative loss 1 and 8 days after learning, and 1 day before retest. Swenson (1941), after reviewing the results available at the time of her survey, concluded that interpolation is more effective in producing interference when it is adjacent either to original learning or to recall of original learning than at other points.

Quantity of Material

Both the amount of original material and the amount of interpolated material have been varied experimentally. The early studies of Robinson and Heron (1922) and Robinson and Darrow (1924) found that longer lists produced less interference than shorter lists. Later work by Sand (1939) casts doubt on the generality of their findings. Sand used 7 pairs of associates as the interpolated material and 6, 8, 10, 12, and 15 pairs as the original material. All but the shortest list gave equivalent interference.

At least with verbal materials, it appears that, the greater the amount of interpolated material, the greater the interference. Twining (1940) taught subjects a list of 8 nonsense syllables. Then 1, 2, 3, 4, or 5 lists were interpolated. The more lists used, the more adversely affected were both recall and relearning. Twining's data on recall are presented in Fig. 47. Similar results were reported by Underwood (1945) when the criterion was recall, but reliable differences were not shown in the number of trials required for relearning to mastery.

"Unlearning" Factors in Reproductive Interference

The analysis presented above of the nature of reproductive interference stresses the conflict of responses attributable to the fact

that the same or similar stimuli have been attached to more than one response. Another important factor affecting retention is the fact that the stimulus-response connec-

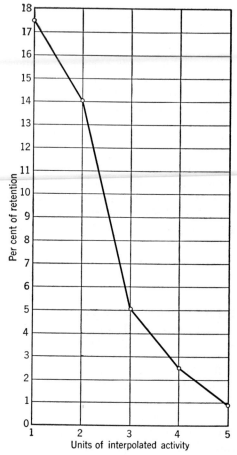

FIG. 47. Reproductive interference with varying numbers of different interpolated lists. (Data from Twining, 1940.)

tion involved in retention may be specifically unlearned. Thus let us suppose that $A \rightarrow B$ is learned; then $A \rightarrow C$ is interposed and the retention of $A \rightarrow B$ is tested. During the $A \rightarrow C$ learning the conditions for unlearning of $A \rightarrow B$ are established (cf. Melton and Irwin, 1940). A good test of the relative importance of this factor as compared with the factor of direct conflict is to compare the retroactive and proactive interference situations:

Retroactive interference paradigm	Proactive interference paradigm
Rest	Learn $A{\to}C$
Learn $A{\to}B$	Learn $A{\to}B$
Learn $A{\to}C$	Rest
Recall $A{\to}B$	Recall $A{\to}B$

These two designs differ primarily in whether the subject gets specific practice in dissociating the learning of A and B through practicing of $A{\to}C$ after learning $A{\to}B$.

The amount of interference with retention produced by these two designs was compared by Melton and Von Lackum (1941). Their subjects learned lists of ten 3-consonant syllables for 5 trials, some with the proactive design and some with the retroactive design. Greater interference was obtained in the recall of the first learned lists. In an experiment by McGeoch and Underwood (1943), consistent but not reliably greater amounts of retroactive than proactive effects were obtained.

In the foregoing studies retention was measured shortly after the learning (ca. 20 minutes). When a 48-hour interval was used by Underwood (1948), the first and second lists were equally well retained. These results, if confirmed, will require modification of the "unlearning" formulation. Underwood proposed that unlearning is analogous to the experimental extinction of a conditioned response. These unlearned verbal associations that have been "unlearned" would then be expected to recover in strength with the passage of time, like extinguished conditioned responses.

McGeoch (1942) was inclined to believe that the unlearning factor can ultimately be interpreted in terms of competition of response, and that the dual character of the theory is simply an acknowledgment of the double locus of the competition. Bugelski (1948) also believed this to be the case. He found that when a series of lists is learned in rapid succession the odd-numbered lists are learned better than the even-numbered lists. The "unlearning" theory would explain this as due to the fact that time spent in unlearning a former list would reduce the time available for learning the new list. But Bugelski pointed out that the results could be explained equally well by McGeoch's interference explanation since a well-learned list could interfere more strongly than one poorly learned. Only further experimentation can determine whether the "competition" factor and the "unlearning" factor are distinctive or are merely different aspects of the same process.

CAUSES OF FORGETTING

Throughout the preceding discussion there have been reported a number of factors whose effect is to reduce retention. A brief attempt will be made here to list more systematically the various factors producing loss in retention with the passage of time.

Disuse

In early discussions of forgetting the most common explanation was that forgetting was a decrease in recall due to lack of use of the material. Using the analogy that a muscle is strengthened through exercise and weakened through disuse, theorists stated that repeated practice strengthens connections and lack of use weakens connections. It is possible that some forgetting does occur owing to physiological changes associated with disuse. Such an explanation has been reiterated by Thorndike and his collaborators (Bregman, Thorndike and Woodyard, 1943) to explain the loss, with time, in the ability of blindfolded subjects to draw lines of appropriate length. The extent to which forgetting can be explained on a physiological basis, however, is much smaller than was earlier thought, and such *ad hoc* explanations should not be invoked when other factors can be isolated.

Reproductive Interference

The earlier discussion of the extent to which recall is affected by intervening learning points up the importance of this factor in accounting for much of forgetting. In our daily life we are commonly learning new responses to stimuli that formerly evoked other responses, the situation most productive of interference.

Research on this problem compares the amount of forgetting with varying intervening activities. The most desirable control comparison would be with absolutely no intervening activity, but this is of course impossible. A close approximation is achieved if the intervening activity is sleep. Forgetting is less rapid when sleep intervenes between learning and recall than when the intervening interval is filled with waking activity. The best-known experiment on this point is that of Jenkins and Dallenbach (1924) on the retention of nonsense syllables during sleep and waking. From their results, presented in Fig. 48, they conclude: "The results of our study as a whole indicate that forgetting is not so much a matter of decay of old impressions and associa-

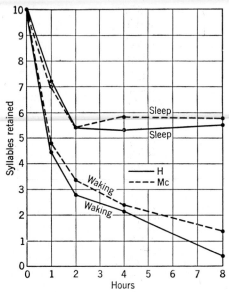

FIG. 48. Retention curves for nonsense syllables following various time intervals of sleep and waking (two subjects). (From Jenkins and Dallenbach, 1924.)

tions as it is a matter of interference, inhibition, or obliteration of the old by the new" (p. 612). Similar results, although with smaller differences, were obtained by Van Ormer (1932). These experiments closely simulate the conditions of real life and indicate that intervening activity is a potent factor in producing forgetting.

Unlearning

Distinguishable in theory but closely linked in actual situations is the factor of unlearning. In the time intervening between learning and recall we are often confronted with some of the relevant stimuli, but we do not make the response initially learned. Thus we practice not making the learned response. Melton and Irwin (1940) have given a clear exposition of the role of this factor and its relation to reproductive interference.

Changed Cues

A fourth important factor in forgetting is the alteration of the stimulating conditions from the time of learning to that of the measurement of retention. Forgetting occurs when some of the stimuli present during the original learning are no longer present during recall, or when new stimuli are present that evoke competing responses sufficiently strong to block those originally learned. Relevant stimuli are both external (like the furniture in the room in which we learn, the apparatus, the experimenter, etc.) and internal (resulting from posture, responses made during learning, etc.). Reduced recall has been shown when learning has been in one location and testing in another (Abernethy, 1940). The gradient of generalization discussed above operates in determining the amount of such transfer. Similarly, when words are learned with one color background, recall is reduced when the background is changed (Dulsky, 1935). Case studies have also shown that a language learned in one context is poorly retained in a different context but is quickly relearned when the original context is restored (Carr, 1925).

Changed Set

Forgetting is sometimes due to the fact that recall occurs with a different set from that operating during the original learning. If one learns material with the expectation that he will have to recall it at a particular later date, attempts to recall it either earlier or later will be less successful. When the method of testing retention is altered, retention is also adversely affected (Postman and Jenkins, 1948). To what extent the explanation of such results coincides with the explanation in terms of changed cues at the time of recall is a problem for further research. A good review of the role of set will be found in J. J. Gibson (1941).

A related aspect of set concerns the relative retention of completed and incompleted tasks. A task that has been finished is less well recalled than one still incomplete, according to Zeigarnik (1927), although there have been a number of failures to confirm the appearance of the phenomenon. Detailed discussion of the results is beyond the scope of the present chapter, but an excellent review is available in Prentice (1944).

The foregoing discussion suggests that a large number of factors influence forgetting. Some may wonder whether they do not "overexplain" the phenomenon of forgetting and raise the question of why we remember things at all. Others may ask whether we ever forget things completely, or whether there exists only temporary interference with recall that could be overcome under appropriate conditions of set, context, etc. These questions cannot be answered at present, not only because we do not know all the factors involved, but more particularly because we have inadequate data concerning the relative contribution of various factors. Here, as throughout the entire field of learning and retention, there is an urgent need and an important opportunity for the kind of theoretical systematization that not only will specify the relevant parameters but will provide quantitative weighting as well.

MATHEMATICAL FORMULATIONS OF LEARNING

Empirical Equations

It was a natural development that, when results from a number of different studies became available, attempts should be made to formulate relations between learning variables in quantitative form. The first attempts were empirical equations that were not based on theory but were merely found to fit the available data. The first proposed was

$$y = a + be^{-cx}$$

where y is a measure of attainment, x is a measure of practice, and a is the limit of attainment as practice increases without limit. This equation was developed by Schükarew (1907) on the analogy of a monomolecular chemical reaction.

A second form is based on the assumption that the rate of learning with respect to the amount of practice is proportional to the product of the amount already learned and the amount still to be learned (the difference between present attainment and the physiological limit; or between total amount to be learned and amount already learned).

$$y = \frac{be^{Ax}}{c + e^{Ax}}$$

where y is a measure of attainment, x is a measure of practice, a is a constant for learner and task, b is the limit of attainment, $A = ab$, and c is a constant of integration. This equation was developed by Robertson (1908) on the analogy of a monomolecular autocatalytic reaction. It was later used by Valentine (1931).

Foucault (1914) used the hyperbola to fit his learning data and later called it "the law of exercise." Thurstone (1917) also suggested using the hyperbola

$$y = \frac{a(x + c)}{(x + c) + b}$$

in which y represents attainment in terms of number of successful acts per unit of time, x is the total number of practice acts, c is previous practice, a is the physiological limit, and b is a number representing the rate of learning. Other empirical equations that have been proposed are discussed in the excellent review by Gulliksen (1934).

Rational Equations

Of greater significance has been the more recent formulation of "rational" equations based on hypotheses concerning the relations among the variables. These are particularly important because they not only summarize data but also permit us to test the agreement between data and theory. One of the earliest important formulations of a rational equation was made by Thurstone (1930b). He assumed that at any one moment "all the acts that the learner is at all likely to initiate in his effort toward a goal may then be arbitrarily divided into two categories, those that lead to success and those that lead either to overt or implicit error . . ." (p. 470).

On the basis of his theory Thurstone developed a rational equation (1933):

$$u = \frac{(\sqrt{m}/ak)R}{R + (\sqrt{m}/k)}$$

where u = cumulative errors, R = number of trials, m and k are constants dependent on the task and learner, respectively, and a is a factor to take care of possible differences in units.

Thurstone found that this equation provided a very good fit to the maze data of Lashley. Parenthetically it should be noted that this equation, derived rationally, is essentially the same as the one suggested earlier by Thurstone on empirical grounds.

An important extension of Thurstone's work has been made by Gulliksen (1934), based on explicit formulation of Thorndike's law of effect. He derives the following equation:

$$u = \frac{g}{c}\left[1 - \left(\frac{\dfrac{h}{k}}{w + \dfrac{h}{K}}\right)^{c/k}\right]$$

where u = cumulative errors, w = cumulative correct responses, g = initial strength of incorrect response, h = initial strength of correct response, c = constant amount deducted from the strength of the incorrect response each time it is repeated and punished, and k = the constant amount added to the strength of the correct response each time it is repeated and rewarded. When k approaches zero, the function becomes exponential similar to the empirical equation presented above. Subsequently Gulliksen and Wolfle (1938) extended this type of treatment to problems of discrimination.

One of the most ambitious attempts at a rational treatment of learning data was made by Hull in his book, *Principles of Behavior* (1943). In contrast to the preceding studies, many more variables are taken into account. The major variables considered are drive, reinforcement, and temporal factors. The relation between strength and habit and number of reinforcements is represented as a positive growth function:

$$sHr = M - Me^{-kN}$$

where sHr = habit strength, M = physiological maximum of habit strength, N = number of reinforcements, and k and e are constants. More detailed formulas take temporal factors and size of incentive more specifically into account (e.g. formula 16, p. 178).

Most of these formulations are of a general character and apply to all types of learning. The deductions from them have often been tested in animal experiments. The most extensive development of a mathematical systemization specifically for human learning is that of Hull et al. (1940) for verbal rote learning. Their deductions dealt with serial position effects, reminiscence, length of lists, massed and distributed prac-

Edwards, A. L. Political frames of reference as a factor influencing recognition. *J. abnorm. soc. Psychol.*, 1941, **36**, 34–50.

Edwards, A. L. The retention of affective experiences: A criticism and restatement of the problem. *Psychol. Rev.*, 1942, **49**, 43–53.

Ehrlich, G. A method of constructing learning curves for a motor skill involving total body speed and accuracy. *J. appl. Psychol.*, 1943a, **27**, 494–503.

Ehrlich, G. The relation between the learning of a motor skill and measures of strength, ability, educability, and capacity. *Res. Quart. Amer. phys. Educ. Ass.*, 1943b, **14**, 46–59.

English, H. B. Reminiscence—reply to Dr. Buxton's critique. *Psychol. Rev.*, 1942, **49**, 505–512.

English, H. B., E. L. Welborn, and C. D. Killian. Studies in substance memorization. *J. gen. Psychol.*, 1934, **11**, 233–260.

Ericksen, S. C. Variability of attack in massed and distributed practice. *J. exp. Psychol.*, 1942, **31**, 339–345.

Flügel, J. C. A quantitative study of feeling and emotion in everyday life. *Brit. J. Psychol.*, 1925, **15**, 318–355.

Foley, J. P., Jr., and C. N. Cofer. Mediated generalization and the interpretation of verbal behavior: II. Experimental study of certain homophone and synonym gradients. *J. exp. Psychol.*, 1943, **32**, 168–175.

Foucault, M. L'étude sur l'exercice dans le travail mental, spécialement dans le travail d'addition. *Année psychol.*, 1914, **20**, 97–125.

Foucault, M. Les inhibitions internes de fixation. *Année psychol.*, 1928, **29**, 92–112.

Franklin, J. C., and J. Brozek. The relation between distribution of practice and learning efficiency in psychomotor performance. *J. exp. Psychol.*, 1947, **37**, 16–24.

Freeman, F. N., and E. M. Abernethy. Comparative retention of typewriting and of substitution with analogous material. *J. educ. Psychol.*, 1930, **21**, 639–647.

Freeman, F. N., and E. M. Abernethy. New evidence of the superior retention of typewriting to that of substitution. *J. educ. Psychol.*, 1932, **23**, 331–334.

Fulton, R. E. Speed and accuracy in learning a ballistic movement. *Res. Quart. Amer. phys. Educ. Ass.*, 1942, **13**, 30–36.

Fulton, R. E. Speed and accuracy in learning movements. *Arch. Psychol., N. Y.*, 1945, **41**, No. 300.

Gardner, L. P. The learning of low grade aments. *Amer. J. ment. Def.*, 1945, **50**, 59–80.

Garrett, H. E. Variability in learning under massed and spaced practice. *J. exp. Psychol.*, 1940, **26**, 547–567.

Gates, A. I. Recitation as a factor in memorizing. *Arch. Psychol., N. Y.*, 1917, **7**, No. 40.

Gentry, J. R. Immediate effects of interpolated rest periods on learning performance. *Teach. Coll. Contr. Educ.*, 1940, No. 799.

Ghiselli, E. Changes in neuro-muscular tension accompanying the performance of a learning problem involving constant choice time. *J. exp. Psychol.*, 1936, **19**, 91–98.

Gibson, E. J. Sensory generalization with voluntary reactions. *J. exp. Psychol.*, 1939, **24**, 237–253.

Gibson, E. J. A systematic application of the concepts of generalization and differentiation to verbal learning. *Psychol. Rev.*, 1940, **47**, 196–229.

Gibson, E. J. Retroactive inhibition as a function of degree of generalization between tasks. *J. exp. Psychol.*, 1941, **28**, 93–115.

Gibson, E. J. Intra-list generalization as a factor in verbal learning. *J. exp. Psychol.*, 1942, **30**, 185–200.

Gibson, E. J., and J. J. Gibson. Retention and the interpolated task. *Amer. J. Psychol.*, 1934, **46**, 603–610.

Gibson, J. J. A critical review of the concept of set in contemporary experimental psychology. *Psychol. Bull.*, 1941, **38**, 781–817.

Gilbert, G. M. The new status of experimental studies on the relationship of feeling to memory. *Psychol. Bull.*, 1938, **35**, 26–35.

Gillette, A. L. Learning and retention: A comparison of three experimental procedures. *Arch. Psychol., N. Y.*, 1936, **28**, No. 198.

Goldmeier, E. Progressive changes in memory traces. *Amer. J. Psychol.*, 1941, **54**, 490–503.

Gordon, K. The recollection of pleasant and unpleasant odors. *J. exp. Psychol.*, 1925, **8**, 225–239.

Grant, D. A. The influence of attitude on the conditioned eyelid response. *J. exp. Psychol.*, 1939, **25**, 333–346.

Grant, D. A. The pseudo-conditioned eyelid response. *J. exp. Psychol.*, 1943, **32**, 139–149.

Gray, S. The influence of methodology upon the measurement of reminiscence. *J. exp. Psychol.*, 1940, **27**, 37–44.

Greene, E. B. An analysis of random and systematic changes with practice. *Psychometrika*, 1943, **8**, 37–52.

Grether, W. F. Pseudo-conditioning without paired stimulation encountered in attempted backward conditioning. *J. comp. Psychol.*, 1938, **25**, 91–96.

Guilford, J. P. *Laboratory studies in psychology.* New York: Holt, 1934.

Gulliksen, H. Transfer of response in human subjects. *J. exp. Psychol.*, 1932, **15**, 496–516.

Gulliksen, H. A rational equation of the learning curve based on Thorndike's law of effect. *J. gen. Psychol.*, 1934, **11**, 395–434.

Gulliksen, H., and D. L. Wolfle. A theory of learning and transfer. I, II. *Psychometrika*, 1938, **3**, 127–149, 225–251.

Guthrie, E. R. *The psychology of learning.* New York: Harper, 1935.

Guthrie, E. R. *The psychology of human conflict.* New York: Harper, 1938.

Haggard, E. A., and G. J. Rose. Some effects of mental set and active participation in the conditioning of the autokinetic phenomenon. *J. exp. Psychol.*, 1944, **34**, 45–59.

Hamilton, R. J. Retroactive facilitation as a function of degree of generalization between tasks. *J. exp. Psychol.*, 1943, **32**, 363–376.

Hanawalt, E. M. Whole and part methods in trial and error learning: Human maze learning. *J. exp. Psychol.*, 1934, **17**, 691–708.

Hanawalt, N. G. Memory trace for figures in recall and recognition. *Arch. Psychol., N. Y.*, 1937, **31**, No. 216.

Harden, L. M. A quantitative study of the similarity factor in retroactive inhibition. *J. gen. Psychol.*, 1929, **2**, 421–432.

Harlow, H. The formation of learning sets. *Psychol. Rev.*, 1949, **56**, 51–65.

Harris, J. D. Forward conditioning, backward conditioning, pseudo-conditioning, and adaptation to the conditioned stimulus. *J. exp. Psychol.*, 1941, **28**, 491–502.

Heese, K. W. A general factor in improvement with practice. *Psychometrika*, 1942, **7**, 213–223.

Heidbreder, E. F. Problem solving in children and adults. *J. genet. Psychol.*, 1928, **35**, 522–545.

Hendrickson, G., and W. H. Schroeder. Transfer of training in learning to hit a submerged target. *J. educ. Psychol.*, 1941, **32**, 205–213.

Hertzman, M., and W. S. Neff. The development of intra-serial relationships in rote learning. *J. exp. Psychol.*, 1939, **25**, 389–401.

Hilgard, E. R., and A. A. Campbell. The course of acquisition and retention of conditioned eyelid responses in man. *J. exp. Psychol.*, 1936, **19**, 227–247.

Hilgard, E. R., and L. G. Humphreys. The effect of supporting and antagonistic voluntary instructions on conditioned discrimination. *J. exp. Psychol.*, 1938, **22**, 291–304.

Hilgard, E. R., and D. G. Marquis. *Conditioning and learning.* New York: Appleton-Century-Crofts, 1940.

Hilgard, E. R., and M. B. Smith. Distributed practice in motor learning: Score changes within and between daily sessions. *J. exp. Psychol.*, 1942, **30**, 136–146.

Hill, L. B., A. E. Rejall, and E. L. Thorndike. Practice in the case of typewriting. *Pedagog. Sem.*, 1913, **20**, 516–529.

Holsopple, J. Q., and I. Vanouse. A note on the beta hypothesis of learning. *Sch. & Soc.*, 1929, **29**, 15–16.

Houlahan, F. J. Immediacy of interpolation and amount of inhibition. *J. educ. Psychol.*, 1941, **32**, 37–44.

Hovland, C. I. 'Inhibition of reinforcement' and phenomena of experimental extinction. *Proc. nat. Acad. Sci., Wash.*, 1936, **22**, 430–433.

Hovland, C. I. The generalization of conditioned responses: I. The sensory generalization of conditioned responses with varying frequencies of tone. *J. gen. Psychol.*, 1937a, **17**, 125–148.

Hovland, C. I. The generalization of conditioned responses: II. The sensory generalization of conditioned responses with varying intensities of tone. *J. genet. Psychol.*, 1937b, **51**, 279–291.

Hovland, C. I. The generalization of conditioned responses. III. Extinction, spontaneous recovery, and disinhibition of conditioned and of generalized responses. *J. exp. Psychol.*, 1937c, **21**, 47–62.

Hovland, C. I. The generalization of conditioned responses. IV. The effects of varying amounts of reinforcement upon the degree of generalization of conditioned responses. *J. exp. Psychol.*, 1937d, **21**, 261–276.

Hovland, C. I. Experimental studies in rote-learning theory. I. Reminiscence following learning by massed and by distributed practice. *J. exp. Psychol.*, 1938a, **22**, 201–224.

Hovland, C. I. Experimental studies in rote-learning theory. II. Reminiscence with varying speeds of syllable presentation. *J. exp. Psychol.*, 1938b, **22**, 338–353.

Hovland, C. I. Experimental studies in rote-learning theory. III. Distribution of practice with varying speeds of syllable presentation. *J. exp. Psychol.*, 1938c, **23**, 172–190.

Hovland, C. I. Experimental studies in rote-learning theory. IV. Comparison of reminiscence in serial and paired-associate learning. *J. exp. Psychol.*, 1939a, **24**, 466–484.

Hovland, C. I. Experimental studies in rote-learning theory. V. Comparison of distribution of practice in serial and paired-associate learning. *J. exp. Psychol.*, 1939b, **25**, 622–633.

Hovland, C. I. Experimental studies in rote-learning theory. VI. Comparison of retention following learning to same criterion by massed and distributed practice. *J. exp. Psychol.*, 1940a, **26**, 568–587.

Hovland, C. I. Experimental studies in rote-learning theory. VII. Distribution of practice with varying lengths of list. *J. exp. Psychol.*, 1940b, **27**, 271–284.

Hovland, C. I. Basic principles of learning and their application in training. *Person. Ser. Amer. Mgmt. Ass.*, 1941, No. 47, 3–14.

Hovland, C. I. Experimental studies in rote-learning theory. VIII. Distributed practice of paired-associates with varying rates of presentation. *J. exp. Psychol.*, 1949, **39**, 714–718.

Hovland, C. I., A. A. Lumsdaine, and F. D. Sheffield. *Experiments on mass communication.* Princeton: Princeton University Press, 1949.

Hsiao, H. H. [An experimental comparison of the whole and the part method of learning.] *Stud. Educ. Psychol., Nat. cent. Univ.*, 1940, **1**, No. 2, 63–70. (Abstracted in *Psychol. Abstr.*, 1941, **15**, No. 2542.)

Huang, I. Experimental studies on the role of repetition, organization, and the intention to learn in rote memory. *J. gen. Psychol.*, 1944, **31**, 213–217.

Hull, C. L. Learning: II. The factor of the conditioned reflex. In C. Murchison (Ed.), *Handbook of general experimental psychology.* Worcester: Clark University Press, 1934. Pp. 382–455.

Hull, C. L. The influence of caffeine and other factors on certain phenomena of rote learning. *J. gen. Psychol.*, 1935, **13**, 249–274.

Hull, C. L. Explorations in the patterning of stimuli conditioned to the G.S.R. *J. exp. Psychol.*, 1940, **27**, 95–110.

Hull, C. L. *Principles of behavior.* New York: Appleton-Century-Crofts, 1943.

Hull, C. L., C. I. Hovland, R. T. Ross, M. Hall, D. T. Perkins, and F. B. Fitch. *Mathematico-deductive theory of rote learning.* New Haven: Yale University Press, 1940.

Humphreys, L. G. The effect of random alternation of reinforcement on the acquisition and extinction of conditioned eyelid reactions. *J. exp. Psychol.*, 1939a, **25**, 141–158.

Humphreys, L. G. Generalization as a function of method of reinforcement. *J. exp. Psychol.*, 1939b, **25**, 361–372.

Humphreys, L. G. Extinction of conditioned psychogalvanic responses following two conditions of reinforcement. *J. exp. Psychol.*, 1940a, **27**, 71–75.

Humphreys, L. G. Distributed practice in the development of the conditioned eyelid reaction. *J. gen. Psychol.*, 1940b, **22**, 379–385.

Humphreys, L. G., J. Miller, and D. G. Ellson. The effect of the inter-trial interval on the acquisition, extinction, and recovery of verbal expectations. *J. exp. Psychol.*, 1940, **27**, 195–202.

Hunter, W. S. Learning: IV. Experimental studies of learning. In C. Murchison (Ed.), *Handbook of general experimental psychology.* Worcester: Clark University Press, 1934. Pp. 497–570.

Hurlock, E. B. An evaluation of certain incentives used in school work. *J. educ. Psychol.*, 1925, **16**, 145–159.

Husband, R. W. A note on maze learning with the time factor constant. *J. gen. Psychol.*, 1929, **2**, 366–369.

Husband, R. W. Intercorrelations among learning abilities: I. *J. genet. Psychol.*, 1939, **55**, 353–364.

Irion, A. L. Retroactive inhibition as a function of the relative serial positions of the original and interpolated items. *J. exp. Psychol.*, 1946, **36**, 262–270.

Jackson, T. A., E. Stonex, E. Lane, and K. Dominguez. Studies in the transposition of learning by children: I. Relative vs. absolute response as a function of amount of training. *J. exp. Psychol.*, 1938, **23**, 578–600.

James, W. *The principles of psychology.* New York: Holt, 1890. Volume I.

Jasper, H., and C. Shagass. Conditioning the occipital alpha rhythm in man. *J. exp. Psychol.*, 1941, **28**, 373–388.

Jenkins, J. G. Instruction as a factor in 'incidental' learning. *Amer. J. Psychol.*, 1933, **45**, 471–477.

Jenkins, J. G., and K. M. Dallenbach. Obliviscence during sleep and waking. *Amer. J. Psychol.*, 1924, **35**, 605–612.

Jenkins, W. O., and F. D. Sheffield. Rehearsal and guessing habits as sources of the 'spread of effect.' *J. exp. Psychol.*, 1946, **36**, 316–330.

Jersild, A. Memory for the pleasant as compared with the unpleasant. *J. exp. Psychol.*, 1931, **14**, 284–288.

Jones, M. C. The elimination of children's fears. *J. exp. Psychol.*, 1924, **7**, 382–390.

Jost, A. Die Assoziationsfestigkeit in ihrer Abhängigkeit von der Verteilung der Wiederholungen. *Z. Psychol.*, 1897, **14**, 436–472.

Judd, C. H. The relation of special training to general intelligence. *Educ. Rev.*, 1908, **36**, 28–42.

Katona, G. *Organizing and memorizing.* New York: Columbia University Press, 1940.

Keller, M. Mediated generalization: The generalization of a conditioned galvanic skin response established to a pictured object. *Amer. J. Psychol.*, 1943, **56**, 438–448.

Kennelly, T. W. The role of similarity in retroactive inhibition. *Arch. Psychol., N. Y.*, 1941, **37**, No. 260.

Kientzle, M. J. Properties of learning curves under varied distributions of practice. *J. exp. Psychol.*, 1946, **36**, 187–211.

Kimble, G. A. Conditioning as a function of the time between conditioned and unconditioned stimuli. *J. exp. Psychol.*, 1947, **37**, 1–15.

Kimble, G. A., and B. R. Horenstein. Reminiscence in motor learning as a function of length of interpolated rest. *J. exp. Psychol.*, 1948, **38**, 239–244.

Kincaid, M. A study of individual differences in learning. *Psychol. Rev.*, 1925, **32**, 34–53.

Kingsley, H. L. *The nature and conditions of learning.* New York: Prentice-Hall, 1946.

Kjersted, C. L. The form of the learning curves for memory. *Psychol. Monogr.*, 1919, **26**, No. 5.

Kline, L. W. Interrelation between habit formation and feeling qualities of voluntary movements. *Psychobiology*, 1920, **2**, 255–328.

Koch, H. L. The influence of some affective factors upon recall. *J. gen. Psychol.*, 1930, **4**, 171–190.

Koffka, K. *Principles of Gestalt psychology.* New York: Harcourt, Brace, 1935.

Köhler, W. *Gestalt psychology.* New York: Liveright, 1929.

Krueger, L. O. The relative effect of interspersing a recall at different stages of learning. *Arch. Psychol., N. Y.*, 1930, **18**, No. 114.

Krueger, W. C. F. The effect of overlearning on retention. *J. exp. Psychol.*, 1929, **12**, 71–78.

Krueger, W. C. F. Further studies in overlearning. *J. exp. Psychol.*, 1930, **13**, 152–163.

Krueger, W. C. F. Rate of progress as related to difficulty of assignment. *J. educ. Psychol.*, 1946, **37**, 247–249.

Krueger, W. C. F. Influence of difficulty of perceptual-motor task upon acceleration of curves of learning. *J. educ. Psychol.*, 1947, **38**, 51–53.

Kulcinski, L. E. The relation of intelligence to the learning of fundamental muscular skills.

Res. Quart. Amer. phys. Educ. Ass., 1945, **16,** 266–276.

Lakenan, M. E. The whole and part methods of memorizing poetry and prose. *J. educ. Psychol.,* 1913, **4,** 189–198.

Larguier des Bancels, J. Sur les méthodes de mémorisation. *Année psychol.,* 1901, **8,** 185–204.

Lashley, K. S. The acquisition of skill in archery. *Pap. Dept. Mar. Biol. Carn. Instn.,* 1915, **7,** No. 211.

Leavitt, H. J. The relation of speed of learning to amount retained and to reminiscence. *J. exp. Psychol.,* 1945, **35,** 134–140.

Leavitt, H. J., and H. Schlosberg. The retention of verbal and of motor skills. *J. exp. Psychol.,* 1944, **34,** 404–417.

Lipmann, O. Methoden der Aussage psychologie. In E. Abderhalden (Ed.), *Handb. biol. Arb-Meth.* Berlin : Urban and Schwarzenberg, 1935, **6,** CII (2), 967–1056.

Littman, R. A. Conditioned generalization of the galvanic skin reaction to tones. *J. exp. Psychol.,* 1949, **39,** 868–882.

Lorge, I. Influence of regularly interpolated time intervals upon subsequent learning. *Teach. Coll. Contr. Educ.,* 1930, No. 438.

Luh, C. W. The conditions of retention. *Psychol. Monogr.,* 1922, **31,** No. 3.

Lumley, F. H. Anticipation as a factor in serial and maze learning. *J. exp. Psychol.,* 1932, **15,** 331–342.

Lyon, D. O. The relation of length of material to time taken for learning and the optimum distribution of time. *J. educ. Psychol.,* 1914, **5,** 1–9, 85–91, 155–163.

Martin, J. R. Reminiscence and gestalt theory. *Psychol. Monogr.,* 1940, **52,** No. 4.

McClelland, D. C. Studies in serial verbal discrimination learning. I. Reminiscence with two speeds of pair presentation. *J. exp. Psychol.,* 1942a, **31,** 44–56.

McClelland, D. C. Studies in serial verbal discrimination learning. II. Retention of responses to right and wrong words in a transfer situation. *J. exp. Psychol.,* 1942b, **31,** 149–162.

McClelland, D. C. Studies in serial verbal discrimination learning. III. The influence of difficulty on reminiscence in responses to right and wrong words. *J. exp. Psychol.,* 1943a, **32,** 235–246.

McClelland, D. C. Studies in serial verbal discrimination learning. IV. Habit reversal after two degrees of learning. *J. exp. Psychol.,* 1943b, **33,** 457–470.

McClelland, D. C., and R. M. Heath. Retroactive inhibition as a function of degree of association of original and interpolated activities. *J. exp. Psychol.,* 1943, **33,** 420–430.

McGeoch, G. O. The intelligence quotient as a factor in the whole-part problem. *J. exp. Psychol.,* 1931, **14,** 333–358.

McGeoch, G. O. The conditions of reminiscence. *Amer. J. Psychol.,* 1935, **47,** 65–89.

McGeoch, J. A. The influence of degree of learning upon retroactive inhibition. *Amer. J. Psychol.,* 1929, **41,** 252–262.

McGeoch, J. A. The influence of associative value upon the difficulty of nonsense-syllable lists. *J. genet. Psychol.,* 1930, **37,** 421–426.

McGeoch, J. A. The influence of four different interpolated activities upon retention. *J. exp. Psychol.,* 1931, **14,** 400–413.

McGeoch, J. A. The direction and extent of intra-serial associations at recall. *Amer. J. Psychol.,* 1936, **48,** 221–245.

McGeoch, J. A. *The psychology of human learning: An introduction.* New York : Longmans, Green, 1942.

McGeoch, J. A., and W. T. McDonald. Meaningful relation and retroactive inhibition. *Amer. J. Psychol.,* 1931, **43,** 579–588.

McGeoch, J. A., F. McKinney, and H. N. Peters. Studies in retroactive inhibition : IX. Retroactive inhibition, reproductive inhibition and reminiscence. *J. exp. Psychol.,* 1937, **20,** 131–143.

McGeoch, J. A., and A. W. Melton. The comparative retention values of maze habits and of nonsense syllables. *J. exp. Psychol.,* 1929, **12,** 392–414.

McGeoch, J. A., and H. N. Peters. An all-or-none characteristic in the elimination of errors during the learning of a stylus maze. *J. exp. Psychol.,* 1933, **16,** 504–523.

McGeoch, J. A., and B. J. Underwood. Tests of the two-factor theory of retroactive inhibition. *J. exp. Psychol.,* 1943, **32,** 1–16.

McKinney, F. Quantitative and qualitative essential elements of transfer. *J. exp. Psychol.,* 1933, **16,** 854–864.

Melton, A. W. The methodology of experimental studies of human learning and retention : I. The functions of a methodology and the available criteria for evaluating different experimental methods. *Psychol. Bull.,* 1936, **33,** 305–394.

Melton, A. W., and J. McQ. Irwin. The influence of degree of interpolated learning on retroactive inhibition and the overt transfer of specific responses. *Amer. J. Psychol.,* 1940, **53,** 173–203.

Melton, A. W., and G. R. Stone. The retention of serial lists of adjectives over short time-intervals with varying rates of presentation. *J. exp. Psychol.,* 1942, **30,** 295–310.

Melton, A. W., and W. J. Von Lackum. Retroactive and proactive inhibition in retention : evidence for a two-factor theory of retroactive inhibition. *Amer. J. Psychol.,* 1941, **54,** 157–173.

Meltzer, H. The present status of experimental studies on the relationship of feeling to memory. *Psychol. Rev.,* 1930, **37,** 124–139.

Menzies, R. The comparative memory values of pleasant, unpleasant and indifferent experiences. *J. exp. Psychol.,* 1935, **18,** 267–279.

Meumann, E. *The psychology of learning.* (Translated by J. W. Baird from 3rd German edition.) New York : Appleton-Century-Crofts, 1913.

Meyer, W. Über Ganz und Teillernverfahren bei vorgeschriebenem Rezitieren. *Z. Psychol.*, 1926, **98**, 304–341.

Miles, W. R. Abilities of older men. *Person. J.*, 1933, **11**, 352–357.

Miller, J. M. The effect of inhibitory and facilitatory attitudes on eyelid conditioning. *Psychol. Bull.*, 1939, **36**, 577–578.

Müller, G. E., and A. Pilzecker. Experimentelle Beiträge zur Lehre vom Gedächtniss. *Z. Psychol.*, 1900, Ergbd. **1**, 1–288.

Müller, G. E., and F. Schumann. Experimentelle Beiträge zur Untersuchung des Gedächtnisses. *Z. Psychol.*, 1894, **6**, 81–190.

Munn, N. L. Bilateral transfer of learning. *J. exp. Psychol.*, 1932, **15**, 343–353.

Munn, N. L. Learning in children. Chapter 8 in L. Carmichael (Ed.), *Manual of child psychology.* New York: Wiley, 1946. Pp. 370–449.

Münsterberg, H. *Beiträge zur experimentellen Psychologie.* Freiburg: Mohr, 1889. Heft 4.

Myers, G. C. A study in incidental memory. *Arch. Psychol., N. Y.*, 1913, **5**, No. 26.

Newman, E. B. Effect of crowding of material on curves of forgetting. *Amer. J. Psychol.*, 1939, **52**, 601–609.

Northway, M. L. The nature of 'difficulty'; with reference to a study of 'whole-part' learning. *Brit. J. Psychol.*, 1937, **27**, 399–403.

O'Brien, C. C. Part and whole methods in the memorization of music. *J. educ. Psychol.*, 1943, **34**, 552–560.

O'Kelly, L. I., and L. C. Steckle. The forgetting of pleasant and unpleasant experiences. *Amer. J. Psychol.*, 1940, **53**, 432–434.

Orata, P. T. *The theory of identical elements, being a critique of Thorndike's theory of identical elements and a re-interpretation of the problem of transfer of training.* Columbus: Ohio State University Press, 1928.

Orata, P. T. Transfer of training and educational pseudo-science. *Educ. Adm. Supervis.*, 1935, **21**, 241–264.

Orata, P. T. Recent research studies on transfer of training with implications for the curriculum, guidance, and personnel work. *J. educ. Res.*, 1941, **35**, 81–101.

Orbison, W. D. The relative efficiency of whole and part methods of learning paired-associates as a function of the length of list. Ph.D. dissertation, Yale University, 1944.

Osgood, C. E. Meaningful similarity and interference in learning. *J. exp. Psychol.*, 1946, **36**, 277–301.

Osgood, C. E. The similarity paradox in human learning: A resolution. *Psychol. Rev.*, 1949, **56**, 132–143.

Owens, W. A., Jr. A note on the effects of practice upon trait differences in motor skills. *J. educ. Psychol.*, 1942, **33**, 144–147.

Pavlov, I. P. *Conditioned reflexes.* (Translated by G. V. Anrep.) London: Oxford University Press, 1927.

Peak, H. Negative practice and theories of learning. *Psychol. Rev.*, 1941, **48**, 316–336.

Peak, H. Dr. Dunlap on "The technique of negative practice." *Amer. J. Psychol.*, 1942, **55**, 576–580.

Peak, H., J. Brooks, and B. Hobson. Positive and negative practice in the correction of spelling errors. *J. Psychol.*, 1941, **11**, 103–114.

Pechstein, L. A. Whole vs. part methods in motor learning. A comparative study. *Psychol. Monogr.*, 1917, **23**, No. 2.

Pechstein, L. A. Whole versus part methods in learning nonsensical syllables. *J. educ. Psychol.*, 1918, **9**, 381–387.

Pechstein, L. A. The whole vs. part methods in learning: Comparison and summary. *Stud. Educ.* (*Yearb. nat. Soc. Coll. Teach. Educ.*), 1926, **15**, 181–186.

Peixotto, H. E. Proactive inhibition in the recognition of nonsense syllables. *J. exp. Psychol.*, 1947, **37**, 81–91.

Pentschew, C. Untersuchungen zur Ökonomie und Technik des Lernens. *Arch. ges. Psychol.*, 1903, **1**, 417–526.

Perkins, F. T. Symmetry in visual recall. *Amer. J. Psychol.*, 1932, **44**, 473–490.

Perry, H. M. The relative efficiency of actual and "imaginary" practice in five selected tasks. *Arch. Psychol., N. Y.*, 1939, **34**, No. 243.

Peterson, G. M. Negative acceleration with material of varying difficulty. *J. exp. Psychol.*, 1928, **11**, 40–44.

Peterson, H. A. Recitation or recall as a factor in the learning of long prose selections. *J. educ. Psychol.*, 1944, **35**, 220–228.

Peterson, J. Experiments in ball-tossing: The significance of learning curves. *J. exp. Psychol.*, 1917, **2**, 178–224.

Philip, B. R. Proactive and retroactive effects in the recognition of form. *J. exp. Psychol.*, 1940, **26**, 502–513.

Pillsbury, W. B., and H. L. Raush. An extension of the Köhler-Restorff inhibition phenomenon. *Amer. J. Psychol.*, 1943, **56**, 293–298.

Pintner, R., and G. Forlano. The influence of pleasantly and unpleasantly toned words on retention. *J. soc. Psychol.*, 1940, **11**, 147–149.

Pitts, W. A general theory of learning and conditioning: I, II. *Psychometrika*, 1943, **8**, 1–18, 131–140.

Postman, L. The history and present status of the law of effect. *Psychol. Bull.*, 1947, **44**, 489–563.

Postman, L., and T. G. Alper. Retroactive inhibition as a function of the time of interpolation of the inhibitor between learning and recall. *Amer. J. Psychol.*, 1946, **59**, 439–449.

Postman, L., and W. O. Jenkins. An experimental analysis of set in rote learning: The interaction of learning instruction and retention performance. *J. exp. Psychol.*, 1948, **38**, 683–689.

Postman, L., and V. L. Senders. Incidental learning and generality of set. *J. exp. Psychol.*, 1946, **36**, 153–165.

Prentice, W. C. H. The interruption of tasks. *Psychol. Rev.*, 1944, **51**, 329–340.

Pyle, W. H. Concentrated versus distributed practice. *J. educ. Psychol.*, 1914, **5**, 247–258.

Pyle, W. H. *Nature and development of learning capacity.* Baltimore: Warwick and York, 1925*a*.

Pyle, W. H. The relation of sex differences to the kind of material used. *J. educ. Psychol.*, 1925*b*, **16**, 261–264.

Pyle, W. H. *The psychology of learning: An advanced text in educational psychology.* Baltimore: Warwick and York, 1928.

Radossawljewitsch, P. R. *Das Behalten und Vergessen bei Kindern und Erwachsenen nach experimentellen Untersuchungen (Das Fortschreiten des Vergessens mit der Zeit).* (Päd. Monogr. No. 1.) Leipzig: Nemnich, 1907.

Rashevsky, N. Mathematical biophysics and psychology. *Psychometrika*, 1936, **1**, 1–26.

Raskin, E., and S. W. Cook. The strength and direction of associations formed in the learning of nonsense syllables. *J. exp. Psychol.*, 1937, **20**, 381–395.

Ray, W. S. Proactive inhibition: A function of time-interval. *Amer. J. Psychol.*, 1945, **58**, 519–529.

Razran, G. H. S. Attitudinal control of human conditioning. *J. Psychol.*, 1936, **2**, 327–337.

Razran, G. H. S. A quantitative study of meaning by a conditioned salivary technique (semantic conditioning). *Science*, 1939*a*, **90**, 89–90.

Razran, G. H. S. Extinction, spontaneous recovery, and forgetting. *Amer. J. Psychol.*, 1939*b*, **52**, 100–102.

Razran, G. H. S. Decremental and incremental effects of distracting stimuli upon the salivary CRs of 24 adult human subjects (inhibition and disinhibition?). *J. exp. Psychol.*, 1939*c*, **24**, 647–652.

Razran, G. H. S. Studies in configurational conditioning: V. Generalization and transposition. *J. genet. Psychol.*, 1940, **56**, 3–11.

Reed, H. B. Part and whole methods of learning. *J. educ. Psychol.*, 1924, **15**, 107–115.

Reed, H. B., and H. A. Zinszer. The occurrence of plateaus in telegraphy. *J. exp. Psychol.*, 1943, **33**, 130–135.

Restorff, H. von. I. Über die Wirkung von Bereichsbildungen im Spurenfeld. (*In* W. Köhler and H. von Restorff, Analyse von Vorgängen im Spurenfeld.) *Psychol. Forsch.*, 1933, **18**, 299–342.

Reynolds, B. The acquisition of a trace conditioned response as a function of the magnitude of the stimulus trace. *J. exp. Psychol.*, 1945*a*, **35**, 15–30.

Reynolds, B. Extinction of trace conditioned responses as a function of the spacing of trials during the acquisition and extinction series. *J. exp. Psychol.*, 1945*b*, **35**, 81–95.

Riess, B. F. Genetic changes in sematic conditioning. *J. exp. Psychol.*, 1946, **36**, 143–152.

Roberts, K. E. Learning in preschool and orphanage children: an experimental study of ability to solve different situations according to the same plan. *Univ. Ia. Stud. Child Welf.*, 1933, **7**, No. 3.

Robertson, T. B. Sur la dynamique chimique du système nerveux central. *Arch. int. Physiol.*, 1908, **6**, 388–454.

Robinson, E. S. The relative efficiencies of distributed and concentrated study in memorizing. *J. exp. Psychol.*, 1921, **4**, 327–343.

Robinson, E. S. The 'similarity' factor in retroaction. *Amer. J. Psychol.*, 1927, **39**, 297–312.

Robinson, E. S., and M. A. Brown. Effect of serial position upon memorization. *Amer. J. Psychol.*, 1926, **37**, 538–552.

Robinson, E. S., and C. W. Darrow. Effect of length of lists upon memory for numbers. *Amer. J. Psychol.*, 1924, **35**, 235–243.

Robinson, E. S., and W. T. Heron. Result of variations in length of memorized material. *J. exp. Psychol.*, 1922, **5**, 428–448.

Robinson, I. P. The effects of differential degrees of similarity of stimulus-response relations on transfer of verbal learning. *Amer. Psychologist*, 1948, **3**, 250.

Rodnick, E. H. Does the interval of delay of conditioned responses possess inhibitory properties? *J. exp. Psychol.*, 1937, **20**, 507–527.

Rubin-Rabson, G. Studies in the psychology of memorizing piano music: II. A comparison of massed and distributed practice. *J. educ. Psychol.*, 1940*a*, **31**, 270–284.

Rubin-Rabson, G. Studies in the psychology of memorizing piano music: III. A comparison of the whole and the part approach. *J. educ. Psychol.*, 1940*b*, **31**, 460–476.

Rubin-Rabson, G. Studies in the psychology of memorizing piano music: IV. The effect of incentive. *J. educ. Psychol.*, 1941*a*, **32**, 45–54.

Rubin-Rabson, G. Studies in the psychology of memorizing piano music: VI. A comparison of two forms of mental rehearsal and keyboard overlearning. *J. educ. Psychol.*, 1941*b*, **32**, 593–602.

Rubin-Rabson, G. Studies in the psychology of memorizing piano music: VII. A comparison of three degrees of overlearning. *J. educ. Psychol.*, 1941*c*, **32**, 688–696.

Rubin-Rabson, G. Mental and keyboard overlearning in memorizing piano music. *J. musicol.*, 1941*d*, **3**, 33–40.

Ruch, F. L. The differentiative effects of age upon human learning. *J. gen. Psychol.*, 1934*a*, **11**, 261–286.

Ruch, F. L. The differential decline of learning ability in the aged as a possible explanation of their conservatism. *J. soc. Psychol.*, 1934*b*, **5**, 329–337.

Ruediger, W. C. The indirect improvement of mental function thru ideals. *Educ. Rev.*, 1908, **36**, 364–371.

Ruger, H. A. The psychology of efficiency: An experimental study of the processes involved in the solution of mechanical puzzles and in the acquisition of skill in their manipulation. *Arch. Psychol., N. Y.*, 1910, **2**, No. 15.

Ryans, D. G. Changes in variability in "digit-symbol substitution" performance measured at the beginning and at the end of practice. *J. genet. Psychol.*, 1939, **54**, 461–465.

Sand, M. C. The effect of length of list upon retroactive inhibition when degree of learning is controlled. *Arch. Psychol., N. Y.*, 1939, **33**, No. 238.

Schükarew, A. Über die energetischen Grundlagen des Gesetzes von Weber-Fechner und der Dynamik des Gedächtnisses. *Ann. d. Naturphil.*, 1907, **6**, 139–149.

Scripture, E. W., T. L. Smith, and E. M. Brown. On the education of muscular control and power. *Stud. Yale psychol. Lab.*, 1894, **2**, 114–119.

Seagoe, M. V. Qualitative wholes : A re-valuation of the whole-part problem. *J. educ. Psychol.*, 1936a, **27**, 537–545.

Seagoe, M. V. The influence of degree of wholeness on whole-part learning. *J. exp. Psychol.*, 1936b, **19**, 763–768.

Sears, R. R., and C. I. Hovland. Experiments on motor conflict. II. Determination of mode of resolution by comparative strengths of conflicting responses. *J. exp. Psychol.*, 1941, **28**, 280–286.

Sharp, A. A. An experimental test of Freud's doctrine of the relation of hedonic tone to memory revival. *J. exp. Psychol.*, 1938, **22**, 395–418.

Shaw, F. J. Influence of degree of original learning upon associative and reproductive inhibition. *Proc. Ia. Acad. Sci.*, 1942, **49**, 413–417.

Sheffield, F. D. The rôle of meaningfulness of stimulus and response in verbal learning. Ph.D. dissertation, Yale University, 1946.

Shurrager, H. C. The measurement of memory on an absolute scale. *Psychol. Monogr.*, 1940, **52**, No. 3, 21–38.

Siegel, P. S. Structure effects within a memory series. *J. exp. Psychol.*, 1943, **33**, 311–316.

Siipola, E. M., and H. E. Israel. Habit-interference as dependent upon stage of training. *Amer. J. Psychol.*, 1933, **45**, 205–227.

Simrall, D. Intelligence and the ability to learn. *J. Psychol.*, 1947, **23**, 27–43.

Sims, V. M. The relative influence of two types of motivation on improvement. *J. educ. Psychol.*, 1928, **19**, 480–484.

Sisson, E. D. Retroactive inhibition : The influence of degree of associative value of original and interpolated lists. *J. exp. Psychol.*, 1938, **22**, 573–580.

Skaggs, E. B., et al. The optimum number of readings before introducing reading-prompting in verbatim learning. *Arch. Psychol., N. Y.*, 1930, **18**, No. 114, 5–14.

Sleight, W. G. Memory and formal training. *Brit. J. Psychol.*, 1911, **4**, 386–457.

Smith, M. H. Spread of effect is the spurious result of non-random response tendencies. *J. exp. Psychol.*, 1949, **39**, 355–368.

Snoddy, G. *Evidence for two opposed processes in mental growth.* Lancaster : Science, 1935.

Snoddy, G. Evidence for a universal shock factor in learning. *J. exp. Psychol.*, 1945, **35**, 403–417.

Solomon, R. L. The influence of work on behavior. *Psychol. Bull.*, 1948, **45**, 1–40.

Sorge, S. Neue Versuche über die Wiedergabe abstrakter optischer Gebilde. *Arch. ges. Psychol.*, 1940, **106**, 1–88.

Spence, K. W. A reply to Dr. Razran on the transposition of response in discrimination learning. *Psychol. Rev.*, 1939, **46**, 88–91.

Spencer, E. M. The retention of orally presented materials. *J. educ. Psychol.*, 1941, **32**, 641–655.

Spitzer, H. F. Studies in retention. *J. educ. Psychol.*, 1939, **30**, 641–656.

Spooner, A., and W. N. Kellogg. The backward conditioning curve. *Amer. J. Psychol.*, 1947, **60**, 321–334.

Stagner, R. The redintegration of pleasant and unpleasant experiences. *Amer. J. Psychol.*, 1931, **43**, 463–468.

Starch, D. A demonstration of the trial and error method of learning. *Psychol. Bull.*, 1910, **7**, 20–23.

Steffens, L. Experimentelle Beiträge zur Lehre vom ökonomischen Lernen. *Z. Psychol.*, 1900, **22**, 321–382.

Stone, G. R. Retention of nonsense syllables over short intervals of time. *Proc. Indiana Acad. Sci.*, 1946, **55**, 178–181.

Stone, G. R. A note on Postman's review of the literature on the law of effect. *Psychol. Bull.*, 1948, **45**, 151–160.

Strong, E. K., Jr. Two factors which influence economical learning. *J. Phil. Psychol. sci. Meth.*, 1914, **11**, 124–131.

Stroop, J. R. Studies of interference in serial verbal reactions. *J. exp. Psychol.*, 1935, **18**, 643–662.

Stroud, J. B. The role of muscular tensions in stylus maze learning. *J. exp. Psychol.*, 1931, **14**, 606–631.

Stroud, J. B., and R. Maul. The influence of age upon learning and retention of poetry and nonsense syllables. *J. genet. Psychol.*, 1933, **42**, 242–250.

Swenson, E. J. Retroactive inhibition : A review of the literature. *Univ. Minn. Stud. Educ.*, 1941, No. 1.

Swenson, E. J. Generalization and organization as factors in transfer and retroactive inhibition. *Proc. Indiana Acad. Sci.*, 1942, **51**, 248–255.

Swift, E. J. Studies in the psychology and physiology of learning. *Amer. J. Psychol.*, 1903, **14**, 201–251.

Swift, E. J. Beginning a language : A contribution to the psychology of learning. In *Amherst studies in philosophy and psychology, Garman Memorial Volume.* Boston : Houghton Mifflin, 1906a. Pp. 297–314.

Swift, E. J. Memory of skillful movements. *Psychol. Bull.*, 1906b, **3**, 185–187.

Taylor, D. W. Learning telegraphic code. *Psychol. Bull.*, 1943, **40**, 461–487.

Telford, C. W. The refractory phase of voluntary and associative responses. *J. exp. Psychol.*, 1931, **14**, 1–36.

Telford, C. W., and W. J. Swenson. Changes in muscular tension during learning. *J. exp. Psychol.*, 1942, **30**, 236–246.

Thompson, G. G., and S. L. Witryol. The relationship between intelligence and motor learning ability, as measured by a high relief finger maze. *J. Psychol.*, 1946, **22**, 237–246.

Thompson, L. M. The role of verbalization in learning from demonstrations. Dissertation, Yale University, 1944.

Thorndike, E. L. *Animal intelligence. Experimental studies.* New York: Macmillan, 1911.

Thorndike, E. L. *Educational psychology. Volume 2. The psychology of learning.* New York: Teachers College, Columbia University, 1913.

Thorndike, E. L. Mental discipline in high school studies. *J. educ. Psychol.*, 1924, **15**, 1–22, 83–98.

Thorndike, E. L. The law of effect. *Amer. J. Psychol.*, 1927, **39**, 212–222.

Thorndike, E. L., et al. An experimental study of rewards. *Teach. Coll. Contr. Educ.*, 1933, No. 580.

Thorndike, E. L., E. O. Bregman, J. W. Tilton, and E. Woodyard. *Adult learning.* New York: Macmillan, 1928.

Thorndike, E. L., and R. S. Woodworth. The influence of improvement in one mental function upon the efficiency of other functions. (I) ; II. The estimation of magnitudes ; III. Functions involving attention, observation and discrimination. *Psychol. Rev.*, 1901, **8**, 247–261, 384–395, 553–564.

Thune, L. E., and B. J. Underwood. Retroactive inhibition as a function of degree of interpolated learning. *J. exp. Psychol.*, 1943, **32**, 185–200.

Thurstone, L. L. The learning curve equation. *Psychol. Bull.*, 1917, **14**, 64–65.

Thurstone, L. L. The learning curve equation. *Psychol. Monogr.*, 1919, **26**, No. 3.

Thurstone, L. L. The relation between learning time and length of task. *Psychol. Rev.*, 1930a, **37**, 44–53.

Thurstone, L. L. The learning function. *J. gen. Psychol.*, 1930b, **3**, 469–493.

Thurstone, L. L. The error function in maze learning. *J. gen. Psychol.*, 1933, **9**, 288–301.

Tilton, J. W. Intelligence test scores as indicative of ability to learn. *Educ. psychol. Measmt.*, 1949, **9**, 291–296.

Travis, R. C. The effect of the length of the rest period on motor learning. *J. Psychol.*, 1937, **3**, 189–194.

Travis, R. C. Length of the practice period and efficiency in motor learning. *J. exp. Psychol.*, 1939, **24**, 339–345.

Tresselt, M. E., and S. D. S. Spragg. Changes occurring in the serial reproduction of verbally perceived materials. *J. genet. Psychol.*, 1941, **58**, 255–264.

Treverton, M. W. Degree of relatedness and retroactive inhibition. *J. gen. Psychol.*, 1941, **24**, 3–20.

Tsai, C. A comparative study of retention curves for motor habits. *Comp. Psychol. Monogr.*, 1924, **2**, No. 11.

Twining, P. E. The relative importance of intervening activity and lapse of time in the production of forgetting. *J. exp. Psychol.*, 1940, **26**, 483–501.

Underwood, B. J. Associative inhibition in the learning of successive paired-associate lists. *J. exp. Psychol.*, 1944, **34**, 127–135.

Underwood, B. J. The effect of successive interpolations on retroactive and proactive inhibition. *Psychol. Monogr.*, 1945, **59**, No. 3.

Underwood, B. J. Retroactive and proactive inhibition after five and forty-eight hours. *J. exp. Psychol.*, 1948, **38**, 29–38.

Valentine, W. L. A study of learning curves : III. The relationship between a growth curve and the arc cotangent function. *J. gen. Psychol.*, 1931, **5**, 251–255.

Van Buskirk, W. L. An experimental study of vividness in learning and retention. *J. exp. Psychol.*, 1932, **15**, 563–573.

Vandell, R. A., R. A. Davis, and H. A. Clugston. The function of mental practice in the acquisition of motor skills. *J. gen. Psychol.*, 1943, **29**, 243–250.

Van Dusen, F., and H. Schlosberg. Further study of the retention of verbal and motor skills. *J. exp. Psychol.*, 1948, **38**, 526–534.

Van Ormer, E. B. Retention after intervals of sleep and waking. *Arch. Psychol.*, N. Y., 1932, **21**, No. 137.

Volkmann, A. W. Über den Einfluss der Uebung auf das Erkennen raumlicher Distanzen. *Sächs. Akad. Wiss. Ber. Leipzig*, 1858, **10**, 38–69.

Wallach, H., and M. Henle. An experimental analysis of the law of effect. *J. exp. Psychol.*, 1941, **28**, 340–349.

Wallach, H., and M. Henle. A further study of the function of reward. *J. exp. Psychol.*, 1942, **30**, 147–160.

Wallen, R. Size changes in remembered figures. *J. exp. Psychol.*, 1943, **32**, 464–472.

Ward, L. B. Reminiscence and rote learning. *Psychol. Monogr.*, 1937, **49**, No. 4.

Warden, C. J. The relative economy of various modes of attack in the mastery of a stylus maze. *J. exp. Psychol.*, 1924, **7**, 243–275.

Waters, R. H. The interpretation of Ebbinghaus's retention values. *Amer. J. Psychol.*, 1941, **54**, 283–286.

Watson, W. S., and G. W. Hartmann. The rigidity of a basic attitudinal frame. *J. abnorm. soc. Psychol.*, 1939, **34**, 314–335.

Webb, L. W. Transfer of training and retroaction. *Psychol. Monogr.*, 1917, **24**, No. 3.

Welsh, B. L., and R. H. Waters. Finger versus stylus learning of the same maze. *J. gen. Psychol.*, 1944, **31**, 283–286.

Werner, H. Development of visuo-motor performance on the marble-board test in mentally retarded children. *J. genet. Psychol.*, 1944, **64**, 269–279.

Whitely, P. L. The dependence of learning and recall upon prior intellectual activities. *J. exp. Psychol.*, 1927, **10**, 489–508.

Wickens, D. D. Studies of response generalization in conditioning. I. Stimulus generalization during response generalization. *J. exp. Psychol.*, 1943, **33**, 221–227.

Williams, O. A study of the phenomenon of reminiscence. *J. exp. Psychol.*, 1926, **9**, 368–387.

Winch, W. H. Should poems be learnt by schoolchildren as 'wholes' or in 'parts'? *Brit. J. Psychol.*, 1924, **15**, 64–79.

Witasek, S. Über Lesen und Rezitieren in ihren Beziehungen zum Gedächtnis. *Z. Psychol.*, 1907, **44**, 161–185, 246–282.

Wolfle, H. M. Time factors in a conditioning finger-withdrawal. *J. gen. Psychol.*, 1930, **4**, 372–378.

Wolfle, H. M. Conditioning as a function of the interval between the conditioned and the original stimulus. *J. gen. Psychol.*, 1932, **7**, 80–103.

Woodrow, H. The effect of type of training upon transference. *J. educ. Psychol.*, 1927, **18**, 159–172.

Woodrow, H. Interrelations of measures of learning. *J. Psychol.*, 1940, **10**, 49–73.

Woodrow, H. The ability to learn. *Psychol. Rev.*, 1946, **53**, 147–158.

Woodward, P. An experimental study of transfer of training in motor learning. *J. appl. Psychol.*, 1943, **27**, 12–32.

Woodworth, R. S. *Experimental psychology.* New York : Holt, 1938.

Wulf, F. Über die Veränderung von Vorstellungen (Gedächtnis und Gestalt). *Psychol. Forsch.*, 1922, **1**, 333–373.

Wylie, H. H. An experimental study of transfer of response in the white rat. *Behav. Monogr.*, 1919, **3**, No. 16.

Yoshioka, J. G., and H. E. Jones. An analysis of children's maze learning, in terms of stages of learning. *J. genet. Psychol.*, 1945, **67**, 203–214.

Youtz, A. C. An experimental evaluation of Jost's laws. *Psychol. Monogr.*, 1941, **53**, No. 1.

Yum, K. S. An experimental test of the law of assimilation. *J. exp. Psychol.*, 1931, **14**, 68–82.

Zeigarnik, B. III. Das Behalten erledigter und unerledigter Handlungen. In K. Lewin (Ed.) Untersuchungen zur Handlungs- und Affektpsychologie. *Psychol. Forsch.*, 1927, **9**, 1–85.

Zirkle, G. A. Success and failure in serial learning. II. Isolation and the Thorndike effect. *J. exp. Psychol.*, 1946, **36**, 302–315.

18.

Theoretical Interpretations of Learning

KENNETH W. SPENCE

The State University of Iowa

A theory in science serves to bring order and meaning into a particular realm of events. The task of ordering a set of events consists in discovering relations among them, or, as we say, in finding empirical laws. In the initial phases of this search we employ the process of inductive generalization from observation and experiment. In the physical sciences this process is straightforward enough, for the scientist in this area is able to arrange for simple systems of observation that permit the isolation and control of a relatively small number of variables. Unfortunately the behavior of living organisms does not yield so readily to simplification and control. The greater complexity of psychological phenomena makes difficult, if not impossible, the experimental isolation and measurement of the relevant variables. Consequently psychologists have found it necessary to guess or theorize much more than physicists had to at this stage of development in their field of knowledge.

As a consequence of the very different stages thus far reached in their development, quite different conceptions of the meaning of the term theory exist in psychology and physics. A theory in present-day physics is a system of highly abstract constructs used to integrate sets of empirical laws that without the theory would appear to be quite unrelated. Examples of such integrating devices are the electromagnetic theory of radiation and the kinetic theory of gases. In contrast, what passes for theory in the be-

havior sciences serves primarily as a device to aid in the formulation of descriptive laws.

Theory in psychology, then, consists primarily in the introduction or postulation of hypothetical constructs to represent the unknown or uncontrolled factors in a situation under observation. The relations of these constructs to the experimental (measured) variables are, in effect, hypothetical guesses at psychological 'laws.' Tolman (1938a) has suggested the term "intervening variable" as a name for these theoretical constructs in psychology because they are assumed to *intervene* between the independent environmental variables on the one hand and the dependent response measures on the other.*

The Task of the Learning Theorist

The task confronting the theorist in the field of learning involves (1) the specification of the experimental variables, environmental and organic, that determine the observed behavioral changes that occur with practice, and (2) the formulation of the functional interrelations (laws) holding between these sets of variables. It is the second of these tasks that has required an extensive use of the intervening variable type of theoretical construct.

Indeed, learning itself is just such a hypothetical construct. This meaning of the term

* A more complete discussion of the various types of theorizing in science and the differences between theory in physics and in psychology may be found in Bergmann (1943), Spence (1945, 1948), and Stevens (1939).

690

is exemplified in the distinction made by many psychologists between the concepts "performance" and "learning." Performance has reference to the observable, measurable response, a purely empirical concept. Learning refers to a hypothetical factor which is assumed, on the one hand, to be the product of the past interactions of the indi-

Figure 1 shows the relations between this type of hypothetical learning construct L, other intervening variables, such as drive D, and the various experimental variables, e.g. present environmental events S, past environmental events, or antecedent conditions AC, and response R. As we shall see, various learning theorists have differed markedly in

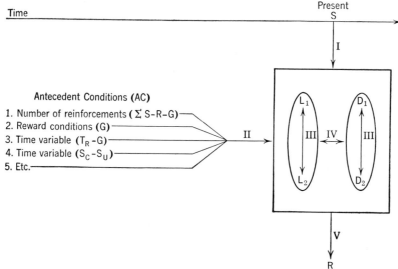

FIG. 1. The relations between intervening theoretical constructs and experimental variables, environmental and response. L and D represent two classes of intervening variables that are assumed to be defined in terms of the antecedent and present environmental variables. They are interrelated with each other and are related to an empirical response measure.

vidual with his environment, and, on the other, to be one of the conditions that determines his performance at any moment. In this sense learning is similar to other constructs representing hypothetical states of the organism, such as drive, fatigue, drug condition, etc., which are assumed to be among the determinants of performance. The learning theorist, in other words, ascribes the progressive changes in behavior that occur in a learning experiment to changes that develop in this hypothetical learning state as a result of previous experiences in the situation. This assumes, of course, that he has taken proper care to control all other factors that affect performance.

the way they have conceived their hypothetical constructs. Some have inferred them entirely from behavior changes or from phenomenological introspection, and have not attempted to tie them up with antecedent environmental conditions. Others have introduced them in terms of antecedent conditions (type II relation in Fig. 1) but have neglected to specify their relations to other nonlearning factors (e.g. drive state, type IV) or even to the response variable (type V). A few have concerned themselves primarily with an account of learning in terms of neurophysiological changes, or have emphasized primarily their intrinsic properties (type III relations). In addition to these differences there have been disagreements as to the method of specifying operationally the antecedent conditions essential for the learning to take place. And last, but probably most confusing, rich and varied jargons have been employed, in which many terms appear to refer to essentially similar notions.

CLASSIFICATION OF LEARNING THEORIES

The Major Issues Dividing Learning Theorists

The classification of learning theories is a purely arbitrary matter. Depending upon the criteria chosen, quite different classificatory schemas may be developed (Dashiell, 1935; Tolman, 1934; Spence, 1942). The distinctions to be made in the present treatment are based upon what appear to be the two major issues dividing learning theorists today. (1) The first of these has to do with the nature of the fundamental concepts (intervening variables) employed to represent the hypothetical changes that take place in learning. (2) The second issue is concerned with the conditions assumed to be necessary for the hypothetical learning changes to occur.

If we designate the rival theories in terms of the type of theoretical construct they favor, we may divide them into perception or S-S (sign-significate) theories on the one hand, and S-R (stimulus-response) theories on the other. If we divide them according to "necessary conditions" we get three groups: (1) reinforcement or law-of-effect theories, (2) theories that do not hold reinforcement to be necessary for learning, and (3) two-factor theories, which assume that there are two basically different learning processes, one governed by the principle of reinforcement, and the other occurring independent of reinforcement.

When we consider the two issues together, we note that there is a marked tendency for those who adopt the same position on the first issue to stick together on the second. Thus most S-S (perception) theorists support the nonreinforcement position, whereas the majority of S-R theorists believe in a law of reinforcement either as a universal law or as a law governing all learning except certain forms of the conditioned response. However, as we shall see, there are a number of exceptions to this tendency, and we find some psychologists who qualify as S-R nonreinforcement theorists and some who propose a theory of learning that is essentially an S-S reinforcement theory.

S-S versus S-R Learning Theories

The characteristics of the two main types of learning theory may be outlined briefly. One group of theorists (Köhler, 1929, 1940; Koffka, 1935; Lewin, 1936, 1942; Tolman, 1932, 1934; Adams, 1931; Zener, 1937) takes the position that learning is to be conceived in terms of the organization (or reorganization) into some kind of functional whole of the perceptual systems of the subject. In sharp contrast is the conception, held by a different group (Thorndike, 1935; Hull, 1943; Guthrie, 1930, 1935; Miller and Dollard, 1941; Spence, 1936) that learning is to be conceived in terms of alterations in the strengths of hypothetical intervening variables, variously referred to as S-R connections, associations, habits, or tendencies.

Learning as perceptual reorganization. The essential notion underlying the S-S theory is that learning is part of a larger problem of organization, including, as a most important aspect, perceptual organization. Instead of thinking of learning in terms of stimuli, responses, and modifiable associative connections, these theorists all agree on emphasizing its perceptual character. Referring to the simple type of learning involved in the conditioned-response situation, Zener writes:

> According to the sign-urge conception [the name he applies to his variation of the theory], the essential structural modification consists in a reorganization into some kind

of functional whole of the perceptual systems (relatively afferent, if you will) corresponding to the conditioned and unconditioned stimuli; and in the functional relation of this organized system to the urge or tension system originally excited by the unconditioned stimulus. [1937, p. 386.]

Koffka (1935) describes learning as equivalent to a perceptual reorganization in which perceptual processes and their traces become organized into complex structures exhibiting field properties. Koffka's treatment of latent learning in the maze provides another good example of this emphasis. He writes:

> What the animal has developed during its "latent learning" is a trace of the maze; this trace, being in communication with the present activity, regulates it more or less as the perception of the maze would. [1935, p. 588.]

Adams (1931), Tolman (1932, 1934, 1936, 1938a), and Lewin (1942) likewise emphasize that learning involves primarily the structuring of the cognitive field of the subject, i.e. the formation and modification of cognitive patterns corresponding to the stimulus relations in the environment. According to Tolman, the most active contributor among the S-S theorists, learning involves the development under the guidance of the principle of contiguity of what he calls a sign-Gestalt-expectation. This is one of his hypothetical intervening variables. It may be thought of as a cognitive pattern in which are organized the successive perceptual processes occurring in a behavior sequence.

As a final example of the perceptual approach to learning, let us consider the following paragraph from White's article (1943) in which he attempted to describe in everyday language the Tolman-Lewin interpretation of learning:

> The perceptual-learning postulate implies the importance of *perceptual 'field' conditions at the time of the original perception,* rather than any subsequent reward or 'rein-

forcement.' This difference is both an affirmation and a denial. It affirms the importance in relation to learning, and not merely in relation to perception, of all those field conditions which have been experimentally shown to influence perceptual organization: temporal contiguity, spatial contiguity, visual continuity, common contrast, embeddedness, exploratory motivation, etc. All of these factors, except temporal contiguity, have been given less emphasis by S-R psychologists. [1943, p. 166.]

Learning as modification of S-R tendencies. The S-R theories formulate their account of learning in terms of stimulus-response connections (bonds, associations, habits, tendencies). Unfortunately these different terms have no clear-cut, single meaning. For some (Gates, 1942; Guthrie, 1942) they seem to refer to a purely empirical concept: the observed functional relation between a situation and a response. At times Thorndike (1940) seems also to have used the concept of S-R bond in this nontheoretical sense.

On the other hand, these terms sometimes refer to a hypothetical learning state (intervening variable). Hull (1943) and Thorndike (1913) have both employed one or another of these concepts in this sense. In effect, Thorndike's three major laws of learning provided definitions of his concept of S-R bond in terms of the experimental conditions, variation of which led to changes in the strength of this hypothetical learning factor. Later, in connection with his experimental studies with human subjects, Thorndike (1932) introduced six additional experimental variables that must, he believes, be taken into account in determining the strength of an S-R bond. These are belongingness, impressiveness, polarity, identifiability, availability, and mental systems (set). It is rather interesting to note that most of these variables are of the type emphasized by the perception-learning theorists, particularly the Gestalters. They refer to the content of the material learned rather than to relations — e.g. temporal — between the contents.

Thorndike's major interest has been in the identification of the experimental conditions that are responsible for the occurrence of learning. In particular he has attempted to discover and describe the properties of a reinforcing state of affairs. He has not been particularly at pains to specify the nature of the functional relation between his hypothetical intervening variable, the S-R bond, and the antecedent experimental conditions. In sharp contrast is Hull's treatment of learning (1943). Hull's theoretical construct, *habit* ($_sH_R$), is very precisely introduced by way of specific equations that relate it to the relevant antecedent experimental conditions — e.g. number of previous reinforcements, quantity of the goal object, time of delay of the reward. In addition, Hull specifies certain additional relations between *habit* and other similarly hypothesized intervening variables (drive, excitatory potential, inhibition, etc.), and he ends by relating all the latter to the several empirical response measures used in conditioning experiments.

So far as emphasis upon the association's being between stimulus and response is concerned, the most explicit of all theorists in this group is Guthrie. He writes:

> Our position is that what is associated is a stimulus and a response. It would perhaps be more exact to say that what is associated is some stimulation of sense organs and a corresponding muscular contraction or glandular secretion. By calling them associated we mean that the stimulation has become the occasion for the response because of a past association of the two. [1942, p. 43.]

Guthrie here seems to use the word "association" in two senses. One refers to the condition of contiguity essential to the establishment of the relation. The other meaning appears to be comparable to the nontheoretical meaning of Thorndike's S-R bond— i.e. the observable relation between stimulus and response. At still other times Guthrie seems to have reference to a more theoretical notion — one roughly comparable to an afferent-efferent tie-up in the nervous system rather than an afferent-afferent connection. Guthrie himself avoided all reference to the nervous mechanisms underlying learning, but his writings imply that the functional tie-up is between sensory events and motor events rather than between the sensory events resulting from the conditioned and unconditioned stimuli.

The Reinforcement — Nonreinforcement (Contiguity) Issue

The second of the two major issues dividing learning theorists is concerned with the conditions deemed essential for the occurrence of the hypothetical learning changes, whether conceived in terms of variations of the strengths of S-R tendencies or as cognitive restructurings. Although the origins of the issue may be traced back to the earliest speculations of philosophers, its modern form dates from the beginning of laboratory investigations near the start of the present century. Out of the studies of Pavlov (1927), Thorndike (1898), and others, there have gradually developed three different positions with respect to the conditions that are essential for learning.

1. One point of view makes the assumption that learning requires some kind of motivating state, primary or secondary, and the occurrence of a reinforcing situation, variously described as drive reduction, satisfying after-effect, success, pleasure, and primary or secondary rewards. Although Thorndike's name has been most prominently associated with this *law-of-effect* type of theory, Thorndike did not himself hold strictly to the view that *all* learning involves the law of effect. Hull (1943), on the other hand, has attempted to develop a theory in which all instances of learning are subsumed under a common principle, the law of effect, or, as he prefers to designate it, the principle of reinforcement.

2. Diametrically opposed to this reinforcement theory may be grouped a number of

theorists whose views on the nature of learning are otherwise quite divergent (Tolman, 1937, 1938b; Lewin, 1942; Guthrie, 1935, 1942; Rexroad, 1932, 1933). They share the belief that reinforcement is not necessary for learning to occur. Although they recognize a number of conditions important for learning to occur — e.g. frequency, recency, and certain perceptual conditions — they emphasize in particular contiguity in experience. Those theorists in the group who consider themselves associationists look upon the law of association by contiguity (and not the law of effect) as the main principle of learning.

3. The third position taken on this theoretical issue represents something of a compromise between the first two. Learning theorists in this category (Thorndike, 1932, 1935; Schlosberg, 1937; Skinner, 1938; Razran, 1939b; Maier and Schneirla, 1942; Stephens, 1942; Tuttle, 1946; Mowrer, 1947) hold that there are two basically different learning processes. To one, the law of effect applies. To the other, reinforcement is unnecessary. Learning under this second process is assumed to be governed by the law of association by contiguity.

These different attitudes toward reinforcement will be discussed in more detail below. But first let us consider their relation to certain types of simple experimental situations.

Classical conditioning, instrumental conditioning, and selective learning (problem solving). Ever since laboratory investigation was first directed at understanding the fundamental nature of the learning process, two experimental techniques have predominated. One involves the so-called trial-and-error (problem-box) situation introduced into the psychological laboratory by Thorndike (1898, 1911), and the other is the classical conditioned-response experiment developed by the Russian physiologists, Pavlov (1902, 1927) and Bekhterev (1932). These two methods have been outstanding not only for the empirical data they have provided but,

more important still, for the extent to which they have influenced learning theory.

The early studies with the problem box gave rise to the law-of-effect interpretation of learning. In this type of situation a selection from among the subject's initial repertory of responses occurs. Thorndike's law of effect accounted for this selection in terms of the different effects or consequences of each response. Satisfying effects were assumed to strengthen the S-R bond or tendency of a response to occur; unsatisfactory or annoying consequences were supposed to have an opposite result. How the concepts of motivation and reward came to dominate the interpretations of the findings obtained with this experimental technique is easily understandable when we stop to consider the important role that each of these factors plays in the situation. The motivation of the subject is an obvious and important determiner of the initial responses made in the situation; variation of the drive produces marked changes in the hierarchy of strengths shown by the different responses. Similarly the environmental consequences of responses, particularly their goal or nongoal character, would seem to bear some kind of relation to the selection process, even if not that postulated by the reinforcement theorists.

In the classical conditioned-response experiment, on the other hand, the emphasis is not upon the effects of the responses and their relation to the motivating state. Instead, a single, measurable aspect of response, the occurrence of which is strictly under the control of the experimenter, is studied. Furthermore the administration of the new stimulus (conditioned) which is to acquire the property of eliciting this response is also under the exact control of the experimenter. The main interest here is in the temporal relation of the conditioned stimulus to the response. The simultaneous occurrence, or close temporal sequence of the events, CS, US, and UR, was regarded by the early experimenters employing this method as the most important factor operating in this situation. Although Pavlov appreciated the necessity for having his subjects motivated, he and other early students of the conditioned response did not stress this factor. The expression, "reinforcement by the unconditioned stimulus," had for Pavlov the physiologist's connotation of facilitation of action rather than that of retroactive strengthening of a response.

In introducing his new behavioristic doctrine, Watson (1914) seized upon the conditioned reflex as the basic unit of behavior. He proposed that the main principle of learning was revealed by this technique to be that of association by contiguity of stimulus and response. Watson claimed this principle held not only for conditioning but also for the more complex trial-and-error type of learning. For the latter he also made use of two subprinciples — frequency and recency. Thus he reasoned not only that the correct response was always the most recent one to occur but also that it would, on the average, occur more frequently than any other response because it takes place at least once on every trial. However, this interpretation assumed erroneously that an incorrect response would occur only once in a trial. In many instances of trial-and-error learning, incorrect responses occur much more frequently than the correct rewarded one, and yet the latter is finally selected and learned. It was primarily this kind of finding that led to the law-of-effect type of explanation of selective learning.

When American experimenters began to investigate CR learning, however, there soon appeared evidence to indicate that the role of motivation and reward had been sadly overlooked by the earlier experimenters. A large number of studies (e.g. Loucks, 1935; Loucks and Gantt, 1938; Culler, 1938; Brogden, 1939a; Brogden, Lipmann, and Culler, 1938) have clearly shown the importance of these factors in the establishment and maintenance of conditioned responses. With this recognition of the role of motivation and reward in the classical conditioning experi-

ment there developed a tendency to regard this type of learning as being essentially similar in nature to problem-solving learning. Following this line of thought, Hull (1937, 1943) reversed the direction of Watson's theorizing and attempted to extend the principle of reinforcement (his formulation of the law of effect) to account for the facts of classical conditioning.

Also helping to bring about this unification of conditioning and problem-box learning has been the development of a new type of experiment known as instrumental conditioning. As was described in a previous chapter, three different experimental arrangements — reward, escape, and avoidance — are usually included under this class of learning situation. The basis on which the three are subsumed under a single category is that, in each, the learned response is *instrumental* in bringing about the goal situation — reward, escape from pain, or avoidance of pain. Actually, the instrumental-avoidance experiment represents a modification of the classical conditioning setup in the direction of the trial-and-error situation. Instead of the noxious US always being administered by the experimenter at a fixed interval after the CS, the CR in this situation may be instrumental in avoiding the US, provided the CR occurs soon enough.

On the other hand, instrumental reward and escape are essentially limiting cases of trial-and-error learning. The selection phase of trial-and-error learning is eliminated, or at least minimized, by arranging for the correct, goal-attaining response to be the response most likely to occur from the beginning. This arrangement, like the classical conditioning setup, permits us to isolate the acquisition process from the complicating effects of the extinction and the spontaneous recovery of erroneous responses. In so far as we succeed in doing this, the situation approaches the classical conditioning setup in its simplicity. Indeed, Hilgard (1936a, b, 1937) has pointed out that the two procedures are essentially the same in terms of the responses that take place. But different responses are measured in the two situations. In instrumental conditioning, the response R_1 that brings the reward — e.g. depressing the lever in the Skinner box — is measured, and the response R_2 to the goal object or US — e.g. chewing the food, salivating, etc. — is ignored. In Pavlov's classical situation, on the other hand, the response R_2 (salivation) to the US, food in the mouth, is measured, and the response R_1 (orienting to the food pan, etc.) is ignored. Theoretical opinion clashes on the issue: can the learning of the two different types of response be explained in terms of the same set of laws, or does it represent two entirely distinct processes governed by quite different laws?

CLASSICAL AND INSTRU-MENTAL CONDITIONING

Reinforcement Theories of Conditioning

The stimulus-response interpretation (Hull). In his *Principles of Behavior*, Hull (1943) has offered a stimulus-response treatment of the findings obtained in the several types of conditioned-response experiments. On the constructs and principles put forward by Pavlov and Thorndike to interpret their original experimental findings, Hull builds a detailed explicit theoretical structure. He looks upon his formulation not only as an account of the phenomena of conditioning, themselves, but also as a theoretical basis for the integration and interpretation of more complex learning phenomena. The relatively simple and highly controlled nature of the conditioned response makes it, Hull believes, the ideal place to look for fundamental mechanisms and principles underlying behavior modification.

Hull sets up a series of postulates that introduce and define a number of intervening variables in terms of the experimental variables that have been shown to play a role in conditioning experiments. These intervening variables are then related to one another and finally to empirical response measures by means of further postulates. One of his fundamental assumptions, the principle of reinforcement, makes explicit the role of motivation and reward in conditioning. In abbreviated form it may be stated as follows: *whenever a response of a motivated organism is followed by a reinforcing state of affairs, there results an increment in the habit strengths ($_SH_R$) of the temporally coincident stimulus components (S_c) to evoke the response.*

A critical part of this formulation is, of course, the notion, "reinforcing state of affairs." A number of different interpretations of this concept have been offered in the past, including Thorndike's earlier hedonistic state of pleasure (1913) and his later definition in terms of objective behavioral criteria (1935). Hull's meaning requires that we first consider the concepts of need, drive, and drive stimulus.

In considering the meaning of Hull's theoretical constructs, we must keep in mind his proclivity for defining them in two different ways—first as an intervening variable introduced in terms of environmental events, and second in physiological terms. We shall for the most part stick to the first definition, adding the physiological meaning whenever it will add to the understanding. Defined in a general manner, need is a state of the organism that results from any deviation of the environment from the optimum biological conditions necessary for survival. More specific needs are defined in terms of specific antecedent conditions in the environment that are under the control of the experimenter — e.g. feeding schedule, administration of noxious stimulus, etc. The concepts, drive D and drive stimulus S_D, are, in turn, defined as hypothetical variables (states) functionally dependent upon the existing need states and hence indirectly upon the antecedent environmental conditions. Physiologically, drive is conceived as a general condition of the nervous system contributed to by all the specific needs of the moment.

Drive stimulus, on the other hand, refers to specific afferent neural impulses aroused by a particular need. There are, presumably, as many different types of drive stimuli as there are primary needs in the organism. The interrelations between these several concepts, with arrows indicating the direction of definition, are shown in Fig. 2.

As a tentative hypothesis Hull proposes to identify his "reinforcing state of affairs" with a reduction in the drive level D or possibly

forcing agents are the familiar appearance of a goal box or food cup, the sight and smell of food, etc.

Unlike Thorndike's law of effect, Hull's principle of reinforcement does not insist that the reinforcing state of affairs is necessarily an effect of a response. It merely states that stimulus-response events occurring in close temporal conjunction with a reinforcing event acquire an increment of habit strength. This, of course, is just what hap-

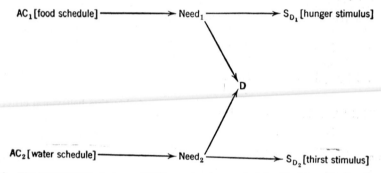

AC₁[food schedule] ⟶ Need₁ ⟶ S_{D₁} [hunger stimulus]

D

AC₂[water schedule] ⟶ Need₂ ⟶ S_{D₂} [thirst stimulus]

Fig. 2. The interrelations between Hull's constructs—need, drive D, drive stimulus S_D, and the antecedent conditions AC in the environment defining them.

with a diminution in the associated drive stimulus S_D. With each need, a response of the organism to some aspect of its environment initiates a sequence of events that culminates in a diminution of the drive. This, in turn, changes the habit strength $_sH_R$. One of the clearest examples of such a primary reinforcing state of affairs is the cessation of a noxious stimulus — e.g. escaping from an electric shock. Supplementing this notion of primary reinforcement, Hull also suggests that there are secondary reinforcing states of affairs. Citing a number of different experiments — e.g. higher-order conditioning, delayed reward, etc. — Hull postulates that all those stimulus-receptor events that have regularly and consistently been associated in time with the reduction in a primary need (or any other stimulus previously so associated) themselves acquire the capacity of acting as reinforcing states of affairs. Examples of such secondary rein-

pens in the Pavlovian CR. The trace of the conditioned stimulus is present at the time the unconditioned response of salivation occurs, and the two are concurrent with the reinforcing event — the receipt of food. The difference between this situation and the typical instrumental and problem-box tasks is that the food produces both the response being learned (conditioned) and the reinforcing state of affairs. As Hull (1942, p. 68) has pointed out, theorists who have not accepted the view that the law of effect holds for Pavlovian conditioning have failed to realize that "food in the mouth" constitutes a reinforcing state of affairs, very possibly a secondary one, by virtue of the past association of this stimulation with primary hunger-drive reduction. According to this interpretation, the Pavlovian conditioned response is merely a special case of the principle of reinforcement.

Similarly Hull (1943, Chapter VI) has shown how the other types of classical and instrumental conditioning are all special cases of learning under the principle of primary or secondary reinforcement. One difference between classical and instrumental conditioning is that in classical conditioning new stimulus-response associations $_sH_R$ are established, whereas in instrumental conditioning (also selective learning), already existent habits are merely strengthened further. As Hull concludes, "the differences between the

In formulating these postulates, Hull has been guided by the available experimental evidence.

The first postulate states how habit strength $_sH_R$ grows or develops with successive reinforced trials N. Hull assumes that the function is exponential: a growth curve in which the increments per trial Δ_sH_R are always a constant fraction of the potential growth still possible. Figure 3

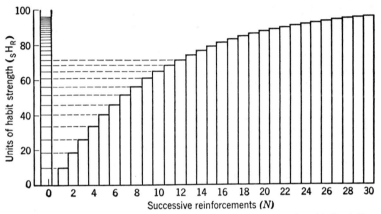

FIG. 3. Diagrammatic representation of the growth of habit strength. At the left are shown the successive increments of habit strength for successive reinforcements. The bars represent the accumulated habit strength at the successive reinforcements. (From Hull, 1943.)

two forms of learning are superficial in nature — i.e. they do not involve the action of fundamentally different principles or laws, but only differences in the *conditions* under which the principle operates" (1943, p. 78).

Hull's principle of reinforcement defines the necessary conditions (motivation and reward) that must hold for the hypothetical learning factor $_sH_R$ to develop. In an operational sense it defines one of the main variables of a learning experiment — the number of reinforcements or trials N. Hull then goes on to specify by means of four subprinciples the experimental variables that determine the strength of a habit or association. These subprinciples or postulates represent attempts on his part to guess at the "laws" or functional relations (type II) holding between the construct of habit $_sH_R$ and the independent experimental variables.

(taken from Hull, 1943, p. 116) provides a picture of this theoretical growth function. At the left of the graph are shown the successive increments of habit for successive reinforcements. The increasing columns to the right represent the amount of accumulated habit strength at the successive reinforcements. An imaginary smooth line joining the tops of each of these columns provides a picture of the hypothetical curve of habit growth that Hull postulates. The equation describing the function is

$$_sH_R = M'(1 - e^{-iN}) \qquad (1)$$

where $M' =$ the limit to which the habit would grow under the particular conditions of the experiment, $N =$ the number of reinforced trials, $i =$ an empirical constant determining the rate of approach of the function to its maximum, and $e =$ the logarithmic base.

The three remaining postulates have reference to experimental conditions that have been found to affect learning. They are: (1) the magnitude (quality) of the reward W — e.g. amount of food reward; (2) the time of delay of the reward T; and (3) a time variable relating the onset of the conditioned stimulus to the occurrence of the response T'. Typically the last variable occurs only in classical conditioning: the time between the conditioned and unconditioned stimulus. The other time variable T has not been varied in conditioning experiments, although it conceivably could be.

On the basis of experimental studies, Hull assumes that each of these variables determines the limit to which the habit will grow with an unlimited number of reinforcements. The assumptions may be stated as follows:

1. Magnitude of the reinforcement. Other things being equal, the limit to which the habit will grow is a positive exponential function of the magnitude of the reinforcing agent.

$$M' = M_o(1 - e^{-kW}) \qquad (2)$$

where M' = limit of habit growth under the particular conditions of the experiment, M_o = limit of habit growth under optimum conditions, W = some objective measurable property describing quantity or quality of goal object, and k = empirical constant.

2. Time of delay of reinforcement. Other things being equal, the limit to which the habit will grow is a negative exponential function of the time between the response and the subsequent occurrence of the reinforcement.

$$M' = M_o e^{-jT} \qquad (3)$$

where T = the time of delay of the reinforcement, and j is an empirical constant. Hull suggests that there is a *primary gradient of reinforcement* of limited extent (from 20 to 40 seconds in the rat) beyond which learning would not occur if the influence of secondary reinforcement could be eliminated from the experimental situation. That is to say, the effect of secondary reinforcement is to extend the actual period of delay in which learning can take place. This secondary extended gradient is Hull's old goal-gradient principle (1932). Spence (1947) has recently proposed that there is no primary gradient of reinforcement but that all learning involving a delay of reward occurs as the result of immediate secondary reinforcement which develops in the situation.

3. Time between the onset of the CS and the occurrence of the US. Other things being equal, the limit to which the habit will grow is a negative exponential function of the time between the onset of a continuously acting conditioned stimulus and the occurrence of the unconditioned stimulus.

$$M' = M_o e^{-u(T'-c)} \qquad (4)$$

where T' = the time between the onset of the conditioned stimulus and the occurrence of the unconditioned stimulus, c = an empirical constant that determines the time interval at which conditioning is optimum (when T is less than c, the terms in the parentheses should be reversed $c - T'$), and u = an empirical constant.*

By substituting in equation 1 the several values for M' given in equations 2, 3, and 4, a single equation stating habit strength as a function of four variables may be obtained as follows:

$$sH_R = M_o(1 - e^{-kW})e^{-jT}e^{-u(T'-c)}(1 - e^{-iN})$$

Hull does not, of course, consider that this equation is either complete or final. Recognizing that there are possibly other factors that enter into the determination of habit strength in simple conditioning, the present equation is offered merely as a point of departure for further experimental analysis.†

* In trace conditioning the time interval T'' is between the cessation of the conditioned stimulus and the onset of the unconditioned stimulus. The equation is $M' = M_o e^{-hT''}$.

† A number of other theorists have offered mathematical equations purporting to describe the hypothetical changes going on in learning or the resultant of these changes (Graham and

In addition to this hypothetical learning construct $_sH_R$, Hull introduces certain other intervening variables in terms of experimental conditions that have been shown to affect the strength of the conditioned response. As these are nonlearning factors, we shall not treat them in detail but shall merely indicate in general terms their interrelations with the other hypothetical and experimental variables.

It is well known that the strength of the measured response is a function of the drive strength present at the moment (Warden, 1931; Perin, 1942). An instrumental or conditioned response may be greatly weakened, even eliminated, if the drive strength on which it is based is reduced. Hull has assumed that habit and drive interact in a multiplicative manner to determine the strength of a response, and he introduces another hypothetical construct, excitatory potential $_sE_R$, to represent the combined action or effects of these two factors. That is,

$$_sE_R = f(H \times D)$$

Note that this conception of Hull's does not ascribe any response-evoking properties to habits (associations) independent of the drive.

Motivation or need also enters into Hull's formulation in a second manner. It provides a component S_D of the stimulus complex which acquires $_sH_R$ to evoke the response. This particular motivational concept was emphasized in Hull's earlier theoretical articles (Hull, 1930b, 1931).

Another factor that may under certain conditions be an important determiner of response strength is identified by Hull under the concept of inhibitory potential I_r. This hypothetical state is assumed to result from the occurrence of the response itself, the amount of inhibition generated being a function of the amount of work involved in the act, the number of occurrences, and the degree of massing

Gagné, 1940; Thurstone, 1930; Gulliksen and Wolfle, 1938; Wiley and Wiley, 1937; Pitts, 1943; Spence, 1936).

or distribution of the trials. If the situation is one in which the response does not involve much work and the interval between trials is long, then this factor is relatively unimportant and can be ignored. When inhibitory potential is generated it is assumed to oppose excitatory potential, and their algebraic summation is designated by Hull as effective excitatory potential $_s\bar{E}_R$. These relations may be stated as follows:

$$I_r = f(N, W, F)$$

$$_s\bar{E}_R = {_sE_R} - I_r$$

where N = the number of trials in which response has occurred, W = amount of work involved in performance of the act, and F = the frequency of occurrence of the response per unit of time, i.e. rate.

The two remaining theoretical constructs employed by Hull in his treatment of simple learning are behavioral oscillation $_sO_R$ and reaction threshold $_sL_R$. Behavioral oscillation is introduced in order to take care of the well-known phenomenon that measures of response, even when showing no systematic change, nevertheless exhibit marked variability. From the fact that such measures tend to distribute themselves according to the normal probability function, Hull has ascribed normal variability to this construct. He further conceives of $_sO_R$ as an oscillating inhibitory potential, which acts against effective reaction potential $_s\bar{E}_R$ to produce at any moment what he terms the momentary effective reaction potential, $_s\dot{\bar{E}}_R$. Thus

$$_s\dot{\bar{E}}_R = {_s\bar{E}_R} - {_sO_R}$$

The presence of such an uncontrolled oscillation factor in living organisms is a major perturbation that makes it difficult to discover laws concerning behavior. It precludes the possibility of predicting the exact momentary behavior of a single organism and necessitates the use of a number of subjects or a number of observations of a single subject.

The concept of threshold $_sL_R$ is defined as the minimal value of the momentary effective reaction potential $_s\dot{\bar{E}}_R$ that will evoke an observable response. The value of $_s\bar{\dot{E}}_R - _sL_R$ must be greater than zero for a response to occur. This construct of $_sL_R$, like that of $_sO_R$, is not defined by Hull in terms of antecedent environmental conditions, but is rather to be regarded as a parameter characteristic of individual subjects. As yet Hull has not made clear whether $_sL_R$ is the same for all response systems in a subject or whether it varies from one response system to another.

With these intervening theoretical constructs, defined in the manner described above, Hull next completes his theory by relating them to the several empirical response measures employed in conditioning experiments, i.e. frequency of responses occurring in a block of trials, resistance to extinction in terms of number of trials to an extinction criterion, amplitude or magnitude of response, and latency of response. We shall consider only one of these measures as an example of Hull's procedure.

REACTION PROBABILITY (R_p) AS A FUNCTION OF THE EFFECTIVE REACTION POTENTIAL $_s\bar{E}_R$. Other things being equal, the probability p of a response occurring to the conditioned stimulus is related by the normal probability integral to the extent to which the effective reaction $_s\bar{E}_R$ exceeds the reaction threshold $_sL_R$. This relation is not arbitrarily assumed at this point but follows from the earlier definitions of the oscillating inhibitory potential $_sO_R$, the reaction threshold $_sL_R$, and the effective reaction potential $_s\bar{E}_R$. As $_s\bar{E}_R$ increases above the value of $_sL_R$, the percentage of momentary effective reaction potentials $_s\bar{\dot{E}}_R$ that remain above $_sL_R$ after the depressing effect of $_sO_R$ will increase. Moreover this increase will follow the normal probability integral, since the $_sO_R$ values are assumed to be distributed according to the bell-shaped normal probability function. The frequency (percentage) of occurrence of responses as a function of $_s\bar{E}_R$ will be the same as that of the $_s\bar{\dot{E}}_R$'s, since a response occurs on each occasion that an $_s\bar{\dot{E}}_R$ is above the threshold value $_sL_R$. A corollary of these relations is that the curve of frequency of conditioned responses, as a function of the number of reinforcement

trials [$R_p = f(N)$], will be either S-shaped or negatively accelerated, depending upon certain conditions which the theory is able to specify.

There are a number of other constructs and principles in Hull's treatment of conditioning, such as the principle of primary generalization, with its associated construct of effective habit strength $_s\bar{H}_R$, the principle of afferent neural interaction, the principle governing the summation of excitatory tendencies, etc. By means of these various postulates Hull is able to account for most of the phenomena of conditioning. Indeed the whole system of related constructs is based on the findings in this relatively highly controlled type of experimental situation. It represents an attempt to guess at the main variables and laws governing changes in response. The value of the formulation may be measured not only in terms of its success in explaining the phenomena of conditioning but also in terms of the extent to which the same constructs and principles may be used to integrate the phenomena of more complex learning. Finally, Hull's system possesses the virtue that all learning is governed by a common fundamental principle—the principle of reinforcement—rather than by a number of exclusive principles.

S-S reinforcement theory (*Woodworth*). Although most S-S theorists do not stress the role of reinforcement, Woodworth (1947) offers an interpretation that emphasizes both the perceptual nature of learning and the principle of reinforcement. Applied to conditioning, Woodworth's view is that reinforcement is responsible for the hypothetical learning change, but that this change is not to be thought of in terms of the strengthening of the connection between the CS and the CR. Instead, Woodworth employs the concept of *expectancy* and states that the definiteness of the expectancy is what is reinforced. Expectancy is further described as involving a perception or registration of the sequence of stimulus events. As Woodworth writes, "The new learning, the conditioning, is sensory and not motor. The change that takes place in him during the process of conditioning is a change in his way of receiving, or perceiving, the sequence of stimuli" (1947, p. 122).

In addition to recognizing the usual reinforcing role of goal objects for which the subject is motivated, Woodworth also postulates that simple perceptual learning is motivated by "a direct, inherent motive which might be called the will to perceive" (1947, p. 123). The attainment of a clear perception is itself a reinforcing event, according to Woodworth.

Contiguity Theories of Conditioning

S-R contiguity theory (Guthrie). One of the most persistent attempts to develop a theory of learning that has no recourse whatever to a reinforcement principle is that of Guthrie (1930, 1935, 1942). Relating his formulation to the earlier doctrines of the English associationists (Locke, Hume, Mill, etc.), Guthrie suggests that his version of associationism might best be described as "behavioristic associationism." For the older notion of association between subjective mentalistic events Guthrie substitutes the concept that the principle of association applies to observable stimulus and response events.

Starting with the phenomena of classical conditioning, Guthrie first carefully distinguishes between two concepts of response — movement and act. Movement refers to specific glandular and motor patterns of action such as salivary secretion, foreleg flexion, etc. An act, on the other hand, is a class of movements, defined in terms of its effects or end results, regardless of the particular pattern of effector activity involved. Examples of the latter are: opening a door, pulling at a loop, and depressing a lever. It is the latter concept of response, it will be observed, that is employed in instrumental and trial-and-error learning, whereas classical conditioning is concerned with movements. Guthrie begins his theoretical formulation with the phenomena of

classical conditioning because he believes that the basic laws of learning apply directly to movements and not to acts or accomplishments.

The main principle governing the development of associations between stimulus and response movements is *association by contiguity.* This principle states, *"A stimulus pattern that is acting at the time of a response will, if it recurs, tend to produce that response"* (1942, p. 23). The essential and sufficient condition for learning, according to this principle, is simultaneity of stimulus pattern and responses. Motivation, in the form of a drive state such as hunger, and the US serve merely to assure that the response to be conditioned will occur. Their function is that of a "forcer" of the response rather than that of a "reinforcer" of a connection.

Guthrie's principle of association, it will be observed, is an empirical generalization referring to observable stimulus and response events and relations between them. As such it is quite different from Hull's principle of reinforcement which introduces and defines a hypothetical learning factor — habit ($_sH_R$). Although Guthrie is inclined to keep his theorizing at the level of "observable and namable items" as he describes it, he nevertheless goes on to speculate on how such secondary experimental variables as frequency and vividness operate to affect the strength (probability) of a tendency to respond. He offers this theory in place of the more traditional physiological hypothesis of variation of resistances at synaptic connections in the nervous system.

According to Guthrie's theory, association is established in a single trial. This means that all the stimulus cues (elements) present on the occasion of a particular response become associated in an all-or-none manner with this response. If exactly the same pattern of cues were present on the next occasion, the response would inevitably occur and conditioning would be said to have occurred in a single trial. Although conditioning may on occasion occur in a single trial, it more typically develops only gradually. The explanation of this apparent contradiction is to be found in Guthrie's hypothetical construct, stimulus cues or elements. It is these elements, exteroceptive, proprioceptive, and interoceptive, that are assumed to become associated in an all-or-none manner with the response, and they remain so associated unless a different response is made to occur in their presence because of the activity of different stimulus elements. The gradual increase in the probability of occurrence of a conditioned response with successive trials results from the fact that more and more of the potential stimulus elements in the stimulating situation become associated with the response. In the classical situation the unfailing occurrence of the unconditioned response, due to the administration of the unconditioned stimulus, insures that eventually all or a sufficient majority of the cue elements will become associated with the response and insure its evocation.

Guthrie's concept of stimulus cue and his assumption of association between these cues and response movements are certainly not observable, point-at-able events. They are typical theoretical constructs put forward to account for the phenomena of behavior.*

The instrumental conditioned response and the successful response in trial-and-error learning are likewise acquired by the principle of association by contiguity. Unlike the setup in classical conditioning, however, there is no unconditioned stimulus in these situations to force the occurrence of the to-be-learned response from the beginning of the experiment. In the problem box the subject makes a series of trial responses. Each one, Guthrie assumes, becomes associated in all-or-none fashion to the particular pattern of concurrently acting stimulus cues and then becomes disassociated as another different response occurs and replaces it as the associated response. Finally the response

leading to success — i.e. the goal situation — occurs, and the sequence stops. In instrumental learning, as described previously, the trial sequence is minimized and the successful goal-attaining response occurs more promptly in the sequence, possibly even from the beginning. In either case the attainment of the goal ends the sequence, whereas the process continues after each nongoal-attaining response.

Recognizing that success, rewards, goal attainment, etc., play an important role in such learning, Guthrie nevertheless rejects the notion that these effects in any way act to establish the association between the situation and the appropriate response. The role of the after-effects of the successful response is to change the situation and make this response the last one to occur. Being the last to take place in the situation, this response will remain associated with it and will tend to recur when the situation occurs again. Reinforcing events thus serve to preserve one among the set of associations established by the principle of association.

There are a number of ways in which the successful response may change the stimulus complex. It might lead to escape from a distressing stimulus, such as getting out of a cage with a grid floor. The attainment of food in a problem box would likewise change the stimulus situation. Here Guthrie does not conceive of the food as immediately relieving the primary hunger drive but as eliminating a state of excited restlessness, annoyance, or conflict present before the food was reached.

Guthrie and Horton (1946) cite extensive experimental data to support this theory. Other experiments and discussions bearing on the theory are those of Seward (1942, 1943) and O'Connor (1946). The latter believes that the occurrence of learning when the reward is delayed is contradictory to Guthrie's theory and supports a reinforcement theory.*

* For a discussion of certain experimental data that tend to support Guthrie's hypothetical picture of classical conditioning, see Spence (1942, p. 303).

* Only one other writer, Rexroad (1932, 1933), has proposed an interpretation of learning along

The S-S contiguity interpretation (Tolman). Most S-S perception theorists emphasize contiguity and depreciate reinforcement. Tolman's extensive writings (1932, 1934, 1936, 1937, 1945) best exemplify this point of view. Tolman introduces explicitly a number of theoretical constructs to aid his formulation of the laws of behavior. His main construct is variously termed sign-Gestalt-expectation, cognition, hypothesis, or expectancy. It is described as a cognitive set or pattern within the subject which reflects relations in the experienced environment. In classical conditioning an expectation is built up to the effect that the first stimulus (called a sign) is going to be followed without further activity on the part of the subject by the second stimulus (called a significate). The expectation in the case of instrumental conditioning includes not only the knowledge of the sequence of the two stimulus events but also a further cognition relating to the behavior necessary to bring about the significate. Such a sign-Gestalt-expectation reveals itself by the fact that, given adequate motivation, the subject continues to exhibit the appropriate behavior as long as the particular arrangement of events in the environment actually obtains.

The experimental conditions assumed by Tolman to underly the acquisition of these expectancies constitute his definition of this theoretical construct. Recognizing that our knowledge is as yet incomplete, Tolman does not attempt the very specific type of postulate employed by Hull. Instead he discusses, in a very general fashion, three classes of variables and laws that he believes are important determiners of the formation of cognitions:

1. Gestalt laws relating to stimulus organization. These laws refer to conditions such as visual continuity, embeddedness, belongingness, fusibility, etc., which influence per-

ceptual organization and hence learning. Very little is known as yet about how these factors relate to conditioning.

2. Laws concerned with the sequence of sign, behavior and significate. Here Tolman mentions factors such as the frequency and recency with which the three components of a sign-Gestalt-expectation — sign, behavior, and significate — have been experienced in the past. Other variables included in this group are such temporal factors as the time between the conditioned and unconditioned stimulus in classical conditioning, and the delay of the reward in instrumental conditioning. Tolman's fundamental law of association should also be included here, for according to him these hypothetical expectancies are acquired because sign, behavior, and significate follow one another in experience. This sequence is a necessary condition for learning; other factors facilitate or inhibit the process.

3. Laws specifying motivational conditions. The findings of latent learning lead Tolman to reject the reinforcement principle. Accepting the observed fact that the reward value of the significate may affect performance, Tolman nevertheless denies that it plays a part in learning per se—i.e. in the formation of the sign-Gestalt-expectations. The law of effect, he believes, is a law of performance rather than a law of learning. Since the organism's performance B is a joint function of its cognitions C and its motivational states M — i.e. $B = f(C, M)$ — its performance varies with different significates, depending upon the extent to which they are "demanded." The "demand" value of a significate depends, in turn, upon the momentary needs of the subject. Thus a response that leads to a significate the subject needs will be stronger than a response leading to an indifferent significate.

A motivational variable that may affect the acquisition of sign-Gestalt-expectations is the vividness or emphatic character of the conditions accompanying either the sign or the significate, or both. Either pleasant or

the general lines of Guthrie's theory. Watson was an S-R association theorist, but his conception differed on many details from that of Guthrie.

painful experiences may accelerate learning, but it is because of their emphasizing or compelling character, not their attendant success or failure. Studies showing that learning speeds up when an electric shock follows the correct response provide a basis for the law of emphasis.

In addition to sign-Gestalt-expectation (the hypothetical learning change) Tolman introduces other intervening variables defined in terms of independent experimental conditions, including environmental and subject variables. Among these are the constructs of demand, appetite, differentiation, and biases. Presumably, when the theory is completed there will be further "second-line," "third-line," and possibly even more highly derived intervening variables. As Tolman writes: "These latter are further displaced toward the final behavior and they depend not only upon certain independent variables but also upon combinations of various of the preceding 'first-line' and 'second-line' variables" (1936, p. 99). Eventually the response measures are to be stated as functions of these intervening variables, thus completing the theorizing.

It should be realized that Tolman is not offering a finished theory of even simple learning phenomena, but only a blueprint outlining the formal structure of a theory. His treatment of the functions (definitions) specifying his second- and third-line intervening variables is even more vague than his description of such constructs as sign-Gestalt-expectation and demand. He is content to suggest that Lewin's topological and dynamic constructs indicate the most promising approach to an adequate formulation.

In this connection it is rather interesting to note that White (1943), in attempting to implement Tolman's theory with more specific postulates, suggested that cognitions and needs combine in a multiplicative manner to determine response strength. This assumption is precisely the same as Hull's (1943). It is the writer's opinion that, as Tolman's theory is developed, the essential similarity

of its formal structure to that of Hull's theory will become more and more apparent. The most fundamental difference between them at the moment is the question whether or not reinforcement is a necessary condition for the development of the hypothetical learning factor.

Two-Factor Theories of Conditioning

In contrast to the foregoing attempts to account for classical and instrumental conditioning by a single set of laws, a number of psychologists have stressed the differences between them and have held to the view that they cannot be reduced to a single system. Skinner (1935, 1938) was one of the first to distinguish carefully between the two types of conditioning. His earlier article implied, although not too explicitly, that one type of response (instrumental) is acquired on the basis of the law of effect, whereas the other type (classical) is acquired on the basis of the principle of conditioning (presumably contiguity). In *The Behavior of Organisms* he definitely adopted this position (1938, p. 111). Referring to the two types of conditioned response as type R (instrumental) and type S (classical), Skinner made the further suggestion that a rough topographical distinction could be made between them: the type R responses are largely skeletal, whereas the type S responses involve primarily those types of effectors, smooth muscles and glands, that are controlled by the autonomic nervous system.

One of the most explicit early treatments of conditioning as involving two different kinds of learning is that of Schlosberg (1937). Certain experimental comparisons between classical (defense) conditioning and the avoidance type of conditioning led Schlosberg to propose two distinct types, governed by two quite different basic laws: (1) simple conditioning (classical) in which the principal law is temporal contiguity of the stimulus and response, and (2) 'effect' learning in which the success or satisfying consequences of the response determines the learning. Schlosberg also differentiated between the types of response learned in the two kinds of conditioning. The type of CR governed by contiguity was described as diffuse, preparatory activity, and from the examples given (changes in electrical skin resistance, breathing rhythm, etc.) it is apparent that his conception was very close to Skinner's notion that they are autonomically controlled. Conditioned responses acquired on the basis of the law of effect — i.e. success — were described as involving the more precise skeletal musculature.

Schlosberg was not entirely sure, however, that the distinction he offered was basic. He looked upon it primarily as an aid to the present understanding of certain experimental findings in the field of conditioning, and he recognized the possibility that the instances of conditioning for which he invoked the law of effect might eventually be explainable by the principle of conditioning (contiguity).

This dual interpretation of conditioned response learning has been taken up again by Mowrer (1947), heretofore a vigorous supporter of the notion that all learning operates under the law of effect. In his earlier writings (1938, 1940, 1946) Mowrer attempted to show how all the various types of classical conditioning could be explained in terms of the same basic law (effect) that governs instrumental and problem-solving learning. In particular, his concepts of anxiety as a secondary drive and anxiety-reduction as reinforcement demonstrated how it was possible to bring the avoidance type of conditioned response — e.g. eyelid conditioning to air puff, finger and leg withdrawal from grid, etc. — within the realm of the law of effect. According to this conception the subject acquires during the early stages of practice a conditioned fear response (anxiety) to the conditioned stimulus as signal. During this period the overt defense response also occurs to the shock stimulus and becomes conditioned to the signal by reason of the primary reinforcement provided by

the cessation of the shock. When this latter response occurs prior to the onset of the shock, it leads, of course, to avoidance of the shock and the failure of primary reinforcement. The fact that such conditioning is benefited by this failure of primary reinforcement seemed to be unexplainable by a law-of-effect theory. The solution suggested by Mowrer was that it is the reduction of the secondary (anxiety) drive with the cessation of the conditioned stimulus that provides for the reinforcement.

Mowrer still believes that classical conditioned responses involving skeletal-muscle activity (eyelid response, leg flexion, etc.) are mediated by drive termination (satisfaction) but that emotional conditioning involving responses controlled by the autonomic nervous system is not. The conditioning of autonomic responses is governed, he believes, by contiguity. Accordingly the major differentiation should be between classical emotional conditioning on the one hand, and instrumental and classical conditioning involving skeletal responses on the other. The latter are merely special cases of problem solving and are acquired in the same way — i.e. through the action of the law of effect.

Other writers, Razran (1939b), Maier and Schneirla (1942), Stephens (1942), and Tuttle (1946), have also suggested some form of dual interpretation of conditioning. Finally, attention should be called to the fact that Thorndike (1931), for all his emphasis upon the law of effect, never held strictly to the belief that all learning occurs as a consequence of reinforcement. Even in his favorite experiments — trial-and-error learning — he recognized that mere repetition of an S-R connection might in time result in some small amount of strengthening, provided other conditions, such as belongingness, were adequate. On the basis of Thorndike's own experiments, however, it would appear that exercise without reinforcement has little or no strengthening effect on responses. Indeed, failure of reinforcement to occur seems to lead to an actual weakening (extinction) of a response tendency.

So far as the Pavlovian type of conditioned response is concerned, Thorndike has held to the view that it is a special instance of learning. He has not been convinced that this experiment would ever throw much light on the general principles governing learning. Conditioning was likened by Thorndike to a form of learning, *associative shifting*, in which the selective or trial-and-error process is eliminated. A simple instance of such associative shifting is the learning of a cat to approach at the call of "kitty, kitty" after these sounds have been combined on a number of occasions with the sight of a bowl of milk. However, both belongingness and satisfaction usually operate in ordinary associative shifting, whereas Thorndike claimed that Pavlov and his followers regarded the time relations alone as adequate for the establishment of conditioned reflexes. The following quotation from the Messinger Lectures sums up Thorndike's evaluation of the conditioned reflex studies:

> If we observe the two sorts of learning side by side, we shall, I think, find that the trial-and-success learning is more important for learning in general than the acquisition of conditioned reflexes. Indeed, I venture, though somewhat timorously, the prophecy that the phenomena of the pure conditioned reflex will teach us more about excitability than about learning. [1932, p. 112.]

The Reinforcement-Contiguity Issue

Types of reinforcement theories and the empirical law of effect. Considerable confusion in discussions of the reinforcement theory has resulted from failure to differentiate clearly between the law of effect (1) as an empirical statement, (2) as a general theory of reinforcement, and (3) as special hypotheses concerning the nature of reinforcers and their mode of acting. Critics have often cited evidence to refute reinforcement theory, which was relevant, if at all,

only to one of the special hypotheses as to the nature of a reinforcing state of affairs. In this section we shall examine the distinction between the law of effect and the various types of reinforcement theories.

McGeoch gives the following statement of an empirical law of effect: "Acts are fixated and eliminated as functions of their effects" (1942, p. 574). This formulation may be elaborated to say that responses leading to certain types of environmental consequences (called "rewards") become stronger and are retained, whereas responses leading to certain other types of after-effects (named nonrewards) become weaker and eventually disappear.

Contrary to common claims, there is nothing circular about this statement. It merely states the observed fact that different things subsequently happen to responses that are followed by different environmental consequences. Two different classes of environmental after-effects can be identified and named. The terms applied (reward and nonreward) need not carry with them any implication whatsoever that the after-effects act in a retroactive manner on stimulus-response bonds. Thorndike has called attention to the fact that very similar, possibly the same set of stimulus events (rewards and nonrewards) may also be differentiated from one another by a behavior test that is independent of the learning experiment. Thus he points out that a reward situation (he called it a satisfier) is "one which the animal does nothing to avoid, often doing such things as to attain and preserve it." A nonreward, or annoying situation, to use Thorndike's term, "is one which the animal does nothing to preserve, often doing things which put an end to it." (Thorndike, 1913).

Such formulations are purely empirical. They state relations between observed response happenings and two different classes of observable environmental events. At this point a general theory of reinforcement may be introduced to account for these observations. The theory might make the assumption that the two different types of environmental after-effects of responses operate, *in some unspecified manner*, to change (strengthen or weaken) the functional connections of the responses with their stimuli. The assumption is also usually made that the action of the after-effect on the learning change (S-R connection, S-S cognition, etc.) is direct (Thorndike) and automatic (Hull). Thorndike's latest treatment of reinforcement theory (1935) comes closest to being just such a purely general theory of reinforcement. He makes no assumption about the nature of a satisfier (reward), specifically stating that it is independent of sensory pleasure. A satisfier is assumed by him to arouse an unknown confirming reaction called the OK reaction. The arousal of this reinforcing process strengthens the connection upon which it impinges. In contrast to such a general theory of reinforcement, supporters of a nonreinforcement (contiguity) theory would deny that the change, increment in the strength of the response, is contingent on the subsequent occurrence of the satisfier. Thus Guthrie would say that the occurrence of the response itself results in an increase in its strength (really an increase in the number of potential cues that are associated with the response). For Guthrie the satisfier serves only the function of protecting these associations by eliminating the maintaining stimuli.

Going beyond this general theory of reinforcement are special hypotheses that attempt to specify (1) the nature of the reinforcing state of affairs and/or (2) the manner in which they strengthen the connection or association. The earliest hedonistic theories contained a special hypothesis concerning the differential nature of after-affects. Pleasant experiences were assumed to strengthen responses they followed, whereas unpleasantness led to weakening. Troland (1928) worked out a hedonistic theory that involved not only the psychological factors of pleasantness and unpleasantness but also a parallel physiological account. Different situations following action were assumed to stimulate one of three types of receptors: beneceptors, neutroceptors and nociceptors. Nociception was assumed to lead by retroflex action of the thalamus to a decrease in the conductance of the then-operating cortical adjustors (synapses). Beneceptor activity, on the other hand, was supposed to increase the conductance of the operating cortical adjustors. Finally, pleasantness was identified with increase of conductance and unpleasantness with decrease.

Another group of theorists (Kuo, 1921; Perrin and Klein, 1926) described the reinforcing situation in terms of the re-establishment of equilibrium or relief from drive. In his *Principles of Behavior* (1943) Hull adopted this type of hypothesis. A primary reinforcing state of affairs is identified by Hull with either the reduction in drive level D or a reduction in the intensity of the drive stimulus S_D. Whenever such a reduction occurs, it presumably sets off the reinforcing machinery (unspecified). According to Hull, secondary reinforcing agents consist of stimulus events that, having consistently and repeatedly occurred in conjunction with drive-stimulus-reduction in the past, apparently have acquired the capacity to activate the reinforcing machinery.

Because Hull's concept of secondary reinforcement does not involve drive reduction, it has been claimed that he is not a consistent reinforcement theorist. This criticism fails to note, however, that Hull does not abandon a reinforcement position in the case of secondary reinforcement, but only the special hypothesis that reinforcement always involves drive-stimulus reduction.

Miller and Dollard (1941) take a consistent stand on the question of the nature of reinforcement. They hypothesize that all reinforcement, both primary and secondary, involves drive-stimulus reduction. Secondary reinforcement, like that involved in anxiety reaction, is assumed to involve a reduction in the intensity of the response-produced stimuli constituting the secondary drive. Like Hull, these writers do not speculate on the nature of the physiological mechanisms by which the increase in habit strength is brought about.

The essential point to note here is that the various interpretations of reinforcement vary greatly in the extent to which they make special hypotheses about the nature of a reinforcing state of affairs. Many of the criticisms of reinforcement theory are really directed at these special hypotheses and are not relevant to the more general theory.

Experimental evidence on the reinforcement-contiguity issue. A final decision on the issue of whether some form of reinforcement principle is required to account for learning must await further experimental investigation. There are, however, some data already available that support the interpretation that reinforcement is a necessary element, at least in the conditioning of skeletal responses. Loucks (1935) reported an experiment in which he failed to obtain conditioning, to a buzzer, of a leg flexion elicited by direct faradic stimulation of the motor cortex of a dog. When food (reinforcement) was given following the leg flexion, however, conditioning took place. Another study pointing in the same direction is that of Loucks and Gantt (1938). These investigators found that leg flexion, elicited by electrical stimulation in the region of the spinal cord carrying kinesthetic fibers, could not be conditioned to a buzzer signal. When the shock was applied to the posterior root ganglion, thus involving pain fibers, the conditioning did occur. This result seems to show that some kind of motivational condition must be provided. The reinforcement theorist — e.g. Hull — would say that the pain drive and its reduction (reinforcing state of affairs) were necessary for the learning to occur. These two experimental studies lend strong support, then, to the view that reinforcement plays a critical role in the acquisition of conditioned responses involving skeletal systems. They do not, how-

ever, bear on the question whether emotional conditioning is or is not dependent on reinforcement.*

One type of experimental evidence that has been cited as embarrassing for the reinforcement view, and as favoring a contiguity interpretation, is the phenomenon of sensory preconditioning. Brogden (1939b, 1947) and Karn (1947) have shown that, if prior to conditioning a stimulus (e.g. a tone) to evoke a response it is presented simultaneously for a number of trials with a second stimulus (e.g. a light), the latter will, in subsequent tests, also tend to evoke the conditioned response. Control conditions have ruled out the possibility that the phenomenon is one of sensory generalization, and it has been interpreted as evidence that some connection, some sensory conditioning, was established during the original combined presentation of the two stimuli. There is reason to question, however, whether this evidence is critical for the reinforcement view. In the first place the conditioning is very weak, and in the human experiments it is not entirely clear whether it represents genuine conditioning or whether the responses occur as the result of complex voluntary sets established in the subject. Brogden has explicitly recognized this possibility and has concluded: "The experimental conditions of the phenomenon of sensory preconditioning are not necessarily critical for any learning theory" (1947, p. 538). But even should it be shown that some form of sensory conditioning is established in this type of experiment, there remains the possibility that one or the other of the two stimuli is sufficiently intense to produce a mild drive state, and hence for its cessation to produce a reinforcing state of affairs. The employment of very weak forms of stimulation and the elimination of any tendency of the stimuli to produce startle responses are necessary conditions if the ex-

---

* These two studies have been conspicuous by their absence from discussions of this problem by pychologists unsympathetic toward the reinforcement view (Hilgard, 1948; Leeper, 1944; Postman, 1947).

periment is to be critical for reinforcement theories.

Another experimental finding that has been interpreted as contradictory to the view that the strength of a conditioned response is a function of the number of reinforcements is that obtained in studies in which partial or intermittent reinforcement has been employed. A number of investigations (Humphreys, 1939, 1940, 1943; Finger, 1942a, b; Mowrer and Jones, 1946; and others) have shown that partial (50 per cent) reinforcement may lead (1) to as much conditioning, and (2) to greater resistance to extinction than reinforcement on every trial. Such evidence has been interpreted by a number of writers (Humphreys, 1943; Postman, 1947; Hilgard, 1948) not only as refuting the reinforcement interpretation but also as evidence that the relevant variable determining response strength is the number of trials on which the response occurs.

Hull (1940–41) suggests that the greater resistance to extinction found in the experiments with human subjects is to be explained partly in terms of stimulus patterning. He points out that when the shift is made from conditioning to extinction there is less change in the stimulus pattern to which the response is conditioned in the 50-per-cent group than in the 100-per-cent group. With this lesser change in the stimulus pattern, the conditioned response is stronger and more resistant to extinction in the 50-per-cent group. The explanation for the greater change in the stimulus pattern of the 100-per-cent group is that the trace of the unconditioned stimulus is no longer present in the stimulus during the extinction period. In the partial reinforcement group, on the other hand, such a stimulus pattern (i.e. one lacking trace of the previous unconditioned stimulus) is present and is reinforced on some of the original conditioning trials.

Denny (1946) has also shown that such partial reinforcement experiments have another factor inherent in them which must be taken into consideration. When care is taken to control (eliminate) secondary reinforcement in the learning of a T-maze by a group of subjects receiving 50-per-cent reinforcement, learning is definitely slower than in the case of the 100-per-cent group. In fact, the 50-per-cent group required exactly twice as many trials (and hence the same number of reinforcements) to learn the T-maze as did the 100-per-cent group. Denny's experiment clearly shows the defect of the earlier studies and supports the view that learning is a function of the number of reinforcements rather than the number of practice trials.

Finally, passing mention should be made of the so-called latent learning studies (Blodgett, 1929; Tolman and Honzik, 1930; etc.) although they have involved a more complex learning situation than the conditioned response. Tolman's assumption of the contiguity principle is based primarily on these studies, which show that, when reward is introduced after a number of unrewarded trials in a maze, the error curve typically exhibits a sudden, marked drop greatly exceeding the usual effects of a single reward. Tolman explains the sudden improvement on the basis of the learning or acquisition of sign-Gestalt-expectations during the earlier unrewarded trials. These cognitions are utilized, according to his view, only when a reward is introduced into the goal box, thereby setting up a differential demand. Granting the genuineness of the latent learning phenomenon, there still remains to be explained the rather remarkable speed with which the critical cognition, "that food is in this particular locus," i.e. the goal box, was acquired. That more evidence is needed in order to settle the reinforcement-contiguity issue is shown by the findings of Reynolds (1945), Karn and Porter (1946), Spence and Lippitt (1946), and Kendler (1947). All these studies appear to be in conflict with Tolman's contiguity interpretation and even with some of the earlier experimental findings.

Theories of Response Elimination (Inhibition)

Internal inhibition theory (Pavlov). In addition to what they tell us about the acquisition process, conditioning experiments tell us a lot about how responses are weakened or eliminated. Pavlov aimed much of his experimentation at this phenomenon, and on the basis of his findings he elaborated his theory of *internal inhibition*. According to this conception, experimental extinction, or the weakening of a conditioned response with failure of reinforcement by the unconditioned stimulus, and other related inhibitory phenomena result from an active, independent, inhibitory state I. This state of inhibition counteracts (negates) the excitatory process E established by conditioning; the algebraic resultant of the two processes determines the strength of the tendency to make the response at a given moment.

Although inhibition, like excitation, was regarded by Pavlov as some kind of neural process, he defined its properties primarily in terms of certain experimental operations. In the first part of his book (Pavlov, 1927) he seems to have assumed that the essential condition for the development of inhibition is failure of occurrence of the unconditioned stimulus. However, on the basis of other studies, particularly the occurrence of a decrement in the strength of the response during conditioning with massed trials, Pavlov later (1927, p. 234) suggested that inhibition develops with each presentation of the conditioned stimulus. During conditioning trials, inhibition is more than offset by the developing excitatory state resulting from reinforcement, but with cessation of the unconditioned stimulus and continued presentation of the conditioned stimulus the inhibitory state becomes stronger and stronger. Eventually it offsets completely the excitatory state, and response ceases.

Pavlov assumed further that the inhibitory state is weaker and more labile than excitation, and that it dissipates with the passage of time. On the basis of these assumptions he was able to account for a great variety of inhibitory phenomena — e.g. differential inhibition, conditioned inhibition, disinhibition, inhibition of delay, inhibitory aftereffect, etc.

The success of Pavlov's theory in explaining his experimental findings is due largely to the fact that the theory was tailored to fit — i.e. he inferred the hypothetical properties of his construct of inhibition from his data. This is, of course, no criticism of the theory, for all scientific theories begin with the data they are to explain. The initial *ad hoc* character of a theory is lost when it develops new experimental implications that are verified by test. Pavlov's theory of internal inhibition has been very successful in this regard. Not only has it served to integrate (explain) a wide range of experimental data, but it has also been successful in accounting for new experimental findings.

Interference or counterconditioning theories of inhibition. A number of psychologists (Wendt, 1936; Guthrie, 1930, 1935; Culler, 1938) have objected to the Pavlovian theory of inhibition on the grounds that it is unnecessary to postulate the concept of inhibition I. Differing in details, these theorists all reject Pavlov's concept of internal inhibition and attempt to account for the decrement and elimination of a learned response in terms of the development of a competing response. Figure 4 contrasts these two views. The upper diagram represents the Pavlovian view with its conception of two different processes, excitation E and inhibition I, jointly determining the response. The lower figure gives the interference interpretation. The inhibitory factor depressing the original conditioned response R_1, in this instance, is conceived of as a competing excitatory process leading to another, incompatible response R_2. The latter is assumed to act in a more or less algebraic manner to depress the strength of the first response. This theory views experimental extinction and other forms of inhibition as the learning of a new, incompatible response or, as it has been aptly described, as counter-conditioning.

Major difficulties with these interference theories of inhibition are the problems: what makes the competing response occur initially, and how does it eventually become stronger than the originally learned response? When the extinction procedure involves the introduction of some new stimulus that evokes the new, competing response, this difficulty does not arise. Thus Culler's example (1938)

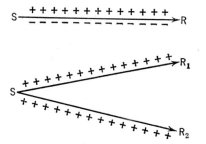

Fig. 4. The upper diagram represents the Pavlovian conception of excitation (+) and internal inhibition (−). The lower figure gives the interference interpretation of inhibition.

of the extinction of a child's fear response to a rabbit by presenting the child with food while the rabbit is kept at a sufficient distance to prevent the fear response from being elicited is easy to understand as a simple instance of counter or redirected conditioning. The feeding responses in the presence of the rabbit, reinforced by the presentation of food, gradually become stronger and supplant the fear response. The extinction of an approaching response to some stimulus object by the introduction of shock (punishment) is another example of the elimination of a response by means of a stronger, competing response elicited by a new stimulus.

In the typical experiment on extinction, however, the unconditioned (reinforcing) stimulus is merely withheld and no new stimulus is introduced. Recognizing the need for some auxiliary postulate to account for the initial occurrence of the competing response, Guthrie at first pointed out that

Pavlovian experimental extinction was a special phenomenon and that most inhibitory conditioning involved the type of counter-conditioning described above. In attempting to account for the Pavlovian phenomenon itself, Guthrie (1935) first postulated that with the withholding of the unconditioned stimulus there is a change of set or attitude on the part of the subject, and the response decreases or ceases altogether. Subsequently this temporary set or postural pattern becomes conditioned to "not responding" — i.e. stopping salivation. In a later discussion Guthrie (1937) modified his theory to accord with a suggestion made by Winsor (1930), namely, that the absence of the food (unconditioned stimulus) leads to irritation and excitement. Such activation of the sympathetic branch of the autonomic nervous system reciprocally inhibits the salivary response, which is under the control of the parasympathetic system. Such an explanation serves only, of course, for responses under the control of the parasympathetic system and is not satisfactory for conditioned defense reactions such as the eyelid reflex.

Apart from these difficulties there are other experimental facts incompatible with the theory that extinction results only from the conditioning of a new, competing response. One of the most embarrassing findings is the fact that the massing of trials has opposite effects on conditioning and extinction. Whereas conditioning is superior under spaced trials (Hilgard and Marquis, 1940), extinction is faster (or as fast) under massed trials (Reynolds, 1945; Reyna, 1946; Rohrer, 1947). If extinction is fundamentally identical with conditioning, no such difference should be found. Other experimental findings embarrassing to the interference type of theory are the absence of positive correlations between conditioning and extinction measures (Hilgard and Marquis, 1940), the differential effects of an extra stimulus on responses extinguished to different degrees (Razran, 1939c), the different types of extinction curves following massed and distributed conditioning (Hilgard and Marquis, 1940), the extinction of a conditioned pupillary response in a curarized cat (Harlow and Stagner, 1933), and even the phenomenon of spontaneous recovery. Still other difficulties confronting this type of inhibition theory may be found in Razran's (1939a) thorough discussion of the problem.

Mention should be made of the fact that, although Tolman and other believers in cognition learning do not have an explicit theory of inhibition, their position falls implicitly in line with the interference or counterlearning type of interpretation. Just as Tolman does not conceive of conditioning as the strengthening of a response but as the acquiring of a cognitive structure concerning the sequence of psychological events, so he does not conceive of experimental extinction as the weakening of a response. Instead, when the unconditioned stimulus stops, a new environmental sequence (conditioned stimulus followed by no stimulus) occurs, and, corresponding to it, a new, different cognition develops. Presumably this new cognition interferes or is confused with the first for a period of time, and then finally becomes clear as the representative of the new environmental situation.

Compound work-inhibition — interference theory. An interpretation of inhibitory phenomena that combines some of the properties of Pavlov's concept of internal inhibition I with the interference theory has been offered by Beritoff (1927) and by Hull (1943). According to Hull's version, experimental extinction of a conditioned response involves the development of inhibitory potential $\dot{I}_R$. The latter, in turn, is composed of two components: reactive inhibition I_R and conditioned inhibition $_SI_R$. Reactive inhibition is a hypothetical condition or state that is assumed to develop in a response system upon its activation. In the properties assigned it, this concept is very similar to Pavlov's concept of internal inhibition. Reactive inhibition is assumed to accumulate with the

occurrence of each response and to dissipate during intervals between responding. The amount of work (energy consumption) involved in the response also plays an important role in determining the rate of development of reactive inhibition. As with his other hypothetical constructs, Hull has made mathematical guesses about the functions relating reactive inhibition to the determining experimental variables.*

It is by means of this construct I_R that Hull is able to account for the phenomenon of spontaneous recovery and for the dissimilar effects, on conditioning and extinction, of the time interval between trials. Reactive inhibition occurs with every response and hence is present in conditioning as well as in extinction. Distributed practice aids conditioning because longer intervals between trials provide more time for dissipation of the inhibition. On the other hand, experimental extinction should be hastened by the massing of trials, because the inhibition then has less opportunity to dissipate.

The second part of Hull's theory of inhibition is like the interference or incompatible-response hypothesis. He assumes that reactive inhibition acts as a primary negative motivational state (need for rest) comparable to pain or tissue injury. Cessation of the activity — i.e. ceasing to make the response — results in alleviation of this motivational state and thereby provides a reinforcing state of affairs that leads to a conditioning of the competing (cessation) response to the stimulus complex. This conditioned tendency of "not responding" is Hull's conditioned inhibition $_SI_R$. It is really an excitatory phenomenon involving a habit structure and a drive, and it could be designated as $_SE_R = (_SH_R \times D)$, in which R represents

---

* Physiologically, the two concepts are quite differently conceived. Pavlov regards his internal inhibition as a state or condition of the sensory analyzers (cortex), whereas for Hull the locus of the inhibition is in the effector mechanism. Actually neither makes much use of these topographical speculations.

a response that is antagonistic to the original response.

By means of this second component of his theory, Hull is able to account for such phenomena as generalization of inhibition to other stimuli, incompleteness of spontaneous recovery, the finding that recovery becomes less and less with successive extinction, external inhibition of the conditioned response, etc. His theory fails, however, to account satisfactorily for disinhibition unless he assigns different properties to the habit $_sH_R$ involved in $_sI_R$ from those he ascribes to it in connection with his other uses of this construct.

More experimental work on the various problems of inhibition is needed before the issues between these rival theories can be settled. Research is especially difficult in this area and the results so far obtained have been complicated by the fact that the conditions under which the original learning occurred have not always been taken into consideration. An example of the importance of this factor is Reynold's finding (1945) that the effect of the time interval between trials upon the rate of extinction depends upon the time interval employed in the original conditioning.

THEORETICAL ISSUES IN COMPLEX LEARNING

The types of conditioned responses that we have been considering all consist of a simple response tendency that is acquired or lost (experimental extinction). From the study of conditioned responses have come laws and guesses at laws (hypotheses), and it is the belief of most students of conditioning that these same laws, along with others, apply to the more complex types of learning. Examples of more complex learning are (1) the process of discovery of the adaptive response in the problem box and in discrimination experiments, (2) the integration of a series of responses in maze and rote learning; and

(3) the processes by which new patterns of motor coordination (skills) are acquired.

Although there exists a considerable body of experimental data concerning these more complex processes, we shall confine our discussion to a few of the more important theoretical issues.

Insight versus Trial and Error in Problem Solving

One of the major concerns of theorists interested in the more complex learning problems has been the process known as *discovery*. The problem has to do with the factors responsible for the first occurrence of the adequate response in a novel situation, and its subsequent dominant status in the response repertory of the subject. One group of theorists believes that the correct goal-attaining response is arrived at through a process known as *insight;* another group thinks it is attained by a process of *trial and error.*

The issue gets itself confused by the fact that the term 'insight' has been used in two quite different senses: (1) as a descriptive term referring to a kind of behavior sometimes observed in problem-solving situations, and (2) as the name of a hypothetical process that is assumed to control behavior and to result in a different kind of problem solution when it is present than when it is absent. The criteria that are said to distinguish insightful from noninsightful solutions are: (1) the suddenness with which the successful response is adopted — e.g. sudden drops in error curves; (2) the readiness with which the correct response is repeated — e.g. the absence of further erroneous responses; and (3) the resistance of the response to forgetting (Yerkes, 1927). There can, of course, be no question that these phenomena occur in certain kinds of learning. They contrast with learning in which the errors are only gradually eliminated and the correct response only gradually adopted. Actually, however, problem solutions vary all the way between these two extremes. As Melton (1941) has pointed out, all three of the criteria for insight refer to behavior characteristics that vary in a continuous manner. Consequently, they do not imply a dichotomy of modes of problem solution — blind trial-and-error solutions as against intelligent insightful solutions.

Turning to the theoretical notion of insight, one finds little to help him understand the different varieties of problem solution. The hypothetical properties ascribed to the concept are either inferred from the observed behavior itself or are arrived at through introspective reports of the subject at the time of the problem solution. In either event one has only a response-inferred construct which, until its hypothetical relations to environmental events, past and present, are specified, is of no great theoretical value. To say that the subject suddenly responds correctly because he suddenly, and for the first time, perceives the situation in a new way (reorganizes his perceptual field) does not provide a satisfactory answer for the learning theorist, although it may be quite true that the change in behavior is the result of such a change in the perceptual response to the situation. This answer, however, merely pushes the problem of explaining the learning back a step, for the theorist must now answer the question: what made the subject perceive it in the new way? What are the factors (variables) that are responsible for the perceptual reorganization? This, it will be seen, is merely a restatement of the problem of learning.

Furthermore, although it may be true for human subjects that sudden drops in the error curve are at times accompanied by introspective reports of suddenly "seeing into" the relevant relations, it does not necessarily follow that sudden changes in animal learning curves involve comparable experiences of insight. Indeed, Spence (1939) has reported an experiment involving multiple choice in which the subjects (chimpanzees) often adopted erroneous responses suddenly and persisted in making them for some time.

If suddenness and persistence indicate the presence of a process of insight, or intelligent "seeing into," in the case of the correct response, it must mean that these subjects were also having intelligent insights when they adopted and persisted in the erroneous responses. It need hardly be pointed out that this latter interpretation does not agree with our usual understanding of the meaning of intelligent behavior.

Although the explanatory concept of insight has not, in the opinion of the writer, been a particularly fruitful concept, the perception theorists, particularly the Gestalt group, have, nevertheless, made a notable contribution to our knowledge of the type of learning known as problem solving. This contribution has consisted primarily in the design and use of new types of problem situations which differed markedly from those that had been employed by most other learning psychologists. The basic plan of these problems involves the presentation to the subject of a novel situation in which the direct approach to the lure is blocked but an indirect route is left open. The problem is arranged in such a manner that its various parts, and the relations among them, are clearly visible to the subject. It is thus possible to perceive the relation of any part of the situation to the lure. Examples of this type of experimental arrangement are the roundabout or *umweg* problems involving the fabrication of implements, and problem situations in which the subject employs some object, for example, sticks, boxes, etc., as an implement to obtain the lure. In these situations it is found that solutions are not always gradual and do not always involve a long, persistent series of erroneous responses. Sudden solutions (insight) and solutions with few or no erroneous trials are, then, genuine-enough phenomena in problem solving. Furthermore they require explanation just as do the instances of learning in which the presolution period is marked by the repeated occurrence of a number of erroneous responses and the gradual adoption of the correct response.

When we turn to the stimulus-response theorists' discussions of problem solving or selective learning, we find that their earlier treatments (Thorndike, 1913; Watson, 1914) were primarily concerned with explaining the gradual type of trial-and-error learning that occurred in the kind of problem box they employed. Quite contrary to the statements of some writers (Krechevsky, 1932), however, these early interpretations of this kind of learning did not view the presolution period as a blind, random, undirected affair. Moreover later theoretical treatments of the discovery process in selective learning by Hull (1930a, 1937) and in discrimination learning by Spence (1936) have explicitly assumed that the genesis, the range, and the order of occurrence of the trial responses are strictly determined, lawful, systematic processes. These theorists have assumed that the subject exhibits an initial hierarchy of responses, the individual strengths of which vary (1) with innate factors such as preference for dark over white alleys, etc., (2) with the past reinforcement experiences of the subjects with similar environmental situations (principle of generalization or transfer), and (3) with the particular motivational state of the moment, coupled with the past relations between various responses and the satisfaction of particular drives. Experimental confirmation of the genesis of these trial responses in the past experience of individual subjects has been experimentally demonstrated in selective learning by Hull (1939) and in discrimination learning by Spence (1937b).

In the typical problem box the subject, motivated toward a goal object, is confronted with a situation to which a variety of responses to various parts or aspects of it can be made. One of these responses is 'successful' in the sense that it leads to the goal object. When this 'correct' response is low in the response hierarchy of the subject, so-called trial-and-error activity ensues.

That is to say, the subject typically makes a number of different responses, often repeating the same one a number of times, until the successful one occurs. On subsequent occasions the number of erroneous responses decreases, until finally the correct response is made at the very start of the trial. No further erroneous responses occur, and the problem is said to be solved.

The explanation offered by the stimulus-response psychologist of this type of trial-and-error learning is that the subject's initial responses are those that are strongest by virtue of his past experience in similar situations. With failure of reinforcement the incorrect responses are gradually weakened until their strength is below that of the correct response, which is strengthened on its occurrence. The recurrence of incorrect acts after the correct response has been 'discovered' is accounted for in terms of 'spontaneous recovery' from the effects of non-reinforcement. Eventually the correct response, as the result of the reinforcements it receives each time it occurs, reaches a level of strength above that to which the weakened erroneous responses recover. This, of course, represents only the most schematic outline of a very complex set of events. Other factors that play a role in the variability of the behavior in the presolution period are refractory phase, punishment, variable stimulation resulting from the responses of the subject, etc. Experimental studies bearing on this theoretical interpretation of simple trial-and-error learning may be found in Hull (1939) and in Hull and Spence (1938).*

* Maier, (1939, 1940) has proposed that the variability of responses exhibited in the presolution period of trial-and-error learning results from a need or tendency to vary for the sake of variation. He also refers to an ability to vary. Subjects showing a lesser tendency to vary their responses are said to have a weaker need to vary or a poorer ability in this respect. Such circular reasoning is to be contrasted with the interpretation given above in which variability of behavior is recognized as a behavioral phenomenon to be explained in terms of principles (inhibition, spontaneous recovery, and reinforcement)

A good part of the issue of gradual versus sudden solution in problem solving is thus seen to be based upon differences in method. Undoubtedly both types of solution occur in learning. In the kind of problem employed by the early S-R psychologists the consequences of a response — i.e. whether correct or incorrect — could not be ascertained except by actual trial. The situation may in this sense be described as blind. In contrast, the 'insight' proponents used an 'open' situation, one in which the consequences of the alternative acts could be anticipated without actual carrying out of the act. The two kinds of situations have led to different kinds of behavioral phenomena, gradual solutions predominating in the 'blind' situation and sudden solutions occurring more frequently in the 'open' situation. It should be clearly understood, however, that considerable trial-and-error activity may occur in the 'insight' type of problem and that there are many instances of sudden learning in the supposedly 'blind' problems. Spence (1938, 1939) has shown that it is quite possible to explain, in terms of the type of theoretical schema outlined above, the sudden instances of learning in 'blind' problems as discrimination and multiple-choice learning. The greater frequency of 'insightful' solutions in the 'open' problem would seem to be explainable by this theory in terms of the fact that the occurrence of the correct response in open situations probably depends on the subject's making a particular receptor-exposure adjustment. That is, once this particular orientation of the sense organs (particularly eyes) occurs, the subject will, because of past learning, make the appropriate perceptual response that leads directly to the correct overt act. Much of the learning in this situation, then, probably consists in trial-and-error sense-organ adjustments which the experimenter usually fails to observe and record. Attention should also be called to

discovered in an entirely different type of experimental situation (i.e. the conditioned response experiment).

the fact that with human subjects there is probably considerable implicit (symbolic) trial-and-error activity that is not recordable. It still remains highly questionable, however, whether some new higher-order process (insight?) must be invoked to explain such instances of sudden learning in animal subjects.

In concluding this discussion, it should be pointed out that there are certain, still more-complicated types of problem solution that stimulus-response theorists like Hull would agree differ from trial-and-error learning. Thus the reasoning experiments of Maier (1929) and the Tolman-Honzik 'insight' maze (1930) probably involve mechanisms different from those involved in the ordinary problem box, maze, and discrimination set-ups. Hull's treatment (1935) of these problems in terms of stimulus-response principles is to be contrasted with those of Maier (1940) and Tolman (1932, 1937).

Continuity versus Noncontinuity Theories of Discrimination Learning

Experimental studies of discrimination learning have shown that the period prior to the attainment of solution is an organized lawful process, marked by the occurrence of systematic response tendencies or, as they have been termed by one investigator (Krechevsky, 1932), 'hypotheses.' Two sharply contrasting interpretations of these systematic behavior tendencies have developed. One, referred to as the noncontinuity theory, had its origins in a suggestion of Lashley (1929), to the effect that these systematic responses (consistent response to the left, simple alternation, etc.) represent more or less insightful attempts at solution on the part of the subject. According to this view (Krechevsky, 1932, 1938; Lashley, 1942) the animal selects and responds, in turn, to certain aspects of the situation and does not acquire any differential response tendencies to the relevant cue until just at or just preceding the time of solution. That is, during the occurrence of the incorrect hypotheses the subject may be learning something concerning the particular discriminanda involved in these hypotheses, but he is not learning anything about the relevant set of discriminanda.

In contrast to this conception, the continuity interpretation (Spence, 1936, 1937a, 1940, 1945; McCulloch, 1939; McCulloch and Pratt, 1934) insists that, so long as the subject is receiving discriminably different stimulation from the positive and negative discriminanda during the presolution period, differential associative tendencies will be developed with respect to them. According to this theory, discrimination learning is conceived as a cumulative process of building up the excitatory strength (habit, associative strength) of the positive cue as compared with the competing excitatory strength of the negative cue. This process is assumed to continue until the difference between the excitatory strengths of the two cues is sufficiently great to offset any other differences in excitatory strength that may exist between the stimulus complexes of which the cues are members. Thus, according to this conception, when an animal is responding always with a left-going hypothesis, it receives reinforcement every time the positive cue (e.g. white stimulus) is on the left side, but it is not reinforced when the negative cue (e.g. black stimulus) is on the left. As a result of this differential reinforcement the white cue gradually acquires a greater excitatory strength than the black, but the subject continues to choose the left side predominantly because the difference in excitatory strengths between the left and right positional cues is greater than the difference in the excitatory strengths of the cue stimuli. Eventually, with continued differential reinforcement, this latter difference becomes greater than that between the positional cues, and the subject gives up the left-going hypothesis and adopts the correct white-going hypothesis.

As a critical test of the two opposed theories an experimental design has been employed in which the significance of the stimulus cues during a preliminary period of trials, in which the subject is responding with some irrelevant hypothesis, is the reverse of that used in the subsequent learning problem (i.e. the positive cue is made negative, and vice versa). According to the noncontinuity theory this preliminary training should have no effect on the subsequent learning of the reverse problem. In contrast the implication of the continuity theory is that the learning of such a reversed group would be retarded as compared with a control group that did not have such initial reversed training but instead was given 50-per-cent reinforcement on each of the relevant cues for the same period of trials.

Three experimental studies employing this design have been reported. Two of them (McCulloch and Pratt, 1934; Spence, 1945) obtained results that confirmed the continuity theory; the third (Krechevsky, 1938) found that one group (40 preliminary trials) supported the continuity theory and another (20 preliminary trials) the noncontinuity theory.

Krechevsky employed pattern discrimination, whereas the more simple brightness discrimination was employed in Spence's study (1945). The latter has the advantage that no special receptor-exposure adjustments must first be learned in order to provide discriminably different proximal stimulations from the two stimulus cards. In the case of the black-white discrimination the animals cannot help but receive discriminably different retinal stimulation from the very first trial, and, because of the differential reinforcement, differential associative strengths with respect to the two stimulus cards develop from the beginning. Such is not necessarily the case, Spence contends, in pattern discrimination, particularly in the Lashley type of jumping apparatus. In the preliminary training with this apparatus the subject learns to jump to an open window, and it acquires the habit of fixating the lower ledge to which it must jump. Although this fixation undoubtedly brings the stimulus cards into the visual field of the subject, it does not guarantee that discriminably different retinal patterns of stimulation will be received from the stimulus cards. Under such conditions no differential learning with respect to the two cards would take place. The subject must first learn to make the appropriate receptor-orienting acts that will lead to the reception of retinal stimulus patterns that are discriminable. Krechevsky's subjects presumably failed to do this in the 20 preliminary trials but did so in 40 trials. Hence the former group showed no retardation, whereas the latter did.

Experimental confirmation of the foregoing analysis has been obtained by Ehrenfreund (1948). When the jumping platform of a Lashley type discrimination apparatus was placed (as is customary) at the same level as the bottom of the stimulus window, and the stimulus forms (upright and inverted triangles) were placed slightly above the center of the stimulus card, Ehrenfreund obtained results comparable to Krechevsky's 20-trial group. That is to say, the preliminary reversal of the reward value of the cues led to no retardation in the subsequent learning of the reversed problems. However, in a strictly parallel experiment, except that the jumping platform was raised so that the rats jumped directly to the stimulus card at the level of the forms rather than to the bottom of it, the experimental results were just the opposite. Under this condition, in which coincidence of the initial fixation point and the cue was approximated from the first, the reversed group showed significant retardation in the learning test as compared with the control group.

The experimental findings of this and earlier studies clearly show, then, that differential learning with respect to the relevant cues can occur, as the continuity theory states, while the subject is responding on the basis of an irrelevant 'hypothesis.' Beyond the level of the simplest perceptual situations, however, there is no guarantee that differentiation will develop with respect to all the cue differences present in the stimulus situation. Such complex pattern discrimination apparently involves, as an important component, the preliminary acquisition of receptor-exposure adjustments that provide the discriminably different retinal stimulation necessary for learning. Perceptual factors obviously play a very important role in this type of learning.

Cognitive versus Response Theories of Simple Maze Learning

For the learning of problems that offer alternative pathways and demand the making of a choice (e.g. the maze), two radically opposed theoretical analyses of the underlying mechanisms have been proposed. One, favored by the S-S or perception theorists (Woodworth, 1947; Tolman, 1932, 1934; Leeper, 1935, etc.), conceives of the learning in terms of the development of cognitions that are representative of the stimulus relations in the environment. Thus maze learning is described as the acquisition of knowledge about the various parts and aspects of the maze, including the sequences and relations among the paths. In the simple T-maze, involving a single choice-point, the subject is assumed to learn the difference between the two alternative alleys in terms of what they signify, if entered. Thus one alley entrance comes to be a sign for a dead end, whereas the other comes to signify food or some other goal object. In terms of Tolman's concepts, sign-Gestalt-expectations or cognitions are built up to the effect that one alley (e.g. left) leads to the significate, food C_{L-F}, whereas the other alley leads to nothing C_{R-0}. Tolman, of course, assumes that these cognitions develop as the result of mere sequence in experience of the stimulus events, whereas Woodworth believes that reinforcement also is an important factor.

The development of a differential response — e.g. preference for the alley leading to food over that leading to a dead end — is not to be accounted for, according to the cognitive theory, in terms of a stronger cognition of the left response than of the right. Rather it is due to the greater demand value of the food than of the empty alley. Given sufficiently clear cognitions or 'significate-expectations' with respect to the two alternative alleys, the one leading to the significate that has the higher demand value will be taken. The demand value of the significates will depend, in turn, upon the motivational state of the subject. This theory may be stated briefly, as follows:

$$B_F > B_0, \text{ if } C_{L-F} \text{ and } C_{R-0} \text{ exist, and } \Delta F > \Delta_0$$

In contrast to this interpretation, the typical S-R associationistic theory accounts for the development of the preference for the rewarded (food) alley in terms of a building up of the associative connection to the left response, whereas no such association is developed to the response of going to the nonrewarded alley. Thus, if we were to extend to selective learning the constructs and principles that Hull has developed for classical and instrumental conditioning, we might say that the habit strength of the left-alley response becomes greater than that of the right-alley response. As both habit strengths are multiplied by the same existing D (drive) strength, this leads to the implication that the excitatory potential for the left-going response will be greater than that for the right-going response ($_sE_{R \text{ left}} > _sE_{R \text{ right}}$). The learning criterion (e.g. 100 per cent) is attained, according to this view, when the difference between the competing excitatory potentials reaches a value that is greater than the range of oscillation of the excitatory potentials.

Although this treatment in terms of Hull's constructs is adequate as far as it goes, it is not complete, for consideration must still be given to a theoretical mechanism that Hull does not treat in his *Principles of Behavior*, but one that figured prominently in his earlier theoretical articles on maze learning (1930b, 1931, 1932). Reference is made here to the fractional anticipatory goal reaction r_g

and its proprioceptive cues s_g which Hull has hypothesized as playing an important role in the integration of the various responses in the maze sequence.

In a symposium paper on simple maze learning, Spence (1941) attempted to show how, under certain conditions, this fractional anticipatory goal mechanism would play a decisive role in selective learning. An experiment carried out by Kendler (1946) will serve to explain this function. Employing a single T-maze, with food at the end of one alley (e.g. left) and water at the end of the other, Kendler gave white rats, motivated for *both* goal objects, a total of 14 trials to each side. Test trials were then given in which the subjects were *either* hungry or thisty. It was found that the animals were able to respond appropriately (85-per-cent correct) on these test trials. When hungry they tended to go to the food side, and when thirsty they chose the alley leading to water. Now, whether we assume that the habit strengths of the two responses were built up equally, or that they were more strongly built up on one side, it is not possible, on the basis of the theoretical S-R analysis given above, to account for the successful differential responses on the different test trials.

The explanation suggested by Spence (1941) was as follows: During the training series the stimuli in the water box and in the water alley become conditioned to anticipatory drinking acts r_w and, in turn, the proprioceptive components s_w resulting from these anticipatory acts themselves become conditioned to the response of entering and continuing locomotion in this alley. In a similar manner, anticipatory eating responses r_f develop and their cues s_f become conditioned to the response of entering the alley leading to food. During the test series when only one drive is operative, the anticipatory act related to the goal for which the subject is motivated is much stronger than the other and hence produces stronger proprioceptive cues. Thus, when the subject is hungry, pro-

prioceptive cues from anticipatory eating responses are stronger than those for drinking.
As these cues become conditioned to the response of entering the food alley, they tend
to throw the balance of habit strength to
the food-alley response. According to this
view, the relative excitatory strengths are a
function of the strength of this fractional
anticipatory goal reaction and its habit relations, as well as a function of the other
intervening variables assumed by Hull in his
Principles of Behavior. Thus the functions
for the $_sE_R$ values would be as follows:

$$_sE_{R_f} = f(_sH_{R_f}, D, r_f \rightarrow {}_{s_f}H_{R_f})$$

$$_sE_{R_w} = f(_sH_{R_w}, D, r_w \rightarrow {}_{s_w}H_{R_w})$$

Strictly conceived, the role ascribed here
to the fractional anticipatory goal reaction
$(r_g - s_g)$ should also apply to instrumental
conditioning. The writer believes that it
does so operate, and he would employ it to
explain the fact that stronger instrumental
responses occur when the goal object is increased in amount (Crespi, 1944). This
hypothesis is to be contrasted with Hull's interpretation (1943) that magnitude of the
reward determines the strength of response
through determination of the limit to which
$_sH_R$ grows (postulate 1, p. 699). Finally,
the possible motivational role of this $r_g - s_g$
mechanism should not be overlooked. It is
conceivable that the occurrence of these
fractional goal responses, in the sequence
leading up to the goal, results in a certain
amount of conflict, and hence in tension. It
is entirely possible that heightened tension
contributes to an increase in the existing
state of generalized drive D.

In concluding this discussion, attention
should be called to the possibility that the
$r_g - s_g$ mechanism as proposed above is
essentially the same thing as Tolman's sign-
Gestalt-expectation (cognition). The present treatment has attempted to show the
manner in which such expectations might operate to produce differences in response. As
such it escapes the criticism that Guthrie

(1935) and Thorndike (1946) have made of
Tolman's conception, namely, that it does
not specify how expectations are related to
action.

Summary and Evaluation of S-S versus S-R issues

The preceding discussion of representative
theoretical issues in problem solving, discrimination learning, and maze learning has
tried to show the extent to which disagreement centers around the issue of S-S versus
S-R. Perceptual learning theorists like
Koffka, Köhler, Lewin, Maier, and even
Tolman have emphasized at one time or
another the concept of insight in their attempts to explain problem solving, although
all have not meant the same thing by the
term. In contrast, the stimulus-response
psychologists have consistently rejected an
insight hypothesis and have offered in its
place some variant of the trial-and-error interpretation. Similarly the disagreements
concerning discrimination and maze learning
stem primarily from these two opposed theoretical positions. A few further comments
on these two theories will be given in order
to summarize some of the basic issues involved.

In addition to picturing the hypothetical
learning modifications as changes in the perceptual or cognitive states of the subject, the
S-S theorists vigorously reject the concept
of association. There are, it is true, a few
conspicuous exceptions. Thus Tolman (1937)
and Maier (1939) explicitly accept a principle of association although they postulate
that the functional relations established by
sequence in experience (principle of contiguity) are not between S's and R's but between the successive stimulus-aroused events.
As Tolman (1938b) has acknowledged, his
associationism is essentially a return to the
eighteenth century concept of "association of
ideas."

The main opposition to association theory
comes from the original Gestalt group
(Köhler and Koffka) and from Lewin.

Köhler and Koffka emphasize that learned cognitive fields (trace systems, etc.) do not consist of separate items merely coupled or joined together by bonds. Rather they are conceived as organized dynamic structures in which the relations between the terms are determined only in part by contiguity. Much more important are differences in the *intrinsic* qualities of the items being organized. Field properties also exert their special effects in the process of organization and in the process of reproduction. Most of the criticisms by this group, however, are directed against the associationistic doctrines of the German school (Mueller, 1924) and are not always relevant to current associationistic theories in America. For example, Lewin has offered the criticism that an association should not be interpreted as a force that can produce responses. It must only be thought of as providing for the organization of cognitions which must in turn be energized by the motivational systems of the individual before action. As we have seen, Hull's concept of habit (associative) strength essentially complies with Lewin's view; the habit strength alone cannot produce a response but must be combined with the co-existing drive state in order to do so.

Reference by these psychologists to the intrinsic properties of the hypothetical psychological fields brings us to another characteristic exhibited by many of the theories falling in this class. The learning theories of the Gestalt group, in particular, are marked by an extensive discussion of the intrinsic nature of their hypothetical intervening variables. Thus Koffka treats at length the various kinds of hypothetical factors he assumes — e.g. processes, traces, trace systems, behavioral environment, ego systems, etc. He theorizes about the possible nature of the interactions (interrelations) among them and, more important, between them, and the behavior they determine. Lewin's theorizing shows this same tendency. Indeed he has emphasized the need for psychological theorists to concentrate more on what he calls the conceptual properties of their theoretical constructs as distinguished from their operational definitions (1940). Finally, Zener seems to imply that this is the only task of the learning theorist. In introducing his theory he states: "We are concerned with the conception of the permanent structural change produced, not with the process of acquisition" (1937, p. 386).

Our diagram (Fig. 1) showing the various types of relations between the theoretical and experimental concepts in psychology may help to clarify this last point. Of the functional relations shown in this figure, the Gestalt discussions of learning theory consist primarily of types III, IV, and, to a lesser extent, of type V. Conspicuous by their complete absence in Lewin's treatment, and by their sparsity in Koffka's and Köhler's theorizing, are relations of type II. Koffka, it is true, mentions some of the experimental variables that he believes to be important in determining the properties of his hypothetical learning variables. For the most part, however, his treatment consists in references to the experimental variables in the present stimulus situation that play an important part in the perceptual processes (type I relations). The implication is usually given that analagous relations (laws) will be found to hold for traces, and hence for learning. The belief on the part of the Gestalt psychologist that learning is merely a part of the larger problem of perceptual organization provides much of the rationale for this appeal to the laws of perception.

A criticism persistently directed at the Gestalt theorists' concern with the *inherent* dynamics of hypothetical learning organizations is that their treatments are speculations with no empirical reference. This criticism is not entirely justified, however, for their constructs are derived from experience, from the observed behavior changes in the learning experiment, and particularly from the phenomenological introspection of their subjects.* Together these sources provide an empirical basis for making guesses as to the nature of hypothetical learning processes.

From the point of view of learning theory, however, an important problem is usually left untackled by the S-S, particularly the Gestalt, theorists. This is the specification of the relations between the hypothetical learning factors of the *present* and the experimental conditions of the *past*. The formulation of such historical laws constitutes the peculiar task of the learning psychologist, for it is these laws that provide the means of controlling behavior changes.

The approach of the Gestalt psychologists to the problem of learning theory probably reflects their preference for the mediational type of explanation of psychological events. For Köhler, in particular, explanation of psychological events is to be sought in the underlying neurophysiological processes. Köhler attempts to indicate the isomorphic relations of his hypothetical trace fields to electrical brain fields. In contrast, the more behavioristic-minded psychologists tend to direct their interests toward explanations that refer to events in the physical and social environment, past and present.

An outstanding exception to this tendency on the part of S-S theorists to concern themselves with the intrinsic properties of their theoretical fields is Tolman's sign-Gestalt formulation. One of the first psychologists to enlist the aid of the intervening variable in the formulation of laws in psychology, Tolman has always insisted that these theoretical constructs must be defined in terms of the independent (environmental) variables and in terms of the resulting behavior. Tolman's theorizing is almost completely free of physiological speculation.

* Snygg (1941) has proposed a theoretical system of learning that is based exclusively on phenomenological introspection. He believes that attempts like those of the Gestaltists to develop theoretical systems based both upon an objective frame of reference and upon the phenomenological approach lead only to confusion.

Likewise, it should be observed that, so far as the meaning of their defining equations is concerned, Hull's theoretical constructs are not concerned with the intrinsic properties (physiological or introspective) of the hypothetical learning changes. As a matter of fact the mathematical equation defining the construct of habit $_sH_R$ does not identify it as either an S-S or an S-R concept. Coupled with this purely mathematical definition of habit, however, is a further treatment of learning in neurophysiological terms. Here Hull refers to receptor-effector connections' $(_sC_R)$ being strengthened by reinforcement, and he identifies (coordinates) this concept with his mathematical concept of habit $_sH_R$. It is only by virtue of this additional neurophysiological theorizing, then, that Hull falls into the S-R group. Actually he makes little or no use of the physiological properties he ascribes to his theoretical constructs.

Attention should also be called to the fact that Thorndike likewise invokes a physiological hypothesis concerning the nature of his concept, the S-R bond. He identifies the change in strength of a bond with changing synaptic conduction between neurons. Interestingly enough, it is primarily these superfluous physiological interpretations of Hull and Thorndike that the cognitive-field theorists object to as being mechanistic and elementaristic. Apparently there has been a failure to appreciate the fact that little or no use is made of the physiological aspects of these constructs by the S-R theorists in their actual attempts to explain learning data.

So far as the experimental evidence is concerned, there is little data bearing on the question whether the functional tie-up is between sensory-motor events or between successive sensory events. It would seem entirely possible that certain kinds of learning, particularly simple perceptual learning, might well involve sensory-sensory associations or combinations, whereas other more complex learning, such as problem solving, might involve primarily the development of sensory-motor integrations. In this connection, Maier and Schneirla (1942) have cited the experiment of Loucks (1935) as support for the view that learning involves sensory-sensory connections. Loucks, it will be recalled, reported finding that a dog could not be conditioned to a buzzer when the unconditioned response of flexing the hind leg was produced by faradic shock applied directly to the motor area of the cortex. This procedure, of course, by-passed the usual sensory system (pain from shock to the limb) involved in normal conditioning. The association between the sensory event resulting from the sounding of the buzzer and the sensory event aroused by the shock could not occur since the latter did not occur.

That conditioning could and did take place when the sensory process corresponding to the unconditioned pain stimulus was absent was, nevertheless, demonstrated by a variation on the experiment. When reinforcement in the form of food was given the subject each time the leg flexion occurred, conditioning followed. An S-R theorist would interpret this to mean that the association was between afferent-efferent events. The connection or association did not occur in the first part of the experiment because of the absence of reinforcement. With the introduction of reward, the association was established. The results of the two experiments taken together are thus seen to favor the S-R interpretation rather than the S-S. Girden (1943) has provided further evidence in favor of the assumption that a response must occur during the training series in order for learning to take place. Girden found that, when complete striated muscle paralysis was induced by injection of the drug erythroidine, no conditioning involving these muscular responses took place. On the other hand, changes in blood pressure and pulse rate, autonomically controlled responses occurring in the drug state, did become conditioned.

In the opinion of the present writer, too much attention has been given to this issue of S-S versus S-R. If we employ constructs introduced by mathematical definition, in the manner of Hull, the problem of the nature of the intrinsic physiological properties of the changes underlying learning does not, for the present at least, even arise. We should be able to work out the laws governing behavioral changes without having to stop and consider such physiological matters. What is needed most at the present time in the study of learning is the continued and persistent pursual of the type of integration of theory and experiment that will lead to the discovery and formulation of laws of learning in terms of environmental and behavioral variables. When such a body of knowledge is available we shall be in a better position to evaluate the adequacy of competing physiological hypotheses. Perhaps by that time, also, the physiologically oriented psychologists will have at hand independent hypothetical physiological mechanisms whose properties are not themselves inferred from the learning phenomena they purport to explain.

REFERENCES

Adams, D. K. A restatement of the problem of learning. *Brit. J. Psychol.*, 1931, **22**, 150–178.

Bekhterev, V. M. *General principles of human reflexology.* (Translated by E. and W. Murphy from the Russian of the 1928 Ed.) New York: International, 1932.

Bergmann, G. Outline of an empiricist philosophy of physics. I and II. *Amer. J. Physics,* 1943, **11**, 248–258, 335–342.

Beritoff, J. Über die individuell-erworbene Tätigkeit des Zentralnervensystems. *J. Psychol. Neurol. Lpz.,* 1927, **33**, 113–335.

Blodgett, H. C. The effect of the introduction of reward upon the maze performance of rats. *Univ. Calif. Publ. Psychol.,* 1929, **4**, 113–134.

Brogden, W. J. Unconditioned stimulus-substitution in the conditioning process. *Amer. J. Psychol.,* 1939a, **52**, 46–55.

Brogden, W. J. Sensory pre-conditioning. *J. exp. Psychol.,* 1939b, **25**, 323–332.

Brogden, W. J. Sensory pre-conditioning of human subjects. *J. exp. Psychol.,* 1947, **37**, 527–540.

Brogden, W. J., E. A. Lipman, and E. Culler. The role of incentive in conditioning and extinction. *Amer. J. Psychol.,* 1938, **51**, 109–118.

Crespi, L. P. Amount of reinforcement and level of performance. *Psychol. Rev.,* 1944, **51**, 341–357.

Culler, E. Recent advances in some concepts of conditioning. *Psychol. Rev.*, 1938, **45**, 134–153.

Dashiell, J. F. A survey and synthesis of learning theories. *Psychol. Bull.*, 1935, **32**, 261–275.

Denny, M. R. The role of secondary reinforcement in a partial reinforcement learning situation. *J. exp. Psychol.*, 1946, **36**, 373–389.

Ehrenfreund, D. An experimental test of the continuity theory of discrimination learning. Ph.D. thesis, University of Iowa, February, 1947.

Ehrenfreund, D. An experimental test of the continuity theory of discrimination with pattern vision. *J. comp. Psychol.*, 1948, **41**, 408–422.

Finger, F. W. The effect of varying conditions of reinforcement upon a simple running response. *J. exp. Psychol.*, 1942a, **30**, 53–68.

Finger, F. W. Retention and subsequent extinction of a simple running response following varying conditions of reinforcement. *J. exp. Psychol.*, 1942b, **31**, 120–132.

Gates, A. I. Connectionism: Present concepts and interpretations. In National Society for the Study of Education, *The forty-first yearbook*. Bloomington, Ill.: Public School Publishing Co., 1942.

Girden, E. Role of the response mechanism in learning and in 'excited emotion.' *Amer. J. Psychol.*, 1943, **56**, 1–20.

Graham, C. H., and R. M. Gagné. The acquisition, extinction and spontaneous recovery of a conditioned operant response. *J. exp. Psychol.*, 1940, **26**, 251–281.

Gulliksen, H., and D. Wolfle. A theory of learning and transfer. *Psychometrica*, 1938, **3**, 127–149, 225–251.

Guthrie, E. R. Conditioning as a principle of learning. *Psychol. Rev.*, 1930, **37**, 412–428.

Guthrie, E. R. *The psychology of learning.* New York: Harper, 1935.

Guthrie, E. R. *Psychology of human conflict.* New York: Harper, 1937.

Guthrie, E. R. Conditioning: A theory of learning in terms of stimulus, response, and association. In National Society for the Study of Education. *The forty-first yearbook.* Bloomington, Ill.: Public School Publishing Co., 1942.

Guthrie, E. R., and G. P. Horton. *Cats in a puzzle box.* New York: Rinehart, 1946.

Harlow, H. F., and R. Stagner. Effect of complete striate muscle paralysis upon the learning process. *J. exp. Psychol.*, 1933, **16**, 283–294.

Hartmann, G. W. The field theory of learning and its educational consequences. In National Society for the Study of Education, *The forty-first yearbook.* Bloomington, Ill.: Public School Publishing Co., 1942.

Hilgard, E. R. The nature of the conditioned response. I. The case for and against stimulus-substitution. *Psychol. Rev.*, 1936a, **43**, 366–385; II. Alternatives to stimulus-substitution. *Ibid.*, 1936b, **43**, 547–564.

Hilgard, E. R. The relationship between the conditioned response and conventional learning experiments. *Psychol. Bull.*, 1937, **34**, 61–102.

Hilgard, E. R. *Theories of learning.* New York: Appleton-Century-Crofts, 1948.

Hilgard, E. R., and D. G. Marquis. *Conditioning and learning.* New York: Appleton-Century-Crofts, 1940.

Hull, C. L. Simple trial-and-error learning: A study in psychological theory. *Psychol. Rev.*, 1930a, **37**, 241–256.

Hull, C. L. Knowledge and purpose as habit mechanisms. *Psychol. Rev.*, 1930b, **37**, 511–525.

Hull, C. L. Goal attraction and directing ideas conceived as habit phenomena. *Psychol. Rev.*, 1931, **38**, 487–506.

Hull, C. L. Goal gradient hypothesis and maze learning. *Psychol. Rev.*, 1932, **39**, 25–43.

Hull, C. L. Special review: Thorndike's *Fundamentals of learning.* *Psychol. Bull.*, 1935, **32**, 807–823.

Hull, C. L. Mind, mechanism and adaptive behavior. *Psychol. Rev.*, 1937, **44**, 1–32.

Hull, C. L. Simple trial-and-error learning—an empirical investigation. *J. comp. Psychol.*, 1939, **27**, 233–258.

Hull, C. L. Psychology seminar memoranda. 1940–41 (unpublished manuscript in Yale Library).

Hull, C. L. Conditioning: Outline of a systematic theory of learning. In National Society for the Study of Education, *The forty-first yearbook.* Bloomington, Ill.: Public School Publishing Co., 1942.

Hull, C. L. *Principles of behavior.* New York: Appleton-Century-Crofts, 1943.

Hull, C. L., and K. W. Spence. "Correction" vs. "non-correction" method of trial-and-error learning in rats. *J. comp. Psychol.*, 1938, **25**, 127–145.

Humphreys, L. G. The effect of random alternation of reinforcement on the acquisition and extinction of conditioned eyelid reactions. *J. exp. Psychol.*, 1939, **25**, 141–158.

Humphreys, L. G. Extinction of conditioned psychogalvanic responses following two conditions of reinforcement. *J. exp. Psychol.*, 1940, **37**, 71–78.

Humphreys, L. G. The strength of a Thorndikian response as a function of the number of practice trials. *J. comp. Psychol.*, 1943, **35**, 101–110.

Karn, H. W. Sensory pre-conditioning and incidental learning in human subjects. *J. exp. Psychol.*, 1947, **37**, 540–545.

Karn, H. W., and J. M. Porter, Jr. The effects of certain pre-training procedures upon maze performance and their significance for the concept of latent learning. *J. exp. Psychol.*, 1946, **36**, 461–469.

Kendler, H. H. The influence of simultaneous hunger and thirst drives upon the learning of two opposed spatial responses of the white rat. *J. exp. Psychol.*, 1946, **36**, 212–220.

Kendler, H. H. A comparison of learning under motivated and satiated conditions in the white rat. *J. exp. Psychol.*, 1947, **37**, 545–549.

Köhler, W. *Gestalt psychology.* New York: Liveright, 1929.

Köhler, W. *Dynamics in psychology.* New York: Liveright, 1940.

Koffka, K. *The principles of Gestalt psychology.* New York: Harcourt, Brace, 1935.

Krechevsky, I. 'Hypotheses' in rats. *Psychol. Rev.*, 1932, **39**, 516–532.

Krechevsky, I. A study of the continuity of the problem-solving process. *Psychol. Rev.*, 1938, **45**, 107–133.

Kuo, Z. Y. Giving up instincts in psychology. *J. Phil.*, 1921, **18**, 645–664.

Lashley, K. S. *Brain mechanisms and intelligence.* Chicago: University of Chicago Press, 1929.

Lashley, K. S. An examination of the 'continuity theory' as applied to discrimination learning. *J. gen. Psychol.*, 1942, **26**, 241–265.

Leeper, R. The role of motivation in learning: A study of the phenomenon of differential motivational control of the utilization of habits. *J. genet. Psychol.*, 1935, **46**, 3–40.

Leeper, R. Dr. Hull's *Principles of behavior*. *J. genet. Psychol.*, 1944, **65**, 3–52.

Lewin, K. *Principles of topological psychology.* New York: McGraw-Hill, 1936.

Lewin, K. Studies in topological and vector psychology I. Part one: Formalization and progress in psychology. *Univ. Ia. Stud. Child Welf.*, 1940, **41**, 9–45.

Lewin, K. Field theory and learning. In National Society for the Study of Education, *The forty-first yearbook.* Bloomington, Ill.: Public School Publishing Co., 1942.

Loucks, R. B. The experimental delimitation of neural structures essential for learning: The attempt to condition striped muscle responses with faradization of the sigmoid gyri. *J. Psychol.*, 1935, **1**, 5–44.

Loucks, R. B., and W. H. Gantt. The conditioning of striped muscle responses based upon faradic stimulation of dorsal roots and dorsal columns of the spinal cord. *J. comp. Psychol.*, 1938, **25**, 415–426.

Maier, N. R. F. Reasoning in white rats. *Comp. Psychol. Monogr.*, 1929, **6**. No. 3.

Maier, N. R. F. The specific processes constituting the learning function. *Psychol., Rev.*, 1939, **46**, 241–252.

Maier, N. R. F. The behavior mechanisms concerned with problem solving. *Psychol. Rev.*, 1940, **47**, 43–58.

Maier, N. R. F., and T. C. Schneirla. Mechanisms in conditioning. *Psychol. Rev.*, 1942, **49**, 117–133.

McCulloch, T. L. Comment on the formation of discrimination habits. *Psychol. Rev.*, 1939, **46**, 75–85.

McCulloch, T. L., and J. C. Pratt. A study of the pre-solution period in weight discrimination by white rats. *J. comp. Psychol.*, 1934, **18**, 271–290.

McGeoch, J. *Psychology of human learning.* New York: Longmans, Green, 1942.

Melton, A. W. Learning. In *Encyclopedia of educational research.* New York: Macmillan, 1941. Pp. 667–683.

Miller, N. E., and J. Dollard. *Social learning and imitation.* New Haven: Yale University Press, 1941.

Mowrer, O. H. Preparatory set (expectancy)—a determinant in motivation and learning. *Psychol. Rev.*, 1938, **45**, 62–91.

Mowrer, O. H. Anxiety-reduction and learning. *J. exp. Psychol.*, 1940, **27**, 497–516.

Mowrer, O. H. The law of effect and ego psychology. *Psychol. Rev.*, 1946, **53**, 321–334.

Mowrer, O. H. On the dual nature of learning—a reinterpretation of "conditioning" and "problem-solving." *Harvard educ. Rev.*, 1947, **17**, 102–148.

Mowrer, O. H., and H. Jones. Extinction and behavior variability as functions of effortfulness of task. *J. exp. Psychol.*, 1943, **33**, 369–386.

Mueller, G. E. *Abriss der Psychologie.* Goettingen: Vandenboeck and Ruppricht, 1924.

O'Connor, V. J. Recency or effect? A critical analysis of Guthrie's theory of learning. *Harvard educ. Rev.*, 1946, **16**, 194–206.

Pavlov, I. P. *The work of the digestive glands.* (Translated by W. H. Thompson.) London: Griffin, 1902.

Pavlov, I. P. *Conditioned reflexes.* (Translated by G. V. Anrep. London: Oxford University Press, 1927.

Perin, C. T. Behavior potentiality as a joint function of the amount of training and the degree of hunger at the time of extinction. *J. exp. Psychol.*, 1942, **30**, 93–113.

Perrin, F. A. C., and D. B. Klein. *Psychology.* New York: Holt, 1926.

Pitts, Walter. A general theory of learning and conditioning. *Psychometrica*, 1943, **8**, 1–18, 131–140.

Postman, Leo. The history and present status of the law of effect. *Psychol. Bull.*, 1947, **6**, 489–563.

Razran, G. S. The nature of the extinctive process. *Psychol. Rev.*, 1939a, **46**, 264–297.

Razran, G. S. The law of effect on the law of qualitative conditioning. *Psychol. Rev.*, 1939b, **46**, 445–463.

Razran, G. S. Decremental and incremental effects of distracting stimuli upon the salivary conditioned responses of 24 adult human subjects. *J. exp. Psychol.*, 1939c, **24**, 647–652.

Rexroad, C. N. Outline of the conditions under which learning occurs. *Psychol. Rev.*, 1932, **39**, 174–183.

Rexroad, C. N. An examination of conditioned reflex theory. *Psychol. Rev.*, 1933, **40**, 457–466.

Reyna, L. J. Experimental extinction as a function of the interval between extinction **trials**. Ph.D. thesis, University of Iowa, 1946.

Reynolds, B. Extinction of trace conditioned responses as a function of the spacing of trials during the acquisition and extinction series. *J. exp. Psychol.*, 1945, **35**, 81–95.

Rohrer, J. H. Experimental extinction as a function of the distribution of extinction trials and response strength. *J. exp. Psychol.*, 1947, **37**, 473–493.

Schlosberg, H. The relationship between success and the laws of conditioning. *Psychol. Rev.*, 1937, **44**, 379–394.

Seward, J. P. An experimental study of Guthrie's theory of reinforcement. *J. exp. Psychol.*, 1942, **30**, 247–256.

Seward, J. P. Reinforcement in terms of association. *Psychol. Rev.*, 1943, **50**, 187–202.

Skinner, B. F. Two types of conditioned reflex and a pseudo-type. *J. gen. Psychol.*, 1935, **12**, 66–77.

Skinner, B. F. *The behavior of organisms.* New York: Appleton-Century-Crofts, 1938.

Snygg, D. The need for a phenomenological system of psychology. *Psychol. Rev.*, 1941, **48**, 404–424.

Spence, K. W. The nature of discrimination learning in animals. *Psychol. Rev.*, 1936, **43**, 427–449.

Spence, K. W. The differential response in animals to stimuli varying within a single dimension. *Psychol. Rev.*, 1937a, **44**, 430–444.

Spence, K. W. Analysis of the formation of visual discrimination habits in the chimpanzee. *J. comp. Psychol.*, 1937b, **23**, 77–100.

Spence, K. W. Gradual versus sudden solution of discrimination problems by chimpanzees. *J. comp. Psychol.*, 1938, **25**, 213–214.

Spence, K. W. The solution of multiple choice problems by chimpanzees. *Comp. Psychol. Monogr.*, 1939, **15**, No. 3.

Spence, K. W. Continuous versus non-continuous interpretations of discrimination learning. *Psychol. Rev.*, 1940, **47**, 271–288.

Spence, K. W. Symposium: Learning as related to need, and the subsequent motivation of such learned behavior. *Psychol. Bull.*, 1941, **38**, 721.

Spence, K. W. Theoretical interpretations of learning. In F. A. Moss (Ed.), *Comparative psychology* (Revised Ed.). New York: Prentice-Hall, 1942.

Spence, K. W. The nature of theory construction in contemporary psychology. *Psychol. Rev.*, 1944, **51**, 47–68.

Spence, K. W. An experimental test of the continuity and non-continuity theories of discrimination learning. *J. exp. Psychol.*, 1945, **35**, 253–266.

Spence, K. W. The role of secondary reinforcement in delayed reward learning. *Psychol. Rev.*, 1947, **54**, 1–8.

Spence, K. W. The postulates and methods of behaviorism. *Psychol. Rev.*, 1948, **55**, 67–78.

Spence, K. W., and R. O. Lippitt. An experimental test of the sign-Gestalt theory of trial-and-error learning. *J. exp. Psychol.*, 1946, **36**, 491–502.

Stephens, J. M. Expectancy vs. effect-substitution as a general principle of reinforcement. *Psychol. Rev.*, 1942, **49**, 102–116.

Stevens, S. S. Psychology and the science of science. *Psychol. Bull.*, 1939, **36**, 221–263.

Thorndike, E. L. Animal intelligence: An experimental study of the associative process in animals. *Psychol. Monogr.*, 1898, **2**, No. 8.

Thorndike, E. L. *Animal intelligence: Experimental studies.* New York: Macmillan, 1911.

Thorndike, E. L. *Educational psychology:* Volume II. *The psychology of learning.* New York: Teachers College, Columbia University, 1913.

Thorndike, E. L. *Human Learning.* New York: Appleton-Century-Crofts, 1931.

Thorndike, E. L., et al. *The fundamentals of learning.* New York: Teachers College, Columbia University, 1932.

Thorndike, E. L. *The psychology of wants, interests, and attitudes.* New York: Appleton-Century-Crofts, 1935.

Thorndike, E. L. *Human nature and the social order.* New York: Macmillan, 1940.

Thorndike, E. L. Expectation. *Psychol. Rev.*, 1946, **53**, 277–281.

Thurstone, L. L. The learning function. *J. gen. Psychol.*, 1930, **3**, 469–493.

Tolman, E. C. *Purposive behavior in animals and men.* New York: Appleton-Century-Crofts, 1932.

Tolman, E. C. Theories of learning. In F. A. Moss (Ed.), *Comparative Psychology.* New York: Prentice-Hall, 1934.

Tolman, E. C. Operational behaviorism and current trends in psychology. *Proc. 25th Anniv. Celebration Inaug. Grad. Stud.* Los Angeles: University of Southern California, 1936. Pp. 89–103.

Tolman, E. C. The acquisition of string-pulling by rats—conditioned response or sign-Gestalt? *Psychol. Rev.*, 1937, **44**, 195–211.

Tolman, E. C. The determiners of behavior at a choice point. *Psychol. Rev.*, 1938a, **45**, 1–41.

Tolman, E. C. The law of effect: A roundtable discussion. II. *Psychol. Rev.*, 1938b, **45**, 200–203.

Tolman, E. C. A stimulus-expectancy need-cathrexis psychology. *Science*, 1945, **101**, 160–166.

Tolman, E. C., and C. H. Honzik. "Insight" in rats. *Univ. Calif. Publ. Psychol.*, 1930, **4**, 215–232.

Troland, L. T. *The fundamentals of human motivation.* New York: Van Nostrand, 1928.

Tuttle, H. S. Two kinds of learning. *J. Psychol.*, 1946, **22**, 267–277.

Warden, C. J. *Animal motivation studies.* New York: Columbia University Press, 1931.

Watson, J. B. *Behavior, an introduction to comparative psychology.* New York: Holt, 1914.

Wendt, G. R. An interpretation of inhibition of conditioned reflexes as competition between reaction systems. *Psychol. Rev.,* 1936, **43,** 258–281.

White, R. K. The case for the Tolman-Lewin interpretation of learning. *Psychol. Rev.,* 1943, **50,** 157–186.

Wiley, L. E., and A. M. Wiley. Studies in the learning function. *Psychometrica,* 1937, **2,** 1–19, 107–120, 161–164.

Winsor, A. L. Observations on the nature and mechanism of secretory inhibition. *Psychol. Rev.,* 1930, **37,** 399–411.

Woodworth, R. S. Reinforcement of perception. *Amer. J. Psychol.,* 1947, **60,** 119–124.

Yerkes, R. M. The mind of a gorilla. *Genet. Psychol. Monogr.,* 1927, **2,** 1–193, 375–551.

Zener, K. The significance of behavior accompanying conditioned salivary secretion for theories of the conditioned response. *Amer. J. Psychol.,* 1937, **50,** 384–403.

19.

Cognitive Processes

ROBERT LEEPER

University of Oregon

Although the psychology of cognitive processes — their nature and their role in human behavior — raises many problems of definition, it seems best to start our discussion, not directly with a set of definitions, but with a description of the experiments that must ultimately set the bounds of meaning on the terms we use. When we start in this way we are assuming, of course, that useful definitions are those that enable us to classify phenomena on the basis of empirical evidence of functional similarities.

To some extent, cognitive processes have always been defined partly in this functional manner. But they have also been defined as though it were possible to identify cognitive processes as such — to discern their qualitative characteristics as conscious experiences. It was thought by some that the two modes of definition are compatible, but this assumption did not stand up under experimental investigation.

For example, it was thought that cognitive processes, as *conscious* processes, are used to compare the pitch of two tones heard in succession or to compare the weights of two objects lifted successively. The theory was that, on the second stimulation, the person experiences a conscious image of the first stimulus and makes a comparison between this conscious image and the perception of the second stimulus. But, as early as the experiments by Schumann in 1898 and Marbe in 1901, this hypothetical process was not confirmed by careful introspective observa-

tion (see, for example, the review of this work by Needham, 1934). There was, in truth, some process that yielded rather accurate comparisons. But the subjects could typically detect no images or conscious representations of the first stimulus at the time the second was given. They reported merely that, as an immediately experienced fact, the second tone, say, was heard as higher or lower in pitch than the first. If cognitive processes were responsible for the judgments, those cognitive processes were not in themselves conscious, even though they yielded a conscious end product.

The same finding resulted from experiments that sought to investigate more complex cognitive processes. Ach (1905) presented to his subjects pairs of digits such as 7, 3; 9, 2. Sometimes the subjects were told to add the numbers; at other times, they were told to multiply or to subtract. The subjects at first had some conscious representation of each new task, but the consciousness of the task faded as the work on each series continued. And yet the subjects responded appropriately. Watt (1905) found similar results. He used single words as stimuli. In different series he asked his subjects, given a word like "tree," to name a larger class, a subclass, or a coordinate class. Or the subject was asked to name a whole when given the name of a part, to name a part when given the whole, or to name another part when given the name of a part.

What he found, as Woodworth summarized the study, was:

When the same task had continued for a series of stimulus words, the conscious awareness of the task faded out even from the foreperiod and was reduced to a mere feeling of readiness. The preparation lost its specificity as a conscious state, but not as an adjustment, for it still insured correctness of response according to the task. With practice the set became at once less conscious and more efficient. [1938, p. 791.]

There were, of course, conscious experiences in the intervals before the response words appeared: the subjects might note a feeling of fatigue, an odor in the room, or what not. But there were no distinctive and relevant conscious processes to which the final response could plausibly be attributed.

Woodworth noted the same phenomenon in his early experiment on voluntary movement (1906). His subjects developed their specifications for such movements by a series of conscious perceptions and thoughts, but these specifications were carried over and used without any clear consciousness of the set thus employed.

Since Ach and Watt were members of the "Würzburg school," which is known chiefly for its concept of "imageless thought," and since Titchener questioned so vigorously the evidence for this concept, it is apt to be forgotten that he heartily agreed with their contribution that conscious processes are often determined by not-conscious processes. In fact, Titchener's views on imageless thought led him to emphasize this finding in unequivocal terms:

But is meaning always conscious meaning? Surely not: meaning may be carried in purely physiological terms. In . . . the rendering of a musical composition, without hesitation or reflection, in a particular key . . .; in these and similar cases meaning has, time and time again, no discoverable representation in consciousness. . . . This predetermination of consciousness by influences that, during the course of conscious-

ness, are not themselves conscious, is a fact of extreme psychological importance. . . . [1910, pp. 369–370.]

In later experiments on "concept formation" an even more drastic conclusion was demonstrated. This conclusion was not reached in the early experiments on concept formation, because in these experiments the subjects were told that they were to search for common elements and to report introspectively how they developed generalizations (Grünbaum, 1908; Moore, 1910; Fisher, 1916). In experiments by Hull (1920) and later workers, however, a different procedure has typically been used. The subjects are given no instructions to form concepts. They are told merely that they are to learn the names of a series of Chinese characters that will be shown them, or of a series of geometrical designs, or whatever. Actually, however, the materials fall into classes that contain common features, and the same name is given as each member of a class is presented to the subjects. Many of the subjects in these experiments soon recognize that they can best handle their task by searching for such common features and by associating the names with them. Some of the subjects, however, develop the ability to name new examples without being able to say how they do it, even when the necessary formulations lie well within the limits of their vocabularies. Hull gives only a meager report of the introspective observations of his subjects, so it is impossible to say to what extent this effect occurred in his study. In later work, however, as in the studies of Heidbreder (1924, 1946, 1947), Smoke (1932), Rees and Israel (1935), Snygg (1935), Heidbreder, Bensley, and Ivy (1948), and Bouthilet (1948), this unconscious process is abundantly demonstrated. The conclusion from these studies, in other words, goes even beyond the findings of Ach, Watt, and Woodworth. For these studies indicate not merely that responses may be governed by sets or determining tendencies, initially established by conscious processes and later dropped from consciousness, but also that complex guiding processes can be formed, retained, and used without the person's being aware of the process at any step. The subject is aware, of course, of the concrete materials and of his efforts to link names with concrete configurations. But he forms more generalized means of naming the figures without realizing that he is doing it.

All these experiments show that unconscious processes are often the means of accomplishing results that were formerly attributed just to conscious cognitive processes. These experiments show that definitions of cognitive processes in terms of the functional properties of psychological processes would not coincide with definitions of cognitive processes as conscious states.

There was also another outcome of the early introspective experiments that cast doubt on the value of definitions of cognitive processes in terms of conscious experience. This was the discovery that it is exceedingly difficult to describe conscious experiences as such.

For example, one of Titchener's students (Perky, 1910) tried to determine the differences between images and sensory perceptions. She instructed her subjects to construct conscious images, projecting them, as it were, on a ground-glass screen in front of them, and then to describe introspectively the nature of the images. At some points, however, without telling her subjects, she caused faint pictures actually to be projected onto the screen from the other side. These stimulations were faint, but not subliminal. Her subjects, however, could not distinguish between these sensory experiences and the images that they themselves projected. They remarked with surprise, sometimes, that their "images" were not what they would have expected. Thus, the banana that was being "imaged" was placed vertically, whereas they said it would seem more natural for the image of this object to lie horizontally. But they could not distinguish introspectively between images and sensory perceptions.

Perky's results have often been regarded as evidence that there is no useful distinction between perceptual and imaginal processes. This conclusion does not follow. Her results suggest, however, that the distinction must be made in terms of functional relations — particularly in terms of the different origins of the two types of processes — and that it cannot be made by introspective observations of the two processes as such.

Much the same conclusion was suggested by the long controversy regarding "imageless thought." The studies by Watt and Ach did not reach merely the one conclusion that some of the controlling processes are unconscious. The introspective reports indicated also that the conscious experiences are not always describable in terms of images, feelings, and sensations but include also "conscious attitudes" of readiness, hesitation, certainty or uncertainty, and the like. This suggestion was carried further in studies with still more complex thought processes by Binet (1903), Bühler (1907), and others. For example, Bühler first read a series of proverbs to a subject to give him a body of material he could use. Then, to provide the process to be described introspectively, he read another proverb similar in sense to one of these, but different otherwise. The subject was asked to recall the related proverb and then to describe the conscious processes involved in this recall. The subjects reported that they often recalled the "meaning" or sense of the required proverb before they could recall its words or before they had any imagery related to it. They claimed they had conscious "thoughts" in terms that were neither sensory nor imaginal.

Moore (1919) supported the same conclusion in a series of reaction-time studies of different sorts of conscious processes. For instance, he flashed single printed words before his subjects and asked them in some cases to react as soon as they were conscious of the "meaning" of the word, in other cases to respond as soon as some conscious visual image appeared. Visual images, on the average, took about twice as long to appear as did a consciousness of the meaning of the word. The differences were not so great in another study with simple pictures as stimuli and with instructions to respond to conscious meaning in one case and to the consciousness of some word association (such as the name of the object) in the other case. But, here again, meaning was reported more quickly.

In his *Lectures on the Experimental Psychology of the Thought Processes*, however, Titchener (1909) said that the alleged "imageless thoughts," in so far as they were actually conscious processes, were reducible to sensory and imaginal materials (often slight kinesthetic sensations) which the advocates of imageless thought had failed to discern. He did not deny that "meanings" were aroused in thought experiments like Bühler's. But, he said, Bühler's subjects failed to distinguish between the actual content of their conscious experience and the content they inferred it must have in view of their recall, e.g. of the appropriate proverb. In other words Titchener insisted that conscious experience is much more meager, much more sketchy and senseless in character, than we would have suspected from everyday observation. Meaning, he said, was carried in great part "physiologically" (by processes that were not conscious) rather than by conscious experience.

To this argument the advocates of imageless thought (see Woodworth, 1915, and 1938, pp. 783–800) replied that their subjects actually were describing their conscious experiences. They claimed that the structuralists were deciding the outcome of their observations in an a priori manner by refusing to allow their subjects to report conscious meanings that existed only as such.

Pratt (1928) claimed that the introspective studies on this problem had led to a general acceptance of the view that conscious thought contains such "impalpable"

materials as imageless thoughts. This possibly has been the general tenor of opinion. But another lesson was suggested even more forcibly — namely, that it is apparently much harder to describe cognitive processes as such than to study them in terms of their functional relations. For neither Titchener nor his opponents doubted the existence of processes that carry an elaborate meaning. What they could not agree on was the extent and character of the conscious experience involved in this process.

During this period in which the controversy raged over imageless thought, two new types of psychological research were demonstrating that cognitive phenomena may be studied without reference to considerations of consciousness. One was the work with intelligence tests, starting with Binet and Simon in 1905. This work indicated that it is possible to explore intellectual activity by a procedure that does not concern itself with the conscious aspects of the thought processes involved.

The other development was derived from the evolutionary-biological research in England. Thus the English biologist, Hobhouse (1901), using problems analogous to many of those later employed by Yerkes and Köhler, reported an ingenious array of studies with monkeys. He found that monkeys seem to "think," because they solve many problems with a relative independence of overt trial and error. Although most of the animal psychologists in the United States followed the example set by Thorndike (1898), who emphasized that animals do not use "representative" processes, a number of experiments supported the evidence of Hobhouse's work. Thus Hunter (1913) used a "delayed-reaction experiment" with several species of animals. The animals were trained to go from a restraining cage to whichever door was designated by a brief illumination. Then, during the test trials, the animals were restrained for several seconds or minutes after the light was turned off, and the animal had to remember which door had been designated. Hunter found that rats and dogs could respond successfully only when, during the delay, they preserved their bodily orientation toward the exit to be used. On the other hand, raccoons handled delays up to about 20 seconds, even though they moved around restlessly in the restraint compartment.

Tinklepaugh carried this work further with monkeys and chimpanzees. He allowed a chimpanzee to watch him hide a bit of food under one of a pair of containers in one room and then to watch the same process in a second room, a third room, etc. Under these conditions Tinklepaugh found that chimpanzees could respond without error after having watched as many as 10 placements on one "trial." What is more, with both monkeys (1928) and chimpanzees (1932), he showed that, if the animals had seen a preferred food hidden, they reacted with strong frustration when this had been secretly replaced with a less-preferred food before the moment of choice. In other words, without going through the overt process of choosing a container and without experiencing directly the reward associated with it, these animals were able to establish some guiding process that represented both the nature and the location of the food.

Furthermore elaborations of the experimental methods favored by Thorndike showed that, even with mazes and latch boxes, the habits that are learned cannot be described in terms of connections between the stimuli and the overt movements present during the learning. Rats can traverse a maze accurately by swimming after they have been able only to wade through the maze during training (Macfarlane, 1930). They can negotiate a maze when they have been badly crippled by cerebellar injuries after the learning (Lashley and McCarthy, 1926) or by spinal-cord injuries (Lashley and Ball, 1929). Muenzinger (1928) demonstrated that normal guinea pigs show a lot of variability in the means by which they move a lever that gives them access to food.

These studies indicate that maze habits and problem-box habits are comparable to the variable adaptive responses of human beings that we explain by saying that the person "knows" what effect has to be attained.

Furthermore these experiments emphasize that the controlling processes involved ought to be studied primarily in terms of their functional properties and only incidentally, if at all, in terms of whether they are conscious processes.

HOW ARE COGNITIVE PROCESSES TO BE DEFINED?

The problem here is broader than the problem of defining the one term "cognitive processes." It is a problem also of the conception and definition of an important group of subordinate terms like perception, concept, thinking, expectation, and mental activity.

The older view in psychology, derived from everyday experience, was that almost all mental processes are conscious and may be observed introspectively. Thus G. F. Stout's *Manual of Psychology* says:

> . . . there are three ultimate modes of being conscious of an object: knowing, feeling, and striving; the cognitive attitude, the feeling attitude, and the conative attitude. . . . The word *cognition* . . . covers all modes and degrees of being aware of or cognizant of an object. [1899, p. 56.]

Stout recognized, of course, that there are "psychological facts" or processes that are not "psychical facts" or conscious processes. He was familiar with the stereoscope and knew that there must be some process, even though it is not introspectively observable, whereby the disparate stimulations of the two retinas are combined to produce the three-dimensional experience. But, in spite of such examples, Stout regarded conscious mental activity as encompassing most of the processes by which we adapt, and he regarded introspection as the key to the observation of these processes.

This emphasis on consciousness in the definition of cognitive processes is seen in Warren's *Dictionary of Psychology* (1934):

Cognition = a generic term used to designate all processes involved in knowing. It begins with immediate awareness of objects in perception and extends to all forms of reasoning.

Even more clear is this tendency in the definition of perception:

1. the awareness of external objects, qualities, or relations which ensues directly upon sensory processes, as distinguished from memory or other central processes; 2. a mental complex or integration which has sensory experiences as its core; 3. awareness of present data . . .

The same emphasis is placed on consciousness by Humphrey (1948). He emphasizes some of the same experiments we have discussed above and says that there is often an interval of "organic processes" between the presentation of a problem and the solving of it. But, he then says (and he apparently intends this as his own definition too): "By 'directed thinking' or reasoning is usually understood the *conscious* side of these intervening processes" (p. 12, italics added). The same slant appears in his brief description of methods of research on thinking (pp. 6–7). Humphrey speaks as though the only available methods are variations of introspective techniques: such methods as the recording of (1) the spontaneous remarks of children as they work on problems, and (2) the retrospective reports of thinking after it has been completed.

These definitions of cognitive processes in terms of consciousness are not, however, an outgrowth of experimental studies on cognitive processes. They can be traced back, instead, to the time before such studies had been made. They are based on the assumption that our responses and our conscious processes are accounted for by previous conscious processes in a much fuller measure than has proved experimentally to be the case. They are based on the assumption that the nature of conscious experiences can be described introspectively with much more certainty and facility than has proved possible in practice. And they are derived from definitions that were formulated before new methods of research had demonstrated the possibility of fruitful study of cognitive processes in children, animals, and other subjects incapable of adequate introspective reports.

In a situation like this we have to make a choice. Either we must devise new terms to reflect the fruits of experimental work or we must redefine the old terms. A few new terms have, in fact, been proposed and used, such as "set" and "determining tendency." But not much progress has been made in this way.

The chief problem arises from the fact that, as Woodworth says, it seems possible for the same process to become "at once less conscious and more efficient." In other words the functional properties of many processes (aside from the one property of being conscious) seem to be the same even though the process is conscious in one case and unconscious in another. The question is, therefore, whether we should define cognitive processes, perception, thinking, concept formation, and the like in terms of *conscious* processes exclusively, or whether we should say that consciousness may be present or absent, as the case may be, and that all these processes are to be defined in terms of their other functional relations.

This latter alternative has been rejected by some psychologists on the grounds that to speak of "unconscious concepts" or "unconscious perceptions" is equivalent to speaking of "unconscious consciousness." But this does not necessarily follow. Although the concept of consciousness emphasizes a property antithetical to "unconsciousness," such concepts as thinking and perception need not refer at all to conscious properties but merely to the origins and to the effects of the processes in question.

For the purposes of this chapter we will follow the suggestion that cognitive processes must be redefined without mention of consciousness. This is apparently the procedure that has appealed to experimenters on pragmatic grounds. Thus it has become typical for experimenters on concept formation to use a criterion of "correct naming of new examples" as the criterion of the attainment of concepts even when the subjects could not say why the name fitted that new stimulus.

In adopting this point of view we are not rejecting introspective observation as having no place in the picture. We use it whenever it seems valuable. It remains true, furthermore, that one of our key problems concerns the difference it makes whether a cognitive process is conscious or not. Another question is why cognitive processes are conscious in some cases and not in others. But it does not seem helpful to include the characteristic of consciousness in the definition of cognitive processes.

A few of the workers who have reintroduced the term "cognitive process" into psychology have defined it as the process whereby there is created, for the individual, a "psychological environment" (Lewin, 1946) or a "behavioral environment" (Koffka, 1935), to which the individual responds. The same notion is embodied in the suggestion of a number of writers that the individual should be thought of as responding to his "phenomenological field" (see Snygg, 1941; MacLeod, 1947; Krech and Crutchfield, 1948). This conception has led to a fruitful attack on certain problems, but it has not proved relevant to all the problems of cognitive processes. It seems better, therefore, to avoid narrow definitions and to say that cognitive processes include all the means whereby the individual represents anything to himself or uses these representations as a means of guiding his behavior. It is in this broader sense that the term "cognitive processes," after virtually disappearing from the vocabulary of psychology, has been re-appearing in the writings of such psychologists as Adams (1931), Tolman (1932), Heidbreder (1945), and Hilgard (1948).

METHODS FOR THE STUDY OF COGNITIVE PROCESSES

As we have said, the view prevailed originally that cognitive processes could be studied only by the method of introspection. Other methods have since been developed, but it still remains true that introspection has considerable value. In the experiments on concept formation, for example, introspective reports have disclosed that the subjects typically engage in an extremely active exploratory process, often formulating, testing, and discarding hypotheses within single trials. Thus Heidbreder described some of the means that her subjects used to help them link the nonsense-syllable names with the drawings she presented:

> Mnemonic devices . . . were very frequent. . . . For example, several definitions of *ling* . . . which was represented in the first series by a drawing of two stockings, reported that the word was remembered as the sound of Christmas bells and associated with Christmas stockings. . . . a definition of *silm* (bird) . . . contained the comment: "This seemed a queer word. I first learned it by associating it with slim and thinking of the bird's slim legs." . . .
>
> Many definitions of *fard* (circle), which in none of the three experiments was represented in the first series by a pictured object, included such comments as: . . . "The first one made me think of the perfectly round moon in a picture of Welch poets and *bards*, bard rhyming with fard." [1947, pp. 112–113.]

Conceivably, by means of large and elaborate tests given after each trial, an experimenter might determine *objectively* just what processes had gone on within his subject, but, as a practical matter, this is not possible. The verbal reports provide evidence that can hardly be gotten in any other way.

Actually many studies of cognitive processes in recent decades have suffered because the experimenter neglected to collect verbal reports to show how the subjects understood their task and how they worked on it. Thus, even though Hull (1920) tried to have his subjects think of his experiment with Chinese characters as a memory experiment rather than as an experiment on concept formation, his comments indicate that many of the subjects came to realize that concepts could be formed and used. But no information is given as to how many subjects came to realize this, or at what points, or with what influence on their behavior.

As was brought out above, however, the introspective method cannot be the sole approach to the study of cognitive processes. There are too many processes that, even though once conscious, fade out of consciousness and yet continue to function effectively. And there are too many cases, as in the concept-formation experiments, in which concepts are formed and used without ever having been conscious.

Another limitation on introspective observation is suggested by Maier (1931) who found that perceptions themselves may sometimes elude introspection. His subjects were brought into a room in which two cords hung from the ceiling, so far apart that, while holding to one cord, the subject could not reach the other one. A few other things were present in the room, such as a chair, a piece of wire, and a pair of pliers. The subjects usually were able to get two possible solutions — reaching for the second cord by means of the wire, and tying the one cord to the chair to bring it closer while they approached it with the other cord. But, when told to search for still a third solution, most of them failed. It required that they tie an object to one string and set it swinging like a pendulum so that it would swing within their reach while they held the other cord. Maier gave them a clue by walking past the second string and brushing against it so as to set it swinging.

Of the 38 subjects who had been unable to solve the problem up to that point, 23 got the solution in an average of 42 seconds. However, only 7 of these 23 were able to report, even after specific questioning, that the movement of the string had given them the clue. As Maier says, retrospective accounts obviously did not indicate the clue that had helped them solve the problem, even though there must usually have been a conscious perception or conscious representation of the swinging string.

It would seem, then, that there is no one method for the investigation of cognitive processes. There are several methods, and their essential feature is the observation of behavior *as precisely and completely as possible and under as great a diversity of conditions as possible.* It is only in this way that we can get dependable and worthwhile information about the cognitive processes that lie back of behavior.

Many studies of learning are unsatisfactory as studies of cognitive processes because the observations are secured under such a small range of conditions that we are left in ignorance of the cognitive processes involved. For example, it has long been observed that, in many discrimination situations, the "error curve" drops more rapidly on successive trials if the animals are "rewarded for correct responses and punished for wrong responses" than when no extra punishment, such as shock, is added to the wrong responses. From this observation it was concluded that punishment "stamps out" the nervous connections leading to the punished responses. But Muenzinger raised the question of what would happen if the grid were placed in a T-maze right after the choice point, *but in the correct alley rather than in the wrong one.* When the rats were given both punishment and reward for right responses, the error curve dropped even more rapidly than when they were punished for wrong responses (Muenzinger, Bernstone, and Richards, 1938).

An experimental example from Spence (1939) illustrates both the great possibilities for cognitive study that come from precise observation and also the uncertainties of interpretation that come from insufficient variation of conditions. In a multiple-choice

Not only did Spence report precisely the behavior exhibited, but he tested the animals under new conditions and related the observations to the previous findings. That is, he tried the animals on the other three possible settings of 5 boxes. The 5 chim-

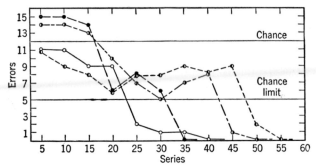

FIG. 1. Error curves for one of the 10 chimpanzees that learned *separately* each of the four original settings on a multiple-choice problem. (Spence, 1939, p. 22.)

experiment, Spence found that his chimpanzees had considerable difficulty in learning to select the *middle* box from different groups of 5 adjacent boxes. The apparatus had 11 boxes that could be lifted into position, and Spence used four different settings in the original training. Correspondingly, he drew, for each chimpanzee, a curve of its errors on *each* of the four settings. The result was that he found two distinctly different outcomes. With 10 of his 15 subjects, the curve for each setting came down separately, as in Fig. 1. With 5 of the chimpanzees, however, the error curves are typified by the graph shown in Fig. 2. That is, 10 subjects had learned each setting separately. The other 5 subjects apparently learned some more generalized habit. From observing the latter animals, moreover, Spence noted that they ". . . usually went to the far side of the cage between trials and thus approached the apparatus from a distance. . . . also . . . , as these subjects approached, they gave the appearance of attempting to place themselves equidistant from the two ends of the setting" (1939, p. 47).

panzees that had learning curves like those in Fig. 2 were still able to select the correct (middle) box with more than 80-per-cent accuracy. None of the other animals made more than 55-per-cent correct choices with the new settings.

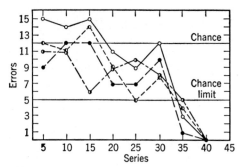

FIG. 2. Error curves for one of the 5 chimpanzees that learned *simultaneously* the four original settings on a multiple-choice problem. (Spence, 1939, p. 22.)

This experiment provides a striking example of the fact that different subjects may learn either more particular or more generalized habits in the same objective situation, and it shows how significant this fact may be in tests of transfer.

The study also indicates how we are often left with uncertainties that can be resolved only if the conditions are varied even further. Thus Spence suggests that the more generalized habit was perhaps dependent on the motor pattern of withdrawing to the opposite end of the cage and approaching from a distance. This suggestion might have been tested by forcing the five "generalizers" to choose from a position as close to the boxes as that usually assumed by the "particularizers."

Not only do we need good methods for the study of cognitive processes, we also need to develop a constructive theory. Too much of the work in this field has been done at random, as it were, or just on *negative* problems. Thus a lot of research and discussion has been devoted to the propositions that not all conscious thought is carried by images, that not all thought is accomplished by words, that not all problem solving is accomplished by trial and error, that not all problem solving is accomplished by insight. This work has value, of course. But it would be still more valuable if we could hypothesize the factors that are responsible and plan our experiments in relation to them. Thus Heidbreder, in a survey of methods, concludes:

> It would be misleading, however, to close this account without stating explicitly that these methods, however effective in specified conditions, have led to little knowledge of thinking that is at once broadly significant, solidly grounded in fact, and unequivocal in meaning. It would be misleading, too, to omit the suggestion that this state of affairs may be due, not so much to a lack of suitable procedures, as to failure to ask effective questions. . . . scientific research . . . is basically an inquiry into significant problems. [1948, pp. 121–122.]

Similarly, Gibson and McGarvey end their review with the statement:

> There have been amazingly few attempts to formulate an hypothesis and test it in carefully planned experiments. There should

be a great revival of interest in the psychology of thinking when investigations in the field become truly critical experiments. [1937, p. 345.]

Not all the research on cognitive processes needs to be aimed at theoretical issues, however. There has been a scarcity, also, of what might be called adequate *ecological* studies. For example, there has been discussion, for centuries, of the various types of errors that conceivably can be made in deductive arguments. But there have been few, if any, studies to determine to what extent each of the logically possible errors is actually found in human thinking. Piaget (1929, 1930) has made some noteworthy studies of this ecological sort with reference to the thinking of children, and some anthropologists have gathered such material with reference to primitive people (e.g. Paul Radin, 1927). But there is need of much more extensive material of this sort.

COGNITIVE PROCESSES AS MEANS OF LEARNING

Earlier in this chapter various incidental references have been made to cognitive processes as means of learning or acquisition. We now turn to the task of pulling these strands together and of indicating more adequately how cognitive processes figure in the phenomena of learning. We will confine ourselves to three matters: inductive concept formation, deductive concept formation, and inventive concept formation. These three processes do not cover all of learning. They do not cover the phenomena of memorizing, the acquisition of sensory-organization habits, or the acquisition of motor-coordination habits. They do cover, however, a great portion of the field of learning.

INDUCTIVE CONCEPT FORMATION

Most of the experiments that are commonly thought of as experiments on inductive concept formation have been experiments on classification. The subject learns that certain stimuli should be classed together on the basis of some common property and that all these stimuli have the same name. Actually, however, inductive concept formation is a very broad and common psychological process, and its nature is indicated only partially by these experiments on class concepts.

What then do we mean by inductive concept formation? Partly we mean a process that is defined by what it produces — namely, concepts. It is the process of developing a habit or a cognitive mechanism that permits a person to respond to an object or event in terms of some property of which he may or may not be immediately aware. Furthermore, we cannot say that a concept is present unless there is some *generality* of application of the habit, and some *differentiation* of those cases to which the concept applies. In general, the experimental psychologist has always found it necessary to study concepts in the sense of "propositions" and not in the sense merely of single terms.*

* It may be well to note that this is not the old philosophical definition of "concepts." In the older philosophical literature the idea was that a conceptual process is a cognition or apprehension of a quality or characteristic *as such.* To have a concept of *red* a person would have to think of "redness" apart from any red objects. This philosophical usage, however, has not been useful to experimental psychology, because it has not been apparent how to measure "apprehension of universals as such." But it has been possible to distinguish between the knowledge of an attribute that is linked specifically to some one object and the knowledge of an attribute that is readily recognized in new specimens that possess it. Thus a small child can learn to say correctly that he has a "red wagon." But, even at 3 or 4 years of age, he is not likely to be able to employ the word "red" appropriately when he is shown rubber balls of different colors. We know, from his inability to apply the word in new situations, that he did not "know what is meant by *red*." He did not have the concept of *red*. This is a simple example, but it illustrates the definition of "concepts" or "conceptual processes" that has been employed, pragmatically at least, by virtually all the experiments on concept formation.

By inductive concept formation we also mean the *process* by which concepts are formed. Inductively formed concepts originate in experiences and observations that provide the organism with a wealth of perceptual materials. Inductive concept formation is the process of recognizing, from this material, that certain features of the material are related to certain other features.

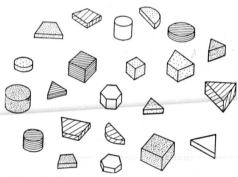

FIG. 3. The blocks used in the Vigotsky or Hanfmann-Kasanin test of concept formation. Colors of the blocks are indicated thus: unmarked = white; light stippling = yellow; heavy stippling = orange; light crosshatching = green; heavy crosshatching = blue. (Adapted from Hanfmann and Kasanin, 1937.)

This process of inductive concept formation may end in a verbal formulation of the concept, but not necessarily. Furthermore, even when some verbal formulation is achieved, it is not always true that the concept is acquired by verbal means. This is demonstrated especially well in a study by Hanfmann (1941) with the test that has come to be known as the Vigotsky or Hanfmann-Kasanin test, which uses the blocks shown in Fig. 3. The subject is told to sort the blocks into four groups that will match names printed on the hidden or bottom sides of the blocks. Hanfmann found that some of her subjects worked out their groupings primarily by moving the objects around and by observing them. Thus she tells of one subject:

The subject noticed two small blocks that happened to lie close to each other, started adding other small blocks to them, all the while saying in an astonished tone of voice: "I really do not know why, but I just feel like putting this one with them, and this one, and this one." Only after she had grouped all the blocks correctly, she said, as if discovering something: "Oh, I see. Of course it is size!" This sequence of events — grouping first and formulating the principle after, or at least during, the process— is typical of the approach that is guided by perception . . . [1941, p. 318.]

The process of inductive concept formation, then, is the experiencing of one thing after another and the selective perception of certain aspects of the material as common to several objects.

As was mentioned above, most of the experimental studies of inductive concept formation have studied the formation of class concepts. These experiments correspond, therefore, to the analysis of thinking given by the older or formal logic. According to traditional logic, deduction is concerned primarily with matters of inclusion and exclusion — as though all deductive thinking had a form like this:

Mr. J lives in Boston
All of Boston is included within Massachusetts.
Therefore Mr. J lives in Massachusetts.

Actually, however, most of our deductive thinking takes one or the other of these forms:

(1)

Calcium-deficient diets produce rickets.
This diet is deficient in calcium.
Therefore this diet will produce rickets.

(2)

Yellow fruits and vegetables are rich in vitamin A.
These peaches are yellow.
Therefore these peaches are rich in vitamin A.

The second proposition in each example is a class concept. But the first proposition in (1) is a concept of cause and effect, and in (2) it is a sign-significate relation. And, indeed, since our definitions and classifications, both in science and in everyday life, depend primarily on our knowledge of functional properties, it follows that most of our class concepts are acquired from the observation of cause-and-effect and sign-significate relations. Accordingly it is true enough that inductive concept formation ought to be studied and interpreted as a process that is related to deductive thinking. But the typical content of deductive thinking suggests a broader territory than has usually been conceived as the field for studies of inductive concept formation.

How widely, then, does inductive concept formation occur? Is it restricted just to cases of technically sophisticated thinking? The answer is that inductive concept formation is found in a much vaster area. It is a great part of the learning of everyday life, as when a person "learns what another individual is like." It is found in small children as well as in adults (witness the fact that the small child typically uses a host of regularly formed words that he has never heard others use, such as "eated," "drinked," "goodest," and "unfavorite"). Furthermore it is not found solely in human beings. Some experiments by Harlow (1949) will later be described that give a fine demonstration of this sort of learning in monkeys. Even on less complex matters than those Harlow has explored, however, it also appears that many aspects of animal learning are examples of inductive concept formation. Specifically this seems to be the case in conditioning, discrimination learning, and much of so-called "trial-and-error learning." For example, a dog in a conditioning experiment faces a complex and confusing situation. He receives a welter of stimulation from the walls of the room, from noises, from pressures of the harness, from odors, etc. And then, without any special factor that distinguishes the "signal" from other stimuli, he is given the signal and, perhaps 2 seconds later, receives a shock. As both Klüver (1933, pp. 344–349) and Mowrer (1947) have pointed out, the dog "learns" something immediately. He does not make merely an isolated foot withdrawal while the shock continues. When the shock ceases he still acts as though he had learned that the whole situation is threatening. He whines, struggles to escape from the harness, etc. As Mowrer says:

> These latter responses are commonly referred to as "spontaneous," or "interval," responses, and are usually regarded as an uninteresting nuisance, to be minimized if possible and, if not, ignored. [1947, p. 110.]

The dog finally quiets down and waits. Then, once more, without any special warning so far as he is concerned, he gets the shock. As both Klüver and Mowrer go on to explain, the learning task for the dog is not primarily a task of building up a habit of fear in response to the grosser aspects of the situation. That is acquired immediately. The "conditioning," so-called, is a matter, instead, of acquiring a finer differentiation between two constellations of stimulation — the one that heralds the reinforcement, and the other that exists between trials. The dog has to learn the property common to the shock situations and absent from the others. We diagram such learning as though merely two stimuli were involved. But actually the dog's problem is comparable to the problem that confronts a human subject in an experiment on inductive concept formation. In both cases the learning depends upon the differentiation of some aspect of the situation, and in both cases the learning has some generality of application to new instances.

It might be asked, of course, what advantages we would gain if we considered discrimination learning, conditioning, and some "trial-and-error learning" as examples of inductive concept formation that should be grouped with the traditional concept-formation experiments. One advantage is economy.

Science aims to group together those things that have similar properties. A second advantage is that, when we thus group tentatively those phenomena that seem to have properties in common, we are more likely to generate fruitful research questions about one of the phenomena because we know something already about the others. Thus the traditional studies of concept formation indicate that human subjects are exceedingly active in forming, testing, and revising hypotheses, and that this is partly the process whereby the concepts are formed. Introspective reports are the chief source of evidence for this conclusion, but nonverbal evidence confirms it at a number of points. The studies of conditioning and discrimination learning in animals, however, have not yielded the same conclusion. But — and this point is vital — it is not that this conclusion has been tested and ruled out empirically in animal learning. The issue has not been clearly faced and checked.

Another reason why the territory of inductive concept formation is broad is that it properly includes many cases in which it seems that the concept is acquired on "one trial" or "one experience." Thus, in some of Piaget's research on the thinking of children, he presented some simple situation and asked the child to explain the effect observed. Piaget found that there is a tendency to seize upon some more or less obvious quality of the object to "explain" what has been seen. A chip of wood floats "because it is light"; a battleship floats "because it is big and strong." But even here the concept is not really formed from the single perceptual experience. In selecting the property that he emphasizes, the child draws upon his past observations. This is seen especially clearly in animistic responses given to such questions as: "Why does the wind blow?" The property of purpose, or "wanting to go somewhere," that the child cites as the explanation is not a directly perceived property of the wind. Here the child integrates his present perception with past experiences of his own reactions, and perhaps of those of other persons.

The difference between the "explanations" of children and of scientifically trained adults, therefore, is not that the child uses only present perceptual material. Both of them go back to past experiences as well. The difference is partly that the adult has more memory materials to draw upon and partly that he has learned to search with more diligence for a wider variety of past observations out of which he can distill some satisfactory proposition.

In defining inductive concept formation, we might finally ask whether this process is simply the "paring away" or "omitting" of unnecessary features. It seems better to say, as Smoke (1946) suggests, that concept formation can also involve the enrichment of concepts. For example, a person can learn additional properties of some main class of things such as "dogs." Or he may acquire more knowledge about "subclasses" within a larger class and learn to know more of the particular properties of each subclass. Or a person may extend the range of cases that he can identify as instances of the main class.

Experimental Findings in Inductive Concept Formation

The results of several studies in this area have already been mentioned, but we will now try to summarize the experimental findings more systematically:

1. Several experiments show that concepts may be formed, retained, and used "unconsciously." This statement does not imply that the subjects are not conscious of the perceptual materials before them. It implies merely that sometimes the subjects do not consciously recognize what properties they use to group or classify the materials. An experiment by Rees and Israel (1935) might be added to those already cited. In one of their series the subjects were asked to rearrange into words a set of 30 anagrams. The first 15 were anagrams like nelin, nedoz,

and sdlen. Each of these had one possible solution and a uniform letter order (5, 4, 1, 2, 3). The last 15 were anagrams like klsta, nolem, and dlsco. Each of these had two possible solutions. However, the subjects who had worked first on the "5, 4, 1, 2, 3" anagrams gave corresponding solutions in 95 per cent of the cases; whereas control subjects gave only 47 per cent of such solutions. But 6 of the 10 experimental subjects had no conscious idea that a uniform arrangement was involved. And yet 91 per cent of their solutions for the ambiguous anagrams were of the determined sort. Another group of subjects was originally given anagrams that represented phenomena of "nature," such as nirsa (rains), sargs (grass), metss (stems). They were then given anagrams that might be solved either by "nature" words or by other words. About two-thirds of the 34 subjects did not realize that any such selection was involved, and yet their responses showed that they had adopted a definite set.

Indeed, even when the subject comes to realize that there is a "system" involved, it appears that he frequently develops the generalization and uses it for a while before he is able to recognize consciously what he is doing. For instance, the subject notices that the anagrams are getting "easier." If he seeks the reason for this he may come to realize that he has been using a particular pattern, or a certain area of association, or whatever.

2. The introspective reports of the subjects commonly disclose an exceedingly active process: they form hypotheses, test them against present perceptions and against memory, and revise them. The process often occurs so rapidly that it would be practically impossible to discover, except by verbal reports, the successive concepts that the person explores.

3. Some of the difficulties encountered in concept formation occur because the perceptual processes of the subject have the same highly selective character that we ac-

cept as characteristic of conceptual reactions. That is to say, the subject does not respond to a drawing, for example, in terms of all its easily discriminable aspects, but only in terms of a few of its aspects. He fails to form some concepts that he might form, and the reason, so he is likely to report, is that he "just didn't notice those other features of the stimulus." Lashley has expressed this principle by saying:

> The mechanism of nervous integration is such that when any complex of stimuli arouses nervous activity, that activity is immediately organized and certain elements or components become dominant for reaction while others become ineffective. This constitutes a "set" to react to certain elements. . . .
> In any trial of a training series, only those components of the stimulating situation which are dominant in the organization are associated. [1942, p. 242.]

This statement is good, but it is too restrictive to fit all the evidence from concept-formation experiments. For, even though the subjects do not retain an impression of many aspects of the stimuli, they do retain and later use more than just the "components . . . dominant for reaction" at that time. This is indicated especially well in an experiment by Heidbreder (1924) in which some rather full verbal reports are quoted from her subjects. These reports often indicate that the subjects were able to "think back" and to say, for example, "Come to think of it, I believe all the ones that have been correct had curved lines in them" (even though the subject, on the earlier trials, had guided his reactions by the hypothesis that some other property was the crucial one).

There is, therefore, some greater *retained* richness of perceptual processes than is involved in the main perceptual reactions of the moment. It is often out of this extra margin of richness that new perceptual and conceptual reactions can be developed. But this extra margin is meager indeed in comparison with what we might expect when we consider the large number of aspects of the stimulus materials and the large number of habits of the person that are relevant to these different aspects.

4. The concepts that are developed and used do not depend upon any simple quantitative effects of reinforcements. This has been shown most strikingly by some *insoluble* problems used by Krechevsky (1932) and Spence (1939), and by some problems in which, conversely, it was impossible for the subjects to make errors (Witkin, 1940, 1941). Krechevsky trained rats in a 4-unit discrimination apparatus. In the 12 trials of each day, the position and illumination of the correct side at each choice-point were so randomly shifted that, no matter what "hypothesis" the rat adopted, it could not be successful in more than 50 per cent of its choices. With equal amounts of reinforcement and punishment for each possible systematic mode of response, it was nevertheless found that each rat would typically try two or even three systematic modes of response in succession. At the beginning the choices had no general character, but within a few days the rat would begin to choose the right or the left side, or perhaps the dark tunnel. Sometimes all the choices for several days would be of one sort. Then that type of response would die out, and a second would gradually appear. Spence (1939) demonstrated the same phenomenon with chimpanzees when he presented them with an insoluble problem on the multiple-choice apparatus.

Witkin used an apparatus much like Krechevsky's, except that the rats were free at each choice-point to choose either side to progress toward the goal. The rats soon learned to run swiftly and unhesitatingly. They did not run at random, however, but, as in Krechevsky's experiment, they soon developed a systematic mode of responding. What is more noteworthy, though, is the fact that, just as in Krechevsky's experiment, they typically shifted to a second or even to a third pattern of response. The shifts that

Krechevsky and Spence observed, therefore, cannot be attributed solely to the frustrations attendant upon the "wrong" choices.

5. Different persons, or the same person at different times, may form concepts by basically different methods in the same objective situation. We have already mentioned Hanfmann's observations with the Vigotsky test of concept formation (1941). In her control group of 64 college graduates, she found that about half the subjects went at the problem of classifying the blocks by formulating verbal hypotheses, with little resort to manipulation of the objects. Such subjects typically counted the number of colors on the blocks, and, since there were five colors, they said that color could not be the basis for the required fourfold classification. The subjects might then work with aspects of shape. When they finally discovered the correct solution, they usually expressed dissatisfaction with it as having a rather arbitrary and unnatural character. In contrast with these subjects who relied mainly on abstract thinking and verbalizations, the other subjects relied more on perceptual and situational factors and helped themselves more with tentative overt groupings of the material. This approach seemed to favor an emphasis on different qualities from those most naturally stressed by the "thinking" group. When these subjects discovered the solution they were typically pleased by it and regarded it as very appropriate. The scores for these subjects were about twice as good as for the subjects who used the more abstract or verbal approach. Hanfmann points out, however, that this result is presumably due to the nature of the imposed problem. If the test had called for a classification on the basis of shapes, rather than on the basis of a combination of height-plus-area, the "abstract thinkers" would have made the better scores. Hanfmann noted further, however, that the most effective work was done by those subjects who were apparently able to employ both modes of approach, alternating between them.

In her original experiment on thinking, Heidbreder (1924) noted a similar effect when the subjects had to figure out the rules for marking different geometrical designs. When the problems were difficult, the subjects sometimes shifted over to what she called "spectator behavior." The subject would say, for instance, "I'm just lost. I'm just marking at random, because I've tried everything I could think of and I can't imagine what the rule would be here." And yet, out of such responses, seemingly just passively made, the subjects were usually able to reach solutions.

Bouthilet (1948) has also demonstrated this effect. She had her subjects try to learn paired associates like:

elephant—path
recognize—zero

After the presentation of 30 pairs she gave a multiple-choice test like this:

elephant—(1) been, (2) front, (3) very, (4) felt, (5) path.
recognize—(1) goat, (2) ruin, (3) zero, (4) dime, (5) frail.

Among these multiple-choice items were 30 new pairs not included within the learning series. The subjects were told to guess, if necessary, but to try to determine the correct item in each case. The results fell into two distinct categories. Some subjects explored one abstract hypothesis after another. Their successes tended to remain at the chance level until they hit upon the correct hypothesis (that the associated word always was formed from letters included within the stimulus word), and then rose sharply to about 100-per-cent correct. Some of the subjects, however, improved gradually over a longer period of trials. These subjects typically said that they "felt" that such and such response words were correct, but that they didn't know why.

Apparently, therefore, there are fundamentally different ways in which inductive concept formation may occur. It would be interesting to know the advantages of each of these procedures for different tasks and the reasons why different individuals use one or the other.

6. Concept formation is sometimes helped by starting with materials that reveal the principle in an extremely clear form. Hull (1920) made this point when he worked with Chinese characters drawn with the root character in red as contrasted with the black of the other strokes. The same phenomenon has been extensively demonstrated in conditioning experiments. Thus "differentiation training" is rapid if it begins with a to-be-distinguished stimulus that is markedly different from the stimulus that is to remain the positive stimulus. It is also well known that long "trace conditioned responses" can be formed only if the animal is first permitted to learn, with a small time interval, to respond to the particular stimulus. Similarly, with the jumping apparatus, Lashley (1938) has demonstrated that rats may require more than 150 trials, say, to learn a discrimination between a lighter and a darker gray. But if trained first to discriminate black from white, which they learn in perhaps 10 trials, they are then able to transfer without further training to the difficult pair of grays. In other words, out of clearly different materials the animals can learn something in a few trials that then can be applied to a more difficult problem on which more training would have been required.

7. Inductive concept formation may be made either easier or more difficult by previous training on related problems. And which of these opposite effects will occur may be predicted from the relation between the present task and the perceptual-conceptual emphasis acquired in the earlier learning.

An excellent illustration of how previous learning facilitates later concept formation is reported by Harlow (1949). His monkeys were required to discriminate small everyday objects like oilcans, matchboxes, and padlocks. On each trial an opaque screen was lifted at the front of the cage, a board was slid within reach of the monkey, and the monkey was permitted to reach out and lift one or the other of the pair of objects to try to secure the food hidden in a small depression under one of them. After a series of trials on one pair of stimulus objects, a second series was given with another new pair of objects, and so on until the monkey had learned more than 300 different discriminations.

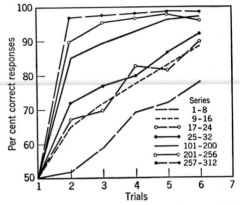

Fig. 4. Showing how monkeys learn to discriminate simple objects on the first six trials of successive series of problems. After the first hundred problems the monkeys almost mastered the discrimination completely on the first trial of the series. (After Harlow, 1949, p. 53.)

Even at the beginning of training, the problem was not difficult. But the remarkable thing is that, as the training continued, the monkeys improved more and more until their learning became almost instantaneous. As is shown in Fig. 4, after the first hundred problems, the monkeys were able to learn new discriminations on the first trial with each new set of objects. A fact that makes this more remarkable, but that is not mentioned in Harlow's article, is that all the studies used a noncorrection method. Even though the monkeys were necessarily wrong on about 50 per cent of their first choices, and even though they were not allowed to lift more than one of the objects on each trial, they were able to learn the object-discriminations from both their failures and their successes. Thus, as is shown in Fig. 4, about 97 per cent of the second trials were correct after the 256th series. Harlow says: "In the final phase of our discrimination series with monkeys there were subjects that solved from 20 to 30 consecutive problems with no errors whatsoever following the first blind trial . . ." (1949, p. 56).

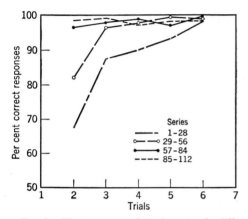

FIG. 5. The responses of monkeys on the "discrimination reversal problem." From the first or "informing" trial on the later series of problems the monkeys achieved almost complete mastery. (Harlow, 1949, p. 57.)

Eight monkeys, trained as described above, were then given a "discrimination reversal problem." With each new pair of objects, the monkey was first given 7 to 11 trials. Then the previously correct object was made the wrong choice, and vice versa; and training continued for 8 trials. On the first reversed trials, of course, almost all the responses were wrong. But, as is shown in Fig. 5, the monkeys gradually built up a generalized "learning set," as Harlow calls it. With increasing training, they made fewer and fewer errors and finally practically no errors after the first "informing" trial.

A set to utilize a special aspect of the stimulus materials, however, will interfere with the learning of sign-significate relations of other aspects of the situation. Lashley (1942) showed this interference in rats. On the jumping apparatus his rats

first learned, in an average of 95 trials, to choose a circle 10 centimeters in diameter and to avoid a 6-centimeter circle. Then they were given 210 trials with the same small circle versus a triangle 10 centimeters on each side. They transferred so readily to these new stimuli that there were only 1.5 errors, on the average, in the 210 trials. Lashley then tested them with an 8-centimeter circle versus a triangle of equal area. All four rats reverted to the use of position habits. Tested with a large circle versus a small triangle, they all chose the circle. In other words, the original training had taught them to look for relative largeness. As long as a basis for size discrimination was present, its use prevented the development of shape discrimination.

In such a case, of course, there would probably be a shift to a new basis of discrimination if circumstances made it hard to continue on the former basis, especially if there were a very ready cue that the subjects could use instead. Lashley had a case of this sort. He says:

In the one instance where a suggestion of association with the new aspect of the stimulus appeared, the patterns added to the original size difference were conspicuously different and of such a character as to obscure somewhat the difference in size; a six-pointed star with long points vs. a triangle of larger surface area but smaller linear dimensions. [1942, p. 259.]

Other Factors Affecting Inductive Concept Formation

The history of science and of culture in general shows striking differences in the speed with which various concepts have been achieved. Perhaps it would be worth while to explore these cases of unequal cultural advance and to try to define the governing factors that operate. We tend to say, for instance, that the slow development of some parts of knowledge, such as the social sciences, is due to institutional resistance or to the fact that they concern emotionally laden problems. These may well be real factors. But when we note how much time had to pass before the concept of vitamins was clearly established, we are warned against accepting too easy explanations.

From an examination of cultural development it appears that the following are some of the factors that impede the discovery of cause-and-effect relations:

1. A separation in time between cause and effect (as between mosquito bites and malaria).

2. Perceptual incongruities between the cause and effect (as the difference between flies and maggots, in the case of the old theory of "spontaneous generation").

3. Already existing habits that cause a misleading organization of the items in the situation (as the knowledge that led early workers on beri-beri to search persistently for the transmission of bacteria from one affected person to another).

4. Relative intangibility of either the cause, or the effect, or both (as the elusiveness of wind resistance as a factor in the inefficiency of trains at high speed).

5. The existence of interdependent causes (as the fact that neither sufficient calcium nor sufficient vitamin D can prevent rickets by itself, but that both must be present).

6. Motivational factors that work against acceptance of a conclusion (as when Semmelweiss's fellow obstetricians in the 1840's refused to accept his demonstration that puerperal or child-bed fever was due to the transmission of some material from one woman to another by the obstetricians themselves).

DEDUCTIVE CONCEPT FORMATION

Deductive thinking, or deductive concept formation, is a very common process. We often fail to appreciate this fact because we conceive of deductive thinking solely in terms of the fully stated syllogism. Actually it occurs most often in everyday life as the enthymeme. Thus a child says, "I don't want to eat that because it's burned." The major premise is assumed, rather than stated. But psychologically it is playing its role as truly as though it were stated. When we recognize the deductive process in cases like this, we can readily see that it is characteristic of small children as well as of adults, and that it is a typical mode of thinking of people of all social and educational levels.

To study deductive thinking we need the help of both logic and psychology. Each field has its distinct contribution to make. Logic, for instance, is like mathematics (see Chapter 1). It describes the transformations by which the conclusion may be secured from the premises. It identifies and describes the types of errors that can be made in such transformations, and it describes the rules by which sound transformations can be made.

From the rules of logic, however, we get no adequate comprehension of the psychological processes involved in deductive thinking nor of the many psychological factors that affect these processes. What is more, we get an inadequate idea of the functions served by deductive thinking. The concepts of logic tend to suggest that deductive thinking is legitimate and profitable only when both premises have been adequately established. But this in turn leads to the discouraging conclusion that deductive thinking must generally be tautological. Thus, consider the syllogism: "All communicable diseases are caused by bacteria; this is a communicable disease; therefore it must be caused by bacteria." This conclusion cannot be drawn unless we already know, from prior study, that this particular communicable disease, as well as all others, is caused by bacteria. Most of our deductive thinking in real life, however, occurs in cases in which, to tell the truth, we have only very sketchy evidence for the propositions from which the conclusion is drawn. The premises are hypotheses, in short. And the conclusions drawn from them are also hypotheses, although we often fail, in ordinary life, to appreciate their tentative status.

Why do we use deductive thinking if it is as uncertain as all this? From a psychological point of view, several reasons may be suggested:

1. It is often true that we need to act in practical matters on conclusions that have not been reached by an adequate process of inductive concept formation. Thus a psychologist may be asked by a parent for advice regarding the toilet training of his baby. The psychologist tells him there are no good studies of what effects occur from what methods of dealing with this problem. "But," the parent insists, "I must do something. What should I do?" Accordingly, the psychologist might reason that "maturation makes learning problems easier; toilet training is a matter of learning; therefore it would be well to postpone such training till a later age than is usually done." In so reasoning, he has to go beyond his knowledge. He does not know whether all things are learned more easily at 2 years, say, than at 1, or whether this is one of the exceptions to such a general rule. Nevertheless it is by deductions such as this that most of the practical decisions in politics, business, religion, child care, and many other practical matters have to be made.

2. Deductive thinking is often a means of formulating fruitful scientific questions. Thus Hill and his co-workers reasoned: "All physiological processes seem to involve heat production; the conduction of nerve impulses is a physiological process; therefore it probably involves heat production." Their work that grew out of this deduction is a classical example of how a deductive argument, persistently followed up, led to the final establishment of the conclusion even though the initial research yielded only negative results.

3. Deductive arguments are used in many situations because our knowledge can be put more economically into the form of abstract statements. It is difficult to learn and remember many specific items of information. It is more economical, instead, to learn, say, that all cases of levers obey such and such laws and then to learn that such and such cases may be thought of as levers even though, superficially, they seem to be quite different.

4. Deductive arguments are also used because strong motivational values get established with reference to general propositions, and, by deductive argument, these motivational values are carried over to specific cases. Thus people build up emotionalized attitudes with reference to such propositions as "Democratic procedures are better than autocratic procedures," or "Gambling is wrong." Then, when it is argued that a given concrete case is an instance of such a broad class, there tends to be a carry-over of the motivational value to the specific case.

Unfortunately the number of experimental investigations of deductive thinking is small (see Woodworth, 1938, pp. 807–817). The neglect of this type of cognitive process may be partly due to its entanglement with logic and to the consequent belief that deductive thinking is more a logical than a psychological problem. Actually, however, there are many purely psychological issues that could well be approached, as suggested above, by methods other than logical analysis. Not much is gained by the mere logical analysis of possible sources of error in deductive thinking. Our greatest need, perhaps, is to start with an empirical investigation of the kinds of deductive thinking people use in actual life, and the kinds of logical mistakes they are likely to make, and under what circumstances. Such "ecological" studies of deductive thinking may not seem to be part of experimental psychology in a narrow sense, but it is probably safe to predict that investigations of this sort would soon lead to really significant experimental problems.

INVENTIVE CONCEPT FORMATION

The process that occurs in problem solving or in trial-and-error situations may or may not be inventive concept formation. For in such situations either of the two means of concept formation may occur that we have discussed above. Thus deductive thinking is often used in an effort to solve baffling problems, as when the research workers on beri-beri argued that, since the symptoms were comparable to those of bacterial origin, probably bacteria were to blame for beri-beri also. In other instances the problem solving may be mainly a matter of inductive concept formation, as when it was noticed that chickens fed on table scraps developed symptoms like those of beri-beri, but that these symptoms cleared up when the chickens happened to be fed on brown rice. The only way to solve some problems is to follow this vague rule: observe and try various things and try to determine, from the perceptual experiences, what factors are related to what other factors.

In some problem situations, however, another type of process is possible. The subject can draw upon his stock of knowledge and on his present perceptual experiences to construct a representation of the solution, or at least an anticipation or representation of *part* of the solution. When the evidence indicates that the subject does this before actually trying out a new technique or a new arrangement of the materials, we say that the subject has engaged in inventive thinking or inventive concept formation.

It is possibly true that there is no fundamental difference between inductive and inventive concept formation. The inductive process often requires a high order of discernment to determine what common properties run through a series of situations. Especially when he tries to "explain" an event (which we grouped under inductive concept formation), the subject has to draw on related knowledge in a way that is highly reminiscent of what he does in inventive thinking. Because of these similarities, much of what has been said about inductive concept formation applies also to inventive concept formation. On the other hand, there may well prove to be at least some principles peculiar to the behavior of the subject who has to think of how to use familiar materials in new ways, or even has to construct new tools not previously in existence. The wiser procedure seems to be to classify these cases as a distinct group.

It is customary, in studies of inventive thinking, to employ problems that the subject is at first unable to solve, because we often have to rely on this initial failure as evidence that the problem is new to the person. However, it is a mistake to insist that there must be this initial blockage. For sometimes the evidence is fairly definite that the individual did not learn his specific response previously and yet is able to produce it almost instantaneously, as when one small child spoke unhesitatingly of a museum as a "dead zoo" and another child spoke of shavings as "carpenter peelings." And, conversely, the initial inability to respond is not always evidence that there was no past learning. Thus we frequently hesitate over a name but recall it after an interval. We surely would not say that we get the name by inventive thinking rather than by past learning. In the same way, it sometimes happens that a subject believes he is doing original inventive thinking when, as it turns out later, he has recalled a solution learned previously.

A lot of interest has been focused on the problem of whether new solutions, or at least new part-solutions, can be achieved by a process of "insight." Usually this has been understood in the sense of "foresight" — i.e. in the sense of a process that yields a representation of a more or less complete solution before the actual manipulation of materials could facilitate the representation perceptually. However, as some writers like Woodworth (1938) have pointed out, a subject often gets a solution by chance but does not discern what happened. So, Woodworth says, "insight" may sometimes be a matter of "hindsight" and yet be a considerable cognitive accomplishment at that. It seems doubtful that these cases should be called inventive thinking. But, if not, they certainly emphasize once more the continuity between inventive thinking and other sorts of concept formation.

A number of careful studies have demonstrated that the taking of new steps in inventive problem solving is often dependent on prior learning. Thus Cleveland (1907) demonstrated that learning to play chess depends on getting a mastery of successively more complex configurations. Guanella (1934) made a careful study of how small children learn to build with blocks and showed what a gradual development of constructive ability is manifested here. Durkin (1937) used puzzles in which flat pieces had to be fitted together to make larger geometrical designs and showed how the solution of more complex problems was facilitated by prior experience with simpler problems. For that matter, Köhler (1925) recognized this phenomenon in chimpanzees. Not until after they had learned to rake in food with one stick could they solve the problem of using a short stick to rake in a longer stick that might, in turn, be used to secure food. In the box-stacking problem, where the chimpanzee had to pile one box on another in order to reach some food hanging high in the air, Köhler recognized a series of steps. First the chimpanzees learned to use a single box. Then they got the notion of employing a second box, but they did no more than to bring it near the first box that had been placed under the food or to hold it up in the air toward the suspended food. Later they learned to place the second box on the first. Even after that, however, the animals still had to learn to adjust the second box well enough to make it usable — and their progress on this last task was so irregular and fumbling that Köhler believed it was

learned by trial and error rather than by insight.

Many studies give evidence that the development of solutions, or the steps of inventive thinking, often depends upon some favorable constellation of physical stimuli or upon some chance exploratory activity that *almost* gives the solution. When one of Köhler's chimpanzees solved the problem of fitting one stick into the end of the other to make a longer one with which to reach, he did so partly as a result of the fact that, when fumbling with the sticks, he seemingly by chance got them in a straight line with each other and almost touching.

Although inventive processes may rest in part on previous learning and in part on favorable external conditions, it is also true that subjects are able to transcend, to some extent, what is given by past experience and by external stimulation. There is some process that is contributed by the organism, some process that runs ahead of what is given by past experience or present environmental stimulation.

The problem of inventive concept formation, however, is not disposed of by the mere demonstration that there are steps or developments that run beyond what is given environmentally and by past experience. The main question is: what factors permit such steps to occur and permit them to be larger in some cases than in others, and what factors tend to impede inventive concept-formation?

A number of factors have been shown to *help* inventive thinking:

1. Some species are clearly more capable of inventive thinking than are others. Klüver (1933) showed that Cebus monkeys considerably surpass Rhesus monkeys, even though the two species do not differ greatly in their manipulative equipment. Yerkes (1927) found that the gorilla is not so gifted as the chimpanzee.

2. Inventive thinking depends strongly on motivation. Indeed, without motivation there often "is no problem" so far as the

subject is concerned. Rossman (1931) found that men who were known as inventors typically attributed part of their progress to their strong desires to accomplish one thing or another. It is likely, however, that this contribution of motivation to inventive thinking can be analyzed more specifically. Thus it is now accepted that motivation helps not solely in the acquisition of habits but also in governing the use or reinstatement of what was learned previously (Tolman, 1932; Hull, 1943). Strong motivation also tends to inhibit responses to factors in the situation that would otherwise distract the problem solver.

3. Inventive thinking often requires long-continued effort. It is not true that solutions come either quickly or not at all. This factor too, however, invites further study, because it would be important to know the factors that are introduced by such long-continued efforts, but that are not present in briefer attempts. It is obvious, of course, that long periods give more time for the occurrence of favorable chance constellations of physical stimulation or of memories and associations. The longer periods also give more time for the mastery of subordinate aspects of the problem, so that the thinker is better able to attempt larger integrations. It may be, however, that long-continued effort causes readjustments of the nervous processes even aside from these influences, just as long-continued viewing of the same stimuli permits an individual to get binocular-rivalry effects and reversible-illusion effects that he would not otherwise see.

4. Inventive thinking is helped by a background of relevant knowledge and skills. A rather striking indication of this fact has been given by the sociologist, Ogburn (1922), who has listed a long series of instances that show that identical inventions and scientific discoveries frequently have been made independently within a few years of one another.

5. An analysis of the nature and function of the solution of a problem may help to solve it. Duncker (1926) reported that, when his subjects were first presented with new problems, they typically tried to find a concrete solution immediately and directly. But when they found themselves blocked they tended to resort to intermediate processes: a closer diagnosis of the source of the difficulty, and, even more important, a "definition of the functional value that the solution would have to serve.".

It is noteworthy that at least one field of practical inventive thinking (architecture) has come to rely explicitly on this intermediate process (see Cooper, 1946). The student of architecture is taught not to strive for a concrete design immediately but to study first what the house is for, the purpose of each room, and the kind of family for whom it is intended. Work on the concrete solution should follow only after this definition of functional values has been determined.

6. The proper mental set may speed the solution of a problem. Maier has demonstrated in a number of experiments (1930, 1931) that, even when subjects have the necessary background knowledge for solving a problem, they may be unable to do so if they lack the proper "direction," or the proper *general* idea of how to solve the problem. His notion here is much the same as one of the key ideas emphasized by Wertheimer (1945), that one of the main processes in thinking is often a *recentering* of the materials, so that something that was formerly a background item becomes an object of central interest. This phenomenon of direction needs further analysis. It seems that Duncker's "definition of functional value" is a form of "direction." But there seem also to be "directions" in other senses as well, and our understanding of inventive thinking would be furthered if the "direction phenomenon" were made more definite.

Most of the factors that *hamper* inventive thinking are simply the lack of the facilitating influences listed above. However, several items deserve specific attention:

1. Birch (1945) demonstrated with chimpanzees a point previously mentioned by Köhler, that a motivation of more than moderate intensity may decrease rather than increase the chances of solution.

2. Duncker (1945) identified an additional specific aspect of the phenomenon of "direction" by his discovery that a subject is less likely to use an object if it is "functionally embedded" in a context other than that of the problem, even though the conditions that create this "functional embeddedness" actually increase the subject's contacts with the object. He gave his subjects the task of making a board stay in position across an open doorway. The materials given provided no means of fixing the board in place except by using a cork as a wedge between one end of the board and the door jamb. The problem was made much more difficult when the cork was present as the stopper in an inkwell than when it was lying, with other materials, out on the table. This was true even when Duncker increased the amount of contact with the cork by requiring the subjects to remove it from the inkwell for the purpose of writing.

3. Some remarkable demonstrations of the hampering effect of *faulty* directions on thinking were given by Luchins (1942), following some exploratory work started by Zener in 1927. His subjects were first given a short series of problems of this type: "If you had three empty jars that hold 21, 127, and 3 quarts, respectively, tell how you might measure accurately 100 quarts of water." These problems established the procedure of getting the required amount by filling the largest vessel and emptying from it with the aid of both the other jars until the required amount was left in the largest jar. Following five or six problems of this sort, other problems were given, such as: "Given three jars that hold, respectively, 23, 49, and 3 quarts, tell how to get 20 quarts." His control subjects showed (if any proof were needed!) that, when no contrary "set" had been established, this type of problem was always solved by a simple subtraction or addition with two jars, rather than by the use of all three. But the previous experience with the other problems caused 81 per cent of one group of college students to solve these problems by the more involved method. Another group of 86 students had been instructed to write "Don't be blind" on their papers before starting on these further problems. Moreover, Luchins explained to them: "This is to make you aware of the fact that you must be cautious; you must watch out and see that you do not act foolishly while solving the subsequent problems . . ." (1942, p. 5). Yet 55 per cent of the subsequent solutions used the unnecessarily involved procedure. The experiment yielded similar results with large groups of subjects of different ages and educational backgrounds. Furthermore a ninth problem was given (to get 25 quarts, given three jars of 28, 76, and 3 quarts capacity) that could not be solved by the involved method but could be solved by simple subtraction. In half of the 29 groups who were thus tested, 66 to 87 per cent of the subjects were unable to solve this problem within the 2½ minutes allowed for it.

In order to get light on the factors affecting this phenomenon, Luchins explored a large number of conditions, and the part of his monograph (1942, pp. 38–86) that describes these experiments is a model of experimental method. He found that the mechanization or "Einstellung" effect was markedly decreased when, during the original training, he gave alternately tasks that called for the long indirect procedure and tasks that introduced the procedures of adding the contents of two jars in one case and of subtracting them in another (p. 41). He also found the effect lessened when there was an interval of 8 days between the original problems and the test problems. But IQ, age, educational status, and many variations of mode of presentation of the task were unrelated to the appearance of the effect. In fact, the degree to which the effect occurred was almost incredible in some cases. Thus with five groups of high school and junior college students he followed the original training with this problem: given jars that hold, respectively, 3, 64, and 29 quarts, tell how to measure out 3 quarts. He found that from 52 to 85 per cent of the subjects proposed filling the 64-quart jar, emptying 29 quarts from it twice and 3 quarts once, thus ending with 3 quarts! When he gave this problem in one public school class he told the subjects, "Using one, two, or three of these jars, get the required volume of water." Yet 80 per cent of the 30 subjects went through the long procedure (pp. 72–73). Nor was this because the subjects believed that they were necessarily required to use one procedure rather than another. For, when he showed the subjects how they might have proceeded, ". . . nearly all of these subjects regretted that they had not previously seen it, and many of them bewailed their blindness and stupidity" (p. 73). The effect was increased somewhat when he presented the tasks as speed tests and when he created a competitive atmosphere. From his behavioral observations and from comparisons among different schools he concluded that strong mechanization effects could be attributed partly to mechanical methods of work and unfavorable emotional atmospheres established in the regular school work.

It is certain, therefore, that experience can exert a surprising hampering effect on subsequent problem solving. But it would be a mistake to emphasize too strongly this hampering influence. We may not have as much "experimental" evidence of the contrary effect, but we certainly see, in the whole breadth of educational work by which students learn to use scientific methods, learn to seek comprehensive theories rather than piecemeal formulations, and so on, that past experience can also help to produce exceedingly complex cognitive activities that would otherwise lie far beyond human reach.

SUMMARY

Experimental work indicates that we need to redefine cognitive processes. The older definitions were phrased both in terms of the functional relations of these processes and in terms of their supposed attributes as conscious experiences. However, experiments on successive comparison, complex associations, and concept formation indicate that cognitive processes are often either not conscious or not describable in terms of their conscious attributes, even when these exist. Furthermore research in intelligence testing and animal psychology has shown that fruitful concepts of cognitive processes can be defined solely in terms of functional properties.

Nevertheless in the study of cognitive processes it is still true that introspective reports provide valuable data. Through them we know of the exceedingly active processes by which inductive concept formation generally occurs. The introspective method is not in itself a sufficient means of studying cognitive processes, however, (1) because experiments have demonstrated that processes with the same functional properties continue to exist even when introspectively they are no longer observable, and (2) because some aspects of cognitive activity are from the beginning inaccessible to introspective observation.

Experiments on inductive concept formation have usually been planned as though all inductive concept formation is a matter of forming class concepts. This emphasis on class concepts is consistent with traditional logic, but it is inconsistent with our present knowledge that actual deductive thinking usually starts from a premise that states certain cause-and-effect relations or certain sign-significate relations. Inductive concept formation therefore must be understood in the broader sense of the learning of concepts (the learning of representations that have some generality of application) by means of a process of recognition of some usually recurrent aspect of perceptual materials as a factor related to some other aspect. Inductive concept formation therefore includes not merely the traditional concept formation experiments with human beings, but also conditioning experiments, discrimination experiments, and many trial-and-error experiments with animals.

Experiments on inductive concept formation have shown that: (1) concepts may be formed, retained, and used unconsciously; (2) concepts frequently result from very active processes in which the subject formulates and tests many hypotheses; (3) difficulties of concept formation are often the result of the meager and selective nature of perceptual processes, even though perceptions usually yield traces of more than just the main attribute emphasized at the moment; (4) concept formation is not determined in simple ways by conditions of reinforcement; (5) two rather different means of concept formation, one a more passive utilization of perceptual experiences, and the other a more active and abstract searching process, occur in different persons or within the same person at different stages, and these two types of process make rather different sorts of contribution to concept formation; (6) concept formation sometimes is helped by an initial use of emphatic examples that "give the subject the idea," as it were; (7) previous learning makes the subject stress and utilize some aspects of the stimulus materials more than others, and this may make later concept formation much easier or much more difficult.

The investigation of deductive thinking has been dominated too much by the principles of formal logic. Deductive thinking is a psychological process, distinct from logic, and it follows rules that can be discovered only empirically. From the point of view of logic, it appears that deductive thinking should not be used except where the major premises are adequately established. Actually it seems that deductive thinking in real life is used most often in cases where the premises are not well established. Deductive thinking is used because we often have (1) to act on matters that lie beyond the area of adequate inductive study, (2) to get hypotheses in as-yet-unexplored areas, (3) to economize in the utilization of past inductive work, and (4) to mobilize motivational factors previously associated with major propositions. Psychological research on deductive thinking ought to explore the functions subserved by it, and it ought to determine what sorts of errors actually occur, and under what conditions, in the actual use of deductive thinking.

Inventive concept formation is a good deal more narrow than problem solving in general. It has many similarities to inductive concept formation, but it involves more the element of using familiar materials in new ways. Many studies have shown the dependence of inventive thinking on prior mastery of part-solutions and often on fortunate constellations of physical stimulation. There seem to be steps, however, that transcend what is thus given by training and stimulation. Inventive concept formation is favored especially by: (1) certain species characteristics, (2) adequate motivation, (3) long-continued effort, (4) relevant knowledge and skills, (5) definition of the functional value the solution must serve, and (6) favorable "directions." Inventive thinking often is handicapped, on the other hand, by the lack of these. Several studies call attention particularly to the hampering influence of (1) too strong motivation, (2) a "functional embeddedness" of elements needed for the solution, and (3) faulty "directions."

REFERENCES

Ach, N. *Ueber die Willenstätigkeit und das Denken.* Göttingen : Vandenhoeck and Ruprecht, 1905.

Adams, D. K. A restatement of the problem of learning. *Brit. J. gen. Psychol.,* 1931, **22,** 150–178.

Binet, A. *L'étude experimentale de l'intelligence.* Paris : Schleicher Frères, 1903.

Birch, H. G. The role of motivational factors in insightful problem-solving. *J. comp. Psychol.*, 1945, **38**, 295–317.

Bouthilet, L. The measurement of intuitive thinking. Ph.D. thesis, University of Chicago Library, 1948.

Bühler, K. Tatsachen und Probleme zu einer Psychologie der Denkvorgänge. *Arch. ges. Psychol.*, 1907, **9**, 297–365 ; 1908, **12**, 1–123.

Cleveland, A. A. The psychology of chess and of learning to play it. *Amer. J. Psychol.*, 1907, **18**, 269–308.

Cooper, D. *Inside your home.* New York : Farrar, Straus, 1946.

Duncker, K. A qualitative (experimental and theoretical) study of productive thinking. *Pedagog. Sem.*, 1926, **33**, 642–708.

Duncker, K. On problem-solving. (Translated by L. S. Lees from the 1935 original.) *Psychol. Monogr.*, 1945, **58**, No. 270.

Durkin, H. E. Trial-and-error, gradual analysis, and sudden reorganization : An experimental study of problem solving. *Arch. Psychol., N. Y.*, 1937, **30**, No. 210.

Fisher, S. C. The process of generalizing abstraction ; and its product, the general concept. *Psychol. Monogr.*, 1916, **21**, No. 90.

Gibson, E. J., and H. R. McGarvey. Experimental studies of thought and reasoning. *Psychol. Bull.*, 1937, **34**, 327–350.

Grünbaum, A. A. Ueber die Abstraktion der Gleichheit. *Arch. ges. Psychol.*, 1908, **12**, 340–478.

Guanella, F. M. Block building activities of young children. *Arch. Psychol., N. Y.*, 1934, **26**, No. 174.

Hanfmann, E. A study of personal patterns in an intellectual performance. *Character & Pers.*, 1941, **9**, 315–325.

Hanfmann, E., and J. Kasanin. A method for the study of concept formation. *J. Psychol.*, 1937, **3**, 521–540.

Harlow, H. F. The formation of learning sets. *Psychol. Rev.*, 1949, **56**, 51–65.

Heidbreder, E. An experimental study of thinking. *Arch. Psychol., N. Y.*, 1924, **11**, No. 73.

Heidbreder, E. Toward a dynamic psychology of cognition. *Psychol. Rev.*, 1945, **52**, 1–22.

Heidbreder, E. The attainment of concepts. I. Terminology and methodology. II. The problem. *J. gen. Psychol.*, 1946, **35**, 173–189, 191–223.

Heidbreder, E. The attainment of concepts. III. The process. *J. Psychol.*, 1947, **24**, 93–138.

Heidbreder, E. Studying human thinking. Chapter 4 in T. G. Andrews (Ed.), *Methods of Psychology.* New York : Wiley, 1948. Pp. 96–123.

Heidbreder, E., M. L. Bensley, and M. Ivy. The attainment of concepts : IV. Regularities and levels. *J. Psychol.*, 1948, **25**, 299–329.

Hilgard, E. R. *Theories of learning.* New York : Appleton-Century-Crofts, 1948.

Hobhouse, L. T. *Mind in evolution.* New York : Macmillan, 1901.

Hull, C. L. Quantitative aspects of the evolution of concepts : An experimental study. *Psychol. Monogr.*, 1920, **28**, No. 123.

Hull, C. L. *Principles of behavior.* New York : Appleton-Century-Crofts, 1943.

Humphrey, G. *Directed thinking.* New York : Dodd, Mead, 1948.

Hunter, W. S. The delayed reaction in animals and children. *Behav. Monogr.*, 1913, **2**, No. 6.

Klüver, H. *Behavior mechanisms in monkeys.* Chicago : University of Chicago Press, 1933.

Koffka, K. *Principles of Gestalt psychology.* New York : Harcourt, Brace, 1935.

Köhler, W. *The mentality of apes.* New York : Harcourt, Brace, 1925.

Krechevsky, I. "Hypotheses" vs. "chance" in the pre-solution period in sensory discrimination-learning. *Univ. Calif. Publ. Psychol.*, 1932, **6**, 27–44.

Krech, D., and R. Crutchfield. *Theory and problems of social psychology.* New York : McGraw-Hill, 1948.

Lashley, K. S. The mechanism of vision : XV. Preliminary studies of the rat's capacity for detail vision. *J. gen. Psychol.*, 1938, **18**, 123–193.

Lashley, K. S. An examination of the "continuity theory" as applied to discriminative learning. *J. gen. Psychol.*, 1942, **26**, 241–265.

Lashley, K. S., and J. Ball. Spinal conduction and kinesthetic sensitivity in the maze habit. *J. comp. Psychol.*, 1929, **9**, 71–105.

Lashley, K. S., and D. A. McCarthy. The survival of the maze habit after cerebellar injuries. *J. comp. Psychol.*, 1926, **6**, 423–433.

Lewin, K. Behavior and development as a function of the total situation. In L. Carmichael (Ed.), *Manual of child psychology.* New York : Wiley, 1946.

Luchins, A. S. Mechanization in problem solving : The effect of Einstellung. *Psychol. Monogr.*, 1942, **54**, No. 248.

Macfarlane, D. A. The role of kinesthesis in maze learning. *Univ. Calif. Publ. Psychol.*, 1930, **4**, 277–305.

MacLeod, R. B. The phenomenological approach to social psychology. *Psychol. Rev.*, 1947, **54**, 193–210.

Maier, N. R. F. Reasoning in humans. I. On direction. *J. comp. Psychol.*, 1930, **10**, 115–143.

Maier, N. R. F. Reasoning in humans. II. The solution of a problem and its appearance in consciousness. *J. comp. Psychol.*, 1931, **12**, 181–194.

Moore, T. V. The process of abstraction. *Univ. Calif. Publ. Psychol.*, 1910, **1**, 74–179.

Moore, T. V. Image and meaning in memory and perception. *Psychol. Monogr.*, 1919, **27**, No. 119.

Mowrer, O. H. On the dual nature of learning—a re-interpretation of "conditioning" and "problem-solving." *Harvard educ. Rev.*, 1947, **17**, 102–148.

Muenzinger, K, F. Plasticity and mechanization of the problem box habit in guinea pigs. *J. comp. Psychol.*, 1928, **8**, 45–69.

Muenzinger, K. F., A. H. Bernstone, and L. Richards. Motivation in learning. VIII. Equivalent amounts of electric shock for right and wrong responses in a visual discrimination habit. *J. comp. Psychol.*, 1938, **26**, 177–185.

Needham, J. G. The time-error in comparison judgments. *Psychol. Bull.*, 1934, **31**, 229–243.

Ogburn, W. F. *Social change.* New York: Huebsch, 1922.

Perky, C. W. An experimental study of imagination. *Amer. J. Psychol.*, 1910, **21**, 422–452.

Piaget, J. *The child's conception of the world.* New York: Harcourt, Brace, 1929.

Piaget, J. *The child's conception of physical causality.* New York: Harcourt, Brace, 1930.

Pratt, C. C. Experimental studies of thought and reasoning. *Psychol. Bull.*, 1928, **25**, 550–561.

Radin, P. *Primitive man as philosopher.* New York: Appleton-Century-Crofts, 1927.

Rees, H. J., and H. E. Israel. An investigation of the establishment and operation of mental sets. *Psychol. Monogr.*, 1935, **46**, No. 210.

Rossman, J. *The psychology of the inventor.* Washington: Inventors' Publishing, 1931.

Smoke, K. L. An objective study of concept formation. *Psychol. Monogr.*, 1932, **42**, No. 191.

Smoke, K. L. Concept formation. In P. L. Harriman (Ed.), *Encyclopedia of psychology.* New York: Philosophical Library, 1946. Pp. 97–100.

Snygg, D. The relative difficulty of mechanically equivalent tasks. I. Human learning. *J. genet. Psychol.*, 1935, **47**, 299–320.

Snygg, D. The need for a phenomenological system of psychology. *Psychol. Rev.*, 1941, **48**, 404–424.

Spence, K. W. The solution of multiple choice problems by chimpanzees. *Comp. Psychol. Monogr.*, 1939, **15**, No. 75.

Stout, G. F.. *A manual of psychology.* New York: Hinds, Noble, and Eldredge, 1899.

Thorndike, E. L. Animal intelligence. *Psychol. Monogr.*, 1898, **2**, No. 8.

Tinklepaugh, O. An experimental study of representative factors in monkeys. *J. comp. Psychol.*, 1928, **8**, 197–236.

Tinklepaugh, O. Multiple delayed reaction with chimpanzees and monkeys. *J. comp. Psychol.*, 1932, **13**, 207–243.

Titchener, E. B. *Lectures on the experimental psychology of the thought processes.* New York: Macmillan, 1909.

Titchener, E. B. *A textbook of psychology.* New York: Macmillan, 1910.

Tolman, E. C. *Purposive behavior in animals and men.* New York: Appleton-Century-Crofts, 1932.

Watt, H. J. Experimentelle Beitrage zu einer Theories des Denkens. *Arch. ges. Psychol.*, 1905, **4**, 289–436.

Wertheimer, M. *Productive thinking.* New York: Harper, 1945.

Witkin, H. A. "Hypotheses" in rats: An experimental critique. I. The genesis of systematic behavior in linear situations. *J. comp. Psychol.*, 1940, **30**, 457–482: II. The displacement of responses and behavior variability in linear situations. *Ibid.*, 1941, **31**, 303–336.

Woodworth, R. S. The cause of a voluntary movement. In *Studies in philosophy and psychology (Garman).* Boston: Houghton Mifflin, 1906. Pp. 351–392.

Woodworth, R. S. Imageless thought—a revision. *Psychol. Rev.*, 1915, **22**, 1–27.

Woodworth, R. S. *Experimental psychology.* New York: Holt, 1938.

Yerkes, R. M. The mind of a gorilla. *Genet. Psychol. Monogr.*, 1927, **2**, 1–193, 377–551.

20.

The Psychophysiology of Learning

CLIFFORD T. MORGAN

The Johns Hopkins University

Almost everything we can say about the physiology of learning concerns the nervous system. There are some phenomena allied to learning in unicellular animals, which have no nervous system, but we cannot be sure yet just what these phenomena mean. In general only animals that possess nervous systems are capable of learning, either simple or complex. This chapter, therefore, is about the nervous system and learning.

EXPLORING THE NERVOUS SYSTEM

Most of us, psychologists and laymen alike, are accustomed to thinking that learning goes along with the brain, that learning requires not just a nervous system in general but a particular part of the nervous system, the brain. For a good many years, in fact, we went further than that. We thought learning required the highest center of the nervous system, the cerebral cortex. Pavlov, the famous father of conditioned reflexology, thought the cortex was the site of all conditioning and higher learning processes. And his notions have tended to hang on in behavioristic learning theory and in neurophysiological conceptions of brain functions.

In this chapter it was convenient for the author to use some of the text prepared for the book *Physiological Psychology* (2nd Ed.) by C. T. Morgan and Eliot Stellar (New York: McGraw-Hill, 1950). The quotations are not acknowledged individually but are used with the permission of the publisher.

It is quite true that most of the learning in which we are interested involves the brain, and particularly the cerebral cortex. Since 1935, however, several workers, not contented with the classical dogma, have examined other parts of the nervous system that may be concerned in learning. In the first part of this chapter we shall look at their exploratory experiments and at their attempts to study conditioning in the spinal cord. Later we shall come to the more intensive study of cortical and subcortical functions in learning.

The Neural Locus of Conditioning

The classical phenomena of conditioning, systematically explored by Pavlov and later by many others, may not be so simple as they appear on the surface. The conditioning technique, however, is a handy one for investigating learning phenomena in animals. It consists of (1) an unconditioned stimulus, such as the sight of food or the shocking of a limb, (2) an unconditioned response, such as salivation or the flexing of a paw to shock, and (3) some conditioning stimulus, such as a bell, a light, or some pressure stimulus applied somewhere to the animal's body. This technique has been used almost exclusively to hunt for the parts of the nervous system and its effectors that are fundamental in learning. The purpose has been to determine what routes in the nervous system are set up in the course of learning, what centers are of special importance, and, in a word, where in the nervous system we can look for the locus of learning. There is a considerable group of studies pointed at this general problem. The problem, like most scientific questions, breaks down into a series of problems.

What route? A first question is whether learning takes place in the route of the unconditioned stimulus or of the conditioning stimulus. Kellogg (1941) has some interesting observations on this point. They do not rest on any surgical disturbance of the nervous system but come from purely behavioral experiments with dogs. The point of them is that conditioned reactions, once formed, may be temporarily lost while the unconditioned response remains intact. In the typical buzz-shock experiments — dogs giving paw-flexure responses to avoid shock when a buzzer is sounded — the dogs appear sometimes to doze off for brief intervals. When they do, their conditioned responses disappear, but their unconditioned responses to shock do not. Similarly, if the dogs are given a light dose of some soporific drug, such as nembutal, they may lose their conditioned responses but not their shock-escape unconditioned responses. Kellogg concludes that there must be different neural centers involved in the conditioned and unconditioned responses.

Is the unconditioned response necessary? Other experiments attack more directly different parts of the unconditioned- and conditioned-response pathways. Several, for example, concern the question whether it is necessary for the unconditioned response to occur in order for learning to take place. In one set of experiments (Kellogg et al., 1940; Light and Gantt, 1936) the muscles involved in the conditioned response were paralyzed during conditioning by crushing the motor nerves leading to them. A complete conditioning procedure was carried out while the dog could not respond. Then time was allowed for the nerves to regenerate, and when it was clear that the muscles could respond again the animals were tested for condition-

ing. They showed by the appropriate flexure of the paw to the conditioning stimulus that learning had taken place while the muscles were paralyzed. These experiments are subject to criticism, because the paralysis did not prevent the animals from giving generalized struggle responses centering about the limb during the original conditioning. These generalized responses were conditioned, and it is possible that it was through them that the correct response was made after nerve regeneration.

Other experiments giving similar results, however, are not open to this objection. In one of them (Crisler, 1930) morphine was employed as the unconditioned stimulus for evoking salivation in the typical Pavlovian type of conditioning. The salivation, however, was blocked by giving the animal atropine during the conditioning trials. Testing later without the atropine produced conditioned responses of salivation to the conditioning stimulus. In a similar study (Finch, 1938) acid was used as the unconditioned stimulus for salivation, but salivation was again prevented with atropine. When conditioning tests were made later without atropine, the animal showed conditioned responses. These experiments, involving the artificial blocking of the motor response, show clearly that response need not occur in order for learning to take place. The parts necessary for learning, therefore, lie upstream from the muscles or glands involved in the execution of the learned response.

Taking a step backward to the motor routes of the spinal cord, we find that these too are not the locus for learning. Loucks and Gantt (1938), instead of evoking paw flexure by the conventional shock to the foot, did it by stimulating directly the motor roots of the spinal cord with an electric current. There was no sign of learning with this technique.

Are motor centers the locus of learning? Pushing even farther back into the nervous system, we come to the motor areas of the cerebral cortex, which are rather essential in carrying out any voluntary or learned response. In higher mammals, extirpation of the motor cortex causes serious paralysis. But by stimulating the motor cortex electrically, we can evoke the various kinds of movements that occur in conditioned responses. In Loucks' experiment (1936), after an appropriate number of such electrical stimulations, tests were made of whether conditioning had taken place. None had.

Harlow and Bromer (1942), rather than employing stimulation of the motor cortex, used a technique for paralyzing it. During the usual conditioning trials a large area of the cortex of the monkey was 'frozen' by the use of a special drug. This drug prevented responses of the limb to the unconditioned shock stimulus, and there was a complete flaccid paralysis. After the drug used for freezing wore off, however, conditioned responses were observed. These were not movements of the limb, but responses of the eyelids and head and neck, which naturally appear in response to shock. These responses now occurred when the conditioned stimulus, a bell, was sounded. Thus it was clear that learning had occurred, although the complete motor system, from the cerebral cortex on down, had been paralyzed.

From these various experiments on motor systems and pathways we can form the definite conclusion that the locus of conditioning is some place other than the motor pathways of the nervous system. To see what the other places may be, we turn to other studies that attack the role of sensory centers and pathways in learning. These give us some hints, but unfortunately they do not give us the final conclusion. The main idea in all experiments of this type is the use of direct electrical excitation of some part of the nervous system in place of either the unconditioned or the conditioning stimulus. By seeing whether such substitutions could successfully be made at various points, we might hope to get some idea of the centers and routes important for conditioning.

Unconditioned stimulus. Several studies show that stimulation in any part of the sensory system normally activated by the unconditioned stimulus, up to and including the cortex, will suffice for conditioning. When Loucks and Gantt (1938) stimulated the spinal roots, in place of using shock-evoked leg flexion, they noticed that, if the intensity of the stimulation was great enough to spread over into the sensory pathways, conditioning to the buzzer was established. The electrical stimulus, they decided, had served as a substitute for foot shock in activating the pain pathways leading upward to the brain.

In another study, by Brogden and Gantt (1942), there is a very interesting result. Direct electrical stimulation of the *cerebellum* of the dog was substituted for the usual unconditioned shock to the foot pad. As usual, a sound was the conditioning stimulus. The cerebellar stimulation evoked movements of the same sort as those evoked by stimulation of the motor cortex. Strangely enough, after a normal number of conditioning trials pairing buzzer and cerebellar stimulation, a conditioned flexion of the limb to buzzer appeared. That is extremely interesting, but we cannot be sure what it means. The investigators assure us that the cerebellar stimulation was not spreading to the cerebral cortex, and we can rule out that possibility. It has been shown, however (Dow and Anderson, 1942; Snider and Stowell, 1944), that sensory impulses reach the cerebellum, and it is possible that the effect was through sensory pathways. Thus we do not know whether electrical stimulation of the cerebellum serves effectively as an unconditioned stimulus because it activates sensory pathways or because it directly arouses motor responses.

Conditioned stimulus. In all the studies in which an electrical stimulus to the nervous system is substituted for the conditioning stimulus, we find positive results. In Loucks' (1936) study with the dog, a hind-leg movement produced by cortical stimulation could serve as the conditioned stimulus for a re-action of the forelimb, when shock was the unconditioned stimulus. Anatomists tell us (Bucy, 1944) that there is representation of cutaneous sense in the motor cortex, and we may assume that the result was due to cortical sensory stimulation. Loucks confirmed this assumption when he completely narcotized the hind limb during the conditioning series, so that no movement could occur. Conditioning still took place. This fact, plus the other results with direct motor stimulation, makes it plain that in Loucks' experiment the sensory effects produced by the stimulation were serving as the conditioning stimulus.

In another part of the same study Loucks demonstrated that the forced movement of a limb could serve as the conditioning stimulus. He produced a *hind-limb* movement by electrical stimulation, then followed this with a shock to the *forelimb*. Conditioning occurred. This is quite easy to understand, however, for it simply means that the kinesthetic impulses arising from the forced movement of one limb could serve as a signal for the conditioned response of another limb.

Finally, let us note another fact that is very much to be expected (Loucks, 1938). Direct electrical stimulation of the visual area of the cerebral cortex can serve as the conditioning stimulus. This was tried and proved true in two different conditioning situations, the salivary response to food and the flexor response to shock. It means simply that one can substitute direct excitation of the visual cortex for stimulation by means of a light.

Here is where this part of the story ends, although it is by no means a satisfying closure. All we have learned is that the locus of conditioning is some place in front of the final common motor path from the cortex. We do not know whether the neural changes that occur in learning are in the centers for the unconditioned stimulus, in those for the conditioning stimulus, in some third 'association' center, or in some combination of all three. Back in 1938, the hope was entertained for a brief moment that learning might be found in special association centers. Culler (1938) reported that a spot on the anterior ectosylvian gyrus, not normally concerned in bell-shock conditioning, would evoke the conditioning response if it were stimulated electrically after conditioning trials. It now appears that this was an artifact of a changing sensitivity of the cortex through repeated stimulation. At any rate there have been no further claims for this association center, either by Culler or by others. So we are still in the dark. Much work and ingenuity are called for if we are to pin down the areas and pathways in which simple learning takes place in the nervous system.

Spinal Conditioning

Although we shall later take up cortical and subcortical functions in learning, let us first consider some exploratory experiments on the possible role of lower centers of the nervous system in learning.

Only a few investigators have looked into the question of spinal conditioning — whether simple learning can take place at the level of the spinal cord. What data we have today we owe chiefly to two investigators, Kellogg and Shurrager. Of these, only Shurrager reported affirmatively. But the two investigators used different techniques, and it is quite likely that the technique has something to do with the results.

Techniques. Shurrager's (1940) method required special surgical procedures to study the conditioning. He stripped out a portion of the semitendinosus muscle from the hind limb of a dog, taking care to keep nerve and blood supply intact. He then looked at this nerve-muscle preparation, either with the naked eye or with the aid of a recording stylus attached to a rotating drum. Whenever the muscle twitched, he could see it. In fact, extremely small reactions, probably involving only one neuromuscular unit, could be observed. As the unconditioned stimulus for this response he applied an electric shock to the foot pad of the same limb from which the muscle had been dissected. Since the muscle was a flexor muscle, it twitched on application of this noxious stimulus. As a conditioning stimulus he applied either gentle pressure or a weak electric shock to the tail of the dog. Before beginning the experiments, however, he transected the spinal cord at the lumbar level to separate it from nervous influences of higher centers. Such operated animals, as Shurrager used them, do not live very long, and all his work demonstrating spinal conditioning was done with acute preparations.

Kellogg et al. (1947), on the other hand, used only chronic preparations — dogs, with their spinal cords transected, that survived the operation for many days. Instead of watching the twitch of a single muscle, he observed the flexor twitch of the whole leg. His unconditioned stimulus was the same as Shurrager's, an electric shock to the foot pad of the same leg. But his conditioned stimulus was different. It was a shock applied to the opposite hind limb of the animal rather than a stimulus on the tail.

Results. With this technique, Kellogg and his colleagues have failed so far to obtain spinal conditioning. Repeated pairing of the conditioned and unconditioned stimuli for hundreds of trials did not 'stamp in' any learned response to the conditioning shock alone. For such a negative result there are several possible explanations: (1) spinal conditioning does not take place in the dog; (2) spinal conditioning cannot be observed in the gross response of the limb when it might be seen in the twitch of a small muscle; and (3) the conditioned stimulus, a shock to the contralateral limb, brings out an unconditioned crossed extension reflex in the other limb — such responses were actually observed — which interferes with the formation of a conditioned flexion response.

With Shurrager's technique, however, data were obtained that have been called spinal conditioning (Shurrager and Culler, 1940,

1941; Shurrager and Shurrager, 1941, 1946). Paired applications of the stimuli to the foot pad and to the tail gave an increasing percentage of twitches in the semitendinosus muscle to the tail stimulus alone. Initial conditioning occurred in 20 to 120 trials and, on the average, in 51 trials. This 'learning' could be extinguished by presenting the tail stimulus without reinforcement, and it could be reestablished by pairing the tail and foot stimuli. For some reason, however, only 98 of 219 dogs in the experiment could be conditioned.

This report of spinal conditioning is remarkable. Even more interesting, however, are some of the other phenomena of spinal conditioning that Shurrager reports. We must run over them rapidly. (1) Conditioned responses may be extinguished and reconditioned (Shurrager and Culler, 1940). Repeated conditionings and extinctions get faster and faster. The rate of extinction, moreover, is proportional to the rate of conditioning preceding it. (2) Normal reflexes may be permanently extinguished (Shurrager and Culler, 1941). An unconditioned response to tail stimulation of the semitendinosus in one leg gradually extinguishes and stays extinguished when the semitendinosus response of the leg on the other side is conditioned to tail stimulation. (3) A conditioned response can be converted into a permanent 'normal' reflex by cutting the roots on the side of the spinal cord opposite to the conditioned semitendinosus response (Shurrager and Shurrager, 1941). (4) All-or-none twitches of the semitendinosus, presumably representing the response of one neuromuscular unit, can be seen in the early stages of spinal conditioning (Shurrager and Shurrager, 1946). Shurrager believes these responses to represent conditioning taking place at a single synapse. The form of the learning curve for the 'synaptic unit' is rectilinear. From this fact Shurrager suggests that the 'true' learning curve is a straight line and that all other forms of learning curves are due to the compounding of units.

We can accept these facts. We may, however, wonder about their interpretation. The meaning of some of the experiments would have been clearer if appropriate controls had been run. In addition, Kellogg and his colleagues (Kellogg, 1947; Kellogg et al., 1947) suggest that these spinal phenomena are not true conditioning but something that might better be called reflex sensitization. They point to the fact that there is an unconditioned response of the semitendinosus muscle to stimulation of the tail. This, they suggest, may become sensitized by repeated applications of the unconditioned foot stimuli. Only more research will tell us whether this or some other interpretation is the correct one.

Subcortical Learning

Even if we are left puzzled by the data on spinal conditioning, we can be confident that some forms of learning can take place at subcortical levels. Several learning experiments have been conducted with decorticate animals (Culler and Mettler, 1934; Girden et al., 1936; Poltyrev and Zeliony, 1930). Both dogs and cats lacking all significant parts of the cortex have been taught to respond in some manner or other to visual, auditory, or cutaneous stimuli. This learning exhibits certain characteristic deficiencies (Culler and Mettler, 1934). We cannot be sure about monkeys and higher primates, however, because we have no learning experiments conducted on such animals without the cortex. After this drastic operation, primates are very hard to keep alive and healthy.

BASIC LEARNING CAPACITIES

There are many ways of presenting the content of this subject, and one may be as good as another. Before we finish, we shall meet many complex and baffling problems. To understand even the problems, let alone the possible answers to them, we need an elementary understanding of the organization of the brain in simple learning. It seems best, therefore, first to take up questions of simple sensory-motor capacity, simple motor and discriminative learning, and their relations to centers and pathways of the brain.

Visual Learning

Although the visual system of the brain includes many centers and pathways, all we need to consider here are two centers: the striate area of the cortex, sometimes called Brodmann's area 17 or simply the visual area, and the main subcortical visual center, the superior colliculus of the midbrain. Worth noting in passing is the fact that another area, the peristriate area or Brodmann's 18, also has some visual associative functions.

Pattern discrimination. On the striate area of the cortex depends the capacity to perceive differences in visual detail, patterns of visual stimuli, and, in fact, nearly all aspects of visual stimuli except simple differences in visual intensity. This is true in the rat (Lashley, 1931), the cat (Smith, 1938), the dog (Marquis, 1934), the monkey (Klüver, 1936, 1937), and man (Hines, 1942). Presumably it is also true of all other animals in the mammalian series. The evidence rests on experiments in which the total striate areas were extirpated and the animals were tested for their ability to discriminate differences in visual detail. Experiments have been done to see whether any subcortical centers are also of importance in detail vision, but these do not give clear-cut results (Brown and Ghiselli, 1938).

Relevant to the role of the visual cortex in detail vision are a number of other studies of cortical lesions and detail vision. Lashley (1939) demonstrated nicely that very small remnants of the visual cortex can be used in pattern discrimination. He (1942) made it clear, too, that no other part of the cortex outside the visual area is concerned in pattern vision. An earlier study by Kirk (1936) purported to show that nonvisual areas are important in complex pattern discriminations, but Lashley, after going over Kirk's results, concluded that these discriminations are probably due to interruptions of the macular projections to the visual cortex.

It seems safe to conclude then that the visual cortex exclusively possesses the capacity to discriminate differences in visual detail. The visual area, and no other, provides animals with their basic capacity to see patterns in their visual environment. If then, the visual cortex provides the capacity for discrimination, what happens, we may ask, when we partially destroy this capacity by taking out part of the visual area, either before or after a habit has been learned?

If very much of the visual cortex is removed, there is usually some disturbance of visual habits. A study by Settlage (1939) with monkeys shows, however, that these disturbances are not due to a disturbance in learning or memory. He took out the occipital cortex on one side in seven animals, thus producing cortical blindness for about half of the visual field. There was a temporary loss, but no final loss, in visual discrimination habits. The trouble seemed to be that the monkeys at first retained their preoperative habits of visual orientation and of fixation of visual objects. This was incompatible with the existence of a large gap in the operated animals' visual world. As time went on, however, the operated animals improved by stages in their ability to make visual discrimination, presumably because they were learning new habits of visual fixation and 'filling in' their visual world.

To test this hypothesis, Harlow (1939) kept some of these monkeys, with half their striate cortex out, in the dark for a period of 10 days following the operation. He then compared their ability in pattern-discrimination tests with those of animals kept in the light. When brought out of the dark, the monkeys showed no recovery of ability to do pattern-discrimination tests. If left

in a lighted cage for a few days, however, with the opportunity to build up experience with visual fixations, the animals regained their ability to discriminate detail.

These studies with various animals add up to one fairly clear conclusion: any loss by an animal of ability to learn or to remember discriminations of visual detail, when its striate cortex is removed, is a loss in ability to see visual space, not a loss in learning or memory capacity.

Spatial vision. So far we have dealt only with pattern discriminations: the capacity to tell the difference between a triangle and a circle or between an upright triangle and an inverted triangle, and so on. The capacity to see these spatial differences, and as a consequence to learn to discriminate them, is clearly dependent on the striate cortex. But there are aspects of spatial vision other than pattern discrimination, and we may ask to what degree are other kinds of spatial vision dependent on the striate cortex.

One study of the cat (Smith, 1938) shows that there is left a little capacity to discriminate spatial orientation afer removal of the striate cortex. Smith was able to demonstrate that the cortically blind cat can learn eventually to tell the difference between an upright bar of light and a horizontal bar, but only if the cat is trained an unusually long time and if the stimuli are presented in total darkness. This, however, is a very primitive capacity and amounts to the ability to tell that there is more light in one sector of the visual field than in another sector. It is only the most primitive type of spatial vision.

Klüver (1942) has done the only really exhaustive studies of the limits of spatial vision in cortically blind animals. He used monkeys. Every aspect of visual space perception, he concluded, is virtually destroyed in monkeys lacking the striate cortex. They have no ability to discriminate differences in visual patterns, they cannot discriminate circles of different size, provided the amount of light coming from the circles is kept constant, nor is there left any depth perception — the ability to tell the relative distance of visual objects. In a word, monkeys without the striate cortex have lost completely their appreciation of visual space.

Intensity discrimination. So much for spatial vision and the striate cortex. Let us turn now to intensity vision and to the subcortical visual center, the superior colliculus. It so happens, as a matter of technique, that the superior colliculus is hard to get at without injury to the visual cortex or to other areas of the brain. Consequently most of what we know about the superior colliculus we have learned by removing the visual cortex and seeing what visual learning capacities are left. The remainder, it turns out, is a capacity for learning intensity differences rather than spatial differences.

Two different techniques have been used to study visual intensity learning in animals. One is the usual conditioning technique in which a light is flashed or a change in light intensity is presented as a signal for the animal to make a conditioned reaction. The other technique is a discrimination method in which two lighted panels are placed in front of the animal and he is trained to choose either the lighter or the darker one to obtain the food reward. Unfortunately many experimenters have been inclined to call the animal's performance in this situation a brightness discrimination. Actually, two panels of the same size, lighted with different intensities, differ in two respects: luminous flux (the total intensity of light emitted) and brightness (the amount of light per unit area). It turns out, in the monkey at least, that there is one neural mechanism for discriminating total flux and a separate one for discriminating brightness. It is safer, therefore, to speak here of intensity differences, and to mean differences in either or both brightness and flux.

All conditioning methods using animals in which the superior colliculus is intact but in which the striate cortex has been removed show that the animals can react to differ-

ences in the intensity of light. Marquis (1934) and Marquis and Hilgard (1936) got this result when they used a conditioned eye-wink reaction, in which the closure of the eyelid to a puff of air was the conditioned reaction to a light signal. So did Wing and Smith (1942) when they used retraction of the hind limb to shock, conditioned to the onset of a light. Wing (1946), using this same technique, conditioned dogs to respond to a change in light intensity, as well as to the onset of a light, and found no effect of the removal of the striate cortex upon either the memory or the learning of this differential conditioned response. Finally, Wing (1947), using reward conditioning, in which the animal is taught to lift his leg to a light signal in order to receive food, found dogs to be capable of learning either a simple reaction to onset of light or a differential reaction to change of intensity of light, with the superior colliculus intact and the visual cortex removed.

Discrimination techniques have been used with other animals with similar results: the rat (Lashley, 1929, 1935b), the cat (Smith, 1937), and the monkey (Klüver, 1936, 1942). Cortically blind animals are capable of learning to discriminate the difference when faced with two lighted panels of the same size but differing in intensity. Klüver (1942), however, working with the monkey, has been able to show that the learning capacity is one of reacting to differences in flux, not to differences in brightness. When he varied the size of equally bright panels, the monkeys were no longer able to perform the discrimination. Reaction to brightness, he points out, requires some sort of space perception, in addition to intensity discrimination. This space perception, he has shown in other connections, is dependent on the striate cortex, not on the superior colliculus. There is no reason to believe that the monkey is different from the dog or the cat in this respect, and we can generalize the conclusion to these animals.

We can summarize these results in a single sentence: with the exception of learning based on crude visual orientation, all learning that involves spatial vision — including brightness discrimination per se — depends on the intact striate cortex, and only learning that depends solely on reaction to flux can be handled by the subcortical centers.

This conclusion, it is interesting to note, explains an otherwise puzzling fact reported a few years ago by Smith (1937). He discovered that, although cats deprived of their striate cortex can make intensity discriminations under ordinary conditions of illumination, when he lighted up the room and surrounded the visual panels with a highly illuminated surface, the cats could no longer learn to make the discrimination, even with hundreds of trials of training. This can be explained by the fact that the cortically blind cats can discriminate only gross differences in flux, not brightness. When the general illumination surrounding the panels is raised to a very high level, the value of $\Delta I / I$ in terms of flux falls to the point where it cannot be discriminated.

Auditory Learning

There have been several studies of the ability of animals lacking an auditory cortex to learn simple auditory discriminations based on intensity. After the removal of this cortex, rats learn to localize the position of a buzzer or a tone (Pennington, 1935). They also learn to avoid shock by shuttling from one platform to another when a tone is used as a signal (Pennington, 1937). Cats, too, readily learn a conditioned movement response to avoid shock when a buzzer or a tone is sounded (Raab and Ades, 1946). So we know that simple learning, dependent on changes in the intensity of sounds, does not depend on the auditory cortex, but on subcortical centers, of which the inferior colliculus is most suspect. Unfortunately we have no data to tell us whether the learning or retention of a frequency discrimination depends upon the auditory cortex.

Somesthetic Learning

Coming now to somesthetic learning — learning based on the use of cutaneous or kinesthetic cues — we again find that there are not enough facts for us to come to decisive conclusions.

We meet a somewhat different situation in somatic sensibility. In the rat (Smith, 1939), so far as we know, there is no one well-defined area that is essential for the discrimination of roughness — a measure of cutaneous intensitive capacity. In monkeys (Ruch, Fulton, and German, 1938), ablation of the postcentral gyrus does not destroy the capacity; neither does injury to the precentral gyrus. Complete parietal lobectomy on one side causes some deficit in capacity to discriminate roughness. But there are no experiments in which such lobectomy has been made bilateral. And we know that there is some bilateral projection in the cutaneous fields.

It is possible to demonstrate somatic form discrimination in monkeys and chimpanzees by giving them such things as wedges and pyramids or cones and pyramids to feel in the dark (Ruch, Fulton, and German, 1938). That such form or spatial discrimination is dependent in part on the posterior parietal lobe is demonstrated by the fact that the chimpanzee in which this lobe has been removed cannot learn to discriminate between a wedge and a pyramid, which are rather similar in form. They can, however, after prolonged training learn to distinguish such dissimilar forms as pyramids and cones. How completely dependent spatial discrimination is on any part or all of the cortical somatic areas has not been accurately determined.

Motor Learning

Research workers have devised an endless variety of motor problems for animals to learn. The possibilities for the rat are more limited than those for primates because rats are low in manipulative skill, but even here several problems have been devised and used in studies of motor learning. The problems fall into two main classes.

Locomotor learning. There are locomotor problems that can be solved by the rat's running and climbing movements. The double-latch box, used by Lashley (1935a), is one of these. In order to obtain food the animals simply depress two platforms in the correct order. Lashley has made lesions, large and small, in various parts of the rat's cortex before putting this problem to them. Compared with normal rats, these operated animals with lesions involving up to 58 per cent of the cortex are capable of normal learning. And, no matter where the lesion is, there is still no appreciable impairment of learning ability. Lashley has concluded, therefore, that there are no crucial areas for simple locomotor learning in the rat.

Manipulative learning in rats. A second class of motor problems, those involving more manipulative skill, gives different results (Lashley, 1935a). Four problems of this type have been used: one requires that a lever be depressed, thereby releasing the latch of a door that admits the animal to food; another requires that a paper strip be cut or torn by the animal before he can obtain food; in a third, the door to food can be opened only by pulling a handle; and, in the fourth, a chain must be pulled to secure food. In all problems of this type, sizable injury to the cortex impaired learning ability. In fact, the amount of retardation in learning was roughly proportional to the size of the cortical lesions. Correlations between retardation and extent of lesion ranged between 0.48 and 0.72. The locus of the lesion seemed to be of no special importance. Why there is a correlation with mass, but not with locus of the lesion, is a vexing problem, which we shall take up more seriously later in the chapter.

Manipulative learning in primates. Experiments with monkeys and chimpanzees give a different but clear and understandable result (Jacobsen, 1931, 1932, 1939). Monkeys have been given manipulative problems calling for the use of sticks, rakes, chains, ropes, etc. Simple learning of this sort has been studied in relation to lesions in different parts of the cortex. Lesions in the posterior cortex and in the precentral cortex do not impair this kind of learning ability. Those in the motor and premotor areas, however, do cause some interference, but, as we shall see in a moment, the interference is with motor skill, not with learning or memory.

The motor area (precentral gyrus) is the area of the cortex through which 'voluntary' movements are initiated. The capacity for skilled movement depends primarily on this area. When it is removed, a monkey shows great difficulty in learning or remembering skilled movements, such as those involved in manipulating sticks and ropes to get food. But it is very clear that the monkey's learning or remembering has not been impaired; only his dexterity has suffered. If the injury has not been too severe, a period of recovery will witness a gradual return of the skill. Then the animal will be able to learn the required patterns or to show that he remembers them if he has learned them previously.

The functions of the premotor area of the extrapyramidal system are difficult to describe briefly. Their removal causes some slight paralysis and interference with ability to make skilled movements, but that is not their primary function. They have something to do with the organization of the components of a skilled movement. For example, when a monkey, deprived of its premotor areas, is faced with a problem of pulling a rope latch, the animal may pick up the rope, but he may not do the next obvious thing, namely, pull the rope. Thus, lack of this part of the motor system interferes to some extent with the skill of an animal, but, after a period of training, he can learn to carry out manipulative skilled movements.

When both the motor and premotor areas are removed simultaneously, there is considerable interference with skilled movements, but it turns out that this is due to the almost complete paralysis that the removal produces. As far as monkeys are concerned, it is fair to conclude, therefore, that neither the premotor nor the motor area of the cortical motor system is concerned in learning ability for motor problems. They are, however, involved in the capacity of the animal to carry out the required manipulations, if it has succeeded in learning what they are.

NEURAL EQUIVALENCE

What has baffled students of brain function for many years is that they cannot put their finger on the particular areas and pathways responsible for any particular learning performance. For simple learning capacities, as we saw in the last section, the essential cortical and subcortical areas have been identified in most cases. But there is more to the problem than that. What happens over and over again is this: An animal is trained to make some particular discrimination or to solve some problem. A certain area is removed. The animal loses the memory for, or the ability to solve, the problem — but only temporarily. In the course of time or with retraining, the animal regains the habit. In other words, the habit, in the normal animal, appears to depend on one area. It is lost when the area is removed. But, afterwards, some other area or part of the brain apparently steps in to furnish the necessary mechanisms for relearning the habit. This is certainly a very handy mechanism to have — it is a kind of insurance policy against the irrevocable loss of a learning capacity. But it is a little hard to understand.

This substitution of one part for another has been called equivalence, for it is a kind of equivalence of parts of the brain in doing the same job. This is a central problem in our field. So far in this chapter we have avoided it, but it is now time to come to grips with it.

Recovery of Motor Functions

A good example of equivalence in brain functions is seen in motor paralysis due to brain injury. In primate animals, such as the monkey, the chimpanzee, and man, voluntary movement is dependent on the motor cortex (area 4), lying just in front of the central sulcus. Also involved in voluntary movement is the premotor cortex (area 6), lying just in front of the motor area, and a part of the somesthetic cortex, the postcentral gyrus (area 3-1-2). The entire motor areas are topographically organized according to regions of the body, with the leg being represented most dorsally, the arm somewhat to the side of the leg area, and the head and face in the extreme lateral portions of the area. Most of the fibers leaving these areas, leading downward to the spinal motor horn cells, are so crossed that the motor cortex on one side of the brain controls movements of the body on the other side.

Complete bilateral extirpation of all the areas concerned with voluntary movement, including 4, 6, and 3-1-2, results in complete motor paralysis of all voluntary movements in man, chimpanzee, and monkey. From such profound paralysis there is no recovery. If, however, the experimental injuries are made to only a part of the crucial cortical areas, there is some improvement in function and effacing of the paralysis over a period of months following the operation. This recovery of motor functions has been known for a long time, but only recently has research thrown some light on how and why it occurs.

Postcentral gyrus. One study (Ades and Raab, 1946) shows that the postcentral gyrus (3-1-2) may be responsible for some recovery after the removal of the precentral cortices (area 4). Ordinarily, when the motor cortex is removed simultaneously on both sides, a rather profound paralysis results. If, however, a lesion is made on only one side and a period of 3 or 4 months is allowed to elapse before taking out the other side, we do not get the usual paralytic signs of bilateral injury. Obviously there has been compensation taking place in the interval between the removal of one cortex and the second operation. Moreover this compensation must involve some areas other than those of the motor cortex (area 4). It turns out that the postcentral gyrus (3-1-2) is responsible for this compensation, for, if it also is removed along with the corresponding precentral cortex, paralysis occurs after the second operation just as it would have if both sides had been removed in one simultaneous operation.

Injury in infancy. We see compensation at work when we compare the effects of cortical removal in infant and adult monkeys (Kennard, 1938, 1942). It is interesting that, when cortical areas 4 and 6, the motor and premotor areas, are removed from infant monkeys, there is very little immediate effect on motor performance; there is no paralysis. As time goes on and the monkeys grow older, some signs of paralysis make their appearance, but these are much more moderate than when the injury is made in adult monkeys. From this study it is possible to draw several conclusions: some kind of reorganization of brain functions goes on after the removal of the motor areas; this reorganization is greater in the young monkey than in the mature animal, occurring to the greatest extent in the first 6 months of life. Apparently the parts of the cortical motor system left uninjured are responsible for the reorganization.

To test this hypothesis, Kennard and her colleagues carried out an excellent set of experiments. They made use of three distinctly different methods for determining what reorganization has taken place. One method employed a stimulant during the period of recovery following the operation. A second involved a sedative, and a third used a test of the electrostimulability of the cortical areas before and after the operation.

Stimulants. The stimulant used was strychnine (Ward and Kennard, 1942). This is a well-known nervous stimulant and probably acts by interfering with cholinesterase activity at the site of transmission of nervous impulses. Ward and Kennard also used two other chemicals that are known to have a stimulating action on the nervous system: thiamin (vitamin B_1) and doryl. By using these drugs postoperatively, singly or in combination, they observed that all animals suffering removal of the cerebral cortex on one side were aided considerably in both the rate and degree of recovery of their motor functions. They concluded that this increased rate of recovery was due to the fact that the stimulus accelerated the rate of functional reorganization in the parts of the motor system remaining after operation.

Sedatives. The opposite result was observed with the use of sedatives (Watson and Kennard, 1945). Several monkeys were deprived of their motor and premotor cortices (areas 4 and 6) on one side and were then treated with sedatives such as phenobarbital and dilantin during the postoperative period. It turned out that phenobarbital, in doses so small that they had no observable effect on the cage behavior of the monkeys, produced a very marked slowing in the rate of recovery of motor functions. In fact, the animals never reached the level of recovery typical of other monkeys subjected to this lesion without the use of sedatives. The investigators concluded, in this case, that the sedatives interfered with the reorganization of remaining tissues of the cortical motor system.

Electrical stimulability. To be noted finally is a study of the electrical stimulability of motor areas before and after operation (Kennard and McCulloch, 1943). Areas 4 and 6 were removed from monkeys in infancy, and the animals were then allowed a long time for recovery. Later, similar operations were performed on older monkeys, and shortly thereafter the two groups were compared with respect to the threshold of electrical stimulus required to produce a movement in various parts of the body.

They found that "the cortex of the animal with motor areas removed in infancy has greater excitability in the region surrounding areas 4 and 6," namely, the posterior lip of the central sulcus (precentral gyrus) and areas 6b and 6a, which lie just in front of area 6, "than has either the normal macaque cortex or that of the animal from which the motor areas have been removed in later age. No regions other than those known to be excitable in the normal animal were found to be excitable in these preparations."

There have been many attempts to explain the phenomena of recovery of motor functions. For a discussion of them the reader should refer to Lashley (1938a). The view taken by Lashley, after a critical review of the data on both animal and man, is that recovery of functions depends upon reorganization of the nervous tissue remaining in the system concerned with the function. Kennard's work on motor functions makes Lashley's view appear correct. In her work it seems clear that the recovery of motor functions depends upon remnants of the motor system remaining intact.

Auditory Equivalence

An interesting demonstration of the equivalence of cortical and subcortical mechanisms in auditory learning comes from experiments using curare and erythroidine. Curare is a poison, used by Indians on arrowheads, that is extracted from various poisonous plants. Actual samples of it vary greatly in strength and purity. The active ingredient, curarine, is an alkaloidal compound with an approximate formula of $C_{19}H_{21}NO_4$. Because the impurity of curare gives varying results in experiments (sometimes underdosing the animal, sometimes killing it), investigators have sought other substitute materials. The drug erythroidine has now been prepared in relatively pure form, and, though it is not chemically identical with curarine, it has similar physiological properties. Thus, experiments in the 1930's used curare, but more recent ones have employed erythroidine.

Conditioning techniques. The outstanding property of these drugs, known for a long time, is that they produce muscular paralysis without affecting appreciably the sensory functions. Physiological experiments have indicated that the site of action is at the neuromuscular juncture. Curare seems to produce its paralytic effects by blocking the transmission of impulses from the motor axon to the muscle fibers. It is this property that first prompted its use by psychologists (Harlow and Stagner, 1933). They wanted to use it as a means of paralyzing an animal during conditioning to see whether it is necessary for responses actually to occur in order for conditioning to take place. In these experiments they gave conditioning training to animals under the influence of curare and tested them for conditioning after the curare had worn off. They found no conditioning, and they concluded that "conditioned reflexes are only possible if a response is made, and do not result merely from stimuli presented simultaneously."

A few years later it was to become clear why this result had been obtained. Girden and Culler (1937) devised a new technique for studying conditioning under curare. They dissected out the semitendinosus muscle of the hind limb, keeping the blood and nerve supply intact. When they applied shock to the hind leg, they could observe muscle contractions in the dissected muscle, even though gross flexor responses of the limb did not occur. By pairing the sound of a bell with the application of a shock they were able to observe conditioning taking place in the semitendinosus muscle under curare. Henceforth, in a series of studies, they used this technique in both normal and curarized animals to observe the course of conditioning and retention in the two states, normal and curarized.

Dissociation. But the most interesting point — the main point of this section — is that the responses conditioned under curare vanished when the animal was returned to the normal state. In the normal state the animal showed no sign of the retention of the conditioning it had acquired under curare. Conversely, conditioning established in the normal animal disappeared when the animal was put under curare. Thus there was a complete amnesia in one state for conditioning in the other state. This fact has now been verified many times (Culler et al., 1939; Girden, 1940, 1942a, b, c).

Once having established the dissociation of skeletal conditioning in normal and curarized animals, the investigators went on to see whether the same rule also held for autonomic responses. It was easily shown that pupillary conditioned responses to a bell could be established under curare (Harlow, 1940; Harlow and Settlage, 1939). Preliminary experiments indicated too that there was no dissociation of the conditioned reactions established in the normal and curarized state (Harlow and Stagner, 1933). More thorough research later, however, made it seem that the apparent carry-over of conditioning of pupillary reactions from curarized to normal state was an artifact. It now looks as though the pupillary reactions under curare were actually unconditioned reactions to the bell. At any rate, when a light was used for conditioning pupillary dilation, there was a dissociation of conditioning like that seen in skeletal responses. This finding has been established with the use of both curare and erythroidine (Girden, 1942b). Moreover, conditioned reactions of blood pressure to shock, carried out in normal state and under erythroidine, show a clear dissociation (Girden, 1942a). Thus the story is now simple and clear. Conditioning reactions, whether skeletal or autonomic, established under curare or erythroidine, do not carry over to the normal state, and vice versa.

Equivalence. The next question concerns the physiological interpretation of these effects. The explanation comes from a study of the effects of curare upon different parts of the nervous system. Culler et al. (1939), suspecting that the curare was doing more to the nervous system than simply paralyzing neuromuscular transmission, examined the excitability of the cerebral cortex and the spinal reflex paths in normal and curarized states. They found that the threshold was raised, and the time for excitation was lengthened, for evoking responses in the semitendinosus muscle by cortical stimulation. In a word, the excitability of the motor cortex, and probably that of the cortex as a whole, was considerably depressed. Stimulation of the motor roots leading to the semitendinosus muscle made it clear that curare had not changed the excitability of the neuromuscular response. At first thought this might seem to contradict the idea that curare paralyzes neuromuscular junctures. There is no contradiction, however, because it turns out that curare does paralyze many of these junctions; on the other hand, it seems to sensitize some of the fibers not knocked out. The end result is no net change in excitability.

The conclusion, then, from these electrophysiological studies is that curare considerably depresses cortical excitability but does not affect spinal excitability. This suggests that the dissociation of conditioning seen in curarization is due to a depression of the cortex. Going further, one might conclude that normal conditioning involves the cerebral cortex, whereas conditioning under curare, with accompanying depression of the cortex, is effected through subcortical routes. This subcortical conditioning, then, gets suppressed when the cortex returns to normal.

This hypothesis has been tested and confirmed. Girden (1940), because he was using a bell as the conditioning stimulus, removed the auditory cortex of dogs before conducting the typical experiments with curare. According to the hypothesis above, the auditory cortex, in addition perhaps to other cortical structures, would be involved in the normal state but would be suppressed in curarization. If, however, the auditory cortex were removed, then it could not function in either the normal or the drugged state. All conditioning whether normal or under drugs would be subcortical, at least in respect of the bell stimulus. One would expect no dissociation under these conditions. This expectation was realized. The conditioned response of the semitendinosus muscle established in either the normal or drugged state carried over to the other state.

The conclusion to this story seems perfectly clear. In the conditioning of skeletal and autonomic responses in normal animals, the cortex is involved, and certain essential parts of the conditioning are not subcortical. Under the drug state, which depresses the cortex and leaves subcortical centers at some level more or less unaffected, conditioning takes place subcortically. There is a dissociation between these two conditionings. The cortex and subcortex are alternates for each other — they are equivalent — but not at the same time. When one is working, the other is not, and vice versa.

Auditory memory. Although that ends the story about curare, there is still a bit more to say about neural equivalence in auditory learning. Unfortunately there is relatively little data on auditory capacities and the memory functions of the auditory cortex, but what there is points to a few conclusions. A series of studies on rats (Pennington, 1935, 1937; Wiley, 1932, 1937) shows that rats without auditory cortex are capable of learning simple auditory habits, like localizing a sound in the correct box, or jumping in response to a tone. Yet animals that learn such responses preoperatively show an amnesia for the habit after removal of the auditory cortex (which is poorly defined in the rat). Another study on cats by Raab and Ades (1946), with conditioned responses to tones, gives a similar conclusion:

Auditory conditioned responses are normally mediated cortically by an all-or-none mechanism of the auditory cortex. In the absence of the projection areas, these habits may be relearned at a midbrain level and are

mediated by the inferior colliculi (discharging through the superior colliculi) with no loss of acuity.

In a word, what all these studies point to is an equivalence of cortical and subcortical centers in auditory learning; when the cortex is intact, it is crucial to the learning; when it is not, subcortical centers mediate the learning.

Visual Learning

In an earlier section we saw that visual space perception, including all capacity to learn or remember spatial cues, is abolished with complete removal of the striate cortex. We saw, too, that all mammalian animals (with the possible exception of man) are capable of learning intensity discriminations in the absence of the striate cortex. The whole story, however, was not told. There are some interesting examples of neural equivalence between cortical and subcortical centers of vision in the learning and retention of visual intensity discriminations. The interesting thing is that we find such equivalence when a discrimination technique is used, but in simple conditioning procedures we do not.

Conditioning. We have already reviewed the studies showing that the conditioning of an intensitive discrimination is not impaired by removal of the visual cortex. The main point to add here is that memory, too, for visual conditioned responses is not significantly affected by total extirpation of the visual cortex. This is true both of simple conditioning to onset of light and of conditioned responses to changes in light intensity. It appears, then, that the learning and retention of such visual learning is normally mediated at subcortical levels and does not normally involve the visual areas of the cortex.

Discrimination. It is when we consider studies in which animals are taught to discriminate differences in intensities of lighted panels that we encounter equivalence phenomena. Under this method there have been many experiments with different animals, including the rat (Ghiselli, 1938; Ghiselli and Brown, 1938; Lashley, 1935b), the cat (Smith, 1937), the dog (Marquis, 1934), and the monkey (Klüver, 1942). The central fact in all these experiments is that the destruction of the visual area of the cortex abolishes a discrimination once it has been learned, but it does not interfere with the relearning of this discrimination. Animals that are operated upon after they have learned the discrimination show a complete amnesia for the learning, but they are capable of relearning it. Apparently then, the visual cortex is normally involved in the learning of an intensity discrimination, but in its absence subcortical centers take over this function.

Somesthetic Learning

As we have seen before, the field of somesthetic learning has not yet provided us with very satisfactory data. In the only available study of tactile discrimination in the rat (Smith, 1939), rats were required to discriminate the roughnesses of two sandpaper surfaces. They were subsequently operated upon in such a way that various lesions, taken together, covered the entire cortex. One area, when removed, caused partial loss or complete loss of the discrimination, and this was presumed to be the somesthetic projection area. Animals that lacked it, however, were capable of relearning the discrimination in relatively few trials. Thus it seems that other cortical or subcortical centers could, if necessary, take over the functions normally subserved by this cortical area. Considerably more work on this problem is needed, but the results so far point to a neural equivalence such as we have met in the other sense modalities.

We also find some evidence of neural equivalence in kinesthetic discrimination in monkeys (Ruch, 1935). Monkeys were trained to discriminate difference in weight, and the effect upon retention of the discriminative habit was measured after removal of the precentral, postcentral, and the posterior parietal areas, taken separately and in combination. After the separate removal of any one of these areas, there was some loss of memory for the discrimination, but the discrimination could be remastered after retraining. The memory loss was much less after removal of the precentral and postcentral areas than after destruction of the posterior parietal areas. Combined lesions of the precentral and postcentral areas also resulted in some memory loss, but this could be recouped by training. Thus we meet again the phenomenon of equivalence: areas normally involved in learning are not necessary for learning, for their functions can be 'taken over' by other areas remaining in the somesthetic cortex.

Similar experiments have been done with the tactile discrimination of roughness in the chimpanzee (Ruch, Fulton, and German, 1938). There is no need to go into them in detail, however, for they present the same general results as those for kinesthetic weight discrimination in the monkey. They all point to neural equivalence in somesthetic learning. In many respects, however, both sets of experiments are incomplete. They leave us uncertain of the degree to which different parts of the somesthetic areas are equivalent, and they tell us very little about the role of subcortical centers in somesthetic learning.

The tactile discrimination of form, stereognosis, has been studied in the chimpanzee in combination with lesions to the somesthetic areas of the cortex (Ruch, Fulton, and German, 1938). Abolition of the posterior parietal lobule (areas 5 and 7) can cause complete amnesia for stereognosis. In the case of complex form discrimination, no amount of retraining will get the animal to master the discrimination. Less difficult discriminations may be learned with retraining; for example, the chimpanzee whose posterior parietal lobe has been removed may again learn to distinguish a cone from a pyramid, but the capacity to distinguish between a pyramid and a wedge, which are more alike than a cone and a pyramid, is apparently never regained, no matter how many trials are given the animal.

This relearning of simple tactual form discriminations after removal of the posterior parietal areas is another case of equivalence. The stereognostic learning ability apparently depends on the posterior area when it takes place in the normal animal, but after removal of the area some other structure takes over part, but not all, of the learning function. Unfortunately the relevant data are not available to tell us whether this other structure is subcortical or cortical.

SELECTION AND VARIABILITY

We have not heard the last of neural equivalence. There will be more of it in this section. Neural equivalence is seen not only within the centers of a particular sensory or motor system but also in the relation of different areas of the cortex to one another. In this section, however, the emphasis will shift from neural equivalence to behavioral equivalence. Equivalence of function is seen in sensory and motor learning behavior, just as it is in nervous function. The two forms of equivalence, neural and behavioral, seem in fact to be different aspects of the same basic organization of brain functions. What is meant by this statement will become clearer as we proceed.

It is a little hard to choose the best terms to describe behavioral equivalence. There are several terms used to denote different aspects of the phenomenon. In some kinds of discriminative learning and in maze learning, an animal has several cues available to him. There may be lights, odors, tactile cues, or spatial cues. He does not need to use all these cues. One or another of them will usually do. Thus these different cues are equivalent. In practice the animal often selects certain cues to use and does not use the others unless it is forced to, and in this case we may speak of *selection* rather than

of equivalence of cues, but we mean essentially the same thing. The concept of *variability* applies to some equivalence phenomena. If the animal does not consistently select a given cue, we can say that it displays variability in behavior. If it sticks to one of two equivalent cues, its behavior is not variable in this respect. To some forms of behavioral equivalence, the term *hypothesis* — a rather anthropomorphic term — has been applied. If from one trial to another the animal varies the cue to which it reacts, one can say that it uses different hypotheses.

There may be objections to some of these terms, but they have been used by one or another of the authors working in the field of neural functions and behavior. The important thing, however, is to recognize the fundamental psychophysiological processes that they denote. In every case they point to organizing or selective processes in the brain in which only certain aspects of a stimulus or stimulus situation are reacted to and only certain responses of many possible responses are given by the subject. These organizing processes can be called selections or hypotheses. In experiments on learning we test our animals in such a way as to find out which of many selections are made.

Spatial versus Visual Hypotheses

A number of experiments have been designed to disclose which of two cues, visual or spatial, the rat had used during learning. Most of these studies were made by Krechevsky, who chose the term 'hypothesis' to describe this selective behavior. His instrument was a maze, made in four units from start to goal box, that could be solved either by entering all lighted alleys or by using a simple directional tendency.

In the first experiment (Krechevsky, 1933) it was demonstrated that rats tend to use different hypotheses in running such a maze. Some react consistently to spatial cues, some to visual cues, and some to both. This could be determined by analyzing the pattern of turns made by the animal on each trial in the maze. It is interesting to note in passing that, when a bright strain of animals was compared with a dull strain, the dull animals were the ones that used visual cues most extensively.

'S' and 'V' areas. The next interesting question concerns the effect of brain lesions on hypotheses in rats (Krechevsky, 1935). Lesions of various sizes were placed at different locations on the cortex so that the whole cerebral cortex was explored. The conclusion: cortical lesions reduce the number of hypotheses in rats. Whereas normal animals tend to use both visual and spatial hypotheses and to vary from one to another, animals subjected to operation were inclined to take one hypothesis and stick to it. The reason for this became clear when the brains were analyzed. It turned out that a cortical area corresponding fairly exactly with the striate (visual) area of the cortex was responsible for the visual hypothesis; when it was removed, animals shifted to the use of spatial hypotheses. On the other hand, an area a little front of center on the cortex, corresponding to motor and somesthetic areas, was crucial for spatial hypotheses; animals with this area removed preferred to use visual hypotheses. This is a simple, understandable result.

Mass action. The same type of maze can, of course, be used to study intensity discrimination simply by arranging the lights over the correct alleys and eliminating spatial cues. Krechevsky (1936) made relatively small lesions, involving about 10 to 12 per cent of the cortex and overlapping the visual area in most cases. Ghiselli (1938a) made lesions of varying size involving up to 55 per cent of the total surface of the cortex. Both investigators found that such lesions considerably retarded the learning of a brightness discrimination. This is strange because in previous studies (Lashley, 1929, 1935b) based on a simple discriminative technique lesions in the cortex did not impair learning ability, although those in the striate cortex did cause amnesia for the habit. Even

more interesting is Ghiselli's statistical analysis of his cases. There was a correlation of about 0.80 between retardation in learning and the size of the cerebral lesion, whereas the position of the lesion was of no importance.

This correlation between size of lesion and degree of retardation in learning has been called *mass action.* This is the second time we have encountered it in this chapter, but we shall get more of it later. Why the amount of cortex is important in learning the intensity-discrimination maze is rather puzzling, especially since the cortex is of no importance in simple intensity discrimination. Apparently there must be some new factors of significance in learning the maze that do not appear in a simple intensity discrimination.

Spatial Hypotheses

There are some more studies dealing with the brain mechanisms of spatial hypotheses. These do not use the four-unit maze but employ various other techniques. One (Krechevsky, 1937a) was a 'block-maze' in which there were several different routes to the goal, all correct and all of the same length. Errors could be made only by the animal's turning away from the general direction of the goal box or by his entering a blind at the side of the maze. Normal animals were compared with animals suffering lesions of different sizes in various parts of the cortex. The normal animals took many more different paths — nearly twice as many — than did operated animals. Normal animals (run only one trial a day) also shifted from one path to another much more than did the operated animals. Thus the number of hypotheses was cut down by the cortical operations. The decrease correlated rather highly with the size of the cortical lesions ($r = 0.67$ to 0.37). Mass action again!

Quite similar in principle is a study by Morgan and Wood (1943). They ran rats in a simple T-maze with reward on both sides and counted the number of times the rats alternated right and left choices. Normal animals, as has been demonstrated several times (Dennis, 1939; Heathers, 1940), took alternate paths about 80 per cent of the time. Some operated animals cut down their variability considerably and consistently chose either the left or the right path. Examination of the lesions indicated some localization of function. All animals with lesions in the frontal areas adopted the stereotyped behavior, and some animals with parietal lesions did, too; but animals with occipital lesions in the vicinity of the striate cortex maintained a high degree of alternation.

There are still other experiments by Krechevsky on variability in spatial hypothesis as related to cortical function. In one of them (1937b), he ran rats in an apparatus where two paths to food were available. One was a variable path through a block maze similar to the one described above; the other was a standard path involving turns in simple alternation. The animal was permitted to choose on each trial whether to take the standard path or the variable path. Taking the variable path in this case was of no particular advantage or disadvantage in getting the food reward. Normal animals, Krechevsky found, tended to vary their responses more than did operated animals. They chose the variable path about 50 per cent of the time and the standard path about 50 per cent. The operated animals, though they started out in the first few trials at about 50 per cent, gradually reduced their choices of the variable path to about 20 per cent, taking the standard path 80 per cent of the time. Even minor cortical injuries seemed to cause this stereotyping of behavior. No correlation, however, between the size of the lesion or its locus and any of the measures of variability could be found.

Krechevsky was concerned over the fact that the standard path, being about the same length as or perhaps shorter than the variable path, might have something to do with the results. He therefore ran another experiment (Krechevsky, 1937c), identical with the one before, except that the standard path was longer by a ratio of 1.54 than the average variable path. In this test his operated animals did not develop the preference for the standard path. They were, however, less variable in their choices than the normal animals and tended to perseverate on one choice longer than the normals. He obtained correlations of −0.36 between the size of the cortical lesions and the number of times the variable path was taken; also he found a correlation of −0.59 between size of lesion and the variability in the choices of the animal.

Somewhat different but still related to spatial hypothesis is a study of *umweg* behavior and brain lesions (Krechevsky, 1938). His apparatus was so constructed that at the first choice-point the rat had to make an intensity discrimination, choosing the path toward a light. It could choose between a long spiral path along which the food and light were visible all the time and a short path through a tunnel directly to the food. This short path, however, was psychologically the *umweg* path because the animal had to leave the field where the light and the food were visible. He found that operated animals made vastly more choices of the spiral longer path (58.9 versus 17.1 per cent of the time). In a control experiment, however, in which the intensity discrimination was eliminated and the animals simply chose the tunnel versus the spiral path, the operated animals chose the spiral path only 12 per cent of the time whereas the normals chose it 18 per cent. This means that the brightness discrimination presented no difficulty to the operated animals. It means also, however, that the operated animals tended to depend on the light cue much more than did the normal.

Variability in Manipulative Behavior

A rough classification, useful for many purposes, divides behavior into locomotor and manipulative behavior. In locomotor behavior the animal moves his whole body in one direction or another. That is what we have been talking about above in respect of spatial hypotheses. We have really been considering locomotor hypotheses and variability. In contrast to that kind of behavior we can think of patterns in which a more specific movement of the hands or limbs is made in the solution of a problem. There are relatively few data on the neural functions involved in the learning and retention of such problems. Those there are point to the importance of variation and stereotyping of such patterns in learning.

There are two studies, worth mentioning briefly, of changes in handedness in manipulative problems. Lashley (1938a) observed that monkeys readily shifted from one hand to another when neural injury paralyzed one side. Animals were taught a manipulative problem in which they used only one hand. The motor cortex responsible for that limb was then removed, partially paralyzing the monkey. Upon preoperative testing the animal promptly used the other, unparalyzed limb to solve the problem. Lashley cites this as an example of equivalence in motor functions. Peterson (1934) reported a similar phenomenon for rats. He first demonstrated that most rats show some hand preference, either left or right. He then located a point on the cortex, corresponding to the motor cortex in primates, which when injured or removed would shift the preference to the other side. Though the limb originally used was not paralyzed by the operation, it probably was made less usable.

More directly related to the problem of variability in manipulative behavior are Lashley's studies of latch-box behavior in rats (1935a). He prepared a series of different problem boxes on which he trained a group of rats. Four of these problems were distinctly manipulative problems. They required a string to be pulled, a paper strip to be torn in the right way, and so on. One box contained a double platform, and the animal had to step on both platforms in order to get food. The effects of brain lesions were different for the two types of problems. The ability of animals to learn the double-platform (locomotor) problem was not affected by cortical lesions of considerable magnitude, even up to 58 per cent. Rate of learning was not correlated with the magnitude of any lesions made. However, with other boxes — those requiring manipulative behavior — there was considerable retardation in learning with cerebral lesions. The correlations between the extent of lesion and the amount of damage to the cortex ranged from 0.48 to 0.72.

It is easy to understand why lesions did nothing serious to learning in the double-platform problem. Its solution requires relatively simple locomotor behavior, no complicated hypotheses, and no skilled movements. The other boxes required variable behavior and reasonably good sensory-motor coordination on the part of the animal. It had first to stumble on to the correct solution and later to develop the specific reactions of manipulating latches. It had then to reduce the time spent in exploring particular items in the situation. It is reasonable, therefore, that almost any kind of lesion might affect the behavior and reduce the probability of the rapid solution of the problem. Lashley's observations of his operated animals and his analysis of results convinced him that the difficulty encountered by the operated animals in the manipulative problem boxes was basically a matter of variability in behavior. The number of exploratory acts (motor hypotheses) was cut down.

Mass Action of the Cerebral Cortex

We come now to the concept that has been so widely publicized in recent years — mass action. Almost every student of elementary psychology has at least heard the words. They represent both a concept and a result. The result is what Lashley and others (Lashley, 1929; Lashley and Wiley, 1933) obtained in studying the effects of brain lesions on maze learning and retention in rats. In brief, they are as follows: The learning ability of rats is retarded in proportion to the size of lesions made in their cerebral cortices. If the lesion is large, the retardation is great; if the lesion is small, little damage to learning ability follows. There is, in general, an exponential relation between size of lesion and degree of retardation, so that the difference between a 50- and a 60-per-cent lesion is much greater in terms of retardation of learning than between lesions of 10 and 20 per cent. It does not matter where the lesion is; the results are the same. It is the mass of the cortex, not its locus, that is important in maze-learning ability. Many people have obtained this result in many different maze situations, and there can be no doubt of it.

The question is, what does it mean? Lashley (1929) interpreted it to mean that cortical tissue, in addition to any specific functions it might have, also possesses general, nondifferentiated functions which it shares with other areas of the cortex. He made mass action into a conceptual property of the cerebral cortex. Hunter and others, however, immediately pointed out another interpretation, that one might expect mass-action results without a concept of mass action. The results might be simply the statistical effect of discrete sensory deprivations.

Supporting this point of view are the studies in which animals have been deprived of various sensory cues. In one (Honzik, 1936), several combinations of sensory deprivation were tried; blindness alone; blindness and deafness; blindness and anosmia; and blindness, deafness, and anosmia. These produce considerable retardation in learning. Blindness alone causes appreciable effect; blindness combined with deafness or anosmia causes even more; and an animal that is deaf, blind, and anosmic shows practically no learning at all, even in a reasonably easy maze. Since peripheral sensory deprivation retards learning, does not cortical injury in various sensory areas cause a similar effect for the same reason?

There can be no doubt that this interpretation is in part true. Animals use many cues in a maze. If all are available, they pick and choose the ones they will use. If a few are taken away, they can still get along reasonably well; but, when too few cues are available, their ability to learn is injured. And we know that only through the cortex can certain cues be utilized.

But, granting that removal of parts of the cortex is equivalent to taking away cues that are needed in learning, there is still the question whether the facts of mass action are entirely accounted for in terms of sensory deprivation. To test this question, Tsang (1934) devised an experiment in which he compared the effect on learning of removing the visual cortex with the effect produced by blinding the animals. If mass action is a factor operating in addition to sensory deprivation, the animals with cortical lesions should be more affected than those blinded. That was the finding in the experiment. He showed that removal of the visual cortex, in addition to blindness, caused more retardation than did blindness alone.

Tsang's data raise certain questions, however. In his effort to remove completely the visual cortex, he made relatively large lesions which, on the average, invaded other cortical regions in addition to the striate area itself. We do not yet know just what these areas outside the striate area do. Electrophysiological evidence indicates that they are secondary visual areas of some sort (see Woolsey, 1947). Homology with the primate cortex indicates that they correspond to one or both of areas 18 and 19, which are concerned apparently with a system of spatial coordination, tied in with vision but not restricted entirely to vision. So there is the possibility that the greater effect of removal of the visual area is due to involvement of other areas which have their own specific functions in learning.

To control this possibility Finley (1941) carried out another experiment similar to Tsang's but in several respects more thorough. In doing so she made sure not to make lesions outside the striate areas. Since cortical operations in the rat are by no means precise, the result was that most of her lesions did not take out all the visual area. Thus, though the visual cortex includes about 20 per cent of the cortex, her lesions averaged only about 10 per cent. Tsang's lesions had averaged more than 20 per cent. Finley found no mass action. Her rats with cortical lesions got along better in learning than did blinded rats. In experiments in which visual cues were not necessary for maze learning (in the dark), her operated animals were just as good as the normal animals.

This might seem to settle the issue against mass action. Not satisfied with Finley's results, however, Lashley (1943) repeated the experiment, attempting to make his lesions small. He again found evidence of mass action. But again his lesions were too big. Though not so large as Tsang's, they covered slightly more than the area of the visual cortex, and many of them ran well over into adjacent areas.

As matters stand at present, it is not possible to make a final decision about mass action. Further experiments are called for. It would be helpful if we knew about the functions of areas adjacent to the visual cortex. That might resolve the issue as to whether running lesions over into these areas is responsible for the difference in results. Another possibility is a comparison of lesions of approximately the same size made entirely within the visual area with those made adjacent to the visual area to see whether those extending into adjacent areas, though of the same size, are more deleterious to learning than those within the striate area. Specific comparisons of this sort have not yet been made.

Visual Selection

We have previously reviewed the role of the striate cortex in the ability of the rat and higher animals to discriminate patterns. The striate cortex, and that area alone, is essential for such ability. There is another aspect of visual detail discrimination that is of interest. This is visual equivalence.

Lashley (1938b) has made a thorough study of the learning of detail discriminations in the normal rat. He used a great variety of visual patterns with all sorts of details in them that could be used by the animals to make the discrimination. After learning, the animals were tested with various patterns that had in them certain elements of the original patterns. By finding out which patterns were discriminated — which ones were equivalent to the ones originally learned — he could determine the parts of the patterns that had been selected as cues in the original learning. Lashley concluded that abstraction of certain details, and the neglect of certain others, is fundamental to the normal learning process. Some animals selected one detail, some others.

To sum up his results and conclusions, it is best to quote directly from Lashley:

> Discrimination was found to be based upon the abstraction of certain general properties of the figure which are then recognized in non-identical figures. Ease of discrimination depends upon the presence of certain relational properties, such as predominant direction, in the figures. Differences in the ease of discrimination and recognition of different figures indicate that the rat's visual system functions most efficiently in spatial orientation — the recognition of relative distance and direction — and that the identification of objects or forms, though possible, is secondary to a system of space coordinates. [1938b, pp. 187–188.]

Other studies of visual equivalence in complex visual forms were made by Maier

(1939). He found that different rats learned different things when there were several possibilities of reacting to cues in the visual patterns. In general, however, if they could, the rats chose to rely on intensity differences. They could and would sometimes use size differences, independently of intensity differences. And sometimes they chose some absolute property of one of the stimulus cards.

After this initial study of the equivalence reactions of the normal rats, Maier went on to study the effect of cortical injuries (1941). He used a standard pair of cards for original learning, then constructed a series of other cards to use in equivalence tests. From the scores on the equivalence tests he could determine what factors the animals had used in their original learning. Also, the percentage of cards that were equivalent for a rat could be used as the rat's index of visual equivalence. Two results stand out in Maier's study of cortical injury: First, the equivalence scores of animals decreased simply as a function of repeated testing. That is to be expected because equivalence cannot be run without involving some kind of learning or change of response on the part of the animals. Second, however, the effect of cortical injuries was to increase the equivalence reactions of the rats, an effect directly opposite to the effects of repeated testing. This increase in visual equivalence in operated animals occurred for animals whether or not the lesion was in the visual area. Wapner (1944), in a similar but more extensive study, got similar results. Equivalence reactions were increased after brain lesions and decreased with repeated testing. He did not find any correlation between the size of the lesion and the equivalence scores (though Maier did). He was able to show that the equivalence reactions were due to the rat's using some combination of intensity and size. The intensity factor became less important on retesting and more important as a result of operation.

LOCALIZATION OF MEMORY FUNCTIONS IN THE BRAIN

There is a vast literature concerning memory losses in human beings suffering lesions of the brain. As one might expect, most of the studies were conducted under clinical conditions in which it is hard to get either adequate tests of the psychological deficit or precise data on the parts of the brain affected. We shall take a brief look at this material later in this section. Several investigators have realized that it would be valuable to conduct well-controlled studies of the brain localization of memory functions in those primates that resemble man most closely in brain structure and mental capacity. There are now several such studies. The majority of them, it turns out, have to do specifically with functions of frontal lobes, and we shall, therefore, take them up in a special section.

Prefrontal Functions

Clinical observations of the effects of removal of the prefrontal lobes have been on record for many years. In the 1930's, however, a special interest in the prefrontal areas began to grow up. This was sparked by clinical reports that the removal of these areas could be used as therapy in certain kinds of psychotic cases — a practice widely applied in later years. Moreover a series of experimental studies with monkeys was begun that pointed to special functions of the prefrontal areas in memory.

Delayed response. Jacobsen's studies (1935) with monkeys have now become classic. He used the delayed-response test that had been developed earlier by Hunter and others. Monkeys were shown where food was hidden under either the right or the left of two cups, then were forced to wait several seconds before they could reach for the cup, remove it, and get the food. Jacobsen's findings were very simple. Normal monkeys could delay for 30 seconds without much difficulty and still select the correct cup. Monkeys with bilateral lesions of the prefrontal areas could not solve the delayed response if required to delay more than 1 or 2 seconds.

Jacobsen's study and others showed that this loss was a characteristic function of the prefrontal areas. The removal of these areas did not affect learning or retention for simple visual discrimination habits or for simple problem boxes. But capacity for delayed memory depended on the prefrontal areas. Jacobsen and Elder (1936) demonstrated that this capacity did not depend on temporal lobe lesions, and Jacobsen and Haslerud (1936) also found no effect of motor or pre-motor lesions on the delayed response.

These results made it appear that the prefrontal areas function in immediate memory. Jacobsen and others suggested that other disturbances of more complex memory functions (see below) could be broken down into one simple disturbance — of recent memory. That the matter is not so simple as that, however, has been well demonstrated by a series of recent experiments.

The memory trace. One possible interpretation of the memory deficit in prefrontal lobectomy could be made in terms of a waning of the memory trace. The trace of a memory might fade away more rapidly in the prefrontal animals than in the normal animals. To test this possibility, Finan (1939) ran prefrontal monkeys in several kinds of learning problems in which memory traces had to last some time in order for the animal to make the correct choice. In one problem, monkeys had to shuttle from one grill to another for several seconds after a signal had been presented. In another they learned a temporal maze in which one route took a longer time than the other. Both prefrontal and normal monkeys solved these problems, though they could not solve the delayed response. Finan concluded that the prefrontal monkey had no basic disability in holding memory traces. Whatever was wrong in the delayed reaction must have had some other basis.

Attentive functions. A second possibility is that prefrontal animals have difficulty in establishing the 'correct connection' in the delayed-response situation, that they do not note well where the food is placed to begin with and therefore have nothing to remember during the delay interval. This factor is probably not the whole story, but many experiments indicate that it is of some importance. In another study, for example, Finan (1942) gave the monkeys pre-delay reinforcement. He let them get food in the correct place before the delay as well as after it. With this procedure prefrontal monkeys succeeded in solving the delayed-response problem. In fact, one prefrontal animal could delay for several seconds on the Jacobsen nonreinforced procedure if it had first had training with pre-delay reinforcement. This kind of result points to a difficulty in 'attention' in the prefrontal animal, a difficulty in noting the original relation between the food and the correct cup.

Supporting this interpretation is another study by Wade (1947), who was able to get prefrontal monkeys to solve the delayed reaction without pre-delay reinforcement by keeping them under light sedatives (nembutal or Dial) while working the problem. The sedative apparently slowed the animal down and let him pay more attention to the placing of the food under the correct cup. At any rate, prefrontal animals under sedative could solve the delayed-reaction problem. Again, as in Finan's case, one of the animals was able to continue solving the problem after it was returned to the normal procedure without sedatives.

Another experiment (Spaet and Harlow, 1943) using, in effect, pre-delay reinforcement also showed positive solution of the delayed-reaction problem by monkeys. In this case, a matching-from-sample technique was used. A sample object was presented to the animal and under it was placed food, which the animal was allowed to get by shoving aside the sample object. Then, after a delay, two dissimilar objects were presented, one exactly like the sample. The prefrontal animal, like the normal one, could pick the correct one. This again points to the ability of the monkey to solve the problem if he is made to pay enough attention to it.

Although Jacobsen's original results have been confirmed many times, it is possible, apparently, for some monkeys to solve the delayed-reaction problem without pre-delay reinforcement and without sedatives. Campbell and Harlow (1945) report that two out of six prefrontal monkeys were eventually able to solve a delayed reaction when they used a method essentially the same as the original Jacobsen technique.

An experiment by Malmo (1942) also points to some disturbance in attention in prefrontal animals. He used the Jacobsen technique (no pre-delay reinforcement) but shut off all lights in the room during the delay interval, then turned them on again at the end of the delay. Under these conditions, prefrontal animals could solve the problem. Attention was apparently a crucial element in the problem.

In fact, all these results seem to show that the prefrontal monkey has difficulty with attention. More specifically, it would look as though there is greater interference from other stimuli and other processes than in the normal animal. Anything that cuts down distractibility or interference, like shutting off the lights or slightly drugging the animal, increases memory ability. And anything that combats interference and forces attention to the task, such as pre-delay reinforcement, assists memory.

That there are disturbances in attention in prefrontal animals is shown in several other types of experiments. In visual discriminations, for example (Harlow and Dagnon, 1943), although the animals can learn and master all ordinary discriminations, there are some signs of deficit. A thorough analysis of their performance on visual discriminations indicates that they make more errors than normal monkeys. Then, when one attempts to reverse the problem by making the correct stimuli incorrect and vice versa, prefrontal animals make more errors than normal ones in a ratio of about four to one.

To be mentioned finally is a rather simple test that also indicates difficulty in attention (Harlow and Johnson, 1943). It was almost a reaction-time test. A piece of food was exposed to the animal for a given number of seconds; if he did not take it in the time allowed, he lost it. Both normal and prefrontal animals can make the response within all reasonable time intervals, but there is a considerable difference in success when the interval is just 1 second long. Normal monkeys can react within 1 second; prefrontal animals cannot.

Other Memory Functions of the Prefrontal Areas

There are several other kinds of memory functions that have been studied in relation to the prefrontal areas. Both rats and monkeys have been used as subjects. It is hard to interpret the findings because the details of the various problems are different, and we do not know how to break them down into the psychological factors involved in each of them. It is well, therefore, not to attempt an interpretation but simply to review the facts.

Delayed alternation. There are two experiments in which delayed alternation has been studied. In each of them, the correct response for the rat, after a delay of several seconds, was to make a turn opposite to that made before the delay. In an experiment by Loucks (1931), the capacity for delayed alternation survived cortical lesions in the middle and posterior parts of the rat's cortex, but it was abolished by lesions in the frontal third. In another experiment that took advantage of these spontaneous alternations of rats (Morgan and Wood, 1943), a similar result was obtained. Lesions in the prefrontal cortex always reduced considerably the capacity for delayed alternation, whereas those in the back part of the brain did not.

Anticipatory functions. Another experiment with rats shows the localization of some sort of function in the prefrontal regions of the rat's cortex (Stellar, Morgan, and Yarosh, 1942). In a maze consisting of a long runway from which six alleys led off to the left, the rats were supposed to turn left at the fourth alley to obtain food. The maze was rotated in the room from time to time in order to eliminate the use of exteroceptive cues. Normal animals were compared with operated animals having lesions in various parts of the cortex. Although the results are not entirely clear-cut, the removal of prefrontal areas most severely and most consistently damaged the capacity to solve this problem. In another experiment (Epstein and Morgan, 1943), prefrontal rats lacking control lesions in other parts of the cortex showed a consistent and complete loss of the anticipatory goal gradient (see Hull, 1934) whereas the goal gradient of speed of locomotion was not affected.

Complex problems. In some of the studies on prefrontal functions in primates, learning problems have been used in which the solution calls for more than one act to be performed in a correct order (Jacobsen, 1935). In one problem, for example, the animal is required to pull a rope, push a lever, and undo a latch, in that order. In another he is required to respond to three different platforms in the correct order. In a third the monkey must use a short rake in order to secure a longer rake that will enable him to pull in food that is placed at a distance outside his cage. The problem may be compounded in complexity by increasing the number of rakes that must be obtained successively in order to get food. The results on all these problems can be summarized very simply: the animal with bilateral extirpation of prefrontal areas is unable to solve them. The prefrontal monkey can learn to perform the individual acts necessary for the solution, but it cannot perform them in the correct order when a series of them is required for solution.

Memory Functions of Other Cortical Areas

For many years there have been wide differences of opinion about the localization of memory functions in man. There have been extreme localizationists, like Henschen (see Teitelbaum, 1943), who argued that each kind of memory can be localized on some rather specific area of the cortex. At the other extreme are writers like Goldstein (1944) who recognize practically no localization of memory functions but hold that any memory is a function of the whole cortex.

The difficulties lie both in the data and in their interpretation. Often the extent of damage to the cortex in human cases is not known, and systematic tests of memory deficit are usually lacking. Even when there is a serious attempt to make careful measures, it is not certain that the classification of memory disorders is a proper one to apply to cases of cerebral damage. In addition to difficulties in obtaining good data, there are often quite different interpretations of the same facts. The data, for example, that Henschen used to support extreme localization were analyzed again by Teitelbaum (1943) with rather different interpretation.

A widely used classification of memory disorders in man is as follows. Memory disorders involving language are called *aphasias*. These, in turn, are divided into two types, receptive aphasias and motor (or expressive) aphasias. Nonlinguistic memory disorders are divided into two categories, the *agnosias*, which are nonlinguistic disorders of perception, and the *apraxias*, which are nonlinguistic disorders of memory for motor acts.

Visual agnosia. There has been relatively little work with complex memory functions in the primates below man. Much can and undoubtedly will be done, but it will require new techniques and extensive training procedures. In addition to the studies of learning and retention of rather specific discriminations and skills discussed in an earlier section, there is one case of visual agnosia in monkeys that is of interest and importance (Klüver and Bucy, 1939). Lesions in the temporal lobes of monkeys produce a variety of symptoms, some of them not related to memory, but one of them is a 'psychic blindness' or visual agnosia for all sorts of objects. The monkeys do not seem to recognize even food objects by sight but must taste and smell and bite them in order to know whether or not they are edible. Preliminary analysis of the brains indicates that there is no primary visual lesion and that the memory deficit is due to cortical destruction in the temporal lobe.

The rest of the data to be reviewed briefly come from human cases. Though many investigators have believed in rather extreme localization, such views have tended to disappear. Weisenberg and McBride (1935), who made a study of a series of cases, came to the conclusion that receptive disorders were primarily localized in the posterior part of the cortex, and that motor memory disorders were primarily associated with anterior lesions — as one might expect from the general organization of the cortex. But beyond that they do not support a very specific localization of kinds of memory in different areas.

Later attempts to wrestle with the problem have taken a middle course that makes some sense out of the data and promises some possibility of arriving at a systematic notion of how the cortex works in complex memory. Lashley (1937) has proposed that different areas of the cortex have relatively specific functions in memory, but that these functions cut across any particular kind of memory test. He suggests that some areas are concerned in spatial aspects of memory, others in intensitive aspects, and so on. Any particular memory test that we ordinarily use, however, is not a pure test — it does not measure the factor, and only the factor, that might be localized in any given area. Lashley proposes that we might find localization

in terms of memory factors (cf. Thurstone) but not in terms of particular memories.

A little different approach, not incompatible with Lashley's, is that of Teitelbaum (1941, 1942, 1943). He has gone over the data of many other workers and in addition has carried out some ingenious experiments comparing psychogenic amnesias (produced by hypnosis) with organic amnesias due to brain lesions. He suggests that there are primary focal areas for different memory functions but that we do not see particular memory losses localized in these areas because there is an interdependence of memory functions. Thus there is a focal area in the temporal lobe, near the acoustic area, in which we tend to get an auditory aphasia. But we find other aphasias and other memory disorders, he suggests, because the ability to understand spoken words is also involved in other aspects of linguistic memory.

This is not the place to go into an extensive review of the vast literature on this subject. The views of Weisenberg and McBride (1935), Lashley (1937), and Teitelbaum (1942) point the direction in which we may finally make some interpretation of localization of functions in the cortex. The interested reader should turn to their discussions and to the bibliographies they cite. Here let us simply note that there is no simple localization of particular memories in different areas of the brain. We may eventually find, however, that *factors* are localized in particular areas but that each factor is involved in several kinds of memory.

REFERENCES

Ades, H. W., and D. H. Raab. Recovery of motor function after two-stage extirpation of area 4 in monkeys (Macaca mulatta). *J. Neurophysiol.*, 1946, **9**, 55–60.

Brogden, W. J., and W. H. Gantt. Intraneural conditioning: Cerebellar conditioned reflexes. *Arch. Neurol. Psychiat., Chicago*, 1942, **48**, 437–455.

Brown, C. W., and E. E. Ghiselli. Subcortical mechanisms in learning. VI. Pattern vision discrimination. *J. comp. Psychol.*, 1938, **26**, 287–300.

Bucy, P. C. (Ed.). *The precentral motor cortex.* Urbana : University of Illinois Press (1st Ed.), 1944. (2nd Ed., 1949.)

Campbell, R. J., and H. F. Harlow. Problem solution by monkeys following bilateral removal of the prefrontal areas. V. Spatial delayed reactions. *J. exp. Psychol.,* 1945, **35,** 110–126.

Crisler, G. Salivation is unnecessary for the establishment of the salivary conditioned reflex induced by morphine. *Amer. J. Physiol.,* 1930, **94,** 553–556.

Culler, E. A. Observations on direct cortical stimulation in the dog. *Psychol. Bull.,* 1938, **35,** 687–688.

Culler, E., J. D. Coakley, P. S. Shurrager, and H. W. Ades. Differential effects of curare upon higher and lower levels of the central nervous system. *Amer. J. Psychol.,* 1939, **52,** 266–273.

Culler, E., and F. A. Mettler. Conditioned behavior in a decorticate dog. *J. comp. Psychol.,* 1934, **18,** 291–303.

Dennis, W. Spontaneous alternation in rats as an indicator of the persistence of stimulus effects. *J. comp. Psychol.,* 1939, **28,** 305–312.

Dow, R. S., and R. Anderson. Cerebellar action potentials in response to stimulation of proprioceptors and exteroceptors in the rat. *J. Neurophysiol.,* 1942, **5,** 363–371.

Epstein, M. A., and C. T. Morgan. Cortical localization of symbolic processes in the rat : III. Impairment of anticipatory functions in prefrontal lobectomy in rats. *J. exp. Psychol.,* 1943, **32,** 453–463.

Finan, J. L. Effects of frontal lobe lesions on temporally organized behavior in monkeys. *J. Neurophysiol.,* 1939, **2,** 208–226.

Finan, J. L. Delayed response with pre-delay reenforcement in monkeys after the removal of the frontal lobes. *Amer. J. Psychol.,* 1942, **55,** 202–214.

Finch, G. Salivary conditioning in atropinized dogs. *Amer. J. Physiol.,* 1938, **124,** 136–141.

Finley, C. B. Equivalent losses in accuracy of response after central and after peripheral sense deprivation. *J. comp. Neurol.,* 1941, **74,** 203–237.

Freeman, W., and J. W. Watts. *Psychosurgery.* Springfield, Ill. : Thomas, 1942.

Ghiselli, E. E. Mass action and equipotentiality of the cerebral cortex in brightness discrimination. *J. comp. Psychol.,* 1938a, **25,** 273–290.

Ghiselli, E. E. The relationship between the superior colliculus and the striate area in brightness discrimination. *J. genet. Psychol.,* 1938b, **52,** 151–157.

Ghiselli, E. E., and C. W. Brown. Subcortical mechanisms in learning: III. Brightness discrimination. *J. comp. Psychol.,* 1938, **26,** 93–107.

Girden, E. Cerebral mechanisms in conditioning under curare. *Amer. J. Psychol.,* 1940, **53,** 397–406.

Girden, E. Generalized conditioned responses under curare and erythroidine. *J. exp. Psychol.,* 1942a, **31,** 105–119.

Girden, E. The dissociation of blood pressure conditioned responses under erythroidine. *J. exp. Psychol.,* 1942b, **31,** 219–231.

Girden, E. The dissociation of pupillary conditioned reflexes under erythroidine and curare. *J. exp. Psychol.,* 1942c, **31,** 322–332.

Girden, E. Role of the response mechanism in learning and in "excited emotion." *Amer. J. Psychol.,* 1943, **56,** 1–20.

Girden, E., and E. Culler. Conditioned responses in curarized striate muscle in dogs. *J. comp. Psychol.,* 1937, **23,** 261–274.

Girden, E., F. A. Mettler, G. Finch, and E. Culler. Conditioned responses in a decorticate dog to acoustic, thermal, and tactile stimulation. *J. comp. Psychol.,* 1936, **21,** 367–385.

Goldstein, K. The mental changes due to frontal lobe damage. *J. Psychol.,* 1944, **17,** 187–208.

Harlow, H. F. Recovery of pattern discrimination in monkeys following unilateral occipital lobectomy. *J. comp. Psychol.,* 1939, **27,** 467–489.

Harlow, H. F. The effects of incomplete curare paralysis upon formation and elicitation of conditioned responses in cats. *J. genet. Psychol.,* 1940, **56,** 273–282.

Harlow, H. F., and J. A. Bromer. Acquisition of new responses during inactivation of the motor, premotor, and somesthetic cortex in the monkey. *J. gen. Psychol.,* 1942, **26,** 299–313.

Harlow, H. F., and J. Dagnon. Problem solution by monkeys following bilateral removal of the prefrontal areas. I. The discrimination and discrimination-reversal problems. *J. exp. Psychol.,* 1943, **32,** 351–356.

Harlow, H. F., and T. Johnson. Problem solution by monkeys following bilateral removal of the prefrontal areas : III. Test of initiation of behavior. *J. exp. Psychol.,* 1943, **32,** 495–500.

Harlow, H. F., and P. Settlage. The effect of curarization of the fore part of the body upon the retention of conditioned responses in cats. *J. comp. Psychol.,* 1939, **27,** 45–48.

Harlow, H. F., and T. Spaet. Problem solution by monkeys following bilateral removal of the prefrontal areas. IV. Responses to stimuli having multiple sign values. *J. exp. Psychol.,* 1943, **33,** 500–507.

Harlow, H. F., and R. Stagner. Effect of complete striate muscle paralysis upon the learning process. *J. exp. Psychol.,* 1933, **16,** 283–294.

Heathers, G. L. The avoidance of repetition of a maze reaction in the rat as a function of the time interval between trials. *J. Psychol.,* 1940, **10,** 359–380.

Hebb, D. O. The effect of early and late brain injury upon test scores, and the nature of normal adult intelligence. *Proc. Amer. phil. Soc.,* 1942, **85,** 275–292.

Hines, Marion. Recent contributions to localization of vision in the central nervous system. *Arch. Ophthal.*, *N. Y.*, 1942, **28**, 913–937.

Honzik, C. H. The sensory basis of maze learning in rats. *Comp. Psychol. Monogr.*, 1936, **13**, No. 64.

Hull, C. L. The rat's speed-of-locomotion gradient in approach to food. *J. comp. Psychol.*, 1934, **17**, 393–422.

Hunter, W. S. A consideration of Lashley's theory of the equipotentiality of cerebral action. *J. gen. Psychol.*, 1930, **3**, 455–468.

Hunter, W. S. Lashley on "cerebral control versus reflexology." *J. gen. Psychol.*, 1931, **5**, 230–234.

Jacobsen, C. F. A study of cerebral function in learning. The frontal lobes. *J. comp. Neurol.*, 1931, **52**, 271–340.

Jacobsen, C. F. Influence of motor and premotor area lesions upon the retention of skilled movements in monkeys and chimpanzees. *Res. Publ. Ass. nerv. ment. Dis.*, 1932, **13**, 225–247.

Jacobsen, C. F. Functions of the frontal association areas in primates. *Arch. Neurol. Psychiat.*, *Chicago*, 1935, **33**, 558–569.

Jacobsen, C. F. Studies of cerebral function in primates: I. The functions of the frontal association areas in monkeys. *Comp. Psychol. Monogr.*, 1936, **13**, No. 63, 3–60.

Jacobsen, C. F. The effects of extirpations on higher brain processes. *Physiol. Rev.*, 1939, **19**, 303–322.

Jacobsen, C. F., and J. H. Elder. Studies of cerebral function in primates: II. The effect of temporal lobe lesions on delayed response in monkeys. *Comp. Psychol. Monogr.*, 1936, **13**, No. 63, 61–65.

Jacobsen, C. F., and G. M. Haslerud. Studies of cerebral function in primates: III. The effect of motor and premotor area lesions on delayed response in monkeys. *Comp. Psychol. Monogr.*, 1936, **13**, No. 63, 66–68.

Jacobsen, C. F., and H. W. Nissen. Studies of cerebral function in primates: IV. The effects of frontal lobe lesions on the delayed alternation habit in monkeys. *J. comp. Psychol.*, 1937, **23**, 101–112.

Kellogg, W. N. Experimenthal data on different neural mechanisms for learned and unlearned responses. *J. exp. Psychol.*, 1941, **29**, 334–341.

Kellogg, W. N. Is "spinal conditioning" conditioning? Reply to "A comment." *J. exp. Psychol.*, 1947, **37**, 264–265.

Kellogg, W. N., J. Deese, N. H. Pronko, and M. Feinberg. An attempt to condition the chronic spinal dog. *J. exp. Psychol.*, 1947, **37**, 99–117.

Kellogg, W. N., V. B. Scott, R. C. Davis, and I. S. Wolf. Is movement necessary for learning? *J. comp. Psychol.*, 1940, **29**, 43–74.

Kennard, Margaret A. Reorganization of motor function in the cerebral cortex of monkeys deprived of motor and premotor areas in infancy. *J. Neurophysiol.*, 1938, **1**, 477–496.

Kennard, Margaret A. Cortical reorganization of motor function. Studies on series of monkeys of various ages from infancy to maturity. *Arch. Neurol. Psychiat.*, *Chicago*, 1942, **48**, 227–240.

Kennard, Margaret A., and W. S. McCulloch. Motor response to stimulation of cerebral cortex in absence of areas 4 and 6 (Macaca mulatta). *J. Neurophysiol.*, 1943, **6**, 181–190.

Kirk, S. A. Extra-striate functions in the discrimination of complex visual patterns. *J. comp. Psychol.*, 1936, **21**, 146–159.

Klüver, H. An analysis of the effects of the removal of the occipital lobes in monkeys. *J. Psychol.*, 1936, **2**, 49–61.

Klüver, H. Certain effects of lesions of the occipital lobes in macaques. *J. Psychol.*, 1937, **4**, 383–401.

Klüver, H. (Ed.). *Visual mechanisms* (Biological symposia, VII). Lancaster: Jaques Cattell, 1942.

Klüver, H., and P. C. Bucy. Preliminary analysis of functions of the temporal lobes in monkeys. *Arch. Neurol. Psychiat.*, *Chicago*, 1939, **42**, 979–1000.

Krechevsky, I. Hereditary nature of "hypotheses." *J. comp. Psychol.*, 1933, **16**, 99–116.

Krechevsky, I. Brain mechanisms and "hypotheses." *J. comp. Psychol.*, 1935, **19**, 425–468.

Krechevsky, I. Brain mechanisms and brightness discrimination learning. *J. comp. Psychol.*, 1936, **21**, 405–445.

Krechevsky, I. Brain mechanisms and variability: I. Variability within a means-end-readiness, *J. comp. Psychol.*, 1937a, **23**, 121–138; II. Variability where no learning is involved. *Ibid.*, 1937b, **23**, 139–163; III. Limitations of the effect of cortical injury upon variability. *Ibid.*, 1937c, **23**, 351–364.

Krechevsky, I. Brain mechanisms and umweg behavior. *J. comp. Psychol.*, 1938, **25**, 147–173.

Krieg, W. J. S. Connections of the cerebral cortex. I. The albino rat. A. Topography of the cortical areas. *J. comp. Neurol.*, 1946, **84**, 221–276.

Lashley, K. S. *Brain mechanisms and intelligence.* Chicago: University of Chicago Press, 1929.

Lashley, K. S. The mechanism of vision: IV. The cerebral areas necessary for pattern vision in the rat. *J. comp. Neurol.*, 1931, **53**, 419–478.

Lashley, K. S. Studies of cerebral function in learning: XI. The behavior of the rat in latch box situations. *Comp. Psychol. Monogr.*, 1935a, **11**, No. 52, 5–42; XII. Nervous structures concerned in the acquisition and retention of habits based on reactions to light. *Ibid.*, 1935b, **11**, No. 52, 43–79.

Lashley, K. S. Functional determinants of cerebral localization. *Arch. Neurol. Psychiat.*, *Chicago*, 1937, **38**, 371–387.

Lashley, K. S. Factors limiting recovery after central nervous lesions. *J. nerv. ment. Dis.*, 1938a, **88**, 733–755.

Lashley, K. S. The mechanism of vision: XV. Preliminary studies of the rat's capacity for detail vision. *J. gen. Psychol.*, 1938*b*, **18**, 123–193; XVI. The functioning of small remnants of the visual cortex. *J. comp. Neurol.*, 1939, **70**, 45–67; XVII. Autonomy of the visual cortex. *J. genet. Psychol.*, 1942, **60**, 197–221.

Lashley, K. S. Studies of cerebral function in learning. XII. Loss of the maze habit after occipital lesions in blind rats. *J. comp. Neurol.*, 1943, **79**, 431–462; XIII. Apparent absence of transcortical association in maze learning. *Ibid.*, 1944, **80**, 257–281.

Lashley, K. S., and L. E. Wiley. Studies of cerebral function in learning. IX. Mass action in relation to the number of elements in the problem to be learned. *J. comp. Neurol.*, 1933, **57**, 3–55.

Light, J. S., and W. H. Gantt. Essential part of reflex arc for establishment of conditioned reflex. Formation of conditioned reflex after exclusion of motor peripheral end. *J. comp.* *Psychol.*, 1936, **21**, 19–36.

Loucks, R. B. Efficacy of the rat's motor cortex in delayed alternation. *J. comp. Neurol.*, 1931, **53**, 511–567.

Loucks, R. B. The experimental delimitation of neural structures essential for learning: The attempt to condition striped muscle responses with faradization of the sigmoid gyri. *J. Psychol.*, 1936, **1**, 5–44.

Loucks, R. B. Studies of neural structures essential for learning: II. The conditioning of salivary and striped muscle responses to faradization of cortical sensory elements, and the action of sleep upon such mechanisms. *J. comp. Psychol.*, 1938, **25**, 315–332.

Loucks, R. B., and W. H. Gantt. The conditioning of striped muscle responses based upon faradic stimulation of dorsal roots and dorsal columns of the spinal cord. *J. comp. Psychol.*, 1938, **25**, 415–426.

Maier, N. R. F. Qualitative differences in the learning of rats in a discrimination situation. *J. comp. Psychol.*, 1939, **27**, 289–331.

Maier, N. R. F. The effect of cortical injury on equivalence reactions in rats. *J. comp. Psychol.*, 1941, **32**, 165–189.

Malmo, R. B. Interference factors in delayed response in monkeys after removal of frontal lobes. *J. Neurophysiol.*, 1942, **5**, 295–308.

Marquis, D. G. Effects of removal of the visual cortex in mammals with observations on the retention of light discrimination in dogs. *Res. Publ. Ass. nerv. ment. Dis.*, 1934, **13**, 558–592.

Marquis, D. G., and E. R. Hilgard. Conditioned lid responses to light in dogs after removal of the visual cortex. *J. comp. Psychol.*, 1936, **22**, 157–178.

Marquis, D. G., and E. R. Hilgard. Conditioned responses to light in monkeys after removal of the occipital lobes. *Brain*, 1937, **60**, 1–12.

Morgan, C. T., and W. M. Wood. Cortical localization of symbolic processes in the rat: II. Effect of cortical lesions upon delayed alternation in the rat. *J. Neurophysiol.*, 1943, **6**, 173–180.

Pennington, L. A. The auditory localizing behavior of the white rat in relation to cerebral function. *J. genet. Psychol.*, 1935, **46**, 264–283.

Pennington, L. A. The function of the brain in auditory localization. II. The effect of cortical extirpation upon original learning. *J. comp. Neurol.*, 1937, **66**, 415–442.

Pennington, L. A. The effects of cortical destruction upon responses to tones. *J. comp. Neurol.*, 1941, **74**, 169–191.

Peterson, G. M. Mechanisms of handedness in the rat. *Comp. Psychol. Monogr.*, 1934, **9**, No. 46.

Peterson, G. M. The influence of cerebral destructions upon the handedness of the rat in the latch box. *J. comp. Psychol.*, 1938, **26**, 445–459.

Poltyrev, S. S., and G. P. Zeliony. Grosshirnrinde und Assoziationsfunktion. *Z. Biol.*, 1930, **90**, 157–160.

Porteus, S. D., and R. D. Kepner. Mental changes after bilateral prefrontal lobotomy. *Genet. Psychol. Monogr.*, 1944, **29**, 3–115.

Raab, D. H., and H. W. Ades. Cortical and midbrain mediation of a conditioned discrimination of acoustic intensities. *Amer. J. Psychol.*, 1946, **59**, 59–83.

Ruch, T. C. Cortical localization of somatic sensibility. The effect of precentral, postcentral and posterior parietal lesions upon the performance of monkeys trained to discriminate weights. *Res. Publ. Ass. nerv. ment. Dis.*, 1935, **15**, 289–330.

Ruch, T. C., J. F. Fulton, and W. J. German. Sensory discrimination in monkey, chimpanzee and man after lesions of the parietal lobe. *Arch. Neurol. Psychiat.*, *Chicago*, 1938, **39**, 919–937.

Settlage, P. H. The effect of occipital lesions on visually-guided behavior in the monkey: I. Influence of the lesions on final capacities in a variety of problem situations. *J. comp. Psychol.*, 1939, **27**, 93–131.

Shurrager, P. S., and E. Culler. Conditioning in the spinal dog. *J. exp. Psychol.*, 1940, **26**, 133–159.

Shurrager, P. S., and E. Culler. Conditioned extinction of a reflex in the spinal dog. *J. exp. Psychol.*, 1941, **28**, 287–303.

Shurrager, P. S., and H. C. Shurrager. Converting a spinal CR into a reflex. *J. exp. Psychol.*, 1941, **29**, 217–224.

Shurrager, P. S., and H. C. Shurrager. The rate of learning measured at a single synapse. *J. exp. Psychol.*, 1946, **36**, 347–354.

Smith, D. E. Cerebral localization in somaesthetic discrimination in the rat. *J. comp. Psychol.*, 1939, **28**, 161–188.

Smith, K. U. Visual discrimination in the cat: V. The postoperative effects of removal of the striate cortex upon intensity discrimination. *J. genet. Psychol.*, 1937, **51**, 329–369; VI. The relation between pattern vision and visual acuity and the optic projection centers of the nervous system. *Ibid.*, 1938, **53,** 251–272.

Snider, R. S., and A. Stowell. Receiving areas of the tactile, auditory, and visual systems in the cerebellum. *J. Neurophysiol.*, 1944, **7,** 331–357.

Spaet, T., and H. F. Harlow. Problem solution by monkeys following bilateral removal of the prefrontal areas: II. Delayed reaction problems involving use of the matching-from-sample method. *J. exp. Psychol.*, 1943, **32,** 424–434.

Stellar, E., C. T. Morgan, and M. Yarosh. Cortical localization of symbolic processes in the rat. *J. comp. Psychol.*, 1942, **34,** 107–126.

Teitelbaum, H. A. Psychogenic body image disturbances associated with psychogenic aphasia and agnosia. *J. nerv. ment. Dis.*, 1941, **93,** 581–612.

Teitelbaum, H. A. The principle of primary and associated disturbances of the higher cortical functions as applied to temporal lobe lesions. *J. nerv. ment. Dis.*, 1942, **96,** 261–273.

Teitelbaum, H. A. An analysis of the disturbances of the higher cortical functions, agnosia, apraxia, and aphasia. *J. nerv. ment. Dis.*, 1943, **97,** 44–61.

Tsang, Y. C. The functions of the visual areas of the cerebral cortex of the rat in the learning and retention of the maze. I. *Comp. Psychol. Monogr.*, 1934, **10,** No. 50.

Wade, Marjorie. The effect of sedatives upon delayed responses in monkeys following removal of the prefrontal lobes. *J. Neurophysiol.*, 1947, **10,** 57–61.

Wapner, S. The differential effects of cortical injury and retesting on equivalence reactions in the rat. *Psychol. Monogr.*, 1944, **57,** No. 262.

Ward, A. A., Jr., and Margaret A. Kennard. Effect of cholinergic drugs on recovery of function following lesions of the central nervous system in monkeys. *Yale J. Biol. Med.*, 1942, **15,** 189–229.

Warden, C. J., S. E. Barrera, and W. Galt. The effect of unilateral and bilateral frontal lobe extirpation on the behavior of monkeys. *J. comp. Psychol.*, 1942, **34,** 149–171.

Watson, C. W., and Margaret A. Kennard. The effect of anticonvulsant drugs on recovery of function following cerebral cortical lesions. *J. Neurophysiol.*, 1945, **8,** 221–231.

Weisenberg, T., and K. E. McBride. *Aphasia.* New York: Commonwealth Fund, 1935.

Wiley, L. E. The function of the brain in audition. *J. comp. Neurol.*, 1932, **54,** 109–141.

Wiley, L. E. A further investigation of auditory cerebral mechanisms. *J. comp. Neurol.*, 1937, **66,** 327–331.

Wing, K. G. The role of the optic cortex of the dog in the retention of learned responses to light: Conditioning with light and shock. *Amer. J. Psychol.*, 1946, **59,** 583–612.

Wing, K. G. The role of the optic cortex of the dog in the retention of learned responses to light: Conditioning with light and food. *Amer. J. Psychol.*, 1947, **60,** 30–67.

Wing, K. G., and K. U. Smith. The role of the optic cortex in the dog in the determination of the functional properties of conditioned reactions to light. *J. exp. Psychol.*, 1942, **31,** 478–496.

Woolsey, C. N. The somatic functions of the central nervous system. *Annu. Rev. Physiol.*, 1947, **9,** 525–552.

21·

Speech and Language

GEORGE A. MILLER

Harvard University

Verbal behavior proceeds word by word. Talking, writing, reading, listening are all embedded in the time continuum. But verbal behavior is not the simple function of time that makes it possible to predict the behavior exactly from one moment to the next. If a man's words could be predicted in advance, he would not need to speak them. On the other hand, verbal behavior is not like the gambler's die, nor like the urn full of marbles that the statistician uses to discuss the probability of equally improbable events. It is a function lying somewhere between the completely determined and the completely random — the connections between successive events limit the range of possibilities, but they do not hold the events strictly to a single path. These connections constitute what we call the verbal context.

In a single chapter it is impossible to treat adequately the entire field of speech and language. In fact, such a treatment hardly seems necessary, for good reviews of many areas are already available.* The following

discussion will restrict itself to the subject of verbal context. The relations among successive verbal responses pose problems that range from phonetics through the psychology of thought, and a consideration of contextual dependencies reveals indirectly many of the crucial aspects of verbal behavior.

A DEFINITION OF VERBAL CONTEXT

Context is usually defined by psychologists to include the totality of conditions that affect an individual at a given time. In this sense the word is similar to "frame of reference" or "behavioral environment" or "life space." If material learned in one situation is not recalled until the learner is again in the same situation, we speak of contextual aids to memory. If a gray looks yellow on one ground and blue on another, we refer to

This chapter was prepared at the Psycho-Acoustic Laboratory, Harvard University, under contract with the U. S. Navy, Office of Naval Research (Contract N5ori-76, Project NR142-201, Report PNR-77).

* The problem of speech development has been discussed thoroughly by McCarthy (1946). Physiological aspects of phonetics are reviewed by Russell (1931), and even Scripture (1902) is not completely out of date. Katzenstein (1930) gives a comprehensive survey of the experimental techniques and procedures, and Negus (1929) discusses the larynx. Acoustic aspects of phonetics can be found in Fletcher (1929), Paget (1930), Potter, Kopp, and Green (1947), or Joos (1948), and the perception of speech is discussed in Chapter 26 of this volume. Phonetic transcription is treated in Jones (1939), and an Americanized version is given by Kenyon (1932). Philosophical discussions of language are somewhat outside the scope of experimental psychology, but the interested reader will find an excellent bibliography in Morris (1946). Statistical analysis is considered in some detail by Zipf (1935, 1949) and, from a somewhat different point of view, by Gray and Leary (1935). Head (1926) and Weisenberg and McBride (1935) provide detailed treatments of aphasia. Speech pathology is summarized by West, Kennedy, and Carr (1947), and Johnson (1946) discusses the role of language in personal adjustment.

the effects of context on perception. If a situation misleads the subject in the solution of a problem, we often talk of the effects of context upon thinking. This notion of context is so broad as to be almost useless, however, and before we can use the notion, therefore, we must pare it down to fit our particular needs.

Verbal context is less general than context alone. Verbal contexts are the communicative acts that precede and follow the verbal response under consideration, and so the verbal context is limited to the temporal sequence of verbal responses.

What a man says depends upon many factors. Their importance is obvious, and their implications have been discussed in detail by Skinner (1947). In this sense the current state of the man and of his environment forms a large portion of the context of the man's remarks. Viewed in this light, verbal behavior is subject to exactly the same influences as all other behavior, and a discussion of the complete context would be a general psychology that drew upon verbal behavior only for its illustrations. In order to restrict the discussion we shall direct our attention to the influence of linguistic structure upon the form of the verbalization.

The Statistical Approximation to English

In order to illustrate the problem of context we shall borrow a useful device from Shannon (1948).

Suppose that we had no knowledge of English, and that we were presented with a list of all the words in the language and told to compose statements or messages. The best we could do would be to draw words at random from the list. The zero-order approximation to English might run something like this: "nautical pillory alas prolix temporal depraved migrates irritability callous oil cent," etc. Our employer would probably regard this as a poor performance, but in order to improve it we need more facts about the language. Suppose we are provided with a statistical tabulation, like those

of Dewey (1923) or Thorndike and Lorge (1944), that tells how often each word is used in normal discourse. We now select words according to their relative frequency of use, and so produce a first-order approximation that might read, "situation our describe the the of however pattern before test is excess in day if to greater the," etc.

The first-order approximation is nothing to be proud of, so we ask for further data. If we select a certain word, what words might reasonably follow it? We need a tabulation of pairs of words according to their relative frequencies of occurrence. With the half-million words in the *Oxford English Dictionary* we could construct $(500,000)^2$ pairs, which makes the job discouraging. But suppose the information is available. We then draw a pair and discover we have the words "they are." Next we take all the pairs beginning with "are" and draw one of them. "Are here" turns up, and our message now reads "they are here." Then we draw from the pairs that have "here" as the first word, and so proceed to construct the message. This second-order approximation might turn out to be, "they are here is not large feet are the happy days and so what is dead weight," etc.

The improvement is enough to encourage us to go on to sequences of 3 or 4 or more words. For a fourth-order approximation we might start with "we are going to," then draw from the set starting with "are going to" and obtain "are going to see," and so proceed to construct "we are going to see him is not correct to chuckle loudly and depart quietly for home," etc. Higher-order approximations to English do not qualify as great literature, but they come close to something somebody might say, given the proper situation. It would be interesting to compare these higher-order approximations with the speech of aphasics or psychotics. A fourth- or fifth-order approximation might be mistaken for automatic writing if it were not for the strong perseverative tendencies in such productions.

Observe what has been done in order to increase the credibility of this imitation English. The necessary information is statistical and consists of the relative frequencies of occurrence of units or sequences of units. The choice of the word as the unit in this process is not crucial, for the same thing can be done with the 26 letters of the alphabet and a space.

We have, therefore, a method for generating statistical approximations to English. The rules of formation require that each unit be selected on the basis of its probability of occurrence after the preceding n units. Viewed from the statistician's side we have a time series with a alternatives at each point but with dependent probabilities of occurrence. The pattern of dependent probabilities — the statistical relations among units — provides a statistical definition for verbal context.

The Amount of Information

Rather than work with a set of 500,000 words, or of 26 letters, consider a very simple example with only two alternatives, A and B. Each alternative might be assigned to one of two possible events. Then it is possible to communicate about the two events by using one of the two symbols, and the person who receives the symbol will be able to make a *decision* between the two alternatives. If four events must be represented, we would have to use combinations, AA, AB, BA, and BB, to represent them. With sequences of three symbols we can represent eight events, and in general a^n events can be represented by sequences of n symbols selected from a alternatives.

If a listener recognizes, as Seashore and Eckerson (1940) say he might, 150,000 words, and if we speak in 10-word sentences, there are $(150,000)^{10}$ or about 10^{52} different events that can be represented, *if we can select each word independently of every other word.* We could, with this language of independent words, convey in 10 words a staggering amount of information, enough

information to enable the receiver to select one from among 10^{52} possibilities. Obviously, English does not work this way. Dependencies among successive words reduce the number of possible sentences and so reduce the number of alternatives that can be represented. In a very real sense, therefore, contextual restrictions reduce the amount of information that can be conveyed by a sequence of n symbols.

We can represent a sequence of dependent probabilities by a discrete Markoff process. Imagine two urns, both filled with black and white marbles, but with different proportions in each. The probability of drawing a white marble from urn I is $p_w(w)$, and the probability of drawing a white marble from urn II is $p_b(w)$. We play the game as follows. Each time we draw a white marble from either urn, we draw next from urn I. Each time we draw a black marble from either urn we draw next from urn II. Thus $p_w(w)$ is the probability that, once we have drawn a white and so must draw next from urn I, we will draw next a white. The probability of drawing a white is therefore different if we have just drawn a white, and so must draw next from urn I, than it is if we have just drawn a black and so must draw from urn II.

The urns represent the different "states" the process can get into; that is to say, they represent the cumulative influence of the preceding events. The model can be generalized by increasing the number of urns and the rules for drawing from them to represent cumulative influences extending over any length sequence with any number of differently marked marbles.

Here we have, then, a statistical model to represent the sequential dependencies observed in human speech. Once we have said certain words, grammar, usage, and sense restrict the range of possible continuations and make some possibilities more probable than others.

By calling the successive items in the sequence "symbols" we imply that they represent something and carry a certain amount of information. We can quantify the information per symbol in a convenient manner if we assume it is proportional to the logarithm of the number of possible alternatives. If there are a alternatives, each symbol in the sequence carries an amount of information proportional to log a, and a sequence of n such symbols in a row would carry an amount proportional to n log a. The value of log a — the information per symbol — can be expressed in terms of probabilities. If all alternatives are equally likely, then $p = 1/a$, and $-$ log $p =$ log a.

As we have seen, however, the alternatives are not always equally likely, and in order to take this situation into account Shannon (1948) writes the equation

$$I = -k \sum_{1}^{a} p_i \log p_i$$

where I is the information per symbol, p_i is the probability of occurrence of the ith of a alternatives, and k determines the unit of measurement. This equation represents the "expected value" (mean value) of log p_i.

In a sequence of symbols the distribution of p_i will, if successive symbols are not independent, vary according to which symbols have preceded. This additional complication puts us into the situation described above by the Markoff process. There are a finite number of states that a Markoff process can get into, and the equation tells us how to compute the amount of information per symbol for any particular state. To represent a sequence of changing states, therefore, what we need is the average information per symbol, where the average is taken over all the states and weighted according to their probability of occurrence. This is given by

$$I = \sum_{j} P_j I_j = -k \sum_{i,j} P_j p_j(i) \log p_j(i)$$

where I is the average information per symbol, I_j is the information of a symbol generated when the process is in state j, P_j is the probability that state j will occur, and

$p_j(i)$ is the transitional probability that when the process is in state j the ith of the a alternative symbols will occur. According to Wiener (1948) this formulation is different from but substitutable for Fisher's (1946) definition of amount of information.

From the equation we see that there is no information in a message if there is only one alternative possible in each of the states, for then $p_j(i)$ is 1, and log 1 is zero. If the message can be predicted exactly in advance, then the message contains no new information. At the other extreme, the information is maximal if successive symbols are independent and all the alternatives are equally likely. In this case there is only one state and P_j is 1, and $p_j(i)$ is equal to $1/a$. If we substitute these values into the equation we get $(-ka/a)$ log $(1/a)$, or k log a. Thus for this case the complicated formula reduces to the simple one with which we began.

This definition of information can be crudely illustrated by a comparison of normal and Basic English. Basic uses 850 different words to do the job that a non-Basic writer might need 10,000 words to do. To make the very simplest comparison, assume that all words are equally likely and independent. Then the information per word in Basic is proportional to log 850, and in normal English it is proportional to log 10,000. How long would a Basic text have to be in order to represent the same amount of information as a non-Basic text? The answer is given by the ratio of these two logarithms, and we conclude that about 1.36 words drawn from the limited vocabulary of Basic English are needed for every word drawn from the larger vocabulary of ordinary English. In practice Basic can improve this ratio by judicious editing, and since Basic words are short the number of pages required for a novel might be quite comparable for the two languages. Critics of Basic have complained that it seems verbose and roundabout, but an increase by a factor of 1.36 may be a small price to pay for the savings obtained in learning the vocabulary.

The statistical model is a useful one. It enables us to represent the statistical relations among the component symbols of a language and to state in a quantitative way how these relations affect the amount of information — the number of decisions per symbol — the language can convey. The idea that the amount of information in a sequence of symbols is a function of the number of possible alternative sequences of symbols says both a little more and a little less than we ordinarily mean by information. Once the quantitative definition becomes familiar, however, it is very convenient to judge what a man says against the yardstick of all the things he might have said but didn't.

THE EFFICIENCY OF THE SPEECH MECHANISM

A message is a sequence of events (symbols) strung together in time according to a pattern. The most widely used generator of such events is the human larynx, and so we shall examine its capacities and limitations for producing messages. We could perhaps examine the flagman's arms or the typist's fingers with the same idea in mind, but these message generators are of secondary importance.

Rate of Production of Speech Sounds

In order to estimate maximal articulatory rates, Hudgins and Stetson (1937) asked talkers to repeat simple syllables as rapidly as possible in rhythmic groups. "Tat, tat, tat, *tat*," for example, was used to measure the speed of articulatory movements made with the tongue. Their results showed that 8.2 syllables per second could be produced with the tip of the tongue, 7.3 with the jaw, 7.1 with the back of the tongue, and 6.7 with the velum and with the lips. Kaiser (1934) has pointed to the relation between speed and the innervation of the various muscle groups. He found that muscles of the face and lips, innervated by the facial nerve,

could be moved only 2.5 to 3 times each second. To produce a more rapid series of labial sounds the talker relies upon the more rapid movements of the jaw, innervated by the trigeminal nerve, to carry the lips along. The tongue, supplied by the hypoglossal nerve, is clearly the most mobile articulator.

These maximal rates cannot be maintained indefinitely, for speech is an 'overlaid' function of the respiratory system. The talker must stop to breathe. In quiet respiration the *I-fraction* — the duration of inhalation divided by the duration of the entire respiratory cycle — averages, according to Fossler (1930), between 0.40 and 0.45. Thus the top rate would be cut in half were it not for the decrease of the I-fraction to 0.16 during speech.

The maximum speed may also be slightly less when articulatory positions are changed for each syllable. If we take 7 syllables per second as the average of Hudgins and Stetson's data, subtract 1 syllable per second to leave time for breathing and 1 to permit changes in articulatory position, we arrive at 5 syllables per second as a reasonable estimate of the speed at which the speech musculature works.

With the aid of the tabulations given by French, Carter, and Koenig (1930) we can estimate the average number of speech sounds contained in 5 syllables. Of all syllables tabulated, consonant-vowel-consonant (CVC) syllables formed 33.5 per cent, CV 21.8, VC 20.3, V 9.7, CVCC 7.8, CCVC and VCC both 2.8, CCV 0.8, and CCVCC 0.5 per cent. These figures indicate that the average syllable must contain approximately 2.5 speech sounds. Thus 5 syllables per second represents 12.5 speech sounds per second. (A similar figure for sounds per syllable is obtained from Dewey's tabulations.)

Number of Different Speech Sounds

If we knew the number of available speech sounds, we could calculate the maximum amount of information carried by 12.5 speech sounds per second. Phonetic transcription of spoken English can be accomplished with about 40 symbols, 15 for vowels and 25 for consonants. The number varies with the skill and intent of the transcriber, but 40 is a fair average for broad transcription. Table 1 shows the classification of consonant sounds by their place and manner of articu-

whereas p is voiceless. The sounds b and m are formed in the same place and both are voiced sounds, but they differ because b releases the air pressure by a sudden opening of the lips whereas m releases the pressure through the nasal cavity. Other cells of the table can be similarly interpreted.

TABLE 1

ENGLISH CONSONANTS

Manner of Articulation	Place of Articulation							
	Bilabial	Labio-dental	Lingua-dental	Lingua-alveolar	Palatal-alveolar	Palatal	Velar	Glottal
Voiced plosive	b			d			g	?
Unvoiced plosive	p			t			k	
Nasal	m			n			ŋ (siŋg)	
Lateral				l				
Rolled				r				
Voiced fricative		v	ð (then)	z	ʒ (azure)			
Voiceless fricative	ʍ (whip)	f	θ (thin)	s	ʃ (she)			h
Continuants	w					j (yes)		

lation. The place of articulation is determined by the speech organs principally involved, and the manner of articulation is determined by the movements these organs make. The sounds represented by b, p, m, and w, for example, are called bilabial because they are articulated with the lips. All these consonants are formed in the same articulatory position, but they differ in their manner of production. Thus p and b differ in that b is accompanied by phonation

The classification of English vowel sounds is usually made in terms of the position of the tongue. In this way the back vowels in words like *boot* or *book* are distinguished from the front vowels in *beet* or *bit*. A vowel diagram with key words is given in Fig. 1. Intermediate positions on this diagram are often encountered in other languages and in the imprecise speech of the workaday world.

The classification given includes 23 consonants and 15 vowels. One of these consonants, the glottal stop ?, is not used in normal English speech, but we should probably add two more: tʃ in *choke*, and dʒ in *joke*. This gives a total of 39 different speech sounds. If we assume that these 39 sounds are all equally likely and might occur in any order at a rate of 12.5 per second, the amount of information per second is 12.5 *k* log 39.

Shannon suggests that, when *k* = 1 and logarithms are taken to the base 2, the re-

example, are greatly overworked, and Dewey estimates that 9 sounds form over 50 per cent of normal utterance. The histogram in Fig. 2 represents the results of Dewey's count of the relative frequencies of occurrence of 41 speech sounds. Voelker's (1935) data are quite similar.

The reason for the preference shown for some sounds seems to be that they are easier to produce and easier to discriminate. Note that the first 8 consonants listed by Dewey

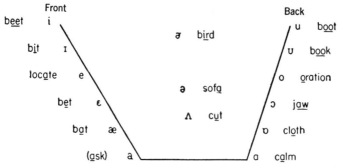

FIG. 1. Schematic representation of the vowel sounds of English according to their place of articulation. Key words indicate the phonetic values of the symbols.

sultant units of information be called *bits*, short for binary digits. A bit is the amount of information necessary for the listener to make a decision between two equally probable alternatives, and 10 bits would be the information required for 10 successive choices between two alternatives. With this unit there are 12.5 $\log_2$ 39 = 67 bits, or successive decisions, per second. In slightly different words, a talker generating randomly any one of 39 phonemes at a rate of 12.5 phonemes per second might speak any one of 2^{67} (about 100,000,000,000,000,000,000) different sequences of sounds each second, and the listener who used the information efficiently would be able to select one from among 2^{67} possible referents.

Frequency of Sounds, Syllables, and Words

Obviously the foregoing estimate is astronomically large and completely unrealistic. For one thing, speech sounds do not occur equally often. Some sounds, ɪ, n, t, r, for

are lingua-alveolar — produced with the tip of the tongue near the gum ridge. These hard-working sounds are produced with the very agile tip of the tongue while the other articulators remain relatively immobile. The consonants used least are those that require the cooperation of the less agile articulatory muscles. The preference for consonants formed in the same place is convenient for the listener as well as for the talker. Analysis of the confusions made by listeners in articulation tests conducted with nonsense syllables shows that the principal confusions occur among sounds formed in the same manner. Consonants produced in the same place but in a different manner are seldom confused. Thus p is often confused with other voiceless plosives, t or k, but not with the voiced plosive b, the nasal m, or the continuant w, all formed in the same position.

Zipf (1935) has also interpreted phonetic favoritism in terms of articulatory complexity. For example, he argues that a voiced consonant represents a greater degree of complexity in its production than does a voiceless consonant. (This argument can be disputed. See Lightoller, 1925.) Presum-

based upon the relative number of errors deaf children make in learning the various sounds. Their data for 192 children enable them to rank the sounds in order accord-

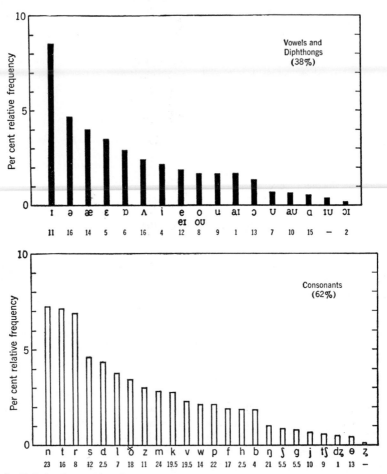

FIG. 2. Relative frequencies of occurrence (after Dewey, 1923, p. 125) for the vowels and consonants in English are indicated by the height of the bars. Numbers under the bars indicate the difficulty score developed by Hudgins and Numbers (1942).

ably, voiceless sounds should occur more frequently than voiced sounds. Zipf presents evidence drawn from 12 languages showing that the voiceless plosives, t, p, and k, occur more frequently than their voiced counterparts, d, b, and g.

Hudgins and Numbers (1942) have proposed an independent scale of difficulty

ing to difficulty, and this ranking is indicated by the numbers below the phonetic symbols in Fig. 2. The low numbers indicate the most difficult sounds. A rank-order correlation coefficient of -0.41 was found between the scale of difficulty for consonants and the frequency of use reported by Dewey. The correlation has the expected sign and may be construed as evidence supporting the notion that our language avoids the difficult phonemes.

It can be shown that the most frequently used sounds are not the ones babies babble earliest or most often. Irwin (1947, 1948) has compiled extensive data on the relative frequencies of the speech sounds as a function of age. In the babbling of 2-month-old babies the glottal plosive ? and the glottal fricative h make up 87 per cent of the consonants, and ɛ, i, and ʌ comprise 96 per cent of the vowels. As the child matures he employs an increasingly wide range of sounds, and at 2.5 years the distribution is very similar to that for adults. There is no striking correlation between the first appearance of the sound, its eventual frequency of use, and the scale of difficulty.

The effect of phonetic favoritism upon the rate at which the speech mechanism encodes information into speech sounds can be calculated by substituting Dewey's tabulation, Fig. 2, for the assumption of equal probability. The equation, $I = -\Sigma p_i \log_2 p_i$, along with Dewey's values for p_i (the probability of occurrence of each of the speech sounds), gives approximately 60 bits of information per second. In the sense of the discussion of the preceding section, the values of p_i give us a first-order approximation to the phonetic structure of English. With this closer approximation it appears that the potential amount of information per second is only 60/67, or 91 per cent, of what it might be if English did not favor the easily produced speech sounds. This ratio of actual to maximum information can be conveniently termed the relative information. One minus the relative information is the *redundancy*. For the first approximation, therefore, the redundancy is $1 - 0.91$, or 9 per cent. Our partiality for certain speech sounds requires us on the average to make 9 per cent more sounds in order to represent as many alternatives as could be represented if we used each sound equally often.

The next step in discovering where our potential information capacity is dissipated is to examine the relative frequencies of occurrence of pairs of phonetic symbols. The pairs that occur frequently, like ðə, ʌv, ɪn, are those that permit an easy shift in articulatory position. Pairs that are seldom or never used involve difficult articulatory transitions, and preferences for certain sequences are even more striking than preferences for certain phonemes.

French, Carter, and Koenig show that we use a wider variety of consonants at the beginning than at the end of our words, and that there is a tendency for division of labor. Some consonants (w, j, h, b, g, f, p, ð, and θ) are used principally at the beginning, others (ŋ, z, v, r) principally at the end of words. The division is not perfect because some consonants (t, n, l, m, d, k) are handy on either end of a vowel, and others (ʃ, tʃ, dʒ, ʒ) are seldom used in any position. The strongest evidence for preferred sequences comes from the casual observation that consonants and vowels tend to alternate in speech. This tendency is so marked that one is tempted to think of the laryngeal and articulatory muscles as antagonistic muscle groups.

Unfortunately, however, all we have are hints, for the actual frequencies of phonetic digrams have not been tabulated. The best we can do is to make some approximations based on Dewey's count for syllables. In a sample of 100,000 words Dewey found 4400 different syllables, and 4500 seems a safe estimate for the number of syllables in English. Next we fit a curve to the distribution obtained ($p_i = 1/8.4r_i$ gives a fair approximation, where r_i is the rank of the ith syllable with respect to frequency of occurrence) and integrate $p_i \log_2 p_i$ between 1 and 4500. The result is 9.2 bits per syllable, and, if we continue to regard 5 syllables per second as the maximum rate, this gives 46 bits per second. Apparently the statistical dependencies among the phonemes used to form syllables restrict us to 46/67, or about 70 per cent, of the information that could be encoded with the same phonemes in the absence of sequential dependencies.

Longer sequences of phonemes can be studied by considering the statistics of word frequencies. Zipf, following a suggestion made by Condon (1928), uses the equation $p_i = 1/10r$ to represent the relative frequencies of occurrence of English words. Thus Eldridge's (1911) count of 43,989 words from

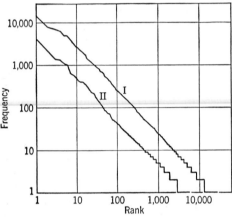

FIG. 3. Frequency of occurrence is plotted against the rank order with respect to frequency for (I) words in Joyce's *Ulysses*, and (II) words in American newspapers. (From Zipf, 1945.)

American newspapers should give 4399 occurrences of the most frequent word, 2199 occurrences of the second most frequent, 1466 occurrences of the third most frequent, etc. The actual results of the count fit rather well, and with a large sample of words it is probably justifiable to use Zipf's equation. Figure 3 shows rank-frequency distributions for Eldridge's data and for a count of James Joyce's *Ulysses* (Hanley, 1937). Zipf's equation is a rectilinear function on these log-log coordinates.

The real difficulty comes when we try to decide the size of the vocabulary from which the words are drawn. The available estimates range all the way from 2822 (the number of different words used in telephone conversations counted by French, Carter, and Koenig) to 500,000 (the number of

lexical units in the *Oxford English Dictionary*). If we assume that their frequency of occurrence follows Zipf's rule, and that the probabilities sum to 1.0, then we must have 22,000 word types, for the definite integral of $1/10r_i$ is 1.0 between the limits of 1 and 22,000. So we integrate $(\log_2 10r_i)/10r_i$ between 1 and 22,000. The result gives 10.6 bits per word.

Just how many words a talker can say per second is also hard to decide. Many of the words are polysyllabic, but the frequently used words are principally monosyllabic. The inverse relation between frequency of use and length is striking in all languages that have been studied, and because of this inverse relation the efficiency of verbal communication is substantially increased. If the average word length is about 1.7 syllables, the talker can pronounce 3 words, or about 32 bits, per second. The maximum efficiency within the restrictions imposed by the phonetic structure of English words, therefore, is about 50 per cent.

Practical Estimate of Rate of Encoding Information

So much for maxima. If we look at the actual performance of human talkers in a conversational situation we find that their rate of encoding information into speech sounds is far below the maximum. To make some realistic assumptions, take the average rate of talking to be about 1.5 words per second, and the speaking vocabulary to be about 5000 words. Under these assumptions a talker could average about 12 bits per word, or 18 bits per second, if the words could be chosen independently and equally often.

We cannot leave it here, however, for words are not chosen without regard to preceding words. If we consider the structure of the language over sequences of several words, the estimate will probably be reduced to about 5 or 6 bits per word. Said differently, a subject shown a sequence of 100 words from everyday English and told to add the 101st word that might reasonably follow these 100 will have, on the average, the equivalent of 40 or 50 alternatives from which to choose. (The actual number may be larger, but the various responses will not be equally likely.) He will not be free to combine speech sounds at random, or to draw blindly from the dictionary. The range of possible choices will vary widely for different sequences, and 5 or 6 bits is only an average value. After "the man saw the," many possibilities are available, but, after "should I stand up or sit," anything but "down" would represent an unusual choice of words. An experimental consideration of the range of possibilities might well show that some words are relatively free of the verbal context, and that others are relatively determined. The context-free words would be, presumably, the nouns, verbs, adjectives, and adverbs, and these would carry most of the information. The articles, prepositions, and conjunctions would be determined largely by context and so could carry relatively little information.

To summarize, the average talker generates information very inefficiently in comparison with the "physiological limit" that might be obtained. Ease of articulation restricts his choice of phoneme sequences, but the principal limitation is probably the inability of the central nervous system to collect, collate, and pass on instructions to the speech mechanism at a more rapid rate. Instead of choosing freely among all possible words, the speech-producing system cannot do much better than to select one from about 70 possibilities per second. Within this range of possibilities, motivational and environmental variables have room to operate, and with the additional help of these psychological factors it may eventually be possible to make short-term predictions of verbal behavior with considerable accuracy.

The redundancy of our normal speech is not a complete waste of time. The redundancy involved in the contextual clues means that we repeat everything we say, but repe-tition is our insurance against errors. By using only a small fraction of the available symbol patterns we make it likely that an error will transform the pattern into some highly improbable pattern and thus enable us to detect the mistake. If all possible sequences were used, an error would transform the message into another meaningful pattern, and the mistake would be hard to discover. (For further discussion of this and related topics, see Chapter 26.)

TALKING AND LEARNING

In order to speak a language, a person must know (1) the semantic rules for a large number of vocal noises, and (2) the syntactic rules for stringing these noises together in patterns. These requirements can be stated in terms of the Markoff process used as the statistical model. The model has urns full of marbles, and rules governing the order in which marbles are drawn from the various urns. Similarly, the talker obeys rules that say "having spoken such-and-such words, the next word must be selected from this limited set." A talker who does not know these rules, or who cannot remember from one instant to the next which verbal marbles he has drawn, cannot know what verbal urn to draw from next. If we do not grant these two abilities to our talker, he will not talk sense.

A device to handle information must deal with (1) a variety of different symbols (2) arranged in a variety of patterns. The 40 speech sounds we use could be reduced to 2 if we were willing to use these 2 as we use the *dit* and *dah* of telegraphic code. By stringing these 2 alternatives together in sequences of 6, we would have more distinctions (64) than we can achieve with one of 40 alternative sounds. Communication would be slower, however, and patterns would have to extend over a longer period of time. It is only when we consider the decoding and storage of information that it becomes clear that some combinations of elements and patterns are more efficient than others, and that pattern and range are substitutable only within rather narrow limits.

Since the span of immediate memory is not infinite, the lengths of the patterns we can use easily in communication are limited. When the length of the pattern is limited, it is necessary to increase the number of different components used in the pattern in order to increase the range of differentiations the language can make. Forty speech sounds combined in patterns extending over approximately 100 successive sounds may be about the most a human being can organize in advance and speak extemporaneously. We can imagine languages with 2 different sounds combined in longer patterns, or with 10,000 sounds in shorter patterns. These imaginary languages could contain as many possible distinctions as does the language we actually use, but they are not designed to hold the information in the form most useful to the human nervous system.

Experimental Studies of Intraverbal Connections

The need for a better understanding of the connections among words has been clearly recognized by the psychologists of language. It is true that some of the early behaviorists — Watson, F. H. Allport, A. P. Weiss, to name a few — had more to say about how our urns get filled with verbal marbles than about the rules for drawing successively from different urns. More recently, however, men like Cofer and Foley (1942), Morris (1946), and Skinner (1947) have carried the analysis further and have outlined a large and important discipline dealing with why words are glued together in some ways and not in others.

It is convenient to refer to the learning underlying the dependencies shown statistically by the name "intraverbal associations," or "intraverbal connections." Such an association or connection means that when one symbol occurs there is a greater than chance likelihood that its associate will

follow shortly. There is more than the word-counters' evidence to make the existence of such connections seem probable. Some of these sources of evidence will be briefly reviewed.

1. *Word-association tests.* One of the oldest and simplest methods of revealing intraverbal connections is the word-association test made famous by Jung (1918). In the usual form of the test the subject hears a stimulus word and is told to respond with the first word that occurs to him. The responses obtained show a large overlap in the associations of different people. For example, Kent and Rosanoff (1910) found that 650 out of their 1000 subjects responded to the word "lamp" with the word "light." Most words show less uniformity, but in every case a limited number of popular responses can be defined. Although the instructions impose no sentence structure on the responses, the distribution of relative frequencies is quite similar to that obtained for words in sentences (Skinner, 1937). There is a limited range of likely responses, and within this set some are used more than others.

Intraverbal connections, as revealed by word-association tests, are well standardized within a given linguistic group. Uniformity is even greater if the responses from members of a single professional group are compared. Foley and Macmillan (1943) found that lawyers respond more like other lawyers than like doctors. Among members of the same family the correspondences are even more striking, especially between parents and their children of the same sex (Jung). The children differ more from their father than from their mother. In short, the more the subjects' past experiences with language overlap, the greater the similarity of their word associations.

There have been many attempts to classify word associations, but the responses are so various that no single classification has gained universal favor. Antonyms (wet–dry), synonyms (pain–hurt), subordinates (fruit–apple), coordinates (apple–peach), superordinates (apple–fruit), assonants (pack–tack), completions (forward–march), egocentrisms (success–I must), syntactic changes (run–ran), and many other classes have been distinguished. The dimensions along which intraverbal connections get formed are very numerous.

2. *Sentence-completion tests.* A subject asked to complete a sentence has a slightly better defined task, but he may have to contribute a more extensive sample of his verbal behavior. Like word associations, incompleted sentences have proved a useful tool for the clinical psychologist.

In one form of the test a group of sentences that have a certain word in common are selected. This word is deleted, and the subjects are asked to read the sentences one at a time and to guess the missing word. Commonly used words require only one or two sentences before the accumulating context makes the correct intraverbal connections obvious. Infrequently used words are more difficult. Analysis of the responses that precede the final decision reveals words that have intraverbal associations very similar to those of one another and to those of the missing word. For example, in a group of sentences where *sorrow* had been removed, readers substituted *anger, hatred, loneliness, longing, confusion, destruction, horror, fear, grief, pain, anxiety, doom.* When the missing word was *red*, the presolution responses included *pale, bright, hot, large, green, brown,* etc.

3. *Conditioned responses.* Several investigators have reported that a response conditioned to an object generalizes to the name of the object, and that a response conditioned to the name generalizes to the object (Cofer and Foley, 1942). Of more direct concern for us are the studies showing generalization from one word to other words.

Razran (1935) used his salivary reflex to obtain a quantitative estimate of his familiarity with the Russian, English, German, French, Spanish, Polish, and Gaelic languages. He measured the amount of saliva secreted when the word for saliva was perceived and thought of in each of the various languages. The magnitude of the response varied with his familiarity as measured by reading speed. Encouraged by this result Razran (1939) proceeded to condition human subjects to salivate to the words *style, urn, freeze,* and *surf.* After conditioning, the subjects were tested with the homophones *stile, earn, frieze,* and *serf,* and with the synonyms *fashion, vase, chill,* and *wave.* Their responses showed generalization to the new words, and the generalization was greater for synonyms than for homophones. Essentially the same results were obtained by Riess (1940) with the GSR. Riess' later results (1946) indicate that children tend to generalize more readily to homophones, but this tendency disappears at about 11 years of age.

Diven (1937) asked his subjects to respond as in the word-association test, and to continue free association until told to stop. One of the stimulus words on the list, *barn,* was always followed by shock after the subject had made several responses. The subjects quickly began to show a GSR whenever the word *barn* was presented. This was true for all subjects, although half of them were unable to report at the end of the experiment that *barn* was the critical word. The response to the stimulus word generalized to other rural words on the list, but the generalized responses were smaller in magnitude. Diven's results support the idea that a response conditioned to one stimulus word generalizes to all words intraverbally related.

4. *Transfer effects in memorization.* Quite similar to the conditioning studies are the experiments that explore the effects of one kind of verbal learning on another. Transfer effects for verbal learning have been discussed in Chapter 17, and it is sufficient for our purposes to note that these studies also indicate a highly organized set of intra-

verbal connections. The similarities among the two sets of materials that are learned influence the amount of transfer, and associative spread can be used to gauge the strength and extent of word relations.

5. *Automatic writing.* One of the most dramatic and least explored methods for intraverbal inquiry is usually referred to as automatic writing. In 1896 L. M. Solomons and Gertrude Stein published an account of

6. *Verbal summator.* Skinner (1936) has developed a projective technique for studying the latent verbal responses that would normally be censored and edited before they appear. In a sense the verbal summator is the most free of all free word-association tests, for the stimulus words are not words at all but only faint, mumbled vowels. In his attempt to make sense of these liminal sounds, the subject supplies short statements

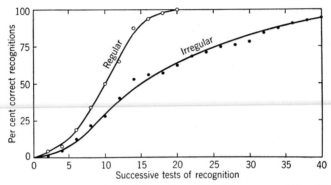

FIG. 4. Learning curves for regular and irregular artificial languages. (After Wolfle, 1932.)

their experimental studies of motor automatism. By concentrating on an interesting task while carrying on a dull one, they developed the ability to write sequences of words without having any recall for what was written. Miss Stein often found it sufficient distraction to read what her arm wrote, but following three or four words behind her pencil. These investigators noted a strong perseverative tendency, as if a verbal response had to be 'extinguished' by repetition before another response could displace it.

A sample production: "This long time when he did his best time, and he could thus have been bound, and in this long time, when he could be this to first use of this long time," etc.

Automatic writing may be the result of shortening the range of statistical dependencies and so may give a glimpse of the verbal processes almost completely stripped of their normal contextual determiners.

of his own invention. As in automatic writing, perseverative tendencies are strong.

7. *Artificial languages.* Studies with artificial languages suggest experimental techniques to chart the development of these dependent probabilities. Esper (1925) and Wolfle (1932) taught subjects to identify visual figures by names composed of pairs of nonsense syllables. The figures came in four shapes, and each shape in four colors or sizes. Each shape had its name, each color or size had its name, and the name for the figure was compounded according to the appropriate names for its attributes. To make the situation more closely analogous to language they introduced irregularities — a shape name might be modified slightly when used with one of the color names, but not modified with the other three colors. Figure 4 shows the average learning curves obtained by Wolfle with regular and irregular languages. The more complex dependencies were more difficult to learn.

Learning Meaningful Materials

If subjects come to the verbal learning experiments with an intricate background of response tendencies, their ability to learn new materials must depend in some way upon the degree of correspondence between these tendencies and the statistical structure of the materials to be learned. The materials used to study verbal learning can be considered with respect to the number of different symbols and the lengths of the patterns. We might ask, for example, how to get n bits of information memorized most efficiently. If we used two symbols, 0 and 1, each symbol in the list could carry one bit, but a long sequence of these two symbols would be very difficult to learn. On the other hand, if the n bits are coded into language, the learner's task is to remember which words were chosen. The order of the words requires little additional learning, and the information is mastered much more readily. Learning a new pattern is much harder than learning which items to fit into a familiar pattern.

The meaningfulness of the materials to be learned is one of the most important factors in verbal learning. Whether or not verbal meaning can be identified with verbal context is debatable, but certainly the two have many aspects in common. We might let meaning refer to the totality of conditions affecting the verbal behavior and retain context for the purely verbal environment of the response. Within the narrow frame of verbal learning experiments, therefore, it seems reasonable to speak of nonsense syllables or digits as having little contextual determination and much new information per symbol, and to speak of prose or poetry as having much contextual determination and little new information per symbol. The relative ease of learning prose or poetry reflects a high positive transfer of response patterns, whereas negative transfer is at its worst when the pattern of symbols is arbitrary or unfamiliar.

A notable characteristic of meaningful learning is its selectivity. When we are faced with a problem that demands new information, we do not open an encyclopedia at random and start reading. We seek out the particular passage we need. Similarly, when messages come to us gratuitously, we do not attempt to memorize them all. We learn only those parts that may be of use to us later. Newman (1939) demonstrated experimentally that not all parts of a prose passage are equally important to a learner. His subjects studied stories constructed to include a number of phrases not essential to the plot. The memory was much better for the essential than for the unessential parts. To explain the learning and remembering of meaningful materials Newman concludes that it is necessary to consider the *nature* of the contextual relations. Equivalence, inclusion, superordination, subordination, centeredness, symmetry, etc., can be distinguished. Not all intraverbal connections have the same functional roles, and so long as these qualitative aspects are ignored it is difficult to understand why one part of a meaningful passage is remembered and another forgotten. Postman and Senders (1946) have demonstrated that the subject's set is a powerful determiner of which bits of information are remembered, and that a variety of sets can be used to produce a variety of selections of information.

The selectivity of human learning should not come as a surprise, however. The whole development of our present concept of context and information hinges on this matter of selectivity. A sequence of symbols carries information because it is one selected from a set of possible sequences. In order to represent any particular situation we must figuratively search through this set of possible sequences until we find the particular sequence that does the job. The searching is guided by the motivation, the situation, and the audience. It is natural that this searching and selecting process should continue to operate during the recall of learned materials.

Readability

How much can a person learn from a paragraph by reading it once? Obviously the answer depends upon what paragraph he reads, for some paragraphs are simple and direct whereas others would tax the wisdom of Solomon. Some symbol patterns present information to the nervous system in a usable form, and others do not.

Difficulty is a dimension of verbal behavior that has received considerable attention. The approach has been to establish relations between the statistical structure of the verbal material and some measure of the reader's success in remembering the contents. The usual procedure is to establish the readability of a passage by the scores on a comprehension test. Various characteristics of the material are then determined, and the results are analyzed in a multiple correlation study.

Gray and Leary (1935) settled on five variables for their predictions: the number of different words, the percentage of uncommon words, the number of personal pronouns, the number of prepositional phrases, and the average sentence length. The multiple correlation of these variables and the criterion was 0.644. Lorge (1944) obtained a multiple correlation coefficient of 0.767 using only three variables: the average sentence length, the number of prepositional phrases, and the number of uncommon words. Flesch (1943, 1946) based his estimate of readability on the average sentence length, the number of affixes (prefixes and suffixes), and the number of personal references. In a later study Flesch (1948) proposed to base "reading ease" on average sentence length and number of syllables per 100 words, and to assess "human interest" separately by an index based on the number of personal words and personal sentences.

These several investigations agree in pointing to two basic variables, and perhaps a third can be added. (1) Long sentences are more difficult than short sentences. (2) Short, familiar words are easier than long, unfamiliar words. (3) Personal references make reading easier because readers are apt to be interested in people. In the first two variables, which all agree are important, we recognize the problems of length of pattern and range of alternatives. Actually the importance of restricting the range of alternatives has been deprecated by Flesch. He feels that the real difficulty with uncommon words is that they are likely to have affixes and so look like one thing while they say something else.

TALKING AND THINKING

The importance of verbalization in thinking is an unsettled issue in psychology. Opinions range from Watson's, who said that thought is implicit movement of the speech musculature, to Wertheimer's, who wrote his penetrating analysis of productive thinking with scarcely a reference to its verbal aspects. Certainly there are individual differences among people in their use of words, images, analogies, etc., for solving problems. The most we can say is that many people converse with themselves, and if they are interrupted they will say they are thinking. These monologues may not constitute all that we want to call thinking, but they are common enough to merit attention.

Determining Tendencies

In the associationistic framework of the early experimental psychology, thought seemed to be the succession of ideas that passed through consciousness. Introspective examination of the process upset this simple view, however, for it became apparent that subjects could arrive at a correct response without any conscious content to report, without any notion of where the response came from. Out of these observations, which the Würzburg School initiated, grew the long, lively, and fruitless controversy over imageless thought (see Titchener, Woodworth). The positive contribution of the work came via the concept of the set and the determining tendency. According to the Würzburg formulation, the *task* gives the subject a particular *set*, and his set influences his associative sequence by means of unconscious *determining tendencies* that guide the process through to its proper completion.

Watt's (1905) experiments can be used to illustrate the sort of observations that supported the Würzburg formulation. Watt used a variation of the word-association test in which the subjects are told to respond with a word that stands in a certain relation to the stimulus word. If the relation is that of subordination, the stimulus word "animal" might lead to the response "dog." Watt had his subjects pay attention to and report on a small segment of the total process, either the preparatory period, the appearance of the stimulus word, the search for the reaction word, or the occurrence of the reaction word. The surprising result was that little conscious content could be reported during the period of search — the word usually came without hesitation. The experiments were later repeated and amplified by May (1917) with similar results. It was natural to conclude that the preparation during the foreperiod represented the critical part of the thought process. Hence the emphasis on the task and the set.

A process of constrained association, or something very like it, must go on in the extemporaneous patching together of words in ordinary speech. The specific words are seldom chosen before the talker begins, yet they usually occur as they are needed without much conscious searching. The task is to verbalize, the topic provides a set for the talker, and the set determines which response tendencies are weakened and which are strengthened as the verbalization proceeds. In the preceding sections of this chapter the changing response tendencies were described as an array of probabilities that shifted as a function of the preceding responses. Watt's experiment must reflect a similar array of probabilities — the subject's set is the same as though he had spoken all of a sentence but the last two words. The occurrence of the reaction word should be almost as natural and automatic as the occurrence of a word in a sentence. The determining tendency is made of the same sort of stuff as the transitional probabilities in human speech (cf. Selz).

Syllogistic Reasoning

Since the simple word-association experiment does not produce thoughts for the scientist to study, more complicated tasks are needed. Störring (1908) met the need by introducing the syllogism. He showed his subject the two premises from which a conclusion was to be drawn. The subject read these carefully and gave an introspective account of how he reached the conclusion. For example, the subject would be given

> All i belong to
> the class o. All z
> belong to the class i.
> Therefore . . .

The subject read the premises, and then introspected, "What are you doing with the second statement? You have to relate it to the first premise. How do you do that? Where was i mentioned in the first premise?" He then found the phrase "all i," and so went on to see that the z belong to the i, and therefore z is to be put in place of i. All this went on without any particular reference to the class o.

With syllogistic problems Störring was able to collect extensive protocols. Sometimes the subject visualized the solution; sometimes the conclusion was reached by purely verbal means. The results do not seem to lead to any generalizations about how people think or where successful hypotheses come from, but they show that the laws of logic are not the laws of thought. The syllogism is a reconstruction of a devious psychological process.

The verbal context has a marked effect upon the syllogizing reasoner, and some conclusions are drawn because the answer 'sounds all right.' For example, one of the premises can be given and the subject asked to continue. What can you say about B if you know that all A are B? Such questions tend to be completed as follows (Wilkins, 1928; Eidens, 1929):

(a) If all A are B, then all B are A.
(b) If no A are B, then no B are A.
(c) If some A are B, then some B are A.
(d) If some A are not B, then some B are not A.

The subjects convert the statements into like statements, and for the letters A and B the conversions sound plausible. But, if words are properly substituted, the habitual verbal associations make the false conversions sound ludicrous. The person who accepts (a) would never accept "If all dogs are animals, then all animals are dogs." Nor would the person who accepts (d) find it natural to say, "If some dogs are not collies, then some collies are not dogs." The statements rephrased with words are not structurally different — the subject recognizes the conclusion as acceptable or unacceptable, regardless of the logical form. Reverse the substitution, "If some collies are not dogs, then some dogs are not collies," and the conversion is apt to be accepted.

The experiments on syllogistic reasoning are full of demonstrations that the particular choice of words used to frame the question has an important effect upon the verbal reply. Perhaps the best illustration of the way verbal habits lead us astray is to be found in what Woodworth and Sells (1935) have called "the atmosphere effect." To exemplify this notion they point to careless constructions like "The laboratory equipment in these situations were in many instances . . . ," where the plural *were* appears

incorrectly because of the atmosphere of plurality created by the two words immediately preceding. Atmosphere effect is another name for intraverbal connections, determining tendencies, or the dependent probabilities of occurrence of verbal units. More specifically, Woodworth and Sells argue that the words "all," "no," and "some" in the premises of a syllogism give a verbal atmosphere that calls for a corresponding conclusion. Sells' (1936) experimental data confirmed this conclusion, and he was able to show that the effect was slightly more pronounced with his bright subjects than with his dull ones. Almost anyone can be trapped into this kind of error. For instance, *POLK* is pronounced *poke*, the *l* is silent, and *FOLK* is pronounced *foke*, also with a silent *l*, and the white of an egg is pronounced . . . ? It is a rare subject that responds "albumen."

In these examples verbal habits operate as a substitute for thought. Habits that function faithfully for the illogical events of daily life are tricked and betrayed by a syllogism. In the realm of logic the most improbable sequences of words are acceptable: "If two is smaller than three, then snow is white." Most nonlogicians regard this sentence as a strange use of "if-then." The fact is that logic is a formal system, just as arithmetic is a formal system, and to expect untrained subjects to think logically is much the same as to expect preschool children to know the multiplication table.

Configurational Theories of Thinking

Modern thought about thinking has developed far beyond the word association and the syllogism. More complex materials have been used, and more complicated interpretations have been proposed. The fullest accounts of thinking seem to be those of Duncker (1935) and of Wertheimer (1945). These men speak of the pattern in which the component parts of the problem are arranged, the reorganizing principles or directions imposed upon the components, and the eventual restructuring of the components in a form that coincides with the form of the desired solution.

In order to understand the configurational interpretation of thinking we need an example. This we will borrow from Wertheimer who, in the course of determining the area of a parallelogram, manages to introduce most of the puzzles that a theory of thinking must contend with. What, he asks, is the best way to teach school children to determine the area of a parallelogram?

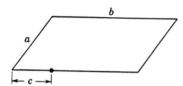

FIG. 5. Wertheimer's parallelogram problem.

One way, an ugly but quite correct way, is to express the area according to the formula $b\sqrt{(a-c)(a+c)}$. The terms a, b, and c are identified as in Fig. 5, and the solution is presented in a series of steps: (1) subtract c from a, (2) add a and c, (3) multiply the sum and difference, (4) take the square root of the product, (5) multiply the root by b. Children can memorize these five steps. They can generalize them to other parallelograms of different dimensions. They get the correct answers. And yet, Wertheimer protests, the method is ugly and the teaching is terrible.

What is wrong with this method of teaching? The principal trouble is that the students are given no opportunity to grasp the inner structure of the situation. They do not understand what they are doing. If you ask them, "Can you show that the answer obtained in this way is really right?" they have no way to answer.

If the area of the parallelogram is given as a problem to children who have just learned to find the area of a rectangle, some do not respond, some try to remember, some start making speeches, some begin to think. For those who think, the trouble with the

parallelogram soon focuses on the two lopsided ends. Resolution comes when they see that one end needs just what is too much at the other end. If one end is cut off and fitted into the other end, the parallelogram becomes a familiar rectangle. The problem is solved.

The example draws a sharp contrast between "blind connections" and a "structural grasp." If thinking were nothing more than behaving in accordance with habits or conditioned responses, there would be little choice between these two methods of teaching. Associative bonds are associative bonds, and one is as good as another. In the simplest form of association theory there is nothing to say that one set of bonds is easier or better to learn than another set of bonds. A configurational view, on the other hand, recognizes trouble regions that must be manipulated and transposed according to the structural requirements of the solution.

We note that the problem is itself a visual problem. Does the visual nature of the task account for such terms as "structure," "form," "see the answer," etc.? For a nonvisual example we can use Duncker's problem, "Why are all numbers of the form $abcabc$ divisible by 13?" In this example the subject who cannot get past the visual symmetry of $abcabc$ may waste considerable time before he abandons this fact and searches for a new structural property. This new property emerges when the thinker encounters the number 1001, for then he sees $abcabc$ as abc thousands plus abc units. Duncker tried various aids during the process of solution — these aids, along with the percentages of subjects who solved the problem in each case, are as follows:

1. (59%) The numbers are divisible by 1001.
2. (50%) 1001 is divisible by 13.
3. (15%) If a common divisor of numbers is divisible by 13, then they are all divisible by 13.

4. (14%) If a divisor of a number is divisible by p, then the number is itself divisible by p.

5. (0%) Different numbers can have in common a divisor which is in turn divisible.

6. (15%) Look for a more fundamental common character from which the divisibility by 13 becomes evident.

7. (8%) No aid.

Aids 1 and 2 which involve a specific mention of the number 1001 are the most effective, and the other aids are of no aid at all. Duncker found that it was helpful to give 1001 even in a disguised form, for if the numbers he used to state the problem were 276,276 and 277,277, the solution was easier than if the numbers were 276,276 and 591,-591. Duncker's interpretation of this and other examples is that the material given is restructured according to the demands of the situation.

The subjects in these examples have several advantages over thinkers outside the laboratory. They are assured that they have all the relevant information and that there is a configuration of this information that fits the requirements. The practical case is less well defined. We encounter a situation for which we have no appropriate response. We try those habit patterns that are easily available, but if none of them works we begin to realize that we face a problem. The redundancy of our verbal habits constrains us to familiar and perhaps unsuccessful formulations of the problem — our language forces our thought in certain directions. We struggle to reformulate the problem and to obtain the necessary information. But even then we cannot be sure that there is an answer or that the problem will not need to be reformulated. Structural aspects may guide the process, but it is not always so clean and pretty as when the experimenter underwrites the happy ending.

Verbal material has configurational properties of two sorts, and these properties influence the transformations that the thinker will apply. There is, first, the contextual, or syntactic, pattern discussed in this chapter. The answer must come out in a sequence of words that sounds probable against the background of our intraverbal associations. Transformations of the problem materials that lead to improbable sequences of words are distrusted and are often discarded as opposed to common sense. Mathematicians and logicians have found that common sense is a poor guide, for if common sense must verify each step in a solution it is very difficult to arrive at any new conclusion unexpected by common sense. To avoid the traps that implicit linguistic habits can lead us into, scientists make up new languages that have explicitly defined symbols and relations among symbols.

The second configurational property that guides the thinker's transformations depends upon the semantic rules that relate the words or sentences to things or events. The full meaning of the problem extends beyond the contextual pattern of the words that state the problem, and transformations that are not permissible for the referents are usually not permissible for the symbols. Much of our thinking is directed toward this second kind of transformation, which is governed by essentially nonverbal restrictions.

Some of the confusion in the psychology of thinking arises because these two aspects are not distinguished. The experiments of Watt and of Sells reveal intraverbal influences upon the way the thinker restructures verbal material. Duncker and Wertheimer were interested in referential restrictions upon the restructuring transformations.

The difference between these two kinds of restrictions can be illustrated by Huxley's famous group of six monkeys that typed at random for millions and millions of years and eventually produced all the books in the British Museum. If these animals operated according to the transitional probabilities of normal verbal behavior, they could reduce the time required by several million years. If you could wait, the monkeys would eventually produce the answer to almost any verbal question you could pose. The problem is how the monkeys would know when they had produced an answer. The recognition of a solution depends upon factors other than purely contextual intraverbal habits, and it is the determination of these factors that an adequate theory of thinking must accomplish.

REFERENCES

Allport, F. H. Social psychology. Boston: Houghton Mifflin, 1924.

Cofer, C. N., and J. P. Foley. Mediated generalization and the interpretation of verbal behavior: I. Prolegomena. Psychol. Rev., 1942, 49, 513–540.

Condon, E. V. Statistics of vocabulary. Science, 1928, 67, 300.

Dewey, G. Relative frequency of English speech sounds. Cambridge: Harvard University Press, 1923.

Diven, K. Certain determinants in the conditioning of anxiety reactions. J. Psychol., 1937, 3, 291–308.

Duncker, K. Zur Psychologie des produktiven Denkens. Berlin: Springer, 1935. Translated by Lynne S. Lees and published in Psychol. Monogr., 1945, 58, No. 5.

Eidens, H. Experimentelle Untersuchungen über den Denkverlauf bei unmittelbaren Folgerungen. Arch. ges. Psychol., 1929, 71, 1–66.

Eldridge, R. C. Six thousand common English words. Buffalo: Clement Press, 1911.

Esper, E. A. A technique for the experimental investigation of associative interference in artificial linguistic material. Language Monogr., 1925, 1, 1–47.

Fisher, R. A. Statistical methods for research workers. (10th Ed.) Edinburgh: Oliver and Boyd, 1946.

Flesch, R. Estimating the comprehension difficulty of magazine articles. J. gen. Psychol., 1943, 28, 63–80.

Flesch, R. The art of plain talk. New York: Harper, 1946.

Flesch, R. A new readability yardstick. J. appl. Psychol., 1948, 32, 221–233.

Fletcher, H. Speech and hearing. New York: Van Nostrand, 1929.

Foley, J. P., and Z. L. Macmillan. Mediated generalization and the interpretation of verbal behavior: V. 'Free association' as related to differences in professional training. J. exp. Psychol., 1943, 33, 299–310.

Fossler, H. R. Disturbances in breathing during stuttering. Psychol. Monogr., 1930, 4, No. 1.

French, N. R., C. W. Carter, and W. Koenig. The words and sounds of telephone conversations. Bell Syst. tech. J., 1930, 9, 290–324.

Gray, W. S., and B. E. Leary. What makes a book readable. Chicago: Chicago University Press, 1935.

Hanley, M. L. Word index to James Joyce's Ulysses. Madison, Wis., 1937.

Head, H. Aphasia and kindred disorders of speech. New York: Macmillan, 1926. Volumes I and II.

Hudgins, C. V., and F. C. Numbers. An investigation of the intelligibility of the speech of the deaf. Genet. Psychol. Monogr., 1942, 25, 289–392.

Hudgins, C. V., and R. H. Stetson. Relative speed of articulatory movements. Arch. néerl. Phon. exp., 1937, 13, 85–94.

Irwin, O. C. Infant speech: Consonantal sounds according to place of articulation. J. Speech Disorders, 1947a, 12, 397–401; Infant speech: Consonantal sounds according to manner of articulation. Ibid., 1947b, 12, 402–404.

Irwin, O. C. Infant speech: Development of vowel sounds. J. Speech & Hearing Disorders, 1948, 13, 31–34.

Johnson, W. People in quandaries. New York: Harper, 1946.

Jones, D. An outline of English phonetics. (6th Ed.) Leipzig: B. G. Teubner, 1939.

Joos, M. Acoustic phonetics. Language, Suppl., 1948, 24, 1–136.

Jung, C. G. Studies in word-association. London: William Heinemann, 1918.

Kaiser, L. Some properties of speech muscles and the influence thereof on language. Arch. néerl. Phon. exp., 1934, 10, 121–133.

Katzenstein, J. Methoden zur Erforschung der Tätigkeit des Kehlkopfes sowie der Stimme und Sprache. In E. Abderhalden (Ed.), Handb. d. biol. Arbeitsmethoden. Berlin: Urban and Schwarzenberg, 1930. Abt. 5, Teil 7, pp. 261–418.

Kent, G. H., and A. J. Rosanoff. A study of association in insanity. Amer. J. Insanity, 1910, 67, 37–96.

Kenyon, J. S. American pronunciation: A textbook of phonetics for students of English. Ann Arbor, Mich.: George Wahr, 1932.

Lightoller, G. H. S. Facial muscles. J. Anat., 1925, 60, 1–85.

Lorge, I. Predicting readability. Teach. Coll. Rec., 1944, 45, 404–419.

May, M. A. The mechanism of controlled association. Arch. Psychol., N. Y., 1917, 5, No. 39.

McCarthy, Dorothea. Language development in children. In L. Carmichael (Ed.), Manual of child psychology. New York: Wiley, 1946. Pp. 476–581.

Morris, C. W. Foundations of the theory of signs. In O. Neurath (Ed.), International encyclopedia of unified science. Chicago: University of Chicago Press, 1938. Volume 1, No. 2.

Morris, C. W. *Signs, language and behavior.* New York: Prentice-Hall, 1946.

Negus, V. E. *The mechanism of the larynx.* St. Louis: Mosby, 1929.

Newman, E. B. Forgetting of meaningful material during sleep and waking. *Amer. J. Psychol.*, 1939, **52**, 65–71.

Paget, R. A. *Human speech.* New York: Harcourt, Brace, 1930.

Postman, L., and V. L. Senders. Incidental learning and generality of set. *J. exp. Psychol.*, 1946, **36**, 153–165.

Potter, R. K., G. A. Kopp, and H. C. Green. *Visible speech.* New York: Van Nostrand, 1947.

Razran, G. H. S. Salivating, and thinking in different languages. *J. Psychol.*, 1935, **1**, 145–151.

Razran, G. H. S. A quantitative study of meaning by a conditioned salivary technique (semantic conditioning). *Science*, 1939, **90**, 89–90.

Riess, B. F. Semantic conditioning involving the galvanic skin reflex. *J. exp. Psychol.*, 1940, **26**, 238–240.

Riess, B. F. Genetic changes in semantic conditioning. *J. exp. Psychol.*, 1946, **36**, 143–152.

Russell, G. O. *Speech and voice.* New York: Macmillan, 1931.

Scripture, E. W. *The elements of experimental phonetics.* New York: Scribner, 1902.

Seashore, R. H., and L. D. Eckerson. The measurement of individual differences in general English vocabularies. *J. educ. Psychol.*, 1940, **31**, 14–38.

Sells, S. B. The atmosphere effect. *Arch. Psychol.*, *N. Y.*, 1936, **29**, No. 200.

Selz, O. *Zur Psychologie des produktiven Denkens und des Irrtums.* Bonn: Cohen, 1922.

Shannon, C. E. A mathematical theory of communication. *Bell Syst. tech. J.*, 1948, **27**, 379–423, 623–656.

Skinner, B. F. Has Gertrude Stein a secret? *Atlant. Mo.*, January 1934, **153**, 50–57.

Skinner, B. F. The verbal summator and a method for the study of latent speech. *J. Psychol.*, 1936, **2**, 71–107.

Skinner, B. F. The distribution of associated words. *Psychol. Rec.*, 1937, **1**, 71–76.

Skinner, B. F. *Verbal behavior.* William James Lectures, Harvard University, 1947. (To be published by the Harvard University Press.)

Solomons, L. M., and G. Stein. Normal motor automatism. *Psychol. Rev.*, 1896, **3**, 492–512.

Stetson, R. H. Motor phonetics. *Arch. néerl. Phon. exp.*, 1928, **3**, 1–216.

Stetson, R. H., and C. V. Hudgins. Functions of the breathing movements in the mechanism of speech. *Arch. néerl. Phon. exp.*, 1930, **5**, 1–30.

Störring, G. Experimentelle Untersuchungen über einfache Schlussprozesse. *Arch. ges. Psychol.*, 1908, **11**, 1–127.

Thorndike, E. L., and I. Lorge. *The teacher's word book of 30,000 words.* New York: Bureau of Publications. Teacher's College, Columbia University, 1944.

Titchener, E. B. *Lectures on the experimental psychology of the thought-processes.* New York: Macmillan, 1909.

Voelker, C. H. Technique for a phonetic frequency distribution count in formal American speech. *Arch. néerl. Phon. exp.*, 1935, **11**, 69–72.

Watson, J. B. *Psychology from the standpoint of a behaviorist.* (2nd Ed.) Philadelphia: Lippincott, 1924.

Watt, H. J. Experimentelle Beiträge zu einer Theorie des Denkens. *Arch. ges. Psychol.*, 1905, **4**, 289–436.

Weisenberg, T., and K. E. McBride. *Aphasia.* New York: The Commonwealth Fund, 1935.

Weiss, A. P. *A theoretical basis of human behavior.* Columbus, Ohio: R. G. Adams, 1929.

Wertheimer, M. *Productive thinking.* New York: Harper, 1945.

West, R., L. Kennedy, and A. Carr. *The rehabilitation of speech.* (2nd Ed.) New York: Harper, 1947.

Wiener, N. *Cybernetics.* New York: Wiley, 1948.

Wilkins, M. C. The effect of changed material on the ability to do formal syllogistic reasoning. *Arch. Psychol.*, *N. Y.*, 1928, **16**, No. 102.

Wolfle, D. L. The relation between linguistic structure and associative interference in artificial linguistic material. *Language Monogr.*, 1932, **11**, 1–55.

Woodworth, R. S. *Experimental psychology.* New York: Holt, 1938.

Woodworth, R. S., and S. B. Sells. An atmospheric effect in formal syllogistic reasoning. *J. exp. Psychol.*, 1935, **18**, 451–460.

Zipf, G. K. *The psycho-biology of language.* Boston: Houghton Mifflin, 1935.

Zipf, G. K. The repetition of words, time-perspective, and semantic balance. *J. gen. Psychol.*, 1945, **32**, 127–148.

Zipf, G. K. *Human behavior and the principle of least effort.* Cambridge, Mass.: Addison-Wesley, **1949.**

22

Basic Correlates of the
Visual Stimulus

DEANE B. JUDD
National Bureau of Standards

The adequate stimulus to a visual perception is a spatial and temporal pattern of radiant energy impinging on the retina. In order to be effective as a stimulus, an ele-

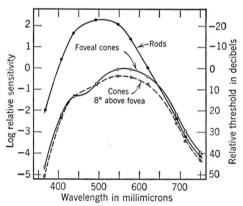

FIG. 1. Reciprocal thresholds in log units (left-hand scale) and thresholds in decibels (right-hand scale) for dark-adapted foveal cones, peripheral rods, and peripheral cones, according to Wald (1945). All thresholds are relative to the minimum for the fovea near wavelength 555 mμ. Note that the thresholds for all types of receptors are but little different for wavelengths greater than 650 mμ.

ment of this pattern must bring to the receptors (rods and cones) a certain minimal energy. The minimal energy effective in half the presentations is called the absolute threshold. Its value depends upon the spectral composition of the energy. Figure 1 shows how the absolute threshold for nar-

row bands in the spectrum depends upon wavelength (Wald, 1945). Further work (Griffin, Hubbard, and Wald, 1947) has extended these curves to the vicinity of 1000 millimicrons (mμ), far into the infrared, where the threshold energy is approximately a million times (60 decibels) greater than it is at 750 mμ. It is similarly true that the retina responds to energy of wavelength near 320 mμ, far into the ultraviolet. This has been shown (Goodeve, 1934) by tests on eyes from which the crystalline lens had been taken out. The visible spectrum thus extends over a range greater than 320 to 1000 mμ and includes much of the ultraviolet and infrared. The extreme limit depends on how much eye injury due to overheating and overexposure to actinic rays the subject is willing to tolerate.

Radiometric Terms

The absolute threshold depends upon the temporal and spatial character of the stimulus. This character of radiant energy requires for its description various radiometric terms.

For extremely brief presentations (less than 0.01 second) and point sources (subtending less than about 10 minutes of arc) the total amount of radiant energy is the important stimulus variable. It does not matter how the energy is distributed in time throughout the 0.01-second interval; it may

TABLE 1

VARIABLES, SYMBOLS, AND UNITS FOR THE VISUAL STIMULUS IN TERMS OF RADIANT ENERGY

Experimental Condition	Stimulus Variable Applying to Retina	Symbol	Unit	
			cgs	mks
Point-source flash	Radiant energy	U	erg	joule
Extended-source flash	Areal density of radiant energy	U/A	erg/cm^2	$joule/m^2$
Steady presentation of point source	Radiant flux	P	erg/sec	watt
Steady presentation of extended source	Irradiance	H	$erg/sec \times cm^2$	$watt/m^2$
External element	Stimulus variable applying to an external element			
Point source	Radiant intensity	J	$erg/sec \times \omega$ *	$watt/\omega$
Extended source	Radiance	N	$erg/sec \times \omega \times cm^2$	$watt/\omega \times m^2$
Transmitting element	Spectral transmittance	T_λ		
Reflecting element	Spectral reflectance	R_λ		

* The symbol ω refers to solid angle.

all occur in the first 0.001 second, or it may be uniformly distributed over the whole 0.01 second. The same amount of radiant energy is required for a threshold stimulus. The most sensitive part of the retina is not, however, the center (cones only) but rather the zone between 20 and 30 degrees away from the center (rods and cones). Measurements by Hecht, Shlaer, and Pirenne (1942) indicate that the absolute energy threshold is about 3×10^{-10} erg.

If the size of the field is increased up to 1 degree, the absolute threshold is still found not to depend on how the energy is distributed in time, up to 0.01 second (law of Bloch or Bunsen-Roscoe). In this case the important stimulus variable is the areal density of the radiant energy (ergs per square millimeter) incident on the retina (Graham, Brown, and Mote, 1939; Tschermak, 1929).

For steady stimulation of small parts of the retina (less than 10 minutes of arc), the absolute threshold depends almost wholly (law of Ricco) on the time rate of incidence of radiant energy (ergs per second). It scarcely matters how the areal density of radiant energy varies within the spot subtending 10 minutes of arc (Graham, Brown, and Mote, 1939; Tschermak, 1929).

But for presentations longer than about 1 second, and for fields subtending more than about 1 degree, the absolute threshold depends upon both the time rate of incidence of the radiant energy and its areal density. Ordinarily, therefore, it is appropriate to express a uniform stimulus in terms of areal density of incident radiant flux,* often called irradiance.

Table 1 summarizes the stimulus variables and the units appropriate to various kinds of stimulation by narrow bands of the spec-

* For definitions of terms, see the Glossary at end of chapter.

trum. The terms, symbols, and units are those adopted by the Optical Society of America (OSA, 1944*a*). The symbols agree with those adopted by the American Standards Association (1943).

It is not possible, of course, to measure these radiant quantities at the retina itself. The approximate retinal pattern has to be computed from the external pattern by taking into account the properties of the lens system of the eye. The exact retinal pattern at any instant is usually unknown because the eye muscles, like other muscles, exert a fluctuating tension. On this account the focus of the lens and the direction of its axis are always changing. It is often, therefore, more useful to correlate visual responses with measurements of the external stimulus.

The stimulating properties of a point source may be expressed in terms of its radiant intensity in the direction of the pupil. Those of an extended source may be expressed in terms of the areal density of point sources of unit radiant intensity to which the extended source is equivalent. This areal density is known as radiance. For either the point source or the extended source the density of the radiant flux incident on the cornea of the observer's eye, known as irradiance, is a useful quantity for correlation with the visual response.

Since the absolute threshold, and indeed all response variables, depend upon the spectral composition of the radiant energy reaching the retina, the foregoing quantities must be given for each wavelength throughout the visible spectrum. When the wavelength has been specified, the quantities are called spectral radiant flux, spectral radiance, spectral irradiance, and so on. The effect of an external transmitting (or reflecting) element may be expressed in terms of its spectral transmittance (or spectral reflectance), that is to say, the ratio of energy transmitted (or reflected) to the energy incident. If the spectral distribution of radiant energy incident on a clear element, such as a goggle lens, is known, we can compute from its spectral transmittances how the energy leaving the lens will be distributed according to wavelength. Spectral reflectance serves the same purpose for a mirror or a diffuse reflector such as a painted surface. Table 1 summarizes these quantities also.

TABLE 2

SPECTRAL TRANSMITTANCE OF OCULAR MEDIA

Wave-length, mμ	Spectral Transmittance of Cornea, Lens, and Aqueous and Vitreous Humors, (Ludvigh-McCarthy)	Spectral Internal Transmittance of Macula Lutea (Wald)	Spectral Transmittance of Ocular Media Including the Macula Lutea
360	0.052 *	0.859	0.045
370	0.056 *	0.826	0.046
380	0.062 *	0.762	0.047
390	0.069 *	0.695	0.048
400	0.086	0.577	0.050
410	0.106	0.506	0.054
420	0.160	0.396	0.063
430	0.248	0.316	0.078
440	0.318	0.305	0.097
450	0.388	0.212	0.082
460	0.426	0.206	0.088
470	0.438	0.299	0.131
480	0.458	0.250	0.115
490	0.481	0.263	0.126
500	0.495	0.516	0.256
510	0.510	0.798	0.407
520	0.525	0.935	0.491
530	0.543	0.968	0.526
540	0.559	0.977	0.546
550	0.566	0.985	0.557
560	0.572	0.989	0.566
570	0.583	0.989	0.577
580	0.594	0.989	0.587
590	0.602	0.989	0.595
600	0.610	1.000	0.603
610	0.619	1.000	0.619
620	0.631	1.000	0.631
630	0.641	1.000	0.641
640	0.649	1.000	0.649
650	0.657	1.000	0.657
660	0.664	1.000	0.664
670	0.676	1.000	0.676
680	0.690	1.000	0.690
690	0.698	1.000	0.698
700	0.705	1.000	0.705
710	0.707	1.000	0.707
720	0.708	1.000	0.708
730	0.710	1.000	0.710
740	0.711	1.000	0.711
750	0.713	1.000	0.713

* Extrapolated.

The effects of the ocular media may be expressed in terms of their spectral transmittance. Table 2 gives the spectral transmittance of these media (Ludvigh and McCarthy, 1938; Wald, 1945).

Photometric Terms

When the stimulus consists of a single part of the spectrum, it may be adequately specified in terms of radiant energy alone. But, if the stimulus consists of two or more parts of the spectrum impinging on the same retinal area, it does no good to add together the radiant energies of the components. It is true that the simple sum gives the radiant energy of the composite stimulus, but the rods and cones respond differently to the different parts of the spectrum, as is indicated by the absolute thresholds. Consequently, in order to obtain a useful measure of a composite visual stimulus, immediate account must be taken of the spectral sensitivity of the receptors. These spectral sensitivities are the reciprocals of the radiant quantities required to produce a threshold response (see Fig. 1). They are also known as luminosity (formerly, visibility) functions. A measure of the effective stimulus is obtained, therefore, by the use of luminous or photometric quantities rather than by the use of the radiant quantities themselves.

Table 3 lists these quantities together with the symbols and units by which they are expressed. It also shows diagrams of the geometrical ideas involved. Note that irradiance and illuminance both refer to the areal density of flux incident on a surface. No restriction on the direction of this flux is implied except that it must all fall on one side of the object. Intensity (both radiant and luminous) refers only to sources so small, compared to the distance of the receiver, that they can be considered as points. Since intensity is flux per unit solid angle, it may depend on the direction of view. Although we may think of the ideal uniform point source, all actual sources vary importantly in intensity, depending on the direction of

view. Radiance refers to extended sources, as does also, of course, its photometric analogue, luminance. The extended source is specified by the number of point sources of unit intensity required per unit area to give the equivalent irradiance or illuminance, as the case may be. The area taken, however, is not necessarily the actual area of the extended source but is always the projection of that area onto a plane perpendicular to the line of sight. Radiance and luminance vary with the direction of view. Many primary sources (furnaces, incandescent filaments, fluorescent tubes, gaseous discharge tubes) and many secondary sources (blotting paper, magnesium oxide) are almost perfectly diffusing, however. For these sources radiance and luminance vary but little with the angle of view.

From the definitions of these terms it is easy to see how each varies with distance away from the source. The total energy from a point source or an extended source is independent of distance. All that leaves the source eventually gets to the stated distance if the medium is a vacuum or some equivalent. It just takes time, and for ordinary distances not too much time at that, the speed of radiant energy being about 3.0×10^{10} centimeters per second. The areal density of energy, however, varies inversely as the square of the distance of the receiving plane from a point source. But, if the source is uniform and of infinite extent, the areal density of energy, like the energy itself, is independent of distance. The same applies to irradiance and illuminance: for point sources, the inverse-square law; for infinite sources, constant. Total flux, like total energy, is constant regardless of distance from any kind of source. Intensity and radiance (luminance, photometric brightness), being characteristic of sources, do not depend on the distance of the receiver by which they are evaluated. It is easy to see that the intensity of a point source in a given direction does not depend on the distance of the receiving plate. That distance is taken into

TABLE 3

VARIABLES AND UNITS FOR THE VISUAL STIMULUS IN LUMINOUS TERMS

Geometry	Corresponding Radiant Term	Luminous Term	Symbol	Unit, mks
	Radiant energy	Luminous energy	Q	talbot
	Areal density of radiant energy	Areal density of luminous energy	Q/A	talbot/m^2
	Radiant flux	Luminous flux	F	lumen
	Irradiance	Illuminance (illumination)	E	lumen/m^2 (lux)
	Radiant intensity	Luminous intensity	I	lumen/ω (candle)
	Radiance	Luminance (photometric brightness)	B	lumen/$\omega \times$ m^2 (candle/m^2)
	Radiant transmittance	Luminous transmittance		
	Radiant reflectance	Luminous reflectance		

account in evaluating intensity. But students often find it hard to understand why the luminance of an extended source should not increase as the observing distance is reduced. As the aperture of a photometer is moved closer to a uniform extended source, it is true that the flux entering the aperture from each element of the source directly in front of the aperture increases according to the inverse square law. But it is also true that elements of the source seen near the edge of the aperture progressively disappear across the edge of the aperture and contribute nothing. For a uniform extended source these two effects exactly cancel.

A common way to evaluate the luminance of an extended source is to measure the illuminance produced by it at a considerable

TABLE 4

CONVERSION FACTORS FOR PHOTOMETRIC UNITS (TAKEN CHIEFLY FROM Z7.1-1942, AMERICAN STANDARDS ASSOCIATION, 1942)

The total flux from a uniform point source of 1 candle is 4π lumens. The illuminance at a distance of 1 foot is 1 foot-candle.

Units of Illuminance (Illumination) in Terms of Foot-candles

Unit	Number of Foot-Candles	Decibels re 1 Foot-Candle
Lumen/m² (lux)	0.0929	−10.32
Lumen/cm² (phot)	929	29.68
Milliphot	0.929	−0.32
Lumen/ft² (foot-candle)	1	0.00

Units of Luminance (Photometric Brightness) in Terms of Millilamberts

Unit	Number of Milli-lamberts	Decibels re 1 Milli-lambert
Candle/m²	0.3142	−5.03
Candle/cm² (stilb)	3142	34.97
Apostilb		
International units	0.1	−10.00
Hefner units	0.09	−10.46
Candle/ft²	3.380	5.29
Candle/in²	487	26.88
Foot-lambert (equivalent foot-candle)	1.076	0.32
Lambert	1000	30.00
Millilambert	1	0.00
Microlambert	0.001	−30.00

distance away so that it may be considered as a point source. A distance ten to fifteen times the largest dimension of the source is usually considered adequate. The intensity of the extended source in candles is thus found by the inverse-square law, and the luminance is expressed as the number of candles per unit projected area of the source. This practice has given rise to many different units of luminance and illuminance. Table 4 gives conversion factors by means of which a measurement in terms of one photometric unit may be converted to any of the others. These factors are taken from ASA Z7.1-1942 (American Standards Association, 1942).

A point source of luminous intensity I supplies an illuminance E at a distance D by the inverse-square law:

$$E \text{ (foot-candles)} = \frac{I \text{ (candles)}}{D^2 \text{ (square feet)}} \quad (1)$$

provided the observing conditions are such that they yield cone vision. The luminance B of a perfectly diffusing surface illuminated by E foot-candles is obtained directly in foot-lamberts (equivalent foot-candles) by multiplying by the luminous reflectance R of the surface; thus,

$$B \text{ (foot-lamberts)} = RE \text{ (foot-candles)} \quad (2)$$

As was noted above, this luminance B is independent of the distance from which the observer views the surface, and if it were an ideal perfectly diffusing surface the luminance would also be independent of the direction of view. The luminance of an actual surface in foot-lamberts is numerically equal to the product of its luminous directional reflectance R_θ by its illuminance in foot-candles, thus:

$$B \text{ (foot-lamberts)} = R_\theta E \text{ (foot-candles)} \quad (2a)$$

This luminance, of course, is also independent of the distance between the surface and the observer, but it depends upon the angle, θ, between the perpendicular to the surface and the line of sight. For nearly perfect diffusers, R_θ is nearly constant and less than 1; for any surface that forms mirror images, R_θ rises to indefinitely large values for the direction of mirror reflection as the angular spread of the illuminating beam approaches zero (OSA, 1944a).

When the lens forms a sharp image on the retina, each external element perpendicular to the line of sight is duplicated by a retinal area of the same angular extent. For every surface of luminance B in the visual field of the observer, there corresponds a retinal area illuminated to a retinal illuminance E. This illuminance depends upon the apparent diameter d of the pupil and upon the luminous transmittance T of the ocular media (see Table 3), thus (OSA, 1944a):

$$E \text{ (lux)} = Td^2 \text{ (square centimeters)} \times$$

$$B \text{ (millilamberts)}$$

$$= 0.929Td^2 \text{ (square centimeters)} \times$$

$$B \text{ (foot-lamberts)} \qquad (3)$$

Since luminous transmittance T of the ocular media of any living eye has yet to be determined, considerable use has been made of a unit of retinal illuminance originally called the photon but now called the *troland* after its originator (OSA, 1944a). The retinal illuminance E in trolands is computed from the apparent area A of the pupil in square millimeters and the luminance B of the viewed surface expressed in candles per square meter, thus:

$$E \text{ (trolands)} = A \text{ (square millimeters)} \times$$

$$B \text{ (candles per square meter)} \quad (3a)$$

Retinal illuminance in lux is usually estimated from retinal illuminance in trolands by the formula:

$$E\text{(lux)} = 0.004 \; TE\text{(trolands)} \qquad (3b)$$

where T is the internal transmittance of the ocular media (see Table 2). This estimate is based on a schematic eye having the nodal point separated from the retinal image by 15.5 mm.

It has been known for some years, however, that the direction as well as the flux density of the light striking the retina influences the brightness perceived (Stiles, 1933). Light striking the retina on the slant from the edge of the pupil may have as little as 20 per cent of the effectiveness of that from the center of the pupil, which strikes the retina perpendicularly. If the natural pupil is used, it may be important to take this property of the eye (known as the Stiles-Crawford effect) into account. If an artificial pupil is used, precautions should be taken to center it with the natural pupil.

Photometric Scales

The conversion of a stimulus specification from radiant to luminous terms is based upon the additivity "law" of luminance: if a stimulus of luminance B_1 (such as is produced by a spot of light on a screen) is added to a second stimulus of luminance B_2 (such as is produced by a second spotlight shining on the same screen), the luminance B of the combination stimulus is defined as the sum of the luminances of the component stimuli; that is, $B = B_1 + B_2$. This law has frequently been studied because it is the basis of photometry (Dresler, 1937; Kohlrausch, 1935; Urbanek and Ferencz, 1942). It has been found to fail unless the eye is kept throughout the series of comparisons essentially in a fixed state of adaptation. That is to say, the law fails unless there is pure cone vision, pure rod vision, or some constant combination of the two. Some reports indicate that it fails anyhow.

If a spot of red light is adjusted to the same brightness as a spot of yellow light, and a spot of green light is similarly adjusted to match the brightness of a second yellow light, the red and green lights added together are often found to be darker than the sum of the two yellow lights (Dresler, 1937). Since it is impossible for an observer to report with high precision and reproducibility which of two spots of light of widely different chromatic character is the brighter, these failures of the law have not been taken very seriously. The usual explanation

is that the observer mistook the high saturation of the red field, relative to that of the
yellow, for brightness and so obtained a
spuriously high estimate of its luminance in
the first place. The next time the observer
tests the additivity law his observations are
somewhat conditioned by the first experience, and soon he has learned to make photometric settings in accordance with the law.
Thus the additivity law provides a basis for
a convenient photometric technique that correlates excellently, though not perfectly, with
visual experience.

In photometric experiments, cone vision is
usually assured by use of a 2-degree field
centrally fixated and supplying a retinal illuminance of 100 or more trolands. An additional safeguard is to use a surrounding field
nearly as bright as the photometric field.
Rod-vision photometry is carried out by
photometric fields (Teele, 1945) subtending
at least 5 degrees at the observer's eye,
because most observers have a central rod-
free area of about 2 degrees.

If it is desired to convert the radiant flux
(watts) entering the pupil of the eye to
luminous flux (lumens), the additivity law is
applied. The radiant flux is analyzed spectrally so that for each portion $\Delta\lambda$ of the
spectrum the spectral radiant flux $P\lambda$ is
known. Then, by multiplying the spectral
radiant flux by the absolute luminosity $K\lambda$
(lumens per watt) for that wavelength region, we find the spectral distribution of
luminous flux. But, by the additivity law,
the total luminous flux F is equal to the
sum of the parts making up this spectral
distribution, thus:

$$F = \sum_0^\infty P_\lambda K_\lambda \, \Delta\lambda \qquad (4)$$

where $\Delta\lambda$ is a wavelength interval so small
that further reduction fails to alter the sum
significantly. Similar formulas serve to convert specifications in other radiant terms
(radiant intensity, radiance, etc.) into the
corresponding luminous terms (luminous intensity, luminance, etc.). If $E_0{}^\lambda$ is the spectral irradiance of an object, $R_{\theta\lambda}$ its spec-

directional reflectance, and $T_{\theta\lambda}$ its spectral
directional transmittance, then its luminous
directional reflectance and luminous directional transmittance, respectively, may be
computed as:

$$R_\theta = \frac{\sum_0^\infty E_{0\lambda} R_{\theta\lambda} K_\lambda \, \Delta\lambda}{\sum_0^\infty E_{0\lambda} K_\lambda \, \Delta\lambda} \qquad (4a)$$

$$T_\theta = \frac{\sum_0^\infty E_{0\lambda} T_{\theta\lambda} K_\lambda \, \Delta\lambda}{\sum_0^\infty E_{0\lambda} K_\lambda \, \Delta\lambda} \qquad (4b)$$

Table 5 gives the absolute luminosities
characteristic of the average normal eye for
adaptation to fields ranging from 10,000 foot-
lamberts (snow in sunlight) to 0.00001 foot-
lambert (overcast moonless sky) supplied by
Jones (1942) for an emergency war standard.
The data for intermediate levels were obtained by an arbitrary method of interpolation described by Weaver (1949). Although
these intermediate data are subject to revision on the basis of further experimental
study, they have served very satisfactorily
and may be provisionally recommended. The
luminosity function recommended in 1924 by
the International Commission on Illumination (ICI) applies well to the luminance
range from 1 to 10,000 foot-lamberts. For
more dimly illuminated adapting fields the
photometric scale is extended to apply to
combinations of rod and cone vision by the
arbitrary choice of a standard light to which
the inverse-square law by definition shall
apply (see equation 1). The choice is light
of the spectral composition obtained from a
small hole in an inclosure uniformly heated
to a temperature of 2,360 degrees on the
absolute or Kelvin scale. Such a light is said
to have a color temperature of 2,360° K. By
definition, formulas 1, 2, and 3 apply to such
lights regardless of the adaptive state of the
observer, but these formulas apply to lights
of any other spectral composition only for
cone vision (adaptation to 1 foot-lambert or
more).

TABLE 5

ABSOLUTE LUMINOSITIES (LUMENS/WATT) (FROM WEAVER, 1949)

Wave-length mμ	ICI	Logarithm of Adapting Luminance, Foot-Lamberts						
		−0.5	−1.0	−1.5	−2.0	−3.0	−4.0	−5.0
350							0.30	0.39
360						0.37	0.81	1.07
370					0.23	1.04	2.18	2.82
380	0.03	0.03	0.05	0.20	0.68	2.82	5.49	7.06
390	0.08	0.08	0.16	0.59	2.00	7.00	12.8	16.3
400	0.25	0.28	0.51	1.76	5.37	16.4	28.0	34.7
410	0.75	0.89	1.59	4.84	12.8	33.9	55.6	68.1
420	2.50	2.79	4.66	11.9	25.5	64.4	101	122
430	7.25	7.69	11.1	22.8	46.0	113	169	202
440	14.4	15.2	20.3	38.7	77.5	178	266	308
450	23.8	25.0	33.1	63.2	124	264	381	436
460	37.5	39.8	52.3	99.4	184	378	520	585
470	56.9	60.8	79.4	149	274	520	678	741
480	86.9	92.5	121	225	393	673	842	918
490	130	139	185	333	539	818	1001	1083
500	202	216	281	471	678	962	1143	1219
510	314	332	416	598	798	1071	1219	1284
520	444	460	534	698	879	1113	1197	1225
530	539	553	614	759	911	1059	1085	1090
540	596	608	660	781	882	938	914	896
550	622	632	674	758	807	777	716	683
560	622	629	656	701	692	604	515	469
570	595	598	612	610	562	428	346	313
580	544	545	541	506	426	288	224	199
590	473	470	454	398	303	185	138	121
600	394	391	367	292	204	113	82.5	71.9
610	314	311	281	201	129	66.9	47.7	41.7
620	238	232	199	131	76.9	38.3	27.6	24.2
630	166	158	133	79.4	43.7	21.6	15.6	13.5
640	109	103	82.5	46.1	24.6	11.9	8.56	7.38
650	66.9	62.5	47.9	25.5	13.4	6.38	4.55	4.05
660	38.1	35.5	26.3	13.6	7.13	3.45	2.47	2.13
670	20.0	19.2	13.9	7.00	3.73	1.86	1.34	1.16
680	10.6	9.69	6.94	3.59	1.96	0.98	0.69	0.59
690	5.13	4.85	3.51	1.86	1.01	0.49	0.34	0.29
700	2.56	2.43	1.79	0.97	0.52	0.24	0.17	0.14
710	1.31	1.23	0.91	0.48	0.26	0.12		
720	0.66	0.61	0.46	0.24	0.12			
730	0.33	0.30	0.22	0.11				
740	0.16	0.15	0.11					
750	0.08	0.07						
760	0.04							
770	0.02							

In the evaluation of a stimulus in luminous terms by application of equation 4, a method of successive approximation may have to be used. If the stimulus to be evaluated has significantly influenced the adaptive state of the observer, an estimate of which luminosity function in Table 5 is applicable must first

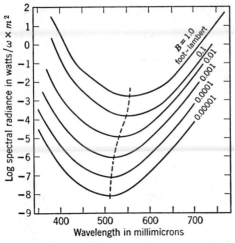

Fig. 2. Contours of equal brightness corresponding to constant values of adapting luminance B. These contours show, for 10-decibel intervals in adapting luminance, the relative values of the radiance, in watts, required to produce equal brightness at different wavelengths (Weaver, 1949). The dotted line passing through the minima of these contours shows how the wavelength of maximum luminous efficiency increases with the luminance to which the observer is adapted (Purkinje effect). The top curve represents the reciprocals of the ICI values of Table 5; the other curves have been shifted downward by successive intervals of 10 decibels (1 log unit).

be made. A trial computation may show that the first estimate was wrong, so that a recomputation based on another selection of luminosity function from Table 5 may be needed.

Figure 2 shows equal-brightness contours on a spectral-radiance wavelength plot for values of adapting luminance at 1.0, 0.1, 0.01, 0.001, 0.0001, and 0.00001 foot-lambert. These contours, separated by 10 decibels in luminance, refer to the level of adaptation of the observer to the field itself. For example, the upper contour indicates the spec-

tral radiances required to give a luminance of 1 foot-lambert measured by an observer adapted to a luminance of 1 foot-lambert. The dotted line passes through the minima of the curves and shows how the wavelength of maximum luminous efficiency increases with the luminance to which the observer is adapted. This increase is known as the Purkinje effect and is caused by the transfer from rod to cone vision. The lowest curve specifies spectral stimuli close to the absolute threshold. The other curves correspond to adapting luminances equal to snow illuminated by starlight, quarter moon, full moon, deep twilight, and twilight with the sun a few degrees below the horizon, respectively.

EQUIVALENT COLOR STIMULI

If a normal observer attempts to adjust one controllable element (subtending 1 degree or more) of his central visual field so that it matches the color of a neighboring element, he will discover that three independent adjustments have to be at his disposal. If he is trying to match one spot of light by shining several spotlights of different color onto a neighboring spot of a screen, he finds, in general, that three lights of fixed spectral composition are required. The same rule applies to rotary mixture on a sector disk; four sectors, giving three independent adjustments, are necessary and sufficient. Similarly in pigment combination at least three pigments are necessary. Examples are the red, yellow, and blue paints of the primary grade school, and the magenta, yellow, and cyan colorants used in color photography, lithography, and color printing. Normal color vision is tridimensional.

Since the color vision of a normal observer is tridimensional, it follows that a color specification is expressible by three numbers. For normal observers three numbers are necessary; for partially color-blind observers only two numbers are necessary; and for totally color-blind observers, only one.

Three-Part Classifications

In the examples given (spotlights, sector disks, colorants) the observer, by adjusting three variables, obtains a color match; he sets up a second stimulus equivalent to the first. Except by accident, however, the ternary or binary mixture does not match the first stimulus in spectral composition. The second stimulus appears the same as the first in color, but it is different in spectral composition. The two stimuli form what is known as a metameric pair: they exhibit metamerism. Difference in spectral composition, however, is a matter of degree. When a painted panel is matched by a mixture of red, yellow, and blue paints, the degree of metamerism is likely to be only moderate. But if the paint panel, illuminated by daylight, is matched by shining on a white card three spotlights, each of which contains energy restricted to a narrow wavelength band (such as spectrum red, green, and blue), the degree of metamerism will be extreme. Normal observers may disagree widely on highly metameric matches. Variations in ocular pigmentation (see Table 2) from observer to observer are largely responsible for these disagreements (Sinden, 1923; Wright, 1929). But all observers, normal and color-blind, must, of course, agree on nonmetameric matches.

Normal visual system. To a normal observer the spectrum appears as a series of chromatic colors varying from dim red through orange, yellow, brilliant yellow-green, green, blue, to dim violet. From a study of spectral metamers it has been found possible to summarize concisely the properties of a reasonably average normal eye. This summary utilizes the principles known as Grassman's laws, foreshadowed by Newton's laws of color mixture (Grassman, 1853). If a light composed of known amounts of three components (called primaries) is equivalent in color to another light, the three known amounts may be used

as a color specification for this light. These amounts are called tristimulus values of the color. Grassman's laws state:

1. When equivalent lights are added to equivalent lights, the sums are also equivalent.

2. When equivalent lights are subtracted from equivalent lights, the differences are also equivalent.

3. Lights equivalent to the same light are equivalent to each other.

Thus, when an unknown spot of color is matched by shining on the same spot of a white screen two component spotlights of tristimulus values, X_1, Y_1, Z_1, and X_2, Y_2, Z_2, respectively, by Grassman's first law, the tristimulus values, X, Y, Z, of the unknown color spot are simply

$$X = X_1 + X_2$$

$$Y = Y_1 + Y_2 \tag{5}$$

$$Z = Z_1 + Z_2$$

Any three lights may be used as primaries in a tristimulus system provided only that no one of them is equivalent to a combination of the other two. Tristimulus values, X, Y, Z, of any color expressed in this system of primaries may be transformed into specifications, R, G, B, relative to any other set of primaries. If R_x, G_x, B_x are the tristimulus values of one unit of the X-primary, R_y, G_y, B_y those of one unit of the Y-primary, and R_z, G_z, B_z those of one unit of the Z-primary, then by Grassman's first law a combination of X-units of the X-primary plus Y-units of the Y-primary plus Z-units of the Z-primary will also be equivalent to the additive combination of R_xX, G_xX, B_xX, R_yY, G_yY, B_yY, R_zZ, G_zZ, and B_zZ. Any stimulus equivalent to the combination of X-units of the X-primary plus Y-units of the Y-primary plus Z-units of the Z-primary will by Grassman's third law also be equivalent to the additive combination of these nine components. By segregating the triads referring to the R-, G-, and B-primaries we find

$$R = R_x X + R_y Y + R_z Z$$

$$G = G_x X + G_y Y + G_z Z \qquad (6)$$

$$B = B_x X + B_y Y + B_z Z$$

The conditions that no one of the RGB set of primaries is equivalent to a combination of the other two may be written

$$D \equiv \begin{vmatrix} R_x & R_y & R_z \\ G_x & G_y & G_z \\ B_x & B_y & B_z \end{vmatrix} \neq 0 \qquad (6a)$$

If condition 6a is not met, that is to say, if the determinant of equation 6a is equal to zero, then equation 6 does not, in general, give a specification of the color, X, Y, Z, because the RGB system is incapable of expressing a three-dimensional variation. One of R, G, and B is not independent of the other two but is a weighted sum of them.

The reverse transformation equations can be found by solving for X, Y, and Z from equation 6:

$$DX = (G_y B_z - G_z B_y)R + (R_z B_y$$
$$- R_y B_z)G + (R_y G_z - R_z G_y)B$$

$$DY = (G_z B_x - G_x B_z)R + (R_x B_z$$
$$- R_z B_x)G + (R_z G_x - R_x G_z)B \qquad (6b)$$

$$DZ = (G_x B_y - G_y B_x)R + (R_y B_x$$
$$- R_x B_y)G + (R_x G_y - R_y G_x)B$$

where D, as in equation 6a, is the determinant of the system

$$D = R_x G_y B_z + R_y G_z B_x + R_z G_x B_y$$
$$- R_z G_y B_x - R_x G_z B_y - R_y G_x B_z$$

Since in the derivation of equation 6 it was assumed that the primaries of the XYZ system could be matched by positive amounts of the primaries of the RGB system, it follows that the gamut of colors producible by the latter system is larger than that of the former. If we take the specifications, R, G, B, of one of the colors producible by the RGB system, but not by the XYZ system, and transform them by equation 6b to the XYZ system, it will be found that one or two of X, Y, and Z is less than zero. Thus equation 6b seems to state that the color RGB is also equivalent to some fraction of unit X plus some fraction of unit Y minus some fraction of unit Z. The meaning of the addition of a negative quantity of a primary to one side of the field of a colorimeter is simply that this quantity is added to the other side. Thus, what equation 6b really states, in this case, is that the color RGB plus some fraction of unit Z is equivalent to a weighted sum of the X-primary and the Y-primary. The original statement can be restored by application of Grassman's second law.

The principles expressed in Grassman's laws have been established by repeated experiment over a wide middle range of retinal illuminance (Hering, 1885) for all types of vision, normal and abnormal. They break down for very high retinal illuminance approaching that sufficient to produce a permanent change in the eye (Wright, 1936). And they break down if the illuminance of the whole retina continues for 10 minutes or more to be so slight that vision by the retinal rods intrudes significantly (König, 1887; Ladd-Franklin, 1929). Between these two extremes, however, Grassman's laws hold independent of the adaptive state of the eye. Thus, if two stimuli of different energy distributions are once responded to alike by the eye, they will be seen alike even after exposure of the eye to another stimulus sufficient to change considerably the appearance of the two equivalent stimuli.

For example, if a portion of the spectrum near 640 mμ (red) is superposed on a portion near 550 mμ (yellowish green), it will be found possible to obtain the color of this combination from an intermediate portion of the spectrum, say 590 mμ (orange). If the retina is then highly illuminated by light of wavelength near 640 mμ, and if its sensitivity to radiant flux of this wavelength is considerably reduced in this way, it is found that, although neither of the equivalent

TABLE 6

1931 ICI Standard Observer for Colorimetry

Wave-length, mμ	Tristimulus Values of Equal-Energy Spectrum			Wave-length, mμ	Tristimulus Values of Equal-Energy Spectrum		
	$\bar{x}_\lambda$	$\bar{y}_\lambda$	$\bar{z}_\lambda$		$\bar{x}_\lambda$	$\bar{y}_\lambda$	$\bar{z}_\lambda$
380	0.0014	0.0000	0.0065	585	0.9786	0.8163	0.0014
385	0.0022	0.0001	0.0105	590	1.0263	0.7570	0.0011
390	0.0042	0.0001	0.0201	595	1.0567	0.6949	0.0010
395	0.0076	0.0002	0.0362	600	1.0622	0.6310	0.0008
400	0.0143	0.0004	0.0679	605	1.0456	0.5668	0.0006
405	0.0232	0.0006	0.1102	610	1.0026	0.5030	0.0003
410	0.0435	0.0012	0.2074	615	0.9384	0.4412	0.0002
415	0.0776	0.0022	0.3713	620	0.8544	0.3810	0.0002
420	0.1344	0.0040	0.6456	625	0.7514	0.3210	0.0001
425	0.2148	0.0073	1.0391	630	0.6424	0.2650	0.0000
430	0.2839	0.0116	1.3856	635	0.5419	0.2170	0.0000
435	0.3285	0.0168	1.6230	640	0.4479	0.1750	0.0000
440	0.3483	0.0230	1.7471	645	0.3608	0.1382	0.0000
445	0.3481	0.0298	1.7826	650	0.2835	0.1070	0.0000
450	0.3362	0.0380	1.7721	655	0.2187	0.0816	0.0000
455	0.3187	0.0480	1.7441	660	0.1649	0.0610	0.0000
460	0.2908	0.0600	1.6692	665	0.1212	0.0446	0.0000
465	0.2511	0.0739	1.5281	670	0.0874	0.0320	0.0000
470	0.1954	0.0910	1.2876	675	0.0636	0.0232	0.0000
475	0.1421	0.1126	1.0419	680	0.0468	0.0170	0.0000
480	0.0956	0.1390	0.8130	685	0.0329	0.0119	0.0000
485	0.0580	0.1693	0.6162	690	0.0227	0.0082	0.0000
490	0.0320	0.2080	0.4652	695	0.0158	0.0057	0.0000
495	0.0147	0.2586	0.3533	700	0.0114	0.0041	0.0000
500	0.0049	0.3230	0.2720	705	0.0081	0.0029	0.0000
505	0.0024	0.4073	0.2123	710	0.0058	0.0021	0.0000
510	0.0093	0.5030	0.1582	715	0.0041	0.0015	0.0000
515	0.0291	0.6082	0.1117	720	0.0029	0.0010	0.0000
520	0.0633	0.7100	0.0782	725	0.0020	0.0007	0.0000
525	0.1096	0.7932	0.0573	730	0.0014	0.0005	0.0000
530	0.1655	0.8620	0.0422	735	0.0010	0.0004	0.0000
535	0.2257	0.9149	0.0298	740	0.0007	0.0003	0.0000
540	0.2904	0.9540	0.0203	745	0.0005	0.0002	0.0000
545	0.3597	0.9803	0.0134	750	0.0003	0.0001	0.0000
550	0.4334	0.9950	0.0087	755	0.0002	0.0001	0.0000
555	0.5121	1.0002	0.0057	760	0.0002	0.0001	0.0000
560	0.5945	0.9950	0.0039	765	0.0001	0.0000	0.0000
565	0.6784	0.9786	0.0027	770	0.0001	0.0000	0.0000
570	0.7621	0.9520	0.0021	775	0.0000	0.0000	0.0000
575	0.8425	0.9154	0.0018	780	0.0000	0.0000	0.0000
580	0.9163	0.8700	0.0017		21.3713	21.3714	21.3715

stimuli any longer appears orange, they still give identical colors. They may yield identical yellows or identical greenish yellows. The eye thus cannot be trusted to yield the same color perception from a given stimulus; simultaneous and successive induction affect it profoundly. But it is still a satisfactory null instrument, and it obeys Grassman's laws.

Standard observer. Any beam of light, whether it originates from a self-luminous body, or comes by transmission, scattering, or reflection, from a nonself-luminous object, may be considered as made up of a large number of bands of the spectrum. The spectral irradiances of these various bands may be determined by spectrophotometry. The tristimulus specification, $\bar{x}_\lambda$, $\bar{y}_\lambda$, $\bar{z}_\lambda$, of each of these bands of vanishingly small wavelength interval have been determined for a number of normal observers (Guild, 1931; Wright, 1929). Average values are given in Table 6 in arbitrary units for every 5 mμ for a spectrum of unit spectral irradiance per unit wavelength (the so-called equal-energy spectrum). The units are chosen so that an equal-energy source will be equivalent to equal amounts of the first primary X, the second primary Y, and the third primary Z; that is to say, so that $\int_0^\infty \bar{x}_\lambda \, d\lambda = \int_0^\infty \bar{y}_\lambda \, d\lambda = \int_0^\infty \bar{z}_\lambda \, d\lambda$. These specifications for the standard observer are plotted in Fig. 3.

The amounts, X, Y, Z, of the primaries required to produce a stimulus equivalent to any spot of light may be found by Grassman's first law simply by adding together the tristimulus values of the various parts of its spectrum. In this way there is provided a three-part classification of stimuli reasonably valid for all observers with normal vision. All stimuli that are equivalent for the standard observer will be characterized by identical values of X, Y, and Z. In general, for each such color there will be an infinite number of physically different stimuli. The triad of numbers, X, Y, Z, serves as a label for each of this infinity of stimuli and

indicates that they are equivalent to each other.

The tristimulus values, X, Y, Z, of any stimulus producing at the cornea of the ob-

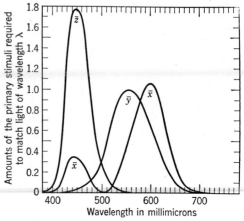

FIG. 3. Tristimulus values of spectrum stimuli of unit irradiance according to the standard observer and coordinate system recommended by the International Commission on Illumination in 1931 (the ICI or CIE system). The $\bar{y}$-function is the relative luminosity function for daylight vision (see Table 5). At each wavelength the amounts of the three primaries required in an additive combination to color match the spectrum at that wavelength may be found from the curves. For example, equal amounts of the X- and Y-primaries combine to produce for the standard observer a close match for the color of the spectrum at 578 mμ.

server's eye the spectral irradiance $E\lambda$ may be computed as:

$$X = \sum_0^\infty E_\lambda \bar{x}_\lambda \, \Delta\lambda$$

$$Y = \sum_0^\infty E_\lambda \bar{y}_\lambda \, \Delta\lambda \tag{7}$$

$$Z = \sum_0^\infty E_\lambda \bar{z}_\lambda \, \Delta\lambda$$

where $\bar{x}_\lambda$, $\bar{y}_\lambda$, $\bar{z}_\lambda$ are the tristimulus values of the spectrum colors (see Table 6) of the standard observer. The $\bar{y}$-function is the standard luminosity function (see Table 5) expressed relative to its maximum value. The Y-value of a stimulus is therefore its luminous value, in this case the illuminance of the cornea. If radiometric quantities other than irradiance are used in equation 7, the Y-value will give the corresponding luminous quantity. Thus, if the radiometric quantity is the radiance of a surface in the direction of the observer's eye, Y will evaluate the luminance of the surface. Or, if the radiometric quantity is the radiant intensity of a source, Y will evaluate its luminous intensity in a unit proportional to the candle, and so on. The tristimulus values, X, Y, Z, serve as a three-part classification of visual stimuli for the central 2 degrees of the normal retina. They will continue to serve until data still more representative have been gathered and adopted.

When two stimuli combined additively are equivalent to a stimulus yielding an achromatic or neutral color perception, they are said to be complementary and to correspond to complementary colors. Since it is possible to test by equation 7 whether or not any two stimuli are equivalent for the standard observer, it is possible to derive the spectral complementaries for that observer. That is to say, it is possible to find which pairs of spectrum colors mix to a match for the neutral color ordinarily perceived to correspond to unit amount of the equal-energy stimulus for which $X = Y = Z = 1$. If $\bar{x}_1, \bar{y}_1, \bar{z}_1$, are the tristimulus values of the first spectrum component, it is necessary merely to find a second portion of the spectrum such that the tristimulus values, $\bar{x}_2, \bar{y}_2, \bar{z}_2$ satisfy simultaneously the three conditions:

$$a\bar{x}_1 + b\bar{x}_2 = 1$$

$$a\bar{y}_1 + b\bar{y}_2 = 1 \tag{8}$$

$$a\bar{z}_1 + b\bar{z}_2 = 1$$

where a and b are the amounts in radiometric terms of the spectrum components, 1 and 2, respectively. Table 7 gives a few of the spectral complementaries, together with the corresponding values of a and b computed by a method worked out by MacAdam (OSA, 1944*b*).

It will be noted from Table 7 that the components $a\bar{y}_\lambda$ and $b\bar{y}_\lambda$ in photometric

TABLE 7

WAVELENGTHS (λ_1, λ_2) OF THE SPECTRAL COMPLEMENTARIES AND THEIR AMOUNTS IN BOTH RADIOMETRIC (a, b) AND PHOTOMETRIC ($a\bar{y}_\lambda$, $b\bar{y}_\lambda$) TERMS IN ARBITRARY UNITS REQUIRED TO MATCH UNIT AMOUNT OF THE EQUAL-ENERGY STIMULUS

Wavelength, mμ		Proportions for Unit Amount of the Equal-Energy Stimulus			
λ_1	λ_2	Radiometric Terms		Photometric Terms	
		a	b	$a\bar{y}_\lambda$	$b\bar{y}_\lambda$
400	569.72	14.58	1.042	0.00583	0.99417
410	569.76	4.858	1.043	0.00583	0.99417
420	569.85	1.545	1.043	0.00618	0.99382
430	570.07	0.721	1.042	0.00836	0.99164
440	570.49	0.572	1.040	0.01319	0.98681
450	571.22	0.563	1.037	0.02140	0.97860
460	572.41	0.598	1.030	0.0359	0.9641
470	574.70	0.776	1.012	0.0706	0.9294
480	580.40	1.229	0.957	0.1709	0.8291
490	600.00	2.148	0.877	0.4468	0.5532
570	427.17	1.042	0.835	0.99248	0.00752
580	479.56	0.961	1.201	0.8361	0.1639
590	486.75	0.891	1.794	0.6744	0.3256
600	490.00	0.877	2.148	0.5532	0.4468
610	491.69	0.937	2.359	0.4715	0.5285
620	492.61	1.106	2.481	0.4214	0.5786
630	493.12	1.476	2.555	0.3911	0.6089
640	493.46	2.119	2.601	0.3708	0.6292
650	493.65	3.353	2.629	0.3588	0.6412
660	493.76	5.764	2.647	0.3516	0.6484
670	493.81	10.89	2.653	0.3486	0.6514
680	493.85	20.35	2.660	0.3460	0.6540
690	493.88	41.97	2.663	0.3442	0.6558
700	493.89	53.9	2.663	0.3438	0.6562

terms sum to unity. This follows from Grassman's law (see equation 5), as well as from the additivity "law" of luminance, since one of the conditions taken was that the equal-energy stimulus is of unit amount ($X = Y = Z = 1$). The components a and b expressed in radiometric terms were found by dividing by the luminosity $\bar{y}_\lambda$. They do not, of course, sum to unity; and indeed it may be seen that when one of the spectrum components is near either the short-wave or the long-wave extreme of the spectrum the energy input rises high. This rise reflects the insensitivity of the eye. It is worth noting, however, that the smallest energy input required to reduce the complementary to neutral is near 450 mμ where the luminance is low ($\bar{y}_{450} = 0.038$; see Table 6). And in photometric terms the luminance of component a near the short-wave extreme may drop as low as $\frac{1}{170}$ of the luminance of the complementary (greenish yellow). The short-wave extreme of the spectrum is chromatically strong but luminously weak.

Spectrum stimuli in the wavelength range from about 494 to 569 mμ have no spectrum complementaries. In order to form with these wavelengths an additive combination equivalent to the equal-energy stimulus, we need at least two additional components, one chosen near the short-wave extreme of the spectrum, the other near the long-wave extreme. The amounts required in order for any given choice of such three-part stimuli to be equivalent, for the standard observer, to the equal-energy stimulus may also be computed from Table 6.

As an example of the use of Table 6 a check of one of the pairs of spectral complementaries given in Table 7 is included. Table 7 indicates that a combination of 2.148 radiometric units (irradiance of the cornea, radiance of an extended source, etc.) of wavelength 490 mμ with 0.877 unit of wavelength 600 mμ is found by the standard observer to be equivalent to unit amount of an equal-energy stimulus ($X = Y = Z = 1$). From Table 6 the tristimulus values, $\bar{x}_\lambda$, $\bar{y}_\lambda$, $\bar{z}_\lambda$, of the spectrum for unit amount in radiometric terms may be read for 600 and 490 mμ, multiplied by 2.148 and 0.877, respectively, and summed as follows:

Wavelength, mμ	$\bar{x}_\lambda$	$\bar{y}_\lambda$	$\bar{z}_\lambda$
490	0.0320	0.2080	0.4652
600	1.0622	0.6310	0.0008

Amount, N	$N\bar{x}_\lambda$	$N\bar{y}_\lambda$	$N\bar{z}_\lambda$
2.148	0.069	0.447	0.999
0.877	0.931	0.553	0.001
Totals	1.000	1.000	1.000

This computation shows that the components a and b satisfy equation 8 for this pair of complementary wavelengths. A similar check has been applied throughout Table 7.

The acceptance of the ICI standard observer makes it possible to compute the answers to many problems that heretofore have been solved rather unsatisfactorily by direct experiment only. Direct experimental results are unsatisfactory because of doubt regarding the representativeness of the vision of the observer used. To repeat such experiments with a large number of observers is impractical. The computation above is an example of the use of the standard observer and of the three-part classification of stimuli afforded by it. Equally fundamental three-part classifications may be found by use of primaries other than those of the ICI colorimetric coordinate system. That is to say, any numbers, R, G, B, found by any choice of the nine constants in equation 6 satisfying equation 6a can serve in the place of X, Y, Z. The superiority of the ICI colorimetric coordinate system is chiefly that it is widely used, but it is also convenient for the routine reduction of radiometric data to colorimetric terms because (1) there are no negative quantities (see Table 6), and (2) the $\bar{y}$-function yields an explicit correlate of the luminous aspect of the response separated from the chromatic aspect. The $\bar{x}$- and the $\bar{z}$-functions correlate solely with the chromatic aspect of the response; they are unassociated with the luminous aspect (Judd, 1933).

A corollary to the freedom of our choice of R, G, and B to yield a fundamental three-part classification of visual stimuli for the normal observer is that any function not expressible in terms of R, G, and B will fail to yield the same groupings of equivalent stimuli. Such functions therefore will group together as equivalent some stimuli that the observer of normal vision would find not to be equivalent, and they cannot be used to represent normal vision. Such functions represent anomalous vision.

Anomalous systems. There are three recognized kinds of anomalous vision: protanomalous, deuteranomalous, and tritanomalous (Judd, 1943).

An observer who requires in a red-green mixture more red than normal to match a given yellow is called protanomalous.

An observer who requires in a red-green mixture more green than normal to match a given yellow is called deuteranomalous.

An observer who requires in a blue-green mixture more blue than normal to match a given cyan is called tritanomalous.

These abnormalities of vision cannot be accounted for by abnormal coloration of the eye media. No matter what spectrally selective filter is looked through by an observer of these types, his vision cannot be made normal (Sinden, 1923). If he is only mildly anomalous, his description of the spectrum will agree rather well with that of the normal. But, if he is extremely anomalous, it will scarcely differ from that of a color-blind observer. The distinctions made by such an observer are light-dark, yellow-blue, and red-green. But his ability to make one of the chromatic distinctions (red-green for prot- and deuter-, blue-yellow for tritanomalous) is relatively weak.

Anomalous trichromats are intermediate in their ability to make chromatic distinctions between normal and dichromatic observers of the protanopic, deuteranopic, and tritanopic types, respectively. Thus, an anomalous trichromat can make with difficulty the distinctions that the corresponding dichromat cannot make at all. However, in other respects anomalous trichromatism is not intermediate between normal trichromatism and dichromatism. For example, the luminosity function of protanomalous observers (McKeon and Wright, 1940) of all degrees is depressed at the long-wave end like that of the protanope (see Fig. 4).

There is no way of setting up a single three-part classification of visual stimuli that will be valid for each of the three types of anomalous trichromatism in the same way that the standard observer serves for normal trichromatism. Anomalous trichromats differ from one another much more than do normal trichromats. The most that can be said about anomalous trichromats is that visual stimuli can be given a three-part classification, valid for each observer separately, by means of functions significantly different from any of the triple infinity of sets (see equation 6) suited for normal trichromatism.

Two-Part Classifications

An observer requiring a mixture of but two lights to produce all the colors that he is capable of experiencing is said to possess a dichromatic visual system. He can make two kinds of visual discrimination, one achromatic (light-dark) and one chromatic (either yellow-blue or red-green). Dichromatic observers are therefore said to be partially color-blind.

Partial color blindness. The spectrum to an observer having red-green blindness appears in two hues only: the short-wave end of the spectrum appears blue; the long-wave end, yellow. These two bands are separated by a region near 495 mμ that, like average daylight, has no hue at all. This region is called the neutral point. From zero at the neutral point the saturations of the spectrum colors increase toward both the long-wave and the short-wave ends. There are two subtypes of red-green blindness: one characterized by abnormally low luminosity of the long-wave portion of the spectrum and by inability to distinguish what to the normal is red and blue-green from gray (protanopia); the other characterized by a substantially normal luminosity function and by inability to distinguish what to the normal is purplish red and green from gray (deuteranopia).

The spectrum to an observer having yellow-blue blindness appears in but two hues, red and green. There are two subtypes of yellow-blue blindness: one characterized by inability to distinguish what to the normal is purplish blue and greenish yellow from gion at or just beyond the short-wave extreme of the spectrum. To a tetartanope, the long-wave portion of the spectrum appears red at the long-wave end, green in the middle, and red again at the short-wave end, with neutral regions near 580 and 470

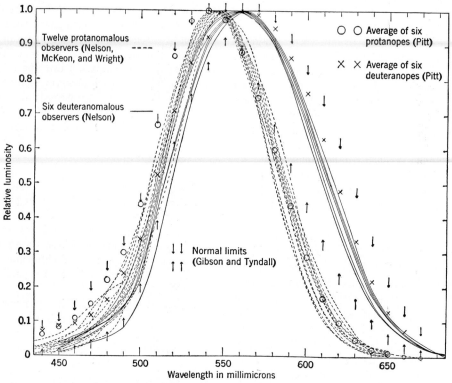

FIG. 4. Relative luminosity functions of anomalous trichromats (6 deuteranomalous, 12 protanomalous) compared to averages for dichromats and to limits for normal trichromats.

gray (tritanopia); the other by inability to distinguish what to the normal is blue and yellow from gray (tetartanopia). Both types have a normal or nearly normal luminosity function. A possible slight defect on the short-wave end is hard to separate from the effect of abnormally heavy ocular pigmentation (see Table 2). To a tritanope the short-wave half of the spectrum appears green; the long-wave, red, with a neutral region near 570 mμ. But the saturation of the short-wave green diminishes with wavelength as if there were a second neutral re-

mμ. This type is rare and is associated with impaired ability to distinguish red from green so that many students of vision treat it in connection with total color blindness (Sloan and Newhall, 1942).

An important characteristic of dichromatic vision is that metameric pairs set up for normal vision are also equivalent stimuli for the dichromat. Dichromatic systems on this account are called reduction systems of normal vision. It is therefore possible to set up two-part classifications for dichromatic vision by means of the same functions used to set up three-part classifications for normal vision. For example, the $\bar{y}$-function and the $\bar{z}$-function taken together isolate all the visual stimuli that are equivalent for deuteranopic vision, except for variations ascribable to abnormally heavy or abnormally light ocular pigmentation. The $\bar{y}$-function alone evaluates the luminous aspect of the stimulus, and the

Figure 5 shows the wavelength distribution of these functions (Judd, 1945).

Stimuli of small angular extent. The normal retina yields trichromatic vision only for large centrally fixated fields. For stimuli subtending less than 10 minutes of arc the normal retina responds with tritanopic vision (Hartridge, 1947). A two-part classification

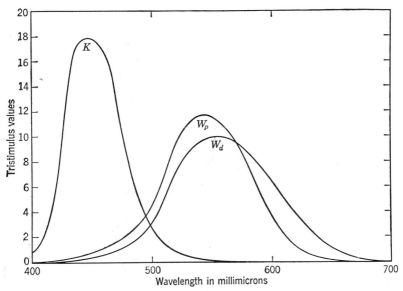

Fig. 5. Tristimulus values of spectrum stimuli of unit irradiance according to a dominator-modulator form of the three-components theory. The primaries, K, W_p, and W_d, are close to the color process whose absence corresponds, respectively, to tritanopia, deuteranopia, and protanopia. These primaries are also close to those of the Helmholtz and the later König theories.

ratio of $\bar{y}$ to $\bar{z}$ evaluates the yellow-blue aspect of the stimulus. Two stimuli having identical values of Y and Z are equivalent stimuli for an average deuteranope.

A two-part classification of visual stimuli for protanopic vision may be formed by combining the $\bar{z}$-function with $-0.460\bar{x} + 1.359\bar{y} + 0.101\bar{z}$. Tritanopia may be represented by a combination of this same function with the $\bar{y}$-function. Since these three functions, taken together, can also yield (by equation 6) the three-part classification suited for normal vision, they form the basis of an explanation of the relation between normal and dichromatic vision similar to that proposed by Young and elaborated by Helmholtz and König.

of stimuli suited to tritanopia thus serves fairly well for the normal receptors stimulated one small group at a time. If the stimulus falls outside the macular pigment, however, account must be taken of the resulting higher transmittance of the ocular media (see Table 2).

Peripheral stimuli. For a given size of stimulus, say 2 degrees, and a given luminance, say 1 foot-lambert, there is a distance from the center of the fovea beyond which red-green distinctions can no longer be made, but light-dark and yellow-blue distinctions can be (Tschermak, 1929). For stimulation of this portion of the periphery the normal retina responds with deuteranopic vision.

Since no one can make precise distinctions of any sort between stimuli applied as eccentrically as these, it is not known whether the same functions that serve to yield a two-part classification of stimuli for deuteranopic vision also serve precisely for eccentric stimulation of the normal retinas. But if account is taken of the effect of macular pigmentation the same functions may be used without introducing notable contradictions.

One-Part Classifications

An observer requiring but a single light to produce all the colors that he is capable of experiencing is said to possess a monochromatic visual system. Since he can match any two stimuli merely by adjusting them to equal brightness, the luminosity function applying to his visual system is a sufficient basis for one-part classification of his visual stimuli. He is capable of light-dark discrimination but of no chromatic discrimination whatsoever. His spectrum does not have merely one or two neutral points; if any point is neutral, all are neutral. On this account the visual system of most monochromats can be called achromatopsia or achromatopia (Sloan and Newhall, 1942).

Total color blindness. The most common form of monochromatism is often called cone blindness since it is universally ascribed to nonfunctioning of the retinal cones (Müller, 1922-23, 1924, and Tschermak, 1929). The most common designation is congenital total color blindness. The luminosity function is the same as that of the dark-adapted normal observer (see Table 5, last column, and Fig. 1).

There are two less-common forms of monochromatism, both of which are thought to arise solely from disease of the eye and the optic nerve. Unlike cone blindness, these forms are characterized by normal visual acuity as well as by good foveal vision. The first type is characterized by a normal or deuteranopic luminosity function (see Table 5, first column, or $\bar{y}_\lambda$ of Table 6); the second, by

a protanopic luminosity function whose maximum is at about 540 mμ (see curve of $W_p = -0.460\bar{x}_\lambda + 1.359\bar{y}_\lambda + 0.101\bar{z}_\lambda$ in Fig. 5). The second form is regarded as the result of a person's being born with protanopic vision and then acquiring tritanopia as a result of disease (Müller, 1924).

Twilight vision. The normal retina adapted to fields of luminance in the neighborhood of 0.0001 foot-lambert responds with monochromatic vision. Since this luminance is below the threshold of the retinal cones, this monochromatic vision is ascribable to the retinal rods. The visual stimuli for this condition can be evaluated by means of the rod luminosity function alone (see last column, Table 5; Müller, 1930; Tschermak, 1929).

Theoretical Implications

The one-, two-, and three-part classifications of visual stimuli appropriate to various types of observers and observing conditions that may be derived from the standard observer, combined with the luminosity function for rod vision, are basic to theories of color vision. These classifications are the best established of all visual functions, and the first criterion of any attempt to explain visual phenomena is whether it yields them correctly.

It is fairly well accepted that the rods and cones of the retina are the immediate organs of vision and that they contain substances or mixtures of substances that absorb radiant energy incident on these receptors. The receptors respond by initiating nerve impulses that find their way to the fibers of the optic nerve. It is well established that the response of the rods is due to the photochemical substance known as rhodopsin (Hecht and Williams, 1922), but the substances giving the cones their spectral sensitivities are still matters of conjecture, as are the combinations of cone responses effective in producing impulses in the optic nerve.

TABLE 8

Summary of a Few of the Better-Known Visual Theories

Name	Anatomical Location	Fundamental Colors	Relation to Standard Observer	Chief Limitation
Young, three components	Cone pigments	Red Green Violet	$+3.1956X + 2.4478Y - 0.6434Z$ $-2.5455X + 7.0492Y + 0.4963Z$ $+ 5.0000Z$	Fails to explain dichromatic vision as intended.
Helmholtz, three components	Cone response	Red Green Violet	$+0.070X + 0.945Y - 0.015Z$ $-0.460X + 1.359Y + 0.101Z$ $+ 1.000Z$	Fails to explain color perceptions of protanopes and deuteranopes.
Dominator-modulator, late König	Cone response	Red Green Violet	$+ 1.000Y$ $-0.460X + 1.359Y + 0.101Z$ $+ 1.000Z$	Fails to explain color perceptions of protanopes and deuteranopes.
Ladd-Franklin, three components, early König	Cone response	Red Green Blue	$+3.7656X + 1.4635Y - 0.2291Z$ $-1.3973X + 6.1289Y + 0.2683Z$ $+ 5.0000Z$	Implies that the blue function has a negative luminosity for normals and deuteranopes, positive for protanopes.
Hering, opponent colors	Optic nerve	Red-green Yellow-blue White-black	$+1.000X - 1.000Y$ $+ 0.400Y - 0.400Z$ $+ 1.000Y$	Fails to give an account of protanopia and tritanopia.
Von Kries-Schrödinger, zone or stage	Cone response	Red Green Blue	$+3.7656X + 1.4635Y - 0.2291Z$ $-1.3973X + 6.1289Y + 0.2683Z$ $+ 5.0000Z$	Implies that the blue function has a negative luminosity for normals and deuteranopes, positive for protanopes; fails to give an account of tritanopia.
	Optic nerve	Green-red Blue-yellow White-black	$-3.537X + 3.196Y + 0.341Z$ $+1.341X - 5.884Y + 4.542Z$ $+ 1.000Y$	
Adams, zone or stage	Cone pigments	Red Green Violet	$+3.1956X + 2.4478Y - 0.6434Z$ $-2.5455X + 7.0492Y + 0.4963Z$ $+ 5.0000Z$	Explanations of protanopia and tritanopia based on subsidiary assumptions.
	Cone response *	Red Green Blue	$+1.000X$ $+ 1.000Y$ $+ 1.000Z$	
	Optic nerve *	Red-green Blue-yellow White-black	$+1.000X - 1.000Y$ $- 0.400Y + 0.400Z$ $+ 1.000Y$	
Müller, zone or stage	Cone pigments	Red Green Violet	$+3.1956X + 2.4478Y - 0.6434Z$ $-2.5455X + 7.0492Y + 0.4963Z$ $+ 5.0000Z$	Implausible explanation of protanopic luminosity by resort to luminosity of the yR cone response and luminosity-inhibiting action of the bG cone response, both of which disappear with the yR-bG cone response to produce protanopia.
	Cone response *	yR-bG gY-rB Luminosity	$+5.741X - 4.601Y - 1.140Z$ $-0.932X + 2.750Y - 1.819Z$ $+ 1.000Y$	
	Optic nerve *	Red-green Yellow-blue White-black	$+6.325X - 6.325Y$ $+ 2.004Y - 2.004Z$ $+ 1.000Y$	

* The theory allows for a nonlinear dependence of the responses upon the stimulus in addition to the linear dependence indicated here.

Equation 6, when combined with the properties of the standard observer, is the key to all such conjectures. It serves not only for normal vision but also for all reduction forms (dichromatism, acquired total color blindness). It also has a powerful negative implication for anomalous vision (protanomaly, deuteranomaly, tritanomaly) in the sense that no explanation in terms of functions

(1905), and Müller (1930) theories, respectively. These functions show how the various assumed processes depend on the spectral distribution of energy incident on the cornea of the observer. The corresponding dependence on the energy incident on the retina may be found by dividing by the spectral transmittance of the ocular media (see Table 3, last column).

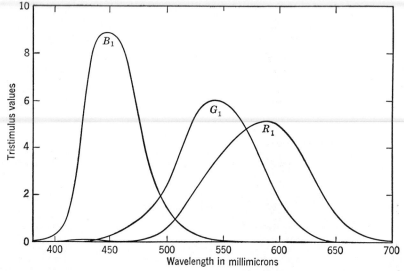

Fig. 6. Tristimulus values of spectrum stimuli of unit irradiance according to the primaries of the Young theory.

defined by equation 6 is admissible for these types of vision. Combinations of these functions yield exactly the same implications as the functions for the standard observer. They yield the same spectral complementaries, etc. (see Table 7).

Table 8 indicates the particular coefficients of equation 6 used for the theories that have attracted most attention so far. It also gives the name by which the theory is known, the particular structure whose activity the functions are now considered to describe, an indication of the color associated with the function, and an indication of the chief limitations of the theory. Figures 6, 7, 8, and 9 show the spectral distributions of the functions listed in Table 8 for the Young (Helmholtz, 1911), Ladd-Franklin (1929), Hering

Figure 5 corresponds to König's later views (1897) and also serves to illustrate the Helmholtz theory. By the Helmholtz theory the deuteranopic luminosity function is located slightly to the long-wave end of the spectrum compared to normal, but the amount, too small to be statistically significant from the number of deuteranopes so far studied, is likewise too small to be seen at all easily on Fig. 5. König was the first to point out that the deuteranopic luminosity function, being almost normal, requires that the red function for the normal be likewise almost identical with the luminosity function. The idea that there is a separate receptor or dominator for the luminous aspect of the visual response has recently been proposed by Granit (1943) under the name of domi-

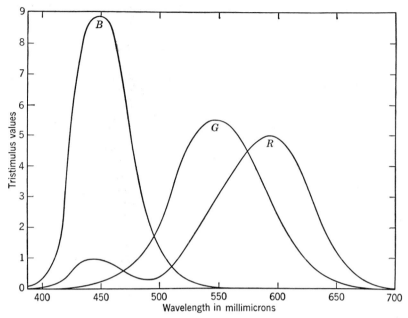

FIG. 7.   Tristimulus values of spectrum stimuli of unit irradiance, according to the primaries of the early König theory and the Ladd-Franklin theory.

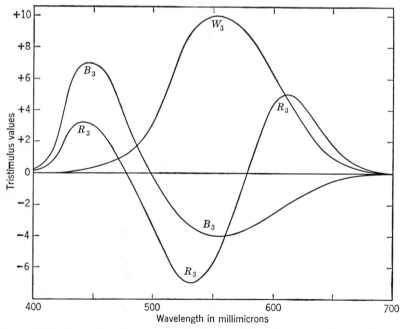

FIG. 8.   Tristimulus values of spectrum stimuli of unit irradiance, according to the primaries of the Hering theory.

nator-modulator theory. This proposal is based on evidence obtained through measurements of the nerve activity of single fibers isolated by a microelectrode.

sidiary assumptions (not published in detail) elaborate the theory to meet these requirements without sacrificing any of the structure. Figure 10 is a diagram of the retinal

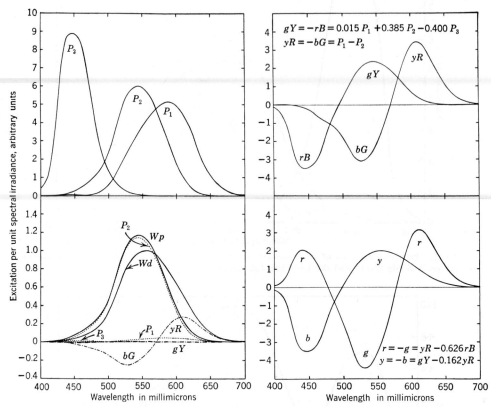

Fig. 9. Tristimulus values of spectrum stimuli of unit irradiance, according to the three stages of the Müller theory (Judd, 1949). Upper left: initial photosensitive-substance stage (same as the Young theory). Upper right: stage of the chromatic retinal sensory processes. Lower right: chromatic processes in the optic-nerve fiber stage (same as the Hering theory). Lower left: components in the luminosity functions (solid lines) for normal and deuteranopic vision (W_d) and for protanopic vision (W_p). The direct contributions to luminosity from the initial photosensitive-substance stage are shown in dotted lines; the indirect contributions from the retinal sensory process stage in dot-dash lines. Protanopic luminosity (W_p) differs from normal luminosity through absence of the indirect contribution from the yR-bG retinal sensory process. The tristimulus values of the spectrum for the first stage are given directly by the excitations, P_1, P_2, P_3 (upper left); those for the last two stages are made up of the luminosity function combined with the chromatic functions shown on the right.

The E. Q. Adams (1923, 1942) stage theory is probably the first dominator-modulator theory. It antedates the coining of the phrase by twenty years. The coordinate systems listed in Table 8 for this theory do not themselves give a simple account of protanopia and tritanopia, but plausible sub-

nerve connections on which the Adams theory is based. It is assumed that there are rods (S) and three kinds of cones (R, W, and B) in the retina. The rods and the W-cones have a direct connection to the W-fibers of the optic nerve and produce a white sensation. The R- and B-cones modulate the response of the W-cones by means of assumed lateral connections. Only an excess of R-response over W-response can reach the R-fiber of the optic nerve and so produce a red sensation. If the W-response is in excess, the R-fiber responds with the negative of red, which is green. Similarly the blue fiber may respond either yellow or

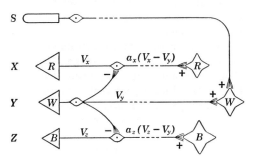

Fig. 10. Diagram of the retinal nerve connections on which the Adams theory is based. It is assumed that in the retina there are rods S and three kinds of cones, R, W, B. The photosensitive pigments contained in these receptors are the first stage of the theory. The receptors themselves are the second stage, represented by the tristimulus values, X, Y, Z, of the standard observer. The final stage is produced by lateral nerve connections in the retina whereby the responses of the R and B cones are opposed by the W responses, giving the net responses $a_x(V_x - V_y)$ and $a_z(V_z - V_y)$, which correspond exactly with the Hering theory.

blue. This is the same as the Hering formulation. Although it is assumed that the photochemical decomposition of the pigments in the R-cone is measured by the X tristimulus value, the response of the R-cone V_x is assumed to be nonlinearly related to X. The Adams theory is a very promising suggestion and is the only stage theory so far that yields fruitful results from the assumption of a nonlinear connection between stages.

The Helmholtz theory is the simplest and most widely followed of visual theories. It states that whenever all three receptors are equally excited a neutral or achromatic color is perceived. Also, if the receptors yielding violet are unstimulated or only weakly stimulated, and those yielding red and green are

about equally excited, a color perception of yellow hue will result. Protanopia is explained by failure of the red receptors to function; deuteranopia, by failure of the green; and tritanopia, by failure of the violet. This leads to the prediction that protanopes should experience simply blends of green and violet, and that deuteranopes should experience simply blends of red and violet. But evidence from observers colorblind in only one eye indicates that both protanopes and deuteranopes experience blends of blue and yellow (Müller, 1924).

Adherents of the Helmholtz theory regard the prediction of the wrong color perceptions for protanopes and deuteranopes as a very minor drawback. Some take the position that the names by which an observer describes his color experiences are subject to change by education, and that such data have therefore relatively little interest compared to the data on equivalent color stimuli and should not be allowed to complicate the representation of those facts. Such adherents ignore the evidence based on a stimulus found to produce the same color perception for the normal and for the dichromatic eye of a unilaterally color-blind observer.

Other adherents of the Helmholtz theory resort to an ingenious suggestion by Fick (1879) modifying the Helmholtz explanation of dichromatic vision. According to Fick we should consider the possibility that dichromatic vision is due to failure to segregate properly the photosensitive substances in the two types of receptors. If both red and green cones are supplied with the substance or mixture of substances proper to the red cones, the observer will have a luminosity function nearly or quite equal to the normal luminosity function. But since both red and green cones have identical spectral sensitivities they must always be equally stimulated, and this is the condition for the perception of colors of yellow hue. This type of vision is deuteranopic and an analogous explanation yields protanopic vision. This suggestion by Fick resembles a stage theory of vision because it deals separately with the cone substances and the cone responses.

The Hering (1905) theory of opponent colors has come to be fairly well accepted as the most likely description of color processes in the optic nerve and cortex. Thus this theory reappears as the final stage in the stage theories of von Kries-Schrödinger (von Kries, 1905; Schrödinger, 1925), Adams (1923, 1942), and Müller (1924, 1930). By far the most completely worked out of these stage theories is that of Müller. It takes at least qualitative account of nearly every known visual phenomenon and is noteworthy on that account alone. Its structure, based partly on conjecture, is formidable, and many aspects of it are implausible. There is slight chance that all of the conjectures are correct, but, even if some of the solutions proposed by Müller prove to be unacceptable, he has nevertheless made a start toward the solution of important problems that will eventually have to be faced by other theorists.

PERCEPTIONS ARISING FROM A KNOWN VISUAL FIELD

By means of his visual sense a human observer is able to perceive positions, sizes, shapes, motions, textures, and colors of objects in his environment. He also perceives the difference between opaque, translucent, and transparent objects. He can tell whether a surface is glossy or matte. And he can even make some estimate of the amount and color of illumination pervading space. This information comes from the relation between the colors of the elements that make up the visual field and the momentary changes that they undergo as a result of object movements and movements of the observer.

Many aspects of these perceptions can be predicted from the characteristics of the environment. Before presenting the basic correlates of the visual stimulus, let us consider the attributes of visual perceptions. Colors may be perceived in various modes; they may belong to objects, or to lights; they may be perceived as filling a hole in a screen, or as belonging to the illumination filling an illuminated space (Katz, 1930; Martin, 1922). The color of an opaque object is perceived as belonging to its surface; the color of a translucent or transparent object belongs partly to its interior and therefore consists partly of surface color and partly of volume color.

There are normally three attributes to the perception of the color of an aperture. These attributes are hue, saturation, and brightness, although, alternatively, an aperture-color perception may be described in terms of redness (whose opposite is greenness), yellowness (whose opposite is blueness), and brightness (whose opposite is dimness). The color perception of an object, however, is closely linked with other aspects of the perception. It is convenient to start the presentation of basic correlates with a classification of the nonshape, nontemporal attributes of visual perception for the more important modes of appearance (OSA, 1943). (See Table 9.)

The chromatic attributes of an object-color perception are the same as those of aperture-color perception. The achromatic attributes of an object-color perception may be lightness (whose opposite is darkness) varying from black to white, or they may be directly stated in terms of whiteness and blackness, or they may be further analyzed in terms of whiteness, grayness and blackness. By this latter method, proposed by Dimmick and Holt (1929), an achromatic object-color perception is expressed in terms of two neighbors in the achromatic series (either white and gray, or gray and black). And a chromatic object-color perception is expressed in terms of these two neighbors in the achromatic series combined with two neighbors in the closed series of chromatic colors, red, yellow, green, blue (red). Thus, a light tan might be expressed as 25 per cent each of white, gray, red, and yellow.

TABLE 9

NONSHAPE, NONTEMPORAL ATTRIBUTES OF VISUAL PERCEPTION

Classification of Visual Perception	Mode of Appearance	Nonshape, Nontemporal Attribute
Nonlocated in depth	Aperture	Hue, saturation, brightness (alternatively: red-green, yellow-blue, bright-dim).
Located in depth	Illuminant	Hue, saturation, brightness, transparency (alternatively: red-green, yellow-blue, bright-dim, transparent-opaque).
	Object	
	1. Volume	Hue, saturation, lightness, transparency (alternatively: red-green, yellow-blue, black-white, transparent-opaque).
	2. Surface	Hue, saturation, lightness, transparency, glossiness (alternatively: red-green, yellow-blue, black-white, transparent-opaque, glossy-matte).

Some of the attributes listed in Table 9 have stimulus correlates that have already been mentioned. The correlate for the brightness perceived to belong to an aperture or self-luminous area is luminance. The perceived brightness varies from very dim to very bright as the luminance varies from the absolute threshold to a value beyond which the observer can detect no further increments in brightness. Fechner pointed out that the function relating brightness to luminance is approximately logarithmic, but the precise nature of this relation has not been determined. The logarithmic relation is closely approximated for limited middle ranges of luminance when the observer is adapted to the average luminance of the two fields being compared (E. Q. Adams, 1922). In other words, under these conditions the decibel scale of luminance relative to the threshold corresponds to the psychological scale of brightness more closely than does a linear scale of luminance.

The lightness of the color perceived to belong to a surface approaching the ideally diffusing surface may be predicted with good reliability from the luminous reflectance of the surface. Under ordinary viewing conditions the perceived lightness varies from black to white as the luminous reflectance varies from zero to one. For actual surfaces (glossy and semiglossy) luminous reflectance must be replaced by luminous directional reflectance in this correlation. Again, too, a better perceptual scale is yielded by functions of luminous directional reflectance similar to the logarithmic, such as $(R_\theta)^{1/2}$ or $R_\theta/(R_\theta + R_f)$, where R_f is the average for the visual field (E. Q. Adams, 1922).

The glossiness perceived to belong to a surface (Bixby, 1926) is correlated with the degree to which the surface reflects light regularly, so that it forms mirror images. There are several kinds of glossiness, all of which may be correlated with various functions of luminous directional reflectance. Table 10 lists five of these kinds of glossiness (Hunter, 1937) together with the functions of luminous directional reflectance with which they correlate. Note that the correlates for the last three kinds of glossiness explicitly indicate that the observer views the specimen from two different directions. This double direction of view is implied in the first two cases also. Vitreous glossiness (luster) corresponds to a moderately bright highlight of the same chromaticity as that of the illuminant. Metallic glossiness (luster) corresponds to a bright highlight not necessarily of the same chromaticity as that of the illuminant.

The transparency perceived to belong to a volume is correlated with the degree to

TABLE 10

Various Kinds of Glossiness and Their Correlates

Kind of Glossiness	Correlate in Terms of Luminous Directional Reflectance	Diagram of the Angular Conditions
Specular	Ratio of $R_{60,-60}$ for the specimen to that of a perfect mirror.	
Sheen	Ratio of $R_{85,-85}$ for the specimen to that of a perfect mirror.	
Contrast	Ratio of $R_{60,-60}$ (specular) to $R_{60,0}$ (diffuse).	
Distinctness of image	Rate of change of $R_{i,-\theta}$ with angle of incidence, i, where the angle of view $-\theta$ differs by a few minutes of arc from that of mirror reflection, $-i$.	
Absence of bloom	Ratio of $R_{i,-i}$ to $R_{i,-\theta}$, where the angle of view $-\theta$ differs from the angle of mirror reflection $-i$ by a few degrees.	

which the elements of the volume transmit light regularly, so that it forms images. Transparency is correlated with luminous directional transmittance in the direction of regularly transmitted light. The ratio of this luminous directional transmittance to the average of the directional transmittances in all other directions (diffuse transmittance) is also a useful measure. The attribute of transparency is closely related to the question whether a volumic appearance is produced at all. Transparency of volumic perceptions approach but do not reach zero. Continuous gradients of luminance (as opposed to discontinuous breaks) often are a sufficient stimulus to a volumic appearance of nearly zero transparency (Fry, 1931). For nearly perfect transparencies the correlate most often used is the ratio of the average directional transmittance for all directions different from that of the regularly transmitted beam to the average for all di-

rections. This ratio, diffuse transmittance to transmittance, is sometimes called haze (American Society for Testing Materials, 1945), and is said to correlate with the haziness of the perceived volume. Haziness is related inversely to transparency and is often applied to nearly clear air or nearly clear plastics. The more transparent a volume is perceived to be, the less hazy.

The transparency perceived to belong to a surface is correlated with the degree to which the surface transmits light regularly. All the stimulus variables applying to the transparency of volumes are also applicable to surfaces. In addition, for transparencies approaching zero, the ratio of luminous reflectance of the surface with a black backing to the luminous reflectance of the surface with a standard white backing is widely used (paint-films, paper) under the name, contrast ratio (Judd, 1938). Contrast ratio may also be of some use as a stimulus correlate for the transparency of volumes having a front surface parallel to the back surface, but account must be taken of the light lost through the sides of the volume (edge effect).

The transparency perceived to belong to a light source is probably correlated with the fraction of the total number of elements in unit projected area of the illuminant that are luminous. A light source is probably never perceived as perfectly opaque (Kreezer, 1930). Even an incandescent filament is transparent in the sense that no front surface is perceived for it: it can be looked into but not through. Nor is a light source ordinarily perceived as perfectly transparent. Between these limits the transparency of a light source correlates with a contrast ratio of the luminance of the light source backed by a white backing to its luminance when backed by black. This is a relatively unexplored field.

Color perception for all modes of appearance has the attributes hue and saturation (see Table 9). There is one additional attribute for each mode. For the aperture and illuminant mode this additional attribute is brightness, varying from dim to very bright. For the (nonself-luminous) object modes this additional attribute is lightness, varying from black to white. A plot of hue, lightness, and saturation in cylindrical coordinates yields the psychological surface-color solid. Lightness is plotted as distance above the base plane; hue by angle about the central black-white axis, and saturation as distance from the axis. An alternative way to plot this solid is by use of rectangular coordinates, red-green being one horizontal coordinate, yellow-blue the other. The boundaries of this solid, often called the color pyramid, are determined by the properties of the visual mechanism. These boundaries are roughly those of a rounded rhomboid with saturated yellow being high in lightness, and saturated blue, low.

Other attributes of object-color perception are insistence and pronouncedness (Katz,

1935; MacLeod, 1932). Pronouncedness does not belong exclusively to the perceived object, however, but relates to the combination of object-color perception and illumination-color perception. It correlates with the illuminance of the scene. Insistence correlates with the luminance of the object and would seem to be nearly the same as the brightness of the aperture-color perception that could be derived from the object by interposition of a screen with a hole in it (reduction screen).

Analysis of the chromatic aspect of color perception in terms of blue, yellow, red, and green, alternative to the use of the terms, hue and saturation, is preferred by many. Anyone who practices this kind of analysis soon learns to think of colors as combinations of various amounts of these primaries and even to experience color directly in these terms. With sufficient practice fairly reproducible estimates may be made. These estimates indicate that blue and yellow cancel, so that a bluish yellow is usually not reported. Nor is a reddish green usually reported. One may, for example, have a yellowish red or a bluish red, but it is considered illogical to experience a red that is at once bluish and yellowish, though such reports are not unknown. This basis for the analysis of chromatic experiences is so universal that blue, yellow, red, and green have become known as the psychological color primaries. These are the fundamental colors taken to describe color processes in the optic nerve by all four of the theories listed in Table 8.

Other bases for the analysis of color experience may, however, be learned with greater or less difficulty. That which accords with the primaries of the Ladd-Franklin theory (see Table 8) is easy to learn, since it differs only in the one respect that red and green are yellow-forming instead of canceling. It is difficult, however, to learn to analyze color in terms of the Young-Helmholtz-König primaries, red, green, and violet.

Color Perception for Adaptation to Daylight

There have been many attempts to determine stimuli corresponding to color perceptions of the unitary hues, red, yellow, green, and blue. Spectrum stimuli and binary mixtures of such stimuli are used because of the comparative ease of specifying them. The appearance of the spectrum, however, depends upon the type of vision possessed by the observer, the size and location of the retinal region stimulated, the retinal illuminance, and the pre-exposure stimulus. Table 11 summarizes the chief results of these attempts to find stimuli for the unitary hues

TABLE 11

STIMULI FOR COLOR PERCEPTIONS OF UNITARY HUE (CF. DIMMICK AND HUBBARD, 1939a)

		Wavelength in Millimicrons			
Experimenter	Date	Red	Yellow	Green	Blue
Bezold	1874	760–656	578	532	468
Donders	1884		582	535	485
Hess	1888		575	495	471
Rood	1890	700	581	527	473
Hering	1898		577	505	470
Voeste	1898		577	505	470
von Kries	1907		574	503	
Westphal	1909		574	506	479
Dreher	1911		575	509	477
Ridgway	1912	644	577	520	473
Goldytsch	1916				468
Bradley	1920	656	579	514	469
Goldmann	1922		568	504	468
Priest	1926	680	583	515	475
Brückner	1927		578	498	471
Schubert	1928		574	500	467
Purdy	1931		571	506	474
Ornstein, Eymers, Vermeulen	1934	630	578	528	487
Verbeek, Bazen	1935		580	530	
Schouten	1935		576	512	472
Dimmick, Hubbard	1939	495c	582	515	475
Theory (Table 8)					
Hering		498.2c	578.1	498.2	477.0
Ladd-Franklin		495.7c	574.3	510.6	468.9
von Kries, Schrödinger		495.7c	574.3	495.7	468.9
Müller		498.2c	578.1	498.2	477.0

(Dimmick and Hubbard, 1939a, b). In these studies the observers were either presumed to be normal or found by test not to be seriously anomalous. They looked directly at the spectrum stimuli so that a region near the center of the retina was used. The spectrum was neither too bright nor too dim to prohibit the characteristic appearance, and the pre-exposure stimulus was darkness, sunlight, overcast-sky light, or some other stimulus chosen with intent to avoid chromatic adaptation.

Analysis in terms of primary color perceptions. For adaptation to stimuli of nearly equal energy distribution (such as daylight, or noon sunlight) various of the functions given in Table 8 correlate well with measurements of the primary colors, red, yellow, green, and blue. Table 11 shows the spectrum stimuli corresponding to color perceptions of the unitary hues according to four of the theories listed in Table 8. The stimuli for unitary red (combinations of the short-wave and long-wave extremes of the spectrum) are identified by the wavelength of the complementary (relative to the equal-energy stimulus, see Table 7). The experimental result by Dimmick (495c in Table 11) is given on this basis also, so that it will be comparable. It will be noted that these theoretical stimuli agree quite well with the experimental results both for yellow and for blue, but they tend to indicate stimuli for red and green that experiment has shown would be called slightly bluish red and slightly bluish green, respectively.

The functions taken to represent the Ladd-Franklin theory correlate with experiment better than the other three because this theory conforms to the principle that red and green are yellow-forming rather than canceling. As may be seen from Table 11, this principle seems to accord with experiment; that is to say, the wavelength for unitary green is higher (more toward yellow) than the complement of unitary red, but it has never been fitted into an acceptable theory. Work by Tschermak and his associates (1929) indicates that failure of observers to be adapted to an achromatic color accounts for the failure of red and green to cancel exactly. But careful work by Dimmick and

TABLE 12

CHROMATICITY COORDINATES (x, y, z) OF THE SPECTRUM COLORS

Wavelength, mμ	Chromaticity Coordinates			Wavelength, mμ	Chromaticity Coordinates		
	x	y	z		x	y	z
380	0.1741	0.0050	0.8209	550	0.3016	0.6923	0.0061
385	0.1740	0.0050	0.8210	555	0.3373	0.6589	0.0038
390	0.1738	0.0049	0.8213	560	0.3731	0.6245	0.0024
395	0.1736	0.0049	0.8215	565	0.4087	0.5896	0.0017
				570	0.4441	0.5547	0.0012
400	0.1733	0.0048	0.8219				
405	0.1730	0.0048	0.8222	575	0.4788	0.5202	0.0010
410	0.1726	0.0048	0.8226	580	0.5125	0.4866	0.0009
415	0.1721	0.0048	0.8231	585	0.5448	0.4544	0.0008
420	0.1714	0.0051	0.8235	590	0.5752	0.4242	0.0006
				595	0.6029	0.3965	0.0006
425	0.1703	0.0058	0.8239				
430	0.1689	0.0069	0.8242	600	0.6270	0.3725	0.0005
435	0.1669	0.0086	0.8245	605	0.6482	0.3514	0.0004
440	0.1644	0.0109	0.8247	610	0.6658	0.3340	0.0002
445	0.1611	0.0138	0.8251	615	0.6801	0.3197	0.0002
				620	0.6915	0.3083	0.0002
450	0.1566	0.0177	0.8257				
455	0.1510	0.0227	0.8263	625	0.7006	0.2993	0.0001
460	0.1440	0.0297	0.8263	630	0.7079	0.2920	0.0001
465	0.1355	0.0399	0.8246	635	0.7140	0.2859	0.0001
470	0.1241	0.0578	0.8181	640	0.7190	0.2809	0.0001
				645	0.7230	0.2770	0.0000
475	0.1096	0.0868	0.8036				
480	0.0913	0.1327	0.7760	650	0.7260	0.2740	0.0000
485	0.0687	0.2007	0.7306	655	0.7283	0.2717	0.0000
490	0.0454	0.2950	0.6596	660	0.7300	0.2700	0.0000
495	0.0235	0.4127	0.5638	665	0.7311	0.2689	0.0000
				670	0.7320	0.2680	0.0000
500	0.0082	0.5384	0.4534				
505	0.0039	0.6548	0.3413	675	0.7327	0.2673	0.0000
510	0.0139	0.7502	0.2359	680	0.7334	0.2666	0.0000
515	0.0389	0.8120	0.1491	685	0.7340	0.2660	0.0000
520	0.0743	0.8338	0.0919	690	0.7344	0.2656	0.0000
				695	0.7346	0.2654	0.0000
525	0.1142	0.8262	0.0596				
530	0.1547	0.8059	0.0394	700	0.7347	0.2653	0.0000
535	0.1929	0.7816	0.0255	705	0.7347	0.2653	0.0000
540	0.2296	0.7543	0.0161	710	0.7347	0.2653	0.0000
545	0.2658	0.7243	0.0099	715	0.7347	0.2653	0.0000

Hubbard (1939*a*, *b*) still shows unitary red and green to be yellow-forming instead of canceling.

Chromaticity diagram (Maxwell triangle). For adaptation to daylight or other nearly neutral light a convenient and widely used correlate of the chromatic aspects of the perception is the chromaticity diagram or Maxwell triangle (Hardy, 1936; Judd, 1933). The tristimulus values, X, Y, Z, in the standard coordinate system (or any transformation by equation 6, such as those given in Table 8) are expressed as ratios of their total: $X/(X + Y + Z)$, $Y/(X + Y + Z)$, $Z/(X + Y + Z)$. These ratios are called chromaticity coordinates, x, y, z, because they correlate well with the chromatic aspect, or chromaticness, of the color perception. (Note that $x + y + z = 1$.) Table 12 gives the chromaticity coordinates (x, y, z) of the spectrum colors at intervals of 5 mμ. Figure 11 shows the chromaticity diagram formed by plotting the second of these ratios, y, against the first, x. This is probably the most widely used chromaticity diagram. Chromaticity diagrams have also been aptly called mixture diagrams because they indicate in a very simple way the chromaticity of the color resulting from the additive combination of any two lights. The point representing this chromaticity is found on the straight line connecting the points representing the two lights.

The primaries of the system are represented by points at the corners of a triangle. (Maxwell used an equilateral triangle, whereas Fig. 11 shows a right triangle, obtained by extending the line $x + y = 1$ from $x = 1$ to $y = 1$.) Every point within the triangle represents the chromaticity of a mixture of primary lights whose proportions are indicated by the chromaticity coordinates. [It is not necessary to plot z, because $z = 1 - (x + y)$.] In Fig. 11 the spectrum colors are shown by a curve known as the spectrum locus. They are identified by wavelength in millimicrons. It will be noted that the spectrum locus is substantially straight from 540 mμ to the long-wave extreme. This means that the standard observer would find binary mixtures of, say, 550 mμ with 700 mμ, closely equivalent to some intermediate portion of the spectrum. But the spectrum locus from 540 mμ to the short-wave extreme is convex. This means that for the standard observer a binary mixture of 540 mμ with, say, 400 mμ would differ importantly in chromaticity from the intermediate parts of the spectrum.

By drawing straight lines through any central point (such as $x = y = \frac{1}{3}$, representing the stimulus whose spectrum has constant irradiance per unit wavelength, the so-called equal-energy stimulus) and extending them until they cut the spectrum locus, we find the spectral complementaries relative to a stimulus represented by that point. That is to say, we may find the two parts of the spectrum that, when combined in proper proportions, will for the standard observer be equivalent to the central stimulus (see Table 7).

The straight line in Fig. 11 joining the extremes of the spectrum locus represents the chromaticities of the mixtures of the two extremes of the visible spectrum. The area bounded by the closed curve made up of the spectrum locus and this straight line is the locus of all physically realizable chromaticities. Note that the points representing the primaries of the standard coordinate system, the apices of the triangle ($x = 1$, $y = z = 0$; $x = 0$, $y = 1$, $z = 0$; $x = y = 0$, $z = 1$) all fall outside this area; that is to say, the primaries have chromaticities that are imaginary and not physically realizable.

Most of the primaries defined in Table 8 share this property. They are intended to indicate independent processes in the visual mechanism that are usually such that no part of the spectrum or combination of parts can succeed in stimulating them to the exclusion of the other processes. The three exceptions are the red processes in the Young theory and in the initial stages of the Adams and Müller theories. The long-wave extreme of the spectrum is assumed to release these

spectrum locus comes close to this line. This means that although a short-wave spectrum stimulus has the power to elicit in the stand-

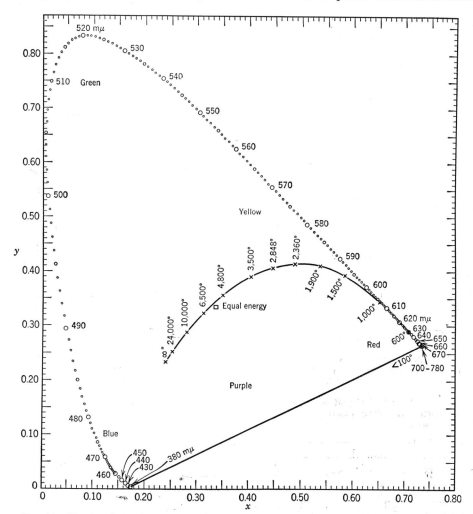

FIG. 11. The (x, y)-chromaticity diagram of the ICI system. The abscissa is the ratio of the tristimulus value X to the sum of all three $(X + Y + Z)$. The ordinate is the ratio of Y to this sum. The parts of the spectrum locus are identified by wavelength in millimicrons. The region bounded by this locus and the straight line (purple border) joining its extremes represents all chromaticities producible by actual stimuli. The central curved line represents the chromaticities of the complete radiator and is called the Planckian locus. Points on this locus are identified by the temperature of the radiator expressed on the Kelvin scale.

processes but to leave unstimulated the other processes of the systems.

The line, $y = 0$, is unassociated with luminosity and is known as the Alychne or lightless line. The short-wave extreme of the

ard observer considerable X and Z response, resulting under ordinary observing conditions in a vivid bluish purple color, radiant flux of wavelength 380 to 420 mμ is only slightly luminous. Note in Table 7 how very small the complementary proportions are for this spectral region expressed in photometric terms. Since both the X and Z primaries fall on the Alychne, they are quite unassociated with the luminous aspect of the response, and refer only to the chromatic aspect.

maticity coordinates x, y, z are important correlates of the visual stimulus.

On the (x, y)-chromaticity diagram (Fig. 11) colors perceived under conditions of near daylight adaptation as grayish are represented near the center $(x = y = z = \frac{1}{3})$. Vivid colors are represented far from the

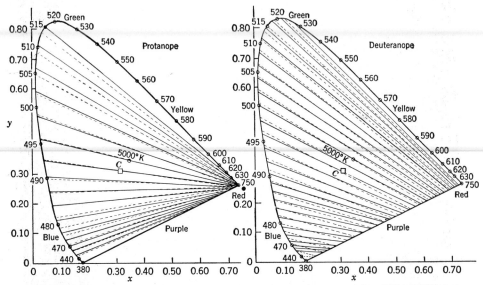

FIG. 12. Chromaticity confusions of the protanope and deuteranope (after Pitt, 1935) shown on the (x, y)-chromaticity diagram. The dotted lines connect points representing chromaticities found experimentally to be indistinguishable by the partially color-blind. The solid lines correspond to the latter König theory and to the Müller theory. Either set of lines indicates, for example, that the typical protanope will not be able to distinguish daylight (C) from a part of the spectrum near 493 mμ (normally perceived as bluish green).

The chromaticity diagram is the most convenient way to show the chromaticity confusions of dichromatic observers. It was pointed out by Maxwell in 1855 that all chromaticities confused by a dichromat with some given chromaticity are represented by points falling on a straight line on the chromaticity diagram. Figure 12 shows the families of straight lines on the (x, y)-chromaticity diagram that represent the chromaticity confusions of protanopic and deuteranopic observers according to Pitt (1935). The chromaticity diagram thus shows very completely the relation between the chromatic aspects of normal and dichromatic vision, and on this account alone the chro-

center. Thus this diagram forms a map on which the relations of the various chromaticities can be seen at a glance. The diagram, however, is considerably expanded in the green portion relative to the other portions, much as the Mercator projection of the earth's surface is expanded near the poles. Thus the saturation of the color perception correlates rather poorly with distance between the center of the (x, y)-diagram and the point representing the chromaticity.

Figure 13 shows the so-called uniform-chromaticity-scale diagram formed by plotting in triangular coordinates the ratio, $R/(R + G + B)$ called r, against the ratio, $G/(R + G + B)$ called g, where

$$R = 3.1956X + 2.4478Y - 0.1434Z$$
$$G = -2.5455X + 7.0492Y + 0.9963Z \quad (9)$$
$$B = 0.0000X + 0.0000Y + 1.0000Z$$

For colors having luminance equal to about 10 millilamberts and a gray surrounding field

The uniform-chromaticity-scale diagram has sometimes been used to derive hue and saturation scales and combination scales that are approximately uniform (OSA, 1944*b*). It indicates that the most saturated spectrum-color perception for a luminance of about

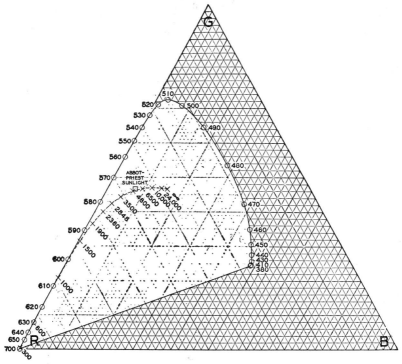

Fig. 13. Uniform-chromaticity-scale (UCS) triangle, according to Judd (1935). The primaries, *R, G, B*, are represented at the apices of the triangle; for example, the *R*-primary corresponds to *r* = 1, *g* = *b* = 0; and the line *BG* corresponds to *r* = 0. On this triangle the distance between two points is approximately proportional to the number of just perceptible chromaticity steps between the two chromaticities represented by the points. For example, it may be seen that Abbot-Priest sunlight is more confusable with the wavelength band near 570 m*μ* than it is with any other part of the spectrum.

of about the same luminance, the distance between a point representing the illuminant (such as Abbot-Priest sunlight, *r* = 0.461, *g* = 0.466, *b* = 0.073) on this diagram and the point representing the chromaticity of the color correlates somewhat better with the saturation of the color perception. If there is a considerable difference between the luminance of the color and of its surroundings the correlation again becomes poor.

10 millilamberts is that belonging to the long-wave extreme; the least saturated, that belonging to some point in the spectrum near 570 m*μ*. For colors of considerably lower luminance (say 0.1 millilambert), the most saturated color perception would probably belong to the short-wave extreme (Haupt, 1922; Martin, Warburton, and Morgan, 1933; Purdy, 1931*a*). Work in this field is fragmentary.

Dominant wavelength and purity. A stimulus yielding an achromatic color perception for daylight adaptation will be found to be represented on the standard chromaticity diagram (Fig. 11) somewhere near to $x = 0.310$, $y = 0.316$ (ICI standard illuminant C, representative of average daylight). If straight lines are drawn from this point to the extremes of the spectrum locus, the area of the diagram representing physically realizable chromaticities will be divided into two parts. That part touching the spectrum locus is said to contain all the spectral colors because these chromaticities can be produced by mixing the achromatic light with light from some part of the spectrum. That part touching the purple boundary is said to contain all the nonspectral (or purple) colors because these chromaticities cannot be so produced. The hue perceived for a spectral color correlates fairly well with the wavelength of the part of the spectrum required to match it by mixture with the achromatic light. This wavelength is called the dominant wavelength of the spectral color. It can be found graphically from the chromaticity diagram (Fig. 11) by drawing a straight line from the point representing the achromatic light through the point representing the color and extending it until it cuts the spectrum locus. The wavelength of this intersection is the dominant wavelength.

The hue perceived for a nonspectral or purple color similarly correlates with the wavelength of that part of the spectrum required to be mixed with the color in order to match the achromatic light. This wavelength is called the complementary wavelength. It is likewise found graphically from the chromaticity diagram by drawing a straight line from the point representing the color through the point representing the achromatic light and extending it until it cuts the spectrum locus.

Both dominant wavelength and complementary wavelength can be found with reference to any fixed light, regardless of whether the observer is so adapted as to make the fixed light appear neutral. But if the observer, who judges the hue belonging to the color, is so adapted that he perceives the fixed light importantly different from neutral or achromatic, it is obvious that the correlation between hue and dominant (or complementary) wavelength must break down. For a dark surrounding field the usual choice of fixed light is that having an equal-energy spectrum. This light has a chromaticity close to that judged to be neutral with a dark surrounding field. But, if the color refers to a surface perceived as a part of a surface-color environment, the illuminant of this environment is chosen as the fixed light.

In the color systems patterned after the opponent-colors theories (Table 8) constant dominant wavelength corresponds to a constant ratio of neighboring chromatic primaries (constant ratio of red to yellow, constant ratio of yellow to green, and so on) provided the sensitivities of the processes remain constant. Similarly, in the color systems (Table 8) patterned after the three-components theories, constant dominant wavelength may correspond to constant ratio of the amounts of the two highest primary processes. With isolated exceptions colors of equal dominant wavelength and unequal purities are perceived as having somewhat different hues, even by an observer adapted approximately to daylight. The correlation is therefore only approximate. It has been pointed out by Adams (1942) that in his stage theory of vision this correlation can be improved by assuming a nonlinear dependence on the stimulus of the processes in the cone response stage; for higher stimulations it is assumed that the sensitivities of the processes diminish.

The degree of approach of an unknown color to the spectrum color of the same dominant wavelength is commonly indicated by the ratio of the amount of the spectrum color to the total amount of the two-part combination. This ratio is called purity, and if the amounts are specified in luminance units the ratio is called colorimetric purity.

Colorimetric purity for nonspectral colors has been defined in two ways, both awkward, and little used in actual practice. By far the most common convention is to express the amounts in units of the excitation sum, $X + Y + Z$, the resulting ratio being called excitation purity (Hardy, 1936; OSA, 1944b).

Excitation purity corresponds simply to distance ratios on the chromaticity diagram of the standard coordinate system. But, in general, excitation purity has more complicated correspondences in transformations of the standard system. This distinguishes it from colorimetric purity which has a meaning apart from the coordinate system and is therefore invariant in transformations.

It is also conventional to define excitation purity for nonspectral colors by assigning to colors that fall on the line connecting the extremes of the spectrum locus a value of excitation purity equal to unity. Excitation purity p_e is thus defined simply in terms of the chromaticity coordinates, x_b, y_b, of the border (be it spectrum locus or purple boundary) at the intersection of the straight line connecting the point, x, y, representing the unknown color with the point, x_w, y_w, representing the fixed light, thus:

$$p_e = \frac{x - x_w}{x_b - x_w}$$

or

$$p_e = \frac{y - y_w}{y_b - y_w} \tag{10}$$

Ordinarily both these expressions yield the same result. But if, as may easily be, both y and y_b are nearly the same as y_w, the y-expression reduces to the ratio of two very small numbers, each of which is uncertain because of rejection errors in the computation. Excitation purity should be computed from the expression having the larger denominator because this one will be less affected by rejection error.

Colorimetric purity p_c can be computed from the same chromaticity coordinates, thus

$$p_c = \frac{(y_b/y)(x - x_w)}{x_b - x_w}$$

or

$$p_c = \frac{(y_b/y)(y - y_w)}{y_b - y_w} \tag{10a}$$

whichever is determinable with the least rejection error. Formulas converting excitation purity to colorimetric purity, and the reverse, have been worked out (OSA, 1944b).

Both forms of purity arbitrarily assign all colors on the border of the chromaticity diagram the same maximum value (100 per cent). Since the spectrum colors are perceived as having different saturations, good correlation between the purity of the color and the saturation of the color perception can exist only within a group of colors of constant dominant wavelength. It is also true, as for the chromaticity diagram just discussed, that the approximate correlation holds only for colors of nearly identical luminance. The two forms of purity are alike in these respects, but colorimetric purity for dominant wavelengths less than 460 mμ yields saturation scales that are perceptually less uniform than those yielded by excitation purity. In the former scales large purity differences near the spectrum are almost imperceptible whereas small differences near zero purity are easily perceptible. Dominant wavelength and purity have been used rather widely in spite of their limited correlation with the hue and saturation of the perceived color (Hardy, 1936).

Munsell hue, value, and chroma. The most generally applicable correlates of hue, lightness, and saturation of object colors in daylight are the recently developed definitions of Munsell hue, value, and chroma (Newhall, Nickerson, and Judd, 1943). They apply to an observer adapted approximately to daylight and viewing objects in an object-color environment such that the average luminous directional reflectance of the surroundings is not less than 10 per cent. They do not apply well to object colors viewed with dark surroundings, nor to self-luminous areas in fields whose elements differ in luminance by factors much above 100.

Table 13 gives the definition of Munsell value in terms of luminous directional reflectance relative to magnesium oxide. If the object is transparent, Y_V should be taken as its luminous transmittance. Munsell value correlates better with the lightness of the color perception than does luminous directional reflectance (or luminous transmittance in the case of a transparent object) in the sense that it gives a scale perceptually more uniform. Equal value intervals are about equally easy to distinguish, whereas a given difference in luminous directional reflectance near 100 per cent is much harder to distinguish than the same difference near 1 per cent. Munsell value thus plays for objects in an object-color environment a role similar to that played for aperture colors by the

decibel scale of luminance when the observer is approximately adapted to the luminance of the field. Actually the Munsell value scale differs from the scale of log reflectance by

TABLE 13

Luminous Directional Reflectance or Transmittance Y_V Corresponding to Various Munsell Renotation Values V

V	$Y_V\%$	V	$Y_V\%$	V	$Y_V\%$	V	$Y_V\%$	V	$Y_V\%$
0.0	0.000	2.0	3.126	4.0	12.00	6.0	30.05	8.0	59.10
0.1	0.120	2.1	3.391	4.1	12.66	6.1	31.23	8.1	60.88
0.2	0.237	2.2	3.671	4.2	13.35	6.2	32.43	8.2	62.71
0.3	0.352	2.3	3.968	4.3	14.07	6.3	33.66	8.3	64.57
0.4	0.467	2.4	4.282	4.4	14.81	6.4	34.92	8.4	66.46
0.5	0.581	2.5	4.614	4.5	15.57	6.5	36.20	8.5	68.40
0.6	0.699	2.6	4.964	4.6	16.37	6.6	37.52	8.6	70.37
0.7	0.819	2.7	5.332	4.7	17.18	6.7	38.86	8.7	72.38
0.8	0.943	2.8	5.720	4.8	18.02	6.8	40.23	8.8	74.44
0.9	1.074	2.9	6.128	4.9	18.88	6.9	41.63	8.9	76.53
1.0	1.210	3.0	6.555	5.0	19.77	7.0	43.06	9.0	78.66
1.1	1.354	3.1	7.002	5.1	20.68	7.1	44.52	9.1	80.84
1.2	1.506	3.2	7.471	5.2	21.62	7.2	46.02	9.2	83.07
1.3	1.667	3.3	7.960	5.3	22.58	7.3	47.54	9.3	85.33
1.4	1.838	3.4	8.471	5.4	23.57	7.4	49.09	9.4	87.65
1.5	2.021	3.5	9.003	5.5	24.58	7.5	50.68	9.5	90.01
1.6	2.216	3.6	9.557	5.6	25.62	7.6	52.30	9.6	92.42
1.7	2.422	3.7	10.134	5.7	26.69	7.7	53.94	9.7	94.88
1.8	2.642	3.8	10.734	5.8	27.78	7.8	55.63	9.8	97.39
1.9	2.877	3.9	11.356	5.9	28.90	7.9	57.35	9.9	99.95
								10.0	102.56

giving larger reflectance intervals near zero (black). This may be seen by plotting the values in Table 13. It reflects the higher threshold of an observer adapted to a daylight illuminated gray of 10 per cent directional reflectance compared to a nearly dark-adapted observer.

In Figs. 14, 15, and 16 the definitions of Munsell hue and chroma are given in terms of the standard (x, y)-chromaticity diagram for dark (Munsell value = 1/), middle (Munsell value = 5/), and light (Munsell value = 9/) colors. Similar definitions for other Munsell values are given by Newhall, Nickerson, and Judd (1943). Note that the loci of constant Munsell hue are curved and

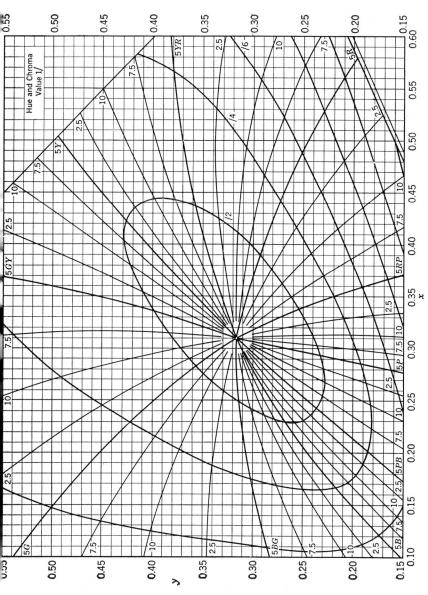

FIG. 14. Definition of Munsell hue and chroma for dark colors (Munsell value = 1/) in terms of the (x, y)-chromaticity diagram. The slightly curved lines intersecting at the point representing standard source C (x = 0.310, y = 0.316; representative of average daylight) correspond to constant Munsell hue. The approximately elliptical closed curve corresponds to Munsell chroma /2. The elliptical curve surrounding this curve and intersecting the spectrum locus near Munsell hue 7.5YR corresponds to Munsell chroma /4. Parts of the loci for Munsell chromas /6, /8, /10, and /12 are also shown. For colors darker than Munsell value 1/ (daylight reflectance equal to 0.0121), these loci become progressively farther from the source-C point. And as Munsell value (and daylight reflectance) approaches zero, the distance between the source-C point and all points on these loci becomes indefinitely great. (From Newhall, Nickerson, and Judd, 1943.)

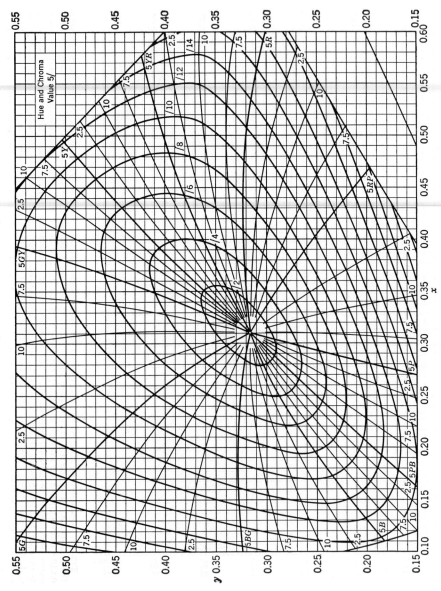

Fig. 15. Definition of Munsell hue and chroma for middle colors (Munsell value = 5/, or daylight reflectance equal to 0.1977) in terms of the (x, y)-chromaticity diagram. Note that the part of the spectrum having the lowest Munsell chroma corresponds to Munsell hue of about 9Y (573 mμ, upper right-hand corner). (From Newhall, Nickerson, and Judd, 1943.)

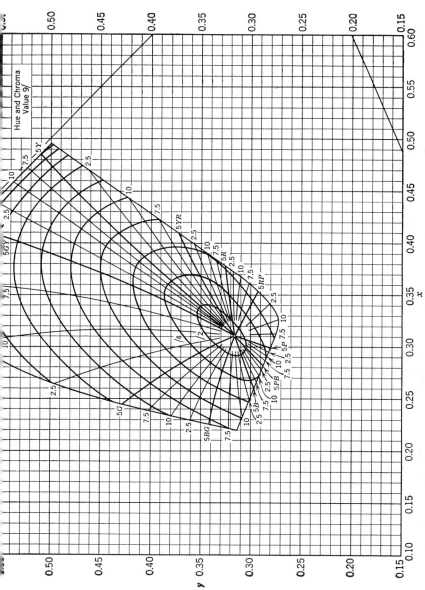

Fig. 16. Definition of Munsell hue and chroma for light colors (Munsell value = 9/) in terms of the (x, y)-chromaticity diagram. It will be noted that the hue loci drift somewhat from one Munsell value to another, and that the chroma loci become progressively smaller with increase in Munsell value. Furthermore the chromaticity range for which definitions of Munsell hue and chroma are given is much smaller at value 9/ than it is at lower values (see Figs. 14 and 15). This is because it is not possible to produce chromaticities outside this range by means of diffusely reflecting specimens and still have the Munsell value come up to 9/ (daylight reflectance equal to 0.787); that is to say, chromaticities outside this range correspond to Munsell value 9/ only if the spectral reflectance is greater than 1.000 for some parts of the spectrum. These boundaries between real and imaginary colors are called the MacAdam limits (OSA Committee on Colorimetry, 1944b). (From Newhall, Nickerson, and Judd, 1943.)

deviate from lines of constant dominant wavelength, which are straight on the chromaticity diagram. To a first approximation, Munsell hue compensates for the failure of dominant wavelength to correlate with the hue of the color perception.

Note that the chroma loci on Figs. 14, 15, and 16 do not parallel the course of the spectrum locus, as would lines of constant purity. On the contrary, Fig. 15 indicates that the colors of the spectrum in the neighborhood of hue $9Y$ (about 573 mμ) yield color perceptions of considerably lower saturation than those of other portions of the spectrum. To a first approximation, Munsell chroma corrects the failure of purity to correlate with saturation by its arbitrary assignment of the same designation (100 per cent) to all spectrum colors.

Note also that the locus defining chroma /2 for dark colors (Munsell value of 1/; Fig. 14) embraces a much larger fraction of the chromaticity diagram than that defining chroma /2 for light colors (Munsell value 9/; Fig. 16). This disparity between the two loci reflects the experimental fact that, of two chromatic colors of identical chromaticity, the light color yields a color perception of considerably higher saturation than the dark. On this account the Munsell chroma of an object color represents, to a first approximation, the saturation of the perception of object colors of all hues and lightnesses.

To summarize, Munsell hue, value, and chroma may be taken as the correlates of the hue, lightness, and saturation, respectively, of object colors when the observer is adapted to daylight. These correlates have the further advantage of being related approximately linearly to the magnitudes of the corresponding subjective attributes. Thus Munsell hue, value, and chroma reflect the psychological facts of object color to a good approximation, whereas dominant wavelength, luminous directional reflectance, and excitation purity reflect them only to a poor approximation. The Munsell notation

for an object color may be obtained by calculation from its reflectance (or transmittance) and its chromaticity coordinates (x, y) as in Table 13 and Figs. 14, 15, and 16, or it may be estimated by direct visual comparison with the color scales of the *Munsell Book of Color*.

Table 14 summarizes the stimulus correlates for the perception of color for (1) self-luminous areas, (2) transparent objects, and (3) matte, opaque objects. The fact that it is possible to list photometric and colorimetric variables that are in close correspondence with the attributes of color perception emphasizes the great strides made in visual psychophysics since 1900. Expressed in terms of radiometric quantities, the attributes of color perception are complicated interdependent functions of wavelength. In the standard luminosity function we have a simpler correlate for lightness and brightness, for all modes of appearance. But the precise functional relation between perceived brightness and luminance has not yet been determined as explicitly as has the relation between loudness and sound intensity, for example. Hue and saturation of object colors correlate closely with Munsell hue and Munsell chroma, respectively, which depend upon the firm establishment of colorimetry on the basis of X- and Z-chromatic functions of the standard observer. Further work remains to develop correlates yielding better agreement than dominant wavelength and purity with the hue and saturation perceived to belong to colors of self-luminous areas against a dark surrounding field.

Color Perception for Any Adaptation

The discovery of photometric and colorimetric functions by means of which we might predict the color perception belonging to any element or aspect of any visual field is the goal of theories of color perception. This goal is far from reached. But some of the relations already developed have considerable generality.

TABLE 14

SUMMARY OF STIMULUS CORRELATES FOR THE PERCEPTION OF COLOR BY A
DAYLIGHT-ADAPTED OBSERVER

Radiometric	Photometric and Colorimetric	Perceptual
Spectral radiance	Luminance	Brightness (dim to bright)
	Dominant wavelength and purity, or chromaticity coordinates	Hue and saturation, or red-green, blue-yellow
Spectral transmittance	Luminous transmittance	Lightness (dark to clear)
	Dominant wavelength and purity, or chromaticity coordinates	Hue and saturation, or red-green, blue-yellow
Spectral directional reflectance	Luminous directional reflectance	Lightness (black to white)
	Dominant wavelength and purity, or chromaticity coordinates,	Hue and saturation, or red-green, blue-yellow
	or Munsell value	Lightness (black to white)
	Munsell hue	Hue } { red-green
	Munsell chroma	Saturation } { blue-yellow

Retinal adaptation (negative after-image, Bezold-Brücke phenomenon). When a light gray spot on a uniform field of darker gray is fixated steadily for more than a few seconds, it is perceived to grow darker and thus approaches more closely the appearance of the background. In the same way the difference perceived between a dark gray spot on a lighter gray field decreases with steady fixation and finally reaches a state of equilibrium in which the difference in lightness is far below what it was at the start. Sometimes the difference falls below threshold, and the spot disappears momentarily. Any slight movement of the eyes restores the originally perceived difference. A few involuntary random eye movements may cause the spot to be perceived as a ring differing much from the background, and surrounding a center differing little. These temporal changes are usually attributed to depletion of photosensitive substance in the retina and are said to be the result of retinal adaptation.

Similarly, if the spot is chromatic, say saturated yellowish red, it is seen to lose its chromatic character with continued steady fixation, becoming less and less saturated until it approaches gray. This transition from a saturated yellowish red to a nearly gray color does not, however, yield a series of colors of constant hue. There is a hue change toward yellow as well as a loss of saturation. The hues that are invariant during adaptation are close to the unitary red, green, yellow, and blue (see Table 11), and according to Tschermak (1929) they correspond to them exactly if precautions are taken to have the observer adapted initially to a background truly gray.

When a spot on a background is fixated for a time and then removed, a negative after-image is perceived, a dark image for a light spot, a greenish image for a red spot, and a bluish image for a yellow spot. Since the hue of the negative after-image is approximately the psychological opposite of that of the original spot, it is said to be complementary. But the hue deviates both from the opposite hue and from the complementary shown in Table 7 by being more reddish blue.

The chief aspects of the negative after-image resulting from local chromatic adaptation may be accounted for qualitatively according to the three-components theory of vision, and moderate degrees of general adaptation can be accounted for quantitatively in much the same terms. This explanation is expressed by the so-called coefficient law enunciated by von Kries (1905).

It is a corollary of Grassman's laws that the components of a metameric pair will remain a match over a wide range of luminances and states of retinal adaptation. The appearance of each component may change from light to dark or even from red to green, depending on the adaptive state of the retina and on the background against which both members of the metameric pair are viewed. But, for a wide middle range of luminance they change appearance together. This behavior would be expected in a visual mechanism that starts with three independent photochemical processes, each having a sensitivity dependent on the concentration of a photosensitive substance.

The particular concentration present in a given retinal area at a given moment would be the result of a balance between the decomposing action of radiant energy previously incident on that area and the nutritive action of the retina. If a given stimulus produces in a rested portion of the retina the activities R, G, and B (see Fig. 7), and if S_r, S_g, and S_b are coefficients (less than 1) expressing diminished sensitivity of a pre-adapted retina or portion of the retina, then the coefficient law states that the appearance of the stimulus for the nonrested retina will be indicated by the products, $S_r R$, $S_g G$, and $S_b B$, just as the appearance for the rested retina is indicated by R, G, and B. Thus, if a color match is set up for a pair of stimuli between a rested and a nonrested retinal area, a comparison of the respective values of R, G, and B for the two stimuli will serve to evaluate the sensitivity coefficients, S_r, S_g, and S_b, and so to define the state of chromatic adaptation. Once these sensitivity coefficients are known they may be used to determine by computation whether any other pair of stimuli, one for the rested, the other for the nonrested retinal area, will be equivalent.

Wright (1934) has verified this coefficient law in the course of an attempt to determine the primaries referred to by R, G, and B. He was able, by application of the law, to deduce primaries that would be perceived to change in brightness alone, without any chromatic change during adaptation. The R- and G-primaries are not far different from those of the Ladd-Franklin theory (see Fig. 7), and the B-primary, less well determined, may not depart much either. The functions given in Table 8 for the Ladd-Franklin theory would therefore be the correlates for retinal adaptation in so far as it is described by the von Kries coefficient law.

There are reasons to believe, however, that the adjustment of the sensitivities of the initial receptor processes is only a part of the explanation of local and general color adaptation. Studies by Schouten and Ornstein (1939) on the change in retinal sensitivity resulting from stimulation of neighboring areas indicate that sensitivity changes may spread over the retina too rapidly to be explained by photochemical processes. Electrical action or nerve action influencing retinal sensitivity and taking place laterally in the retina is suggested. A momentary flash of strong light yields a complicated series of after-images (Judd, 1927) that also requires an explanation involving more than photochemical changes.

The coefficient law does not account for the failure of the color of the negative after-image to be an exact complementary to the color of the primary image. It does not account for the hue change with duration of stimulus, nor for an aspect of the negative after-image known as the Bezold-Brücke phenomenon.

The Bezold-Brücke phenomenon refers to the fact that the hues of most stimuli change with luminance. Spots of red, yellow, green, or blue often exhibit a decreased saturation but little or no hue change when luminance is increased. But yellowish red and yellowish green spots are yellower at high luminance, and bluish red and bluish green are bluer. It should be noted that in order to obtain this hue change the observer may fixate one spot of light while it is changed from a high luminance to a low. Or he may fixate the brighter spot, then the darker. By either procedure he projects the afterimage of the first spot onto the second. The Bezold-Brücke phenomenon is thus usually obtained as an aspect of the negative afterimage produced by retinal adaptation. Only if the time interval between presentation of the bright and dark spots is too prolonged would there be no after-image involvement.

The best attempt to explain the Bezold-Brücke phenomenon by the three-components theory of vision rests on a simple and likely assumption (Purdy, 1931b). The perception of a yellowish red light, produced, say, by 610 mμ, results from a major activity in the red-generating process and a minor activity in the green-generating process (see Figs. 5, 6, and 7). It is therefore assumed that the retina will become desensitized chiefly by loss of red-generating substance and only slightly by loss of green. For a portion of the retina partially adapted to light of 610 mμ, the appearance of this light should therefore incline toward that of shorter-wave light (toward yellow). For spectral regions near the crossing points of the curves of spectral sensitivity (Figs. 5, 6, and 7) the corresponding two photosensitive substances are assumed to be depleted equally, and no hue change is to be expected. By this argument, the original forms of the Young-Helmholtz theory (Figs. 5 and 6) do not work, because the crossing points fall at the wrong places in the spectrum. In order to account for the invariant hue found experimentally near 470 mμ we have to use the primaries of the Ladd-Franklin, or early König, theory (Fig. 7). But we find by this theory that a red-

dish-blue spot should change toward red (Purdy, 1931b) with increase in luminance, the reverse of the experimental result. The simple account of the Bezold-Brücke phenomenon in terms of the three-components formulation has, therefore, to be given up.

Since the invariant hues correspond well with the psychologically unitary hues (red, yellow, green, and blue), the Hering theory is often used as a basis not only for stating the facts of retinal adaptation but also for explaining them. Figure 17 shows Purdy's results (1931b) on the Bezold-Brücke phenomenon compared with the wavelength change corresponding in the Hering theory (see Table 8) to a hue change equivalent to a reduction of 20 per cent in the red-green response relative to the yellow-blue response. The ratio of the amounts of the two neighboring primary processes (red to yellow, yellow to green, green to blue, blue to red) is the correlate of hue. It will be seen that Purdy's results on the hue change due to an increase in retinal illuminance from 100 to 1,000 trolands may be described as closely equivalent to a 20-per-cent reduction in the red-green response relative to the yellow-blue. The basic determiners of this phenomenon are therefore the red-green and yellow-blue responses whose expressions are given in Table 8. This explanation does not prove that an adjustment of retinal sensitivities in the sense of the von Kries coefficient law is nonexistent; it simply indicates that the essential mechanism of the Bezold-Brücke phenomenon is to be found later in the chain of events.

The lower sensitivity of the red-green response compared to the yellow-blue response is ascribable to a nutritive preponderance of the yellow-blue process (Müller, 1930). This nutritive preponderance of the yellow-blue process leads to a prediction that the hue of a color should vary with duration in a manner analogous to the change with luminance. This prediction is borne out fairly well by experiment.

As already mentioned, there is a similar, but not exactly analogous, change in hue when a chromatic color is mixed with an achromatic color. The chromaticities produced by this mixture are shown by straight lines on the chromaticity diagram (Fig. 11). These lines

Y/Y_0, and Z/Z_0, called chromatic reflectances, in which X_0, Y_0, Z_0, are the tristimulus values of a standard white surface. The third stage is evaluated by the numbers, V_x, V_y, and V_z, found from Table 13 by substituting in succession the chromatic reflectances, in per

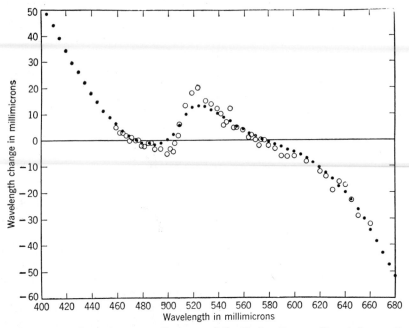

FIG. 17. Bezold-Brücke phenomenon in terms of the Hering theory. The circles are Purdy's experimental determination of the wavelength difference corresponding to the hue change caused by increasing retinal illuminance from 100 to 1000 trolands. The dots are derived from the Hering theory. The index of hue is the ratio of chromatic excitation for neighboring chromatic primaries (red to blue, blue to green, green to yellow, yellow to red). The dots show the hue change corresponding to a reduction of the red-green excitation by 20 per cent relative to the yellow-blue.

correspond to constant dominant wavelength. The experimental facts are shown fairly well on Figs. 14, 15, and 16 on which the lines of constant Munsell hue are seen in general to be curved instead of straight. The two exceptions are found near Munsell hue $10Y$ (about 572 mμ) and $5P$ (complementary to about 560 mμ). Adams has applied his theory to this problem and has shown that it can be closely solved by the assumption of a non-linear dependence of the third stage on the second. The second stage of the Adams theory (Table 8) is given directly by X/X_0,

cent, for Y_V. By plotting amount of blue-yellow process, $0.4(V_z - V_y)$, against amount of red-green process, $V_x - V_y$, we obtain a chromatic-value diagram on which the loci of constant hue should appear as straight lines passing through the origin, and those of constant saturation as circles. Figure 18 shows the hue and chroma contours for the ideal Munsell colors plotted on this diagram. The chroma contours do indeed approximate circles. The contours of constant Munsell hue show significant deviations from straight lines, but there is some basis for believing that straight lines on the chromatic-value plot correlate better with color perceptions of constant hue than does Munsell hue, itself.

Postretinal adaptation (simultaneous color contrast, color constancy, color transformation). Color contrast is the name given to by projection of a negative after-image of the red background onto the gray. Simultaneous color contrast thus seems superficially to correspond to a weak exertion of processes that yield retinal adaptation and, indeed, is sometimes called simultaneous in-

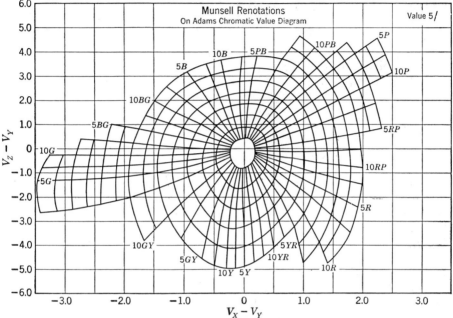

FIG. 18. Munsell renotations on the Adams (1942) chromatic-value diagram (after Nickerson, 1947). The abscissa $(V_x - V_y)$ refers to the optic-nerve-fiber stage of the Adams theory (see Fig. 10) and evaluates the red-green response. The ordinate $(V_z - V_y)$ similarly evaluates the blue-yellow response. Lines of constant hue on this diagram are straight lines passing through the origin which represents an achromatic color. Lines of constant saturation correspond to circles centered on the origin. Note that the experimental data expressed by the Munsell renotations, and intended to be in accord with the ideal Munsell system, support the Adams theory remarkably well, though not perfectly.

the effect exerted on the appearance of a portion of the visual field by the stimulation of the retinal regions corresponding to the neighboring portions of the field. If a small piece of medium gray paper is placed on the background of a large sheet of red paper and its center fixated, the gray paper takes on a greenish-gray appearance. Similarly a green background induces purple, and a yellow background induces blue.

If the fixation point is shifted from time to time, the appearance of the gray paper changes to a rather saturated bluish green duction to emphasize its similarity to successive induction often ascribed to retinal adaptation. The explanation that accords with this view is that the red-generating substance is used up in the surrounding retinal areas, the deficiency being supplied from the central area by a process of diffusion, leaving the central region relatively blue-green sensitive. This, in turn, makes the gray take on a greenish appearance.

The evidence is against this view, however. Color contrast is too nearly instantaneous to arise from a process of diffusion of retinal fluids or substances. It is enhanced rather than diminished by elimination of clearly defined contours. Binocular simultaneous color contrast can occur (Tschermak, 1929). Likewise there can be obtained under some conditions the contrast color for the area corresponding to the blind spot, the exit point of the optic nerve. Further evidence is available from pathological cases (Müller, 1930). Simultaneous color contrast is accordingly considered to have its chief seat in the nerve processes outside the retina, and to be of the same nature as other contrast phenomena involving not only the eye but also other sense organs. Electro-adaptation of the retina (Schouten, 1939) probably also contributes to it, but diascleral light and light diffracted, scattered, and reflected within the eyeball opposes it.

When the illumination of a room is changed from daylight to candlelight, the observer perceives readily that there is a reddish-yellow character in the illumination not present before. After about 5 minutes, presumably because of retinal adaptation, this reddish-yellow character is perceived much less definitely. Even at the instant of change, however, objects perceived to be white in daylight are usually perceived to be white, or nearly white, in candlelight, despite the fact that the spectral composition of the radiant energy reaching the eye of the observer has changed markedly. The transformation of an object color perceived under chromatic illumination from the appearance proper to the spectral composition of the radiant energy leaving it back nearly to its daylight appearance is called color transformation (Jaensch, 1921).

Color transformation depends on the grasp of the situation by the observer. If he perceives that the illumination is reddish yellow, he also automatically adjusts his perception of object color accordingly. Color transformation has therefore been described as an automatic discounting of the illumination color. The perception of illumination color is drawn from the organization of the visual field itself. If the observer fails to make an organization that includes objects illuminated by reddish-yellow light, he will perceive the object colors to be quite different (more reddish yellow) than in daylight, or he may even fail to organize the visual field into objects in an illuminated space at all. Such failure may come from destruction of cortical tissue as by a gunshot head wound (Gelb, 1920) or from an insufficiently structured visual field. Changes from one organization to another take place rapidly, much as the reversible-staircase picture changes from a bottom view to a top view. Color transformation is therefore ascribed to cortical processes, but these processes are rapid and largely automatic rather than deliberate like those of intellectual judgment.

In studies of color transformation, and also in studies of the effects of local changes in the amount and spectral composition of the illumination (as when an object in shadow is compared with another outside the shadow), the most striking result is the tendency of object colors to be perceived as of the same hue, lightness, and saturation, regardless of the illuminant. Often the object-color constancy (Gelb, 1929; MacLeod, 1932, 1940) is virtually perfect, but it is possible for the same observer to respond to the stimulus in very different ways. If he regards an element of the object merely as a patch of color, his responses may exhibit only a slight tendency toward constancy with change in the illuminance of the working plane. His estimates of lightness may correlate better with luminance (see Table 14) than with luminous directional reflectance, or his estimates may correlate with some intermediate factor. But if he judges the object color relative to others in the field of view, his estimates of lightness will correlate well with luminous directional reflectance.

The observer will, of course, perceive a difference between a highly illuminated object and a poorly illuminated one. The former is sometimes reported as having a more pronounced color (Katz, 1930). Pronouncedness is an attribute of the colors perceived to belong to all objects in a uniformly illuminated space. It correlates with the average luminance of the visual field corresponding to the illuminated space, or with the illuminance of the observer's eye by light from the illuminated space, or with some other equivalent photometric quantity (Bocksch, 1927; Bühler, 1922; Gelb, 1929; Katz, 1930; Koffka, 1935; Pikler, 1931, 1932).

By color transformation an observer is able to make object-color perceptions immediately that accord well with what he obtains a few minutes later after he has become completely adapted to the new illuminant. Also by color transformation an observer is able to perceive an object in shadow or colored light as having a color resembling that perceived to belong to it when it is taken out of the local deviating illumination and viewed by the general illumination (MacLeod, 1932, 1940). Simultaneous color contrast also tends in the direction of preserving object-color constancy, though to a much smaller degree, according to Jaensch (1921).

Another factor tending to preserve the color constancy of visual objects is memory color (G. K. Adams, 1923). If the room is full of familiar objects, recognition of the object in an unfamiliar illumination will often cause its color to be perceived as it would be in the usual kind of illuminant, say daylight. Substitution of an object of the same size and shape but of considerably different color may often go unrecognized. Memory color leads to perfect color constancy of visual objects and is ascribed to cortical processes. Sometimes the phenomenon of color transformation has been falsely ascribed to memory color. But color transformation occurs in a regular way, including regular deviations from color constancy. Furthermore the phenomenon can be obtained characteristically with quite unfamiliar test objects. It is probably true, however, that in daily life color transformation and memory color work together to promote recognition

of objects in unfamiliar illuminations and to prevent disorientation. In producing this effect they are aided greatly by retinal adaptation, and somewhat by simultaneous color contrast.

Indices of the attributes of color perception. Perfect correlates of the attributes of color perception have yet to be worked out. There are two methods of approach to this problem. One is the analytical approach; another is the configurational approach.

In the analytical approach an attempt is made first to evaluate the direct contribution from the element of the visual field under consideration, then to evaluate the indirect contribution to the color of this element induced by other elements neighboring in space and immediately preceding in time. The sum of these contributions gives the perceived color. By this view the basic correlates are the expressions for white-black, yellow-blue, and red-green given in Table 8. White, black, yellow, blue, red, and green take on the nature of elementary sensations and apply not only to matte opaque objects but also to elements of the visual field perceived to belong to self-luminous objects and to elements perceived as film or aperture color. According to this view both the lightness of a nonself-luminous object and the brightness of an aperture or self-luminous object are to be correlated with the white-black response. Hue is to be correlated with the ratio of responses of neighboring chromatic primaries (red to yellow, yellow to green, green to blue, and blue to red). Saturation is to be correlated with the fraction of the total chromatic response relative to the total achromatic plus chromatic.

The advantage of this view is that it sanctions experimentation, with simple, controlled conditions of observation, for the purpose of building up a store of information regarding the color inductions produced by various pre-exposure and surrounding fields (Müller, 1930; Tschermak, 1929). It gives an insight into the working of the visual mechanism by ascribing various portions of the induced contribution to such elements as changes in sensitivity of the initial photochemical processes, to contrast, and to nutritive differences among the assumed neural processes. The chief disadvantage of using the analytical method exclusively is that it has so far proved to be impossible to put the pieces together so as to predict successfully the color perceptions belonging to elements of a complicated field. It is not clear whether the present limitations of the analytical method are ascribable to errors in evaluating the relative importance of the various components, or whether the analysis has itself caused an essential aspect of color perception to be ignored.

In the configurational approach an effort is made to take direct account of the total stimulating situation, simple or complex. The basic idea is that color perception correlates with gradients in the visual field relative to some frame of reference rather than with an absolute response to each element separately (Koffka, 1935). Explicit account is taken of the mode of appearance of the color. For the aperture and illuminant modes of appearance, brightness is correlated with the luminance of the spot relative to a function of the average luminance of the whole visual field (Kardos, 1935). Hue and saturation are similarly correlated with the chromaticity of the spot considered in relation to a function of an average chromaticity of the whole visual field (Judd, 1940).

For colors perceived to belong to nonselfluminous objects it has been found possible to deal successfully with complicated experimental situations in which the various matte objects are in a visual space that is perceived to be uniformly and diffusely illuminated (Helson, 1938, 1940). The color change perceived when the illuminant, or the background, or the state of adaptation is changed has been termed *color conversion* by Helson (1938). The principle of color conversion for object colors is that objects whose luminous directional reflectance is above a certain critical value, called the

adaptation reflectance, tend toward the hue of the illuminant color, and those whose reflectance is below this value tend toward the after-image complementary of the illuminant hue. In this configurational approach the reference point is the adaptation reflectance. It is found to be about half the average luminous directional reflectance of all objects in the visual field (Judd, 1940).

The lightness of the object-color perception was found to correlate well with $R_\theta/(R_\theta + R_f)$, where R_θ is the luminous directional reflectance of the object, and R_f is the average luminous directional reflectance of all objects in the visual field. R_θ is computed from equation 4f by using the actual spectral irradiance of the (usually nondaylight) illuminant.

The fundamental reference point on the chromaticity diagram for estimates of hue and saturation is the point corresponding to an achromatic color. As a first approximation this point corresponds to that representing the chromaticity of the illuminant. That is to say, a series of spectrally nonselective (gray) papers appears nearly gray under any kind of illumination. However, for strongly chromatic illuminants a nonselective surface whose reflectance is close to adaptation reflectance appears slightly off-gray in the direction of reddish blue. The point corresponding to an achromatic color is therefore slightly on the green side of the illuminant point for surfaces whose reflectance is close to adaptation reflectance. For lighter and darker objects the achromatic point deviates in a regular way from this region slightly on the green side of the illuminant point.

Work by Judd (1940) shows that hue is indicated approximately by the direction on the UCS triangle (see Fig. 13) of the line connecting the achromatic point with the point representing the object color, and that saturation is indicated approximately by the length of this line. More careful work by Bouma and Kruithof (1947) indicates, however, that hue does not correlate perfectly with the direction of this line on the UCS triangle, or with any transformation of it.

Unpublished work by Helson and his associates has also led to a principle of color conversion for aperture or illuminant color. The reference point on which this principle is based is the adaptation luminance, which is found to be about half the average luminance of the visual field. This principle states that parts of the field above adaptation luminance tend toward the color of that part viewed under daylight adaptation, and parts below the adaptation luminance tend toward the after-image complementary. The Bezold-Brücke phenomenon is a special case of this principle of color conversion for aperture and illuminant color.

For visual space perceived to be directionally illuminated, the color perceptions of opaque objects depend upon how the observer perceives their surfaces to be oriented with respect to the chief direction of the illumination. Luminous directional reflectance fails under these circumstances to be a reliable correlate of the lightness of the perceived color, and no substitute for it has yet been worked out. If there are glossy surfaces in the field of view, some of them may have luminous directional reflectances greatly exceeding unity. In a rough way any excess of luminous directional reflectance above unity correlates with the glossiness of the perception. But other aspects of the situation, such as the shape and character of the mirror images seen by light reflected from the surfaces relative to other shapes in the field, have a bearing on the glossiness of the object perception. These same aspects also influence the lightness of the color perception of glossy objects. Similarly it is known qualitatively that the shape and character of the transmitted images determine the transparency perceived to belong to volumes and surfaces. Color perception of objects is interrelated with the perception of their transparency and glossiness in ways that have not yet been evaluated quantitatively.

GLOSSARY

ABSOLUTE LUMINOSITY. Luminosity (which see) expressed in absolute terms, such as lumens per watt (see Table 5); distinguished from relative luminosity (see $\bar{y}$ of Table 6).

ACHROMATIC COLOR. Color perceived to have no hue, same as neutral color.

ACHROMATOPIA. Type of vision by which all colors are perceived as achromatic.

ACHROMATOPSIA. Same as achromatopia.

ADAPTATION REFLECTANCE. Reflectance above which spectrally nonselective surfaces tend toward the hue of the illuminant, and below which the hue tends toward the after-image complementary; equal to about half of average of the luminous directional reflectances of the surfaces filling the visual field.

ALYCHNE. Line on the chromaticity diagram (outside the area representing physically realizable colors) corresponding to zero luminosity; lightless line.

ANOMALOUS TRICHROMATISM. Trichromatic type of vision possessed by an observer whose metamers depart from normal in a way not to be explained by abnormal ocular pigmentation.

APERTURE COLOR. Color perceived as filling a hole in a screen; same as film color (see Table 9).

APOSTILB. Unit of luminance equivalent to 1/10 millilambert (see Table 4).

BEZOLD-BRÜCKE PHENOMENON. Change of hue with luminance.

BLIND SPOT. Exit point of the optic nerve; also the part of the visual field corresponding to this point.

BLOOM. Appearance of haze near the highlight of a glossy specimen.

BRIGHTNESS. Psychological attribute of aperture and illuminant-color perceptions in terms of which they may be ordered on a scale from dim to bright.

CANDLE. Unit of luminous intensity; a source of 1 candle in all directions emits 4π lumens (see Table 4).

CANDLE PER SQUARE CENTIMETER. Unit of luminance equivalent to 1000π millilamberts; same as stilb (see Table 4).

CANDLE PER SQUARE FOOT. Unit of luminance equivalent to 3.380 millilamberts (see Table 4).

CHROMATIC ADAPTATION. Process by which the visual mechanism comes to equilibrium under the influence of a stimulus of nondaylight chromaticity.

CHROMATIC COLOR. Color perceived to have a hue.

CHROMATICITY-CONFUSION LINES. Lines on the chromaticity diagram indicating the normal chromaticities confused by a partially color-blind observer (see Fig. 12).

CHROMATICITY COORDINATES. Ratio of one of the tristimulus values of a color to the sum of all three (see Table 12, Figs. 11 and 13, and equation 8).

CHROMATICITY DIAGRAM. Plane diagram obtained by plotting one of any set of chromaticity coordinates against one of the other two coordinates of the same set (see Figs. 11 to 16).

CHROMATICNESS. Aspect of a color perception determined by its hue and saturation taken together; psychological correlate of chromaticity.

CHROMATIC REFLECTANCE. Name given by Adams (1942) to the ratios X/X_0, Y/Y_0, and Z/Z_0, where X, Y, Z are the tristimulus values of the light reflected from a surface, and X_0, Y_0, Z_0 are the tristimulus values of the light reflected from a standard white surface such as magnesium oxide, similarly illuminated and viewed.

CHROMATIC VALUES. Name given by Adams (1942) to the differences, $0.4(V_z - V_y)$ and $V_x - V_y$, where V_x, V_y, V_z are the Munsell values found by substituting chromatic reflectance in percentage ($100X/X_0$, $100Y/Y_0$, $100Z/Z_0$) for Y_V in percentage in Table 13.

COLOR. Characteristics of light other than spatial and temporal inhomogeneities.

COLORIMETRIC PURITY. Ratio of the luminance of the spectral component of a mixture to luminance of the mixture, itself.

COMPLEMENTARY COLORS. Colors whose additive combination in some proportion is equivalent to some arbitrary choice of achromatic color.

COMPLEMENTARY WAVELENGTH. Wavelength of the spectral band that when mixed with the color produces a match for some arbitrary choice of achromatic color.

CONTRAST RATIO. Ratio of the luminance of an object backed by black to that backed by white; a correlate of transparency.

DECIBEL. A logarithmic measure of the ratio between two quantities. The number of decibels denoting the ratio is 10 times the logarithm to the base 10 of the ratio. (The decibel is widely used as a measure of ratios between electric powers and between acoustic powers, less widely used for photometric quantities such as luminance.)

DEUTERANOMALY. Type of anomalous trichromatism.

DEUTERANOPIA. Type of partial color blindness.

DIASCLERAL LIGHT. Light entering the eyeball through the sclerotic coat.

DICHROMATISM. Type of vision requiring two primaries to duplicate by addition the colors seen; partial color blindness.

DIRECTIONAL REFLECTANCE. The reflectance that a perfectly diffusing surface would have to possess in order to yield the same luminance as the object in question under the same illuminating and viewing conditions (see equation 2a).

DIRECTIONAL TRANSMITTANCE. Ratio of the luminance (candle per unit area) of the second surface of a light-transmitting specimen to the illuminance (lumens per unit area) of the first surface.

DOMINANT WAVELENGTH. Wavelength of the spectral band that when mixed with some arbitrary choice of achromatic color produces a match for the chromatic color.

DOMINATOR-MODULATOR THEORY. Visual theory based on the assumption that a separate dominating receptor exists for the brightness aspect of vision with chromatic distinctions introduced by receptors modulating the dominant response (see Table 8).

EQUAL-ENERGY STIMULUS. Stimulus whose irradiance per unit wavelength is constant throughout the spectrum.

EQUIVALENT COLOR STIMULI. Stimuli producing identical colors.

EXCITATION PURITY. Ratio of two distances on the standard chromaticity diagram (see Fig. 11), the first distance being that between the point representing some arbitrary choice of achromatic color and the point representing the chromatic color to be specified, and the second being that between the achromatic point and the point on the border of physically realizable colors (spectrum locus, line connecting its extremes) of the same dominant or complementary wavelength as the chromatic color to be specified.

FOOT-CANDLE. Unit of illuminance; the illuminance produced by a uniform point source of 1 candle on a surface every point of which is 1 foot away from the source (see Table 4).

FOOT-LAMBERT. Unit of luminance equivalent to 1.076 millilamberts; a perfectly reflecting, perfectly diffusing surface illuminated with an illuminance of 1 foot-candle has a luminance of 1 foot-lambert, regardless of the direction of view (see equations 2 and 2a, and Table 4).

FREQUENCY. Rate of vibration of electromagnetic radiation; frequency in cycles per second is found by dividing the velocity of electromagnetic radiation (3.0×10^{17} millimicrons per second) by its wavelength. Under ordinary conditions the highest frequency to which the eye responds is that corresponding to 380 mμ or about 790×10^{12} cycles per second; the lowest frequency corresponds to 780 mμ and is about 385×10^{12} cycles per second.

GLOSSINESS. Attribute of surface perception ranging from matte to glossy. There are various kinds of glossiness: absence-of-bloom glossiness characterized by absence of haze near the highlight; contrast glossiness characterized by brightness of a highlight judged relative to that of the surrounding area; distinctness-of-image glossiness; specular gloss characterized by brightness of the highlight; sheen characterized by brightness of the highlight seen at grazing incidence; metallic glossiness or luster characterized by an intense highlight not necessarily achromatic; and vitreous glossiness or luster characterized by a moderately intense achromatic highlight.

HAZE. Characteristic of light-transmitting specimens, specifically the difference between its transmittance and its regular transmittance divided by its transmittance, thus: $(T - T_r)/T$; correlate for transparency.

HUE. The attribute of a color perception that determines whether it is red, yellow, green, blue, purple, or the like (see Tables 9 and 14).

ILLUMINANCE. Areal density of incident luminous flux; formerly called illumination; the most common unit of illuminance is the foot-candle (see Tables 3 and 4).

ILLUMINANT COLOR. Color perceived as belonging to a self-luminous object (see Table 9).

ILLUMINATION. Process of supplying an area with luminous flux.

ILLUMINATION COLOR. Color perceived as belonging to the illumination pervading a space.

IMAGINARY CHROMATICITY. Chromaticity not producible by any part of the spectrum or any combination thereof; chromaticities conceived as corresponding to some one process in the visual mechanism in the absence of activity of other processes are usually imaginary.

INSISTENCE. Attribute of object-color perception correlated with its luminance; closely allied to and perhaps identical with the brightness of the aperture-color perception derivable from the object by interposition of a screen with a hole in it (reduction screen).

INTERNAL TRANSMITTANCE. Ratio of the flux reaching the second surface of a specimen to that penetrating the first (see Table 2).

IRRADIANCE. Areal density of incident radiant flux; radiometric analogue of illumination (see Table 1).

LAMBERT. Unit of luminance equal to that of a perfectly diffusing surface emitting or reflecting light at the rate of 1 lumen per square centimeter (see Table 4).

LIGHT. That aspect of radiant energy of which a human observer is aware through the visual sensations that arise from the stimulation of the retina of the eye.

LIGHTNESS. Attribute of an object-color perception ranging either from black to white (surface) or from black to perfectly clear (non-light-diffusing volume). See Table 9.

LUMEN. Unit of luminous flux equal to that through a unit solid angle (steradian) from a uniform point source of 1 candle; the total flux emitted by such a source is 4π lumens (see Table 4).

LUMINANCE. Luminous flux emitted per unit solid angle (steradian) and unit projected area of source; formerly called photometric brightness; the most common unit of luminance is the millilambert (see Tables 3 and 4).

LUMINOSITY. Ratio of any photometric quantity to the corresponding radiometric quantity in standard units (such as the ratio of luminous flux to radiant flux in lumens per watt; see Table 3); formerly called visibility or radiant luminous efficiency.

LUMINOUS DIRECTIONAL REFLECTANCE. See Directional reflectance; also equation 2a and 4a.

LUMINOUS DIRECTIONAL TRANSMITTANCE. See Directional transmittance; also equation 4b.

LUMINOUS FLUX. Rate of transfer of luminous energy (see Table 3).

LUMINOUS INTENSITY. Flux luminated per unit solid angle in a given direction from a point source (see Table 3).

LUX. Unit of illuminance equal to that produced at a surface, all points of which are at a distance of 1 meter from a uniform point source of 1 candle; same as meter-candle or lumen per square meter; equivalent to 0.0929 foot-candle (see Table 4).

MAXWELL TRIANGLE. Chromaticity diagram.

MEMORY COLOR. Color perception based on recognition of the object.

METAMERIC PAIR. Pair of stimuli having the same color but different spectral composition.

METAMERISM. The property exhibited by a metameric pair; if the members of the pair are of greatly different spectral compositions, they are said to exhibit a high degree of metamerism.

MILLILAMBERT. The most commonly used unit of luminance; one-thousandth of a lambert (see Table 4).

MILLIMICRON (m_μ). Unit of length equal to one-thousandth of a micron, or one-millionth of a millimeter, or one billionth of a meter, or 10 Angstroms; unit of length most frequently used to specify wavelength of visible radiant energy.

MILLIPHOT. Unit of illuminance equal to one-thousandth of a lumen per square centimeter, or one-thousandth of a centimeter-candle, or one-thousandth of a phot (see Table 4).

MODE OF APPEARANCE. Characterization of a color according to whether it is perceived to belong to an aperture, a surface, a volume, an illuminant, or the like (see Table 9).

MONOCHROMATISM. Type of vision requiring only one primary to duplicate the colors seen.

MUNSELL BOOK NOTATION. Munsell hue, value, and chroma of a color estimated by interpolation and extrapolation from the color scales of the *Munsell Book of Color*.

MUNSELL CHROMA. Expression of the degree of departure of an object color from the nearest gray color on arbitrary scales defined in terms of its Y-value (luminous reflectance, or luminous transmittance) and its chromaticity coordinates (see Table 13, and Figs. 14, 15, and 16).

MUNSELL HUE. Correlate of hue on arbitrary scales defined in terms of Y-value (luminous reflectance, or luminous transmittance) and chromaticity coordinates (see Table 13, and Figs. 14, 15, and 16).

MUNSELL RENOTATION. Munsell hue, value, and chroma of an object color obtained by reference to the definition of the ideal Munsell system (see Table 13, and Figs. 14, 15, and 16).

MUNSELL VALUE. Expression of the luminous reflectance, or transmittance, of an object on an arbitrary scale giving approximately uniform perceptual steps under usual conditions of observation; correlate of lightness (see Table 13).

NEUTRAL COLOR. See Achromatic color.

PHOT. Unit of illuminance equal to that produced at a surface, all points of which are at a distance of 1 centimeter from a uniform point source of 1 candle; same as centimeter-candle; same as lumen per square centimeter (see Table 4).

PHOTOMETRIC BRIGHTNESS. See Luminance.

PHOTON. See Troland.

PROTANOMALY. Type of anomalous trichromatism.

PRIMARY COLOR PERCEPTIONS. Color perceptions in terms of which all color perceptions are analyzed; usually black, white, blue, yellow, green, and red, but sometimes middle gray is added (see Tables 9 and 14).

PRONOUNCEDNESS. Attribute of nonself-luminous object-color perceptions correlated with illuminance of the objects in the field of view.

PROTANOPIA. Type of dichromatism.

PURITY. Degree to which a color approaches that of the spectrum at the same dominant wavelength; approximate correlate to saturation. Two scales of purity have been widely used: colorimetric purity, and excitation purity (which see).

RADIANCE. Radiant flux radiated per unit solid angle (steradian) and unit projected area of source; radiometric analogue of luminance (photometric brightness). See Tables 1 and 3.

RADIANT ENERGY. Energy traveling through space in the form of electromagnetic waves of various lengths (see Table 1).

RADIANT FLUX. Time rate of transfer of radiant energy; the most common unit is the watt (see Table 1).

RADIANT INTENSITY. Radiant flux radiated per unit solid angle (steradian) about a source (see Table 1).

REDUCTION SYSTEM. Visual system differing from the normal trichromatic system simply by nonfunction of one or two of the three processes.

REFLECTANCE. Ratio of reflected to incident flux; see equation 2.

RELATIVE LUMINOSITY. Luminosity expressed relative to maximum (near 555 mμ for daylight vision); see $\bar{y}$-function of Table 6.

REVERSE TRANSFORMATION COEFFICIENTS. Coefficients of transformation required to return tristimulus values from a transformed color system back to expression in terms of the original system (see equation 6b).

SATURATION. The attribute of any color perception, possessing a hue, that determines the degree of its difference from the achromatic color perception most resembling it (see Table 9).

SPECTRAL COMPOSITION. Distribution of any radiant quantity as a function of wavelength (see Table 1).

SPECTRAL REFLECTANCE. Ratio of reflected to incident radiant flux of narrow wavelength range.

SPECTRAL TRANSMITTANCE. Ratio of transmitted to incident radiant flux of narrow wavelength range.

SPECTRUM LOCUS. Locus of points on a chromaticity diagram representing the chromaticities of the spectrum colors (see Figs. 11, 12, and 13).

STAGE THEORY. Theory of vision in which separate account is taken of processes at various stages or zones of the visual mechanism (photosensitive substances, receptors, retinal nerve fibers, optic-nerve fibers, etc.); same as zone theory.

STILB. Unit of luminance equal to 1 candle per square centimeter; equivalent to 1000π millilamberts (see Table 4).

TETARTANOPIA. Controversial form of partial color blindness.

TRANSFORMATION EQUATIONS. Equations whereby tristimulus values expressed in terms of one set of primaries may be transformed into those expressing the same color relative to another set of primaries (see equations 6 and 6b).

TRANSFORMATION COEFFICIENTS. The coefficients of a set of transformation equations (see equations 6 and 6b, and Table 8).

TRANSMITTANCE. Ratio of transmitted to incident flux.

TRANSPARENCY. Perceptual quality of a volume correlated with the degree to which the elements of the volume transmit light in an image-forming state.

TRICHROMATISM. Type of vision requiring three primary lights to duplicate the colors seen; normal vision is trichromatic.

TRISTIMULUS VALUES. Amounts of the primaries required to produce a match with the sample, either by addition of all three, or addition of one primary to the sample to match any pair of primaries, or the addition of any pair to the sample to match the remaining primary; amounts of a primary added to the sample are indicated by a negative algebraic sign.

TRITANOMALY. Form of anomalous trichromatism.

TRITANOPIA. Form of partial color blindness.

TROLAND. Unit of retinal illuminance equal to that produced by viewing a surface whose luminance is 1 candle per square meter through an artificial pupil whose area is 1 square millimeter centered on the natural pupil (see equation 3).

UNIFORM-CHROMATICITY-SCALE DIAGRAM. Maxwell triangle within which the separation of two points is an approximate measure of the perceptibility of the difference between the chromaticities represented by them (see equation 8 and Fig. 13).

UNITARY HUE. Hue perceived as having no admixture of neighboring hues; the unitary hues are red, yellow, green, and blue (see Table 11).

WAVELENGTH. Distance traversed by spectrally homogeneous radiant energy during a single period of vibration.

ZONE THEORY. Same as stage theory.

REFERENCES

Adams, E. Q. A comparison of the Fechner and Munsell scales of luminous sensation value. *J. opt. Soc. Amer. and Rev. Sci. Instr.*, 1922, **6**, 932.

Adams, E. Q. A theory of color vision. *Psychol. Rev.*, 1923, **30**, 56.

Adams, E. Q.   *X-Z* planes in the 1931 I.C.I. system of colorimetry.   *J. opt. Soc. Amer.*, 1942, **32**, 168.

Adams, G. K.   An experimental study of memory color and related phenomena.   *Amer. J. Psychol.*, 1923, **34**, 359.

American Society for Testing Materials.   Haze of transparent plastics by photoelectric cell. ASTM Designation D672-45T, ASTM Standards, 1945, Supplement, Part III.   Philadelphia, 1945.   P. 362.

American Standards Association.   Illuminating engineering nomenclature and photometric standards.   American Standard Z7.1-1942, Feb. 27, 1942.

American Standards Association.   Letter symbols for heat and thermodynamics including heat flow.   American Standard Z10.4-1943, June 1943.

Bixby, F. L.   A phenomenological study of luster. *J. gen. Psychol.*, 1926, **1**, 136.

Bocksch, H.   Duplizitätstheorie und Farbenkonstanz.   *Z. Psychol.*, 1927, **102**, 343.

Bouma, P. J., and A. A. Kruithof.   Chromatic adaptation of the eye.   *Philips Tech. Rev.*, 1947–48, **9**, 257.

Bühler, K.   Die Erscheinungsweisen der Farben. In *Handb. d. Psychol.*   Jena: Fischer, 1922. Heft 1, Teil 1.

Commission Internationale de l'Éclairage.   Proc. 8th Session, Cambridge, England, September 1931.   Pp. 19–29.

Dimmick, F. L., and C. H. Holt.   Gray and the color pyramid.   *Amer. J. Psychol.*, 1929, **41**, 284.

Dimmick, F. L., and M. R. Hubbard.   The spectral location of psychologically unique yellow, green, and blue.   *Amer. J. Psychol.*, 1939a, **52**, 242.

Dimmick, F. L., and M. R. Hubbard.   The spectral components of psychologically unique red. *Amer. J. Psychol.*, 1939b, **52**, 348.

Dresler, A.   Über den Einfluss von Farbton und Sättigung auf die Messung verschiedenfarbiger Lichter.   *Das Licht*, 1937, **7**, 203.

Fick, A.   Die Lehre von der Lichtempfindung. In L. Hermann (Ed.), *Handb. d. Physiol.* Leipzig: Vogel, 1879.   Heft 3, Teil 1, p. 139.

Fry, G. A.   The stimulus correlate of bulky color. *Amer. J. Psychol.*, 1931, **43**, 618.

Gelb, A.   Die "Farbenkonstanz" der Sehdinge. In A. Bethe (Ed.), *Handb. d. normalen u. path. Physiol.*   Berlin: Springer, 1929.   Volume XII/1, p. 594.

Gelb, A., and L. Goldstein.   *Psychologische Analysen hirnpathologischer Fälle.*   Leipzig, 1920. Volume I; *Z. Psychol.*, 1920, **84**, 193.

Gibson, K. S., and E. P. T. Tyndall.   Visibility of radiant energy.   *Sci. Pap. Bur. Stand. Wash.*, 1923, **19**, 131; S475.

Goodeve, C. F.   Vision in the ultraviolet.   *Nature, Lond.*, 1934, **134**, 416.

Graham, C. H., R. H. Brown, and F. A. Mote, Jr. The relation of size of stimulus and intensity in the human eye.   I. Intensity thresholds for white light.   *J. exp. Psychol.*, 1939, **24**, 555–573.

Granit, R.   A physiological theory of colour perception.   *Nature, Lond.*, 1943, **151**, 11–14.

Grassman, H.   Zur Theorie der Farbenmischung. *Pogg. Ann. Physik.*, 1853, **89**, 69; *Phil. Mag.* (Ser. 4), 1853, **7**, 254.

Griffin, D. R., R. Hubbard, and G. Wald.   The sensitivity of the human eye to infra-red radiation.   *J. opt. Soc. Amer.*, 1947, **37**, 546–554.

Guild, J.   The colorimetric properties of the spectrum.   *Philos. Trans.*, 1931, **A230**, 149.

Hardy, A. C.   *Handbook of colorimetry.*   Cambridge, Mass.: Technology, 1936.

Hartridge, H.   The visual perception of fine detail.   *Philos. Trans.*, 1947, **B232**, 538.

Haupt, I. A.   The selectiveness of the eye's response to wavelength and its change in intensity.   *J. exp. Psychol.*, 1922, **5**, 347.

Hecht, S., and R. E. Williams.   The visibility of monochromatic radiation and the absorption spectrum of visual purple.   *J. gen. Physiol.*, 1922, **5**, 1.

Hecht, S., S. Shlaer, and M. H. Pirenne.   Energy, quanta, and vision.   *J. gen. Physiol.*, 1942, **25**, 819.

Helmholtz, H. von.   *Handbuch der physiologischen Optik.*   (3rd Ed.)   Leipzig: Voss, 1911.   Volume 2, p. 122.

Helson, H.   Fundamental problems in color vision. I. The principle governing changes in hue, saturation, and lightness of non-selective samples in chromatic illumination.   *J. exp. Psychol.*, 1938, **23**, 439.

Helson, H., and V. B. Jeffers.   Fundamental problems in color vision.   II. Hue, lightness, and saturation of selective samples in chromatic illumination.   *J. exp. Psychol.*, 1940, **26**, 1.

Hering, E.   *Ueber individuelle Verschiedenheiten des Farbensinnes.   Lotos, Prague*, 1885, New Series, *6; Zbl. prakt. Augenhlk.*, November 1885.

Hering, E.   Grundzüge der Lehre vom Lichtsinn. In Graefe-Saemisch (Eds.), *Handb. d. ges. Augenhlk.*   (2nd Ed.), 1905.

Hunter, R. S.   Methods of determining gloss. *J. Res. Nat. Bur. Standards*, 1937, **18**, 19; RP958.

Ives, H. E.   Studies in the photometry of lights of different colours.   *Phil. Mag.* (Ser. 6), 1912, **24**, 149, 352, 744, 845, 853.

Jaensch, E. R.   Ueber den Farbencontrast und die sogenannte Berücksichtigung der farbigen Beleuchtung.   *Z. Sinnesphysiol.*, 1921, **52**, 165.

Jones, L. A.   Summary of American opinion BS/ARP 18, British standard specification for fluorescent and phosphorescent paint.   Transmitted to Dr. P. G. Agnew, Secretary, American Standards Association, June 2, 1942.

Judd, D. B.   A quantitative investigation of the Purkinje after-image.   *Amer. J. Psychol.*, 1927, **38**, 507.   (Bibliography of 30 titles.)

Judd, D. B. The 1931 I.C.I. standard observer and coordinate system for colorimetry. *J. opt. Soc. Amer.*, 1933, **23**, 359.

Judd, D. B. A Maxwell triangle yielding uniform chromaticity scales. *J. Res. Nat. Bur. Standards*, 1935, **14**, 41; RP756; *J. opt. Soc. Amer.*, 1935, **25**, 24.

Judd, D. B. The specification of light-scattering materials. *J. Res. Nat. Bur. Standards*, 1937, **19**, 287; RP1026; *Paper Trade J.* (Tech. Sect.), 1935, **106**, 5; also *Tech. Assoc. Papers* (Ser. 21), 1938, 474.

Judd, D. B. Hue, saturation, and lightness of surface colors with chromatic illumination. *J. Res. Nat. Bur. Standards*, 1940, **24**, 293; RP1285; *J. opt. Soc. Amer.*, 1940, **30**, 2.

Judd, D. B. Color systems and their inter-relation. *Illum. Eng. N. Y.*, March 1941, **36**, 336.

Judd, D. B. Facts of color-blindness. *J. opt. Soc. Amer.*, 1943, **33**, 294. (Bibliography of 62 titles.)

Judd, D. B. Standard response functions for protanopic and deuteranopic vision. *J. Res. Nat. Bur. Standards*, 1944, **33**, 407; RP1618; *J. opt. Soc. Amer.*, 1945, **35**, 199.

Judd, D. B. Response functions for types of vision according to the Müller theory. *J. Res. Nat. Bur. Standards*, 1949, **42**, 1; RP1946.

Kardos, L. Versuch einer mathematischen Analyse von Gesetzen des Farbensehens. Nähere Bestimmung des funktionalen Verhältnisses zwischen Farbenerlebnis und Reizgesamtheit. *Z. Sinnesphysiol.*, 1935, **66**, 188.

Katz, D. *The world of color.* London: Kegan Paul, Trench, Trubner, 1935. (Translation of *Der Aufbau der Farbwelt.* Leipzig: Barth, 1930.)

Koffka, K. *Principles of Gestalt psychology.* New York: Harcourt, Brace, 1935.

Kohlrausch, A. Zur Photometrie farbiger Lichter. *Das Licht*, 1935, **5**, 259, 275.

König, A. Ueber Newtons Gesetz der Farbenmischung und darauf bezügliche Versuch des Hrn. Eugen Brodhun. *Sitzber. Akad. Wiss. Berlin*, Mar. 31, 1887, p. 311; also in *Gesammelte Abhandlungen.* Leipzig: Barth, 1903. p. 108.

König, A. Ueber "Blaublindheit." *Sitzber. Akad. Wiss. Berlin*, July 8, 1897, p. 718; also in *Gesammelte Abhandlungen.* Leipzig: Barth, 1903, p. 396.

König, A., and C. Dieterici. Die Grundempfindungen in normalen und anomalen Farbensystemen und ihre Intensitätsverteilung im Spectrum. *Z. Psychol.*, 1892, **4**, 241; also in *Gesammelte Abhandlungen.* Leipzig: Barth, 1903, p. 214.

Kreezer, G. Luminous appearance. *J. gen. Psychol.*, 1930, **4**, 247.

Kries, J. von. Die Gesichtsempfindungen. In W. Nagel (Ed.), *Handb. d. Physiol. des Menschen.* Braunschweig: Vieweg, 1905. Volume 3, p. 269.

Ladd-Franklin, C. Eine neue Theorie der Lichtempfindungen. *Z. Psychol. u. Physiol. Sinnesorg.*, 1892, **4**, 211; *Colour and colour theories.* New York: Harcourt, Brace, 1929, p. 219.

Ludvigh, E., and E. F. McCarthy. Absorption of visible light by the refractive media of the human eye. *Arch. Ophthal.*, 1938, **20**, 37.

MacLeod, R. B. An experimental investigation of brightness constancy. *Arch. Psychol., N. Y.*, 1932, **21**, No. 135.

MacLeod, R. B. Brightness-constancy in unrecognized shadows. *J. exp. Psychol.*, 1940, **27**, 1.

Martin, L. C., F. L. Warburton, and W. J. Morgan. Determination of the sensitiveness of the eye to differences in the saturation of colours. Medical Research Council, Report of the Committee on the Physiology of Vision, XIII, Special Report Series, No. 188. London, 1933.

Martin, M. F. Film, surface, and bulky colors and their intermediates. *Amer. J. Psychol.*, 1922, **33**, 451.

Maxwell, J. C. Experiments on colours, as perceived by the eye, with remarks on colour-blindness. *Trans. roy. Soc., Edinb.*, 1855, **21**, 275.

McKeon, W. M., and W. D. Wright. The characteristics of protanomalous vision. *Proc. phys. Soc., Lond.*, Part 4, 1940, **52**, 464.

Müller, G. E. Zur Theorie des Stäbchenapparates und der Zapfenblindheit. *Z. Sinnesphysiol.*, 1922–23, **54**, 9, 102.

Müller, G. E. *Darstellung und Erklärung der verschiedenen Typen der Farbenblindheit.* Göttingen: Vandenhoeck and Ruprecht, 1924.

Müller, G. E. Ueber die Farbenempfindungen. *Z. Psychol.*, 1930, *Ergänzungsbd.* **17–18**. Pp. 46, 508.

Newhall, S. M., D. Nickerson, and D. B. Judd. Final Report of the OSA subcommittee on the spacing of the Munsell colors. *J. opt. Soc. Amer.*, 1943, **33**, 385.

Nickerson, D. Interrelation of color specifications. *Paper Trade J.*, July-December, 1947, **125**.

OSA Committee on Colorimetry. The concept of color. *J. opt. Soc. Amer.*, 1943. **33**, 544.

OSA Committee on Colorimetry. The psychophysics of color. *J. opt. Soc. Amer.*, 1944*a*, **34**, 246, 254, 255.

OSA Committee on Colorimetry. Quantitative data and methods for colorimetry. *J. opt. Soc. Amer.*, 1944*b*, **34**, 665, 672, 677, 682.

Pikler, J. Das Augenhüllenlicht als Mass der Farben. *Z. Psychol.*, 1931, **120**, 189; 1932, **125**, 90.

Pitt, F. H. G. Characteristics of dichromatic vision. Medical Research Council, Report of the Committee on the Physiology of Vision, XIV, Special Report Series, No. 200. London, 1935.

Purdy, D. McL. On the saturations and chromatic thresholds of the spectral colours. *Brit. J. Psychol.* (Gen. Sect.), 1931*a*, **21**, 283.

Purdy, D. McL. Spectral hue as a function of intensity. *Amer. J. Psychol.*, 1931*b*, **43**, 541.

Schouten, J. F., and L. S. Ornstein. Measurements on direct and indirect adaptation by means of a binocular method. *J. opt. Soc. Amer.*, 1939, **29,** 168.

Schrödinger, E. Ueber das Verhältnis der Vierfarben- zur Dreifarbentheorie. *Sitzber. Akad. Wiss. Wien* (Math.-Nat. Kl., Abt. 2a), 1925, **134,** 471.

Sinden, R. H. Studies based on spectral complementaries. *J. opt. Soc., Amer.*, 1923, **7,** 1123.

Sloan, L. L., and S. M. Newhall. Comparison of cases of atypical and typical achromatopsia. *Amer. J. Ophthal.*, 1942, **25,** 945.

Stiles, W. S., and B. H. Crawford. *Proc. roy. Soc.*, 1933, **B112,** 428.

Teele, R. P. Photometer for luminescent material. *J. Res. Nat. Bur. Standards*, 1945, **34,** 325; RP1646.

Tschermak, A. Licht- und Farbensinn. In A. Bethe (Ed.), *Handb. d. normalen. u. path. Physiol.* Berlin: Springer, 1929. Volume XII/1, pp. 322, 342, 345, 351, 381, 489, 497.

Urbanek, J., and E. Ferencz. Report of the Hungarian Secretariat Committee. Sur la Photométrie Visuelle. *Internationale Beleuchtungskommission, Proc. 10th Session. Scheveningen, 1939,* 1942, **1,** 44.

Wald, G. Human vision and the spectrum. *Science,* June 29, 1945, **101,** 653.

Weaver, K. S. The visibility of radiation at low intensities. *J. opt. Soc. Amer.*, 1937, **27,** 36.

Weaver, K. S. A provisional standard observer for low level photometry. *J. opt. Soc. Amer.*, 1949, **39,** 278.

Wright, W. D. A re-determination of the trichromatic mixture data. Medical Research Council, Report of the Committee on the Physiology of Vision, VII, Special Report Series, No. 139. London, 1929.

Wright, W. D. The measurement and analysis of colour adaptation phenomena. *Proc. roy. Soc.*, 1934, **B115,** 49.

Wright, W. D. The breakdown of a colour match with high intensities of adaptation. *J. Physiol.*, 1936, **87,** 23.

23.

Visual Perception

C. H. GRAHAM
Columbia University

Historically considered, the problems of visual perception have centered about such topics as span of perception, size constancy, fluctuations of perception, illusions, grouping of stimuli, precision of perception, and influence of context. These topics entail such questions as the following: (1) Within what limits do stimuli, arranged according to a given numerical classification and exposed for a short duration, elicit "number" responses that meet certain criteria of classification? (2) What is the relation between response and retinal image size? (3) What are the stimulus variables that underlie response alternation? (4) In what manner are certain changes in stimulus configuration associated with a change in response? (5) How does the spatial and temporal ordering of stimuli affect response? (6) What change on a stimulus dimension is required to produce a change in response? (7) How does previous stimulation influence the response to a present stimulus?

The questions as formulated call for an experimental program, one that seeks to determine specific, explicitly stated relations between stimulus, response, and whatever hypothesized variables become logically necessary.

The stimulus-response relations of the perception experiment derive from the experimental methods involved. Consider first the

This account was prepared under Project NR142-404, Contract N6onr-271, Task Order IX, between Columbia University and the Office of Naval Research, U. S. Navy.

matter of response specification; in particular, let the discussion center about a specific case: the determination of a visual threshold. When a visual threshold is determined by the method of constant stimuli, the subject's responses may be restricted by the "instruction stimulus" to two categories: * "Yes (I see it)" and "No (I don't see it)." We accept these responses as different, if for no other reason than that one is an affirmation and the other a negation, although it is true, but probably not crucial, that their physical sound-wave properties are also different.

* In using the psychophysical methods, we restrict the subject's responses by means of the "instruction stimulus." When specific instructions to restrict response categories are not given, the subject's responses are relatively uncontrolled and are in the nature of introspective verbal reports. Such responses usually demonstrate so many degrees of freedom that their classification is difficult or impossible.

In general it seems desirable to concentrate our unknown variables in the instruction stimulus and to restrict responses. When such a procedure is followed, it may, with some reason, be assumed that the conditions of the organism are constant for a given instruction stimulus; and for the constant condition we may quantify restricted responses in a way that is not possible with unclassifiable responses. Perhaps it may turn out that unknown conditions of the organism, due to instruction, may be specifiable as parameters of observable stimulus-response relations. Such an outcome would present a great advance over our present knowledge, for it is certain that instruction stimuli are now specifiable only at the level of social conversation; i.e. no instruction stimulus may be related to another within a framework of quantitative relations.

It turns out in an experiment of this sort that, as we vary the energy of the physical stimulus, the frequency of occurrence of each response follows a different function. Because of this fact we no longer have to specify response differences on the basis of conversational "significances," but may explicate such differences more reliably and more specifiably by the operation of plotting response frequencies. Similarly, in using the psychophysical methods of single stimuli, limits, and sense distances, we are provided with various types of frequency distributions of contrasting responses plotted as functions of stimulus variables. The method of adjustment which strictly speaking involves only one class of response — adjustment — may be made to provide an *arbitrary* specification of response classes on the basis of the distribution of stimulus settings (e.g. on the basis of the standard deviation).*

Now consider the classification of stimuli. Various classifications exist at the present time; but all are subject to the condition that the specified variables must be unequivocally related to response.

In certain areas of sensory psychology it can be shown that stimulus energies are important correlates of response, and one measures stimulus strength in the proper units. For example, a description of visual stimuli may involve classifications with respect to wavelength, distance from fovea, and amount of energy. In this type of classification, stimuli are specified in terms of a system (e.g. physics) that has little or no reference to the response elicited; the light may be described whether or not a subject is present. However, reference to response enters as soon as we consider the determination of stimulus values that have response parameters (e.g. thresholds).†

At another level of stimulus specification, measurement of the stimulus may be made in terms that have direct or indirect reference to response. For example, in measuring thresholds of stereoscopic vision, we make use of a difference in visual angles η as our primary stimulus datum. The use of η is based upon a theory of how stimulation of "disparate points" influences response; it is, as it were, a "second-order" measurement, given in terms of some mathematical concepts appropriate to a psychological theory.

At more complex levels physical specification of stimuli may not, at present, be especially significant. For example, the physical characteristics of sound waves that constitute words are not closely related to response; a subject may give the same response to a whisper as to a shout. In such a case the basis of stimulus classification must reside in adequate psychological theory rather than in physical measurement.

Our discussion makes it clear that the observable variables of the psychophysical experiment are response on the one hand and stimulus operations on the other; in particular the data describe how differential restricted responses relate to such stimulus operations as the presentation of objects, words, and energies. Such data are discrimination data (Graham, 1950).‡ When pro-

---

* It might be worth while to differentiate between the behavior, i.e. discrimination behavior, that is observable in experiments employing the methods of constant stimuli, single stimuli, limits, and sense distances, and the behavior observable in the method of adjustment, i.e. "matching" behavior. Such differentiation would be precise, but in what follows we shall not always make the distinction.

It may be argued that any given adjustment, under the method of adjustment, involves a serialized set of discriminations involving different responses and changing stimuli. This is a theoretical position and calls for specification of the response components of the adjustment. No data on the problem exist at present, and an answer can be reached only by direct observation of a subject in the psychophysical experiment.

† In determining thresholds, theory may dictate the particular function of the stimulus variable to plot on the abscissa axis of a psychophysical curve. In such cases the plot may involve a numerical transformation of a measured energy. On problems that occur with the use of numerical transformations, see Mueller (1949).

‡ For different approaches to problems of perception see Brunswik's account of the "representative" experiment (1947) and Thurstone's description of his factor analysis investigations (1944).

cedures other than the psychophysical methods are used, and, in particular, when responses are not restricted, the data are in terms of "introspective" reports and are neither easily interpretable quantitatively nor classifiable at a level higher than social conversation.

In what follows, a "subjective" terminology will sometimes be used, not because the terms with which it deals are unspecifiable in behavior concepts but because, in the interest of avoiding circumlocution, such words as "apparent," "perception," "see," "detect," etc., are convenient. Nevertheless it is asserted that the behavior functions of which these words are descriptive are discriminations except, possibly, in cases that involve unrestricted responses.*

VISUAL SPACE PERCEPTION

Many of the concepts and measures of space perception are based on elaborate theoretical considerations. Even such a seemingly simple measure of stimulus as visual angle may involve a complex theory of the eye as an optical instrument.

Historically (Carr, 1935; Hering, 1861–64; Helmholtz, 1924) the specification of stimulus conditions for space perception has been formalized in terms of so-called cues, and these cues, in turn, have been divided into two types: monocular and binocular. Mo-

* The present discussion does not attempt to differentiate between "sensation" and "perception." From the point of view of analysis of consciousness, sensation is an irreducible element; perception is an aggregate of sensations. From the point of view of behavior, a specification of what a subject does when he analyzes "sensation" and what he does when he "perceives" is not now available and probably will not be available for a long time. In any case it is doubtful if such specialized behavior would be of great interest. Other attempts to differentiate sensation and perception on the basis of physiological and psychological mechanisms seem unfruitful. In general, it seems that the term sensation has been applied to those discussions for which some relevant sense organ theory exists, and the term perception to those for which no such theory exists. No basis for differentiation exists in the psychological functions obtained.

nocular cues are those that elicit spatial discriminations on the basis of vision with a single eye. Binocular cues require the coordinated activity of the two eyes.

The monocular cues are the following:

1. *Relative size.* Our discrimination of distances is dependent on the size of the retinal image provided by an object and by our past experience with objects of the same class. A small retinal image provided by a member of a class of objects called automobiles results in the response, "Distant automobile."

2. *Interposition.* The cue of interposition occurs when an overlapping object is said to be nearer than an overlapped object. The cue that exists in these circumstances is based on the fact that the contour line of the overlapping object does not change its direction discontinuously at a point where it joins the contour of the overlapped object. On the other hand, the contour line of the overlapped object does change direction discontinuously at the same point. The discrimination of continuity of contour change from discontinuity of contour change is the essential cue.

3. *Linear perspective.* The stimulus condition for this cue is determined by the fact that a constant distance between points subtends a smaller and smaller angle at the eye as the points recede from the subject. A subject reports that lines formed by car tracks, telephone wires, etc., seem to approach each other in the distance.

4. *Aerial perspective.* When surface details of an object do not provide conditions for requisite visual contrasts, a subject reports that the object seems far off.

5. *Monocular movement parallax.* When a subject's eyes move with respect to the environment, or when the environment moves with respect to a subject's eyes, a differential angular velocity exists between the line of sight to a fixated object and the line of sight to any other object in the visual field. This condition of differential angular velocity leads to such discriminations as are

concerned with the response that *near* objects move *against* the direction of movement and *far* objects move *with* the direction of movement (of the head or environment).

6. *Light and shade.* Various combinations of shadow and highlight are reported as objects having various dimensions and lying at different distances.

7. *Accommodation.* Differential aspects of "blur circles" in a retinal image may elicit spatial discriminations, although probably not for objects at distances greater than a few yards.

The two binocular cues are convergence and stereoscopic vision.

1. *Convergence.* When an object is at a great distance, lines of fixation to the object are parallel. When the object is near at hand, the subject's eyes are turned in a coordinated manner so that the lines of fixation converge on the object. Convergence may serve as a cue for depth responses. A large amount of convergence may lead to the response "nearby object," and slight convergence may lead to the response "far-off object." Convergence cues cannot be differentially effective for objects at distances greater than about 20 yards.*

2. *Stereoscopic vision.* When a subject regards an object in space, the retinal image in the right eye is different from the retinal image in the left eye. The difference in retinal images serves as the basis for many spatial discriminations. Theoretically the essential stimulus condition for stereoscopic vision is a difference in convergence angles between (*a*) lines of sight from the two eyes that converge at a fixated object point, and (*b*) those that converge at another object

point. (Note that the term *convergence angles* does not imply the response of convergence. It is used in a geometrical sense.)

Of the visual cues for space, relative size, linear perspective, monocular movement parallax, accommodation, interposition, and stereoscopic vision are most specifiable in quantitative terms. The cues of aerial perspective, and light and shade are conveniently specifiable, at present, only in terms of the subject's response. However, some studies, such as those of Blackwell (1946) and Hardy (1946), may clarify our concepts of specifiable contrasts and other variables in aerial perspective and may indicate an approach to some problems of illumination gradients in light and shade. Finally, the reader is referred to Schlosberg's account (1941) of the very striking depth effects, dependent only on monocular cues, that may be obtained under proper conditions of monocular viewing.

Except for a very short account of some of the better known "illusions," little attention will be paid in what follows to cues classifiable on a response basis. Rather the attempt will be made to show the manner in which theoretical concepts and analysis aid in the specification of stimuli. Finally, we shall make a survey of experimental findings on controlling variables of the stimulus-response relations of space perception.†

---

* It might be argued that, since the subject cannot report on his condition of convergence (Ludvigh, 1936), convergence is not a cue for space. It is true, however, that convergence enters as a parameter of other space discriminations (see e.g. Matsubayashi, 1938*d*). Thus, in the sense that it is an influencing variable, convergence is, in fact, a cue. The requirement that a cue be capable of eliciting a verbal report is unnecessary.

† The mathematical analysis of binocular vision by Luneburg (1947) is of considerable interest to the present discussion. Luneburg has been concerned with finding the mathematical form of the metric of the "visual space." He concludes that the geometry of the visual space is the hyperbolic geometry of Lobachevski. Luneburg's treatment expresses the general hypothesis that, for an individual observer, the apparent size of a line element is uniquely determined by its physical coordinates; thus the judgment of visual size depends not only upon angular relations but also upon the location of the line element. On this basis Luneburg discusses such problems as the horopter problem and the alley problem.

It is to be noted that Luneburg's treatment, in a sense a sophisticated "phenomenological" account, is based upon a psychometric coordination that attempts to introduce the concept of a metric in a manifold of "sensations." From the point of view of the present discussion, Lune-

Visual Angle

Visual angle is a basic variable in experiments concerned with the cues of relative size and linear perspective; in fact it may be conveniently employed whenever visual extents and positions must be designated. Thus it is a measure applicable in one way or another to all visual experiments.

In Fig. 1 the line e represents a distance relating to some aspect of the stimulus situation (e.g. a length of line, a diameter, a separation between points, etc.). We wish to specify the visual angle subtended.

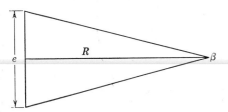

Fig. 1. Diagram representing the concept of visual angle.

For the condition that the line of regard bisects e, the visual angle β is given by

$$\tan \frac{\beta}{2} = \frac{e}{2R} \tag{1}$$

where R is the distance to e along the line of regard.

When β is small (so that $\tan \beta = \beta$, approximately)

$$\beta = \frac{e}{R} \tag{2}$$

in radians, or

$$\beta = \frac{57.3e}{R} \tag{3}$$

in degrees.

Equations 2 and 3 overestimate β by 1 per cent at a value of 10 degrees, and by 3 per cent at a value of 17 degrees. When line e is curved, so that all its points are equidistant from the reference point of the eye, equations 2 and 3 hold perfectly. If line e is tilted with respect to R, more com-

burg's hypothesized coordination is the very problem for which an experimental answer is sought. Its relation to behavior requires analysis.

plex calculations, analogous to those used for asymmetric convergence (see section on Convergence), must be employed.

Equations 2 and 3 are probably applicable to most situations in which visual angles must be determined. Where the equations are not applicable, good experimental design would often require that conditions be changed so that they become applicable. For example, in the peripheral retina a stimulus area should be disposed at the same distance R as the fixation point. Under these conditions accommodation is the same for the test area as it is for the fixation point, and equations 2 and 3 may be used.

The distance R is most practicably measured from the front surface of the cornea. If it is desired to calculate retinal image size, the reference point at the vertex of angle β (at or in the eye) must be specified. In any event visual angle computations should be accompanied by a statement as to (1) absolute stimulus size, and (2) position of reference point (e.g. corneal surface) from which the distance R is measured. Given these two variables it is possible to recalculate the data for any other reference point (e.g. anterior principal point) dictated by the particular form of image equation applicable to the experimental conditions. The considerations that apply under various circumstances are discussed by Southall (1933).

Discrimination of sizes. It has been known for a long time (Martius, 1889) that, under certain conditions, when a subject has been instructed to adjust the size of a comparison stimulus at constant distance until it matches a standard stimulus at a variable distance, the resulting "match" is not one that would be predicted on the basis of retinal image theory. Instead the size of the comparison stimulus changes little with increase in distance of the standard. This effect has been termed "size constancy."

Holway and Boring (1941) have performed the most adequate investigation of the conditions that influence "equation settings" for size discrimination. Their method was the following: A comparison stimulus, a uniformly illuminated circular light image, was viewed by the subject at a distance of 10 feet. The image diameter S_c could be continuously varied in size by means of an iris diaphragm. The standard stimulus, which varied in distance from 10 to 120 feet from the subject's eyes, was always of a diameter S_s that subtended a visual angle of 1 degree. Brightnesses of the two stimuli were identical for any one series of measurements, but the level varied in different series.

Results were plotted on graphs showing the diameter S_c of the comparison stimulus as the ordinate, and D_s (the distance of the standard stimulus) as the abscissa. In this type of graph, performance that results in an equating of the comparison stimulus with the standard stimulus on the basis of visual angle is represented by a horizontal line (law of the visual angle).

The law of the visual angle is based on the following reasoning. The visual angle given at the eye by S_c (variable diameter) is arctan $S_c/2D_c = \beta_c/2$; and the angle given by S_s (variable in distance) is arctan $S_s/2D_s = \beta_s/2$. For $\beta_c = \beta_s$, $S_c/D_c = S_s/D_s$. But S_s/D_s is constant ($= 2 \tan 0.5°$) and so is D_c ($= 10$ feet). Therefore, for an adjustment based on $\beta_c = \beta_s$,

$$S_c = \left(\frac{S_s}{D_s}\right) D_c = \text{Constant} \qquad (4)$$

and, when S_c is plotted against D_s, the curve must be a straight line of zero slope.

For the law of size constancy, $S_c = S_s$. But $S_s = D_s (2 \tan 0.5°)$, and so

$$S_c = D_s(2 \tan 0.5°) \qquad (5)$$

Equation 5 means that, if the law of size constancy applies to the data of Holway and Boring, S_c should be linearly related to D_s by way of a slope constant equal to $2 \tan 0.5°$ and an intercept constant of zero.

Figure 2 summarizes the data of the experiment for four conditions of observation. With binocular comparison the data are found to be in accord with expectations based on the law of size constancy. (There

may even be overcompensation as shown by the fact that the data fall above the line for "constancy." Holway and Boring tentatively attribute this effect to a possible "space error.")

With monocular regard, a condition that excludes cues contributed by stereoscopic vision, the data still adhere to the law of size constancy. With monocular vision through an artificial pupil (1.8 millimeters in diam-

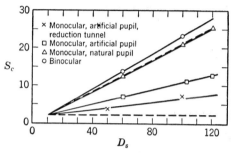

FIG. 2. The diameter of the comparison stimulus S_c plotted against the distance of the standard stimulus D_s for the conditions of observation in Holway and Boring's experiment (1941). The inclined dashed line represents an expectation based on size constancy. The horizontal dashed line represents an expectation based on the law of the visual angle.

eter), the slope of the experimental function is reduced and the curve lies about halfway between the curves representing the two laws; i.e. the constancy effect is reduced. Finally, when observations are made monocularly through an artificial pupil and a long dark tunnel constructed to eliminate faint extraneous reflections, the experimental function approaches the law of the visual angle even more closely.

The experiments of Holway and Boring show that constancy behavior may be expected when conditions of stimulation are "complex," a fact emphasized by Thouless (1931a, b) and by Woodworth (1938) with respect to color and brightness constancy. When stimuli are restricted to a condition that involves a minimum number of parameters, the phenomena of constancy appear in slight degree, if at all.

In a later experiment Taylor and Boring (1942a) used two subjects, each of whom was blinded in one eye. The two subjects, long experienced in making monocular discriminations, gave data that more closely approximate the law of the visual angle than do the data of temporarily monocular subjects.

Vernon (1937), Koffka (1935), and Boring (1942) give excellent discussions of experiments on size constancy, and Boring relates them to research on the geometry of afterimages and the early "alley" experiments (Hillebrand, 1902; Blumenfeld, 1913). The work of Köhler (1915) on chimpanzees and Götz (1926) on chickens shows that discrimination of sizes in lower animals tends to be of the "constancy" type; that is, for the conditions examined the responses are more in accord with expectations based on the law of size constancy than on the law of the visual angle. Beyrl (1926) and Frank (1928) obtained similar findings with young children, although deviations from the law of the visual angle were not so marked with their subjects as was true in earlier experiments on adults.

Holaday (1933) examined the question of "attitude" and found that a "betting" attitude is conducive to obtaining a size constancy function. Conditions for obtaining the constancy function are improved when extraneous objects are placed between the stimuli and the subject. The experiments of Schur show that deviation from the law of the visual angle is a function of elevation of regard, and this same influence is emphasized by Boring (1943) in considering the "moon illusion" (i.e. the fact that a subject reports the moon at the horizon to be larger than the moon at the zenith). After participating in three experiments (Holway and Boring, 1940a, b; Taylor and Boring, 1942b), Boring (1943) says:

It (the moon illusion) is not due to physical causes outside the visual mechanism. It is not due to the greater brightness of the moon in elevation, when atmospheric haze

is diminished. It depends on raising or lowering the eyes. Movements of the head, neck, and body do not cause it.

Discrimination of shapes. In an extensive series of experiments dealing with various types of constancy, Thouless (1931a) studied the responses subjects made to obliquely viewed objects. In a first experiment he had subjects regard circles or squares laid on a table top at distances of 54.5, 109.0, and 163.5 centimeters from the subject's end of the table. Each square was oriented so that one diagonal was parallel to the subject's line of regard, and the figures were viewed from a point 48.5 centimeters above the table. The subject was instructed to "reproduce" each square or circle in a drawing. Such an instruction calls for a complex, serialized response, probably uncertainly specifiable on the basis of selected dimensions of the "drawing."

The results show that the ratios of the short to the long axis in the "drawings" were 1⅓ to 2⅓ times as large as would be predicted by the laws of retinal image theory. In other words the reproduced ellipses and squares were much closer to being true circles and squares than were the elliptical and trapezoidal retinal images of the circles and squares. When the subject was given actually elliptical disks to reproduce in direct vision, the ratios of short to long axes in the "drawings" were very close to the true ratios. Similar results were obtained by a matching method.

Thouless performed an additional experiment to discover how deviations from retinal image theory vary with the angle of object inclination. A white circular disk 29.7 centimeters in diameter was mounted on a turntable with its axis of rotation horizontal and at right angles to the subject's line of vision. Turning the turntable presented the disk to the subject at varying angles of inclination. The subject's task was to match the inclined circle to a standard ellipse. Measurement of the axes for each condition of inclination of the circle was performed by a photographic method.

Results are presented in Fig. 3, which shows the ratio of short to long axes of comparison ellipses as a function of angle of inclination of the circle. The solid line with a slope of 45 degrees is the line relating the two variables on the basis of retinal image theory. The experimental data fall above

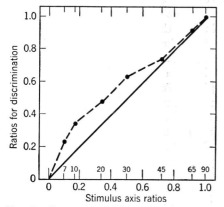

FIG. 3. Shape comparisons of an ellipse and a tilted circle. Adjusted axis ratio of the comparison stimulus (ellipse) is plotted as a function of axis ratio of the standard stimulus (circle) for various inclinations of the latter. Upper abscissa units give angular inclinations of the circle in degrees. The solid inclined line gives the expectation based on the law of the retinal image. (After Thouless, 1931a.)

the "image theory" line, and we see that obtained ratios of short to long axes of the comparison ellipse are generally larger than would be expected on the basis of the geometry of the retinal image.

A later experiment (Thouless, 1931b) was concerned with the elimination of cues. In general it may be said that Thouless' experiments give results analogous to those that appear in researches on size "matchings." When stimulus cues are present in addition to the presumably single discriminative stimulus, matching values are influenced by the total constellation. What the laws are that govern perception in the presence of cue constellations is a question that sets a program of research. When the constellation is

restricted, matchings are predictable on the basis of retinal image theory.

Stavrianos (1945) performed an experiment on the relation between matchings made with respect to object inclination and matchings made with respect to object shape.

The hypothesis tested predicts that changes in the accuracy with which inclination is judged will be accompanied by changes in the accuracy of shape perception such that, when the inclination of an object is accurately perceived, its apparent shape will coincide with the actual shape; when inclination is underestimated (when in the extreme case, an object appears frontal-parallel though it is actually tilted), the apparent shape will deviate from the actual in the direction of the retinal shape; and when the inclination of the object is overestimated, the apparent shape will deviate from the actual in the direction of greater than object match or overconstancy.

The experimental data are, in general, not in agreement with the hypothesis. Stavrianos says:

We may conclude from our investigation that perception of shape may be roughly related to explicit judgment of inclination. However, in order to provide a crucial test of our hypothesis, further experiments are required in which explicit judgments of inclination and shape are made with approximately the same attitude and conditions as the implicit registration of tilt and shape.

The experiment that most nearly demonstrates a relation between tilt matchings and shape matchings is Stavrianos' Experiment III, in which errors in tilt adjustments were accompanied by the expected errors in shape adjustments for some of the subjects. In this experiment the subject was required to designate which of a series of seven rectangles appeared square. The rectangles varied in altitude from rectangles "taller than wide" to rectangles "shorter than wide." Each rectangle had a base of 5 centimeters. The background on which the rectangles were placed was presented in a frontal-parallel position and at deviations of 15, 30, 45, and 55 degrees from the frontal parallel. The subject's task was to adjust the rectangle at his right until its tilt was considered equal to that of the background containing the rectangular forms, and then to designate which of the seven rectangular forms was seen as square. Binocular vision was used.

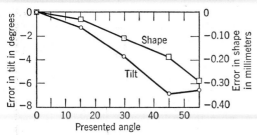

Fig. 4. Constant errors for tilt adjustments and for judgments of squareness plotted against angular inclination of the standard stimulus. The tilt setting of the comparison stimulus deviates more and more from the tilt of the standard stimulus as the tilt of the latter increases. In addition, the constant error of shape matching increases as the degree of tilt of the standard stimulus increases. Data are from Stavrianos' Experiment III (1945).

Constant errors for tilt and shape were determined and are shown in Fig. 4. The figure shows that the tilt setting of the comparison stimulus deviates more and more (in the direction of smaller tilt) from the tilt of the standard stimulus as the tilt of the latter increases. In addition the constant error of shape matching increases as the degree of tilt of the standard stimulus increases. At a zero-degree tilt the square designated is in fact very nearly a true square (5 × 5 centimeters). As tilt increases, the designated square becomes a rectangle with increasing height; i.e. the rectangle must become increasingly higher to be responded to as a square.

The status of size and shape discriminations. It is no exaggeration to say that the facts of size and shape discriminations are poorly understood. The lack of understanding may be due to a number of causes. In

the first place, experiments have often been demonstrational rather than analytic. In particular a long series of researches has not resulted in those systematically determined functional relations which, as Holway and Boring (1941) say, are "wanted and wanting." In the second place, theoretical considerations have often outrun experimental data with the consequent development of a theoretical structure weak in operational specification and definition. Despite these difficulties the problems of size and shape discrimination are important and require understanding.

What can we say about the experiments on size? For one thing they clearly show that size matches are dependent on the presence or absence of stimuli other than those that may be naïvely considered to be *the* discriminative stimuli (Holaday, 1933; Holway and Boring, 1941). Second (Köhler, 1915; Götz, 1926; Beyrl, 1926), the experiments show that the constancy effect holds, within unknown limits, in children and lower animals. Third, Holaday (1933) and Sheehan (1938) have demonstrated that the form of instruction stimulus and "attitude" affect the precise form of the discrimination function. Finally, the researches by Schur and by Holway and Boring focus attention on the influence of elevation of regard.

The experiments do not bring the measure *visual angle* into question as a stimulus specification. What is brought into question is the *relation* (as in Holway and Boring's experiment) between an adjusted *diameter* of a comparison area (or calculated visual angle) and the *distance* of an object subtending a given visual angle. The slope of the function relating the two variables changes as a function of certain controlling circumstances, e.g. presence of "extraneous" stimuli. In the absence of such additional stimuli the function approximates the law of the retinal image.

The facts of shape matching may be similarly summarized. Discrimination of shapes is dependent on the presence or absence of "additional" stimuli (Thouless, 1931*b*). The constancy effect is improved with binocular vision (Thouless, 1931*b*; Eissler, 1933). "Attitude" influences the degree of constancy shown (Klimpfinger, 1933). On the theoretical side Koffka's contention (1935) that the relation between matched shape and matched tilt is an invariant relation of shape perception is not unequivocally supported by the work that Koffka himself describes, nor by the experiments of Stavrianos (1945).

In general it seems that an adequate basis for theorizing about size and shape can be provided only when we have accumulated analytic data, covering large-enough ranges of specifiable parameters, on conditions influencing the forms of the discrimination functions. Analyses should probably progress from conditions where certain parameters (e.g. specifiable aspects of additional stimuli) have zero value to conditions where the same variables assume values other than zero. (A new method of psychophysical treatment by Helson, 1947, may prove valuable in researches of this kind.) Thus we shall be interested in knowing how various intensities, durations, and areas of additional stimuli influence the functions. We shall be interested in knowing how angular separation and angular elevation of the comparison and standard stimuli determine the shape of the functions; and we shall probably want to examine the effect of the temporal interval between standard and comparison stimuli. From a somewhat different point of view we may wish to study the effect of presentation of the comparison and standard stimuli to different eyes, and we might consider results obtained by flicker comparisons, although this type of analysis may provide only a limiting case of the temporal interval between standard and comparison stimulus. Above all, we shall be interested in the problem of functional relations between stimulus variables and responses rather than in further demonstrational experiments on unspecified stimulus constellations.

Finally, and not least, it is probable that size and shape discriminations must be related to conditioning, learning, and concept formation (Hull, 1920; Heidbreder, 1945). For example, the response "Circle" (in the shape experiment) is the end product of a type of learning that must involve an elaborate interplay of generalization and discrimination. The response develops, as a language reaction, in situations that present circles in many positions and under conditions involving the presence or absence of other stimuli. Thus a geometric circle as a stimulus has its influence upon an already elaborated response which shows a high degree of stimulus generalization.

And so it is important that the constancies be studied in relation to conceptual learning. In the course of this program we may ask such questions as the following: Given groups with different past histories with respect to a class of figures, what are the influences of the different past histories upon the responses made to figures within the class? Is it possible to set up experimentally a training procedure whereby different groups of subjects develop different responses to the same figure? What is the influence of such training on later discriminations?

Monocular Movement Parallax

When a human being who is moving through space fixates an object that is not moving, a differential angular velocity exists between the lines of sight to the fixated object and some other stationary object. If the objects move while the observer remains motionless, the same situation of differential angular velocity exists. Further, the differential angular velocity occurs if the observer is stationary but moves his head while looking at objects that do not move. An exhaustive list of situations giving rise to monocular movement parallax is given by Tschermak (1939). The present account will consider some of the more common examples.

Circular movement. Conditions giving rise to the differential angular velocity may be readily described for a situation in which the objects move.

An object (Fig. 5) at distance R from the center of rotation of the eye C moves from m through a distance L, along the arc of the circle of radius R, at a constant velocity. Another object (farther away and not neces-

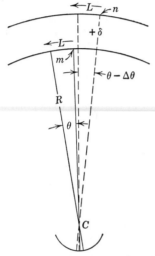

FIG. 5. Geometrical representation of monocular movement parallax for circular movement. Explanation in text.

sarily on the same visual axis as the object at distance R) is at distance $R + \delta$ from the center of rotation of the eye. At the start of the movement (which takes place at the same constant rate as in the case above) the object is at position n. (As an alternative possibility, a nearer object, at distance $R - \delta$, may move from position p through distance L at the same linear velocity as the object at distance R.) We are interested in knowing the differential angular velocity, $\omega = d\,\Delta\theta/dt$, which exists between the moving lines of sight to the two objects.

In Fig. 5 the object moving from m has passed through distance L in a given period of time. This distance corresponds to an angle θ given (in radians) by

$$\theta = \frac{L}{R} \tag{6}$$

On differentiating equation 6 we obtain

$$d\theta = -\frac{L\,dR}{R^2} \tag{7}$$

and, if we consider small values of δ, not too far from threshold δ_t, then dR may be taken equal to δ, and $d\theta$ may be considered equal to $\Delta\theta$. Thus,

$$\Delta\theta = -\frac{\delta \cdot L}{R^2} \tag{8}$$

or, from equation 6,

$$\Delta\theta = -\frac{\delta \cdot \theta}{R} \tag{9}$$

Consequently

$$\omega = \frac{d\,\Delta\theta}{dt} = -\frac{\delta}{R} \cdot \frac{d\theta}{dt} \tag{10}$$

For constant change of θ with time (a case of greatest interest to the psychologist)

$$\omega = -\frac{\delta}{R}\left(\frac{\theta - \theta_0}{t - t_0}\right) \tag{11}$$

where θ_0 is a reference value of θ when t equals t_0. ω has the dimensions of radians per unit of time. Thus, if t is in seconds, ω has the dimensions of radians per second. For ω to be expressed in seconds of arc per second, the right-hand side of equation 11 must be multiplied by 206,265. At threshold,

$$\omega_t = -\frac{\delta_t}{R}\left(\frac{\theta - \theta_0}{t - t_0}\right) \tag{12}$$

Movement parallel to the interocular axis. An equally common case involves movement from m which is parallel to the line between the centers of rotation of the two eyes. Under these conditions equations must be written to represent θ, $\theta - \Delta\theta$, and $\theta + \Delta\theta$ by the appropriate arctan functions (see section on Convergence). Appropriate calculations may be carried out when the functions are expanded in series form. However, for the range where tan θ may be taken equal to θ, equations 9, 10, 11, and 12 apply to the first approximation.

Figure 6 represents the situation in which the objects move (usually at a constant rate) from positions that fall initially on the visual axis. The figure also shows another feature. When the eye rotates to maintain fixation upon the object at distance R, the differential angular velocity occurs with reference to an unchanging line of regard; i.e. that for the fixated object. If the eye does not "fol-

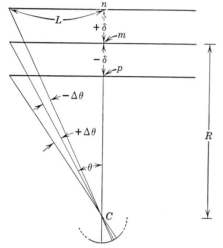

FIG. 6. Geometrical conditions existing in monocular movement parallax for movement parallel to the interocular axis. (From Graham, Baker, Hecht, and Lloyd, 1948.)

low," then the differential angular velocity exists with reference to object images that pass into more and more peripheral positions on the retina.

Moving head, stationary objects. It may be shown that equations 11 and 12 may be expected to hold when the head moves and the objects remain stationary. The assumptions are made that the head movement is essentially a lateral translatory movement at constant rate, that it is small with respect to R, and that δ is also small with respect to R. Under these conditions L is the extent of head movement, θ is the angle formed by the rotation of the visual axis around point m, and $\Delta\theta$ is the angle formed at the center of rotation of the eye by the lines of sight from the two objects. $\Delta\theta$ is equal to

the difference in apex angles formed around points m and n (or m and p) by the lines of sight.

Experimental data. Graham et al. (1948) investigated some factors that influence thresholds for monocular movement parallax, i.e. differential size of comparison stimuli, intensity of illumination, rate of movement of objects, and axis of movement.

The experimental situation used was one in which the subject remains stationary while the objects move. It may be understood with the help of Fig. 7.

The subject regards, through an aperture in a screen, two needles, one above the other. The upper needle is firmly placed; the lower may be adjusted, by means of a micrometer, in a plane parallel to the principal line of sight through the apparatus (indicated by the dashed line). The needles move in a plane perpendicular to the principal line of sight at a constant rate. The subject, "following" the needle movement in monocular vision, adjusts the distance of the variable needle until the two needles are matched in the same depth plane while they move from right to left and left to right at a constant rate across the screen aperture. The needles are regarded against a uniformly illuminated background.

The method of adjustment is used, and the standard deviation of "equality" settings is taken to be δ_t of equation 12. In addition to obtaining precision of settings, it is also possible to determine the constant error. Graham et al. (1948) report that the constant error of setting did not vary systematically under their experimental conditions.

Objects of the same dimensions placed at different distances subtend different visual angles at the eye. Since in these experiments differences in visual angle are unavoidable, because of the fact that the movable needle must be placed at different distances from the subject's eye during the course of a setting, the authors examined influences that might be attributed to differential needle size.

Three different sizes of needles were used in the fixed position, the movable needle always being 0.025 inch in diameter. δ_t (the SD of settings) and the "equality" position for the two needles were determined under the three conditions of needle diameter.

The effect of level of illumination on ω_t is shown in Fig. 9. The curve drawn through the data indicates that, in general, log ω_t decreases with an increase in intensity. The rate of decrease is rapid at low intensities, but the curve seems to flatten out and ap-

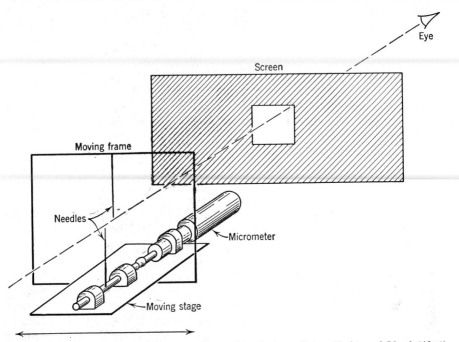

FIG. 7.   Schematic diagram of the apparatus used by Graham, Baker, Hecht, and Lloyd (1948). The needle driven by the micrometer is adjustable in a plane parallel to the line of sight. The subject adjusts this needle until it is in the same plane as the fixed, upper needle. The moving stage, containing the needles and accessory equipment, moves in a plane perpendicular to the line of sight.

Figure 8 gives the data of the experiment on "equality" settings. The experimental values lie on a horizontal line, and not on the line that would correspond to constant visual angle. This means that, whatever the size of needle, the equality setting was always made at the same distance from the eye. The fact that the average distance of setting remained constant under the three conditions indicates that differential size of stimuli played little part in the discrimination. However, it had some influence on precision of settings, since δ_t (and hence ω_t) was found to be smallest when the fixed and movable needles had the same diameter.

proach a final level for intensities above about 100 millilamberts. The total change in log ω_t is approximately 0.8 log unit over the range of intensities used and for a speed of needle movement of about 7 degrees per second.

The curve fitted to the data, as a first approximate description, is Hecht's intensity discrimination (1935) equation,

$$\frac{\Delta I}{I} = c \left[1 + \frac{1}{(KI)^{\frac{1}{2}}} \right]^2 \qquad (13)$$

in which I is intensity; ΔI is the least discriminable intensity increment, and c and K are constants. Log ω_t has been set equal to log $\Delta I/I$; and this treatment implies that, in order to discriminate a threshold parallax, a threshold rate of separation ω_t is required, which, in a small interval, dt, allows a discriminable separation, $d\,\Delta\theta$, to appear between the lines of sight to the needles, each of which provides its diffraction pattern on

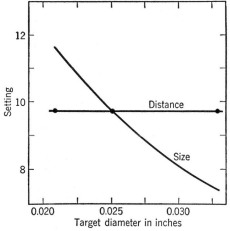

FIG. 8. Distance of setting of the movable needle as a function of the diameter of the stationary needle. The stationary needle was at a distance 9.75 inches from the eyepiece lens. The oblique line (marked Size) represents the theoretically expected curve for settings made on the basis of visual angle. The horizontal line (marked Distance) is the experimentally obtained curve for discriminations made on the basis of distance of the stationary needle. (From Graham, Baker, Hecht, and Lloyd, 1948.)

the retina. The small difference, $d\,\Delta\theta$, is required before a differential diffraction pattern may be established to signal a threshold parallax. Thus ω_t becomes a measure of a difference in diffraction exposures which, in a given short time, provides a ΔI that is discriminated against a general illumination I. Much more work, based on this analysis, must be carried out.

Figure 10 represents the data of an experiment on rate of needle movement. It shows the threshold for differential angular velocity in seconds of arc per second (log ω_t) as a function of rate of movement of the needles (in a line perpendicular to the principal line

of sight) in radians per second. Log ω_t increases with increase in the rate of movement of the stimulus needles. The curve is negatively accelerated and appears to be approaching an asymptote for rates greater

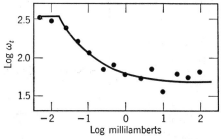

FIG. 9. Threshold values of the differential angular velocity ω_t, in seconds of arc per second, as a function of intensity. The threshold for monocular movement parallax is high for low intensities and decreases as intensity increases. (From Graham, Baker, Hecht, and Lloyd, 1948.)

than about 0.35 radian per second. On the logarithmic scale the overall change in log ω_t is about half a log unit, corresponding to a factor of about 3.

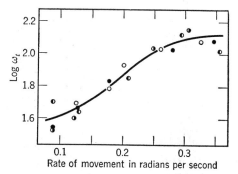

FIG. 10. Threshold values ω_t as a function of the rate of movement of the stimulus needles. The threshold for monocular movement parallax is low for slow rates of needle movement and increases as the rate of the needle movement increases. Data for different subjects are indicated by different symbols. (From Graham, Baker, Hecht, and Lloyd, 1948.)

A final experiment of the report is concerned with the influence of the axis of movement on ω_t. An eyepiece, with artificial pupil of 3-millimeter diameter and holding a Dove prism, was substituted for the eyepiece of the previous experiments. Rotation of the Dove prism allowed for any desired rotation of the axis of movement. Determinations were made for axes, separated by steps of 30 degrees, through a 360-degree rotation of the field.

The experimental data are given in Fig. 11. The curve through the data shows that, when the axis of movement is horizontal (zero or 180 degrees), ω_t is at a minimum. When the axis of movement is vertical (90 or 270 degrees), ω_t is at a maximum. For

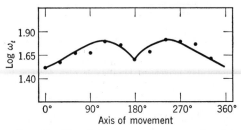

Fig. 11. Threshold values of ω_t as a function of axis of movement. Thresholds for monocular movement parallax are least for horizontal movement and greatest for vertical movement. (From Graham, Baker, Hecht, and Lloyd, 1948.)

axes of movement between the horizontal and vertical, ω_t assumes intermediate values.

When appropriate corrections are made for different viewing distances, the δ_t values obtained by Tschermak (1939) in his experiment employing unknown rates of head movement are found to be of the same order of magnitude as those of Graham et al. (1948). Thus both experiments substantiate the view that the thresholds for monocular movement parallax are smaller for the horizontal axis of movement than for the vertical. The difference in thresholds may be due to differences in the effectiveness of eye muscle pairs which control the various axial movements, or it may be due to differences in retinal gradients of cone densities along the various foveal-peripheral axes.

Zegers (1948) has been concerned with the influence on ω_t of the following parameters: (1) rate of movement of stimuli; (2) size of visual field in which the moving

stimuli appear; (3) amount of "offset" (defined as the instantaneous visual angle of separation, $\Delta\theta$, existing between the comparison and variable stimuli); and (4) conditions of fixation.

Zegers finds, as was true in the earlier experiment of Graham et al. (1948), that δ_t and ω_t increase with an increase in the rate of stimulus movement up to a limiting rate. He interprets this result to mean (1) that high rates of stimulus movement interfere with proper "following" of the stimuli by the eye, and (2) that, at high speeds, intensity effects in individual cones are decreased.

When conditions are provided to allow for good "pickup" of the stimuli as they emerge in the visual field, and for improved visual pursuit of the stimuli, the size of the visual field has little or no influence on ω_t.

In another series of experiments Zegers found that a constant visual field, providing a stimulus excursion of 3.58 degrees, and placed at increasing angular displacements from the principal line of sight, gave values of ω_t according to the rule: the greater the angular displacement, the lower the threshold for differential angular velocity. Calculations of the threshold "offset" $\Delta\theta$ in these experiments lead to the conclusion that threshold of monocular movement parallax is determined when, for a given rate of movement, $\Delta\theta$ reaches a critical value. This means that the threshold is determined for monocular movement parallax when a threshold value of visual angle separates the comparison and test stimuli. The critical value of $\Delta\theta$ varies as a function of the rate of stimulus movement, and this fact leads one to consider the reciprocal relations of time and intensity factors, relations reminiscent of those implied by the Bunsen-Roscoe law.

Accommodation

When the eye is fixated on a point in space, that point is sharply focused on the retina. All points nearer or farther than the fixated point are blurred. The blur circles formed for points not in focus have diameters that vary as a function of pupil size. They also vary as a function of the distance between the fixated point and the point not fixated (Southall, 1933, 1937).

The discrimination of the clearly focused image from the blurred image probably serves as a distance cue, although the process of discriminating must be quite complex and certainly has never been adequately investigated. Presumably such factors as the discrimination of detail and retinal image size combine with the subjects' reactions to the accommodation performance itself to provide the cue.

Interposition

Interposition is often defined as the cue for the discrimination of the relative distances of two objects that results when one object partially obscures or overlaps the outline of another object. The overlapping object is reported as nearer. As Ratoosh (1949) points out, such a definition is not satisfying, for it appeals to an unspecified factor: the basis for discriminating between the object that obscures and the object that is obscured. Helmholtz (1924) describes the cue when he says "the mere fact that the contour line of the covering object does not change its direction where it joins the contour of the one behind it, will generally enable us to decide which [object] is which."

Helmholtz's statement is not precise and is improved by Ratoosh.

Consider a projection of figures onto a plane perpendicular to the visual axis such that the nodal point of the eye is the point of projection. In such a perspective transformation all objects will be represented by simple closed curves. (Without any loss in generality only two figures will be treated here; the same reasoning may be extended to apply to any number of objects.)

A necessary condition for interposition to become effective as a cue is that the curves of the two objects in the plane of projection have a common boundary. A point at which the boundaries of the curves meet will be called a point of intersection. Clearly there will be two points of intersection for a common boundary.

Helmholtz's specification implies that the behavior of the functions represented by the closed curves at the points of intersection alone determines which object will be seen as nearer. More specifically Helmholtz's assertion may be taken to indicate that continuity of the first derivative of the object's contour at the points of intersection is the sole determiner of relative distance. (A first derivative, $f'(x)$, of a function, $f(x)$, is continuous at a point p if and only if for any $\epsilon > 0$, there exists a δ such that $|f'(x) - f'(p)| < \epsilon$ in the interval $|x - p| < \delta$.)*

This formulation predicts that what happens at one point of intersection is independent of what happens at the other. That is to say, both points of intersection may give the same cue, both may offer no cue, only one may give a cue, or each may provide a cue which contradicts the other. If, at a point of intersection, the contours of both objects are the same with respect to continuity of their first derivatives, no cue will be provided at that point of intersection; if this occurs at both points of intersection, interposition will afford no cue for the relative distances of the two objects.

Some examples of interposition are shown in Fig. 12.

In Fig. 12A, one boundary's first derivative is continuous at both points of intersection. The other boundary has a discontinuous intersection at both points of intersection. The figure whose boundary has a continuous first derivative at the point of intersection, i.e. the left-hand figure, is seen as nearer; the figure whose boundary has a discontinuous first derivative, i.e. the right-hand figure, is seen as farther away. The same cue is provided at both points of intersection.

In Fig. 12B, one function possesses a continuous first derivative at one point of inter-

* To be continuous at a point, the first derivative must be defined at that point. Accordingly, in the examples given in Fig. 12, the coordinate axes must be taken in such a way that neither is parallel to the sides of the figures containing **a** point of intersection.

section and a discontinuous one at the other, whereas the other function's first derivative is discontinuous at both points of intersection. No cue is given at point a where both first derivatives are discontinuous. At point b, however, the outline of the right-hand figure has a discontinuous first derivative and the outline of the left-hand figure has a

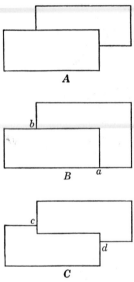

Fig. 12. Examples of interposition as a cue for the perception of relative distance. A and B give obvious cues; C gives conflicting cues. (From Ratoosh, 1949.)

continuous first derivative. Thus the left-hand figure is seen in front of the right-hand figure.

Figure 12C gives a complex case: a cue is provided at each of the two points of intersection, but the two cues contradict each other; the point of intersection at c indicates that the right-hand figure is nearer, whereas that at d indicates that the left-hand figure is nearer. This situation results because the first derivative of each function is continuous at one point of intersection and discontinuous at the other, and each derivative is continuous at that point of intersection at which the other is discontinuous.

Convergence

Symmetric convergence (Southall, 1937). The angle of convergence is represented as angle α in the diagram of Fig. 13, and a is the distance between the centers of rotation

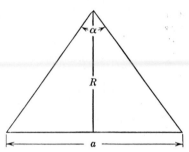

Fig. 13. Angular relations in symmetric convergence. Explanation in text.

of the two eyes (equal to the interpupillary distance). When, as is often the case (symmetric convergence), the two lines of fixation intersect each other at a point in the median plane perpendicular to a,

$$\tan \frac{\alpha}{2} = \frac{a}{2R} \qquad (14)$$

In this equation R represents the distance along the perpendicular bisector of a to the point of intersection of the lines of fixation. For small angles of α the relation of equation 14 is given approximately, in radians, by

$$\alpha = \frac{a}{R} \qquad (15)$$

or, in degrees, by

$$\alpha = \frac{57.3a}{R} \qquad (16)$$

α is overestimated by equations 15 and 16 in the same manner as is β by equations 2 and 3. For large angles and accurate determinations of α, computations based on equation 14 should be used.

Asymmetric convergence. Suppose that we are not dealing with the case of symmetric convergence but rather with the situation represented in Fig. 14 (asymmetric convergence). We wish to obtain an expression for α.

Let a ($= Z_1Z_2$) be the distance between the centers of rotation of the two eyes, and PM the perpendicular bisector of a. Draw $P'L$ perpendicular to the extension LZ_1 of Z_1Z_2. Let $(LZ_1 + Z_1M)$ equal s, and let $P'L$ equal R. Finally, let $b = a/2$ ($= Z_1M = MZ_2$). Note that θ' is the angle that may be used to designate the angular position of P with respect to PM.

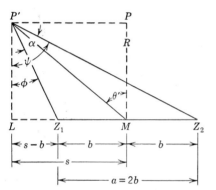

FIG. 14. Angular relations in asymmetric convergence.

In Fig. 14 it may be seen that $P'P = LM = s$; $Z_1M = MZ_2 = b$; and $MP = LP' = R$. Also, $\psi = \arctan (s + b)/R$; $\phi = \arctan (s - b)/R$; and $\alpha = \psi - \phi = \arctan (s + b)/R - \arctan (s - b)/R$.

The expansion of the difference $\psi - \phi$ by Maclaurin's series is [for $(s + b) < R$]

$$\alpha = \frac{2b}{R} - \frac{2b(3s^2 + b^2)}{3R^3}$$
$$+ \frac{2b(5s^4 + 10s^2b^2 + b^4)}{5R^5} - \cdots \quad (17)$$

On dropping all terms but the first and recognizing that $a = 2b$, we obtain

$$\alpha = \frac{a}{R} \quad (18)$$

as an approximate statement of the value of α (in radians).

For an alternating convergent series such as equation 17, the remainder for one term

is less than the second term; i.e. remainder $<$ $\left| \dfrac{2b(3s^2 + b^2)}{3R^3} \right|$, and the error is $\dfrac{\text{remainder}}{\text{preceding term}}$ $< \dfrac{3s^2 + b^2}{3R^2}$. Thus, equation 18 overestimates α by 1 per cent when

$$\frac{3s^2 + b^2}{3R^2} = 0.01$$

Other percentage errors may be calculated. When necessary, terms beyond the first in equation 17 may be used for more accurate estimation of α.

Stereoscopic Vision

Single vision and the horopter. Singleness and doubleness of vision with two eyes are best understood in terms of a geometrical construct, the horopter (Southall, 1937; Boring, 1942; Helmholtz, 1924; Hering, 1861–64; Luneburg, 1947).

Johannes Müller (1826) was not the first to consider the facts of single binocular vision — Vieth anticipated him — but he discussed the problem so thoroughly that his name is inseparably associated with early theoretical developments.

According to Müller, singleness of object vision occurs when the object lies at the point of intersection (in the external field) of a pair of straight lines drawn through the nodal point of each eye, *provided* the lines meet the retinas at a pair of corresponding points. If the lines do not meet the retinas at corresponding points, (1) the object will be seen as double if the disparity between points is great enough, or (2) if the disparity is not great, the object will be seen as single but as nearer or farther away than a fixated object.

Theoretically, corresponding points are those retinal points that would be coincident if one retina could be placed over the other with vertical and horizontal axes through the fovea superimposed. We know that such a hypothetical construction is an approximation at best. Nevertheless it provides a basis for systematization not otherwise available.

The locus of points giving rise to single vision for a given attitude of the two eyes is called the horopter. As shown in Fig. 15 the horopter, for one particular case, is a circle, the Vieth-Müller horopter circle.

It may be proved that the Vieth-Müller construction is a circle in the following manner. The points o and o' are the centers of rotation of the two eyes. (The centers may

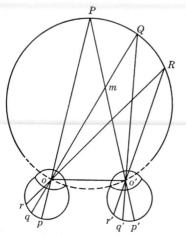

Fig. 15.   The Vieth-Müller horopter circle. Only if the points P, Q, and R lie on a circle will their images fall on corresponding points in the two retinas.   The proof is given in the text. (From Boring, 1942.)

be considered nearly coincident with the nodal points.) The eyes fixate P and form images on corresponding points p and p'. Let Q form images on corresponding points q and q'; and similarly let R form images on corresponding points r and r'. Under these conditions, angle qop = angle $q'o'p'$, and angle rop = angle $r'o'p'$.

Consider angles qop and $q'o'p'$. Angle $qop = QoP$ and angle $q'o'p' = Qo'P$. Therefore angle QoP = angle $Qo'P$. But the opposite angles at m are also equal. Therefore triangles Pmo and Qmo' are similar, and angles oPo' and oQo' are equal.

For the condition that two triangles Poo' and Qoo' have a common side oo' opposite equal angles, it is necessary that the points at the vertices of the equal angles lie on a

circle. (All triangles erected upon a chord of a circle to a point on the circumference have equal angles opposite the chord.) Thus points P and Q lie on a circle. A similar proof would demonstrate that R falls on the same circle, and so would any other point whose images fall on corresponding points. If conditions of fixation change, the size of the circle also changes.

The Vieth-Müller horopter circle is based on the notion that, with the fovea centralis of each eye as origin, corresponding points occur at equal distances along radii rotated about the origin through equal angles from the horizontal. A generalized horopter drawn on the basis of this concept is a sphere generated by the revolution of the Vieth-Müller circle around one of its diameters.

We know that this conception of the horopter is oversimplified, and Helmholtz (1924) and Hering (1861–64) worked out the form of a general horopter which appears in Fig. 16. This horopter contains the Vieth-Müller circles as a special case; i.e. for horizontal regard. Work by Hering and Hillebrand showed that the horopter varies with different conditions of fixation, being much less curved than the Vieth-Müller circle for strong convergence. For weak convergence (fixation at about 2 meters), the curve becomes a straight line perpendicular to the median plane; and for fixation distances greater than about 2 meters, the horopter curve becomes slightly convex towards the face (Southall, 1937). For a more detailed historical summary, see Glanville (1933).

When an object is fixated, another object, not lying on the horopter of the fixated object, is discriminated as double, provided that it lies far enough from the horopter of the fixated object so that the degree of non-correspondence of the retinal images exceeds the range for binocular fusion. If the object lies beyond the point of fixation, a condition known as "uncrossed" retinal images obtains; i.e. with his left eye open, a subject says that the object lies to the left of the fixated object. With his right eye open, the subject says that the object lies to the right of the fixated object. When the object lies nearer than the point of fixation, the retinal images

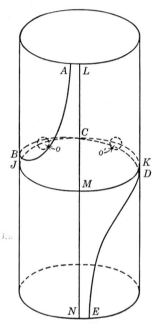

FIG. 16. The generalized horopter line, according to Helmholtz and Hering. The general horopter is a curve, symmetrical above and below, plotted on the surface of a cylinder. The curve is asymptotic to the line *LMN*. The eyes, with their optical centers at *o* and *o'*, are represented by the dashed circles at the back of the cylinder. The horopter line is *ABCDE*. The part of the line that passes through the eyes is dotted, *BCD,* and defines a region of invisibility. In a limiting case, horizontal regard, this horopter becomes the Vieth-Müller horopter circle, *CKMJ*. (From Boring, 1942.)

are "crossed"; i.e. the subject, with his left eye open, reports that the object lies to the right of the fixation object. With his right eye open, he reports that the object lies to the left of the fixated object. The geometry of crossing and lack of crossing of the retinal images is readily deducible from geometric theory (Southall, 1937).

A subject reports on the direction of an object, responded to as single in binocular vision, as if the object were on a line drawn from the point of fixation to the point midway between the two eyes. Hering (1942), in particular, has been interested in this problem, and the reader is referred to his book for a more detailed account than can be given here.

Objects viewed in space with the unaided eyes. Suppose that a subject regards, with the left eye alone, the scene represented in the left side of Fig. 17; i.e. two flagpoles

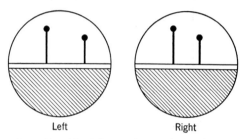

Left   Right

FIG. 17. The left-eye view and the right-eye view of two flagpoles behind a stone wall. The lateral separation of the flagpoles is seen as smaller in the right-eye view than in the left-eye view.

behind a stone wall. For vision with the left eye alone the subject cannot tell which of the two flagpoles is nearer. After looking with the left eye, the subject closes that eye and regards the flagpoles with the right eye. The "right-eye view" is shown in the right side of the same figure. Although the subject may state that the lateral separation of the flagpoles seems smaller in the right-eye view than in the left, neither type of monocular viewing allows him to state which flagpole is nearer.

After regarding the scene with each eye alone, the subject looks at the scene with both eyes and can immediately state that the right-hand flagpole is nearer than the left-hand flagpole. The binocular discrimination of difference in distance is brought about by one of the well-known cues for depth perception, retinal disparity (Helmholtz, 1924; von Kries, 1924; Southall, 1937; Graham, 1943), and the geometric considerations that underlie the concept are represented in Fig. 18.

In Fig. 18, a represents the interocular distance, and F (the left-hand flagpole) is the object fixated. F' represents the right-hand object. R is the distance to F along a perpendicular to the interocular axis, and δ is the difference in distance along this perpendicular between F and F'. Angle θ_2 is the visual angle formed by the lines of sight

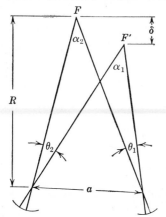

FIG. 18. The geometry of the binocular perception resulting from stimulation as in Fig. 17. The left-hand flagpole is farther from the subject than the right-hand flagpole.

to the two objects in the left eye, and angle θ_1 is the angle between the lines of sight in the right eye. Angle α_2 is the apex angle for the intersection of the lines of sight from the two eyes to F, and angle α_1 is a similar angle for the lines of sight to F'.

It may be observed that $\theta_2 - \theta_1$ is a difference in visual angles subtended in the two eyes by the lines of sight to the two objects; hence, $\theta_2 - \theta_1$ is (ideally) a measure of the retinal separation of the two object images in angular measure.

In Fig. 18,

$$\theta_2 - \theta_1 = \alpha_1 - \alpha_2 \qquad (19)$$

that is, the difference in visual angles is the difference in convergence angles with changed sign.

The determination of α_1 and α_2 is, for the general case, similar to the determination of α

in the case of asymmetric convergence (see equation 17) and requires a calculation based on a series expansion for the appropriate α and its corresponding ψ and ϕ. However, in the great majority of cases, where R is many times greater than either a or δ, and where F' is not too far from the perpendicular to a on which F lies,

$$\alpha_2 = \frac{a}{R} \qquad (20)$$

and

$$\alpha_1 = \frac{a}{R \pm \delta} \qquad (21)$$

in radians. Therefore, if we call

$$\alpha_2 - \alpha_1 = \theta_1 - \theta_2 = \eta \qquad (22)$$

then

$$\eta = \frac{a\delta}{R^2} \qquad (23)$$

an expression in which a term $(R \pm \delta)$ is considered equal to R. For calculations in seconds of arc, the radian values must be multiplied by 206,265.

At threshold one measures η_t which is determined on the basis of δ_t, i.e. $\eta_t = a\delta_t/R^2$. The term δ_t may be determined, e.g. in the Howard-Dolman apparatus (Howard, 1919), as an average of threshold differences in the settings of two sticks (one the standard, and the other the comparison), and for settings made toward the subject and away from the subject.

The telestereoscope. In a telestereoscopic viewing system, the distance a is effectively increased by providing a system that reflects the images of the objects viewed from mirrors placed farther apart than the distance between the two eyes (Graham, 1943). The distance between the two mirrors is called the baselength B. Since a, as previously discussed, is a special case of baselength, the interpupillary distance, equation 23 may be rewritten in more general form for lines of sight converging on an object from any baselength. The resulting equation is

$$\eta = \frac{B\delta}{R^2} \qquad (24)$$

When there is magnification M it multiplies (in the ideal case) the right side of equation 24, which then becomes

$$\eta = \frac{BM\delta}{R^2} \qquad (25)$$

Many factors serve to diminish the influence of M at high magnifications (Riggs, Mueller, Graham, and Mote, 1947).

The limit of stereoscopic vision. The limiting range, R_{lim}, of stereoscopic vision is the greatest distance at which an object can be just detected as nearer than an object at infinity. Suppose that α_1 is the apex angle for the object at infinity; i.e. $\alpha_1 = 0$. Then, if we take the least discriminable difference, η_t as 30 seconds of arc (a large figure), we find, by equation 22, that $\alpha_2 = 30/206,265$ radians. On substituting this value of α_2 in equation 20 and assuming an average value of a to be 0.072 yard (65 millimeters), we find R_{lim} to be 495 yards. Of course, the computation of R_{lim} varies with the value of η_t taken, as well as with the interpupillary distance assumed. Nevertheless the calculation emphasizes the fact that stereoscopic vision acts as a space cue through a considerable range of distance.

Binocular vision in the stereoscope. In looking into a stereoscope, we look with the left eye at a presentation (e.g. a photograph) which is different from the one for the right eye.

Consider two stereograms, one the left view in Fig. 17 and the other the right view in the same figure. They are mounted together in the stereoscope in such a way that the right view is presented to the right eye and the left view to the left eye. Under these conditions, the two flagpoles F and F' are designated F_L and F'_L for the left eye and F_R and F'_R for the right eye. The geometrical theory of binocular vision that applies to these circumstances can be made out with the help of Fig. 19.

The angular disparity in the separation of the two flagpole images is $\theta_2 - \theta_1 = \eta$. Now, in radians,

$$\theta_2 = \frac{\overline{F_L F'_L}}{R} \qquad (26)$$

and

$$\theta_1 = \frac{\overline{F_R F'_R}}{R} \qquad (27)$$

Therefore

$$\eta = \frac{\overline{F_L F'_L} - \overline{F_R F'_R}}{R} = \frac{g}{R} \qquad (28)$$

in radians; and for threshold, the quantities η and g are η_t and g_t, i.e. $\eta_t = g_t/R$. Where θ_2 and θ_1 are large, it is necessary to use the

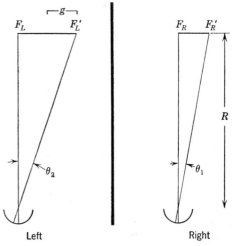

Fig. 19. Geometrical relations existing for the flagpole scenes as presented in stereograms, one to the left eye and the other to the right. Theoretical considerations are discussed in the text.

appropriate arctan functions as discussed in the section on convergence.

When, in the stereoscope, the attempt is made to line up a "target" with a fiducial line, the fiducial lines F_L and F_R in the two views are "fused" and the variability of setting [in terms of lateral movement of F'_L (or F'_R) in the plane at distance R] is taken to be g_t, a datum that accords with a conventionally determined just noticeable difference.

When the eyes are accommodated for infinity by a lens in each eye piece, R is taken as the focal length of the lens.

Experimental data. Howard (1919) has performed a well-known research on the determination of the threshold difference angle, η_t. The apparatus he used has become known as the Howard-Dolman apparatus, although it is essentially similar to the earlier one of James (1908).

The apparatus presents two vertical rods, one stationary and the other movable. The subject looks through a rectangular aperture (20×12 centimeters) in a screen at the two rods (each 1 centimeter in diameter) which may be seen side by side in uniform illumination. The viewing distance is usually 6 meters, a distance great enough to minimize effects due to convergence and accommodation.

One design of the Howard-Dolman apparatus allows the subject to move the adjustable rod toward him or away from him by means of strings. In the original experiment Howard set the variable rod at various positions and determined η_t on the basis of a least depth difference δ_t that could be discriminated 75 per cent of the time. The values of η_t varied from subject to subject over a wide range of stereoscopic acuity. Of 106 subjects tested, the 14 with the best stereoscopic acuity had values of η_t lying between 1.8 and 2.07 seconds; the 24 with the worst acuity had values between 10.6 and 136.2 seconds.

It is clear that, as the variable rod is moved back and forth in space, the size of its retinal image varies. The difference in retinal image size might account for the depth discrimination, and so Howard performed an additional experiment to determine the influence of this factor. The method involved monocular viewing, which, of course, eliminated all cues but size difference. Nine subjects gave an average depth difference value, δ_t, in the binocular experiments of 14.4 millimeters, and, in the monocular experiments, 285 millimeters. In other words, a least depth difference discriminated on the basis of image size is, for a viewing distance of 6 meters, about twenty times as great as one discriminated on the basis of stereoscopic vision.

Woodburne (1934) has made a careful determination of η_t under conditions where retinal image size is invariable. He presented the subject with two illuminated slits, one stationary and the other variable with respect to distance. By means of an ingenious apparatus, it was so arranged that, as the distance of the variable slit increased, the actual size of the slit also increased, the visual angle for length and width remaining the same in all positions. The viewing distance was 2 meters and single observations were restricted to exposures of 1.5 seconds. The method of constant stimuli was used, and by this method η_t turned out to be 2.12 seconds for the averaged "near" and "far" thresholds for 7 subjects. This value is similar to the one found by Howard for his best subjects.

Matsubayashi (1937, 1938) published a series of papers in Japanese (abstracts in German) on factors that influence stereoscopic acuity. He used a two-rod and a three-rod apparatus in various experiments. The three-rod apparatus had a movable middle rod and two stationary outer rods.

One important factor that influences the magnitude of the threshold difference angle η_t is the distance (or visual angle) separating the stationary and variable rods in the three-rod and the two-rod apparatuses (1937b). As the outer rods vary in angular separation from the variable rod, η_t becomes larger and larger as shown in Fig. 20, which presents a graph of Matsubayashi's data. The constant error of setting may also be influenced by angular separation. Matsubayashi says that it may be opposite in sign for some separations as contrasted with others.

In other experiments Matsubayashi examined influences due to length of rods and thickness of rods. With a decrease in length of rod from 2.5 degrees to 38 minutes η_t increases slowly, until with further decrease to 17 minutes η_t increases rapidly (1938a). A thickness of about 2.4 minutes gives the lowest values of η_t (1938b).

Distance of observation, with its associated conditions of convergence, also seems to influence η_t (1938d). η_t is greater for an observation distance of 2.5 meters than it is for 15 meters. For example, with a 30-minute lateral separation of rods, η_t, determined by the method of constant stimuli,

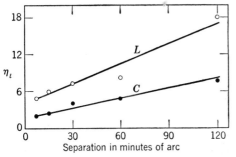

FIG. 20. Data from Matsubayashi (1937b) on the threshold difference angle for stereoscopic vision (η_t in seconds of arc) as it is influenced by the visual angle (in minutes of arc) separating the stationary and variable rods. Curve L presents data obtained, by the method of limits, with the 2-rod apparatus. Curve C represents data obtained, by the method of constant stimuli, with the 3-rod apparatus.

is 3.86 seconds at 2.5 meters and 2.51 seconds at 15 meters. These data are averages for 6 subjects.

Artificial visual defect, produced by placing a gelatin filter over one eye, seems to have little influence on the threshold difference angle η_t until the acuity of the covered eye is very low (1938e). With acuity normal in one eye at 1.2 and reduced to 0.3 in the other eye, η_t is slightly increased. Further reduction of acuity in the eye covered by the filter to 0.2 causes a great increase in η_t. With a decrease in acuity of the covered eye to 0.1, depth perception becomes impossible.

A number of interesting experiments were performed by Langlands (1926) and his report presents a good survey of earlier investigations.

Langlands obtained stereoscopic acuity values comparable to those obtained by other investigators; i.e. values ranging from about 2 to 40 seconds of arc, depending on the conditions of experimentation. He found that good space discriminations may be made for differently shaped objects in continuous illumination, η_t for his subjects being of the order of 1.5 to 6.0 seconds. With short flashes of light produced by a spark of about 10^{-5} second's duration, objects were spatially discriminated when η_t varied, for two well-trained subjects, from about 20 to 40 seconds. Discrimination was better with an 8-degree field than with a 1-degree field.

Langland's results do not mean that the discrimination is made in the short period of the flash. Obviously the duration of flash simply determines amounts of retinal initiating processes, and discrimination may be based on events that last for a time after the flash has ceased. Langlands maintains that the discriminations of his subjects were not based on the positive after image.

A series of exploratory experiments on stereoscopic acuity at 2 degrees from the fovea demonstrate that the probability of detection of a spatial difference is lower for this location than it is for the center of the fovea.

In addition to making observations in the "real depth" situation, Langlands determined η_t in a stereoscope, where η_t, as found with exposure by an electric spark, was slightly higher than that found in "real depth," but, as Langlands says, "I have no doubt that with improved apparatus and greater practice finer binocular acuities could be reached."

Mueller and Lloyd (1948) determined the influence of illumination on η_t for observations with a stereoscope. The stereoscope they used provided movement of a vertical line in the right-eye field while a comparable line in the left-eye field remained stationary. The "fused" line that resulted was compared spatially with three short "fused" fiducial lines, produced by paired vertical lines in the right and left fields. Mueller and Lloyd found, for observations lasting from 5 to 10 seconds, that η_t is small (i.e. discrimination is "good") at high photopic illuminations and increases with a decrease in illumination to cone threshold. Figure 21 gives the data. Cone threshold is taken to occur at the discontinuity of the curve. It will be observed that η_t is nearly constant over much of the range of photopic illumination and rises as

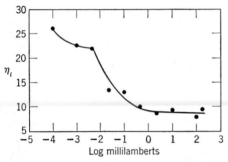

FIG. 21. The threshold for stereoscopic vision (η_t in seconds of arc) as a function of intensity of illumination. Determinations were made with the stereoscope. Thresholds are high for low illuminations and decrease as illumination increases. (From Mueller and Lloyd, 1948.)

intensities decrease to cone threshold. Below the cone threshold, space discrimination is still maintained, presumably by the rods, but in a relatively ineffective way, as shown by the high values of η_t.

Mueller and Lloyd's results for the stereoscope are similar to some obtained by Berry, Riggs, and Duncan (1950), Holway (1947), and Ludvigh (1947) in experimental conditions involving a comparison of object distances in "real depth" (e.g. as in the Howard-Dolman apparatus). η_t is high at low intensities, decreases as intensity increases, and finally approaches a low limiting value at high illuminations.

The observations of Matsubayashi on the effect of lateral distance between rods have been verified for the stereoscope by Graham, Riggs, Mueller, and Solomon (1949). Observations were made in an apparatus comparable to that used by Mueller and Lloyd, and

η_t was determined as it is influenced by the separation of the variable line from a constant reference line. η_t increases when the lateral distance between reference line and variable line increases in the frontal plane.

Berry compared threshold acuities for vernier, real-depth, and stereoscopic tasks under similar conditions (1948). Two black cylindrical rods, one above the other in the median vertical visual plane, were viewed through an aperture. Under the vernier condition the subjects were required to tell whether the bottom rod was to the right or left of the upper one (i.e. the subjects had to discriminate an "offset"). In the real-depth situation the discrimination was based on the bottom rod's being behind or in front of the upper rod. In the third condition, stereoscopic depth, two sets of vernier objects were viewed through right angle prisms, the view of each set being restricted to a single eye. The method of constant stimuli was employed. An essential question concerned the manner in which the three types of acuity vary as a function of the vertical separation between the rods. The separations employed varied between 3.6 and 891 seconds.

The results show that, for a small rod separation, vernier acuity is best. However, as the vertical separation is increased to more than 135 seconds, stereoscopic-depth acuity and real-depth acuity become superior to vernier acuity.

Many factors in daily life must influence the effectiveness of stereoscopic vision. For example: a condition of asymmetric convergence means that the retinal image in one eye must be different in size from the retinal image in the other eye, due to the fact that one eye is farther removed from the observed object than the other. Ogle (1939) has shown that the expected size difference does not produce anomalous stereoscopic effects. He assumes that some sort of compensatory effect must occur to offset the difference in distance from the object to the eyes in asymmetric convergence.

It is obvious that if size differences exist between the two images, complex stereoscopic effects will ensue, because the points along contours do not lie on corresponding points. This problem has engaged the attention of workers at the Dartmouth Eye Institute (Ames, 1946; Ogle, 1939), and many elaborate and useful studies have been made upon phenomena resulting from aniseikonia, the condition under which the two retinal images are different in size. There is an excellent theoretical account of aniseikonia by Ogle and Boeder (1948). Their discussion relates aniseikonia to a geometrical theory of space perception in a convincing manner.

Effects due to size difference show up in such manifestations as an apparent horizontal rotation of the visual field around a vertical axis at the point of fixation. If the relative shapes of the two ocular images are distorted, the visual field, instead of being rotated, will appear concave or convex. Differences in size of about 0.25 per cent may be distinguished (Ames, Gliddon, and Ogle, 1932).

Differences in the size and shape of the two retinal images may be introduced by two sources: by a change in the dioptric image, and by a change in the anatomical positioning of the retinal elements. Differential effects due to both sources may be expected in the two eyes. For example, (1) differential conditions of accommodation may produce aniseikonia; (2) there is a change in the asymmetric distribution of corresponding retinal points from distant to near vision (Hering-Hillebrand horopter deviation); (3) there seems to be a disparity of corresponding points in certain abnormal conditions of the eyes associated with phoria; and, finally, (4) there is some evidence that ocular images change in size when one looks left or right of the median plane (Ames, Gliddon, and Ogle, 1932).

An interesting effect, called the induced size effect (Ogle, 1940), occurs when a difference in the vertical dimensions of the images occurs. The effect appears as an apparent rotation of the observed object about the point of fixation and is opposite in direction to the rotation introduced by a difference in the horizontal dimensions of the retinal images. Complex effects may also be introduced when the aniseikonia involves an oblique axis (Burian and Ogle, 1945), and an instrument, the space eikonometer (Ogle, 1946), has been developed to measure the declination error between the images in the two eyes as well as image size differences in the vertical and horizontal meridians.

Graham, Hammer, Mueller, and Mote (1949) have shown theoretically that, under certain conditions of varying convergence, a stereoscopic observer may align a target with a reticle at more than a single value of apparent range. Theory predicts that multiple alignments may occur when the visual angle, $\Delta\beta$, existing between adjacent, equally spaced reticle marks is sufficiently small. If we designate the angular difference existing between a given alignment setting and the "true" alignment setting as η, then the condition for alignment is fulfilled when $\eta = n\,\Delta\beta$, where n, an integral number, represents the degree of "false" fusion. The effect described is, of course, the "wallpaper" effect discussed by Woodworth (1938). Experimental data are in accord with theory.

Conditions of attitude of the eyes may be expected to influence stereoscopic vision. For example, certain torsional effects (Hermans, 1943; Ogle and Ellerbrock, 1946) may occur due to the manner in which the muscles of the eyes are attached to the eyeball. The net result of such effects would be to make the upper part of a vertical line appear farther from the observer in stereoscopic vision than the lower part of the line. Undoubtedly, many other factors are important in stereoscopic vision, and some may influence our behavior in everyday life.

The Pulfrich effect. If a subject with a not-too-dense filter in front of one eye regards an object oscillating in simple harmonic motion in the frontal plane, the physically rectilinear movement of the object is reported as generating a curve, not unlike an ellipse, whose plane is perpendicular to the frontal plane and parallel to the floor. Best results are obtained when fixation is maintained in the median plane.

The phenomenon is explained in the following way by Pulfrich (1922) who uses a suggestion by Fertsch: Stimulation of a given point on the retina is signaled after a latent period that varies as a function of light intensity. Now the latency of visual effect for the uncovered eye is shorter than for the eye covered by a filter, and so the covered eye signals a position of the moving object that "lags" behind the position signaled by the uncovered eye. Thus at any moment the reaction of a subject is based on stimulations from noncorresponding points, and the discriminated position of the object at any time is dependent on the amount and sign of the retinal disparity. Banister (1932), Liang and Piéron (1947), and Lit (1949) have made quantitative measures of the effect and on the basis of their results have computed the difference in latencies for the two eyes as a function of intensity differences. For a good summary of the history of the Pulfrich effect and related phenomena, see Lit (1949).

Binocular Rivalry

When two figures, different according to some system of classification, are presented, one to one eye and the other to the other eye, in a stereoscope, the subject reports that now one and now the other figure appears in alternating sequence. Sometimes, when the two stimuli are not "incompatible," the subject reports that they present a view that is a combination of both. For example, under certain circumstances the figure of a fence presented to one eye and a figure of a pony presented to the other results in the report of a pony jumping over the fence. The rivalry of binocular color mixture is well known and has played a role in the development of color theory (Hecht, 1928).

Illusions

"Illusions" of reversible perspective have been known since Euclid's time. Boring (1942) ascribes to Necker (1832) the first scientific observation on reversible perspective, and Necker's well-known cube is shown in Fig. 22. Schröder's staircase (1858) and Sinsteden's windmill (1860) are other famil-

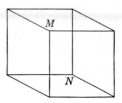

FIG. 22. Necker's cube as an example of reversible perspective. Fixation of M gives one perspective; fixation of N, the reverse. (From Boring, 1942.)

iar reversible figures; both are presented in Boring (1942). Rubin (1921) studied a number of "ambiguous" configurations and on the basis of his analysis formulated the Gestalt principle of "figure and ground." The reader is referred to Boring's discussion for a fuller treatment of these interesting but unexplained phenomena.

Papers on illusions are not as numerous as they once were, but occasionally one appears. Finger and Spelt (1947), for example, analyzed the effects due to the bisection of a line in a figure that shows the horizontal-vertical illusion.

The overestimation of verticals with respect to horizontals was, together with the illusion of interrupted extents, the first to be studied. Wundt (1862) called attention to the tendency to overestimate the vertical as compared to the horizontal, and Oppel (1854–55) showed that interrupted extents are reported as greater than "empty" extents.

The Poggendorff figure was described by Zöllner (1860), and his modification of the illusion provided a more striking effect.

Hering (1861–64) presented the figure that bears his name, and a companion figure was published by Wundt (1898). All these figures are reproduced in Boring (1942).

By far the most famous geometrical illusion of all is the Müller-Lyer figure (1896) shown in Fig. 23. The Müller-Lyer figure has been used to test almost all the theories of illusions that have been advanced, and it, together with other common designs, has been presented over and over in the psychological texts of the past fifty years.

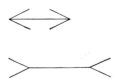

FIG. 23. Müller-Lyer figure. The horizontal line segment appears longer when the arrows point out. (From Boring, 1942.)

Theories concerning the mode of action of the various figures have been inconclusive. As Boring (1942) says, "The problem of the geometrical illusions is not a special problem of space perception. When the general laws are known, the illusions will also be understood."

PERCEPTION OF MOVEMENT

The field of movement perception includes studies of real and apparent movement. An adequate theory of movement perception must include both topics, but at present we are in a position to do little more than systematize and summarize experimental results. For this reason, in what follows we shall consider the two types of movement independently.

Real movement. Experiments on real movement involve a stimulus that moves through a distance s at a rate ds/dt. Theoretically, thresholds for changing velocity may be determined, but, in fact, the literature on real movement is almost entirely restricted to the examination of constant, or nearly constant, speeds.

Two types of threshold have been of primary concern: (1) the rate threshold, for which a threshold value of ds/dt is determined while s remains constant, and (2) the displacement threshold (Gordon, 1947), for which a threshold value of s is determined while ds/dt remains constant.

Aubert (1886) determined the lower threshold for rate under several conditions. He found that when the threshold for moving objects, such as the fine lines of millimeter paper, a long vertical line, etc., was determined with fixation on the moving object and in the presence of clearly seen stationary parts of the apparatus, the threshold turned out to be of the order of 1 to 2 minutes of arc per second. When the stationary parts of the apparatus were screened from view, the movement threshold rose to about ten times this figure, that is, to 10 to 20 minutes per second.

Bourdon (1902) verified these observations, and Grim's data (1910), obtained under conditions similar to Aubert's "screening" experiments and with circular movement, are in accord with the figures of Aubert.

The threshold for peripheral movement is higher than the threshold for central vision; for example, in one of Aubert's experiments the threshold for movement at 9 degrees in the periphery turned out to be 18 minutes of arc per second, whereas the threshold for central vision was 54 seconds per second. As for the discriminable difference between two different basic rates, Aubert interpreted it to be of the order of 1 to 2 minutes per second, a figure that resulted from a rejection of data for high speeds.

The results of Graham et al. (1948) on monocular movement parallax may be thought of as rate discrimination data and hence may be compared with Aubert's results. The discriminable difference rate (about 30 seconds of arc per second) found by Graham et al. (1948) for low speeds is lower than the figures given by Aubert. The difference threshold, about 100 seconds per second, obtained at high velocities, is near Aubert's figure and holds for much higher velocities (about 17 degrees per second) than he used. Presumably, differential rate thresholds obtained in the experiments on monocular movement parallax are not complicated at high speeds by factors that may have appeared in Aubert's double drum arrangement.

An experiment by Basler (1906) is representative of research on the minimum discriminable extent of movement — the displacement threshold. Basler found the displacement threshold to be of the order of 20 seconds of visual angle in photopic illuminations. Such a small angle is less than the angle required for the resolution of two acuity objects. (See also the earlier date of Exner, 1875, for peripheral vision.) In contrast to Basler, Stern (1894) and Gordon (1947), working in dim illumination, found that the displacement and acuity thresholds are similar; and Stratton (1902) determined that the displacement threshold is no smaller in foveal vision than the threshold for vernier ("offset") acuity. In view of the fact that the threshold is a function of rate of stimulus movement (Basler, 1906), the question of the relation between acuity and displacement threshold becomes meaningless in the absence of a rate specification.

Basler's experiments were neither systematic nor exhaustive; for example, he did not provide satisfactory measures and controls of rate and illumination. Nevertheless we may probably accept his qualitative results as showing an influence on threshold of the following variables: (1) Illumination: the displacement threshold is lower for high illuminations than for dim illuminations. (2) Rate of movement: the displacement threshold is low for high rates (probably not too high) and increases as rate decreases. (3) Retinal position: peripheral thresholds are higher than foveal thresholds. Data on the latter variable are now relatively satisfactory in comparison with results on rate and illumination. For example, Gordon (1947) has shown that the displacement threshold increases systematically with increase in the peripheral angle of regard.

Some experiments by Brown (1931) are important because they specify several types of movement threshold and demonstrate the influence of certain variables on the thresholds.

Brown used small black squares pasted at 20-centimeter intervals on an endless white paper band, the spaces appearing in a diaphragm opening of dimensions varying from 15×2 centimeters to 3.75×1.25 centimeters. A fixation point was provided in the center of each field.

Brown found that, as the physical velocity of the moving square is increased continuously from zero to 200 centimeters per second, the following thresholds are ascertainable: (1) just discriminable movement; (2) movement reported as a reversed movement; e.g. when a square moves to the top of the field, disappears, and the succeeding square appears at the bottom of the field; (3) movement reported as equivalent to movement of two or more squares; (4) movement reported as equivalent to a continuous gray band (i.e. at "stimulus fusion").

Brown determined the threshold rate for each of these aspects of movement. He found a lower threshold for just discriminable movement (threshold 1) which ranges from 0.11 to 0.30 centimeter per second, depending on field dimensions. These figures correspond to angular velocities of about 2 to 6 minutes of arc per second.

It may be observed that Brown's lower figure is equal to Aubert's upper figures, previously discussed. Length and width of field of view enter as important parameters to determine threshold magnitude, as do size and, presumably, distance between objects. These variables affect not only the lower threshold, but all other thresholds that Brown determined.

As for the other thresholds: the threshold for reversed movement (threshold 2), which Brown refers to as a threshold for a phi movement, varies from 10 to 30 centimeters per second (about 3 to 9 degrees per second) depending upon field dimensions, size of stimulus objects, and distance between stimulus objects. Threshold 3, for increase in the number of moving objects, varies under different conditions from about 25 to 50 centimeters per second (7 to 15 degrees per second). Threshold 4, for "fusion," varies with different conditions from about 50 to 115 centimeters per second (12 to 32 degrees per second). Another specification of these results, which emphasizes the fact of repeated stimulation, is in terms of critical fusion frequency; this turns out to be about 6 to 8 stimulations per second.

All the thresholds determined by Brown show an effect of field dimensions and stimulus dimension parameters. Thresholds are low for small fields, small stimulus objects, and small separations between stimulus objects. More extensive analyses of these factors are needed.

Brown's investigation of "band" movement (threshold 4) followed an earlier research by Cermak and Koffka (1922) on the effects of illumination and field size on "band" movement threshold. Cermak and Koffka caused a narrow line of light, 35 millimeters in length, to rotate behind a screen containing an open sector which was variable in angular size. The authors determined, for each sector width, the speed of rotation of the line of light that was required just to cause an equivalent "band" discrimination. Under these conditions threshold speed of rotation was found to vary as a function of sector angle (or arc) according to the approximate empirical description $v = (KB)^{1/2}$, where v is speed of rotation, B is length of arc; and K is a parameter depending on line illumination. In examining the influence of illumination on traversal time, $e\ (= B/v)$, Cermak and Koffka obtained results that may be described by the empirical expression $e = b - a \log I$, where b and a are parameters representing influences that include size of exposure opening.

Data on the effects of intensity on movement discrimination are sparse and unsystematic. Crook (1937) determined the intensity threshold for the detection of direction of movement with rate of movement and width of stimulus grating bars as parameters. Crook's data show that the intensity threshold for the discrimination of the direction of movement passes through a minimum for fairly slow rates and then increases as rate increases. Intensity thresholds decrease as the width of the grating bar increases.

Our cursory survey of data on real movement shows that our knowledge of the relevant parameters is at an elementary stage of analysis. Complete functional descriptions of the relevant relations are badly needed, as are careful considerations of variables. In studying movement thresholds, we must take care that parameters are not confounded, a danger that arises only too readily from the fact that velocity itself involves the variables of distance and time. In any given experiment the variables of time, distance, interval between stimuli, and cycle of repetition of stimuli must be clearly analyzed before we can be confident that unequivocal data may be obtained.

Apparent movement. The most important type of apparent movement * arises under the following conditions. A given stimulus (a dot, a line, an illuminated area, etc.) is presented to the subject for a duration extending from a few milliseconds up to about

* Presumably the study of apparent movement involves the determination of the critical values of the variables that determine the conditions under which a subject's response will be equivalent to one made in the presence of real movement. Apparent movement, then, is a problem in response equivalence for various conditions of stimulation. Conversely, if the responses are restricted by instructions, the problem becomes one of determining thresholds, based on contrasting responses, for given variables in the presence of a given instruction stimulus.

A discussion of "apparent" movement in terms of behavior does not involve insurmountable difficulties. It is clear, however, that an agreed-upon vocabulary would be valuable in specifying the stimulus and response relations in the various kinds of perception experiments.

400 milliseconds. Then a second stimulus, similar to or different from the first, follows after a pause and in a new location. The length of the pause p may be varied as well as: (1) the duration d_1 of the first stimulus; (2) the duration d_2 of the second stimulus; (3) the intensities i_1 and i_2 of the respective stimuli; (4) the spatial interval s between the two stimuli; (5) the shapes and sizes of the two stimuli; (6) the wavelength distributions of the two stimuli, and (7) the conditions of instruction. (See Koffka, 1931, for a detailed discussion of variables.)

The determinations of greatest interest are those made under an instruction to perceive "optimal movement" (Wertheimer, 1912) where, presumably, the problem is to determine conditions that lead to a response equivalent to one produced by "real" movement (Neuhaus, 1930).

Under certain conditions it is also possible to determine thresholds of p for a report of simultaneity of stimuli and succession of stimuli. The report of simultaneity occurs with pauses p that are shorter than those holding for "optimal" movement. Reports of stimulus succession appear with pauses longer than those providing optimal movement. In addition, Wertheimer maintained that he was able to demonstrate the existence of what he called phi movement. The pause threshold for phi movement lies between the threshold for optimal movement and for succession. Phi movement is reported under an ill-defined class of instructions to the subject to respond to "pure" movement, i.e. "movement that does not involve object movement."

It will be impossible in this short review to give a thorough account of the confused, sprawling literature on apparent movement. Good reviews by Higginson (1926), Koffka (1931), Neff (1936), and Boring (1942) are available. It is sufficient to say that, although several stroboscopic devices had been perfected before 1835 by Faraday, Plateau, Stampfer, and Horner (cf. Boring, 1942), it was not until 1875 that Exner's experiments

showed the relevance of apparent movement to psychological theory.

Exner presented an analysis in which he claimed that movement, because of its irreducible nature, is a true "sensation"; and thus began a long series of papers by various authors. In the next few years Exner's view was supported by Vierordt (1876) and Aubert (1886), but Stern (1894) vigorously combated Exner's assertion and treated movement as a complex of psychological processes. Marbe (1898) presented an analysis of movement in terms of peripheral and central physiological mechanisms, and a short time later Dürr (1900) attempted to get along without the central mechanisms. These men and others, for example, Linke (1918) and Schumann (cf. reference to Lasersohn, 1912, a student of Schumann's) who worked before and after Wertheimer, are of some interest for their psychological analyses. However, it was not until the appearance of Wertheimer's paper that psychologists came into possession of enough data to specify essential controlling variables for apparent movement.

Wertheimer's paper appeared in 1912. With its systematic implications — its treatment of the perception of movement as simple unanalyzable experience — we shall not deal. Nor shall we consider the implications of Wertheimer's theory of cortical activity. From the point of view of the present discussion the paper is important because it contributed to the systematization of the study of apparent movement.

Wertheimer's experimentation set the pattern for much of the later work in the field. His method consisted of the tachistoscopic presentation of two stationary stimuli in such a way that they might be made to appear as simultaneous, overlapping in time, or successive. In Wertheimer's experiments, many variables were found to determine the class of response: exposure time of stimuli, interval between stimuli, characteristics of the stimuli (form, shape, wavelength distribution, intensity, etc.), as well as influences due to conditions of the subject (attitude, instructions, etc.).

Wertheimer paid particular attention to the influence of the temporal interval between stimuli. On the basis of his observations he specifies three types of apparent movement response which may be made as a function of stimulus interval.

With intervals up to about 30 milliseconds the two stimuli are reported as occurring simultaneously. With intervals near 60 milliseconds subjects report the appearance of "optimal movement." Stimulus succession appears at about 200 milliseconds. "Part movements" of stimuli may be reported at temporal intervals lying between those for optimal movement and for simultaneity; and phi movement appears between optimal movement and succession.

In addition to his observations on the various responses obtainable with variations in the temporal pause, Wertheimer investigated the effects of eye movements and changes in the subject's attitude and compared certain phenomena of real and apparent movement.

Immediately after Wertheimer's work, adherents of the Gestalt school, particularly workers in Koffka's laboratory, instituted a program concerned with the specification of (phenomenal) variables and the laws of movement perception. For example, Kenkel (1913), using Wertheimer's methods, examined figures of the "illusory" type, especially various forms of the Müller-Lyer illusion.

Kenkel reports that on successive presentation of the figures subjects may report three different types of movement, alpha, beta and gamma. The alpha movement is an apparent change in the size of an object under successive presentation. Beta movement is the apparent movement of an object from one position to another, the type of effect indicated by Wertheimer's "optimal movement." Gamma movement is the apparent expansion and contraction of an object as illumination is increased or decreased. (It is possible that gamma movement may

be due, in some cases, at least, to an increase and decrease in diffraction-pattern intensities.)

Finally, another type of apparent movement, delta movement, was obtained by Korte (1915), who found that under certain conditions of intensity of illumination, size of objects, distance between objects, and length of pause, a report of reversed movement can be obtained. The essential requirement is that the later stimulus be brighter than the earlier. Under these circumstances movement is reported to occur in the direction of late stimulus to early stimulus. Problems of latency have to be considered in an adequate theory of this effect.

In his experiments Korte (1915) examined beta movement as well as delta movement and, on the basis of his results, propounded the "laws" that bear his name. These laws do not express precise functional relations, and they are confusing with respect to stimulus specification. At best they are limited descriptions of trends for short ranges of stimuli.

Before considering the laws in detail, it will be well to consider one of Korte's terms that causes confusion. Korte used i to refer to a variable that he called *Intensität der Reize*. This variable sometimes refers to light intensity, e.g. as it is varied by the interposition of one, two, or three sheets of white paper between the stimulus patch and the light source. In other cases i refers to stimulus area or shape; e.g. a stimulus of large area or one "strengthened" by "crossbeams" is said to have a higher i value than one having a smaller area or lacking the crossbeams. It is obvious that the term i is ambiguous. For a precise formulation of his results Korte required two types of laws: one that stated the relation between physically measured light intensity and other variables, and another that stated the relation between stimulus area and other variables.

And now consider the laws. Let us call s the spatial distance between stimuli; i_1 the "intensity" of the earlier stimulus, and i_2 the "intensity" of the later; t_1 and t_2, the exposure times of the stimuli; and p the temporal pause between stimuli. Since, for beta movement, $i_1 = i_2$ and $t_1 = t_2$, we may refer to i $(= i_1 = i_2)$ and t $(= t_1 = t_2)$ without subscripts, and the descriptions may be formulated in the following way:

For a report of optimal beta movement:

I. s increases as i increases; p and t remaining constant.

II. i decreases as p increases; s and t remaining constant.

III. s increases as p increases; i and t remaining constant.

IV. t decreases as p increases; i and s remaining constant.

The first variable given for each rule is to be read as the critical value of s, i, t, etc., required for the report of optimal movement. If the independent variable becomes the dependent, then the rule is restated so that the appropriate critical value of the new dependent variable is treated as a function of the formerly independent variable.

The application of these laws to delta movement is brought about by a fifth rule, in which d stands for the absolute difference between I_2 and I_1, the respective light intensities of the two stimuli. Since i_1 does not equal i_2, it is necessary to designate the appropriate i-variable (the intensity of the later stimulus) with a subscript. In Korte's experiments $t_1 = t_2$, and so the t-variable may be written without subscripts.

V. d increases as i_2 increases; p, s, and t remaining constant.

The fifth law refocuses attention on the confusion centering about the use of the term i. The light intensity measures I_2 and I_1 do not always have the dimensions of i_1 and i_2, which may refer to spatial extent. Again, the need for rules concerning the effect of area is obvious.

Two more laws complete the case for delta movement:

VI. d increases as s increases; p, t, and i_2 remaining constant.

VII. d increases as p increases; s, t, and i_2 remaining constant.

The outstanding study on conditions of apparent movement was performed by Neuhaus (1930). Neuhaus felt it essential to vary stimulus conditions over large ranges of relevant variables, and his apparatus, for the first time, allowed such variation. He investigated a number of problems, many of which had been discussed and worked on by earlier investigators, and on the basis of his experiments drew the following conclusions. (1) If exposure time t and distance between stimuli s are kept constant, a proper choice of temporal interval p is required for the report of optimal movement. There is, however, a large range of p values within which variation in p has little effect. For certain values of t and s, optimal movement may be reported over a range of 80 to 400 milliseconds. This finding destroys the generality of Wertheimer's figure of 60 milliseconds. (2) If t is constant and p and s are varied, the spatial separation s for optimal movement increases with an increase in p. This finding is in accord with Korte's third law. Further increases in s may be made by increasing t. (3) If the distance between stimuli, s, is held constant, t increases as p decreases. This finding is in line with Korte's fourth law. In addition, if t_1 represents the exposure time of the first stimulus and t_2 the exposure time of the second, variation in t_2 has little effect. (4) Optimal movement may occur under conditions of temporal overlap of stimuli, but only if t is larger than a certain value. (5) Variation of stimulus intensity over a considerable range results in no need for change in other variables. This finding is in contradiction to Korte's first and second laws. (6) Movement may be reported with differently colored lights and with lights of different intensity.

In addition to examining stimulus conditions, Neuhaus made observations on states of the subject as they influence his reports. Unpracticed subjects, he says, report simultaneity or succession for temporal intervals that, for practiced subjects, result in a report of movement. With continued training, subjects give more and more consistent reports of movement.

Effect of instructions is also important. Direct instructions to see movement elicit the appropriate response in subjects who had not previously given it. Thus for Neuhaus, conditions of the subject, such as "attitude" and "set," are important influences in determining responses to movement.

Our discussion of apparent movement suggests that the field may be greatly improved by new analyses and new investigations. Early research was important for breaking new ground, but it has certainly not left us free of confusion. Where then do we stand at present? What are the generally agreed-upon conditions for the perception of apparent movement? What are the points of disagreement?

The following discussion attempts to contrast, by a topical consideration of variables, those facts that are undisputed and those problems that are foci of disagreement. Neff (1936) presented a similar discussion in his valuable review, and the present treatment makes considerable use of Neff's analyses.

1. *Length of pause between stimuli.* There is general agreement that the length of the interval is fundamental in determining apparent movement. It is certain, however, that Wertheimer's figure of 60 milliseconds for the occurrence of optimal movement is not appropriate to all conditions. Korte's laws have been shown by Neuhaus to be inadequate descriptions of the relations between length of pause and other variables.

2. *Duration of stimulus exposure.* Neuhaus presents data to demonstrate that duration of stimulus exposure is important. Certainly it must be for short exposures below a critical duration (Graham and Margaria, 1935). A change in exposure time necessitates a change in other variables for movement to appear optimal.

3. *Distance between stimuli.* Korte and Neuhaus have shown that distance between stimuli, a basic variable, must be increased as the pause between stimuli increases.

4. *Form.* Linke and others have shown that stimulus form enters as a complex determiner of apparent movement. (See Koffka, 1931, for a detailed consideration of such things as tridimensional effects.) Korte's data show that an increase in area or change in shape of the stimulus patches (see the discussion of his i variable) requires increase in the distance and a decrease in the pause.

5. *Relative differences in intensity.* Korte reports delta movement when the second stimulus is more intense than the first. This observation awaits confirmation.

6. *Wavelength distributions.* Movement may be obtained with stimuli of different colors. Quantitative analyses are wanting.

7. *Conditions of the subject.* States of the subject determined by past history with respect to a given stimulus (providing stimulus "insistence," "conventionality," "familiarity," etc.) operate to influence apparent movement. Attitude, self-instructions, and instructions presented by the experimenter are of fundamental importance in determining the nature of apparent movement.

In general this topic could benefit greatly from good experimentation and careful analysis. Careful exploration of the relevant variables over wide ranges of values will be required before we shall be in a position to improve the rigor of a field that has suffered from too much generalization and too little experimentation and analysis.

SPAN OF PERCEPTION

In introducing their study of the "span" of visual discrimination, Hunter and Sigler (1940) describe the theoretical interests of earlier workers in the following words.

The psychological literature contains many experimental studies on the span of visual discrimination which have been interpreted by their authors as studies of the span either of attention or apprehension. These interpretative labels and their accompanying discussions indicate clearly that the problem was viewed as one whose investigation would illuminate such phases of mental life as the following: How many objects can be grasped in a single moment of consciousness? How many levels of clearness are there? What is the difference between attention, cognition, and apprehension? How does the span of attention vary with the instructions given the subject, with the character of the material used, and with the age and training of the subject?

So far as we can discover no investigator has viewed the experiment as one on visually controlled behavior. . . .

Hunter and Sigler do view the problem in these terms, but before we consider their work it will be profitable to give a short account of some of the earlier "span" experiments.

The history of early work on the span of attention is given in a concise manner by Whipple (1924), and Garrett and Schneck (1933) present a valuable short summary of some later investigations.

The span-of-discrimination experiment employs a variety of stimulus objects: figures, letters, nonsense syllables, dots, etc. Various numbers of objects within a given class are presented to the subject for *short* durations (of the order of 200 milliseconds and less) and the number of objects correctly responded to half the time is determined by the method of constant stimuli. Of course, the number correctly responded to may be influenced by various factors: intensity and duration of stimulus, instructional stimuli, class of objects, age of subjects, previous amount of practice, etc.

Whipple summarizes some of these influences. Age, according to Freeman's work, has some effect on the span of discrimination: children 8 to 10 years of age give correct responses to five objects 22 per cent less frequently than adults. Practice has little influence on the threshold for span of discrimination once an "habituation" period is passed. Little relation exists between span and intelligence score. Different forms and combinations of stimuli give different threshold spans.

When a series of "unrelated" objects is exposed, the threshold is of the order of 4 to 8. When objects may be "grouped" (as letters in words, part figures in larger figures, etc.), the threshold remains at 4 to 8 units of the new class of grouped stimuli. These latter findings demonstrate the great need for an adequate theory of grouping and of relatedness. Why must one specify *words* as the appropriate stimulus units in one situation and *letters* in another? Such description clearly implies a need for an understanding of behavior processes that depend on different classes of discriminative stimuli.

When durations of exposure of the order of several seconds are used, the experiment becomes the span of apprehension experiment. Presumably complex behavior, such as counting, can take place during intervals of the order of 3 seconds and longer, and it seems fairly certain that, whatever form behavior analysis must take in the future, it must reckon with complexities for the long exposures that do not exist for the short.

Durations between about 80 milliseconds and 2000 milliseconds are beyond the range where an increase in duration increases intensity effects in the visual process (Graham and Kemp, 1938). Hence it is not surprising that for durations below about 3 seconds and with many classes of stimulus materials (e.g. nonsense syllables), the span of discrimination is little better for long durations than for short. With other stimulus classes, such as words, the span approximately doubles (Whipple, 1924) for a duration of 3 seconds as contrasted with a duration of about a second. For durations of the order of 10 seconds and more it is clear that the span would be limited only by the amount of counting, verbal repetition, etc., that may be accomplished.

Whipple reports that practice has little effect on the span of apprehension for adults. Dallenbach (1914) found that a 17-week period of daily drills resulted in an increased span for children aged 7 to 10 years, with performance reaching its maximum by the seventh week.

The 1920's were the heyday of systematic theorizing about attention, particularly by workers of the Cornell and Pennsylvania laboratories, who set their findings in a context of structural psychology. Dallenbach (1920) performed an elaborate introspective analysis of levels of clearness. Fernberger (1921) emphasized the need for application of psychological methods to the "span of attention" experiment. He found himself in agreement with Whipple (1924; Fernberger refers to the 1914 edition) and Dallenbach (1914, 1920) that, since more than one degree of clearness was discriminated by subjects within the "focal consciousness," the "range of attention" experiment should rightly be called the "range of apprehension" experiment. Oberly (1924), on the basis of introspective studies, divided the conscious content of the span experiments into three characteristic processes: a first, *immediate* process; a second, *grouping* process; and a third, *counting* process. To these three processes, Oberly gave the names attention, cognition, and apprehension, respectively. Much controversial writing occurred at this time concerning the processes and the question of "clearness" (Cooper, 1928; Wever, 1928; Dallenbach, 1928).

The first study of the span of discrimination from the point of view of behavior was performed by Hunter and Sigler (1940). They determined, by the method of constant stimuli and for binocular vision, the number of dots giving a 50-per-cent correct response for a given intensity and duration of light. The dots were small black figures on an illuminated field. Psychophysical functions were determined, each for a given intensity, with duration employed as a parameter that fixed the position of each curve. The durations of the exposures varied from 4 to 4000 milliseconds.

Hunter and Sigler's data show that, for a constant duration of exposure, the number of dots correctly responded to 50 per cent of the time increases with intensity (cf. also Schlegel, 1929). Figure 24 shows this result and also demonstrates the influence of dura-

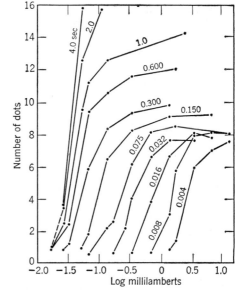

FIG. 24. Curve showing the number of dots correctly discriminated 50 per cent of the time at different intensities. The number attached to each curve gives the duration of exposure. (After Hunter and Sigler, 1940.)

tion. The curve for the 4-millisecond duration is farthest to the right, indicating that a high illumination is required in order to discriminate the dots at this short duration. The curve for the 8-millisecond duration is to the left of the curve for 4 milliseconds; and the curves for successively longer durations, up to 4000 milliseconds, are successively shifted in the direction of lower intensities. Up to a duration of about 75 milliseconds the maximum number of dots correctly discriminated seems to be fairly constant; i.e. the maxima of the curves are similar. However, for durations greater than about 75 milliseconds the maximum becomes greater and greater with an increase in duration.

Hunter and Sigler continued their analysis by relating their data to the Bunsen-Roscoe law. This law states that a constant photolytic effect is determined by a constant amount of energy of stimulation, which may be spread over a shorter or a longer duration of time. Specifically, $I \cdot t = C$, where I is intensity, t is duration, and C is a constant.

In visual research it is convenient to test for the Bunsen-Roscoe law by plotting log $I \cdot t$ against log t. A slope of zero on such a graph indicates that the Bunsen-Roscoe law holds; a slope of unity represents the relation $I = $ Constant. In experiments on responses to short flashes of light it has been found that the equation $I \cdot t = C$ gives way to $I = $ Constant at a critical duration (Hartline, 1934; Graham and Margaria, 1935; Karn, 1936). Hartline has discussed the implications of the critical duration most adequately. He states that where a given constant response, for example a constant initial rate of nerve impulses, is determined by light stimulation, the product of intensity and time may be expected to be constant up to that critical duration at which the sensory event is completed. Any increase in time beyond this critical duration has no influence since the event in question is over. Beyond this critical point, intensity alone is the determining factor.

In Fig. 25 the data of Hunter and Sigler are plotted in terms of log $I \cdot t$ versus log t. It may be observed that the lowest curve, the curve for discrimination of a single dot, lies lowest on the graph and that, as the constant effect is taken to be 2, 4, 6, etc., dots, the total energy (product of intensity and duration) required for the discrimination increases. All the curves up to the curve for 7 dots seem to give data that fit the Bunsen-Roscoe law for short durations; i.e. the curves have zero slope. Beyond a certain duration the slope of each curve changes gradually to a slope of unity, and the equation becomes $I = $ Constant.

The relations described are not obeyed by the curves for 9, 10, 12, and 14 dots. These curves have initially negative slopes, which become positive only at long exposure times. On this problem Hunter and Sigler say:

The construction of the graph is such that a negative slope indicates that time is a more important factor in determining span

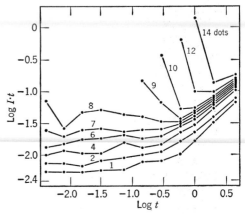

FIG. 25. Curves showing the total energy ($I \cdot t$) required for the discrimination of various numbers of dots as a function of exposure duration. On this graph a horizontal line would represent the Bunsen-Roscoe law. A line with a slope of unity would represent the relation $I = $ Constant. The curves are derived from those of Fig. 24. (After Hunter and Sigler, 1940.)

than is intensity. Since we are certain that the discrimination of a large number of dots, let us say 12, involves counting and therefore that time is an important factor, we are led to infer that even the span of 8 dots has taken us over the boundary of a single discriminatory event and into the counting area because its curve also has a negative slope. In spans of 8 dots and over we have not left the field of sensory determination of response as indicated by the role of the Bunsen-Roscoe law, but we have obscured that rôle by dealing with more than one event at a time. [P. 177.]

Hunter and Sigler summarize the implications of their work in the following terms:

These results are interpreted to mean that where the span is a single discriminatory event (1–7 dots) as opposed to several such events, as in the necessary counting of more than 7 dots, the Bunsen-Roscoe law holds up to that duration at which the sensory contribution is complete. Stating this in other words, we may say: the span of a single discriminative event may vary from 1–7 dots depending upon the intensity and duration of the stimulation; and up to the duration at which the sensory contribution is completed, a constant amount of sensory energy is required to produce the event. Beyond that critical duration, intensity is more important than time. The 'span of attention' thus resolves itself into a span of discrimination, a form of behavior which in the field of vision is controlled on the receptor side by time and intensity factors.

In a later analysis of the Hunter-Sigler data Schlosberg (1948) was concerned with the problem of why the number of dots correctly responded to increases with the energy of the stimulus. Schlosberg sets forth the hypothesis that, in a response to a given configuration of dots, the contribution of each dot to the discrimination is an independent event, so that, for example, the probability of seeing 2 dots at a given energy is less than the probability of seeing either alone. Schlosberg attempted to fit the psychophysical functions of Fig. 24 by a theory based on the simple formulation that the probability of seeing N dots is the Nth power of the probability of seeing a single dot at the same light value. This simple formulation fits the data for low intensities quite well but does not fit the data for the higher intensities.

For a more precise formulation Schlosberg attempted to compound the probabilities by assuming that the binocular data of the Hunter-Sigler experiment are the end product of events taking place in the two eyes. The Hunter-Sigler data are fitted by the resulting equation for 2 to 3 dots. However, when the curve passes to 5 or 6 dots, the deviation of data from theory is considerable.

Because of the failure of the simple formulations Schlosberg developed two somewhat more complex hypotheses: (1) Any dot will be discriminated if it stimulates either eye. On this assumption the resulting probability expression is mathematically similar to one of the simple formulations. (2) Two or more dots will be discriminated *only* if they all stimulate the same eye. On this assumption lower frequencies of correct response are predicted than by hypothesis 1.

When the curves given by the mathematical treatments of (1) and (2) are applied to the Hunter-Sigler data, it is found that treatment 1 fits the data for 1, 2, or 3 dots, but that treatment (2) fits the data for 4, 5, 6, and 7 dots. (Schlosberg is not interested in applying the theory to more than 7 dots. He says that the "span of apprehension," with new controlling events, enters beyond this number.)

Taken at face value, Schlosberg's treatment may imply that the subject "can interpret two or three dots, even though they stimulate different eyes." However, "five or six dots must *all* stimulate the same eye if they are to be perceived."

Undoubtedly other hypotheses might account for the data as well as or better than those employed by Schlosberg. Nevertheless his analysis is interesting, and its further application may elucidate data in an informative way. Already, in fact, Casperson and Schlosberg (to be published) have found that Schlosberg's simplest formulation fits new data for the *monocular* viewing of dots.

Hunter and Sigler's experiments and Schlosberg's analysis signal new approaches to the old span experiments. The points of view and the methods exemplified in their work may stimulate a new approach to this old problem.

FLUCTUATIONS OF PERCEPTION

If a subject regards a weak light, under instructions to report when the light is visible and when it is not, his behavior shows an alternating character: positive responses

("The light is visible") alternate with negative ("The light is not visible"). Oscillating behavior of this sort, traditionally called "fluctuations of attention," may continue in a more or less rhythmical way for many cycles. Fluctuations of behavior occur not only to weak visual stimuli but to weak stimuli in the other senses. Guilford (1927) gives an excellent summary, not only for the field of vision, but for other senses as well.

Münsterberg (1889) was not the first to work on the problem of fluctuations but he formulated it in terms that led to later work; hence, he is probably the most important of the early investigators. On the side of analysis his work is significant chiefly because of his conclusion that fluctuations to visual stimuli are due to changes in accommodation and fixation.

Münsterberg's theory was soon brought into question by Pace (1893) who treated one eye of a subject with atropine and found just as frequent fluctuations in that eye as in the untreated eye. Slaughter (1901) used an aphakic subject (one without a lens) and found fluctuations of normal period. Ferree (1913) also found normal fluctuations in aphakic subjects.

The experiments of Pace, Slaughter, and Ferree indicate that accommodation changes do not account for the oscillations. Pace introduced the concept of light adaptation as a determinant of fluctuations, and Hammer (1905) and, later, Ferree (1913) added eye movements as complementary influences. Presumably eye movements, in causing stimulation to shift to new portions of the retina, operate to restore sensitivity, which, in turn, is diminished by adaptation.

As against the eye movement theory, Liddell (1919) failed to show any relation between eye movements and fluctuations, a fact that was later verified by Guilford (1927). Troland (1921) suggested that the fluctuations might be connected with changes in pupil size, but the suggestion has not yet received experimental verification. At present we must regard as untenable theories

that emphasize eye movements and changes in accommodation.

Early in the present century considerable interest was shown in the problem of how fluctuations of response relate to the various bodily rhythms. Slaughter (1901), on the basis of some inconclusive data, reported relations among fluctuations of response, breathing rate, and the Traube-Hering waves of blood-pressure change. Bonser (1903) interpreted some of his results as substantiating the Traube-Hering relation, and Griffitts and Gordon (1924) concluded that visibility of a light occurs during the trough and upward slope of the Traube-Hering waves.

Guilford criticized the work of Griffitts and Gordon on the grounds that they did not correlate the response period with the Traube-Hering period. At present it seems that any theory that interprets response fluctuations as correlates of bodily rhythms will have to be decisively bolstered before it can be accepted with confidence.

In the most adequate study of oscillating visual discrimination, Guilford (1927) showed that fluctuations of response are phenomena associated with the visual threshold. First, he demonstrated that the percentage of time a weak light is discriminable varies with the light intensity in a manner comparable to the "frequency of seeing" function obtained by the method of constant stimuli. Second, he showed that the stimulus value that is visible 50 per cent of the time is near the threshold value found in the usual manner when allowances are made for adaptation occurring with long stimulus exposures. Like thresholds themselves, fluctuations of response to weak visual stimulation are a matter of "probability of seeing."

FIGURAL AFTER-EFFECTS

In 1933 Gibson reported the interesting observation that, when we look steadily at a curved line, the line seems to become progressively less curved. In addition, when a straight line is presented immediately after exposure to the curved line, the straight line seems to be curved in a direction opposite to the original curvature. Quantitative measurement gave an indication of the degree of curvature imposed on a straight line, in order for it to be seen as straight, after preceding stimulation by a curved line.

a straight line, moderately tilted from the horizontal or vertical, and then regard a horizontal or vertical line, the position of the objectively horizontal or vertical line is reported to be tilted in a direction opposite to the tilt of the original line. Gibson and

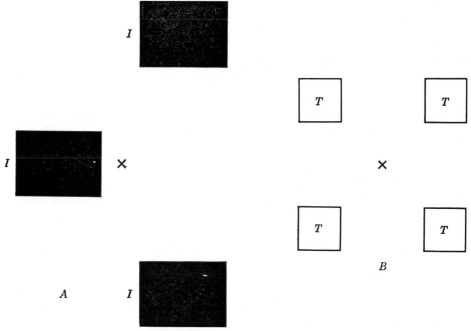

FIG. 26. Inspection configurations used by Köhler and Wallach (1944) to demonstrate displacement effects. Regard the fixation cross of *A* at a distance of about 18 inches for 40 seconds, and then look at the fixation cross of *B*. After *A* has been observed, the right-hand squares of *B* appear nearer the central horizontal axis of this figure than do the left-hand squares. Inspection of the left-hand *I*-figure in *A* causes the left-hand squares of *B* to move apart vertically; and inspection of the right-hand *I*-figures of *A* causes the right-hand squares of *B* to move together. Test figures are displaced away from previous inspection figures.

ceding stimulation by a curved line. (See also Bales and Follansbee, 1935.)

In another series of experiments Gibson examined straight lines that joined at the vertex of an obtuse angle. When, after stimulation by such a bent line, the subjects regard a straight line, they report that the straight line appears bent into lines whose contained angle is opposite in sign to the angle of the original bent figure.

A further effect was observed by Gibson (1937), M. D. Vernon (1934), and Gibson and Radner (1937). When subjects inspect

Gibson and Radner interpreted the tilted-line effect as due to the deviation of inspected objects from vertical and horizontal "norms" (Gibson and Mowrer, 1938).

Köhler and Wallach (1944), on the other hand, have demonstrated that a displacement effect is basic to an understanding of figural after-effects.

Consider the design shown in Fig. 26*A*. The solid rectangles, marked *I*, are presented to the subject, together with their fixation cross, on a separate card. After a period of regard lasting about 40 seconds, the inspection objects are withdrawn and the subject is confronted with the test objects shown in *B*. The subject is instructed to report on the heights of the right-hand squares relative to the left-hand squares. The almost universal response under these conditions is that the upper right-hand square is lower than its paired left-hand square, and the lower right-hand square is higher than its paired left-hand square.

On the basis of many related experiments, Köhler and Wallach demonstrated that, in general, subjects report that test objects are seen as displaced in space from the positions of previously viewed inspection objects. In the experiment under consideration, the shift of each right-hand *T*-object toward the center of the field is a displacement away from the associated *I*-object; and the movement of each left-hand *T*-object away from the center of the field is also a displacement away from the associated *I*-object.

It is clear that any adequate theory of the displacement effect requires a description of the manner in which displacement varies as a function of the distance that separates the inspection and the test object. Köhler and Wallach performed such an experiment. Their method is described as follows:

> Our *T*-objects were two outline squares which lay at equal distances on the left and on the right side of a fixation mark. On the right side — and in one experiment on both sides — an *I*-figure was first shown which affected the relative height of the two squares. The position of one *T*-square was varied in a random order and the subjects reported in each case which square, if any, appeared higher. From a table of such judgments the most probable equivalence point was inferred.

One experiment done under these conditions gave the results shown in Table 1. (The *I*-figure was a single solid oblong placed at various distances above the right-hand test square.)

It will be observed in the table that when the *T*-square is separated from the *I*-oblong

TABLE 1

DISTANCE THROUGH WHICH THE SUBJECTS MOVED THE LEFT-HAND TEST SQUARE DOWN SO THAT IT APPEARED AT THE SAME HEIGHT AS THE RIGHT-HAND SQUARE. *I*-OBJECT IS A SOLID OBLONG ABOVE THE RIGHT-HAND SQUARE

Distance of *I*-Object above Right *T*-Square (in 20ths of an Inch)	Movement of Left-Hand Square in Millimeters			
	Subject K	Subject B	Subject W	Subject M
2	2.2		1.8	0.8
3.5	2.0	1.6	2.1	1.8
5	3.0	2.8	2.3	1.8
6.5	2.0		1.7	0.5
8	1.8	2.1		

by $\frac{5}{20}$ inch, the displacement of the *T*-square with respect to the comparison square is greatest. When the *T*-square is separated from the *I*-object by $\frac{2}{20}$ inch, the displacement is less, and, when it is at a distance of $\frac{8}{20}$ inch, the displacement is again small. This means that displacement is a function of the distance separating the *T*-object and the *I*-object. The displacement function passes through a maximum at intermediate distances and has low values at small and great distances.

Observations on the displacement function are important and only in terms of it can many of Köhler and Wallach's results be explained. The reader is referred to their account for a full treatment.

It will be recalled that Gibson (1937) and Gibson and Radner (1937) had explained certain tilted-line effects as due to deviations from vertical and horizontal "norms." (See also Gibson and Mowrer, 1938.) Köhler and Wallach disagree with this interpretation and believe that tilted-line effects can be explained as special cases of the displacement principle without resort to the concept of norms.

Their method was as follows:

> An *I*-line was inspected in a given orientation, and then a *T*-line was shown in an-

other orientation, so that a small angle lay between the two lines. Parallel to this T-line there were on both sides and at some distance two other lines which served as comparison objects. The position of the T-line in the middle was not actually constant. As one inspection period followed another this line was shown in slightly varying positions, and in each case the subject compared its direction with that of the fixed lines. The method of constant stimuli was used throughout.

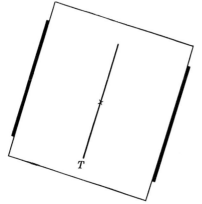

FIG. 27. The T-line used by Köhler and Wallach (1944) in one of their tilted-line experiments. The I-object (not shown) is a straight line (with fixation point) which may be presented to the subject on any retinal axis.

Figure 27 represents the test figures shown to the subject. The line marked T can be rotated about the point of fixation, and the whole configuration can be presented so that the two outer lines fall on any one of a number of chosen retinal axes. The I-object was a straight line (with fixation point) that could be presented to the subject on any retinal axis, the only consideration being that the I-line varied 10 degrees (plus or minus) from the orientation of the succeeding T-line.

Table 2 gives the averaged data of the experiment; they "indicate by what angle the T-line had to deviate from the direction of the standards if the T-line was to appear parallel to them; i.e., if compensation for the after-effect was to be obtained horizontally

TABLE 2

NECESSARY ROTATION OF THE T-LINE AT VARIOUS ORIENTATIONS OF THE I-LINE IN ORDER FOR THE T-LINE TO APPEAR PARALLEL TO THE OUTER COMPARISON LINES. ORIENTATION OF THE I-LINE AND INITIAL ORIENTATION OF T-LINES ARE GIVEN IN TERMS OF ANGLES MEASURED COUNTERCLOCKWISE FROM HORIZONTAL. AVERAGE OF THREE SUBJECTS

Orientations of I- and T-Lines in Degrees		Rotation of T-Line in Degrees
I	T	
10	0	1.22
0	10	1.27
35	45	2.73
100	90	1.34
85	95	1.46
90	100	1.46

the T-line had to be turned toward the direction of the I-line" by the amounts given in the table. In other words, the presence of the I-line caused the later T-line to appear out of parallel with the standard lines, and the subjects then had to rotate the T-line by the amounts indicated.

Köhler and Wallach interpret the results of Table 2 to mean that Gibson and Radner's account of visual after-effects in terms of deviations from horizontal or vertical norms is invalid. Angular displacements comparable to those of Table 2 may presumably occur for any visual axis; in fact, they are greatest in Table 2 for the 45-degree axis. Thus there is no need to consider norms; the tilted-line effect is a special case of displacement.

Hammer (1949) studied some temporal aspects of frontal plane after-effects: (1) their development during the inspection period and (2) their disappearance after the inspection period. Specifically she examined the way in which figural displacements vary as functions of (1) the time interval between inspection and test periods and (2) the duration of inspection period.

Her procedure consisted in having her subjects, during the test period, make a vertical alignment of a short upper black comparison line with a lower black test line. Prior to each alignment (i.e. during the inspection period) an inspection line had been presented to the left or right of the position of the subsequently presented lower test line. The measure of the after-effect produced was the deviation of a setting of the upper line from a zero point (i.e. a point of "subjective" equality based on alignment set-

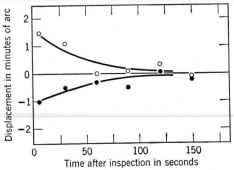

FIG. 28. The disappearance of figural after-effects as a function of time after inspection. Positive angular displacements are to the subject's right of the zero point; negative, to the left. Curves have been fitted by inspection. (From Hammer, 1949.)

tings made in the absence of prior stimulation by the inspection lines).

Hammer's experiment shows that, as regards the time course of disappearance of figural after-effects, such effects are at a maximum immediately after the inspection period and decrease rapidly with increase of time after inspection, reaching zero at approximately 90 seconds, and remaining constant with further increases in time after inspection. The experimental data are presented in Fig. 28. Displacements from zero are a function of the position of the I-figure with respect to the T-figure. When the I-figure is to the right of the T-figure (solid circles), the displacement is to the left; when the I-figure is to the left of the T-figure, the displacement is to the right (open circles).

The time course of development of figural after-effects is presented in Fig. 29. Figural after-effects, tested immediately after the

inspection period, increase with increase in the duration of the inspection period to a maximum at approximately 1 minute. With further increase in inspection time, displacements remain relatively constant.

Köhler and Wallach present an exhaustive theoretical account of figural after-effects, an account that seems to follow from Köhler's earlier "brain field" theory (Köhler, 1920). (See also Ségal, 1939.) To what extent the theory may be important in producing a rational account of figural after-effects must remain a question until many more experiments are directed at estimating magnitudes of essential variables. For some important criticisms of the theory, see Smith (1948).

In a later research Köhler and Emery (1947) investigated figural after-effects in the third dimension. They demonstrated that tilted-line effects occur in the third dimension as well as in the frontal plane.

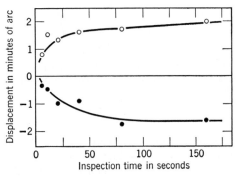

FIG. 29. Angular displacement as a function of inspection time. Signs of displacement and symbols have the same significance as in Fig. 28. (From Hammer, 1949.)

One of their experiments consisted in presenting an inspection line tilted at 20 degrees to the frontal plane. When a later test line was shown in the frontal plane, subjects reported that they saw it tilted in a direction opposite to the tilt of the original inspection line. Several other experiments have demonstrated that tilted-line effects occur even more strikingly in the third dimension than in the frontal plane.

Displacements also occur for objects in the third dimension, a fact that may be demonstrated in the following manner. A subject is instructed to inspect a white square placed in front of the homogeneous background provided by a large black screen. After removal of the inspection object a similarly sized test object (white screen) is placed in front of the location of the now absent inspection object, and the subject is instructed to compare its distance with the distance of another white screen, placed to the left of the test object but physically at the same distance from the eye. Under these conditions subjects report that the test object appears nearer than the left-hand "neutral" comparison object.

If the test object is placed farther away than the inspection object, the subject reports that it seems at a greater distance than a neutral object physically at the same distance. Köhler and Emery combine both demonstrations; and the subject sees a test object nearer than the previous inspection object as closer to him than its associated neutral object, whereas a test object farther away than the previous inspection object appears to be at a greater distance than its neutral object.

Thus the same rule holds for the third dimension as for the frontal plane: subjects report that a test object appears displaced from a previous inspection object. Quantitative experiments show that the displacement is at a maximum for a medium distance in space and becomes less for great and small distances.

Another series of experiments was concerned with displacements as related to conditions of fixation. In one of the experiments a subject regarded, during the inspection period, a fixation point in the same frontal plane as the inspection object. After the inspection period the inspection object served as test object, and a neutral comparison object, at the same distance as the test object (previously the inspection object) was inserted in the field. The subject had

been instructed to change fixation, after the inspection period, to a mark either in front of or behind the fixation point of the inspection figure and to report on the position of the test figure with reference to the neutral figure.

Under these circumstances it was found that, when fixation is changed, after the inspection period, to a point nearer the subject, the subject reports that the test object is seen as farther away than the "neutral" object. If fixation changes to a point farther away than the fixation point of the inspection period, the test object appears nearer than the neutral object. In other words the direction of apparent spatial displacement of a given test object depends on the relation between fixation distances in the inspection and test periods, and the subject's report is made with reference to the geometry of the horopter.

Köhler and Emery do not relate their results immediately to a theory of space perception. They describe some interesting experiments on "stereoscopic distortions" and conclude that contours are important determiners of space perceptions. It is probable that some of these latter phenomena have much in common with problems investigated by workers on aniseikonia.

PERCEPTION AND CONDITIONS OF THE ORGANISM

It has been known for a long time that discriminations are influenced by the condition of the organism at the time the discriminations are made. The multitude of experiments on attention, apperception, Einstellung, and preparatory set attest the universal appreciation of this fact. On the side of psychological theory, many writers, e.g. Woodworth (1945) and Dashiell (1937), reserve an important central position for factors of this sort in their systematic presentations. In a similar vein, in our earlier discussion of size and shape, we pointed out that a subject's responses are determined not only by the stimuli present at a given moment but also by the nature of the subject's history of past stimulation. The present chapter is not the place to consider a de-

of language, or, as they say, by "those processes of the organism that are initiated by language." A set of twelve relatively ambiguous figures was prepared, seven of which are shown in Fig. 30. Two names were assigned to each of the figures. The same

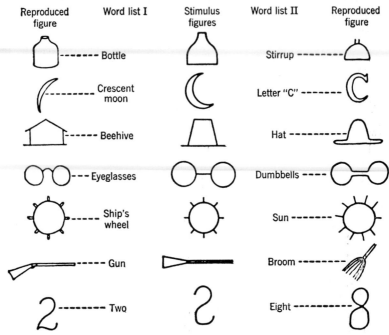

FIG. 30. Figures used by Carmichael, Hogan, and Walter (1932) in their experiment on the influence of speech upon perception. The stimulus figures appearing in the middle column were presented to one group of subjects with the associated words of word list I and to another group with the associated words of word list II. The reproduced figures given by the two groups are shown in the two outer columns. Differences in the drawings for each stimulus figure may be attributed to differences in conditions set up within the subjects by the different words announced. (From Dashiell, 1937.)

tailed treatment of this topic, but it does seem necessary to indicate its relation to perception in more than a passing way.

Experimental facts, as they exist, do little more than set the problem. It has often been shown that different conditions of the organism, aroused in many different ways, lead to different responses to similar stimuli. Experiments on reproduced forms are of interest here (cf. e.g. Wulf, 1921; Gibson, 1929).

Carmichael, Hogan, and Walter (1932) attempted to control reproduction by means

visual figures were presented to all subjects, but one list of names (word list I) was given when the figures were presented to the 48 subjects of group I, and the other list of names (word list II) was given when the figures were presented to the 38 subjects of group II. Each subject was instructed that he must draw the figures as accurately as possible after the series was over. Just before each figure was presented, the experimenter said, "The next figure resembles . . ." (giving one of the two names of the figure).

The figures as reproduced were judged, without consultation, by two of the authors, and the drawings were rated upon a 5-point scale. Drawings rated 5 "included figures which were almost completely changed from the original." All the analyses of the report were performed on drawings of this grade.

Based on the ratings of the two judges, 74 per cent of the figures that had been named by word list I were found to be similar to "what may be termed the visual representation of the figure named in List I." Seventy-three per cent of the figures named by word list II "were like the visual representations of the figure named in List II."

In summarizing their experiment, Carmichael, Hogan, and Walter make the following statement:

It seems that if a subject has just heard, for example, the word "eyeglass," certain processes in his organism have been started that initiate certain processes which are possible because of the past experience of that individual with *eyeglasses* as words and as objects. If, while these processes are in progress, a figure of two visual circles connected by a line is presented to the subject, this figure may later be reproduced in a manner (different from what would be the case) if the processes present in the individual at the time of the same visual presentation had been evoked by the word "dumbbell." In other words, without recourse to any elaborate theory, one who wishes to make an empirical statement of fact may say: If a verbal stimulus-form and a visual stimulus-form are presented to a subject in certain temporal relationships, the processes in question may be modified, or rather a new total process may result, which is in certain respects unlike either of the previous sets of processes. On subsequent arousal by any "part" stimulus the "reproduction" is thus a complexly determined total, and not either of its component processes.

Specification of such a "complexly determined total" and conditions of which it is representative is, of course, fundamental to a science of psychology.

Sherif (1935, 1936) performed a widely known experiment on the influence of social factors in perception. Subjects were brought into a dark room and instructed to regard a small stationary spot of light. Under such circumstances an effect called the autokinetic phenomenon occurs; i.e. the subject reports that the stationary spot seems to move erratically in all directions.

Sherif studied the reported extent of the autokinetic effect with subjects tested singly and in groups. Among single subjects, as might be expected, the estimates of movement showed wide variation from subject to subject. But, when the individual subjects were grouped in two's and three's, the data for each individual tended to approach the average of the group. In other words, "social factors," deriving from the fact of grouping, influenced individual subjects to make estimates in line with those of their fellows.

Sherif (1936) relates these findings to a concept of social norms.

The experiments, then, constitute a study of the formation of a norm in a simple laboratory situation. They show in a simple way the basic psychological process involved in the establishment of social norms. They are an extension into the social field of a general psychological phenomenon that we found in perception and in many other psychological fields; namely, that our experience is organized around or modified by frames of reference participating as factors in any given stimulus situation. [See also an experiment by Schonbar, 1945.]

A number of experiments have tested the influences of reward and punishment upon discrimination. Proshansky and Murphy (1942) rewarded subjects for estimating the weights of objects or lengths of line with a given bias, the subjects showing significant response shifts in the rewarded direction. Reward may also influence responses to "figure" and "ground" relations (Schafer and Murphy, 1943). Frequency and extent of movement of the autokinetic phenomenon in a given reported direction is increased by "reinforcement," by "active participation" by the subject, and by instructions that the light would move (Haggard and Rose, 1944). Ellson's experiments (1941*a*, *b*) on "sensory conditioning," in which subjects were conditioned to "hear" a tone on the presentation of a light, are also of considerable interest.

The experiments of Bruner and Goodman (1947) show the influence on discrimination of conditions presumably set up by "economic deprivation." Groups of "rich" and "poor" children were instructed to set the area of a variable circular aperture equal to the area of a simultaneously presented penny, nickel, dime, quarter, or half-dollar. The subjects also made matches against cardboard disks equal in size to the various coins.

In the matches made against the cardboard disks the subjects showed only slight error in the adjustment of the diaphragm aperture; but with the coins the error increased with coin denomination to a maximum for the twenty-five-cent piece. The error was in the direction of overestimating coin size and rose to 35 per cent for the quarters.

When the data were broken down (Fig. 31) into scores for the "rich" and "poor" groups, it was found that the "poor" children overestimated in much higher degree than did the "rich" children. (The children were described as 10-year-olds of "normal intelligence." One would like data on the intelligence scores of the two groups.)

Bruner and Goodman interpret their results as affirming the hypothesis that perceptual behavior deviates from "physiologically determined behavior" as a function of subjective need for socially valued objects. Thus the greater overestimation of the "poor" children is a manifestation of habits relating to money, conditioned by "economic" factors in the lifetime of the subject. In an experiment with similar orientation, Ansbacher (1937) found that, in matching a variable number of stamps or coins with respect to a standard number, the number

required to make a match depends upon the values of the stamps and coins.

The problem with which we have been concerned in the present section is the following: How are discriminations influenced by different conditions of the organism? The correlated question of how the conditions may be specified is probably a more

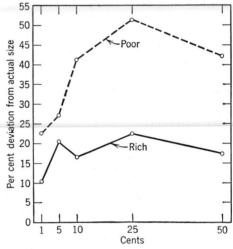

FIG. 31. Size adjustments made by "rich" and by "poor" 10-year-old subjects for various coin denominations. Note that the poor children overestimated coin size more than did the well-to-do. (From Bruner and Goodman, 1947.)

important one; it is certainly more important as soon as we progress beyond the stage of demonstrating that various conditions cause different discriminations. Without operational or theoretical specification of "conditions" it is unlikely that we can give a satisfying answer to the first question. Although it may be true that specification of the organism's state as love, pain, attentive set, need, anxiety, joy, etc., may, at the conversational level, establish the existence of a problem, we hope to develop behavioral theory to the point where these unknown conditions may be described in such form that their quantitative influences on behavior are predictable. One of our first duties is probably to see that definitions of the various "conditions" are anchored to definable antecedents and consequents.*

CONCLUDING REMARKS

The present account has considered the problem of specification of variables in considerable detail but has said little about theory. This emphasis is justifiable at the present time, for it is probably true enough that significant theory cannot exist in the absence of proper specification. Nevertheless the search for adequate theory must remain an overshadowing endeavor of the scientist; and, as regards the field of perceptual discrimination, the need for useful theory is great. This is not to say that the field has lacked theorists in the past. It has had plenty of theorists but little adequate theory. Exceptions to this statement, of course, come to mind, notably the brilliant but limited systematization available in the geometrical theory of space perception.

Close examination of the many theories advanced reveals that they do not usually specify test operations and that, very often, the number of facts explained is no greater than the number of assumptions made. Theories exhibiting these deficiencies may be of interest for other reasons, but they are not a satisfactory stopping place in a scientific program.

It would probably be unprofitable to attempt an a priori judgment on the nature of theories that might advance the field of visual perception. In general terms, however, it would seem that an ultimately adequate theory must make specific the general relations implied in the equation

$$R = f(a, b, c, d \cdots n \cdots t \cdots x, y, z) \quad (29)$$

The first letters of the alphabet (a, b, c, etc.) refer to properly specified aspects of stimuli; the last letters ($\cdots x$, y, z), to properly

---

* A number of articles dealing with the topic of perception as influenced by conditions of the subject has appeared since this account was written. Pastore (*J. Psychol.*, 1949, **28**, 457–475) presents a critical review of some of the later work.

specified conditions of the organism; R, to response; n, to number of presentations; and t, to time.

In a program of research that might eventually explicate these relations, it can be foreseen that theories of vision (Hecht, 1937; Granit, 1947), which tell something of initiating events and limiting conditions, will be desirable; and behavior theories (Hull, 1943; Skinner, 1938), which can describe conditions of the organism, will clearly be advantageous.

Psychologists have sometimes reacted against theories couched in terms of physiological mechanisms. There can be little doubt that a theory that uses a physiological vocabulary adds nothing to a theory using a psychological vocabulary if the former theory specifies no test beyond what may be specified by the latter.

On the other hand, there is no reason why well-established phenomena, describable by a physiological vocabulary and demonstrating functional dependencies of the sort required by a necessary inferred variable, may not be used for a quantitative account when due attention is paid to transformation relations; in fact, the joining of vocabularies may result in an increased number of testable statements. (The need for attention to transformation relations is not unique to a transition from a physiological to a psychological vocabulary. The same consideration applies to generalization of results obtained in a particular behavior situation to principles presumably applicable to a class of situations.) On the practical side, the existence of ready-made physiological models may lead, in the hands of some workers, to a more rapid adoption of appropriate inferred variables. Generalization beyond this point is probably unwarranted; the essential point is that variables related in the context of a given vocabulary need not be excluded from the systematic considerations of another vocabulary.

Finally a statement may be made concerning the general field of perception. The study of perception has, since its beginnings, come a long way. It still has a long way to go. Improved experimentation, performed with attention to problems of specification and designed to provide a broad base for theory, will hasten the day when psychology will be provided with an inclusive system of relations to define and explain the phenomena of this important field.

REFERENCES

Ames, A. Binocular vision as affected by relations between uniocular stimulus-patterns in commonplace environments. *Amer. J. Psychol.*, 1946, **59**, 333–357.

Ames, A., G. H. Gliddon, and K. N. Ogle. Size and shape of ocular images. I. Methods of determination and physiologic significance. *Arch. Ophthal.*, 1932, **7**, 576–597.

Ansbacher, H. Perception of number as affected by the monetary value of the objects. *Arch. Psychol., N. Y.*, 1937, No. 215.

Aubert, H. Die Bewegungsempfindung. *Arch. ges. Physiol.*, 1886, **39**, 347–370.

Bales, J. F., and G. L. Follansbee. The aftereffect of the perception of curved lines. *J. exp. Psychol.*, 1935, **18**, 499–503.

Banister, H. Retinal action time. In *Report of a joint discussion on vision held on June 3, 1932, at the Imperial College of Science by the Physical and Optical Societies*. London : Physical Society, 1932. Pp. 227–235.

Basler, A. Über das Sehen von Bewegungen. I. Die Wahrnehmung kleinster Bewegungen. *Arch. ges. Physiol.*, 1906, **115**, 582–601.

Berry, R. N. Quantitative relations among vernier, real depth and stereoscopic depth acuities. *J. exp. Psychol.*, 1948, **38**, 708–721.

Berry, R. N., L. A. Riggs, and C. P. Duncan. The relation of vernier and depth discrimination to field brightness. *J. exp. Psychol.*, 1950, **40**, 349–354.

Beyrl, R. Ueber die Grössenauffassung bei Kindern. *Z. Psychol.*, 1926, **100**, 344–371.

Blackwell, H. R. Contrast thresholds of the human eye. *J. opt. Soc. Amer.*, 1946, **36**, 624–643.

Blumenfeld, W. Untersuchungen über die scheinbare Grösse im Sehraume. *Z. Psychol.*, 1913, **65**, 241–404.

Bonser, F. G. A study of the relations between mental activity and the circulation of the blood. *Psychol. Rev.*, 1903, **10**, 120–138.

Boring, E. G. *Sensation and perception in the history of experimental psychology.* New York : Appleton-Century-Crofts, 1942.

Boring, E. G. The moon illusion. *Amer. J. Physics*, 1943, **11**, 55–60.

Bourdon, B. *La perception visuelle de l'espace.* Paris : Librairie C. Reinwald, 1902. P. 442.

Brown, J. F. The thresholds for visual movement. *Psychol. Forsch.*, 1931, **14**, 249–268.

Bruner, J. S., and C. C. Goodman. Value and need as organizing factors in perception. *J. abnorm. soc. Psychol.*, 1947, **42**, 33–44.

Brunswik, E. Systematic and representative design of psychological experiments. University of California Syllabus Series No. 304, 1947.

Burian, H. M., and K. N. Ogle. Meridional aniseikonia at oblique axes. *Arch. Ophthal.*, 1945, **33**, 293–309.

Carmichael, L., H. P. Hogan, and A. A. Walter. An experimental study of the effect of language on the reproduction of visually perceived form. *J. exp. Psychol.*, 1932, **15**, 73–86.

Carr, H. A. *An introduction to space perception.* New York : Longmans, Green, 1935.

Cermak, P., and K. Koffka. Untersuchungen über Bewegungs- und Verschmelzungsphänomene. *Psychol. Forsch.*, 1922, **1**, 66–129.

Cooper, S. F. The effect of brightness in the range of attention experiment. *Amer. J. Psychol.*, 1928, **40**, 254–274.

Crook, M. N. Visual discrimination of movement. *J. Psychol.*, 1937, **3**, 541–558.

Dallenbach, K. M. The effect of practice upon visual apprehension in school children. *J. educ. Psychol.*, 1914, **5**, 321–334, 387–404.

Dallenbach, K. M. Attributive vs. cognitive clearness. *J. exp. Psychol.*, 1920, **3**, 183–230.

Dallenbach, K. M. Attention. *Psychol. Bull.*, 1928, **25**, 493–512.

Dashiell, J. F. *Fundamentals of general psychology.* New York : Houghton Mifflin, 1937. P. 455.

Dürr, E. Über die stroboskopischen Erscheinungen. *Philos. Stud.*, 1900, **15**, 501–523.

Eissler, K. Die Gestaltkonstanz der Sehdinge bei Variation der Objekte und ihrer Einwirkungsweise auf den Wahrnehmenden. *Arch. ges. Psychol.*, 1933, **88**, 487–550.

Ellson, D. G. Hallucinations produced by sensory conditioning. *J. exp. Psychol.*, 1941a, **28**, 1–20.

Ellson, D. G. Experimental extinction of an hallucination produced by sensory conditioning. *J. exp. Psychol.*, 1941b, **28**, 350–361.

Exner, S. Über das Sehen von Bewegung und die Theorie des zusammengesetzten Auges. *Sitzber. Akad. Wiss. Wien* (Math.-nat. Kl., Abt. 3), 1875, **72**, 156–190.

Fernberger, S. W. A preliminary study of the range of visual apprehension. *Amer. J. Psychol.*, 1921, **32**, 121–133.

Ferree, C. E. Fluctuation of liminal visual stimuli of point area. *Amer. J. Psychol.*, 1913, **24**, 378–409.

Finger, F. W., and D. K. Spelt. The illustration of the horizontal-vertical illusion. *J. exp. Psychol.*, 1947, **37**, 243–250.

Frank, H. Die Sehgrössenkonstanz bei Kindern. *Psychol. Forsch.*, 1928, **10**, 102–106.

Garrett, H. E., and M. R. Schneck. *Psychological tests, methods and results.* New York : Harper, 1933. Chapter III.

Gibson, J. J. The reproduction of visually perceived forms. *J. exp. Psychol.*, 1929, **12**, 1–39.

Gibson, J. J. Adaptation, after-effect and contrast in the perception of curved lines. *J. exp. Psychol.*, 1933, **16**, 1–31.

Gibson, J. J. Adaptation, after-effect, and contrast in the perception of tilted lines. II. Simultaneous contrast and the areal restriction of the after-effect. *J. exp. Psychol.*, 1937, **20**, 553–569.

Gibson, J. J., and O. H. Mowrer. Determinants of the perceived vertical and horizontal. *Psychol. Rev.*, 1938, **45**, 300–323.

Gibson, J. J., and M. Radner. Adaptation, after-effect and contrast in the perception of tilted lines. I. Quantitative studies. *J. exp. Psychol.*, 1937, **20**, 453–467.

Glanville, A. D. The psychological significance of the horopter. *Amer. J. Psychol.*, 1933, **45**, 592–627.

Gordon, D. A. The relation between the thresholds of form, motion and displacement in parafoveal and peripheral vision at a scotopic level of illumination. *Amer. J. Psychol.*, 1947, **60**, 202–225.

Götz, W. Experimentelle Untersuchungen zum Problem der Sehgrössenkonstanz beim Haushuhn. *Z. Psychol.*, 1926, **99**, 247–260.

Graham, C. H. Visual space perception. *Fed. Proc. Amer. Soc. exp. Biol.*, 1943, **2**, 115–122.

Graham, C. H. Behavior, perception and the psychophysical methods. *Psychol. Rev.*, 1950, **57**, 108–120.

Graham, C. H., K. E. Baker, M. Hecht, and V. V. Lloyd. Factors influencing thresholds for monocular movement parallax. *J. exp. Psychol.*, 1948, **38**, 205–223.

Graham, C. H., E. R. Hammer, R. D. Mueller, and F. A. Mote. Steroscopic settings with reticles providing multiple reference ranges: The perception of spatially repeating patterns. *J. Psychol.*, 1949, **27**, 209–216.

Graham, C. H., and E. H. Kemp. Brightness discrimination as a function of the duration of the increment in intensity. *J. gen. Physiol.*, 1938, **21**, 635–650.

Graham, C. H., and R. Margaria. Area and the intensity-time relation in the peripheral retina. *Amer. J. Physiol.*, 1935, **113**, 299–305.

Graham, C. H., L. A. Riggs, C. G. Mueller, and R. L. Solomon. Precision of stereoscopic settings as influenced by distance of target from a fiducial line. *J. Psychol.*, 1949, **27**, 203–207.

Granit, R. *Sensory mechanisms of the retina.* New York: Oxford University Press, 1947.

Griffitts, C. H., and E. I. Gordon. The relation between the Traube-Hering and attention rhythms. *J. exp. Psychol.*, 1924, **7**, 117–134.

Grim, K. Über die Genauigkeit der Wahrnehmung und Ausführung von Augenbewegungen. *Z. Sinnesphysiol.*, 1910, **45**, 9–26.

Guilford, J. P. 'Fluctuations of attention' with weak visual stimuli. *Amer. J. Psychol.*, 1927, **38**, 534–583.

Haggard, E. A., and G. J. Rose. Some effects of mental set and active participation in the conditioning of the autokinetic phenomenon. *J. exp. Psychol.*, 1944, **34**, 45–59.

Hammer, B. Zur experimentellen Kritik der Theorie der Aufmerksamkeitsschwankungen. *Z. Psychol.*, 1905, **37**, 363–376.

Hammer, E. R. Temporal factors in figural after-effects. *Amer. J. Psychol.*, 1949, **62**, 337–354.

Hardy, A. C. Atmospheric limitations on the performance of telescopes. *J. opt. Soc. Amer.*, 1946, **36**, 283–287.

Hartline, H. K. Intensity and duration in the excitation of single photoreceptor units. *J. cell. comp. Physiol.*, 1934, **5**, 229–247.

Hecht, S. On the binocular fusion of colors and its relation to theories of color vision. *Proc. nat. Acad. Sci., Wash.*, 1928, **14**, 237–241.

Hecht, S. A theory of visual intensity discrimination. *J. gen. Physiol.*, 1935, **18**, 767–789.

Hecht, S. Rods, cones and the chemical basis of vision. *Physiol. Rev.*, 1937, **17**, 239–290.

Heidbreder, E. Toward a dynamic psychology of cognition. *Psychol. Rev.*, 1945, **52**, 1–22.

Helmholtz, H. von. *Physiological optics.* (Translated by J. P. C. Southall.) Optical Society of America, 1924, Volume 3, pp. 281–369, 400–488.

Helson, H. Adaptation-level as frame of reference for prediction of psychophysical data. *Amer. J. Psychol.*, 1947, **60**, 1–29.

Hering, E. *Beiträge zur Physiologie.* Leipzig: W. Engelmann, 1861–64. P. 358.

Hering, E. *Spatial sense and movements of the eye.* (Translated by C. A. Radde.) Baltimore: The American Academy of Optometry, 1942.

Hermans, T. G. Torsion in persons with no known eye defect. *J. exp. Psychol.*, 1943, **32**, 307–324.

Higginson, G. D. The visual apprehension of movement under successive retinal excitations. *Amer. J. Psychol.*, 1926, **37**, 63–115.

Hillebrand, F. Theorie der scheinbaren Grösse bei binocularem Sehen. *Denkschr. Acad. Wiss. Wien* (Math.-Nat. Kl.), 1902, **72**, 255–307.

Holaday, B. E. Die Grössenkonstanz der Sehdinge bei Variation der inneren und äusseren Wahrnehmungsbedingungen. *Arch. ges. Psychol.*, 1933, **88**, 419–486.

Holway, A. H. 1947 (personal communication).

Holway, A. H., and E. G. Boring. The moon illusion and the angle of regard. *Amer. J. Psychol.*, 1940a, **53**, 109–116.

Holway, A. H., and E. G. Boring. The apparent size of the moon as a function of the angle of regard: Further experiments. *Amer. J. Psychol.*, 1940b, **53**, 537–553.

Holway, A. H., and E. G. Boring. Determinants of apparent visual size with distance variant. *Amer. J. Psychol.*, 1941, **54**, 21–37.

Howard, H. J. A test for the judgment of distance. *Amer. J. Ophthal.*, 1919, **2**, 656–675.

Hull, C. L. Quantitative aspects of the evolution of concepts. *Psychol. Monogr.*, 1920, **28**, No. 1.

Hull, C. L. *Principles of behavior.* New York: Appleton-Century-Crofts, 1943.

Hunter, W. S., and M. Sigler. The span of visual discrimination as a function of time and intensity of stimulation. *J. exp. Psychol.,* 1940, **26,** 160–179.

James, B. Measurements of stereoscopic visual acuity. *Lancet,* 1908, 1763.

Karn, H. W. Area and the intensity-time relationship in the fovea. *J. gen. Psychol.,* 1936, **14,** 360–369.

Kenkel, F. Untersuchungen über den Zusammenhang zwischen Erscheinungsgrösse und Erscheinungsbewegung bei einigen sogenannten optischen Täuschungen. *Z. Psychol.,* 1913, **67,** 358–449.

Klimpfinger, S. Über den Einfluss von intentionaler Einstellung und Übung auf die Gestaltkonstanz. *Arch. ges. Psychol.,* 1933, **88,** 551–598.

Koffka, K. Die Wahrnehmung von Bewegung. In A. Bethe (Ed.), *Handb. d. normalen u. pathol. Physiol.* Berlin: Springer, 1931. Volume XII/2, pp. 1166–1214.

Koffka, K. *Principles of Gestalt psychology.* New York: Harcourt, Brace, 1935.

Köhler, W. Optische Untersuchungen am Schimpansen und am Haushuhn. *Abh. preuss. Akad. Wiss.* (Phys.-math. Kl.). 1915, No. 3.

Köhler, W. *Die physischen Gestalten in Ruhe und im stationären Zustand.* Braunschweig: Vieweg, 1920.

Köhler, W., and D. A. Emery. Figural aftereffects in the third dimension of visual space. *Amer. J. Psychol.,* 1947, **60,** 159–201.

Köhler, W., and H. Wallach. Figural after-effects. *Proc. Amer. phil. Soc.,* 1944, **88,** 269–357.

Korte, A. Kinematoskopische Untersuchungen. *Z. Psychol.,* 1915, **72,** 193–296.

Kries, J. von. Notes. In H. von Helmholtz, *Physiological Optics.* (Translated by J. P. C. Southall.) Optical Society of America, 1924. Volume 3, pp. 369–450; 488–593.

Langlands, H. M. S. Experiments in binocular vision. *Trans. opt. Soc. London,* 1926, **28,** 45–82.

Lasersohn, W. Kritik der hauptsächlichsten Theorien über den unmittelbaren Bewegungseindruck. *Z. Psychol.,* 1912, **61,** 81–121.

Liang, T., and H. Piéron. Recherches sur la latence de la sensation lumineuse par la méthode de l'effet chronostéréoscopique. *Année psychol.,* 1942–43, **43–44,** 1–53 (Published 1947).

Liddell, H. S. Eye-movement during the fluctuation of attention. *Amer. J. Psychol.,* 1919, **30,** 241–252.

Linke, P. *Grundfragen der Wahrnehmungslehre.* Munich: E. Reinhardt, 1918. Pp. 269–360.

Lit, A. The magnitude of the Pulfrich stereophenomenon as a function of binocular differences of intensity at various levels of illumination. *Amer. J. Psychol.,* 1949, **62,** 159–181.

Ludvigh, E. Ocular proprioceptive sense concerned in vision. *Arch. Ophthal.,* 1936, **15,** 1037–1049.

Ludvigh, E. 1947 (personal communication).

Luneburg, R. K. *Mathematical analysis of binocular vision.* For the Dartmouth Eye Institute [by the Princeton University Press], Princeton, 1947.

Marbe, K. Die stroboskopischen Erscheinungen. *Philos. Stud.,* 1898, **14,** 376–401.

Martius, G. Ueber die scheinbare Grösse der Gegenstände und ihre Beziehung sur Grösse der Netzhautbilder. *Philos. Stud.,* 1889, **5,** 601–617.

Matsubayashi, A. Forschung über die Tiefenwahrnehmung. I. *Acta Soc. Ophthalm. Jap.,* 1937a, **41,** 1289–1312 (German abstract, ibid., 94–95; and *Ber. ges. Physiol.,* 1938, **106,** 135).

Matsubayashi, A. Forschung über die Tiefenwahrnehmung. II. *Acta Soc. Ophthalm. Jap.,* 1937b, **41,** 2055–2074 (German abstract, ibid., 150–151; and *Ber. ges. Physiol.,* 1939, **110,** 464).

Matsubayashi, A. Forschung über die Tiefenwahrnehmung. III. *Acta Soc. Ophthalm. Jap.,* 1937c, **41,** 2151–2162 (German abstract, ibid., 158; and *Ber. ges. Physiol.,* 1939, **110,** 464–465).

Matsubayashi, A. Forschung über die Tiefenwahrnehmung. IV. *Acta Soc. Ophthalm. Jap.,* 1937d, **41,** 2257–2268 (German abstract, ibid., 167; and *Ber. ges. Physiol.,* 1939, **110,** 465).

Matsubayashi, A. Forschung über die Tiefenwahrnehmung. V. *Acta Soc. Ophthalm. Jap.,* 1938a, **42,** 2–21 (German abstract, ibid., 1; and *Ber. ges. Physiol.,* 1939, **110,** 465).

Matsubayashi, A. Forschung über die Tiefenwahrnehmung. VI. *Acta Soc. Ophthalm. Jap.,* 1938b, **42,** 230–241 (German abstract, ibid., 15; and *Ber. ges. Physiol,* 1939, **110,** 465).

Matsubayashi, A. Forschung über die Tiefenwahrnehmung. VII. *Acta Soc. Ophthalm. Jap.,* 1938c, **42,** 366–377 (German abstract, ibid., 26–27; and *Ber. ges Physiol.,* 1939, **110,** 465).

Matsubayashi, A. Forschung über die Tiefenwahrnehmung. VIII. *Acta Soc. Ophthalm. Jap.,* 1938d, **42,** 480–491 (German abstract, ibid., 31–32; and *Ber. ges. Physiol.,* 1939, **110,** 465–466).

Matsubayashi, A. Forschung über die Tiefenwahrnehmung. IX. *Acta Soc. Ophthalm. Jap.,* 1938e, **42,** 1920–1929 (German abstract, ibid., 133; and *Ber. ges Physiol.,* 1939, **112,** 290–291).

Matsubayashi, A. Forschung über die Tiefenwahrnehmung. X. *Acta Soc. Ophthalm. Jap.,* 1938f, **42,** 1185–1196 (German abstract, ibid., 82–83; and *Ber. ges. Physiol.,* 1939, **112,** 291).

Mueller, C. G. Numerical transformations in the analysis of experimental data. *Psychol. Bull.,* 1949, **46,** 198–223.

Mueller, C. G., and V. V. Lloyd. Stereoscopic acuity for various levels of illumination. *Proc. nat. Acad. Sci., Wash.,* 1948, **34,** 223–227.

Müller, J. Beiträge zur vergleichenden Physiologie des Gesichtsinnes. Leipzig: Cnobloch, 1826. P. 46.

Müller-Lyer, F. C. Ueber Kontrast und Konfluxion. Z. Psychol., 1896, 9, 1–16 ; 10, 421–431. See also: Optische Urteilstäuschungen. Arch. Anat. Physiol. Lpz. (Physiol. Abt.), Ergänzungsbd., 1889, 263–270.

Münsterberg, H. Beiträge zur experimentellen Psychologie. Freiburg: J. C. B. Mohr, 1889. Heft 2, p. 234.

Necker, L. A. Observations on some remarkable phaenomena seen in Switzerland; and an optical phaenomenon which occurs on viewing of a crystal or geometrical solid. Phil. Mag. (Ser. 1), 1832, 3, 329–337.

Neff, W. S. A critical investigation of the visual apprehension of movement. Amer. J. Psychol., 1936, 48, 1–42.

Neuhaus, W. Experimentelle Untersuchung der Scheinbewegung. Arch. ges. Psychol., 1930, 75, 315–458.

Oberly, H. T. The range for visual attention, cognition and apprehension. Amer. J. Psychol., 1924, 35, 332–352.

Ogle, K. N. Relative sizes of ocular images of the two eyes in asymmetric convergence. Arch. Ophthal., 1939, 22, 1046–1067.

Ogle, K. N. The induced size effect. J. opt. Soc. Amer., 1940, 30, 145–151.

Ogle, K. N. Theory of the space-eikonometer. J. opt. Soc. Amer., 1946, 36, 20–32.

Ogle, K. N., and P. Boeder. Distortion of stereoscopic spatial localization. J. opt. Soc. Amer., 1948, 38, 723–733.

Ogle, K. N., and V. J. Ellerbrock. Cyclofusional movements. Arch. Ophthal., 1946, 36, 700–715.

Oppel, J. J. Ueber geometrisch-optische Täuschungen. Jber. phys. Ver. Frankfurt, 1854–55, 34–47.

Pace, E. Zur Frage der Schwankungen der Aufmerksamkeit nach versuchen mit der Masson'schen Scheibe. Philos. Stud., 1893, 8, 388–401.

Proshansky, H., and G. Murphy. The effects of reward and punishment on perception. J. Psychol., 1942, 13, 295–305.

Pulfrich, C. Die Stereoskopie im Dienste der isochromen und heterochromen Photometric. Naturwissenschaften, 1922, 10, 533–564, 569–601, 714–722, 735–743, 751–761.

Ratoosh, P. On interposition as a cue for the perception of distance. Proc. nat. Acad. Sci., Wash., 1949, 35, 257–259.

Riggs, L. A., C. G. Mueller, C. H. Graham, and F. A. Mote. Photographic measurements of atmospheric "boil." J. opt. Soc. Amer., 1947, 37, 415–420.

Rubin, E. Visuell Wahrgenommene Figuren. Copenhagen: Gyldendalska Boghandel, 1921.

Schafer, R., and G. Murphy. The role of autism in a visual figure-ground relationship. J. exp. Psychol., 1943, 32, 335–343.

Schlegel, W. Die Abhängigkeit des Umfanges der tachistoskopischen Neuauffassung von der In-

tensität des Reizes. Arch. ges. Psychol., 1929, 70, 463–520.

Schlosberg, H. Stereoscopic depth from single pictures. Amer. J. Psychol., 1941, 54, 601–605.

Schlosberg, H. A probability formulation of the Hunter-Sigler effect. J. exp. Psychol., 1948, 38, 155–167.

Schonbar, R. A. The interaction of observer-pairs in judging visual extent and movement. Arch. Psychol., N. Y., 1945, No. 299.

Schröder, H. Ueber eine optische Inversion bei Betrachtung verkehrter, durch optische Vorrichtung entworfener, physischer Bilder. Ann. Phys. Chem., 1858, 181, 298–311.

Ségal, J. Les interactions des éléments corticaux et la théorie de la forme. J. Psychol. norm. path., 1939, 21–35.

Sheehan, M. R. A study of individual consistency in phenomenal constancy. Arch. Psychol., N. Y., 1938, No. 222.

Sherif, M. A study of some social factors in perception. Arch. Psychol., N. Y., 1935, No. 187.

Sherif, M. The psychology of social norms. New York: Harper, 1936. Chapter 6.

Sinsteden, W. J. Ueber ein neues pseudoskopisches Bewegungsphänomen. Ann. Phys. Chem., 1860, 187, 336–339.

Skinner, B. F. The behavior of organisms. New York: Appleton-Century-Crofts, 1938.

Slaughter, J. W. The fluctuations of the attention in some of their psychological relations. Amer. J. Psychol., 1901, 12, 313–332.

Smith, K. R. The satiational theory of the figural after-effect. Amer. J. Psychol., 1948, 61, 282–285.

Southall, J. P. C. Mirrors, prisms and lenses. New York: Macmillan, 1933. Chapter 13.

Southall, J. P. C. Introduction to physiological optics. New York: Oxford University Press, 1937. Chapters 2, 5, and 6.

Stavrianos, B. K. The relation of shape perception to explicit judgments of inclination. Arch. Psychol., N. Y., 1945, No. 296.

Stern, L. W. Die Wahrnehmung von Bewegungen vermittelst des Auges. Z. Psychol., 1894, 7, 321–385.

Stratton, C. Visible motion and the space threshold. Psychol. Rev., 1902, 9, 433–447.

Taylor, D. W., and E. G. Boring. Apparent visual size as a function of distance for monocular observers. Amer. J. Psychol., 1942a, 55, 102–105.

Taylor, D. W., and E. G. Boring. The moon illusion as a function of binocular regard. Amer. J. Psychol., 1942b, 55, 189–201.

Thouless, R. H. Phenomenal regression to the real object. I. Brit. J. Psychol., 1931a, 21, 339–359. Phenomenal regression to the real object. II. Ibid., 1931b, 22, 1–30.

Thurstone, L. L. A factorial study of perception. Chicago: University of Chicago Press, 1944.

Troland, L. T. The colors produced by equilibrium photopic adaptation. J. exp. Psychol., 1921, 4, 344–390.

Tschermak-Seysenegg, A. Über Parallaktoskopie. *Pflüg. Arch. ges. Physiol.*, 1939, **241**, 454–469.

Vernon, M. D. The perception of inclined lines. *Brit. J. Psychol.*, 1934, **25**, 186–196.

Vernon, M. D. *Visual perception.* New York: Macmillan, 1937.

Vierordt, K. Die Bewegungsempfindung. *Z. Biol.*, 1876, **12**, 226–240.

Wertheimer, M. 1912. Experimentelle Studien über das Sehen von Bewegung. *Z. Psychol.*, 1912, **61**, 161–265.

Wever, E. G. Attention and clearness in the perception of figure and ground. *Amer. J. Psychol.*, 1928, **40**, 51–74.

Whipple, G. R. *Manual of mental and physical tests. Part I: Simpler processes.* Baltimore: Warwick and York, 1924. Chapter VII.

Woodburne, L. S. The effect of a constant visual angle upon the binocular discrimination of depth differences. *Amer. J. Psychol.*, 1934, **46**, 273–286.

Woodworth, R. S. *Experimental psychology.* New York: Holt, 1938.

Woodworth, R. S. *Psychology.* (4th Ed.) New York: Holt, 1945.

Wulf, F. Beiträge zur Psychologie der Gestalt: über die Veränderung von Vorstellungen (Gedächtnis und Gestalt). *Psychol. Forsch.*, 1921, **1**, 333–373.

Wundt, W. *Beiträge zur Theorie der Sinneswahrnehmung.* Leipzig und Heidelberg: C. F. Winter'sche Verlagshandlung, 1862.

Wundt, W. Die geometrisch-optischen Täuschungen. *Abh. sächs. Ges. (Akad.) Wiss. Lpz.* (Math.-phys. Kl.), 1898, **24**, 53–178.

Zegers, R. T. Monocular movement parallax thresholds as functions of field size, field position, and speed of stimulus movement. *J. psychol.*, 1948, **26**, 477–498.

Zöllner, F. Ueber eine neue Art von Pseudoskopie und ihre Beziehungen zu den von Plateau und Oppel beschrieben Bewegungsphänomenen. *Ann. Phys. Chem.*, 1860, **186**, 500–525.

24

The Psychophysiology of Vision

S. HOWARD BARTLEY

Michigan State College

The psychophysiology of vision may be thought of as the study of the mechanisms whereby the discriminative reactions of vision are brought about. Obviously, since these mechanisms are means to ends, both structure and function are involved, and we are faced with anatomical as well as with physiological problems.

Vision involves at least five major kinds of mechanisms: (1) optical, (2) anatomical, (3) photochemical, (4) neurophysiological, and (5) oculomotor. This division of the subject of vision into topics on the basis of mechanisms is different from a classification on the basis of primary functions, such as adaptation, brightness discrimination, visual acuity, etc. These functions will be discussed in several places in this chapter, i.e. at as many places as there are different mechanisms crucially involved.

OPTICAL MECHANISMS

Optical mechanisms fall into three subgroups those having to do with image formation, those that pertain to the relations between the object, the image, and the sensory end result, and those that produce stray light within the eye.

Image formation has to do with clearness of vision, with visual acuity, with the size of the retinal area stimulated, and (when the two eyes are considered in relation to each other) with the apparent localization of objects. Not so long ago small differences in the sizes of the retinal images of the two

eyes had no more than academic interest. But, since it has been shown that these small differences have a marked effect on spatial localization, retinal image size has become a matter of importance.

The human eye may evidence refractive error (become ametropic) in at least two, if not three, ways: (1) by a change in the axial length of the eyeball, (2) by a change in the power of the diopteric system through alterations in the curvature of the cornea or lens surfaces, through shifts in the separation between cornea and lens, or through changes in the indices of refraction of the several ocular media, and (3) through some change in the innervation that alters the power of the lens. The first type of defect, or ametropia, is called *axial;* the second, *refractive;* and the third, *accommodative* or *functional.* Although the first two are taken for granted by most investigators, the third is still controversial.

The retinal image size in the corrected axially ametropic eye remains unchanged by the application of spectacles and is the same as though the eye were normal. In the refractive ametropic eye the image after "correction" is different from that of the normal or emmetropic eye, so that if the experimenter wishes to deal with precise values he must take steps to determine the effect of the corrections used.

Image Formation

A point source of light used as an "object" is not focused on the retina as a point.

TABLE 1

RETINAL LIGHT DISTRIBUTION FOR A POINT AND A LINE (FROM HARTRIDGE, 1947)

Distance from Center of Image in Microns	Distance in Cone Units	Relative Intensity		Color	
		(a) Point	(b) Line	(a) Point	(b) Line
0	0	∞	∞	Yellow	Yellow
1.8	0.5	34.0	40.0	Yellow	Yellowish white
3.6	1.1	13.0	15.0	Yellow	Cream
5.4	1.6	5.3	8.0	Yellow	Cream
7.2	2.1	2.3	4.5	Yellow	Cream
8.9	2.7	1.0	2.0	Yellowish white	White
10.7	3.2	0.4	0.8	Greenish white	White
12.5	3.7	0.2	0.5	Greenish white	White
14.3	4.3	0.1	0.2	Greenish white	Greenish white
16.1	4.8	....	0.1	Bluish white	Bluish white
18.0	5.4	....	....	Purple	Purple
19.5	5.8	....	....	Purple	Purple
21.5	6.4	....	....	Blue	Blue
25.0	7.5	....	....	Blue	Blue

TABLE 2

EDGE OF A BRIGHT AREA ON A DARK SURROUND (FROM HARTRIDGE, 1947)

	Distance from Edge of Image in Microns	Distance in Cone Units	Relative Intensity	Color
	10	3.0	.....	Black
	9	2.7	0.2	Deep violet
	8	2.4	0.4	Deep violet
	7	2.1	1.1	Dark blue
Outside edge (blue)	6	1.8	2.3	Dark blue
	5	1.5	3.9	Dark blue
	4	1.2	6.2	Blue
	3	0.9	9.6	Blue
	2	0.6	13.9	Blue
	1	0.3	28.0	White
Edge	0	0.0	50.0	Yellow
	1	0.3	72.0	Yellow
	2	0.6	86.1	Yellow
	3	0.9	90.4	Yellow
	4	1.2	93.8	Pale yellow
Inside edge (yellow)	5	1.5	96.1	Pale yellow
	6	1.8	97.7	Pale yellow
	7	2.1	98.9	Cream
	8	2.4	99.6	Cream
	9	2.7	99.8	Cream
White	10	3.0	100.0	White

Although it is true that actual point sources are never points in the mathematical sense, they may be very restricted in area. Ideally such a point source would focus in a restricted and sharply defined area on the retina. Table 1 (from Hartridge, 1947) gives the retinal effect of a point source and a 4-millimeter pupil. The first column indicates various distances from the center of the retinal image in microns. The same information is given in the second column, but in cone units. The cone unit is approximately 3 microns. In the third and fourth columns are the relative intensities of the image at the various indicated distances from the center of the image for a point (*a*) and for a line (*b*). The fifth and sixth columns indicate the color of the light at various distances from the image center for a point (*a*) and for a line (*b*).

Table 1 shows that there are differences between the image of a point source and the image of a line source: (1) the intensity of the line does not decline so rapidly as a function of distance on the retina, and (2) more white light is present in the central parts of the line image, owing to overlap between the yellow and the blue disks.

The image of an extended test object or source differs from that of a narrow line and a point source in that it is composed largely of white light. Color fringes are found only near its edges. The dimensions of such fringes are given in Table 2 for a 4-millimeter pupil.

The characteristics of the image of a black dot on a bright surround is the negative of a bright point source on a dark ground (Table 3). The image of a bright point source on a black ground is an intense yellow center surrounded by a dark blue-violet annulus. The image of a black point source on a bright ground is a blue center surrounded by a pale pinkish yellow annulus. Images of black lines of various widths also manifest the expected differences from white lines.

TABLE 3

THE RETINAL LIGHT DISTRIBUTION OF A BLACK POINT ON A LIGHTED GROUND (FROM HARTRIDGE, 1947)

Distance from Image Center in Microns	Distance in Cone Units	Relative Intensity	Color
0	0	0	Blue
1.8	0.5	66.0	Blue
3.6	1.1	87.0	Pale blue
5.4	1.6	94.7	Pale blue
7.2	2.1	97.7	Bluish white
8.9	2.7	99.0	Bluish white
10.7	3.2	99.6	Very pale pink
12.5	3.7	99.8	Very pale pink
14.3	4.3	99.9	Very pale cream
16.1	4.8	....	Very pale cream
18.0	5.4	....	White
19.5	5.8	....	White
21.5	6.4	....	White
25.0	7.5	....	White

Relation to illumination. In strong illumination many individuals adjust monocular optical instruments to a negative focus. Instruments whose focus can be adjusted are usually calibrated in both directions from a zero point. The zero point indicates the adjustment that ought to function for an accommodation for infinity or supposedly for an emmetropic (normal) eye. A negative adjustment indicates that the individual using the instrument is acting as though he needed lenses of negative power (concave) in order to see. It appears that, whether or not the individual is visually abnormal, he tends to accommodate in order to achieve maximum visual acuity. Accordingly, he compensates for his accommodation by adjusting the instrument. Within the 4- or 5-diopter range of the usual instrument, the average setting is 1 to 2 diopters more negative than the refractive corrections of the observers themselves. In view of this fact, fixed focus instruments often incorporate corrections of -0.5 to -1.5 diopters.

With binocular instruments the tendency to focus negatively is usually absent. In both binocular and monocular settings, however, there is a tendency to set instruments negatively under *low* illumination.

Wald states that a change of about −0.4 diopter is justifiable on the basis of the chromatic aberration of the eye and the Purkinje shift. Furthermore the deviation from optimal setting can be this large without producing a marked functional detriment.

subtend the same visual angle at the eye as some other object differently oriented with relation to the eye. Figure 1, for example indicates that there is an infinite number of surfaces, differently oriented with reference to the line of regard, that may produce a

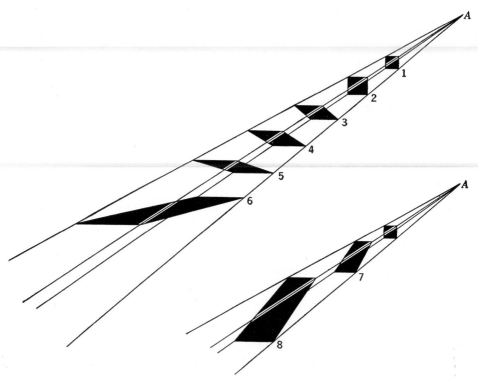

Fig. 1. A diagram to show that a number of objects may subtend the same visual angle at *A* as does square 1 and therefore may be perceived as a square when collateral cues are absent. (Bartley and Chute, 1947.)

Object, image, and sensory end result. Even when the optical properties of the eye as an image-forming system are known, the relations between the geometry of the object, the image on the retina, and the sensory end result are not directly deducible. Although the relations between the three are lawful, they are not always discoverable without experiment.

First of all, there is some degree of ambiguity or "freedom" between the shapes of objects and the shapes of the retinal images cast on the eye. An object of one shape may

retinal image of the same shape. This and related problems are discussed in Chapter 23.

Entoptic Stray Light

Another optical fact about the eye is that stray light reaches the retina (Bartley, 1941). Were the amount of this light trivial relative to that falling on the retinal image, mention of it would be of little interest. It happens, however, that the slight stimulation of the myriads of receptors in the retina outside the image may sum up to a greater recordable electric effect than the receptor activity in the image itself, except when the image is very large. Seldom is retinal stimulation confined to a small area. Either the image covers a part of the retina and is accompanied by stray light over the whole retina, or else the image is large and covers the retina, in which case the whole retina receives both focused and unfocused light.

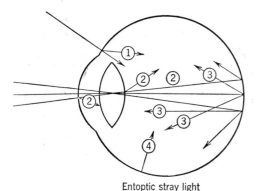

Entoptic stray light

Fig. 2. Diagram of eye to indicate the sources of stray light within. The stray light that falls on any specific part of the retina comes initially either through the pupillary aperture or through the coats of the eyewall. However, it is helpful to classify the sources into four: (1) the passage of diffuse light through the eyewall; (2) diffraction and scattering in the media, particularly the boundaries between the cornea and the humor, and the lens and the humor; (3) reflection from the retinal image; and (4) reflection from one portion of the retina to another.

The sources of internal (entoptic) stray light are indicated in Fig. 2.

The existence of a considerable amount of stray light on the retina may be observed in an excised eye of an albino rabbit. When the image of a disk of intense light (the surrounding field being dark) is thrown upon the retina, not only is the disklike image seen through the coats of the eye, but the whole eye becomes an internally illuminated globe. One set of measurements on the rabbit's eye indicated that with an artificial pupil 5 millimeters in diameter a test object whose brightness was 342 candles per square foot formed an image whose brightness,

through the coats of the eye, was 9.5 candles per square foot. The average brightness of the area not covered by the image was 0.266 candles per square foot or close to ⅟₃₆ the value of the image.

When the pupil of the eye was masked by an opaque disk, the light falling on the eyeball from a 7-degree test object whose brightness was 1500 candles per square foot provided a noticeable illumination of the retina. This shows how much the eye may be illuminated by light passing through its relatively opaque walls.

Several other means have been used to demonstrate or to measure entoptic stray light. The *first* of these is the measurement of the effect upon the differential threshold at the fovea, induced by a light whose image falls on the periphery of the retina. The *second* is the measurement of the critical flicker frequency of the visual field surrounding the intermittently illuminated test object. When the flicker of the field to one side of the test object is measured, the critical flicker frequency (cff) * is found to be lower than that of the test object. Checks to determine whether this critical flicker frequency is caused by neural spread from the test object or by stray light shows that it is attributable to stray light.

The *third* method is electrophysiological. The electric effect of the light in the image is compared with that of light falling outside it. In one experiment equivalent electroretinograms were produced by two different stimuli, (1) a small but intense spot of intermittent light, and (2) a homogeneous whole-field illumination applied intermittently. The size and intensity of the spot was set to provide stray-light illumination of the retina equal to the whole-field illumination. The two conditions, in yielding the same-sized electroretinograms, indicated that

* Critical flicker frequency (cff) is the lowest rate of stimulus intermittency required to produce a sensation of uniform illumination.

the retinal field outside the image produced virtually the whole response, even in the presence of an intense image.

The *fourth* method also utilizes the electro-retinogram as an indicator. In this experi-

single disk, the major factor producing the electroretinogram is fluctuation in stray light. When the stray light is constant, the conditions for producing a series of waves in the electroretinogram are absent.

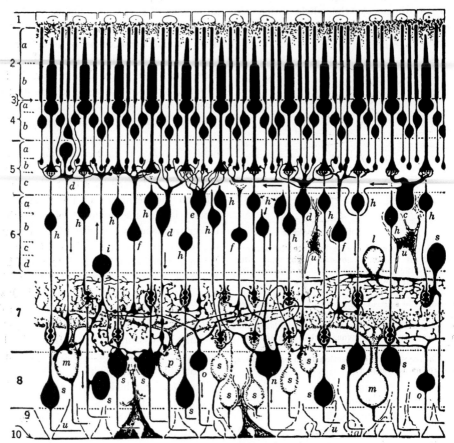

FIG. 3.   The structure of the primate retina.   The numbers and letters at the left indicate various layers and zones.   The other letters indicate elements as follows: c, horizontal cell; d, mop bipolar; e, brush bipolar; f, flat bipolar; h, midget bipolar; i, centrifugal bipolar (amacrine cell); l, internal association cell (amacrine cell); m, o, and p, diffuse ganglion cells; n, short ganglion cell; s, midget ganglion cell; u, "radial fibers" of Müller.   (Polyak, 1941.)

ment disks of light in different positions alternate with each other. As one disappears, the other appears, thereby providing a constant level of stray light in the retina. Under conditions of slow alternation — in which one would expect a series of responses if the images were the effective cause — no responses occur. This indicates that, with a

Stray light measured in the human eye by the first of these four methods has indicated that a peripheral light, 5 degrees from the test object, produces 0.00408 troland of retinal stray light per candle per square foot of brightness per millisteradian (unit of solid visual angle) per square millimeter of pupillary aperture.

ANATOMICAL MECHANISMS

The vertebrate eye handles light by means of a focusing mechanism, which forms an image of an external pattern upon the sensitive carpet called the retina. The compound eyes of certain subvertebrate forms use mainly unfocused light. The compound eye is composed of a number of tubelike cells (ommatidia) closely packed together and arranged so as to present their distal ends in the form of a spherical grid. The light that penetrates to the proximal or sensitive ends of the tubes reaches there primarily by virtue of its being in line with the axis of the tube. Hence a light source moving across the animal's visual field strikes some of these elements earlier than others.

The photoreceptors of the compound eye are functionally separate. The fiber processes leading from them form a bundle that does not reach a synapsing center until it arrives at the animal's nerve axis, some distance from the eye. Electrodes can therefore be placed on the fiber bundle, and presynaptic effects can be recorded. Furthermore separate fibers can, in some cases, be teased out so that the activity of single receptors can be studied.

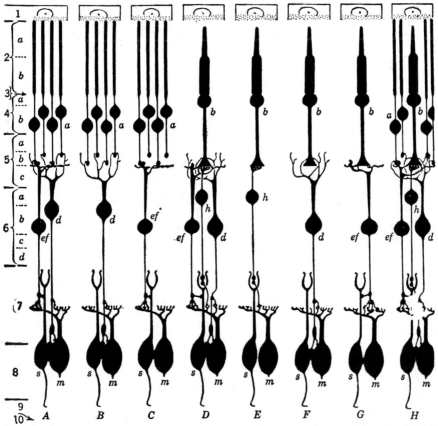

FIG. 4. The grouping of the primate retinal cells into functional systems. (For the identification of elements, see Fig. 3.) A, rod system; B, rod system with a single intermediate link (mop bipolar); C, rod system with only the brush or flat bipolar as the next link; D, cone system; E, pure cone system with midget bipolar as intermediate link; F, cone with mop bipolar as intermediate link; G, cone system with either the brush or flat bipolar cell as intermediate link; H, common rod-and-cone system. (Polyak, 1941.)

Some vertebrates possess one kind of photoreceptor (cones), some another (rods), and still others possess both kinds. Some animal forms have two kinds of cones. Because of their peculiarities and differences these several animal forms provide a means for the analysis of receptor function not otherwise available.

ately connected and compact tissue system (see Figs 3 and 4).

According to Polyak (1941), the *rod system* consists of three links: (1) the rods, (2) mop bipolars, and some brush bipolars

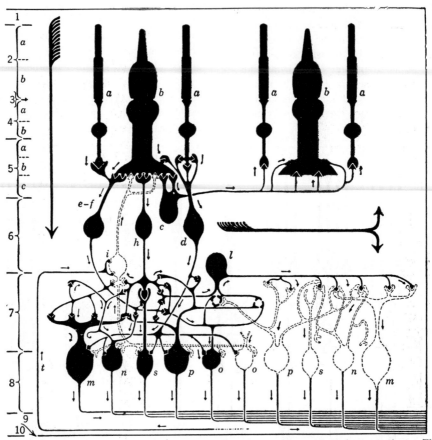

FIG. 5. A schema of the essential elements of the primate retina with their connections. The schema indicates the direction of propagation of impulses from the receptors to other elements in the retina, to the brain, and back to the retina. For identifications, see Fig. 3. (Polyak, 1941.)

eral animal forms provide a means for the analysis of receptor function not otherwise available.

In the human retina there are two kinds of receptors (rods and cones). The rods and cones differ in their functions and in their interconnections with each other, with the other elements of the neuroretina, and with the brain centers. Notwithstanding their difference in function, they form an intimate

and flat bipolars, and (3) all varieties of ganglion cells. The rod system does not involve the midget bipolars, the association cells, or the amacrine cells.

The *cones* may synapse with all types of centripetal bipolars, which may in turn synapse with all types of ganglion cells. Just as in the rod system, the cone receptors are not completely separate from one another, owing to the overlapping of the bipolar and ganglion cells. Only in the fovea where the "pure" cone system exists are there no diffuse ganglion cells. There the mop bipolars are also absent, and the cone impulse is conducted to a midget bipolar, then to a midget ganglion cell, without lateral or transverse overlapping (convergence and divergence). This is the old "private line" system of the cones according to the classical description.

retinal system, consisting of the horizontal cells, the centrifugal bipolars, and presumably the amacrine cells.

Figure 5 indicates the direction of the propagation of impulses through the retina, according to Polyak. Discharges from receptors *a* and *b* reach the horizontal cells and are carried to the surrounding receptors. The discharges from the receptors reach also

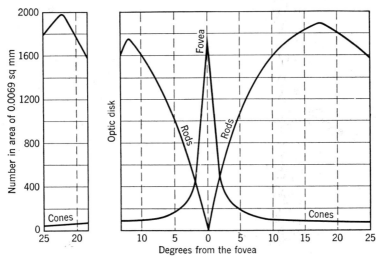

Fig. 6. Diagram to show the number of receptors (cones and rods) at various distances from the fovea. The number of cones drops rapidly with increasing distance from the fovea, and the rod density rises. (Østerberg, 1935.)

There is also the *mixed rod-and-cone* type of system. It involves as the first link both rods and cones, as the second link all kinds of bipolars, and as the third all types of ganglion cells. In such a system each diffuse bipolar is associated with a densely packed group of receptors. These groups, of course, fuse with one another, owing to the overlapping of the dendrites of the various bipolar and ganglion cells. Even the midget bipolars, which form a part of the pure cone conduction at the fovea, are constituents in this mixed system. The mixed system is active at levels of illumination where rods and cones are both activated.

In addition to the "line" conduction from receptor to brain, there is a definite intra-

the bipolars (*d, e, f, h*) which act as analyzers. Thence the impulses pass to all types of ganglion cells which in turn discharge into their axons, the optic nerve fibers. Impulses from the bipolar and ganglion cells also reach the centrifugal bipolar cell (*i*) which sends impulses to the receptors. This cell connects with afferent fibers in the optic nerve and acts as the main link in the conduction path carrying impulses from the brain to the receptors. The amacrine cells (*l*) presumably receive impulses from the bipolars and "diverge" them among ganglion cells (*m, n, o, p, s*).

The distribution of the rods and cones across the human retina is obviously a matter of functional importance. Figure 6 indicates their distribution across the horizontal meridian of the human retina, according to Østerberg.

The Stiles-Crawford Effect

Stiles and Crawford (1933) showed that rays passing through the edge of the pupil

be laid to the retina itself. Figure 7 indicates the loss in effectiveness as we pass from the center nasalward, and templeward. It was found that the effect appears only in the light-adapted eye. It is definitely related to cone vision, for it is found at all levels of adaptation when measurements are re-

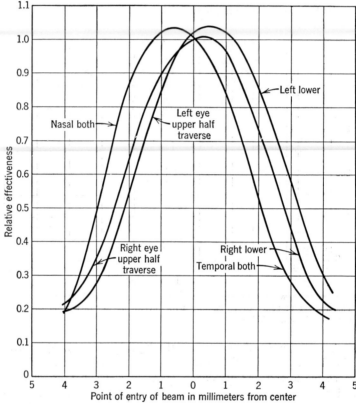

FIG. 7. The Stiles-Crawford effect. Light falling on different parts of the pupil is not equally effective in producing a sensory end result, even though the light reaches the same point on the retina. The data are those for B. H. Crawford's eye. (Stiles and Crawford, 1933.)

stimulate the retina less than those passing through the center of the pupil. To a very small extent this reduction in the effect of peripheral rays may arise from losses at the margins of the refracting media. Rays entering the edge of the pupil and those passing through its center do not encounter equivalent conditions along their paths to a given point on the retina. The greater part of the Stiles-Crawford effect, however, must

stricted to the fovea. The effect is also found in any part of the retina when the illumination is deep red. Thus it is apparent that, in order to obtain the effect, the response must be predominantly that of the cones.

Of the exact origin of the Stiles-Crawford effect, we are not sure. Several authorities ascribe it either to the shape of the cones or to the direction in which they point. O'Brien says that the total internal reflection within the conical part of the cones may be responsible for a concentration of the light in the outer segments. If the cone pigment is concentrated largely in the outer segments, and if the refractive index of the cones is higher than that of their surrounds, the Stiles-Crawford effect would necessarily follow. The fact that the Stiles-Crawford effect does not occur in pure rod vision is then to be ascribed to differences between cones and rods in shape, in refractive index, and in distribution of the photoreceptive pigments. The diameters of the rods are almost constant throughout their lengths, and this alone might account for the absence of the effect were it not for the morphological similarity of the rods and the *foveal* cones. Moon and Spencer (1944) have calculated in detail the quantitative features of the Stiles-Crawford effect.

Factors in Visual Resolution

The retina contains a layer of light-sensitive elements (the receptors) that form a *mosaic*. In order for objects (areas of different luminance in the visual field) to be differentially responded to, they must produce images of varying intensity on the retina. The ability of the individual to see two portions of the visual field (let us say, two dark bars on a light ground) as spatially separated is called visual acuity, and it is based, in part, upon the resolving ability of the retinal mosaic.

The two major hypotheses advanced to account for the limits of visual acuity concern (1) geometrical factors and (2) diffraction patterns. These hypotheses have to do with the way the anatomical and the sensitivity features of the retinal mosaic function to provide for fine resolution. In order for spatial distinctions to be perceived, the geometrical hypothesis would insist that the retinal image must not possess a fineness of detail exceeding the diameter of individual retinal receptors. The second hypothesis relies upon the gradients in the diffraction pattern of the image. The diffraction pattern must not taper so slowly that it fails to excite adjacent receptors differentially.

The necessary precision of perception, as it relates to visual acuity, can be accounted for if it is assumed that small differences in light intensity are reacted to by adjacent receptors. It first seemed as though the intensity difference to be accounted for was not less than 10 per cent. But Hecht and Mintz found that a single line on a homogeneous background of considerable extent could be resolved when it subtended a visual angle of only 0.5 second of arc. This necessitated a revision downward, to 5 per cent, in the magnitude of the difference between the stimulation of neighboring receptors.

The relation between cross-section sizes of the receptors and the sizes of the retinal images of fine wires is indicated in Fig. 8. The taper of the images can be seen to involve not one row of receptors, but several, although with unequal intensities of light. The finest detectable wire actually subtends a visual angle covering less than a single cone. Since the breadth of its image covers several cones, some sort of a differential response between rows of cones is necessary in order to explain how a fine wire is seen in contoured form.

There are four primary factors limiting visual acuity: (1) diffraction of light at the pupil, (2) aberrations of the eye, (3) fineness of the retinal mosaic, and (4) ability of the nervous mechanism, from the receptor onward, to utilize differences in excitation. Of these the first two are optical, the third is anatomical, and the fourth is neural. Factors 1 and 2 are to some extent interrelated: diffraction results in image deterioration, especially with small pupils, and aberrations induce deterioration, especially with large pupils. Accordingly, between the limits of large and small pupils definition is maximum. Factors 3 and 4 are not obviously interrelated. With a grating test object, resolution might be inadequate for one of two different reasons: (1) because the light and dark bars are too nearly alike in shade of gray, or (2) because the bars are so close together that the entire width of two adjacent bars falls on a single receptor. In this event all receptors would be stimulated equally.

The following methods can, as Hartridge (1947) points out, be used to determine

it were initially low. This would be expected to increase the fineness of the retinal mosaic.

4. Finally, if visual acuity is low on account of too little difference between the light and dark parts of the test object, it can be improved by increasing these differences.

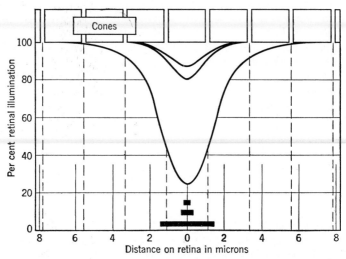

Fig. 8. Diagram to indicate the relation of the retinal mosaic (cones, in this case) to the retinal images of three narrow lines (diameters indicated by black bars at bottom). The cones are shown at the top of the diagram. It will be seen that more than single rows of cones are involved in the illumination pattern and that adjacent rows are not equally intensely illuminated. The differential in this illumination is presumed to be a crucial factor in accounting for the perception of a sharp line. (Modified from Hecht and Mintz, 1939.)

which of the four determiners of acuity is operating:

1. If diffraction underlies the failure of resolution, matters will be improved by enlarging the pupil, or by using light of shorter wavelength.

2. If aberration is the cause, acuity will be improved by substituting monochromatic light for white light.

3. If the retinal mosaic is responsible, it might be expected that the use of monochromatic light would reduce visual acuity, for, according to current theories, monochromatic light would activate fewer receptors. This would coarsen the retinal mosaic. A procedure for increasing visual acuity would be to increase the stimulus intensity, especially if

Shlaer concluded that the limiting factor in the visual resolution of a grating is the diameter of the pupil when it is less than 2.3 millimeters, and the size of the cones when the pupil is larger than this. Hartridge disagrees.

Other patterns that have been used in the laboratory to study visual acuity are broken circles (Landolt C's) and paired bars. The width of such bars is a critical factor in the visual resolution of the space between them. Fry and Cobb (1935) used two sets of paired bright bars on a dark field. The angle subtended by the width of the bars in the narrower set was 168 seconds; in the broader, 1000 seconds. The length of the bars in both cases subtended 2000 seconds.

As the intensity of the narrow bars was increased from a low value up to 3 candles per square foot, visual acuity increased rapidly at first, but finally declined again. For the broad bars the initial rapid rise was followed by a maintained slow ascent. To explain this these authors utilized the principle previously announced by Fry and Bartley, namely, that parallel borders interfere with each other's formation. The sides of the bars are parallel to each other, and, the broader the bars, the less the borders interfere. Hence the adjacent borders of two broad bars can come closer together before they cease being neurally "resolvable."

The Visual Pathway

The main bundle of optic tract fibers invades the medial and posterior surfaces of the ventral nucleus of the geniculate body and envelops the ventral and posterior surfaces of the dorsal nucleus. When the optic radiation fibers passing to the visual cortex leave the lateral and anterior surfaces of the nucleus, they are structured as a 3-layered S-shaped sheet. The part of the optic tract just described as entering the geniculate contains most of the largest fibers as well as some of the smaller fibers of the optic nerve.

The tract not entering the geniculate consists of medium-sized fibers and many more small fibers than are contained in the tract to the dorsal nucleus. There are indications that, in general, the smaller fibers pass toward the colliculus before synapsing. Between the tract fibers entering the geniculate and the small fibers passing toward the colliculus are the medium-sized fibers that seem to supply various structures such as the pulvinor, the lentiform nucleus, and the pretectal area.

Pathways for Pupillary Response

The central nervous connections for the various pupillary reflexes are not completely known. The two arcs, the sphincter (constrictor) and the dilator, are under control of the parasympathetic and sympathetic segments of the autonomic nervous system, respectively (see Fig. 9).

The fibers mediating the light reflex of the pupil by-pass the geniculate and hence do not synapse there as do optic fibers passing to the occipital cortex. These pupillomotor fibers pass through the superior colliculus to

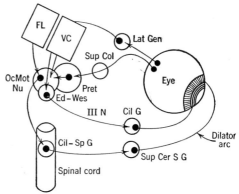

FIG. 9. The pathways for dilatation and constriction of the pupil. FL is the frontal lobe of the cerebrum; VC, the visual cortex; Sup Col is the superior colliculus; Lat Gen is the lateral geniculate body, through which the sensory arc passes and synapses; OcMot Nu is the oculomotor nucleus; Pret is the pretectal area; Ed-Wes is the Edinger-Westphal center of the oculomotor nucleus; III N is the third or oculomotor nerve; Cil G is the ciliary ganglion from which the short ciliary nerves reach the eye; Cil-Sp G is the ciliospinal ganglion; Sup Cer S G is the superior cervical sympathetic ganglion. The two kinds of fibers in the ciliary muscles are the radial (dilator) and the annular (sphincter).

the pretectal region. After synapsing there, the pathway divides. One part passes through the anterior commissure to the opposite side of the nervous system. The other part passes around and ventral to the cerebral aqueduct. Here it divides again, one fraction entering the oculomotor nucleus of the same side, the other going to the oculomotor nucleus on the other side.

The efferent part of the pupillomotor pathway consists of two parts, the sphincter and the dilator arcs. The sphincter arc is as follows: From a part of the oculomotor nucleus called the Edinger-Westphal center the path passes along the oculomotor nerve to the ciliary ganglion behind the eyeball, and from there through the short ciliary nerves to the sphincter muscle fibers of the iris. Cortical influences on pupil constriction are mediated by cerebral connection with the Edinger-Westphal center.

The dilator arc is more complex. Both the frontal cortex and the visual cortex may initiate the reflex through a midbrain center close to the Edinger-Westphal center in the

the visible spectrum, and its limits depend upon the intensity of the radiation involved. Near the middle of the visible spectrum the wavelengths are most effective in eliciting a visual response. The efficacy of the various wavelengths diminishes as the limits of the visible spectrum are approached. The curve representing this phenomenon is called a *visibility curve*, or a *luminosity curve*. It is obtained by a method of comparison in

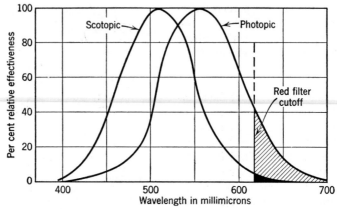

Fig. 10. Luminosity curves for scotopic (rod) and photopic (cone) vision. Since the maxima are arbitrarily set at 100, these curves give no information about the relative sensitivity of the rods and cones. The vertical line indicates the place at which a common red filter cuts off. It transmits $\frac{1}{10}$ of the light involved in the cone curve, and $\frac{1}{100}$ of that in the rod curve. (Hecht and Yun Hsia, 1945.)

oculomotor nucleus. The dilator pathway leads to the inferior ciliospinal center in the constrictor arc. The pathway passes next to the superior cervical sympathetic ganglion, the homologue of the ciliary ganglion of the constrictor arc. It is thought possible that these two ganglia have some connecting pathway, though its existence and function are unknown. The pathway from the superior cervical sympathetic ganglion passes to the radial muscle fibers of the iris.

PHOTOCHEMICAL MECHA-NISMS

The human eye is sensitive only to the limited spectral band of radiation that has been called light. This band is spoken of as

which the visible brightnesses of the various wavelengths in the spectrum are matched by adjusting their intensities. In Fig. 10 two luminosity curves are plotted. One is for moderate levels of illumination at which the cones are definitely functioning. It is called a photopic luminosity curve, and its maximum is at 554 mμ. The other curve is for levels at which only rods are functioning. It is called a scotopic luminosity curve. Its maximum lies more toward the blue end of the spectrum, at about 511 mμ. It is believed that luminosity curves bear some relation to the absorption spectra of the pigments found in the eye. A pigment called visual purple is found in the rods, and it possesses an absorption spectrum similar to the scotopic luminosity curve.

Wavelengths shorter than those at the violet end of the spectrum are spoken of as ultraviolet. Wavelengths longer than those at the red end of the visible spectrum are known as infrared. Questions regarding the more precise effects of both ultraviolet and infrared are still being raised and studied.

Sensitivity to Infrared Radiation

Although it is customary to specify the limits of the visible spectrum as lying between 400 and 750 mμ, it has been shown by Griffin, Hubbard, and Wald (1947) that with sufficient energy the eye can be stimulated well beyond these limits.

The most recent measurements of the infrared extend to 1050 mμ (Fig. 11). In the visible range from 550 to 700 mμ, the rods decline in sensitivity faster than the cones. In the far red the fovea is the most sensitive area of the retina. However, at still longer wavelengths this relation is reversed. Beyond 800 mμ, under the conditions used by Griffin, Hubbard, and Wald, the rods are considerably more sensitive than the cones. At the threshold of the dark-adapted eye infrared radiation is seen only with the peripheral retina and is colorless. It should be noted that in Fig. 11 the foveal and peripheral functions coincide between 675 and 740 mμ. This is an apparent contradiction to the statement that in the extreme red the fovea is more sensitive than the periphery (by about 0.2 log unit). The difference is occasioned by the fact that the exposure time in the earlier experiments was 0.04 second, and in the later measurements, 1 second.

Although the customary limits assigned to the visible spectrum have been extended by increasing the energy of the stimulus, this does not mean that the range is limitless. At some point, the eye would cease to function as a specialized visual sense organ and be no more sensitive to radiant energy than is the body surface in general. The human skin can respond to radiation both visible and infrared. The sensation is that of

warmth. For example, the threshold for the skin to radiant energy varies from 0.019 g-cal/cm²/sec for a small area (0.2 square centimeter on the forehead) to 0.00015 g-cal/cm²/sec for a large area (the whole dorsal surface). It has been shown that the threshold for rods at 510 mμ is 1.85×10^{-16} g-cal/cm²/sec.

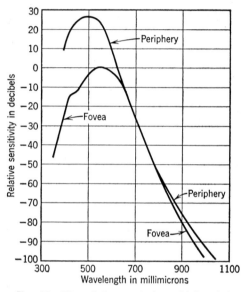

FIG. 11. The relative spectral sensitivity of the dark-adapted fovea and the peripheral retina. The curves represent 1-degree test objects either fixated or placed 8 degrees above fixation, and exposed for 1 second. (From Griffin, Hubbard, and Wald, 1947.)

It is to be noted from Fig. 11 that at 1050 mμ the retina is 125 decibels or 3.3×10^{12} less sensitive than it is at 510 mμ. At 1050 mμ the threshold is 0.00061 g-cal/cm²/sec, which is a little higher than the value for the whole dorsal body surface, but definitely lower than for small cutaneous areas. An additional factor working in favor of the skin is the absorption spectrum of water. It is negligible below 950 mμ, but at 1150 mμ all but about 16 per cent of the radiation entering the eye is absorbed by the water in the various media before it reaches the retina. At 1200 mμ even less reaches the retina (about 8 per cent). It would be expected that 1150 to 1200 mμ would mark the limit at which radiant energy would cease to be seen and would be more readily felt as heat.

The effect of wavelengths in the ultraviolet region will be discussed in the section on dark adaptation. Exposure to ultraviolet radiation apparently produces effects on the visual system that have been detected in the form of raised thresholds of dark adaptation.

Cone Function and Color Response

While we are on the subject of the selective sensitivity of the receptors (particularly the cones) let us consider the matter of color vision. Many theories regarding the mechanism of color vision have cluttered up our textbooks for several generations (see Chapter 22), but it is only now that we are beginning to lay an experimental foundation for dealing with the problem. Even now not too much can be said. There have long been two contending hypotheses regarding the functioning of foveal cones: (1) the single receptor theory, and (2) the triple receptor theory. According to theory 1, all receptors are able to respond to all parts of the spectrum. According to theory 2, the receptors belong to one of three groups: they may be sensitive to red, green, or blue. In addition to these two hypotheses, two others have emerged, namely, (3) the polychromatic hypotheses of Granit and of Hartridge, and (4) the cluster hypothesis of Hartridge.

According to Granit (1945), there are not three groups of receptors, there are many groups, each sensitive to a band of frequencies. At present it is thought that one group of receptors, the "dominators," is activated by white light, whereas the other groups, the "modulators," are activated by light near the wavelengths 600, 580, 520, 500, 460, and 430 mμ. Using a microelectrical recording technique, Granit found evidence for this variety of receptors in the retinas of a number of animals. Thus far

these techniques have not been applied to man.

Hartridge (1947) points out that his cluster hypothesis does not conflict with any of the first three hypotheses. It adds, rather, an important feature to either the triple-receptor idea or the polychromatic idea. Were the single-receptor hypothesis proved, the cluster hypothesis would be unnecessary.

According to the cluster hypothesis, receptors of a given variety tend to group together. Hence at one retinal point there may be a cluster of "dominators"; at another point, some blue-sensitive receptors; and at still another, some green-sensitive receptors. This nonuniform distribution would function as follows: Let the test object be a broken circle (C). When red light is used, the fixation of the test object is such that the image of a critical portion is caused, by an appropriate adjustment of the extrinsic eye muscles, to coincide with the red fixation point. This implies that there are several possible fixation points, an idea for which Hartridge feels he has some evidence.

Granit found two types of receptor in the light-adapted eyes of such animals as frogs and snakes: (1) receptors with restricted spectral response, and (2) those with broad response. The former he called "modulators," and the latter he called "dominators." It was found that the luminosity curve of the dominator was quite like, if not identical with, the luminosity curve of the light-adapted human eye. Dominators were not found in the eyes of those animals devoid of cones, such as rats and guinea pigs. This led to the idea that cones are essential in the dominator response.

Granit also found that the dominator can be split into the individual modulators of which it consists, provided selective adaptation is used. He also synthesized the human photopic luminosity curve on the basis of three fundamental sensation curves, red, green, and blue. (The red is made up of two modulators, MY and MR.) This concept that the dominator is a complex of several modulators connected with the same nerve fiber is consistent with Polyak's finding that both rods and cones converge on the same optic nerve fiber. Granit found all dominators to be identical in their response curves. Hence he concluded that they must be similarly constituted. All of them must be made up of four modulators: one blue, one green, and two red.

Visual acuity based on dominator action must be grosser than that provided for by a modulator, since the former is a cluster of receptors acting together as a physiological unit. Accordingly, were dominators to be present in large numbers, visual acuity would suffer. Since it is firmly believed that visual acuity in the human fovea can be accounted for only if each receptor is connected to its own nerve fiber, few, if any, of Granit's dominators can exist in the human fovea.

Hartridge, on the other hand, came to the revolutionary conclusion that all foveal cones give the "white" or dominator response. This is to say that every cone is a dominator. This concept implies that the same receptor may be at one time a modulator and at another a dominator. It is a dominator when the light reaching it is weak and covers a small visual angle. It becomes a modulator, able to differentiate parts of the spectrum, when the stimulated retinal area is larger and the light more intense. This idea will require considerable investigation in order to verify it. If it is proved, then in some way the retinal receptors would seem to be under a control by which, at one time, they can respond equally to all wavelengths of light, and at other times they can respond quite critically to some restricted portion of the spectrum.

Hartridge's (1948) polychromatic theory postulates two kinds of units in addition to the tricolor unit of the single receptor theory. One of these is called the Y-B unit and possesses receptors most vigorously responsive to wavelengths for yellow and blue. The other unit he labels R-BG-R. It contains two kinds of receptors responding most vigorously to wavelengths in the red and blue-green parts of the spectrum. The "red" receptors also have a secondary characteristic of being sensitive in the extreme violet part of the spectrum. This he indicates by the extra R in the symbol for the unit. There is also the conventional tricolor unit. Thus according to this theory there are three response units, with a total of seven types of receptor. Since the one type displays a secondary curve of sensitivity, there is a total of eight response curves that may be activated in any one of several combinations. There are, then, different responses for high, medium, and low intensity ranges of stimulation, and for the fovea and periphery, which, of course, differ in behavior. Whereas Granit developed his theory from electrical recording from the retina with microelectrodes, Hartridge obtained most of his evidence from the sensory impressions that occurred when he used the fovea, the periphery, and several levels of illumination as variables. It would seem, however, that Hartridge was considerably influenced by Granit's findings.

In the fovea, according to Hartridge, all seven types of units may be brought into action, depending upon intensity and kind of stimulation. All these units function when white light is used. If the intensity is very high, only the Y-B unit functions. If the intensity of the white light is low, or the visual angle very small, only the R-BG-R unit functions. In the periphery the Y-B unit is all that ever functions.

When colored light (a restricted band of the spectrum) is used, the receptors activated depend upon the response curves that correspond to the portion of the spectrum used. Hartridge gives the example of what would happen for stimulation by the wavelength of 650 mμ. Certain receptors in each of the three units would be activated, namely, the long wavelength receptor of the tricolor unit, the red receptor of the R-GB-R unit, and the yellow receptor of the Y-B unit.

Here again, if the intensities are very high, only the *Y-B* unit is activated. The result is a sensation of yellow. If moderate intensities are used, all three receptors just mentioned are activated, the combined effect giving a sensation of orange-red. When

to rods and cones through polysynaptic ganglion cells and bipolar neurons. Others make connections to cones through midget ganglion and bipolars. Some cones are connected to both types of fibers. These connections are indicated in Fig. 12.

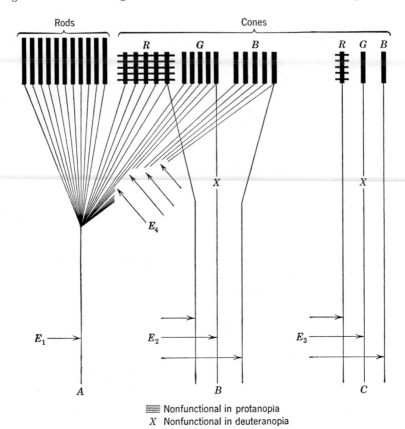

Fig. 12. A diagram to represent the supposed neural connections between modulators, dominators, and rods. Points marked E_1, E_2, E_3, and E_4 are recording positions. *R*, *G*, and *B* stand for red, green, and blue. (Jahn, 1946*a*.)

low intensities are used, only the *R-BG-R* unit is involved, and it provides for the sensation of purplish crimson, owing to the involvement of both the primary and secondary response curves.

Jahn (1946*b*) combines Granit's data and what is known about synaptic connections in the retina to form a very simple account of the mechanism of color vision and its defects. Some fibers in the optic nerve are connected

Jahn proceeds from the premise that modulators and dominators refer to ganglionic axons rather than to types of cones. Accordingly the fibers of the polysynaptic ganglion cells are the dominators. Modulators are then of six or seven kinds, which for convenience are divided into three groups, red, green, and blue. The algebraic summation of the modulator sensitivity curves is equivalent to the dominator curve. On this account, the dominator fiber can be considered to be connected to the receptors as in A of Fig. 12, and the dominator response would be obtained from a recording electrode at E_1. Modulator fibers may be connected with cones as in C, or with certain cones that are connected with the dominator as in B. In such cases the modulator responses would be experimentally recorded at E_3 and E_2, respectively. A sensitivity curve recorded from a set of fibers as in E_4 could be identical to a modulator curve.

Jahn (1946b) also assumes that the usual luminosity curve is the overall effect of dominator and modulators, rather than simply the dominator curve as Granit proposed. Jahn also assumes that hue discrimination is determined by modulators alone.

Though it is not the purpose of this section to deal at length with color vision and its defects, the kind of explanation given deuteranopia will indicate one of the possibilities of Jahn's version of the polychromatic theory. In deuteranopia red-green hue discrimination is poor, although the luminosity curve is almost normal. There could exist a deficiency in the "green" modulator units (midget bipolars or midget ganglion cells) or in the "green" cones connected with them. In either case the pathways indicated by X in the figure would become nonfunctional, whereas pathways between some of the "green" cones and their dominator fibers would still be functional. This would account for a decided decrease in hue discrimination associated with only a small shift in spectral sensitivity, such as actually occurs. The fact that nerve fiber degeneration may result in deuteranopia but not in protanopia is also cited by Jahn in support of this theory.

Photoreceptor Processes

The processes that occur in the photoreceptor have for some time been assumed to determine the quantitative features of processes further along in the optic pathway.

Certain features of photochemistry are known and others have been postulated to account for the known sensory end results. Hecht (1934), whom we shall follow in the first part of this section, points out that we know three things regarding the *primary* photochemical process: (1) that certain material is decomposed by light falling on it, (2) that some of the resulting products are transported from the site of action, so that the full photochemical result is never utilized, and (3) that the initial sensitive material is replenished in the dark and supposedly even in the light. It would appear that this synthesis occurs from two other substances that disappear in the process.

In addition to the primary or light process, there is a *secondary* or "dark" process intimately related to it. The secondary process is unable to initiate the nerve impulse until the primary process has, through the action of light, produced the necessary products. The rate of the secondary reaction is proportional to the concentration of these products.

The situation may be represented by a pseudoreversible reaction as follows:

$$ S \xrightarrow[\text{"dark"}]{\text{light}} \begin{array}{l} P + A + B \\ P + A + C \end{array} \qquad (1) $$

in which B is a product of the primary reaction, and C is a substance developed in excess and supplying the means for recombination of A and P. Hecht puts it as follows.

Imagine light falling on S. Through its decomposition its original concentration a will be changed to concentration $a - x$ (x equaling the concentration of S changed into P). The rate of this process may be written as

$$ v_1 = k_1 I (a - x) \qquad (2) $$

in which k_1 is the velocity constant including the absorption coefficient. This rate is proportional to the concentrations of the already-mentioned substances, P, A, B (and possibly others, with reactions x, x^2, or x^n, depending upon the number of photolytic products).

Then

$$v_2 = k_2x^n \qquad (3)$$

must be subtracted from the velocity of the primary reaction in order to describe the actual velocity

$$\frac{x}{t} = k_1I(a - x) - k_2x^n \qquad (4)$$

with which the products accumulate in the receptor. The equation may be rearranged so as to indicate more directly the relation between intensity of light, the time it acts, and the production of a given amount x of photochemical products, in which case we have

$$It = \frac{x}{k_1(a - x)} + \frac{k_2x^n}{k_1(a - x)}t \qquad (5)$$

Since x is presumed to be constant, $(a - x)$ is constant, and equation 5 may be simplified to

$$It = C + Dt \qquad (6)$$

D, representing k_2, becomes negligible for threshold values of x and for short exposure times, so that the equation reduces to

$$It = C \qquad (6a)$$

which is the Bunsen-Roscoe law. Despite the occurrence of the extra reaction removing P, the relation between *time* and *intensity* follows the simple equation 6a for short exposures, and the slightly more complex equation 6 for more extended exposures.

When intensity is the limiting factor determining a threshold reaction, $t \to \infty$, and $S \rightleftharpoons P + A$ reaches a stationary state. Then the velocity $dx/dt = 0$, and equation 4 becomes

$$\frac{k_1}{k_2}I = \frac{x^2}{(a - x)} \qquad (7)$$

in which time is eliminated. The equation also describes the concentration in the photosensory system when adaptation to I has occurred. Exposure to an additional momentary illumination subjects the system to the sum of I and I_s (the adapting and the stimu-

lating intensities). The stationary state then no longer exists, and additional S is decomposed with a velocity represented by

$$\frac{dx}{dt} = k_1(I + I_s)(a - x) - k_2x^2 \qquad (8)$$

If the intensity is reduced to some fraction of its original value, the following will result:

$$\frac{k_1}{k_2} \cdot \frac{I}{p} = \frac{x_p{}^2}{a - x_p} \qquad (9)$$

Here x_p indicates a particular value of x in equation 7 determined by I/p. Whereas the total effect of I is reduced by a reduction in its intensity, its effectiveness may also be reduced by shortening the time of action, e.g. by means of a sector disk. When such a disk is used, the photosensory system is subjected to alternate periods of light and darkness. Figure 13 will aid in picturing what happens. During the light period (light fraction of the cycle) the velocity of the process is represented by equation 4, and during this time the concentration of x rises. During the dark phase of the cycle only the "dark" reaction occurs. Its velocity is given by equation 3. If the alternation is continued, a pseudostationary state is maintained. In it the light phase and the dark phase produce equal but opposite effects, and the concentration of x fluctuates equally above and below a mean value. The more rapid the alternation, the smaller is the fluctuation of x, until at last a point is reached at which the fluctuation is no longer sufficient to produce physiological effects leading to a sensation of flicker. That is to say, Δx becomes too small to be effective.

During the short light phase the velocity of the light reaction is

$$\frac{\Delta x}{\Delta t} = k_1I(a - x) - k_2x^2 \qquad (10)$$

and the speed of the "dark" reaction during the short interval $(p - 1) \Delta t$ is

$$\frac{\Delta x}{(p - 1) \Delta t} = k_2x^2 \qquad (11)$$

which may be rearranged so that

$$\frac{\Delta x}{\Delta t} = (p - 1)k_2x^2 \qquad (12)$$

and since this may be equated with equation 10 the result becomes

$$k_1I(a - x) - k_2x^2 = (p - 1)k_2x^2 \qquad (13)$$

which becomes

$$\frac{k_1}{k_2} \cdot \frac{I}{p} = \frac{x^2}{a - x}$$

which is equation 9. This means that a reduction in exposure time by the fraction $1/p$, obtained by rapid alternations of light and dark periods, is equivalent to a reduction, by the same fraction, of the intensity of a steady illumination. This, of course, is Talbot's law.

The situation is not so simple, however, as the derivation indicates. First of all, observed flicker rates and rates of stimulus

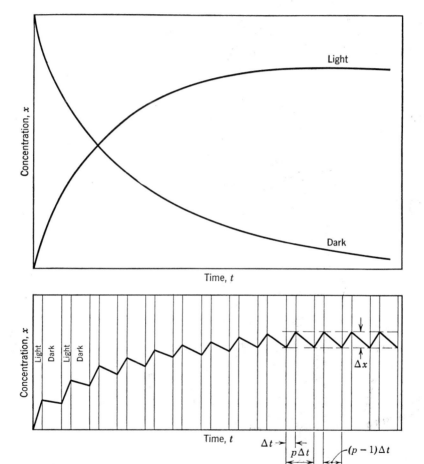

FIG. 13. Diagrammatic derivation of Talbot's law. The upper two curves represent the course of light adaptation and of dark adaptation. Dark adaptation is in reality many times slower than light adaptation. The two processes are here made roughly alike for diagrammatic purposes, since the actual values do not enter into the derivation of Talbot's law as given in Hecht's equations. In the lower graph the alternation of light and dark periods is such that the light period is given by the small time Δt, the total cycle of light and dark by $p\Delta t$, and the dark period by $(p - 1)\Delta t$. The fluctuation in concentration Δx in the stationary state is quite small in relation to the concentration x, and is incapable of producing sensory fluctuations. (Hecht, 1932.)

intermittency ("flash" rates) do not, under all conditions, coincide. Second, subjective uniformity (the steady state) may be reached by the use of short light intervals and long dark intervals, or vice versa, at nearly the same critical flicker frequencies. The explanation of the first fact involves certain intrinsic properties of ganglion cells; the second fact involves specifically the off-effect in retinal discharge. These effects will be discussed in the section on neurophysiological considerations.

Hecht derives an equation for critical flicker frequency as follows. Since the concentration of the photo products is x, the rate of the secondary dark reaction is

$$\left(\frac{\Delta x}{\Delta t}\right) \text{ secondary } = k_3 x \qquad (14)$$

where k_3 is a velocity constant. At the disappearance point of flicker he supposes that $\Delta x = c'$, i.e. that the change Δx in the dark time Δt is constant at a value just too small to induce a physiological change sufficient to cause a change in the sensation of brightness. Let the critical fusion frequency F be defined as the number of light-and-dark cycles per second. Let $F = 1/2 \Delta t$. Substituting for Δx and Δt in equation 14, the result is

$$F = cx \qquad (15)$$

where $c = k_3/2c'$. This means that the critical flicker frequency is directly proportional to the concentration of the photo products in the stationary state represented by

$$\frac{k_1 I}{k_2 p} = \frac{x^2}{a - x} \qquad (16)$$

Since in equation 15 F is a linear function of x, F may be substituted for it in the equilibrium equation, where at the same time F_{max} may be exchanged for a. We let m and n indicate the order of the reaction of $S \to P + A$ and $P + A \to S$, respectively. Equation 16 then becomes

$$\frac{k_1 I}{k_2 p} = \frac{F^n}{(F_{max} - F)^m} \qquad (17)$$

or, by rearrangement,

$$F = \left[\frac{k_1 I}{k_2 p} (F_{max} - F)^m\right]^{1/n} \qquad (18)$$

or, by shifting the absolute value of k_2,

$$F = \frac{1}{pk_2} (k_1 I)^{1/n} (F_{max} - F)^{m/n} \qquad (19)$$

Jahn (1946a) has pointed out that several difficulties arise in the use of equation 19 to account for the relation between fusion frequency F and intensity I. (1) When the temperature is changed in lower animals the effect is opposite to prediction. (2) The effect of a change in the light-dark ratio (LDR) is opposite to prediction. (3) It is necessary to assume that the photochemical reaction is bimolecular in order for the data on human observations to fit the equation. This is contrary to the chemical evidence we have. (4) The flicker results for certain animals do not fit equation 14; (e.g. *Pseudemys, Sphaerodactylus,* and the low illumination results for *Asellus*). (5) On a purely logical basis, it is taken as probable that the concentration of S, instead of the concentration of $P + A$, directly determines critical flicker frequency.

It is thought that the amount of "new" $P + A$ needed for excitation at threshold is the same for all frequencies and intensities. The quantity of light needed for a given small photochemical result is inversely proportional to the concentration of S. Thus if the amount of photosensitive material is increased, as for instance by raising temperature, or by increasing time in the dark, critical flicker frequency should rise, and the intensity of light needed for a given cff should drop. This is what actually occurs. The cff equations of Hecht appear to be open to criticism mainly because the concentration of the active catalyst ("new" $P + A$), the direct antecedent of stimulation, is not taken into account. "Old" $P + A$, indicated by x, has no active part in stimulation, and it is possible that the observed correlation between F and x is fortuitous. On account of the difficulties listed, equations 17 to 19 require modification.

Two assumptions may be made in modifying the formulations: (1) that F varies as the reciprocal of light phase needed to produce a given critical catalytic effect of "new" $P + A$ (an amount just too small to be effective in ultimate sensation); and (2) that the maximum F is determined by some factor outside the sense cell (which is not affected by temperature) rather than by photochemical changes in the sense cell itself.

Whereas P and A represent "old" or inactive substances, active materials may be denoted by E whose concentration is w. Accordingly the photochemical cycle becomes $S \rightarrow E \rightarrow P + A \rightarrow S \cdots$. The reaction resulting in nerve stimulation is determined by the concentration of E, whereas the process of dark adaptation depends on the concentration of P and A.

It is supposed that the formation of E varies with intensity I, with the amount of S present, i.e. $(a - x)$, and with the duration of illumination t. The amount of E formed by a single light period ("flash") is thus

$$k_1I(a - x)t \qquad (20)$$

It is assumed that, with some exceptions, E is small relative to $a - x$. The secondary reaction $(L \rightarrow T)$ depends upon the concentration of E, and of L (denoted by l) and the velocity constant k_4 of the catalyzed reaction. Accordingly the rate of the reaction is k_4lw, and the amount of L changed to T is approximated by k_4lwt. It may be assumed that for critical flicker frequency either this or k_4lw is a constant and may be represented by C. Since $L \rightarrow T$ is either cyclic or reversible, it may be assumed that its rate must attain a threshold value $(k_4lw = C)$. Thus

$$C = k_4l[k_1I(a - x)]t \qquad (21)$$

For any chosen value of p (light fraction of the cycle), the critical flicker frequency F should vary as the reciprocal of the time needed to produce the required constant physiological effect. Thus F varies as $1/t$.

$$\frac{1}{t} = \frac{k_4l}{C}[k_1I(a - x)] \qquad (22)$$

Assuming $L \rightarrow T$ to be any kind of change resulting in nerve stimulation, we may assume that the concentration of L varies considerably during a light-dark cycle, decreasing during the light phase and increasing during darkness. At the start of the light phase, the available l varies as a function of the duration of the previous dark period $(l = fp)$. As a first approximation, l may be considered a linear function of p. As a consequence, p may replace l in equation 22. The proportionality constant C, now C', may also be included.

$$\frac{1}{t} = \frac{k_4p}{C'}[k_1I(a - x)] \qquad (23)$$

The equation for flicker frequency may be written thus:

$$F = \frac{k_4p}{C'}[k_1I(a - x)] \cdot f(F) \qquad (24)$$

In this equation $f(F)$ does not have to do with the chemical process by which the receptor is stimulated, but rather with the mechanism by which the experience of flicker approaches the fusion frequency when the frequency of intermittent stimulation is increased. The critical process for this phenomenon may (as far as the equation is concerned) lie anywhere in the chain of events from the sense organ process to the central nervous effects. One simple expression for this function may be $(F_{max} - F)^r$. Consequently one form of equation 24 is

$$F = \frac{k_4p}{C'}[k_1I(a - x)]q(F_{max} - F)^r \qquad (25)$$

where q probably pertains to the mechanism by which photo product E is used in the sense cells.

Jahn (1946a) points out that the data for *Pseudemys*, *Sphaerodactylus*, and *Asellus* which are not well fitted by Hecht's equation 17 can, because of the flexibility of equation 25, be fitted reasonably well by it. Equation 25 also predicts the shift observed when the LDR is changed.

In order to explain brightness discrimination, Jahn has set up the following equations: In the photochemical cycle $S \to E \to P + A \to S \cdots$, the concentration of E is denoted by w, the concentration of P and A by x, and the concentration of S by $a - w - x$.

In the stationary state the rates of the three reactions implied above are equal, so that

$$k_1 I(a - w - x) = k_2 w = k_3 x^2 \qquad (26)$$

where k_1, k_2, and k_3 are velocity constants. The outcome is that

$$\Delta I = \frac{(C/k_4 l)^{1/q} - w}{k_1(a - w - x)t} \qquad (27)$$

which becomes, on dividing by I,

$$\frac{\Delta I}{I} = \frac{(C/k_4 l)^{1/q} - w}{k_1 I(a - w - x)t} \qquad (28)$$

But since in equation 26 $k_1 I(a - w - x) = k_3 x^2$

$$\frac{\Delta I}{I} = \frac{(Ck_4 l)^{1/q} - w}{k_3 x^2 t} \qquad (29)$$

And since from equation 26 $w = k_3 x^2 / k_2$

$$\frac{\Delta I}{I} = \frac{(C/k_4 l)^{1/q}}{k_3 x^2 t} - \frac{1}{k_2 t} \qquad (30)$$

Since the minimum visual angle alpha (α) varies as $\Delta I/I$, the form of the present equation for visual acuity is

$$\alpha = C_1 \frac{(C/k_4 l)^{1/q} - w}{k_3 x^2 t} \qquad (31)$$

in which C_1 is a proportionality constant. This equation fits all the data that can be fitted by Hecht's (1935) equivalent formula

$$\frac{\Delta I}{I} = C \left[1 + \frac{1}{(kI)^{\frac{1}{2}}} \right]^2 \qquad (32)$$

Response of a Single Receptor

Jahn's modification (1946a, c) of Hecht's equations for the activity of the photoreceptor has been applied by Fry and Alpern to the response of the dark-adapted receptor of the Limulus (horseshoe crab) to a flash of light. From it they derive equations for predicting the sequence of impulses. Accord-

ing to Jahn's proposal the initiation of an impulse depends upon the presence of the catalyst E. Thus, to predict the sequence of impulses elicited by a flash of light, the changes in the concentrations of E and the original photosubstance S must be known. Equations for the course of these changes at various times after the onset of the flash were derived. It is assumed that the secondary reaction $(L \to T)$ is produced in one part of the photoreceptor and must diffuse to another part before it can produce nerve impulses. This takes time, and there is a lag between the production of T and its arrival at the point of effectiveness. In order to account for the failure of low intensities of light to produce a response regardless of duration, it must be supposed that T is constantly being dissipated. It must also be supposed that a fixed quantity of T must be accumulated before the photoreceptor can initiate a nerve impulse. When the receptor discharges, all the accumulated T is consumed. Fry and Alpern derive an equation for the frequency of impulses

$$F = \frac{1}{\Delta t}$$

where Δt is the time required for the concentration of T at the point of nerve stimulation to rise from zero to threshold value. In general the frequency is proportional to the rate of accumulation of T at the point of nerve stimulation.

Fry and Alpern also account for the initial burst of impulses in the receptor and the subsequent "silent period." They explain why reaction time lengthens when the duration of the stimulus is shortened to within the critical value, and they explain the relation between the peak of the curve for concentration of E and the instant at which maximum frequency of impulses is produced. Their formulations deal also with light and dark adaptation and with the effects of a brief increase in light intensity.

Dark Adaptation

The ability of the human eye to become more sensitive during a stay in the dark is known as dark adaptation. Its readjustment when it returns to high illumination levels is millilambert, its threshold after a few minutes in bright light is 0.005 millilambert, a diminution in sensitivity equal to 37 decibels, or a reduction to $\frac{1}{5000}$ of the previous sensitivity.

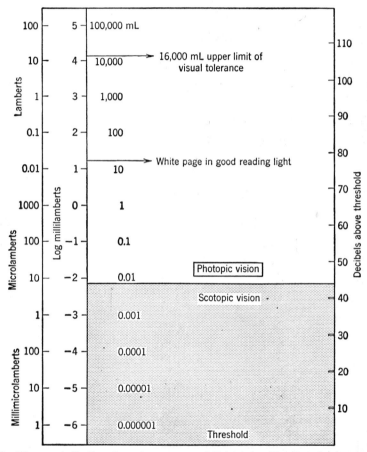

FIG. 14. Diagram indicating the extreme range of light intensities that the human eye confronts and the relation between the levels of cone and rod vision. The scale on the right shows that the range of visible intensities covers approximately 100 decibels, or a ratio of intensities equal to 10 billion to 1.

known as light adaptation. It is obvious from Fig. 14 that there is an enormous range between the threshold level of sensitivity and the brightness of snow in noonday sun. The range is actually something like 1 to 10 billions, or close to 100 decibels (10 logarithmic units). Whereas the threshold of the eye after 10 to 12 hours in darkness is 0.000001

Figure 15 indicates the relation between log luminance in microfoot-lamberts (1 foot-lambert = 1.076 millilamberts) and the angular relation of the sun to the horizon. The curve was constructed from readings made at four different times of the year. For the latitude (42.5 degrees) at which the readings were made, the light reflected from a test object not in shadow is definitely related to the angular elevation of the sun.

Figure 16 shows both the decline of outdoor brightness during twilight and the dark-adaptation curves for rods and cones. The adaptation curves are thresholds obtained under the usual condition of complete dark-

The distribution of the rods and cones for 25 degrees on either side of the fovea, along the horizontal meridian, was previously indicated in Fig. 6. Figure 17 shows the dark-adaptation curves obtained with centrally fixated fields of various sizes from 2 to 20 degrees. It will be noted that the centrally

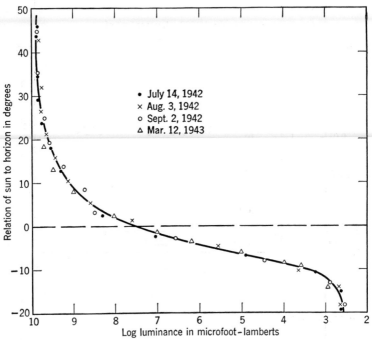

FIG. 15. The intensity (luminance) of a test object as a function of angular height of the sun at different times of the year. (Beebe-Center, Carmichael, and Mead, 1944.)

ness between readings. Hence dark adaptation induced by gradually declining illumination may not be so rapid as pictured. Nevertheless it is thought to be as rapid as the normal decline in daylight illumination, if not more so.

Owing to the difference in the distribution of the rods and cones over the retina, dark-adaptation threshold curves vary in shape in accordance with the area of the test object and, if small, with its location on the retina. The dark-adaptation curve also depends on the intensity level of preadaptation, the duration of preadaptation, and the portion of the spectrum used.

fixated 2-degree test object indicates little adaptation aside from the initial cone effect which is complete within the first few minutes. Progressively larger test objects involve a relatively greater proportion of rods, and the curves show greater adaptation. Figure 18 pictures the dark-adaptation curves for a test object of 2 degrees placed at various distances from the fixation point. Figure 19 shows the thresholds (reached after 30 minutes in darkness) for test objects of different diameters, and for a 2-degree test object placed at different distances from the fixation point. The behavior of the retina with regard to dark adaptation is shown in another way in Fig. 20, which represents the effects of a 20-degree annulus test object and a 20-degree disk test object. From these results it would seem that the outcome depends more upon where

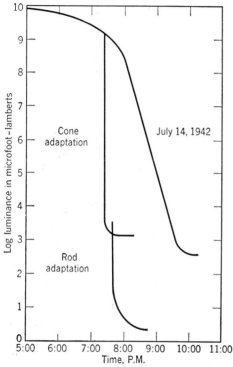

the image of the outer border of the test object falls on the retina than upon the total area involved in the image.

Figure 21 shows the rate of dark adaptation following exposures to 5-second flashes at various intensities and following exposure to the very short flash of a photoflash lamp. Figure 22 indicates the progress of dark adaptation as measured with violet light (480 mμ and below) following 2-minute exposures to preadapting intensities of various

levels. A violet color was seen above threshold, whereas at threshold the light was colorless. Figure 23 shows the various rates of dark adaptation following preadaptation to

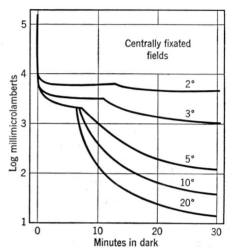

FIG. 17. Threshold curves showing dark adaptation for centrally fixated areas of different size. (Hecht, Haig, and Wald, 1935.)

different durations of a luminance at a level of 333 millilamberts.

From both practical and theoretical points of view the effect on dark adaptation of

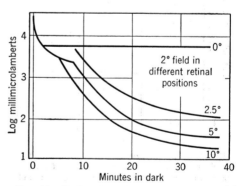

FIG. 18. Dark adaptation as measured with a 2-degree test object placed at various angular distances from the fixation point. (Hecht, Haig, and Wald, 1935.)

exposure to red light is of interest. In order to explain why red filters (goggles) enable a person to become dark adapted while ex-

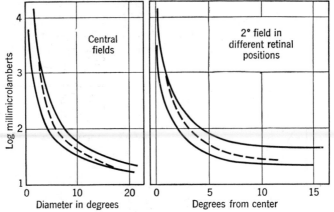

FIG. 19. The threshold level reached in 30 minutes of dark adaptation for retinal fields of different size and location, for three different observers (each curve for a single observer). The left-hand graph shows the results for test objects coaxial with the fixation point (central field). The right-hand graph is for a 2-degree field placed at different distances from the fixation point. (Hecht, Haig, and Wald, 1935.)

posed to ordinary indoor levels of illumination, we must inspect the characteristics of rods and cones as they bear on this matter. The luminosity curves based on rod and cone

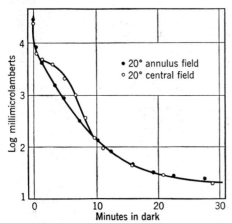

FIG. 20. A comparison between thresholds under dark adaptation for a centrally fixated 20-degree field and for a narrow 1-degree annulus, 20 degrees in diameter. (Hecht, Haig, and Wald, 1935.)

functions are effectively dissimilar (see Fig. 10). Spectral sensitivity curves plotted in terms of threshold, as in Fig. 24, express in another way the dissimilarity between rods and cones.

Were we to use exposure to red light as provided by a filter with a cutoff at about 620 mμ (see Fig. 25), we should be exposing the two classes of receptors (rods and cones) to different fractions of the total spectral ranges to which they are sensitive. This is one of the principal factors involved in dark adaptation when red filters are used. To illustrate, we may again refer to the two luminosity curves (Fig. 10) where the portions of the two curves eliminated by the red filter are shown by the unshaded areas. It will be seen that a greater portion of the scotopic curve (rod) is eliminated than is taken from the photopic curve (cone). The red filter passes $\frac{1}{100}$ of the effective flux for the rods and $\frac{1}{10}$ of that for the cones. This is a 10 to 1 difference, and it means that by wearing the red filter goggles the individual reduces the effective flux of light to the rods more than to the cones. For cone vision, if white light is to be reduced in effectiveness until it is equal to the red, the light of all wavelengths must be reduced to $\frac{1}{10}$ their value. Through a red filter, then, the cones receive enough light for the individual to see to do his work, but the light to the rods is greatly reduced. By adjusting the spectrum of the light source we may further augment the 10 to 1 difference between the stimulation of the rods and cones. The difference may become as great as 50 to 1.

preadaptation and the time required in darkness for the eye to reach a threshold 0.5 log unit (5 decibels) above its final value. The

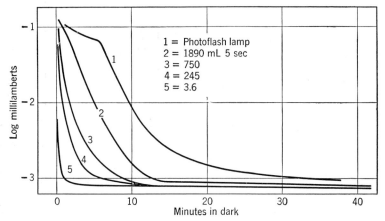

Fig. 21. Dark adaptation following short exposures to various intensities. The initial dark adaptation of the rods increases in velocity as the preadapting intensity decreases. (Wald and Clark, 1937.)

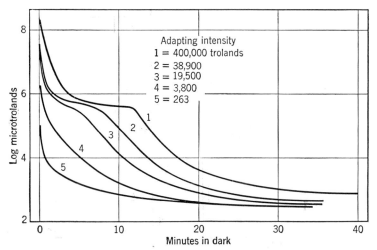

Fig. 22. The influence of light adaptation on subsequent dark adaptation of the eye. The thresholds during dark adaptation were measured with violet light following different amounts of preadaptation. (Hecht, Haig, and Chase, 1937.)

Figure 26 shows the rate of dark adaptation following preadaptation to white and red lights. It is obvious that preadaptation to red light provides for more rapid dark adaptation. Figure 27 shows the relation between the intensity of the light used for

curve for red preadaptation is about 1.5 log units to the right of the curve for white. To obtain the same dark adaptation in the same time the eye can be exposed to thirty times as much red light as white. In aviation where vision at low intensities is often

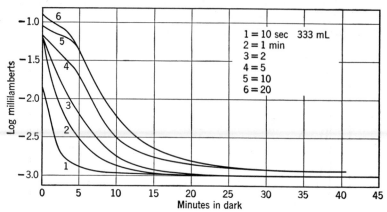

FIG. 23. Threshold curves showing dark adaptation following various lengths of exposure to a luminance of 333 millilamberts. As light adaptation proceeds, the visual threshold rises and the rate of rod adaptation declines. (Wald and Clark, 1937.)

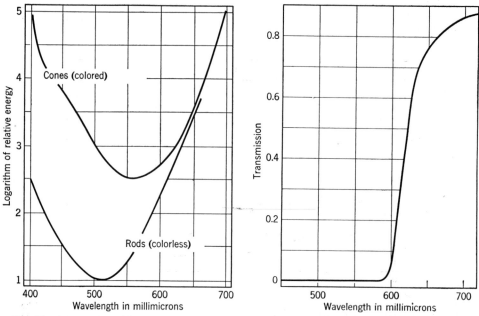

FIG. 24. Spectral sensitivity curves for rod and cone vision, showing the relative energy required to produce a threshold response. The actual energy increment above the threshold for the appearance of color (cone function) varies for different parts of the retina. In the parafovea it is between 0.1 and 1.0 log unit. The distance between the two curves represents the *photochromatic interval*. (Hecht and Yun Hsia, 1945.)

FIG. 25. Transmission of the red plastic material commonly used in red goggles. The part of the spectrum transmitted by the material is in the right-hand side of the diagram. (Hecht and Yun Hsia, 1945.)

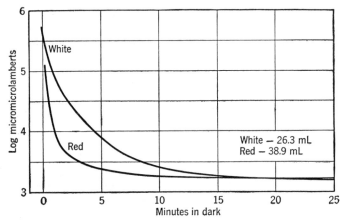

FIG. 26. Dark adaptation following preadaptation to white light and to red light of about equal photopic brightness. It is clear that, following white preadaptation, dark adaptation (which here is purely rod) is slower than that following red preadaptation. (Hecht and Yun Hsia, 1945.)

very necessary, and where restricted areas in the visual field may at the same time intrude with higher levels of illumination, red light may be used to advantage.

Preadaptation to lights containing various amounts of ultraviolet radiation has been tested for its effect upon subsequent dark adaptation. Young chicks were used for this

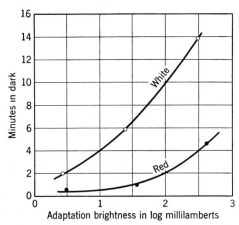

FIG. 27. Relation between the brightness of the preadaptation and the subsequent dark interval required for the eye to reach a threshold 0.5 log unit above the final threshold. The curve for red is nearly 1.5 log units to the right of the curve for white. This means that, in order to secure the same dark adaptation in the same time, the eye must be exposed to thirty times as much red light as white. (Hecht and Yun Hsia, 1945.)

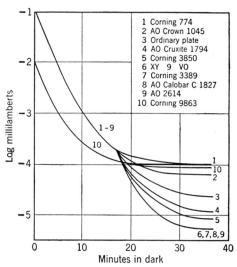

FIG. 28. The course of the dark adaptation of the eye of the young chick after pre-exposure to light containing different amounts of the ultra-violet spectrum. In proportion to the increase of the ultraviolet component below 365 mμ, the final dark-adaptation thresholds are raised, indicating a reduction in potential dark adaptation by the ultraviolet. Wavelengths above 365 mμ do not produce such effects. Curves 1 to 9 represent the effects of filters that pass a progressively decreasing range of ultraviolet radiation. The final threshold is affected less and less. Curve 10 is for an ultraviolet filter that transmits all the ultraviolet radiation. This filter shows the greatest effect on the final threshold. (Wolf, 1945.)

study. The results are shown in Fig. 28. Apparently ultraviolet radiation below 365 mμ raises the threshold in proportion to the amount of ultraviolet involved.

Dark Adaptation of the Color Anomalous

For a long time it was held that the dark-adaptation curves for both types of dichromats, for anomalous trichromats, and for dark-adaptation curves resulting from red, reddish-orange (Red II in the figure), yellow, and white lights are higher than are the corresponding sections of the curves for the color normal. The discrepancy decreases as one proceeds from the long to the short wavelengths. The curves for the protanopes resulting from the use of green and violet light are essentially normal.

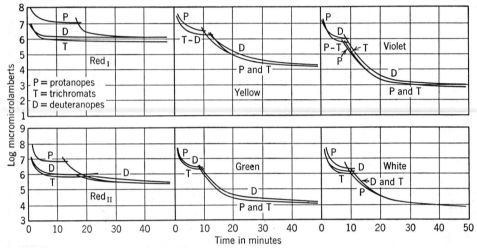

FIG. 29. Composite data from two dark-adaptation curves for each of four protanopes, four trichromats, and three deuteranopes, using various 3-degree spectral test lights placed 7 degrees temporally in the visual field. The various types of observers are indicated by the letters, P, D, and T, and the spectral colors are designated in each case. Red_I is red, and Red_II is a reddish-orange. (Chapanis, 1947.)

normal individuals were similar, but, either the data for these assertions were never published, or else the experimental conditions left something to be desired. Since it is known that protanopes are less sensitive to long wavelengths than are deuteranopes or color-normal persons, it would be expected that dark-adaptation curves measured with red light would be different for the protanope.

Measurements on the dark adaptation of the color anomalous with red, reddish orange, yellow, green, violet, and white lights gave results as shown in Fig. 29. It will be seen that the dark-adaptation curves for the deuteranopes are essentially like those of the trichromats (normals). The protanopic

Brightness Discrimination

Absolute threshold. In brightness discrimination there are several major considerations, of which the relation between area and the absolute visual threshold is of first importance. One assumption is that a constant number of retinal elements must be stimulated in order for a threshold response to occur. Wald used fields placed 15 and 25 degrees above the fovea and found close agreement between his findings and the results expected from the assumption just stated.

An expression used to describe such data is the following:

$$(A - n_t)^k I = C$$

where A is area, n_t is a constant threshold number of elements, and C and k are constants. This, in its simplest form, $AI = C$, is Ricco's law, applying to foveal vision. When k chances to take the value 0.5, it becomes Piper's law, which pertains to the peripheral retina

$$I\sqrt{A} = C$$

It happens, however, that investigators who have studied the area-threshold relation throughout a large area range have found that the simple rules just stated do not hold precisely. Ricco's law holds, for both fovea and periphery, when the angular size of the test object is no greater than 10 minutes. Piper's law holds for the periphery for visual angles within the range of 2 to 7 degrees.

Graham, Brown, and Mote (1939) surveyed the area-threshold relation. In the fovea they used test objects with diameters ranging from 1.86 minutes to 1 degree. In the periphery they used test objects ranging from 1.86 minutes to 25 degrees and 6 minutes. In explaining their findings and in considering the possible mechanisms involved, they recognized the fact that, although a retinal image may be more or less uniform from its center to its periphery, the excitation of the retina by the image tapers from center to periphery. This introduces complications in formulating the relation between area and stimulus intensity for threshold response. The authors assumed that at threshold only the center of the retinal area is involved. All other parts of the retina within the image are excited subliminally, but they nevertheless make some contribution to the effect E at the center. The excitatory contribution of each elemental area away from the center will be inversely proportional to a power p of the distance from the center r. Therefore the excitatory contribution dE is proportional to I/r^p.

In the fovea the unit area of effect may be a single cone, but in the periphery it is a more complex affair. If e is a constant intensity effect in each elemental area, e may be considered as being either (1) the photochemical effect occurring as a function of the intensity of the light in each receptor unit, or (2) the impulse frequency in the nerve fibers leading from the unit. Therefore e might be considered as

$$e = k_2 \log \frac{I}{I_0}$$

where k_2 is a proportionality constant, I_0 the constant threshold intensity of the receptor unit, and I the intensity of the light involved.

$$E = cR^{2-p} \log \frac{I}{I_0}$$

where $c = (2\pi k_1 k_2)/(2 - p)$, k_1 is a proportionality constant that was used in another equation (not given here) in connection with e, and R is the radius of the circle. The simplest assumption regarding threshold is that it is a constant, and the equation above becomes

$$\log \frac{I}{I_0} = CR^{p-2}$$

where $C = E/c$.

The constants found for this equation yield the specific expressions as follows: $\log I/I_0 = 1.61R^{-0.51}$ for the fovea when $\log I_0 = -2.9$; and $\log I/I_0 = 6.92R^{-0.54}$ for the peripheral retina whose $\log I_0 = -5.95$.

Differential thresholds. Brightness discrimination involves not only absolute thresholds but differential thresholds as well. Here the major consideration is the ratio of ΔI to I, but the area of the test object must be taken into account at the same time. Figure 30 shows the results when the angular size of the test object is varied from 23.5 minutes to 24 degrees. Figure 31 shows the values of $\Delta I/I$ for very small test objects (2 to 28 minutes) stimulating the fovea.

The differential threshold is also dependent upon the duration of stimulation. Here it may be said that the value of $\Delta I/I$ for constant intensity is highest for the shortest durations. It decreases as the duration is extended and reaches a limiting constant value at long durations. The duration at which the limiting value is reached is a function of intensity. It shortens as intensity increases.

Holway and Hurvich plotted log $I/\Delta I$ against the visual angle subtended by the

from the cornea and amounts to about 4 per cent. The second loss occurs in the ocular media between the outer surface of the cornea and the retina. For a wavelength of 510 mμ a loss of approximately 50 per cent is sustained in the media. The percentage of the energy reaching the retina, where it

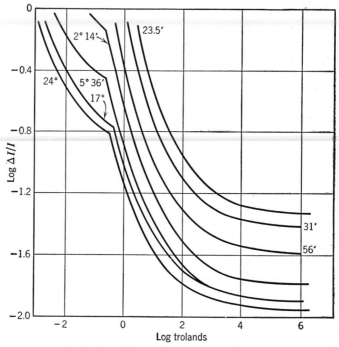

FIG. 30. Human intensity discrimination as dependent upon illumination and size of test object. Each curve is for a separate size of test object. The visual angles subtended are indicated on the curves. (Steinhardt, 1936.)

test object and found a linear relation for intensities lying between 0.000625 and 500 millilamberts, a range of 59 decibels.

Minimum visible energy. The matter of threshold stimulation has been studied from another point of view, that of determining the absolute amount of energy needed to produce a perceptual end result. It has been demonstrated that very little energy is required to reach the absolute threshold of visual response. The amount of energy in the stimulus outside the eye is, of course, greater than the amount that reaches the retina. The first loss is due to reflection

is finally absorbed by the receptors, has been estimated to range from 4 to 20 per cent of the energy incident on the cornea. The best estimate, according to Hecht (Hecht, Shlaer, and Pirenne, 1941), is about 10 per cent. The initial 58 to 148 quanta reaching the cornea (Hecht) dwindle to a number between 5 and 14 before they actually become effective within the receptors. The estimated number of rods in the field used by Hecht was 500. It was considered improbable that any single rod would receive more than 1 quantum. It was therefore concluded that, in order to initiate a visual sensation, only a single quantum of light needs to be absorbed by each of 5 to 14 rods.

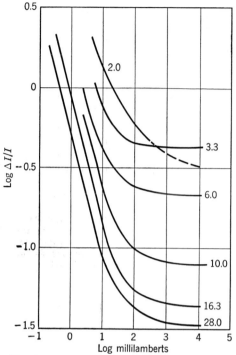

FIG. 31. The influence of area on foveal intensity discrimination. The values on the curves give the radii of the test objects in minutes of visual angle. (Graham and Bartlett, 1940.)

Additional factors. Not only the size of the test object, but also the degree of contrast between the test object and its surrounds, is important to discrimination. A study of these relations requires that we vary both the size of the test object and the level of its surrounds, as well as the contrast between the test object and its surrounds. An extensive study of this sort was made at the Tiffany Foundation and published by Blackwell (1946). Findings from this work are shown in Figs. 32, 33, 34, and 35. Let B_o represent the apparent brightness of the surrounds, and ΔB the increment either added to or subtracted from B_o to form the brightness of the transient

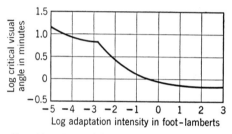

FIG. 33. The "critical" visual angle in minutes as a function of adaptation level. The critical visual angle is the angle at which area times intensity of test object ceases to be a constant. The contour of this function is similar to that relating threshold contrasts and adaptation level. (Blackwell, 1946.)

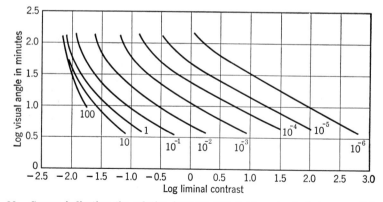

FIG. 32. Curves indicating the relation between threshold contrast (between a disk and its background) and disk area, at various adaptation levels. Each curve represents a separate adaptation level. Adaptation level is that produced by the intensity level of the field. Targets appear in any one of eight positions in an imaginary circle at the center of the field. There were five sizes of test object (disk). (Blackwell, 1946.)

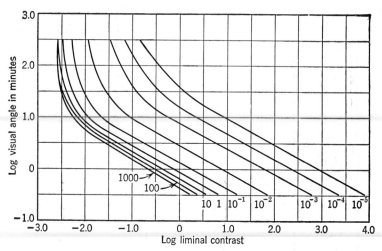

FIG. 34. Each curve represents the relation between threshold contrast and area of test object for a given adaptation level. The curve for each different adaptation level is determined by the intensity level of the field. The ordinate indicates the size of the target. The abscissa indicates the threshold contrast. The target was always at the center of the field, whereas for Fig. 32 the target was in one of eight positions in an imaginary circle on the field. (Blackwell, 1946.)

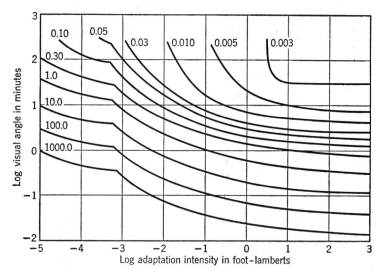

FIG. 35. The relation between test-object area and adaptation level for test objects of threshold contrast with their background (field). Adaptation level is that produced by the stated intensity level of the field given on the abscissa. (Blackwell, 1946.)

stimulus, or test object, B_s. Contrast is designated as follows:

$$C = \frac{B_s - B_0}{B_0} \quad \text{(test objects brighter than surrounds)}$$

$$C = \frac{B_0 - B_s}{B_0} \quad \text{(test objects less bright than surrounds)}$$

Values ranging from $C = 0$ to $C = \infty$ were used for test objects brighter than the sur-

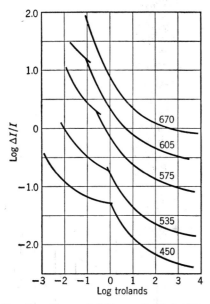

FIG. 36. Human brightness discrimination for the red, orange, yellow, green, and blue parts of the spectrum. The labeling on the ordinate applies to the data for yellow (575 mμ). The orange and red curves have been raised 0.5 and 1.0 log unit, respectively, and those for green and blue have been lowered 0.5 and 1.0 log unit, respectively. (Hecht, Peskin, and Patt, 1938.)

rounds, and $C = 0$ to $C = +1$ for test objects darker than the surrounds. Figure 32 shows the relation between the liminal contrast (in log units) and the logarithm of the visual angle in minutes of arc. Each curve represents the relation between threshold contrast and test object area for a given adaptation brightness. Some of the curves possess a linear portion indicating that the product of area and brightness ΔB is a constant. Test objects whose areas put them

on the linear parts of the curves are in effect "point sources." The critical visual angle is taken as the angle at which the product of area times brightness ceases to be constant. Critical visual angle is pictured in Fig. 33. The character of this function is similar to that relating liminal contrast and adaptation brightness. The curves for this latter relation are not given here, but they form the basis for the curves in Fig. 34. Figure 35 pictures the relation between test object area and the adaptation level for test objects of a number of contrasts.

When differential sensitivity is tested with isolated portions of the spectrum, the relation $\Delta I/I$ is shown to vary with intensity in the manner indicated in Fig. 36. The measurements with 670 mμ (red) exhibit a continuous function, whereas the measurements with 605 mμ (orange) begin to manifest a break because both rods and cones are involved.

Effect of anoxia on brightness discrimination. Anoxia produces a decreased differential sensitivity (see Fig. 37). The effect is marked at 15,000 feet and detectable considerably below that altitude. Impairment of brightness discrimination begins slowly and accelerates as higher altitudes are reached. It varies inversely with light intensity. Whereas the deterioration is most obvious with low intensities, it becomes negligible at full daylight levels. The oxygen lack affects vision in both the fovea and the periphery, and the general form of the relation between $\Delta I/I$ and I is the same for all oxygen concentrations. As shown in Fig. 37, anoxia merely shifts the curve along the intensity axis. This is taken to indicate that anoxia does not affect the photoreceptor system but affects rather the visual pathway beyond it.

Visual Acuity

The ability of the human visual mechanism to distinguish small spatial separations between portions of the visual field has been

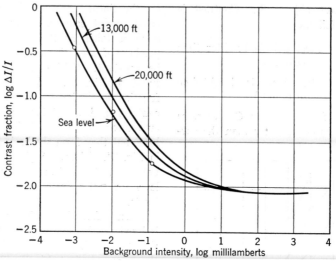

FIG. 37. The relation between just perceptible contrast $\Delta I/I$ and the prevailing I for each of three simulated altitudes. The curves are theoretical. (Hecht et al., 1946.)

studied in various ways. In most cases the test object has been characterized by abrupt transitions. That is to say, there are abrupt gradients (contours) between the intensity levels of the various parts of the visual field. Contours are usually seen as sharp, although the gradients in the retinal image are gradual and not infinitely steep. The kinds of test object commonly used include gratings, paired parallel bars or rectangles, single fine lines, illuminated single slits, and such figures as open circles or C's. In all cases spatial resolution is the central problem. The variation in fineness of resolution is studied in relation to intensity of illumination, state of adaptation, and duration of stimulation.

Visual acuity is defined as the reciprocal of the minimal effective visual angle in terms of minutes of arc. This notation is used in order to make high numerical values of acuity reflect high degrees of excellence in visual acuity, rather than the reverse.

A typical study is that of Shlaer (1937) whose results are pictured in Fig. 38. He used both a grating, whose overall visual angle was 4 degrees, and a C-shaped figure. He obtained somewhat different results in the two cases. Below about 30 trolands, the

grating yields better visual acuity. At higher levels, the C is better than the grating. Figure 39 is a plot of the visual acuities for the same two test objects, but here the

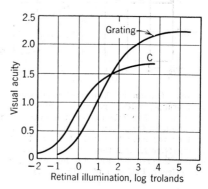

FIG. 38. The relation between visual acuity and retinal illumination for two kinds of test object— a grating, and a C, or broken circle. See Fig. 39 for theoretical curves on a log-log plot. (Shlaer, 1937.)

logarithm of visual acuity is plotted on the ordinate (hence a log-log plot). In this type of graph the cone and rod portions of the curves show up more distinctly than when visual acuity is plotted on a linear scale.

When parallel bars are used to test visual acuity, several factors are effective. They

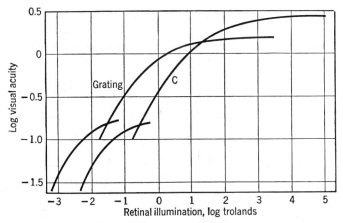

FIG. 39. Curves showing visual acuity for two different test objects. On this log-log plot each curve appears to be composed of two segments. The lower segment represents rod function; the upper segment represents cone function. Below approximately 30 trolands the grating yields better visual acuity values, whereas the C is superior at higher intensities. At low intensities about ten times more light is necessary for the C than for the grating. (Shlaer, 1937.)

include the intensity relations between bars and surround (light bars on dark field or dark bars on light field) and the widths of the bars themselves. Wilcox found that visual acuity continued to increase with increases in the level of the ground when dark bars were seen against a light ground. As the intensity of the light bars was raised, however, visual acuity first improved, then reached a maximum, and finally declined (see Fig. 40). In order to explain this effect the ideas of *irradiation* and *negative irradiation* were used.

Fry and Cobb (1935) showed that the width of two bright bars on a dark field affects visual acuity. With both wide and narrow bars visual acuity initially improves as the intensity of the bars is increased. With the wide bars the initial rapid improvement changes to a slower improvement. With the narrow bars it changes to an actual decline in visual acuity.

Not only paired bars but also single fine lines have been used to determine visual acuity. Hecht and Mintz used a fine wire bisecting a homogeneous lighter visual field that subtended a large visual angle. They found that the finest resolvable line at the highest illuminations subtended a visual

angle of only 0.5 second. In terms of actual visual acuity this is 120 times greater than the "standard acuity" of 1 minute and about

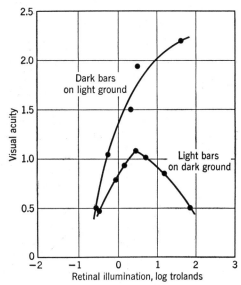

FIG. 40. Curves showing visual acuity as measured by parallel bars. (Modified from Wilcox; Bartley, 1941.)

60 times greater than the acuity obtained with a C or a grating. It is shown in Fig. 41.

Niven and Brown used a bright slit on a dark ground to determine the relations among three variables: the minimal visual angle, the duration of exposure, and the intensity of the slit illumination. The results

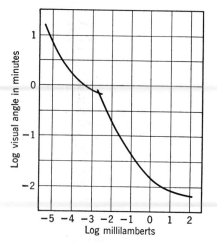

FIG. 41. The relation between intensity of background and the visual angle subtended by the thickness of wire when it is just resolved against its background. The upper section of the curve is for rod vision; the lower section is for cone vision. (Hecht and Mintz, 1939.)

are shown in Fig. 42. Each curve is for a single duration. Increasing the duration of the exposure simply displaces, to the left, the curves showing the relation between log visual angle and log intensity.

Figure 43 indicates the effect of selected portions of the spectrum, and pupils of con-

trolled size, on measurements of visual acuity. When red light (predominantly 670 mμ) is used, there is no break apparent between rod and cone levels of function. When blue light (predominantly 450 mμ) is used, the break shows up very plainly.

Flicker

Not only dark adaptation and various forms of stationary brightness discrimination, but also the discrimination of intermittent stimulation, has been studied for its possible contribution to photochemical theory. Figure 44 (left) indicates the findings when a 2-degree test object is studied. The critical flicker frequency (cff) is the flicker rate in flashes per second at which the field just becomes steady. It will be seen that the curve tends to reverse after reaching its maximum, especially with the 10-degree surround. This tendency is even greater with no illuminated surround whatsoever.

Figure 44 (right) shows the outcome when the area of the test object is varied.

Figure 45 (left) shows the results of shifting the original 2-degree test object to positions away from the fixation point. Figure 45 (right) represents the outcome of using a test object having a 19-degree diameter and different wavelengths. The intensity range covered by the red (670 mμ) is the narrowest. Hecht and Shlaer (1936) state

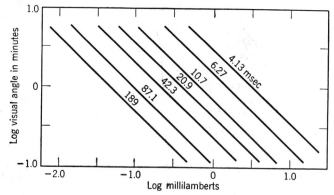

FIG. 42. The relation between the logarithm of the visual angle subtended by the test object (illuminated slit) and the threshold intensity for exposures of various durations. The subject's task was to determine the direction of orientation of the slit. (Niven and Brown, 1944.)

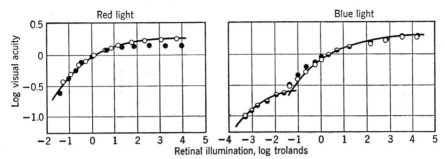

FIG. 43. *Left.* A typical curve showing the relation between visual acuity and retinal illumination when red light and a grating test object are used. The filled circles are for a 2-millimeter pupil. The open circles are for a 3-millimeter pupil. *Right.* Same relation but for blue light and a 2-millimeter pupil. The open circles are for one subject, and the solid circles for another. All points below a log I value of -1.5 were made in a subjectively colorless field and represent pure rod function. (Shlaer, Smith, and Chase, 1942.)

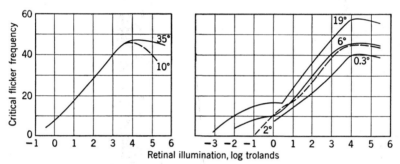

FIG. 44. *Left.* Critical flicker frequency as a function of the illumination. The experiment employed central fixation of a 2-degree flickering field with a 10-degree surround and with a 35-degree surround. (Hecht, 1938.) *Right.* Influence of the area of the test field on the relation between critical flicker frequency and retinal illumination. (Hecht and Smith, 1936.)

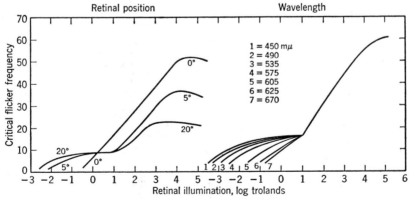

FIG. 45. *Left.* The relation between cff and log I for white light with a 2-degree field in three different retinal locations : at the fovea, and at 5 and 20 degrees above the fovea. (Hecht, 1938.) *Right.* The relation between cff and log I for different parts of the spectrum. Eye of S. Hecht. (Hecht and Shlaer, 1936.)

that the measurements are faithfully described by two similar equations. One of these is for the rods; the other for the cones. Both equations are derived from the stationary state equation he uses for other visual functions.

NEURAL MECHANISMS

Even though the visual sense cell is a photoreceptor, its behavior is described here rather than in the previous section, which dealt with photochemical considerations. The sense cell also manifests electrical activity, and therefore its behavior is allied to that of the neural units succeeding it in the visual pathway.

Electrical Effects in Single Receptors

Hartline and co-workers (Hartline, 1940) have determined the temporal characteristics of the electrical discharge of single receptors under various conditions. They used the horseshoe crab, Limulus, which has compound eyes whose neural connections lie at some distance from the receptors. This permits recording from receptor units prior to the development of neurally produced complications.

In the undivided nerve of the horseshoe crab the response to light consists of slow potential changes upon which are superimposed rapid irregular fluctuations (impulses). When the nerve is divided into sufficiently small strands, a regular sequence of uniform nerve impulses appears. These are taken to be the successive discharges of a single fiber, the result of stimulating a single ommatidium. The discharge of a single fiber may reach a frequency as high as 130 impulses per second at the outset of stimulation.

Since the eye of this crab does not possess lateral connections analogous to the internuncial neurons of the vertebrate retina, it may be used for studying the "area effect." The ommatidia respond with the same latent period regardless of how many are stimulated. This is true over an intensity range

of from 1 to 10,000 (40 decibels). The magnitude of the retinal potential, however, is directly proportional to the number of elements illuminated, up to one-half the area of the eye. Beyond this the response increases less rapidly, owing to the angular displacement of the peripheral elements.

Each receptor of a compound eye exhibits a luminosity (visibility) curve just as does the human eye taken as a whole. Figure 46

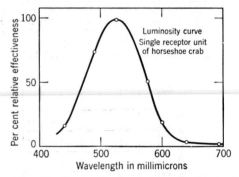

FIG. 46. Luminosity curve for a single visual cell. Relative effectiveness of each spectral band is the reciprocal of the relative intensity necessary to produce a specified burst of impulses. Value at 530 mμ set equal to 100 per cent. (Data from Graham and Hartline, 1935; Hartline, 1940.)

shows a typical curve for a single receptor cell of the horseshoe crab. It is not greatly different from the curve for the human eye, except that the curve for the single receptor cuts off earlier toward the longer wavelengths.

The discharge rate in a single receptor following the onset of steady illumination is pictured in Fig. 47 (left). The rate is high at first, but it falls quickly to a much lower value. The very strongest illuminations result not only in the "initial burst" just described but also in a momentary pause in the discharge following the burst. This is called the "silent period." Low illuminations may yield records that show acceleration of the discharge rate from the very start, with no silent period.

Discharge rate is related positively to level of illumination, as indicated in the right-

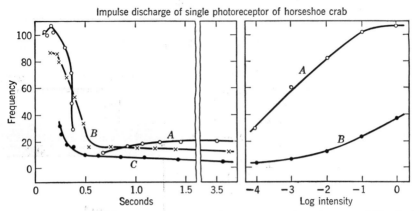

Impulse discharge of single photoreceptor of horseshoe crab

FIG. 47. *Left.* Frequency of impulses per second **versus** time after the onset of illumination. Curve *A* is for an intensity of 0.1. Curve *B* is for an intensity of 0.001. Curve *C* is for an intenstiy of 0.0001. Intensity is in arbitrary units (1 unit = 630,000 meter-candles on surface of eye). The points give the average frequency of four successive impulses. The time value is assigned to the second impulse. *Right.* The relation between frequency of impulse and intensity of stimulating light, in arbitrary units. Curve *A*, frequency of the initial maximum discharge. Curve *B*, frequency of discharge 3.5 seconds after onset of illumination. (Hartline and Graham, 1932.)

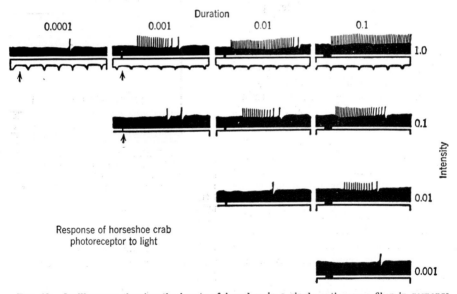

Response of horseshoe crab
photoreceptor to light

FIG. 48. Oscillograms showing the bursts of impulses in a single optic nerve fiber in response to short pulses of light of various intensities and durations. Relative intensity for each horizontal row is given on the right (1.0 = 3 x 10⁶ meter-candles). Duration of pulse for each vertical column is at the top, in seconds. Signal of light pulse blackens the white line above the time marker (arrows mark position of signal for very short pulses). Time marked in ⅕ second. (Hartline, 1934.)

hand diagram of Fig. 47. Two curves are included: A, for the frequency of the initial maximum, and B, for the rate 3.5 seconds after onset of illumination.

For very short pulses of light it is the quantity of light that counts. The amount of light required to reach threshold or to elicit a given number of impulses is the product of the intensity and the duration of the pulse, $I \times t = c$. An actual demonstration of this reciprocity between intensity and duration is provided in Fig. 48.

Increasing the intensity of a pulse of constant duration reduces the time elapsing before the response occurs (latent period) and increases the frequency and the total number of impulses discharged. For various features of the response, such as the initial or the maximal frequency of discharge, only those pulse durations that are shorter than the time required for the appearance of the features themselves can be considered. When the pulses are shorter than the latent period, the lengthening of a pulse of fixed intensity acts as does an increase of intensity. For both initial and maximal impulse frequency the reciprocity relation ultimately fails and is replaced, at a critical duration, by the condition in which intensity alone determines the response. Since this critical duration is considerably shorter than the time that elapses before the appearance of the response impulses, it is inferred that the impulses are determined within the sense cell earlier than the time indicated by the appearance of the impulses at the recording site.

The process of adaptation in a single sense cell is shown in Fig. 49. In this figure, responses to a test pulse at each of four intervals during the sense cell's stay in the dark is pictured.

If pulses, ΔI, are added at random intervals to a steady illumination, I (which elicits a steady discharge of impulses), additional impulses will result. Significant information regarding receptor behavior can be obtained by varying the intensity of the pulses and by varying the level of the steady

illumination. Pulses of light added to a steady (adapting) light increase the impulse discharge frequency. This effect occurs throughout the interval from the twentieth to the eightieth second of light adap-

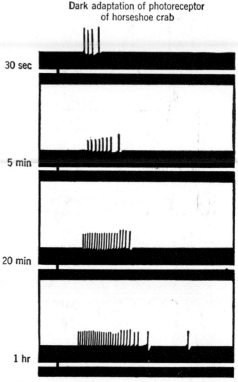

FIG. 49. Dark adaptation of a visual sense cell. Bursts of impulses in an optic nerve fiber in response to a test pulse of 0.01 second ("flash") thrown upon the eye at various times (given at left), following an adapting exposure. Signal of pulse appears on white line in the record. (Hartline, 1940.)

tation and declines slowly during the remainder of the adaptation period (see Fig. 50).

The value of ΔI that just elicits an additional single impulse with a given latency varies with the time elapsed since the appearance of the preceding impulse resulting from the steady "adapting" illumination (Riggs and Graham, 1945). This interval is called the "recovery time." As this interval increases, the value of ΔI necessary to elicit the single extra impulse decreases. As ΔI is made more intense, the frequency and the total number of impulses in response to it increase at any constant adapting illumination. The latency of the ΔI response likewise diminishes. When ΔI is intense, the response to it is followed by a "silent period." Increasing the level of the adapting illumination increases the value of ΔI needed

Retinal Ganglion Cell Discharge

In the vertebrate retina it is next to impossible to obtain records from single receptors. While this goal is being approached, the chief record now obtainable is from the ganglion cell axons. The ganglion cell discharge is not related so simply to intensity and timing of stimulation as is the discharge recorded from receptors of the horseshoe crab.

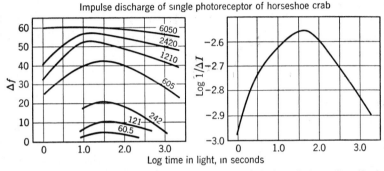

Impulse discharge of single photoreceptor of horseshoe crab

Fig. 50. *Left.* Increment Δf in impulse frequency as a function of time after the beginning of light adaptation. Each curve represents a designated value for ΔI, the increment in illumination responsible for Δf, the increment in impulse frequency. Adaptation intensity 49 foot-candles. *Right.* Logarithm of the sensitivity of the photoreceptor (defined as the reciprocal of the value of ΔI required to make the impulse frequency reach 30 per second) as a function of the time following the beginning of light adaptation. ΔI is the intensity of the flash above that of the steady illumination used to adapt the receptor. (Riggs and Graham, 1940.)

to elicit a response and changes the maximal interval within which recovery is measurable.

For constant added response (response to ΔI) the following relations hold: (1) At any level of adapting illumination, the latency diminishes as recovery time increases. (2) The value of ΔI needed to produce a constant response is small for low values of I and increases as I is raised. (3) At low adapting illuminations the minimal latency of the constant added response (response to ΔI) tends to be long. (4) As I and the ΔI used with it rise, latencies tend toward smaller minimum values. (5) With increase in I and ΔI, the change of latency with recovery time increases. (6) As I and ΔI increase, maximum recovery time shortens.

In the frog, three kinds of discharge have been found. Some ganglion cell fibers exhibit trains of impulses only during the absorption of light by the receptors. Other cells discharge only at the beginning of illumination and just following its cessation. A third kind of discharge arises only after cessation of illumination and continues longer than the "off" discharge in the second group. The first kind of discharge has been called the maintained or X type; the second, the on-off or Y type; and the third, the off or Z type. About 20 per cent of the fibers belong to the X, 50 per cent to the Y, and 30 per cent of the Z type (see Fig. 51).

In the guinea pig retina, where there are only rods, the vast majority (90 per cent) of the elements begin their discharge at the onset of illumination. Whereas they all continue to discharge throughout receptor illumination, some possess a definite after-discharge. About 8 or 9 per cent of the elements are the on-off type, and 1 or 2 per cent are the pure off-type.

In the duplex (rods and cones) retina of the cat, the great majority of the elements

quency is compressed. On this account, frequency-intensity curves for the light-adapted state rise more rapidly. In both the cat and the guinea pig spontaneous activity in isolated elements is demonstrable, and its suppression is taken to be an indication of inhibition.

Impulse-discharge vertebrate eye of frog
Single optic nerve fiber

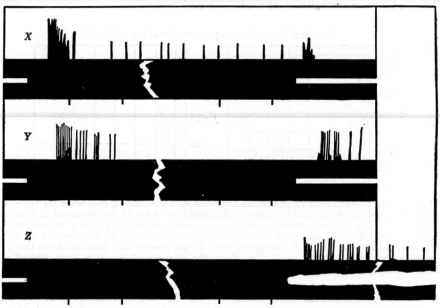

Fig. 51. Somewhat schematic oscillograms showing the discharge of impulses in single optic nerve fibers of the vertebrate eye (frog), illustrating the three most common types of response to illumination of the retina. Onset and termination of stimulation are indicated by the white line in the center of the black bands. Time marked in ⅕ second. (Hartline, 1938.)

appear to be the on-off type. Pure off-elements are very rare.

It would appear that the proportion of the on-off discharges recorded in the cat varies greatly with stimulus conditions. Light adaptation tends to affect the activity in the following ways: (1) It raises the thresholds of the various elements. (2) It shortens the duration of the after-discharge, if any. (3) It decreases the number of impulses at the onset and termination of illumination. And (4) it does not alter the maximum rate of discharge. Since the threshold is raised, the intensity range effective in varying fre-

Each optic nerve fiber (ganglion cell axon) is fed from a *receptive field* of the retina. A single fiber responds to retinal stimulation anywhere within a limited area. The limits of such a field have been mapped by Hartline, by means of a very small spot of light whose location could be accurately manipulated. The receptive field is smallest under threshold illumination. It is then somewhere between 0.25 and 0.50 millimeter in diameter. When intensities are raised to 100 or to 1000 times the threshold, the area doubles. The effectiveness of a small spot is greatest when the spot is near the center of the receptive field. Two spots of light placed within the receptive field summate in effect. Fibers carrying Y or Z responses respond to the movement of a bright spot or to a shadow produced within the receptive field.

The Electroretinogram

The electroretinogram is one of several types of record indicating features of the neural mechanism in the retina. The electroretinogram (ERG) is the overall pattern of potential elicited by momentary illumination of the retina and is recorded by placing one electrode on the cornea and one on the back of the eyeball. It does not exist as a recordable wave pattern during continuous illumination, nor when intermittent illumination reaches a high frequency. It is not a highly differentiated response, although it does vary with stimulus conditions and with internal conditions of the eye, such as degrees of asphyxia, drug application, etc. The ERG consists of a small, brief negative deflection (the a wave) a much larger positive wave (the b wave), and a second slow rise called the c wave. The c curve follows the decline of the b wave. The first two waves are the *on* response. At the cessation of illumination, if a c wave exists, an *off* response develops as a slight positive hump and a rapid decline to the base line.

From an analysis of these waves the existence of three components, PI, PII, and $PIII$, has been deduced. PI is a prolonged positive deflection, largely the c wave; PII is largely the b wave; and $PIII$ is a negative component. Since $PIII$ develops at the onset of stimulation, its initial negative swing is uncompensated and appears in the record as the a wave. From the way the components behave under various stimulus conditions, deductions concerning facilitative and inhibitive processes in the neuroretina have been made.

One significant result sometimes obtained with intermittent stimulation is that a b wave (the main feature of the response in such cases) is not elicited by each pulse of light but only by alternate pulses. If the frequency of intermittent stimulation is reduced, a small b wave may appear as a response to each flash that formerly produced no wave. As the frequency is further reduced, the initially small wave increases in size. With low enough frequencies all pulses are followed by b waves of equal size. This phenomenon is taken by some (Bartley, 1939) to indicate that the recovery of elements responding to the first pulse is not accomplished by the time the second pulse is presented. If a little more time between pulses is allowed, a small response is possible; with still more time, a larger one. This "alternate-response" phenomenon does not always occur, nor would it be expected to. Under some conditions all pulses quite soon are responded to by equal numbers of elements, regardless of pulse rate, each pulse activating a fraction of the elements. Succeeding pulses would activate similar fractions, in keeping, of course, with the length of the actual activity-recovery cycle of the elements. That these elements are neural complexes, and not simply receptors themselves, is indicated by the length of the cycles involved.

In certain subfusional ("flicker") experiments it was found that the flashes or fluctuations seemed to have a rate one-half that of the stimuli. Hence there is a definite perceptual counterpart of the ERG phenomenon just described.

The ERG of the human eye elicited by a brief pulse of light can be divided into two parts, based on the dissimilar behavior of the scotopic and photopic mechanisms of the retina. The photopic part is a short diphasic potential, the cornea initially negative. This response is elicited by white light, or by any monochromatic light except blue. It is manifested in the light-adapted eye and is little augmented by dark adaptation. The scotopic part is a more prolonged monophasic potential (0.3 to 0.4 millivolts), and the cornea is positive. All parts of the spectrum except the deep red will elicit it. It is not elicited in the light-adapted eye, and it varies in size in keeping with the degree of dark adaptation, quite parallel to the increase in visual sensitivity.

The two response components, scotopic and photopic, can be elicited in pure form by deep blue and deep red illumination, respectively. The form of the responses does not change with intensity of illumination, whereas the size does. White light and wavelengths intermediate between red and blue give rise to a compound response containing the two response components. As might be expected, the photopic response is more dependent upon the intensity of illumination of the central part of the retina, and the scotopic upon that of the retinal periphery. Furthermore the scotopic response has not been detected when a brief light pulse is added to a field already steadily illuminated at a level of two apparent footcandles, but is present when the level is reduced to 0.3 foot-candle. With repeated pulses the scotopic component diminishes quickly after the first few pulses.

The Optic Nerve Discharge

The optic nerve discharge provides another method for determining something about the behavior of the visual pathway. The optic nerve discharge is highly manipulable, and the responses to a series of light pulses disclose aspects of dark adaptation, as well as a number of other features related to brightness vision (see Bartley, 1942).

Pulses that are just suprathreshold elicit merely a single small wave in the optic nerve record. (Owing to the method of recording, all waves are monophasic.) Pulses that are either stronger or longer (greater quantity of light) elicit a larger wave that soon becomes somewhat bimodal and sharp-crested. The progress of these changes as the pulses are intensified or increased in length is shown in Fig. 52.

A perceptual counterpart of the secondary wave S in Fig. 52 has been demonstrated by Bartley (1942). Within a certain range of stimulus intensities and durations, a second flash is seen, although only a single pulse of light is actually presented. Too little or too much light, in the form of either intensity or duration, elicits only the subjective end result of a single flash. The conditions that produce an *on* response with a secondary wave S are comparable to those that produce the impression of a pair of flashes. The S wave is presumably the basis for the second flash of the pair.

It is possible to arrange the stimulus conditions so as to bring out numerous other variations in the discharge record of the optic nerve. In the foregoing example, however, we have a demonstration of the possibility of correlating sensory outcome with neural events.

The Response of the Optic Cortex

It is possible to record electrical responses from the surface and from the underlying layers of the optic cortex in experimental animals and to correlate some characteristics of these responses with features of the sensory end result (in man) obtained with the same stimulus setup. The optic cortex, like other parts of the brain, is continuously active. One feature of the activity is the periodic fluctuation called the alpha rhythm. In the rabbit this rhythm is at a rate of about 5 per second; in the cat, 7 or 8 per second; and in man, about 10 per second.

The electrical response of the optic cortex to pulses of light indicates that it is made up of three components (Bishop and O'Leary, 1938): (1) a series of rapid small waves of the order of axon spikes; (2) a larger diphasic or triphasic wave (surface initially positive); and (3) a longer triphasic series of undulations of the temporal order of the alpha rhythm. The first of the small waves or spikes is interpreted as the activity of the axons in the afferent radiation. The second indicates the activity within the cortex analogous to the spread of activity in the intercalary neurons in the spinal cord. The third seems to signal the cortifugal discharge, perhaps in the pyramidal cells, to various regions including the superior colliculus; it can be recorded at depths below the cortex.

Experimental procedures may alter the waves of the second major component in the elements responsible for the second component of the cortical response is enhanced.

The cortical response manifests both an *on* and *off* response to intermittent stimulation, and in this and other ways it forms a useful indicator for certain experimental purposes.

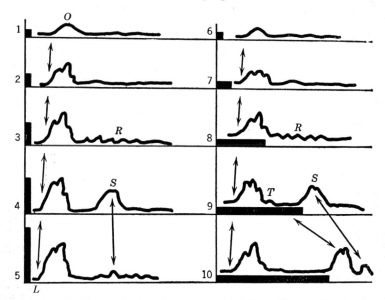

FIG. 52. A schematic diagram to show the components of the optic nerve discharge in response to pulses of light (black bars) varying in intensity (1st column) and in duration (2nd column). Record 1 is the response to a just suprathreshold stimulus. *O* is the *on* response. The succeeding records are the responses to light pulses of progressively greater intensity. *R* is the series of small irregular waves or ripples. *S* is a secondary wave that emerges to replace the ripples within a critical range of stimulus intensities. *S* reduces to a mere vestige, as shown in record 5. The second column shows that *S* also emerges as duration (quantity of light) of the pulse is increased. *S* is not to be mistaken for the off response *T* shown in records 9 and 10. *L*, in each record, represents latency or point of onset of response. *T* in record 9 indicates the first appearance of an off response, which in 10 has become longer and later. In 9 it precedes *S*, and in 10 it precedes the vestige of *S*. (Bartley, 1942.)

ways different from those in which the third or slow component is altered. Strychnine applied directly to the cortex obliterates the third and augments the second component. The spikes in the record, produced by application of strychnine to the cortex are quite like those seen in the human electroencephalogram (EEG) in epileptic seizures, and this has led to the conclusion that in such seizures it is *not* the alpha rhythm that is being augmented. Rather the alpha rhythm has disappeared, and the activity of

Intermittent Stimulation

The use of the factor of timing in stimulation, particularly as it is involved in the presentation of paired or serial light pulses, has yielded considerable information about the functioning of the visual pathways. It has led also to correlations between neural events and the sensory end result. A number of these findings have disclosed phenomena not explainable by photochemical theory. Major examples of such phenomena are brought together in what follows.

The studies of some workers have led them to reject the photochemical determination of the sensory outcome as affirmed by Hecht and others. Crozier and colleagues, Wolf and Zerrahn-Wolf, have studied the responses of a number of animal forms to in-

mal. The following are the animals used, according to the kinds of retinas possessed: (1) those having rods only (gecko, horned lizard); (2) those having cones only (turtle, bird); (3) those having both (duplex retinas) (frog, fish, man); (4) those pos-

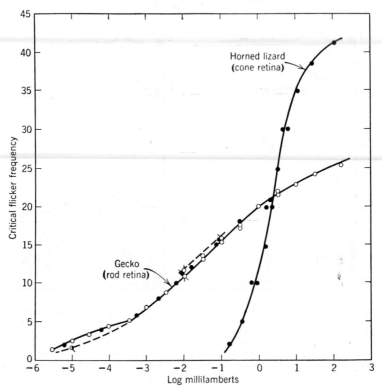

Fig. 53. The cff curves for the horned lizard and the gecko. The horned lizard possesses a cone retina; the gecko a rod retina. The curves for both resemble probability integrals. With the gecko, certain techniques had to be employed to compensate for eyelid behavior that modified the cff. When the proper compensations were made, the cff at low intensity levels was taken to be that represented by the broken line. (Crozier and Wolf, 1939a; 1941.)

termittent stimulation and have outlined a neurostatistical rather than a photochemical picture of the underlying mechanisms at work. In their experiments the test animals are placed inside a rotating cylinder possessing alternate opaque and transparent vertical bands. Light of measured intensity shines through the transparent stripes, and the speed of the cylinder and the intensity of the light are so adjusted as just to produce the required reaction of the ani-

sessing three groups of receptors (two kinds of cones plus the rods) (newt); and (5) those possessing compound eyes (crayfish, dragonfly, bee).

The attempt throughout was to measure precisely the cff for the separate retinal receptor populations. When the activities of the rods and cones are separated, the curve representing the activity of each describes an integral of the normal probability curve. Accordingly, Crozier and his colleagues developed a *statistical* theory to account for the results obtained.

The following are some of the assumptions that underly their theory: (1) Visual brightness is a function of the total "neural effect" * reaching a certain crucial station in the nervous system. (2) A jnd, whether that any increase in stimulus intensity can be expected to produce is, in part, determined by the difference between the effect then existing and the maximum possible effect. This is called the *availability principle*. Presumably the amount of effect representing a jnd is constant, whereas the amount of

Fig. 54. *Left.* Cff for the sunfish (*Lepomis*). The two curves are for two procedures: (1) in which the rotation of the stripes was held constant, and the illumination was varied to obtain the cff (open circles), and (2) in which illumination was held constant at each of the various levels, and the rotation speed was varied to obtain the cff. *Right.* Cff for man. Same type of apparatus used as with lower animals, i.e. a revolving drum with alternate black and white stripes. The data shown were taken on a series of successive days, after considerable practice. Each plotted point is the mean of ten readings. (Crozier, Wolf, and Zerrahn-Wolf, 1937b.)

absolute or differential, is the result of the addition or subtraction of a certain amount of neural effect to or from that already existing by virtue of the standard stimulus. (3) The threshold intensity (in logarithmic terms) for initiating nerve impulses varies from unit to unit and in the same unit from time to time in a random fashion. (4) There is a maximum neural effect that can be set up in any group of neural units under the most favorable conditions. (5) The effect

* This neural effect is not exclusively one of frequency of impulses, for it must also involve spatial distribution (ultimately, total number per unit time). Nevertheless the principles of Crozier's theory can be made clear by the expedient of description in terms of impulse frequency.

stimulation required to set up this additional neural effect is a function of the additional impulse frequency or other neural effect left *available* before the maximum is reached.

The following curves illustrate the statistical nature of the visual responses in different types of retinas. Figure 53 presents the "flicker curve" for the rod retina of the gecko and for the cone retina of the horned lizard. Similar curves for duplex retinas (sunfish and man) are shown in Fig. 54. These are composite curves resolvable into two parts, one for the rods (at low intensities) and one for the cones (at high intensities). Each of these parts has the shape of a normal probability integral.

The cff curve for a retina having three types of functional units is shown in Fig. 55. Here we have a composite curve resolvable into three probability integrals.

ommatidia are not pointed toward the light coming from a single direction. Thus, especially when illumination is low, a sizable fraction of the ommatidia will not be act-

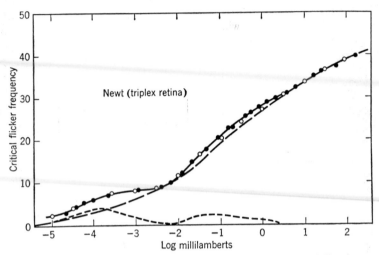

FIG. 55. Cff for the newt (*Triturus viridescens viridescens*). The dashed line is a probability integral. The left-hand dotted curve represents the rod contribution. The right-hand dotted curve corresponding to the bulge between log $I = -2.0$ and log $I = 0.5$ presumbably represents the activity of a third group of receptor units. (Crozier and Wolf, 1940.)

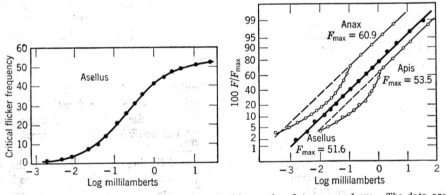

FIG. 56. *Left.* Cff for the *Asellus*, an isopod with a rather flat compound eye. The data are fitted to a probability integral. *Right.* A comparison of the curves for the *Anax*, the bee (*Apis*), and the isopod *Asellus.*. The departures from the probability expectations in the first two cases and the strict adherence in the third are made graphic by the plotting of the data on a probability grid, in which the numbers on the ordinate are so spaced that a probability integral plots as a straight line. F is critical flicker frequency. F_{max} is maximal critical flicker frequency. (Crozier, Wolf, and Zerrahn-Wolf, 1939b.)

Figure 56 depicts the cff response for three animals having compound eyes. Some of these eyes are quite convex, and all their

ivated, and a departure of the cff curve from the normal probability integral will ensue. This is especially true for *Anax* and *Apis*. I contrast, a strict adherence to the probability function is shown in the isopod *Asellus,* whose eye is relatively flat.

Discrepancy between Flicker and Stimulus (Flash) Rate

When flash rate is low, the subjective alternation between light and dark follows the stimulus, but this principle does not hold when frequencies approach cff. Bartley (1938a) showed that even when (with feeble illumination) cff was as low as 4 per second, the subjective or perceived flicker manifested a relatively high rate. By a comparison method it was concluded that this rate lay in the neighborhood of 20 per second. When, at higher intensities, the cff was about 50 per second, the perceived flicker appeared to occur at the same frequency as in the former case, namely about 20 per second (see Fig. 57). This phenomenon is not predicted by present-day photochemical theory. It would appear to be based upon the inherent discharge rate of the retinal ganglion cells. Hence it is an example of the participation of the neuroretina in visual brightness discrimination.

Spontaneous Activity in the Retina

Granit (1941) has recorded what he calls rotational activity and spontaneous rhythms

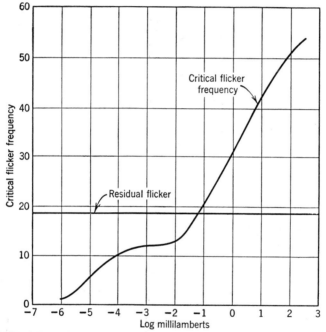

FIG. 57. Residual flicker is the last vestige of flicker just before a visually steady field is produced. The rate of this flicker is not related to the cff but remains nearly steady at a rate supposedly in the neighborhood of 20 per second. This result is attributed to the determination of residual flicker by the intrinsic discharge characteristic of the retinal ganglion cells, rather than by the flash rate. (Bartley, 1941.)

from the retina. By means of a microelectrode technique, he has found that single activity units, as well as many individual active elements, exhibit definite rotation by pausing and again resuming activity at random intervals. He states that spontaneous activity in such elements is of two types: (1) discharges that can be temporarily or indefinitely inhibited by illumination or momentarily stopped by discontinuance of illumination, and (2) discharges that persist irrespective of the presence or absence of illumination. Spontaneous rhythms can be set up or enhanced by rhythmic stimulation. In these facts we see a possible basis for the discrepancy, found by Bartley, between the stimulus frequency and the sub-

hancement is at its maximum. This rate coincides with the alpha rhythm. That this is not a mere coincidence is suggested by the fact that optic nerve stimulation and light pulses to the retina are both maximally effective in producing responses at the optic cortex when supplied at the rate of the alpha rhythm. This and a number of other facts

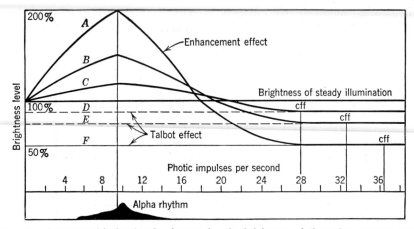

FIG. 58. At some subfusional pulse frequencies the brightness of the pulses appears greater than the brightness of steady illumination of the same physical intensity. This enhancement is maximum in the neighborhood of 10 pulses per second. The three curves represent three different LDR's. $A = \frac{1}{1}$; $B = \frac{7}{2}$; $C = \frac{8}{1}$. D, E, and F are the Talbot brightnesses for these ratios. The Talbot brightness is the brightness predicted by Talbot's law: rapid intermittent stimuli produce a brightness equal to that produced by a steady stimulus having the same average intensity. (Bartley, 1939.)

jective frequency of intermittent stimulation described in the preceding section.

Brightness Enhancement

Another phenomenon that has not as yet been explicitly dealt with in photochemical theory is known as brightness enhancement (see Fig. 58). It is possible for an observer to match the brightness produced by a series of light pulses to the brightness produced by a steady light. This is done by adjusting the physical intensity of one or the other. For subfusional pulse rates it is found that the average physical intensity of intermittent light need not be so great as that of the continuous illumination in order to be equally effective. When the pulsation rate is in the neighborhood of 10 per second, en-

indicate that a major component of the optic-cortex response to light involves the same cortical elements as the alpha activity.

Relation between LDR and Cff

One of the most significant findings in this area is illustrated in Fig. 60, which shows a number of cases in which the light periods are long and the unstimulated (dark) periods are short, and vice versa. This information was taken from Fig. 59. The question is: why, with a fixed intensity of light pulse, may the LDR vary so greatly with only a small variation of cfi (critical flicker interval, or $1/cff$)?

The problem is to explain why a slight shortening of the light fraction of the cycle, when the fraction is great, produces flicker;

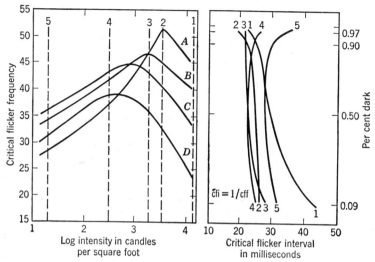

FIG. 59. *Left.* The relation between cff and stimulus intensity for four different light-dark ratios (LDR). Each curve represents a different LDR. *A* = 0.97 of cycle in darkness, *B* = 0.90, *C* = 0.50, and *D* = 0.09. When the intensity is raised, the cff increases to a peak and then declines. The dashed lines numbered from 1 to 5 represent points at which values on the ordinate were taken to plot curves 1 to 5 in the figure at the right. *Right.* The abscissa represents critical flicker interval (cfi), or 1/cff. The ordinate represents the percentage of the cycle occupied by the dark phase. Each curve is for a different pulse (flash) intensity. (Bartley, 1937.)

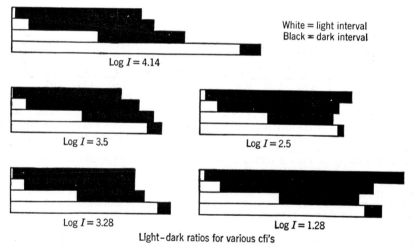

FIG. 60. The times occupied by the lighted and unlighted portions of the various cfi's represented in Fig. 59. For example, the dashed line labeled 4 in Fig. 59 cuts curves *A*, *B*, *C*, and *D* at the same intensity level (log *I* = 2.5). These curves represent closely similar cff's and cfi's. This fact is represented in the present figure by the closely similar lengths of the bars in the group labeled log *I* = 2.5. Each bar represents the actual cfi or the time occupied by a light-dark sequence (a "flicker cycle"). The white portion represents the light interval; the black portion represents the dark interval. Despite the closely similar values of cfi the fractions of the cycle occupied by the light and dark phases may be quite dissimilar. Thus for log *I* = 1.28, the cfi may be shorter when the light pulse occupies most of the cycle than when it occupies a trivial fraction of it. (Bartley, 1937.)

because no flicker exists when the light fraction in a cfi of almost the same length is very short. Figure 60 pictures cases of this kind for pulses of several different intensities. Although the results are not quite the

nation of this curious fact is that shortening the long pulse allows enough time for an *off* response to occur at each repetition of the cycle. This off response would be expected to result in flicker. An off response does not

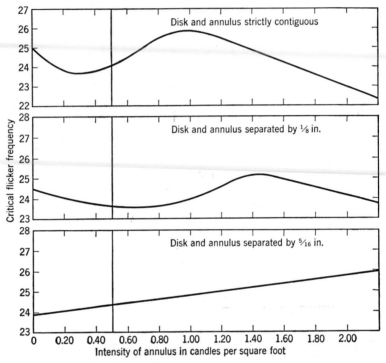

FIG. 61. The relation between the cff of an area and the intensity of a surrounding annulus. The Talbot brightness of the disk is indicated by the vertical line at 0.5 candle per square foot. The curves indicate that a steady stimulus applied to one area of the retina affects the cff of a stimulus in another region. As the intensity of the steady stimulus rises from zero the cff also rises, but it falls again when a critical point is reached. Apparently the steadily stimulated area depresses activity in the intermittently stimulated area. Below a critical intensity it depresses the weak phases of activity and thus raises the cff. Above this critical intensity it depresses the strong phases also and thus lowers the cff. When the distance between the two stimuli is sufficient, the critical intensity lies beyond the range investigated and no reversal appears. (Fry and Bartley, 1936.)

same for all intensities, the general principle just implied is pretty well illustrated in all the examples.

If, for a given cfi, the very short pulse just succeeds in eliminating flicker, it might be expected that a long pulse would provide more light than needed for fusion. But shortening the long pulse may abolish fusion and give rise to flicker. A possible expla-

occur when the light portion of the cycle is very short. On the other hand, short light pulses are able to produce uniform firing of impulses throughout the cfi's represented. Long light pulses certainly are able to do the same. They even provide for more rapid firing of impulses and induce sensations of greater brightness. But when these long pulses are shortened just enough for off responses to develop, the result is an alternation of *on* and *off* responses. This produces flicker.

Interarea Effects

A steady illumination of one part of the retina influences the activity in an adjacent portion illuminated intermittently. The results pictured in Fig. 61 indicate that, as the ferential between the weak and strong phases of the fluctuation cycle.

Another interarea effect of retinal stimulation shows up as contour formation. If the test object is a disk within an annulus, and if the disk is illuminated intermittently while the illumination of the annulus is kept constant, the following phenomena is observed. For flash frequencies below 10 per

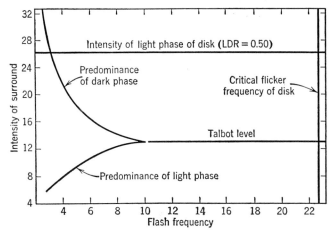

Fig. 62. The intensity of an annulus surrounding a flashing disk has certain effects on the disk's contour. If the intensity of the surround is above the Talbot level, the disk's dark phase is predominant and contoured, and the light phase is uncontoured. If the intensity of the surround is below the Talbot level, the light phase is predominant and contoured, and the dark phase is uncontoured. Cff for the disk is designated by the perpendicular at the extreme right. The Talbot level is the level of the steady stimulus that is equivalent to the flashing stimulus in effective brightness. (Bartley, 1939.)

intensity of the steady illumination (annulus) is raised from zero, the cff of an enclosed disk undergoes significant changes. As the distance between the two retinal areas involved is increased from zero, the intensity of the annulus for which the cff of the dish is maximal becomes greater and finally lies above the range of intensities tested. This phenomenon is taken to mean that the steadily stimulated area depresses the activity in the fluctuating area. Below the critical intensity it depresses the weak phases of activity and thereby raises the cff. Above the critical intensity the strong phases of the fluctuation cycle are depressed also, and the cff is lowered by diminution of the dif-

second, a predominance of either the dark or the light phase can be produced by changing the luminance of the annulus. If the intensity of the annulus surround is raised, the dark phase becomes predominant and contoured. If the intensity of the surround is dropped, the light phase is contoured. The results are pictured in Fig. 62. Beyond a frequency of 10 per second, both phases become partially fused.

If, with the test object just described, the flash rate is varied from low to high, a point is reached at which *both* the light and the dark phases are seen *simultaneously*, the one behind the other. The light phase appears as a translucent surface through which the dark phase is seen lying behind it. This is an example of how temporal factors in stimulation affect spatial factors in sensation.

OCULOMOTOR MECHA-NISMS

Oculomotor responses may be divided into three categories: (1) movements of the extrinsic eye muscles for convergence and for cyclofusional adjustments of the eyeballs; (2) accommodative processes in adjusting the lens for best focus; and (3) pupillary adjustments. The neural pathways involved in some of these processes were sketched in a previous section.

Convergence

Convergence, or the pointing of the two eyes at an object of regard occurs in conjunction with accommodation, or the focusing of the dioptic systems of the eyes. Normally there is some kind of "coupling" between the convergence and the accommodation mechanisms. Not all convergence is, however, induced by accommodation; part of it is supposedly brought about by a fusion center in the brain and is called fusional convergence. Some convergence is also supposed to be controlled by still other factors, but the isolation of these is not satisfactory at present.

Cyclofusional Movements

Cyclofusional movements of the two eyes to maintain single binocular vision can occur, particularly in forced optical conditions like those involved in vision through a stereoscope.

Suppose the eyes **are** fixating a line perpendicular to the line of regard and that the line appears vertical to the observer. The retinal images in the two eyes fall on corresponding points. If the top of the line is then tilted toward the observer, the retinal images are no longer vertical. Each has been displaced in an opposite direction around the axis of fixation, and the line should appear to be inclined (cf. Chapter 23). But this predicted appearance does not always occur. There is said to be a "compulsion" toward fusion of the two disparate retinal images, and this induces a cyclotorsional eye movement that compensates for the declination. The eyes rotate about their axes until the two images lie on corresponding points in the two retinas. This may obliterate the initial declination of the images and obliterate the *seen* inclination of the line. Such tendencies for the eyes to take compensatory positions must be recognized when we attempt to explain certain visual effects.

Accommodation

Theories of accommodation have, from time to time, proposed changes in the axial length of the eyeball, in the corneal curvature, or in the position of the crystalline lens to account for the changes in degree of blurredness of vision. Some writers have insisted that nothing but changes in axial length could account for certain phenomena in aphakic vision (vision without the lens, as in eyes that have undergone cataract removal). The more general tendency has been, however, to rely upon changes in the *curvature* of the lens to account for changes in the dioptric power of the eye. The three most prevalent theories of accommodation have been spoken of as the "hydraulic theory," the "theory of increased tension," and the "theory of decreased tension."

The hydraulic theory asserts that accommodation is accomplished by a properly balanced transfer of fluid from the front to the peripheral regions of the lens, brought about by the ciliary muscle. This causes the lens to become more convex.

According to the theory of increased tension, in distant vision the ciliary muscle is relaxed and the lens is free from stress. For the eye to focus on a near object, the ciliary mucle contracts and exerts pressure on the vitreous humor, thereby causing the lens to bulge.

The theory of decreased tension states that the capsule of the lens is elastic and under perpetual tension by the suspensory ligaments, even when the eye is focused on a distant object. Accommodation for a nearby object involves the contraction of the ciliary muscle. This counteracts the pull exerted by the suspensory ligaments upon the elastic lens, which is thereby permitted to assume a more highly curved form. This is Helmholtz's theory and is the one most prevalently held.

Each theory has its difficulties. The objections to them have led more recent investigators to look for reciprocal innervation in the ciliary muscle system. It now seems that this has been proved, although no sympathetic innervation of the ciliary muscle fibers has been disclosed. The latest theory postulates that the sympathetic system supplies a tonal background via vascular innervation and that it is upon this that increased or decreased innervation via the oculomotor nerve supplies the variations spoken of as positive and negative accommodation. The tonal background sets the "level" of accommodation, and the oculomotor nerve innervation provides the specific adjustments.

Pupillary Behavior

There are several considerations regarding pupillary light response that are pertinent here: (1) At what rate does the pupil constrict, when subjected to an increase in light intensity? (2) At what rate does the pupil dilate in the dark after exposure to various light intensities? (3) What are the expected pupillary apertures during protracted exposure to various levels? (4) What are some of the important factors evidencing relations between pupillary and sensory behavior? (5) What are the facts regarding pupillomotor areas in the retina? The following information from Talbot answers some of these questions.

Contraction of the pupil to pulses of light shows the following typical characteristics. Contraction begins at a latency of about 0.25 second. The contraction is at first very rapid, but at about 0.60 second a jog occurs. From there on the contraction slows up until at about 0.93 second a rebound or reversal carries the contraction to a value that is roughly maintained, except for irregular variations or oscillations. This picture may be described as one of overshooting. A second jog or irregularity in the curve of contraction at about 1 second is quite usual. With intermediate stimuli the response fails to develop a reversal, and after the first second the curve depicting pupillary behavior becomes quite flat. In general the reversal is over within 12 seconds. Some say that, for all durations of light pulse, equilibrium is arrived at within 6 seconds. Questions of this sort pertain only to long stimuli, however, whereas we are here concerned with the results of pulses of not more than 2.5 seconds.

Contraction latency is related to strength of stimulus, but only in a "statistical" manner. The course of the contraction varies systematically with the initial diameter of the pupil, independently of the strength of the stimulus or of the retinal adaptive state. Contraction always displays the same general form, regardless of the shortness of the stimulating pulse. There is a minimum duration of the contraction beyond which it does not diminish, regardless of the shortness of the pulse. This seems to be of the order of 1.1 seconds for a pulse producing a contraction of 1.5 millimeters. Speed of contraction is apparently not a reliable feature of the pupillary response. Naturally the response to intense light diminishes when the initial pupillary aperture is smaller, for the pupil is already nearer its minimum aperture value.

The pupillary response depends upon the size and location of the retinal area stimulated. The macula seems to have ten times the pupillomotor sensitivity possessed by areas 10 degrees from the fovea. The area of the retina stimulated must be increased faster than the intensity is decreased in order for the amplitude of the pupillary response to remain constant.

The first jog in the course of the pupillary contraction occurs earlier as the initial size of the pupil diminishes. The latency of the first jog does not vary systematically with stimulus strength as do the second jog and the latency of the initial contraction. This points to an independent mechanism for the

Then the stimulus patch was illuminated for 1 second, at the end of which a picture was taken. Four pictures were taken at the end of successive 7-second intervals. For these the same test-object area was used, but different intensities of illumination were employed. The adapting conditions were then repeated, and three additional pictures were taken at the same time intervals. Thus,

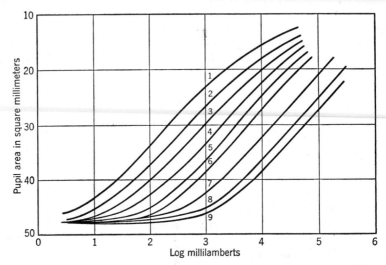

FIG. 63. Pupil area as a function of intensity for foveal stimulation by test objects of different sizes. The radii of the test objects in minutes of angle subtended are as follows: 1 = 30.6, 2 = 17.9, 3 = 12.7, 4 = 8.21, 5 = 4.86, 6 = 3.0, 7 = 2.03, 8 = 1.28, and 9 = 0.97. The values obtained are those produced by flashes 1 second in duration and represent maximum constrictions for the stimuli used. (Page, 1941.)

first jog. The second jog also arises earlier as the initial size of the pupil increases.

Dilation latency appears generally to be shorter with small initial pupil sizes, and to be more or less independent of the intensity change producing it. Light adaptation also reduces pupillary sensitivity, and much greater intensity is necessary for a given amplitude of response.

As an answer to question 3 concerning the relation of light intensity to pupil size, we have the work of Page, which is illustrated in Fig. 63. The subjects were light adapted for 15 seconds. This was followed by 105 seconds of dark adaptation prior to the taking of the first photograph of the pupil.

seven pictures, each at a different stimulus intensity, were taken for each of the nine different test objects whose radii subtended visual angles ranging from 0.97 second of arc to 30.6 seconds of arc. The right eye alone was measured, and the left eye was left uncovered. The order of taking pictures was always from the smallest area and the lowest intensity upward. The whole procedure was repeated twenty times for each of the subjects.

Figure 64 shows the earlier results of Reeves in which he plotted the relation between pupil size and level of illumination. Although Reeves' data did not cover the same intensity range, the shape of the curve in Fig. 64 is somewhat similar to that of curves obtained by Page. Reeves used full-field illumination, rather than small test objects, and he preadapted his subjects to 15

A Pupillary Parallel to Brightness Sensation

An investigation that has disclosed a fundamental property of pupillary behavior made use of the fact that a pupil exposed

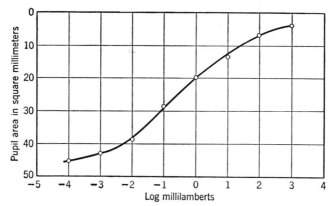

FIG. 64. Relation between pupil size (area) and level of general illumination. (From the data of Reeves, 1920.)

minutes of darkness before subjecting them to the test levels.

Figure 65 shows how the area of the pupil changes with the duration of the illumination.

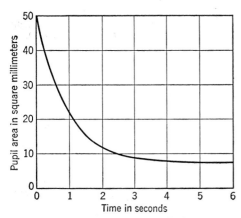

FIG. 65. Relation between pupil area and duration of exposure to light of 100 millilamberts. (From Reeves, 1920.)

Exposure of one eye alone to light induces constriction of both pupils. The constriction in the unexposed eye is called the *consensual reflex.*

to a sequence of increasing light intensities can be photographed in infrared illumination and the course of its constriction can be plotted. When a high intensity had been reached *in one eye,* it was maintained in that eye and the *corresponding area* of the other retina was exposed to the same sequence of intensities. These increments of light, added via the second eye, did not at first induce further constriction. Instead they resulted in dilatation. But as more and more light was added, the dilatation reached a peak and then subsided. The ultimate result was a constriction beyond the amount existing at the moment of initial stimulation of the second retina. For a picture of this, see Fig. 66. This is an oculomotor parallel of Fechner's paradox.

Fechner's paradox is the sensory result when two eyes are independently exposed to *unequal* amounts of light. When the light falls on corresponding areas of the two retinas, it is seen as a single light or object. But instead of the stimulation of the two eyes combining to yield a brighter object, it results in an object (or surface) whose brightness level lies somewhere between the

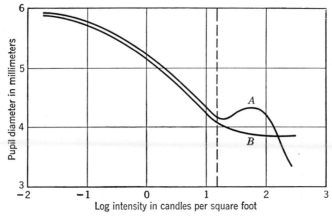

Fig. 66. The relation between pupil diameter and intensity of a disk test object. Curve A indicates the behavior when part of the light is presented to one eye and the remainder is then presented to the other eye. The broken perpendicular line indicates the level reached by the stimulus to the first eye before the presentation of light to the second eye. In each eye the illumination was at first feeble and was increased step by step. The light presented to the second eye evoked dilatation at first. Curve B indicates pupil behavior when all the light was given to one eye. (Bartley, 1943.)

brightnesses of the two lights seen separately. On the other hand, when the intensities of the stimuli to both eyes are equal, the combined subjective effect is greater than from one stimulus alone.

Actually the sequence of events in the pupillary response described above results not only from stimulating *corresponding* areas of the two retinas but also from stimulating *noncorresponding* areas. In fact, essentially the same pattern of behavior accrues from the stimulation of two areas on the same retina.

REFERENCES

Bartley, S. Howard. The neural determination of critical flicker frequency. *J. exp. Psychol.,* 1937, **21,** 678–686.

Bartley, S. Howard. Subjective brightness in relation to flash rate and the light-dark ratio. *J. exp. Psychol.,* 1938a, **23,** 313–319.

Bartley, S. Howard. Subjective flicker rate with relation to critical flicker frequency. *J. exp. Psychol.,* 1938b, **22,** 338–349.

Bartley, S. Howard. Some factors in brightness discrimination. *Psychol. Rev.,* 1939, **46,** 337–358.

Bartley, S. Howard. *Vision: A study of its basis.* New York: Van Nostrand, 1941.

Bartley, S. Howard. The features of the optic nerve discharge underlying recurrent vision. *J. exp. Psychol.,* 1942, **30,** 125–135.

Bartley, S. Howard. Some parallels between pupillary 'reflexes' and brightness discrimination. *J. exp. Psychol.,* 1943, **32,** 110–122.

Bartley, S. Howard. Studying vision. In T. G. Andrews (Ed.), *Methods in psychology.* New York: Wiley, 1948.

Bartley, S. Howard, and E. Chute. *Fatigue and impairment in man.* New York: McGraw-Hill, 1947.

Beebe-Center, J. G., L. Carmichael, and L. C. Mead. Daylight training of pilots for night flying. *Aeronaut. Eng. Rev.,* 1944, **3,** 1–10.

Bishop, G. H. Fiber groups in the optic nerve. *Amer. J. Physiol.,* 1933, **106,** 460–474.

Bishop, G. H., and J. L. O'Leary. Potential records from the optic cortex of the cat. *J. Neurophysiol.,* 1938, **1,** 391–401.

Bishop, G. H., and J. L. O'Leary. Electrical activity of the lateral geniculate of cats following optic nerve stimuli. *J. Neurophysiol.,* 1940, **3,** 308–322.

Blackwell, H. R. Contrast thresholds of the human eye. *J. opt. Soc. Amer.,* 1946, **36,** 624–643.

Brown, R. H., and J. I. Niven. The relation between the foveal intensity threshold and length of an illuminated slit. *J. exp. Psychol.,* 1944, **34,** 464–476.

Byram, Geo. M. Physical and photochemical basis of visual resolving power. II. *J. opt. Soc. Amer.,* 1944, **34,** 718–738.

Chapanis, A. The dark adaptation of the color anomalous measured with lights of different hues. *J. gen. Physiol.,* 1947, **30,** 423–437.

Coleman, H. H., and M. F. Coleman. Theoretical resolution angles for point and line test objects in the presence of a luminous background. *J. opt. Soc. Amer.,* 1947, **37,** 572–576.

Crozier, W. J., and E. Wolf. The flicker response contour for the gecko (rod retina). *J. gen. Physiol.*, 1939a, **22**, 555–566.

Crozier, W. J., and E. Wolf. Flicker response curve for the crayfish I. *J. gen. Physiol.*, 1939b, **23**, 1–10.

Crozier, W. J., and E. Wolf. The flicker response contour for the frog. *J. gen. Physiol.*, 1939c, **23**, 229–237.

Crozier, W. J., and E. Wolf. The flicker response curve for *Fundulus*. *J. gen. Physiol.*, 1940, **23**, 677–694.

Crozier, W. J., and E. Wolf. The flicker response contour for *Phrynosoma* (horned lizard; cone retina). *J. gen. Physiol.*, 1941, **24**, 317–324.

Crozier, W. J., and E. Wolf. The wavelength sensitivity function for the zebra finch. *J. gen. Physiol.*, 1942, **25**, 381–390.

Crozier, W. J., E. Wolf, and G. Zerrahn-Wolf. On critical frequency and critical illumination for response to flickered light. *J. gen. Physiol.*, 1936, **20**, 211–228.

Crozier, W. J., E. Wolf, and G. Zerrahn-Wolf. Critical illumination and flicker frequency in related fishes. *J. gen. Physiol.*, 1937a, **21**, 17–56.

Crozier, W. J., E. Wolf, and G. Zerrahn-Wolf. Intensity and critical frequency for visual flicker. *J. gen. Physiol.*, 1937b, **21**, 203–221.

Crozier, W. J., E. Wolf, and G. Zerrahn-Wolf. Critical illumination and flicker frequency as a function of flash duration: for the sunfish. *J. gen. Physiol.*, 1938a, **21**, 313–334.

Crozier, W. J., E. Wolf, and G. Zerrahn-Wolf. Critical intensity and flash duration for the response to flicker: with *Anax* larvae. *J. gen. Physiol.*, 1938b, **21**, 463–474.

Crozier, W. J., E. Wolf, and G. Zerrahn-Wolf. Temperature and the critical intensity for response to visual flicker. *Proc. nat. Acad. Sci., Wash.*, 1938c, **24**, 216–221.

Crozier, W. J., E. Wolf, and G. Zerrahn-Wolf. The flicker response curve for the turtle *Pseudemys*. *J. gen. Physiol.*, 1939a, **22**, 311–340.

Crozier, W. J., E. Wolf, and G. Zerrahn-Wolf. The flicker response contour for the isopod *Asellus*. *J. gen. Physiol.*, 1939b, **22**, 451–462.

Fry, G. A. Photoreceptor mechanism for the modulation theory of color vision. *J. opt. Soc. Amer.*, 1945, **35**, 114–135.

Fry, G. A., and Matthew Alpern. Theoretical implication of the response of a photoreceptor to a flash of light. *Amer. J. Optom.*, 1946, **23**, 509–525.

Fry, G. A., and S. H. Bartley. The effect of steady stimulation of one part of the retina upon the critical flicker frequency in another. *J. exp. Psychol.*, 1936, **19**, 351–356.

Fry, G. A., and P. W. Cobb. A new method of determining the blurredness of the retinal image. *Trans. Amer. Acad. Ophthal. Otolaryng.*, 1935, **40**, 423–428.

Graham, C. H. Vision III. Some neural correlations. In C. Murchison (Ed.), *Handbook of general experimental psychology*. Worcester: Clark University Press, 1934.

Graham, C. H., and N. R. Bartlett. The relation of size of stimulus and intensity in the human eye: III. The influence of area on foveal intensity discrimination. *J. exp. Psychol.*, 1940, **27**, 149–159.

Graham, C. H., R. H. Brown, and F. A. Mote, Jr. The relation of size of stimulus and intensity in the human eye: I. Intensity thresholds for white light. *J. exp. Psychol.*, 1939, **24**, 555–573.

Graham, C. H., and H. K. Hartline. The response of single visual cells to lights of different wave lengths. *J. gen. Physiol.*, 1935, **18**, 917–931.

Granit, R. The components of the retinal action potentials in mammals and their relation to the discharge in the optic nerve. *J. Physiol.*, 1933, **77**, 207–239.

Granit, R. Rotation of activity and spontaneous rhythms in the retina. *Acta Physiol. Scandinav.*, 1941, **1**, 370–379.

Granit, R. A physiological theory of colour perception. *Nature, Lond.*, 1943, **151**, 11–14.

Granit, R. The color receptors of the mammalian retina. *J. Neurophysiol.*, 1945, **8**, 195–210.

Griffin, D. R., R. Hubbard, and G. Wald. The sensitivity of the human eye to infra-red radiation. *J. opt. Soc. Amer.*, 1947, **37**, 546–554.

Hartline, H. K. Intensity and duration in the excitation of single photoreceptor units. *J. cell. comp. Physiol.*, 1934, **5**, 229–247.

Hartline, H. K. The response of single optic nerve fibers of the vertebrate eye to illumination of the retina. *Amer. J. Physiol.*, 1938, **121**, 400–415.

Hartline, H. K. Nerve messages in the fibers of the visual pathway. *J. opt. Soc. Amer.*, 1940, **30**, 239–247.

Hartline, H. K., and C. H. Graham. Nerve impulses from single receptors in the eye. *J. cell. comp. Physiol.*, 1932, **1**, 277–295.

Hartridge, H. The visual perception of fine detail. *Philos. Trans.*, 1947, **B232**, 519–671.

Hartridge, H. Recent advances in color vision. *Science*, 1948, **108**, 395–404.

Hecht, S. Vision II. The nature of the photoreceptor process. In C. Murchison (Ed.), *Handbook of general experimental psychology*. Worcester: Clark University Press, 1934.

Hecht, S. A theory of visual intensity discrimination. *J. gen. Physiol.*, 1935, **18**, 767–789.

Hecht, S. The nature of the visual process. *Bull. N. Y. Acad. Med.*, 1938, **14**, 21–45.

Hecht, S., C. Haig, and A. M. Chase. The influence of light adaptation on subsequent dark adaptation of the eye. *J. gen. Physiol.*, 1937, **20**, 831–850.

Hecht, S., C. Haig, and G. Wald. Dark adaptation of retinal fields of different size and location. *J. gen. Physiol.*, 1935, **19**, 321–337.

Hecht, S., C. D. Hendley, S. R. Frank, and C. Haig. Anoxia and brightness discrimination. *J. gen. Physiol.*, 1946, **29**, 335–351.

Hecht, S., and E. U. Mintz. The visibility of single lines at various illuminations and the retinal basis of visual resolution. *J. gen. Physiol.,* 1939, **22,** 593–612.

Hecht, S., J. C. Peskin, and M. Patt. Intensity discrimination in the human eye. II. Relation between $\Delta I/I$ and intensity for different parts of the spectrum. *J. gen. Physiol.,* 1938, **22,** 7–19.

Hecht, S., and S. Shlaer. Intermittent stimulation by light. V. The relation between intensity and critical flicker frequency for different parts of the spectrum. *J. gen. Physiol.,* 1936, **19,** 965–977.

Hecht, S., S. Shlaer, and M. H. Pirenne. Energy at the threshold of vision. *Science,* 1941, **93,** 585–587.

Hecht, S., and E. L. Smith. Intermittent stimulation by light. VI. Area and relation between critical frequency and intensity. *J. gen. Physiol.,* 1936, **19,** 979–988.

Hecht, S., and E. Wolf. Intermittent stimulation by light. I. The validity of Talbot's law for *Mya. J. gen. Physiol.,* 1932, **15,** 369–389.

Hecht, S., and Yun Hsia. Dark adaptation following light adaptation to red and white lights. *J. opt. Soc. Amer.,* 1945, **35,** 261–267.

Helmholtz, H. von. *Physiological optics.* (Translated by J. P. C. Southall from the 3rd German edition.) Optical Society of America, 1924. Volumes I, II, and III.

Holway, A. H., and L. M. Hurvich. Visual differential sensitivity and retinal area. *Amer. J. Psychol.,* 1938, **51,** 687–694.

Jahn, T. L. Visual critical flicker frequency as a function of intensity. *J. opt. Soc. Amer.,* 1946a, **36,** 76–82.

Jahn, T. L. Color vision and color blindness: A mechanism in terms of modern evidence. *J. opt. Soc. Amer.,* 1946b, **36,** 595–597.

Jahn, T. L. The kinetics of visual dark adaptation. *J. opt. Soc. Amer.,* 1946c, **36,** 659–665.

Klüver, Heinrich. *Visual mechanisms* (Biological symposia VII). Lancaster: Jaques Cattell, 1942.

Lamar, E. S., S. Hecht, S. Shlaer, and C. D. Hendley. Size, shape and contrast in detection of targets by daylight vision. I. Data and analytical description. *J. opt. Soc. Amer.,* 1947, **37,** 531–545.

Moon, P., and D. E. Spencer. On the Stiles-Crawford effect. *J. opt. Soc. Amer.,* 1944, **34,** 319–329.

Niven, J. I., and R. H. Brown. Visual resolution as a function of intensity and exposure time in the human fovea. *J. opt. Soc. Amer.,* 1944, **34,** 738–743.

O'Brien, Brian. Theory of the Stiles-Crawford effect. *J. opt. Soc. Amer.,* 1946, **36,** 506–509.

O'Leary, J. L. A structural analysis of the lateral geniculate nucleus of the cat. *J. comp. Neurol.,* 1940, **73,** 405–430.

Østerberg, G. Topography of the layer of rods and cones in the human retina. *Acta Ophthal. Suppl.,* 1935, **61,** 1–102.

Page, H. E. The relation between area of stimulation and intensity of light at various levels of visual excitation as measured by pupil constriction. *J. exp. Psychol.,* 1941, **29,** 177–200.

Polyak, S. L. *The retina.* Chicago: University of Chicago Press, 1941.

Reeves, P. The response of the average pupil to various intensities of light. *J. opt. Soc. Amer.,* 1920, **4,** 35–43.

Riggs, L. A., and C. H. Graham. Some aspects of light adaptation in a single photoreceptor unit. *J. cell. comp. Physiol.,* 1940, **16,** 15–23.

Riggs, L. A., and C. H. Graham. Effects due to variations in light intensity on the excitability cycle of the single visual sense cell. *J. cell. comp. Physiol.,* 1945, **26,** 1–13.

Sheard, C. Dark adaptation. *J. opt. Soc. Amer.,* 1944, **34,** 464–508.

Shlaer, S. The relation between visual acuity and illumination. *J. gen. Physiol.,* 1937, **21,** 165–188.

Shlaer, S., E. L. Smith, and A. M. Chase. Visual acuity and illumination in different spectral regions. *J. gen. Physiol.,* 1942, **25,** 553–569.

Steinhardt, J. Intensity discrimination in the human eye. I. The relation of $\Delta I/I$ to intensity. *J. gen. Physiol.,* 1936, **20,** 185–209.

Stiles, W. S., and B. H. Crawford. The luminous efficiency of rays entering the eye pupil at different points. *Proc. roy. Soc.,* 1933, **B112,** 428–450.

Stiles, W. S., and B. H. Crawford. The liminal brightness increment for white light for different conditions of the foveal and parafoveal retina. *Proc. roy. Soc.,* 1934, **B116,** 55–102.

Talbot, S. A. *Pupillography and the pupillary transient.* Ph.D. thesis, Harvard University, 1938.

Troland, L. T. Vision I. Visual phenomena and their visual correlates. In C. Murchison (Ed.), *Handbook of general experimental psychology.* Worcester: Clark University Press, 1934.

Wald, George. Area and visual threshold. *J. gen. Physiol.,* 1938, **21,** 269–287.

Wald, George, and A. B. Clark. Visual adaptation and the chemistry of the rods. *J. gen. Physiol.,* 1937, **21,** 93–105.

Walls, G. L. *The vertebrate eye.* Bloomfield Hills, Mich.: Cranbrook Institute of Science, 1942.

Walls, G. L. Factors in human visual resolution. *J. opt. Soc. Amer.,* 1943, **33,** 487–505.

Wilcox, W. W. The basis of the dependence of visual acuity on illumination. *Proc. nat. Acad. Sci., Wash.,* 1932, **18,** 47–56.

Wolf, E. Effects of exposure to ultra-violet light on subsequent dark adaptation. *Proc. nat. Acad. Sci., Wash.,* 1945, **31,** 349–355.

25·

Basic Correlates of the
Auditory Stimulus

J. C. R. LICKLIDER
Massachusetts Institute of Technology

In hearing, as in other fields of psychology, the problem has been to understand the stimulus. Our aims in the first part of this chapter will therefore be to consider a few of the fundamental characteristics of sound vibrations and to develop a language that will allow us to describe them effectively.

Waveform

When the diaphragm of a loudspeaker vibrates to and fro, it alternately compresses the air and allows it to expand. The pressure built up, during compression, in the layer of air next to the diaphragm is passed on to more distant layers, and waves travel out from the loudspeaker. In this process the air particles themselves do not move far from their original positions, but the sound wave — the compression and the rarefaction — travels far and fast. In air at ordinary temperatures the speed of sound is a little over 1100 feet per second (330 to 340 meters per second). These sound waves strike our eardrums and become the stimulus to hearing. They can be recorded with the aid of a microphone fitted with a narrow probe tube, the end of which we can place within a millimeter of the eardrum. By plotting the alternating sound pressure as a function of

This chapter was prepared at the Psycho-Acoustic Laboratory, Harvard University, under contract with the U. S. Navy, Office of Naval Research (Contract N5ori-76, Project NR142-201, Report PNR-78).

time, we obtain a representation of the acoustic stimulus that we shall call the *pressure waveform at the eardrum.*

Recording the pressure variations near the eardrum has the advantage of getting us near the auditory receptors, but we purchase this advantage at a price. First, the measurement is difficult to make. Second, we do not yet have probe microphones that give us faithful reproductions of complex sound waves. And third, what we measure in this way depends to some extent upon the characteristics of the eardrum.

An alternative method of specifying the sound pressure as a function of time achieves independence of the listener's characteristics by getting him out of the way so that the measurements can be made in a free sound field, i.e. in an anechoic (echo-free) space like that shown in Fig. 1. The sound pressure is measured at the point at which the center of the listener's head was, or where it will be when he returns to serve as a subject. The resulting graph of pressure against time is the *free-field pressure waveform.*

Although the sound pressure is what we usually measure, it is by no means the only aspect of the sound vibration. We might equally well plot, as a function of time, the displacement of the air particles from their normal positions (*displacement waveform*) or the velocity of their vibratory motion

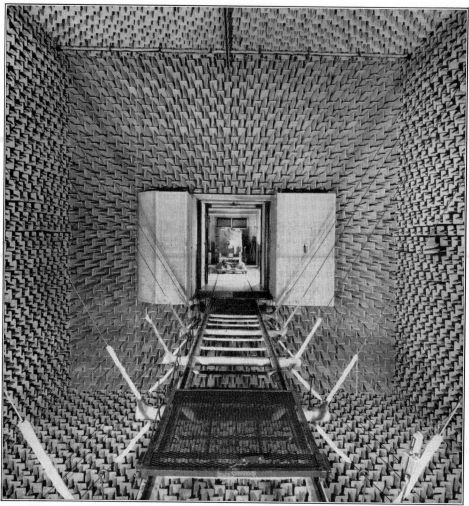

FIG. 1. An anechoic chamber for research in acoustics and hearing. The wedge-shaped fingers protruding from the floor, ceiling, and walls are of Fiberglas, covered with muslin. As sound waves approach the boundaries of the room, they are trapped, as it were, in the fibrous, weblike structure of the wedges. Since very little sound is reflected, echoes and standing waves are negligible. The chamber provides the 'free-field' conditions that are required for many of the fundamental measurements in psychoacoustics. (From Beranek, Sleeper, and Moots, 1945.)

(*velocity waveform*). But — and herein lies the beauty of the situation — if we know the properties of the medium, all three waveforms give us the same information. In a free field the pressure waveform and the velocity waveform of a plane wave are identical in shape, and the displacement waveform is the time integral of either of the other two.

The waveform represents a *time analysis* of the acoustic signal. It has two dimensions, *amplitude* (which we shall use as a general term for pressure, velocity, or displacement) and *time*. The information it contains is all we need in order to specify the stimulus to (monaural) hearing. It is not, however, the only form in which this information can be presented.

Spectrum

An alternative method, based on *frequency analysis*, stems from the discovery by Fourier (1822) that any waveform of the type with which we shall be concerned can be analyzed into, or synthesized from, a series of sinusoidal waveforms. We must,

angle. The frequency is the number of to-and-fro oscillations per unit time: it is specified in cycles per second (cps). The Amplitude is the maximum displacement from the zero position. And the phase angle, which has meaning only in relation to an arbitrarily selected reference instant, des-

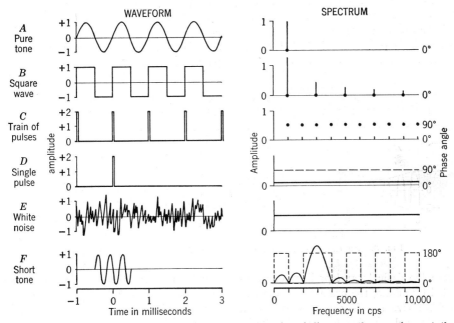

FIG. 2. Waveforms and spectra. In each of the six pairs of diagrams the waveform at the left showing amplitude as a function of time provides exactly the same information as the spectrum at the right showing both Amplitude and phase angle as functions of frequency. The waveform graphs are to be thought of as extending indefinitely in both directions. The spectrum graphs are to be thought of as extending indefinitely to the right. Amplitude (solid lines) is specified in arbitrary units, and phase angle (dashed lines or heavy dots) in degrees.

therefore, examine the properties of sinusoidal waves with some care.

The word *sinusoidal* refers to the class of simple harmonic motions — the most elementary vibratory motions — of which the sine wave (*A* in Fig. 2) is the most familiar member.

Any sinusoidal wave may be described in terms of three characteristics: its frequency, its maximum Amplitude,* and its phase

ignates the part of its cycle in which, at the reference instant, a point on the wave finds itself.† In order to have a convenient method of specifying the phase, we divide the full cycle into 360 degrees or 2π radians, beginning with the upward crossing of the zero line. If the reference time ($t = 0$) falls at the beginning of a cycle (0 degrees) as it does in Fig. 2A, we refer to the sinusoid as a *sine wave*. If $t = 0$ corresponds to the

---

* The maximum amplitude (Amplitude) will be distinguished from the varying instantaneous amplitude (amplitude), the capital letter 'A' being used for the former, the lower case 'a' for the latter.

† In the expression $a = A \sin (2\pi ft + \phi)$, **the** whole quantity $2\pi ft + \phi$ is the instantaneous phase angle. It is the constant part ϕ to which we refer here as the third parameter of the sinusoid.

maximum of the waveform (phase angle of 90 degrees), we refer to the wave as a *cosine wave*. If neither of these coincidences occurs, we state the phase angle at $t = 0$ in degrees or in radians.

The task of frequency analysis is to break up a complex wave into sinusoidal components of various frequencies, then to represent the complex wave in terms of the Amplitudes and the phases of the components. This process is illustrated in Fig. 3. The complex waveform that oscillates

are sine waves (zero phase angle at time $t = 0$).

Relation between Waveform and Spectrum

The spectrum, with its three dimensions (frequency, Amplitude, and phase), describes the wave completely and uniquely, just as does the waveform with its two dimensions (amplitude and time). Almost always, however, one or the other of the two representations is the more convenient for a given purpose. Consequently the conversions from

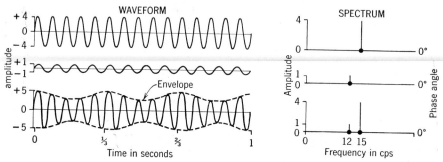

FIG. 3. An example of the transformation from waveform to spectrum.

between the dashed *envelope* lines was constructed by adding the ordinates of the two sinusoids above it. In order to perform a frequency analysis, therefore, we break the complex wave down into its components (photoelectric and mechanical analyzers and purely mathematical methods have been developed for this purpose). For each component we describe the frequency, the Amplitude, and the phase angle at time $t = 0$. The representation of the complex wave in terms of its spectrum is then obtained by placing the component spectra side by side, as in the lower right-hand corner of the figure. The vertical lines are located at 12 and 15 cps on the frequency scale because there are 12 full cycles of one wave and 15 of the other in each second. The heights of the lines indicate the Amplitudes of the sinusoidal components, and the fact that the heavy dots are side by side on the zero line indicates that the two components

waveform to spectrum and from spectrum to waveform, called the Fourier transformations, are important tools in the study of hearing. We cannot, here, go into the mathematical details of the process, but we can extend our intuitive grasp of the problem by examining the paired diagrams of Fig. 2.

We have already considered the sine wave A with its periodic oscillations and its single-component spectrum. We note now that the square wave has as one of its components a sinusoid of the same frequency and phase as that of A, but of slightly greater Amplitude. Added to this fundamental component (first harmonic) are a series of higher harmonics, sinusoids with frequencies equal to integral multiples of the fundamental frequency. Note that, in this particular instance, the multipliers are all odd integers: the frequencies are 1000, 3 times 1000, 5 times 1000, etc. Note also that the harmonics are all sine waves (0-degree phase angle), and that their Amplitudes are inversely proportional to their frequencies. In order to give an accurate graphical representation of the spectrum of the square wave, we would have to extend the figure indefinitely to the right because, although the high-frequency components are very weak, all the odd harmonics would be present in an ideal square wave. Ideal square waves never occur in nature, because air particles have finite mass and hence cannot be given the infinite acceleration that the square corners on the wave imply.

It is of interest to compare the train of pulses (*C* in Fig. 2) with the square wave on the one hand and with the single pulse on the other. The train of pulses has even harmonics as well as odd, the components are cosine waves (90-degree phase angle) instead of sine waves, and, to a first approximation, all the harmonics shown in the figure are equally strong — or, more aptly, equally weak. The presence of even harmonics in the pulse spectrum is related to the fact that the pulse waveform does not oscillate about the center axis in a self-balancing way as the square wave does, and the presence of cosine components instead of sine components is due to the fact that the waveform is symmetrical about a vertical line through time $t = 0$. The uniformity of the pulse spectrum is related to the brevity of the pulses. By making the pulses short enough, we can make the spectrum as nearly uniform as we please up to any desired frequency.

Even if we have only one pulse (Fig. 2D), the spectrum is still uniform. Now, however, it consists not of concentrations of energy at particular frequencies, but of a continuous distribution of energy along the frequency scale. This is called a *continuous spectrum*, whereas the spectra of the sine wave, the square wave, and the train of pulses are called *line spectra*. The Amplitude scale of the single-pulse spectrum is not calibrated because apportioning the energy of the single pulse among an infinitude of

frequency components leaves only an infinitesimal Amplitude for each component. The phase-angle scale, however, can be labeled as before; all the components are cosine waves.

White noise (Fig. 2E), or random fluctuation noise as it is often called, is of peculiar significance because it is always present. The thermal movements of the molecules of the air produce a noise that is only a little too weak to be audible. The fluctuations of electrons in conductors and in vacuum tubes give rise to the familiar 'hiss' of radio sets and public address systems. The distribution of instantaneous amplitudes in the waveform follows the normal distribution curve. The spectrum is uniform in Amplitude and random in phase. One way to picture the relation between the waveform and the spectrum is to think of superimposing an infinitude of waves, each of a different frequency. Because there is no orderly phase relation among the sinusoids, they reinforce one another or cancel one another in an entirely haphazard way.

Finally, the short tone (Fig. 2F). One of the reasons why short tones are of practical importance in research on hearing is that, in an actual experiment, we cannot present a stimulus for the eternity that would be required to make a pure tone ideally a *pure* tone. Whenever we turn it on or off, we sully its purity. Whenever we change its frequency or its Amplitude or its phase, we spread energy along the frequency scale. The spectrum of Fig. 2F is an example. Instead of finding the energy concentrated at 3000 cps, as we might expect since there are 3 cycles in 1 millisecond, we find an almost continuous distribution of energy from 0 to 10,000 cps. This is, admittedly, an extreme case; for longer tones the spectral energy is concentrated more closely around a center frequency. But the essential fact remains: whenever we change anything about a pure tone, we cease to have an ideally pure tone.

Power Spectrum and the Autocorrelation Function

The spectrum of white noise, we have seen, contains the same (infinitesimal) amount of energy at each frequency within the frequency interval under consideration, but the phase angles of the component sinusoids are distributed at random. In dealing with signals like white noise, therefore, we can adopt a representation that omits information concerning phase. Such a representation is achieved by giving the mean-square amplitude instead of the Amplitude and the phase of each of the components. Since, in resistive media, power is proportional to the square of amplitude, the plot of mean-square amplitude against frequency is called the *power spectrum*. Note that, because the spectrum of white noise is uniform within the interval represented in Fig. 2E, the substitution of the mean-square amplitude for the maximum amplitude of the components changes the picture only to the extent that the ordinate scale must be relabeled.

An alternative way of expressing the information contained in the power spectrum is to give the *autocorrelation function* of the waveform. The autocorrelation function is obtained by drawing the waveform twice, the second time below the first, and determining the correlation between corresponding ordinates of the two curves. If the second waveform is directly below the first, the correlation is, of course, unity. If, however, the second waveform is shifted in time relative to the first by an amount τ_i, the correlation in general becomes less than unity. The correlation between the original wave and the shifted wave, plotted against the amount of the shift, τ, gives us a useful picture of the signal. This plot relating r (the coefficient of correlation) to τ (the shift) is the normalized autocorrelation function. It is called normalized to distinguish it from the closely related function that relates the mean square product of the original and the shifted waveforms to the amount of the shift. The latter, called the

unnormalized autocorrelation function, is equal to the former multiplied by the mean square ordinate of the original wave and is the Fourier transform of the power spectrum. It thus bears to the power spectrum the same relation that the waveform bears to the spectrum that specifies Amplitude and phase.

In Fig. 2E, for example, we see that the waveform zigzags up and down so rapidly that the correlation between the original wave and the same wave shifted by even a small amount will almost certainly approach zero in the long run: there is practically no relation between the amplitude at one instant and the amplitude a short time later. In an ideal random noise, with its power spectrum uniform to indefinitely high frequency, there would be *no* relation. This means that the autocorrelation function derived from the waveform to Fig. 2E will drop from unity, for zero shift, to zero for any appreciable shift. The autocorrelation function for white noise will therefore have approximately the same shape as the waveform shown in Fig. 2D. To check the rule that the power spectrum is the Fourier transform of the autocorrelation function, we can compare the spectrum of 2D, which is the Fourier transform of the waveform of 2D and thus the Fourier transform of the autocorrelation function of the waveform of 2E, with the spectrum of 2E. We find that they are both horizontal lines. Since the ordinate scales of both graphs are arbitrary, the two horizontal lines are functionally identical, and the rule is checked. Autocorrelational methods are being used more and more widely in communication and related fields. A comprehensive discussion of them is given by Wiener (1949b).

Steps and Pulses as Elemental Waveforms

In addition to the method of representing a complex waveform as the sum of a number of elementary sinusoidal components, there are other methods in which the elements are nonsinusoidal. In the 1880's,

Oliver Heaviside worked out a method of analyzing the characteristics of communication lines and cables with transient instead of steady test signals. His elemental waveform was a single, abrupt step of amplitude, like the rise or fall of a square wave. Any complex wave can be regarded as the result of superimposing a sufficient number of such step-waves, for any curve can be approximated as closely as desired by a stairstep pattern. Studying the mathematical foundation of Heaviside's method, J. R. Carson (1920) showed that it was closely related to a way of representing mathematical functions that had been developed by Laplace. In Laplace's calculus, the elemental waveform is an impulse (cf. Fig. 2D) of negligible duration but with sufficient amplitude to make the area under the curve equal to unity. Because of their roles in the operational calculus, which has been developed around the methods of Heaviside and Laplace, acoustic stimuli consisting of steps and impulses are of interest in experiments on hearing.

Intensity-Frequency-Time Patterns

As we have seen, the waveform deals with instants in time and says not a word about frequency; the spectrum deals with points along a frequency scale and fails to distinguish between events that happen at different instants in time. Although time analysis and frequency analysis have provided the foundation upon which the science of communication has grown, neither method bears a one-to-one correspondence with the actual behavior of any physical analyzing system. No physical system can single out and record the event of a mathematical instant, and no physical system can wait the eternity required for the isolation of a mathematical sinusoid.* What we should like to have in the study of hearing

* The cathode-ray oscillograph provides what is for our purposes an excellent approximation to time analysis, and the harmonic wave analyzer or narrow-band filter performs a reasonably good frequency analysis. Neither is perfect.

is a compromise method of analysis, a method that would represent sounds the way we hear them. Such a method must distinguish to some extent between events occurring successively in time (sounds follow one another in auditory experience) and must distinguish also between signals that differ in frequency (a 1000-cycle tone sounds quite different from a 2000-cycle tone).

The musical notation is, of course, just such a method of describing patterns of sound in frequency and in time. It is better for art than for science, however, for it leaves a great deal to the imagination of the interpreter. For the purpose of describing auditory stimuli, we need a notation that allows us to set down in unambiguous form all the relevant information. We can get an idea of how we might achieve this goal by considering a simple model.

The standard at the left-hand side of Fig. 4 carries a series of weighted springs. All the springs are equally stiff, and all the damping constants are equal. Because the weights are heavy at the bottom of the series and light at the top, the bottom springs vibrate slowly when struck while the top springs vibrate rapidly. The natural frequency of each tuned vibrator is indicated in the figure. Now let us suppose that all the springs are hit in exactly the same manner at $t = 0$ on the time scale at the bottom of the figure. The small diagram A at the right-hand side of the figure shows what we can call the pressure waveform of the blow; it is simply a brief pulse. Diagram B shows its spectrum (cf. Fig. 2E). The question is, how do the weighted springs respond? This question is of interest because we have here a physical model that can perform neither perfect time analysis nor perfect frequency analysis. Its behavior should give us insight into the compromise method of representing the pulse.

The vibrations of the eleven springs are traced out in terms of their waveforms in the plots in the center of the figure. Each spring goes through a damped oscillation that dies down to 1/2.718 (= 1/e) of its maximum amplitude in about 1 millisecond and eventually becomes negligible. The dashed curves show the *envelopes* of the oscillations. If we deal only with the envelopes, we lose some detail, but we retain a good indication

gram *C* at the right-hand side of Fig. 4. Now we apply the pulse to the infinite set of resonators and represent the amplitudes of the envelopes of their oscillations by stippling more or less densely in the frequency-time plot. This gives us a pattern with the three

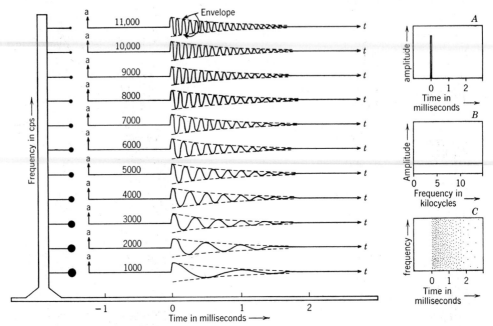

FIG. 4. An intensity-frequency-time pattern. The standard at the left supports a number of resonators, equally damped and tuned to the frequencies indicated. Simultaneously, the resonators are struck an impulsive blow, the force-versus-time pattern of which is shown at *A*, the spectrum at *B*. The oscillatory responses of the resonators to the blow are shown in the velocity-versus-time plots (*a* versus *t*) in the center of the figure. The envelopes of these responses can be used to provide a picture of the original signal itself, i.e. of the impulsive blow. This picture, schematized at *C*, is a compromise between *A* and *B*. It indicates at least approximately the time of occurrence of the blow, and it shows that energy is distributed uniformly along the frequency scale.

of the magnitude of the disturbance, and we greatly simplify the picture. The picture now says simply that the same thing happens at each frequency (i.e. to each weighted (spring).

Now let us imagine, instead of eleven springs, an infinite set of springs so constructed that, after equal excitations, their oscillations decay at equal rates, and so ordered that their natural frequencies form a frequency scale. At right angles to the frequency scale we set a time scale, as in diagram

dimensions, *intensity* (the amplitude of the envelope), *frequency*, and *time*. This pattern represents the pulse almost as exactly as does the waveform or the spectrum. We lost some detail by neglecting the phases of the oscillations when we turned our attention to the envelopes.

The same method of analysis can, of course, be applied to any input wave, and the resulting pattern provides a convenient representation of the signal. It is the basis of the Sound Spectrograph, the development of the Bell Telephone Laboratories (Koenig, Dunn, and Lacy, 1946) that produces "visible speech" (cf. Chapter 26). The Sound Spectrograph uses electrical resonators, of course, instead of weighted springs, but the important thing is that the method of analysis gives us pictures of sounds that show what goes on both in time and in frequency.

If we could find a convenient way of showing not merely the amplitudes of the envelopes but the actual oscillations of the array of resonators, we would have a notation (cf. Gabor, 1946) of even greater generality and flexibility, one that would reduce under certain idealizing assumptions to the spectrum and under others to the waveform. For example, let us imagine the resonators of Fig. 4 to be entirely frictionless, so that the oscillations, once started, will never stop. Here we would have perfect frequency analysis; the idealized arrangement records the spectrum of the applied signal. Or we can assume that the viscous friction of the fluid in which the resonators are immersed is so great that their tendency toward oscillation is negligible. All the elements would then behave in exactly the same way; each would vibrate only while the input signal is acting, and each would yield with a velocity proportional to the applied force. As a result, the arrangement would provide perfect time analysis — it would trace out the input waveform.

It should now be clear that to any given wave there corresponds not just one pattern in intensity, frequency, and time, but an infinite number of patterns. Between pure time analysis and pure frequency analysis we can strike any compromise we choose. Although the human auditory system is by no means so simple as the series of tuned circuits we have been considering, it too must strike a compromise. The nature of its solution to the time-frequency problem is, in fact, one of the central problems in the psychology of hearing.*

* The problem can be formulated alternatively by contrasting the waveform and its autocorrela-

Although in the foregoing analysis we get both time and frequency into the picture we do so at a cost. In a sense, we lose precision in specifying one as we gain precision in specifying the other. The analogy has often been drawn between the time-frequency problem, which we have been examining, and the position-momentum and energy-time problems that led Heisenberg in 1927 to state his uncertainty principle. The formal analogy is very close:

$$\Delta p \cdot \Delta q \geq h \text{ (Heisenberg)};$$

$$\Delta t \cdot \Delta E \geq h \text{ (Heisenberg)};$$

$$\Delta t \cdot \Delta f \sim 1 \text{ (Hartley, 1928)}; \text{ or}$$

$$\Delta t \cdot \Delta f \geq \frac{1}{2} \text{ (Gabor, 1946)}.$$

Here Δ is the interval of uncertainty, p is momentum, q is position, E is energy, t is time, and f is frequency. This analogy has led Gabor to suggest that we may find the solution to the time-frequency problem in quantum mechanics, and it has led Joos (1948) to speak of the "smear" (region of uncertainty) in intensity-frequency-time plots of acoustical waves. It should be noted, however, that there is no uncertainty about the spectrum that corresponds to a given waveform, no matter how brief the waveform. The only sense in which there is uncertainty about the frequency of a short wave is that a short wave has many frequency components. Conversely, narrow-band spectra imply stretched-out waveforms, but the waveform corresponding to a given narrow-band spectrum is quite precisely determined.

Sound Intensity and Decibels

The intensity of a sound wave, as we have seen, is usually measured with a pressure-

tion function instead of the waveform and its spectrum. The compromise representation is then a 'running' autocorrelation function. R. Fano and W. H. Huggins have suggested (personal communications) that it may turn out that the auditory mechanism can be understood better as an autocorrelator than as a frequency analyzer.

indicating instrument and specified in pressure units, i.e. in dynes per square centimeter. It is sometimes advantageous, however, to specify sound intensity in units of power or of energy.* The relation between the pressure of a plane sound wave in a free field and acoustic power is a simple one because open air is an almost purely resistive medium. In resistive media, the so-called volume velocity v is always proportional to the pressure a. Since power P is equal to pressure times volume velocity, we have the relations

$$v = ca \qquad P = va \qquad P = ca^2$$

where c is the reciprocal of the acoustic resistance of the air. From the third equation, we see that the power is proportional to the square of the pressure.

The *decibel* scale is essentially a logarithmic form of the power or energy scale. In order to obtain units of convenient size, the *bel* (the logarithmic unit) is divided into 10 decibels. Hence the number of decibels corresponding to a given ratio of acoustic power or energies is

$$N_{(db)} = 10 \log_{10} \frac{P_1}{P_0}$$

Thus if one sound intensity P_1, measured in power or energy units, is ten times as great as another sound intensity P_0, also measured in power or energy units, P_1 is said to be 10 db greater than P_0. Note that the expression *10 db* represents an intensity *ratio*, not an absolute intensity. In order to specify the absolute intensity of a sound in terms of the decibel notation, it is necessary to state that the intensity P_1 of the sound is N decibels above or below a given *reference intensity* P_0.

The reference intensities most commonly used are 1 dyne per square centimeter and

* In physical acoustics the word *intensity* almost always means power or energy — or, more precisely, energy flux density. In this chapter, however, we shall find it convenient to use intensity as a generic term for amplitude, pressure, voltage, power, energy, etc.

0.0002 dyne per square centimeter. These values, however, are given in *pressure* units, and we have seen that the decibel scale is essentially a logarithmic form of the *power* scale. We can, of course, circumvent the difficulty by converting the reference intensity from pressure units into power units; we can note, for example, that 0.0002 dyne per square centimeter is equivalent in open air to 10^{-16} watt per square centimeter. It is often more convenient, however, to adapt the decibel notation so that it expresses ratios of pressure as well as ratios of power. This is done by recalling that, in resistive media, $P = ca^2$, where P is power, a is amplitude (pressure), and c is a constant. It then follows that

$$N_{(db)} = 10 \log_{10} \frac{P_1}{P_0} = 10 \log_{10} \frac{ca_1{}^2}{ca_0{}^2} = 20 \log_{10} \frac{a_1}{a_0}$$

Thus we see that, since a tenfold increase in pressure (amplitude) corresponds to a hundredfold increase in power, it is represented by +20 db. Other decibel equivalents for power and amplitude ratios are given in Table 1. (For a discussion of the decibel notation see Rao, 1944.)

TABLE 1

RELATIONS BETWEEN POWER RATIOS, AMPLITUDE RATIOS, AND DECIBELS

Amplitude Ratio	Power Ratio	Decibels	Decibels	Amplitude Ratio	Power Ratio
1.00	1.00	0	0	1.00	1.00
0.89	0.79	−1	+1	1.12	1.26
0.79	0.63	−2	+2	1.26	1.59
0.71	0.50	−3	+3	1.41	2.00
0.50	0.25	−6	+6	2.00	3.98
0.32	0.10	−10	+10	3.16	10.00
0.10	0.01	−20	+20	10.00	100.00

AUDITORY THRESHOLDS

The intensity at which a sound is just discriminable from silence is called the *absolute threshold* for that sound. To simplify matters, experimenters have worked chiefly with pure tones, and they have tried to minimize differences among observers by using as listeners young adults without obvious defects of hearing. But their methods of measurement and their ideas of what to measure have varied. Some experimenters have presented

in Fig. 5. This graph contains twelve curves, of which six show the absolute threshold of hearing as a function of the stimulus frequency. The vertical scales indicate the root-mean-square * sound pressure relative to the two widely used reference intensities.

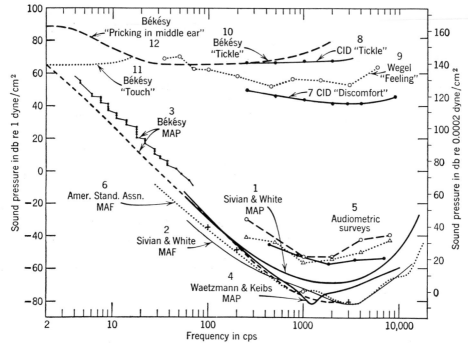

FIG. 5. Determinations of the threshold of audibility and the threshold of feeling. Curves 1 to 6 represent attempts to determine the absolute threshold of hearing at various frequencies. MAP = minimum audible pressure at the eardrum; MAF = minimum audible pressure in a free sound field, measured at the place where the listener's head had been. Curves 7 to 12 represent attempts to determine the upper boundary of the auditory realm, beyond which sounds are too intense for comfort, and give rise to nonauditory sensations of tickle and pain, etc.

the tone monaurally; others have presented it binaurally. Some have delivered the tone via an earphone and have measured the sound pressure at the listener's eardrum (*minimum audible pressure*); others have delivered the tone via a loudspeaker and have measured the sound pressure, after removing the listener from the sound field, at the center of the region that had been occupied by his head (*minimum audible field*).

Absolute threshold curves. Some of the discrepancies among the determinations of the absolute intensive threshold are shown

Curve 1 is a summary curve prepared by Sivian and White (1933) to represent the weighted mean of a number of determina-

* 'Root-mean-square sound pressure' is a short form of 'the square root of the mean of the squares of the instantaneous sound pressures.' To make it still shorter, 'root-mean-square' will be abbreviated to 'rms.' The reasons for using the rms pressure instead of simply the mean pressure or the mean absolute pressure (mean without regard for sign) are (1) that the mean pressure over an integral number of cycles of a sinusoidal sound wave is, of course, zero, and (2) that the rms is more tractable than the mean absolute pressure in computations involving complex waves.

tions of the minimum audible pressure (MAP). Curve 2 represents, in a similar way, the minimum audible field (MAF). Curve 1 is for monaural listening, curve 2 for either monaural or binaural listening. The fact that the two curves do not coincide is due in part to the fact that the sound pressure measured in a free field at the place to be occupied by the listener's head is not the same as the pressure developed at his eardrum when he is listening (see Chapter 27, p. 1079). This effect would not be expected to account for the discrepancy at frequencies below 1000 cps, however.

More recent laboratory determinations of the monaural MAP have yielded values somewhat lower than those of Sivian and White's summary curve. Curves 3 and 4 show the threshold pressure at the eardrum as determined by Békésy (1936a, b) in Budapest, and by Waetzmann and Keibs (1936a, b) in Breslau. Békésy generated intense sinusoidal pressure variations at very low frequency and found that the lower frequency limit of hearing is far below 20 cps, the value usually given in textbooks. The irregular line, for one of Békésy's listeners, shows that, as frequency is varied, the absolute threshold changes in jumps. This effect suggests that auditory sensitivity may actually be "quantal" in nature. Additional evidence on this point will be described later.

The curves marked 5 in Fig. 5 show the results of audiometric surveys made under less ideal conditions than are usually provided for laboratory measurements. The solid line represents the median values for listeners 20 to 29 years of age who took the hearing tests at the Bell Telephone Company's exhibits at the New York and San Francisco World's Fairs in 1938 and 1939 (Steinberg, Montgomery, and Gardner, 1940). They agree reasonably well with the neighboring dashed and dotted curves obtained, respectively, by the Bell Telephone Laboratories (Montgomery, 1932), and by the United States Public Health Service (Beasley, 1938); and they are consistent

with criteria for "normal hearing" adopted in clinical work with audiometers. It is possible that some part of the discrepancy between the curves marked 5 and the other absolute threshold curves of Fig. 5 is due to the fact that, in the audiometric surveys, the listener held the earphone to his ear as though he were using a telephone. Brogden and Miller (1947) found that the act of holding the receiver produces a measurable amount of low-frequency noise in the ear canal — the 'noise of the sea' that one hears in a sea shell.

Since the parametric value of the threshold has not been pinned down very closely, the American Standards Association has decided somewhat arbitrarily that the MAF at 1000 cps shall be taken (until further measurement indicates otherwise) as 0.0002 dyne per square centimeter. The ASA has, in fact, adopted a "standard" MAF curve (curve 6 in Fig. 5). Note that this curve crosses the 1000-cycle ordinate at 0 db on the right-hand scale.

Variations in absolute sensitivity. In asking about differences among listeners, we risk the semantic hazard of trying to distinguish between normal variations in the absolute threshold and partial deafness. It is clear from the United States Public Health Surveys that the thresholds even of young listeners without known otological pathology cover a considerable range. But it is by no means certain where to draw a line of division between normal and abnormal. In Fig. 6, for example, we see that there is no discontinuity in the distribution of thresholds. The median of this distribution is represented in Fig. 5, curve 5, by the filled circle at 880 cps.

Although for most listeners the absolute thresholds for low-frequency tones remain essentially constant throughout the span of life, the thresholds for high-frequency tones increase markedly with advancing age. This fact is illustrated in Fig. 7, which shows typical *audiograms* for various ages. Note that the ordinate scale in this figure is the number of decibels by which it differs from the average for listeners 20 years of age. This method of representation is widely used in audiometry.

We have as yet no detailed analysis of the day-to-day variations in the absolute thresh-

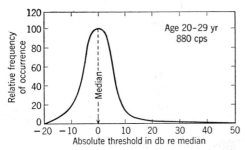

Fig. 6. Distribution of auditory sensitivity among individuals 20 to 29 years of age. The data are measurements of the absolute thresholds of 35,589 subjects for an 880-cycle tone. (After Steinberg, Montgomery, and Gardner, 1940.)

old, but we know that the variations are significant. When we compare the overall variance (variability) of a set of threshold measurements taken over a period of days with the average of the variances of the daily

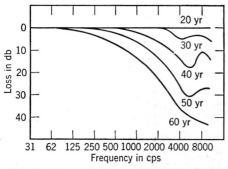

Fig. 7. Progressive loss of sensitivity at high frequencies with increasing age. The audiogram at 20 years of age is taken as a basis of comparison. (From Morgan, 1943, after Bunch, 1929.)

subsets, we find that the overall variance is three or four times as large as the average (Pollack, unpublished data; Goodfellow, 1938). During a test session of an hour's duration, the threshold of a well-motivated

listener may show no consistent trend either upward or downward, but there are variations of as much as 5 db from one half-minute to the next (Békésy, 1947b).

Even within an interval as short as 5 seconds the threshold appears to fluctuate. If the stimulus consists of five 0.4-second bursts of tone separated by intervals of 0.6 second, the listener may hear all five bursts, or four, or three, $\cdots$, or none. The lowest intensity at which all five are heard is about 6 db higher than the highest intensity at which none are heard (Lifshitz, 1939).

Finally, the absolute threshold depends to a considerable extent upon how long the observer has been listening. Tones of very high frequency tend to disappear, as Lord Rayleigh several times observed, even if they are, at the onset, well above what is then the threshold. Rosenblith and Miller (1949) find, in fact, that the threshold of a 4000-cycle tone may change with continued listening by as much as 20 db.

The thresholds of discomfort, tickle, feeling, etc. We can map the upper boundary of the auditory realm by determining how intense the tones of various frequency can be made before they give rise to reactions that indicate that the auditory mechanism is being overloaded. Because there are several alternative criteria of overload, several end points can be distinguished.

These upper boundaries are represented in Fig. 5 by curves 7 to 12. Curves 7 and 8 were obtained by Silverman, Harrison, and Lane (1946) at the Central Institute for the Deaf (CID), in St. Louis. Curve 7 shows the intensity level at which, after an extended period of getting used to intense acoustic stimulation, the listeners reported "discomfort," and curve 8 marks the onset of "a tickling sensation." The earphones broke before some of the experienced listeners complained of "pain." Before the listeners had become hardened to the rigors of the experiment, however, they complained of discomfort and tickle at levels 5 to 10 db lower than those shown in the curves, and they reported "pain" at about 140 db above 0.0002 dyne per square centimeter. It appears, therefore, that listeners develop a certain amount of tolerance for intense sounds. This may explain the fact that Wegel's (1932) curve for feeling (curve 9) lies below the CID curve (8) and the curve (10) obtained by Békésy (1936b). Békésy was able to explore the boundaries of the "auditory area" in the very-low-frequency range. He found that at frequencies below 15 cps his listeners could report consistently in terms of two criteria. Curves 11 and 12, labeled "touch" and "pricking in middle ear," show the central tendencies of the judgments.

The listener's subjective impression is that the criteria for the 'upper boundary' thresholds are chiefly nonauditory. As the names imply, feeling, tickle, touch, and pricking seem to be tactile. This impression is supported by the observation that the tickle, etc., remains localized in the ears when the sound itself is shifted from one position to another in phenomenal space. The sensations are probably to be accounted for in such terms as the stretching of the drum skin and contact between the ossicles and the wall of the middle ear. Discomfort is the exception; it appears to be a characteristic of the auditory sensation.

Other nonauditory effects of intense acoustic stimulation have been noted in connection with work with ultrasonic sirens (e.g. Allen and Rudnick, 1947). Exposure to a siren-generated sound of 20 kilocycles at 1 watt per square centimeter kills cockroaches in 3 to 4 minutes, mice in 1 minute, and mosquitoes in 10 seconds. They are literally cooked to death. The operators of the siren have to be careful, when they place objects in the sound field, to hold their fingers wide apart lest heating between the fingers, where they almost touch, cause burns. Even when they are wearing earplugs, the operators experience a slight dizziness when they get near the siren, and they report a "cool sizzling sensation" in the mouth and an unpleasant tingling in the nasal passages. Similar effects have been observed at lower frequencies (Parrack, Eldredge, and Koster, 1948).

DIFFERENTIAL THRESHOLDS

The *differential threshold*, or difference limen (DL), is an inverse measure of discriminatory capacity. It answers the question: how small a change in the stimulus can an average observer detect? This question is important because we can communicate with one another only by means of *changing* signals.

Differential threshold for intensity. Let us consider, first, changes in sound intensity. On first thought, it would appear that the following procedure, used by Knudsen (1923) to determine the differential intensity threshold, is unequivocal: A tone is switched abruptly from one intensity level to another, and listeners report whether or not they can detect the change. The intensity difference is varied until, for the average listener, the change is just detectable. This intensity difference is taken as the differential threshold. We have already seen, however, that it is impossible to change the intensity of the tone without spreading energy along the frequency scale, and we might ask whether it is the intensity change or the spread of energy along the frequency scale that is detected by the listener.

We cannot avoid the problem posed by this question, but we can try to minimize the difficulty by changing the intensity in such a way as to cause as little spread of energy as possible along the frequency scale. Riesz (1928) introduced the change in intensity by adding to a steady tone a second tone differing in frequency from the first by 3 cps. The second tone sometimes augmented the first and at other times partially canceled it, thereby introducing recurrent variations of amplitude at a rate of three per second. These variations at suprathreshold levels give rise to the sensation of beats (cf. Fig. 3). Riesz' results are shown in Fig. 8. The upper surface of the solid figure defines the just noticeable increment in intensity as a function of the frequency and of the intensity * of the standard to which the increment was added. It is

switch the oscillator abruptly from 1000 cps to 1003 cps, we produce not two frequencies, but an infinitude of frequencies. The trouble is that we try to use time language and frequency language both in the same sentence, and that is very difficult to do correctly.

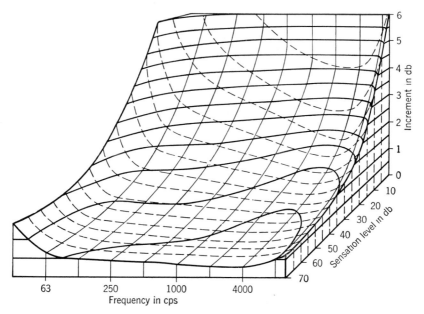

FIG. 8. Three-dimensional surface showing the differential intensity threshold as a function of the frequency and the intensity of the standard tone. The threshold is represented as the difference in decibels between the standard intensity and the standard plus the increment. Following the contour lines from 1000 cps and 30 db, we see, by way of illustration, that the intensity of a 1000-cycle tone must be raised 1.0 db from a level 30 db above threshold before the average observer can detect the change. If we start with levels 60 or 70 db above threshold, we find that an increment of less than 0.5 db is detectable. (Based on the data of Riesz, 1928.)

important to note that the differential threshold is given in decibels. The difference limen (DL) in decibels = 10 log $(1 + \Delta I/I)$, where I is measured in terms of energy flow.

Differential threshold for frequency. The concept of a threshold change in frequency brings us up against the same difficulty that we faced in the case of the differential threshold for intensity. Again, it is impossible to change any of the parameters of a pure tone and leave the tone pure. If we

---

* The *sensation level* of a sound is the intensity of the sound in decibels above its absolute threshold level.

Despite its inherent difficulties, the question of frequency discrimination has been studied for many years and by many methods (see Boring, 1940). Probably the best procedure would be to vary the dial of an oscillator smoothly (sinusoidally) back and forth between two frequency settings and determine how far apart the settings have to be to make the average listener report 'change' in half the trials. This would be sinusoidal frequency modulation, and it would have the advantage that both the waveform and the spectrum of the frequency-modulated tone are easy to describe.

Shower and Biddulph (1931) used almost, but not exactly, the procedure just outlined. They modulated the frequency of the test tone in the way that would be achieved if the oscillator dial were moved sinusoidally from one frequency to the other and were then allowed to rest a moment before being moved back.

cps from 60 to 1000 cps, beyond which point it increases rapidly. Above 1000 cps, the *relative DL* ($\Delta F/F$) is approximately constant.

Factors influencing the DL's for intensity and for frequency. As we shall see when we examine temporal and binaural effects in hearing, the size of the DL depends to some

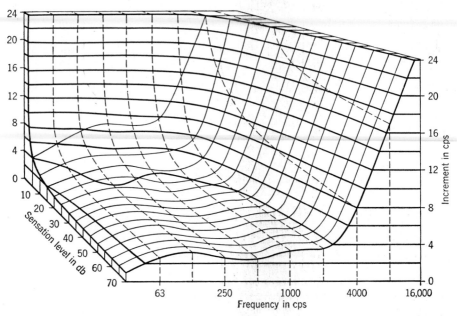

Fig. 9.   Three-dimensional surface showing the differential frequency threshold as a function of the frequency and the intensity of the standard tone. Frequency discrimination is poor at intensity levels near the absolute threshold (rear part of figure) and at high frequencies (right-hand part of figure). At sensation levels above 30 db and at frequencies below 1000 cps, however, a change of about 3 cps can be detected. (Based on the data of Shower and Biddulph, 1931.)

They tried various rates of modulation and found that the sharpest discriminations were made when the frequency was varied back and forth about twice a second. They then determined DL's at various frequencies and intensities, for subjects listening monaurally, binaurally, and via bone conduction. The monaural results are shown in Fig. 9.

It is important to note that in Fig. 9 it is the absolute frequency change ΔF that is represented on the vertical scale. This method of representation emphasizes the fact that, at sensation levels above 30 db, the *absolute DL* is roughly constant at 2 or 3

extent upon the duration of the stimulus and upon whether it is presented to one ear (Figs. 8 and 9) or to both ears. The DL is influenced also by the mode of transition between the standard and comparison tones. Rawdon-Smith and Grindley (1935) have dramatized the latter fact by presenting to the listener a tone that periodically jumps upward in intensity, then falls slowly to the initial level. Subjectively, the sound seems to grow ever louder: the DL's are lower for abrupt than for gradual transition. Intervals of silence between the standard and comparison tones make the DL's larger, but

Harris (1948) has found that listeners can make surprisingly accurate discriminations of frequency with intervals as long as 25 seconds. Finally, as we should expect, the listener can make more accurate discriminations if he controls the switch that introduces the increment to be detected than if he has no way of concentrating his attention at the critical moment.

Quantization in the Auditory Process

In the simplest conceptual neurology, the stimulus threshold owes its existence to the effect of a small barrier, a threshold in the root sense of the word, between successive stages in the sequence of neural processes that underlie hearing. Actually it is difficult to determine whether or not the differential threshold is, in this sense, a true threshold, because the measured threshold is influenced by small but unavoidable fluctuations in the stimulating apparatus and in the listener himself. Nevertheless the overcoming of a barrier (or barriers) is fundamental to the concept of threshold. If the DL is more than a statistical artifact, the neural mechanism must function in a stepwise or quantal manner.

The best evidence of the existence of true barrier-determined thresholds in audition comes from experiments in which the transition from the standard to the comparison stimulus is abrupt. (In a short interval of time there is little opportunity for the occurrence of extensive fluctuations of sensitivity that might obscure the true threshold.) The curves of Fig. 10 show Békésy's (1930b) results on differential sensitivity to intensity. Plot B was obtained with highly sensitive, well-trained listeners, plot A with less sensitive or less well-trained listeners. The discontinuous and rectilinear nature of the curves suggests strongly that differential sensitivity to itensity is quantal (cf. Chapter 1). Experiments by Stevens, Morgan, and Volkmann (1941), by Flynn (1943),

and by Miller and Garner (1944) have confirmed Békésy's observations and have further defined the conditions under which the quantal effect appears. The discovery of quantization in the psychometric function leads us to ask whether or not quanta can actually be heard. Some of Békésy's

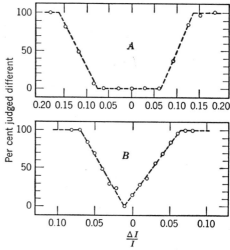

Fig. 10. Evidence of quantization in intensity discrimination. The data (especially in curve B) are fitted better by straight lines than by ogive curves. The V-shaped and trapezoidal graphs are just what we should expect on the assumption of (1) fluctuating transmission efficiency and (2) a quantal discriminatory process. (From Stevens and Davis, 1938, after Békésy, 1930b.)

(personal communication) observations are of interest in this connection. A tone of very slowly declining intensity sounds as though it jumps down every so often. Very slow but continuous changes in frequency also produce subjective jumps. In the vicinity of the absolute threshold the almost discontinuous nature of sensation is, in Békésy's experience, especially marked (cf. Fig. 5, curve 4). The physiological basis of the quantization, however, is not clear. Stevens, Morgan, and Volkmann (1941) attribute it to a central rather than to a peripheral process.

DIMENSIONS OF TONAL EXPERIENCE

The intensity and the frequency of a tone can be measured, if need be, by entirely automatic apparatus, far removed from the nearest listener. The loudness and the pitch of a tone, on the other hand, are attributes of the tone as heard and reacted to by a listener. Loudness and pitch are thus dimensions of auditory experience, whereas intensity and frequency are dimensions of the

concept of independent variability if the number of subjective attributes is greater than the number of stimulus dimensions. He suggests instead that the test for an attribute is its independent constancy or its invariance in the face of changes in the other attributes.

The Loudness of Pure Tones

In order to handle loudness quantitatively, we should like to have a ratio scale of loud-

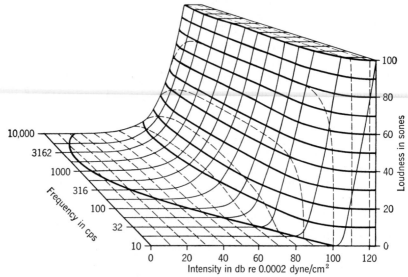

Fig. 11. Three-dimensional surface showing loudness as a function of intensity and frequency. Subjective loudness in sones is represented vertically above the intensity-frequency plane. The heavy curves coursing from front to rear in the diagram are equal-loudness contours for pure tones. (After Stevens and Davis, 1938.)

tensity and frequency are dimensions of the acoustic stimulus. These distinctions between loudness and intensity and between pitch and frequency have not always been observed.

The term *subjective* attributes as used by Külpe and by Titchener referred to a rather limited set of the characteristics of subjective experience, characteristics that were regarded as inseparable (e.g. if there is no pitch, there is no sensation of tone) and independently variable (e.g. pitch can vary while loudness remains constant and vice versa). Stevens (1934a, b, c) has pointed out, however, that there is a difficulty in the

ness such that a sound of 1 loudness unit is twice as loud as a sound of ½ loudness unit, half as loud as a sound of 2 loudness units, etc. (cf. Chapter 1). Whether or not such a scale can be constructed is, of course, an empirical question best answered by trying.

Several experimenters (Ham and Parkinson, 1932; Geiger and Firestone, 1933; Churcher, King, and Davies, 1934) measured the intensities at which one tone sounds twice as loud, half as loud, etc., as another tone; and Békésy (1929) and Fletcher and Munson (1933) performed experiments from which the intensities required for half-loudness can be inferred. Putting these data together with other data obtained by measuring the intensity levels at which tones of different frequencies are equally loud, Fletcher and Munson (1933) constructed a ratio scale of loudness. As a name for the unit of loudness of this scale, Stevens' (1936) term *sone* has been widely adopted, one sone being the loudness of a 1000-cycle tone, 40 db above threshold. Other tones can be compared in loudness with a 1000-cycle tone by referring to the three-dimensional surface shown in Fig. 11.

The solid curves running from front to back in Fig. 11 are *equal-loudness contours.* We note, for example, that a tone of 10 cps, 120 db above 0.0002 dyne per square centimeter, has for the average listener the same loudness (80 sones) as a tone of 1000 cps at 100 db. It is thus evident that loudness is a function of frequency as well as of intensity. Following the dashed lines, we see that, for a given intensity, the loudness is greater in the middle range of the frequency scale than it is at either extreme. And, following the solid curves that sweep upward from left to right, we see that, as the intensity is increased uniformly along the logarithmic scale, loudness increases slowly at first, then more and more rapidly. The loudness is in fact over three times as great at 100 db as it is at 80 db. This is, however, by no means a violation of the law of diminishing returns: the stimulus power is 100 times as great at 100 db as it is at 80 db.

The Pitch of Pure Tones

The pitch analogue of the loudness scale shown in Fig. 11 would be a surface representing the pitch of each audible tone as a function of its intensity and of its frequency. The variation of pitch with intensity, however, is small (Zurmühl, 1930; Stevens, 1935; Snow, 1936; and Morgan and Garner, 1947), and a single function relating pitch to frequency will suffice, as a first approximation, as a pitch scale for all inten-

sities. Such a scale was determined by Stevens, Volkmann, and Newman (1937) and later modified by Stevens and Volkmann (1940) with the aid of the fractionation and the bisection procedures. The 1940 scale is shown in Fig. 12. The function is plotted twice, once against a linear frequency scale

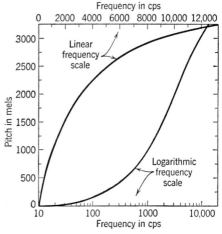

Fig. 12. Pitch as a function of frequency. The upper curve shows that subjective pitch (in mels) increases less and less rapidly as the stimulus frequency is increased linearly. The lower curve shows that subjective pitch increases more and more rapidly as stimulus frequency is increased logarithmically. (The musical scale is a logarithmic scale.) The pitch of a 1000-cycle tone, 40 db above threshold, is defined as 1000 mels. (After Stevens and Volkmann, 1940.)

(top of graph) and once against a logarithmic frequency scale (bottom of graph).

There are many claims and some evidence that, in addition to the ordinary type of pitch perception to which the pitch scale just described refers, there is another type of pitch perception that endows the musical note C with a certain 'C-ness,' that makes middle C more like the C an octave higher than like the D that is only an interval removed along the musical scale. This quality, which characterizes tones of frequencies below 5000 cps, we may call *tone chroma,* or *tonality,* to distinguish it from ordinary pitch — realizing, however, that there is probably no field of psychology in which the terminology has been more confused (cf. Boring's summary, 1942). Bachem (1948) has restated the view, held earlier by Révész (1913) and by Max Meyer (1914), that individuals with "genuine absolute pitch" are able to identify tonal frequencies with great accuracy because the "tone height" (ordinary pitch) points out the proper octave and the "tone chroma" locates the note within

Volume, Brightness, and Density of Pure Tones

In addition to loudness and pitch, tones differ from one another in such dimensions as *volume* (size, extensity), *brightness*, and *density* (compactness). The tones of a tuba sound bigger than those of a piccolo, and a bugle blast appears to be hard and compact and to have a luster that is lacking in the

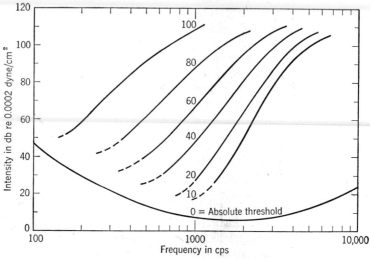

Fig. 13. Equal-volume contours for pure tones. Those tones are judged equal in volume whose frequency and intensity coordinates fall along one of the curves. The upper left-hand curve represents the largest volume, the lower right-hand curve represents the smallest, but the subjective volume ratios have not been determined. The parameter is the sensation level (number of decibels above threshold) of the 1000-cycle tone in each contour. (After Thomas, 1949.)

the octave. "Genuine absolute pitch" is quite different, according to Bachem, from the "quasi-absolute pitch" developed by musicians who learn to estimate the frequencies of tones in relation, for example, to the lowest notes they can sing. The recent discussion of absolute pitch by Neu (1947, 1948) and Bachem (1948) serves to emphasize, however, that we must have (1) agreement on a definition of absolute pitch and (2) careful measurements with controlled stimuli on (3) an adequate sample of listeners before we can be sure that there is reason to postulate a special mechanism for absolute pitch. We do not, for example, postulate a special kind of vision to account for unusual accuracy in color naming.

more diffuse sound of an organ. It is true, of course, that we visualize the sound source as larger in the case of the tuba and as shinier and more compact in the case of the bugle, but the subjective dimensions are held to refer to the sounds themselves and not to their sources. The question is, do listeners react confidently and consistently when they compare sounds in respect of the dimensions, volume, brightness, and density?

In early experiments on the question of tonal volume, Rich (1919) and Halverson (1924) determined the DL's for volume as functions of frequency and intensity, respectively, and concluded that volume is, as an attribute of tonal experience, separate and distinct from pitch and from loudness.

The inconsistent results later obtained by Gundlach (1929), Gundlach and Bentley (1930), and Zoll (1934), however, made it appear for a time that volume is not a characteristic upon which different listeners can agree. Nevertheless, by giving the listeners control over the variable stimulus, and by determining equality rather than differential sensitivity, Stevens (1934a, b) was able to obtain consistent determinations of equal-volume contours, and Thomas (1949) has extended these contours over a wide range of frequencies and intensities.

Figure 13 shows smoothed equal-volume curves based on Thomas' data. Knowing that the volume of a sound increases as we raise its intensity, we can tell from Fig. 13 that the increase is very rapid as soon as we elevate low-frequency tones above their absolute thresholds. High-frequency tones, on the other hand, must be raised to intensities far above their absolute thresholds before they attain any appreciable volume. We should like to be able to label each of the equal-volume contours of Fig. 13 with the appropriate parameter in volume units, but we do not yet have the data needed to construct a subjective ratio scale of volume. Hence we designate each contour with the sensation level of the 1000-cycle tone to which the other tones are equal in volume.

Stevens (1934b, c) employed the equating procedure to determine not only equal-volume contours but equal-density and equal-brightness contours. His results indicate that volume and density are separate attributes, different from each other and from pitch and loudness. Boring and Stevens (1936) later suggested that brightness and density might well be different words for the same attribute.

MASKING AND FATIGUE

When we say we hear two tones at once, we give evidence of having made an analysis of the acoustic stimulation, for, even though the air vibrations at the eardrums represent the superposition of waves from two separate sources, they constitute one physical sound, not two. It is a remarkable fact that our auditory mechanisms can analyze compound acoustic stimuli into components, that we can describe the loudness or the pitch or the location of one component while effectively ignoring another.

However, analysis is not perfect. A weak tone is audible in a quiet room, but not in a noisy one, where the tone is *masked* by the noise. Masking is thus the opposite of analysis; it represents the inability of the auditory mechanisms to separate the tonal stimulation into components and to discriminate between the presence and the absence of one of them.

The degree to which one component of a sound is masked by the remainder of the sound is usually determined by measuring two thresholds. Let us call the part that does the masking the primary component, and the part that is masked the secondary component. First we find the intensity at which the secondary component is just audible in the presence of the primary; this is its masked threshold. Then we find the intensity at which the secondary component is just audible when sounded alone; this is its absolute threshold. The ratio of these two intensities, expressed in decibels and referred to as the threshold shift, we take as a measure of the masking.

Masking of pure tones by pure tones. Wegel and Lane (1924) made a study of the masking of one pure tone by another. They worked chiefly with a single listener but covered a wide range of frequencies and intensities. Their results are shown in Figs. 14 and 15. Figure 14 describes what is heard when a primary tone of 1200 cycles, 80 db above its threshold, is used to mask a secondary tone of variable frequency and intensity. When the secondary tone is above its masked threshold, the sensation cannot be described simply as a pair of tones; it is complicated by the presence of beats, subjective harmonics, and combination tones.

Figure 15 presents the results in greater detail, showing how much the threshold for the secondary tone is shifted when the primary tone is turned on.

The main facts about masking, evident in Figs. 14 and 15, are these: (1) Masking tends to be greater for tones of neighboring frequencies than for tones widely separated

Masking of pure tones by white noise. As we have already seen (Fig. 2E), white noise contains components of all the audible frequencies, sounding simultaneously. When a pure tone is presented against a background of white noise, therefore, it is masked, as it were, by all of Wegel and Lane's masking tones at once. We should,

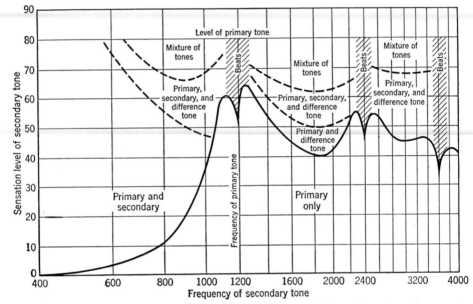

FIG. 14. The various sensations produced by a two-component tone. The primary component is a sinusoid of 1200 cps, 80 db above threshold. The secondary component is a sinusoid of the frequency and sensation level indicated by the coordinates. When the secondary component falls below the solid curve it is masked. When the secondary component is above its masked threshold, however, the auditory sensation may be quite complex, as indicated by the descriptions in the several regions of the graph. (From Fletcher, 1929, after Wegel and Lane, 1924.)

along the frequency scale. (2) Low-frequency tones effectively mask high-frequency tones, whereas high-frequency tones are much less effective in masking low-frequency tones. (3) The rate at which masking increases as the masking tone is raised in intensity depends upon the frequencies of the tones. When the masked tone is applied to one ear and the masking tone to the other ear, very little masking occurs (Wegel and Lane, 1924). What little masking is observed can be attributed largely to leakage of the masking vibration around the head (Békésy, 1948).

of course, expect the resultant masking to be much less critically a function of the frequency of the masked tone than was the masking produced by a single pure tone.

This expectation is confirmed by the results of Hawkins and Stevens (1950), shown in Fig. 16. The lowest contour is the absolute-threshold curve, and the other contours mark the monaural thresholds for pure tones heard against a background of white noise. The parameter is the intensity of the noise, expressed in terms of level per cycle. The level per cycle, or spectrum level, as it is often called, is the amount of

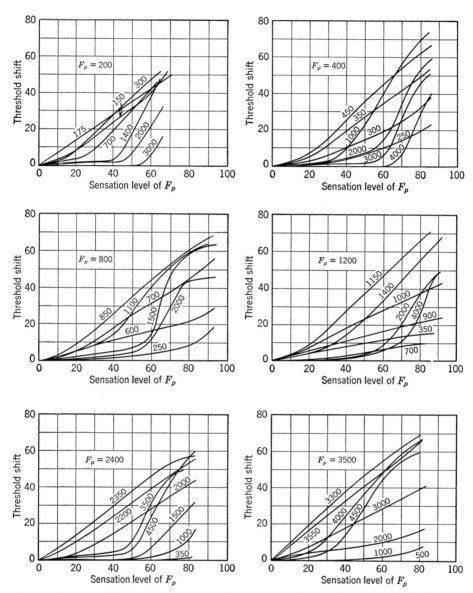

FIG. 15. The masking of secondary by primary components. The frequency of the primary component F_p is given in each plot, and the frequency of the secondary component is attached to the curve. Note that the growth of masking with increasing intensity of F_p is approximately linear only when the two components are nearly equal in frequency. (From Fletcher, 1929, after Wegel and Lane, 1924.)

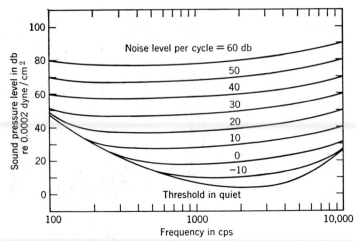

FIG. 16. The masked threshold for pure tones presented against a background of white noise. The ordinate gives the sound pressure that the sinusoid must reach to be audible against random fluctuation noise of the spectrum level shown as the parameter. (From Hawkins and Stevens, 1950.)

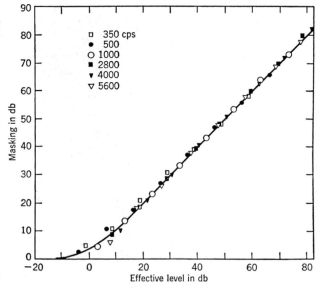

FIG. 17. The relation between the masking produced by a white noise and the effective level of the noise. The effective level is the amount of noise power in a narrow frequency band, the "critical band" (see text), centered about the frequency of the masked sinusoid. It is expressed in decibels relative to the absolute threshold (in power units) at that frequency. When the intensity is given in terms of effective level, the function shown in the graph is essentially independent of the frequency of the masked sinusoid. (From Hawkins and Stevens, 1950.)

sound energy in the small fraction of the noise spectrum that lies between two frequency limits 1 cycle apart. Since the spectrum of the noise was uniform within the frequency limits set by the earphones, the total noise energy is equal to the level per cycle multiplied by the total bandwidth.

Since masking is the shift in threshold produced by the masking sound, we can find

by Fletcher and Munson (1937). Instead of a white noise, however, they used a random noise with a nonuniform spectrum. The spectrum was so adjusted that it produced approximately the same amount of masking at each frequency. This adjustment had, of course, to be determined empirically.

Having established the shape of the spectrum that produces uniform masking,

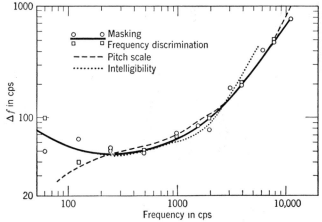

FIG. 18.   Four functions relating Δf to f. The critical band function (circles and solid curve) shows the width of the band of noise that contributes to the masking of a sinusoid at the center of the band. In the frequency-discrimination curve (squares and solid curve), Δf is 20 times the jnd (cf. Fig. 9, approximately 70-db sensation level). The curve based on the pitch scale gives the width in frequency of intervals that are 50 mels wide in pitch. The curve based on intelligibility data shows the widths of frequency bands that contribute equally—2 per cent of the total—to the intelligibility of speech (cf. Chapter 26). The similarity of the curves suggests that they have a common basis in the auditory mechanism. (Based on the data of Fletcher, 1940 ; Shower and Biddulph, 1931 ; Stevens and Volkmann, 1940 ; and French and Steinberg, 1947.)

from Fig. 16 how much a white noise of given intensity masks a pure tone of given frequency by noting the separation of the masked-threshold and the absolute-threshold contours. This separation increases as we go from the left-hand side of the graph to the center. No matter what the frequency of the masked tone, however, the amount of masking increases at an almost constant rate as we make the noise more and more intense. The relation between masking and noise intensity is shown in Fig. 17.

The Concept of Critical Bands

An experiment quite similar to that of Hawkins and Stevens was performed earlier

Fletcher (1940) was able to derive, with the aid of an important assumption, the relation that tells us the width of the critical band mentioned in the legend of Fig. 17. Fletcher's assumption can be stated in two parts: (1) that we can neglect the masking produced by all the components of the noise except those whose frequencies lie within a narrow band around the frequency of the masked tone; and (2) that, when the tone is just audible against the background of noise, the acoustic power of the tone is the same as the acoustic power of the noise components within the narrow band. We cannot go into the details of Fletcher's reasoning, but we can get an idea of the fundamental nature of his critical band function by comparing it (Fig. 18) with three other basic psychophysical functions that relate a frequency bandwidth to a center frequency. In Fig. 18 the critical band function is marked by the circles and approximated by the solid curve. The other three functions are based on (1) Shower and Biddulph's data on frequency discrimination (squares

19 gives, for comparison, what might be called the critical band function for the basilar membrane. It is derived by measuring the frequency intervals (Δf) between the half-amplitude points of the frequency-selectivity curves in Fig. 31 of Chapter 27, which describe the vibration of the cochlear partition as seen through a microscope by Békésy.

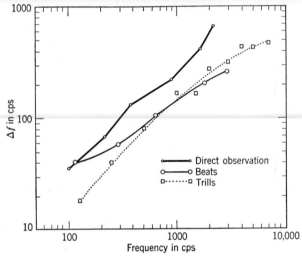

FIG. 19. The heavy solid curve shows the widths (between half-amplitude points) of the selectivity or resonance curves at various points along the basilar membrane, as observed by Békésy. The difference between this curve and those of Fig. 18 argues against the interpretation of the psychophysical data (of Fig. 18) as reflecting directly the mechanical frequency-resolving of the cochlea. The functions for beats and trills, however, are roughly parallel to the heavy solid curve. These are referred to later in the text. (Based on the data of Mayer, 1894; Békésy, 1943; and Miller and Heise, 1949.)

and solid curve), (2) Stevens and Volkmann's pitch scale (dashed line), and (3) French and Steinberg's curve showing the importance of various frequencies for the intelligibility of speech (dotted lines; cf. Chapter 26).

The fact that the four curves of Fig. 18 follow such parallel courses suggests that they stem from a common source, the frequency-resolving characteristic of the auditory system. They are no doubt related to the function that describes the sharpness of tuning of the cochlear mechanism, but probably not in the very direct way suggested by Fletcher (1940). The solid curve of Fig.

Masking and differential sensitivity. If we compare the operations that we perform when we measure the masked threshold with those we perform when we measure the differential threshold for intensity, we find that we do essentially the same things in the two experiments. The principal differences lie in our selection of signals and in our interpretation of the measurements. If we recall, for example, Riesz's procedure for determining the just noticeable increment in intensity, we note that he actually measured the masking of one tone by another 3 cycles removed along the frequency scale. In fact, his data were used in preparing that part of Fig. 14 that shows how much tones near 1200 cycles are masked by a 1200-cycle tone.

G. A. Miller has recently pointed out that this equivalence of operation holds also for (1) the masking of white noise by white noise and (2) the differential threshold for noise intensity. Miller's results are presented in Fig. 20. The figure shows how large the increment in the intensity of a

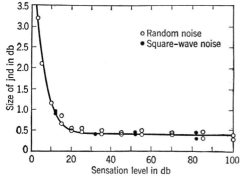

FIG. 20. The differential intensity threshold for white noise. The open circles are for the type of noise illustrated in Fig. 2E. The closed circles are for noise consisting of rectangular waves of irregular lengths. The square-wave noise sounds like white noise and has essentially the same jnd's. (After G. A. Miller, 1947.)

white noise, heard binaurally, must be before a listener can detect a change. Regarded from the point of view of intensity discrimination, his data indicate that an increment of about 0.4 db can be heard to produce a change when it is added to a fairly intense white noise. Regarded from the point of view of masking, Miller's data indicate that one fairly intense white noise is entirely masked by another white noise 12 db more intense.

Auditory Fatigue

Masking refers, as we have seen, to the elevation of the threshold for one tone by a second tone sounding simultaneously. The threshold for a tone may be elevated also by prior stimulation. The post-stimulation depression of sensitivity is called auditory fatigue or adaptation, temporary hearing loss, or permanent hearing loss, depending

upon its persistence. Here we shall consider only the effects of relatively short duration. Previous work has been summarized by Banister (1934) and by Stevens and Davis (1938).

Measurements of short-duration auditory fatigue following tonal stimulation have been made by de Maré (1939), by Gardner (1947), by Caussé and Chavasse (1947), and by Lüscher and Zwislocki (1947). These experimenters used variations of the same basic procedure, which runs as follows: A fatiguing tone of fixed duration is presented to the listener. After the fatiguing tone has been turned off and an interval of silence has elapsed, a short burst of tone is applied to test the momentary sensitivity of the

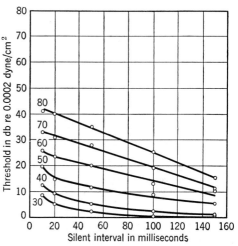

FIG. 21. The momentary threshold at various intervals after a burst (0.4 second) of fatiguing or preconditioning tone. The parameter is the intensity of the preconditioning tone in decibels re 0.0002 dyne per square centimeter. (After Lüscher and Zwislocki, 1947.)

auditory system. The test is repeated with fatiguing tones and with test tones of various frequencies and intensities. The curves of Figs. 21 to 23 illustrate the results, showing the degree to which the threshold for the test tone was shifted by the previous stimulation. We see (Fig. 21) that, when the fatiguing tone and the test tone are applied to the same ear, the after-effects of even moderate stimulation persist for over a tenth of a second. There is little or no depression of sensitivity when one ear is fatigued and the other tested.

The results shown in Figs. 21 to 23 are for listeners with normal hearing. Listeners with so-called nerve deafness yield curves of a characteristically different shape. Listeners with conductive deafness yield curves

given in terms of phase difference), the amount by which the masking wave shifted the threshold for the masked wave. Typical results are shown in Fig. 25. For masked frequencies higher than the masking frequency, we see that masking is greatest when the masked tone *precedes* the masking tone by about $\pi/4$ radians, i.e. about 2 milliseconds. This result appears reasonable

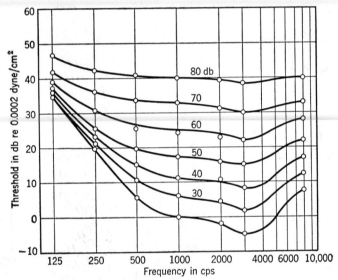

FIG. 22. Frequency characteristic of the momentary threshold 20 milliseconds after a 0.4-second preconditioning tone. The parameter is the intensity of the preconditioning tone in decibels re 0.0002 dyne per square centimeter. (After Lüscher and Zwislocki, 1947.)

similar to those of normal subjects except that their thresholds are shifted upward by a number of decibels equal to the conductive hearing loss.

Retroactive masking. Since one tone can raise the threshold for a second presented either at the same time or after a short delay, it is natural to ask what happens when the masked tone is presented before the masking tone. R. L. Miller (1947) has obtained data on this question in an experiment with pulsed tones. Both the masked tone and the masking tone were turned on and off periodically as shown in Fig. 24. With the Amplitude of the masking wave fixed, Miller found, for each of a number of time intervals (in the figure, the time is

when we consider the fact that the synaptic facilitation lets intense neural activity proceed up the auditory pathways at a faster pace than weak neural activity. Apparently the activity set off by the intense masking pulse catches up with that set off by the weak masked pulse by the time the latter activity reaches the auditory cortex.

Sensitization. Following a procedure very much like that used in the experiments on auditory fatigue except for the use of sharp clicks instead of short tones, Buytendijk and Meesters (1942) obtained results that point to the existence of what might be called negative masking (cf. Bronstein, 1936). A moderately intense click makes another click, presented either a little earlier or a little later, sound *louder* than it would have sounded had it been presented alone. If the facilitative effect depends upon central rather than cochlear processes, we might expect the augmentation to be greater when

An Auditory After-Image?

The problem of an analogue in hearing for the visual after-image has interested many investigators. The most nearly comparable phenomenon is the tinnitus, the an-

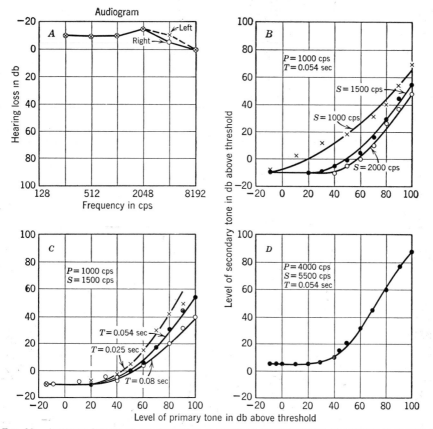

FIG. 23. Auditory fatigue at one frequency *S* produced by stimulation at another frequency *P*. Diagram *A* is a conventional audiogram; it shows that the ears of the listener are more sensitive than average. The other three diagrams show the elevations of the threshold for the secondary burst of tone *S* (second in time) that are produced by primary (preconditioning) bursts of tone *P*. The frequencies of the two tones and the duration of the interval between them are indicated in the diagrams. (From Gardner, 1947.)

the clicks are led to opposite ears than when they are applied to the same ear — this because there is very little 'cross masking,' and the binaurally separated clicks would not tend to mask each other. Buytendijk and Meesters found, indeed, that the facilitative effect was especially marked when one click is led to one ear, the other to the other.

noying ringing in the ear that often follows exposure to deafening sounds; but tinnitus may persist for hours, is often pathological in origin, and resembles spots before the eyes more than a true after-image.

Although perhaps not technically an after-*image*, an after-effect of acoustic stimulation observed by Rosenblith et al. (1947) is of considerable interest. After listening for

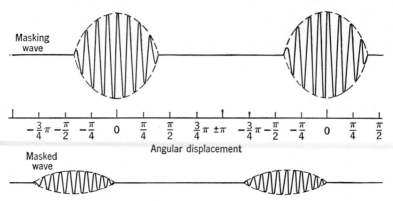

FIG. 24. The stimuli used to study the temporal spread of masking are repeated spindles of tone. The masked spindles can be made to come a little early (as shown in the figure) or a little late. With a given time (or phase) interval, the Amplitude of the masked spindle is adjusted until the listener can just notice its presence. For comparison the threshold of the masked wave is also determined in quiet. (From R. L. Miller, 1947.)

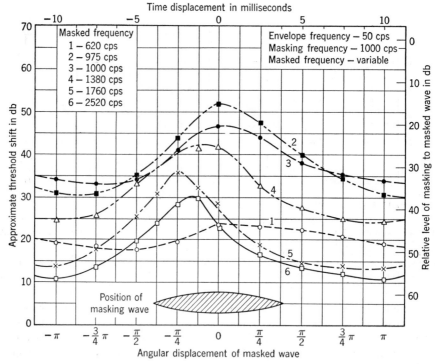

FIG. 25. Masking as a function of the temporal separation of the masked and masking waves illustrated in Fig. 24. Note that for masked frequencies greater than the masking frequency (1000 cps) masking is greatest when the masked wave arrives slightly earlier than the masking wave. (From R. L. Miller, 1947.)

some seconds to a train of sharp pulses (cf. Fig. 2*C*), the listener finds that familiar noises do not have their expected quality. Instead, they sound "jangly" or "twangy" as though they were being modulated in an unusual manner. This effect is noted after the pulses are turned off, and it continues for some seconds (Fig. 26*A*), depending upon the intensity and duration of the pulses. The after-effect does not manifest itself in the absence of acoustic stimulation, but it impresses itself upon almost any familiar sound. The characteristics a sound must have in order to set up the after-effect are not yet thoroughly understood, but it appears that the sound must contain relatively strong high-frequency components and that the overall sound pressure must undergo sudden jumps about 100 times a second.

BEATS, AURAL HARMONICS, AND COMBINATION TONES

If we stimulate the ear with two equally intense sinusoids and gradually increase their separation along the frequency scale, we find that the sound passes through four stages (Wever, 1929). First, a single subjective tone is heard; its loudness waxes and wanes. When the difference between the frequencies reaches 6 or 7 cps, we cease to hear the waxing and waning: the tone takes on an intermittent, throbbing quality like a violinist's vibrato. At about 25 cps we can no longer make out the individual throbs, and the sound has the rough quality of a Scotsman's burr. This third stage lasts until the two sinusoids are separated by a frequency interval, Δf, shown in Fig. 19 by the curve marked "beats," which is based on the data of Mayer (1894). In the fourth and final stage, the listener hears two smooth tones and, if the sinusoids are intense, a mixture of harmonics and combination tones.

According to Helmholtz' widely accepted theory, we hear beats only because the cochlear mechanism provides imperfect fre-

quency analysis. The essential condition for beats is that the two frequency components of the stimulus affect overlapping segments of the basilar membrane. In the region of overlap, two oscillations are superimposed, and the pattern of vibration is similar to that shown in Fig. 3. Outside the region of overlap, on the other hand, the oscillation is

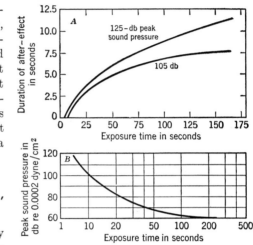

FIG. 26. Characteristics of the auditory after-effect. *A.* The duration of the after-effect depends upon the duration and upon the intensity of the preconditioning stimulation. *B.* To produce a constant duration (2 seconds) of after-effect, the intensity and duration of the preconditioning stimulation (140 pulses per second) must be related in the way shown by the curve. (From Rosenblith et al., 1947.)

principally attributable to a single frequency component.

Historically, beats and difference tones have been regarded as closely related phenomena because they are always characterized by the same frequency of recurrence (cf. Boring, 1942). It would appear, however, that their underlying processes are quite different. Beats occur whenever two tones are superposed. Combination tones (of which difference tones form a subgroup) occur only when two tones are superposed in a nonlinear system.

With difference tones, therefore, we come to the general question of nonlinear effects in hearing (see also Chapter 26). The output of a nonlinear circuit characteristically contains frequency components not present in the input. This effect is illustrated in Fig. 27 in which the input is a single-frequency tone: the output contains frequencies that are integral multiples of the input frequency. These are called harmonics or overtones. When the input consists of two beating tones, the output contains not only the two input frequencies and their harmonics, but components whose frequencies are sums and differences of the input frequencies and their integral multiples.

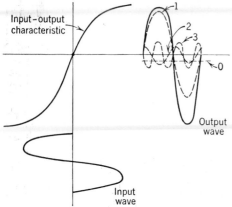

FIG. 27. Nonlinear distortion in the sound-transmission apparatus of the ear. By projecting points from the input waveform up to the characteristic curve, then over to the proper time position in the output plot, we see that the sinusoidal input is transformed into a complex output. The latter can be analyzed into a steady component (dotted line 0) and harmonics (dotted lines 1, 2, 3, •••) of the input frequency.

monics or overtones. When the input consists of two beating tones, the output contains not only the two input frequencies and their harmonics, but components whose frequencies are sums and differences of the input frequencies and their integral multiples.

The peripheral auditory mechanism is nonlinear when driven to high amplitudes of oscillation. The nonlinearity appears to be of the type represented in Fig. 27. It is only to be expected, therefore, that, when the intensity of an acoustic stimulus is sufficient to drive the system into the curved part of its characteristic, the resonant mechanism should analyze the complex into components, and that we should hear pitches corresponding to multiples and to combinations of the stimulus frequencies.

SUBJECTIVE ATTRIBUTES OF COMPLEX SOUNDS

A sound that is acoustically complex, i.e. one that has more than one frequency component, may or may not give rise to a complex sensation. Complexity also has interesting effects on the attributes, loudness, pitch, and volume, and may even give rise to new attributes.

The loudness of complex sounds. Experiments with acoustically complex tones (Fletcher and Munson, 1933; Fletcher, 1935; Howes, 1949) have shown that, if the components are sufficiently separated from one another along the frequency scale, the total loudness is equal to the sum of the loudnesses of the individual components presented separately. If the frequency components of the complex tones are not widely separated, however, the total loudness is somewhat less than the sum of the individual loudnesses. The failure of simple additivity is due to the fact that the cochlear or neural activities set up by the several components overlap. Following this reasoning to the extreme case, we should expect the growth of loudness (with increasing intensity) to be slowest for a single-component tone, because all the activity would be concentrated in one region of the basilar membrane and one channel of the auditory system. As is shown in Fig. 28, noises grow in loudness more rapidly than does a tone.

The pitch of complex sounds. We have already seen that there is not a direct, one-to-one relation between pitch and frequency, because pitch depends also upon intensity. But the variation of pitch with intensity is less marked for complex tones than for pure tones (Fletcher, 1935). The main problem to consider, therefore, is: to what aspect of the spectrum of a sound is pitch so closely (though not uniquely) related? Is it, indeed, the fundamental frequency?

Fletcher (1935) has pointed out that almost everyone hears the complex tone consisting of components 700, 800, 900, and 1000 cps as having approximately the same pitch as a 100-cycle pure tone. Although it has no energy at 100 cps, the 700-800-900-1000-cycle tone has by definition a fundamental frequency of 100 cps: the highest frequency of recurrence of the waveform is 100 cps.

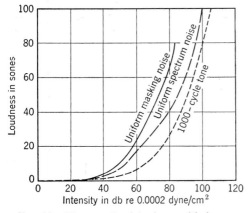

FIG. 28. The growth of loudness with increasing intensity. Loudness increases most rapidly for the uniform masking noise, which distributes excitation as widely as possible. The increase is least rapid for the pure tone, which produces a maximal concentration of excitation. The uniform spectrum noise (white noise) is intermediate. (Based on the data of Fletcher and Munson, 1937, and Pollack, 1948c.)

However, since the common difference frequency is also 100 cps, the observation that the pitch is approximately that of a 100-cycle tone does not decide between the two possible determiners of pitch, fundamental frequency and common difference frequency. Schouten (1940) resolves this question by asking listeners the pitch of a tone consisting of components at 300, 500, 700, 900, ···, cps. This tone has a fundamental of 100 cps and a common difference frequency of 200 cps. The listeners say that the pitch is approximately that of a 100-cycle pure tone, thus deciding in favor of the former alternative, that the fundamental frequency (or, as Schouten puts it, the periodicity of the waveform) is the important thing,

whether there is energy at the fundamental or not.

If we accept this conclusion, that pitch depends upon the fundamental frequency whether there is energy at the fundamental or not, we find ourselves on the verge of rejecting the place theory of pitch perception. We can reconcile the two theories only by arguing that, although in the acoustic stimulus there is no energy at the fundamental frequency, energy is shifted to the fundamental by nonlinear processes that intervene between the vibration of the eardrum and the excitation of the neurons of the auditory nerve. However, Schouten does not think the place theory can be rescued so easily. He points out that pitch is determined by the "missing fundamental" even at intensity levels so low that little or no nonlinear distortion should occur.

It might be possible, of course, for the central nervous system to determine the fundamental frequency from the neural correlates of the higher harmonics. Schouten thinks, however, that the clue for pitch is transmitted to the central nervous system as an actual periodicity. How the periodicity of the waveform can be preserved despite the analytical action of the cochlear mechanism is illustrated in Fig. 29. This figure is similar to Fig. 4 except that a train of input pulses has replaced the single pulse, and that here each low-frequency resonator responds only to a narrow band of the pulse-train spectrum, whereas each high-frequency resonator responds to a band wide enough to include several harmonics. The periodicity of the waveform is retained, therefore, in the responses of the high-frequency resonators. Schouten reports that a complex wave consisting entirely of frequency components above 3000 cps is heard as having a pitch of 200 cps if its components are spaced along the frequency scale at multiples of 200 cycles.

Schouten's theory applies, however, only within limits. If the period between recurrences of the complex wave is too long — a second, for example — we should not expect the pitch to be determined in any simple way by the periodicity. Ekdahl and Boring (1934) have shown, in fact, that the pitch of a tonal mass (e.g. 236, 244, 252, 260, 268, 276, 284, and 292 cps) is, as we should expect on the basis of the resonance-place theory, equal to the pitch of a pure tone lying near the midfrequency of the mass. The same result appears to hold for bands

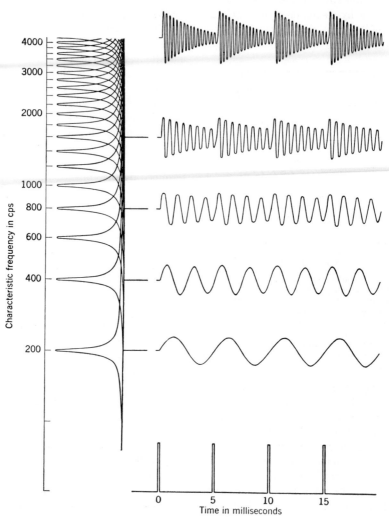

FIG. 29. The preservation of a periodicity corresponding to the fundamental frequency of a complex input wave of 200 pulses per second. The pulses are applied to each of the frequency-selective (resonant) circuits for which selectivity curves are shown. These resonant circuits differ from those of Fig. 4 in that they have equal Q's rather than equal damping constants. (The selectivity of the auditory system is intermediate between these two.) Only a single component of the input wave gets through the low-frequency resonators, but several pass through the higher resonators. These several components beat together and produce a periodic, complex output. If the auditory nerve fibers respond to this output, they may preserve the periodicity of the original pulse train. Eliminating the low-frequency components of the pulse train would have no effect upon this periodicity. (After Schouten, 1940.)

of random noise, for which the fundamental frequency is zero, i.e. the waveform never recurs.

A question arises as to how rigorously we should interpret Schouten's term, periodicity. If the component frequencies are incommensurable, the signal is not rigorously periodic, yet its *envelope* may be recurrent. We have evidence from experiments by Mathes and R. L. Miller (1947) that periodic recurrence of the envelope is sufficient, that rigorous periodicity of waveform is by no means an essential, to give the sound a pitch or at least a subjective attribute very much like pitch.

An instance in which a totally aperiodic sound appears to have a definite pitch has been described by G. A. Miller and Taylor (1948). They used a white noise turned on and off at various rates. When the rate of interruption was very low, the noise appeared to come, of course, in successive bursts. But when the rate was increased to about 40 per second, the noise took on a fairly definite pitch — this despite the fact that the intensity of the 40-cycle component of the interrupted noise was no stronger, and no less strong, than any other component. Listeners were able to match the interrupted noise in pitch to a pure tone with reasonable accuracy until the interruption rate exceeded 200 per second. Thus we have an instance in which pitch appears to depend solely upon fluctuations in the rms pressure of the sound wave.

On the basis of the foregoing evidence, we are justified in looking for two different bases for subjective pitch. The pitch of a pure tone — of a high-frequency tone, at any rate — appears to be related to the place within the higher nervous centers at which it excites activity, whereas the pitch of a complex tone of fundamental frequency between approximately 25 and 300 cps may depend principally upon the rate at which the fluctuations of this activity occur. (Note that the frequency region between 25 and 300 cps is a region of poor mechanical

frequency analysis, described in Chapter 27, Fig. 44.)

The volume of complex sounds. In the same experiment in which he determined equal-loudness contours for various bandwidths of white noise, Thomas (1949) had his listeners make equal-volume judgments. From the equal-volume contours, we can infer that as we increase the bandwidth of a uniform, continuous-spectrum noise, holding the total noise power constant, the volume of the noise grows even faster than the loudness does. This is especially true at high intensity levels. On the basis of Thomas' results we might hypothesize that volume is more dependent upon the spread of neural activity and less dependent upon the intensity of that activity than loudness is.

The timbre of complex sounds. The timbre of a complex sound has usually been defined as the subjective quality that depends upon the complexity or overtone structure of the physical sound. We have seen, however, that both the loudness and the pitch of a complex tone are influenced to some extent by its overtone structure. We must, therefore, fall back upon the ill-defined notion that timbre has to do with the distribution or pattern of pitch and loudness in the total sensation. Until careful scientific work has been done on the subject, it can hardly be possible to say more about timbre than that it is a "multidimensional" dimension.

The annoyance value of complex sounds. Noises are often annoying. Upon what factors does their annoyance value depend? Everyday observation tells us that annoyingness is usually bound up with meaning (the knock or sputter of an automobile engine, the honk of the car behind), with the state of the listener (the robin stomping on the lawn in the early morning), with repetitiveness (the incessant tick of the clock, the footsteps on the bare floor of the apartment upstairs), with intensity (the subway, the elevated), and with frequency (the squeak

of the chalk on the blackboard, of the finger-
nail on the window pane).

Despite the obvious practical importance
of accurate knowledge on these points, only
the last two factors have been studied in the
laboratory. Laird and Coye (1929) studied
the annoyance value of tones as related to
pitch and loudness, and Reese and Kryter
(1944) (also Kryter, 1948*b*) determined

duce effects. We should anticipate, therefore, that the process of stimulation must
involve some sort of accumulation of excitation. The question is, what are the rules
that govern this accumulation?

One of the principal methods employed
in attempts to answer this question has been
to determine the relation between the duration of a sound and the intensity it must

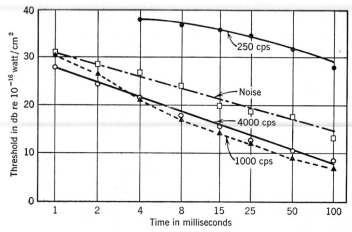

FIG. 30. Temporal integration at the absolute threshold. The curves show how the threshold
power decreases as the duration of the acoustic stimulus increases. (After Garner, 1947*a*.)

equal-annoyance and equal-loudness contours for narrow frequency bands of random
noise. The two experiments agree in indicating that annoyance goes up with loudness
and that high-frequency sounds are more
annoying for a given loudness than are low-
frequency sounds.

TEMPORAL EFFECTS IN HEARING

Up to this point we have been concerned
principally with sustained sounds, sounds of
sufficiently long duration that the question
of changes in their duration is of little concern. Now, however, we must examine more
closely the temporal dimension of hearing.

Temporal integration. Acoustic power
alone does not activate the auditory mechanism. The power must be expended for
some length of time: it takes energy to pro-

have to reach the absolute threshold. This
method has been used by Hughes (1946),
Garner (1947*b*), G. A. Miller (1948), and
de Vries (1948). From their results, shown
in part in Fig. 30, we see that, within the
range of durations studied, the threshold decreases as the duration increases.

If we had only the 4000-cycle curve of
Fig. 30 to consider, we might set up the
hypothesis that the auditory mechanism
simply integrates the stimulus power, that
the threshold expressed in terms of the time
integral of power, i.e. in terms of *energy*, is
constant. In simplest form,

$$It = \text{Constant}$$

where I is intensity and t is duration. According to this hypothesis, however, all the
curves should fall 1 log unit (10 db) in
intensity for each log unit increase in duration, and we see that the slope of the noise

curve is only about −8 db per log unit of duration. A second difficulty is that the 250-cycle curve levels off instead of continuing upward to the left as the duration is decreased. And, finally, common sense tells us that all the curves must level off instead of continuing downward to the right if only we make the stimulus durations long enough.

Therefore we must modify the hypothesis of simple integration. There is, of course, an infinitude of possible variations, two of which have been considered for the masked threshold by Garner and Miller (1947). The first, we can call the diverted input hypothesis. Briefly, it says that a constant portion of the stimulus power I_0 is diverted from the excitation process and is not integrated. The threshold function is therefore given by

$$(I - I_0)t = \text{Constant}$$

The second variation is the auditory analogue of Crozier's (1940) statistical theory of visual sensitivity. This formulation leads, however, to a prediction so similar to the one just mentioned that the data are not capable of discriminating between the two. As is so often the case, both hypotheses are tenable, and neither is proved to be correct.

We have as yet no real understanding of the difference between the curve for noise and the curve for the 4000-cycle tone. We can say only that the accumulation process is influenced by the frequency bandwidth of the acoustic signal. The peculiar behavior of the 250-cycle curve, on the other hand, is explicable. As the tone is made shorter, energy is spread along the frequency scale. Some of this energy falls within a frequency range in which auditory sensitivity is considerably higher than it is at 250 cycles. This increases the audibility of the tone and makes the curve less steep at short durations.

Not only the absolute threshold but also the masked threshold (Garner, 1947a) and the differential thresholds (Garner and Mil-

ler, 1944; Turnbull, 1944) of tones are dependent upon duration. The relation between the differential threshold for intensity and the duration of the increment added to an otherwise steady tone is shown in Fig. 31. The differential threshold for frequency also grows larger as the duration of the increment decreases.

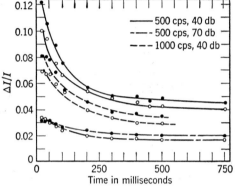

Fig. 31. The differential threshold for intensity as a function of the duration of the added increment. $\Delta I/I$ is the ratio of the sound-pressure increment to the standard sound pressure. Increments that last 0.5 second are as readily detectable as longer ones, but shorter durations require greater intensity. The open and the closed circles distinguish two listeners. (From Garner and Miller, 1944.)

The rise and fall of loudness. When we listen to a short sound, we hear its loudness build up rapidly, reach a maximum, and then decline. The problem of determining the temporal course of the sensation has interested several investigators (Metzger, 1932; Roelofs, 1939; Buytendijk and Meesters, 1942), but the measurement of loudness at instants closely spaced in time has proved very difficult. It has been possible, however, to answer questions phrased more directly in terms of the stimulus. How must we vary the intensity of a tone to compensate for changes in its duration? How long must a sound last before it gets to be as loud as it will ever become? How slowly can we turn a sound off and still have it appear to terminate abruptly? (Békésy (1933), Lifshitz (1933), and Munson (1947) have studied these questions with tonal stimuli, and G. A. Miller (1948), taking advantage of the uniform spectrum of white noise in order to avoid the problem of the 'impurity' of short tones, has studied them with bursts of noise.

Békésy found that, in order to hold the loudness of short tones constant, he had to

or noise with varying degrees of abruptness, and to find the highest rate of decay that could be distinguished from instantaneous cessation. Békésy's and Miller's results agree in indicating that, regardless of the intensity of the sound, the length of time required for the sensation to disappear is approximately constant. However, the noise

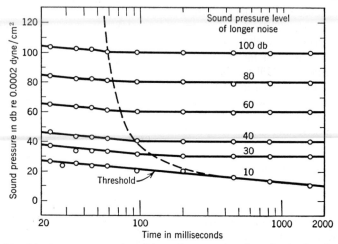

FIG. 32. Equal-loudness contours for white noise as a function of stimulus duration. The sound pressure of a short burst of noise that sounded equal in loudness to a standard 1.0-second burst is plotted as a function of the duration of the short burst. The dashed curve indicates the shortest duration for which loudness is independent of duration. (After G. A. Miller, 1948.)

trade intensity (I) for duration (t) according to the rule, $\log I = -k \log t + c$. Loudness did not increase further, however, after the duration of an 800-cycle tone reached 180 milliseconds. Munson, using tones of 125, 1000, and 5650 cps, arrived at a slightly larger value, 250 milliseconds, for the critical duration. Miller's results (Fig. 32) indicate that the critical duration for white noise depends to a considerable extent upon the intensity, but it is shorter than Békésy's and Munson's values for tones. By studying the responses of two subjects lacking both the muscles and the ossicles to which they are normally attached, Miller was able to show that the dependence upon intensity is not due to contraction of the middle ear muscles.

The method used in studying the decay of auditory sensation was to turn off the tone

takes only about half as long to disappear as the tone. One way to explain how an intense sensation can disappear as fast as a weak one is to suppose that the individual elements of the auditory system operate in parallel, not in series. Except for differences in latency and rate of conduction, therefore, it should take no longer to set up activity in all the elements, or to stop that activity once it has been set up, than to start or to stop a single element. The reason why a noise disappears faster than a tone is not entirely clear, but it may be related to the fact that noise activates substantially the entire auditory system whereas a tone activates only a part of it. When a tone is turned off, activity declines in the part of the system that had been activated, but a trace of the activity may remain for some time. This trace stands out, it is reasonable to suppose, against the background of quiescence (or of neutral activity) of the unstimulated tissue. When noise is turned off, however, there is no background with which the trace can contrast.

Closely related to the questions of the rise and the decay of auditory sensation is the question of the loudness of short impulses. This question has been studied by Steudel

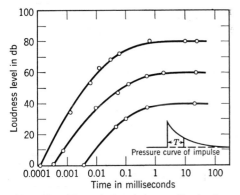

FIG. 33. The relation between the loudness level of a declining exponential impulse and its time constant. The loudness level is defined as the sensation level (decibels above threshold) of the 1000-cycle tone judged to have the same loudness. (From Stevens and Davis, 1938, after Steudel, 1933.)

(1933), who had his subjects judge the loudness of the clicks that resulted when he applied electrical impulses of various shapes and magnitudes to a loudspeaker. Steudel's results are illustrated in Fig. 33. The time constant T of the impulse is the length of time the impulse takes, in its exponential decay, to reach an amplitude equal to $1/e$ (about 37 per cent) of its initial amplitude.

Steudel interpreted his results as indicating that the important part of the click is the first 0.3 millisecond and that the loudness of the click is proportional to the integral of the pressure over that time interval. Bürck, Kotowski, and Lichte (1935), however, determined the spectra of Steudel's clicks and found that they could account for Steudel's results, as well as results obtained

with clicks of other shapes (see Fig. 34), by taking into account the distribution of the stimulus energy in frequency rather than in time. Garner (1947a) later used this approach to account for the audibility and loudness of interrupted tones. Thus far, however, there have been no successful efforts to handle loudness as a function both of frequency and of time.

The pitch of short tones. As the duration of a sinusoidal tone is increased from 2 or 3 milliseconds to 0.5 second or more, three stages can be distinguished in its subjective quality. These have been described by Bürck, Kotowski, and Lichte (1935) and by Doughty and Garner (1947) as (1) the stage

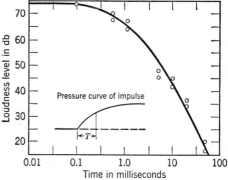

FIG. 34. The relation between the loudness level of a rising exponential impulse and its time constant (the length of time required for the impulse to reach approximately 63 per cent of its final amplitude). The impulse grows fainter as the time constant is increased beyond about 0.3 millisecond, because a slowly rising impulse (large time constant) has most of its energy concentrated at very low frequencies, for which the auditory mechanism is insensitive. (From Stevens and Davis, 1938, after Bürck, Kotowski, and Lichte, 1935.)

in which the subject hears only a click, (2) a stage in which the sound is a click with discernible tonal quality, and (3) the stage in which there is an on-click and an off-click with a tonal part of easily identifiable pitch in between.

In order to understand the stimulus basis of these three stages, it is helpful to think of the short tone in terms of its intensity-

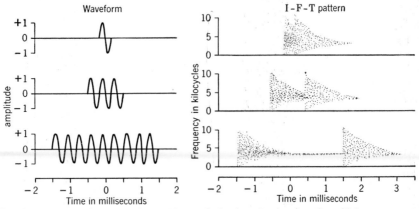

FIG. 35. Intensity-frequency-time patterns of short segments of a sinusoidal pressure wave. These patterns are of the type illustrated in Fig. 4. The visual appearances of the patterns are closely analogous to the auditory impressions obtained by listening to the three stimuli.

frequency-time pattern. This pattern, shown schematically in Fig. 35, makes it clear that the concentration of energy in the frequency dimension depends markedly upon the duration of the sinusoidal segment. In the upper pair of diagrams the energy is spread so diffusely along the frequency scale that there is no basis on which the auditory system can arrive at a judgment of pitch. In the middle pair, however, there is a discernible concentration of energy at 3000 cps. And in the lower pair the concentration is almost as clear-cut as it is in a pure tone. When we look at the stimulus from this point of view, what we see corresponds closely to what the listener hears.

Doughty and Garner have determined the shortest duration at which the listener can just discern "click pitch" and the shortest duration at which the listener can hear "tone pitch." Threshold durations determined at moderately high intensity are shown in Fig. 36. At lower intensities the threshold durations are somewhat greater.

Monaural detection of differences in phase. The responsibility for the statement that a listener "cannot perceive phase" is often attributed to Helmholtz. In fact Helmholtz did write, in his *Sensations of Tone,* that

. . . the quality of the musical portion of a compound tone depends solely on the num-

ber and relative strength of its partial simple tones, and in no respect on their differences of phase. [P. 126.]

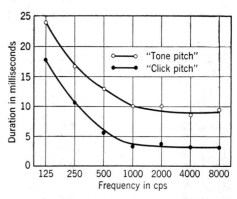

FIG. 36. The duration thresholds for two degrees of 'pitchedness' as functions of frequency. Below 1000 cps, two or three cycles of the wave must be heard for the sound to have any predominant pitch at all, whereas above 1000 cps the threshold is not a fixed number of cycles but a fixed length of time. (From Doughty and Garner, 1947.)

But Helmholtz also said:

We were not able to embrace these [nonmusical tones with upper partial tones close together along the frequency scale] in our experiments, and hence we must leave it for the present doubtful whether in such dissonating tones difference of phase is an element of importance. Subsequent theoretic

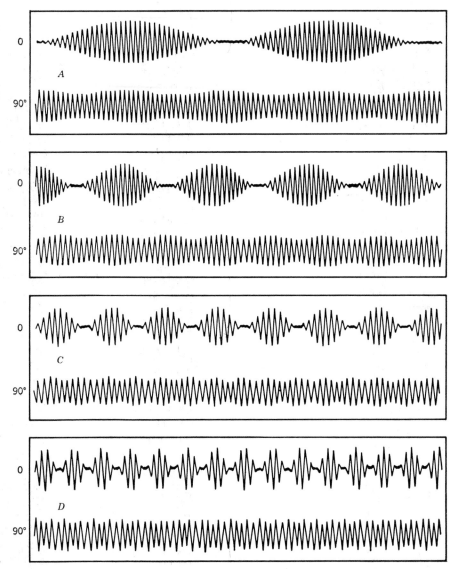

FIG. 37. Stimuli used to study monaural discrimination of phase differences. Both members of each pair of waveforms have the same Amplitude-vs-frequency characteristic. Each wave consists of three components, 1000 − ƒ, 1000, and 1000 + ƒ, where ƒ is designated as the "signal frequency." The only difference between members of a pair is that in one the 1000-cycle component has one phase angle, in the other it is retarded 90 degrees. This phase shift makes a clear and obvious difference in the subjective sound. The upper wave sounds rougher and lower in pitch than the lower wave. (From Mathes and Miller, 1947.)

considerations will lead us to suppose that it . . . [probably] is. [P. 127.]

Little note of this latter statement appears to have been taken by the pioneers in auditory research (Koenig excepted). With Helmholtz' prestige misplaced behind it, the theory that we are 'phase deaf' was generally accepted (for references, see Boring, 1942).

We see how unfounded the theory was when we recall that phase differences are simply time differences. When we shift the phases of components of a complex wave, we advance them or retard them in time. Now everyday experience tells us that the auditory system is capable of distinguishing temporal differences. Therefore it cannot be entirely phase deaf. To prove the point conclusively, we need only consider again the white noise and the single pulse of Fig. 1. Both sounds have 'flat' spectra. The only difference is one of phase: the various frequency components of the white noise are assigned their phase angles at random; the frequency components of the single pulse all reach their maximum amplitudes at the time $t = 0$, and they cancel one another at all other times. As a result, we hear the white noise as *sshhhh* and the single pulse as *pt*.

Mathes and R. L. Miller (1947) studied a wide variety of stimuli devised to show up phase effects in monaural perception. In one of their experiments, they used stimuli of the type shown in Fig. 37. In each pair of tracings the pronounced difference in waveform is due solely to difference in phase; the Amplitude-versus-frequency patterns are identical. Nevertheless there were decided differences in the sensations evoked by the stimuli. The waveform characterized by the wider fluctuations of the envelope sounded rough. When the second waveform was substituted, the listeners noticed a marked diminution in the roughness. They also reported that the "apparent pitch sensation" increased markedly.

Mathes and Miller found several other pairs of stimulus patterns that differed only

in phase, yet were readily distinguishable by ear. Three conditions appear to be prerequisite to the monaural phase effects. First, the important components of the stimulus must be close together in frequency (as Helmholtz thought). Second, there must not be too many frequency components. And third, the phase changes must make clear-cut differences in the envelope of the waveform.

SOUND LOCALIZATION

Thus far we have restricted our attention to what has been called *monotic* and *diotic* hearing.* Now, however, we must take into account the fact that the auditory system has two input channels. *Dichotic* stimulation is especially involved in the spatial localization of sounds.

The localization of actual sources. Stevens and Newman (1934, 1936a) noted that much of the earlier work on sound localization (see Boring, 1942) suffered from the defect that the listener was in a reverberant room and therefore received sounds from all sides, no matter where the source might be located. They tried, therefore, to get away from sound reflections by seating the observer in a chair at the top of a post rising above the roof of a building. The sound came from a loudspeaker located at the end of a rotatable boom and at the same level as the listener's ears. The loudspeaker was always set at the listener's right, and at an integral multiple of 15 degrees azimuth. The average errors of two observers are shown in Fig. 38A. This figure, which does not take into account confusion between symmetrical locations in the front and rear quadrants, shows that the errors of localization increased with the frequency of the stimulus

---

* *Monotic:* stimulus applied only to one ear; *diotic:* same stimulus to both ears; *dichotic:* different stimuli to the two ears. Binaural stimulation may be dichotic in respect of several dimensions or in respect of one dimension, e.g. dichotic in phase but diotic in Amplitude and frequency.

tone up to about 3000 cps, then decreased until they were again quite small for tones of 10,000 cps. The front-rear confusions are shown in Fig. 38B. The two curves, taken together, support the observations of Rayleigh (1907) and of von Hornbostel and Wertheimer (1920) that there are two bases for localization, one for high-frequency tones

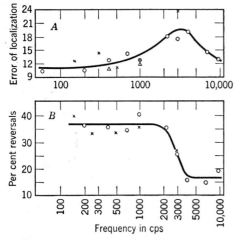

Fig. 38. Errors made in judging the direction of a sound source in the horizontal plane. Plot *A* shows the average of the errors, in degrees, for various tonal frequencies. The circles and the crosses are for two different series of observations with pure tones. The triangles are for impure tones. Plot *B* shows the percentage of confusions between front and rear quadrants. (After Stevens and Newman, 1936b.)

and the other for low-frequency tones. At frequencies near 3000 cps, evidently neither mechanism is effective, and the errors of localization are greatest.

A pure tone, emanating from a source to the right of the listener, travels a somewhat shorter and more direct path to the listener's right ear than to his left. Consequently the pressure waves in the two ear canals differ both in phase (or in time of arrival of a given phase) and in Amplitude. The Amplitude differences are considerable only at high frequencies because the head and the auricles act more efficiently as barriers against high frequencies than against low. The phase differences are, as we shall see, detectable

only at low frequencies. It is an easy inference, therefore, that one mechanism of (pure-tone) sound localization operates on the basis of intensive clues, the other on the basis of temporal clues.

When the physical sound is complex, each frequency component has *both* a characteristic interaural phase difference and a characteristic interaural Amplitude ratio. Furthermore it is not certain that the phase effect is restricted to low frequencies when the stimulus is complex. It is not surprising, therefore, that complex sounds are more readily localized than pure tones.

Intensive clues. In order to investigate the mechanism of sound localization, it is of interest to separate the intensive from the temporal variables and to study them individually.

One thing that we should like to know is how much more intense a tone must be made in one ear than in the other before the listener notices a shift in the apparent source of the tone. Upton (1936) determined that this differential threshold varied as a function of intensity. The differential dichotic sensitivity was greatest when the tone (800 cps) was between 70 and 100 db above threshold; at these levels the jnd was approximately 1 db, which is about twice the monaural jnd for intensity determined by Riesz. Ford (1942) got results that agree fairly well with Upton's. When the difference between the intensities at the two ears is increased beyond threshold, the apparent source of sound waves moves farther toward the side with the greater intensity. The rule, followed approximately, is that the angle measured from the midline is proportional to the logarithm of the Amplitude ratio (Stewart, 1920a, 1922, 1930, 1932).

Temporal clues (phase and time of arrival). Many experiments have been conducted to determine the relation between the interaural phase difference and the phenomenal location of tones, but the results have been equivocal. The more recent results agree, however, in restricting the importance of the interaural phase of pure tones to frequencies below 1500, or in any event below 2000, cps (Langmuir et al., 1944; Hirsh, 1948a, c). The tone tends to be localized toward the side to which the wave leading in phase is delivered. The degree of lateralization increases with increasing interaural phase difference until the sound appears to be localized in one ear. Stewart (1920b, 1922) reported that the angle of deviation from the midline is proportional to the interaural phase difference.

Using a 100-cycle tone as a stimulus, Monnier and Viaud (1946) found that the threshold for interaural phase difference was less than 3 degrees (time difference: 100 microseconds) for subjects practiced in locating aircraft by aural means. When pulses or clicks are used as stimuli, the just detectable interaural time difference is even smaller than it is with low-frequency tones (von Hornbostel and Wertheimer, 1920; Bennett, 1927; Wallach, Newman, and Rosenzweig, 1949). Results obtained by the latter experiments are illustrated in Fig. 39A. The graph indicates that a listener may tend to report localizations to one side when the interaural time difference is zero, but that a time difference of 30 or 40 microseconds clearly predominates, in a statistical sense, over his bias. If the time difference is increased to 2 or 3 milliseconds, the listener hears a double click, and longer time differences give rise to reports of two clicks with different localizations.

A listener in a reverberant room is stimulated not only by the sound wave transmitted directly to him from the source but also by echoes from the walls. A single pulse at the source becomes a series of pairs of pulses at the listener's ears. And each pair has its own interaural time difference. What happens in a situation of this kind has been investigated by Békésy (1930), by Langmuir et al. (1944), and by Wallach, Newman, and Rosenzweig (1949). The results can be summarized by describing two effects. First, similar impulsive sounds fuse into a single auditory sensation if they are closely spaced in time. Second, the first wave to arrive at the listener's ears tends to preempt the mechanism of localization. For example, consider the stimulus situation schematized in Fig. 39B. The two pairs of 1-millisecond pulses are described by giving the interaural time difference of the first pair, the interaural time difference of the second pair, and the interval between the two pairs. If the interval is more than 2 or 3 milliseconds (and if the time differences are considerably shorter than the interval), the listener reports that he hears two clicks. As the interval is made shorter, the two clicks fuse into a double click, then a single click, the subjective location of which is approximately that occupied by the first click when, with the longer interval, two clicks had been heard. The predominance, in determining localization, of the first pair of pulses over the second is illustrated in Fig. 39C, which shows how great the first interaural time difference must be to neutralize a second interaural time difference of given magnitude and opposite sign. The fusion and precedence effects offer an explanation of the fact that sound sources are localized reasonably well, even in highly reverberant rooms.

Externalization. In experiments in which the intensive and the temporal clues are separated, it is necessary to lead the two tones individually to the two ears. Earphones are usually employed for this purpose. It is interesting to note, therefore, that the tones are characteristically localized within or very near the head, which is quite different from the localization that is made when the tone is transmitted to the ears through the air from an actual source. Wallach (1938, 1939, 1940) proposed the theory that the externalization of the sound in the latter case is related to the fact that the listener can change the interaural phase and intensity relations by moving his head, whereas in the laboratory situation the earphones follow the head movement, and there is therefore no concomitant variation in the acoustic stimulation.

Clues to elevation. If sounds were localizable only in terms of right and left, only in the horizontal plane, we should have to

stationary, judgments of elevation are very poor. The listener must move his head in order to determine the angle of elevation.

Wallach (1939) has shown that (when vision is ruled out) head movements give us

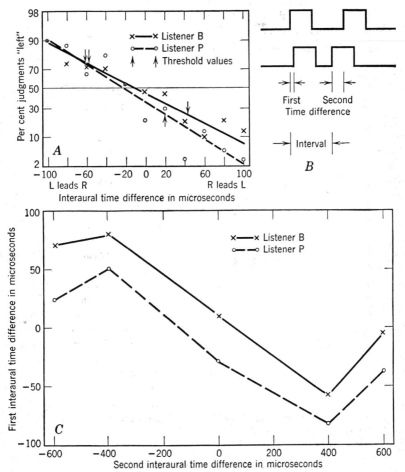

FIG. 39. The influence of interaural time differences upon the localization of impulsive sounds. If a single pulse is presented to one ear slightly before the other, it is localized to the side of prior stimulation as shown in *A*. If the stimulus is complicated by adding a second time-dichotic pulse after an interval of 1 millisecond (*B*), it is heard as a single click, and the localization of the sound image is determined to some extent by the second time difference but mainly by the first (*C*). (After Wallach, Newman, and Rosenzweig, 1949.)

look no further for sensory data than the intensitive and temporal relations just mentioned. However, sounds can be localized also in respect of elevation. The key to the problem of elevation is that, when both the sound source and the listener's head are held

the sensory data on the basis of which we make the judgments of elevation, quite as they give us the data on the basis of which we project the sound into the external world. Wallach found that, if he made the source of sound rotate with the listener's head in the horizontal plane, the listener reported that the sound appeared to come from above. Directly above and perhaps directly below, Wallach points out, are the only source locations for which horizontal rotation of the head normally produces no change in interaural phase and intensitive relations. Thus it appears that the mechanism of sound localization takes into account not only auditory data but also data from other sense systems as well.

Stereophonic sound localization. The effort to increase the realism of sound reproduction has led to experiments in two-channel sound transmission and in stereophonic sound reproduction. The idea of the simplest two-channel scheme is to record the sounds with two microphones, placed in the positions of the two ears of a dummy listener. When these sounds are led to a remote listener and applied to his ears via earphones, he gets almost exactly the same auditory picture that he would get if he were in the dummy's position. The effect is very compelling. When someone with hobnailed boots walks past the dummy, the listener pulls in his feet to keep them from getting stepped on. If loudspeakers are used to transduce the sound, the problem is considerably more complicated. It has been found, however, that a reasonably realistic reproduction can be achieved by recording the sound through two or more microphones and reproducing it with two or more loudspeakers (Steinberg and Snow, 1934; de Boer, 1940).

OTHER BINAURAL EFFECTS

Binaural summation at the absolute threshold. The question of binaural summation — whether or not the binaural threshold is lower than the monaural threshold — has been asked, and answered equivocally, for many years. Tarchenow, Preyer, and Körting (see Hirsh's review, 1948a), reported individually that, with both ears, they could hear sounds inaudible to either ear alone.

But the weight of authority — Fechner, Stumpf, and von Hornbostel — was behind a negative answer to the question, and we find Sivian and White (1933) deciding on the basis of what we should probably call inadequate evidence (comparable measurements on only two listeners) that their curve for the monaural MAF (Fig. 5) was equally representative of the binaural MAF.

When we turn to more recent experiments (Gage, 1932; Hughes, 1938; Caussé and Chavasse, 1942a; Shaw, Newman, and Hirsh, 1947; Keys, 1947; and Pollack, 1948b), we find emphasized the principal reason (originally mentioned by Urbantschitch in 1893) for the earlier divergence of opinion. These experiments show definitely that the binaural threshold for pure tones, expressed in terms of sound pressure developed at the eardrum, is lower than the monaural threshold. They show also, however, that, unless the two monaural thresholds are nearly equal, the difference between the binaural threshold and the threshold of the more sensitive ear is very small. Since the two ears of the average listener differ in sensitivity by almost 6 db, the amount of binaural summation actually found (about 1 db) is approximately what we should expect on the basis of perfect power summation. If we happen to find a listener whose ears are equally sensitive (or if, in applying the sound stimuli, we handicap the more sensitive ear, making the two ears artificially equal in sensitivity), we find that the binaural threshold is about 3 db lower than the monaural threshold. This again is perfect power summation: the listener is just able to detect the sound, no matter whether we offer all the acoustic power to one ear or divide it equally between the two. Hughes finds, in fact, that the rule holds for other than equal divisions of the total acoustic power, but Pollack's (1948b) data indicate that, both for a 1000-cycle tone and for white noise, binaural summation runs a little short of what would be expected on the power-summation hypothesis.

Binaural versus monaural DL's. Binaural DL's are somewhat smaller than monaural DL's. One explanation attributes this superiority of binaural hearing to what might be called binaural supplementation: (1) both ears are continually varying in sensitivity; (2) sometimes the right ear is the more acute, sometimes the left; (3) the central nervous system takes advantage of the better of the two incoming signals.

A more quantitative explanation has been formulated by Crozier, who views the sensory systems as statistical problem solvers for which the determination of the DL is the problem of finding a difference that just reaches a predetermined level of statistical significance. Two ears are better than one, according to this notion, because the sample (of neural elements) is twice as large. Since doubling the sample divides the standard error by $\sqrt{2}$, differences that would fall short of statistical significance for the monaural system are significant for the binaural system. Actually the binaural DL for intensity has been reported to be about 3 db lower than the monaural DL (Upton and Holway, 1937). Since 3 db corresponds to a voltage ratio of $\sqrt{2}$, the result is just what the statistical theory would predict.

Binaural summation of loudness. Early observations by Seebeck, by Mach, by Fechner, and by Docq (see Hirsh's review, 1948a) indicated that tones sound louder to both ears than they do to one, and that the binaural summation of loudness is more evident than binaural summation at the absolute threshold. But these observations did not carry as much weight as did Stumpf's dictum to the effect that the greater clarity, fullness, and volume of binaural sounds lead to an *illusion* of greater loudness. Stumpf's conclusion was not challenged successfully until 1929, when Békésy took the sound step of thinking that, if loudness is the listener's subjective reaction, it must *include* the illusion. Békésy made monaural-binaural loudness matches, obtaining the quantitative

evidence of summation shown in Fig. 40. We see that, for maximal summation, the tones delivered to the two ears must be of the same frequency. This is quite the opposite of what we noted in the case of monaural summation of loudness: when two tones are led to the same ear, they must be widely separated in frequency if their loudnesses are to add up.

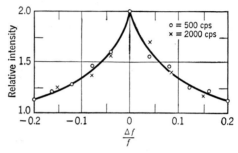

FIG. 40.   Binaural summation of loudness. Two tones of equal sound pressures, one presented to one ear, the other to the other ear, sound as loud as a single monaural tone of the relative sound pressure shown by the ordinate. The abscissa gives the relation between the frequencies of the two tones. Their sensation levels were 40 db. (From Stevens and Davis, 1938, after Békésy, 1929.)

In more recent experiments, Fletcher and Munson (1933) and Caussé and Chavasse (1942b) determined, for various monaural intensities, how much weaker than the monaural tone a binaural tone can be and still give rise to the same loudness. The results are not in complete agreement, but it is clear that binaural summation increases with intensity level, at least up to 60 db. Regardless of the intensity level, Fletcher and Munson found that a tone heard binaurally seems just twice as loud as the same tone heard monaurally.

Interaural phase and masking. We have seen that two ears are better than one when it comes to distinguishing between sound and silence. Are two ears better than one when the signal must be heard against a background of noise? In exploring this question, Hirsh (1948b) presented the tone first to one ear, then to both, *but he left the mask-*

ing noise in both ears all the time. To his surprise, he found that, in the tests with intense low-frequency tones, two ears were *worse* than one — worse by as much as 7 db. This effect he called "interaural inhibition" because it appeared that applying the tone to the second ear set up a process that, in some way, interfered with the process already going on. As indicated in Fig. 41, interaural inhibition is found only when the

to one side of the ball. When, on the other hand, the noise delivered to one of the ears was reversed in polarity so that both eardrums moved together toward the right, then back toward the left, the noise sounded spread out, and the tone was most audible when it was diotic in phase and had, therefore, a central localization.

Hirsh (1948c) worked out the functions relating audibility to interaural phase and

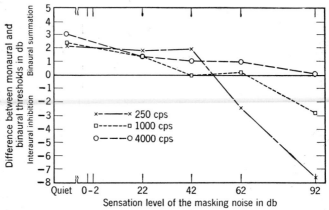

Fig. 41. Binaural summation and inhibition. Binaural inhibition occurs only with the 250- and 1000-cycle tones and in the presence of fairly strong masking noise. The masking noise was always presented binaurally. (From Hirsh, 1948a.)

stimulus tone is low in frequency and when the masking noise is high in intensity. Under other conditions some degree of binaural summation is found.

A related observation that throws light on Hirsh's interaural inhibition was described, more or less incidentally, in a report by Langmuir et al. (1944) on binaural effects in sound localization. They found that the audibility of a tone heard against a background of random noise was dependent upon the interaural phase relations of the tone and of the noise. When the noise was presented in such a way that it made the two eardrums move inward together toward the center of the head, then outward together, the noise sounded as though it were a compact ball in the center of the head, and the tone was most audible when it was sufficiently dichotic in phase to be localized, subjectively,

found that, under certain conditions, changing the interaural phase relations can shift the masked threshold by as much as 14 db. His results are illustrated in Fig. 42. This demonstration that interaural relations are so important in determining masking upsets the notion that masking is exclusively peripheral in origin. Evidently, masking is by no means determined entirely by cochlear processes: events taking place in the central nervous system, at or beyond the point at which the two afferent channels come together, have a considerable influence upon the degree to which the total excitation can be analyzed into parts.

Loudness, too, is influenced by interaural phase relations. Hirsh and Pollack (1948) found that the loudness of a tone, heard against a background of intense noise, is considerably greater if the tone and noise have

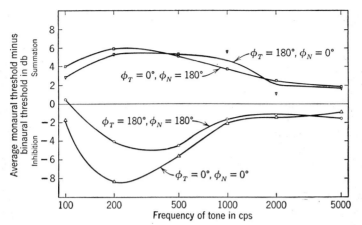

FIG. 42. The influence of interaural phase relations upon binaural summation and inhibition. The ordinate shows the relation between the monaural and binaural masked thresholds for pure tones of the frequencies indicated along the abscissa. The masking was by white noise at a sound pressure level of 59 db re 0.0002 dyne per square centimeter. The tones in the two ears were sometimes in phase ($\Phi_T = 0$ degrees), sometimes 180 degrees out of phase ($\Phi_T = 180$ degrees). The noise waveforms were sometimes the same in both ears ($\Phi_N = 0$ degrees), sometimes right-side up in one ear and upside down in the other ($\Phi_N = 180$ degrees). Thus there were four different interaural phase relations and, corresponding to them, four different curves of binaural summation and/or inhibition. (From Hirsh, 1948c.)

opposite interaural phase relations than if they have similar interaural phase relations. In the quiet, however, interaural phase has no effect upon loudness, nor upon the absolute threshold (Hirsh, 1948b).

Binaural pitch disparity — diplacusis. Otologists have long been familiar with a condition, known as *diplacusis binauralis*, in which the patient hears one pitch when his right ear is stimulated with a pure tone, another pitch when his left ear is stimulated with the same tone. But little note was taken of the early observations of von Liebermann and Révész (1914), and for many years it was not generally realized that a moderate degree of binaural pitch disparity is the rule rather than the exception. Diplacusis is measured by finding how much the stimulus frequency has to be changed, as the tone is switched from one ear to the other, to hold the pitch constant. Typical data (Stevens and Egan, 1941) are shown in Fig. 43. The amount of diplacusis depends upon the intensity of the stimulus: it decreases as the intensity is raised.

Diplacusis is most apparent after one ear has been subjected to intense stimulation. Pitch disparities amounting to as much as an

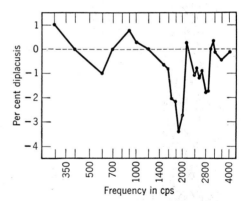

FIG. 43. The displacusis of a 'normal' listener. The frequency of the tone delivered to the left ear had to be changed to make the left-ear pitch match the right-ear pitch. The ordinate shows the percentage of change in frequency required. (From Morgan, 1943, based on the data of Stevens and Egan, 1941.)

octave were found by Davis et al. (1944) in listeners who had been exposed for several minutes to tones 130 to 150 db above 0.0002 dyne per square centimeter. Sometimes, in fact, the sound heard with the affected ear had not one pitch but two pitches: one higher, the other lower, than the pitch heard with the previously unstimulated ear. Rüedi and Furrer (1945, 1946, 1947) found that the pitch tends to be shifted upward if the preconditioning tone is below 4000 cps in frequency, downward if the preconditioning tone is above 4000 cps.

Diplacusis provides the place theorist with excellent ammunition to use against frequency theories of hearing. If one is to maintain that pitch depends upon neural frequency, he must explain how neural frequency gets out of step with stimulus frequency; he must reject the notion of synchrony between the acoustic stimulus and the neural response. In terms of the place theory, on the other hand, the facts of diplacusis almost explain themselves. We need assume only that a small segment of the basilar mechanism is relatively insensitive — for example, as a result of previous stimulation. When we apply a weak tonal stimulus that would normally excite the nerve fibers that innervate this segment, nothing happens. As we raise the intensity, nerve fibers innervating an adjacent region are activated before the elevated thresholds of the local fibers are reached. The neighboring fibers give rise to a pitch that is characteristic of their 'place,' hence slightly different from the pitch normally associated with the stimulus frequency.

AUDITORY THEORY

The principal tasks of auditory theory are (1) to explain the psychophysics of hearing in terms of aural mechanics and neurophysiology, (2) to give audition its proper setting in a general theory of communication, and (3) to provide a calculus of response to auditory stimulation. In this chapter we have been concerned principally with the third of the three objectives. The first and second considerations set the pattern for the chapters that follow. Now is the time, therefore, to see how near we are to having an auditory calculus. Can we start with data about the listener and the acoustic stimulus, and from these data calculate the listener's auditory experience or response? Can we parallel the auditory process by manipulating symbols?

In some situations, we can — with fair approximation. If the stimulus is simple enough or nearly enough like stimuli with which we have had experience, we can take advantage of empirically determined relations and predict, for example, the loudness in sones and the pitch in mels. The calculation involved in making the prediction (usually little more than graphical interpolation) is admittedly primitive, but it is a start.

The next question is, how do we proceed when we encounter acoustic stimuli that are complex and unfamiliar? Must we make empirical tests with these new sounds or others nearly like them, or may we reason from our knowledge based on simpler stimuli? This question brings us up against one of the greatest obstacles to the study of psychology: it is difficult to calculate from components to the whole when the system under consideration is nonlinear.

We should like to break the complex stimulus down into familiar components, to look up the expected responses to these components, and then to arrive at a prediction for the complex stimulus by adding up the component responses. The trouble is that, knowing we are dealing with a nonlinear mechanism, we cannot count on linear additivity. We must take into account the possibility of interactions among components, and there is no way to learn about the interactions except through experiment. Except in the few instances (e.g. loudness of complex tones, masking) in which interactions have been rather thoroughly studied, we must admit that we have not yet reduced psychoacoustics to symbols.

This admission need not discourage us; it is evidence of approaching maturity that the question of a calculus should even arise. What we should see, actually, is this: it is patently not feasible to explore experimentally the infinitude of acoustic stimuli that may some day prove to be of interest. We must learn to predict the complex from knowledge of the simple; we must learn to combine components. The first step, logically, is to choose the right basic components. The next is to study their interactions.

Actually, it will probably take considerable study of interactions to determine what are the right basic components. Sinusoids, for all their mathematical beauty, are probably not the right ones because transient changes are so important in hearing. It may turn out that exponentially declining spindles of the type illustrated in Fig. 4, or perhaps pulses with envelopes the shape of the normal distribution curve, may turn out to be the proper building blocks. At any rate, as the later parts of the chapter have indicated, we have already put behind us the preoccupation with pure tones that characterized the early period of research in hearing. Perhaps in reaction we have adopted as a favorite stimulus that most complex of all sounds, white noise. In order to achieve a calculus of psychoacoustics, however, we must do extensive work in the intermediate region — work with simple combinations of simple components — so that we can learn the rules of interaction.

REFERENCES *

Allen, C., and I. Rudnick. In *Atmospheric physics and sound propagation*. Progress Report 17, Acoustics Laboratory, Pennsylvania State College, 20 Oct. 1947. Pp. 3–7.

* Reports prepared under contract with the Office of Scientific Research and Development usually bear an OSRD number. In addition, many carry a PB number, which indicates that they may be obtained from the Office of Technical Services, U. S. Department of Commerce, Washington 25, D. C.

Bachem, A. Note on Neu's review of the literature on absolute pitch. *Psychol. Bull.*, 1948, **45**, 161–162.

Banister, H. Audition: I. Auditory phenomena and their stimulus correlates. In C. Murchison (Ed.), *Handbook of general experimental psychology*. Worcester: Clark University Press, 1934. Chapter 16.

Beasley, W. C. National Health Survey, Hearing Study Series, Bulletin 5. The United States Public Health Service, 1938.

Békésy, G. von. Zur Theorie des Hörens. Über die eben merkbare Amplituden- und Frequenzänderung eines Tones. Die Theorie der Schwebungen. *Physik. Z.*, 1929, **30**, 721–745.

Békésy, G. von. Zur Theorie des Hörens. Über das Richtungshören bei einer Zeitdifferenz oder Laustärkenungleichheit der beiderseitigen Schalleinwirkungen. *Physik. Z.*, 1930a, **31**, 824–835, 857–867.

Békésy, G. von. Über das Fechnersche Gesetz und seine Bedeutung für die Theorie der akustischen Beobachtungsfehler und die Theorie des Hörens. *Ann. Physik*, 1930b, **7**, 329–359.

Békésy, G. von. Bemerkungen zur Theorie der günstigsten Nachhalldauer von Räumen. *Ann. Physik*, 1931, **8**, 851–873.

Békésy, G. von. Über die Hörsamkeit der Ein- und Ausschwingvorgänge mit Berücksichtigung der Raumakustik. *Ann. Physik*, 1933, **16**, 844–860.

Békésy, G. von. Über akustische Rauhigkeit. *Z. techn. Physik*, 1935, **16**, 276–282.

Békésy, G. von. Über die Herstellung und Messung langsamer sinusförmiger Luftdruckschwankungen. *Ann. Physik*, 1936a, **25**, 413–432.

Békésy, G. von. Über die Hörschwelle und Fühlgrenze langsamer sinusförmiger Luftruchschwankungen. *Ann. Physik*, 1936b, **26**, 554–566.

Békésy, G. von. Über die Resonanzkurve und die Abklingzeit der verschiedenen Stellen der Schneckentrennwand. *Akust. Z.*, 1943, **8**, 66–76.

Békésy, G. von. The recruitment phenomenon and difference limen in hearing and vibration sense. *Laryngoscope*, 1947a, **57**, 765–777.

Békésy, G. von. A new audiometer. *Acta otolaryng., Stockh.*, 1947b, **35**, 411–422.

Békésy, G. von. Vibration of the head in a sound field and its role in hearing by bone conduction. *J. acoust. Soc. Amer.*, 1948, **20**, 749–760.

Bennett, A. L. A measurement of the efficiency of the ears as a means of detecting short time intervals. *J. opt. Soc. Amer.*, 1927, **14**, 342–345.

Beranek, L. L., H. P. Sleeper, Jr., and E. E. Moots. The design and construction of anechoic sound chambers. *OSRD Report 4190*, Harvard University, 1945.

de Boer, K. Stereophonic sound reproduction. *Philips Tech. Rev.*, 1940, **5**, 107.

Boring, E. G. The size of the differential limen for pitch. *Amer. J. Psychol.*, 1940, **53**, 450–455.

Boring, E. G. *Sensation and perception in the history of experimental psychology.* New York: Appleton-Century-Crofts, 1942.

Boring, E. G., and S. S. Stevens. The nature of tonal brightness. *Proc. nat. Acad. Sci., Wash.,* 1936, **22,** 514–521.

Brogden, W. J., and G. A. Miller. Physiological noise generated under earphone cushions. *J. acoust. Soc. Amer.,* 1947, **19,** 620–623.

Bronstein, A. J. Sensibilization of the auditory organ by acoustic stimuli. *Bull. Biol. Méd. exp., U.R.S.S.,* 1936, **1,** 274–275, 276–277; **2,** 347–349.

Bunch, C. C. Age variations in auditory acuity. *Arch. Otolaryng.,* 1929, **9,** 625–636.

Bürck, W., P. Kotowski, and H. Lichte. Die Lautstärke von Knacken, Geräuschen und Tönen. *Elek. Nachr.-Techn.,* 1935, **12,** 278–288.

Buytendijk, F. J. J., and A. Meesters. Duration and course of the auditory sensation. *Commentationes Pontif. Acad. Sci.,* 1942, **6,** 557–576.

Carson, J. R. *Electric circuit theory and the operational calculus.* New York: McGraw-Hill, 1920.

Caussé, R., and P. Chavasse. Recherches sur le seuil de l'audition binauriculaire comparé au seuil monauriculaire. *C. R. Soc. Biol., Paris,* 1942*a,* **135,** 1272–1275.

Caussé, R., and P. Chavasse. Différence entre l'écoute binauriculaire et monauriculaire pour la perception des intensités supraliminaires. *C. R. Soc. Biol., Paris,* 1942*b,* **136,** 405.

Caussé, R., and P. Chavasse. Etudes sur la fatigue auditive. Note Technique No. 1057. Paris: Centre National d'Etudes des Télécommunications, 10 Dec. 1947. Pp. 29*ff.*

Churcher, B. G., A. J. King, and H. Davies. The minimum perceptible change of intensity of a pure tone. *Phil. Mag.,* 1934, **18,** 927–939.

Crozier, W. J. The theory of the visual threshold. I. Time and intensity. *Proc. nat. Acad. Sci., Wash.,* 1940, **26,** 54–60.

Davis, H., et al. Final report on physiological effects of exposure to certain sounds. OSRD Report 889, Harvard University, 1942 (PB M 19786).

Doughty, J. M., and W. R. Garner. Pitch characteristics of short tones. I. Two kinds of pitch threshold. *J. exp. Psychol.,* 1947, **37,** 351–365.

Ekdahl, A. G., and E. G. Boring. The pitch of tonal masses. *Amer. J. Psychol.,* 1934, **46,** 452–455.

Fletcher, H. *Speech and hearing.* New York: Van Nostrand, 1929.

Fletcher, H. Newer concepts of the pitch, the loudness and the timbre of musical tones. *J. Franklin Instit.,* 1935, **220,** 405–429.

Fletcher, H. Auditory patterns. *Rev. mod. Phys.,* 1940, **12,** 47–65.

Fletcher, H., and W. A. Munson. Loudness, its definition, measurement, and calculation. *J. acoust. Soc. Amer.,* 1933, **5,** 82–108.

Fletcher, H., and W. A. Munson. Relation between loudness and masking. *J. acoust. Soc. Amer.,* 1937, **9,** 1–10.

Flynn, B. M. Pitch discrimination: The form of the psychometric function and simple reaction time to liminal differences. *Arch. Psychol., N. Y.,* 1943, **280,** 1–41.

Flynn, J. P., and S. J. Goffard, et al. Auditory factors in the discrimination of radio range signals, collected informal reports. OSRD Report 6292, Psycho-Acoustic Laboratory, Harvard University, 1945 (PB 19811).

Ford, A. Dynamic auditory localization: I. The binaural intensity disparity limen. *J. acoust. Soc. Amer.,* 1942, **13,** 367–372.

French, N. R., and J. C. Steinberg. Factors governing the intelligibility of speech sounds. *J. acoust. Soc. Amer.,* 1947, **19,** 90–119.

Gabor, D. Theory of communication. *J. Inst. elec. Eng.,* 1946, **93,** Part 3, 429–457.

Gage, F. H. A note on the binaural threshold. *Brit. J. Psychol.,* 1932, **23,** 148–151.

Gardner, M. B. Short duration auditory fatigue as a method of classifying hearing impairment. *J. acoust. Soc. Amer.,* 1947, **19,** 178–190.

Garner, W. R. The effect of frequency spectrum on temporal integration of energy in the ear. *J. acoust. Soc. Amer.,* 1947*a,* **19,** 808–815.

Garner, W. R. Auditory thresholds of short tones as a function of repetition rates. *J. acoust. Soc. Amer.,* 1947*b,* **19,** 600–608.

Garner, W. R. Accuracy of binaural loudness matching with repeated short tones. *J. exp. Psychol.,* 1947*c,* **37,** 337–350.

Garner, W. R., and G. A. Miller. The masked threshold of pure tones as a function of duration. *J. exp. Psychol.,* 1947, **37,** 293–303.

Geiger, P. H., and F. A. Firestone. The estimation of fractional loudness. *J. acoust. Soc. Amer.,* 1933, **5,** 25–30.

Goffard, S. J., and J. C. R. Licklider. Effects of static on radio range performance. Report PNR-10, Psycho-Acoustic Laboratory, Harvard University, 21 Mar. 1946.

Goodfellow, L. D. The stability of auditory and vibro-tactile thresholds. *J. gen. Psychol.,* 1938, **18,** 49–55.

Gundlach, R. H. Tonal attributes and frequency theories of hearing. *J. exp. Psychol.,* 1929, **12,** 187–196.

Gundlach, R. H., and M. Bentley. The dependence of tonal attributes upon phase. *Amer. J. Psychol.,* 1930, **42,** 519–543.

Halverson, H. M. Diotic tonal volumes as a function of phase. *Amer. J. Psychol.,* 1922, **33,** 526–534.

Halverson, H. M. Tonal volume as a function of intensity. *Amer. J. Psychol.,* 1924, **35,** 360–367.

Ham, L. B., and J. S. Parkinson. Loudness and intensity relations. *J. acoust. Soc. Amer.,* 1932, **3,** 511–534.

Harris, J. D. Pitch discrimination and absolute pitch. Progress Report 1, Medical Research

Dept., U. S. Submarine Base, New London, Conn., 30 Jan. 1948.

Harris, J. D., and C. K. Meyers. Detection thresholds and tonal thresholds in auditory acuity. *Amer. Psychologist*, 1947, **2**, 433.

Hartley, R. V. L. Transmission of information. *Bell Syst. tech. J.*, 1928, **7**, 535–563.

Hawkins, J. E., Jr., and S. S. Stevens. The masking of pure tones and of speech by white noise. *J. acoust. Soc. Amer.*, 1950, **22**, 6–13.

Heisenberg, W. Über den anschaulichen Inhalt der quantentheoretischen Kinematik und Mechanik. *Z. Physik*, 1927, **43**, 172–198.

Hirsh, I. J. Binaural summation—a century of investigation. *Psychol. Bull.*, 1948a, **45**, 193–206.

Hirsh, I. J. Binaural summation and interaural inhibition as a function of the level of masking noise. *Amer. J. Psychol.*, 1948b, **61**, 205–213.

Hirsh, I. J. The influence of interaural phase on interaural summation and inhibition. *J. acoust. Soc. Amer.*, 1948c, **20**, 536–544.

Hirsh, I. J., and I. Pollack. The role of interaural phase in loudness. *J. acoust. Soc. Amer.*, 1948, **20**, 761–766.

von Hornbostel, E. M., and M. Wertheimer. Über die Wahrnehmung der Schallrichtung. *S. B. preuss. Akad. Wiss.*, 1920, **20**, 388–396.

Howes, D. H. The loudness of multicomponent tones. *Amer. J. Psychol.*, 1950, **63**, 1–30.

Hughes, J. W. The monaural threshold: Effect of subliminal contralateral stimulation. *Proc. roy. Soc.*, 1938, **B124**, 406–420.

Hughes, J. W. The threshold of audition for short periods of stimulation. *Proc. roy. Soc.*, 1946, **B133**, 486–490.

James, H. M., N. B. Nichols, and R. S. Phillips, *Theory of servomechanisms*. New York: McGraw-Hill, 1947.

Joos, M. Acoustic phonetics. *Language* (J. linguistic Soc. Amer.), 1948, **24** Suppl., 1–136.

Kendall, M. G. *The advanced theory of statistics.* London: Griffin, 1946. Volume II.

Keys, J. W. Binaural versus monaural hearing. *J. acoust. Soc. Amer.*, 1947, **19**, 629–631.

Knudsen, V. O. The sensibility of the ear to small differences in frequency and intensity. *Phys. Rev.*, 1923, **21**, 84–103.

Koenig, W., H. K. Dunn, and L. Y. Lacy. Sound spectrograph. *J. acoust. Soc. Amer.*, 1946, **18**, 19–49.

Kryter, K. D. Effects of high altitude on speech intelligibility. *J. appl. Psychol.*, 1948a, **32**, 503–511.

Kryter, K. D. Loudness and annoyance value of bands of noise. *Oralism and Auralism*, Transactions, Thirtieth Annual Meeting, National Forum on Deafness and Speech Pathology, March 19–20, 1948b, 26–28.

Laird, D. A., and K. Coye. Psychological measurement of annoyance as related to pitch and loudness. *J. acoust. Soc. Amer.*, 1929, **1**, 158–163.

Langmuir, I., V. J. Schaefer, C. V. Ferguson, and E. F. Hennelly. A study of binaural perception of the direction of a sound source. OSRD Report 4079, 30 June 1944 (PBL 31014).

Liebermann, P. von, and G. Révész. Die binaurale Tonmischung. *Z. Psychol.*, 1914, **69**, 234–255.

Lifshitz, S. Two integral laws of sound perception relating loudness and apparent duration of sound impulses. *J. acoust. Soc. Amer.*, 1933, **5**, 31–33.

Lifshitz, S. Fluctuation of hearing threshold. *J. acoust. Soc. Amer.*, 1939, **11**, 118–121.

Lüscher, E., and J. Zwislocki. The decay of sensation and the remainder of adaptation after short pure-tone impulses on the ear. *Acta oto-laryng., Stockh.*, 1947, **35**, 428–445.

Mach, E. Über einige der physiologischen Akustik angehörige Erscheinungen. *Sitzber. Akad. Wiss. Wien* (Math.-nat. Kl., Abt. 2), 1864, **50**, 342.

de Maré, G. Audiometrische Untersuchungen. *Acta oto-laryng., Stockh.*, Suppl. 1939, **31**.

Mathes, R. C., and R. L. Miller. Phase effects in monaural perception. *J. acoust. Soc. Amer.*, 1947, **19**, 780–797.

Mayer, A. M. Researches in acoustics. IX. *Phil Mag.* (Ser. 5), 1894, **37**, 259–288.

Metzger, W. Versuch einer gemeinsamen Theorie der Phänomene Fröhlichs und Hazelhoffs und Kritik ihrer Verfahren zur Messung der Empfindungszeit. *Psychol. Forsch.*, 1932, **16**, 176–200.

Meyer, M. F. [Review of] *Zur Grundlegung der Tonpsychologie*, by G. Révész. *Psychol. Bull.*, 1914, **11**, 349–352.

Miller, G. A. Sensitivity to changes in the intensity of white noise and its relation to masking and loudness. *J. acoust. Soc. Amer.*, 1947, **19**, 609–619.

Miller, G. A. The perception of short bursts of noise. *J. acoust. Soc. Amer.*, 1948, **20**, 160–170.

Miller, G. A., and W. R. Garner. Effect of random presentation on the psychometric function: Implications for a quantal theory of discrimination. *Amer. J. Psychol.*, 1944, **57**, 451–467.

Miller, G. A., and G. A. Heise. Study of melodic patterning. In *Periodic Status Report VIII*, Psycho-Acoustic Laboratory, Harvard University, 1 Jan. 1949.

Miller, G. A., and W. G. Taylor. The perception of repeated bursts of noise. *J. acoust. Soc. Amer.*, 1948, **20**, 171–182.

Miller, G. A., F. M. Wiener, and S. S. Stevens. *Transmission and reception of sounds under combat conditions.* Summary Technical Report of Division 17, NDRC. Washington, D. C., 1946. Volume 3.

Miller, R. L. Masking effect of periodically pulsed tones as a function of time and frequency. *J. acoust. Soc. Amer.*, 1947, **19**, 798–807.

Monnier, A. M., and G. Viaud. Recherches sur l'acuité de la perception binaurale. *Arch. int. Physiol.*, 1946, **54**, 107–116.

Montgomery, H. C. Do our ears grow old? *Bell Lab. Rec.*, 1932, **10**, 311.

Morgan, C. T. *Physiological psychology.* New York: McGraw-Hill, 1943.

Morgan, C. T., and W. R. Garner. Further measurements of the relation of pitch to intensity. *Amer. Psychologist,* 1947, **2,** 433.

Munson, W. A. The growth of auditory sensation. *J. acoust. Soc. Amer.,* 1947, **19,** 584–591.

Neu, D. M. A critical review of the literature on "absolute pitch." *Psychol. Bull.,* 1947, **44,** 249–266.

Neu, D. M. Absolute pitch—a reply to Bachem. *Psychol. Bull.,* 1948, **45,** 534–535.

Parrack, H. O., D. H. Eldredge, and H. F. Koster. Physiological effects of intense sound. Report MCREXD-695-71B, Aero-Medical Laboratory, 24 May 1948.

Pollack, I. The atonal interval. *J. acoust. Soc. Amer.,* 1948a, **20,** 146–149.

Pollack, I. Monaural and binaural threshold sensitivity for tones and for white noise. *J. acoust. Soc. Amer.,* 1948b, **20,** 52–57.

Pollack, I. Studies in the loudness of complex sounds. Ph.D. dissertation, Harvard University, 1948c.

Rao, V. V. L. *The decibel notation.* Madras: Addison, 1944.

Rawdon-Smith, A. F., and G. C. Grindley. An illusion in the perception of loudness. *Brit. J. Psychol.,* 1935, **26,** 191–195.

Rayleigh, Lord (J. W. Strutt). On our perception of sound direction. *Phil. Mag.* (Ser. 6), 1907, **13,** 214–232.

Reese, T. W., and K. D. Kryter. The relative annoyance produced by various bands of noise. Report IC-65, Psycho-Acoustic Laboratory, Harvard University, 17 March 1944.

Révész, G. *Zur Grundlegung der Tonpsychologie.* Leipzig: Veit, 1913. Pp. 4–75.

Rich, G. J. A study of tonal attributes. *Amer. J. Psychol.,* 1919, **30,** 121–164.

Riesz, R. R. Differential intensity sensitivity of the ear for pure tones. *Phys. Rev.,* 1928, **31,** 867–875.

Roelofs, C. O. Ist die Wahrnehmungszeit messbar? *Z. Psychol.,* 1939, **145,** 212–235.

Rosenblith, W. A., and G. A. Miller. The threshold of hearing for continuous and interrupted tones. (Abstract) *J. acoust. Soc. Amer.,* 1949, **21,** 467.

Rosenblith, W. A., G. A. Miller, J. P. Egan, I. J. Hirsh, and G. J. Thomas. An auditory afterimage? *Science,* 1947, **106,** 333–334.

Rüedi, L., and W. Furrer. Tonhöhenempfindung und akustisches Trauma. *Experientia,* 1945, **1,** 201–202.

Rüedi, L., and W. Furrer. Akustisches Trauma und Funktion des Innerohres. *Acta oto-laryng., Stockh.,* 1946, **33,** 460–470.

Rüedi, L., and W. Furrer. Traumatic deafness. Chapter X in E. P. Fowler, Jr. (Ed.), *Medicine of the ear.* New York: Nelson, 1947.

Schouten, J. F. The perception of pitch. *Philips tech. Rev.,* 1940, **5,** 286–294.

Seebeck, A. Beiträge zur Physiologie des Gehör- und Gesichtsinnes. *Ann. Phys. Chem.,* 1846, **68,** 449–458.

Shannon, C. E. A mathematical theory of communication. *Bell Syst. tech. J.,* 1948, **27,** 379–343, 623–656.

Shaw, W. A., E. B. Newman, and I. J. Hirsh. The difference between monaural and binaural thresholds. *J. exp. Psychol.,* 1947, **37,** 229–242.

Shower, E. G., and R. Biddulph. Differential pitch sensitivity of the ear. *J. acoust. Soc. Amer.,* 1931, **3,** 275–287.

Silverman, S. R., C. E. Harrison, and H. S. Lane. Tolerance for pure tones and speech in normal and hard-of-hearing ears. OSRD Report 6303, Central Institute for the Deaf, St. Louis, 1946 (PB L 58239).

Sivian, L. J., and S. D. White. On minimum audible sound fields. *J. acoust. Soc. Amer.,* 1933, **4,** 288–321.

Snow, W. B. Change of pitch with loudness at low frequencies. *J. acoust. Soc. Amer.,* 1936, **8,** 14–19.

Steinberg, J. C., H. C. Montgomery, and M. B. Gardner. Results of the World's Fair hearing tests. *J. acoust. Soc. Amer.,* 1940, **12,** 291–301.

Steinberg, J. C., and W. B. Snow. Physical factors in auditory perspective. *Bell Syst. tech. J.,* 1934, **13,** 247–260.

Steudel, U. Über Empfindung und Messung der Lautstärke. *Hochfrequenztechn. u. Elektroakust.,* 1933, **41,** 116–128.

Stevens, S. S. The volume and intensity of tones. *Amer. J. Psychol.,* 1934a, **46,** 397–408.

Stevens, S. S. The attributes of tones. *Proc. nat. Acad. Sci., Wash.,* 1934b, **20,** 457–459.

Stevens, S. S. Tonal density. *J. exp. Psychol.,* 1934c, **17,** 585–592.

Stevens, S. S. The relation of pitch to intensity. *J. acoust. Soc. Amer.,* 1935, **6,** 150–154.

Stevens, S. S. A scale for the measurement of a psychological magnitude: loudness. *Psychol. Rev.,* 1936, **43,** 405–416.

Stevens, S. S., and H. Davis. *Hearing, its psychology and physiology.* New York: Wiley, 1938.

Stevens, S. S., and J. P. Egan. Diplacusis in "normal" ears. (Abstract) *Psychol. Bull.,* 1941, **38,** 548.

Stevens, S. S., C. T. Morgan, and J. Volkmann. Theory of the neural quantum in the discrimination of loudness and pitch. *Amer. J. Psychol.,* 1941, **54,** 315–335.

Stevens, S. S., and E. B. Newman. The localization of pure tones. *Proc. nat. Acad. Sci., Wash.,* 1934, **20,** 593–596.

Stevens, S. S., and E. B. Newman. The localization of actual sources of sound. *Amer. J. Psychol.,* 1936a, **48,** 297–306.

Stevens, S. S., and E. B. Newman. On the nature of aural harmonics. *Proc. nat. Acad. Sci., Wash.,* 1936b, **22,** 668–762.

Stevens, S. S., and R. Sobel. The central differentiation of synchronized action potentials in the auditory nerve. *Amer. J. Physiol.*, 1937, **119**, 409–410.

Stevens, S. S., and J. Volkmann. The relation of pitch to frequency: a revised scale. *Amer. J. Psychol.*, 1940, **53**, 329–353.

Stevens, S. S., J. Volkmann, and E. B. Newman. A scale for the measurement of the psychological magnitude pitch. *J. acoust. Soc. Amer.*, 1937, **8**, 185–190.

Stewart, G. W. The function of intensity and phase in the binaural localization of pure tones. I. Intensity. *Phys. Rev.*, 1920a, **15**, 425–431.

Stewart, G. W. The function of intensity and phase in the binaural localization of pure tones. II. Phase. *Phys. Rev.*, 1920b, **15**, 432–445.

Stewart, G. W. The intensity logarithmic law and the difference of phase effect in binaural audition. *Psychol. Monogr.*, 1922, **31**, No. 1, 30–44.

Stewart, G. W. Binaural hearing. *J. acoust. Soc. Amer.*, 1930, **1**, 344–347.

Stewart, G. W. *Acoustics.* New York: Van Nostrand, 1932.

Tarchenow, J. Das Telephon als Anzeiger der Nerven- und Muskelströme beim Menschen. *St. Pet. med. Wschr.*, 1878, **43**, 353.

Thomas, G. J. Equal-volume judgments of tones. *Amer. J. Psychol.*, 1949, **62**, 182–201.

Thompson, S. Phenomena of binaural audition. *Phil. Mag.*, 1877, **4**, 274–276.

Tuller, W. G. Theoretical limitations on the rate of transmission of information. Ph.D. dissertation, Massachusetts Institute of Technology, 1948.

Turnbull, W. W. Pitch discrimination and tonal duration. *J. exp. Psychol.*, 1944, **34**, 302–316.

Upton, M. Differential sensitivity in sound localization. *Proc. nat. Acad. Sci., Wash.*, 1936, **22**, 409–412.

Upton, M., and A. H. Holway. On the psychophysics of hearing: I. Monaural differential sensitivity and exposure time. II. Binaural differential sensitivity and exposure time. *Proc. nat. Acad. Sci., Wash.*, 1937, **23**, 29–34.

de Vries, H. The minimum audible energy. *Acta oto-laryng., Stockh.*, 1948, **36**, 230–235.

Waetzmann, E., and L. Keibs. Hörschwellenbestimmungen mit dem Thermophon und Messungen am Trommelfell. *Ann. Physik.*, 1936a, **26**, 141–144.

Waetzmann, E., and L. Keibs. Theoretischer und experimenteller Vergleich von Hörschwellenmessungen. *Akust. Z.*, 1936b, **1**, 3–12.

Wallach, H. Über die Wahrnehmung der Schallrichtung. *Psychol. Forsch.*, 1938, **22**, 238–266.

Wallach, H. On sound localization. *J. acoust. Soc. Amer.*, 1939, **10**, 270–274.

Wallach, H. The role of head movements and vestibular and visual cues in sound localization. *J. exp. Psychol.*, 1940, **27**, 339–368.

Wallach, H., E. B. Newman, and M. R. Rosenzweig. The precedence effect in sound localization. *Amer. J. Psychol.*, 1949, **62**, 315–336.

Wegel, R. L. Physical data and physiology of excitation of the auditory nerve. *Ann. Otol., Rhinol., Laryngol.*, 1932, **41**, 740–779.

Wegel, R. L., and C. E. Lane. The auditory masking of one pure tone by another and its probable relation to the dynamics of the inner ear. *Phys. Rev.*, 1924, **23**, 266–285.

Wever, E. G. Beats and related phenomena resulting from the simultaneous sounding of two tones. *Psychol. Rev.*, 1929, **36**, 402–418, 512–523.

Wiener, N. *Cybernetics.* New York: Wiley, 1948.

Wiener, N. A new concept of communication engineering. *Electronics*, 1949a, **22**, 74–76.

Wiener, N. *Extrapolation, interpolation, and smoothing of stationary time series.* New York: Wiley, 1949b.

Zoll, P. M. The relation of tonal volume, intensity, and pitch. *Amer. J. Psychol.*, 1934, **46**, 99–106.

Zurmühl, G. Abhängigkeit der Tonhöhenempfindung von der Lautstärke und ihre Beziehung zur Helmholtzschen Resonanztheorie des Hörens. *Z. Sinnesphysiol.*, 1930, **61**, 40–86.

26·

The Perception of Speech

J. C. R. LICKLIDER   and   GEORGE A. MILLER

Massachusetts Institute of Technology   *Harvard University*

Although the perception of speech is a psychological problem, it remained for telephone engineers interested in the adequacy of their equipment to develop procedures for the quantitative investigation of speech perception. These procedures were evolved, principally by the Bell Telephone Laboratories, without reference to the traditional problems and methods of experimental psychology. The concern was with intelligibility rather than perception, and the results were used to evaluate equipment rather than listeners. Although the question "What must the equipment do?" can be rephrased to "What can the listener do?" the marks of the engineers' original interests will be unmistakable in the following summary.

ACOUSTIC CHARACTERISTICS OF SPEECH

We can begin with a brief summary of the physical dimensions of vocal stimuli. A large and respectable body of experimental literature exists in this area, and we shall have space to consider only a few of the more important studies.

Speech Power

The *average power* radiated by a talker during conversational speech, when this

This chapter was prepared at the Psycho-Acoustic Laboratory, Harvard University, under contract with the U. S. Navy, Office of Naval Research (Contract N5ori-76, Project NR142-201, Report PNR-79).

average is taken over a long period of talking and includes pauses between phrases, is about 10 to 20 microwatts. If the pauses are omitted in averaging, the figure increases about 50 per cent (Sacia, 1925; Dunn and Farnsworth, 1939). When one talks as loudly as possible, the average speech power increases to about 1000 microwatts. The faintest voice possible without whispering is 0.1 microwatt, and a whisper may radiate as little as 0.001 microwatt. Thus from the faintest whisper to the loudest shout there is a range of about 60 db.

When the power is averaged over short periods of time — 0.01 second, for example — the rise and fall of the average power during the course of a syllable can be determined. Sacia and Beck (1926) have made such measurements during conversational speech with a variety of speakers. The maximum value of the average power reached during the course of a given sound was taken to represent the power in that sound, and values for different talkers were averaged to give the results summarized in Table 1.* Since the measurements were made for conversational speech, these averages include values for both accented and unaccented occurrences of the sounds. Several consonants were omitted from the analysis because their power was insufficient for measurement.

* The phonetic symbols in this chapter are the same as those in Chapter 21.

TABLE 1

CONVERSATIONAL VALUES OF AVERAGE POWER
OF SPEECH SOUNDS IN MICROWATTS (SACIA AND
BECK, 1926)

Vowels		Diph-thongs		Semi-vowels		Conso-nants	
u	13	oʊ	22	l	0.33	d	0.08
ɔ	47	aɪ	20	ŋ	0.35	t	0.14
ɑ	34			n	2.11	k	0.34
æ	9			m	1.85	v	0.03
ɛ	17					f	0.08
ɪ	9					dʒ	0.47
i	12					tʃ	1.44
ð	10					ʃ	1.83
ʌ	15					z	0.72
						s	0.94

Instantaneous power has been measured
at random instants during conversational
speech. From a large number of such meas-

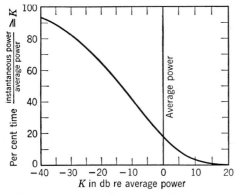

FIG. 1. Statistical distribution of instantaneous
speech power. (After Sivian, 1929.)

urements a statistical distribution can be
drawn showing the percentage of the time
the instantaneous power equals or exceeds
a given value. The results of Sivian's (1929)
measurements for men's voices are so plotted in Fig. 1. The instantaneous power has
a relatively low value most of the time, but
occasionally it rises to very high peak values.
According to Dunn and White (1940), the
distribution of instantaneous pressures is
very nearly a normal distribution similar to
that obtained from similar measurements
with random noise.

Dunn and Farnsworth (1939) have shown
that the sound is radiated best in front of
and slightly below the talker's lips. Especially for the high-frequency components of
speech, radiation is poorest in back of the
head.

The Speech Spectrum

The various methods for analyzing speech
into its component frequencies can be classified under two headings, the graphic and the
electric. The graphic procedures, which
employ Fourier analysis of the waveform,
are summarized in convenient form by
Budde (1930). Electric methods have been
discussed by Trendelenburg (1930), Dunn
and Farnsworth (1939), and Stevens, Egan,
and Miller (1947). In its usual form the
electric analysis employs 10 or 15 band-pass
filters which divide the range from about 30
to 12,000 cps into contiguous bands of frequencies. The talker is located in an anechoic (echo-free) room. The microphone is
placed at a known distance directly in front
of the talker's lips, and the inverse square
law is applied to relate intensity (power)
and distance. The output voltage of the
microphone is passed through the filters, and
the output of each filter is measured and
averaged. The measured voltages are then
converted to the sound pressure levels that
would have been obtained if each of the
filters had had a pass band 1 cycle wide.

Figure 2 shows the average spectra measured by Dunn and White (1940) for six
men and five women, and by Rudmose et al.
(1944) for seven men. (See also Clark et al.,
1948). Over a long period of time most of
the speech energy is found in frequencies
below 1000 cps. For brief periods of time,
however, the energy distribution may be
quite different, and it is these changes in the
distribution of speech energy that carry the
perceptual clues to which we react.

Graphic analysis provides a more detailed
picture of the changes in the distribution of
speech energy as a function of time. Figure

3, for example, shows a series of harmonic analyses made by Steinberg (1934) of the successive periods of the vowel in the word *out*. The heights of the darker lines represent the amplitudes of component vibrations at those frequencies. The dotted lines mark the regions of resonance, or formants, which change continuously throughout the produc-

ordinate, time on the abscissa, and intensity as the brightness of the record. Figure 4 illustrates the basic principle of this device (cf. also Fig. 4 in Chapter 25). The technical aspects of the Sound Spectrograph have been discussed in a series of papers from the Bell Telephone Laboratories (Steinberg and French, 1946; Koenig, Dunn, and

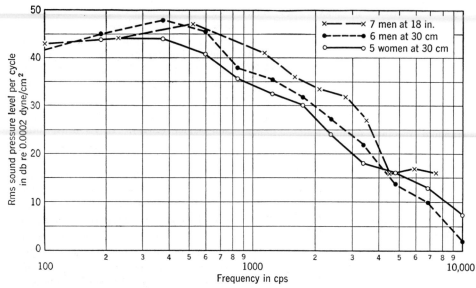

FIG. 2. Average speech spectra. The overall levels, not indicated in the graph, were as follows: 18 inches in front of the seven male talkers, 74 db; 30 centimeters in front of the six male talkers, 76 db; and 30 centimeters in front of the five female talkers, 73 db. (After Dunn and White, 1940, and Rudmose et al., 1944.)

tion of the sound. Similar analyses have been reported by Gemelli and Pastori (1933), Lewis (1936), Black (1937, 1939), Laase (1937), Kaiser (1943) and others. The generation of such a series of graphs for a whole sentence requires a formidable amount of labor.

An electric device that indicates the changes in the intensity-frequency pattern as a function of time is called a Sound Spectrograph (Potter, 1945). The speech is passed through a set of filters, and the output voltages from each pass band are used to control the brightness of small lamps that leave traces on a moving belt of phosphor. A record is obtained with frequency on the

Lacy, 1946; Riesz and Schott, 1946; Dudley and Gruenz, 1946; Kopp and Green, 1946; Koenig and Ruppel, 1948; Kersta, 1948), and in a book by Potter, Kopp, and Green (1947).

Figure 5 illustrates the kind of spectrogram that is obtained for speech. The dark bars indicate the major vocal resonances, and these bars shift from sound to sound, vanish, and reappear as the sentence progresses. The different sounds have different spectrograms, but the formants in the same sounds, as pronounced by different people, are quite similar. The pitch of the voice, whether soprano or bass, has little effect upon the relative positions of the vocal resonances, and upon the durations of the phonemes. Adjacent sounds interact, and the spectrograms of some consonants are considerably modified by the vowels that precede or follow them. The most susceptible are the consonants k, g, h, ŋ, l, and r. These

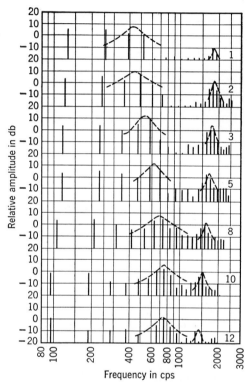

FIG. 3. The results of graphical analysis of the diphthong in the word "out." The numbers 1 to 12 indicate successive periods of the fundamental. Note changes in vocal resonance with time. (From Steinberg, 1934.)

consonants are produced in the back of the mouth and thus are more affected by the positions of the vocal cavities than are consonants produced in the front of the mouth.

In Fig. 6 the spectrograms are shown for six different vowels. The greatest differences appear in the relative positions of the two lowest resonant areas. Potter and Peterson (1948) suggest that these differences among the vowels can be represented conveniently by plotting the center frequency of the first

resonance against the center frequency of the second resonance (Fig. 7). The sustained vowels appear as points on this plot, and the diphthongs are represented as movements from one sustained vowel to another. The dotted line indicates the boundaries of the vowel region — normal speech traces paths through this region but seldom passes outside it. These plots suggest a new method for vowel designation that is particularly adaptable to quantitative analysis.

QUANTITATIVE EVALUATION OF INTELLIGIBILITY

There are several possible ways to measure the efficiency of speech communication. If standard messages are adopted, the time required for their transmission provides an index of efficiency. Or it is possible to count the number of times the listener asks the talker to repeat. Subjective scaling procedures are also available, and the listener can rate different systems on the basis of "pleasantness," "naturalness," or "intelligibility." All these methods have been discussed and occasionally used, but the great bulk of experimental data have been obtained by *articulation testing methods* (Fletcher and Steinberg, 1929; Egan, 1943, 1948). An announcer reads lists of syllables, words, or sentences to a group of listeners, and the percentage of items correctly recorded by these listeners is called the *articulation score*.

Articulation tests have proved useful for comparing communication equipments, for evaluating the effects of noise on communication, for determining the basic audibility of different words, and for rating and training communication personnel. The experimental variables involve the announcer (quality and intensity of voice, pronunciation, use of equipment), the test material (phonetic composition and item difficulty), the communication link (fidelity, noise, intensity of speech, etc.), and the listener (ability to hear sound, to discriminate speech sounds, and to resist masking noises). Such a list indicates the extensive matrix of variables that affects the results of an articulation test.

The early research is summarized by Fletcher (1929), and more recent work is

nience of training the listeners to use phonetic notation is avoided. Still higher scores are obtained with polysyllabic words. Dissyllabic words with a spondaic stress pattern (bloodhound, oatmeal, etc.) have been used

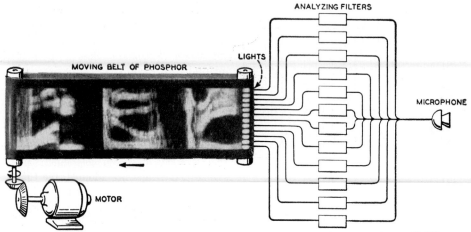

FIG. 4.   Principle of the Sound Spectrograph.   (From Potter, Kopp, and Green, 1947.)

discussed by Miller, Wiener, and Stevens (1946).

Test material. For most purposes it is desirable to have the test material reflect the relative frequencies of occurrence of the different phonemes in English speech. Non-

extensively because they provide lists of relatively homogeneous items. Figure 8 shows results obtained with spondaic dissyllables, unselected (trochaic or iambic) dissyllables, and phonetically balanced monosyllables. The homogeneity of the spondees

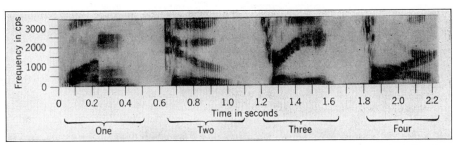

FIG. 5.   Spectrogram of the words, "one, two, three, four." Horizontal and vertical directions represent time and frequency, respectively. Variations in intensity are shown by shades of gray. The heavy dark bands or bars show the frequency regions that are reinforced by the vocal resonances.   (From Steinberg and French, 1946.)

sense syllables are often used for test material. They have the advantage that scores for the different speech sounds can be compared. Somewhat higher scores are obtained with monosyllabic words, but the inconve-

is reflected in the steeper slope of the function relating articulation score to intensity of speech.

Sentences present certain problems in scoring. One procedure designates key words in

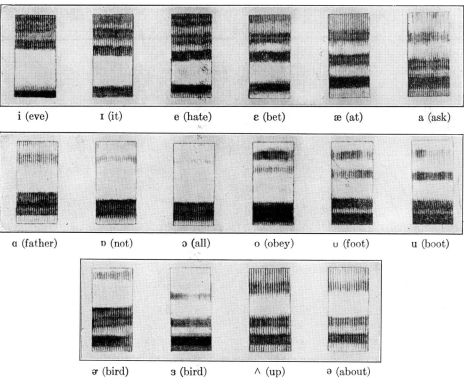

| i (eve) | ɪ (it) | e (hate) | ɛ (bet) | æ (at) | a (ask) |

| ɑ (father) | ɒ (not) | ɔ (all) | o (obey) | ʊ (foot) | u (boot) |

| ɚ (bird) | ɜ (bird) | ʌ (up) | ə (about) |

Fɪɢ. 6. Spectrograms of the vowel sounds. (From Kopp and Green, 1946.)

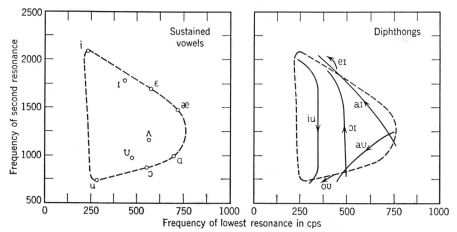

Fɪɢ. 7. The frequency of the lowest vocal resonance is plotted against the frequency of the second vocal resonance for ten vowels. Such a plot defines a "vowel area" for human speech. (From Potter and Peterson, 1948.)

each sentence and then scores according to the percentage of these words correctly recorded. Another procedure is to use a simple question which the listener must answer. Sentence scores are usually higher than word or syllable scores obtained under identical conditions.

When continuous discourse is used, a common procedure is to permit the listener to adjust the intensity of the continuous speech

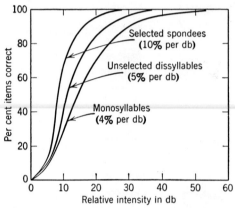

FIG. 8. Comparison of results obtained from articulation tests conducted with three kinds of words. The percentage of items heard correctly is plotted against the relative intensity of speech in decibels. (From Hudgins et al., 1947.)

until it is just detectable (threshold of detectability), or just intelligible (threshold of intelligibility). This procedure stands in the same relation to the formal articulation test as does the method of adjustment to the method of constant stimuli in classical psychophysics.

Suitable test materials have been published by Egan (1948a) and by Hudgins et al. (1947). Collard (1929) has attempted to account for the quantitative relations among sound, syllable, and word articulation scores.

Personnel. Most experimenters have found large individual differences among talkers and listeners. Announcers should be selected who are able to enunciate the fundamental speech sounds in a "normal" manner, where the criterion for normality is one of common sense. Unless regional dialects are to be

studied specifically, talkers and listeners are usually chosen for General American pronunciation. Articulation scores obtained with inexperienced listeners show improvement with practice. Figure 9 gives a typical learning curve obtained in the presence of a loud masking noise. After 2 to 3 hours of practice each day for 5 successive days, this crew reached a relatively stable level of performance.

The number of listeners needed depends upon the reliability desired. The mean articulation score obtained from a well-trained crew of six to eight listeners will usually be sufficiently stable for most purposes. Talker variability is a more important source of instability.

Experiments designed especially to measure the effects of fatigue indicate that there

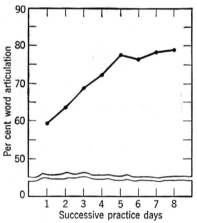

FIG. 9. Showing the effect of practice upon articulation score. Each point represents the average score on twelve tests for a crew of ten listeners. Both the announcer and the listeners were located in an intense airplane noise. (From Egan, 1948a.)

is little or no change in articulation scores obtained in the presence of intense noise over a period of several hours.

Equipment. Articulation tests are sometimes conducted with nothing but the air intervening between talker and listener, but more often the talker's speech is picked up by a microphone, amplified, modified according to the variables being studied, and passed along to the listener via loudspeakers or headphones. Thus it is necessary to have a high-fidelity system with sufficient flexibility to permit the substitution of special components. Calibrating and monitoring equipment should be available to permit a precise description of the speech stimuli that reach the listener's ears. Test methods and equipment have been reviewed by Miller, Wiener, and Stevens (1946).

Statistical methods. A program of articulation testing should be designed in advance to permit statistical analysis. Analysis of variance can be used to estimate the potencies of the different sources of variation in the scores (Goffard and Egan, 1947). Examples of such statistical analysis can be found in a series of papers by Licklider, Bindra, and Pollack (1948), Licklider and Pollack (1948), and Licklider (1948).

RELATION BETWEEN INTENSITY AND INTELLIGIBILITY

When the announcer and the listener are linked together by an intercommunication system, it is a simple matter to control the intensity of the speech at the listener's ear by controlling the amplification in the system. As the speech level is increased above the threshold of detectability the articulation score increases, as shown in Fig. 8, until a level is reached where nearly all words are correctly heard. For greater intensities of speech the articulation score remains high until the threshold of pain is reached.

A statement of the threshold of detectability for speech should take into account the differences in the intensities of the various speech sounds (Table 1). It is customary to state the threshold in terms of an average, but, since some sounds exceed the average consistently, these sounds will determine the threshold value. Thus Fletcher (1929) estimates that the vowel ɔ is just detectable in a free field when the long-interval, root-mean-square pressure for the

speech is 0 db re 0.0002 dyne per square centimeter, but that the consonant θ does not become audible until this level is raised 25 or 30 db. Kryter (1946) reports that the presence of about half the words can be detected in a free field of 5 db. Estimates based upon the minimum audible pressure under earphones tend to run slightly higher; Hawkins and Stevens (1950) used the same criterion as Kryter but obtained 10 db as the minimum audible speech pressure at the entrance of the ear canal.

The speech level necessary in order to identify half the test items correctly depends upon the type of speech material tested. A free-field determination of 31 db for monosyllabic words has been reported by Kryter. French and Steinberg (1947) found 50 per cent of nonsense syllables correctly recorded at approximately 30 db. Davis (1947, p. 150) reported that a level of 33 db is necessary in order to hear correctly half the monosyllabic words when earphones are used, and that spondees can be heard correctly half the time at only 22 db. Shaw, Newman, and Hirsh (1947) found that spondees were reported 50 per cent of the time at 17 db monaurally, and at 14 db binaurally. Hawkins and Stevens found that connected discourse heard through earphones could be followed by the listener when the speech level was 24 db.

At the other end of the scale listening becomes uncomfortable, even for experienced listeners, when the intensity of the speech reaches 130 db, and at 135 db listeners report a tickling in their ears (Silverman *et al.*, 1946). Considering the threshold of intelligibility as about 25 db and the threshold of tickle as 135 db, the usable range of intensities is well over 100 db.

Fletcher (1929) has published curves showing the articulation scores for individual speech sounds as a function of intensity (Fig. 10). The consonants are usually harder to recognize correctly than the vowels. Fletcher estimates that the sounds v, f, and

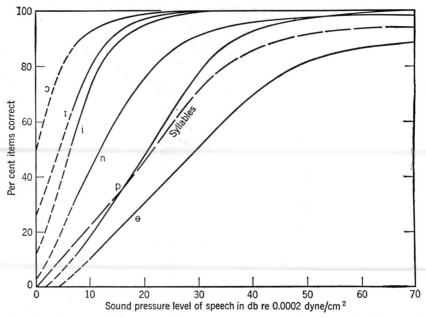

FIG. 10. Articulation data for nonsense syllables were analyzed to determine the percentage of times each speech sound was correctly identified. Results for whole syllables and for six individual sounds are shown. The abscissa is the level of average speech, not of the individual speech sounds. (After Fletcher, 1929.)

θ count for more than half the phonetic mistakes made in listening to ordinary conversation.

THE MASKING OF SPEECH

In most situations speech is accompanied by other sounds. Masking, the shift in the threshold due to the presence of an interfering sound, is a serious problem in many situations, and the masking produced by a wide variety of sounds has been explored (Miller, 1947).

Masking by pure and complex tones. The effects of pure and complex tones upon the threshold of intelligibility have been investigated by Stevens, Miller, and Truscott (1946). They found that low-frequency tones are much more disruptive than high-frequency tones. Intense sine waves produce the most masking when their frequency is about 300 cps, whereas for weaker sine waves the most effective frequency is about 500 cps. This result is what we should expect on the basis of the results obtained in the masking of one pure tone by another: masking is greatest at and above the frequency of the masking tone.

The complex tones studied by Stevens, Miller, and Truscott included rectangular pulses and square waves. These complex waves are built up of many harmonics; consequently they mask the entire range of speech frequencies at lower intensities than do pure tones. At high frequencies, however, pure and complex tones are equally ineffective for masking speech.

Masking by noise. When a noise with a continuous spectrum throughout the range of audible frequencies is used as the masking sound, the noise must be specified in terms of the distribution of energy in the frequency range under consideration. The noise that is easiest to describe is one that has a uniform level per cycle over the range of speech frequencies. When such a *white noise* is used to mask speech, the results shown in Fig. 11 are obtained. In this figure the shifts in the thresholds of detectability and intelligibility are plotted as a function of the intensity of the noise (Hawkins and Stevens, 1950). When the sound pressure level of the noise is greater than 40 db, the threshold shift is directly proportional to

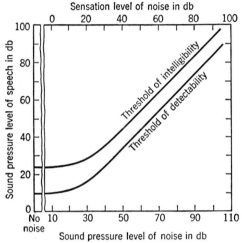

FIG. 11. Showing the thresholds of intelligibility and detectability as functions of the intensity of the masking noise. (From Hawkins and Stevens, 1950.)

the intensity of the noise (cf. Fig. 17 in Chapter 25). Similar results were reported by Fletcher (1929) on the basis of more formal articulation tests with nonsense syllables. Kryter's (1946) experiments yielded comparable results for monosyllabic words.

This relation between masking and noise intensity is often expressed by saying that the *speech-to-noise* ratio (the ratio of the average speech power to the average noise power, which we shall abbreviate S/N) at the masked threshold is constant over a wide range of intensities. Only at the very low and possibly at very high noise levels must S/N be increased. For most noises encountered in practical situations, S/N should exceed 6 db for satisfactory communication, although the presence of speech is detectable for S/N as low as −18 db. If

the speech is distorted, higher values of S/N may be necessary.

The effects of different masking signals can be compared by stating the S/N necessary for a certain articulation score. For instance, if masking noise A gives the same articulation score when the speech is at n db as does masking noise B when the speech is at m db, then n − m is the decibel difference in the masking effectiveness of the two noises.

The results obtained when speech is masked by narrow bands of noise (Miller, 1947) can be used to illustrate this kind of comparison. Highly discriminative filters were inserted into the noise channel to provide the eight adjacent pass bands indicated in Fig. 12. The narrow bands of noise were then mixed with the speech (monosyllabic words) and articulation tests were run. The results are shown in Fig. 12. Curve A, for a wide-band masking noise, shows the most effective masking of speech. At the low noise levels, the high-frequency bands were more effective than bands below 1000 cps. At the high noise levels, however, the low-frequency bands were more effective. The low-frequency noise, like the low-frequency masking tones discussed above, can mask the entire speech range if it is intense enough.

Licklider (1948) has shown that the phase relations of the speech and the noise at the two ears affect the articulation scores obtained at a given S/N. These phase relations are considered in detail in Chapter 25 for the case where tones are masked by noise, and it is sufficient here to note that similar results are obtained when the masked sound is human speech. When either the speech waves or the noise waves at the two ears are 180 degrees out of phase, word articulation scores are as much as 25 percentage units higher than when both the speech waves and the noise waves at the two ears are in phase. These experiments indicate that masking is by no means a wholly peripheral process. An apparently related fact was Egan's (1948) discovery that the loudness of

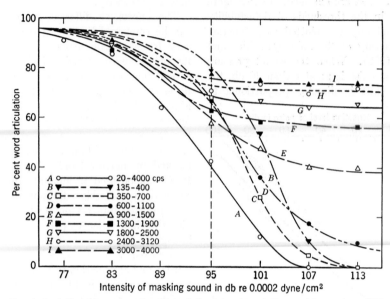

Fig. 12. Articulation score as a function of the intensity of the masking noise. Filters were used to provide the narrow bands of noise. The speech was not filtered, and its level was held constant at 95 db. (From Miller, 1947.)

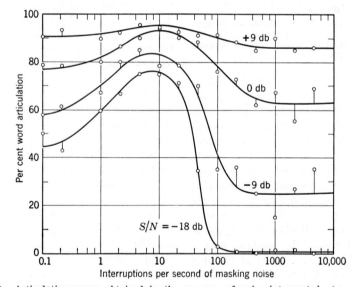

Fig. 13. Articulation scores obtained in the presence of noise interrupted at various rates. The noise was on half the time, off half the time. The parameter is the signal-to-noise ratio in decibels.

speech in one ear is enhanced by introducing noise into the opposite ear.

A further parameter influencing the masking effectiveness of a noise is its temporal continuity. Since many noises — static, intermittent noise of machinery, etc. — are not continuous, it is of some practical interest to determine the effect of interruptions upon masking. In general, turning the masking noise off periodically decreases its masking effectiveness, but just how much this decrease amounts to depends upon the noise-time fraction and the rate of interruption. Figure 13 summarizes the results obtained by Miller and Licklider (1950) when monosyllabic words at 90 db were masked by interrupted random noise at four intensities. The noise-time fraction was 0.50, and other noise-time fractions would give similar families of curves. When the noise is interrupted

FREQUENCY SELECTIVITY

We have considered two general ways in which the speech signal is altered during its passage from the talker to the listener. In the first instance, the speech was simply amplified or attenuated. In the second, noise was added to the speech. We are ready now to examine a third class of alterations to which the speech may be subjected, the class of distortions due to the *selective* action of the transmission system.

Three types of selective action are especially important. In each of these certain parts of the signal are favored and other parts are discriminated against. The basis upon which the signal is analyzed into parts (frequency components, amplitude levels, or temporal segments) is indicated in the first column of Table 2. The second and third

TABLE 2

CLASSIFICATION OF COMMON DISTORTIONS

Distinguishing Parameter	Discriminative Operation	Affected Parameter	Designation
Frequency	Amplification Delay	Amplitude Phase angle	Frequency distortion Phase or delay distortion
amplitude Instantaneous Rms or running average	Amplification Amplification	amplitude amplitude	Nonlinear or amplitude distortion Compression, expansion
Time	Amplification	amplitude	amplitude modulation

more than 200 times per second it is effectively continuous. Between 1 and 200 interruptions per second it is possible to patch together the bits of speech heard between the bursts of noise, and therefore the masking effectiveness of such noises is rather low. At very slow rates of interruption whole words or groups of words may be masked, and the perception is more nearly "all or none."

columns tell us what the selective operation is and what characteristic of the signal is affected by that operation. The name given to the type of distortion (last column) is the one currently used in this country. To illustrate the use of Table 2, let us consider frequency distortion. The circuit is selective on the basis of *frequency* (column 1), introducing different amounts of *amplification* (column 2) at different points along the scale of frequency (column 1), with the effect that the pattern of *Amplitudes* * (column 3) is changed.

Designations other than those given in the last column of Table 2 are often encountered, especially in the older literature.

Frequency Distortion

A system that is selective with respect to frequency is called a filter. If high frequencies are selected and low frequencies rejected, it is called a high-pass filter. Similar definitions apply to low-pass, band-pass, and band-rejection filters. With such filters it is possible to remove portions of the speech spectrum and so to evaluate the relative importance of the different frequencies to intelligibility.

French and Steinberg (1947) reported results of articulation tests with both men's and women's voices passed through various filters (Fig. 14). Orthotelephonic gain (Inglis, 1938) is merely the transmission of a system relative to that of a standard system consisting of a talker and a listener who face one another at a distance of 1 meter in open air. For normal conversational levels, 0-db orthotelephonic gain corresponds to approximately 65-db sound pressure level at a distance of 1 meter in front of the talker.

The articulation scores in Fig. 14 rise rapidly as the orthotelephonic gain is increased. Optimal scores are obtained for each of the filter conditions at about the same point, roughly +10 db. Apparently the low frequencies contribute little to intelligibility in spite of the fact that they carry most of the speech power. When all the components of speech below 1000 cps are attenuated by a high-pass filter, the speech power is reduced approximately 80 per cent but the articulation score falls only 10 per cent. It should be noted that the frequencies above 1900 cps give approximately the same syllable

* The maximum amplitude (Amplitude) will be distinguished from the varying instantaneous amplitude (amplitude), the capital letter being used for the former, the lower case for the latter.

articulation as do the frequencies below 1900 cps.

These data have been analyzed to show the effects upon each of the individual speech sounds (Fletcher, 1929). Eliminating the high frequencies affects consonant articulation scores more than vowel articulation scores. Eliminating the low frequencies affects the vowels more than the consonants.

Pollack (1948) studied the effects of filtering upon word intelligibility under the special circumstance of a background of white masking noise. The noise was introduced electrically into the earphones at an overall sound pressure level of 81.5 db, and the intensity of the filtered speech was varied. For Pollack's talkers 0-db orthotelephonic gain corresponded to a sound pressure level of 68 db. In Fig. 15 the results are plotted in a form comparable to that used in Fig. 14 for quiet conditions. The effect of the noise is to shift the zero score from about −50 db to +5 db. In the presence of noise the relative importance of the different frequency components seems to shift as a function of speech level. At the lower intensities the low frequencies are relatively more important than they are at the higher intensities. It is also interesting to note that Pollack's data do not indicate that the articulation score decreases at very high intensities.

Egan and Wiener (1946) studied the intelligibility of narrow bands of speech in the presence of noise, and they summarized their results in terms of equal-articulation contours. By considering all the band-pass conditions that gave a given syllable articulation score, Egan and Wiener constructed the family of curves shown in Fig. 16. On the ordinate 0 db is the intensity of the speech in a wide-band system, and the results with the narrow-band systems are plotted relative to the level in the wide-band system. The figure is used in the following way. Suppose we wish to substitute a narrow-band system, 850 to 1700 cps, for a high-fidelity system, but must maintain a syllable articulation score of 60 per cent in the presence of white

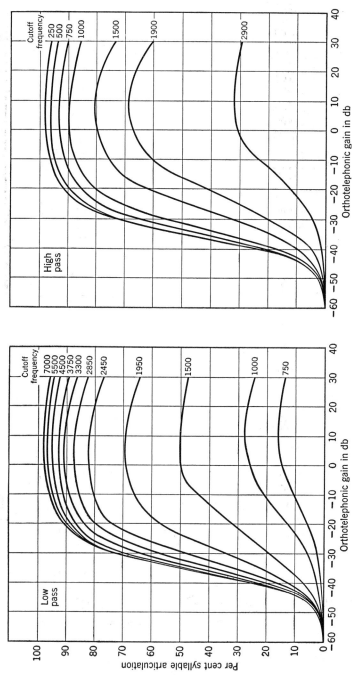

Fig. 14. Functions relating syllable articulation scores for filtered speech to orthotelephonic gain, with the cutoff frequency of the filters as the parameter. (From French and Steinberg, 1947.)

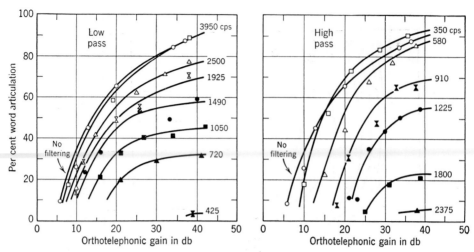

FIG. 15. Functions relating articulation scores for filtered speech and orthotelephonic gain. The cutoff frequency of the speech filters is the parameter. The overall pressure level of the white masking noise (100 to 700 cps) was 81.5 db. (From Pollack, 1948.)

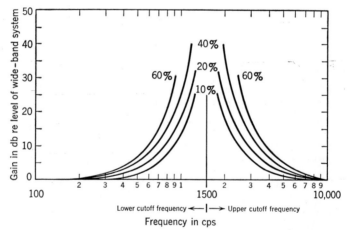

FIG. 16. Generalized equal-articulation contours plotted for band-pass systems all having a center frequency of 1500 cps. If the bandwidth is decreased, the intensity must be increased in order to hold the articulation score constant. (From Egan and Wiener, 1946.)

noise. Figure 16 tells us that the filtered speech must be 25 db more intense than speech via the broad-band system. In order to economize in terms of the frequency range of the system it is necessary to spend more on amplification. This generalized family of equal-articulation contours was constructed with a center frequency of 1500 cps, but to a reasonable approximation the same con-

tours can be used for other center frequencies by shifting the entire family horizontally.

PHASE OR TIME-DELAY DISTORTION

When some of the frequency components of a speech wave are delayed more than others — i.e. when the phase shifts are not proportional to the frequencies of the shifted components — the waveform and the spectrum of the speech are of course modified. That this modification sometimes affects intelligibility was evident from experience with the early long-distance telephones. If the high-frequency *sh* of the word shoe is considerably delayed with respect to the low-frequency *ooh*, for example, the listener will hear the word backwards: *oosh!*

Unfortunately, we cannot yet specify the conditions under which phase distortion produces serious impairment of intelligibility. Most of the experiments that have been conducted have shown that intelligibility is highly resistant to distortion of this type (Steinberg, 1929, 1930; van der Pol, 1930). The frequency components above 1500 cps, for example, can be delayed 0.1 second relative to the components below 1500 cps without reducing the sound articulation score below 90 per cent. However, severe phase distortion has a pronounced effect upon the sound of speech (Steinberg, 1929). When different components of the speech arrive at different times, the listener frequently hears "birdies" or "tweets." The annoyingness of phase distortion can be reduced by narrowing the range of frequencies passed by the system, but, as we have seen, narrowing the frequency range too far may seriously impair intelligibility.

EMPIRICAL EQUATIONS FOR ARTICULATION

Articulation measurement is a tedious and expensive business, and considerable attention has been devoted to the development of a computational device to replace, or at least to supplement, the laborious testing procedures. The rationale for such a device, as described by Collard (1930), involves weighting the contribution to intelligibility of the speech components as a function of their frequency and intensity. Various methods have been elaborated by Pocock (1939), French and Steinberg (1947), Beranek (1947), and

Fletcher and Galt (1950), but the basic assumptions of all these workers have been very similar.

Basic assumptions. We have seen that articulation scores depend upon the test materials used. It is desirable, therefore, to obtain a more fundamental measure of communication efficiency. Sentence, word, syllable, and sound articulation scores can then be related to this fundamental index, so that all four can be predicted once the index has been computed. Let the articulation index, A, assume values between 0 and 100, where 0 is assigned when all speech components are attenuated below the listener's threshold, and 100 is assigned to the performance of the orthotelephonic reference system. In order to divide this scale up into equal units, the articulation test is used as the operation for establishing equality; i.e. two systems have equal articulation indexes if they give equal articulation scores. Take the reference system ($A = 100$) and insert a filter that passes only the frequencies in the range from 20 to 500 cps. This system will yield a word articulation score of about 20 per cent. Next, change the filter so that it passes only frequencies in the range from 500 to 800 cps. The word articulation score will again be about 20 per cent, and by adjusting the range of the band-pass filter we can obtain exactly the same score for the two circuits. By repeating this process we can obtain n circuits such that each alone gives the same articulation score, and taken all together they constitute the original high-quality circuit. In so far as the contributions of the several bands of frequencies are equal and independent, the articulation index of each band is $100/n$.

The contribution of a given band of frequencies depends upon the intensity of the speech in the band, as well as upon the width of the band. If the intensity of the speech in a given band is below the threshold of hearing at those frequencies, the band makes no contribution to intelligibility, but as its intensity is increased the contribution increases until the maximum, $100/n$, is reached. This fact is expressed by a weighting factor, w, which varies from 0 to 1.0 as a function of the sensation level of the band of speech frequencies. We can then summarize the computational procedure by

$$A = \sum_{i=1}^{i=n} w_i \frac{100}{n} = \frac{100}{n} \sum_{i=1}^{i=n} w_i$$

This equation expresses the notion that a narrow band of speech frequencies of a given

A is 50 the syllable articulation score is 68 per cent. Another point can be obtained by returning to Fig. 14 at the orthotelephonic gain that gives an articulation score of 68 per cent. If the articulation scores are now plotted as a function of filter-cutoff frequencies for this gain setting, these functions cross at a point that defines $A = 25$. By continuing this procedure the complete function relating A to syllable articulation can be plotted. This has been done in Fig. 18,

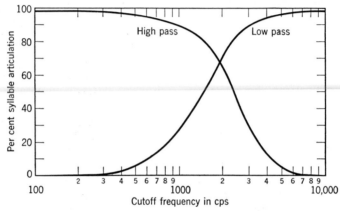

Fig. 17. Syllable articulation for high-pass and low-pass systems operating in the quiet with optimal gain. These functions are derived from the curves of Fig. 14 for an orthotelephonic gain of 10 db. (From French and Steinberg, 1947.)

intensity carries a contribution to the total index that is independent of the other bands with which it is associated, and that the total contribution of all bands is the sum of the contributions of the separate bands.

Dividing the frequency scale. French and Steinberg (1947) attempted to establish the relation between frequency and articulation index with the data shown in Fig. 14. If we cut through these two families of curves at an orthotelephonic gain of +10 db and plot articulation as a function of the cutoff frequency, we obtain the curves shown in Fig. 17. It is evident from these curves that as much of the total intelligibility is carried by frequencies below 1900 cps as is carried by the frequencies above 1900 cps. This establishes the value of 50 for the articulation index, and it appears that when

where the cumulative contribution to the articulation index is shown as a function of the upper cutoff frequency. The *slope* of this function shows the relative importance of the various frequencies in their contribution to intelligibility. With this information the range of important speech frequencies can be divided into a number of bands each of which contributes equally to the articulation index. Computations are normally made on the basis of 20 bands, each contributing a maximum ΔA of 5.

Weighting according to intensity. French and Steinberg estimate that a band of frequencies begins to contribute to intelligibility when it is about 6 db above the threshold of audibility, and that w increases linearly with a slope of 0.033 per decibel up to a sensation level, for the band, of about 30 db. The maximum contribution is not made until the band of speech is 50 db above its threshold, but as a first approximation,

$$w_i = \frac{\text{(Sensation level of band in decibels)} - K}{30}$$

where w_i is limited to unity as a maximum value, and K is about 6 db. This approximation will tend to overestimate the contributions of bands more than 30 db above the threshold.

db. For noisy conditions, therefore, the approximated weighting factor becomes

$$w_i = \frac{\text{(S/N of band in decibels)} + 12 \text{ db} - K}{30}$$

This approximation cannot be used when the masking sound is a tone or a narrow band of noise, because these sounds spread their masking effects outside the range of frequencies of a single band.

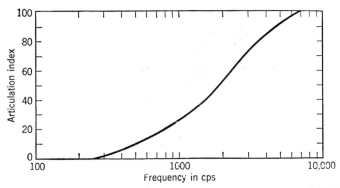

Fig. 18.   Articulation index as a function of frequency.   (From French and Steinberg, 1947.)

It is usually assumed that the relation between w_i and intensity is approximately the same for all bands, although Pollack's results do not support the assumption.

When noise is present it will have the effect of raising the threshold of hearing. In this case the computations are made as before, but the masked threshold of hearing is used instead of the quiet threshold. If the masking sound is a noise with a continuous spectrum throughout the range of speech frequencies, it is possible to compute the masked threshold from the spectrum of the noise (Fletcher, 1938a, b; Fletcher and Munson, 1937). According to Fletcher, the masking produced by such a noise at a given frequency depends upon the intensity of the noise in the frequency region immediately adjacent to that frequency. The masking of a band of speech frequencies, therefore, will depend upon the value of S/N in that band. The sensation level of the band in the presence of the noise is 0 db when S/N is −12

Detailed examples are provided by Pocock (1939), Beranek (1947), and Fletcher and Galt (1950). The procedure is simple and straightforward once the speech spectrum and the noise spectrum at the listener's ears are known. Then S/N is stated for each band, the values of w_i are computed and totaled for the n bands, and the total is divided by $(100/n)$. The value of K seems to vary with different listeners; French and Steinberg used 6 db, but Beranek (1947) obtained more accurate predictions with K equal to 0 db. If all that is desired is a comparison of two proposed communications systems, the value of K does not affect the comparison and the computational procedure gives satisfactory results. If an accurate prediction of the articulation score is needed, however, the procedure does not seem to take sufficient account of individual differences in talkers and listeners.

The computational procedure is appropriate when the only difficulties in the communication system are noise and frequency selectivity. Unfortunately, many other types of distortion occur, and for these there is at present no substitute for articulation testing methods.

AMPLITUDE SELECTIVITY

The most prevalent type of amplitude distortion is the one that discriminates against the high-amplitude parts of the speech wave.

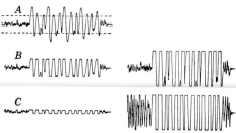

FIG. 19.   Diagram *A* is a schematic representation of the waveform of the word *Joe*. *B* shows what is left after 6-db peak clipping, i.e. after reduction to one-half the original peak-to-peak amplitude. *C* illustrates 20-db peak clipping. At the right, the waves of *B* and *C* are shown reamplified until their peak-to-peak amplitudes are equal to the peak-to-peak amplitude of *A*. (From Licklider, Bindra, and Pollack, 1948.)

Reduced to its simplest form, this type of amplitude distortion is called peak clipping. It is illustrated in Fig. 19. The results of a number of experiments on peak clipping agree in indicating that, although peak clipping degrades the quality and naturalness of the speech, a surprisingly large fraction of the speech wave can be eliminated before intelligibility is affected (Fletcher, 1929; Strecker, 1936; Gemelli, 1938; Licklider, 1944). This resistance to the effects of peak clipping is shown by the solid line in Fig. 20. We find, for example, that more than 95 per cent of monosyllabic words are heard correctly even after 24-db peak clipping, i.e. after all but 1/16 of the speech wave nearest the center axis has been clipped away. In fact, as indicated at the right-hand side of the figure, about 70 per cent of the words

can be understood after the speech wave has been subjected to 'infinite peak clipping,' which reduces it to a succession of rectangular waves (Fig. 21).

The opposite of peak clipping is center clipping (Fig. 22). As is evident in Fig. 20, center clipping is disastrous. Clipping out only one-quarter of the speech wave (2.5-db center clipping) reduces word articulation to about 30 per cent, and clipping out one-half of the wave (6 db) leaves something that resembles static more than speech.

Comparing the effects of peak and center clipping, we are led to ask what it is about the center part of the speech wave that makes it so important for intelligibility. We do not have to go far for an answer: the center part contains the consonant sounds. Only a small percentage of our vocal energy goes into consonants, but that small portion conveys a disproportionate amount of information.

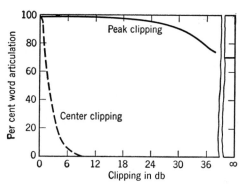

FIG. 20.   The effects of peak clipping and center clipping upon intelligibility. When peak clipping is infinite, the articulation score is approximately 70 per cent.

It is evident from the observations on peak clipping and center clipping and from the results of other experiments with other types of amplitude distortion (Licklider, 1944) that the dimensions of the waveform, *amplitude* and *time*, are not, as such, the ones in terms of which the auditory system responds. If they were, we should not be able (as, e.g., by clipping off the peaks) to render the waveform unrecognizable without imparing intelligibility more severely. Nor are the dimensions of the spectrum, *Amplitude, frequency,* and *phase,* the 'auditory' dimensions: the auditory system obviously analyzes along the temporal dimension, hearing "one," "two," "three," and "four" as

changed by infinite peak clipping, the general plan is by no means rendered unrecognizable. In the lowermost diagram, on the other hand, all trace of the general pattern has been lost. Clearly, the recognizability of the intensity-frequency-time pattern parallels the intelligibility of the speech.

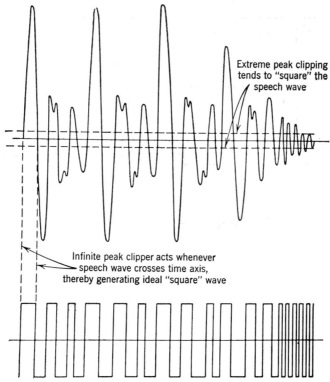

FIG. 21. Showing how speech may be transformed into rectangular waves by means of a circuit that acts whenever the speech wave crosses the time axis. This transformation may be thought of as infinite peak clipping. (From Licklider, 1944.)

separate words, not as a steady spectrum. We turn, therefore, to *intensity, frequency,* and *time,* i.e. to the representation described above and illustrated by the visible speech pattern. In Fig. 23, we see an intensity-frequency-time plot of the word "shoe-bench," showing how it looks (1) when faithfully reproduced, (2) after infinite peak clipping, and (3) after 6-db center clipping. Comparing the middle diagram with the uppermost diagram, we see that, although many of the details of the pattern are

Amplitude selectivity and noise. When noise gets into an amplitude-selective speech transmission system, three aspects of the situation are of critical importance: (1) the characteristics of the noise; (2) the characteristics of the nonlinear circuit; and (3) whether the noise enters the system at a point preceding or at a point following the nonlinear circuit.

If the noise gets into the system at the talker's end of the line, the noise must pass with the speech through the nonlinear circuit. The resulting intermodulation is detrimental to intelligibility. Only when the noise consists of sharp pulses or clicks and the nonlinear circuit is a peak clipper is the

tortion products, and the listener judges the distortion to be less severe than it actually is.

Since every speech transmission system has an overload point where the peaks of the

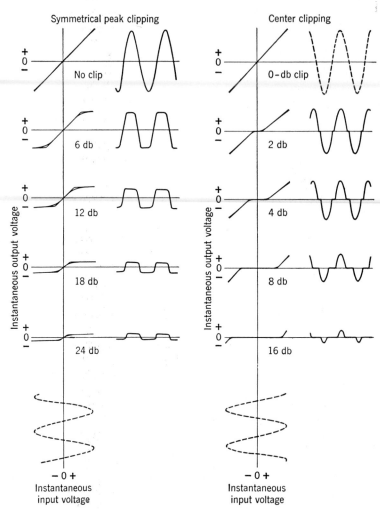

FIG. 22. The diagrams illustrate various degrees of symmetrical peak clipping (left) and symmetrical center clipping (right). For each type and amount of clipping, the nonlinear input-output characteristic is shown, and opposite each nonlinear characteristic the effect upon a sine wave is illustrated. (From Licklider, 1944.)

interaction at all favorable: peak clipping then gets rid of more noise than speech.

If, on the other hand, the noise enters the system at a point following the nonlinear circuit, the noise tends to cover up the dis-

speech waves are clipped, the question arises, what is the best compromise between amplification and distortion? The answer stems from experiments on peak clipping (Licklider, 1944): if a communication system has insufficient amplitude-handling capability to pass the peaks of the speech wave and at the same time to provide an adequate in- (Kryter and Stein, 1944; Licklider and Roberts, 1945; W. W. Smith, 1946; Gross and Licklider, 1946; Miller and Mitchell, 1947),

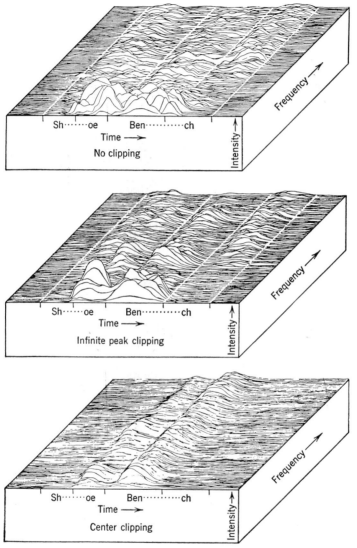

Fig. 23. Intensity-frequency-time patterns contrasting the effects of infinite peak clipping and 6-db center clipping. (From Licklider, Bindra, and Pollack, 1948.)

tensity level, maximal intelligibility is obtained by clipping off the peaks and using the available power for the remainder of the wave (see Fig. 24). This principle has been applied to the design of radio transmitters and the design of hearing aids (Davis et al., 1946, 1947). The principle appears to be of wide applicability because a considerable improvement in intelligibility can often be obtained with as little as 12-db peak clipping, and that amount does not seriously impair speech quality.

Amplitude selectivity and frequency selectivity. When we have both frequency selectivity and amplitude selectivity in the same

obtained with various arrangements of two frequency-selective circuits (differentiator and integrator) and one amplitude-selective circuit (infinite peak clipper). The differen-

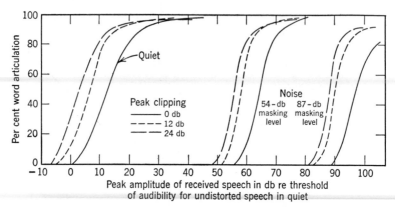

Fig. 24. The advantage provided by peak clipping when the amplitude-handling capability of the communication system limits performance. When clipped and unclipped speech waves are equated in peak-to-peak amplitude, the clipped waves are much more intelligible than the unclipped waves. (From Licklider, 1944.)

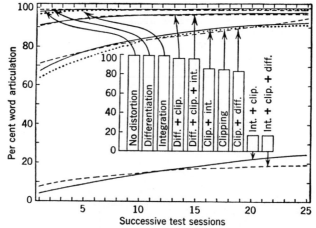

Fig. 25. The effects of various combinations of differentiation, integration, and infinite peak clipping upon intelligibility. The smooth curves show the course of the articulation scores through the 25 test sessions. The heights of the bars of the inset diagram indicate the overall averages for the ten arrangements of the distorting circuit. (From Licklider and Pollack, 1948.)

tivity and amplitude selectivity in the same communication system, we face another problem of interaction. The total effect upon intelligibility is by no means the sum of the individual effects of the two distortions. Figure 25 shows, for example, the results

tiator passes the high frequencies but attenuates the low frequencies by an amount that increases 6 db per octave as we go down the frequency scale. The integrator does just the opposite. The frequency-selective circuit preceding the clipper has a marked influence upon intelligibility, whereas the one following the clipper has almost no effect upon intelligibility. It is apparent from Fig. 25, incidentally, that the listener improves rapidly in his understanding of distorted speech; only about one-third of this improvement can be attributed to increasing familiarity with the particular word lists used in the test.

TIME SELECTIVITY

Steinberg (1936) describes an experiment in which the listener was prevented from hearing the first part of the nonsense syllable spoken by the talker. Steinberg used a voice-operated relay that did not complete the communication circuit until some fixed interval after the nonsense syllable had begun. The average duration of the initial

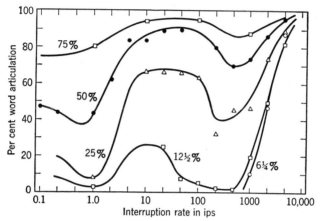

Fig. 26. Effects of regularly repeated interruptions upon the intelligibility of speech. The percentage of the time that the speech was left on is shown by the figure adjacent to each curve.

Amplitude selectivity, frequency selectivity, and noise. Since the effect of amplitude distortion depends markedly upon the type of frequency distortion to which the speech has previously been subjected, it is reasonable to assume that some combination of the two might provide a greater advantage than that obtained with peak clipping alone. This possibility was investigated, with somewhat disappointing results, in some of the experiments already mentioned. It turns out, however, that frequency-selective circuits are useful in suppressing low-frequency noise that enters the system at a point preceding the nonlinear circuit (Kryter and Stein), and that speech in airplanes at high-altitude can be made to sound more natural by attenuating its low-frequency components (Miller and Mitchell).

consonants was normally about 0.16 second. When the first 0.08 second of this consonant was lopped off, the listeners still recorded the sound correctly about half the time. With the first 0.12 second gone the listeners were right about 25 per cent of the time.

Several investigators have performed the experiment of turning speech on and off periodically and noting the effect upon intelligibility (Poirson, 1920; Marro, 1936; Montani, 1946; Miller and Licklider, 1950). As shown in Fig. 26, the effect of the interruptions upon intelligibility depends upon the two variables, *interruption rate* and *speech-time fraction.* If the rate of interruption is sufficiently high, almost all the words can be understood even though the speech-time fraction is very low. This result may appear surprising at first thought, but it is exactly what amplitude-modulation theory predicts, and we need appeal to no unusual properties of the auditory mechanism to understand it. The part of the signal that falls within the frequency range important for intelligibility is, in fact, essentially undistorted. The dip in the curve between 100 and 3000 interruptions per second (ips) is also to be expected on the basis of modulation theory. The plateau between 10 and 100 ips, however, tells us something about the dynamics of auditory perception. We find that, under certain conditions, the auditory mechanism is capable of getting the whole story even though it hears the speech only half the time, provided only that the interruptions are so spaced in time that few of the fundamental speech sounds are entirely eliminated. When the interruptions occur at a rate of 15 per second, for example, the loudness of the signal fluctuates in step with the interruption. The 'sense' of the interrupted speech, however, is perceived quite independently of the loudness. In fact, intelligibility remains high even when the gaps in the speech are filled with intense bursts of noise that sound much louder than the speech.

Observations have been made also with aperiodic or random interruptions (Miller and Licklider, 1950). These observations show that, if the average rate of interruption and the average speech-time fraction are held constant, changing from regular to random interruption has relatively little effect upon intelligibility. The subjective sound of the interrupted speech, however, is quite different: regularly interrupted speech seems to be heard against a somewhat tonal background; irregularly interrupted speech seems to be heard against a background of white noise or static.

PRACTICAL APPLICATIONS

Three quantities of great economic importance in the communication world are frequency, power, and time. Since power is proportional to the square of amplitude,

it is evident that these quantities are essentially the ones we have been discussing. The practical utility of frequency, amplitude, and time selectivities may be judged, therefore, in terms of the savings that they may permit us to achieve in frequency, power, and time.

The way to save space along the frequency scale is, of course, to minimize the bandwidth of the transmitted signal. We have seen that intelligibility is impaired only slightly by the elimination of the very high and the very low frequency components of speech. Advantage is taken of this fact in practical telephone and radio communications: the speech spectrum extends from below 100 to above 7000 cps, but only those parts between about 250 and 3500 cps are usually transmitted. This frequency selectivity permits a saving of approximately one-half in bandwidth.

As we saw in Fig. 24, 24-db peak clipping allowed us to achieve a given level of intelligibility with about 13 db less peak signal power than would be required if we insisted on distortionless transmission. We can therefore substitute a 1-watt peak-clipping amplifier for a 20-watt linear amplifier. Advantage of this fact is taken in military and commercial communication by building premodulation clippers into the radio transmitters. In broadcast work, simple peak clipping cannot be used because it impairs the quality of music; compression or volume-limiting amplifiers (which preserve quality better, but provide a less marked saving in power) are used instead.

A possible application of time selectivity, suggested by Marro, takes advantage of the high intelligibility of speech interrupted at a low rate in such a way that it is on only half the time (cf. Fig. 26). By alternating between two conversations 15 times per second, it is possible to provide intelligible two-way communication on a single channel, thereby achieving double use of the communication facilities, which is in a sense equivalent to halving the bandwidth of the signal.

OTHER TYPES OF DISTOR-
TION

Of considerable practical interest are several special types of distortion that we should consider briefly. These are the distortions due (1) to reverberation in enclosures with reflecting walls, (2) to expansion, contraction, or modulation of the time scale, and (3) to displacement of the speech spectrum along the frequency scale.

tailed analysis. Steinberg found that the sounds most affected were short vowels, nasal consonants, and stop consonants. Long vowels and sustained fricative consonants were, as might be expected, considerably less affected.

We should not conclude, however, that because extreme reverberation impairs intelligibility all reverberation is undesirable. (Note the maxima in the curves in Fig. 27.) Anyone who has listened inside an anechoic

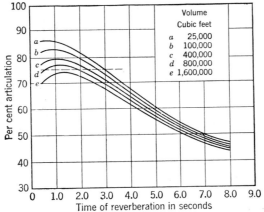

FIG. 27. The effect of reverberation upon the intelligibility of speech. The data were obtained with nonsense-syllable tests in a series of auditoriums having about the same shape and volume, but different reverberation times. (From Knudsen, 1929.)

Reverberation. The reverberation of sound in a 'live' room leads to a piling up of echoes in such a way that both frequency and phase distortion are introduced. The individual speech sounds tend to lose their individuality, to run together into an unintelligible blur. The effect is especially pronounced in the waiting rooms of railroad stations.

The impairment of intelligibility caused by reverberation has been measured by Knudsen (1929) and by Steinberg (1929). Knudsen's results are shown in Fig. 27. The reverberation time is the length of time required for the sound to decay to $\frac{1}{1000}$ of its initial rms amplitude (60 db). Clearly, severe reverberation is highly deleterious to intelligibility. Knudsen's results are confirmed, in the main, by Steinberg's more de-

chamber knows the oppressive feeling of 'acoustic deadness' and remembers the unfamiliar sound that familiar voices have when there is no reverbation.

In an effort to express in a quantitative way the characteristic of a room or auditorium that determines the naturalness of speech or music, Maxfield and Albersheim (1947) developed a formula for liveness. According to this formula, liveness is proportional to the square of the reverberation time, to the square of the distance between the sound source and the listener, and, inversely, to the volume of the enclosure. One of the principal advantages of liveness over reverberation time is that the optimal liveness is a constant, whereas the optimal reverberation time increases, approximately as the $\frac{1}{6}$ power of the volume of the room.

Time-scale distortion. We ordinarily think (or at least Newton thought) of time as flowing by at a constant rate. Neverthe-

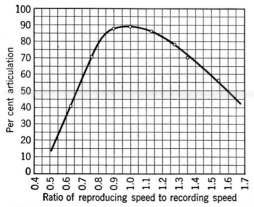

Fig. 28. The effect upon intelligibility of compressing or expanding the time scale. The data were obtained by recording speech and playing it back faster or slower. (From Fletcher, 1929.)

less we can change the time scale by recording a signal and playing it back at another rate. This operation also affects the frequency scale, of course: when we increase the record speed by a factor N, all frequencies of the signal components are multiplied by N.

The relation between intelligibility and the factor N is shown in Fig. 28. Ordinary speech has, we see, a fairly high tolerance for distortion of this type. The tolerance is by no means so high, however, as the tolerance for the speeding up or slowing down that the talker can achieve simply by altering the rate at which he talks (cf. Fig. 30).

Probably the most drastic form of time-scale distortion is produced by making time, i.e. a phonograph record, run backwards. Backward speech is so completely unintelligible at first hearing that it makes good nonsense material for experiments on learning (Lewis, 1946). English sounds like Chinese. The words seem to follow one another at a rapid pace. The talker is surprised to find that he has generated *h*'s during what he thought were pauses between words (Kellogg, 1939). These unfamiliar effects occur, of course, despite the fact that the Amplitude-frequency pattern is not changed by reversing the time scale. There is perhaps no more convincing evidence that the auditory mechanism "perceives phase" (cf. Chapter 25).

Frequency-shift distortion. When speech is sent from one point to another by means

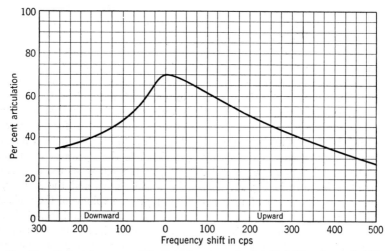

Fig. 29. The effect of frequency-shift distortion upon the intelligibility of speech. The speech spectrum was shifted bodily along the frequency scale by the number of cycles indicated on the abscissa. (From Fletcher, 1929.)

of single side-band transmission, an unusual effect is produced in the received speech if the two stations are not precisely synchronized. The whole speech spectrum is shifted bodily up or down the frequency scale, a constant number of cycles being added to or subtracted from the frequency of each component. The effect of this frequency-shift distortion upon intelligibility is shown in Fig. 29. We see that the auditory mechanism can tolerate an upward frequency shift of 100 cps with an articulation loss for nonsense syllables of less than 10 percentage units. Because frequency-shift distortion changes harmonic relations into inharmonic relations, however, it is highly deleterious to music.

INDIVIDUAL DIFFERENCES

If the talker and the listener both speak the same language, word articulation measured in the quiet and in the absence of distortion is almost always above 90 per cent. We should be careful, however, not to jump to the conclusion that individual differences among talkers and among listeners are therefore small. We need only apply a little stress in the form of noise or distortion to make it apparent how great the variations among talkers actually are. In one experiment the average articulation scores of twelve representative talkers in the presence of simulated airplane noise with standard military communication equipment were found to range from 44 to 85 per cent (Abrams et al., 1942).

The question naturally arises, what are the characteristics of the talkers, or of their speech waves, that determine the differences? This question was studied by Abrams et al. (1944) in the following way: First, they used word and sentence articulation tests to determine intelligibility scores for each of 47 talkers. Then, from phonographically recorded samples of their speech they made measurements of (1) speech intensity, (2) the distribution of speech energy along the frequency scale, (3) the 'pitch' of the voice (fundamental frequency of the vowel sounds), and (4) the 'peak factor' (peakedness) of the speech waveform. In addition they had a group of five judges make subjective ratings of (1) consonant strength, (2) consonant precision, (3) appropriateness of rate of speaking, (4) duration of words, (5) steadiness of rate of speaking, (6) steadiness of level and

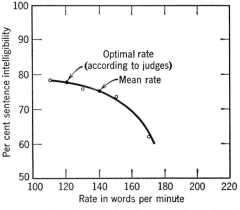

FIG. 30. The relation between the rate of speaking and average sentence intelligibility. (From Abrams et al., 1944.)

emphasis, (7) noise-penetrating quality, (8) deviation from General American dialect, and (9) overall intelligibility. Finally they determined the degree of correlation between measured intelligibility and each of the parameters just mentioned. Besides intensity, which is almost always the most important variable determining intelligibility in noise, the important factors proved to be the noise-penetrating quality (which itself is a function of intensity, pitch, and peak factor), the strength and precision of the consonants, and the dialect.

It is perhaps surprising that normal variations in rate of speaking do not have much effect upon intelligibility. As shown in Fig. 30, sentence intelligibility fell off only slightly as the rate was increased until the talker was emitting almost 160 words per minute; approximately 120 words per minute was rated optimal by five judges.

One of the psychologist's contributions to communication theory is the idea that the talker and the listener are parts of the communication system. Directly from this notion stems the question: can we train talkers to speak intelligibly? Black and Mason (1946) have answered it in the affirmative; they found that they could do more to improve communication by training the talker than the engineers could do by developing new and better microphones. In order to improve a talker's intelligibility over an interphone or radio link operating in a noisy location, they simply taught the talker (1) to handle his microphone properly, (2) to get his speech level up as high as he could without straining his voice, and (3) to articulate precisely. In an hour they found it possible to improve the intelligibility of aviation personnel talking over an aircraft interphone system by about 7 percentage units (a control group improved less than 1 percentage unit). A 4-hour course led to improvements ranging from 12 to 24 percentage units.

Variations among listeners. It goes almost without saying that a good listener understands the language and has normal auditory acuity. (See Carhart, 1946, on the relation between the audiogram and the capacity to hear weak speech.) The other characteristics of the listener that determine his ability to understand speech, however, are difficult to elucidate. The principal trouble is that, whereas we can analyze the speech wave that the talker produces, the only thing that we can do with the listener's response is to check it to see whether or not it is correct. The role of the listener must be studied, therefore, by varying the stimulus and/or by varying the listener.

Here again, most of the interest has been in the ability to understand speech in noise. That there are wide individual differences in this ability was shown by Abrams et al. (1942). Karlin et al. (1944) studied the nature of these individual differences by varying the nature of the speech material, the equipment over which it was transmitted, and the noise against which it was heard. Using a large number of subjects, they found that there was only one significant factor in the situation. This factor, surprisingly, is uncorrelated (actually, $r = -0.17$) with ability to receive telegraphic code in noise. Moreover, the correlations between listening ability and intelligence, memory span, and speaking ability are all quite low.

We have already seen (Fig. 25) how markedly listeners improve with practice in their understanding of distorted speech. Similar results have been obtained with undistorted speech heard in the presence of noise (cf. Fig. 9). There appears to be no better way to teach listeners than to motivate them and have them listen. Even after extensive training, however, normal listeners differ considerably in their ability to understand speech under difficult conditions.

DISCUSSION

The preceding summary has shown that vocal communication is highly resistant to distortion. Apparently no single dimension of the speech is critical. Speech power can be varied over a range of a billion to one. Conversations are intelligible with only the upper half of the speech spectrum, but there is nothing unique about this half because we can throw it all away and get along equally well with only the lower half. The waveform can be distorted to a series of square waves or turned off half the time without severe effects. The listener does not seem to depend upon amplitude alone, nor upon frequency or time alone. The fundamental acoustic determinant of his response is the distribution of energy at the different frequencies as a function of time: the intensity-frequency-time pattern. Types of distortion that alter the listener's ability to respond correctly are those that change the intensity-frequency-time pattern. Changes in the intensity, the fundamental frequency, the waveform, the envelope of the wave, or the spectrum do not affect intelligibility until the change is so great the spectrographic pattern is markedly altered. The resistance of this pattern to the commonly encountered distortions makes vocal communication possible under adverse circumstances.

It is interesting to note that the attempts to translate speech into tactual or visual patterns for the benefit of the deaf have not succeeded unless they have presented intensity-frequency-time patterns to the new modality. An oscillogram of the waveform, for example, presents speech to the eye in a graph of amplitude versus time, and quite different oscillograms can have very similar spectrographic patterns. If the waveform is applied with a vibrator to the skin, the subject can discriminate changes in the envelope of the wave, but the complete pattern is not available (Gault, 1926; Gault and Goodfellow, 1937; Weichbrodt, 1932). The pattern must be presented in the appropriate dimensions before we recognize it readily.

Since speech can be severely distorted without becoming unintelligible, it is reasonable to suppose that the normal stream of speech contains many more discriminative clues than are necessary. If distortion removes or confuses some of these clues, the others carry the message. An important aspect of any message is the extent to which the component elements are interrelated. As long as each element is unrelated to the others, each element can carry a separate parcel of information, but the listener is required to make no mistakes. If some relation exists, the amount of information per element of the message is reduced, but the listener's job is simplified. If the listener hears any one of the related elements, he knows something about the others. By sending related elements in the message the talker is, in effect, repeating himself. From the point of view of efficiency, human speech seems a poor device, but what is lost in efficiency is regained in resistance to distortion. If the speech stimulus contains many more discriminative clues than the listener really needs, distortions in the stimulus must be extreme in order to obliterate all traces of the message.

In almost all the work on the perception of speech, the yardstick has been a scale on which 100 per cent represents a perfect echo: the listener writes down or repeats what the talker says. Currently, however, communication theorists are developing a more elegant yardstick (see Chapter 21). The new standard of performance is perfect reproduction, not of what a talker says, but of the information he might transmit if he generated a white noise of the same bandwidth as the speech. In order to make this notion seem reasonable, it is necessary to consider that the information contained in a message does not depend upon what the talker says, but upon what he might say.

In the simplest formulation of the theory, the amount of information contained in one message is equal to the number of decisions, D, between equally probable alternatives that the listener must make correctly in order to tell which of the M possible messages was sent.

$$\text{Amount of information} = D = \log_2 M$$

If there are two possible messages, the listener must make one correct decision. If there are four possible messages, two correct decisions are necessary. Eight possible messages require three decisions, etc.

Now it is possible to estimate how rapidly information, so defined, could be transmitted by a 'white noise' talker to an ideal listener over a reasonably good communication system. Assume (1) that the system passes all the component frequencies within a frequency band B cycles wide and suppresses all others, (2) that the ratio of the talker's speech power to the interfering noise power is 1000/1 (i.e. 30 db), and (3) that in all other respects the system transmits the speech faithfully. The amount of information — number of decisions — that the system can handle in a length of time T is given by the formula *

$$D = BT \log_2 (S/N + 1)$$

Substitute the values of bandwidth (5000 cps), time (1 second), and signal-to-noise ratio (30 db). The system is capable of transmitting

$$5000 \log_2 (1001) \simeq 50,000 \text{ decisions per second}$$

For this representative set of conditions the yardstick places perfect performance at 50,000 bits of information per second.

When normal speech communication is evaluated by this yardstick (cf. Chapter 21), we find that it carries less than 50 usable bits of information per second. Relative to the theoretical ceiling of the system, human beings are less than 0.1 per cent efficient. And if the listener is expected to retain what

---

* Here we accept the formula with only a suggestion as to its derivation. Although the talker's message is only T seconds long, we can imagine a wave of infinite duration made up of endless repetitions of his message. The fundamental frequency of this recurring wave is $f = 1/T$ cps, and the spectrum consists exclusively of integral multiples of f. In the B cycles passed by the system there are $B/f = BT$ harmonics. Associated with each harmonic are two magnitudes, one designating Amplitude, the other phase angle (or two Amplitudes, one of a sine component, the other of a cosine component). Thus $2BT$ numbers are necessary to specify the message completely. Because of the noise these magnitudes cannot be determined exactly. We have, as it were, a scale s units long, but we can read it only to the nearest n units. We can do no more than select the proper mark out of $(s/n + 1)$ alternatives. This selection supplies us with $\log_2 (s/n + 1)$ units of information about each of the $2BT$ magnitudes. Now s and n are linear quantities (like inches), but we want to use quadratic quantities (S, N) in the formula. We therefore note that, if $S/N \gg 1$, $\log_2 (s/n + 1) \simeq \frac{1}{2} \log_2 (S/N + 1)$. In all, then, we have $2BT \log_2 (s/n + 1) \simeq BT \log_2 (S/N + 1)$. More detailed discussions are given by Shannon (1948) and Wiener (1948).

he recognizes, the rate at which information is transmitted must be reduced even further.

It is reasonable to ask why we are so inefficient. A principal reason is that our sensory channels, although sensitive to small differences, do not identify stimuli in an absolute way. The ideal decoding machine would have a capacity not just to detect differences but to identify the frequency components of the messages, their Amplitudes, and perhaps their phases. This capacity is poorly developed in the human listener. In lieu of an absolute calibration, the auditory system must respond to relations. Nevertheless, from the point of view of information theory, response to relations is highly inefficient. If the parts of the signal must form a pattern, if they must be intercorrelated, the total amount of information carried by the signal is necessarily reduced. The necessity for relations among the elements of the signal greatly reduces the number of degrees of freedom in the system.

One final point is of interest here. A spoken message carries information about the talker as well as about the things the talker refers to. Numerous studies (Bonaventura, 1935; Cantril and Allport, 1935; Eisenberg and Zalowitz, 1938; Fay and Middleton, 1939–1943; Herzog, 1933; Pear, 1931; Stagner, 1936; Taylor, 1934) have tested the reliability and validity of personality judgments based solely upon the voice. Table 3 summarizes the results according to the accuracy of the listener's opinion. The listeners often agree among themselves that a talker should be what he is not, and several studies report results significantly different from chance, but in the wrong direction. In other words, stereotypes are common. Not all the listener's information depends upon the talker's choice of words. Whether or not the listener's impression is accurate, it is quite simple to show that he perceives and evaluates vocal information that does not appear in the results of an articulation test.

TABLE 3

Summary from Several Experiments of the Results of Listener's Judgments of a Talker's Personality. Most Accurate Judgments are +++, Least Accurate, 0

	Cantril and Allport	Fay and Middleton	Herzog	Pear	Others
1. Sex			+++	+++	
2. Age	+		++	++	
3. Occupation	+	+	+	+	
4. Height	0		+		
5. Weight			+		
6. Appearance	+	+		+	++
7. Extraversion-intraversion	+	0			0
8. Leadership		0			
9. Dominance	+		+		0
10. Values	+	+			
11. Handwriting	0				
12. Sociability		0			
13. Intelligence		+			
14. Fatigue		0			
15. Lying		0			
16. Summary sketch of personality	++				

REFERENCES*

Abrams, M. H., S. J. Goffard, et al. Speech in noise: A study of factors determining its intel-

* Reports prepared under contract with the Office of Scientific Research and Development usually bear an OSRD Report number. In addition, many carry a PB number, which indicates that they may be obtained from the Office of Technical Services, U. S. Department of Commerce, Washington 25, D. C.

ligibility. OSRD Report 4023, Psycho-Acoustic Laboratory, Harvard University, 1944 (PB 19805).

Abrams, M. H., and J. E. Karlin. Vocabularies for military communication in noise. OSRD Report 1919, Psycho-Acoustic Laboratory, Harvard University, 1943 (PB 22906).

Abrams, M. H., J. E. Karlin, et al. The problem of selecting and training personnel for communication in intense noise. OSRD Report 987, Psycho-Acoustic Laboratory, Harvard University, 1942 (PB 19785).

Bagley, W. C. The apperception of the spoken sentence: A study in the psychology of language. *Amer. J. Psychol.*, 1900, **12**, 80–130.

Beranek, L. L. The design of speech communication systems. *Proc. Inst. Radio Eng.*, 1947, **35**, 880–890.

Black, J. W. The nature of the spoken vowel. *Arch. Speech*, 1937, **2**, 7–40.

Black, J. W. The effect of the consonant on the vowel. *J. acoust. Soc. Amer.*, 1939, **10**, 203–205.

Black, J. W., and H. M. Mason. Training for voice communication. *J. acoust. Soc. Amer.*, 1946, **18**, 441–445.

Bonaventura, M. Ausdruck der Persönlichkeit in der Sprechstimme und im Photogramm. *Arch. ges. Psychol.*, 1935, **94**, 501–570.

Budde, E. Mathematisches zur Phonetik (Klanganalyse). In E. Abderhalden (Ed.), *Handb. d. biol. Arbeitsmethoden.* Berlin: Urban und Schwarzenberg, 1930. Abt. 5, Teil 7, pp. 197–260.

Cantril, H., and G. W. Allport. *The psychology of radio.* New York: Harper, 1935.

Carhart, R. Monitored live-voice as a test of auditory acuity. *J. acoust. Soc. Amer.*, 1946, **17**, 339–349.

Clark, K. C., H. W. Rudmose, J. C. Eisenstein, F. D. Carlson, and R. A. Walker. The effects of high altitude on speech. *J. acoust. Soc. Amer.*, 1948, **20**, 776–786.

Collard, J. A theoretical study of the articulation and intelligibility of a telephone circuit. *Elec. Comm.*, 1929, **7**, 168–186.

Collard, J. Calculation of the articulation of a telephone circuit from the circuit constants. *Elec. Comm.*, 1930, **8**, 141–163.

Collard, J. A new criterion of circuit performance. *Elec. Comm.*, 1933, **11**, 226–233.

Collard, J. The practical application of the new unit of circuit performance. *Elec. Comm.*, 1934, **12**, 270–275.

Crandall, I. B. The sounds of speech. *Bell Syst. tech. J.*, 1925, **4**, 586–626.

Crandall, I. B. Dynamical study of the vowel sounds, Part II. *Bell Syst. tech. J.*, 1927, **6**, 100–116.

Davis, Hallowell (Ed.). *Hearing and deafness.* New York: Murray Hill, 1947.

Davis, H., C. V. Hudgins, R. J. Marquis, R. H. Nichols, Jr., G. E. Peterson, D. A. Ross, and S. S. Stevens. The selection of hearing aids. *Laryngoscope* 1946, **56**, 85–115, 135–153.

Davis, H., S. S. Stevens, R. H. Nichols, Jr., C. V. Hudgins, R. J. Marquis, G. E. Peterson, and D. A. Ross. *Hearing aids: An experimental study of design objectives.* Cambridge: Harvard University Press, 1947.

Dudley, H. W. Remaking speech. *J. acoust. Soc. Amer.*, 1939, **11**, 169–177.

Dudley, H. W., and O. O. Gruenz. Visible speech translators with external phosphors. *J. acoust. Soc. Amer.*, 1946, **18**, 62–73.

Dunn, H. K., and D. W. Farnsworth. Exploration of pressure field around the human head during speech. *J. acoust. Soc. Amer.*, 1939, **10**, 184–199.

Dunn, H. K., and S. D. White. Statistical measurements on conversational speech. *J. acoust. Soc. Amer.*, 1940, **11**, 278–288.

Egan, J. P. Articulation testing methods II. OSRD Report 3802, Psycho-Acoustic Laboratory, Harvard University, 1943 (PB No. 22848).

Egan, J. P. Articulation testing methods. *Laryngoscope*, 1948a, **58**, 955–991.

Egan, J. P. The effect of noise in one ear upon the loudness of speech in the other ear. *J. acoust. Soc. Amer.*, 1948b, **20**, 58–62.

Egan, J. P., M. I. Stein, and G. G. Thompson. The articulation efficiency of nine carbon microphones for use at low altitudes. OSRD Report 3515, Psycho-Acoustic Laboratory, Harvard University, 1944 (PB 22913).

Egan, J. P., and F. M. Wiener. On the intelligibility of bands of speech in noise. *J. acoust. Soc. Amer.*, 1946, **18**, 435–441.

Eisenberg, P., and E. Zalowitz. Judging expressive movement: III. Judgments of dominance-feeling from phonograph records of voice. *J. appl. Psychol.*, 1938, **22**, 620–631.

Fay, P. J., and W. C. Middleton. Judgment of Spranger personality types from the voice as transmitted over a public address system. *Character & Pers.*, 1939, **8**, 144–155.

Fay, P. J., and W. C. Middleton. Judgment of occupation from the voice as transmitted over a public address system and over a radio. *J. appl. Psychol.*, 1939, **23**, 586–601.

Fay, P. J., and W. C. Middleton. Judgment of intelligence from the voice as transmitted over a public address system. *Sociometry*, 1940, **3**, 186–191.

Fay, P. J., and W. C. Middleton. Judgment of Kretschmerian body types from the voice as transmitted over a public address system. *J. soc. Psychol.*, 1940, **12**, 151–162.

Fay, P. J., and W. C. Middleton. The ability to judge the rested or tired condition of a speaker from his voice as transmitted over a public address system. *J. appl. Psychol.*, 1940, **24**, 645–650.

Fay, P. J., and W. C. Middleton. The ability to judge sociability from the voice as transmitted over a public address system. *J. soc. Psychol.*, 1941, **13**, 303–309.

Fay, P. J., and W. C. Middleton. The ability to judge truth-telling, or lying, from the voice as transmitted over a public address system. *J. gen. Psychol.*, 1941, **24**, 211–215.

Fay, P. J., and W. C. Middleton. Judgment of introversion from the transcribed voice. *Quart. J. Speech.*, 1942, **28**, 226–228.

Fay, P. J., and W. C. Middleton. Judgment of leadership from transmitted voice. *J. soc. Psychol.*, 1943, **17**, 99–102.

Fletcher, H. *Speech and hearing.* New York: Van Nostrand, 1929.

Fletcher, H. Loudness, masking and their relation to the hearing process and the problem of noise measurement. *J. acoust. Soc. Amer.*, 1938*a*, **9**, 275–293.

Fletcher, H. The mechanism of hearing as revealed through experiment on the masking effect of thermal noise. *Proc. nat. Acad. Sci., Wash.*, 1938*b*, **24**, 265–276.

Fletcher, H., and R. H. Galt. Perception of speech and its relation to telephony. *J. acoust. Soc. Amer.*, 1950, **22**, 89–151.

Fletcher, H., and W. A. Munson. Relation bettween loudness and masking. *J. acoust. Soc. Amer.*, 1937, **9**, 1–10.

Fletcher, H., and J. C. Steinberg. Articulation testing methods. *Bell Syst. tech. J.*, 1929, **8**, 806–854.

French, N. R., and J. C. Steinberg. Factors governing the intelligibility of speech sounds. *J. acoust. Soc. Amer.*, 1947, **19**, 90–119.

Gault, R. H. The interpretation of speech by tactual and visual impression. *Arch. Otolaryng.*, 1926, **4**, 228–239.

Gault, R. H., and L. D. Goodfellow. Experimental evidence for a basic theory of vibrotactile interpretation of speech. *Arch. Otolaryng.*, 1937, **25**, 190–195.

Gemelli, A. Observations sur le phonème au point de vue de la psychologie. *Acta psychol. Hague*, 1938, **4**, 83–112.

Gemelli, A., and G. Pastori. Elektrische Analyse der Sprache. II. Untersuchungen über die Gestaltung der Wörter und Phrasen. *Psychol. Forsch.*, 1933, **18**, 191–217.

Goffard, S. J., and J. P. Egan. *Procedures for measuring the intelligibility of speech; Sound-powered telephone systems.* Report PNR-33, Psycho-Acoustic Laboratory, Harvard University, Feb. 1, 1947.

Gross, N. B., and J. C. R. Licklider. The effects of tilting and clipping upon the intelligibility of speech. Report PNR-11, Psycho-Acoustic Laboratory, Harvard University, 1946.

Hawkins, J. E., Jr., and S. S. Stevens. The masking of pure tones and of speech by white noise. *J. acoust. Soc. Amer.*, 1950, **22**, 6–13.

Herzog, H. Stimme und Persönlichkeit. *Z. Psychol.*, 1933, **130**, 300–379.

Hudgins, C. V., J. E. Hawkins, J. E. Karlin, and S. S. Stevens. The development of recorded auditory tests for measuring hearing loss for speech. *Laryngoscope*, 1947, **57**, 57–89.

Inglis, A. H. Transmission features of the new telephone sets. *Bell Syst. tech. J.*, 1938, **17**, 358–380.

Kaiser, L. *Biological and statistical research concerning the speech of 216 Dutch students.* Amsterdam: N. V. Noord-Hollandsche Uitgevers Maatschappij, 1943.

Karlin, J. E., M. H. Abrams, et al. Auditory tests of the ability to hear speech in noise. OSRD Report 3516, Psycho-Acoustic Laboratory, Harvard University, 1944 (PB 22847).

Kellogg, E. W. Reversed speech. *J. acoust. Soc. Amer.*, 1939, **10**, 324–326.

Kersta, L. G. Amplitude cross-section representation with the sound spectrograph. *J. acoust. Soc. Amer.*, 1948, **20**, 796–801.

Knudsen, V. O. The hearing of speech in auditoriums. *J. acoust. Soc. Amer.*, 1929, **1**, 56–82.

Koenig, W., H. K. Dunn, and L. Y. Lacy. The sound spectrograph. *J. acoust. Soc. Amer.*, 1946, **18**, 19–49.

Koenig, W., and A. E. Ruppel. Quantitative amplitude representation in sound spectrograms. *J. acoust. Soc. Amer.*, 1948, **20**, 787–795.

Kopp, G. A., and Harriet C. Green. Basic phonetic principles of visible speech. *J. acoust. Soc. Amer.*, 1946, **18**, 74–89.

Kryter, K. D. Effects of ear protective devices on the intelligibility of speech in noise. *J. acoust. Soc. Amer.*, 1946, **18**, 413–417.

Kryter, K. D., and M. I. Stein. The advantage of clipping the peaks of speech waves prior to radio transmission. Report IC-83, Psycho-Acoustic Laboratory, Harvard University, 1944 (PB 22859). (Summarized in Promodulation clipping in *AM* voice communication, *J. acoust. Soc. Amer.*, 1947, **19**, 125–131.)

Laase, L. T. The effect of pitch and intensity on the quality of vowels in speech. *Arch. Speech*, 1937, **2**, 41–60.

Lewis, D. Vocal resonance. *J. acoust. Soc. Amer.*, 1936, **8**, 91–99.

Lewis, D. The learning function. (Abstract) *Amer. Psychologist*, 1946, **1**, 260.

Licklider, J. C. R. Effects of amplitude distortion upon the intelligibility of speech. OSRD Report 4217, Psycho-Acoustic Laboratory, Harvard University, 15 Nov. 1944 (PB 19775). (Summarized under same title in *J. acoust. Soc. Amer.*, 1946, **18**, 429–434.)

Licklider, J. C. R. The influence of interaural phase relations upon the masking of speech by white noise. *J. acoust. Soc. Amer.*, 1948, **20**, 150–159.

Licklider, J. C. R., D. Bindra, and I. Pollack. The intelligibility of rectangular speech-waves. *Amer. J. Psychol.*, 1948, **61**, 1–20.

Licklider, J. C. R., and K. D. Kryter. Articulation tests of standard and modified interphones conducted during flight at 5000 and 35,000 feet. OSRD Report 1976, Psycho-Acoustic Laboratory, Harvard University, 1 July 1944 (PB 5505).

Licklider, J. C. R., and I. Pollack. Effects of differentiation, integration, and infinite peak clipping upon the intelligibility of speech. *J. acoust. Soc. Amer.*, 1948, **20**, 42–51.

Licklider, J. C. R., and G. A. Roberts. A premodulation clipper unit for voice communication transmitters. Report IC-100, Psycho-Acoustic Laboratory, Harvard University, 1945 (PB 19807).

Marro, M. Amplificateur téléphonique duplex employant un phénomène de persistance d'impressions sonores sur l'ouie. *Rev. gén. élect.*, 1936, **39**, 458–461.

Maxfield, J. P., and W. J. Albersheim. An acoustic constant of enclosed spaces correlatable with their apparent liveness. *J. acoust. Soc. Amer.*, 1947, **19**, 71–79.

Miller, D. C. *The science of musical sounds.* New York : Macmillan, 1926.

Miller, G. A. The masking of speech. *Psychol. Bull.*, 1947, **44**, 105–129.

Miller, G. A., and J. C. R. Licklider. The intelligibility of interrupted speech. *J. acoust. Soc. Amer.*, 1950, **22**, 167–173.

Miller, G. A., and S. Mitchell. Effects of distortion on the intelligibility of speech at high altitudes. *J. acoust. Soc. Amer.*, 1947, **19**, 120–125.

Miller, G. A., F. M. Wiener, and S. S. Stevens. *Transmission and reception of sounds under combat conditions.* Summary Technical Report of Division 17, NDRC. Washington, 1946. Volume 3.

Montani, A. Infrasonic switching. *Electronics,* 1946, **19**, No. 3, 214–222.

Paget, R. *Human speech.* New York : Harcourt, Brace, 1930.

Pear, T. H. *Voice and personality.* London : Chapman and Hall, 1931.

Pocock, L. C. The calculation of articulation for effective rating of telephone circuits. *Elec. Comm.,* 1939, **18**, 120–132.

Poirson, E. Sur les déformations systématiques des courants téléphoniques. Application à un procédé de téléphonie secrète. *Bull. Soc. franç. Élect.* (Ser. 3), 1920, **10**, 147–161.

van der Pol, B. A new transformation in a-c theory. *Proc. Instit. Radio Eng.,* 1930, **18**, 221–230.

Pollack, I. Effects of high pass and low pass filtering on the intelligibility of speech in noise. *J. acoust. Soc. Amer.,* 1948, **20**, 259–266.

Potter, R. K. Visible patterns of sound. *Science,* 1945, **102**, 463–470.

Potter, R. K., G. A. Kopp, and H. C. Green. *Visible speech.* New York : Van Nostrand, 1947.

Potter, R. K., and G. E. Peterson. The representation of vowels and their movements. *J. acoust. Soc. Amer.,* 1948, **20**, 528–535.

Riesz, R. R., and L. Schott. Visible speech cathode-ray translator. *J. acoust. Soc. Amer.,* 1946, **18**, 50–61.

Rudmose, H. W., K. C. Clark, et al. Effects of high altitude on the human voice. OSRD Report 3106, Harvard University, 1944 (PB 19820).

Sacia, C. F. Speech power and energy. *Bell Syst. tech. J.,* 1925, **4**, 627–641.

Sacia, C. F., and C. J. Beck. The power of fundamental speech sounds. *Bell Syst. tech. J.,* 1926, **5**, 393–403.

Scripture, E. W. *The elements of experimental phonetics.* New York : Scribner, 1902.

Shannon, C. E. A mathematical theory of communication. *Bell Syst. tech. J.,* 1948, **27**, 379–423.

Shaw, W. A., E. B. Newman, and I. J. Hirsh. The difference between monaural and binaural thresholds. *J. exp. Psychol.,* 1947, **37**, 229–242.

Silverman, S. R., et al. Tolerance for pure tones and speech in normal and hard-of-hearing ears. OSRD Report 6303, Central Institute for the Deaf, St. Louis, Missouri, 1946 (PB L 58239).

Sivian, L. J. Speech power and its measurement. *Bell Syst. tech. J.,* 1929, **8**, 646–661.

Smith, W. W. Premodulation speech clipping and filtering. *QST,* 1946, **30**, 46–50.

Stagner, R. Judgments of voice and personality. *J. educ. Psychol.,* 1936, **27**, 272–277.

Steinberg, J. C. Effects of distortion on the recognition of speech sounds. *J. acoust. Soc. Amer.,* 1929, **1**, 121–137.

Steinberg, J. C. Effects of phase distortion on telephone quality. *Bell Syst. tech. J.,* 1930, **9**, 550–566.

Steinberg, J. C. Application of sound measuring instruments to the study of phonetic problems. *J. acoust. Soc. Amer.,* 1934, **6**, 16–24.

Steinberg, J. C. Tests of speech and music transmission, and Effects of distortion on speech and music. In H. Pender and K. McIlwain (Eds.), *Electrical engineer's handbook, electric communication and electronics* (3rd Ed.) New York : Wiley, 1936. Pp. 9.24–9.36.

Steinberg, J. C., and N. R. French. The portrayal of visible speech. *J. acoust. Soc. Amer.,* 1946, **18**, 4–18.

Stevens, S. S., J. P. Egan, and G. A. Miller. Methods of measuring speech spectra. *J. acoust. Soc. Amer.,* 1947, **19**, 771–780.

Stevens, S. S., J. Miller, and I. Truscott. The masking of speech by sine waves, square waves, and regular and modulated pulses. *J. acoust. Soc. Amer.,* 1946, **18**, 418–424.

Strecker, F. Verständlichkeit und Lautstärke bei Frequenz- und Amplitudenbegrenzung, *Akust. Z.,* 1936, **1**, 174–178.

Stumpf, C. *Tonpsychologie.* Leipzig : Herzel, 1883.

Taylor, H. C. Social agreement on personality traits as judged from speech. *J. soc. Psychol.,* 1934, **5**, 244–248.

Trendelenburg, F. Elektrische Methoden zur Klanganalyse. In E. Abderhalden (Ed.), *Handb. d. biol. Arbeitsmethoden.* Berlin : Urban and Schwarzenberg, 1930. Abt. 5, Teil 7, pp. 787–870.

Weichbrodt, M. Tactual compared with visual discrimination of consonantal qualities. *J. gen. Psychol.,* 1932, **6**, 203–206.

West, W. Telephone transmission testing by subjective methods. *P. O. Elect. Eng. J.,* 1939, **31**, 286–292.

Wiener, N. *Cybernetics.* New York : Wiley, 1948.

27·

The Mechanical Properties
of the Ear

GEORG von BÉKÉSY and WALTER A. ROSENBLITH

Harvard University

Many theories have been proposed to account for the phenomena of hearing. Theorizing has flourished principally because the location and the size of the various parts of the ear make it difficult to measure their physical properties with accuracy. Consequently our knowledge of the mechanical properties of the ear is sketchy, and even more fragmentary is our understanding of the translation of mechanical processes into neural stimuli.

In the following pages we shall be concerned primarily with those phenomena that are accessible to physical measurement. We shall attempt to separate the function of the ear, as a mechanical transducer, from the function of the nervous system, and to examine the mechanical processes in the ear that relate to the theory of hearing. We must, however, point up the danger of generalizing about the whole process of hearing on the basis of measurements made in one range of frequencies. Our measurements demonstrate that the auditory systems of man and higher animals function in many respects as if they were governed by the same general principles. Yet a more detailed quantitative study often brings out important differences in the functioning of cer-

This chapter was prepared at the Psycho-Acoustic Laboratory, Harvard University, under contract with the U. S. Navy, Office of Naval Research (Contract N5ori-76, Project NR142-201, Report PNR-80).

tain parts of these systems. It would appear unwise, therefore, to try to generalize too freely about the workings of the various elements of human and animal auditory systems from certain similarities in their overall response.

GROSS ANATOMY OF THE EAR

Figure 1 represents a schematic drawing of the human ear. (Unless otherwise noted, all drawings and measurements presented in this chapter represent the human ear.) An incident sound wave exerts a pressure upon the drum (tympanic membrane) which sets the three ossicles — the hammer (malleus), the anvil (incus), and the stirrup (stapes) — into motion and thereby transfers the pressure to the inner ear. The air-filled space containing the ossicles is called the middle ear. Since gas inside the body is absorbed by the blood stream, the pressure in the middle ear would gradually fall below normal, were it not for the Eustachian tube which connects the middle ear with the pharynx. The Eustachian tube is usually closed, but it opens when we swallow or yawn. The middle ear pressure and the atmospheric pressure are thereby equalized. This is very important whenever the atmospheric pressure changes rapidly, as in airplanes and elevators. In certain pathological cases the

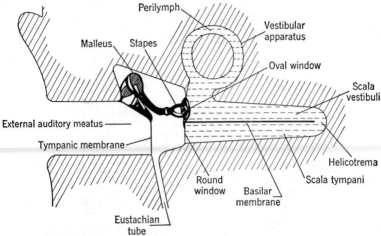

Fig. 1. Schematic drawing of the human ear. Sound waves enter the external meatus, and move the tympanic membrane which sets the three ossicles in motion. When the stapes footplate moves inward, the perilymph inside the cochlea flows in the direction of the helicotrema and makes the round-window membrane bulge outward. All these movements can be observed with the aid of a microscope. (Békésy, 1935.)

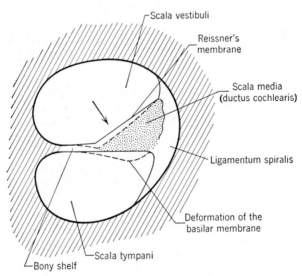

Fig. 2. Schematic cross section of the cochlear channels. When a pressure (direction of arrow) is applied, the ductus cochlearis is bulged into the scala tympani (shown by the dashed lines). (Békésy, 1941b.)

Eustachian tube remains continuously open, and sound then travels directly from the mouth to the middle ear. An unpleasant rumble known as autophony ensues.

The inner ear is filled with liquid. It consists of two parts: the vestibular apparatus and the cochlea. The cochlea is coiled in the manner of a snail shell (hence the name).

By means of an elastic partition, the cochlea is subdivided into two principal perilymph-filled channels. This partition contains the ductus cochlearis, which is filled with a highly viscous, almost gelatinous substance called endolymph (see dotted area in Fig. 2). The partition contains the auditory nerve endings and many other structures whose function is connected with the translation of mechanical into neural

liquid does not flow through the helicotrema and back to the round window. Instead it deforms the cochlear partition as shown by the dashed lines in Fig. 2.

Figure 3 shows an actual section of the human ear. The sound impinges from the

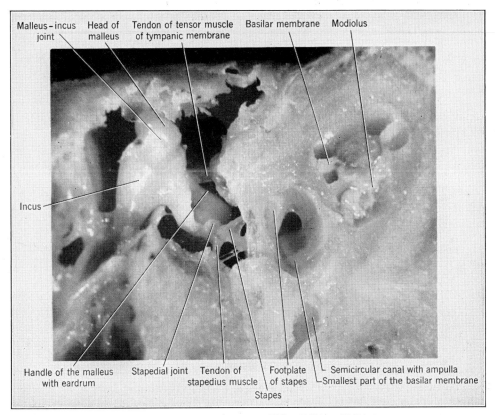

FIG. 3. Middle ear in man. (After Békésy, 1949.)

stimuli (for details see Chapter 28). In spite of its rather heterogeneous inner structure, the partition can, to a first approximation, be treated as a single elastic layer. The helicotrema (see Fig. 1) protects the cochlear partition from one-sided, static pressures. When the stapes moves slowly inward, the liquid flows along the upper channel and through the helicotrema into the lower channel where it finally produces a deformation of the round window. At higher audible frequencies of vibration of the stapes the

back of the figure upon the drum and sets the handle of the malleus into motion. The interlocking of the head of the malleus and the incus is visible, as are also the various ligaments that fasten the ossicles to the middle ear wall. We see a tendon leading to the tensor tympani, a muscle that contracts when the ear is stimulated by a sound. Another muscle, the stapedius, the smallest muscle in the human body, is fastened to the stapedial joint. The stapes footplate is attached by means of very tenuous fibers to the bony wall. This insures a pistonlike motion of the stapes. Figure 4, a histological section of the middle ear of a cat, shows the piston "packing" as well as the stapedius muscle.

Only the outer edge of the cochlear partition is elastic; the inner edge is a bony shelf known as the lamina spiralis ossea (see Fig.

tions (Mangold, 1926). The external ear can be compared to a funnel. For higher frequencies the funnel acts in two different ways: (1) it brings about a pressure transformation making the pressure at the drum greater than the pressure in the free sound field, and (2) it has directional properties such that sounds from one direction are

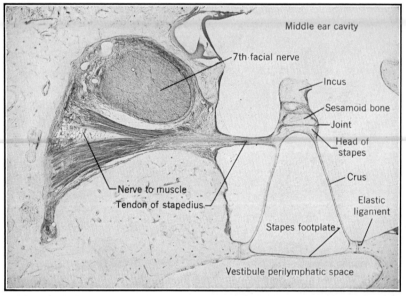

FIG. 4. Cross section of the stapes of a cat. In otosclerotic patients the tenuous elastic ligaments that attach the stapes footplate to the bony capsule of the cochlea become ossified and the stapes becomes immobilized. (We are indebted for this figure to Dr. M. H. Lurie.)

2). The width of the elastic part of the cochlear partition increases uniformly as we go from the stapes to the helicotrema. Since the width of the cochlear partition as a whole remains rather constant, the width of the bony part decreases as we recede from the stapes. To give the reader a feeling for the dimensions and masses in the human ear, the best available data have been summarized in Table 1.

The outer and the middle ear. Many animals possess rather large pinnas which affect particularly their reception of high-frequency sounds. The horse, for instance, has seventeen different muscles that permit him to orient his pinna in different direc-

amplified while sounds from other azimuths are attenuated. Both these properties come into play for wavelengths that are of the order of magnitude of the dimensions of the external ear funnel (the wavelength of a 3000-cycle tone in air is about 11 centimeters). Mach and Fischer (1873) have given a particularly clear and thorough discussion of this matter.

The second half of the nineteenth century produced a whole series of experiments dealing with the modifications of the sound field due to irregularities in the human meatus. The experimenters (Schneider, Kuepper, Harless, Rinne, Kessel, and others) used great ingenuity to get a smooth sound path

TABLE 1

AVERAGE DATA FOR HUMAN EARS (RESULTS OF MEASUREMENTS BY MANY AUTHORS)

Auditory Meatus
Cross section, 0.3–0.5 cm^2
Diameter, 0.7 cm
Length, 2.7 cm
Volume, 1.0 cc

Tympanic Membrane
Area, 0.5–0.9 cm^2
Thickness, about 0.1 mm
Volume elasticity for 10 cps, equivalent
to about 8 cc air
Displacement amplitude 1000 cps tone
(at threshold), 10^{-9} cm
Displacement amplitude for low-fre-
quency tones (threshold of feeling),
about 10^{-2} cm

Middle Ear
Total Volume, about 2 cc
Malleus: weight, 23 mg
length, 5.5–6.0 mm
Incus: weight, 27 mg
Stapes: weight, 2.5 mg
length of footplate, 3.2 mm
width of footplate, 1.4 mm
area of footplate, 3.2 mm^2
width of elastic ligament, 0.015–0.1 mm

Cochlea
Length of cochlear channels, 35 mm
Height of scala vestibuli or scala tympani, about
1 mm (great variability)
Round window: area, 2 mm^2
Basilar membrane: width at stapes, 0.04 mm
width at helicotrema, 0.5 mm
Helicotrema: area of opening, 0.25–0.4 mm^2

to the drum. They introduced glass tubes and filled the hollows of the external ear with wax, oil, or bread dough. Their final conclusions show a good measure of agreement: although the threshold for sounds in the middle range is not much affected, localization suffers when the shape of the external ear is altered. In particular it becomes less easy to distinguish noises originating in front from those in back of the head.

The meatus functions also as a protective device against foreign bodies. Since the thin membranes of the middle ear are very sensitive to changes in humidity, the meatus also serves the purpose of making the humidity in the vicinity of the drum reasonably independent from the humidity of the atmosphere. The same holds for temperature: because of the length of the meatus we find that the temperature close to the drum is independent of the atmospheric temperature and is even 0.2 to 0.3 degree C higher than the temperature in the armpit.

The meatus is a resonator about 2.7 centimeters long. The natural frequency of the resonator is near 3000 cps. Consequently,

for frequencies close to the resonant frequency the sound pressure at the drum is greater than the free-field pressure, but, since this resonator is terminated by a flexible drum and since its outside opening is relatively large, the resonance is not sharp. Even at the resonant frequency the increase in sound pressure is small: in most cases the maximum increase is about 10 db. To this increased sound pressure due to the meatus are added the effects on the sound field produced by the presence of the head and the body.

These phenomena were predicted on theoretical grounds by Ballantine (1930) and Békésy (1932b). Experimental evidence substantiating them came from Wiener and Ross (1946) and Wiener (1947). In order to perform such measurements a probe is inserted close to the drum and the measured sound pressure is compared with the pressure at the entrance of the meatus. Figure 5 shows the most recent results.

The drum and the ossicles. Although with the aid of an ear speculum we can see the drum very clearly, it is not easy to measure its vibratory pattern because the amplitude of vibration of the drum is very small.

In 1872 Mach and Kessel put some shell gold on the drum and succeeded in observing the drum vibrations through a microscope. Similar observations can be made more easily with modern ear microscopes (Waar, 1923). When low frequencies are used, greater amplitudes are obtained, and it becomes simpler to make these observations stroboscopically. Wilska (1935) determined the amplitude of vibration of the

The question is often asked whether the ear responds mainly to pressure changes or mainly to changes in the velocity of the vibrating air particles. In a standing wave pattern a tone is heard loudest when the ear is located at a pressure antinode, while nothing is heard at a velocity antinode. The ear behaves therefore, at low frequencies, as a pressure receiver. For frequencies near 1500 cps, the vibrations of the ossicles give rise to rather irregular resonance phenomena. In this frequency range the drum

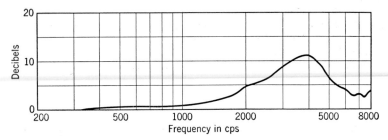

Fig. 5. Effects of resonance in the external meatus. The ordinate shows the ratio in decibels between the sound pressure at the eardrum and the sound pressure at the entrance to the auditory canal. (Wiener, 1947.) For the effects of sound diffraction around the head, see Wiener and Ross (1946).

drum at the threshold of audibility for various frequencies. He glued a light stick directly to the eardrum and then measured the amplitude with which the stick vibrated (Fig. 6).

A series of measurements (West, 1928; Tröger, 1930; Békésy, 1932a, 1936a; Sivian and White, 1933; Geffcken, 1934; Waetzmann and Keibs, 1936a, b; Metz, 1946) were carried out in order to determine the mobility of the drum. More specifically, these workers measured the volume displacement of the drum for pressure changes inside the meatus. The importance of these so-called impedance measurements stems from the fact that once we know the impedance of the drum we are able to calculate how much sound energy is transferred to it (Fig. 7). These impedance measurements show that, at low frequencies, the drum behaves like an elastic membrane whose displacements are proportional to the incident pressure.

reflects practically none of the energy that impinges upon it. Its sensitivity is maximum. It is, however, no longer exclusively a pressure receiver. At the higher frequencies the situation is complicated by the fact that the eardrum vibrates in segments, so that no simple generalizations can be made. The pattern of segmental vibration changes drastically with frequency.

The natural frequency of vibration of the middle ear depends upon the ossicular masses and also upon the elastic properties of the various ligaments that keep the ossicles in place. The small bumps in the curves representing the threshold of hearing would seem to be attributable to small frequency-dependent variations in drum mobility. In 1936 Langenbeck drew attention to the fact that threshold curves for both ears of a given individual show a high degree of similarity, as would be expected from the bilateral symmetry of the face.

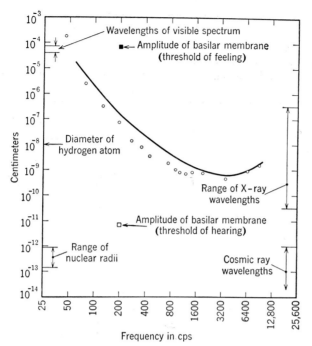

FIG. 6. Amplitudes of vibration of the drum at the threshold of hearing. The circles show the amplitudes determined by Wilska. Békésy measured the amplitude of vibration of the basilar membrane at the threshold of feeling (solid square). The amplitude of the basilar membrane at the threshold of hearing (open square) is an extrapolation, as were Wilska's points. The curve shows the amplitude of vibration of air molecules in a sound wave at threshold as calculated by Stevens and Davis. This curve and Békésy's data are in reasonable agreement with Wilska's findings if allowance is made for the different impedances involved.

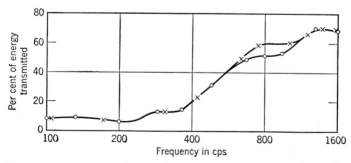

FIG. 7. Transmission of energy at the eardrum. The ordinate values were computed from impedance measurements. They indicate the percentage of the incident sound energy transmitted to the middle ear. The circles refer to the left and the crosses to the right ear of the subject. The difference between the ordinate values and 100 per cent is the amount of energy reflected at the eardrum. (After Waetzmann and Keibs, 1936a.)

Since the shape of facial bones is presumably inherited, we may also assume that the shapes of the ossicles, and hence of the fine structure of threshold curves, are likewise inherited. This was shown by Waetzmann and Keibs (Fig. 8). Threshold curves on identical twins confirm this notion.

be thought of as a piston with a cross section of about 85 square millimeters, out of which about 55 square millimeters are rigidly attached to the handle of the malleus. The pressure upon this piston is finally transmitted to the stapes where the effective area amounts to only 3.2 square millimeters.

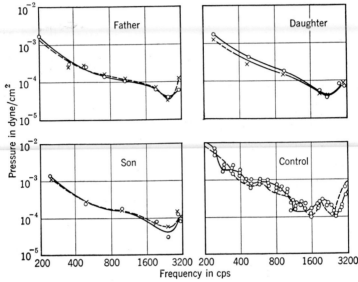

FIG. 8. Family similarities in audiograms (right and left ears). The "control" is for one of Waetzmann's three unrelated subjects. Waetzmann stresses (1) that audiograms tend to be similar for both ears, (2) that audiograms for members of a family are similar, and (3) that unrelated subjects show significant differences. (Békésy, 1935, after Waetzmann, 1935.)

Since the auditory nerve endings are immersed in a liquid, a transducer problem arises: how is the acoustic energy transferred from the air to the liquid? Air, a very light and compressible medium, has a small impedance compared to that of the practically incompressible cochlear liquid. Hence the necessity for a system of levers whose function consists in transforming the large displacements of the air into small displacements of the liquid, while at the same time transforming the small forces acting upon the drum into larger forces acting upon the cochlear liquid.

The anatomical structure of the middle ear seems extremely appropriate for this purpose (Helmholtz, 1868). The drum can

The ossicles are pivoted in a manner that provides a small additional mechanical advantage (about 1.3). From these figures we can calculate that the pressure at the stapes should be about 22 times as large as the pressure at the drum. Frank (1923) made some detailed computations concerning this point. More recently van Esser (1947) reexamined the problem.

Work by Backhaus (1928) on condenser microphones led to a technique that makes it possible to observe in detail the vibrations of the various parts of the middle ear. In a Backhaus microphone one plate of a condenser is fixed while the other plate is attached to a vibrating body (e.g. the eardrum). The fixed plate does not come into contact with the vibrating body. The vibration itself alters the distance between the two plates and produces thereby a change in

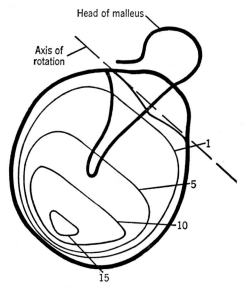

Fɪɢ. 9. Vibration of the human eardrum for a 2000-cycle tone. The closed curves represent contours of equal displacement amplitude on a relative scale. The eardrum moves like a rigid body around the axis of rotation. (Békésy, 1941a.)

the capacity of the condenser. The variable capacitance is used in a circuit to modulate the frequency of a high-frequency signal, and we are thereby able to make measure-

ments on very light, soft bodies without modifying the way in which they vibrate. It is even possible to dispense with the condenser plate usually attached to the vibrating body and to reduce the surface of the fixed plate to a diameter of 2 to 3 millimeters. Hence the displacement amplitude of vibrating bodies can be easily measured without interfering with their motion (Békésy, 1941a).

This method was used to determine how the drum vibrates. Figure 9 shows that for a frequency of 2000 cps the drum vibrates like a solid plate pivoted on an axis (upper right corner). In man the drum vibrates with its greatest amplitude near the lower edge. Detailed anatomical investigations have shown that the great mobility of this part of the drum is made possible by the presence of a small fold. The pattern of vibration remains the same for frequencies up to about 2400 cps. At higher frequencies the drum vibrates in segments.

The same method can be used to measure the vibrations of the stapes footplate after the ear has been opened from the cochlear side. It is also possible to measure the pressure transformation of the middle ear by a null method. A known pressure is applied to the drum and balanced by a pressure on the cochlear side of the stapes footplate so that the latter remains motionless. Figure

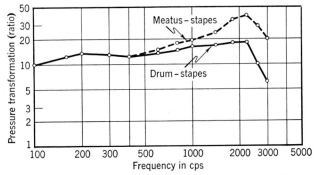

Fɪɢ. 10. Pressure transformation in the middle ear. The pressure at the stapes is increased over the pressure at the meatus (and at the drum) by the ratio shown. This pressure transformation helps to match the impedance of the air to the impedance of the cochlea. At the higher frequencies the ratio of transformation between stapes and meatus is enhanced by the resonance of the meatus (cf. Fig. 5). (Békésy, 1941a.)

10 shows the ratio between the pressure that acts upon the stapes footplate and the pressure acting on the drum (the dashed curve shows the ratio of the pressure at the stapes to the pressure at the entrance of the meatus). As can be seen, the average transformation ratio is 15:1. The agreement with the previously calculated transformation

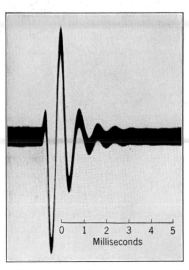

FIG. 11. Response of the malleus handle to a sharp click presented to the ear. The displacements were recorded by means of a light beam reflected from a mirror glued to the handle. It is possible to calculate the natural frequency and the degree of damping from the recorded curve. (Békésy, 1936c.)

ratio could easily be "improved" by using different data for the area of the drum (see, for instance, Stuhlman, 1943, who cites a range of 52 to 90 square millimeters with a mean of 66 square millimeters).

An important datum for the understanding of the functioning of the middle ear is its natural frequency. If a sharp click is produced by means of a spark and the oscillations of the malleus handle are recorded by an oscillograph, we find that the natural frequency lies in the neighborhood of 1300 cps (Fig. 11). There is a good deal of damping in the mechanism of the middle ear, which tends to reduce the distortion of the on-and-off transients of speech waves.

THE MIDDLE EAR AS A PROTECTIVE DEVICE

The structure of the middle ear is rather complicated. One bone, the stapes, would suffice to bring about the appropriate pressure transformation. In birds we find merely this one bone. The presence of three ossicles in mammals is not too easy to understand, and many investigators have been concerned with this problem.*

At first sight it would seem absurd that both the malleus and the incus should be endowed with so much mass (Figs. 12 and 13). But, as Bárány (1938) has pointed out, the symmetrical arrangement of the mass of these ossicles with respect to the axis of rotation contributes to the minimization of bone-conducted sound.

For low frequencies the ligaments are certainly sufficient to keep the axis of rotation

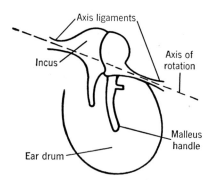

FIG. 12. Arrangement of the ossicles, showing how the mass is distributed around the axis of rotation. As shown in Fig. 9 the maximum displacement of the eardrum occurs at its lower edge. (Bárány, 1938.)

of the ossicles fixed, guaranteeing thereby pressure transformation. At higher frequencies, however, the acceleration forces (which are proportional to the square of the frequency) increase so much that the elastic ligaments tying the ossicles to the membranous wall are no longer able to keep the ossicles precisely in their normal loca-

* For a detailed description of the middle ear, see Fumagalli (1949).

tion. The pivot, however, remains fixed (theorem of the center of mass).

There are also two small muscles in the middle ear. One of them pulls the drum inward in reflex response to an incident sound; the other muscle pulls the stapes out of the

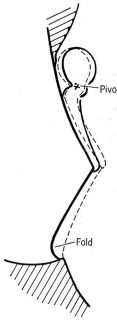

Fig. 13. For lower frequencies the human eardrum is rigid and turns on an axis at its upper rim. A fold on the lower rim permits movement of the rigid eardrum cone. Since the center of gravity is at the point of rotation of the malleus, no bending force acts to deform the eardrum, unless the malleus head is missing. (Békésy, 1941a.)

cochlea. In patients with perforated drums the activity of both muscles is easily observed (Lüscher, 1929). In 1864, Politzer expressed the opinion that the pull exerted by these two muscles reduces the displacement amplitude of the drum. In other words the effect of these muscles is presumably analogous to that of the iris in the eye, in that they protect the cochlea from excessively loud sounds. Many animal experiments (in particular those that make use of cochlear microphonics) support this

view. Under normal circumstances the sound pressure is not reduced as much in man as it is in animals. Kato (1913) showed that the muscles in both ears contract, even if the sound is present in one ear only. Thus it becomes possible to expose one ear to a high-frequency tone and then to examine what happens to the loudness of a low-frequency tone in the other ear. The changes that occur are of the order of 5 to 10 db.

When impedance measurements are used to determine the mobility of the drum in the presence of voluntary muscle contractions, no significant changes in drum mobility are found (Geffcken, 1934).

In any case, the muscles do not seem to offer protection against sharp clicks because their reaction time is about 10 milliseconds, and as war injuries have demonstrated it is during this interval that the damage occurs.

According to Helmholtz there is a mobile joint between the head of the malleus and the incus. This joint loosens up if the malleus vibrates too strongly, and the transmission is reduced. Békésy was, however, unable to observe such a loosening either in fresh post-mortem preparations or during operations on living subjects.

Measurements with very low-frequency tones have shown that there is another effective mechanism at work that protects the inner ear to a certain extent. Beyond a certain point an increase in the sound pressure of a 10-cycle tone does not produce an increase in its loudness. On the contrary, the loudness of the tone decreases suddenly (Békésy, 1936b). When the loudness starts to decrease the subject has a pricking sensation in the middle ear. Closer investigation shows that the whole mode of motion of the ossicles changes at that time, as indicated by Fig. 14. The stapes stops rotating about a vertical axis and no longer presses the fluid into the cochlea. Instead, the stapes footplate turns now about an axis at right angles to the previous axis. This causes the fluid to flow only from one edge of the footplate to the other. Such an arrangement is a really effective protective device. The complicated structure of the ossicular chain now becomes understandable. We are here in the presence of a mechanical system able

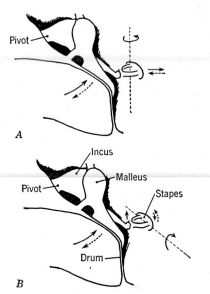

A

B

FIG. 14. The two modes of vibration of the stapes. *A.* Rotation of the footplate about a vertical axis through its far edge occurs in response to weak sounds. The fluid is pressed into the scala vestibuli by the motion of the edge of the stapes nearest the reader. *B.* For intensities above the threshold of feeling, the axis of rotation coincides with the longitudinal axis of the footplate, and the actual volume of fluid pressed into the scala is reduced. (Békésy, 1936c.)

to vibrate in two different modes with a sudden transition from one mode to the other for displacement amplitudes greater than a critical value.

NONLINEAR DISTORTION

Hooke's law states that a deformation is proportional to the force producing it. But this law holds only for small deformations, and as the force increases the deformation deviates from the value predicted by the law. This phenomenon, called nonlinearity, is encountered whenever an elastic system

is investigated over any appreciable range of forces. If tones of two frequencies f_1 and f_2 act simultaneously upon a nonlinear system, harmonics ($2f_1$, $3f_1$, etc.; also $2f_2$, $3f_2$, etc.), difference tones ($f_1 - f_2$, $2f_1 - f_2$, etc.) and summation tones ($f_1 + f_2$, $2f_1 + f_2$, etc.) will make their appearance. Nonlinearity thus gives rise to frequencies previously not present in the stimulus. If the system is one-dimensional and deviates from Hooke's law in a known manner, the amplitudes of the difference and summation tones are related in a lawful manner to the amplitudes of the harmonics (cf. Fig. 27 in Chapter 25).

The ear is apparently not so simple a system, however. Let us consider, for instance, the semihypothetical case of an eardrum connected to a single ossicle. If the eardrum is under negative pressure, so that the eardrum and the ossicle are pulled outward, the system has only one degree of freedom. For a positive pressure, however, the ossicle is in an unstable equilibrium, and it can tilt in various directions so that it has at least three degrees of freedom. The eardrum moving in from left to right tilts the ossicle upward from the middle position. With the movement of the eardrum out to the left, the ossicle comes back to the midline. The next inward movement of the eardrum causes the ossicle to move downward because its kinetic energy carries it through the middle position. Therefore it is evident that, during a full period of the eardrum, the ossicle makes an excursion to only one side. It moves with the half frequency of the eardrum (this gives rise to what are called undertones).

Such a system, having three degrees of freedom, cannot be represented by a single characteristic function describing the relation between input and output, and it is not possible to use the relation among harmonics and difference tones to determine the shape of the input-output function.

Nevertheless the appearance of "new" tones can still be used to determine whether nonlinearity is present in the ear and what type of nonlinearity we are dealing with. If two tones ($f_1 = 2000$ cps, and $f_2 = 2260$ cps) are presented to the ear, a tone corresponding to $f_1 - f_2 = 260$ cps can be heard and clearly distinguished from the two primary tones. (For some frequencies the loudness of the difference tone may equal the loudness of the primary tones.) We can make it easier to detect the difference tone if a search tone of frequency, $f_3 = 261$ cps, is added. This results, of course, in beats between the difference tone and the newly added tone of 261 cps. We must bear in mind, however, that the introduction of a search tone gives rise to new distortion products.

Once the existence of nonlinear distortions in the ear has been established, the question arises: where are they generated? Possibilities of mechanical nonlinearity exist in the drum, in the ossicular joints and ligaments, in the cochlear fluid, and in the cochlear partition.

Is the drum the source of difference tones? This question can be decided in the following manner: two intense tones are presented to the ear, at about 20 db below the threshold of feeling. A very strong difference tone is heard. If this difference tone owes its existence to distortion in the drum, it should be radiated from both sides of the drum and be detectible in the external meatus. Experiments of this kind (Békésy, 1934) led to the conclusion that the difference tones we hear when the primary tones are about 20 db below the threshold of feeling are not generated by the drum. The same negative conclusion applies to the generation of harmonics by the drum.

If we assume that the difference tones originate in the middle ear, their intensity should change when the ossicles are displaced from their normal position (such a displacement would cause the ossicles to vibrate in a mode other than their normal mode). This displacement can be accomplished if a pressure is exerted upon the drum at the same time as a tone is presented.

As shown in Fig. 15, the greatest change in the loudness of difference tones occurs during the time interval in which there is a change in the added pressure, i.e. while the ossicles are being displaced from their normal position. It would therefore appear that

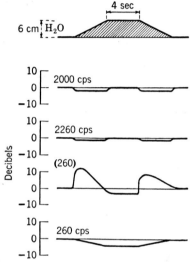

FIG. 15. If the pressure in the meatus is increased by the equivalent of 6 centimeters of water, the changes in the loudness of three primary tones are not striking, but the loudness of the 260-cycle difference tone (2260 minus 2000 cps) increases considerably while the pressure is changing. (Békésy, 1934.)

the origin of difference tones is to be sought in the nonlinearity of the middle ear, at least part of which may be due to the ligaments holding the ossicles in place. It is most probable that these distortion phenomena are in particular related to the vibrations of the stapes footplate.

The origin of the harmonics cannot be localized in this same manner. Application of a unidirectional pressure does not influence their loudness to the same extent.

It seems at present difficult to determine the exact part played by rectification phenomena inside the cochlea in the production of nonlinear distortions. This rectification is probably achieved by means of eddies in the vicinity of the stapes footplate and also further along the cochlear partition.

It seems very surprising that the drum does not give rise to observable nonlinear distortions, for we might expect it to on the basis of its anatomical structure. In particular, we should expect a funnel-shaped membrane to exhibit more distortion than a flat membrane (Fig. 16). On the other

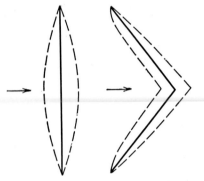

Fig. 16. Vibration of flat and conical membranes (schematic). The flat membrane is deformed symmetrically by positive and negative pressures. The eardrum is like a conical membrane. Positive and negative pressures produce different deformation patterns, thus giving rise to nonlinear distortion. (Békésy, 1939a.)

hand, the actual drum displacements are determined principally by the elastic properties of the volume of air in the middle ear (which acts like an air cushion) and not by its own elastic properties. Since in the human ear the stiffness of the air cushion exceeds that of the membrane (Békésy, 1936a) the nonlinearity of the drum itself is not an appreciable factor. (This same principle of "cushioning" is made use of in the condenser microphone, where a thin aluminum foil is given great stiffness without being put under tension.)

The situation changes if relatively large pressures are exerted upon the drum. Kobrak (1949) has studied the effects of such pressures by measuring the displacements of the round-window membrane for various static pressures in the external meatus.

Figure 17 shows the lack of proportionality between pressure and displacements; it also points up the fact that the displacements are different for positive and negative pressures.

For large alternating pressures the presence of harmonics can be easily detected, especially at low frequencies. Figure 18 shows the waveform present in the meatus for a tone of 20 cps at a pressure of 10^4 dynes per square centimeter (approximately 154-db sound-pressure level). This considerable amount of nonlinear distortion is due to the fact that the ossicles now vibrate in their second stable mode (see Fig. 14). Stuhlman's enlarged model of the ossicles (1937, 1943) permitted him to investigate in detail the nonlinearites that arise when the

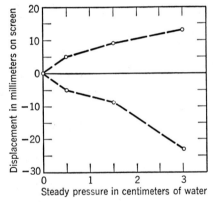

Fig. 17. The effects on the round window of static pressures in the ear canal of a fresh human cadaver. Note the asymmetry of the displacements: negative phases of pressure in the external auditory canal produce greater displacements than positive phases. (Kobrak, 1949.)

ossicles undergo rotational motion of appreciable amplitude.

A question of particular interest is whether nonlinear phenomena can be demonstrated in the vibration of the cochlear partition. Actual measurements (Fig. 19) show that the movement of the basilar membrane is not a linear function of the movement of the stapes when the amplitude is above the threshold of feeling. This non-linearity is not present, however, at sound intensities below the threshold of feeling.

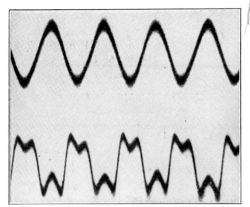

FIG. 18. Waveform generated in the meatus by a tone of 20 cps at a sound-pressure level of 154 db. The upper curve represents the stimulus, and the lower curve shows the waveform, containing a large third harmonic, reradiated from the drum. Part of the fundamental was canceled out in order better to display the distortion. (Békésy, 1936a.)

Among other things the linearity of the movement of the cochlear partition under the impact of moderate sound intensities

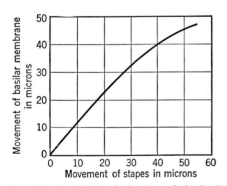

FIG. 19. Amplitude of vibration of the basilar membrane as a function of the amplitude of the stapes. At values far above the threshold of feeling the movement of the basilar membrane ceases to be proportional to the movement of the stapes. (Békésy, 1947.)

rules out nonlinearity as an explanation of the fact that pitch is observed to change with intensity.

THE INNER EAR: HYPOTHE-SES AND THEORIES

Does the cochlea perform a mechanical frequency analysis so as to translate differ-

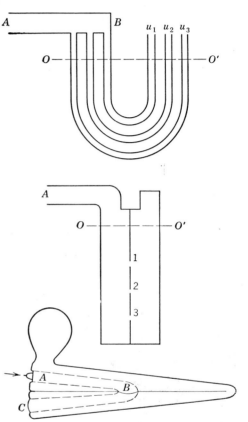

FIG. 20. Models representing fluid motion in cochlea. The series of U-shaped tubes (top figure) are filled with fluid up to the level OO' and form resonating systems one of which responds preferentially to an alternating air pressure in channel AB. The system is thus capable of frequency analysis. In the middle figure the tubes have now been collapsed into a single vessel with several openings; gravity still provides the restoring force in this frequency-analyzing system. In the cochlea (bottom figure), the mass of the resonating system is given by the thread of fluid ABC; and the restoring force comes from the elastic membrane. (After Lux, Budde, and Wilkinson.)

ent tones into different "spatial" stimuli for the nervous system? Helmholtz, in 1863, assumed the presence of a series of resonators in the ear, each tuned to a different frequency, and he thought he was able to explain Ohm's acoustic law according to

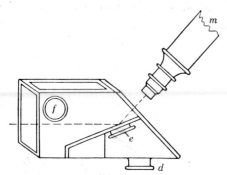

FIG. 21. Ewald's *camera acustica* designed to reproduce the vibrations of the cochlear partition, represented by a thin rubber membrane fastened in the frame *e*, contained in a water-filled box. The opening *d* represents the round window. The sound enters through the opening *f* (the oval window) and sets the rubber membrane into vibration, which brings about changes in the reflection pattern observed through a microscope *m*. (Ewald, 1903.)

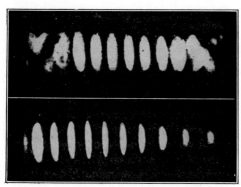

FIG. 22. Typical standing wave patterns observed by Ewald are different for different frequencies. The distance between nodes of the standing waves decreases as the frequency increases. (Ewald, posthumously published.)

which the ear tends to hear the individual components of a complex sound, regardless of their phase relations. The search for these resonators ran, however, into certain difficulties. According to Helmholtz the cochlear partition has what might be called a "piano-chord" structure. This means that

there must be present a membrane characterized by a much larger tension crosswise than in the longitudinal direction.

In the absence of anatomical evidence for such a piano-chord structure of the cochlear partition, Lux developed his hypothesis (described by Budde in 1917) according to which there is a series of U-shaped threads of liquid in the cochlea. All these threads

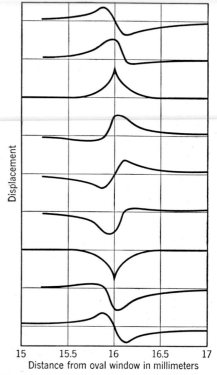

FIG. 23. The deformation patterns of the basilar membrane for one complete cycle of a 1000-cycle tone. The instantaneous patterns of the membrane are for intervals separated by ⅛ of a period. Each wave of vibration passes along the membrane away from the oval window. For 1000 cps the amplitude of vibration is greatest at a location 16 millimeters from the oval window. (After Fletcher, 1930.)

represent resonant systems: the fluid in the thread furnishes the mass, and the elastic cochlear membrane furnishes the elasticity. Figure 20 shows the transition from this system of U-tubes, in which gravity supplies the restoring force, to the cochlea, where the restoring force is the cochlear membrane. Roaf (1922) and Wilkinson (1922) carried this theory further.

We could also have started, however, from an entirely different conception. The cochlear scalae are essentially elastic tubes since they are bounded on one side by the elastic gated along the membrane. Reflection from the far end of the membrane will then give rise to standing waves, with a different standing wave pattern for each frequency. Ewald (1899, 1903) built a detailed theory along this line. He demonstrated his patterns by experiments with models (Figs. 21 and 22).

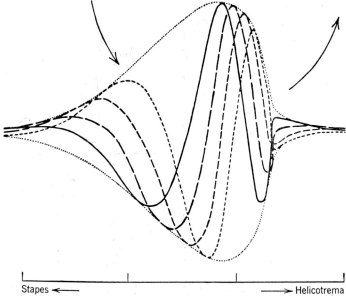

Stapes ◄—————   —————► Helicotrema

FIG. 24. Deformation of the basilar membrane, according to Ranke. This figure should be compared with Fig. 23. The four different patterns are separated by ⅛ of a period. The envelope shows the maximum amplitude obtained at each point. The wave travels from the stapes to the helicotrema, pushing the fluid ahead of the wave front. This gives rise to eddy formation as indicated by the arrows. (Ranke, 1942.)

cochlear partition. Then by analogy with the concepts that have proved useful in work on blood vessels, we can assume that an inward motion of the stapes will give rise to a traveling wave along the cochlear partition. Hurst (1895), Bonnier (1895), and ter Kuile (1900) constructed theories along these lines. They assumed appropriate values for the damping and the wavelength of these traveling waves so as to obtain different loci of maximum displacement on the cochlear partition for different frequencies. It is also possible to assume that the number of waves simultaneously present along the partition is large, and that there is not much damping as they are propa-

If still other assumptions are made concerning the elastic properties of the cochlea, the forms of vibration depicted in Figs. 23 and 24 can be deduced.

In the extreme we could consider the cochlear partition as being very stiff. The wavelength then becomes so large that the entire partition will vibrate in phase in the manner of a telephone diaphragm (Rutherford, 1886).

Wever and Bray (1930) examined the possibilities of combining resonance and frequency theories.*

* Since this chapter was written, Wever (1949) has given a detailed account of his resonance-volley theory.

Measurement of mechanical properties. The various mechanical theories of hearing differ from one another at essentially one point: each of them assumes different values for the elastic properties of the cochlea. The actual measurement of these mechanical characteristics constitutes, therefore, a stepping stone to further progress.

Ewald (1914) was the first who tried to observe the vibrations of the basilar membrane itself. However, his short account of the work does not allow one to draw any conclusions.

When we try to measure the properties of the cochlea, the first question is whether the measurements have to be made in a living animal or whether a post-mortem preparation will suffice. Hence the first step in such an investigation is to determine how the elastic properties of tissues vary post mortem. The eardrum is a very thin membrane and is easily accessible to measurement. The following experiment was therefore performed: The middle ear of a living cat was opened up, and the displacements of the drum for certain sound pressures were measured. After death, observations were made to determine whether there had been any changes. It was possible to show that the drum's mobility can be kept the same throughout several days, provided the ear is kept in a moist chamber. (The elastic properties are definitely affected by the drying-out process.) The preparations were maintained at a temperature of approximately 5 degrees C.

The elasticity of the cochlear partition also remains unchanged for 2 or 3 days, compared with its value 1 hour after the death of the animal. Precautions must of course be taken; i.e. all preparations have to be kept cool, in physiological saline solution, with air excluded. The salt solutions have to be degassed beforehand. Otherwise gas bubbles of microscopic size may form inside the cochlea and hamper the motion of the liquid. Since the elastic properties remained apparently constant for at least 1 day, it ap-

peared possible to measure the properties of the human cochlea during the first hours after death.

In order to make it possible to prepare human cochleas quickly, a special micro-anatomical technique was developed (Békésy, 1941b). The whole procedure takes place

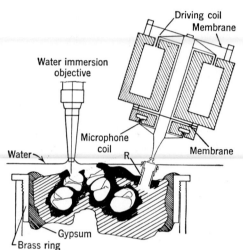

FIG. 25. Setup for the measurement of the amplitude of vibrations of the cochlear partition for known volume displacements of an artificial stapes. The cochlea is mounted under water in plaster and is opened at the apex. A small metal tube *R* is fastened in place of the stapes and covered with a rubber membrane that is driven with a known amplitude by an electrodynamic unit. With a water immersion microscope and stroboscopic illumination it is possible to observe the vibrations of silver crystals dropped on the cochlear partition. (Békésy, 1943.)

under water. The bony parts are removed by means of a dental burr and then carried away by flowing water. It is relatively easy to distinguish the cochlear canal since the bone changes color in the vicinity of the canal. The finer structures are then examined by means of a water-immersion microscope with magnifications ranging from 30 to 70.

The whole setup is portrayed in Fig. 25. After the cochlea has been removed from the skull by means of a cylindrical drill, it is imbedded in gypsum. The place of the stapes is taken by a tube with a small piston in it; and this piston can be driven electro-dynamically in a measureable way. Thus the experimenter can measure displacements of the cochlear partition that correspond to a given displacement of the stapes. In preliminary experimentation the maximum permissible size of the openings was determined. Their presence did not give rise to a modification in the pattern of vibration.

PROPERTIES OF THE COCH-LEAR PARTITION

The cochlear partition is made of an almost completely transparent jellylike substance. It tears when touched only lightly. Berendes (1934) was the first experimenter who tried to determine its elastic properties. *Elastic properties.* The following procedure may be chosen for such an investigation. If a short hair is cemented to a handle and used to exert a pressure upon a surface up to the point at which the hair bends, a certain maximum pressure is produced. A known pressure of a few milligrams produces a certain deformation of the underlying tissue, which permits a determination of the elastic properties of the tissue.

Observations with these hairs show that, near the helicotrema where the basilar membrane is broad, the area of deformation is circular, even when the pressure is not exerted at the center of the membrane. Near the stapes, the deformed area is generally elliptical with the major axis parallel to the longitudinal axis of the cochlear canal. The ratio of the major and minor axes of the ellipse is 2:1, at most. Very thin hairs must be used here, so that the deformed area will remain small compared with the width of the membrane. A microscopic enlargement of about 30× is most suitable.

It follows that the most flexible part of the cochlear partition displays essentially the same elastic properties in the longitudinal and in the transverse directions. This independence of direction in elastic properties of the basilar membrane is partly due to the

existence, in addition to the known radial fibers, of a layer lying upon the basilar membrane (the tympanic covering layer) whose fibers extend longitudinally along the membrane. As W. Roux (1895) has demonstrated, such sets of fibers at right angles to each other occur very often in nature as, for example, in the eardrum.

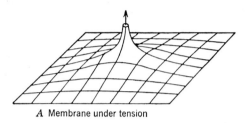

A Membrane under tension

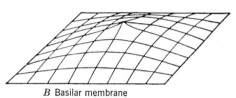

B Basilar membrane

Fig. 26.   Deformation patterns in membranes. *A* shows a uniformly stretched, thin, elastic membrane. Note the fairly steep gradient near the point at which pressure is applied. *B* shows the basilar membrane near the helicotrema when the same pressure is applied. The difference between these two patterns shows that the basilar membrane is not like a thin, stretched membrane. (Békésy, 1941*b*.)

If the hair probe is used not on the basilar membrane but near the bony edge of the cochlear partition, a considerable section of this zone, up to ⅛ of a turn, is displaced simultaneously. At the same time, the basilar membrane is also bent for the same large distance. Therefore the cochlear partition possesses near its bony edge considerable rigidity in the longitudinal direction.

If a rod is pushed into a stretched membrane under uniform tension, the area of deformation that results is illustrated in Fig. 26*A*. Displacement of the membrane increases sharply near the point of pressure. Nothing of the kind is observed in the case of the basilar membrane (Fig. 26B), where the deformed area is much the same as that produced when a pencil point is pressed into the skin.

The basilar membrane, therefore, does not seem to be a membrane under tension, for a large part of its elasticity, when deformed, arises in some other way. The question is whether the basilar membrane at rest exhibits any tension at all.

as free from tension when there was no effective external stimulation.

Had the theory of hearing not started with the notion of a vibrating piano string, the basilar membrane might never have been regarded as under lasting tension at all.

The fine structure of the various parts of the cochlear partition can be examined by the method of pressure deformation patterns. In Fig. 27 the upper portions of the draw-

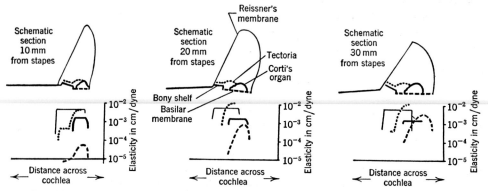

FIG. 27.   Relative stiffness of different membranes belonging to the cochlear partition.   The upper parts of the figures show schematic cross sections through the cochlear partition at different distances (10, 20, and 30 millimeters) from the stapes.   Below is shown the elasticity for each of the structures as a function of distance across the cochlear section.

Both the tectorial and basilar membranes vary in stiffness across the cochlear partition.   The basilar membrane alone shows a large variation in elastic properties as one proceeds from the stapes to the helicotrema.   (Békésy, 1947.)

When a slit is cut in any elastic material or tissue that is under tension, the cut edges gape apart in a lens-shaped opening.   But, when very fine cuts are made in the basilar membrane, transversely or longitudinally, the cut surfaces cannot be observed to draw apart.

These observations indicate that the basilar membrane is apparently not under tension and that it can best be likened to a gelatinous sheet covered by a thin, homogeneous layer of fibers.   The complete lack of tension in the cochlear partition would appear to be important physiologically, inasmuch as the inner structure of the cochlea may, as a consequence, be treated as analogous to the other parts of the labyrinth where the tissues have always been regarded

ings show schematic cross sections of the cochlear partition of man at positions 30, 20, and 10 millimeters from the stapes.   The lower part of each figure presents the depth of impression, expressed in centimeters per dyne, for the positions across the membranes corresponding to the section shown immediately above.   A comparison of the three figures shows that Reissner's membrane has the same elasticity throughout its entire length.

If Reissner's membrane is removed and the material within the cochlear duct is washed away, the elastic properties of the tectorial membrane can be investigated in the same way.   As has been previously indicated, all measurements must be carried out in a physiological saline solution in order to avoid the effects of drying and of capillary forces. The values obtained for the tectorial membrane show that its stiffness is not great and that it increases only slightly in the neighborhood of the stapes. This membrane is noteworthy for the ease with which it may be moved in a direction perpendicular to the basilar membrane. Together with its supporting structure it represents essentially a flat, delicate, very thin-walled tube filled with liquid, which can be rotated about the edge that is attached to the bony shelf of the cochlear partition. The decrease in elasticity at the end near the stapes is a result principally of its narrow breadth.

The values for the elasticity of the organ of Corti (including the hair cells) indicate no dependence whatsoever on location. On the other hand, it can be seen that there are marked differences in the stiffness of the basilar membrane from one position to another. These changes in the basilar membrane produce a continuous change in the volume elasticity along the cochlear partition. These measurements show that it is not the tectorial membrane but, as Hensen and Helmholtz have argued, the basilar membrane that determines the movement of the cochlear partition and the location of the point of maximum vibration.

Except for the tectorial membrane, all the surfaces investigated show circular symmetry in the depressions produced by the test hair. The surface of the tectoria presents a much elongated hollow (Fig. 28). It must therefore be concluded that the tectorial membrane exhibits different elasticities in different directions. In some directions it possesses a substantial stiffness. This may also be recognized from the fact that upon tearing it away from its attachment a considerable segment comes off, whereas the other membranes may be removed in quite small sections.

Microscopic observations of the various parts of the cochlear partition show that they tend to move together. As Fig. 27 indicates, there are relative displacements of

these structures, but as a first approximation we may assume that they all move with the same phase. If one then wants to assess the combined elastic properties of the cochlear partition it becomes necessary to determine the volume displacements for a given pressure difference across the partition. Figure 29 shows how many cubic centimeters of liquid are displaced by a section of the cochlear partition 1 millimeter long for a pressure difference across it equivalent to

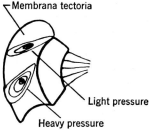

FIG. 28.   Depression patterns at the surface of the tectorial membrane. The only noncircular patterns observed are found at the surface of the tectoria. The contour lines indicate equal amounts of depression. (Békésy, 1947.)

1 centimeter of water. As we can see, the volume displacement at the widest part of the cochlear partition is 200 times the volume displacement at a point 3 millimeters from the stapes.

Since the cochlear partition is bony at the inner edge and soft at the outer edge, the greatest displacements of the partition occur at the outer edge of the cochlea (see Fig. 2).

Vibration pattern. Before describing how the volume displacements in the liquid produced by the stapes vibrations affect the various sections of the cochlear partition, let us determine the transfer characteristic of the entire cochlea as a function of frequency. Figure 30 shows the ratio of the volume displacement of the round window to the sound pressure at the eardrum. The transmission is fairly constant up to 4000 cps. The lower curve in Fig. 30 shows that the structures between the drum and the round window behave like a spring for frequencies below 500 cps, whereas above

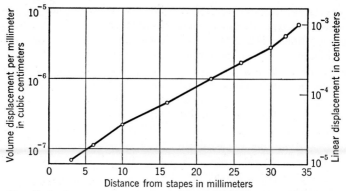

Fig. 29. Overall elastic properties of the cochlear partition. The ordinate scales indicate the volume displaced by a segment of the cochlear partition 1 millimeter long, and also the depth of the bulge, for a difference of pressure across the cochlear partition equivalent to 1 centimeter of water. (Békésy, 1941b.)

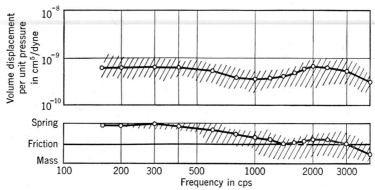

Fig. 30. Overall transfer characteristics of the mechanical structures between the eardrum and the round-window membrane. The upper curve shows the displacements of the round-window membrane for a given sound pressure at the eardrum. The crosshatched area indicates the range of dispersion of the data for ten temporal bones. The lower curve represents the phase angle between the displacement and the applied pressure. At low frequencies the displacement has the same phase as the pressure, and the mechanical structure behaves as a spring whose elastic forces come from the ligaments attached to the stapes footplate and the round window. (Békésy, 1942.)

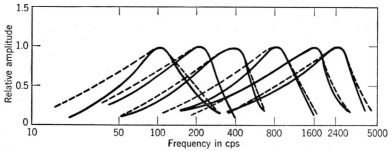

Fig. 31. Resonance curves for six points on the cochlear partition. The solid curves are measured values (Békésy, 1943); the dashed curves are theoretical values calculated by Zwislocki (1948).

1000 cps frictional forces determine the excursions of the round-window membrane.

If the stapes is vibrating sinusoidally with constant amplitude and if the displacements of various points along the cochlear partition are examined under the microscope as a function of frequency, the curves of Fig. 31 are obtained for human ears. We can see quite clearly that each different point on the membrane undergoes its maximum displacement for a particular frequency. And the behavior of the point as a function of frequency resembles a resonance curve.

If we now cut windows into the human cochlea at appropriate places, the vibration pattern of the entire partition can be determined for selected frequencies. Figure 32 shows the results obtained. It is obvious that the maximum response is displaced towards the stapes as the frequency increases. A number of experiments were carried out in order to verify that the windows made in the cochlea had no influence upon the locus of this maximum. If we plot the distance from the stapes of the point of maximum displacement versus frequency, the curve obtained has the general form of the curves that can be inferred from psychophysiological data (Fig. 33). Many measurements have shown that there is little variability in the curves one obtains from different subjects. The structure of the cochlea shows great stability in this respect, in marked contradistinction to the elastic properties of certain parts of the middle ear, for instance.

It was also possible to measure the phase difference between the movement of the stapes and the movement of the membrane. From these data and from the data on displacement amplitudes the deformation pattern of the membrane can be determined.

It is necessary first to determine the amplitude of vibration at a given place along the partition for various frequencies, and then, in a second series of measurements, to measure for each frequency the phase difference between the movement of the stapes and that of the observed point. By combining the

two series of measurements, the displacement (deformation) of the cochlear partition can be determined for the various vibratory states.

Since the cochlear partition cannot be loaded with a measuring instrument because

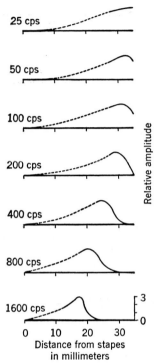

Fig. 32. Displacement amplitudes along the cochlear partition for different frequencies. The stapes was driven at a constant amplitude and the amplitude of vibration of the cochlear partition was measured. The maximum displacement amplitude moves toward the stapes as the frequency is increased. (Békésy, 1943.)

of its delicacy, an optical method of measuring phase is the most useful. Further, since the entire cochlear partition in fresh condition is almost transparent, very small crystals of silver were strewn over it to improve its visibility. Stroboscopic observation shows that these flat crystals follow the movement of the partition quite exactly up to 4000 cps, the highest frequency that was investigated. With the proper illumination on the partition one sees a large number of bright, shiny dots, which spread out into a band when the basilar membrane is in vibration. In order to carry out the measurement accurately, the crystals of silver were made so small that even when enlarged more than 100 times they appeared as quite sharp dots.

zero. The measurement of phase is therefore particularly suited to test the degree to which the cochlea resembles a simple resonant system.

When the phase relations in the movement of the cochlear partition are observed, it can

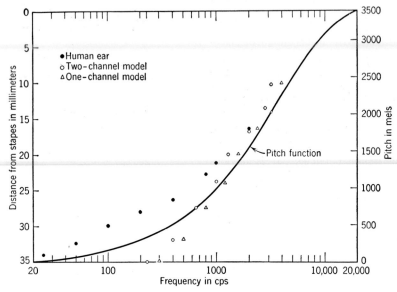

FIG. 33.   Position of maximum vibration of the cochlear partition as observed in ears and in models (Békésy, 1942).   The curve relating pitch to frequency (Stevens and Volkmann, 1940) is drawn for comparison.   The form of this curve is in agreement with "maps" of the basilar membrane derived from several sources: (1) position of maximal electrical activity (Culler et al., 1943); (2) impairment of cochlear microphonic by localized lesions (Stevens, Davis, and Lurie, 1935); (3) degeneration in human cochleas associated with deafness (Crowe, Guild, and Polvogt, 1934); (4) integration of pitch jnd's (Stevens, Davis, and Lurie, 1935); (5) width of critical band in masking (Fletcher, 1940); (6) contribution of various frequencies to total loudness (Fletcher); (7) contribution of various frequencies to speech intelligibility (French and Steinberg, 1947).

The phase relations in the movements of the cochlear partition possess a significant theoretical interest. If we trace, for a given position along the cochlear partition, how the amplitude changes with frequency, a curve is obtained that resembles a resonance curve. Such measurements seem to support the notion of an aural resonator. In a *simple* resonant system like a pendulum or an inductive-capacitative circuit, however, the phase angle must change from $\pi/2$ through zero to $-\pi/2$, as the driving frequency is changed continuously. Furthermore at the point of resonance the phase angle will be

be determined first of all that there are, as stated previously, no microscopically observable phase differences among the movements of the basilar membrane, the organ of Corti and the tectorial membrane. In a fresh preparation, Reissner's membrane also vibrates in phase with the other parts of the partition. At the higher frequencies it may happen that Reissner's membrane does not undergo a simple movement; rather it may vibrate in sections.

In Fig. 34 is presented the amplitude of vibration for a point along the cochlear partition 30 millimeters from the stapes. The amplitude of vibration is shown in the dashed line as a function of frequency when the stapes undergoes movement of constant amplitude. The form of the curve shown is similar to a resonance curve. The solid line

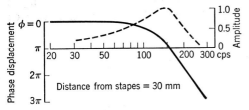

FIG. 34. Resonance curve and phase displacement for a position along the cochlear partition 30 millimeters from the stapes. The phase angle is relative to the movement of the stapes. Its variation from 0 to 3π indicates that we are not concerned with a simple resonating system but with some kind of traveling waves. (Békésy, 1947.)

in this same figure presents measurements of the difference in phase angle between the movement of the stapes and that of the point on the basilar membrane. The phase angle changes, as the resonance curve is traversed, from $\phi = 0$ to $\phi = 3\pi$. These facts, taken together, indicate clearly that we are not dealing with a simple resonance, but with some sort of traveling waves. These waves pass the point at which observations are

made, and it can be seen that their wavelength decreases as the frequency increases.

The distribution along the cochlear partition of displacement amplitude and phase angle are shown for various frequencies in Fig. 35. Below 50 cps the movement of the entire cochlear partition is practically in phase; above 150 cps the traveling wave can be demonstrated. The measurements are quite reproducible in a given cochlea.

The curve for 200 cps in Fig. 35 was used to calculate the detailed form of vibration of the cochlear partition for two different instants in time corresponding to a separation by a phase angle of 90 degrees. The two curves that result are shown in Fig. 36. The measured values compare favorably with those calculated by Ranke (cf. Fig. 24).

Transient response. The Helmholtz resonance theory has stimulated discussion of a controversial problem, namely, the time constant of the so-called resonators in the ear. Many authors have been concerned with this question: Waetzmann (1912, 1922), Meyer and Waetzmann (1925), Hartridge (1921), Hallpike and Rawdon Smith (1934), Hunt (1942) and Pumphrey and Gold (1947, 1948). The difficulties that have arisen are

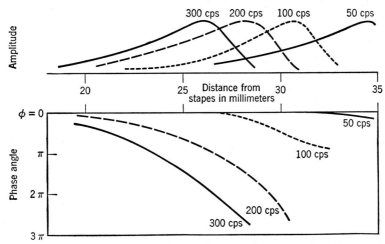

FIG. 35. Amplitude and phase angle of the cochlear partition at various distances from the stapes. For frequencies above 100 cps the difference in phase may exceed π. At 50 cps the membrane vibrates in phase. (Békésy, 1947.)

due largely to the fact that we are dealing with "time constants" obtained by various techniques of measurement: physical, physiological, and psychological. All these different time constants may be presumed to be involved in an auditory sensation. But the fact that they are really different phenomena

the stapes to the helicotrema, and during this time interval there will be stimulation of the nerve endings, provided the wave has not spent too much of its energy.

In order to measure the transient response of the cochlear partition the cochlear liquid is set into vibration and the transients on

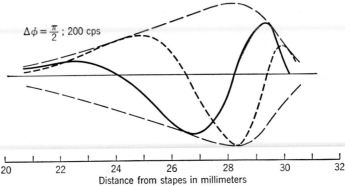

$\Delta\phi = \frac{\pi}{2}$; 200 cps

Distance from stapes in millimeters

FIG. 36.   Traveling wave along the cochlear partition for a 200-cycle tone.   The solid line indicates the deformation pattern at a given instant.   The line with the short dashes shows the same traveling wave ¼ of a period later.   The envelope shows the maximum displacement at each point.   Compare this figure with Fig. 24 calculated by Ranke.   (Békésy, 1947.)

warns us to proceed cautiously when we examine the conclusions that have been drawn.

We are concerned here only with the mechanical contributions to this composite time constant. They are essentially two:

the cochlear partition are then observed directly. This experiment can be carried out by again scattering small silver crystals on the partition, illuminating them so that they stand out as very brilliant points, and then observing them, through a moving micro-

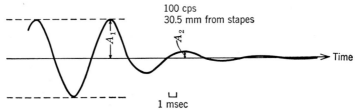

100 cps
30.5 mm from stapes

A_1 A_2

Time

1 msec

FIG. 37.   Decay process in the displacement amplitude of a point of the cochlear partition 30.5 millimeters from the stapes.   (Békésy, 1943.)

(1) one arising in the middle ear, which contributes a damped transient close to its own natural frequency (around 1500 cps), and (2) one constituting a damped traveling wave along the cochlear partition, initiated whenever there is displacement. This wave takes a certain length of time to get from

scope, at a point where a given frequency will produce maximum displacement amplitude. The microscope is made to move at right angles to the direction of the displacement so that the displacements appear spread out, as in Fig. 37. This figure shows the decay curve obtained when the vibration of the stapes footplate is brought to a sudden halt. The values for the decrement agree satisfactorily with values calculated from Fig. 31. This confirms that the inner ear, as a mechanical system, is less than critically damped. Hence it can act as a frequency-analyzing system.

Traveling waves along the cochlear partition. Let the stapes be set into sinusoidal vibration, and let us observe microscopically the vibrations of a sizable section of the cochlear partition under stroboscopic illumination. We then get the impression that the section of the cochlear partition in the immediate vicinity of the stapes is vibrating in the same phase as the stapes. In the vicinity of the region of maximum displacement amplitude we observe traveling waves propagated toward the helicotrema. These waves are so damped that after one or two cycles they are no longer visible. But we can see them clearly enough to detect that the wavelength decreases markedly as they proceed toward the helicotrema. This situation is quite understandable if we remember that near the stapes the stiffness of the partition is relatively great, and that it decreases toward the apical end. The velocity of propagation is much greater for a stiff partition than for a soft one; the decrease in the wave velocity is responsible for the decrease in wavelength [λ (wavelength) = c (wave velocity)/v (frequency)].

In 1933 Békésy established the existence of this travel time by a subjective method. He exposed one ear to a low-frequency tone and the other ear to a high-frequency tone, so as to desensitize the section of the partition close to the helicotrema in one ear and close to the stapes in the other ear. When both ears were then exposed simultaneously to a click, the difference in travel time along the partition led the observers to judge the clicks as "localized" to one side instead of in the median plane.

In order to measure travel times objectively, a small mirror was put on the cochlear partition, the stapes was set into motion,

and the time difference between the onsets of the vibrations of the stapes and of the partition was recorded by means of an oscillograph. An electric spark was used to ini-

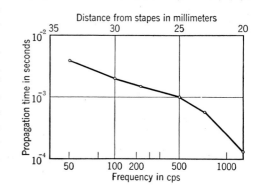

FIG. 38. Propagation times along the cochlear partition. When the stapes is suddenly displaced, a bulge travels along the partition toward the helicotrema. The time intervals plotted are those between the onset of the motion of the stapes and the first detectable displacement at a given point along the partition. The propagation velocity near the stapes is high and is much reduced near the helicotrema. (Békésy, 1943.)

tiate the sudden pressure change with the correct amount of energy.

In Fig. 38 we find plotted the propagation time of the traveling wave. On the abscissa both the distance from the stapes and the

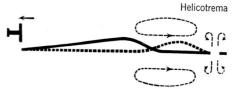

FIG. 39. A sudden displacement of the stapes gives rise to a traveling bulge along the cochlear partition. The dashed line indicates the position of the bulge at a later time. The bulge pushes fluid ahead along the surface of the partition. The bulge disappears at the helicotrema and the fluid flows back to its original position, creating eddies (dotted ellipses). (Békésy, 1933.)

equivalent frequency (taken from the solid curve of Fig. 33) are indicated. The ordinate represents the travel time. As can be seen, it takes the wave about 5 milliseconds to reach the helicotrema.

Figure 39 gives a schematic representation of the way the partition is deformed when there is a sudden short outward movement of the stapes. In a brief interval of time the wave progresses from the position shown by the solid line to that shown by the dashed

increase in length of the basilar membrane, or whether there is an improvement with increase in length. It would be particularly interesting to know whether increased length corresponds only to an extension of the auditory range, so as to include lower and higher

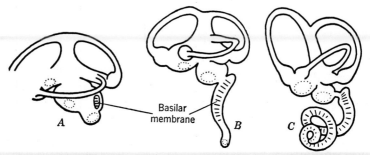

FIG. 40. The membranous labyrinth of (A) turtle, (B) bird, and (C) mammal. The vestibular organ is fully developed in fish, and there has been no further evolution in higher animals. The dotted ellipses represent the otoliths. In higher animals the length of the basilar membrane shows a decided increase as we go from the turtle to the mammal. (Békésy, 1944.)

line. If there are repeated displacements of the stapes to the right and the left, there is an eddy formation in the liquid channel, as shown by the lighter dashed lines in Fig. 39.

frequencies, or whether there is an increase in the resolving power of the ear.

This problem was attacked by the same direct microscopic observation previously

FREQUENCY ANALYSIS

Analysis in the cochleas of various animals. Figure 40 shows the membranous labyrinth of a turtle (A), a bird (B), and a mammal (C). The three semicircular canals are clearly visible. The dotted ellipses indicate the otoliths. The short lines represent the auditory nerve endings along the basilar membrane.

When we compare these three steps in the evolution of the membranous labyrinth, we are struck by the apparent invariance of the semicircular canals, in contrast to a decided increase in the length of the basilar membrane. This increase in length pushes the lowest otolith to the end of a tube (in the bird), until it finally vanishes in the labyrinth of mammals.

The question then arises, to what extent improved hearing ability is related to the

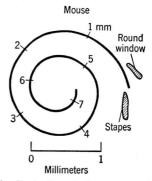

FIG. 41. Projection of the mouse cochlea upon a horizontal plane. The numbers on the curve give distances from the stapes in millimeters. (Békésy, 1944.)

used in man. Fortunately we find that the dimensions of the cochlea do not vary nearly as much from animal to animal as do the body dimensions. Figure 41 shows a map of the cochlea of the mouse, and Fig. 42

gives a map of the cochlea of an elephant. In both cases the projection is in the direction of the axis of the cochlea. The cochlear diameters are in a ratio of 1:7.

For the elephant a change in frequency from 30 to 40 cps produces a shift in the position of the maximum displacement am-

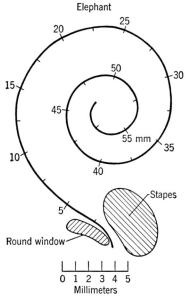

Elephant

FIG. 42. Projection of the elephant cochlea upon a horizontal plane. The numbers give distances from the stapes in millimeters. (Békésy, 1944.)

plitude (Fig. 43). For the mouse this lower limit lies at 400 cps. For frequencies lower than 400 cps the entire cochlear partition of the mouse vibrates in phase.

If the curves of displacement amplitude for different frequencies are plotted along the cochlear partitions of various animals in the manner of Fig. 32, the curves look very much alike for all animals, except that those for the elephant are more pointed. We can therefore use the shift of the point of maximum response along the partition (Δl) for a given ratio of frequency change ($\Delta n/n$) as a measure of the mechanical frequency analysis. This mechanical resolving power

$$\frac{\Delta l}{\dfrac{\Delta n}{n}} = \mathrm{MRP}$$

has been plotted in Fig. 44. As we would expect, the hen possesses the least developed cochlea. In general we can say that the mechanical resolving power increases with the size of the animal. Also, for the higher frequencies this resolving power is practically independent of frequency in most animals. The one exception is the human ear, where the resolving power shows an abrupt change between 500 and 1000 cps. This fact is possibly related to the findings in articulation tests, that the speech sounds below 300 cps are relatively unimportant.

The lower frequency limit for mechanical frequency discrimination has been chosen as

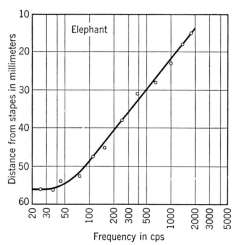

FIG. 43. Locus of maximum displacement amplitude for various frequencies in the elephant. Compare with Fig. 33. (Békésy, 1944.)

the point at which there is no shift in the pattern when the frequency is further decreased.

Figure 44 shows clearly how this lower frequency limit is shifted downward as the animals increase in size. These shifts are not due so much to changes in elastic constants (since practically all the animals examined show the same range of variation of volume elasticity, namely, from 10^{-9} to 10^{-5} cubic centimeter) as to the effective mass that loads the cochlear partition.

The wisdom of nature is evident in all this, because it is certainly important for large animals to hear over great distances. If the sound is propagated along the ground, the absorption will in general affect low-frequency sounds less than high-frequency

The preceding pages contain most of the data necessary to build an uncoiled model of a cochlea having approximately the correct characteristics. Such a model (Fig. 45) shows satisfactory agreement with the actual situation. (The uncoiling of the cochlea seemingly does not influence the vibration along the membrane.) The model is made essentially of three microscope slides, two

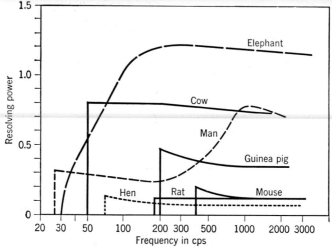

Fig. 44. Mechanical resolving power in the cochlea of man and various animals. The mechanical resolving power is here defined as the shift of the locus of maximum response for a given relative shift in frequency. (Békésy, 1944.)

sounds. Hence the usefulness of favoring the low frequencies.

Frequency analysis in cochlear models. Ear models have been used on several occasions (Ewald, 1914; Wilkinson, 1922; Meyer, 1928) in order to investigate the vibration pattern inside the cochlea. These experiments were, however, based on rather arbitrary assumptions, since most of the relevant mechanical data were unknown at the time. But when use is made of the hydrodynamical laws of similitude — a common procedure in the designing of ships — a good approximation to the real situation can be obtained (Békésy, 1928). In this manner it becomes possible to build an enlarged model of the cochlea.

razor blades, and a rubber membrane. The volume displacement of this rubber membrane, in response to a given rise in pressure in the channel, corresponds to the volume displacement for the same pressure change in the human cochlea. If the channel is filled with a liquid in which small silver crystals are suspended, it becomes possible to observe the motions of the liquid by means of a microscope. If a glass tube is cut lengthwise, and one-half is used to cover the basilar membrane of the model shown in Fig. 45, a more perfect imitation of the actual situation in the cochlea is obtained. This was done in several experiments. Comparing data collected with the two types of models, we find that the only change is a shift in the locus of the maximum response. This shift can be compensated for by a frequency change of about ½ octave.

Although it is true that we are at present able to perform satisfactory measurements on a real ear, models similar to the one described are still very useful, because they

tude is a maximum (see also Fig. 47). The locus remains unchanged when the dimensions of the channel are increased or when the introduction of foreign bodies has made the channel considerably narrower. It was furthermore found that the vibrations of the membrane are largely independent of the

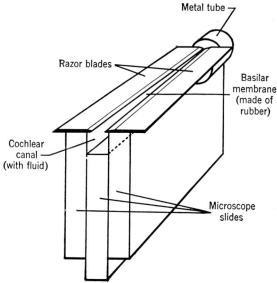

Metal tube

Razor blades

Basilar membrane (made of rubber)

Cochlear canal (with fluid)

Microscope slides

FIG. 45. Model of the uncoiled cochlea. Three microscope slides are set to form a trough having a cross section of 1 square millimeter. A solution of rubber is applied to the V-shaped opening formed by the two razor blades, producing a 'basilar membrane' whose volume displacement corresponds to that measured along the human cochlear partition. The fluid column in the cochlear channel is set in motion by a small metal tube. The other end of the channel, the 'helicotrema,' can be left open because capillary forces keep the fluid (water, or water mixed with honey) in the channel. (Békésy, 1942.)

permit us to investigate the factors that are responsible for the vibration pattern of the cochlear partition. The models also show very clearly the presence of a small eddy at the locus of maximum response (Békésy, 1928). This eddy moves toward the stapes for high frequencies and toward the helicotrema when the frequency is lowered. Since it is possible to observe the center of the eddy with great accuracy, each change in the vibration pattern of the membrane can be determined with satisfactory precision.

Figure 46 illustrates a striking conclusion to be drawn from experiments with ear models: it is extremely difficult to influence the location at which the displacement amplitude

location of the "round" and "oval windows" in the model.

All the experiments with ear models show that even perfectly sinusoidal vibrations of the liquid are accompanied by a "rectified" or unidirectional flow. Any irregularity in the structure of the cochlear model leads to the presence of one or more additional eddies. The eddies that occur regularly at the locus of maximum deformation of the cochlear partition are particularly striking; they change position along the membrane when the frequency changes.

Eddies also occur in the vicinity of the stapes footplate under the influence of strong vibrations. As a matter of fact, a circular eddy occurs at any opening in the cochlear canal or in the semicircular canals. Since the vestibular apparatus is so close by, these eddies may lead to disturbances affecting the

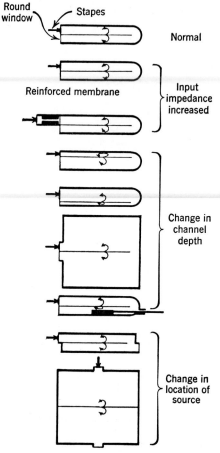

FIG. 46. Measurements on an ear model with the same elastic properties as the human ear showed that the vibration pattern and the location of the eddy do not change under the modifications shown. (Békésy, 1942.)

sense of equilibrium. This effect can be demonstrated very easily with pigeons: if an opening is made in the labyrinth, it becomes possible to produce head motions by means of sounds (Tullio, 1929).

Even for the normal human ear there are noticeable vestibular effects when fairly loud tones are turned on or off. One has the

feeling that one's head is pulled over to the side. These motions have been recorded (Fig. 48) for monaural beats between tones around 1000 cps at a sound pressure of about 120 db (Békésy, 1935).

Frequency analysis in the human cochlea. The measurements of the displacement amplitude along the cochlear partition demonstrate some kind of preliminary mechanical frequency analysis. In particular, they establish two facts: (1) there is a position of maximal stimulation along the cochlear par-

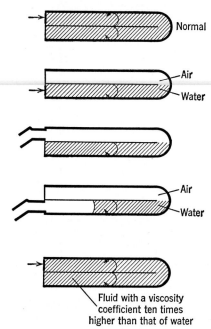

FIG. 47. Under these alterations in the ear model, there is a slight change in the locus of the eddy, which can be restored by lowering the input frequency 15 to 25 per cent. When the fluid in a canal is replaced by air, the model may be driven by airborne sound via the tube shown at the left. Removing the fluid from one channel reduces the model to a one-channel variety. (Békésy, 1942.)

tition, and (2) the location of this maximum sensitivity shifts with frequency.

The curve for man in Fig. 44 subdivides the audible frequencies into essentially four subregions. The first lies to the left of the starting point: there is no mechanical frequency discrimination for tones lower than about 25 cps. For frequencies lower than this, the analysis must be purely neural. Incidentally, man can hear tones as low as 1 cps (Békésy, 1936). The second subregion extends from 25 to about 300 cps. Here we find a moderate amount of mechanical frequency analysis, but probably not enough to account for the precision found in judgments of pitch discrimination. The next region, from about 300 to about 1000 cps is

It was never really possible to throw the entire burden of pitch discrimination on mechanical analysis alone, because, as both Wien (1905) and Fischer (1908) have already pointed out in the case of pure tones, the mechanical excitation falls off much too slowly on both sides of the maximum (i.e. the resonance curve for pure tones is much too flat). It is still not clear by what processes the nervous system increases the apparent sharpness. Gray's (1900) view is

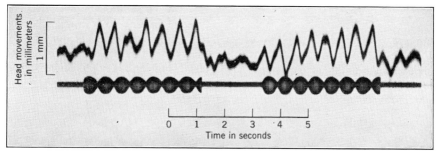

FIG. 48. Head motions induced by loud sounds (about 120-db sound-pressure level). If beats (lower tracing) between two tones of about 1000 cps are presented to one ear, lateral head motions can be recorded from most listeners. (Békésy, 1935.)

a region of transition where mechanical frequency analysis improves rapidly. In this subregion pitch discrimination likewise improves. Unfortunately, for most of the fourth region (the part above 4000 cps) mechanical measurements are not available. For the highest audible frequencies it becomes impossible to observe the vibration pattern on the partition, because amplitudes involved are too small. In models, however, the eddy moves toward the stapes end of the membrane as the frequency increases, and remains there for further increases in frequency.

This summary has attempted to fit together the different observations and measurements made. We are, at present, far from a definite solution of the problem of pitch discrimination. What was attempted here was to demonstrate the possibilities of a purely mechanical frequency analysis in the ear.

slowly gaining, according to which only the position of maximum stimulation counts. The positions that have been stimulated less than maximally are apparently subject to some sort of nervous inhibition in the manner of the law of contrast (Békésy, 1928). In any case, the fact that mechanical time constants are very small compared with overall auditory time constants, as found in psychophysical experiments, must eventually be fitted into the picture of a frequency- and time-analyzing system for which equivalent linear circuits with simple time constants and resonance curves cannot be readily established.

The auditory system includes both mechanical and neural transducers. We know that the latter behave in a radically nonlinear manner. This reason alone would seem to be sufficient to discourage the setting up, for the entire auditory system, of an equivalent circuit made up of passive, linear, time-invariant elements — i.e. a circuit that obeys the principle of superposition. This does not mean, however, that it is impossible to find an equivalent circuit for *parts* of the auditory system. If we restrict the range of variables sufficiently, we might even imitate the behavior of the entire system by an equivalent circuit. We must, however, constantly remain aware of the limitations of such an equivalence.

HEARING BY BONE CONDUCTION

There are two principal ways in which sound can reach the inner ear. The first is by air conduction: the drum is set into vibration, and these vibrations are transmitted via the ossicles. The second involves a direct contact between the human head and a vibrating body. The vibration of the skull produces compressions in the bones, and we might very plausibly assume that these compressions stimulate the auditory nerve directly. If this were so, the vibration pattern of the cochlear partition would lose its importance, and we would find ourselves in the presence of a type of hearing radically different from hearing by air conduction.

It can be shown, however, that for both types of hearing an identical vibration pattern of the cochlear partition is obtained. This can be demonstrated by canceling a tone heard by bone conduction by means of

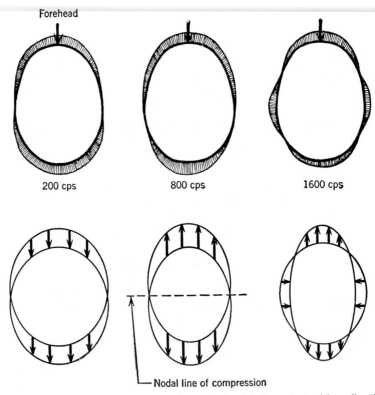

FIG. 49. Vibration pattern of the skull when the forehead is in contact with a vibrating body. Below about 200 cps the skull behaves as a rigid body. Near 800 cps the forehead vibrates in the opposite direction from the back of the head—a type of resonance of the skull with a nodal line of compression. Above 1500 cps the skull vibrates in sections separated by nodal lines. Variations in the thickness of the skull produce variability in the resonance frequency. (Békésy, 1932a.)

another tone (in proper phase and amplitude) heard by air conduction. If the vibration patterns for air and bone conduction were not exactly alike, such a cancellation would prove impossible (Békésy, 1932a; Lowy, 1942).

If a body vibrating at low frequency touches the forehead, the head will undergo displacements that are parallel to those of the vibrating body, i.e. the compression of the skull is very small. But for higher frequencies the back of the head does not follow the vibrations of the forehead because of its inertia. Hence the middle of the head is compressed. The elasticity of the middle of the head and the mass of the back of the head constitute a system that may resonate at a certain frequency. This skull resonance is most easily measured by determining the phase of the vibration at different places on the skull. The phase pattern makes it possible for us to see which part of the bony wall is moving inward and which outward (Békésy, 1948).

For low frequencies the movements of various parts of the head are simple parallel movements in the same direction. Around 800 cps the skull goes through a kind of resonance. The forehead moves forward as the back of the head moves backward, and vice versa. Above about 1500 cps the skull vibrates in several sections very much like a bell (Fig. 49). If the source of vibration is moved to different locations on the head, this pattern rotates with it to some extent.

Figure 50 shows the mandibular joint of the lower jaw in the immediate vicinity of the meatus. If we insert a finger into the meatus, we are able to feel displacements of the lower jaw. When the head and the lower jaw are displaced with respect to each other, the auditory meatus finds itself compressed and dilated. Consequently, if the meatus is plugged by means of a stopper, the loudness of a bone-conducted tone will increase because of the compression of the meatus due to the relative movements of the

skull and the jaw. This is known as Weber's experiment. If the stopper is located inside the bony part of the meatus (as indicated by the stopper in Fig. 50), the vibration of the mandible does not compress the meatus to the same extent as before and the loudness of a bone-conducted sound increases very little.

The inertia of the ossicles prevents them from following the vibrations of the skull.

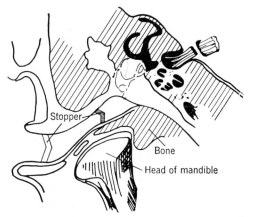

FIG. 50. Schematic longitudinal section through the meatus and the temporal bone. The head of the mandible is close to the ear canal, and its movement produces a deformation of the wall of the meatus. Stoppers at the two positions indicated have different effects. (Békésy, 1941c.)

The ossicles then undergo displacements relative to the bony wall of the middle ear. These relative vibrations are transmitted in the usual manner (i.e. by means of the stapes) to the cochlea.

The bending of the skull capsule results in compressions of the cochlea. Figure 51A shows that this compression would produce no motion of the cochlear partition if both windows were equally mobile (Rejtö, 1914; Herzog, 1930). Actually the membrane of the round window moves more easily than the stapes footplate in the oval window. The basilar membrane is therefore deformed in the manner indicated in Fig. 51B. Deformation of the bones produces a compression, not only of the cochlea, but also of the other parts of the labyrinth. This compression forces liquid into the cochlea close to the stapes footplate, so that the vibration pattern of the cochlear partition is identical

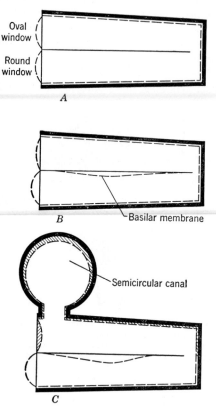

Fig. 51. Compression of the inner ear by bone-conducted sound leads to movement of the basilar membrane. The dashed lines indicate the positions of the various membranes during compression by a sound wave in the skull. *A*. Hypothetical case of symmetrical compression of the cochlea and equal yielding of the membranes of the oval and round windows. No movement of the basilar membrane occurs. *B*. The round window actually yields more than the oval window to equal pressures. The basilar membrane is moved slightly toward the scala tympani. *C*. The semicircular canals are also compressed, and fluid forced into the scala vestibuli causes greater movement of the membranes. (Békésy, 1932a.)

with that obtained when the stapes itself is displaced in the usual manner (Fig. 51C).

In many cases it is difficult to evaluate the relative importance of hearing by bone and by air conduction. For instance, an ear-

phone on one ear produces a sound pressure that is heard by air conduction. But at the same time the vibrating membrane of the earphone sets the housing of the earphone into vibration, and these vibrations are transmitted to the bony part of the skull and heard by bone conduction. Bone-conducted sounds are very easily transmitted from one ear to the other ear, and we have, therefore, the problem of finding out what fraction of the sound energy delivered to one ear by means of an earphone is transmitted to the opposite ear by air conduction and how much is transmitted by bone conduction. For an ordinary earphone, the measured transmission loss from one side of the head to the other is between 40 and 50 db for the frequencies between 100 and 10,000 cycles. By measuring the vibrations of the head produced by an earphone it was possible to show that the loss in cross-hearing by bone conduction is of the order of 90 db (Békésy, 1948). In other words, in order to minimize cross-hearing we should provide the greatest possible insulation for airborne sounds, since the air provides the path of least attenuation.

The construction of an earplug assuring a maximum of acoustic insulation also leads to the problem of distinguishing between air and bone conduction. During the second World War many experimenters came to the conclusion that it was impossible to construct earplugs with an acoustic insulation greater than about 40 db. Therefore it was assumed that the sound waves striking the forehead set the skull into vibration and that these vibrations are heard by bone conduction. If this were the case, above a certain value the amount of mass closing the ear canal would be of no importance. It was, however, possible to increase the insulation provided by earplugs by covering each ear with a cotton-filled tube (Fig. 52). This can be interpreted only by saying that the reduction of the sound field near the ear canal made it possible to improve the insulation. In other words, when we listen to airborne sounds the limiting factor is the sound attenuation of the earplug for these same sounds. Bone conduction plays little or no role in the maximum insulation provided by an earplug, as can be shown by increasing the surface of the head as much as ten times without changing the amount of insulation. The lower drawing in Fig. 52 shows how the effective surface of the head hit by the sound may be increased by biting on a board.

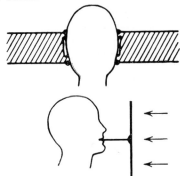

FIG. 52. The upper drawing shows two tubes filled with cotton and pressed upon the ears to improve the acoustic insulation provided by earplugs. In the lower drawing the surface exposed to the sound is enlarged without changing the insulation provided by the earplug. (Békésy, 1948.)

Bone conduction is of considerable importance in the hearing of one's own voice. If the vibrations of the surface of the skin are recorded by means of a pickup at various body locations while the subject sings a vowel, we find (Fig. 53) that the displacement amplitude in the vicinity of the ear is only $1/20$ of the amplitude recorded near the vocal cords. The vibrations of the air in the oral cavity are transmitted to the cheeks and from there to the lower jaw. The attenuation between the oral cavity and the ear canal is about 40 to 50 db. If we introduce a sound into the closed oral cavity through a tube, the sound pressure in the mouth must be about 47 db higher than the sound pressure in the ear canal in order to be heard with equal loudness. From this

we can see that, in the hearing of our own voices, the sound transmitted to the ear by bone conduction and that transmitted by air conduction are of about the same magnitude. Herein lies the explanation for the well-known difference between our speech as heard by ourselves and our speech as heard by others. If we record speech on a phonograph disk, the speaker does not recognize his own voice, since there is a great difference in the timbre of bone-conducted and air-conducted sound, and only air-conducted sound has been recorded.

Middle-ear infections have little influence upon hearing by bone conduction. A pathological condition of the acoustic nerve, on

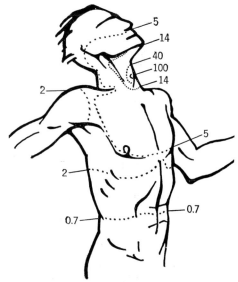

FIG. 53. The decrease in amplitude as the vibrations from the vocal cords travel over the surface of the body. The numbers give relative amplitudes along the dotted contours of equal amplitude. (Békésy, 1939b.)

the other hand, affects the hearing by air conduction and bone conduction in identical manner. Therefore, if a hard-of-hearing individual's hearing by bone conduction remains unchanged, we may conclude that we are dealing with a middle-ear disease. But, if his hearing by air and bone conduction are both affected, we can conclude that we are

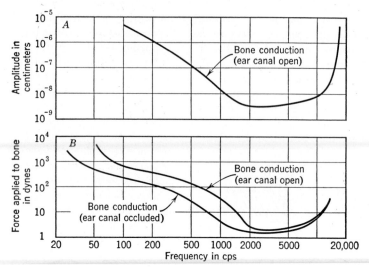

FIG. 54. Bone-conduction thresholds. A vibrating body with a surface area of 0.8 square centimeter was pressed against the forehead. Two sets of threshold curves were obtained: A, the effective amplitude of the forehead; B, the rms force applied to the bone. An occlusion of the ear canal lowered the threshold by about 10 db for frequencies below 2000 cps. (Békésy, 1941c.)

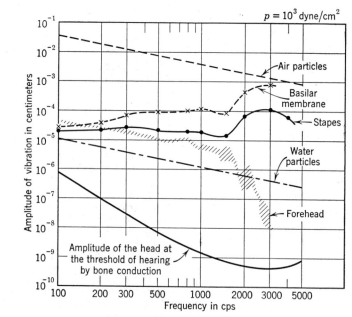

FIG. 55. Amplitudes of vibration of the human head, stapes, and basilar membrane, and also of air and water particles, in response to sound waves having a pressure of 10^3 dynes per square centimeter (134-db sound-pressure level). The lowest curve shows the amplitude of the head at the threshold of hearing by bone conduction. (Békésy. 1948.)

concerned with a nerve condition. Hence the importance of the measure of the bone-conduction threshold for diagnostic purposes.

If bone-conduction thresholds of audibility are measured, two different curves may be obtained, depending upon the type of measurement: in one case the displacement amplitude of the forehead is measured; in the other the alternating force applied to the bone is determined (Fig. 54). It is also of some practical interest to note that the bone-conduction threshold is lowered if the outer ear is stopped off. As shown in Fig. 54, this effect amounts to about 10 db for frequencies below 2000 cps.

A FINAL WORD ABOUT SENSITIVITY

In the preceding pages we have attempted to describe the vibratory phenomena encountered in hearing. Figure 55 presents a quantitative summary of the displacement amplitude of various structures important or related to the process of hearing.

Findings such as those summarized in Figs. 6 and 55 pose a problem. What physical meaning are we to attach to displacements as small as the threshold values in the region of greatest sensitivity of the ear? It would appear from extrapolation that in the case of a very good observer we might be dealing with threshold displacements that are only about tenfold removed from what according to Gamow (1949) might turn out to be a new universal constant of elementary length. In other words, the ear would appear to be responding to displacements not much bigger than the smallest numerical values of distance that can be used in a physical sense to characterize the space separation of two elementary particles. This is an astonishing and baffling conclusion!

It would lead us too far to discuss here the related question of the signal-to-thermal noise ratio at the absolute threshold. Sivian and White (1933) have carried out certain calculations, and more recently the whole subject has been reviewed by de Vries in a series of articles (1948a, b, c) to which the reader may refer.

REFERENCES

Backhaus, H. Über Strahlungs- und Richtwirkungseigenschaften von Schallstrahlern. Z. techn. Physik, 1928, 9, 491–495.

Ballantine, S. Effect of cavity resonance on the frequency response characteristic of the condenser microphone. Proc. Inst. Radio Eng., 1930, 18, 1206–1215.

Bárány, E. A contribution to the physiology of bone conduction. Acta oto-laryng., Stockh., 1938, Suppl. 26, 1–223.

Békésy, G. von. Zur Theorie des Hörens. Die Schwingungsform der Basilarmembran. Physik. Z., 1928, 29, 793–810.

Békésy, G. von. Zur Theorie des Hörens. Über die eben merkbare Amplituden- und Frequenzänderung eines Tones. Die Theorie der Schwebungen. Physik. Z., 1929, 30, 721–745.

Békésy, G. von. Zur Theorie des Hörens bei der Schallaufnahme durch Knochenleitung. Ann. Physik., 1932a, 13, 111–136.

Békésy, G. von. Über den Einfluss der durch den Kopf und den Gehörgang bewirkten Schallfeldverzerrungen auf die Hörschwelle. Ann. Physik, 1932b, 14, 51–56.

Békésy, G. von. Über den Knall und die Theorie des Hörens. Physik. Z., 1933, 34, 577–582.

Békésy, G. von. Über die nichtlinearen Verzerrungen des Ohres. Ann. Physik., 1934, 20, 809–827.

Békésy, G. von. Über akustische Reizung des Vestibularapparates. Pflüg. Arch. ges. Physiol., 1935, 236, 59–76.

Békésy, G. von. Über die Herstellung und Messung langsamer sinusförmiger Luftdruckwankungen. Ann. Physik., 1936a, 25, 413–432.

Békésy, G. von. Über die Hörschwelle und Fühlgrenze langsamer sinusförmiger Luftdruckschwankungen. Ann. Physik., 1936b, 26, 554–566.

Békésy, G. von. Zur Physik des Mittelohres und über das Hören bei fehlerhaftem Trommelfell. Akust. Z., 1936c, 1, 13–23.

Békésy, G. von. Über die mechanisch-akustischen Vorgänge beim Hören. Acta oto-laryng., Stockh., 1939, 27, 281–296, 388–396.

Békésy, G. von. Über die Vibrationsempfindung. Akust. Z., 1939, 4, 316–334.

Békésy, G. von. Über die Messung der Schwingungsamplitude der Gehörknöchelchen mittels einer kapazitiven Sonde. Akust. Z., 1941a, 6, 1–16.

Békésy, G. von. Über die Elastizität der Schneckentrennwand des Ohres. Akust. Z., 1941b, 6, 265–278. (Translation. On the elasticity of the cochlear partition. J. acoust. Soc. Amer., 1948, 20, 227–241.)

Békésy, G. von. Über die Schallausbreitung bei Knochenleitung. *Z. Hals-Nas.- u. Ohrenheilk.*, 1941c, **47**, 430–442.

Békésy, G. von. Über die Schwingungen der Schneckentrennwand beim Präparat und Ohrenmodell. *Akust. Z.*, 1942. **7**, 173–186. (Translation. The vibration of the cochlear partition in anatomical preparations and in models of the inner ear. *J. acoust. Soc. Amer.*, 1949, **21**, 233-245.)

Békésy, G. von. Über die Resonanzkurve und die Abklingzeit der verschiedenen Stellen der Schneckentrennwand. *Akust. Z.*, 1943, **8**, 66–76. (Translation. On the resonance curve and the decay period at various points on the cochlear partition. *J. acoust. Soc. Amer.*, 1949, **21**, 245–254.

Békésy, G. von. Über die mechanische Frequenzanalyse in der Schnecke verschiedener Tiere. *Akust. Z.*, 1944, **9**, 3–11.

Békésy, G. von. Variation of phase along the basilar membrane with sinusoidal vibrations. *J. acoust. Soc. Amer.*, 1947, **19**, 452–460.

Békésy, G. von. Vibration of the head in a sound field, and its role in hearing by bone conduction. *J. acoust. Soc. Amer.*, 1948, **20**, 749–760.

Békésy, G. von. The structure of the middle ear and the hearing of one's own voice by bone conduction. *J. acoust. Soc. Amer.*, 1949, **21**, 217–232.

Berendes, Z. Die Spannung der menschlichen Basilarmembran. *Z. Hals-Nas.- u. Ohrenheilk.*, 1934, **36**, 338–342.

Bonnier, P. De la nature des phénomènes auditifs. *Bull. Scient. du Nord*, 1895, **25**, 367–397.

Budde, E. Über die Resonanztheorie der Hörens. *Physik. Z.*, 1917, **18**, 225–236, 249–260.

Crowe, S. J., S. R. Guild, and L. M. Polvogt. Observations on the pathology of high-tone deafness. *Johns Hopk. Hosp. Bull.*, 1934, **54**, 315–379.

Culler, E. A., J. D. Coakley, K. Lowy, and N. Gross. A revised frequency-map of the guineapig cochlea. *Amer. J. Psychol.*, 1943, **56**, 475–500.

Esser, M. H. M. van. The mechanism of the middle ear: I. The two piston problem. II. The drum. *Bull. math. Biophysics*, 1947, **9**, 29–40, 75–91.

Ewald, J. R. Zur Physiologie des Labyrinths: VI. Eine neue Hörtheorie. *Arch. ges. Physiol.*, 1899, **76**, 147–188.

Ewald, J. R. Zur Physiologie des Labyrinths: VII. Die Erzeugung von Schallbildern in der camera acustica. *Arch. ges. Physiol.*, 1903, **93**, 485–500.

Ewald, J. R. Bemerkungen zur Schallbildertheorie. *Zbl. Physiol.*, 1914, **28**, 756.

Fischer, O. Über ein von Max Wien geäussertes Bedenken gegen die Helmholtzsche Resonanztheorie des Hörens. *Ann. Physik.*, 1908, **25**, 118–134.

Fletcher, H. A space-time pattern theory of hearing. *J. acoust. Soc. Amer.*, 1930, **1**, 311–343.

Fletcher, H. Auditory patterns. *Rev. mod. Physics*, 1940, **12**, 47–65.

Frank, O. Die Leitung des Schalles im Ohr. *Sitzber. bayer. Akad. Wiss., München* (Math.-phys. Kl.), 1923, **53**, 11–77.

French, N. R., and J. C. Steinberg. Factors governing the intelligibility of speech sounds. *J. acoust. Soc. Amer.*, 1947, **19**, 90–119.

Fumagalli, Z. Ricerche morfologiche sull'apparato di trasmissione del suono. *Arch. Ital. Otol.*, 1949, **60**, 1–323.

Gamow, G. And physics tomorrow? *Physics Today*, 1949, **2**, 16–21.

Geffcken, W. Untersuchungen über akustische Schwellenwerte: III. Über die Bestimmung der Reizschwelle der Hörempfindung aus Schwellendruck und Trommelfellimpedanz. *Ann. Physik.*, 1934, **19**, 829–848.

Gold, T., and R. J. Pumphrey. Hearing. I. The cochlea as a frequency analyzer. *Proc. roy. Soc.*, 1948, **B135**, 462–491.

Gray, A. A. On a modification of the Helmholtz theory of hearing. *J. Anat. Physiol.*, 1900, **34**, 324–350.

Hallpike, C. S., and A. F. Rawdon-Smith. The Helmholtz resonance theory of hearing. *Nature, Lond.*, 1934, **133**, 614.

Hartridge, H. A vindication of the resonance hypothesis of audition. *Brit. J. Psychol.*, 1921, **12**, 142–146.

Helmholtz, H. von. *Die Lehre von den Tonempfindungen* (1st Ed.). Braunschweig: Vieweg, 1863.

Helmholtz, H. von. Über die Mechanik der Gehörknöchelchen. *Arch. ges. Physiol.*, 1868, **1**, 1–60.

Herzog, H. Die Mechanik der Knochenleitung im Modellversuch. *Z. Hals-Nas.- u. Ohrenheilk*, 1930, **27**, 402–408.

Hunt, R. S. Damping and selectivity of the inner ear. *J. acoust. Soc. Amer.*, 1942, **14**, 50–57.

Hurst, C. H. A new theory of hearing. *Proc. Trans. Liverpool Biol. Soc.*, 1895, **9**, 321–353.

Kato, T. Zur Physiologie der Binnenmuskeln des Ohres. *Pflüg. Arch. ges. Physiol.*, 1913, **150**, 569–625.

Kobrak, H. G. Round window membrane of the cochlea. *Arch. Otolaryng.*, 1949, **49**, 36–47.

ter Kuile, E. Die Übertragung der Energie von der Grundmembran auf die Hörzellen. *Arch. ges. Physiol.*, 1900, **79**, 146–157.

ter Kuile, E. Die richtige Bewegungsform der membrana basilaris. *Arch. ges. Physiol.*, 1900, **79**, 484–509.

Langenbeck, B. Das Symmetriegesetz der erblichen Taubheit. *Z. Hals-Nas.- u. Ohrenheilk.*, 1936, **39**, 223–261.

Lowy, K. Cancellation of the electrical cochlear response with air-conducted and bone-conducted sound. *J. acoust. Soc. Amer.*, 1942, **14**, 156–158.

Lüscher, E. Die Funktion des musculus stapedius beim Menschen. *Z. Hals-Nas.- u. Ohrenheilk.*, 1929, **23**, 105–132.

Mach, E., and A. Fischer. Die Reflexion und Brechung des Schalles. *Pogg. Ann. Physik,* 1873, **149,** 421–429.

Mach, E., and J. Kessel. Die Funktion der Trommelhöhle und der tuba Eustachii. *Sitzber. Akad. Wiss. Wien* (Math.-phys. Kl., Abt. 3), 1872, **66,** 337–343.

Mangold, E. Das äussere und das mittlere Ohr und ihre physiologischen Funktionen. In A. Bethe (Ed.), *Handb. d. normalen u. path. Physiol.* Berlin : Springer, 1926. Volume XI, pp. 406–435.

Metz, O. The acoustic impedance measured on normal and pathological ears. *Acta oto-laryng., Stockh.,* 1946, Suppl. **63,** 1–254.

Meyer, M. F. The hydraulic principles governing the function of the cochlea. *J. gen. Psychol.,* 1928, **1,** 239–265.

Meyer, E., and E. Waetzmann. Über den Grad der Dämpfung der Ohrresonatoren. *Naturwissenschaften,* 1925, **13,** 268–271.

Politzer, A. Untersuchungen über die Schallfortpflanzung und Schallleitung im Gehörorgane (im gesunden und kranken Zustande). *Arch. Ohrenheilk.,* 1864, **1,** 59–73.

Pumphrey, R. J., and T. Gold. Transient reception and the degree of resonance of the human ear. *Nature, Lond.,* 1947, **160,** 124.

Ranke, O. F. Das Massenverhältnis zwischen Membran und Flüssigkeit im Innenohr. *Akust. Z.,* 1942, **7,** 1–11.

Rejtö, A. Beiträge zur Physiologie der Knochenleitung. *Verh. Deuts. otol. Ges.,* 1914, **23.** *Versammlung,* 268–285.

Roaf, H. E. The analysis of sound waves by the cochlea. *Phil. Mag.,* 1922, **43,** 349–354.

Roux, W. *Gesamte Abhandlungen über die Entwicklungsmechanik der Organismen.* (2 vols.) Leipzig : Engelmann, 1895.

Rutherford, W. The sense of hearing. *J. Anat. Physiol.,* 1886, **21,** 166–168.

Sivian, L. J., and S. D. White. On minimum audible sound fields. *J. acoust. Soc. Amer.,* 1933, **4,** 288–321.

Stevens, S. S., and H. Davis. *Hearing.* New York : Wiley, 1938.

Stevens, S. S., H. Davis, and M. H. Lurie. The localization of pitch perception on the basilar membrane. *J. gen. Psychol.,* 1935, **13,** 297–315.

Stevens, S. S., and J. Volkmann. The relation of pitch to frequency : A revised scale. *Amer. J. Psychol.,* 1940, **53,** 329–353.

Stuhlman, O., Jr. The non-linear transmission characteristics of the auditory ossicles. *J. acoust. Soc. Amer.,* 1937, **9,** 119–128.

Stuhlman, O., Jr. *An introduction to biophysics.* New York : Wiley, 1943.

Tröger, J. Die Schallaufnahme durch das äussere Ohr. *Physik. Z.,* 1930, **31,** 26–47.

Tullio, P. *Das Ohr.* Berlin and Wien : Urban and Schwarzenberg, 1929.

de Vries, H. Brownian movement and hearing. *Physica,* 1948a, **14,** 48–60.

de Vries, H. The minimum audible energy. *Acta oto-laryng., Stockh.,* 1948b, **36,** 230–235.

de Vries, H. Die Reizschwelle der Sinnesorgane als physikalisches Problem. *Experientia,* 1948c, **4,** 205–213.

Waar, A. G. H. Mikroskopische Wahrnehmungen der Funktion der Mittelohrmuskeln beim Menschen. *Acta oto-laryng., Stockh.,* 1923, **5,** 335–358.

Waetzmann, E. *Die Resonanztheorie des Hörens.* Braunschweig : Vieweg, 1912.

Waetzmann, E. Die Resonanztheorie des Hörens. *Naturwissenschaften,* 1922, **10,** 542–551.

Waetzmann, E. Hörtheorien. In A. Bethe (Ed.), *Handb. d. normalen u. path. Physiol.* Berlin : Springer, 1926. Volume XI, pp. 667–700.

Waetzmann, E. Ein erb-biologisches Problem am menschlichen Gehörorgan. *Nachr. Ges. Wiss Göttingen* (Math.-phys. Kl., Biol.), 1935, **1,** 157–161.

Waetzmann, E. Über Symmetrie- und Erblichkeitsfragen am menschlichen Gehörorgan. *Z. techn. Physik.,* 1936, **17,** 549–553.

Waetzmann, E., and L. Keibs. Hörschwellenbestimmungen mit dem Thermophon und Messungen am Trommelfell. *Ann. Physik.,* 1936a, **26,** 141–144.

Waetzmann, E., and L. Keibs. Theoretischer und experimenteller Vergleich von Hörschwellenmessungen. *Akust. Z.,* 1936b, **1,** 3–12.

West, W. Measurements of the acoustical impedance of human ears. *P. O. Elect. Eng. J.,* 1928, **21,** 293.

Wever, E. G. *Theory of hearing.* New York : Wiley, 1949.

Wever, E. G., and C. W. Bray. Present possibilities for auditory theory. *Psychol. Rev.,* 1930, **37,** 365–380.

Wien, M. Ein Bedenken gegen die Helmholtzsche Resonanztheorie des Hörens. In *Festschrift für Wüllner.* Leipzig, 1905. Pp. 28–35.

Wiener, F. M. On the diffraction of a progressive sound wave by the human head. *J. acoust. Soc. Amer.,* 1947, **19,** 143–146.

Wiener, F. M., and D. A. Ross. Pressure distribution in the auditory canal in a progressive sound field. *J. acoust. Soc. Amer.,* 1946, **18,** 401–408.

Wilkinson, G. A note on the resonating system in the cochlea with demonstration of a model illustrating the action of a hitherto neglected factor. *J. Physiol.,* 1922, **56,** II–IV.

Wilska, A. Eine Methode zur Bestimmung der Hörschwellenamplituden des Trommelfells bei verschiedenen Frequenzen. *Skand. Arch. Physiol.,* 1935, **72,** 161–165.

Zwislocki, J. Theorie der Schneckenmechanik. *Acta oto-laryng., Stockh.,* 1948, Suppl. **72,** 1–76.

28.

Psychophysiology of Hearing and Deafness

HALLOWELL DAVIS, M. D.

*Central Institute for the Deaf
and Washington University*

The external ear delivers sound waves through the external auditory canal to the middle ear, and thence they pass to the inner ear. There, in the cochlea, the sensory cells of the organ of Corti are stimulated and initiate nerve impulses in the fibers of the auditory nerve. The impulses pass through a series of nuclei and fiber tracts in the medulla and midbrain to the auditory area of the cerebral cortex; and there, somehow, they generate the sensations that we know subjectively as "sounds."

NEUROANATOMY OF THE AUDITORY SYSTEM

The gross anatomy of the inner ear has been described in the previous chapter. There special attention was given to the cochlear partition, consisting of the spiral lamina and the basilar membrane. The basilar membrane is a structure of special interest because on it rests the organ of Corti, which contains the specialized sensory cells of audition. Somehow these cells, when agitated by the movements of the basilar membrane, set up nerve impulses in the fibers of the auditory nerve.

The author gratefully acknowledges the assistance of Robert Galambos in the writing of various sections, and in the preparation of Figures 4 and 14.

Microscopic Anatomy of the Ear

A typical cross section of the organ of Corti, as seen under the microscope, is shown diagrammatically in Figs. 1 and 2 (Rasmussen, 1943). At the junction of the basilar membrane with the bony spiral lamina, and projecting into the scala vestibuli, stand two relatively stiff structures, the rods of Corti. The rods converge and, with the segment of basilar membrane beneath them, enclose the "tunnel," triangular in cross section, that runs from end to end of the organ of Corti. The rods are about 50 microns in length near the round window and increase progressively to about 90 microns in the apical turn. Internal to the rods, i.e. toward the modiolus and over the edge of the spiral lamina, is located a single row of sensory cells, the internal hair cells. One internal hair cell is seen in a typical cross section of the organ. External to the pillars are three or four rows of external hair cells. The supporting structures, like the rods of Corti, increase progressively in size from the basal to the apical end of the basilar membrane.

Two accessory structures worthy of mention appear in Figs. 1 and 2. The tectorial membrane, attached by its inner edge to the epithelium of the limbus, is located just above the hair cells. In fixed sections it appears homogeneous and fairly dense, but during life it is a soft, delicate, semigelatinous, tubelike mass that seems to be lightly attached to the organ of Corti. The attachment appears to be chiefly through delicate hairlike structures, several of which project from each hair cell into the endolymphatic space. The hairs, entangled in the tectorial membrane, probably excite the sensory cells when they are bent or pulled by movement of the hair cells relative to the tectorial membrane. The tectorial membrane is thus analogous to the cupola of the cristae and maculae in the vestibular portion of the inner ear. (The vestibular structures of the inner ear, i.e. semicircular canals, utricle, and saccule, are concerned with orientation relative to gravity and acceleration. There is no good evidence, in spite of many theoretical suggestions, that they are in any way concerned with the sense of hearing.)

ner's membrane. The canal enclosed by it, the basilar membrane, and the stria vascularis is called the ductus cochlearis or scala media. These structures taken together are called the cochlear partition. The scala media ends as a closed sac at the helico-

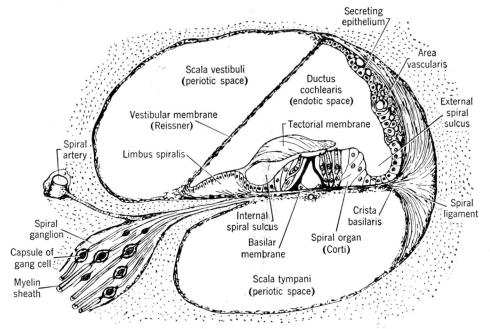

FIG. 1. Diagrammatic cross section of a cochlear canal. The ductus cochlearis (or scala media) contains the organ of Corti with its hair cells, the ultimate end organs of hearing. (From Rasmussen, 1943.)

Above the tectorial membrane is a thin, flexible, dividing partition known as Reiss-

trema, an opening that connects the scala vestibuli and the scala tympani.

The scala media forms part of the membranous labyrinth and is continuous with the vestibule, the saccule, the utricle, and the membranous semicircular canals. The sensory structures of all the sense organs of the inner ear lie inside this inner membranous labyrinth. The membranous labyrinth is filled with endolymph, and another fluid, the perilymph, surrounds the membranous labyrinth. These structures act as a single homogeneous medium in transmitting the movements of the stapes to the basilar membrane.

The ultimate sense organ of hearing, the hair cells of the organ of Corti, forms a long narrow sensory surface, four or five cells wide, and running the length of the basilar membrane. Each inner hair cell is about 12 microns in diameter (viewed from the scala vestibuli) and the external hair cells are about 8 microns in diameter. There are

recognized in this ganglion. Auditory nerve fibers make uninterrupted anatomical and functional connections between the hair cells of the organ of Corti and nerve cells inside the central nervous system. One peculiarity of the neurons of the auditory nerve is that,

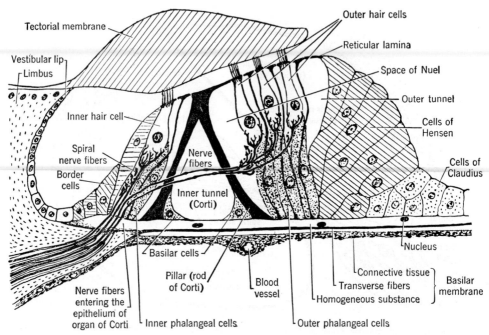

FIG. 2. Diagrammatic cross section of the organ of Corti. The outer hair cells are supported by their respective phalangeal cells, which rest in turn on the movable basilar membrane. The phalangeal cells supporting the inner hair cells rest on bone. Motion of the basilar membrane presumably distorts the hair cells. (From Rasmussen, 1943.)

about 3500 inner hair cells and a total of about 20,000 external hair cells.

The Innervation of the Organ of Corti

The eighth cranial (auditory) nerve consists of a vestibular portion and a cochlear portion. The latter, serving the sense of hearing, runs down the center of the spiral core or modiolus of the cochlea. The cell bodies of its nerve fibers are located within the modiolus and form a long spiral ganglion. This spiral ganglion of Corti contains about 27,000 cells and is analogous to the dorsal root ganglia of the spinal nerves. Its cells are bipolar, and no synaptic connections are

contrary to the usual law of Wallerian degeneration, when the fibers are severed between the medulla and the spiral ganglion the fibers do not regenerate from the cell bodies, but all of each injured neuron, including the cell body, degenerates. As a rule the hair cells innervated by the injured neurons also ultimately degenerate.

The cell bodies of the spiral ganglion are more densely grouped (900 to 1100 per millimeter) along the basal and lower middle turns of the cochlea than along the upper middle and apical turns (about 500 per millimeter), with a gradual transition in the middle turn (Guild, 1932).

The inner hair cells are each innervated by one or two nerve fibers, and each fiber connects with one or two hair cells. The innervation of the external hair cells is more complicated, however, as most of the fibers turn at right angles near the external hair cells and run for a half turn or farther toward the round window. Each fiber makes connections with many external hair cells, as

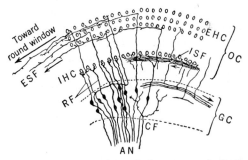

FIG. 3. Innervation of the organ of Corti (cat). Auditory nerve fibers (AN), with their cell bodies in the ganglion of Corti (GC), end in the organ of Corti (OC). Internal hair cells (IHC) receive radial fibers (RF) and collaterals from internal spiral fibers (ISF). External hair cells (EHC) receive collaterals mainly from external spiral fibers (ESF). An external hair cell is innervated by many fibers; an internal hair cell by a few. The function of the internal spiral and centrifugal (CF) fibers is unknown. (From Stevens and Davis, 1938, after Lorente de Nó, 1933.)

is shown in Fig. 3 (Lorente de Nó, 1933). There is also a bundle of internal spiral fibers that parallels the organ of Corti just internal to the internal hair cells, and additional fibers running lengthwise of the organ of Corti within the spiral ganglion have also been described. The origin and connections of the fibers in these spiral bundles, as well as of others in the auditory nerve, are still unknown.

The Auditory Nerve

The fibers in the auditory nerve are arranged in an orderly but complicated fashion. They twist like the strands of a rope around a central core. This core contains the fibers that originate at about the middle of the basal turn. The fibers running to the more apical region twist around the core in one direction, those running to the basal end, in the opposite direction. This arrangement results from the fact that, in embryological development, the nerve fibers are dragged after the organ of Corti as the latter grows out and assumes its ultimate spiral form.

The auditory nerve is short. The distance from the internal auditory meatus to the point of entrance of the nerve into the medulla is only about 5 millimeters. The nerve enters the lower brain stem (medulla oblongata) at the inferior border of the pons, and there its fibers promptly divide. One branch of each primary afferent fiber runs to the dorsal, and the other to the ventral portion of the cochlear nucleus. Here are the first synapses of the auditory system. The fibers of the auditory nerve, and also the cells in the cochlear nucleus on which they impinge, preserve more or less completely the orderly arrangement of the corresponding sensory cells on the basilar membrane. The same general tendency to an orderly arrangement, with its implications for a segregation of high-tone, middle-tone, and low-tone fibers, seems to be maintained throughout the auditory system.

Auditory Pathways and Nuclei of the Brain Stem

The general arrangement of the auditory pathways and nuclei is shown in Fig. 4. The system may be divided into four levels: (1) the group of nuclei in the lower brain stem (including those of the superior olive, the trapezoid body, and the lateral lemniscus), (2) the cerebellum, (3) the inferior colliculus at the upper pontine level, and (4) the medial geniculate body (in the thalamus) and the auditory cortex at the highest level.

Second-order neurons * from the two cochlear nuclei pass by different pathways

* By "second-order" we mean fibers separated by at least one synapse from the sense organ, but we disregard possible longer alternative routes

to other nuclei of the lower brain stem and to the inferior colliculus. From the brain stem nuclei (of the trapezoid body and the superior olive) third-order neurons pass up the lateral lemniscus. Many terminate in

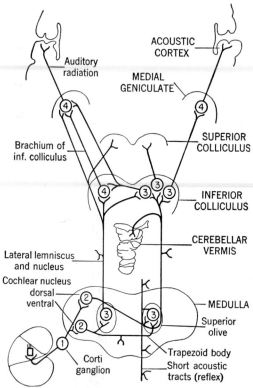

FIG. 4. The afferent acoustic pathways (based mainly on the cat). The locations of important synapses are indicated in capital letters on the right. The "order" of each neuron is indicated by a number. (Cf. Ades; Barnes, Magoun, and Ranson; Cajal; Rasmussen; Cheng and Niemer.)

the inferior colliculus, but a significant fraction also sends collaterals to the medial geniculate body (Cajal, 1909; Ades, 1944). Other third-order neurons originate in the inferior colliculi and pass to the medial geniculate bodies where at least one additional synapse is located. The auditory radiations to the cortex are therefore at least fourth-order neurons.

with more synapses by way of neurons with short axons that lie entirely within a single nucleus.

In addition to the main pathways from cochlea to cortex, three others of known or potential functional importance to the animal may be pointed out.

Some neurons arising from the superior olive ultimately connect with the motor nuclei controlling eye movements, the middle ear muscles, and other reflex responses to sound. Also, neurons from the inferior colliculus pass to the near-by superior colliculus which is an important nucleus of the optic system. Visual and auditory activity may be coordinated here, but this plausible suggestion has not been substantiated experimentally.

Finally, Snider and Stowell demonstrated, in 1944, a strong projection of the auditory system to the vermis of the cerebellum. The vermis responds when visual, tactile, or auditory stimuli are presented to the anesthetized cat, and also when the visual or auditory cortices are stimulated electrically (Hampson, 1949). How the cerebellum is involved in hearing is not at all clear, but speculations that it coordinates impulses from the different sense modalities are not out of order.

In contrast to other sensory systems, each ear appears to be represented bilaterally in the auditory pathway from at least the level of the superior olive upwards. The relative importance of the homolateral and contralateral pathways to the auditory cortex has been variously estimated, both from anatomical and from physiological evidence. At the cortical level the contralateral ear evokes stronger electrical responses than does the homolateral ear in cats (Bremer, 1943) and dogs (Tunturi, 1946). Cats with one cochlea destroyed and one cortex removed show a definite loss in auditory sensitivity. Yet the sensitivity is the same, regardless of whether the homolateral or contralateral cortex has been spared (Brogden et al., 1936). Apparently, then, each ear projects about equally to the two hemispheres. This bilateral projection is accomplished in the numerous places where the auditory tracts cross as they ascend the brain substance. Important crossings occur at every level except the thalamic (medial geniculate), and opportunities for interaction between the two ears are correspondingly numerous. Such interactions are presumably significant for integrating functions, like localization, which depend upon slight differences in the neural inflow from the two ears.

In this connection the inferior colliculus appears to be an important center for auditory reflexes in some forms. It attains a relatively enormous development in bats (Kappers et al., 1936); and in these animals the ability to recognize the direction of incoming sounds, notably the echoes of their own ultrasonic cries, is developed to such an extent as to enable the bats to avoid obstacles while flying in the dark (Galambos and Griffin, 1942). The fact that some authors depreciate, with good reason, the role of the inferior colliculi as reflex centers illustrates our lack of understanding of many aspects of the auditory system (cf. Barnes, Magoun, and Ranson, 1943).

The Auditory Area of the Cortex

The auditory cortex may properly be considered an outgrowth from the medial geniculate body of the thalamus. The auditory radiations to the cortex are the chief outgoing pathway from the medial geniculate nucleus. Nearly all the cell bodies of this nucleus show signs of retrograde degeneration after the auditory cortex has been surgically removed. If only part of the auditory cortex is removed, a corresponding portion of the medial geniculate body shows degeneration (Walker, 1937).

The auditory projection area, where the auditory radiations are distributed in the cerebral cortex, lies in the posterior portion of the superior temporal convolution in man. Most of it is hidden deep in the sylvian fissure. Accurate information concerning both its location and its organization in monkeys, dogs, and cats has been derived from studies of its electrical responses when

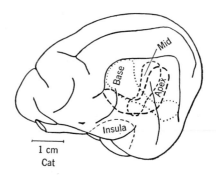

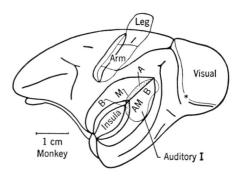

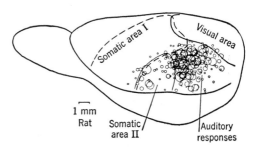

FIG. 5. Auditory areas of cat, monkey, and rat, as determined by the electrical response of the cortical mantle following stimulation of the cochlea. Base (B), mid (M), and Apex (A) refer to regions responding when, in the cochlea, electrical stimuli were applied to the basal, middle, and apical turns, respectively, of the cat and monkey. Circles indicate where electrical responses were evoked by clicks to the ear of the rat, with diameter of circle roughly proportional to amplitude of response (maximum ≈ 2500 microvolts). The active area measures about 4 by 4 millimeters. (From Woolsey, 1947; LeMessurier, 1948.)

the organ of Corti is stimulated electrically or by sound (Bremer and Dow, 1939; Ades and Felder, 1945; Walzl and Woolsey, 1946; Woolsey and Walzl, 1942; Tunturi, 1944, 1945, 1946). Walzl (1947) and Woolsey (1947) have both written useful summaries of this work.

sylvian fissure. There it comes into close relation with somatic sensory area II. Figure 5, from Woolsey, shows the auditory cortical areas for cat, monkey, and rat.

Each projection system in the cortex seems to arise independently from the medial geniculate body. Fibers from the small-cell

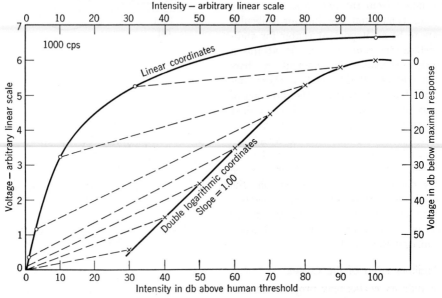

Fig. 6. The voltage of the aural microphonics is plotted as a function of intensity in linear and in double logarithmic coordinates. Corresponding points on the two curves are connected by broken lines. These microphonics were obtained from the round window of a guinea pig and measured with a sharply tuned wave analyzer. (From Stevens and Davis, 1938.)

The auditory area, like other sensory cortical areas that have been similarly analyzed, shows two systematic projections of the sense organ. In the monkey (macaque) one of these projections (auditory area I) lies along the posterior half of the lower bank of the sylvian fissure. Stimulation of nerve fibers from the apical turn of the cochlea gives responses in the anterior lateral part of the area. Stimulation of fibers from the basal turn gives responses in the posteromedial part. In the adjacent auditory area II, the relations are reversed. Apical fibers activate the posteromedial region, and basal fibers the anterolateral. Area II extends to and includes part of the upper bank of the

part of the nucleus (in the cat) apparently go to area I, and fibers from the large-cell portion go to area II (data of Waller, quoted by Woolsey and Walzl, 1942).

In the dog a third auditory area, occupying the ventral end of the anterior ectosylvian gyrus, has been described by Tunturi (1946), who presents some physiological evidence for separate fiber connections from local parts of the cochlea to this area. The localization of responses to high and to low tones is not so clear as in the other two areas, however. The existence of a third cortical projection area is apparently unique among the sensory systems. Many investigators suspect that this third area is an association area rather than a true primary projection area.

THE AURAL MICROPHONIC

If one electrode is placed on the round window of an animal and another anywhere on the tissues of the head or neck, an electrical potential can be measured between the two electrodes when sound waves fall on the animal's ear. The time course of this potential follows closely, although not always precisely, the changes in sound pressure. Thus a pure tone may produce an alternating electrical potential that is very nearly sinusoidal in form. A transient sound, such as a click, produces a train of electrical waves that starts in either the positive or the negative direction, depending on whether the initial sound wave is a wave of positive or of negative pressure. Over a considerable range of pressure the electrical potential is nearly proportional to the sound pressure (Figs. 6 and 7). Usually, however, the slope of the line plotted in double logarithmic coordinates is significantly less than 1.00 (Wever and Bray, 1938). At high sound intensities the potential increases less and less rapidly and finally reaches a maximum. The maximum voltage varies with frequency, and under favorable conditions it may approach as much as a millivolt in the cat or the guinea pig.

This electric response of the cochlea or *aural microphonic* is generated within the cochlea. It is strong at the round window, at the oval window, at the internal auditory meatus, along the auditory nerve, and, in the guinea pig, all over the thin, bony shell that covers the cochlea. It still appears when sound is transmitted to the cochlea by bone conduction, even after surgical removal of eardrum, malleus, and incus, and after the auditory nerve has degenerated following its transection at the internal auditory meatus. The microphonic appears without any apparent latency except for the time required for transmission

of the sound waves into and along the cochlea. The microphonic spreads from the cochlea through the tissues of the head, according to their configuration and electrical conductivity. Its polarity at the round window is opposite that at the oval window, as

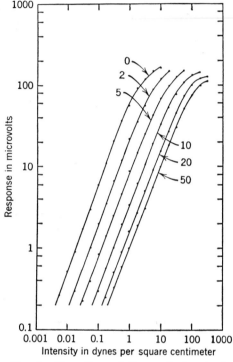

FIG. 7. The voltage of the aural microphonics (cat) plotted against the intensity of a 1000-cycle tone. The numbers on the curves indicate tension in grams applied to the stapedius muscle. Increased tension reduces the response, but the shape of the curve and its slope (= 1) remain constant. (From Wever and Bray, 1942.)

though the 'generator' were located on, and oriented perpendicular to, the basilar membrane.

The aural microphonic does not disappear immediately on the death of the animal, although it begins to fall off rapidly in intensity soon after the blood supply has been interrupted in any way. At a much reduced level the microphonic may persist for several hours after death (Wever, Bray, and Lawrence, 1941*a*).

The aural microphonic was first detected in 1929 by Wever and Bray when they placed an electrode on the auditory nerve of a cat. The microphonic was combined with the action potentials of the auditory nerve, and at first it was not recognized as a separate phenomenon; but soon the dual nature of the electric response (nerve impulses plus aural microphonic) became clear. The microphonic, or, more accurately, the mixture of microphonic and action potentials, is often known as "the Wever-Bray phenomenon." The term *aural microphonic* for the cochlear response (as distinguished from action potentials of the auditory nerve) has been advocated by Stevens and Davis (1938).

Nearly all the characteristics mentioned above serve to differentiate the aural microphonic from the action potentials of nerve. The behavior of the microphonic suggests a purely biophysical phenomenon such as a piezoelectric effect or the movement of an electrically charged structure. The acoustic energy of the sound wave seems to be sufficient to account for the electrical energy that is developed. The microphonic seems to be a pure transduction of acoustic to electrical energy, not a physiological response in the proper sense of the term, which implies a release of stored energy.

Possible Origins of the Aural Microphonic

The mechanism of the aural microphonic is still uncertain. It has been ascribed, by one investigator or another, to nearly every anatomical structure within the cochlea as well as to physical artifacts. Reviews dealing with aural microphonics have been written by Wever (1939), Walzl (1939), Walzl and Bordley (1942), and Stevens and Davis (1938).

The aural microphonic may arise from the movement of a polarized membrane. The generation of the potential would then be very much like the action of a condenser microphone. Reissner's membrane, the basilar membrane, and even the tectorial membrane have been suggested as the polarized structure, and the difference in chemical composition between endolymph and perilymph has been postulated to account for the assumed polarization (Hallpike and Rawdon-Smith, 1934a, b). The polarized-membrane theory has not been completely disproved, but it is rendered improbable by the absence of the aural microphonic in congenitally deaf animals that lack an organ of Corti but have apparently normal basilar and Reissner's membranes. It is still possible that the electrically charged structure is the organ of Corti, and that the charge depends on the integrity of the sensory cells. This is the writer's present working hypothesis.

In a closely allied theory the microphonic is attributed to "streaming potentials," i.e. the potential generated when fluid is forced through small channels in a filter or membrane (Eyster, Bast, and Krasno, 1935). If such movement is to generate a potential, there must be a surface charge between the fluid and the solid. Such a charge is usually present in biological systems. The arguments for and against this theory are very similar to the arguments concerning the movement of polarized membranes, and the theory is not generally accepted.

In considering the various hypotheses, however, we must remember that they need not be mutually exclusive. The aural microphonic may be generated by several different mechanisms simultaneously. In fact, the long persistence of a weak microphonic many hours after death suggests the presence of a second mechanism that is less directly dependent on an adequate oxygen supply than the mechanism that is responsible for most of the microphonic during life.

The most generally accepted hypothesis of the origin of the aural microphonic attributes it to the organ of Corti, and specifically to the hair cells. These cells, oriented nearly perpendicular to the basilar membrane, are thought to develop a difference of electrical potential between their hair-bearing ends and the ends that are in contact with the terminal nerve fibers. The potential is thought to depend on pressure (or deformation or movement or acceleration) in some simple and direct fashion and has been compared with the piezoelectric effect in a quartz crystal (Stevens and Davis, 1938). No more detailed explanation of the transformation of acoustic to electrical energy by the hair cells has been proposed.

An extension of the hair-cell theory makes the aural microphonic the mechanism whereby the sensory cell initiates a nerve impulse in the contiguous basket-like termination of the auditory nerve fiber. The microphonic would thus be analogous to a synaptic potential or, still more accurately, to the local potential that is the electrical aspect of the local excitatory process in a nerve or muscle cell (see Chapter 2). This extension of the hair-cell hypothesis is attractive in its simplicity, but some authors have specifically rejected it in favor of a theory of chemical mediation between the hair cell and the nerve (Derbyshire and Davis, 1935). It is possible that the microphonic originates in the hair cells, and that it plays no part in the initiation of the nerve impulses.

The hair-cell theory rests largely on a general correspondence between the integrity of the hair cells and the presence of the microphonic. For example, in one set of experiments, local degeneration of the hair cells in one region along the basilar membrane, caused by long exposure to a loud tone, was associated with a weakening of the microphonic generated by a particular band of frequencies (Davis et al., 1935). Again, the development of the organ of Corti in the pouch-young opossum begins at the upper end of the basal turn, and in such young opossums the microphonic is present for only a restricted range of medium frequencies (McCrady, Wever, and Bray, 1940). Similar evidence has been found in studies of deaf (or partially deaf) albino cats, waltzing guinea pigs, and Dalmatian dogs (cf. Wever,

1939). The hair-cell theory offers a reasonable explanation of the depression of the aural microphonic by the injection into the cochlea of narcotics and of salt solutions of varying composition, by deprivation of oxygen (Wever, Bray, and Lawrence, 1941a), by partial injury by very small surgical lesions (Walzl and Bordley, 1942), and by exposure to loud tones.

On the other hand, there is evidence that the degree and location of injury to hair cells, particularly the injury caused by brief exposure to loud tones or noise, does not correspond accurately to the frequencies for which the microphonic is impaired. Although in some instances the behavior of the microphonics agrees well with prediction from theory, the exceptions (Bast and Eyster, 1935; Dworkin et al., 1943; Lurie, Davis, and Hawkins, 1944) are too numerous and too well substantiated to be lightly ignored. Although explanations of the exceptions may yet be forthcoming, the hair-cell theory of the origin of the microphonic is still only a theory.

Species differences. The microphonic has been demonstrated in the ear of every species of animal in which it has been sought, but there are great differences in its strength from one species to another. Particularly interesting in this respect is the weakness of the microphonic in monkeys and especially in man. It has been successfully recorded from the round window of human beings, but the strongest reported is less than 50 microvolts. (For references, see Lempert, Wever, and Lawrence, 1947.) As much as 1000 microvolts may be found in cats and guinea pigs.

Parameters of the Aural Microphonic

Frequency. Whatever its origin, the microphonic is closely related to the mechanical events within the cochlea. The microphonic generated by low tones is relatively much stronger at the apex (in the guinea pig) than at the round window, but for high tones it is stronger at the round window. The frequency limits of the microphonic are at least as wide as the range of audible tones, and probably wider. The slow changes of pressure produced by contraction of the intra-aural muscles give a strong microphonic although they do not seem to excite nerve impulses (Wiggers, 1937).

Intensity. At low sound intensities the microphonic seems to reflect quite faithfully the mechanical movements of the basilar membrane. Its relation to sound intensity is nearly linear (see Fig. 6) up to about 40 per cent of its maximum voltage. The microphonic has been used to study the characteristics of the transmission system of the middle ear, the effects of the contractions of the intra-aural muscles (Fig. 7), and the generation of aural harmonics. It has been found, for example, that nonlinear distortion of the ear may be influenced by the contraction of the intra-aural muscles (Stevens and Newman, 1936; Newman, Stevens, and Davis, 1937; Wever and Bray, 1942), but it is also clear that nonlinear distortion of the microphonic takes place in the inner ear (Wever, Bray, and Lawrence, 1940*a, b, c,* and 1941*a, b;* Wever and Lawrence, 1949).

As the intensity of the sound is increased, the microphonic ceases to increase proportionately, and finally reaches a maximum. This suggests a mechanical 'overload' of the vibrating system. The situation is more complicated, however, for further increase in the intensity of the sound causes a *decrease* in the aural microphonic; and after exposure to intense sounds the microphonic produced by a weaker sound is also reduced for some time. This effect has been termed *hysteresis* (Hughson and Witting, 1935; Stevens and Davis, 1938). This phenomenon suggests a biological 'fatigue' or perhaps a mild injury (followed by recovery) of the elements that transform the mechanical into electrical energy.

Interference. A phenomenon called *interference* is closely related to overload, hysteresis, and injury. If a fairly strong stimulating tone is sounded and then a second tone of different frequency is added, the response to the second tone is less than it would be if the second tone were sounded alone. Many details of this interference have been described (Wever, Bray, and Lawrence, 1940*b;* Wever and Lawrence, 1941), and the phenomenon is presumably the same as that reported by Newman, Stevens, and Davis (1937), who found that the presence of a second tone decreases the aural harmonics of a first tone. Wever, Bray and Lawrence (1940*a, b*) interpret their data as showing that interference precedes overloading in the chain of events in the inner ear and thereby tends to protect the hair cells against overload.

ACTION POTENTIALS OF THE AUDITORY NERVE

The human auditory nerve is composed of about 30,000 individual fibers, and the activity of each fiber presumably consists of the familiar all-or-none nerve impulses. All the information transmitted from the ear to the brain must pass through this bottleneck, and a fundamental problem of the neurophysiology of audition is to 'break the code' of the auditory nerve. At the psychophysiological level every auditory discrimination must depend on a corresponding difference in the space-time pattern of nerve impulses in the auditory nerve. Consequently the aspects of neural response that we seek to relate to the parameters of the stimulus are (1) the rates of discharge of impulses in various fibers and (2) the time relations of the impulses in one fiber with respect to the stimulus and to the impulses in other fibers.

Observation of auditory nerve impulses. The electric responses of the auditory nerve as a whole may be studied by means of an electrode inserted into or hooked beneath the eighth nerve where it emerges from the internal auditory meatus of the experimental animal. Unfortunately, the action potentials of the nerve fibers are mixed with the aural microphonic from the cochlea and perhaps also with the responses of cell bodies in the spiral ganglion and in the cochlear nucleus. The unwanted microphonic potentials can be almost completely eliminated by the use of coaxial electrodes (Derbyshire and Davis, 1935b), but the remaining composite potentials are still difficult to interpret in detail.

Action potentials in the nerve are also detected by an electrode placed on the round window. In response to a faint or moderate click they may be large and distinct, but, if a continuous tone is used or if the click is made strong, the neural responses are almost completely obscured by the aural microphonic.

A third type of recording has employed a microelectrode (a very fine pipette with an opening only a few microns in diameter) inserted into the eighth nerve (Galambos and Davis, 1943; Galambos, 1944). With such electrodes unitary neural responses were obtained which were interpreted as action potentials of the axons of first-order neurons running from the cochlea to the medulla. It now appears, however (Galambos and Davis, 1948), that the observed potentials actually originated *in cell bodies of second-order neurons* (see below). We still lack, therefore, direct observations of the activity of single first-order neurons which we would like to relate to the parameters of the stimulus.

From the observations of composite potentials at the round window and from the eighth nerve and from the activity of the second-order neurons we shall draw several inferences as to the activity of the first-order neurons. Many of the following propositions must still be regarded as tentative, however.

Synchronization with the stimulus. The organ of Corti tends to excite nerve impulses during one-half of the cycle of movement of the basilar membrane. Apparently excitation occurs only during the phase of movement of the basilar membrane toward (or the phase of displacement into) the

scala vestibuli. This corresponds to movement of the stapes outward. The result is that for low and medium frequencies the nerve impulses are synchronized with the

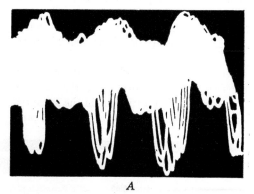

A

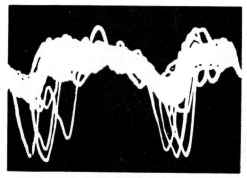

B

Fig. 8. Synchronization of neural response. Each record is the photograph of many sweeps across the oscillograph. The neural responses are downward excursions from the undulating baseline, which is the aural microphonic. The neural responses, from cell bodies of the second order (in the cochlear nucleus), are relatively few in number compared with the sound-wave cycles photographed. The grouping of the neural responses indicates a synchrony that is approximate, but imperfect. The stimulating frequency is 1050 cps in *A*, 500 cps in *B*. (From Galambos and Davis, 1943.)

stimulating sound waves, and therefore with one another. At high frequencies the refractory period of the nerve prevents the fiber from responding to every sound wave, but the tendency toward (nearly) synchronous response to a pure tone in the auditory fibers as a group is very strong. A series of well-defined action-potential waves appears in the auditory nerve and reproduces, up to 2000 or 3000 cps, the frequency of the stimulating tone. This synchronization at the higher frequencies presumably depends upon the ability of the individual nerve fibers to take turns responding to alternate sound waves, or to every third or fourth sound wave.

The approximate synchronization of nerve impulses is carried over into the second-order neurons, but variations in the synaptic delay apparently make it a little less pre-

in the fine, nonmedullated terminals of the fibers, or it may be a true latency at the junction between hair cell and nerve fiber.

ACTION POTENTIALS IN SINGLE SECOND-ORDER NEURONS

The observations of Galambos and Davis (1943, 1944), made with microelectrodes inserted into the eighth nerve of anesthetized cats, were originally interpreted as action potentials of the axons of first-order neurons

"Eighth"   "Nerve"

FIG. 9. Response of a single cell body in the cochlear nucleus (cat) to words spoken about 20 feet from the preparation.

cise than in the first-order neurons. Figure 8 shows the impulses in a single (second-order) neural unit synchronized with the stimulating tone in an approximate but imperfect manner. The responses occur at about the same phase in each cycle, when they do occur, but they vary over a range of about ± 0.13 millisecond. From this figure it is also clear that the responses of a given unit do not occur after *every* sound wave by any means.

Latency. Stimulation with transient sounds (clicks) causes the appearance of impulses in the auditory nerve at the internal auditory meatus about 0.4 to 1.0 millisecond after the arrival of the sound wave at the oval window (Derbyshire and Davis, 1935*b*). Not more than 0.1 millisecond of this latency can be attributed to conduction time in the large medullated portion of the nerve fibers. Much of the latency of the later waves can be explained as the time required for the mechanical wave to travel up the basilar membrane. But even the earliest (high-tone) component of a composite action potential has an unexplained latency of about 0.3 or 0.4 millisecond. This part of the latency may be due to slow conduction

running from the cochlea to the medulla. These authors later assumed (1948) that their unitary action potentials were recorded from cells of the cochlear nucleus separated from those of the spiral ganglion in the cochlea by at least one synapse. We therefore call the neurons of Galambos and Davis "second-order neurons." The response of such a cell body is shown in Fig. 9.

Relation to frequency. Each second-order neuron is 'tuned' to a particular frequency. Less acoustic energy is required at this frequency than at any other to set up impulses. Near threshold the tuning is very sharp, but the neuron responds to a broader and broader band of frequencies as the intensity is increased. If the response area of a fiber is plotted against logarithmic scales of intensity and frequency, the area is unsymmetrical (Fig. 10). It invariably extends more octaves into the lower frequencies than into the higher frequencies as intensity is increased. Also, on this scale, the tuning of the high-frequency neurons tends to be sharper than the tuning of the low-frequency neurons.

Even for fairly strong tones the tuning of each neuron to a particular frequency is still

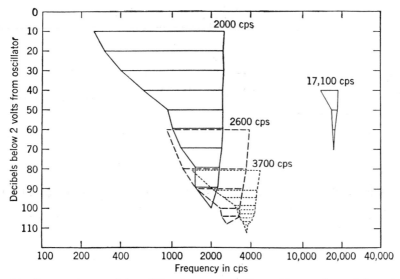

FIG. 10. Response areas of four different neurons in the cochlear nucleus of the cat. The frequency at which the minimal acoustic energy was required for producing discharges is indicated. Energies greater than the minimal elicited discharges over wider frequency ranges. The lower borders of each of the areas represent the threshold curve of response for the neuron. (From Galambos and Davis, 1943.)

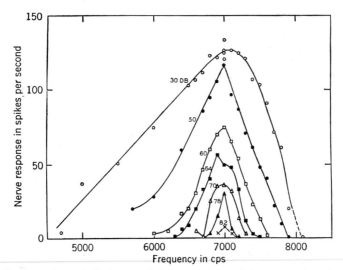

FIG. 11. Number of neural discharges plotted against sound frequency at various intensities (cat). More discharges appear at 7000 cps than at any other frequency. Each point represents the total number of discharges counted in the first second after the start of the tone. The reference level for intensity is the same as in Fig. 10. (From Galambos and Davis, 1943.)

apparent. At its characteristic frequency
the neuron discharges more impulses per
second than at any other frequency, provided, of course, that intensity is constant
(see Fig. 11).

Neurons with characteristic frequencies as
low as 200 cps and as high as 50,000 cps have
been identified in the cat (Galambos, un-

The greater the intensity of a stimulating
tone, the higher the rate of discharge in the
cells of the cochlear nucleus (Fig. 13). A
rate of 400 to 500 discharges per second is
the highest attained by most neurons, and
intensities of 30 db above the threshold for
the neuron are sufficient to produce the
maximum rate. Not infrequently, at high

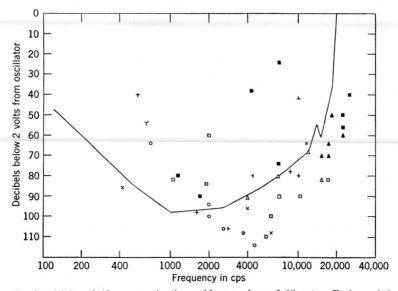

Fig. 12. Sensitivity of 42 neurons in the cochlear nucleus of 12 cats. Each symbol marks
the frequency and intensity at which a particular neuron began to respond. The solid line is
the aural microphonic "threshold" for the animal whose neural thresholds are indicated by open
squares. Some neurons respond at intensities well below that at which the microphonic can be
just detected; others are relatively insensitive. (From Galambos and Davis, 1943.)

published). Neurons tuned to frequencies
below 1000 cps are rarely encountered in the
cochlear nucleus of the cat, but this may be
due to a systematic anatomical distribution
of cell bodies that favors isolation of high-
frequency rather than of low-frequency neurons (Lorente de Nó, 1933).

Relation to intensity. The thresholds for
different neurons tuned to the same frequency differ by as much as 60 db (Fig. 12).
The most sensitive neurons begin to respond
at levels below that at which the aural
microphonic can be detected at the round
window. The less sensitive neurons seem to
be neither more nor less sharply tuned than
the most sensitive neurons.

stimulus intensities, one discharge follows
another with an interval of about 1 millisecond, but intervals shorter than this are
not seen.

Relation to duration. Under the influence
of a steady tone the frequency of discharge
from a second-order neuron soon falls off to
one-half, or less, of its initial rate. Most of
this 'adaptation' takes place within the first
fifth of a second. Most neurons, when
adapted, maintain a steady discharge of between 100 and 200 impulses per second.

Inhibition in the cochlear nucleus. About
half of the cells in the cochlear nucleus discharge at a slow rate in the absence of any
known acoustic stimulus. This 'spontaneous'

discharge can often be checked or *inhibited* by a tone of the proper frequency (Fig. 14*A*). The most effective inhibitor is usually

Similarly, a discharge of impulses in response to a tone of moderate intensity may often be inhibited by a second tone sounded

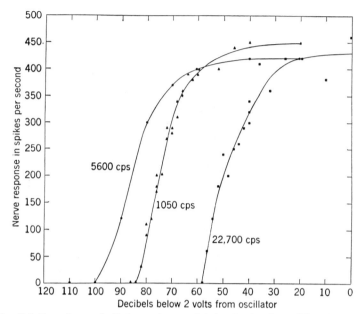

Fig. 13. Relation of neural discharge to sound intensity in three different neurons in the cochlear nucleus (cat). The rate of discharge was established by counting the number of spikes appearing in the first 1/10 second. (From Galambos and Davis, 1943.)

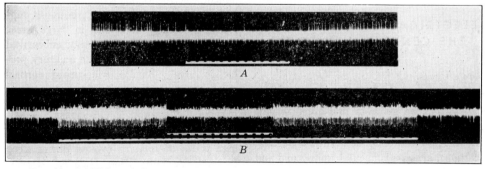

Fig. 14. Inhibition of single neuron responses in the cochlear nucleus. *A*. The notched white line indicates the presentation of a faint tone of 9400 cps to the ipsilateral ear of a cat. This tone inhibits the spontaneous discharge of the neuron. *B*. The lower white line marks the duration of a faint 1300-cycle tone, which excites the neuron. The line above it indicates a 2400-cycle tone which inhibits the discharge resulting from the 1300-cycle tone. Records *A* and *B* are from different cats.

a tone that is slightly *higher* in frequency than that by which the neuron is most easily stimulated, but lower frequencies or noises also sometimes produce inhibition.

simultaneously (Fig. 14*B*). Not every neuron is subject to inhibition, and the effect usually occurs only when both tones are moderate or weak. Increasing the intensity of an inhibiting tone sometimes shifts the effect abruptly from inhibition to excitation. Also the response to a strong tone is difficult to inhibit.

It is noteworthy that facilitation of the central effect of one tone by another is not described. If it occurs it probably is not very dramatic, at least at the level of the cochlear nucleus.

The mechanism of the inhibition is not a physical interference or cancelation of sound waves. The effect is certainly neural and almost certainly occurs at the first synaptic junctions of the auditory tract. As Lorente de Nó has pointed out, each second-order cell body is connected to a large number of auditory nerve fibers by the fine terminal endings of those fibers. Each nerve fiber innervates hundreds of cell bodies, he says, and each cell body is innervated by many nerve fibers. Such a complicated set of synapses should show the properties of all synapses in the nervous system, including the phenomenon of inhibition. We must admit, however, that both the mechanism and the functional significance of central inhibition are still obscure.

ELECTRICAL RESPONSES OF THE CENTRAL AUDITORY SYSTEM

The latency of impulses in the midbrain nuclei and pathways increases systematically as we go from first-order to second-order and then to third-order neurons. The increase in latency associated with each additional synapse is about 1 millisecond and is a little shorter for strong than for weak stimuli (Kemp, Coppée, and Robinson, 1937; Kemp and Robinson, 1937).

The impulses in response to sustained tones do not appear to be so accurately synchronized in the higher auditory pathways as in the auditory nerve. Although isolated clicks may yield brief, clearly defined action potentials from the fourth-order

neurons in the cortex, synchronized impulses at frequencies above about 70 or 100 cps have not been found in the cortex (Bremer, 1943, 1947).

An absolutely unresponsive period of 20 to 100 milliseconds followed by gradual recovery during 100 to 250 milliseconds was found by Tunturi (1946) in the auditory cortex, the auditory radiations, and the medial geniculate bodies of dogs. Stimuli applied to one cochlea rendered the cortex refractory to stimuli applied to the corresponding region of the opposite cochlea. Below the medial geniculate body, however, the unresponsive period lasted only 1 to 2 milliseconds. The evidence suggests that there is a neuron, activated from symmetrical points in the two ears, that runs from the medial geniculate body to all three auditory areas in the cortex.

The electrical response of the cortex to auditory stimulation (even to sharp clicks) is difficult to demonstrate unless cortical activity is reduced or simplified by anesthesia or by sleep (Bremer, 1947). Small action potentials definitely associated with acoustic stimuli have been identified in the waking human electroencephalogram (P. A. Davis, 1939). These responses may, however, represent secondary reactions in large areas of the cortex (and presumably subcortical structures as well) outside the auditory projection area. Similar widespread cortical reactions in anesthetized animals have been produced by electrical stimulation of other sensory nerves (Forbes and Morison, 1939). The clearest generalized cortical response in man is the K-complex evoked during sleep by auditory stimulation (Loomis, Harvey, and Hobart, 1938; Davis et al., 1939). This combination of beta and delta waves probably represents a partial and transient arousal or awakening of the sleeping brain, and perhaps also a synchronous activation of whatever neural elements are responsible for the large slow waves of sleep.

Acoustic stimuli may also cause a transient suppression of the alpha waves in the waking human brain. This effect is apparently related to startle, to the attracting of attention, or even to the specific emotional value of the sounds or words.

Bremer and his colleagues have studied the reactions of the auditory area in the unanesthetized isolated brain of the cat (1947). Disturbing sensory impulses are largely eliminated by cutting the medial lemnisci, and the simplified regularized electrocortico-gram suggests a state of normal repose bordering on sleep and alternating with periods of actual sleep. In the state of waking repose the suppression of regular slow (alpha) waves in all parts of the cortex by acoustic stimuli is very clear. In addition, the auditory cortex, but not other areas, shows an increase of waves (beta) that are faster but still fairly regular. The maximum frequency of the latter is 70 per second. The frequency depends on the intensity, *not* on the frequency, of the stimulating tone. Clicks, up to about 70 per second, give very clear diphasic "primary responses" (Bremer, 1943), followed by an acceleration and regularization of the electrical activity of the auditory area. The first phase of the primary response is surface-positive, and the latency is about 8 milliseconds. Both of these features are compatible with a response in fourth-order neurons of the thalamocortical radiations. Natural sleep and barbiturate anesthesia (unlike ether) depress the after-discharge selectively. They also reduce, slow, and simplify the spontaneous resting activity of the cortex. (Most of the mapping of the auditory cortex mentioned in an earlier section was done with barbiturate anesthesia.) Tonal localization was not observed by Bremer and his associates in the unanesthetized cortez (1943).

Audiogenic seizures. Epileptiform reactions are produced in some rats by acoustic stimuli. The reactions, including tonic seizures, clonic seizures, and racing seizures, resemble those produced by electrical stimulation of the cortex at appropriate intensities (Golub and Morgan, 1945). Generalized electrical seizure patterns have been recorded from the cortex during audiogenic seizures (Lindsley, Finger, and Henry, 1942), but their origin is not specifically from the auditory cortex.

General emotional reactions. The fact that human brain waves are altered by sounds illustrates the general arousing or alerting action of auditory stimuli. In addition, emotional effects of loud sounds (startle, fright, fear) are seen even in newborn infants. A very different emotional reaction is the depression that is characteristic of adults who have suddenly been deprived, by disease or injury to the ear, of normal continual auditory stimulation (Ramsdell, 1947).

AUDITORY REFLEXES

Some of the phenomena mentioned above, such as the startle reaction, general alerting, and possibly audiogenic seizures, are akin to reflex responses. There are other more specific types of auditory reflexes.

Protective auditory reflexes. The tensor tympani and the stapedius muscles contract reflexly when the ear is stimulated by a strong sound. The latent period is about 10 milliseconds (Perlman and Case, 1939). The contraction takes up any slack in the ossicular chain. In more precise terms it adds both stiffness and damping to the transmission mechanism of the middle ear (Wever and Bray, 1937). The net effect of these changes, inferred from observations on cats and guinea pigs, is to raise slightly the natural period of the transmission system, and to reduce considerably the transmission for low tones (Wever and Bray, 1942; Wiggers, 1937). The transmission for high tones is unaffected or slightly reduced. For a band of middle frequencies, near 2000 cps, transmission may be slightly improved. A very vigorous contraction of the stapedius muscle, however, may greatly reduce transmission for all frequencies (Wever and Bray, 1942; cf. also Fig. 7). The reduced transmission of low tones, which are mechanically dangerous because of their greater amplitude, justifies our classifying the reflex as "protective." The reflex is also elicited by tickling the skin in or near the external end of the ear canal.

A twitch of the pinna in response to a sudden sound is characteristic of many small animals, notably the guinea pig. The reaction has frequently been used as a rough test of the ability of the animal to hear. Its functional significance is uncertain, but it may represent a reflex closing of the external canal which protects the ear much as an eye-blink protects the eye.

Conditioned Auditory Reflexes

An effective method of conditioning cats for auditory studies is to place them in a rotating cage and deliver a shock after an auditory stimulus. The animal soon learns to move the cage and thereby avoid the shock whenever he hears the tone. Reliable 'audiograms' and measures of intensity discrimination have been made in this way (Kryter and Ades, 1943; Raab and Ades, 1946).

Complete bilateral removal of the auditory cortex causes total loss of auditory conditioned reflexes. If only a small portion of one auditory area remains, however, the simple avoidance reaction to a pure tone is retained. Raab and Ades consider this function of the cortex to be all-or-none in character.

After removal of the auditory cortex the CR can easily be reestablished, although a few more trials may be necessary than for an intact animal. The relearned response is not abolished by removal of the medial geniculate body, which, by this criterion, seems to have no reflex function. It is, however, abolished by removal of the inferior colliculi or their efferent pathway through the superior colliculi. But removal of the colliculi alone, leaving the lateral lemniscus, the medial geniculates, and the auditory cortex does not abolish the reflex. Apparently the midbrain centers do not mediate the CR normally, but they can be trained to do so after removal of the cortex. The difference limens for intensity are as small for reflexes mediated at the midbrain level as at the cortical level.

Even after the cortex and the midbrain centers have been removed, auditory CR's can still be established. They are, however, less precise, and the latency of response is longer. The threshold is elevated, and intensity discrimination is impaired. The threshold of auditory acuity is elevated about 15 db after removal of the inferior colliculi (Kryter and Ades, 1943). If only the brain stem nuclei below the level of the inferior colliculus remain, the thresholds for motor CR are elevated about 40 db above the normal level.

In a study of auditory conditioned reflexes of dogs, Allen (1945) found that correct conditioned differential responses were abolished after bilateral destruction of all or part of the auditory cortex. They could be reestablished if only the projection areas I and II had been removed bilaterally or if all three areas were removed unilaterally (including Tunturi's area III or C). Bilateral destruction of all three did not prevent the reappearance of correct *positive* responses, but these dogs seemed to lack the ability to make correct *inhibitions*. A similar lack of correct inhibition in differential responses with two sets of general *cutaneous* stimuli was also observed after removal of Tunturi's third auditory area. The full functional significance of the two (and perhaps three) auditory areas is still uncertain, but we may hope for rapid clarification now that the areas have been defined.

A study of auditory conditioned reflexes by Neff (1947) is particularly interesting. The hearing of 11 cats was measured by CR before and after partial section of the auditory nerve on one side and complete destruction of the cochlea on the other. After the operation no hearing losses were detected, at octave frequencies from 125 through 8000 cps, unless at least half of the nerve was sectioned. All losses that were found were extensive high-tone losses, beginning at or (usually) above 1000 cps. These systematic hearing losses resulting from presumably varied lesions are surprising, but they correspond to some very similar clinical observations by Dandy on patients operated for Ménière's disease.

The ears of several of these same cats were studied electrically (5 animals) and histologically (7 animals) by Wever (Wever and Neff, 1947). The aural microphonics were normal for 4 of the 5, and depressed for high frequencies in the fifth. Only in this last animal had any of the hair cells degenerated, and here only in the basal turn. All the ears showed degeneration of some or many nerve fibers, but in all ears that had given evidence of any hearing (by CR) there was at least a short stretch of intact nerve supply at the apical end. This situation corresponds to their retention of normal hearing for the low tones. The data also show that tones below 1000 cycles were heard normally by a cat in which only the last few millimeters at the apical end were normally innervated. The question why the apical nerve fibers were systematically spared remains unanswered.

IMPAIRMENTS OF HEARING

Five main types of auditory impairment are recognized (Davis et al., 1947). We shall consider each of them in turn.

Conductive Deafness

Conductive deafness usually depends on an obvious mechanical abnormality of the conductive system, such as plugging of the external ear by wax, restriction of the movement of the ossicles by abnormal tension on the ear drum (barotrauma) or by pus or fluid or scarlike adhesions (otitis media), loss of drum and/or ossicles (chronic otitis media and radical mastoidectomy), or pathological fixation of the stapes in the oval window (otosclerosis). The hearing loss is in general fairly uniform as a function of frequency, a "flat hearing loss," but either the high or the low tones may be selectively impaired. The conductive impairment may also be analyzed in acoustic terms by measuring the acoustic impedance of the ear (Metz, 1946; Perlman, 1946) and by interpreting the abnormality in terms of changes in the mass, the stiffness, and the resistance of the ear as an acoustic load.

The bones of the skull, as well as the specialized conductive mechanism of the external and middle ear, conduct sound to the inner ear. Even if the acoustic energy is not delivered preferentially to the skull, as by a bone-conduction receiver of an audiometer or a hearing aid, the skull is set in vibration to some extent by airborne sound waves from a headphone or in a free field. The basilar membrane is set in motion by the bone-conducted sound by mechanisms described in the previous chapter, and therefore conductive hearing loss can never be complete.

The movements of the basilar membrane induced by bone conduction may be opposite in phase to those produced by air conduction (Békésy, 1941). It has been suggested, therefore, that at some stage in the development of conductive deafness in otitis media and particularly in otosclerosis there should be a stage of total deafness when the reduced air conduction exactly balances the bone-conducted waves of opposite phase. Clinically such an intermediate stage of very profound deafness is not seen. The suggestion is naïve, however, for it assumes that the relative efficiency of pickup of acoustic energy by bone and by air conduction is constant in amplitude and phase regardless of the orientation of the head to the sound source (cf. Lowy, 1942).

Nerve Deafness

Nerve deafness has both physiological and anatomical bases. The thresholds of some or all of the essential sensory cells of the organ of Corti may be temporarily elevated by fatigue or partial injury; and the sensory cells, auditory nerve fibers, or both, may degenerate entirely. Degeneration may be spontaneous, as in hereditary nerve deafness or the partial high-tone nerve deafness of old age. It may depend on, or be accelerated by, toxic agents (quinine and the toxins of certain diseases such as scarlet fever, measles, etc.). Infection may attack the inner ear directly (meningitis), or the auditory nerve may be mechanically compressed by a tumor. Once a fiber of the auditory nerve has been cut, the entire neuron including the cell body degenerates and does not regenerate. Hair cells deprived of their innervation usually degenerate ultimately — but not immediately, unless their blood supply is also impaired.

Another important cause of degeneration of hair cells is acoustic trauma from loud sounds (Davis et al., 1946; Lurie, Davis, and Hawkins, 1944; Rüedi and Furrer, 1946; Perlman, 1941). A blast or very intense continued sound may disrupt the conductive mechanism, or the organ of Corti, or both. Less intense sounds produce a temporary impairment of function. The external hair cells are more susceptible to permanent injury than the internal, and the cells responsible for the hearing of tones of about 4000 cps are particularly vulnerable. A 'dip' in the audiogram at 4000 cps is often seen in men who have been exposed to very loud sounds from machinery or gunfire, but a similar dip often occurs spontaneously from hereditary or other obscure causes (Wever, 1942).

There are two curious but consistent relations between nerve deafness and sound frequencies perceived. (1) The temporary nerve deafness produced by exposure to an intense pure tone causes hearing loss for tones *above* but not below the frequency of the exposure tone. The maximum loss is from half an octave to an octave above the exposure tone. Sensitivity for the exposure tone may be somewhat impaired, but always to a lesser degree. (2) Permanent nerve

deafness from whatever cause almost always impairs hearing for high tones more than the hearing for lower tones. A partial exception to this rule is the special vulnerability at about 4000 cps, but even in severe congenital or toxic nerve deafness there is likely to be some residual hearing for tones below 1000 cps. The transition from slight or moderate nerve loss for low tones to complete loss for high tones may be gradual, but sometimes it is very abrupt. The audiogram may fall off more than 40 db per octave. Corresponding abrupt low-tone hearing losses do not occur.

The foregoing description of nerve deafness, based on the threshold of hearing, is incomplete. Equal-loudness contours, determined by matching the loudness at various frequencies to the loudness of a standard 1000-cycle tone, become more and more nearly normal as louder and louder levels are explored. As a corollary of this proposition we find that, as the intensity of an exploring tone delivered to a partially nerve-deaf ear is increased, the perceived loudness of the tone increases more rapidly than it does for a normal ear. This effect is known as "recruitment" of loudness or as "regression" (Bruïne-Altes, 1946), and, because of it, nerve deafness is sometimes called "variable" deafness. A practical result of this effect is that a partially nerve-deaf person may hear and discriminate speech sounds better at high intensities than his threshold audiogram would suggest.

The *threshold of discomfort* for loud sounds (about 120 db) is, on the average, about the same for hard-of-hearing as for normal ears (if the tones can be heard at all), even though the ear may show a high-tone hearing loss (Silverman, 1947). The thresholds of *tickle* and of *pain*, mediated by other sense modalities, are also about the same for hard-of-hearing ears as for normals, although there is a scatter of values over a range of about 20 db for both groups.

The mechanism of recruitment is not clear, but apparently recruitment appears when the organ of Corti is abnormal, as in Ménière's disease, but not when the auditory nerve is injured, as by a tumor in the auditory canal (Dix, Hallpike, and Hood, 1948). We may suppose that auditory elements whose thresholds are high may be less susceptible to injury and degeneration than low-threshold elements, and that they may contribute proportionately a much greater share of subjective loudness; or there may be a nonlinear law of central summation of neural activity, analogous to recruitment of motor units in reflex motor responses, that obscures the loss of the low-threshold elements when the total activity becomes great.

Central Deafness

Central deafness may be physiological in origin, sometimes based on definite anatomical abnormalities, or it may be psychological or psychogenic. A psychological or functional hearing loss may be combined with a partial conductive or perceptive hearing loss as an 'overlay.' The functional character of the overlay is demonstrated when the hearing loss is relieved by appropriate psychiatric treatment. It is usually a form of hysteria or a conversion neurosis. This condition was clearly demonstrated in a considerable percentage of cases of hearing loss incurred in military service when they were treated by *narcosynthesis* (Martin, 1946).

Loss of understanding of the meaning of sounds, especially of speech, is another form of central deafness. This condition is termed *aphasia*. It may depend on definite injury to parts of the auditory cortex and/or its association areas. This condition, like psychogenic or hysterical deafness, has its counterparts in other sense modalities. Aphasia and psychogenic deafness are auditory only in their specific manifestations, not in their basic nature. Specific auditory impairments of thresholds, of discrimination, and of conditioned reflexes due to lesions of the auditory pathways (in animals) have been described in a previous section. It must be remembered, however, that in primates and man, according to the principle of encephalization, the auditory impairment caused by cortical injury tends to be more severe than in dogs, cats, and other animals.

Diplacusis

Diplacusis, or false sense of pitch, may depend on a physical abnormality. Apparently edema or "hydrops of the labyrinth" may cause a slight shift of the pattern of vibration on the basilar membrane and a consequent change in the pitch of the sensation aroused by a tone of a given frequency (Shambaugh, 1940). Small differences in the 'tuning' of the two ears can also be found in many, perhaps most, normal individuals (Stevens and Egan, 1941; see also Chapter 25).

Tinnitus

Ringing in the ears and other head noises (except hallucinations, which are considered central in origin) heard in the absence of physical sound are physiological phenomena. They undoubtedly represent a spontaneous discharge of sensory elements in the auditory system. The usual source is an irritation or hypersensitivity of the hair cells or their nerves. A small amount of spontaneous activity is probably normal and presumably accounts for the faint 'white' noise or the faint ringing heard by almost everyone in a very quiet room. Tinnitus may become very loud (and annoying) after exposure to a loud sound. Here it is clearly an aftereffect of mild mechanical injury to some of the hair cells. Tinnitus is often present in ears in which sensory degeneration seems to be in progress, as in progressive high-tone nerve deafness. The pitch of the tinnitus usually corresponds to a frequency for which hearing is impaired but not lost. It is a frequent symptom in otosclerosis, and may be caused (by some unknown mechanism) by irritation in the middle ear and even in the external canal. It is a constant feature and may be very severe in Ménière's disease. Here the symptom of vertigo (abolished by destruction of the labyrinth or section of its nerve) indicates clearly a severe irritation of the labyrinthine sense organs. Mechanical irritation of the cochlear nerve, as by a tumor, may cause very severe, continuous, and distressing tinnitus.

Tinnitus causes a partial hearing loss for tones of the same or neighboring pitch. The hearing loss, measured by audiometer, is usually exaggerated because of the subject's uncertainty as to whether he hears the test tone or his tinnitus. There is usually some true loss of acuity, probably due to a physiological masking by a 'line-busy' effect, but it seldom amounts to more than 15 db, in spite of subjective impressions that head noises are much louder than this.

The pitch of a tinnitus may be very distinct, particularly when it is high pitched, and sometimes it may be accurately matched by an exploring tone. In other cases it resembles a vague low-pitched roar or even a wide band of noise. Attempts have been made to detect beats between a tinnitus and an exploring tone (Davis et al., 1946). All subjects but one have reported that beats are absent, and most investigators view with suspicion the classic positive report (Wegel, 1931).

PSYCHOPHYSIOLOGICAL INTERPRETATIONS

We are still far from a complete auditory theory, particularly in regard to the final psychophysiological steps. The early biophysical steps and some of the physiological correlates of the physical stimulus and of auditory sensation are fairly clear, however. There is good agreement as to the general structure of the physiological code of audition.

The two chief attributes of auditory sensation are pitch (correlated almost uniquely with the frequency of sound waves) and loudness (correlated strongly but not uniquely with their intensity). The out-

standing features of the neuroanatomical and physiological system are:

1. Multiple levels. There are primary, secondary, tertiary, etc., neurons that connect the sense organ with the lowest nerve center, the lowest with the next higher center, and so on. In these centers there are interconnections between neuron chains of the same side and also from one center to its opposite. Here integration can occur.

2. Orderly spatial arrangement of the primary sensory surface and its projection at various levels in the central nervous system.

3. Multiple representation of the primary sensory surface at each level beyond the primary neuron.

4. The all-or-none law of transmission in neurons, and the limitations on frequency of discharge imposed by the refractory period.

5. Summation or integration of neural activity, both excitatory and inhibitory, not only in space (neuronal branching) but also in time (delay paths, after-discharge, and persistent subliminal changes of excitatory state).

6. The possibility of nonneuronal integration (electrical and/or chemical field effects) in nerve centers. This last principle is not yet clearly defined in neurophysiology and should not be invoked in present theory unless absolutely required.

It is generally accepted that movement of the basilar membrane somehow excites impulses in the nerve fibers that innervate the hair cells of the organ of Corti. The activity of single second-order neurons shows just the sort of selectivity in relation to frequency that would be expected from the anatomical distribution of the fibers of the auditory nerve and from direct observation of the regions of maximum amplitude of vibration of the basilar membrane. It is helpful to assume that the thresholds of different hair cells (or their nerve fibers), defined in terms of the amplitude of movement of the basilar membrane, vary in some consistent way. This makes it easier to explain intensity discrimination over a wide range of intensities. The only plausible explanations of intensity discrimination seem to be on the basis of (1) number of fibers activated, or, better, (2) the total number of impulses per second in all fibers, or, still better, (3) a composite of number of impulses per second and a selective contribution to loudness from a class of fibers with relatively high threshold.

Auditory information on its way to the brain passes through its narrowest bottleneck in the auditory nerve. Here, in the first-order neurons, the limitations of the all-or-none law and the refractory period of nerve apply in full force. The pathways have not yet branched to provide the additional possibilities of temporal summation and spatial interaction. The latter may be part of the mechanism for decoding the condensed information transmitted up the nerve. In our present ignorance it is useless to speculate on the elaboration of patterns of neural activity in the nerve centers, or on the physiological basis of sensation. The crux of present auditory theory is the form in which information is conveyed in the auditory nerve, for (except for binaural effects) no information can be added beyond the internal auditory meatus.

For tones up to 1000 cps, or even a little higher, a frequency theory of pitch is possible. The impulses pass up the auditory nerve in well-defined volleys. The frequency of discharge in tactile fibers seems to be the basis of our ability to discriminate different rates of vibration. A frequency theory of pitch for these low tones is certainly possible, and it is favored by several students of auditory physiology as an adjunct to the place principle (Wever, 1939). This theory postulates a gradual transition from the place principle to the frequency principle *somewhere within the audio range* instead of at the transition from the sense of touch to the sense of hearing. In favor of this theory are (1) the very vague localization on the basilar membrane of any area of maximum excursion for low tones, (2) the

difficulty of selectively eliminating low-tone fibers by surgical section, and (3) the perception of periodicity (discussed in Chapter 25).

A few investigators still adhere to the generally discarded notion of a series of lightly damped resonators along the organ of Corti. Light damping allows the theoretical possibility of relatively sharp tuning, but the weight of evidence is heavily on the side of nearly critical damping of the basilar membrane. Pumphrey and Gold (1947) suggest that the damping of the organ of Corti is light and that it varies systematically from apex to base. Their observations on the recognition of the pitch of brief pulses of tone can be interpreted otherwise, however. Galambos' demonstration (1944) of inhibitory interaction between tones only slightly different in frequency provides a theoretical explanation for sharp frequency discrimination. Galambos also demonstrated some very sharp tuning of second-order neurons in cats. The gradient of activity among adjacent second-order nerve fibers can apparently be sharper than would seem likely from the small differences in the amplitude of vibration along the basilar membrane.

REFERENCES

Ades, H. W. Midbrain auditory mechanisms in cats. *J. Neurophysiol.*, 1944, **7**, 415–424.

Ades, H. W., and R. E. Felder. The acoustic projection system : A comparative study. *J. Neurophysiol.*, 1945, **8**, 463–470.

Allen, W. F. Effect of destroying three localized cerebral cortical areas for sound on correct conditioned differential responses of the dog's foreleg. *Amer. J. Physiol.*, 1945, **144**, 415–428.

Anson, B. J. Development of the auditory ossicles. *Laryngoscope*, 1946, **56**, 561–569.

Barnes, W. T., H. W. Magoun, and S. W. Ranson. The ascending auditory pathway in the brain stem of the monkey. *J. comp. Neurol.*, 1943, **79**, 129–152.

Bast, T. H., and J. A. E. Eyster. The function of the apical turns of the cochlea and the symptoms of a lesion in this location. Discussion from the point of view of animal experimentation. *Ann. Otol., Rhinol. and Laryngol.*, 1935, **44**, 792–803.

Békésy, G. von. Über die Schallausbreitung bei Knochenleitung. *Z. Hals-Nas.- u. Ohrenheilk.*, 1941, **47**, 430–442.

Bremer, F.   Étude oscillographique des réponses sensorielles de l'aire acoustique corticale chez le chat. *Arch. int. Physiol.,* 1943, 53–103.

Bremer, F.   L'activité électrique spontanée des centres nerveux et l'électroéncephalogramme. Essai d'interprétation. *J. belge Neurol. Psychiat.,* 1947, **47,** 1–19.

Bremer, F., and R. S. Dow.   The acoustic area of the cerebral cortex in the cat. A combined oscillographic and cytoarchitectonic study. *J. Neurophysiol.,* 1939, **2,** 308–318.

Brogden, W. J., E. Girden, F. A. Mettler, and E. Culler.   Acoustic value of the several components in the auditory system in cats. *Amer. J. Physiol.,* 1936, **116,** 252–261.

Bruïne-Altes, J. C. de.   *The symptom of regression in different kinds of deafness.* Groningen: Wolters, 1946.

Cajal, S. Ramon.   *Histologie du système nerveux de l'homme et des vertébrés.* Paris: Maloine, 1909. Vol. I.

Cheng, S. K., and W. T. Niemer.   Ascending auditory system, a study of retrograde degeneration. (Unpublished.)

Davis, H., et al.   *Hearing and deafness: A guide for laymen.* New York: Murray Hill, 1947.

Davis, H., P. A. Davis, A. L. Loomis, E. N. Harvey, and G. Hobart.   Electrical reactions of the human brain to auditory stimulation during sleep. *J. Neurophysiol.,* 1939, **2,** 500–514.

Davis, H., A. J. Derbyshire, E. H. Kemp, M. H. Lurie, and M. Upton.   Functional and histological changes in the cochlea of the guinea pig resulting from prolonged stimulation. *J. gen. Psychol.,* 1935, **12,** 251–278.

Davis, H., A. J. Derbyshire, M. H. Lurie, and L. J. Saul.   The electric response of the cochlea. *Amer. J. Physiol.,* 1934, **107,** 311–332.

Davis, H., B. E. Gernandt, and J. S. Riesco-MacClure.   Threshold of action potentials in ear of guinea pig. *J. Neurophysiol.,* 1950, **13,** 73–87.

Davis, H., B. E. Gernandt, J. S. Riesco-MacClure, and W. P. Covell.   Aural microphonics in the cochlea of the guinea pig. *J. acoust. Soc. Amer.,* 1949, **21,** 502–510.

Davis, H., C. T. Morgan. J. E. Hawkins, Jr., R. Galambos and F. W. Smith.   Temporary deafness following exposure to loud tones and noise. *Laryngoscope,* 1946, **56,** 19–21. Summary of a report of the Committee on Medical Research, Sept. 30, 1943.

Davis, P. A.   Effects of acoustic stimuli on the waking human brain. *J. Neurophysiol.,* 1939, **2,** 494–499.

Derbyshire, A. J., and H. Davis.   The probable mechanism for stimulation of the auditory nerve by the organ of Corti. *Amer. J. Physiol.,* 1935a, **113,** 35.

Derbyshire, A. J., and H. Davis.   The action potentials of the auditory nerve. *Amer. J. Physiol.,* 1935b, **113,** 476–504.

Dix, M. R., C. S. Hallpike, and J. D. Hood.   Observations upon loudness recruitment phenomenon, with especial reference to the differential diagnosis of disorders of the internal ear and VIII nerve. *Proc. roy. Soc. Med.,* 1948, **41,** 516–526.

Dworkin, S., J. E. Hawkins, Jr., M. H. Lurie, and H. Davis.   The independence of the aural microphonic from auditory function. *Fed. Proc. Amer. Soc. exp. Biol.,* 1943, **2,** 10–11.

Eyster, J. A. E., T. H. Bast, and M. R. Krasno.   Studies on the electrical response of the cochlea. *Amer. J. Physiol.,* 1935, **113,** 40.

Eyster, J. A. E., T. H. Bast, and M. R. Krasno.   The origin of cochlear potentials. *Amer. J. Physiol.,* 1937, **119,** 305. See also *Laryngoscope,* 1937, **47,** 461–479.

Forbes, A., and B. R. Morison.   The cortical response to sensory stimulation under deep barbiturate narcosis. *J. Neurophysiol.,* 1939, **2,** 112–128.

Galambos, R.   Cochlear potentials elicited from bats by supersonic sounds. *J. acoust. Soc. Amer.,* 1942, **14,** 41–49.

Galambos, R.   Inhibition of activity in single auditory nerve fibers by acoustic stimulation. *J. Neurophysiol.,* 1944, **7,** 287–303.

Galambos, R., and H. Davis.   The response of single auditory-nerve fibers to acoustic stimulation. *J. Neurophysiol.,* 1943, **6,** 39–58.

Galambos, R., and H. Davis.   Action potentials from single auditory nerve fibers? *Science,* 1948, **108,** 513.

Galambos, R., and D. R. Griffin.   Obstacle avoidance by flying bats: The cries of bats. *J. exp. Zool.,* 1942, **89,** 475–490.

Golub, L. M., and C. T. Morgan.   Patterns of electrogenic seizures in rats: Their relation to stimulus-intensity and to audiogenic seizures. *J. comp. Psychol.,* 1945, **38,** 239–245.

Guild, S. R.   Correlations of histologic observations and the acuity of hearing. *Acta otolaryng., Stockh.,* 1932, **17,** 207–249.

Guttman, J., and S. E. Barrera.   Persistence of cochlear electrical disturbance on auditory stimulation in the presence of cochlear ganglion degeneration. *Amer. J. Physiol.,* 1934, **109,** 704–708.

Guttman, J., and S. E. Barrera.   The electrical potentials of the cochlea and auditory nerve in relation to hearing. *Amer. J. Physiol.,* 1937, **120,** 666–671.

Hallpike, C. S., and A. F. Rawdon-Smith.   The "Wever and Bray phenomenon." A study of the electrical response in the cochlea with especial reference to its origin. *J. Physiol.,* 1934a, **81,** 395–408.

Hallpike, C. S., and A. F. Rawdon-Smith.   The origin of the Wever and Bray phenomenon. *J. Physiol.,* 1934b, **83,** 243–254.

Hallpike, C. S., and A. F. Rawdon-Smith.   The Wever and Bray phenomenon—a summary of the data concerning the origin of the cochlear effect. *Ann. Otol., Rhinol. and Laryngol.,* 1937, **46,** 976–990.

Hampson, J. L.   Relationships between cerebral and cerebellar cortices in cat. *J. Neurophysiol.,* 1949, **12,** 37–50.

Hughson, W., and E. G. Witting. An objective study of auditory fatigue. *Acta oto-laryng., Stockh.*, 1935, **21**, 457–486.

Kappers, C. U. A., G. C. Huber, and E. C. Crosby. *The comparative anatomy of the nervous system of vertebrates, including man.* New York: Macmillan, 1936.

Kemp, E. H., G. E. Coppée, and E. H. Robinson. Electric responses of the brain stem to unilateral auditory stimulation. *Amer. J. Physiol.*, 1937, **120**, 304–315.

Kemp, E. H., and E. H. Robinson. Electric responses of the brain stem to bilateral auditory stimulation. *Amer. J. Physiol.*, 1937, **120**, 316–322.

Kryter, K. D., and H. W. Ades. Studies on the function of the higher acoustic nervous centers in the cat. *Amer. J. Psychol.*, 1943, **56**, 501–536.

LeMessurier, D. H. Auditory and visual areas of the cerebral cortex of the rat. *Fed. Proc. Amer. Soc. exp. Biol.*, 1948, **7**, 70–71. (Abstract.)

Lempert, J., E. G. Wever, and M. Lawrence. The cochleogram and its clinical application. *Arch. Otolaryng.*, 1947, **45**, 61–67.

Lindsley, D. B., F. W. Finger, and C. E. Henry. Some physiological aspects of audiogenic seizures in rats. *J. Neurophysiol.*, 1942, **5**, 185–198.

Loomis, A. L., E. N. Harvey, and G. A. Hobart. Distribution of disturbance-patterns in the human electroencephalogram, with special reference to sleep. *J. Neurophysiol.*, 1938, **1**, 413–430.

Lorente de Nó, R. Anatomy of the eighth nerve. The central projection of the nerve endings of the internal ear. *Laryngoscope*, 1933, **43**, 1–38.

Lowy, K. The change of phase caused by impedance deafness. *J. acoust. Soc. Amer.*, 1942, **13**, 389–392.

Lowy, K. Some experimental evidence for peripheral auditory masking. *J. acoust. Soc. Amer.*, 1945, **16**, 197–202.

Lurie, M. H., H. Davis, and J. E. Hawkins, Jr. Acoustic trauma of the organ of Corti in the guinea pig. *Laryngoscope*, 1944, **54**, 375–386.

Martin, N. A. Psychogenic deafness. *Ann. Otol., Rhinol. and Laryngol.*, 1946, **55**, 81–89.

McCrady, E., Jr., E. G. Wever, and C. W. Bray. A further investigation of the development of hearing in the opossum. *J. comp. Psychol.*, 1940, **30**, 17–21.

Metz, O. *The acoustic impedance measured on normal and pathological ears.* Copenhagen: Einar Munksgaard, 1946.

Neff, W. D. The effects of partial section of the auditory nerve. *J. comp. Physiol. Psychol.*, 1947, **40**, 203–215.

Newman, E. B., S. S. Stevens, and H. Davis. Factors in the production of aural harmonics and combination tones. *J. acoust. Soc. Amer.*, 1937, **9**, 107–118.

Perlman, H. B. Acoustic trauma in man. *Arch. Otolaryng.*, 1941, **34**, 429–452.

Perlman, H. B. Stiffness lesions of the conducting mechanism. *Laryngoscope*, 1946, **56**, 497–509.

Perlman, H. B., and T. J. Case. Latent period of the crossed stapedius reflex in man. *Ann. Otol., etc., St. Louis*, 1939, **48**, 663–675.

Polyak, S. L., G. McHugh, and D. K. Judd. *The human ear in anatomical transparencies.* Sonotone Corporation, Elmsford, N. Y., 1946.

Pumphrey, R. J. Hearing in insects. *Biol. Rev.*, 1940, **15**, 107–132.

Pumphrey, R. J., and T. Gold. Transient reception and the degree of resonance of the human ear. *Nature*, 1947, **160**, 124–126.

Raab, D. H., and H. W. Ades. Cortical and midbrain mediation of a conditioned discrimination of acoustic intensities. *Amer. J. Psychol.*, 1946, **59**, 59–83.

Ramsdell, D. A. The psychology of the hard-of-hearing and the deafened adult. In H. Davis (Ed.), *Hearing and Deafness.* New York: Murray Hill, 1947.

Rasmussen, A. T. *Outlines of neuro-anatomy.* Dubuque, Ia.: Brown, 1943.

Rawdon-Smith, A. F., and J. E. Hawkins, Jr., The electrical activity of a denervated ear. *Proc. roy. Soc. Med.*, 1939, **32**, 496–507.

Rüedi, L., and W. Furrer. Physics and physiology of acoustic trauma. *J. acoust. Soc. Amer.*, 1946, **18**, 409–412.

Rüedi, L., and W. Furrer. *Das akustische Trauma.* Basel: Karger, 1947.

Shambaugh, G. E., Jr. Diplacusis: A localizing symptom of disease of the organ of Corti. *Arch. Otolaryng.*, 1940, **31**, 160–184.

Silverman, S. R. Tolerance for pure tones and speech in normal and defective hearing. *Ann. Otol., Rhinol. and Laryngol.*, 1947, **56**, 658–677.

Snider, R. S., and A. Stowell. Receiving areas of the tactile, auditory and visual systems in the cerebellum. *J. Neurophysiol.*, 1944, **7**, 331–358.

Stevens, S. S., and H. Davis. *Hearing, its psychology and physiology.* New York: Wiley, 1938.

Stevens, S. S., and J. P. Egan. Diplacusis in "normal" ears. (Abstract) *Psychol. Bull.*, 1941, **38**, 548.

Stevens, S. S., and E. B. Newman. On the nature of aural harmonics. *Proc. nat. Acad. Sci., Wash.*, 1936, **22**, 668–672.

Tunturi, A. R. Audio frequency localization in the acoustic cortex of the dog. *Amer. J. Physiol.*, 1944, **141**, 397–403.

Tunturi, A. R. Further afferent connections to the acoustic cortex of the dog. *Amer. J. Physiol.*, 1945, **144**, 389–394.

Tunturi, A. R. A study on the pathway from the medial geniculate body to the acoustic cortex in the dog. *Amer. J. Physiol.*, 1946, **147**, 311–319.

Walker, A. E. *The thalamus of the rhesus monkey (Macaca mulatta)*. Chicago: University of Chicago Press, 1937.

Walzl, E. M. The effect of chemicals on cochlear potentials. *Amer. J. Physiol.*, 1939, **125**, 688–698.

Walzl, E. M. Representation of the cochlea in the cerebral cortex. *Laryngoscope*, 1947, **57**, 778–787.

Walzl, E. M., and J. E. Bordley. The effect of small lesions of the organ of Corti on cochlear potentials. *Amer. J. Physiol.*, 1942, **135**, 351–360.

Walzl, E. M., and C. N. Woolsey. Effects of cochlear lesions on click responses in the auditory cortex of the cat. *Johns Hopk. Hosp. Bull.*, 1946, **79**, 309–319.

Wegel, R. L. A study of tinnitus. *Arch. Otolaryng.*, 1931, **14**, 158–165.

Wever, E. G. The electrical responses of the ear. *Psychol. Bull.*, 1939, **36**, 143–187.

Wever, E. G. The problem of the tonal dip. *Laryngoscope*, 1942, **52**, 169–187.

Wever, E. G., and C. W. Bray. Action currents in the auditory nerve in response to acoustical stimulation. *Proc. nat. Acad. Sci., Wash.*, 1930, **16**, 344–350.

Wever, E. G., and C. W. Bray. The tensor tympani muscle and its relation to sound conduction. *Ann. Otol., Rhinol. and Laryngol.*, 1937, **46**, 947–961.

Wever, E. G., and C. W. Bray. The nature of the acoustic responses: The relation between stimulus intensity and the magnitude of cochlear responses in the cat. *J. exp. Psychol.*, 1938, **22**, 1–16.

Wever, E. G., and C. W. Bray. The stapedius muscle in relation to sound conduction. *J. exp. Psychol.*, 1942, **31**, 35–43.

Wever, E. G., C. W. Bray, and M. Lawrence. Locus of distortion in the ear. *J. acoust. Soc. Amer.*, 1940a, **11**, 427–433.

Wever, E. G., C. W. Bray, and M. Lawrence. The interference of tones in the cochlea. *J. acoust. Soc. Amer.*, 1940b, **12**, 268–280.

Wever, E. G., C. W. Bray, and M. Lawrence. The origin of combination tones. *J. exp. Psychol.*, 1940c, **27**, 217–226.

Wever, E. G., C. W. Bray, and M. Lawrence. The nature of cochlear activity after death. *Ann. Otol., Rhinol. and Laryngol.*, 1941a, **50**, 317–329.

Wever, E. G., C. W. Bray, and M. Lawrence. The effect of middle ear pressure upon distortion. *J. acoust. Soc. Amer.*, 1941b, **13**, 182–187.

Wever, E. G., and M. Lawrence. Tonal interference in relation to cochlear injury. *J. exp. Psychol.*, 1941, **29**, 283–295.

Wever, E. G., M. Lawrence, and K. R. Smith. The middle ear in sound conduction. *Arch. Otolaryng.*, 1948, **48**, 19–35.

Wever, E. G., and M. Lawrence. The patterns of response in the cochlea. *J. acoust. Soc. Amer.*, 1949, **21**, 127–134.

Wever, E. G., and W. D. Neff. A further study of the effects of partial section of the auditory nerve. *J. comp. Physiol. Psychol.*, 1947, **40**, 217–226.

Wiggers, H. C. The functions of the intra-aural muscles. *Amer. J. Physiol.*, 1937, **120**, 781–797.

Woolsey, C. N. Patterns of sensory representation in the cerebral cortex. *Fed. Proc. Amer. Soc. exp. Biol.*, 1947, **6**, 437–441.

Woolsey, C. N., and E. M. Walzl. Topical projection of nerve fibers from local regions of the cochlea to the cerebral cortex of the cat. *Johns Hopk. Hosp. Bull.*, 1942, **71**, 315–344.

29

Taste and Smell

CARL PFAFFMANN

Brown University

Taste, smell, and the so-called common chemical sense are frequently grouped together because agents that excite them are most readily described and classified by their chemical formulas. There is no proof, however, that stimulation depends primarily upon a chemical reaction between the ions or molecules of the stimulus and some part of the receptor concerned. In certain instances, as in the sense of taste, it is known that the stimulus substance must be in solution. Colloids are tasteless. It has been argued that odor-producing molecules dispersed in a gaseous form must first dissolve in the mucus that covers the olfactory epithelium before stimulation can occur. But efforts to stimulate the olfactory receptors of man by stimulus solutions introduced directly into the nostrils have not been conclusive. In water-inhabiting vertebrates, olfactory stimulation by substances dissolved in the water obviously takes place (Parker, 1922).

Three types of sense organ and sensitivity are included in the chemoreceptor group:

1. The *common chemical sense*, a sensitivity to mildly irritating solutions found on moist mucous membrane surfaces such as the eyeball and nasal and mouth cavities, as well as the external skin of water-inhabiting vertebrates. The nerve endings appear to be undifferentiated free nerve terminations from the nerves of general sensitivity.

2. The sense of *taste* located in man on the tongue and portions of the throat. In certain water-inhabiting vertebrates this sensitivity may be present on barbels and other parts of the body surface. The sense organs are specialized endings called taste buds consisting of modified epithelial cells upon which gustatory afferent nerve fibers terminate.

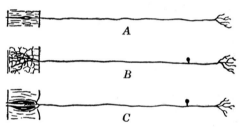

Fig. 1. The three types of chemoreceptor. Olfactory cell (*A*) and free nerve endings (*B*) consist entirely of neural elements; gustatory receptors (*C*) consist of modified epithelial cells upon which the afferent nerve fibers terminate. (From Parker, 1922.)

3. The sense of *smell* which in man is located in the upper recesses of the nasal cavity and in lower animals in olfactory pits or sacs. The end organs consist of long spindle-shaped cells with fine hairs projecting from their distal ends. The proximal end of the cells tapers into fine nerve fibers to form the olfactory nerve.

Of these three classes of sensory cells, only those of the common chemical sense and olfaction are primary neural elements (Fig. 1). The sense cells of taste are modified epithelial cells. When the taste nerves are cut, the taste cells and buds degenerate. When the nerve fibers regenerate and reach the periphery, taste cells and taste buds reform (Olmsted, 1920a, b).

The fact that the chemical sense organs are grouped together at the entrance to the respiratory and alimentary tracts of air-inhabiting animals means that these senses are frequently stimulated in combination. The contribution of each of these senses to the complex experience we call flavor or "taste" of food may be ascertained only by analytical study. These perceptions are further complicated by other components such as warm, cold, touch, and pressure.

For man, vision and hearing appear to be the more important senses, in spite of the fact that the chemical senses have a close relation to food getting, avoidance of certain noxious fumes, and perhaps sexual activity. Loss of taste, ageusia, although disconcerting, is nothing like the loss of vision or hearing. Perhaps taste and smell are of greater importance in animals. In fact, the relatively greater development of certain structures underlying olfaction in some species has led to the designation of these creatures as macrosmatic as opposed to man who is microsmatic.

Recent experiments have reemphasized the importance of the chemical senses in food getting. Animals rendered deficient in one constituent of the diet were found to increase the intake of the needed substance when given access to a wide variety of food substances. The capacity to make such selections seems to depend on taste. Selection of needed substances because they "taste good" may occur in human beings under certain conditions (Richter, 1942).

COMMON CHEMICAL SENSE

The existence of two classes of receptors in the nasal passages has long been recognized: (1) the true olfactory nerve endings of the olfactory cleft and (2) the common chemical sense consisting of the trigeminal nerve endings sensitive to mildly irritating vapors. True odors are typically described by such terms as fruity, foul, fragrant, etc., whereas the trigeminal stimulants cause mild pain and frequently lead to strong reflex effects like sneezing, crying, or coughing. Many olfactory stimulants may affect both systems. Experimental studies on animals with surgical removal of one or the other set of nerves indicate that only such relatively mild agents as oil of cloves, extract of orange, etc., stimulate the sense of smell alone. Oil of wintergreen, xylol, acetic acid, or ammonia stimulate both smell and the free nerve endings (Allen, 1929).

Acids in concentrations far above those required to call out the sour taste will elicit pain from surfaces of the mouth devoid of taste buds, and, in fact, from all exposed or partially exposed mucous membrane surfaces. In lower aquatic vertebrates the whole surface of the body is sensitive to acids and other irritants.

The common chemical sensitivity is said to be distinct not only from touch, but also from pain (Crozier, 1916a). However, the type of afferent impulse elicited by chemical stimulation in the cutaneous nerve preparation of the frog, for example, appears to be much the same as that elicited by scraping, burning, or other injury. These impulses travel in small nerve fibers of slow conduction. Impulses initiated by tactile stimuli are of large potential and are rapidly conducted (Adrian, Cattell, and Hoagland, 1931). Crozier (1916a), utilizing the leg flexion of the frog as an indicator of stimulation, studied the differential effect of cocaine upon the sensitivity to pain elicited by a pinch on the foot and by immersing the foot in acid. After cocainization the acid continued to elicit a response whereas pain had become ineffective. The reaction time to the acid, however, was increased. It might be argued that, since the chemical stimulus covered a large area of the foot, spatial summation occurred to render the chemical more effective. Pain and the common chemical sensitivity appear therefore to be mediated by the same nerve endings.

On the other hand, it is quite clear that such chemical sensitivity is distinct from touch, and, in the mouth and nose, distinct from taste and smell.

Of the three types of chemically sensitive endings, the common chemical sense appears to be the least sensitive. For alcohol, which is an adequate stimulus for all three senses, the threshold values on mouth surfaces devoid of taste buds ranged from 5 to 10 mol.* The mildly sweetish taste of alcohol could be detected at 3 mol, and the odor at a concentration of 0.000125 mol (Parker and Stabler, 1913).

TASTE

Anatomy. The taste end organs consist of spindle-shaped cells grouped together in

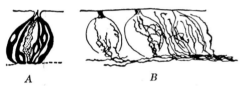

A   *B*

Fig. 2. Golgi preparations of taste buds and associated nerve endings. *A.* Taste cells and a "sustentive" element. *B.* Nerve endings, sense cells not shown (after Retzius). (From Crozier, 1934.)

gobletlike clusters called taste buds. A tiny hair projects from each taste cell toward the taste pore at the open end of the bud. The nerve fibers supplying these taste cells arise from a subepithelial plexus to wind about and terminate on the surfaces of the taste cells. Certain nerve fibers may be seen to bifurcate and to end upon more than one taste cell in either the same or neighboring taste buds (Fig. 2).

On the tongue, the taste buds are primarily located on the dorsal surfaces of the mushroomlike fungiform papillae, in the grooves of the foliate papillae, and in the trenches of the circumvallate papillae at the back of the tongue (Fig. 3). The middorsal tongue region is devoid of taste buds and is

* *Mol* is an abbreviation for molar concentration (see footnote on p. 1148).

insensitive to taste stimuli. Taste buds are also found in somewhat lesser numbers on the palate, the anterior faucial pillars, the pharynx, and the larynx.

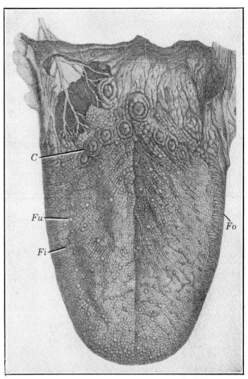

FIG. 3. Dorsal surface of the tongue partially dissected to show the nerves to the posterior part. The circumvallate (*C*), fungiform (*Fu*), and filiform (*Fi*) papillae are shown. The foliate papillae (*Fo*) are not clearly visible in this view since they are on the lateral surface of the tongue. Taste buds occur in *C, Fo*, and *Fu*, not in *Fi*. (From Wenzel, reproduced from Warren and Carmichael, 1930.)

The number and distribution of taste buds change with age. In children many more buds are found over the dorsal tongue surface. With increasing age, the number of taste buds decreases (Arey, Tremaine, and Monzingo, 1935). The reduced sensitivity found in older people is probably associated with this decrease in the number of sense cells (Richter and Campbell, 1940).

The nerve fibers from the taste buds do not travel in a single cranial nerve. Those from the anterior part of the tongue travel in the lingual nerve, a mixed nerve that subserves touch, temperature, and pain sensitivity.

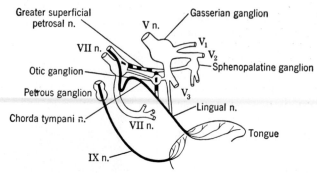

Fig. 4. The nerve supply to the tongue. The solid lines indicate the most common pathways for the taste impulses. The broken line indicates an alternative path from the chorda tympani believed to exist in a limited number of cases. (Modified from Cushing, 1903; Schwartz and Weddell, 1938.)

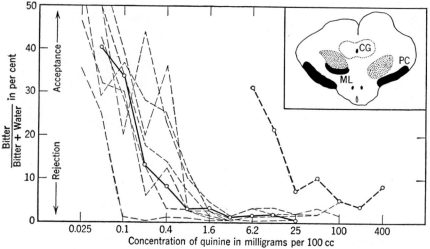

Fig. 5. The effect of lesions near the medial lemniscus on gustatory discrimination. The ordinate shows the percentage of total fluid intake selected from the quinine flavored bottle. Heavy solid and heavy broken lines are the pre- and postoperative threshold curves, respectively, of a rat with the lesion shown in stipple in the inset. Fine broken lines are the threshold curves of seven normal rats. ML, medial lemniscus; PC, cerebral peduncles; CG, central gray matter. (From Patton and Ruch, 1947.)

tivity. The taste fibers, however, leave the lingual nerve to form a small branch, the chorda tympani, which crosses the tympanic membrane of the ear on its way to join the seventh cranial nerve (Olmsted, 1922). This is the typical pathway, although in man clinical evidence has suggested that an alternative pathway may exist (Fig. 4). (See Cushing, 1903; Lewis and Dandy, 1930; Schwartz and Weddell, 1938.) Nerve fibers from the posterior part of the tongue travel in the ninth (glossopharyngeal) nerve. Fibers from the larynx and pharynx may travel with the tenth (vagus) nerve. The lingual nerve supply is essentially homolateral, although there is some evidence for a dual innervation of the circumvallate papilla.

The nerve fibers carrying taste impulses are relatively small in diameter as judged by the amplitude of the action potentials following gustatory stimulation (Hoagland, 1933; Zotterman, 1935; Pfaffmann, 1941).

The gustatory fibers of the seventh, ninth, and tenth nerves form a well-defined tract of the medulla, the tractus solitarius. The secondary gustatory neurons arise from its nucleus. Both histological and behavioral studies indicate that these fibers ascend in the opposite medial lemniscus (Fig. 5). Clinical, anatomical, and physiological observations have indicated that the taste fibers in the thalamus are closely allied with those of general somatic sensitivity of the face in the arcuate nucleus. In the cortex, likewise, taste is localized in relation to the somatic sensitivity of the face and not in conjunction with the olfactory sensitivity as was formerly supposed (Patton and Ruch, 1947). The region concerned lies at the inferior end of the central fissure near the sylvian fissure (Fig. 6).

Taste Qualities

Sour, salty, bitter, and sweet are the typical gustatory qualities elicited by sapid solutions applied to the taste buds. It is commonly held that these four are the primary taste qualities from which all other true tastes are compounded. Although some investigators (Hahn, Kuckulies, and Taeger, 1938) include alkaline with this group, most others believe that alkaline is a combination taste that may include nongustatory components like touch, olfaction, or pain (Oehrwall, 1891; von Frey, 1910; Kloehn and Brogden, 1948). The complex tastes of many stimuli may be duplicated by mixtures of substances that elicit the four basic qualities. The salty-sour bitter taste of potassium chloride, for example, may be matched by an appropriate mixture of sodium chloride, tartaric acid, and quinine hydrochloride (von Skramlik, 1926).

The fungiform papillae on the anterior part of the tongue can be stimulated individually by means of very fine brushes moistened with saturated solutions of quinine sulphate, cane sugar, and sodium chlo-

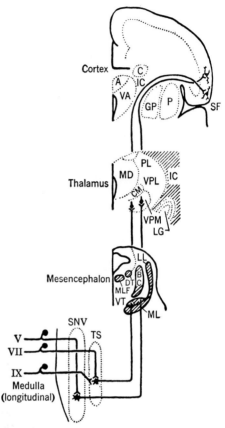

FIG. 6. Schematic diagram of the central pathways of the somatic fibers of the Vth nerve and gustatory fibers of the VIIth and IXth nerves. Important parts are: SNV, spinal nucleus of the Vth nerve; TS, nucleus of the tractus solitarius; ML, medial lemniscus; LL, lateral lemniscus; IC, internal capsule; SF, sylvian fissure. (From Patton and Ruch, 1947.) The results of recent experiments (not shown in the diagram) indicate that some fibers terminate in the opercular and para-insular cortex buried in the sylvian fissure.

ride or a 0.2-per-cent solution of hydrochloric acid. Of 39 papillae tested in this manner, three reacted exclusively to salt, three to acid, seven to sweet, and none to bitter. The others reacted to all or some of these stimuli in various combinations (Oehrwall, 1891; Kiesow, 1898). Punctate stimulation of slightly larger areas on the tongue indicates that salt sensitivity is greatest on the tip and sides, sour on the sides, sweet on the tip and bitter on the back (Kiesow, 1894; Hänig, 1901).

This suggests that the four qualities may be mediated by four different receptor mechanisms present in various combinations in each of the papillae and occurring with varying density in various parts of the tongue. The differential action of certain drugs like

gan with which the stimulus combines before stimulation can take place.

Sour. Of the stimuli for the four fundamental tastes, that for sour has been most clearly defined. The sour taste is a common property of all save the very weakest acids like phenol. The common property of all acids is that in aqueous solutions they ionize into anions and the cation hydrogen.

$$HCl \leftrightharpoons H^+ + Cl^-$$

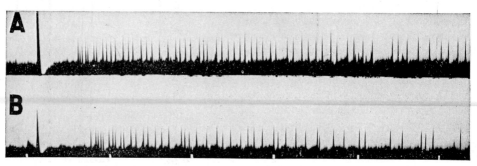

FIG. 7. Oscillographic record of a single nerve fiber preparation responding to acid on the cat's tongue. The large initial upward deflection signals the time of applying the stimulus. This is followed by the train of nerve impulse spikes. *A.* Stimulus 0.5 *N* acetic acid. *B.* Stimulus 0.01 *N* hydrochloric acid. Each interval mark at base of record *B* indicates 1/10 second. (From Pfaffmann, 1941.)

gymnemic acid, which selectively reduces only sweet and bitter sensitivity, is consistent with this view (Shore, 1892; Kiesow, 1894). In a study of the action potentials in the gustatory nerve fibers of the cat, individual nerve fibers were isolated that responded only to acid and not to any other taste stimuli like sodium chloride, sucrose, or quinine (Fig. 7). (See Pfaffmann, 1941.) Two mixed types were found, one that responded to acid and salt, and a second that responded to acid and quinine. No fibers responsive to sugar were found. Since the histological evidence shows that one fiber may supply more than one taste bud, the mixed sensitivity could be accounted for by this fact. It is clear, however, that a specificity for acid stimuli has been demonstrated. Crozier (1934) has suggested that such specificity might be determined by a specific receptive substance in each end or-

In most chemical reactions the strength of an acid is determined by the degree to which this dissociation occurs. Strong acids of equal concentration have a sour taste that is proportional to the degree of dissociation. On the other hand, weak acids like acetic, which are only slightly ionized, have a sour taste greater than would be predicted from the H ion concentration. In one study the threshold for HCl was 0.00125 *N* with a pH of 2.9.* Acetic acid thresholds fell at a con-

* Chemical concentration may be stated in several different ways:

1. Percentage concentration equals the number of grams of solute dissolved in 100 grams of solvent. Where water is the solvent, this is equivalent to 100 cubic centimeters (milliliters) of water. Other ways of specifying percentage concentration are frequently used as, for example, the number of grams of solute in 100 grams of solution.

2. Molar concentration (mol) equals the number of gram molecular weights in 1 liter of solution. The number of grams of solute divided by its molecular weight equals the gram molecular

centration of 0.005 N with a pH of 3.5 (Richards, 1898; Kahlenberg, 1898). It has been suggested that organic acids may penetrate the receptor membranes with greater ease than do strong acids (Crozier, 1916b; Taylor, 1928a). On the other hand, the difference in taste strength of weak and strong acids has been attributed to the buffer action of saliva. A typical buffer system consists of the salt of a weak acid, such as sodium acetate, mixed with acetic acid. The salt, sodium acetate, tends to be highly dissociated, and the partially dissociated acid acts as a reservoir for H ions such that, upon the addition of other H ions, the excess is taken up by an increase in the amount of undissociated acid.

$$NaAc + HAc \leftrightarrows H^+ + Na^+ + Ac^-$$

This reaction, i.e. change in undissociated acid, proceeds to the right when H ions are withdrawn. The total free H ion concentration does not change significantly in such a buffer.

Weak acids and saliva act like such a buffer so that little change in the original pH of the acid itself occurs in the mouth. Acetic acid held in the mouth for 5 seconds showed a pH change from 3.5 to 4.4. Sul-

weight. Equal volumes of equimolar solutions contain an equal number of molecules.

3. Normality N equals the number of gram equivalents in 1 liter of solution. The gram equivalent is usually given by the molecular weight of a compound divided by the total positive or total negative valence without regard to sign. For HCl the molar and normal concentrations are equal. For H_2SO_4 the normality is one-half the molarity because the SO_4 group has a valence of two and requires two hydrogen atoms. Solutions of a given normality always react with exactly equal volumes of any solution of the same normality.

The hydrogen ion concentration is usually stated in terms of pH, the hydrogen ion exponent:

$$pH = \log_{10} \frac{1}{[H \cdot]}$$

where $[H \cdot]$ is the effective H ion concentration in normality. Since the H ion concentration in pure water is $1 \times 10^{-7} N$, or pH 7, water neutrality is indicated by pH 7, acidity by values less, and alkalinity by values greater, than 7. (Findlay, 1933.)

phuric acid, on the other hand, changed from pH 3.5 to 6.3 (von Skramlik, 1926). It has been suggested that sourness can be predicted by the titration capacity of the acid when titrated with a buffer solution (Kenrick, 1931; Beatty and Cragg, 1935), although not all investigators believe that saliva is the buffer. If buffered solutions are employed as stimuli, it can be shown that the same degree of sourness can be elicited at different pH's (Liljestrand, 1922). The taste of the buffer solutions remains as long as the solution is held in the mouth, whereas the taste of dilute acids rapidly disappears. This is attributed to the fact that buffer solutions provide a continuous supply of H ions as they are used up. The sourness of an acid under ordinary methods of tasting depends on, but does not necessarily parallel, the strength of the acid in terms of the free H ion concentration (Harvey, 1920; Paul, 1922; Moncrieff, 1946).

On the other hand, Hahn, Kuckulies, and Taeger (1938) were able to minimize the effects of saliva by means of their Gustometer. This device consists of a U-shaped tube with a round opening at the bend of the U. Taste solutions flow through the device and over the surface of the tongue, which is held lightly against the opening. Preliminary rinsing with water is followed immediately by the acid stimulus. Under these conditions, the threshold determinations for weak acid and strong acids alike yield a value of approximately 0.003 N. The chemical combining capacity of the acid apparently determines the sourness.

These results suggest, therefore, that the anomalous sourness of weak acids under normal conditions of tasting may depend upon the interaction with the saliva. Where this effect is eliminated by prior removal of the saliva, the total acid, i.e. the total H ion available, determines sourness.

Salt. The most characteristic stimulus for the salty taste is sodium chloride, common table salt, which, interestingly enough, is the only agent that will elicit a pure salty taste.

Other salts like sodium bromide or potassium chloride arouse additional qualities like bitter or sweet as well as saline. That the salty taste results primarily from anions like Cl, Br, I, SO_4, NO_3, etc., is generally agreed (Kahlenberg, 1898), but there is less agreement on the relation of stimulating strength to ionic concentration. Some investigators find that, at threshold, the salt taste solutions are equimolecular in terms of the anion (Höber and Kiesow, 1898; Gley and Richet, 1885; Hahn, Kuckulies, and Taeger, 1938). Others, however, report that, in a common cation series like Na_2SO_4, NaCl, NaBr, NaI, $NaHCO_3$, $NaNO_3$, the relative strength of these stimuli is in the order named. Since sodium is common to all these solutions, the anions must account for the differences in stimulating efficiency (von Skramlik, 1926).

That the cations play a role in the salty taste is indicated by the fact that sodium chloride, lithium chloride, and potassium chloride all have tastes that are slightly different from one another. For example, lithium chloride has a slightly sour component, and potassium chloride is slightly sour and bitter. The cations may be arranged in order of their strength of taste as follows:

$$NH^+ > K^+ > Ca^{++} > Na^+ > Li^+$$

This series is probably related to the mobility of the ions, for ammonium is the fastest and lithium the slowest (Frings, 1948). Both cations and anions therefore play a role in stimulating the sense of taste. Similar ionic seriations have been described not only for physiological action (Starling, 1933; Hopkins, 1932; Crozier, 1934) but also for certain physical reactions such as the precipitation of colloids by electrolytes (Findlay, 1933).

Sweet. Unlike the stimuli for sour and salty, those for sweet include among their more common members a number of substances that have no known common physical or chemical property. Many of these are organic substances that, as a rule, are not ionized. Sucrose is a typical example:

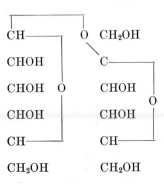

Many sugars such as fructose, and glucose and others in which the CH_2OH group is repeated, have the characteristic sweet taste. On the other hand, saccharin, which is extremely sweet, has the following structural formula:

The sweet taste is presumably due to the anion, for most of the salts are sweet. Other sweet stimuli of a diverse nature are lead acetate and a number of beryllium salts. In these salts, the Be^{+++}ion seems to be responsible for the sweet taste.

An attempt to bring some order into the relations among the many sweet-tasting compounds of the aliphatic series was made by Oertly and Myers (1919). They suggested that the sweet taste is due to two factors in the molecule, a glucophor and an auxogluc. A glucophor is a core grouping of atoms that forms a sweet-tasting compound when combined with a number of other atoms included in a second grouping called auxoglucs. An example of their formulation is provided in Table 1.

TABLE 1

Substance	Formula	Glucophor	Auxogluc
Glycol	CH_2OH-CH_2OH	$CH_2OHCHOH$	H
Glycerol	$CH_2OH-CHOH-CH_2OH$	$CH_2OHCHOH$	CH_2OH
Glycine	CH_2NH_2-COOH	$CHNH_2-COOH$	H

In all, they identified six glucophors and nine auxoglucs. This represents only a beginning, for many substances such as saccharin or dulcin cannot be accounted for.

In general, it may be said that homologues, i.e. substances with similar physical and chemical properties, display a similarity in taste. The homologue of a particular substance may, however, introduce an additional taste. With increasing molecular weight in a homologous series, the taste may change from sweet to bitter (Moncrieff, 1946).

Ethylene glycol	Sweet
Trimethylene glycol	Sweet
Propylene glycol (1.2)	Sweetish
Tetramethylene glycol	Less sweet
Hexamethylene glycol	Bitter

With the increase in molecular weight, the solubility decreases and therefore the concentration available for taste stimulation may be expected to fall off.

As with many physiological reactions, stereoisomerism can be shown to affect taste quality. One of the best examples is that of asparagine

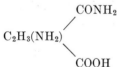

$$C_2H_3(NH_2) \diagup \begin{matrix} CONH_2 \\ \\ \diagdown COOH \end{matrix}$$

which in the dextrorotatory form is sweet but in the laevo form is tasteless. Hence the sweet taste is determined not only by the presence of certain ions or groups of atoms but by the structural arrangement of the molecules themselves.

Bitter. Typical stimuli for bitter are the alkaloids such as quinine or strychnine. As is true for sweet, no one class of chemical agents is characterized by the bitter taste. A number of electrolytes such as magnesium or ammonium salts are bitter. It appears that an increase in the molecular weight of salts is associated with a change from salty to bitter. Bitter is often associated with the sweet taste. As noted above, many substances can be converted with relatively little change in the molecule from sweet to bitter, and many sweet substances have a bitter aftertaste. This relation has led to the theory that the taste mechanisms for bitter and sweet constitute a class distinct from those for acid and salt in which electrolytes constitute the major class of stimuli (Taylor, 1928b). It has even been suggested that a single receptor mechanism may be involved in the bitter-sweet sensitivity. Both are depressed by the action of gymnemic acid, although the major action is upon the sweet. Salt and sour sensitivity is relatively unaffected. Alkaloids and other toxic agents frequently have bitter tastes, as do a number of narcotic agents. Their effects are generally thought to be due to their special affinity for the lipoidal elements in the gustatory cells. The initial action is frequently excitatory followed by an inhibitory action. It is the former that may be basic to the sweet, and the latter that may be associated with the elicitation of the bitter taste.

The laws relating taste quality to chemical constitution are still highly empirical, and, except for the acids and to some extent for the salts, there is no simple rationale to the many relations that have been discovered, particularly among the organic stimuli.

Electrical stimulation. Taste is not particularly responsive to inadequate (non-chemical) stimulation except by electrical currents. When the tongue is stimulated with monopolar electrodes, a characteristic stinging sour quality is elicited at the anode, and a burning alkaline taste occurs at the cathode. Upon breaking the current, a marked sour aftertaste occurs at the cathode. According to one view, first suggested by Humboldt, the sour taste at the anode may be due to H ions, the secondary products of the electrolysis of saliva (von Skram-lik, 1926). It is unlikely, however, that any gross change in the acidity or alkalinity of the saliva takes place. When currents of short duration are employed, the time constant of stimulation by the anode is relatively long compared with that of the cathode (Bujas and Chweitzer, 1934). This suggests that the anodal process is a slow one and that it may involve some electrolytic process acting on the sense cell. The shorter time constant of the cathode may indicate direct stimulation of the nerve. Both processes may occur under certain conditions, as in stimulation by alternating currents (Bujas and Chweitzer, 1937).

The gustatory endings of the cat's tongue can be stimulated by the anode of a constant current, as evidenced by the discharge of nerve impulses in the individual afferent nerve fibers of this preparation. Such discharges have the same general frequency and adaptation rate as those elicited by acids. Thus anodal stimulation resembles very closely the adequate stimulation by acids themselves. However, the latency of the impulse discharge is much shorter with electrical stimuli, probably owing to the rapid development of the ionic concentrations in the neighborhood of the taste cell membranes. The latency of discharge to acid stimuli probably includes the relatively slow diffusion time required for the H ions to reach the surface of the taste cells (Pfaffmann, 1941). Interestingly enough, the cathode has never been observed to stimulate the single fiber preparation. It does, however, tend to reduce any spontaneous discharge that might be under way.

Sensitivity

Measurements of threshold sensitivity by different investigators frequently show wide discrepancies. The method of applying the stimuli, the amount of solution used, the area of tongue involved, and the psychophysical procedures employed may lead to significant differences in threshold, even with

the same group of subjects (Richter and MacLean, 1939). The drop method yielded an average sodium chloride threshold of 0.19 per cent as compared with 0.08 per cent for the choice method in which the subjects were allowed to compare water and salt solutions by sipping.

In addition there are more fundamental variables that may influence sensitivity. For example, changes in the threshold in the same individual have been noted from day to day. In women, during pregnancy, the threshold is elevated particularly for sodium chloride and for acid (Hansen and Langer, 1935). Differences in sensitivity among individuals may reach such magnitudes that some individuals are said to be "taste-blind." This has been found primarily in the sensitivity to a group of substances like phenyl-thiocarbamide which is bitter to some and, except in the highest concentrations, tasteless to others (Fox, 1932; Blakeslee, 1932). This insensitivity appears to be an inherited characteristic. It has also been shown that the acidity of the saliva, which differs in different individuals, may influence the sourness of a weak acid, like acetic acid, when compared with hydrochloric acid (Cragg, 1937).

In spite of such effects, however, it is possible to give a typical order of magnitude for stimulation by certain characteristic taste stimuli (Table 2).

TABLE 2

ABSOLUTE THRESHOLDS

Substance	Per Cent Concentration (approx.)	Molar Concentration
Sucrose	7×10^{-1}	2×10^{-2}
Sodium chloride	2×10^{-1}	3.5×10^{-2}
Hydrochloric acid	7×10^{-3}	2×10^{-3}
Crystallose (sodium salt of saccharin)	5×10^{-4}	2×10^{-5}
Quinine sulphate	3×10^{-5}	4×10^{-7}

According to these figures the four sensitivities may be arranged in order from low to high as follows: salty, sour, sweet, and bitter, where saccharin is used as the sweet stimulus.

For purposes of neurological examination the graded series of taste stimuli shown in Table 3 were found to be suitable (Börnstein, 1940). To the normal subject the

TABLE 3

GRAMS PER 100 CUBIC CENTIMETERS OF H_2O

	Easily Recognizable	Moderately Strong	Very Strong
Sucrose	4.0	10.0	40.0
Sodium chloride	2.5	7.5	15.0
Citric acid	1.0	5.0	10.0
Quinine monohydro-chloride	0.075	0.5	1.0

three intensities shown elicited tastes that were easily recognizable, moderately strong, and very strong, respectively. Tests were carried out by applying single drops to different parts of the tongue surface so that localized impairment of taste sensitivity might be detected. The graded series is valuable because neural lesions might lead to a partial impairment of sensitivity. In mild cases only the weakest stimuli might be ineffective. In severe cases even the strongest stimuli might be without taste.

As already indicated, the gustatory receptors are spread out over a surface so that stimulation may be diffused over the whole tongue or restricted to a small area. Stimulation of small areas is associated with increased reaction times to the stimulus and with elevated thresholds (Holway and Hurvich, 1938; Bujas and Ostojcic, 1941).

Temperature. That temperature influences taste sensitivity has been recognized for a long time. The early workers, however, found little consistent effect except at the extremes (0 to 50 degrees C) (Kiesow, 1896; Chinaglia, 1916). Others reported effects in the intermediate range between 10 and 40 degrees C (Komuro, 1921; Goudriaan, 1930). Hahn and Günther (1932) carried out a systematic temperature analysis by means of the Gustometer. With this device it is possible to bring the tongue

area to the temperature of the taste solution prior to stimulation and to maintain the temperature of the taste solution relatively constant throughout the course of stimulation. Temperature has a typically different effect upon each of the four basic qualities (Fig. 8). But not all stimuli for any one quality are affected in the same

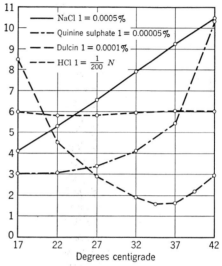

FIG. 8. The effect of temperature on taste thresholds for sodium chloride, quinine sulphate, dulcin, and hydrochloric acid. The ordinate gives the thresholds in arbitrary units. The value of one unit on the ordinate differs for each of the four substances, as shown by the key in the figure. For example, one unit for NaCl equals 0.0005 per cent. (From Hahn, 1936.)

way. The sensitivity for some sweet substances shown in Fig. 8 may rise with a rise in temperature and then decrease above 37 degrees C. Others like glycocol may show no change in threshold, and still others may show intermediate effects.

These relatively complex temperature effects suggest that stimulation cannot be a simple chemical reaction between stimulus and taste cell. Most chemical reactions are enhanced by a rise in temperature. Only for sweet does such a relation appear to exist, and even in this case there are many exceptions, depending upon the substance and the subject.

Internal factors. Particular interest has been aroused by the possibility that changes in the blood stream and body fluids affect, by some direct chemical action, the sensitivity of the taste cells. The intravenous injection of certain drugs (Hartridge, 1945) gives rise to taste sensations after a latent period attributed to circulation time. Pre-

1947; Young and Chaplin, 1949). In order to determine whether a lowering of the gustatory threshold occurs in adrenalectomized rats, a direct physiological study of afferent impulses in the chorda tympani nerve was made when salt solutions were applied to the tongue. The minimal concentration of salt that would just elicit a dis-

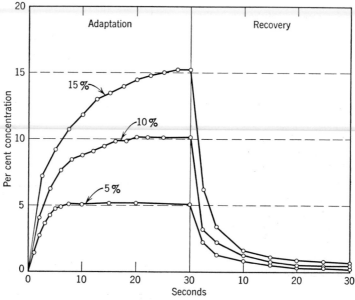

FIG. 9. Adaptation and recovery curves for sodium chloride. The ordinate indicates the threshold concentrations. The course of adaptation to three concentrations of sodium chloride, 5, 10, and 15 per cent, is shown for an adaptation period of 30 seconds and a recovery period of 30 seconds. The unadapted threshold is 0.24 per cent. (From Hahn, 1934.)

sumably these sensations arise from stimulation by the substance circulating in the blood. The further possibility has been advanced that a decrease in the body supply of a specific substance like NaCl may lower the gustatory threshold for that substance. Animals rendered salt deficient by adrenalectomy display an increased preference for salt such that they voluntarily ingest enough extra salt to counteract the usually fatal results of adrenal insufficiency (Richter, 1942). Actually, normal rats prefer weak salt solutions to water when both are available in a free choice situation (Bare, 1949; Chaplin,

charge of afferent impulses was essentially the same in normal and salt-hungry (adrenalectomized) rats. In fact the average threshold for both groups equaled approximately the concentration at which the adrenalectomized animals first displayed a preference for salt. This suggests not only that both groups are equally sensitive but that the salt-needy animals show the preference as soon as they can taste the salt. The normal animals do not (Pfaffmann and Bare, 1949). It seems likely, therefore, that the physiological changes induced by adrenalectomy have relatively little effect on the taste bud. Some change more central in locus must account for the enhanced salt hunger displayed by these animals.

On the other hand, Mayer-Gross and Walker (1946) have shown that the hypoglycemia following the injection of insulin apparently leads to a reduced sensitivity for

Adaptation. It has long been recognized that the intensity of taste decreases as the taste substance is held in the mouth. Such adaptation may be complete (Abrahams, Krakauer, and Dallenbach, 1937; Krakauer and Dallenbach, 1937) or partial (Mayer, 1927; Hahn, 1934). With the aid of the

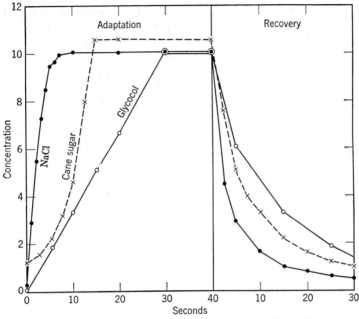

FIG. 10. Adaptation and recovery curves for three substances. The NaCl curve is similar to that labeled 5 per cent in Fig. 9; the adapting solution of cane sugar had a concentration of 10 per cent, and that of glycocol, 1 per cent. The ordinate units are arbitrary; 10 units is equal to the adapting concentration. This makes all three curves more nearly comparable. The adaptation curve for sodium chloride is negatively accelerated; that for sugar, positively accelerated; and that for glycocol, linear. (Modified from Hahn, Kuckulies, and Taeger, 1938.)

sugar. Reduction of the blood-sugar level below 50 milligrams per cent * appeared to render the sense of taste specifically less sensitive to sugar. Sensitivity to other substances was not affected. Subjects in a hypoglycemic condition preferred 30 per cent sucrose solutions, whereas at normal blood-sugar levels this solution was usually rejected as too sweet. These results suggest that a reduction in blood-sugar level may be associated with a decreased taste sensitivity.

* Milligrams per cent equals the number of milligrams per 100 cubic centimeters of solvent.

Gustometer it has been possible to adapt a particular region of the tongue for controlled periods of time and to determine thresholds during and after adaptation. Adaptation is proportional to the strength of the adapting solution (Fig. 9), but the form of the adaptation curve is not always the same (Fig. 10). The adaptation curves within the same quality may be quite different for two chemically different substances. This suggests that the locus of the adaptation process, in part at least, is at the point where the stimulus and the taste cell interact. The recovery curves all have the same general shape and can be fitted with equations that resemble those typical of unimolecular reactions, i.e. where the rate of reaction is proportional to the concentration of only one reactant that is gradually used up. The initial adaptation curves do not all conform to such a model.

The use of such adaptation curves as the basis for a theory of stimulation in terms of some unimolecular chemical model (e.g. as in Lasareff's theory, 1922) is open to question in the light of further results on cross adaptation (Hahn, Kuckulies, and Bissar, 1940). The effect of chemically different substances that aroused the same taste quality was examined. With 24 different salts studied, such as NaCl, NaBr, KCl, CaCl$_2$, etc., adaptation to any one salt did not affect the threshold for any other salt. There was no cross adaptation. On the other hand, all acids would adapt the sour taste for all other acids. Some bitter and sweet stimuli showed cross adaptation; others did not.

Since it does not appear reasonable to assume that there are as many as 24 different receptors for salt, it has been suggested that so-called gustatory adaptation is due to a change in the permeability of the taste cell for the specific agent bathing the cell. The receptor can still respond when another adequate stimulus is applied. This has been characterized as a kind of inhibitory process rather than adaptation. If this conclusion is accepted, the kinetics of gustatory stimulation cannot be inferred from adaptation curves, for adaptation and stimulation are two different processes.

Adaptation has been observed to influence the threshold for stimuli of other qualities. Sensitivity for all qualities was enhanced by prior adaptation to sucrose or sodium chloride. Quinine raised the sensitivity to all qualities but sweet, on which variable results were obtained. Hydrochloric acid adaptation did not affect the other qualities (Mayer, 1927; Dallenbach and Dallenbach, 1943).

Relative sensitivity. Intensity discrimination in taste, according to some investigators, shows the same general relations as in the other senses: relative sensitivity is approximately constant only in the middle ranges (Lemberger, 1908; Holway and Hurvich, 1937). Other workers report that $\Delta I/I$ is nearly constant over the entire range (Saidullah, 1927; Kopera, 1931; Bujas, 1937). The approximate average value of $\Delta I/I$ found for all qualities by most investigators is ⅕.

In one study this function was determined for two different substances, sucrose and crystallose, both of which produce a sweet taste. Since the value of ΔI was obtained for each jnd directly, it was possible to specify for both substances the concentrations that fell at an equal number of discriminable steps above threshold. In addition, equal-sweetness concentrations were independently determined. Concentrations at equal numbers of jnd steps above threshold were not equally sweet. A crystallose solution 9 jnd's above threshold equaled in sweetness a sucrose solution 6 jnd's above threshold (Lemberger, 1908).

The relative sweetness of crystallose and sucrose changes with concentration as shown

TABLE 4

EQUALLY SWEET CONCENTRATIONS (CF. LEMBERGER)

Sucrose	Crystallose	Ratio, Crystallose/Sucrose
0.041 mol	0.000085 mol	1:482
0.053	0.000161	1:330
0.102	0.000273	1:300
0.140	0.00045	1:311
0.164	0.00062	1:265

in Table 4. Crystallose becomes relatively less sweet than sucrose, measured both in jnd's and in physical units of concentration. Certain other substances behave in a similar manner. Figure 11 shows the concentration of different substances that taste as sweet as various concentrations of sucrose (Cameron, 1947). Most of the curves turn upward (slight positive acceleration) which indicates that these substances become relatively more sweet as the concentration increases. Not all sweetness matches follow this rule, however.

Efforts to apply subjective scaling methods to the sense of taste have proved successful (Lewis, 1948; Beebe-Center and Waddell, 1948; MacLeod, 1950). Such studies show, as is true for other senses, that

creases. Exceptions to these trends are occasionally noted. For example, two subjects found sugar in the higher concentrations to be predominantly unpleasant. They reported a dislike for sweet which may have been determined by excessive consumption of sweets in their youth.

It is possible that other factors, such as physiological changes, may affect the pleasantness of various taste stimuli (Beebe-

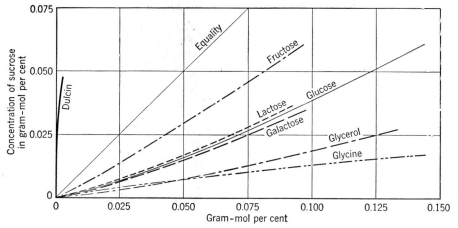

FIG. 11. Curves showing the concentrations at which different substances taste as sweet as various concentrations of sucrose. Gram-mol per cent is $\frac{1}{10}$ the value of the molar concentration. (From Cameron, 1947.)

the size of the jnd increases as the intensity of the stimulus increases. Cross quality matching, that is, matching salty with sweet for magnitude of sensation, indicates that the ratio units of taste are more valid than jnd units (Bujas, 1937).

Affective value. It is of interest that both odors and tastes usually have more affective value than most other sensations except pain. There is almost general agreement that strong bitter is unpleasant and that sweet is pleasant. The degree of pleasantness depends upon the intensity of the stimulus, and, particularly for salty and sour, intensity determines whether the taste is pleasant or unpleasant (Saidullah, 1927; Engel, 1928). Weak concentrations of salt or acid may be definitely pleasant but become unpleasant as the concentration in-

Center, 1932). In fact, change in this aspect of taste rather than change in threshold seems to be a more likely explanation of the craving for salt discussed above. Just how past experience and physiological variables contribute to this pleasantness of taste and how this relates to the needs of the organism for such substances is a problem demanding further investigation.

Theory

Theories of gustatory function may be concerned with either of two aspects: the mechanism of excitation, whether physical or chemical, or the nature of the receptors that underlie different taste qualities. For sour and salty tastes the adequate stimulus appears to have been delineated. The evidence for bitter and sweet is less clear. In

order to account for the similarity in the effects of two such chemically diverse agents as saccharin and sucrose, simplicity of theory would suggest that there is some as yet unrecognized physical property, other than chemical structure, that determines the sweet taste. On the other hand, some unique property of the sensory endings for sweet might account for the fact that these diverse agents give rise to the same quality, if the same endings are concerned in both instances.

Although some writers have stressed the importance of a physical process like adsorption of the taste substance on the surface of the taste cell (Renqvist, 1919) and others have argued for a chemical mechanism (Lasareff, 1922), the present evidence suggests that taste stimulation is not solely one or the other. The fact that stereoisomers have quite different tastes argues against a simple chemical mechanism. Nor can the temperature and adaptation effects previously described be interpreted in this way. Certain additional physicochemical processes, involving the membrane of the taste cell, as well as a chemical reaction with some

substance of the taste cell itself may well be involved (Hahn, Kuckulies, and Bissar, 1940).

The view that there are four basic taste qualities, salty, sour, bitter, and sweet, has been generally accounted for on the grounds that there are four different types of specifically sensitive receptors. Any taste is the result of stimulation of one or more of these basic receptors to a greater or less extent. Efforts to show that there are taste receptors that are specifically sensitive to different chemical agents have been successful (Pfaffmann, 1941). However, whether these receptor types correspond directly with the types postulated from the basic qualities seems doubtful. The details of this specificity remain to be elaborated.

SMELL

The olfactory receptors are located in a small patch (2.5 square centimeters) of yellowish brown pigmented mucous membrane covering the medial wall of the superior concha and the adjacent lateral wall of the nasal septum (Fig. 12). The two receptor

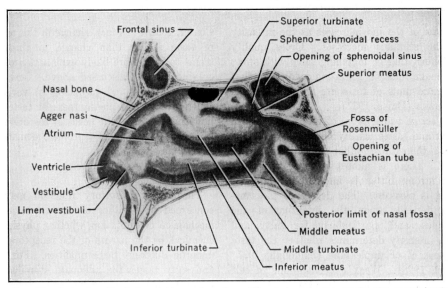

FIG. 12. Lateral wall of the right nasal cavity. The darkened area marks the approximate limits of the olfactory region. (Modified from Piersol, 1923.)

areas, one in each nasal cavity, are ana-tomically distinct, being separated from each other by the nasal septum. The olfactory epithelium is made up of basement and columnar cells which support the long, ovoid olfactory cells. The distal end of each olfac-tory cell terminates in several delicate hairs

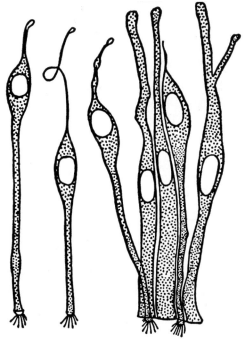

FIG. 13. Olfactory and sustentacular cells from the olfactory epithelium of man. (From Parker, 1922.)

that project out into the mucus covering the nasal epithelium. The fine, unmyeli-nated proximal ends of the cells form the olfactory nerve fibers which enter the olfac-tory bulb of the brain directly after pierc-ing the cribriform plate. The sense cells therefore subserve the functions of both re-ception and conduction (Fig. 13).

During quiet breathing, odorous particles may be carried to the olfactory cleft by slight eddy currents as the air enters the nostrils during inspiration or the posterior nares during expiration. Much odor stimu-lation takes place by way of the latter

route, especially during eating. Sniffing or vigorous inhalation produces a surge or turbulence in the olfactory cleft itself. It is obvious that the impairment of odor sensi-tivity can result from simple mechanical block of these air passages. Closure of the anterior nares will effectively eliminate olfac-tion. Congestion of the mucous membranes during an attack of the common cold may have a similar effect.

The olfactory nerve fibers enter the olfac-tory bulb to end in a series of intricate,

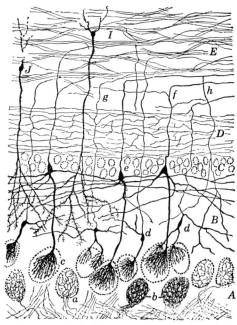

FIG. 14. Section of the olfactory bulb of a kitten. Golgi method. *A*, layer of glomeruli; *C*, layer of mitral cells; *I*, *J*, granule cells; *a*, *b*, glomeruli showing the terminations of the olfac-tory nerve fibers; *c*, glomerulus showing the ter-minal arborization of a dendrite of a mitral cell; *d*, tufted cells; *e*, mitral cell; *h*, recurrent col-lateral from an axon of a mitral cell. (From Ran-son and Clark, 1947.)

basketlike terminations called glomeruli (Fig. 14). At this point in the olfactory pathway occur the first synapses of two dif-ferent types of cells: the large mitral cells and the tufted cells. Axons from both types form the olfactory tract which then passes caudally along the base of tne frontal lobe. In the olfactory bulb the arrangement of cells and axons provides a convergence of pathways and a return route back to the glomerulus itself by way of collaterals, so that a kind of closed reverberating circuit is formed. It is this "feedback" that accounts in part for the great sensitivity of the sense of smell.

The central connections of the olfactory fibers are still to be clearly delineated. Brodal's (1947) review of the evidence concludes, in opposition to the common view, that the hippocampus and cingular gyrus are *not* particularly concerned with olfaction. The fibers from the olfactory bulb travel in two main tracts, the lateral and the medial olfactory tracts. The lateral tract (lateral olfactory gyrus) is continuous with the hippocampal gyrus, and the two together form the pyriform area or lobe (Fig. 15). The fibers from the olfactory bulb, partly with a relay in the anterior olfactory nucleus, are distributed to the nucleus of the lateral olfactory tract, the olfactory tubercle, the anterior part of the pyriform lobe, and certain nuclei of the amygdaloid complex. The anterior olfactory nucleus, situated in the posterior part of the bulb, connects with the corresponding nucleus of the opposite side by means of the anterior commissure. Nuclei of the septal areas probably do not receive primary olfactory fibers. The relation of the hippocampus, the mammillary bodies, the anterior thalamic nuclei, and the cingular gyrus with olfaction is thought to be indirect and slight.

Electrical activity in the pyriform lobe following olfactory stimulation has been recorded in several different species (Hasama, 1934; Allen, 1943; Adrian, 1942). Electrical stimulation of the olfactory bulbs produced definite alterations in the electrical activity of the olfactory tract, the prepyriform cortex, the pyriform area, the anterior perforated space, and parts of the hippocampal gyrus (Rose and Woolsey, 1943; Fox, McKinley, and Magoun, 1944). Potentials

could not be detected in the amygdaloid nucleus or hippocampus.

Experiments in which parts of the CNS were removed have yielded few instances where habits based on olfactory discrimination were disrupted. Neither destruction of the rat cortex up to 85 per cent, nor section of the cortical projection fibers from the anterior thalamic nuclei, impaired olfactory discrimination. Only transection of the rat's olfactory tract has been found to disrupt

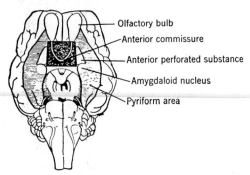

FIG. 15. Ventral view of sheep's brain, pyriform area shaded, and anterior commissure exposed. (From Ranson and Clark, 1947.)

such a habit (Swann, 1935; Lashley and Sperry, 1943). A conditioned leg flexion to odors was not impaired after bilateral temporal lobectomy, removal of the hippocampus, or destruction of the pyriform amygdaloid complex in the dog. A more complex situation where discrimination between cloves and asafetida was required, however, was abolished with bilateral destruction of the pyriform-amygdaloid complex (Allen, 1940, 1941).

Olfactory Qualities

Numerous attempts to describe odor experiences and to reduce them to some orderly arrangement have been made. Since the particular physicochemical property that does the stimulating has not been discovered, all such classifications are primarily psychological. The earliest attempts were largely odor catalogues. Since many odor stimuli also stimulate other sensory endings, like those of the trigeminal and taste, the problem of description is rendered even more difficult.

One of the best-known classifications is that of Henning (1924), who used over 400 scents. In some experiments subjects were instructed to describe and identify the odor. In other experiments odors were to be arranged according to similarity of quality. Henning concluded that there were six basic odor qualities: *fragrant, ethereal, resinous, spicy, putrid,* and *burnt.* The relations among

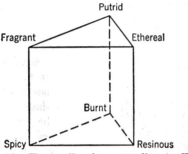

FIG. 16. The smell prism, according to Henning.

these olfactory qualities are indicated by the smell prism (Fig. 16). Although Henning attempted to show that certain chemical structures were related to the FERS face, the prism was designed mainly to show the interrelations among odor sensations. Subsequent studies by other investigators showed that, although this schema describes the general relations among odors, it is far from precise (Dimmick, 1927; Findley, 1924; MacDonald, 1922; Hazzard, 1930). These six basic odors are not to be thought of as corresponding to six different basic receptors, although that interpretation has been made.

More recently, another scheme involving only four basic components, *fragrant, acid, burnt,* and *caprylic,* has been developed, including a semiquantitative treatment of the component intensity (Crocker and Henderson, 1927). The value of each component is indicated on a scale from 0 to 8. Thus, acetic acid may be characterized as 3803

where 3 describes the odor as moderately fragrant, the acid value is 8, the burnt value 0, and the caprylic 3. Each component can be evaluated by comparing a sample with a set of odor standards for which the odor values have been determined. Each standard has a value for each of the four components, but it is used chiefly to characterize the one indicated. The standard for 8 on the fragrant scale is methyl salicylate, but its complete formula is 8453. This system can be used reliably by unpracticed subjects and has proved useful in certain practical applications (Boring, 1928).

Stimulus correlates. It is generally believed that odor depends upon particles or molecules volatilized from odorous substances or liquids. Since these particles must enter the nose to be transported to the olfactory epithelium a necessary condition for olfactory stimulation appears to be volatility. For some substances only a relatively small number of molecules may be required. For example, musk and civetone are relatively involatile; yet they are two of the most potent olfactory stimulants known. For a given odorous substance, increase in volatility will affect the strength of the odor, presumably by increasing the number of molecules impinging on the nose.

In a homologous series such as the saturated fatty hydrocarbons with the general formula C_nH_{2n+2}, there is an increase in odor from the lower to the higher members. Methane, CH_4, is odorless; pentane, C_5H_{12}, has an indistinct odor; decane, $C_{10}H_{22}$, has a strong gasoline odor; whereas the still higher members have less strong odors owing largely to the lower volatility of the large molecules (Moncrieff, 1946).

Although many relations between chemical constitution and odor have been described, it is not possible to predict the odor of a substance from its constitution. Compounds of quite different constitution may have similar odors, and compounds of very similar constitution may have quite different odors. Seven basic chemical elements are odorous.

These are fluorine, chlorine, bromine, iodine, phosphorus, arsenic, and oxygen (as ozone). These elements occur in the high valence groups 5, 6, and 7 of the periodic table. None of the elements occurring free in nature are odorous under normal conditions. Odorous inorganic compounds are largely those made up of the nonmetallic elements. Water and carbon dioxide are odorless, but these substances are normally present in the atmosphere surrounding the sense cells. When sulphur is substituted for oxygen, a strongly odorous substance is formed, H_2S for H_2O.

Organic compounds make up the greatest class of odorous substances. Both total molecular structure and the presence of osmophoric groups and arrangements within the molecule appear to influence odor. Different forms of the same compound, stereoisomers, which have different spatial arrangements of the molecule may have different odors. On the other hand, a series of benzene derivatives all have very similar odors. Substitution of groups in the ring cannot entirely overcome the osmophoric effect of the benzene ring itself. It is of historical interest that the first compounds occurring in nature with the benzenoid structure were found in association with pleasant-smelling compounds like oil of wintergreen, oil of anise, and oil of bergamot, to name but a few. As a consequence these compounds were labeled "aromatic" to distinguish them from the fatty substances.

The natural scent of flowers and fruits depends upon the presence of minute quantities of such highly odorous oils as those named above. These are known as essential oils, for they contain the essence of the flower or fruit. These oils themselves are complex mixtures. Upon chemical analysis they are found to contain a few major constituents of known chemical structure, which are largely responsible for the odor of the essence. The production of synthetic perfumes by mixtures of the pure chemicals is possible. However, the natural essence is usually so complex that its odor can be matched only if a small amount of the natural product is added to the synthetic mixture in order to produce just the right blend (Poucher, 1932).

Sensitivity

In spite of the relative inaccessibility of the olfactory end organs, odorous materials can be detected at extremely low concentrations. Of the chemical senses smell is the most acute. In terms of concentrations of molecules it has been estimated that olfaction is 10,000 times as sensitive as taste (Moncrieff, 1946). Differential sensitivity, on the other hand, is not so great.

Measurement of the physical concentration of odorous vapor present at threshold is not possible by direct methods because the amounts are so small. Threshold values are therefore obtained by the dilution technique. For example, a known quantity of odorous substance may be evaporated in a room of known dimensions and the concentration computed. It was by this method that the oft cited threshold concentration for ethyl mercaptan of 4×10^{-8} milligram per liter of air or 7×10^{-13} mol was found (cf. Moncrieff, 1946). The small glass olfactory chambers (camera inodorata) in which small amounts of odorous material may be evaporated operate on the same principle. More elaborate devices have been employed, with flowmeters to measure the flow of pure air through a chamber containing odorous materials. The concentration in milligrams per liter can be computed from the weight lost to a known volume of air. In other devices the concentration of the odorant has been calculated from the known vapor pressure relations for different substances as streams of air passed through saturating chambers at different temperatures. Comparative tables of threshold values show major discrepancies among the results of different investigators, depending on the methods of dilution, the method of sniffing by the subject, and a number of other variables. However, the relative stimulating efficiency within a series of substances is often independent of the method. The values obtained when the odorants were diluted in alcohol (Passy, 1892) were greater, by a factor of approximately 150, than those found by Allison and Katz (1919) with a flowmeter type of odorimeter (see Table 5).

TABLE 5

THRESHOLD CONCENTRATIONS OF VARIOUS ODOROUS MATERIALS (CF. ALLISON AND KATZ, 1919)

Substance	Boiling Point, degrees C	Milligrams per Liter of Air	Molar Concentration *
Ethyl ether	35	5.83	7.8×10^{-5}
Carbon tetrachloride	76.7	4.53	3.0×10^{-5}
Chloroform	62	3.30	2.8×10^{-5}
Ethyl acetate	77.4	0.69	7.8×10^{-6}
Amyl alcohol	137.8	0.225	2.6×10^{-6}
Nitrobenzene	209.4	0.146	1.2×10^{-6}
Ethyl mercaptan	37	0.046	7.4×10^{-7}
Methyl salicylate	222.2	0.100	6.6×10^{-7}
Pyridine	115.2	0.032	4.0×10^{-7}
Amyl acetate	148	0.039	3.0×10^{-7}
Valeric acid	186.4	0.029	2.9×10^{-7}
Methyl isothiocyanate	119	0.015	2.1×10^{-7}
Butyric acid	162.3	0.009	1.0×10^{-7}
Isobutyl mercaptan	88	0.008	8.9×10^{-8}
Allyl isothiocyanate	151	0.008	8.0×10^{-8}
Propyl mercaptan	67	0.006	7.9×10^{-8}
Phenyl isocyanide	165	0.002	2.0×10^{-8}
Amyl thioether	95–98	0.001	5.8×10^{-9}
Artificial musk	.....	0.00004	....

* Computed as the number of gram molecules in a liter of diluent or, more properly, in a liter of solution, but the concentrations are so low that a negligible error results from considering only the diluent.

In all these studies, thresholds were determined in reasonably odorless environments, but no specific air conditioning was employed. Since the presence of odor in the surroundings would affect threshold values, some of the discrepancies in the results of different investigators might be attributed to the failure to reach "zero" adaptation prior to each threshold determination (Foster and Dallenbach, 1948).

Relative measures can be used for investigating the comparative strength of different agents, the magnitude of individual differences, or the effect of adaptation and other experimental variables. Values obtained with such devices avoid the problem of computing minimal concentrations, since the instruments are calibrated in terms of norms. The best known of these instruments is the olfactometer of Zwaardemaker, which, in its simplest form, consists of a glass tube that slips into a larger odorous tube (Fig. 17). One end of the glass tube is inserted into

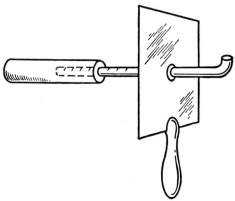

FIG. 17. Zwaardemaker's olfactometer. The bent-up end of the tube is inserted into the nostril. Over the other end of the smaller tube fits the larger stimulus tube made of odorous material. As the subject sniffs, air is drawn through the odor-bearing larger tube and then through the smaller tube to the nostrils. The amount of odor is determined and measured by the length in centimeters of the odor tube exposed to the current of air. This device also exists in the double form to permit dirhinic stimulation.

the subject's nostril. The other is open and exposed to various amounts of the inner surface of the odor-bearing tube. The larger the extent of the odor-bearing tube exposed to the current of air drawn through the device by the subject's inhalation, the stronger the concentration of odorous material. A standard unit, the olfactie, is defined as the length of odor tube in centimeters exposed at threshold. One olfactie of India rubber equals 0.7 centimeter. A number of similar methods have been devised, but in all of them we encounter the difficulty that the subject determines the amount of odorous stimulation by the rate and force of his inhalation.

The blast injection technique overcomes this objection (Elsberg and Levy, 1935). A bottle containing odorous liquid or solid is connected by an outlet tube to a nosepiece inserted in the subject's nostrils (Fig. 18). Various amounts of air may be forced into the bottle by a syringe attached to the inlet

FIG. 18. Elsberg's blast injection device. The bottle contains odorous fluid or solid. The pressure in the bottle can be raised by introducing different volumes of air by means of the hypodermic syringe. Upon release of the pinch clamp on the outlet tube, odorous vapor is injected into the nostrils.

tube. This raises the pressure in the bottle so that, upon release of a pinch clamp, odorous vapor is injected into the nostrils by a sudden pressure pulse. The threshold is given by the volume of odorous vapor injected, although the pressure of injection rather than the volume appears to be the significant factor (Jerome, 1942). Highly volatile substances have smaller thresholds than do involatile substances (Elsberg, Brewer, and Levy, 1935). Volatility, however, is a factor that influences the transport of molecules from an odorous substance to the olfactory epithelium. The blast method

appears to maximize this factor so that the more basic aspects of olfactory stimulation may be masked. The method has been modified so that, during any one stimulating blast, pressure is held constant. However, even with these modifications pressure effects still appear to complicate the results obtained with the blast technique (Wenzel, 1948).

Stimulus variables that might have a direct effect on olfactory sensitivity are difficult to investigate because the stimulation pathway is so indirect and devious. Temperature and humidity influence the strength of odors largely because these factors influence volatility or transport of odorous particles from the source to the observer. In a study of the effect of temperature changes in the odorous gas, as measured at the entrance to the nostrils, the lowest values occurred between 25 and 30 degrees C. An increase of 5 degrees raised the threshold appreciably, a change opposite to what occurs when temperature affects the source itself (Morimura, 1934).

By restricting the stimulus to one nostril (monorhinal stimulation) it is possible to stimulate one patch of olfactory epithelium at a time. Thresholds determined in this way are higher than those determined dirhinally (Henning, 1926; Elsberg, 1936). Differences in the sensitivity of the right and left nostrils may reflect differences in the physical contours of the two nasal passages as well as in their intrinsic sensitivity.

The most common deviation encountered in olfactory acuity is acquired hyposmia as a result of nasal infection. Such hyposmia may be differential; that is to say, the sensitivity for certain substances only may be impaired. A change or distortion in the quality of an odor (parosmia) may also occur.

Normal variations in sensitivity may occur from day to day. In women, hyperosmia occurs just before and during the menstrual period (Elsberg, Brewer, and Levy, 1935). Pregnancy is said to be associated with changes in odor sensitivity. Actual olfactometric tests (Hansen and Glass, 1936) indicate a reduced sensitivity. The presumed hypersensitivity of pregnancy appears to be due to changes in the affective tone of odors. More subtle and less well-recognized differences in sensitivity are thought to occur among normal individuals. Certain floral odors, for example, can be detected only by certain observers. This may be analogous to the taste blindness described above (Blakeslee, 1918).

The existence of a daily cycle in olfactory acuity has been demonstrated by Goetzl and Stone (1947). This cycle appears to bear some relation to hunger and appetite. Olfactory acuity increases from morning until just before lunch. If food is ingested, the threshold becomes elevated, to be followed by a second decline during the afternoon. If lunch is withheld there is no midday rise in the threshold. The administration of amphetamine sulphate in lieu of lunch also produces a midday elevation of the olfactory threshold. This drug reduces both the sensations of appetite and the free caloric intake (Goetzl and Stone, 1948).

Adaptation. Perhaps the best-known physiological process affecting olfactory sensitivity is adaptation to the continued presentation of an odor stimulus. The apparent disappearance of odor soon after we enter a malodorous atmosphere is a common experience. Figure 19 shows how this adaptation proceeds for two different intensities of two different substances. For any one substance, it has been shown that the time required for total adaptation is directly proportional to the vapor pressure exerted by an odorous gas (Woodrow and Karpman, 1917). High vapor pressures are equivalent to large numbers of molecules in the air entering the nose. The degree of adaptation therefore appears to be proportional to the molecular concentrations in the nasal passage.

Qualitative changes in certain odors during the adaptation process were given much consideration by the earlier workers, for it was thought that some clue to the nature of the olfactory receptor might be provided by this information. For example, the odor of nitrobenzol changes from one of bitter almonds to that of tar or pitch. The unpleasant odor of mercaptan changes to a pleasant etherial quality (von Skramlik,

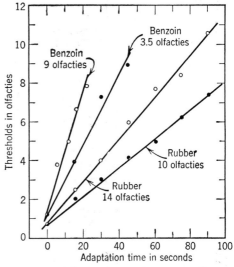

FIG. 19. Olfactory adaptation curves. Increasing adaptation is measured by the increase of the olfactory threshold (in olfacties). Adaptation occurs faster for benzoin than for rubber. With each substance the adaptation is faster for the more intense stimulus. (After Zwaardemaker, 1925.)

1926). Such changes were thought to depend on the differential exhaustion rate of different components of the receptor mosaic. Further evidence along the same line is provided by the classical experiments of Nagel (1897) in which two chemically inert substances were mixed in such proportions that one, vanillin, masked the scent of the other, cumarine. Adaptation to vanillin alone unmasked the cumarine odor of the mixture.

Adaptation to one substance may affect the sensitivity to other stimuli (cross adaptation). Exposure to camphor elevates the threshold for eucalyptol and eugenol. In fact, each of these three substances affects the threshold for the others. There is, therefore, a mutual adaptation effect. This is not simply a generalized fatigue, because the threshold for benzaldehyde is not greatly changed. Benzaldehyde in turn has little effect on the thresholds for the other three (see Fig. 20). Such effects suggest a receptor mosaic made up of groups of sensitive units, each of which is sensitive to different groups of chemical stimuli. Whether such

difficult. When many components are present, analysis becomes even more difficult. Training, however, may markedly influence the ability to analyze odors. The professional perfume chemist is particularly adept at distinguishing many components.

Masking of one odor by another occurs regularly when the intensity of one surpasses that of the other. Concerning another interaction effect, "compensation,"

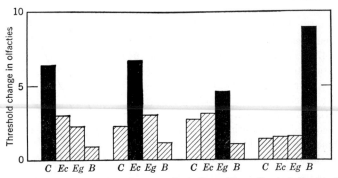

Fig. 20. The selective character of olfactory adaptation. The ordinate indicates the threshold change in olfacties after adaptation by each of four substances (camphor, eucalyptol, eugenol and benzaldehyde) in turn. Self-adaptation is indicated by the solid figure; threshold changes for the other substances, by crosshatching. The threshold for each substance is most influenced by itself. In addition, camphor, eucalyptol, and eugenol all appear to show reciprocal adaptation effects. The sensitivity to benzaldehyde is little affected by these substances. Benzaldehyde has little effect upon their thresholds. (Based on data of Ohma in von Skramlik, 1926.)

adaptation experiments can provide the basis for a theory of the olfactory receptor, however, may be open to question in view of the adaptation experiments described in the section on taste.

Stimulus mixtures. The mixture of odors in certain instances produces effects that agree with the mosaic concept. When two quite different odors are presented simultaneously, the components may be readily identified. The components may appear distinct and unrelated. The more the components resemble each other, the greater the tendency for blending to occur. A unitary blend or fusion may result which, however, resembles the odors of the components. Attention to one or the other of the components individually then becomes extremely

there is less agreement. As first described, the simultaneous presentation of two odors was said to lead to cancelation, so that no olfactory experience occurred. The odor of paraffin and India rubber canceled each other. That this was due to a physiological process was suggested by the fact that compensation could be demonstrated when each odor was presented to each nostril separately (dichorhinal stimulation) (Zwaardemaker, 1925). Since these early observations there has been increasing doubt of the generality of this phenomenon. Numerous examples have been cited of the reduction in strength of an odor with physical mixture of the odorous gases in a chamber prior to inhalation (von Skramlik, 1926). In such instances physical or chemical interaction between the two substances can occur. This, according to Henning (1924), accounts for all cases of so-called compensation.

Differential sensitivity. Although the absolute threshold of olfactory discrimination indicates a reasonably high order of sensitivity, the differential sensitivity is relatively poor. Gamble (1898) found that the Weber fraction for different substances varied between ⅙ and ½, with the average ratio around 38 per cent. Over a wide range of I values the $\Delta I/I$ value was found to be largest at low intensities and to decrease gradually to a minimum of 10 per cent at about 200 olfacties and above (Zigler and Holway, 1935).

Theory

Theories accounting for olfactory function exhibit two aspects. The first deals with the physical nature of the adequate stimulus, whether chemical or physical. The second deals with the nature of the receptor, whether it consists of many specialized different endings or of only a few basic types. Some theories, of course, consider both aspects of the problem.

The more fundamental problem at the present stage of knowledge is the nature of the essential stimulus for smell. Until the essential stimulus has been described in terms of its basic invariances there can be no adequate psychophysics of odor (cf. Chapter 1). It is very probable that no one physical property alone is involved. In man and animals, where the olfactory organ is tucked away in the upper part of the olfactory passage, the penetration of odor particles into this tortuous passage is required. Odorous particles appear to be governed by the gas laws. An increase in the vapor pressure of any one substance increases the intensity of the olfactory stimulation, presumably by increasing the number of molecules of odorous substance. But volatility alone does not determine odor.

Other physical properties, such as solubility in water or lipoid, may be additional important factors in determining the ease with which odor particles are dissolved or absorbed or otherwise brought into contact with the mucosa of the olfactory cleft. All these may be considered transport factors influencing preliminary stages of stimulation (Zwaardemaker, 1926).

Theories that point to such molecular effects as infrared absorption, ultraviolet absorption, Raman effect, etc., to account for the essential step in stimulation have been presented ever since Faraday first noted that many odorous materials strongly absorb radiation in the infrared region of the spectrum. Dyson (1938) placed particular emphasis upon the Raman effect. When monochromatic light shines through pure substances, spectroscopic analysis reveals scattering into the longer and shorter wavelength regions. The difference between the wavelengths of incident and reflected light is the Raman shift. It is independent of the light used and is a unique characteristic of any one substance. Raman shifts between 140 and 350 millimicrons, according to the theory, are odorous. Mercaptan and allied substances have a Raman shift of 250 millimicrons. Even stereoisomers may have different Raman shifts. Such substances frequently have different odors. Many suggestive correlations of this sort have been made; but disturbing exceptions have been found. Glycerin, which has a Raman shift in the critical region, is odorless.

The infrared theory of olfactory stimulation has been restated in a new form in which the absorption of heat in particular wavelength bands is the essential step (Beck and Miles, 1947). Only the infrared band in the range from 4 to 20 microns is considered significant, for this corresponds to the range emitted by the human body. Absorption in this range is said to produce local cooling of certain receptor elements. In a later version of the theory, Beck (1950) introduced additional factors such as water and lipoid solubility, particle size, and infrared scattering. These additions, he believes, will account for different odors of certain optical isomers with the same infrared spectra (Young, Fletcher, and Wright, 1948) and for the fact that some odorous substances like paraffin and carbon disulphide have no infrared absorption. It is well to point out, however, that a correlation between odor and infrared absorption of odorous substances, if established, does not necessarily indicate that stimulation involves cooling.

Infrared spectroscopy is a powerful technique for the analysis of molecular structure. Infrared absorption and the Raman effect both depend on the oscillation of the atoms in the molecule around their mean positions. Because the masses and distances involved in molecular structure are so small, frequencies of oscillation are of the order of 10^{13} to 10^{14} cycles per second. It is this frequency range that determines the infrared absorption. Every organic substance has a unique infrared absorption spectrum which cannot be matched by any other substance. Odorous materials as well as many others have marked infrared absorption (Barnes, Liddell and Williams, 1943). The fact that infrared absorption, Raman shift, and other properties seem to occur largely in odorous materials is suggestive that some property related to the molecular oscillation is concerned in olfaction. But to account entirely for the nature of olfaction, due consideration probably will have to be given to the so-called "transport" factors.

Theories concerning the nature of the olfactory receptor have been based largely upon such indirect evidence as the observations on differential anosmia, differential adaptation, and odor mixture. A direct approach by means of electrophysiological methods has not proved fruitful because of the relative inaccessibility of the primary afferent neurons. Such techniques as punctate or localized stimulation, which in the sense of taste provide some of the strongest evidence for the specificity of receptors, are not applicable because of the relative inaccessi-bility of the receptor surface itself. The indirect evidence that is available, then, points to a multiplicity of recepter units rather than to a few basic types. Olfaction tends to follow the auditory analogue, where complex tones can be subjected to an analysis by the ear alone. The remarkable ability of the trained perfume chemist to identify the components of odor provides a dramatic illustration of the analytical character of the olfactory receptor mechanism.

REFERENCES

The present chapter has not considered chemo-reception in invertebrates. A comprehensive review of this subject will be found in:

Dethier, V. G., and L. E. Chadwick. Chemoreception in insects. *Physiol. Rev.*, 1948, **28**, 220–254.

GENERAL REFERENCES

Crocker, E. C. *Flavor.* New York: McGraw-Hill, 1945.

Crozier, W. J. Chemoreception. In C. Murchison (Ed.), *Handbook of general experimental psychology.* Worcester: Clark University Press, 1934. Pp. 987–1036.

Henning, H. *Der Geruch.* (2nd Ed.) Leipzig: Barth, 1924.

McCord, C. P., and W. N. Witheridge. *Odors: Physiology and control.* New York: McGraw-Hill, 1949.

Moncrieff, R. W. *The chemical senses.* New York: Wiley, 1946.

Parker, G. H. *Smell, taste and allied senses in vertebrates.* Philadelphia: Lippincott, 1922.

Patton, H. D. Olfaction and olfactory pathways. In J. F. Fulton (Ed.), *Howell's textbook of physiology.* Philadelphia: Saunders, 1947. Pp. 402–408.

Patton, H. D., and T. C. Ruch. Taste. In J. F. Fulton (Ed.), *Howell's textbook of physiology.* Philadelphia: Saunders, 1947. Pp. 370–384.

Poucher, W. A. *Perfumes and cosmetics.* New York: Van Nostrand, 1932.

Skramlik, E. von. *Handbuch der Physiologie der niederen Sinne. Bd. 1, Die Physiologie des Geruchs- und Geschmackssinnes.* Leipzig: Thieme, 1926.

Zwaardemaker, H. *L'odorat.* Paris: Doin, 1925.

SPECIFIC REFERENCES

Abrahams, H., D. Krakauer, and K. M. Dallenbach. Gustatory adaptation to salt. *Amer. J. Psychol.*, 1937, **49**, 462–469.

Adrian, E. D. Olfactory reactions in the brain of the hedgehog. *J. Physiol.*, 1942, **100**, 459–473.

Adrian, E. D., M. Cattell, and H. Hoagland. Sensory discharges in single cutaneous nerve fibers. *J. Physiol.*, 1931, **72**, 377–391.

Allen, W. F. Effect on respiration, blood pressure and carotid pulse of various inhaled and insufflated vapors. *Amer. J. Physiol.*, 1929, **88**, 117–129.

Allen, W. F. Effect of oblating the frontal lobes, hippocampi, and occipito-parieto-temporal (excepting pyriform areas) on positive and negative olfactory conditioned reflexes. *Amer. J. Physiol.*, 1940, **128**, 754–771.

Allen, W. F. Effect of oblating the pyriform-amygdaloid areas and hippocampi on positive and negative olfactory conditioned reflexes and on conditioned olfactory differentiation. *Amer. J. Physiol.*, 1941, **132**, 81–92.

Allen, W. F. Distribution of cortical potentials resulting from insufflation of vapors into the nostrils and from stimulation of the olfactory bulbs and the pyriform lobe. *Amer. J. Physiol.*, 1943, **139**, 553–555.

Allison, V. C., and S. H. Katz. An investigation of stenches and odors for industrial purposes. *J. industr. eng. Chem.*, 1919, **11**, 336–338.

Arey, L. B., M. J. Tremaine, and F. L. Monzingo. The numerical and topographical relations of taste buds to human circumvallate papillae throughout the life span. *Anat. Rec.*, 1935, **64**, 9–26.

Bare, J. K. The specific hunger for sodium chloride in normal and adrenalectomized white rats. *J. comp. physiol. Psychol.*, 1949, **42**, 242–253.

Barnes, R. B., U. Liddell, and V. Z. Williams. Infrared spectroscopy, industrial applications. *Industr. and Eng. Chem.*, 1943, **15**, 659–709.

Beatty, R. M., and L. H. Cragg. The sourness of acids. *J. Amer. chem. Soc.*, 1935, **57**, 2347–2351.

Beck, L. H. Osmics: Theory and problems related to the initial events in olfaction. In O. Glasser (Ed.), *Medical physics*. Chicago: The Year Book Publishers, 1950. Vol. II.

Beck, L. H., and W. R. Miles. Some theoretical and experimental relationships between infrared absorption and olfaction. *Science*, 1947, **106**, 511.

Beebe-Center, J. G. *The psychology of pleasantness and unpleasantness*. New York: Van Nostrand, 1932.

Beebe-Center, J. G., and D. Waddell. A general psychological scale of taste. *J. Psychol.*, 1948, **26**, 517–524.

Blakeslee, A. F. Unlike reactions of different individuals to fragrance in verbena flowers. *Science*, 1918, **48**, 288.

Blakeslee, A. F. Genetics of sensory thresholds: Taste for phenyl thiocarbamide. *Proc. nat. Acad. Sci., Wash.*, 1932, **18**, 120–130.

Boring, E. G. A new system for the classification of odors. *Amer. J. Psychol.*, 1928, **40**, 345–349.

Börnstein, W. S. Cortical representation of taste in man and monkey II. *Yale J. Biol. Med.*, 1940, **13**, 133–156.

Brodal, A. The hippocampus and the sense of smell. *Brain*, 1947, **70**, 179–222.

Bujas, Z. La mesure de la sensibilité differentielle dans le domaine gustatif. *Acta Inst. Psychol. Univ. Zagreb.*, 1937, **2**, 1–18.

Bujas, Z., and A. Chweitser. Contribution à l'étude de goût dit électrique. *Année psychol.*, 1934, **35**, 147–157.

Bujas, Z., and A. Chweitser. Goût électrique par courants alternatifs chez l'homme. *C. R. Soc. Biol. Paris*, 1937, **126**, 1106–1109.

Bujas, Z., and A. Ostojcic. La sensibilité gustative en fonction de la surface excitée. *Acta Inst. Psychol. Univ. Zagreb.*, 1941, No. 13, 1–19.

Cameron, A. T. The taste sense and the relative sweetness of sugars and other sweet substances. Scientific Report Series No. 9, Sugar Research Foundation, 1947.

Chaplin, J. P. Preferences of adrenalectomized rats for salt solutions of different concentrations. Ph.D. thesis, University of Illinois, 1947.

Chinaglia, L. Ricerche intorno all 'influenza esercitato della temperatura sulla sensibilita gustativa. *Riv. Psicol.*, 1916, **11**, 198–226.

Cragg, L. H. The relation between sourness and the pH of the saliva. *Trans. roy. Soc. Can.*, 1937, **31** (III), 7–13.

Crocker, E. C., and L. F. Henderson. Analysis and classification of odors. *Amer. Perfum.*, 1927, **22**, 325, 356.

Crozier, W. J. Regarding the existence of the common chemical sense in vertebrates. *J. comp. Neurol.*, 1916a, **26**, 1–8.

Crozier, W. J. The taste of acids. *J. comp. Neurol.*, 1916b, **26**, 453–461.

Cushing, H. The taste fibers and their independence of the nerve trigeminus. *Johns Hopk. Hosp. Bull.*, 1903, **14**, 71–78.

Dallenbach, J. W., and K. M. Dallenbach. The effects of bitter adaptation on sensitivity to the other taste qualities. *Amer. J. Psychol.*, 1943, **56**, 21–31.

Dimmick, F. L. The investigation of the olfactory qualities. *Psychol. Rev.*, 1927, **34**, 321–335.

Dyson, G. M. The scientific basis of odor. *Chem. and Ind.*, 1938, **57**, 647–651.

Elsberg, C. A. Monorhinal, birhinal and bisynchronorhinal smell. The summation of impulses in birhinal smell. *Bull. neurol. Inst. N. Y.*, 1936, **4**, 496–500.

Elsberg, C. A., E. D. Brewer, and I. Levy. Concerning conditions which may temporarily alter normal olfactory acuity. *Bull. neurol. Inst. N. Y.*, 1935, **4**, 31–34.

Elsberg, C. A., E. D. Brewer, and I. Levy. The relation between the olfactory coefficients and boiling points of odorous substances. *Bull. neurol. Inst. N. Y.*, 1935, **4**, 26–30.

Elsberg, C. A., and I. Levy. A new and simple method of quantitative olfactometry. *Bull. neurol. Inst. N. Y.*, 1935, **4**, 5–19.

Engel, R. Experimentelle Untersuchungen über die Abhängigkeit der Lust und Unlust von der Reizstärke beim Geschmackssinn. *Arch. ges. Psychol.*, 1928, **64**, 1–36.

Findlay, A. *An introduction to physical chemistry.* New York: Longmans, Green, 1933.

Findley, A. E. Further studies of Henning's system of olfactory qualities. *Amer. J. Psychol.*, 1924, **35**, 436–445.

Foster, D., and K. M. Dallenbach. The olfactorium, an apparatus for odor research. *Amer. Psychologist*, 1948, **3**, 253.

Fox, A. L. The relationship between chemical constitution and taste. *Proc. nat. Acad. Sci., Wash.*, 1932, **18**, 115–120.

Fox, C. A., W. A. McKinley, and H. W. Magoun. An oscillographic study of the olfactory system of cats. *J. Neurophysiol.*, 1944, **7**, 1–16.

Frey, M. von. Der laugige Geruch. *Pflüg. Arch. ges. Physiol.*, 1910, **136**, 275–281.

Frings, H. A contribution to the comparative physiology of contact chemoreception. *J. comp. physiol. Psychol.*, 1948, **41**, 25–34.

Gamble, E. M. The applicability of Weber's law to smell. *Amer. J. Psychol.*, 1898, **10**, 82–142.

Gley, E., and C. Richet. Action chimique et sensibilité gustative. *C. R. Soc. Biol.* Paris, 1885, **37**, 742.

Goetzl, F. R., and F. Stone. Diurnal variations in acuity of olfaction and food intake. *Gastroenterol.*, 1947, **9**, 444–453.

Goetzl, F. R., and F. Stone. The influence of amphetamine sulfate upon olfactory acuity and appetite. *Gastroenterol.*, 1948, **10**, 708–713.

Goudriaan, J. C. Über den Einfluss der Temperatur auf die Geschmacksempfindung. *Arch. néerl. Physiol.*, 1930, **15**, 253–282.

Hahn, H. Die Adaptation des Geschmackssinnes. *Z. Sinnesphysiol.*, 1934, **65**, 105–145.

Hahn, H. Über die Ursache der Geschmacksempfindung. *Klin. Wschr.*, 1936, **15**, 933–935.

Hahn, H., and H. Günther. Über die Reize und die Reizbedingungen des Geschmackssinnes. *Pflüg. ges. Physiol.*, 1932, **231**, 48–67.

Hahn, H., G. Kuckulies, and H. Taeger. Eine systematische Untersuchung der Geschmacksschwellen. I. *Z. Sinnesphysiol.*, 1938, **67**, 259–306.

Hahn, H., G. Kuckulies, and A. Bissar. Eine systematische Unterschung der Geschmacksschwellen. II. *Z. Sinnesphysiol.*, 1940, **68**, 185–260.

Hänig, D. P. Zur Psychophysik des Geschmackssinnes. *Philos. Stud.*, 1901, **17**, 576–623.

Hansen, R., and L. Glass. Über den Geruchsinn in der Schwangerschaft. *Klin. Wschr.*, 1936, **15**, 891–894.

Hansen, R., and W. Langer. Über Geschmacksveränderungen in der Schwangerschaft. *Klin. Wschr.*, 1935, **14**, 1173–1176.

Hartridge, H. The importance of taste and smell in nutrition. *J. Physiol.*, 1945, **103**, 34–35.

Harvey, R. B. The relation between the total acidity, the concentration of the hydrogen ion, and the taste of acid solutions. *J. Amer. chem. Soc.*, 1920, **42**, 712–714.

Hasama, B. Über die elektrischen Begleiterscheinungen an der Riechsphäre bei der Geruchsempfindung. *Pflüg. Arch. ges. Physiol.*, 1934, **234**, 748–755.

Hazzard, F. W. A descriptive account of odors. *J. exp. Psychol.*, 1930, **13**, 297–331.

Hoagland, H. Specific nerve impulses from gustatory and tactile receptors in catfish. *J. gen. Physiol.*, 1933, **16**, 685–693.

Höber, R., and F. Kiesow. Über den Geschmack von Salzen u. Laugen. *Z. phys. Chem.*, 1898, **27**, 601–616.

Holway, A. H., and L. Hurvich. Differential gustatory sensitivity to salt. *Amer. J. Psychol.*, 1937, **49**, 37–48.

Holway, A. H., and L. Hurvich. On the psychophysics of taste I. *J. exp. Psychol.*, 1938, **23**, 191–198.

Hopkins, A. E. Chemical stimulation by salts in the oyster, *Ostrea virginica. J. exp. Zool.*, 1932, **61**, 13–28.

Jerome, E. A. Olfactory thresholds measured in terms of stimulus pressure and volume. *Arch. Psychol., N. Y.*, 1942, **39**, No. 274.

Kahlenberg, L. The action of solutions on the sense of taste. *Bull. Univ. Wis., Sci. Ser.*, 1898, **2**, 1–31.

Kenrick, F. B. The sour taste of acids. *Trans. roy. Soc., Can.*, 1931, **25** (III), 227–228.

Kiesow, F. Über die wirkung des Cocain und der Gymnemasäure auf die Schleimhaut der Zunge und des Mundraums. *Philos. Stud.*, 1894, **9**, 510–527.

Kiesow, F. Beiträge zur physiologischen Psychologie des Geschmackssinnes. I. *Philos. Stud.*, 1894, **10**, 329–368. IV. *Ibid.*, 1896, **12**, 465–473.

Kiesow, F. Contribution à la psychophysiologie de la cavité buccale. *Arch. ital. Biol.*, 1898, **30**, 377–398.

Kloehn, N. W., and W. J. Brogden. The alkaline taste. *Amer. J. Psychol.*, 1948, **61**, 90–93.

Komuro, K. Le sens du goût a-t-il un coefficient de température? *Arch. néerl. Physiol.*, 1921, **5**, 572–579.

Kopera, A. Untersuchungen über die Unterschiedsempfindlichkeit im Bereiche des Geschmacksinnes. *Arch. ges. Psychol.*, 1931, **82**, 272–307.

Krakauer, D., and K. M. Dallenbach. Gustatory adaptation to sweet, sour, and bitter. *Amer. J. Psychol.*, 1937, **49**, 469–475.

Lasareff, P. Untersuchungen über die Ionentheorie der Reizung III. Ionen theorie der Geschmacksreizung. *Pflüg. Arch. ges. Physiol.*, 1922, **194**, 293–297.

Lashley, K. S., and R. W. Sperry. Olfactory discrimination after destruction of the anterior thalamic nuclei. *Amer. J. Physiol.*, 1943, **139**, 446–450.

Lemberger, F. Psychophysische Untersuchungen über den Geschmack von Zucker und Saccharin. *Arch. ges. Physiol.*, 1908, **123**, 293–311.

Lewis, D., and W. E. Dandy. The course of the nerve fibers transmitting sensations of taste. *Arch. Surg., Chicago*, 1930, **21**, 249–288.

Lewis, D. R. Psychological scales of taste. *J. Psychol.*, 1948, **26**, 437–446.

Liljestrand, G. Über den Schwellenwert des sauren Geschmacks. *Arch. néerl. Physiol.*, 1922, **7**, 532–537.

MacDonald, M. K. An experimental study of Henning's system of olfactory qualities. *Amer. J. Psychol.*, 1922, **33**, 535–553.

MacLeod, S. A scale of sweetness. Ph.D. thesis, Brown University, 1950.

Mayer, B. Messende Untersuchungen über die Umstimmung des Geschmackswerkzeugs. *Z. Sinnesphysiol.*, 1927, **58**, 133–152.

Mayer-Gross, W., and J. W. Walker. Taste and taste selection of food in hypoglycaemia. *Brit. J. exp. Path.*, 1946, **27**, 297–305.

Morimura, S. Untersuchung über den Geruchssinn. *Tohoku J. exp. Med.*, 1934, **22**, 417–418.

Nagel, W. A. Über Mischgerüche und die Komponentengliederung des Geruchsinnes. *Z. Psychol. Physiol. Sinnesorg.*, 1897, **15**, 82–101.

Oertly, E., and R. G. Myers. A new theory relating constitution to taste. *J. Amer. chem. Soc.*, 1919, **41**, 855–867.

Oehrwall, H. Untersuchungen über den Geschmacksinn. *Skand. Arch. Physiol.*, 1891, **2**, 1–69.

Olmsted, J. M. D. The nerve as a formative influence in the development of taste buds. *J. comp. Neurol.*, 1920a, **31**, 465–468.

Olmsted, J. M. D. The results of cutting the 7th cranial nerve in *Amiurus nebulosus. J. exp. Zool.*, 1920b, **31**, 369–401.

Olmsted, J. M. D. Taste fibers and the chorda tympani nerve. *J. comp. Neurol.*, 1922, **34**, 337–341.

Parker, G. H., and E. M. Stabler. On certain distinctions between taste and smell. *Amer. J. Physiol.*, 1913, **32**, 230–240.

Passy, J. Note sur les minimums perceptibles de quelques odeurs. *C. R. Soc. Biol.* Paris, 1892, **44**, 84–88.

Paul, T. Physikalisch-chemische Untersuchungen über die Saure Geschmacksempfindung. *Z. Electrochem.*, 1922, **28**, 435–446.

Pfaffmann, C. Gustatory afferent impulses. *J. cell. comp. Physiol.*, 1941, **17**, 243–258.

Pfaffmann, C., and J. K. Bare. *Gustatory thresholds in normal and adrenalectomized rats. J. comp. physiol. Psychol.*, 1950, **43**, 320–324.

Piersol, G. A. *Human anatomy.* Philadelphia: Lippincott, 1923.

Ranson, S. W., and S. L. Clark. *The anatomy of the nervous system.* Philadelphia: Saunders, 1947.

Renqvist, Y. Über den Geschmack. *Skand. Arch. Physiol.*, 1919, **38**, 97–201.

Richards, T. W. The relation of the taste of acids to their degree of dissociation. *J. Amer. chem. Soc.*, 1898, **20**, 121–126.

Richter, C. P. Self-regulatory functions. *Harvey Lect.*, 1942, Ser. 38, 63–103.

Richter, C. P., and K. H. Campbell. Sucrose taste thresholds of rats and humans. *Amer. J. Physiol.*, 1940, **128**, 291–297.

Richter, C. P., and A. MacLean. Salt taste thresholds of humans. *Amer. J. Physiol.*, 1939, **126**, 1–6.

Rose, J. E., and C. N. Woolsey. Potential changes in the olfactory brain produced by electrical stimulation of the olfactory bulb. *Fed. Proc. Amer. Soc. exp. Biol.*, 1943, **2**, 42.

Saidullah. Experimentelle Untersuchungen über den Geschmacksinn. *Arch. ges. Psychol.*, 1927, **60**, 457–484.

Schwartz, H., and G. Weddell. Observations on the pathways transmitting the sensation of taste. *Brain*, 1938, **61**, 99–115.

Shore, L. E. A contribution to our knowledge of taste sensations. *J. Physiol.*, 1892, **13**, 191–217.

Starling, E. H. *Principles of human physiology.* (6th Ed.) C. L. Evans (Ed.). London: Churchill, 1933.

Swann, H. G. The function of the brain in olfaction. *Amer. J. Physiol.*, 1935, **111**, 257–262.

Taylor, N. W. Acid penetration into living tissues. *J. gen. Physiol.*, 1928a, **11**, 207–221.

Taylor, N. W. A physico-chemical theory of sweet and bitter excitation based on the properties of the plasma membrane. *Protoplasma*, 1928b, **4**, 1–17.

Warren, H. C., and L. Carmichael. *Elements of human psychology.* Boston: Houghton Mifflin, 1930.

Wenzel, B. M. Differential sensitivity in olfaction. *J. exp. Psychol.*, 1949, **39**, 124–143.

Woodrow, H., and B. Karpman. A new olfactometric technique and some results. *J. exp. Psychol.*, 1917, **2**, 431–447.

Young, C. W., D. F. Fletcher, and N. Wright. On olfaction and infra-red radiation theories. *Science*, 1948, **108**, 411–412.

Young, P. T., and J. P. Chaplin. Studies of food preference, appetite and dietary habit. X. Preferences of adrenalectomized rats for salt solutions of different concentrations. *Comp. Psychol. Monogr.*, 1949, **19**, No. 5.

Zigler, M. J., and A. H. Holway. Differential sensitivity as determined by the amount of olfactory substance. *J. gen. Psychol.*, 1935, **12**, 372–382.

Zotterman, Y. Action potentials in the glossopharyngeal nerve and in the chorda tympani. *Skand. Arch. Physiol.*, 1935, **72**, 73–77.

Zwaardemaker, H. Prüfung des Geruchssinnes und der Gerüche. In R. Abderhalden (Ed.), *Handb. d. biol. Arbeitsmethoden.* Berlin: Urban and Schwartzenberg, 1920. Abt. 5, Teil 7, Heft 3.

Zwaardemaker, H. *Odoriferous materials.* International Critical Tables, N. R. C. New York: McGraw-Hill, 1926. Volume I.

30·

Somesthesis

WILLIAM LEROY JENKINS

Lehigh University

In some ways the somesthetic senses are biologically of greater importance than the special senses of sight, hearing, taste, and smell. Helen Keller provides an example of a useful life without sight and hearing, and no doubt she could have managed without taste and smell. But it is hard to imagine how anyone could survive, let alone act like a human being, if totally devoid of kinesthesis for the control of position and movement, of pain for protection against injury, and of the temperature senses which aid in the thermostatic regulation of the blood stream. This chapter attempts to bring into perspective what we know about somesthesis and to highlight the gaps that remain for further research. The cutaneous senses will be considered first, then subcutaneous sensitivity, kinesthesis, and internal sensitivity.

CUTANEOUS SENSITIVITY IN GENERAL

It is commonly assumed that there are four cutaneous senses: touch, pain, warm, and cold. However, this fourfold division has never been universally accepted and is still under attack today. Of only historical interest now is the older view that pain is merely the result of overstimulating other senses. Also abandoned for the lack of experimental confirmation are Head's proposal of a dual system of four epicritic and four protopathic skin senses (Walshe, 1942 *)

and Katz's suggestion of a separate vibration sense (Geldard, 1940). However, Nafe believes that warm and cold are merely kinesthetic sensations from dilating and constricting blood vessels (Nafe and Wagoner, 1936), and Gilmer tentatively suggests that both cold and touch may be mediated by vascular units (Gilmer, 1942*a*, *b*). Furthermore there is some evidence that the terms, touch, pain, warm, and cold, might be written as plurals. There may be as many as three touches, two pains, and just possibly two warms and two colds.

Sensory spots. Since 1883 it has been recognized that the skin is not uniformly sensitive. For example, if an area is mapped with a small stimulator at low temperature, some points are found that respond with a clear cold, whereas the major portion of the area does not. Similarly a stimulator at high temperature reveals warm spots, a sharp needle pain spots, and a fine hair touch spots. Although the number of spots varies with the conditions of mapping (Heiser, 1932), those of high intensity appear to remain stable over long periods of time (Gilmer, 1942*b*, p. 315). Caution demands that the sensory spots should be defined in a purely *operational* way — as points of high sensitivity appearing under certain conditions of mapping. The assumption that any map of spots corresponds point for point with individual receptors is entirely unnec-

---

* Walshe's critical review discusses Head's experiments and other similar investigations and gives an overall view of the whole history of the controversy.

cessary — and probably incorrect, as a study of the histology of the skin will show.

Histology of the skin. The skin consists of two layers: an outer epidermis and an inner dermis. The epidermis in turn is stratified into two parts: an outer corneal layer of dead cells containing neither nerves nor blood vessels, and an inner Malpighian layer having many free nerve endings but no

have been discovered in many different skin regions, but their full distribution has never been systematically investigated.

Of the specialized endings, shown on the right of Fig. 1, no one type is found in all parts of the skin. Basket endings around the hair bulb are associated with practically all hairs but are absent in the hairless parts of the body. Meissner corpuscles are abun-

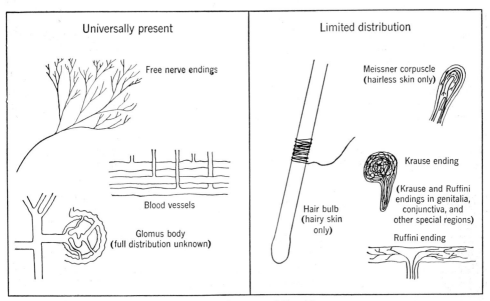

FIG. 1. End organs of the skin.

blood vessels. The dermis, on the other hand, is richly supplied with both nerve endings and blood vessels. It merges without definite boundary into the subcutaneous tissues.

The main types of nerve endings and vascular units are shown diagrammatically in Fig. 1. Note that only free nerve endings and blood vessels are widely distributed. Free nerve endings are abundantly present in the dermis and in the Malpighian layer of the epidermis, and even in the cornea of the eye, which is nonvascular. Blood vessels of varying size and shape are found throughout the dermis but not in the epidermis. Glomus bodies, which are direct arteriovenous connections of larger caliber than capillaries,

dant on the palms of the hands and soles of the feet but are not present in the hairy regions. Krause endings appear only in limited regions such as the conjunctiva of the eye, the nipple, and the genitalia, but not throughout the major portions of the skin. Ruffini cylinders are even scarcer than Krause endings. Indeed, so many intermediate forms of capsulated endings exist that any strict division into types is of dubious merit.

The neural basis. By piecing together information derived from histological, clinical, and physiological studies, we can derive an approximate idea of the neurological scheme underlying cutaneous sensitivity. Any given skin area appears to be innervated by a great number of fibers approaching it from all directions. Each of these fibers, furthermore, branches and rebranches so that the distribution of a single neuron typically spreads over an area of several hundred square millimeters. The result is a complex system of overlapping supply from a multiplicity of fibers.

For example, a single hair bulb is found to have basket endings derived from two or more separate myelinated fibers. Other branches from these same fibers go to form basket endings about other hair bulbs. In addition, around the hair bulb is an accessory innervation of fine unmyelinated fibers, each a branch from a neuron supplying accessory innervation to other hair bulbs. As another instance, the free nerve endings in the Malpighian layer of the epidermis are arranged in extensive nerve nets, each covering an area of several hundred square millimeters and overlapping repeatedly with other similar nets. Nowhere do we find evidence of an isolated receptor serving a limited area and having a private line to the central nervous system — such as we might expect if sensory spots actually corresponded to single receptors. Instead it seems that mapped spots are nothing more than points of functionally high sensitivity, perhaps where the concentration of receptors is greatest.

The older idea of specific and separate fiber types in the peripheral nerve trunks has had to be discarded. Neurons are found to vary in a continuous spectrum of sizes and degrees of myelinization, with corresponding conduction rates. The supposed types are merely modes in a continuous frequency distribution. Nevertheless there is a crude relation between size and sensory function. Starting with the larger myelinated fibers we find in descending order: kinesthesis, cutaneous touch, subcutaneous pressure, pain, warm, cold, and pain again in the smallest unmyelinated fibers. There is considerable overlapping, particularly through the pain-warm-cold region.

Note that pain comes in twice, first in myelinated fibers slightly larger than those for warm and cold, and again in the smallest unmyelinated fibers. The assigned relations between size and function are based on indirect evidence, from the piecing together of the results of studies on human subjects and animals. Direct evidence would require comprehensive action-current records from nerves in conscious human subjects who could simultaneously report their awareness. Such direct studies are as yet beyond the bounds of our technical skill.

In the spinal cord some degree of separation according to function is maintained. The dorsal columns contain fibers mediating kinesthesis and some of those for subcutaneous pressure and cutaneous touch. The spinothalamic tracts carry the balance of the pressure and touch fibers (mostly in the ventral portion) and the neurons for pain, warm, and cold (mostly in the lateral part).

At the level of the thalamus, division according to function is lost and only a topographical representation remains. The posteroventral nucleus of the thalamus shows three distinct regions from the head, the trunk, and the legs. Again, at the level of the cortex, the representation is topographical. Electrophysiological studies on the monkey indicate a considerable degree of point-for-point projection analogous to that of the motor cortex (Marshall, Woolsey, and Bard, 1937). But no study of the cortex has revealed evidence of separate touch areas, pain areas, warm areas, or cold areas. Whatever it is that distinguishes centrally between pain and touch, warm and cold, etc., has so far escaped our research techniques.

Identity of receptors. Returning to the skin, let us examine the problem of the possible receptors for touch, pain, warm, and cold. In cutaneous touch it appears that three different types of receptors are involved. These are the basket endings around hair bulbs, the Meissner corpuscles, and some of the free nerve endings. The basket endings are thought to be touch receptors, because even the light flicking of a single hair can be sensed, and because touch spots on hairy skin are typically found slightly to the windward of the hairs, that is, right over the basket endings. For Meissner corpuscles the evidence is less direct — simply that they are present in densest concentration where touch sensitivity is greatest. That some free nerve endings are involved is indicated by two facts: first, that the cornea has touch sensitivity, but only free nerve endings; second, that touch spots are sometimes found on the hairy parts of the body in positions not related to hair bulbs.

For cutaneous pain, it is almost universally agreed that free nerve endings must be responsible. Throughout the skin only free nerve endings are present in sufficient abundance to account for the great density of pain spots. Also, the cornea shows extreme pain sensitivity and has free nerve endings. Some pain, as Nafe suggests, may arise from the spastic constriction of blood vessels, but even then the free nerve endings associated with the blood vessels are probably directly responsible.

Concerning the receptors for warm and cold our ignorance is profound. Following von Frey's suggestion, some textbooks still proclaim Ruffini cylinders as the receptors for warmth and Krause endings as the receptors for cold. There has never been the slightest evidence connecting Ruffini cylinders with warmth, except that the Ruffini endings are very scarce and warm spots were once thought to be few and far between. In fairness to von Frey, it should be recalled that he was careful to preface his suggestion with a cautious "perhaps" which has too often been lost in reprinting.

The case for the Krause endings as cold receptors appears more plausible at first sight. Krause endings are abundant in the nipple where there is strong sensitivity to cold (Belonoschkin, 1933). The number of Krause endings per square centimeter on the prepuce agrees with the number of mapped cold spots (Bazett et al., 1932). But any correlation of numbers might be purely accidental. More directly, Strughold and Karbe (1925) reported a topographical coincidence of Krause endings and mapped cold spots in the conjunctiva of an eye vitally stained with methylene blue. Careful examination of the data from this dramatic experiment, however, reveals that there were some cold spots without corresponding Krause endings, and some Krause endings without corresponding cold spots. Weddell, examining the tissue beneath a single excised cold spot from the forearm, found ". . . two groups of endings resembling Krause's end bulbs" (Weddell, 1941, p. 355).

In contrast to these scattered positive indications stands a wealth of negative findings. At least six independent studies of numerous excised cold spots have failed to reveal any capsulated endings whatsoever (Dallenbach, 1929). In fact, a systematic histological examination of sections of skin from various hairy regions failed to show any capsulated endings, although the same technique readily revealed Meissner corpuscles on the hairless skin (Gilbert, 1929). Apparently the best that can be said for the Krause ending is that it may be a cold receptor in certain limited regions, but it cannot be *the* cold receptor in the major portion of the skin.

Nor is anything known with certainty about the relative depth of warm and cold receptors. Dubious calculations based on reaction times and supposed rates of thermal conduction have generally placed warm receptors at a greater depth than cold (Bazett et al., 1932), although one calculator arrived at the conclusion that they are equidistant from the surface (Hahn, 1927). In an attempt at direct study Endres (1930) punctured the skin to a known depth and placed a drop of anesthetic on the puncture. He found that the skin had to be pierced to a greater depth on a warm spot than on a cold spot in order to destroy the sensitivity of the spot. On the other hand, Woollard (1935) found three cold spots remaining after successive slicing away of the skin had removed all but the lowest portion of the dermis. This shows, at least, that cold sensitivity must extend to a considerable depth. Other evidence indicates that some warm receptors must be quite superficial. For example, Oppel and Hardy (1937) discovered that nonpenetrating infrared is more effective than penetrating radiation in arousing warmth. Also, Windisch (1931) showed that dry diathermy, which warms principally the skin surface, is far more effective than wet diathermy, which penetrates.

Dissociation as evidence. Although we must admit failure to identify fully the cutaneous receptors, there is considerable evidence that at least four functionally separate systems exist, because they can be dissociated in a variety of ways. The detailed reports are sometimes confusing and contradictory, but the essential fact of dissociation stands forth in study after study. The following paragraphs summarize the chief methods of producing dissociation.

1. Local anesthesia of a section of skin can best be controlled by driving the anesthetic into the skin electrically (Cummings, 1938). The exact order of disappearance and reappearance of sensitivities varies, but generally warm and cold go out first and come back last.

2. Complete loss of sensitivity followed by long-delayed recovery is the outcome of cutting or crushing a nerve branch or of injecting it with alcohol (Lanier, Carney, and Wilson, 1935). Figure 2 shows an example of the dissociation of touch and warmth in one subject. Effects of shorter duration may be obtained by injecting novocaine around a nerve (Bishop, 1944a), by blocking the nerve with pressure (Raffel, 1936), or by cutting off the blood supply (Lewis, 1942). The order of disappearance and reappearance of the specific sensitivities varies considerably with the method, but some dissociation is always found. Dissociation is likewise typical during the recovery of sensitivity in skin grafts (Kredel and Evans, 1933).

3. Dissociation has also been produced by slicing off successive thin layers of skin (Woollard, 1935) and by destroying the outer layers chemically (Bishop, 1944b). In these instances, cutaneous touch in response to stimulation seems the first to go.

4. Statistically significant differences in sensory chronaxy for warm, cold, pain, and touch have been reported (Jones and Jones, 1941). (Sensory chronaxy is the duration of an electrical stimulus of twice threshold

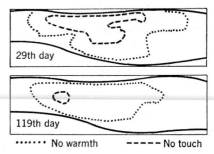

•••••• No warmth   ----- No touch

Fig. 2. Dissociation of warmth and touch. The maps show the state of recovery following nerve block by alcohol injection. (Adapted from Lanier, Carney, and Wilson, 1935.)

strength required to arouse the appropriate sensory experience from a mapped spot.) In studies of chronaxy, all four sensations are produced by the same type of stimulus applied to different spots.

5. Injection of a spinal anesthetic causes some dissociation (Heinbecker, Bishop, and O'Leary, 1934). Nicking the spinal cord can stop pain without interfering with touch from the same area.

6. Pathological conditions also provide striking evidence. At least one case of congenital pure analgesia has been reported, with the senses other than pain intact (Dearborn, 1932). In syringomyelia, a disease that begins in the spinal gray and moves outward, pain is usually lost first, with little or no impairment of the other senses. Then warm and cold disappear, and finally touch.

The overwhelming weight of evidence from dissociation studies provides a basis, other than mere convenience, for the separate discussion of touch, pain, warm, and cold in the following sections.

CUTANEOUS TOUCH

Touch may be aroused without direct contact on the skin simply by moving a hair. Movement of the hair apparently has a dual stimulating action, because destroying the hair root endings reduces but does not obliterate the sensitivity (Stetson, 1923). The movement must directly disturb the basket endings, and must also distort the surface of the skin, which indirectly affects other touch receptors.

Purely cutaneous touch from direct contact with the skin requires the use of very light weights or weak hair stimulators (to avoid the simultaneous stimulation of subcutaneous pressure sensitivity). The adequate stimulus for cutaneous touch is clearly a deformation gradient, and not contact as such. For example, if a finger is inserted in a vessel of mercury, there is contact all over the submerged finger, but touch is felt only at the surface of the liquid where there is a deformation gradient on the skin. The deformation gradient may be produced either by pressure or by pulling. If a small stimulator is glued securely to the skin and lightly pulled and lightly pressed, the average subject cannot distinguish between the two directions.

The *rate* at which the skin is deformed is important. Grindley (1936) showed that the minimal detectable weight is less when the stimulus is applied rapidly than when it is applied slowly. Nafe and Wagoner (1942) found that, when a light stimulator was allowed to sink into the skin, the touch sensation disappeared just when the rate of movement fell close to zero. The exact minimum rate of deformation at which touch was felt varied somewhat with the weight, but it was independent of the area of the stimulator. Using a uniform rate of application von Bagh (1935) found that the threshold was related to the depth of defor-

mation of the skin but that it was independent of the area. Holway and Crozier (1937) thought they had demonstrated that area as such (and not the distortion gradient at the perimeter) was the significant variable in discriminating differences among weights resting on the skin. Their results are inconclusive, however, because they determined difference limens by *gradually* adding weight, and they disregarded the crucial factor of the rate of application of the stimulus. Unless applied pressures are strong enough to stimulate deep pressure sensibility, it appears that the distortion of skin produced at the perimeter of a stimulator is the critical factor.

Vibratory stimulation. Separate touches can be sensed as discrete up to a frequency of about 20 per second — the exact value depending somewhat on the individual subject. Above this frequency, the touches melt into a smooth sense of vibration, which shows characteristics roughly analogous to those of hearing. Maximum sensitivity is in the region of 250 cycles per second, but the upper limit is not known with any certainty because of the technical difficulties of moving the skin at high frequencies (Geldard, 1940, p. 282). Differences between vibration frequencies can be discriminated, but much less adequately than in pitch discrimination by hearing. Thresholds in terms of amplitude of movement of the skin (not the vibrator) can be measured accurately with a binocular microscope, using a slightly mistuned stroboscopic light to slow down the apparent movement. Thresholds thus determined are much lower for touch spots than for areas insensitive to touch, indicating that the same receptors mediate both touch and vibration (Geldard, 1940, p. 279). An artifact in vibration studies is the tendency of the vibration to spread from the stimulated spot to other regions. By using a lightweight phonograph pickup rested on the skin, Weitz (1939) has shown that the vibration may spread a considerable distance from the point of origin.

CUTANEOUS PAIN

For all the vast literature on the subject of pain, relatively little is known for certain about cutaneous pain and how it is aroused. The view seems to be widely held that pain results from direct nerve stimulation of "bare" free nerve endings. It is true that the same excitants arouse pain when applied to the skin and when applied directly to exposed nerves (Lewis, 1942, p. 108). But this merely indicates that pain *might* result from direct nerve excitation, not that it necessarily does. As a matter of fact, the available evidence seems to indicate that pain receptors are just as specific as any others. There are distinct pain spots, and the prick of a needle between them does not arouse pain. Pain can be dissociated from the other skin senses. Later we shall see that some visceral pains cannot be aroused except by tension, indicating that these pain receptors must be specific even to their manner of arousal.

Pain is ordinarily associated with intense stimulation. But under conditions of hyperalgesia a mild temperature or even a light touch may cause excruciating pain. Pain is also commonly connected with tissue damage, but damage is certainly not sufficient and probably not necessary for pain. It is possible for X-rays and certain kinds of freezing to damage the skin severely without causing the slightest pain; so injury is not sufficient. Pain spots may be stimulated by mild electric shocks without any sign of damage to the tissues; so injury is probably not necessary.

Pain has often been considered the opposite of pleasure, and this idea has crept into the psychological literature. But pain is not necessarily unpleasant. Some people derive pleasure from the consumption of hot spices, horseradish, etc., which appear to obtain their distinctive effects by the stimulation of pain receptors.

Bishop (1943) suggests that mild stimulation of pain spots may not be painful at all.

In response to single electric shocks of threshold intensity applied to pain spots, his subjects reported only a vague sense of stimulation too weak to be clearly discriminated. At higher intensities there was a "painless prick." "True pain" was reported only when repeated or strong shocks were employed. Thus Bishop concludes: "Increases in total stimulation of any pattern may have both quantitative and qualitative effects" (Bishop, 1946, p. 95).

Are there two pains? It has been mentioned above that there is some justification for believing that there are two cutaneous pains. The evidence is a number of suggestive but as yet not fully coordinated facts. Various investigators have reported the subjective differentiation of "pricking pain" from "burning pain," although Lewis believes them to differ not in quality but only in latency and duration. A needle prick or a brief contact with a high-temperature stimulator arouses first a brief sting, and is followed after an appreciable interval by a flash of pain of greater intensity. According to Lewis (1942, p. 51) the average lag of the second response is 1.9 seconds at the toe, 1.3 seconds at the knee, and 0.9 second at the top of the thigh. These changes in lag, he points out, correlate with the differences in conduction rate of the two groups of pain nerves disclosed by electrophysiological study (Gasser, 1935). Furthermore, cocainization abolishes the second pain while leaving the first intact, and cocaine is known to affect the small unmyelinated nerves first (Lewis, 1942, p. 51). Lewis believes, therefore, that the two pains are mediated by two sets of fibers, one myelinated and moderately rapid in conduction, the other unmyelinated and slow.

Possibly not connected at all with the foregoing are two other sets of puzzling facts. Schumacher et al. (1940) found the pain threshold for radiant heat to be remarkably uniform in 150 subjects. Yet Lanier (1943) discovered that the pain threshold for electric shock varied greatly in a group of 15 subjects. Whether this discrepancy is related in any way to the two sets of pain fibers is an interesting topic for future research.

CUTANEOUS WARM AND COLD

Warm and cold are almost certainly two separate forms of skin sensitivity: they can be dissociated and their two distributions on the skin show little correlation (Jenkins, 1941b). However, warm and cold can be conveniently discussed together, since they display so many phenomena in common.

Adequate stimulation. The nature of the adequate stimulus for the temperature senses is still a matter of speculation. Normally there is a temperature gradient between the circulating blood (37.5 degrees C) and the skin surface (32 to 33 degrees C on the forearm). Any addition or removal of heat disturbs this gradient. But the actual stimulation might be due to (1) the disturbance of the gradient as such or (2) a change in temperature at the receptors, with the gradient shift purely incidental. At present there is no basis for choosing between these alternatives. We do not even know quantitatively how the temperatures in the skin are altered by brief contact or by radiant stimulation sufficient to arouse warmth or cold. Measurement with buried thermocouples indicates that the temperature at a depth of 1 millimeter is altered only a few degrees by prolonged contact stimulation of the skin at high or low temperatures (Bazett, McGlone, and Brocklehurst, 1930). Estimates of temperature changes at the skin surface following threshold radiant stimulation indicate alterations of a fraction of a degree (Oppel and Hardy, 1937). Neither type of measurement is entirely satisfactory in a quantitative sense, but the evidence is strong that the temperature changes responsible for stimulation may be minute indeed.

Nonadequate stimulation. Strong evidence for the specificity of the temperature receptors is the fact that warm and cold can be produced by several types of stimulation: mechanical, electrical, chemical, and thermal. Jones (1940) showed that a stirring motion of a neutral-temperature rod over a cold spot will frequently produce cold, and over a warm spot, warm. Even the jab of a fine needle is sometimes effective. Electric shock can also arouse warm and cold. (It is interesting to remember that Blix in 1883 first discovered the existence of warm, cold, and touch spots through the use of electrical stimulation.) Chemical arousal of cold by menthol is used commercially in sunburn lotions and in cigarettes. Chloroform and carbon dioxide, when evaporation is prevented, can be used to arouse warmth.

Paradoxical cold — from stimulating a cold spot with an object at about 45 degrees C — has been experienced by many people. Paradoxical warmth — from stimulating a warm spot by a low temperature — is probably also a genuine phenomenon. Its authenticity has been questioned, however, because of the tendency of naïve subjects to call anything "warm" that is not definitely cold.

Radiant versus contact stimulation. The statement that there may possibly be two warms and two colds is based solely on the puzzling differences between the effects of radiant and of contact stimulation. There is no evidence of multiple types of receptors as there is for cutaneous touch. Nor is there any indication of multiple nerve fiber groups as there is for cutaneous pain. But radiant and contact stimulation show some differences so striking that speculation is inevitable.

The effects of radiant stimulation have been exhaustively studied by Hardy and his collaborators, who used a special radiometer to measure the radiant energy with a high degree of accuracy (Hardy and Oppel, 1937). Analogous effects in contact stimulation have been investigated by the method of *seriatim mapping*, designed to check the reliability of subjective reports of intensity (Jenkins,

1940). In seriatim mapping, the squares of a checkerboard pattern are stimulated in random order. The subject reports 0, 1, 2, or 3 to designate increasing degrees of cold (or warm). The mapping is repeated six times to accumulate a score for each square.

Two major differences are found between radiant and contact stimulation:

1. Warmth cannot be sensed at all with small areas of radiant stimulation. In areas less than about 700 square millimeters only pain is experienced when the radiation becomes strong enough to elicit any sensation at all (Hardy and Oppel, 1937, p. 537). In contrast, warm spots may be mapped with a contact stimulator of 1 square millimeter or even less.

2. Positive summation from the combined stimulation of two areas is quite marked with radiant stimulation (Hardy and Oppel, 1937). At threshold the radiant energy per unit area is considerably less when two regions of the forehead are stimulated simultaneously than when either is stimulated alone. There is even a summation effect when radiant stimulation is applied to the backs of the two hands, though none when a hand and the forehead are stimulated together. In contact stimulation, on the other hand, summation appears at best to be only slightly positive and may actually be negative (Jenkins, 1940). When two adjacent areas give equal seriatim scores (say 12 and 12), stimulating them simultaneously gives a slightly higher score (about 13). But, if the two areas have markedly different scores (say 12 and 6), stimulating them simultaneously gives a lower score than the maximum and only slightly higher than the average of the two (in this case about 10).

Such great differences in the effects of radiant and of contact stimulation indicate that the two forms of stimulation must act differently on the same receptor system — or just possibly that they affect two different systems. The latter hypothesis is at present pure speculation.

CUTANEOUS ADAPTATION

The term "adaptation" has been employed in a confusing variety of ways.

1. Most commonly, adaptation refers to the diminution or complete disappearance of sensation under continued stimulation. For example, a light weight resting on the skin is soon not felt at all.

2. Also called adaptation is another negative effect that may be closely related to the first. This is the blunting of response as the result of previous stimulation. For example, dipping a hand into cold water reduces the intensity of sensation produced by a cold stimulator.

3. Positive enhancement is sometimes also called adaptation, particularly in the case of the temperature senses. Dipping an arm into cold water, for instance, makes a stimulator at 30 degrees C feel warm, although this is below the normal skin temperature of the arm.

4. Most confusing of all, it is said that touch shows "rapid adaptation" because successive contacts up to 20 per second can be felt as discrete. However, this does not mean that the sensation has been either diminished or enhanced as in the three preceding cases, but merely that the touch receptors are sufficiently dead-beat in their operation to permit the sensing of a rapid tactual flicker.

Possibly some of the confusion can be alleviated by eliminating this fourth use of the term completely and by using positive adaptation for the third, and negative adaptation to cover both the first and the second. At any rate, that will be done in this chapter.

However, this semantic housecleaning does not clarify the situation completely. Negative and positive adaptation still refer to gross phenomena without regard to the basic causes. Barring central processes, the diminution or enhancement may be due to a change in the *receptors*, or to a change in the effective *stimulus*, or to some combination of the two. Rather than introduce new terms, or new uses for old ones, we may employ the terms negative adaptation and positive adaptation to designate the gross phenomena, and continue to search beyond them for the basic causes.

Touch adaptation. Nafe and Wagoner (1942) have done a real service by demonstrating that the negative adaptation of touch, when a light weight is rested on the skin, is due largely to the cessation of the *stimulus.* They measured kymographically the movement of a weight into the skin while the subject reported on the disappearance of sensation. Consistently the instant of disappearance was related to a rate of movement very close to zero. In short, sensation from the dead-beat receptors stopped as soon as the weight stopped moving. The receptors themselves were still fully sensitive as shown by their immediate response to restimulation.

However, the conclusion of these authors that *all* touch adaptation is due merely to cessation of the stimulus is unsound. Numerous investigators have reported what is called 'threshold lability" (Tschlenoff, 1931). That is to say, a touch spot sometimes fails to respond at all after repeated brief stimulations. In this case it is clearly the *receptors* that have failed. Although studied principally as a symptom of neural disorders, threshold lability has been demonstrated in normal people under conditions of fatigue (Beringer and Ruffin, 1932). Probably related is the slow increase in threshold values when vibratory stimulation is continued for a long time (Geldard, 1940). No clear-cut evidence of positive adaptation (i.e. enhancement) of touch seems to exist.

Pain adaptation. It is common experience that many cutaneous pains do not show negative adaptation but appear to get worse as time goes on. Under carefully controlled conditions, however, complete negative adaptation to needle pricks and to radiant heat has been demonstrated (Burns and Dallenbach, 1933; Stone and Dallenbach, 1934). Since we do not know the nature of painful stimulation, it is difficult to determine whether a cessation of the effective stimulus is involved in these cases. But the fact that pains wax and wane during adaptation without visible external causes suggests that the receptors are responsible at least in part.

The term "positive adaptation" might logically be applied to the condition of *hyper-*

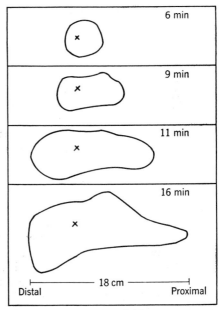

FIG. 3. Spread of hyperalgesia following skin injury. The cross marks the spot at which the skin was injured by pinching, and the heavy line shows the area in which the mildest stimulation caused pain. To account for such an extensive spread of hyperalgesia, Lewis postulates a system of nocifensor nerves that release a pain-producing chemical.

algesia following injury, since there is a definite enhancement of pain. The complexities of this condition have been carefully investigated by Lewis (1942). Ordinarily the hyperalgesic area shows a marked lowering of the threshold for pain. Mild temperatures, friction, and tension readily arouse pain. Sometimes, as is shown in Fig. 3, the hyperalgesia spreads both distally and proximally from the point of injury until it occupies practically the entire area supplied by a main nerve. Significantly the distal spread can be blocked by anesthetizing the nerve at a point distal to the injury. It is known that the sympathetic system is not essential, because such effects can be produced after sympathetic ganglionectomy. On the basis of his findings, Lewis postulated a special system of nocifensor (effector) nerves which release some pain-producing chemical. Antidromic action over the sensory pain nerves has also been used to explain the effects. Concerning the chemical responsible for hyperalgesia, there is no direct evidence. Histamine is released by painful stimulation (Rosenthal and Minard, 1939) and causes pain when injected or painted on raw wound surfaces, but so do many other substances. Lewis believes that histamine is responsible only for the reddening of the skin, and that the hyperalgesia-producing substance remains to be discovered.

Thermal adaptation. Warm and cold show both negative and positive adaptation. Mild thermal experiences tend to fade out completely, and more severe intensities generally are blunted with the passage of time. On the positive side, a precooled hand feels warm and a prewarmed hand cool when both are dipped into water of neutral temperature. Consideration of such effects led to Hering's still widely accepted theory that thermal adaptation is merely a shift of the "physiological zero."

With large areas, a shift of the physiological zero appears to explain adaptation effects fairly well, if certain limits are assumed. The lower limit seems to be about 25 degrees C. Complete negative adaptation, according to Gertz (1921), does not occur to temperatures lower than this. Likewise 25 degrees C seems to be the lowest temperature that can be sensed as warm, no matter how much the skin is precooled (Hahn, 1930). At the upper limit there is some discrepancy. Complete negative adaptation can occur to temperatures as high as 45 degrees C, but it is doubtful whether any temperature higher than 40 degrees C can be made to feel cool by prewarming the skin (Gertz, 1921).

With very small areas, however, the simple shift-of-physiological-zero theory becomes totally inadequate. Small stimulators produce intricate adaptation effects, as the following examples show:

1. Brief intermittent stimulation frequently knocks out a warm or cold spot completely (Levine and Dallenbach, 1936). This is analogous to threshold lability in touch, except that it occurs much more commonly.

2. Spontaneous recovery occurs slowly after a matter of some minutes, but the recovered spot is unstable when subjected to further stimulation. Short contact with a stimulator at 45 degrees C hastens restoration (Jenkins, 1937).

3. When a spot is surrounded with a controllable field, gradual reduction of the field temperature progressively lowers the liminal temperature of the spot for cold. However, when the field temperature reaches about 25 degrees C, the spot is likely to fade out completely and remain unresponsive even to 10 degrees C. Reversing the field temperature sometimes brings the spot almost back to normal (Jenkins, 1937).

4. When the field temperature is gradually raised, the liminal temperature for cold usually goes up, but never above blood temperature. On the contrary, some spots lose sensitivity as the field temperature is raised and are restored by returning the field temperature to normal (Jenkins, 1937).

5. Under continuous stimulation with the smallest stimulators, the time to reach complete negative adaptation to 10 degrees C is a matter of a few seconds. With slightly larger stimulators, the negative adaptation time is lengthened, but in proportion to the perimeter rather than to the area of the stimulator. Thus adaptation time is longer for rectangular and annular stimulators than for circular stimulators of the same area (Jenkins, 1938a).

It is evident from these examples that thermal adaptation is a complex affair, suggestive of some chemical basis for the receptor action.

THEORIES OF CUTANEOUS WARM AND COLD

The complex phenomena of thermal adaptation provide an excellent background for considering theories of cutaneous thermal sensitivity, because enthusiastic proponents have sometimes failed to take account of all the available experimental evidence.

Nafe's vascular theory. Although Nafe has recently attempted a general theory of sensitivity based on movement as the sole form of stimulation (Nafe, 1942), his best-known contribution is the hypothesis that cutaneous warm and cold are merely kinesthetic sensations from dilating and constricting blood vessels. In support of this, Nafe has marshaled a number of facts showing the coincidence of vascular activity and temperature sensations, including the familiar "chills" from screeching sounds (Nafe and Wagoner, 1936). He has also answered point for point certain objections that have been raised (Nafe, 1938). A new twist has been added by Gilmer (1942a, b) who tentatively suggests that the glomus bodies (see Fig. 1) may mediate both cold and touch, because they have been found in close relation to some cold spots and touch spots.

The preponderance of evidence, however, does not fit a vascular theory (Jenkins, 1939). The facts of dissociation and the phenomena of nonadequate stimulation seem to point rather to *specific* receptors. If only blood vessels are involved, they mimic the behavior of specific receptors to the last detail. There is no independent evidence that blood vessels are capable of such versatility.

The spot theory. Since von Frey's original statement in 1895, it has been widely assumed that the mapped sensory spots, particularly warm and cold spots, correspond point for point with individual receptors. Many gross phenomena can be readily ex-plained on this basis. Thus the weaker responses of regions between spots are said to be due to conduction through the skin. The increased sensation experienced from more extreme temperatures is thought to be simply the stronger response from the receptors concerned.

Evidence from seriatim mapping, however, has cast doubt on the validity of the spot theory. Consider, for example, two adjacent squares on a seriatim map, one of high and the other of low score. Suppose that the high score is due to the presence of a receptor, and the adjacent low score to conduction to the same receptor. Then a stimulator covering both areas should yield a score at least as high as the stronger one. But actually the two squares together give a score that is consistently *less* than the stronger and approximately equal to the average of the two scores (Jenkins, 1940). Furthermore the squares of a seriatim map do not respond with a uniform increase in their scores when the stimulating temperature is increased, as they should do if only a relatively few receptors were involved (Jenkins, 1941a). In a typical case, half the squares show no increase in score when the stimulus temperature is raised 3 degrees C, whereas the other half exhibit increases of varying magnitude. An increase of 6 degrees C leaves one-fifth of the scores unaltered, although certain individual squares go from zero to maximum with the same change in temperature. Any system of a few warm receptors per square centimeter is much too inflexible to account for such findings as these.

The concentration theory. To explain these and similar results, a concentration theory has been proposed (Jenkins, 1941a). Figure 4 shows the essence of the theory schematically. Instead of a few warm and cold receptors per square centimeter, it is postulated that there are hundreds of receptors with varying limens. The intensity experienced from a given stimulation depends on the *concentration of active receptors.* Thus simultaneous stimulation of a strong and a weak area yields approximately an average score that corresponds to the overall concentration in the total area. Similarly, different squares of a map may respond quite independently to the same increase in stimulus temperature. In one square, virtually all the receptors are brought into action by mild stimulation, and further increase in temperature can have little or no effect. In another square, most of the receptors may

not be adequately handled in terms of either the vascular theory or the spot theory.

SUBCUTANEOUS OR DEEP SENSITIVITIES

Even after the skin itself has been completely anesthetized, subcutaneous pressure sensitivity and pain sensitivity remain. Under normal circumstances, heavy weights

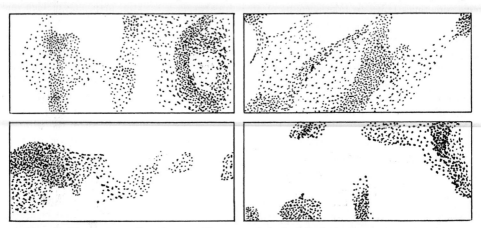

FIG. 4. The concentration theory. The maps show hypothetical distributions of receptors corresponding to scores obtained in seriatim mapping. Warm and cold "spots," according to this theory, do not mark the locus of individual receptors but are points where the concentration of receptors is dense.

be unresponsive except to rather extreme temperatures. An infinite variety of intermediate grades is possible.

It may be objected that the concentration theory offers no possible receptors for warm and cold except free nerve endings, which are thought to mediate pain and probably touch as well. But it is entirely possible that what we loosely call free nerve endings may be differentiated in ways — chemically, for example — that are not revealed by our present histological methods. It appears that they would have to be so differentiated to account for both touch and pain; and the inclusion of warm and cold would be merely another step in the same direction. In any event, the chief merit of the concentration theory as a working hypothesis is that it explains experimental facts that can-

and strong pressures stimulate both cutaneous touch and subcutaneous pressure. Since much longer negative adaptation times are reported for heavy than for light weights, it appears that the subcutaneous pressure receptors are not dead-beat like the cutaneous touch receptors. They continue to respond long after movement of the stimulator into the skin has ceased, although the intensity of the experience diminishes with time.

It is uncertain whether the subcutaneous pressure receptors can sense smooth vibration like that sensed by cutaneous touch. Vibration can be felt when a vibrator is applied to anesthetized skin (Cummings, 1938). But Weitz (1939) has shown that the anesthetized skin tends to move up and down as a unit, and to spread the vibration to unanesthetized areas. Logically it might be expected that the nondead-beat subcutaneous pressure receptors could not respond to vibratory stimulation as do the dead-beat cutaneous touch receptors.

The large Pacinian corpuscles (see Fig. 5) are generally believed to mediate subcutaneous pressure. They are large enough in size to permit the experimental stimulation of an individual corpuscle while nerve action potentials are being simultaneously recorded. Such experiments show that Pacinian corpuscles do respond to pressure stimulation.

In kinesthesis at least three different kinds of receptors are involved — endings associated with the muscles, the tendons, and the joints (see Fig. 5). The muscle endings are arranged in the form of spirals and flower sprays within the muscle spindles. They appear to be normally stimulated only by the *stretching* of a muscle, and not directly by its contraction. The muscle relaxes and lengthens when its antagonist contracts, and it is then that the muscle endings are activated.

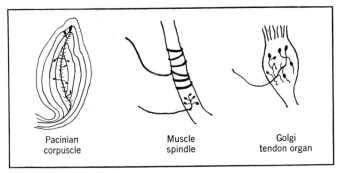

| Pacinian corpuscle | Muscle spindle | Golgi tendon organ |

FIG. 5. Subcutaneous and kinesthetic endings.

Subcutaneous pain can be aroused by extreme pressure and probably also by extreme temperatures (Rein, 1924). Puncture of arteries is generally painful, but veins and subcutaneous fat are relatively insensitive (Bazett and McGlone, 1928). Free nerve endings are believed to be the receptors for subcutaneous pain, but the actual nature of their stimulation is no better understood than is the mechanism of cutaneous pain.

KINESTHESIS

Kinesthesis — the sense of position and movement — is probably the most important sensitivity man possesses. Without kinesthesis a person could not maintain erect posture, let alone walk, talk, and engage in other skilled activities. Yet the existence of kinesthesis is not popularly appreciated, and the word has no counterpart in common language.

The Golgi tendon endings (see Fig. 5) are in the form of spirals around the ends of tendons where they attach to muscles. Their primary stimulation occurs when the muscle *contracts*. Thus muscle spindles and tendon endings complement each other in recording muscular changes.

Sensitivity at joints is still a puzzle. No endings have been demonstrated within the joint surfaces, but Pacinian corpuscles are found in abundance in the immediately surrounding tissues. If these are actually the receptors, then the so-called "joint sense" is reduced to subcutaneous pressure in a particular locus.

The most remarkable feature of kinesthesis is that it gives knowledge of *position* as well as of movement. Movement might be handled by receptors operating in the dead-beat fashion of cutaneous touch. Position demands nondead-beat receptors that can maintain characteristic patterns of nerve impulses.

It has already been mentioned that Pacinian corpuscles are nondead-beat in operation. Electrophysiological studies of nerve impulse patterns from muscles indicate that muscle spindles and tendon endings display the same characteristic.

INTERNAL OR ORGANIC SENSITIVITIES

Because of the difficulties of precise experimentation, relatively little is known about the sensitivity of the internal parts of the body, except for the mouth cavity which reacts in much the same way as the external skin. The esophagus and stomach have specific warm and cold sensitivity but no touch sense in response to light contact (Boring, 1915a, b). Since the esophagus responds to mild distension, it appears to have something analogous to subcutaneous pressure sensitivity. Strong distension arouses a quality similar to subcutaneous pain. In other internal parts there is no clear evidence of specific touch, warm, cold, or pressure senses.

Even the distribution of internal pain does not rest on too secure a foundation. Much of the evidence is derived from not-too-well-controlled clinical studies of human beings or by inference from animal studies where subjective reports are necessarily lacking. It is reasonably certain that such solid organs as the liver, the spleen, and the kidney can be squeezed, cut, and burned without causing pain. Traction upon the hollow viscera is painful, but possibly only because the tension is transmitted to the mesenteries or abdominal walls (Lewis, 1942, p. 9). A similar explanation can be applied to pain from strong contraction of hollow viscera (Lewis, 1942, p. 170). The peritoneum is generally found to be very sensitive to pain from stretching, but not from direct contact. However cloudy the details, one essential fact stands forth; some internal pains must arise from receptors that are more specific than those of the skin. Not only are they specific in yielding only pain, but they can be stimulated only in certain specific ways.

An interesting feature of internal pains is their tendency to be referred to other parts of the body, usually following the segmental distribution of spinal nerves. So standardized are some of these references that they are used in clinical diagnosis. There is also a referred hyperalgesia. For example, attacks of angina pectoris often leave a tenderness in the skin over the left side of the chest (Lewis, 1942, p. 152). Superficially this appears similar to the hyperalgesia from direct skin injury, but of lesser intensity. Morely (1937) and others claim to have abolished shoulder-tip pain from pressure on the diaphragm by local anesthesia of the cutaneous region. However, this finding has not been confirmed by some other investigators and definitely does not hold for many types of visceral referred pains. It is possible for local skin anesthesia to abolish temporarily the referred skin hyperalgesia without interfering with the referred pain.

SOMESTHETIC DISCRIMINATION

Many research studies have been concerned with the systematic measurement of such phases of somesthetic perception as the error of localization, the two-point limen, the discrimination of intensity differences, and the discrimination of form. Here space permits only a brief summary of the broad perspectives, with a complete omission of quantitative data such as may be found in the handbook of von Skramlik (1937).

Localization. If a point on the skin is lightly touched, its location can be designated with a degree of accuracy that varies according to a great number of factors, chiefly the part of the body and the method used to designate the spot. Localization by means of subcutaneous pressure is good but less precise than that for cutaneous touch. Pain from a pinprick can be localized about as accurately as touch, even when the subject reports no simultaneous touch sensation. Warm and cold, whether derived from contact or radiant stimulation, are poorly localized when simultaneous touch cues are excluded.

Two-point limen. The ability to discriminate two simultaneously stimulated points as separate roughly parallels the ability to localize on various parts of the body. The two-point limen is usually found to be two or three times as large as the error of localization. Conflicting results in this connection are sometimes referable to differences in instructions to the subjects. Perceptually the transition from one to two points is not clean-cut but passes through a series of intermediate stages: point, line, circle, oval, dumbbell, etc., before it becomes two clearly separate points. If a subject reports "two" as soon as he gets a hint of departure from singleness, he will show a much smaller limen than if he waits until there is clear duality. By common agreement the latter is considered the true two-point limen.

Discrimination of intensity differences. Kinesthetic-tactual discrimination of weights by lifting is better than the static discrimination of weights rested on the skin. (In static discrimination, it is probable that both cutaneous touch and subcutaneous pressure are involved unless the weights are extremely light.) Appreciation of differences in thermal stimulation is best in the neighborhood of normal skin temperature, and it becomes progressively poorer as the stimulus temperature departs from this level, even when the skin has been exposed to an adapting temperature for some time.

Discrimination of pain intensity is, in general, a difficult topic for psychophysical study because we have so little knowledge of what physical measurements are really significant in relation to most forms of painful stimulation (i.e. needle pricks, pressures, chemicals, etc.). A striking exception is the pain produced by radiant heat. Hardy, Wolff, and Goodell (1948) tested subjects with a series of nine radiant heat intensities varying from the pain threshold to just below a strength that would blister the skin. The stimuli were spaced at intervals of 1 dol, where a *dol* is defined as a unit of painfulness equal in size to two just noticeable differences in pain intensity. The subjects — 73 of them — were exposed to a standard stimulus, corresponding to 8 dols (or 16 jnd's above threshold), and then were asked to judge the intensities of the other stimuli in terms of fractions of the standard. The judgments of apparent fractional intensity were found to agree reasonably well with the dol values of the stimuli. The authors feel, therefore, that the dol scale of pain, originally based on jnd's, can serve as a subjective scale of pain intensity, linearly related to perceived painfulness.

Discrimination of form. Perception of points, lines, and shapes pressed against the skin — usually involving both cutaneous touch and subcutaneous pressure — follows rules that are quite analogous to those for vision, including many of the familiar illusions (Revesz, 1934). Much the same is true when kinesthesis is added by allowing the objects to be handled. On the other hand, thermal discrimination of forms is very poor, and only the grossest differences can be detected (Stone, 1937).

COMPLEX SOMESTHETIC PERCEPTIONS

So far our discussion has dealt with only a few simple somesthetic qualities: touch, pain, warm, cold, subcutaneous pressure, muscular stretch and contraction. In contrast, consider the wealth of phenomenological terms applied to somesthetic experience. Tickle, itch, wet, dry, soft, hard, smooth, rough, oily, greasy, blunt, sharp, and the like refer to the effects of external stimulation. Nausea, suffocation, dizziness, hunger, thirst, and the awarenesses derived from excretory and sexual processes have internal reference.

What can we say about these complex experiences? Are they unique and unanalyzable, requiring the assumption of special sense organs of their own? Or have we succeeded in reducing most of them to patterns of the known simple somesthetic qualities of touch, pain, warm, cold, subcutaneous pressure, and muscular stretch and contraction? Or, in spite of our efforts are we still densely ignorant of their nature?

In our eagerness to avoid postulating special receptors for these complex perceptions there is real danger of our accepting too readily some purely superficial answers. In order to show that a particular pattern of simple qualities provides the basis for a complex experience we must demonstrate that the pattern is both *sufficient and necessary* for the perception. Introspective description cannot do this. Introspection is useful in suggesting the possible composition, but it can never prove that a particular pattern is either sufficient or necessary.

Synthesis can establish sufficiency. Certain complex somesthetic perceptions, or reasonable facsimiles thereof, can be synthesized artificially from simple qualities. For example, artificial wetness from cold plus pressure can be readily demonstrated, even to a naïve subject. Heat, or some unique and interesting experience, can be synthesized from mild warm and mild cold (Burnett and Dallenbach, 1927), although many naïve subjects do not spontaneously call the warm-cold fusion "hot" (Jenkins, 1938b). However, all that such synthetic experiments prove is that a certain pattern of simple qualities is sufficient — provided the artificial product is indistinguishable from the natural perception. They do not show that such a combination, or any part of it, is necessary. To demonstrate necessity requires a subtractive procedure.

Subtraction tests necessity. To prove that a simple quality is necessary, its removal must destroy the complex experience. For example, if mechanically preventing rhythmic contractions of the stomach stops hunger pangs, the contractions are necessary for the experience. Yet this does not mean

that they are sufficient in themselves. They may be only a necessary part of a larger pattern.

In reverse, if removal of a component does not destroy the complex perception, that component is *not necessary*. For example, cold is not necessary for the perception of wetness, because water at neutral temperature feels wet (Lauterbach and Crouser, 1933). Cold is not necessary for the perception of what naïve individuals call "hot," because the latter is consistently reported from small skin areas that are consistently negative to low-temperature stimulation (Jenkins, 1938b).

In summary, then, it seems that we actually know little or nothing about what simple qualities are *both sufficient and necessary* for the various complex somesthetic perceptions. This does not imply that the complex phenomena are unique and unanalyzable, or that there are additional sense organs remaining to be discovered. It does mean that the complex somesthetic perceptions are a rich and almost untouched field calling for further research.

GENERAL REFERENCES

Morgan, C. T. *Physiological psychology.* New York: McGraw-Hill, 1943. Chapters XII and XIII cover the skin senses and proprioception with strong emphasis on the neurological foundations.

Boring, E. G. *Sensation and perception in the history of experimental psychology.* New York: Appleton-Century-Crofts, 1942. Chapters 13 and 14 supply the historical background of the experimental study of the somesthetic senses.

Andrews, T. G. (Ed.). *Methods in psychology.* New York: Wiley, 1948. Chapters 9 and 10 give brief descriptions of the principal research methods used in somesthetic studies.

Fulton, J. F. *Howell's Textbook of Physiology.* Philadelphia: Saunders, 1947. Chapters 16 and 17 for neurological basis.

For a review of cutaneous research between 1930 and 1940, including a bibliography of 262 titles, see two articles by L. J. Stone and W. L. Jenkins: Recent research in cutaneous sensitivity: I. Pain and temperature. *Psychol. Bull.,* 1940, **37**, 285–311. II. Touch and the neural basis of the skin senses. *Ibid.,* 1941, **38**, 69–91. See also Geldard (1940) and von Skramlik (1937) in the list of specific references.

SPECIFIC REFERENCES

Bagh, K. von. Quantitative Untersuchungen auf dem Gebiets der Berührungs- und Druckempfindungen. *Z. Biol.*, 1935, **96**, 153–177.

Bazett, H. C., and B. McGlone. Note on the pain sensations which accompany deep punctures. *Brain*, 1928, **51**, 18–23.

Bazett, H. C., B. McGlone, and R. J. Brocklehurst. The temperatures in the tissues which accompany temperature sensations. *J. Physiol.*, 1930, **69**, 88–112.

Bazett, H. C., B. McGlone, R. G. Williams, and H. M. Lufkin. Sensation: I. Depth, distribution and probable identification in the prepuce of sensory end-organs concerned in sensations of temperature and touch; thermometric conductivity. *Arch. Neurol. Psychiat., Chicago*, 1932, **27**, 489–517.

Belonoschkin, B. Physiologish-Anatomische Untersuchungen über die Empfänger der Kaltempfindung. *Z. zellforsch.*, 1933, **18**, 555–572.

Beringer, K., and H. Ruffin. Sensibilitätsstudien zur Frage des Funktionswandels bei Schizophrenen, Alkoholikern und Gesunden. *Z. ges. Neurol. Psychiat.*, 1932, **140**, 604–640.

Bishop, G. H. Responses to electrical stimulation of single sensory units of skin. *J. Neurophysiol.*, 1943, **6**, 361–382.

Bishop, G. H. The peripheral unit for pain. *J. Neurophysiol.*, 1944a, **7**, 71–80.

Bishop, G. H. The structural identity of the pain spot in human skin. *J. Neurophysiol.*, 1944b, **7**, 184–198.

Bishop, G. H. Neural mechanisms of cutaneous sense. *Physiol. Rev.*, 1946, **26**, 77–102.

Boring, E. G. The sensations of the alimentary canal. *Amer. J. Psychol.*, 1915a, **26**, 1–57.

Boring, E. G. The thermal sensitivity of the stomach. *Amer. J. Psychol.*, 1915b, **26**, 485–494.

Burnett, N. C., and K. M. Dallenbach. The experience of heat. *Amer. J. Psychol.*, 1927, **38**, 418–431.

Burns, M., and K. M. Dallenbach. The adaptation of cutaneous pain. *Amer. J. Psychol.*, 1933, **45**, 111–117.

Cummings, S. B. The effect of local anesthesia on tactile and vibratory thresholds. *J. exp. Psychol.*, 1938, **23**, 321–338.

Dallenbach, K. M. A bibliography of the attempts to identify the functional end-organs of cold and warmth. *Amer. J. Psychol.*, 1929, **41**, 344.

Dearborn, G. V. N. A case of congenital pure analgesia. *J. nerv. ment. Dis.*, 1932, **75**, 612–615.

Endres, G. Punktions-narkose von Rezeptoren. *Z. Biol.*, 1930, **89**, 536–540.

Gasser, H. S. Conduction in nerves in relation to fiber types. *Res. Publ. Ass. nerv. ment. Dis.*, 1935, **15**, 35–59.

Geldard, G. A. The perception of mechanical vibration. *J. gen. Psychol.*, 1940, **22**, 243–308. (Includes a thorough review of research and a bibliography of 214 titles.)

Gertz, E. Psychophysische Untersuchungen über die Adaptation im Gebiet der Temperatursinne und über ihren Einfluss auf die Reiz- und Unterschiedsschwellen. *Z. Sinnesphysiol.*, 1921, **52**, 1–51, 105–156.

Gilbert, R. W. Dermal sensitivity and the differentiated nerve terminations of the human skin. *J. gen. Psychol.*, 1929, **2**, 445–461.

Gilmer, B. v. H. The glomus body as a receptor of cutaneous pressure and vibration. *Psychol. Bull.*, 1942a, **39**, 73–93.

Gilmer, B. v. H. The relation of cold sensitivity to sweat duct distribution and the neurovascular mechanisms of the skin. *J. Psychol.*, 1942b, **13**, 307–325.

Grindley, G. C. The variation of sensory thresholds with the rate of application of the stimulus. II. Touch and pain. *Brit. J. Psychol.*, 1936, **27**, 189–195.

Hahn, H. Die Reize und die Reizbedingungen des Temperatursinnes. II. Die Reizbedingungan des Temperatursinnes. *Pflüg. Arch. ges. Physiol.*, 1927, **217**, 36–71.

Hahn, H. Die psycho-physischen Konstanten und Variablen des Temperatursinnes. II. Die Umstimmung der Erregbarkeit der Temperaturnerven. *Z. Sinnesphysiol.*, 1930, **60**, 198–232.

Hardy, J. D., and T. W. Oppel. Studies in temperature sensation. III. The sensitivity of the body to heat and the spatial summation of the end organ responses. *J. clin. Invest.*, 1937, **16**, 533–540.

Hardy, J. D., H. G. Wolff, and H. Goodell. Studies on pain: An investigation of some quantitative aspects of the dol scale of pain intensity. *J. clin. Invest.*, 1948, **27**, 380–386.

Heinnecker, P., G. H. Bishop, and J. O'Leary. Analysis of sensation in terms of the nerve impulse. *Arch. Neurol. Psychiat., Chicago*, 1934, **31**, 34–53.

Heiser, F. Stimulus temperature and thermal sensation. *Arch. Psychol., N. Y.*, 1932, **21**, No. 138.

Holway, A. H., and W. J. Crozier. The significance of area for differential sensitivity in somesthetic pressure. *Psychol. Rec.*, 1937, **1**, 178–184.

Jenkins, W. L. Adaptation in isolated cold spots. *Amer. J. Psychol.*, 1937, **49**, 1–22.

Jenkins, W. L. Studies in thermal sensitivity: 3. Adaptation with a series of small annular stimulators. *J. exp. Psychol.*, 1938a, **22**, 164–177.

Jenkins, W. L. Studies in thermal sensitivity: 8. Analytic evidence against the Alrutz theory. *J. exp. Psychol.*, 1938b, **22**, 417–422.

Jenkins, W. L. Nafe's vascular theory and the preponderance of evidence. *Amer. J. Psychol.*, 1939, **52**, 462–465.

Jenkins, W. L. Studies in thermal sensitivity: 14. Part-whole relations in seriatim warm-mapping. *J. exp. Psychol.*, 1940, **27**, 76–80.

Jenkins, W. L. Studies in thermal sensitivity: 16. Further evidence on the effects of stimulus temperature. *J. exp. Psychol.*, 1941, **29**, 413–419.

Jenkins, W. L. Studies in thermal sensitivity: 17. The topographical and functional relations of warm and cold. *J. exp. Psychol.*, 1941, **29**, 511–516.

Jones, F. N. The chronaxy of cold and warmth. *Amer. J. Psychol.*, 1940, **53**, 216–228.

Jones, F. N., and M. H. Jones. The chronaxy of pain. *Amer. J. Psychol.*, 1941, **54**, 240–242.

Kredel, F. E., and J. P. Evans. Recovery of sensation in denervated pedicle and free skin grafts. *Arch. Neurol. Psychiat., Chicago*, 1933, **29**, 1203–1221.

Lanier, L. H. Variability in the pain threshold. *Science*, 1943, **97**, 49–50.

Lanier, L. H., H. M. Carney, and W. D. Wilson. Cutaneous inervation: An experimental study. *Arch. Neurol. Psychiat., Chicago*, 1935, **34**, 1–60.

Lauterbach, C. E., and R. E. Crouser. Sensation cues to moisture. *J. exp. Psychol.*, 1933, **16**, 328–338.

Levine, H. A., and K. M. Dallenbach. Adaptation of cold spots under continuous and intermittent stimulation. *Amer. J. Psychol.*, 1936, **48**, 490–497.

Lewis, T. *Pain.* New York: Macmillan, 1942.

Marshall, W. H., C. N. Woolsey, and P. Bard. Cortical representation of tactile sensibility as indicated by cortical potentials. *Science*, 1937, **85**, 388–390.

Morely, J. Visceral pain. *Brit. med. J.*, 1937, **2**, 1270–1273.

Nafe, J. P. Dr. W. L. Jenkins on the vascular theory of warmth and cold. *Amer. J. Psychol.*, 1938, **51**, 763–769.

Nafe, J. P. Toward the quantification of psychology. *Psychol. Rev.*, 1942, **49**, 1–18.

Nafe, J. P., and K. S. Wagoner. The experiences of warmth, cold, and heat. *J. Psychol.*, 1936, **2**, 421–431. (Pertinent experiments are also described on pp. 433–477.)

Nafe, J. P., and K. S. Wagoner. The nature of pressure adaptation. *J. gen. Psychol.*, 1941, **25**, 323–351.

Oppel, T. W., and J. D. Hardy. Studies in temperature sensation. II. The temperature changes responsible for the stimulation of the heat end organs. *J. clin. Invest.*, 1937, **16**, 525–531.

Raffel, G. Recovery of sensitivity to prick and touch after pressure block, with a note on the sensitivity of the hair spots. *J. gen. Psychol.*, 1936, **15**, 13–21.

Rein, H. Beiträge zur Lehre von der Temperaturempfindung der menschlichen Haut. *Z. Biol.*, 1924, **82**, 189–212.

Revesz, G. System der optischen und haptischen Raumtäuschungen. *Z. Psychol.*, 1934, **131**, 296–375.

Rosenthal, S. R., and D. Minard. Experiments on histamine as the chemical mediator for cutaneous pain. *J. exp. Med.*, 1939, **70**, 415–425.

Schumacher, G. A., H. Goodell, J. D. Hardy, and H. G. Wolff. Uniformity of the pain threshold in man. *Science*, 1940, **92**, 110–112.

Skramlik, E. von. Psychophysiologie der Tastsinne. *Arch. ges. Psychol.*, 1937, Ergänzungsbd. **4**. (Chiefly valuable as a source of tabulated data.)

Stetson, R. H. The hair follicle and the sense of pressure. *Psychol. Monogr.*, 1923, **32**, No. 145, 1–17.

Stone, L. J. An experimental study of form perception in the thermal senses. *Psychol. Rec.*, 1937, **6**, 235–337.

Stone, L. J., and K. M. Dallenbach. Adaptation to the pain of radiant heat. *Amer. J. Psychol.*, 1934, **46**, 229–242.

Strughold, H., and M. Karbe. Vitale Färbung des Auges und experimentelle Unterschung der gefärbte Nervenelement. *Z. Biol.*, 1925, **83**, 297–308.

Tschlenoff, L. Sensibilitätsstudien an Nervenkranken. II. Ueber die Schwellenlabilität der Hautsinne. *Dtsch. Z. Nervenheilk.*, 1931, **122**, 89–113.

Walshe, F. M. R. The anatomy and physiology of cutaneous sensibility: A critical review. *Brain*, 1942, **65**, 48–112.

Weddell, G. The pattern of cutaneous innervation in relation to cutaneous sensitivity. *J. Anat. Lond.*, 1941, **75**, 346–367.

Weitz, J. Vibratory sensitivity as affected by local anesthesis. *J. exp. Psychol.*, 1939, **25**, 48–64.

Windisch, E. Untersuchungen über den adäquaten Reiz für die Wärmerezeptoren. *Z. Biol.*, 1931, **91**, 126–136.

Woollard, H. H. Observations on the terminations of cutaneous nerves. *Brain*, 1935, **58**, 352–367.

31·

Vestibular Functions

G. R. WENDT

University of Rochester

The vestibule is the part of the ear that responds to motion and position. Flourens published the first exact experimental observations on the semicircular canals of pigeons in 1824, setting off an accelerating interest. Since Griffith reviewed the field in 1922, listing 1701 experimental studies, there has been an increasing volume of papers. The German, English, and Italian literatures now contain the best of the studies; interest has been decreasing among the French, but increasing among the Portuguese. A number of useful reviews have appeared (Dusser de Barenne; Griffith, 1922; Fischer, 1928; Camis and Creed; McNally and Stuart; Spiegel and Sommer; Tenaglia; and others), but a reasonably complete and unbiased review has still to be written. The review in this chapter is necessarily sketchy and selective.

ANATOMY OF THE VESTIB-ULAR APPARATUS

The entire internal ear is called the *labyrinth*. It consists of the cochlear apparatus and the *vestibular apparatus*. The latter consists of the three *semicircular canals* and the *otolith organs* (*utricle* and *saccule*). The membranous labyrinth lies within a bony labyrinth in the temporal bone, the space between being filled with perilymph.

The preparation of this chapter was aided by funds from a contract between the University of Rochester and the Office of Naval Research.

Since the canals lie in three planes that are roughly at right angles to one another, as shown by the model in Fig. 1, we are able to analyze the turning of the head in any plane. The right and left horizontal canals are in the same plane, tipped back somewhat (Fig. 2). If one tips the head forward so that a line from the corner of the eye to the ear canal is horizontal, the horizontal canals are then brought near the true horizontal. The vertical canals are paired otherwise. The superior canal on one side is in a plane parallel to that of the posterior canal of the other side. These planes form angles of about 45 degrees with the mesial plane of the head. There are, therefore, three pairs of canals: a horizontal pair, a right upper and left rear pair, and a right rear and left upper pair. The canal receptors are in the ampullar swellings of the canals where they join the vestibule (see Fig. 1). The otolith organs in man are found in two sacs: the utricle (or vestibule), from which the canals arise, and the saccule. These chambers lie close together, joined by a short duct. Figure 3 is a diagram of these relations. The endolymph that fills the sacs and canals has a viscosity and specific gravity like that of cerebrospinal fluid.

The anatomy of the receptors has been studied both histologically and by direct observation. Each canal has within its *ampulla* a transverse ridge called the *crista*, which is supplied by a branch of the vestibular nerve. The surface of the crista con-

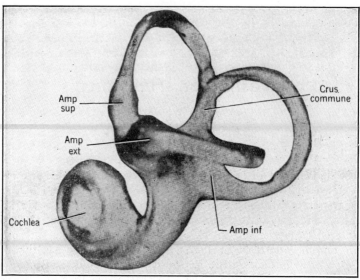

FIG. 1.   Model of left human labyrinth.   The inner ear is shown in the position it would have in the upright head.   This model shows the canals as being more regular in shape than they actually are; normally they follow a somewhat sinuous course, and the geometrical relations of their planes differ slightly among individuals.   The three ampullae are labeled: Amp ext = ampulla of horizontal canal; Amp sup = ampulla of superior canal; Amp inf = ampulla of posterior canal.   (From Spiegel and Sommer.)

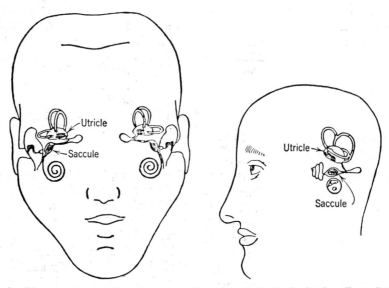

FIG. 2.   Diagrams showing the orientations of the labyrinths in the head.   (From Camis.)

sists of supporting cells and ciliated receptor cells (*hair cells*). The nerve fibers form a plexus about the base of the hair cells. The cilia project into a flattened gelatinous mass, called the *cupula*, which extends from the ridge of the crista to the roof of the ampulla. One can see in live fish that

The utricular receptor is the *macula*, an oval flat thickening of the vestibular wall with supporting cells and ciliated receptor cells on its surface, and nerve fibers forming plexuses about the bases of the hair cells. The hair cells protrude into a thin gelatinous pad. This contains calcareous crystals, the

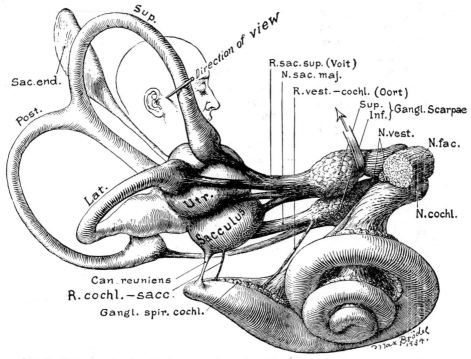

FIG. 3. Nerve supply of vestibular apparatus and cochlea. The seven branches of the vestibular nerve and the cochleosaccular nerve are shown, as described in the text. Lat = horizontal canal. (From Hardy.)

the crista and cupula fill the whole cross section of the ampulla. The cupula acts like a swinging door, hinged on the cilia, and moving because of endolymph pressures. The fit of the cupula in the ampulla is close, so that endolymph does not flow past it. Dye put into the endolymph on one side of this barrier does not seep past it, even during induced motions of the cupula. Although direct observations have not been possible in warm-blooded forms, it is assumed that they have the same cupular structure.

otoliths (oto = ear, lith = stone), up to 14 microns in diameter in mammals. The pad has definite shape and some stiffness, so that it presumably tends to act as a whole. The plane of the utricular macula in man is like that of the horizontal canal (see Fig. 2). The saccule also contains a macula like that in the utricle. Its axis is at right angles to that of the utricular macula. Unlike the canals, which are similar from fish to man, the otolith organs show wide anatomical and perhaps functional variations among animal groups. In fish the saccular organs are believed to be in part vibration (or sound) receptors.

The neurons of the vestibular nerve in man (see Fig. 3) form two main divisions which split into seven branches, one to each of the three ampullae, one to the utricle, two to the saccule, and one (Oort's nerve) to the cochlea. Their cell bodies lie close to the vestibule in Scarpa's ganglion; their fibers travel in the vestibular division of the VIIIth nerve. The vestibular fibers usually make up more than half of the VIIIth nerve and are about 19,000 in number. Most of the fibers are large (10 to 15 microns), but there are fibers as small as 2 microns (Rasmussen). On entering the medulla, fibers end in the vestibular nuclei and possibly in the cerebellum. The place of ending of the fibers from the saccular maculae is unknown. The saccule, in addition to being supplied by *both* divisions of the vestibular nerve, receives a small nerve (cochleo saccular nerve) which appears to come from the cochlear ganglion and presumably enters the medulla by way of the cochlear division of the VIIIth nerve (Hardy).

Neural connections. The bipolar first-order neurons whose dendritic endings are in the cristae and maculae and whose cell bodies are in the vestibular (Scarpa's) ganglion are believed to have their synaptic endings mainly in the vestibular nuclei in the medulla. There are four major nuclei on each side: Deiter's nucleus, Bechterew's nucleus, the medial vestibular nucleus, and the nucleus of the descending vestibular root. Some investigators believe, also, that some first-order neurons go directly to the cerebellar vermis. The details of distribution of fiber endings from the individual cristae and maculae to the various nuclei are not known, nor is the functional organization of these centers. Lorente de Nó believes that each group of receptors has endings in each of the nuclei. Others conceive of a nucleus for each peripheral functional unit (Spiegel and Sommer; Gray).

A complete description of the neural connections of the vestibular apparatus would be extensive since most of the effectors of the body are influenced by it.* Connections go to the spinal motor centers for movements of head, trunk, and limbs, to the motor centers for movement of eyes, to the flocculonodular lobe of the cerebellum, an organ that is phylogenetically and also embryologically an outgrowth of the vestibular nuclei, to the autonomic centers in medulla, midbrain, and thalamus, and to the cerebral cortex. The connections to the autonomic centers and to the cerebral cortex are probably in part direct, but also indirect, by way of the cerebellum. The evidence for cortical representation is physiological rather than anatomical. Spiegel showed that vestibular stimulation changes the electrical activity of a region of the temporal lobe, near the parietal area, and of a region of the frontal lobe, and that strychninization of the temporal area leads to epileptiform seizures on vestibular stimulation.

ACTION OF THE SEMICIRCULAR CANALS

The canals are the chief receptors for rotational movements, being affected by angular accelerations. There is evidence that they are stimulated also to some degree by position and linear acceleration, and by sound. They may also be stimulated calorically (by irrigating the ear canal with warm or cold water, thereby causing convection currents in the endolymph), electrically, chemically, or by direct mechanical means (pneumatic hammer).

The most striking advance in knowledge of the canals came from direct observation of the ampulla in fish. Steinhausen (1933) and Dohlman (1944), using living pike and cod, observed that the cupula moves with

* For detailed descriptions of the anatomy of these systems see Barré (1937) ; Van Gehuchten ; Leidler ; Magnus ; Rademaker ; and Riley.

movement of the endolymph. By direct manometric measurement Dohlman (1941) found cupular movement from pressure changes equal to 0.05 millimeter of water (0.00004 gram). Deviations of the cupula were slowly restored (in about 20 seconds) by its own elasticity. By use of models he tried to show (1938b) that motions of the cupula slacken the hair cells on the side toward the bending and stretch those on the other side.

Apparently no one has yet studied end-organ potentials in the ampullae.* On the other hand, action potentials from the vestibular nerve have been recorded. Lowenstein and Sand, using primitive fish (rays), and leading off either from an ampullar nerve by gross electrodes or from teased-out single fibers, found a spontaneous discharge of impulses during the resting state. This discharge increased on rotation in one direction and decreased on opposite rotation. After a constant state of motion was reached, it took 20 to 40 seconds for the nerve activity to return to normal. These facts correlate well with the direct observations of Steinhausen and Dohlman and show that in fish and frogs the nerve responds to the degree of displacement of the cupula, rather than to the momentary force acting on it. On the other hand, earlier studies on turtles, fish and frogs have given somewhat different results (Mowrer, 1935a; Zotterman; Ross).

There are no directly comparable data on higher animals. However, Adrian took records from the vestibular nuclei of the cat

* The evolutionary development of the cochlea from the vestibular apparatus suggests the desirability of studying the vestibule by the techniques used for the cochlea (thresholds, effects of various frequencies and amplitudes, end-organ potentials, prolonged stimulation, etc.). To some extent this has been done, but not systematically. Guinea pigs have been subjected to prolonged periods (250 hours) of rotation (Jonason, Kyhlstedt, and Nylén), being accelerated for 16 seconds and then decelerated for 16 seconds. Histological examination of the vestibular apparatus, vestibular ganglia, and vestibular nuclei showed degeneration, but the results were inconclusive.

(presumably not from first-order neurons). Acceleration followed by constant movement set up activity lasting up to 25 seconds. With the head at rest there was, in most locations, persistent spontaneous activity. This could be increased by rotation in one direction or suppressed for as long as 30 seconds by opposite rotation. Gernandt, recording from what he believed to be second-order neuron cell bodies in the nerve, got like results. He found units excited by rotation in either direction, others inhibited by rotation in either direction and others affected oppositely by opposite rotations.

How the canals work has been studied in many ways: theoretically, by models, experimentally, and clinically. The chief theories agree that forces act on the canal contents only during *acceleration* of motion (positive or negative). This has been dogma since Mach, Breuer, and Brown simultaneously, but independently, proposed it in 1878 (see Griffith, 1922; Dusser de Barenne). According to the *flow* hypothesis the inertia of the endolymph, acted on by rotary accelerations of the head, causes an endolymph flow that is maximum when the rotation is in the plane of a canal. This hypothesis holds that the cupula is deflected by the force of the stream of endolymph. The *displacement* hypothesis appears to be better supported in view of Steinhausen's and Dohlman's reports that in the fish the cupula fills the entire lumen of the ampulla so that no streaming can take place. Inertia acting on the endolymph and cupular mass is regarded as causing a shift of fluid and thereby displacement of the cupula. Werner suggested that the canals, being of small diameter — 1.4 millimeter in man (Gray) — offer frictional resistance to endolymph movement and thus damp the response of the system.

Rotation mainly affects that canal whose plane is nearest the plane of rotation. But it also affects more than one canal (possibly all to some extent), even when in unfavorable planes. This is shown by theoretical analysis (Summers, Morgan, and Reimann) and by electrical recording from single ampullar nerves (Lowenstein and Sand). Furthermore, rotation in planes other than the primary canal planes may be the most effective stimulus. This is shown by experiments in which the plane of rotation is varied about one of the major canal planes. Travis (1938) found that rotation about the vertical axis is best sensed when the head is upright rather than tipped forward to bring the horizontal canals into the plane of rotation (see also Werner).

It is likely that progressive movements (linear accelerations) stimulate the canals. De Kleyn, Magnus, and Versteegh found that reflexes to linear accelerations were present after the otolith membranes had been thrown off by centrifugation, although Hasegawa doubts their data. Such effects might be produced by a greater specific gravity of the cupula than of the endolymph. Ter Braak has calculated that the difference in specific gravity of cupula and endolymph need be only one part in 10,000 to allow movement of the cupula at linear accelerations of 1g. One may also argue for such stimulation from the fact that proper reflexes are present when the canals are artificially stimulated as if by progressive movements. Bilateral equal caloric stimulation producing opposite stimulation of two canals like that to be expected from forward movements results in a pulsion reflex like that produced by actual forward movement (Fischer, 1928).

Under certain conditions the canals are stimulated by sound, as shown by more than a dozen research papers (Tullio and Canova; Zanzucchi, 1939; Rejtö; Tenaglia). If a hole is drilled in a bony canal, reflexes of the head and eyes proper to the ampulla of the opened canal are produced by sound. The effect occurs over a wide frequency range, but the maximum lies between 400 and 1000 cps. The reflexes are present only for the duration of the stimulus. Such effects have been reported clinically in cases of fistula. Dohlman (1925) recorded eye movements in man from sound stimulation of a fistula. In the intact human ear very loud sounds (10 to 500 dynes per square centimeter) cause head movement by stimulation of the otoliths (Békésy).

The stimulus thresholds of the canals have been measured in a number of ways and found to be very small. Dohlman measured the pressure necessary to move the cupula of fish, finding a value of 0.00004 gram. The threshold can also be thought of as the smallest rate of change (acceleration) that will cause response, or as the lowest speed of movement that causes response at any given rate of acceleration. Ter Braak showed that ocular compensation was produced in rabbits by angular accelerations of as little as 0.09 degree per second per second. The reaction took place in 100 per cent of trials at 0.23 degree per second per second with an average latency of 2.9 seconds. At an acceleration of 0.5 degree per second per second the latency was 1.1 seconds. Mowrer (1935b) found the average acceleration necessary to produce reflex head deviation in the homing pigeon to be 0.8 degree per second per second. The average latency of head movement at this value was 10 seconds. Accelerations of 7.5 degrees per second per second were necessary to reach minimum latency. He found no differences in threshold of a single canal on rotation to right or left (the canal on the other side had been plugged). The thresholds of human subjects for onset of rotation vary with the indicator used and with the method of computation. The threshold as measured by appearance of compensatory eye movements is in all probability lower than that measured by perception of rotation (blindfolded subjects). The lowest values reported for the human threshold are 0.2 degree per second per second (Tumarkin) and 0.5 degree per second per second (Dohlman, 1925; Groen and Jongkees). Allard found an increase of threshold with age in adults.

ACTION OF THE OTOLITH ORGANS

The utricular otolith organs respond to gravity and to linear accelerations. They control static reflexes to position of the head, and dynamic reflexes in response to movements. For experimental purposes they are stimulated by tilting boards, linear accelerators, swings, human centrifuges, and other means.

The evidence for a resting discharge from the utricle is somewhat surer than it is for the ampullae. Electrical records from the nerve of the utricular macula have been made by Lowenstein (1948) with fish, and by Ross with frogs. Adrian recorded from the medulla of cats activity that was presumably set up by utricular stimulation, being gravity controlled. Adrian found a resting activity, the level of which was increased as the head was tilted out of the normal position. The units reacted also to linear accelerations. They maintained these activity levels with only slow adaptation. Lowenstein got the same results from the peripheral units in fish. In addition he found response during rotation at constant speed (presumably due to centrifugal force). Ross' results were concordant with these, but he further believed that there might be two receptors, type I responding when the head was tilted, type II signaling return of the head to the normal position. Magnus showed that the extensor tone of decerebrate rigidity depends on the orientation of the head to gravity; Spiegel found a reduction in postural tone after prolonged exposure of the labyrinth to cold, suggesting the removal of a source of tonic influences.

The way in which the utricle is stimulated is not known. It is of course assumed that the mass of the otolith-laden macula, acted on by gravity or linear acceleration, stimulates the hair cells, but the manner of action is obscure. An interesting lead comes from laboratory studies of motion sickness, which show that wave forces are most effective in producing nausea when they act along the vertical axis of the head, as when a subject is sitting normally (*Aero med. Ass. Proc.*). Other studies of motion sickness have shown that waves are most effective when their frequencies and accelerations are in the mid-range (Alexander et al., 1947).

The functions of the saccular macula are in doubt. Its anatomical similarity to the utricular macula and its arrangement with respect to the head axes suggest that it shares function with the utricle, just as the canals supplement one another. While there is some evidence for this, the weight of present evidence suggests that the saccular macula is a vibratory receptor or low-tone auditory receptor. In lower vertebrates the functions of this as well as of other structures in the labyrinth (lagena, pars neglecta) and the extent to which they are involved in equilibratory, water pressure, vibration, or sound reception are matters of controversy.

Thresholds of the otolith organs are not satisfactorily known either for tilt or for linear acceleration (Travis and Dodge; Gurnee; Travis, 1944, 1945; Tenaglia). The mode of stimulation in the studies of thresholds was such that muscle or skin stimuli gave cues that probably acted before the threshold of the vestibule was reached. Well-controlled studies are needed.

VESTIBULAR CONTROL OF THE EYES

The reflexes that move our eyes do a marvelous job. When the head rotates from side to side or from front to back, the eyes compensate well enough to keep the appearance of perfect fixation. This eye movement is the result of joint control of the eye muscles by four separate sources: vestibular, visual, neck muscle-receptor, and cortical.

During these active head movements there are two main kinds of eye movements. The one, called by Dodge the coordinate compensatory movement, occurs when the head is turned while the visual fixation remains the same. It is interesting that the onset of the head rotation and of the compensatory eye movement are simultaneous, showing that the initial phase of the response, at least, is not vestibular in its control, since it starts without latency with respect to head movement (Dodge, 1921). The other type of eye movement occurs when one starts a shift of fixation (and of head position) to a new object. In such an act a saccadic fixa-

wooden block pressed against the lid over the center of the corneal bulge, and so pivoted that it tips from side to side as it remains tangential to the underlying corneal surface.

In a short arc of passive rotation, say 15 or 65 degrees, the eyes show a nystagmoid movement (slow compensatory drift interrupted by fast return movements) during the period of rotation (see Fig. 4). The plane of the eye movements is the same as the plane of rotation. The reflex latency

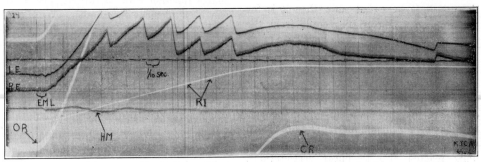

FIG. 4. Reproduction of a strip of photographic paper, 4 in. wide, showing nystagmoid eye movements during a 2-second horizontal rotation through 65 degrees. Recording by Dodge's method described in text. OR = onset of rotation; CR = approximate cessation of rotation; RI = rotation indicator; HM = record of head movement; LE = record of movement of left eye; RE = right eye; EML = eye-movement latency. Note the alternation of slow and fast phases. The recorder reverses the direction of movement; actually the slow phase is opposite to the rotation. (After Wendt, 1936b.)

tion movement and a head movement in the same direction usually begin simultaneously. The eyes, being quicker, reach their "location" before the head; during completion of the head movement the eyes remain on the object, by means of a coordinate compensatory movement (Mowrer, 1932). Both types of eye movement occur when the lids are closed (Wendt, unpublished).

Eye movements during short arcs of rotation. The canals may be stimulated by placing the subject on a rotating chair (with head fixed so as to avoid tonic neck reflexes). In order to study vestibular response without visual reinforcement or inhibition, vision is excluded. Dodge invented a good method for recording horizontal eye movements through closed lids (see Wendt, 1938; and Wendt and Dodge). A band of light is reflected from a mirror mounted on a small

of the slow phase is 50 to 80 milliseconds (Dodge, 1921). The form of the slow phase, except in minor but significant details, faithfully reflects the form of the rotation (Wendt, 1936b). Figure 5 shows this relation by a plot of the amount of slow phase per unit of time (0.1-second units) along with a plot of the amount of rotation. Quantitatively, the compensation is short of complete adequacy, the total angular degrees of slow drift of the eyes being about 60 per cent of the actual rotation of the chair. The eye movement accelerates a little longer than the acceleration of the chair, the deceleration of eye movement takes place more quickly than that of the chair, and the eyes reverse their direction of drift shortly before the actual end of the movement, showing a slow (3 degrees of arc per second) drift after rotation. All this is with eyes closed, so only the vestibule is acting.

The saccadic movements (fast phases) in this nystagmus are variable in both timing and size. The first saccadic commonly occurs about one-third second after onset of the slow phase; subsequent ones are separated by $\frac{1}{10}$ to $\frac{1}{2}$ second. Their usual extent is about 5 degrees, but it varies from as little as a few minutes of arc to perhaps 20 degrees. From one to thirteen fast phases

onset to stop) and observing the post-rotation nystagmus. Or we may accelerate the chair at a subthreshold rate (0.5 degree per second per second is slow enough) to a desired rate, and then stop it. Buys (1924) has shown that the sequence of response after a single acceleratory stimulus is in all ways the same as after a single decceleratory stimulus.

Most of the textbooks in psychology and physiology give incorrect descriptions of such

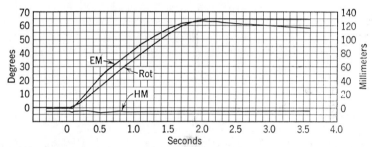

FIG. 5. Slow phase of nystagmus during 65-degree rotation. This graph shows the slow phase of eye movements (EM) plotted on the same time-amount coordinates as the rotation (Rot); HM = head movement. The graph was constructed by averaging, from a number of photographic records like that in Fig. 4, the amount of slow phase in each $\frac{1}{10}$-second interval and then summating these averages. (After Wendt, 1936b.)

occur in each record for a 65-degree rotation lasting 2 seconds.

When visual reinforcement is added to the vestibular effect (one eye seeing objects about the rotating chair), the adequacy of the slow phase is increased from 60 per cent (with eyes closed) to 80 per cent (with eyes open). With visual inhibition (one eye seeing a fixation field that rotates with the chair), the ocular compensation is reduced to 5 per cent.

Single acceleratory stimuli. The sequence of eye movements after a single acceleratory stimulus looks very different from that during short movements where the chair accelerates and then decelerates. Such a stimulus is produced by bringing the chair to a desired speed (usually 180 degrees per second) and then holding it at that speed until the response has run its course. It can also be obtained by stopping a rotation (after waiting for all action started by its

rotation nystagmus. The true sequence of events (after acceleration to 180 degrees per second) is a series of movements lasting several minutes. These consist of a primary nystagmus followed by a long-lasting secondary nystagmus in the opposite direction. The onset of rotation initiates a nystagmus whose slow phase increases in speed for slightly longer than the duration of acceleration and then shows a gradual decrement lasting for 25 to 50 seconds in different subjects (usually about 35 seconds). This is the primary rotation nystagmus (or post-rotation nystagmus) of the textbook descriptions. But this is only part of the story. As the drift of the eyes slows to zero velocity, they immediately (with no detectable pause) begin to drift in the opposite direction and produce an *inverse nystagmus* (or *secondary nystagmus*). The speed of the inverse grows over a period of roughly 80 seconds until its slow phase is at the rate of about 5 degrees per second. It then shows a gradual decrement over a period of about 3 to 10 minutes, until the eyes return to their prestimulus state (which is usually a slow drift). The time of cessation of the original nystagmus, the time of maximum speed of the inverse, and the duration of the inverse show large variations among individuals. The same individual, on the other hand, shows a remarkable constancy in the dura-

The finer details of this sequence of events are in need of careful metrical study in relation to the amounts of power expended on the ear. Of the numerous studies of the primary nystagmus, only that of Buys (1924) shows an approach to technical adequacy. He reported that the duration of this nystagmus showed "little change" over the range of power levels involved in acceleration to velocities of 18 to 360 degrees per

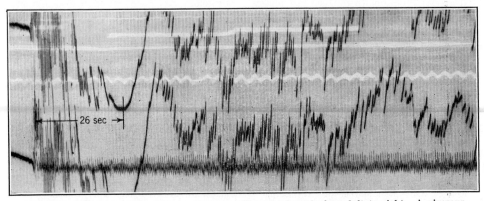

26 sec

FIG. 6.   Primary and secondary nystagmus.   The record reads from left to right.   A vigorous primary nystagmus begins with the acceleratory stimulus.   After 26 seconds this reverses and a secondary nystagmus occurs.   The wavy white line is breathing; the bottom line shows amplitude of pulse in the finger.

tion of the primary nystagmus (i.e. time to reversal of nystagmus) so long as stimuli are properly spaced and the subject is kept alert. Figure 6 shows a sample record of this sequence of events for the 2-minute period following a single acceleratory stimulus to a rotation speed of 180 degrees per second.*

second but that the speed of the slow phase (and consequently the total amount of ocular drift) was directly related to power expended. He also varied accelerations from 0.8 to 81 degrees per second per second and found that the speed of the slow phase was roughly a linear function of acceleration

* The general nature of this response has been known since the studies by Buys (1924). The failure of our texts to mention it is because the literature is confusing to the nonspecialist who writes texts. There are six complicating circumstances. First, in much research visual reinforcement or inhibition of nystagmus was not prevented and its importance was not understood. Second, many investigations have been conducted by the standard method of Bárány, ten rotations performed in 20 seconds, thus having an acceleratory and deceleratory stimulus close together, a method that complicates the response to each stimulus by the presence of the other. Third, direct visual observation of eye movements has often been used, which is totally inadequate to show fine detail. Fourth, interference due to habituation has not been controlled. Fifth, some-

times investigators, confronted by peculiarities of response that did not fit the textbook statements, have apparently been blind to their existence or unwilling to comment on them. And, sixth, unjustified inferences have been made from the subjects' reports of sensations of rotation to the (inferred) presence or absence of eye movements. Although a strong nystagmus is usually accompanied by a corresponding sensation of rotation, slow nystagmus may be accompanied by no sensation or by sensations that do not correspond.

Since the time of Buys' paper a number of other investigators have studied the characteristics of the secondary nystagmus (Pilossian; Woletz; and others), but none with methods as good as those of the original study. Fischer and Wodak (Fischer, 1928) reported that changes of head position during the early part of the pri-

times duration of acceleration; i.e. the "output" in terms of velocity of the eyes is a function of the "input" in terms of power expended on the ear.

M. H. Fischer (1928), who has been most active in the study and discussion of the secondary phases, believes that the sequence of events following a single stimulus is quite protracted, consisting of a continued rhythmical alternation of opposite phases lasting up to 1 hour, each succeeding phase growing progressively briefer and weaker. This belief is based on finding such alternations in subjective reports of the sensation of rotation. Other investigators have not confirmed this finding (Dodge, 1923a; Buys, 1924; Pilossian). My own eye-movement records show satisfactory evidence for only a single inverse phase. In those subjects showing a spontaneous drift of the eyes there may be a pseudo third phase when the spontaneous drift is reestablished at the end of the secondary nystagmus.

The fast phase of nystagmus is in general inversely related to the speed of the slow phase in both frequency and extent. However, the saccadics show great irregularity in both magnitude and temporal separation. In a weak nystagmus there are typically

mary post-rotational phase changed the plane of the response, but there was no change when the head was moved during the secondary or late in the primary phase. One wonders whether the effect of the movement depends merely on intensity of response.

The discovery of an inverse phase of nystagmus was apparently made independently by Dodge in America, by Fischer and Wodak in Germany, and by Bárány in Sweden. The reports of the first two were based on an inverse phase in the sensations following acceleration. The inverse is apparently also found following the original nystagmus induced by caloric stimulation (Fischer and Oldberg). Dohlman (1925), who studied calorically induced nystagmus with a recording mirror attached directly to the eye, published records showing reversals but made no mention of them in the text. Studies of the so-called "oculogyral illusion," the apparent movement of a very faint light in a darkened room, have verified the fact that secondary phases occur as a result of rotation about planes other than the horizontal (Andreas, Brown, and Wendt, unpublished).

also some forward fixation movements, i.e. saccadics in the same direction as the slow phase. In these respects the primary and secondary nystagmus do not differ.

Visual reinforcement or inhibition greatly changes the sequence of response to single stimuli. In a subject rotated with eyes open and in the presence of good fixation objects, a visually induced nystagmus lasts throughout the rotation, whatever its duration, the visual response being dominant over the weak opposing secondary nystagmus of vestibular origin. The post-rotation nystagmus, since it is opposed by still fixation objects, is less vigorous than with eyes closed. It is shortened and has no noticeable secondary phase. When a subject is producing a vestibular nystagmus in the dark, and visual inhibition is suddenly introduced by lighting up a fixation field, the inhibition takes about 1½ seconds to develop fully when the nystagmus is weak. On removal of the fixation by ending the illumination, the vestibular nystagmus is reestablished within ¾ second. The inhibition acts the same on the primary and on the secondary nystagmus (Andreas, Brown, and Wendt, unpublished).

Dodge (1923a) studied conflicting visual and vestibular control of the eyes by rotating vertical stripes about the subject to induce a visuo-ocular reflex nystagmus in one direction while actual bodily rotation at low velocities induced a vestibulo-ocular nystagmus in the opposite direction. When both stimuli started together, the vestibular deviation was the first to appear after its usual brief latency, to be overcome about ¼ second later by a visually induced slow phase in the opposite direction. When vision of the stripes was then cut off, the vestibular response came back immediately. With increased velocities of body rotation, a value was reached where the two stimuli were approximately balanced. Control then shifted alternately from one to the other, each response being weak.

Deceleration preceded by an acceleration. In the common clinical rotation tests (Bárány method), the patient is rotated ten times at a rate of 180 degrees per second, i.e. ten turns in 20 seconds, and then suddenly stopped. Only the post-rotation nystagmus is observed. Here the nystagmus sequence resulting from the start has not run its course by the time the stop occurs. The observed post-rotation nystagmus is therefore the algebraic sum of the response to the start and the response to the stopping. When the time between starting and stopping is systematically varied, this interaction is clearly seen (Buys, 1924; Fischer, 1928). The limiting case is the normal head movement of everyday life, where the deceleratory stimulus follows immediately after the acceleratory. The second stimulus then almost completely cancels the effects of the first.

Rotation about other axes. The plane of the vestibular compensatory eye movement is the same as the plane of the head turning, whether horizontal, vertical, or oblique. If the subject is lying down, so that the axis of rotation passes from the front to the back of the head, a rotary nystagmus develops (Majewsky). Limited observations suggest that secondary nystagmus occurs in each case (Fischer, 1928; Andreas, Brown, and Wendt, unpublished).

Tilt, position, and rectilinear movement. When the head and body are tilted very slowly so as to avoid canal stimulation and stimulation of neck muscle receptors, tonic compensatory eye deviations occur. These are present in man in response to a variety of positions of the head. Fischer (1930) showed that lateral tilt produced a positional "counter-rolling" of the eyes such that 60 degrees of tilt produced 5 to 12 degrees of rotation about the line of regard. But such tonic reflexes are far more readily observed in lower mammals and especially in reptiles and fish, where the positional reflex is large and maintained (Hasegawa, 1940; Dusser de Barenne). Fischer and Veits made limited observations on an elevator, using a visual after-image to indicate ocular deviation during linear acceleration. Only small deviations (estimated at 1½ degrees) were found.

Eye Movements Due to Other than "Adequate" Stimuli

The adequate stimuli for the vestibule are head movements. One may stimulate these receptors experimentally by caloric, mechanical, electrical, or chemical means. No account will be made here of experiments on chemical stimuli.

Caloric stimulation. The caloric method confines stimulation largely to the cupula of a single canal. Irrigation of the external auditory canal with water either warmer or colder than the canal wall (cold water is usually used) produces a heat exchange that is readily transmitted to the vestibule. The heating or cooling of the endolymph causes an upward or downward movement of the fluid which deflects the cupula.

Dohlman's excellent investigation (1925) showed that the temperature change first reaches the horizontal canal. If this canal is oriented vertically, the caloric stimulus produces a horizontal nystagmus. The maximum speed of the slow phase is linearly related to temperature difference and this maximum occurs at about 1 minute after onset of irrigation. The duration is variable among individuals, but of the order of 3 minutes. There is a secondary nystagmus after caloric stimulation (Fischer and Oldberg).

The temperature change also reaches the other canals (at a greater latency) and, if they are vertically oriented, produces a corresponding nystagmus.

Mechanical stimulation. If the bony wall of the vestibule is eroded by infection, it may become perforated with a permanent fistula. Such an ear was used by Dohlman (1925) to show that rapidly alternating pneumatic pressures compressing the canal wall were reflected exactly in corresponding oscillatory deviations of the eyes. Rates of alternation up to 100 per second were reflected in eye movement.

The "pneumatic hammer" method was also used by Ewald in experiments with pigeons to find the effects of fluid displacement in the canals.

Electrical stimulation. There is a large but confusing literature on the effects of "galvanic" stimulation (see review in Spiegel and Sommer). Little of an analytical nature with sharply localized stimulation has been reported. Usually electrodes are placed over the mastoids or in the saline-filled ear canals, and current is passed through the head. It appears to be demonstrated that the main locus of stimulation is the first-order neurons.

On passage of a direct current through the head there is a vigorous nystagmus of brief latency (10 milliseconds, according to Dohlman, 1925) with the slow phase toward the anode. This subsides to a moderate nystagmus within about 2 seconds to continue for the remaining time of current passage. If the current is passed for 2 to 3 minutes, a post-galvanic nystagmus is found, lasting about a minute (Caussé, 1928). Fischer and Wodak (Fischer, 1928) found a sequence of alternating phases in the subjective phenomena. Alternating current passed through the head yields no response, yet alternating current applied directly to the canal receptors produces strong ocular deviation limited to the period of stimulation (Rossi, 1936).

Vestibular "imbalance." Usually some slow conjugate drift of the eyes is present when highly magnified records of horizontal eye movements are obtained from the stationary subject with vision excluded. No systematic study of this has been made, but observations incident to other experiments (Wendt, 1936b) show that its rate and direction differ among individuals and even in the same individual on different days. Related data may be found in a large literature concerning clinical phenomena variously

called spontaneous nystagmus, readiness for nystagmus, vestibular disharmony, and directional preponderance of nystagmus (Alfandary, 1938; Arslan, 1938; Barbey and Morsier; Barré, 1942; Fitzgerald and Hallpike).

Effects of bodily conditions. Only a few of the many studies of the effects of disease and of drugs have value for our present purpose, since such studies are usually made to understand the disease or the drug rather than the vestibular apparatus. Bartels (1910) said that narcosis affects the fast phase of ocular nystagmus before the slow phase. This needs to be checked by experiments with oscillation through small arcs where one can get the slow phase continuously. Angyal and Blackman (1941) found that alcohol increased caloric nystagmus in normal man. Since their subjects had some vision of the surrounds, this effect might be due to a lessened visual interference. (I have found that alcohol slows visual nystagmus.) In the study of Angyal and Blackman, excess CO_2 depressed nystagmus, and low CO_2 increased it. In each case the effects were opposite in schizophrenic patients — the patients without drug show lessened response to stimulation (Claude, Baruk, and Aubry; Angyal and Sherman). Intravenous injection of certain morphine derivatives produces in man a spontaneous vertical nystagmus, with slow phase up (Zum Gottesberge and Sellerbeck). Bulbocapnine, given to the dog (Delmas-Marsalet, 1937), leaves ocular nystagmus unaffected but completely blocks other vestibular reflexes. (For the effects of other drugs, see Camis and Creed.)

VESTIBULAR CONTROL OF NECK MUSCLES

The head shows nystagmus and compensation, much as do the eyes. In many animals, especially among the long-necked reptiles and birds, the head (rather than the eyes) does most of the compensating. Pigeons, for example, show a compensatory head nystagmus during rotation, with slow and fast components. This nystagmus, after single acceleratory stimuli, has a secondary inverse phase (Buys, 1924). In the laboratory, human subjects show little head movement during rotation. Figure 4 demonstrates, however, that at the onset of a strong stimulus there is a small amount of active head compensation with latency like that of the eyes.

Tonic labyrinthine reflexes on the muscles of the neck from changes in orientation to gravity are easily demonstrated in lower mammals, birds, and reptiles. The head turns so as to keep its normal relation to gravity (see reviews by Dusser de Barenne and by Camis and Creed). Magnus and his collaborators have studied the righting reflexes by which an animal, placed in an abnormal posture, reflexly returns to the normal position. These responses are not easy to get in the normal human adult in the laboratory, but they are present in the infant (Landau) and may be assumed to operate in the adult as one of the controls of his normal motor activity.

VESTIBULAR CONTROL OF TRUNK AND LIMBS

The vestibular apparatus is the second most important source of stimuli for postural tonus and body posture. Only the muscle receptors take precedence. Normally the vestibule acts in conjunction with other sources of stimulation, and it is not always easy to separate vestibular effects from other factors.

Effects of rotation. Dusser de Barenne hung a frog by a thread through the praemaxilla and let it rotate, meanwhile watching limb movements. The pattern is complicated, but it involves extension of the trailing limb during the acceleration, and flexion of the leading limb.* Similar re-

* Brazilian investigators (Ozorio de Almeida, Moussatché, and Vianna Dias) have verified this

sponses have been studied in rabbits and in monkeys (Dusser de Barenne).

Fischer and Wodak and others (Fischer, 1928; see review by Lange) have shown the general nature of the body response in human subjects. Suppose we rotate a subject to the right for a while and stop him (the terminal stimulus is then an acceleration acting from right to left). The subject is asked to stand with arms outstretched and to offer no voluntary resistance. The head then turns to the right (compensatory deviation), as do the trunk and arms, the left arm rises while the right is lowered, and there is a tendency for the left leg to extend, the right to flex. The resulting position has been described as that of a discus thrower.

Effects of rectilinear movement. Progressive movements cause responses of the limbs and the trunk muscles. Magnus and de Kleyn (see Magnus) and Bard (1937) have investigated the "vestibular placing reactions." If an animal (e.g. cat) is suddenly lowered, the legs extend and the toes spread. If raised, the legs flex slightly. Fischer (1928) has studied the same thing in human beings stimulated by an elevator. This response is presumably a resultant of stimuli from vestibule and musculature.

Studies of animal righting during a drop from the inverted position show a complex series of responses involving the trunk and limbs — and also the neck and eyes (Rademaker and Ter Braak; Warkentin and Carmichael). These are illustrated (Fig. 7) in the tracings from successive frames of a motion picture of the fall of a young rabbit.

Phenomena probably related to response to progressive movements are found in the pulsion reflexes affecting the limbs (the standing subject makes forward or backward compensatory movements) as a result

by an ingenious preparation in which the head can be rotated while the body is fixed for recording. They remove a section of the frog between head and lower body but retain the connection by the spinal cord.

of bilateral calorization of the ear canals (Fischer, 1928). These are best elicited when the head is about 60 degrees back (or 180 degrees from this position); they are

FIG. 7. Tracings of successive frames of a motion picture (64 frames per second) of a 20-day-old rabbit dropped while upside-down. (From Warkentin and Carmichael.)

absent in the midpositions. Therefore they may be assumed to come from simultaneous stimulation of the two horizontal canals.

Effects of head position. The most important students of the labyrinthine positional reflexes are de Kleyn and Magnus (see Magnus), who systematically studied the contribution of these responses to the righting reflexes of mammals. The nu-

merous studies of geotropic responses in animals are also relevant.

The position of the head affects the extensor tone of the limbs. In the normal standing position of the cat, for example, tone is balanced. Raising the head increases extensor tone of the forelimbs and decreases that of the hind limbs; lowering the head

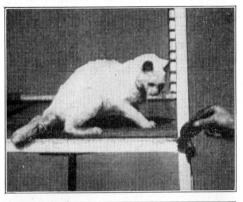

FIG. 8. Influence of head position on extensor tone of forelimbs. Lowering the muzzle reflexly decreases the tone of the forelimbs; raising it extends the forelimbs. In this case reflexes from the neck muscle cooperate with reflexes from the vestibule, causing this change. (From Camis after Magnus.)

decreases the tone in the forelegs. Figure 8 shows this for a normal cat. The positions of maximal effect are 90 degrees away from the normal head position. The nature of the response varies with species. When an animal lies on its side, the down-limbs are extended, the up-limbs flexed (Bieber and Fulton). Similar labyrinthine positional reflexes are seen in human infants and adults lacking cortical motor function (Fischer, 1928; Fulton). They presumably contribute to normal posture, but their demonstration in the normal adult in the laboratory is far from satisfactory.

Tonus. The tonic effects of the labyrinths may also be inferred from experiments showing a slight loss of extensor tone after removal of both inner ears (see McNally and Tait for review). Damage to the vestibular nuclei causes a further severe loss of tone, showing that the continuous activity of these centers is involved. The peripheral source of the tonic impulses may be from spontaneous "canal tonus," otoliths, or both (Cawthorne, Fitzgerald, and Hallpike). A decrease in oxygen consumption after labyrinthectomy may be due to loss of tonus (Ciurlo).

VESTIBULAR CONTROL OF OTHER SYSTEMS

Autonomic effectors. The data in this field * are exceptionally difficult to interpret, as compared to the simpler striped muscle effects. There are various reasons: (1) The recording methods used do not ordinarily permit adequate temporal analysis of the response. (2) The reflexes of the autonomic system are interdependent in complicated ways, having many "feedback" mechanisms. (3) Sequential or simultaneous reaction at a number of neural levels produces effects that may facilitate or inhibit one another. Arguments rage, especially over the role of "psychic" factors. In short, there is no single correct description of these behavior systems; they vary greatly with the conditions of the experiment.

* For general reviews of the autonomic effects of vestibular stimulation see Camis and Creed; Fischer, 1928; Arslan, 1939; Tenaglia; and Spiegel, 1946.

Emotional consequences of vestibular stimulation. There is an extensive literature about the emotional effects of vestibular stimulation, especially of "loss of support" (Carmichael; Armstrong; Buys, 1937; Chavany; Griffith, 1920b, c; Majer; Wendt, 1948; Schilder, 1939). The interests of investigators have included the emotional repertory of infants, the role of the body-image in ego development, and the role of anxiety in motion sickness. Stability of orientation is generally regarded as necessary to feelings of security, and vestibular disturbances or vestibular stimulation lead to feelings of insecurity, anxiety, fear, or panic.

Motion Sickness

World War II stimulated a large volume of research on motion sickness.† Motion sickness occurs, not as an immediate effect of motion, but only after stimulation has lasted for a time. Some have concluded therefore that motion sickness is not a reflex response to motion but rather a secondary result of anxiety produced by motion, or of other psychic factors (Armstrong; Green). That it is solely such a secondary phenomenon seems disproved, however, by Bard's observations that cortical lesions or even decerebration do not affect susceptibility in the dog, and that cerebellar removal prevents vomiting (Bard, personal communication).

Nature of the response. In cats and dogs the onset of sickness is shown by profuse watery salivation, urination, or anxiety behavior. As sickness progresses, the saliva becomes viscous and defecation occurs. Finally there is chop licking, retching, and vomiting. Spiegel (1944) concludes that the gastrointestinal events begin with relaxation of the fundus of the stomach, cessation of contractions, closure of the pylorus, and reverse peristalsis of the duodenum. In vomiting, the pyloric region also contracts, the cardia and esophagus relax, the glottis is

† A review of this work by Bard and Tyler is to be published in *Physiol. Rev.* See also McEachern and Lehman.

closed, with inhibition of breathing. Strong contraction of the striped musculature of the diaphragm and abdominal muscles expels the stomach contents, and other appropriate postures are part of the pattern.

In man the pattern is the same, except that urination and defecation are rare. There is local "cold sweating," distributed differently from thermal sweating (Hemingway). These events in man are usually (but not always) accompanied by unpleasant feelings of depression, by subjective muscular weakness, and by sensations of malaise referable to mouth, abdomen, and head. When the sickness is due to rotation, there may be dizziness. In exceptional cases the discomfort may last for 3 days after the motion has ceased. It is believed that in some people this whole pattern does not occur but that there is only headache.

Pregnant cats that aborted their fetuses after motion showed no signs of motion sickness, yet were harmfully affected by motion. Perhaps we can conclude that the nausea pattern is not the only "sickness" possible from motion (Cramer and Wendt, unpublished).

Factors producing sickness. The vestibule is primarily involved in the production of motion sickness, as is shown by the fact that those deaf people who show no vestibular sensitivity do not get sick (McNally and Stuart). Rotation causes sickness when the acceleration and deceleration are separated in time (Alexander et al., 1945a), as in automobiles on mountain roads or in acrobatic flying, but not when movement phases are short, as in normal head movements. On the rotating chair, nausea is rare so long as the head is fixed (Fischer, 1928; and personal observation), but rotation in several planes favors sickness. Repeated rectilinear accelerations acting along the vertical axis of the head, as for the seated passenger in an airplane in rough air or on a heaving ship, are the most common cause of sickness. Experiments with other motions and other head positions indicate that there can

be little effect of the lateral motion due to the roll of ships (*Aero med. Ass. Proc.*). Waves of moderate frequency and acceleration cause sickness quicker than either very gentle or very rough waves (Alexander et al., 1947). A 7-foot wave of 22 cycles per minute produced sickness in 53 per cent of a group of naval officers within 20 minutes. Yet the head rotations of everyday life and the rough movements of walking and running do not make one sick. The mechanism by which certain waves produce sickness is not yet known.

Common experience shows that other stimuli facilitate or inhibit motion sickness. Moving visual objects or visual disorientation (Witkin), unpleasant odors, and uncomfortable warmth probably facilitate sickness, whereas an interesting task, pleasant odors and comfortable temperature inhibit it. Pilots and drivers, for reasons unknown, rarely become sick; passengers often do.

Psychic factors play a variable role, depending on the person and the situation. The identifiable factors are expectation of sickness, influence of suggestion from others, conditioning by past sickness to the stimuli associated with motion, the protective effects of habituation, effects of concurrent activity, emotional state (anxiety, etc.), conscious or unrecognized desire to become sick, and neurotic patterns of adjustment (Wendt, 1948). These factors probably operate maximally for airsickness, owing to the novelty of air travel, and least for sickness due to the more accepted modes of transportation.

Susceptibility is greatest in childhood, decreasing during adolescence and adulthood, and it is greater in women than in men. At the present time susceptibility is most frequent to airplanes, then to boats, automobiles, streetcars, and trains, in that order. About 20 per cent of college students have never been motion sick, and about 5 per cent suffer often enough to consider it a handicap. It is possible that motion sickness is associated with extreme neuroticism and with migraine, but for the general population it appears to be unrelated to neurotic tendency. Personality correlates of susceptibility other than neuroticism are not, however, excluded. Previous history of motion sickness and frequency of vomiting in other situations are prognostic (Alexander et al., 1945*b*; Wendt, 1946*a, b*; Birren, Fisher, and Stormont).

Prevention. About three-fourths of motion sickness is preventable. When sickness is psychologically influenced, as in a first airplane trip, psychological procedures may help greatly. Habituation helps, but its effects may be temporary if the person has a history of motion sickness. Its effects are probably lasting when the person habituates without allowing sickness ever to occur (Van de Water and Wendt). The laboratory experiments on direction of forces suggest that placing the head so that forces act at right angles to the vertical axis, e.g. by reclining, would prevent sickness. Certain drugs are effective. Hyoscine hydrobromide, a belladonna derivative, 0.6 milligram by mouth, reduces average sickness rates by 60 per cent when given to all passengers 2 hours before motion (Tyler, 1946). An antihistaminic drug, trade-named Dramamine, seems to have not only a fairly good preventive action but also a curative action (Gay and Carliner). How these drugs prevent sickness is not known. By finding how they do it, we may find how motion sickness is brought about.

PERCEPTION OF MOVEMENT AND POSITION VIA THE VESTIBULE

Is there a vestibular sense? Unlike the other senses discussed in this volume, few of the data on the vestibule come from the study of sensations. There is, in fact, no agreement that there are *unique* sensory qualities from rotation, rectilinear motion, or position. There are several reasons for this: (1) We are not sure whether there is a cortical vestibular projection area. (2) It it introspectively hard to distinguish possible vestibular from kinesthetic sensations, especially when reflexes of the trunk and limbs and autonomic systems complicate the experience, or to separate them from vision, when the eyes are open. (3) We lack words in our language to distinguish phenomenal motion from the physical event. (4) This, plus the sheer intellectual difficulty involved in thinking about a set of data where the sensations often have little relation to what is being done to the subject, makes for confusion. These difficulties prevent our knowing whether there is a vestibular sense modality. Griffith (1922), who denied its existence, stated:

> We have found the experience of dizziness or vertigo to be made up of a large number of processes the most prominent of which are (1) kinesthesis from the eyes, neck and in the arms, (2) pressure from the region of the abdominal viscera, the chest and head, and (3) certain vascular processes which supply an obscure background and which give to the whole experience a characteristic shading.

Despite this alternative possibility, it is my tentative opinion that there are unique vestibular sensations from rotation, movement, and position. Spiegel's data on a possible cortical projection area suggest it. And the experience of rotation near threshold, the experience of sinking slowly while under water, and the awareness of the direction of gravity while under water do not appear in my own introspection as kinesthetic. Although, to be sure, there is no proof that the rotational experience is not of extra-ocular muscle origin (since there is nystagmus), such an explanation fits less well the experiences of straight-line movement or position.

A point against the notion of a special vestibular sense is that the experiences of rotation, movement, and position are introspectively similar when the visual field is rotated or moved (as when the train on the next track moves) or given a tilt (as in the tilted-room experiment), or when a sound is rotated about the head (the sound is heard as stationary, cf. Dodge). Since these sensations of body movement or position do not require the vestibule, it is concluded that there need be no vestibular sense. But seen motion is a similar experience whether the moving object is fixated (and thus "seen" to move via the kinesthetic sense) or allowed to move across the visual field (and thus seen to move via changing visual pattern). Arguing from these facts alone we might as well claim that, since the experience of motion requires no kinesthesis (or vision), kinesthesis (or vision) does not exist. Experiments could perhaps be devised to shed light on this question. What, for instance, are the introspections of a subject with complete anesthetization of all extraocular muscles, or of a subject after loss of both eyes?

At any rate, if there are unique vestibular qualities, we may speculate that their major attributes are sensations of rotation, rectilinear movement, and position. Presumably the first two vary also in direction, intensity, and complexity. Holt (1910) found that the common element in rotational experiences at threshold was only a "feeling" of rotation, also described as a "swimming sensation." As speed of movement rises, the experience becomes more complex (Griffith, 1920c). The subject may then call it "dizziness," a term he may also use when visual objects appear to rotate about him. "Vertigo," a complex of sensations with autonomic components and an unpleasant feeling tone, is another term used. This experience is not confined to the results of vestibular stimulation (Witkin). The several sensory qualities aroused by bodily rotation and by the responses to it are introspectively difficult or impossible to tell apart. These difficulties have also been recognized in the problems of space perception and of

the body-image * (Göthlin; Marburg; Schilder, 1942).

Sensations of rotation when vision is allowed. For a subject on a rotating chair with eyes open, the course of events is quite different from that for a subject with closed eyes. When the subject turns at 180 degrees per second and then stops, the sensations are as follows: First he feels that he is turning, the room being fixed. Or he may feel as though he and the room are both rotating within some outer fixed space. After a time this may be replaced by the feeling that he is still while the room whirls around him. On stopping, the subject seems to spin and the room with him. This may be replaced by movement of the room alone. Finally everything seems to come to rest, but he still feels vague sensations, as though he were not back to normal.

When the rotation is done in a dark room with a faint fixation light mounted on the chair, the sensations are the same after acceleration as after deceleration. First, both self and light rotate, then light alone rotates as for full vision. The movement of such a faint light is called "oculogyral movement" (Graybiel et al.). In this case, however, there may be a brief pause at the end of the primary phase of movement of the light, followed by a secondary inverse phase. It seems, then, that a faint light does not inhibit the secondary nystagmus as does full vision.

Instead of a fixation light, one can use an after-image of a strong light as the object whose movement is reported. Its movement is in the same direction as that of the slow phase of nystagmus, being opposite to that produced when the image of an actual light

---

* The literature of "vestibular sensations" is chiefly old, written before adequate recording techniques for analysis of the response systems were devised. Darwin (1801), Purkinje (1820), Crum Brown (1878), Mach (1878), Holt (1910), and Griffith (1920b, c) may be consulted (see Griffith, 1922). More recent work has been done by Travis, and by Fischer and his collaborators (Fischer, 1928). For reviews, see Griffith (1922); Leiri; Fischer (1928).

moves across the retina. In oculogyral movement, the light, although moving constantly, does not seem to change its position, whereas with an after-image the light does change position and returns during the saccadic phase.

DAMAGE TO THE VESTIBULE

The effects of damage to parts of the vestibule, of unilateral or bilateral removal in various animals, and of peripheral disease and removal in man have been studied by many experimental and clinical investigators. The phenomena following such damage are very complex but in some ways most instructive. For reviews, see Dusser de Barenne; Camis and Creed; McNally and Stuart; and others noted below.

Otolith organs. Separate surgical damage to the otolith organs can be done in frogs and some fish, but it is hard or impossible in warm-blooded forms. The heavy otolith membrane may be torn loose (in both low and high forms) by "centrifuging" the animal (Maxwell; Dusser de Barenne; Camis and Creed; McNally and Stuart; Hasegawa, 1935). Extirpation of the saccule is apparently without effect on the labyrinthine compensatory reflexes, but this has not settled the problem of whether it has vestibular functions. Utricular function may be studied by destroying all the canals. In frogs, posture is then nearly normal, righting reflexes are present but slow, and the animal jumps, but somewhat clumsily. If the utricles are taken out, leaving the canals, the righting reflexes are also present and the animals are able to jump, but must be prodded to do so. After the centrifuging off of the otolith membranes of guinea pigs or frogs, tonic labyrinthine reflexes remain (Dusser de Barenne). It seems, then, that reflexes to position and linear acceleration come from both otoliths and canals.

Canals. The experiments using a pneumatic hammer, those on rotation after plugging single canals, and those on electrical recording from the nerve show the contribution to function of each canal. These studies are supplemented by those in which all canals except one are destroyed, or one ear is destroyed and the animal is rotated in different planes. Results are ambiguous, for both lower and higher forms, as to whether each canal is unidirectional, bidirectional, or multidirectional in response to rotation in various planes (Maxwell; Lowenstein, 1937; Camis and Creed; Cawthorne, Fitzgerald, and Hallpike; Sand). It is probable that the horizontal canal is bidirectional but that it causes stronger reflexes on rotation toward its own side. The responses of this canal to rotation in opposed directions need not be of the same nature. The mechanism of the effect of rotation away from the side of the canal may be by suppression of a tonic discharge, whereas opposite rotation may truly stimulate. The vertical canals are less understood but may tentatively be assumed to work like the horizontal canal.

The experiments on injury to single parts of the labyrinth show that the remaining parts, although somewhat impaired or changed, usually support all the reflex responses. This forces us to give up the view that each part alone has a special function and to recognize the functional duplication of parts.

Labyrinthectomy. Animal experiments on the removal of a whole labyrinth (or the cutting of an VIIIth nerve) are more revealing than studies of man. Human cases of loss of the receptor are available as a result of inherited defect, labyrinthine infection (labyrinthitis), Ménière's disease, or surgery.*

---

* A brief statement on the reasons for surgical interference with the human labyrinth is in order, since a large literature exists in this field. This is done for relief of Ménière's syndrome, which may be treated by intracranial cutting of the nerve, by cutting only its vestibular division, by surgical labyrinthectomy, or by alcohol injection into the labyrinth. Ménière's "disease" has been ascribed to many causes. The best present evidence is that it is due to distention of the labyrinth from an

The immediate effects of bilateral labyrinthectomy or VIIIth nerve section vary with phylogenetic status (Maxwell; Camis and Creed). They are quite striking in the pigeon, which shows violent movements and is unable to hold itself upright. After several days some recovery occurs, probably through use of kinesthetic and visual senses to control the movements. The pigeon stands and walks unsteadily and holds up its head except while asleep. It does not fly or feed itself again. The immediate and late effects in mammals are much less striking, decreasing in the higher forms (Dow, 1938; Ferraro and Barrera). There is unsteadiness in standing, tremor of the head, and impaired running, jumping, etc., especially when the eyes are covered.

Deaf people often lack vestibular response. About 20 per cent lack all response, and about another 65 per cent have varying degrees of vestibular deficit (Tenaglia and Scevola; Vastine). They have poor equilibrium, but not poor enough to handicap them noticeably. There is a correlation between extent of hearing loss and of vestibular deficit.

The immediate effects of the loss of one ear also become less as we ascend the phylogenetic scale (Magnus; Dandy and Kunkel; Dow, 1938; Camis and Creed; Ferraro and

overproduction of endolymph. This has been ascribed to allergy, histamine sensitivity, disorders of adrenals, thyroids, or gonads, autonomic imbalance, dietary deficiencies, lack of vitamin B complex, etc. The afflicted patient has occasional sudden violent vestibular "storms" of unilateral peripheral origin (although the disease process is bilateral; cf. Cawthorne, Fitzgerald, and Hallpike), in which usually he falls, has extreme vertigo, and is severely nauseated (Cawthorne; Cawthorne, Fitzgerald, and Hallpike; Crowe). "The overwhelming vertigo, the awful sickness and the turbulent eye movements—all enhanced by the slightest movement of the head—combine to form a picture of helpless misery that has few parallels in the whole field of injury and disease" (Cawthorne, p. 271). In response to the pleas of wretched patients, surgeons have removed the offending source, even though the opposite ear may later become affected. For review of the literature see Altman and Fowler; Brunner, 1939; Grove; McLaurin; Simonton.

Barrera). In the monkey, in the earliest postoperative period, there may be much disturbance when movements are tried. The animal then lies on its side with the remaining labyrinth up, with the head bent away from the good labyrinth and turned toward it. The eyes show a continuous nystagmus (mainly horizontal) with the slow phase away from the good ear. In man the postural effects are usually inhibited (perhaps because the patient is relaxed in bed), but there is nystagmus.

These immediate effects decrease with time in all forms, owing to the development of a central compensation and to increasing dominance of other senses. In animals below mammals postural defects are permanent. Dow (1938) found that in the rhesus monkey nystagmus lasted for a day, then became occasional, and was not seen on the third day. Recovery, at least from the postural defects, was faster in baboons and chimpanzees (see also Northington and Barrera; Ferraro and Barrera). Observations of man conform to this picture (Cawthorne, Fitzgerald, and Hallpike). There is at first a strong spontaneous nystagmus. At this time the nystagmus is strengthened by rotation toward the remaining ear; it is slowed by weak opposite rotation or reversed in direction by stronger stimuli. This spontaneous nystagmus soon comes under the control of vision, but when the eyes are closed it persists in decreasing amount for at least several weeks (Wendt, unpublished). Shaking the head from side to side reestablishes the nystagmus for a time. Even after many years, rotation toward the good ear produces excessive response (Fischer, 1928; Cawthorne, Fitzgerald, and Hallpike). It has been noted that the loss of function in a diseased ear may be so slow that compensation keeps pace with the loss, with the result that no symptoms are noticed by the patient (Fernando and de Ocampo).

Effects of a second labyrinthectomy after compensation for the first. Phenomena of the greatest theoretical importance occur when, after one ear is removed and partial or complete compensation is allowed to occur, the second ear is then removed. In this behavior system there is a good chance to study the neural mechanisms underlying the recovery of function. Bechterew in 1883 cut out one labyrinth from the dog. This operation caused a nystagmus that decreased and in time disappeared. Removal of the second ear (producing an animal with no afferent input from the vestibules) was then followed again by a prolonged nystagmus, opposite in direction to the original. This, too, disappeared within a few days. Bechterew's nystagmus, as it has since been called, has been studied in a number of animal forms (Carréga, Appaix, and Paillas; Dow, 1938; Gatteschi; MacKenzie; Pike). The only reasonable explanation for these eye movements is that the original compensation was due to some change in activity of the nerve centers that counterbalanced the effects of the input from the remaining vestibule. On removal of the second ear this central compensation is left unbalanced, producing a nystagmus.

The central compensation that causes Bechterew's nystagmus is seen in animals after removal of the cortex or the cerebellum (Cawthorne, Fitzgerald, and Hallpike; Ross and Olsen). This, plus the fact that one-sided injury to the vestibular nuclei can cause a nystagmus for which compensation never develops, leads to the hypothesis that the nuclei are the site of the compensation. There are, however, two aspects of this recovery process. One is central compensation for the unbalanced activity of the remaining vestibule. The other is the learning process by means of which visual, kinesthetic, and other stimuli gain dominance over the vestibular reflexes and come to substitute for them. The latter process has apparently not been studied, but it is certainly different from the compensatory process accounting for Bechterew's nystagmus.

Damage to the Central Parts of the Vestibular System *

The vestibular responses are mostly low-level reflexes. One gets nystagmus with both slow and fast phases in the absence of all brain except the vestibular nuclei and ocular motor centers. In an anencephalic child lacking cerebrum, cerebellum, and all except the posterior brain stem, containing the abducens nucleus, and having only abducens muscles, de Kleyn and Schenk recorded a nystagmus contraction pattern. Conversely, damage to the midbrain and medulla produces defects in the righting reflexes and leads to permanent abnormalities of posture and to nystagmus (Buchanan; Falkenberg; Ferraro and Barrera; Lurie and Dempsey; Magnus; Nylén; Rademaker; Seiferth; and reviews). Decortication, decerebration, and decerebellation, or decerebration plus decerebellation leave nystagmus normal and do not change the essential pattern of postural reflexes from the vestibule (Buchanan, 1939; Dow, 1942; Dusser de Barenne; Halstead, Yacorzynski, and Fearing; Yacorzynski, Halstead, and Fearing). The effects of visual stimuli upon the vestibular systems are lessened or lost after decortication or decerebration, and all these procedures reduce habituation to rotation. More limited lesions in the frontal lobes cause changes in the postural effects of the vestibule and lengthen after-nystagmus (Austregesilo and Borges Fortes; Delmas-Marsalet, 1936; Jayle; Kennard and Ectors). Temporal lobe lesions that include the supposed labyrinthine projection area cause a spontaneous nystagmus

* This review will be brief. The reader should consult reviews for details concerning this field. See especially Barré, 1937a, 1938; Dusser de Barenne; Van Gehuchten; Leidler; Magnus; Rademaker; Riley. For reviews and data on the vestibular effects of tumors, concussions, gunshot wounds, and such diseases as Parkinsonism, encephalitis, syringomyelia, and multiple sclerosis, see Barré, 1938; Leidler; Alexander and Scholl; Falkenberg, 1942; Nylén; Brunner, 1936a, b; Delmas-Marsalet, 1936; Fitzgerald and Hallpike; Frazier and Rowe; Gibbs; Jayle; Kolodny; Moruzzi; Müller; Seiferth.

and increase the after-nystagmus (Barré, 1937*b*; Fitzgerald and Hallpike; Kolodny). Such increased after-nystagmus may be due to a reduction in the inhibitory action of vision. Cortical lesions do not prevent formation of conditioned responses to angular acceleration (Oppenheimer and Spiegel).

Search for the mechanism of the fast phase of vestibular nystagmus has been actively pursued, but without complete success. The alternations of direction of eye movement in nystagmus have been attributed to rhythmically alternating peripheral vestibular discharge, but this is most unlikely. The response is not caused by proprioceptive stimulation from the antagonistic eye muscles, as is shown by the following facts (de Kleyn and Schenk; McIntyre; Kollner and Hoffman; de Maré; McCouch and Adler; Dohlman, 1925). (1) A single muscle, the others cut away, shows alternating slow and fast phases. (2) Stretching a muscle produces no stretch reflex and is without any effect on nystagmus. (3) Local anesthetic applied to the efferent and afferent fibers of a muscle, presumed to affect sensory fibers first, has no effect on nystagmus until the motor fibers are affected. The notion that the fast phase is from the cortex was based on the alleged observation that only the slow phase is present under general anesthesia and in coma (Alfandary, 1937; Dohlman, 1938*b*). This observation may be questioned on the ground that the eye deviation is probably not the slow phase. It must first be shown that the slow deviation observed is actually conjugate and is quantitatively related to the stimulus. The present tendency is to localize the centers responsible for the fast phase in Deiter's nucleus and in the reticulate substance (Dohlman, 1938*b*; Spiegel and Price). Lorente de Nó (1939) has proposed a mechanism by which these centers could produce such an alternating response. It seems more reasonable, however, to expect to find this mechanism associated with the ocular muscle nuclei. It is difficult to believe that the slow phases of

both visual and vestibular nystagmus come from the vestibular nuclei, because of the way they interact under conflict. And, if the visual slow phase does not use these nuclei, then the fast phase would be unlikely to come from them. On the other hand, the many functional likenesses between the fast phase of visual and vestibular nystagmus suggest that they have a common source. It seems reasonable to place this at the natural point of convergence of the systems.

Theory of balanced centers. Högyes in 1881 (Sugár, p. 134) suggested that the vestibular centers operate as though in a balance. One may think of the nuclei on each side as being in continuous, partly self-maintained activity. (Tonic impulses from the vestibule may contribute to it.) So long as this activity is equal (i.e. "balanced"), tonus distribution is normal and the eyes do not move. Stimulation raises or depresses the activity of one side of the system (thereby producing reflex change), and the balance is only gradually restored. The evidence for such a theory rests on the presence of circular circuits, on the studies of Bechterew's nystagmus and of compensation after unilateral labyrinthectomy, and on the nystagmus produced by unilateral lesions of the nuclei (Lorente de Nó, 1933; Cawthorne, Fitzgerald, and Hallpike).

MODIFIABILITY OF THE VESTIBULAR SYSTEMS

The vestibular systems are in some ways highly modifiable; in others not at all.

That the postural reflexes are greatly affected by learning is shown by their absence in adults, except as a substrate for coordination, and by the fact that effects due to the loss of one ear are soon overcome. Nystagmus comes under learned control by the use of vision, especially in dancers and acrobats. Voluntary control is possible to some extent by near-fixation or by looking in the direction of the slow phase (Griffith, 1920).

The compensation after loss of an ear may rest on the same mechanism as the "disembarkation syndrome" after a sea trip or other prolonged motion. Others have given anecdotal accounts of this syndrome (Larroudé) and I shall add my own to these. One summer, after 9 days in the most forward cabin of a light cruiser, I felt decreasing effects for 6 days after landing. My bed felt as though I were still at sea, and I was quite unsteady in walking. After the first 2 days I experienced these effects only on waking and for a short time after rising.

Learning experiments in the laboratory have been directed at two phases of the effects of repetition of stimuli, conditioning and habituation. These effects may proceed collaterally, but they are different in nature.

Conditioned responses. Vestibular stimuli have been used both as conditioned stimuli and as unconditioned stimuli. Spiegel and Oppenheimer, using dogs, found that responses based on electric shock to the leg could be conditioned to a rotation stimulus, linear movement, or to a particular position in space. Differentiation and other phenomena were shown. Wendt (1936*b*) used rotation through short arcs as the unconditioned stimulus (human subjects) with sound as the conditioned stimulus. Apparently the slow phase of the response cannot be conditioned. The fast phase, on the other hand, is conditioned, in the sense that anticipatory responses to sound appear before the rotation. There is a "regularization" of timing of saccadics during the rotation, and there is a learned inhibition of saccadics coinciding with the end of rotation. Löwenbach and Gantt used sound as the conditioned stimulus and a galvanic vestibular stimulus as the unconditioned stimulus with dogs, recording the postural adjustments. The characteristic body movements were conditioned.

Habituation. For a time following World War I few subjects could so arouse American psychologists as the question whether there was habituation to rotation (Dunlap, 1919). Disagreements had arisen with Medical Corps otologists, who denied that the Bárány tests of nystagmus used in airplane pilot selection showed reduction on repetition. We can now see that both groups could have been right. Under certain circumstances there is a reduction in the duration of nystagmus (and of all other consequences of stimulation, including sensory and autonomic). In fact, the typical course of events on repetition of stimulation is habituation of all parts to the response (see reviews by Harris; Mowrer, 1934*b*; McNally and Stuart). Under other circumstances the character of ocular nystagmus, at least, may remain wholly unchanged. My own rotation nystagmus, for example, is still normal after 20 years of using myself as subject. Careful investigators such as Dohlman and Buys have obviously obtained repeated records of nystagmus that did not suffer from habituation.

The resolution of this contradiction has not previously been successful. I believe, however, that the reasons for it are clear in the evidence. There are two factors in habituation, two kinds, in fact, which may be present separately or together. The one shows up especially in the usual method of observing after-nystagmus with the subject's eyes open. In this case visual stimuli tend to inhibit the vestibular nystagmus, and with repetition these stimuli become increasingly dominant. Such habituation is probably not preventable. The other shows up even with the eyes closed. In this case loss of nystagmus occurs when the subject fails to remain alert to his external surroundings. This habituation is preventable by keeping the subject attentive to the external surrounds and avoiding inward-directed revery states.

I shall describe the character of this second kind of habituation from my own experiments on human subjects and on monkeys (1936*a*). Highly magnified records of eye movements to rotation, taken simultaneously from both eyes (through closed lids), show that "habituation" occurs as a competition between the vestibular reflex and another system of control of the eyes. This system consists of an autogenous wandering of the eyes in a nonconjugate manner such as has been described in states of sleep, unconsciousness or coma. The reflex and this system compete for control in an almost either-or fashion. There are usually sharp, bilaterally simultaneous transitions from reflex to wandering movement and from wandering movement to reflex. Figure 9 shows such periods of interruption of nystagmus, bracketed for ease of identification. The first appearance of these periods of nonconjugate movement, during a series of rotations, is usually in that portion of a response when nystagmus is weak, as at the end of the primary phase of nystagmus. With continued stimulation it encroaches further, or it may appear several times during the course of a prolonged nystagmus. The records resemble, in abruptness of the rivalry, those taken when strong visual rivalry is introduced and withdrawn, except that the onset of the wandering movement is sharper. These autogenous movements are apparently like those under general anesthesia, in coma, and in normal sleep (Alfandary) and are identical with those present in animals when immobilized, i.e. so-called "animal hypnosis" (Wendt, 1936a).

Not all subjects can avoid such habituation. Usually, however, it can be done. When monkeys are used as subjects, any strange sound (clicking the fingernails, watch tick), blowing lightly against the face, or bringing a piece of banana to the nose will restore nystagmus immediately. Closing the monkey's nostrils with the fingers is a sure way to do it. With human subjects, properly instructed and stimulated, alertness can be maintained for continuous 10-minute periods of recording. The trick is to maintain an environment-directed orientation.

Conversely, factors that favor an inward orientation of attention — such as firm body support, darkness, quiet, regularity, and monotony — favor autogenous movement (Griffith, 1920a, b; Mowrer, 1934a, b;

Dorcus; Wendt, 1936a). Sleeping infants are said to show no nystagmus (see McNally and Stuart). It is also suggestive that catatonic schizophrenics have reduced nystagmus times. The correlation of vestibular response with personality traits relevant to internali-

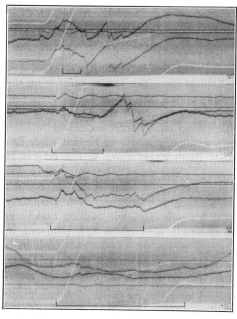

FIG. 9. "Habituation" to 65-degree rotation. Four photographic records of human nystagmus showing periods of interruption (bracketed) by an intruding eye-movement system (habituation). In the lowest record there is a brief return of nystagmus (at the point where a fast phase occurs). Note in this record also that the eyes drift in a nonconjugate way both before and after the rotation.

zation of reference has been made by Buck (1936) and is currently under investigation by Syz and by Witkin and Wapner.

The neural origin of this competing control of eye movements is probably different from that of the slow phase of nystagmus. Were they the same, there could presumably be no sharp alternations between wandering movement and reflex within a single nystagmus sequence. On the other hand, habituation occurs after decerebration and decerebellation. A number of facts suggest likenesses between the wandering movement and the saccadic movement. Perhaps their nerve mechanisms are related.

Dodge (1923a) introduced a disturbing confusion when he stated that habituation is due to loss of the saccadic phase, so that only ocular deviation occurs. This has been repeatedly quoted as fact. This conception confuses two processes, the one a resystematization of the vestibular response, which is an active conditioning process, the other the intrusion of the autogenous wandering due to habituation. The former effect is on the spacing of the fast phases in the vestibular reflex. They become regularized and may either drop out (during oscillating rotation with an alert subject) or become more frequent (with longer turns with a subject in revery). The other effect is due to the dominance of the other system of control, the autogenous wandering. This frequently produces a deviated eye position that looks as though a slow phase had produced it. But the movement toward this position is not the slow phase of the reflex, as Dodge supposed; it is a nonconjugate movement bearing little direct relation to the stimulus. Both processes, resystematization of the nystagmus and competition for dominance by the autogenous movement, may proceed concurrently.

With vision allowed, there is little loss of nystagmus during rotation, but great reduction of the after-nystagmus with repetition. Dodge (1923a) ascribed the latter to the increasing dominance of the visual stimulus; nystagmus is replaced by visual still-fixation (cf. Mowrer, 1934b). However, I have seen (especially in monkeys) the eventual appearance of autogenous wandering of the eyes even when they were open. Most human subjects presumably find the visual surrounds of sufficient interest to hold an environmentally focused body localization. Hence, habituation in human subjects with open eyes is usually due to increased visual dominance, whereas in monkeys both types of habituation may occur.

Much effort has gone into the study of habituation as a learning process. In "well-controlled" experiments, where no instructions about attention are given to the subject and extraneous stimuli that might keep the subject alert are intentionally avoided, habituation, as indicated by lessened duration of after-nystagmus, is at first rapid and then proceeds more slowly. It is favored by spaced repetition and shows some transfer from one type of stimulus to another (Dodge, 1923a; Dorcus; Dunlap, 1925; Fearing; Griffith, 1920a, b, c; King; Maxwell and Pilz; Mowrer, 1934b).

If one adopts the views here presented on the nature of habituation to rotation, most of the quarrels between the psychologists and other groups can probably be resolved. I suspect that many of the latter have used attention-directing devices, thereby avoiding the autogenous eye wandering. When such wandering has occurred, the fact has probably been overlooked. One of Dohlman's published records, for example, appears to show the wandering (Dohlman, 1925, plate I, record 466 at 140 seconds).

REFERENCES

Attention is called to the following sources of information concerning certain topics not covered in the text of the chapter because of limitations on space.

Theory of action receptors, theory of caloric nystagmus (Dohlman, 1925; Schmaltz);

Vestibular images, etc. (de Morsier; Hoff and Pötzl; Schilder);

Body and limb reflexes (Magnus; McNally, 1937; Fischer, 1928; O'Neill; Lange; Angyal and Sherman; Spiegel and Sommer; Dorcus and Mowrer; Galamini; Holsopple; Hirsch; Birren);

Circulatory reflexes (Baitschenko, Krestownikow, and Losanow; Rosselli del Turco; Marinesco; Spiegel, 1946; Patroni; Scevola and Ventura Gregorini; Wojatschek; Streiff, Montandon, and Monnier; Welling; Spiegel, Henry, and Wycis; Tenaglia);

Other autonomic effects (Bozzi and Ciurlo; Welling; Gatteschi and Rodolfo-Masera; Spiegel, 1946; Galamini; Cojazzi; Hitchcock and Ferguson; Mayerson, Sweeney, and Toth; Nielson, Herrington, and Winslow; Alexander et al.; Huxley; Nöel-Patton);

Sense of movement and position (Fischer, 1928); and

Psychoanalytic studies (Isakower; Marburg; Schilder, 1939).

Adrian, E. D. Discharges from vestibular receptors in the cat. *J. Physiol.*, 1942, **101**, 389–407.

Aero med. Ass. Proc., 1948. W. R. Franks (Ed.). (In press.)

Alexander, A., and R. Scholl. Beschwerden und Störungen in Hör- und Gleichgewichtsorgan bei der Nachuntersuchung Schädelverletzter. *Mschr. Ohrenheilk.*, 1938, **72**, 1021–1058.

Alexander, S. J., M. Cotzin, C. J. Hill, Jr., E. A. Ricciuti, and G. R. Wendt. Wesleyan University studies of motion sickness: I. The effects of variation of time intervals between accelerations upon sickness rates. *J. Psychol.*, 1945a, **19**, 49–62. VI. Prediction of motion sickness on a vertical accelerator by means of a motion sickness history questionnaire. *Ibid.*, 1945b, **20**, 25–30.

Alexander, S. J., M. Cotzin, J. B. Klee, and G. R. Wendt. Studies of motion sickness: XVI. The effects upon sickness rates of waves of various frequencies but identical acceleration. *J. exp. Psychol.*, 1947, **37**, 440–448.

Alexander, S. J., J. S. Helmick, C. J. Hill, and G. R. Wendt. III. A second experimental comparison of autonomic responses in individuals susceptible and non-susceptible to motion sickness. In *Studies in motion sickness* (Ser. C). Washington, D. C.: Civil Aeronautics Administration, Division of Research, 1946.

Alfandary, I. Du nystagmus provoqué dans les états comateux. *Rev. d'oto-neuro-opht.*, 1937, **15**, 161–169.

Alfandary, I. Introduction a l'étude de la dysharmonie vestibulaire. *Rev. d'oto-neuro-opht.*, 1938, **16**, 577–605.

Allard, A. Contribution a l'étude de la sensibilité de l'appareil semi-circulaire, par la méthode des petites stimulations primaires, post-rotatoires, realisées au moyen du fauteuil Buys-Rylant. *Ann. d'oto-laryng.*, 1938, **1**, 417–423.

Altmann, F., and E. P. Fowler, Jr. Histological findings in Ménière's symptom complex. *Ann. Otol. Rhinol. Laryngol.*, 1943, **52**, 52–80.

Angyal, A., and N. Blackman. Paradoxical vestibular reactions in schizophrenia under the influence of alcohol, hyperpnea and CO_2 inhalation. *Amer. J. Psychiat.*, 1941, **97**, 894–903.

Angyal, A., and M. A. Sherman. Postural reactions to vestibular stimulation in schizophrenic and normal subjects. *Amer. J. Psychiat.*, 1942, **98**, 857–862.

Armstrong, H. G. *Principles and practice of aviation medicine.* Baltimore: Williams and Wilkins, 1939.

Arslan, K. Introduction a l'étude de la dysharmonie vestibulaire. *Rev. d'oto-neuro-opht.*, 1938, **16**, 649–663.

Arslan, K. Sui rapporti tra sistema nervoso vegetativo e apparato vestibolare. *Riv. clin. Med.*, 1939, **17**, 3–48.

Austregesilo, A., and A. Borges Fortes. Syndrome de déséquilibre et ataxie frontale. *Encéphale*, 1936, **31**, 1–14.

Baitschenko, I. P., A. N. Krestownikow, and N. N. Losanow. Weitere Untersuchungen über den Einfluss des vegetativen Nervensystems auf das Zentrum des vestibularen Nerven. *Fiziol. Zh. S.S.S.R.*, 1936, **21**, 353–366.

Bárány, R. *Physiologie und Pathologie des Bogengangapparates beim Menschen.* Vienna: Deuticke, 1907.

Barbey, E., and G. de Morsier. La prédominance unilaterale de la direction du nystagmus provoqué. *Ann. d'oto-laryng.*, 1938, **1**, 46–59.

Bard, P. Studies on the cortical representation of somatic sensibility. *Harvey Lect.*, 1937–38, **33**, 143–169.

Barré, J. A. Essai sur les syndromes topographiques des voies vestibulaires centrales de l'homme. *Rev. d'oto-neuro-opht.*, 1937a, **15**, 353–432.

Barré, J. A. Les troubles vestibulaires et de l'équilibre statique dans les tumeurs du lobe temporals (d'après huits cas personnels). *J. belge Neurol. Psychiat.*, 1937b, **37**, 238–261.

Barré, J. A. Essai sur les syndromes topographiques des voies vestibulaires centrales de l'homme. *Rev. d'oto-neuro-opht.*, 1938, **16**, 417–509.

Barré, J. A. Sur la dysréflexie vestibulaire croisée. Sa valeur en tant que signe objectif chez les traumatisés craniens. *Rev. neurol.*, 1942, **74**, 311–312.

Bartels, M., and S. Ziba. Über Regulierung der Augenstellung durch den Ohrapparat. *Arch. Ophthal.*, 1910, **76**, 1–97.

Békésy, G. von. Über akustische Reizung des Vestibularapparates. *Pflüg. Arch. ges. Physiol.*, 1935, **236**, 59–76.

Bieber, I., and J. F. Fulton. The relation of the cerebral cortex to the grasp reflex and to the postural and righting reflexes. *Arch. Neurol. Psychiat., Chicago*, 1938, **39**, 435–454.

Birren, J. E. Static equilibrium and vestibular function. *J. exp. Psychol.*, 1945, **35**, 127–133.

Birren, J. E., M. B. Fisher, and R. T. Stormont. Evaluation of a motion sickness questionnaire in predicting susceptibility to seasickness. *Nav. med. Bull., Wash.*, 1945, **45**, 629–634.

Bozzi, E., and L. Ciurlo. Modificazioni volumetriche della milzo in sequito a eccitamento labirintico. *Arch. ital. Otol.*, 1936, **48**, 83–101.

Brunner, H. Beiträge zur otologischen Diagnostik der Hirntumoren. XVI. Ergebnisse der kalorischen Prüfung des Labyrinthes bei Hirntumoren. *Mschr. Ohrenheilk.*, 1936a, **70**, 206–221.

Brunner, H. Beiträge zur otologischen Diagnostik der Hirntumoren. XVII. Ergebnisse der bilateralen Kalorisation bei Hirntumoren. *Mschr. Ohrenheilk.*, 1936b, **70**, 278–288.

Brunner, H. Ménière's syndrome. *Laryngoscope*, 1939, **49**, 877–911.

Buchanan, A. R. Vestibular harmony and disharmony in guinea pigs with lesions in the cerebellum and brain stem. *Mschr. Psychiat. Neurol.*, 1939–40, **102**, 312–326.

Buchanan, A. R. Circling in guinea pigs with lesions in the brain stem. *Proc. Soc. exp. Biol.*, 1940a, **45**, 389–391.

Buchanan, A. R. Nystagmus and eye deviations in guinea pigs with lesions in the brain stem. *Laryngoscope*, 1940b, **50**, 1002–1011.

Buck, H. Ein Beitrag zur Lehre vom Drehschwindel und den Konstitutionstypen. *Untersuch. Psychol. Phil.*, 1936, **11**, No. 2, p. 58.

Buys, E. Contribution à l'étude du nystagmus oculaire de la rotation chez l'homme. *Rev. d'oto-neuro-ocul.*, 1924–25, **2**, 641–659, 721–749; **3**, 10–32, 105–126.

Buys, E. Interrogatorie de l'appareil semi-circulaire par déclanchement d'un nystagmus post-rotatoire "primaire" au moyen du fauteuil Buys-Rylant (Note preliminaire). *Valsalva*, 1937, **13**, 139–144.

Camis, M. *The physiology of the vestibular apparatus.* (Translated and annotated by R. S. Creed.) Oxford : Clarendon Press, 1930. Translation of *Fisiologia dell'apparato vestibolare.* Bologna : Casa Editrice N. Zanichelli, 1928.

Carmichael, L. (Ed.) *Manual of child psychology.* New York : Wiley, 1946.

Carréga, Appaix, and Paillas. A propos d'un cas de labyrinthite aiguë. *Rev. d'oto-neuro-opht.*, 1938, **16**, 704.

Caussé, R. Recherches sur l'épreuve galvanique auriculaire prolongée le nystagmus post-galvanique. *C. R. Soc. Biol., Paris,* 1928, **98**, 1125–1127.

Cawthorne, T. E. Vestibular injuries. *Proc. roy. Soc. Med.*, 1946, **39**, 270–273.

Cawthorne, T. E., G. Fitzgerald, and C. S. Hallpike. Studies in human vestibular function : II. Observations on the directional preponderance of caloric nystagmus ("Nystagmusbereitschaft") resulting from unilateral labyrinthectomy. *Brain*, 1942, **65**, 138–160. III. Observations on the clinical features of "Ménière's" disease : With especial reference to the results of the caloric tests. *Ibid.*, **65**, 161–180.

Chavany, J. A. L'anxiété d'équilibration. *Presse méd.*, 1941, **49**, 1017–1019.

Ciurlo, L. Ricambio gassoso nei colombi slabirintati. *Arch. ital. Otol.*, 1936, **48**, 662–675.

Claude, H., H. Baruk, and M. Aubry. Contribution à l'étude de la démence précoce catatonique : Inexcitabilité labyrinthique au cours de la catatonic. *Rev. neurol.*, 1927, **34**, 976–980.

Cojazzi, L. Ricerche di fisiologia e fisiopatologia vestibolare. Ricerche sperimentali sui riflessi vestibulovegetativi. *Valsalva*, 1938, **14**, 174–191.

Concetti, F., and T. Rodolfo-Masera. Gli effeti dell'eccitazione del labirinto posteriore sull'attività motoria dell'utero di coniglia. *Arch. ital. Otol.*, 1939, **51**, 370–388.

Concetti, F., and T. Rodolfo-Masera. Ricerche sull'attività motoria dell'utero di coniglia in gravidanza ed in puerperio in rapporto all stimolazione del labirinto posteriore. *Riv. ital. Ginec.*, 1939, **22**, 249–272.

Crowe, S. J. Ménière's disease. A study based on examination made before and after an intracranial division of the vestibular nerve. *Medicine, Baltimore.*. 1938, **17**, 1–36.

Dandy, W. F., and P. A. Kunkel. The central connections of the vestibular pathways. An experimental study. *Amer. J. med. Sci.*, 1939, **198**, 149–155.

Delmas-Marsalet, P. Lobe frontal et équilibre. *Encéphale*, 1936, **31**, 15–91.

Delmas–Marsalet, P. Dissociation pharmaco-dynamique des réactions vestibulaires expérimentales. *Rev. d'oto-neuro-opht.*, 1937, **15**, 266–268.

Dodge, R. Five types of eye movement in the horizontal meridian plane of the field of regard. *Amer. J. Physiol.*, 1903, **8**, 307–329.

Dodge, R. The latent time of compensatory eye-movements. *J. exp. Psychol.*, 1921, **4**, 247–269.

Dodge, R. Habituation to rotation. *J. exp. Psychol.*, 1923a, **6**, 1–35.

Dodge, R. Thresholds of rotation. *J. exp. Psychol.*, 1923b, **6**, 107–137.

Dodge, R. Adequacy of reflex compensatory eye-movements including the effects of neural rivalry and competition. *J. exp. Psychol.*, 1923c, **6**, 169–181.

Dohlman, G. Physikalische und Physiologische Studien zur Theorie des kalorischen Nystagmus. A-B. *Acta oto-laryng., Stockh.*, 1925, Suppl. **5**.

Dohlman, G. Towards a new method for quantitative measurement of the functional capacity of the vestibular apparatus. *Acta oto-laryng., Stockh.*, 1935, **23**, 50–62.

Dohlman, G. Zum mechanismus der raschen nystagmusphase. *Acta oto-laryng., Stockh.*, 1938a, **26**, 267.

Dohlman, G. On the mechanism of transformation into nystagmus on stimulation of the semicircular canals. *Acta oto-laryng., Stockh.*, 1938b, **26**, 425–442.

Dohlman, G. The role of the perilymph in vestibular reactions. *Arch. Ohr.-, Nas.-, u. Kehlk-Heilk.*, 1941, **150**, 25–30.

Dohlman, G. Investigations in the function of the semicircular canals. *Acta oto-laryng., Stockh.*, 1944, Suppl. **51**, 211–219.

Dorcus, R. M. A comparison of post-rotation duration for repeated stimulation with the head fixed and free. *J. comp. Psychol.*, 1927, **7**, 177–179.

Dorcus, R. M., and O. H. Mowrer. An experimental analysis of the vestibular pointing test. *Ann. Otol. Rhinol. Laryngol.*, 1936, **45**, 33–57.

Dow, R. S. The effects of unilateral and bilateral labyrinthectomy in monkey, baboon and chimpanzee. *Amer. J. Physiol.*, 1938, **121**, 392–399.

Dow, R. S. The evolution and anatomy of the cerebellum. *Biol. Rev.*, 1942, **17**, 179–220.

Dunlap, K. The nystagmus test and practice. *J. Amer. med. Ass.*, 1919, **73**, 54–55.

Dunlap, K. Adaptation of nystagmus to repeated caloric stimulation in rabbits. *J. comp. Psychol.*, 1925, **5**, 485–493.

Dusser de Barenne, J. G. The labyrinthine and postural mechanism. In C. Murchison (Ed.), *Handbook of general experimental psychology.* Worcester : Clark University Press. 1934. Pp. 204–246.

Ewald, J. R. *Physiologische Untersuchungen über das Endorgan des Nervus octavus.* Wiesbaden : Bergmann, 1892.

Falkenberg, K. Zur Klinik und Pathologie der Vestibularisschädigung bei Syringobulbie. Beitrag zur Lokalisationslehre des Nystagmus. *Arch. Ohr.-, Nas.-, u. KehlHeilk.*, 1941, **150**, 347–367.

Falkenberg, K. Zur lokaldiagnostischen Bedeutung der Nystagmusbeobachtung bei Prozessen der hinteren Schädelgrube. *Arch. Ohr.-, Nas.-, u. GehlkHeilk.*, 1942, **151**, 134–188.

Fearing, F. S. Post-rotational head nystagmus in adult pigeons. *J. comp. Psychol.*, 1926, **6**, 115–131.

Fernando, A. S., and G. de Ocampo. Labyrinthitis : Clinical analysis of fifteen cases. *J. Phil. Is. med. Ass.*, 1937, **17**, 271–286.

Ferraro, A., and S. E. Barrera. Differential features of "cerebellar" and "vestibular" phenomena in Macacus rhesus. *Arch. Neurol. Psychiat., Chicago*, 1938, **39**, 902–918.

Fischer, M. H. Die Regulationsfunktionen des menschlichen Labyrinthes und die Zusammenhänge mit verwandten Funktionen. *Ergebn. Physiol.*, 1928, **27**, 209–379.

Fischer, M. H. Messende Untersuchungen über die Gegenrollung der Augen und die Lokalisation der scheinbaren Vertikalen bei seitlicher Neigung des Gesamtkörpers bis zu 360°. *Graefes Arch. Ophthal.*, 1930, **123**, 476–508.

Fischer, M. H., and E. Oldberg. Abhängigkeit der calorischen Vestibularisreflex vom Zustande der nervösen Zentren Pulsionsreflexe. *Z. Hals-Nas.- u. Ohrenheilk.*, 1932, **30**, 499–523.

Fitzgerald, G., and C. S. Hallpike. Studies in human vestibular function : I. Observations on the directional preponderance ("Nystagmusbereitschaft") of caloric nystagmus resulting from cerebral lesions. *Brain*, 1942, **165**, 115–137.

Fitzgerald, G., and C. S. Hallpike. The effect of certain cerebral lesions upon the caloric responses. *Proc. roy. Soc. Med.*, 1942, **35**, 801–804.

Frazier, C. H., and S. N. Rowe. Certain observations upon the localization in fifty-one verified tumours of the temporal lobe. *Proc. Ass. Res. nerv. ment. Dis.*, 1934, **13**, 251–258.

Fulton, J. F. *Physiology of the nervous system.* New York : Oxford University Press, 1943.

Galamini, A. Effeti della stimolazione de labirinto sulle funzioni circolatoria respiratoria e sul consumo di O. *Fisiol. e Med.*, 1936, **7**, 267–280.

Gatteschi, G. L'influenza dell'insulina sulle reazioni oculair da eccitamento labirintico e sui fenomeni da deficienza e compensatori in animali condistruzioni labirintiche. *Otorino-laring. ital.*, 1939, **9**, 179–204.

Gatteschi, G., and T. Rodolfo-Masera. Il comportamento della glicemia vell'uomo in sequito a stimolazione labirintica. *Arch. ital. Otol.*, 1939, **51**, 105–128.

Gay, L. N., and P. E. Carliner. The prevention and treatment of motion sickness. I. Seasickness. *Science*, 1949, **109**, 359.

Gernandt, B. Response of mammalian vestibular neurons to horizontal rotation and caloric stimulation. *J. Neurophysiol.*, 1949, **12**, 173–184.

Gibbs, F. A. Frequency with which tumors in the various parts of the brain produce certain symptoms. *Arch. Neurol. Psychiat., Chicago*, 1932, **28**, 967–989.

Göthlin, G. F. Wie können bei Bewegungen der Augen bzw. bei Bewegungen dez Kopfes Gegenstände der Umgebung als in Ruhe befindlich aufgefasst werden, trotzdem sich deren Bilder auf den Netzhäuten verschieben? *Skand. Arch. Physiol.*, 1929, **55**, 271.

Zum Gottesberge, A. M., and W. Sellerbeck. Zentrale Nystagmusphänomen. *Arch. Ohr.-, Nas.-, u. KehlHeilk.*, 1943, **152**, 191–196.

Gray, A. A. *The labyrinth of animals.* London : Churchill, 1907. Volume I.

Graybiel, A., B. Clark, K. MacCorquodale, and D. I. Hupp. Role of vestibular nystagmus in visual perception of moving target in dark. *Amer. J. Psychol.*, 1946, **59**, 259–266.

Green, D. M. Airsickness in bomber crews. *J. Aviat. Med.*, 1943, **14**, 366–372.

Griffith, C. R. The effect upon the white rat of continued bodily rotation. *Amer. Nat.*, 1920a, **54**, 524–534.

Griffith, C. R. The organic effects of repeated bodily rotation. *J. exp. Psychol.*, 1920b, **3**, 15–46.

Griffith, C. R. An experimental study of dizziness. *J. exp. Psychol.*, 1920c, **3**, 89–125.

Griffith, C. R. *An historical survey of vestibular equilibration.* Urbana : University of Illinois Press, 1922.

Groen, J. J., and L. B. W. Jongkees. The threshold of angular acceleration perception. *J. Physiol.*, 1948, **107**, 1–7.

Grove, W. E. An evaluation of the Ménière syndrome. *Ann. Otol. Rhinol. Laryngol.*, 1941, **50**, 55–69.

Gurnee, H. Individual differences in sensitivity to vertical motion of the body. *Psychol. Monogr.*, 1938, **47**, No. 212, 108–114.

Halstead, W., G. Yacorzynski, and F. Fearing. Further evidence of cerebellar influence in the habituation of after-nystagmus in pigeons. *Amer. J. Physiol.*, 1937, **120**, 350–355.

Hardy, M. Observations on the innervation of the macula sacculi in man. *Anat. Rec.*, 1934, **59**, 403–418.

Harris, J. D. Habituatory response decrement in the intact organism. *Psychol. Bull.*, 1943, **40**, 385–422.

Hasegawa, T. Labyrinthreflexe nach Abschleuderung der Otolithenmenbranen. *Pflüg. Arch. ges. Physiol.*, 1935, **236**, 589–593.

Hasegawa, T. Über die labyrinthären Augenbewegungen bei Änderung der Kopflage und bei Progressivbewegungen. *Acta oto-laryng., Stockh.*, 1940, **28**, 593–600.

Hemingway, A. Cold sweating in motion sickness. *Amer. J. Physiol.*, 1944, **141**, 172–175.

Hirsch, C. A new labyrinthine reaction: "The waltzing test." *Ann. Otol. Rhinol. Laryngol.*, 1940, **49**, 232–238.

Hitchcock, F. A., and J. K. W. Ferguson. Respiratory and circulatory adjustments to the erect posture. *Amer. J. Physiol.*, 1938, **124**, 457–465.

Hoff, H., and O. Pötzl. Über die labyrinthären Beziehungen von Flugsensationen und Flugträumen. *Mschr. Psychiat. Neurol.*, 1937–38, **97**, 193–211.

Holsopple, J. Q. The importance of analysis of the complete vestibular response. *Trans. Amer. otol. Soc.*, 1925, **18**, 1–10.

Holt, E. B. On ocular nystagmus and the localization of sensory data during dizziness. *Psychol. Rev.*, 1910, **16**, 377–398.

Huizinga, E. The classification of the labyrinthine reflexes. *Acta oto-laryng., Stockh.*, 1939, **27**, 662–667.

Huxley, F. M. On the reflex nature of apnoea in the duck in diving. I. The reflex nature of submersion apnoea. *Quart. J. exp. Physiol.*, 1913, **6**, 147–157, 159–182.

Isakower, O. On the exceptional position of the auditory sphere. *Int. J. Psycho-Anal.*, 1939, **20**, 58–63.

Jarcho, L. W., and W. S. Root. The relation of labyrinthectomy to sensitization of the nictitating membrane in the cat. *Amer. J. Physiol.*, 1939, **128**, 526–531.

Jayle, G. E. Lobe frontal et motilité oculaire de fonction d'après les faits expérimentaux et anatomiques. *Rev. d'oto-neuro-opht.*, 1938, **16**, 1–32.

Jonason, I., S. Kyhlstedt, and C. O. Nylén. Tierversuche mit beschleunigter Rotation. *Acta oto-laryng., Stockh.*, 1940, **28**, 327–339.

Kaneyuki, M. Über den Einfluss der Labyrinthfunktion auf den Calciumgehalt des Blutserums. *Jap. J. med. Sci.* (IV. Pharmacol.), 1939, **12**, 85–92.

Kennard, M. A., and L. Ectors. Forced circling in monkeys following lesions of the frontal lobes. *J. Neurophysiol.*, 1938, **1**, 45–54.

King, B. G. The influence of repeated rotations on decerebrate and on blinded squabs. *J. comp. Psychol.*, 1926, **6**, 399–421.

de Kleyn, A., and V. D. W. Schenk. Ueber den Reflexbogen des vestibulären Augennystagmus beim Menschen. *Acta oto-laryng., Stockh.*, 1931, **15**, 439–450.

de Kleyn, A., and C. J. R. Versteegh. Labyrinthreflexe nach Abschleuderung der Otolithenmembranen bei Meerschweinchen. *Pflüg. Arch. ges. Physiol.*, 1933, **232**, 454–465.

Kollner, H., and P. Hoffman. Der Einfluss des Vestibularapparates auf die Innervation der Augenmuskeln. *Arch. Augenheilk.*, 1922, **90**, 170–194.

Kolodny, A. The symptomatology of tumours of the temporal lobe. *Brain*, 1928, **51**, 385–417.

Landau, A. Ueber einen tonischen Lagereflex beim älteren Säugling. *Klin. Wschr.*, 1923, **2**, 1253–1255.

Lange, O. Valor semiótico da prova dos braços ao diagnostico neurológica. Contribuèção para a sistematicação de suas aplicações ao diagnostico neurológica. *Rev. brasil. Oto-rino-laring.*, 1941, **9**, 315–382.

Larroudé, C. Le mal de débarquement. *Oto-rhino-laryng. int.*, 1940, **24**, 209–211.

Leidler, R. Fragen der Lokalisation innerhalb des zentralen Vestibularsystems. I. Die entzündlichen, nichteitrigen Erkrankungen des Hirnstammes (Enzyphalitis). *Mschr. Ohrenheilk.*, 1936, **70**, 176–187, 472–480, 544–560, 725–736, 801–821. II. Die vestibulär ausgelösten Haltungsänderungen des Kopfes und Oberkörpers. *Ibid.*, **70**, 951–965.

Leiri, F. Über den Schwindel. II. *Z. Hals-Nas.-u. Ohrenheilk.*, 1927, **19**, 139–162.

Levi, L. Observations sur des anomalies du vertige voltaïque. *Rev. neurol.*, 1927, **34**, 997–1000.

Lorente de Nó, R. Vestibulo-ocular reflex arc. *Arch. Neurol. Psychiat., Chicago*, 1933, **30**, 245–291.

Lorente de Nó, R. Transmission of impulses through cranial motor nuclei. *J. Neurophysiol.*, 1939, **2**, 402–464.

Löwenbach, H., and W. H. Gantt. Conditioned vestibular reactions. *J. Neurophysiol.*, 1940, **3**, 43–48.

Löwenstein, O. Effect of unilateral elimination of the horizontal semicircular canal in the pike. *Nature, Lond.*, 1937, **139**, 715.

Löwenstein, O. Oscillographic analysis of the non-acoustic functions of the vertebrate ear. *Nature, Lond.*, 1948, **161**, 652–654.

Löwenstein, O., and A. Sand. The individual and integrated activity of the semicircular canals of the elasmobranch labyrinth. *J. Physiol.*, 1940, **99**, 89–101.

Lurie, M. H., and E. W. Dempsey. Experimentally induced circling (waltzing) in the guinea pig. *Laryngoscope*, 1939, **49**, 565–569.

MacKenzie, J. G. Some functions of the non-acoustic labyrinth (an experimental study). *Ann. Otol. Rhinol. Laryngol.*, 1943, **52**, 400–408.

Magnus, R. *Körperstellung.* Berlin: Springer, 1924.

Majer, E. H. Über die Drehnachempfindungsdauer. *Arch. Ohr.-, Nas.-, u. KchlkHeilk.*, 1941, **149**, 210–218.

Majewski, K. Eine neue Methode der klinischen Nystamographie. *Graefes. Arch. Ophthal.*, 1918, **96**, 140–171.

Malan, A. Sedia rotatoria ad accelerazione subliminate per stimolazione vestibolare. *Valsalva*, 1940, **16**, 201–207.

Malcolm, J. A. Vertigo. *Laryngoscope*, 1943, **53**, 755–758.

Marburg, O. Modern views regarding the anatomy and physiology of the vestibular tracts. *Laryngoscope*, 1939, **49**, 631–652.

Maré, G. de. Kann Dehnung oder elektrische Reizung eines äusseren Augenmuskels des einen Auges eine assozierte Bewegung des anderen Auges auslösen? *Skand. Arch. Physiol.*, 1928, **53**, 203–207.

Marinesco, G. Les réflexes vestibulo-végétatifs chez l'homme. *C. R. Soc. Biol., Paris*, 1931, **106**, 103–105.

Marinesco, G., S. Draganesco, A. Kreindler, and A. Bruch. Recherches sur les réflexes vestibulo-végétatifs chez l'homme. *Rev. d'oto-neuro-opht.*, 1937, **15**, 690–704.

Maxwell, S. S. *Labyrinth and equilibrium.* Philadelphia and London : Lippincott, 1923.

Maxwell, S. S., and G. F. Pilz. On the relation of labyrinthine and retinal excitations in the rabbit. *Amer. J. Physiol.*, 1924, **70**, 118–121.

Mayerson, H. S., H. M. Sweeney, and L. A. Toth. The influence of posture on circulation time. *Amer. J. Physiol.*, 1939, **125**, 481–485.

McCouch, G. P., and F. H. Adler. Extraocular reflexes. *Amer. J. Physiol.*, 1932, **100**, 78–88.

McEachern, G. M., and P. Lehman. Forms of motion sickness ; general review of literature. *War Med.*, 1942, **2**, 410–428.

McIntyre, A. K. The quick component of nystagmus. *J. Physiol.*, 1939, **97**, 8–16.

McLaurin, J. W. Desensitization by histamine (histamine azoprotein) in vertigo, periodic headaches and vasomotor (allergic) rhinitis : Review of the literature and report of 102 personal cases. *Laryngoscope*, 1946, **56**, 253–281.

McNally, W. J. Labyrinthine reactions and their relation to clinical tests. *Proc. roy. Soc. Med.*, 1937, **30**, 905–916.

McNally, W. J., and E. A. Stuart. Physiology of the labyrinth reviewed in relation to seasickness and other forms of motion sickness. *War Med.*, 1942, **2**, 683–771.

McNally, W. J., and J. Tait. Action of the utricular maculae of the frog. *Acta oto-laryng., Stockh.*, 1936, **24**, 52.

de Morsier, G. Les hallucinations. Étude oto-neuro-ophthalmologique. *Rev. d'oto-neuro-opht.*, 1938, **16**, 241–340.

Moruzzi, G. Ricerche sulla fisiologia del paleocerebellum. I riflessi labirintici e cervicali, paleocerebellum e tono posturale. *Arch. Fisiol.*, 1936, **36**, 57–112.

Mowrer, O. H. Concerning the normal function of the vestibular apparatus. *Ann. Otol. Rhinol. Laryngol.*, 1932, **41**, 412–421.

Mowrer, O. H. Influence of "excitement" on the duration of postrotational nystagmus. *Arch. Otolaryng.*, 1934a, **19**, 46–54.

Mowrer, O. H. The modification of vestibular nystagmus by means of repeated elicitation. *Comp. Psychol. Monogr.*, 1934b, **9**, 1–48.

Mowrer, O. H. The electrical response of the vestibular nerve during adequate stimulation. *Science*, 1935a, **81**, 180–181.

Mowrer, O. H. The nystagmic response of the pigeon to constant angular acceleration at liminal and supraliminal intensities. *J. comp. Psychol.*, 1935b, **19**, 177–193.

Müller, E. Otoneurologische Untersuchungen an Kopfschussverletzten. *Arch. Ohr.-, Nas.-, u. KehlkHeilk.*, 1943–44, **153**, 172–186.

Nielsen, M., L. P. Herrington, and C. E. A. Winslow. The effect of posture upon peripheral circulation. *Amer. J. Physiol.*, 1939, **127**, 573–580.

Nöel-Patton, D. The relative influence of the labyrinthine and cervical elements in the production of postural apnoea in the duck. *Quart. J. exp. Physiol.*, 1913, **6**, 197–207.

Northington, P., and S. E. Barrera. Induced nystagmus in monkeys following peripheral vestibular lesions (with clinical observations). *Laryngoscope*, 1937, **47**, 729–754.

Nylén, C. O. The oto-neurological diagnosis of tumours of the brain. *Acta oto-laryng., Stockh.*, 1939, **33**, 1–151.

O'Neill, H. Attitudinal reflexes of Magnus and de Kleijn (tonic cervical and labyrinthine) in thalamic man. *Arch. Otolaryng.*, 1946, **43**, 243–282.

Oppenheimer, M. J., and E. A. Spiegel. Acquisition of conditioned reactions to angular acceleration after cortical lesions. *Proc. Soc. exp. Biol.*, 1940, **45**, 418–420.

Ozorio de Almeida, M., H. Moussatché, and M. Vianna Dias. Sobre o methodo de estudo dos reflexos labyrinthicos va rà. *Brasil-med.*, 1939, **53**, 643–646.

Patroni, A. Sul comportamento dei capillari durante e dopo la calorizzozione del vestibolo. *Valsalva*, 1935, **11**, 708–712.

Peet, E. W. Observations on the semicircular canals. *J. Laryng.*, 1937, **52**, 431–434.

Pike, F. H. The function of the vestibular apparatus. *Physiol. Rev.*, 1923, **3**, 209–239.

Pilossian, C. Le nystagmus post-rotatoire après accélération angulaire négative de petite valeur physique. *Rev. d'oto-neuro-opht.*, 1937, **15**, 680–689.

Rademaker, G. G. J. *Die Bedeutung der roten Kerne.* Berlin : Springer, 1924.

Rademaker, G. G. J. *Das Stehen.* Berlin : Springer, 1931.

Rademaker, G. G. J., and J. W. G. Ter Braak. Das Umdrehung der fallenden Katze in der Luft. *Acta-oto-laryng., Stockh.*, 1935–36, **23**, 313–343.

Rasmussen, A. T. Studies of the VIIIth cranial nerve of man. *Laryngoscope*, 1940, **50**, 67–83.

Rejtö, A. Reizen die Schallwellen auch den statischen Apparat? *Mschr. Ohrenheilk.*, 1938, **72**, 34–39.

Riley, H. A. The central nervous control of the ocular movements and the disturbances of this mechanism. *Arch. Ophthal.*, 1930, **4**, 640–661, 885–910.

Ross, D. A. Electrical studies on the frog's labyrinth. *J. Physiol.*, 1936, **86**, 117–146.

Ross, E. L., and A. Olsen. Readjustment of equilibrium following unilateral labyrinthectomy. *Arch. Otolaryng.*, 1936, **24**, 190–198.

Rosselli del Turco, L. Variazioni pressorie, pletismografiche e del ritmo cardiaco durante le prove calorica e galvomica per l'esame della funzionalita vestibolare. Differenze di comportamento fra l'uomo normale e l'iperteso. *Rass. Neurol. veget.*, 1938, **1**, 211–323.

Rossi, G. Effetti della stimolazione elettrica dei singoli canali del labirinto acustico dei conigli. *Oto-rino-laring. ital.*, 1936, **6**, 140–159.

Roth, G. M., M. Williams, and C. Sheard. Changes in the skin temperatures of the extremities produced by changes in posture. *Amer. J. Physiol.*, 1938, **124**, 161–167.

Sand, A. The mechanism of acustico-lateral sense organs in fishes, with special reference to problems in the physiology of semicircular canals. *J. Laryng., Lond.*, 1940, **55**, 449–458.

Scevola, P., and F. Ventura Gregorini. Contribulò allo studio dei fenomeni labirintovegetativi. *Arch. ital. Otol.*, 1938, **50**, 393–407.

Schilder, P. The relations between clinging and equilibrium. *Int. J. Psycho-Anal.*, 1939, **20**, 58–63.

Schilder, P. *Mind: Perception and thought in their constructive aspects.* New York: Columbia University Press, 1942.

Schmaltz, G. The physical phenomena occurring in the semicircular canals during rotatory and thermic stimulation. *Proc. roy. Soc. Med.* (Sect. Otol.), 1932, **25**, 1–23.

Seiferth, L. B. Commotio cerebri und Lagenystagmus unter Berücksichtigung der übrigen Vestibularis- und Cochlearissymptome. *Arch. Ohr.-, Nas.-, u. KehlkHeilk.*, 1941, **149**, 241–263.

Simonton, K. M. Ménière's symptom complex: A review of the literature. *Ann. Otol. Rhinol. Laryngol.*, 1940, **49**, 60–98.

Spiegel, E. A. Depressor effects of cold upon static receptors of the labyrinth. *Amer. J. Physiol.*, 1944, **141**, 404–409.

Spiegel, E. A. Effect of labyrinthine reflexes on the vegetative nervous system. *Arch. Otolaryng.*, 1946, **44**, 61–72.

Spiegel, E. A., G. F. Henry, and H. T. Wycis. Changes of cerebral circulation induced by labyrinthine stimulation. *Amer. J. Physiol.*, 1944, **142**, 589–593.

Spiegel, E. A., and M. J. Oppenheimer. Conditioned reactions to position and angular acceleration. *Amer. J. Physiol.*, 1939, **125**, 265–275.

Spiegel, E. A., M. J. Oppenheimer, G. C. Henry, and H. T. Wycis. Experimental production of motion sickness. *War Med.*, 1944, **6**, 283–290.

Spiegel, E. A., and J. B. Price. Origin of quick component of labyrinthine nystagmus. *Arch. Otolaryng.*, 1939, **30**, 576–588.

Spiegel, E. A., and I. Sommer. *Neurology of the eye, ear, nose, and throat.* New York: Grune and Stratton, 1944.

Steinhausen, W. Über Sichtbarmachung und Funktionsprüfung der Cupula Terminalis in den Bogengangsampullen des Labyrinthes. *Pflüg. Arch. ges. Physiol.*, 1927, **217**, 247–755.

Steinhausen, W. Ueber die Beobachtung der Cupula in den Bogengangsampullen des Labyrinthes des lebenden Hechts. *Pflüg. Arch. ges. Physiol.*, 1933, **232**, 500–512.

Streiff, E. B., A. Montandon, and M. Monnier. Variations simultanées des pressions artérielle rétinienne et générale en fonction des excitations vestibulaires caloriques. *Confinia neurol.*, 1942, **4**, 347–350.

Sugár, M. Vorwort zu weiland Prof. Andreas Högyes' Arbeiten über den Nervenmechanismus der assoziierten Augenbewegungen. *Mschr. Ohrenheilk.*, 1912, **46**, 681–684.

Summers, R. D., R. Morgan, and S. P. Reimann. The semicircular canals as a device for vectorial resolution. *Arch. Otolaryng.*, 1943, **37**, 219–237.

Tenaglia, G. Fisiologia e patologia dell'apparato otolitico. *Arch. ital. Otol.*, 1940, **52**, 329–383, 387–435.

Tenaglia, G., and P. Scevola. Osservazione sull'adattamento statico nei sordomuti. *Arch. ital. Otol.*, 1940, **52**, 161–169.

Ter Braak, J. W. G. Über die Empfindlichkeit des Bogengangsapparates für Winkelbeschleunigungen. *Pflüg. Arch. ges. Physiol.*, 1936, **238**, 319–326.

Ter Braak, J. W. G. Kann der Bogengangsapparat durch geradlinige Beschleunigung gereizt werden? *Pflüg. Arch. ges. Physiol.*, 1936, **238**, 327–332.

Ter Braak, J. W. G. Untersuchungen über optokinetischen Nystagmus. *Arch. néerl. Physiol.*, 1936, **21**, 310–375.

Travis, R. C. Vestibular sensitivity to intermittent passive rotation of the body. *Psychol. Monogr.*, 1928, **39**, No. 2, 78–91.

Travis, R. C. Protracted passive oscillation and intermittent rotation of the body; variability in perception and reaction. *J. exp. Psychol.*, 1929a, **12**, 40–57.

Travis, R. C. Reciprocal inhibition and reenforcement in the visual and vestibular systems. *J. exp. Psychol.*, 1929b, **12**, 415–430.

Travis, R. C. The effect of varying the position of the head on voluntary response to vestibular stimulation. *J. exp. Psychol.*, 1938, **23**, 295–303.

Travis, R. C. Perception and bodily adjustment under changing rotary acceleration: A new technique. *Amer. J. Psychol.*, 1944, **57**, 468–481.

Travis, R. C. An experimental analysis of dynamic and static equilibrium. *J. exp. Psychol.*, 1945, **35**, 216–234.

Travis, R. C., and R. Dodge. Sensori-motor consequences of passive rotary and rectilinear oscillation of the body. *Proc. nat. Acad. Sci., Wash.*, 1927, **13**, 843–846.

Tullio, P. *Das Ohr.* Berlin : Urban and Schwaetzenberg, 1929.

Tullio, P., and S. Canova. Ricerche comparativa sopia la stimolazione calnica, elettrica, rotatoria, chimica e sonora del labirinto acustico VII. Stimolozione dei canali semicircolari mediante la corrente elettrica modulata col suono delle lettere e delle parole. *Oto-rino-laring. ital.*, 1937, **7**, 114–120.

Tumarkin, I. A. Some observations on the function of the labyrinth. *Proc. roy. Soc. Med.*, 1937, **30**, 599–610.

Tyler, D. B. The influence of a placebo, body position and medication on motion sickness. *Amer. J. Physiol.*, 1946, **146**, 458–466.

Van de Water, M., and G. R. Wendt. How to prevent airsickness. Washington, D. C. : Civil Aeronautics Administration, Division of Research, 1942.

Van Gehuchten, P. Anatomie des voies centrales du système vestibulaire. *Rev. d'oto-neuroopht.*, 1937, **15**, 321–352.

Vastine, M. F. Correlation between vestibular function and hearing in a profoundly deaf child. *Arch. Otolaryng.*, 1944, **39**, 164–171.

Warkentin, J., and L. Carmichael. A study of the development of the air-righting reflex in cats and rabbits. *J. genet. Psychol.*, 1939, **55**, 67–80.

Welling, E. J. Über Änderungen des Blutdruckes und der Blutgerinnungszeit nach Reizung des Vestibularapparates beim Menschen. *Arch. Ohr.-, Nas.-, u. KehlkHeilk.*, 1942, **151**, 294–309.

Wendt, G. R. An interpretation of inhibition of conditioned reflexes as competition between reaction systems. *Psychol. Rev.* 1936a, **43**, 258–281.

Wendt, G. R. The form of the vestibular eye-movement response in man. *Psychol. Monogr.*, 1936b, **47**, No. 2, 311–328.

Wendt, G. R. Methods of recording action. *Arch. Psychol., N. Y.*, 1938, **228**, 2–83.

Wendt, G. R. I. Frequency of susceptibility to motion sickness among young adults. In *Studies in motion sickness, Series B.* Washington, D. C. : Civil Aeronautics Administration, Division of Research, 1946a, Report 60.

Wendt, G. R. IV. Studies of somatic, physiological, and psychological correlates of history of motion sickness. In *Studies in motion sickness, Series C.* Washington, D. C. : Civil Aeronautics Administration, Division of Research, 1946b.

Wendt, G. R. Of what importance are psychological factors in motion sickness? *J. Aviat. Med.*, 1948, **19**, 24–32.

Wendt, G. R., and R. Dodge. Practical directions for stimulating and for photographically recording eye-movements of animals. *J. comp. Psychol.*, 1938, **25**, 9–49.

Werner, C. F. Über die anatomischen und funktionellen Beziehungen zwischen Ampulle und Bogengang. *Arch. Ohr.-, Nas.-, u KehlkHeilk.*, 1937, **143**, 257–270.

Witkin, H. A. The perception of body position and of the position of the visual field. *Psychol. Monogr.*, 1950 (in press).

Witkin, H. A., and S. E. Asch. Studies in space orientation. III. Perception of the upright in the absence of a visual field. *J. exp. Psychol.*, 1948, **38**, 603–614.

Wojatschek, W. Klinische Messung der Otolithenfunktion. *Acta oto-laryng., Stockh.*, 1936, **24**, 11–33.

Woletz, F. Quantitative Untersuchungen über den postrotatorischen Nystagmus. I. *Z. Hals.-, Nas.-, u. Ohrenheilk.*, 1933, **33**, 476–513.

Yacorzynski, G. K., W. Halstead, and F. Fearing. A quantitive method for the measurement of equilibration of pigeons with cerebral, cerebellar, or labyrinthine lesions. *J. gen. Psychol.*, 1941, **25**, 75–83.

Zanzucchi, G. I riflessi sonori vel came. Tenica operatoria. *Arch. ital. Otol.*, 1939, **51**, 73–83.

Zanzucchi, G. Studio sperimentale sui rapporti fra pupilla e labirinto. *Arch. ital. Otol.*, 1940, **52**, 105–158.

Zotterman, Y. The microphonic effect of teleost labyrinths and its biological significance. *J. Physiol.*, 1943, **102**, 313–318.

32.

Time Perception

HERBERT WOODROW
University of Illinois

The data that have been accumulated in the illusive field of time perception show two outstanding characteristics. One is the conflicting nature of the findings of different experimenters; the other is the mentalistic nature of the data. There have been, however, a few studies of physiological influences on judgments of time and of the behavior of animals with respect to temporal stimuli.

The Comparison and Reproduction of Times

Temporal stimuli are ordinarily one of two sorts: (1) what are called empty intervals, for example, two flashes of light or two short sounds, separated by a period of time; and (2) sounds or lights lasting continuously over a period of time. Behavior with respect to these stimuli has been extensively studied by methods that have usually required judgments of the relative length of two empty intervals or of two continuous stimuli presented for comparison, or the reproduction of an interval by taps upon a reaction key. From data on the comparison of the relative lengths of intervals may be calculated such things as differential thresholds and time-order errors; from the data obtained by the method of reproduction may be calculated the mean error, often termed the constant error, and some measure of the variability of the reproductions about their mean.

The accuracy of discrimination of intervals and durations. Among the few questions concerning temporal perception to which fairly definite answers can be given are those concerning the accuracy of discrimination as measured by the differential threshold. Dependable data have been obtained for three types of temporal stimuli: (1) empty intervals, bounded by sound clicks, (2) continuous tones, and (3) continuous lights. In general, the just noticeable difference is smallest at some relatively short magnitude or range of magnitudes and increases both above and below this middle region.

A thorough investigation of the comparison of empty intervals was made by Blakely (1933). His intervals were bounded by the clicks produced by the impacts of an electromagnetic hammer, with a pause of 1.5 seconds between the first and second interval of each compared pair. From data obtained by the method of constant stimuli, with the standard given second as often as first (so as to eliminate the effect of the time-order errors), he calculated relative just noticeable differences (jnd's). He found discrimination to be most accurate at intervals of 0.6 and 0.8 second. At these lengths the relative jnd (taken as the difference giving 75-per-cent correct judgments) was slightly less than 8 per cent of the standard. With shorter standards and also with longer ones the relative jnd was slightly greater, but throughout the range extending from 0.2 to 1.5 seconds, inclusive, it was less than 10 per cent. With longer intervals, 2.0 seconds and 4.0 seconds, the relative differential threshold rose to approximately 16 per cent. With still longer intervals ranging from 6 to

30 seconds, the indications were that the variable would need to differ from the standard by from 20 to 30 per cent to yield 75-per-cent correct judgments. It is obvious from these data that Weber's law does not hold for the range extending from 0.2 to 30.0 seconds. Naturally there are marked individual differences in accuracy of discrimination. Values for the relative differential threshold of a particular subject have been found, with intervals less than 2 seconds, to vary from 1 per cent (Fröbes, 1923, p. 384) to over 20 per cent (Blakely, 1933).

For continuous tones or lights the accuracy of discrimination is almost the same as for empty intervals bounded by clicks. In the case of continuous tones, Stott (1933), using fifteen college students as subjects, obtained the following values for the average relative jnd: approximately 10 to 12.5 per cent, with standards varying from 0.4 to 2.0 seconds; a somewhat larger value for a standard of only 0.2 second; and a considerably larger one for durations varying from 4 to 30 seconds. Accuracy of discrimination of the durations of continuous lights seems to be approximately the same as for continuous tones, with more or less representative values of the relative jnd lying in the range from 7 to 14 per cent for durations varying from 2.0 to 8.0 seconds (Quasebarth, 1924).

Related to the accuracy of discrimination is the accuracy of reproduction. As in the case of discrimination, accuracy is greater for very short intervals than for those of 4.0 seconds or longer. The greatest accuracy for both discrimination and reproduction lies within the range extending from 0.2 to 2.0 seconds. When the same empty interval is presented repeatedly and reproduced at each presentation, the standard deviation of the reproductions is typically, for the most favorable intervals, about 8 per cent of the standard, but it increases to twice this magnitude for intervals of 4 to 30 seconds (Woodrow, 1930).

The indifference interval. No phenomenon connected with short times has been the object of so many investigations as has the indifference interval. Vierordt (1868) first stated as a law that short intervals are overestimated and long ones are underestimated. This statement carries the implication that some intermediate length is neither overestimated nor underestimated. This intermediate length is the indifference interval.

Overestimation, underestimation, and indifference interval are terms that need careful definition. They all refer to values calculated from the results of procedures that require either a comparison of two time intervals presented in succession or the reproduction of an interval presented once. Accordingly we may speak of a comparison indifference interval, and of a reproduction indifference interval. The comparison indifference interval may best be defined as that length of the variable at which the percentage of judgments *meaning* that the variable seems longer than the standard remains the same irrespective of the order in which the variable and the standard are presented. If the frequency of judgments meaning variable longer is plotted separately for the two orders, variable first and variable second, the indifference interval is the length of the variable at which the two curves intersect (see Fig. 1).

By time-order error is meant the effect due to the temporal order of presentation of the standard and the variable. If the frequency of judgments meaning that the variable seems longer is greater when the variable comes first, the time-order error is called positive; if greater when the variable comes second, the time-order error is labeled negative. What is meant by the terms overestimation and underestimation, when applied to the comparison of intervals, is peculiar and misleading and is based on the false assumption that the sole error is in the estimation of the standard. Thus, when the time-order error is positive, the error is called one of overestimation (of the standard); and when the time-order error is negative, the error is called one of underestimation (of the standard). As a matter of fact the errors are in the outcome of the comparison: there is no separate estimate of either the standard or the variable.

Time-order errors in the method of reproduction do not have quite the same meaning as in the method of comparison. When the

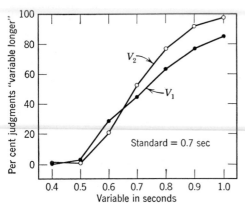

FIG. 1. Graph showing time-order errors. Both curves show the percentage of judgments *meaning* variable longer. The curve showing this percentage when the variable is first is marked V_1, and the one showing this percentage when the variable is second is marked V_2. When the V_1 curve is higher than the V_2 curve, the time-order error is positive. The interval at which the curves intersect is the indifference interval. (Data from Blakely, 1933.)

average length of the reproduction is equal to the stimulus interval, that interval is called the indifference interval; when the reproductions average longer than the stimulus interval, the time-order error is labeled positive, and the standard is said to be overestimated; and, when the reproductions are shorter than the standard, the time-order error is called negative and the standard is regarded as underestimated. As in the method of comparison, the terms overestimation and underestimation are misleading. In neither method does the subject estimate the length of the standard: in one he compares two lengths, and in the other he reproduces a given length.

Over a score of investigators have sought to determine the indifference interval, but

seldom have two investigators found the same value. Perhaps indifference intervals of 0.5 to 0.7 second have been reported more frequently than others, but the range extends from under 0.36 to 5.0 seconds (Woodrow, 1934). Sometimes no indifference interval has been found; sometimes several. Early investigators claimed to find periodic indifference lengths but disagreed on the length of the period. Rather exceptionally, a few investigators, contrary to Vierordt's law, have reported negative time-order errors (underestimation) for intervals shorter than the indifference interval and positive time-order errors (overestimation) for longer intervals. One study, made with relatively large groups of subjects, found a considerable percentage of subjects making positive time-order errors (by the method of reproduction) for all lengths of stimulus intervals from 0.3 to 4.0 seconds (Woodrow, 1934). It follows that, even under fixed experimental conditions, there is no single indifference interval valid for all subjects. A few investigations have been extensive enough to afford an estimate of the average indifference interval for a group of subjects. One study (method of reproduction of empty intervals bounded by short sounds) indicated a mean indifference interval of approximately 0.6 second (Woodrow, 1934); another (method of constant stimuli with empty intervals) indicated a mean indifference interval of approximately 0.7 second (Blakely, 1933); and a third (method of constant stimuli with continuous tonal durations) showed an indifference interval of approximately 0.9 second (Stott, 1935).

Early theorists attempted to identify the indifference interval with the duration of some physiological event, such as the duration of the swing of the leg in walking or the time between two pulse beats. The time per word in talking could also have been suggested. Others have attempted to connect the indifference interval with the duration of an alleged wave of attention, or, quite different, the time required to adjust the attention for the most effective apprehension of a stimulus. On the whole, the full explanation of any indifference interval is still uncertain. Something is known, however, concerning factors that affect the indifference interval; and these factors are of considerable significance for the light they throw upon the processes involved in the temporal comparative judgment. The most important of these influences may be classified under two headings: (1) aspects of the temporal stimuli presented the subject, and (2) the ways in which subjects make comparisons.

The effect of characteristics of the stimuli. The first class of factors affecting judgments and reproductions of temporal intervals and durations may be termed objective or environmental as distinguished from the attitudinal or subjective conditions. Temporal perceptions are reactions to stimuli. Whether the stimuli are continuous or are those bounding empty intervals, they may vary in intensity or quality and, in the case of cutaneous and light stimuli, in area. When two temporal stimuli are presented for comparison, the pause between them, though ordinarily about 1.5 seconds, may be of any desired length, as may also the preparatory interval between the ready signal and the beginning of the first temporal stimulus. Very decided effects upon the comparison of empty intervals are produced by variation in the length of the bounding stimuli and by inequality in their length. For example, two empty intervals, one of which is 0.5 second and the other 0.66 second, may be judged equal, if the 0.5-second interval is bounded by a long initial sound and a short terminal one and the 0.66-second interval is bounded by the same sounds but with the position of the initial and terminal sounds reversed (Woodrow, 1928).

In addition to the objective characteristics attaching to individual comparison pairs, one must consider the whole series of such pairs presented at a single sitting, and even during the entire course of an experiment, extending perhaps over a good many days.

The total range of times used is extremely important because of a tendency to become adapted to an interval repeatedly presented. As a consequence of adaptation to times of one length, judgments at other lengths may be altered. Practice alone may cause a pronounced change in the magnitude of the time-order errors or a reversal in their direction. In the course of a long experiment the indifference interval tends to move towards the average length of the intervals constituting the total series. In one study, for example, 110 subjects were given 120 comparisons of empty intervals with a standard of 1.0 second and variables of 0.8, 0.9, 1.0, 1.1, and 1.2 seconds. The pooled data (see Fig. 2) show that if the indifference interval were calculated from the first 60 trials it would fall below 0.8 second (estimated by extrapolation). During the last 60 trials, however, the responses were what might be expected if the variables were being compared with a standard of about 0.94 second. With practice the indifference interval moved towards the average length of all the intervals presented during the entire sitting, namely 1.0 second.

The effect of attitude. By attitude is here meant not a fixed state but rather the manner in which a subject goes about his task. Information on this matter is available only through introspective reports. It is amazing what variety these reports indicate in the internal activities of a subject when he has been asked simply to tell which of two short temporal stimuli is the longer.

Sometimes the reports suggest a division of subjects into two classes. One class consists of those for whom the two compared intervals form a single pattern, perceived as a whole and described as a whole. Within the total pattern, different subjects may introduce differences in accent, producing differences in rhythm or phrasing. Benussi (1913) has emphasized the effect of this subjective phrasing on the outcome of the judgment in the comparison of empty intervals, particularly when the two intervals are marked off by three short stimuli, the second of which both ends the first interval and begins the second one. A second class of subjects seems to pay attention to the first temporal interval as a separate phenomenon and then in some manner to start reproducing the first as the second begins. The first may be reproduced by the subject through his initiation of a kinesthetic experience of strain or some other process, either sensory or imaginal. The final comparative judgment, then, refers to two simultaneous

ently originate in almost any part of the body. Frequently mentioned are sensations of strain from the arms or hands, from the muscles involved in breathing, and from the vocal organs, the latter being sometimes accompanied by auditory imagery.

Little confidence can be placed in the relation between these impressionistically described attitudes and the errors of comparison supposed to depend upon them, unless the relation is established by the method of

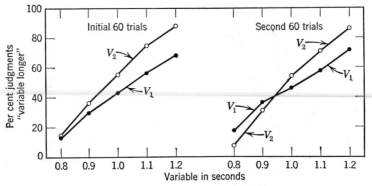

Fig. 2. Graph showing change in the indifference interval with practice. (Data from Woodrow, 1935.)

judgment, then, refers to two simultaneous experiences, one instigated by the subject's own effort to reproduce the first, and the other by the second of the temporal stimuli (see Kastenholz, 1922).

Another classification distinguishes between objective and subjective attitudes (Hülser, 1924, p. 367). In the objective attitude attention is centered upon characteristics of the stimulus, e.g. in the case of two continuous light stimuli, upon area, color, and brightness; in the subjective attitude the subject intentionally abstracts from, or ignores, the objective stimulus and concentrates upon the experience of duration. This subjective attitude may be reported either as a passive waiting or as one of attention to strain. The strain may be described as a feeling, as strain of attention, as strain of expectation, or as a group of kinesthetic sensations. The sensations of strain may appar-

differential instruction. This method consists in instructing or training the subjects in different attitudes, and then having them carry out series of comparisons under those attitudes. Quasebarth (1924, p. 407), by this method, was able to change the direction of the errors made by her subjects. They were first instructed to distinguish between an attitude of passive listening and one of maximal, active attention. Subjects who gave maximal attention to the second of two tones overestimated its duration, whereas subjects who listened passively to the second tone underestimated its duration. Another investigator (Woodrow, 1933) has reported marked effects on the direction of the time-order errors and therefore upon the indifference interval as a result of changing instructions given subjects who, by taps on a key, reproduced empty intervals bounded by instantaneous sounds. The subjects were, in one case, asked to pay attention only to the sounds, to listen to the interval as a pair of sounds, and then, in another set of instructions, to attend to the interval between the sounds as a duration. In the first case the reproductions were much shorter than in the second. For example, in reproducing the interval 4.0 seconds, with attention directed primarily to the bounding sounds, the average error was one of underestimation of the stimulus interval by 0.46 second, whereas, with attention to strain, it changed to one of overestimation by 0.26 second.

Introspective Reports Concerning Single Temporal Experiences

The studies considered in the preceding section have dealt with behavior with respect to two time intervals, one of which is compared with the other or constitutes a reproduction of the other. A second class of data consists of introspective descriptions of experiences of single temporal stimuli. These descriptions, particularly in the case of longer times, may take the form of estimates of duration in terms of seconds or other physical units. They refer ordinarily not to duration as such, which seems scarcely to be describable, but to such things as the following: the absolute impression, as regards length, pleasantness, or other attributes; the characteristics of the stimuli used to present times to the subjects; fading images of these stimuli; feelings of strain, expectation, and surprise; and awareness of breathing, counting to one's self, and a variety of kinesthetic and organic sensations.

The absolute impression. It has generally been supposed that different lengths of time give rise to qualitatively different experiences: adequate, pleasant, long, short, etc. The terms long and short, in spite of their obvious connotation of relativity, are here intended in an absolute, qualitative sense. To what lengths of time they apply has been a subject of particular study. The length at which the judgments change from short to long is termed the absolute judgment indifference interval. It is not necessarily identical with either a comparison or a reproduction indifference interval.

Almost any time, apparently, may be judged either short or long, depending upon the length of preceding temporal stimuli. Benussi (1907), for example, found that, when subjects were presented a series of intervals ranging from 0.09 to 2.7 seconds, the change from judgments of short to judgments of long occurred at three widely different lengths, depending upon whether the series was presented in an ascending order, in a descending order, or in a mixed order. The ascending order gave an indifference interval of about 0.23 second; the descending order, one of 1.17 seconds; and the mixed order, one between 0.58 and 0.72 second. Other ranges of intervals would undoubtedly have produced still other indifference intervals. Thus Abe (1935), using a range of intervals extending from 0.3 to 10.0 seconds, found indifference intervals scattered over a range of 0.75 to 3.4 seconds. These results indicate that the terms short and long probably always carry the implication of a comparison with a standard, though the subject may be unaware of the fact. This standard is largely a function of recent temporal experiences, or of a composite trace left by them. It is worthy of note, however, that the absolute indifference interval is seldom reported as equal to the mean length of the series of times presented the subject for his judgments. It tends to be much closer to 0.6 second. There is no conclusive evidence, then, to rule out the possibility that the "standard" for the absolute judgment of long and short may be a relatively stable one, corresponding to an absolute judgment indifference interval.

The thresholds of unitary duration. If one listens to the ticks of a clock, he may notice that he is aware of several clicks at once. It may be asked, therefore, how many ticks before the last one, or how many successive ticks, can be heard simultaneously.

More generally the problem may be stated as that of the physical time over which stimuli may be spread and yet all be perceived as present. This time has sometimes been termed the temporal span of attention. The question may be better phrased, perhaps, as that of the maximal physical time over which may extend a temporal stimulus pattern, the successive parts of which are perceived as a whole, possessing a unitary property of duration. There is also a minimal time which constitutes the lower duration threshold.

There can be little doubt that the answer to the question here envisaged depends upon the nature of the stimuli that fill the physical time. In any case, however, there are marked individual differences, due in part, perhaps, to ambiguity in the meaning of unity. Unity is by no means an unequivocal term, since unity may be more or less perfect, more or less disjointed, or more or less vague as regards boundaries. Moreover, the answer to this question, like that to any other question of thresholds, should be conceived in statistical terms. There are variations in the probability that a subject will perceive an interval in its entirety, even under fixed external conditions.

Using continuous lights, Quasebarth (1924) concluded that the upper limit of the psychological present, the limit permitting a unitary awareness of duration, is reached when the stimulus has a duration of about 6 seconds. For continuous tones, the duration was about 5 seconds. The introspections indicated that above these limits the light or sound loses its character of being all present at once. On account of the discordant results of several other investigators, however, it is impossible to state definitely the upper limit of the psychological present. The limit probably lies between 2.3 (Kastenholz, 1922, p. 217) and 12.0 seconds (Dietze, 1885), but it is possible that it may under some conditions be considerably higher (Titchener, 1923).

An indirect way of determining the upper limit of the psychological present may be afforded by the study of rhythm. It is possible to determine at how slow a rate certain factors producing rhythmical grouping lose their force. One such factor is a difference in the relative loudness of sounds composing a rhythmical series. For example, if every second sound in a series of equally spaced sounds is louder than the others, and if the rate of sequence of the sounds is moderately slow, the sounds tend to be perceived in trochaic rhythm, that is, in groups of two with the louder sound the first member of the group. However, when the sounds succeed each other at a very slow rate, this segregating effect of loudness may vanish: the subject no longer reports any grouping at all. The rate at which this grouping vanishes has been found to vary from one sound every 3.5 seconds to one sound every 13 seconds (Woodrow, 1909, p. 37). The grouping becomes very feeble and is obtained only with considerable effort at rates slower than one sound every 3.5 seconds. If, now, it is assumed that a rhythmical measure represents a perceptual unity, then these results appear to be in substantial agreement with those obtained by direct introspections on temporal unity.

The preceding discussion pertains to the maximum length of time that may be perceived as a unitary duration. If we ask whether there is also a lower limen, we meet with some complexities. A very short stimulus no doubt gives rise to a unitary experience; but, if it is perceived as momentary or instantaneous, it is usually said to lack the quality of duration. It follows that there exists a lower limen for duration. The values reported for this lower limen have varied with the investigator and with the conditions under which they were determined. For continuous light, Durup and Fessard (1930) obtained duration thresholds varying around 0.12 second, and for continuous sound much lower thresholds, varying from 0.01 to 0.05 second.

Much lower are the limens separating doubleness from singleness. By such a limen is meant the interval at which successive impressions fuse into a single experience. For essentially instantaneous stimuli, Wundt (1903) gives the following mean values, based on the findings of four investigators: sound, 0.002 to 0.016 second; touch, 0.027 second; and light, 0.043 second. If the stimuli follow each other at longer intervals, they are perceived as separate; if at shorter intervals, they fuse into one. In the case of light this interval is called the critical flicker interval. This critical interval decreases with the intensity of the light. When light alternates with darkness, the critical interval between successive light stimuli may vary from more than 0.200 second to less than 0.025 second (Zoethout, 1947).

The estimation of long times. It is a familiar fact that the seeming length of long periods of time depends largely upon the nature of the experiences by which these periods are occupied. In general, a time filled by pleasant, interesting, well-motivated activities seems shorter than one spent simply in waiting. In retrospect, however, the relations may be reversed. A period of idleness and monotony, as in sickness, may seem short when remembered after recovery. This influence upon temporal estimates exerted by the way time is occupied has been the subject of several experiments. Gulliksen (1927), for instance, found that subjects who were required to estimate the time elapsing between two signals gave much longer estimates when they passed the time doing nothing or performing a task of monotonous nature than when they were engaged in work or forced to endure pain. For example, an interval of 200 seconds was estimated at 242 seconds, on the average, when filled with mere waiting, but as only 169 seconds when devoted to work on problems in long division.

It is probable that in many situations the sense of time is more or less completely absent. It is, indeed, possible that this is always the case, with both long and short times, unless there exists an intention to make some temporal judgment. Situations especially favorable to an experience that is subjectively timeless are those characterized by intensely absorbing occupations, such as reading an interesting novel, contemplating the beautiful hallucinations produced by some drugs, or battling for one's life. Ferrari (1909) reports such a timeless experience on the part of three brothers who were entombed for 18 days by the earthquake of Messina in a very narrow space, in which the body of their little sister was putrefying. They remembered only certain facts: how they had been buried, how they ate, how they escaped; but they could not say how much time they had spent underground. When asked to do so, they estimated the time as from 4 to 5 days. It seems likely that the basis of such an enormous error lies in conditions, including those prevailing at the time of the estimate, that have not been clearly set forth. The same may be said when a patient, after hashish intoxication, estimates a period of a quarter of an hour as a century (Pick, 1919). Again, further analysis is needed to understand why a given drug, for example, mescaline, sometimes produces enormous overestimation (Fröbes, 1923) and sometimes enormous underestimation (Favilli, 1937).

A number of physiological influences other than intoxicating drugs have been investigated. In one case an influenza patient with fever was asked to estimate a period of 1 minute by counting to herself at the rate of one per second (Hoagland, 1935). The subject completed the count in considerably less than a minute, particularly when the fever was relatively high. This result indicates that what was actually a minute by physical time seemed longer than a minute to the subject — an interpretation in agreement with the subject's report that time seemed to pass very slowly. That the overestimation of physical time in this case may be attributed to the increased bodily temperature, and perhaps to an increased rate of brain metabolism, is indicated by the fact that a similar result is produced by heightened temperature due to a high-frequency alternating current passed through the body. On the other hand, Gardner (1935) found no significant difference in the temporal reactions of hyper- and hypothyroid subjects. For example, there was no significant difference between two groups, one of which showed a basal metabolism of +25 per cent or more and an average pulse rate of 114 and the other a basal metabolism of −11 per cent or less and an average pulse rate of 80. Schaefer and Gilliland (1938) likewise could find no significant relation between physiological processes and the accuracy of estimation, in terms of seconds, of empty intervals varying in length from 4 to 27 seconds. The physiological processes studied included pulse rate, breathing rate, heart work, lung work, and blood-pressure changes.

The effect of sleep on estimation of time was studied by Boring and Boring (1917), who attempted to ascertain the cues used by subjects in giving the time of night at which they were awakened. Since the subjects knew that the time would not be earlier than 12:15 A.M. nor later than 4:45 A.M., they did not designate times outside these limits. Immediately after estimating the time of night, the subjects wrote down the conscious cues on which their judgment was based. Most frequently mentioned were feelings dependent upon the general bodily state, such as degree of restedness or fatigue and degree of sleepiness. The state of the excretory and digestive functions was less emphasized and appeared to furnish less accurate cues. A secondary cue for some of the subjects was the ease with which they could pick up or remember the topic in mind at retiring. These cues were regarded by the authors as sufficiently definite to obviate the need of assuming an unconscious mechanism of timekeeping, a conclusion that seems very reasonable in view of the large mean error of 50 minutes in the estimated

times. The alleged remarkable accuracy with which some persons can awaken themselves at a time decided upon before going to sleep (Omwake and Loranz, 1933) needs further study, as does the temporal accuracy with which subjects carry out posthypnotic suggestions. Stalnaker and Richardson (1930) required each of nine subjects, both when in a hypnotic trance and when awake, to indicate the lapse, after a signal, of times varying from 1 to 3 minutes. The subjects showed no greater accuracy when hypnotized than when in the normal state.

Rhythm

By rhythm, in the psychological sense, is meant the perception of a series of stimuli as a series of groups of stimuli. The successive groups are ordinarily of similar pattern and experienced as repetitive. Each group is perceived as a whole and therefore has a length lying within the psychological present.

The nature of the perceived grouping is largely, but not entirely, determined by characteristics of the stimulus series. The most important of these characteristics are the relative intensities of the members of the series, their durations, both absolute and relative, and their temporal spacing. It is possible to measure the degree to which any of these factors promotes rhythmical grouping. For example, with equal temporal spacing, and not too fast a rate, and every second sound louder than the others, the series of sounds tends to be heard in groups of two, with the louder sound beginning the group. If, however, the interval following the softer sound is decreased while that before it is correspondingly increased, a point is reached where grouping occurs with the softer sound first and the louder sound second. In other words, the rhythm changes from trochaic to iambic. At some point in this progressive change in the intervals the probability of a report of trochaic just equals that of a report of iambic. The difference between the intervals before and after the louder sound at this neutral point may be used as an index of the tendency towards grouping produced by making alternate sounds louder.

In the same way, the group-producing tendencies of quite different stimulus characteristics, such as duration and pitch, may be determined. The effect of a given factor may therefore be expressed in terms of an index consisting of the difference in duration of the intervals between the members of the stimulus series that must exist in order to neutralize the grouping effect exerted by the factor when the temporal spacing of the members of the series is uniform. With such an index it has been determined that the group-beginning tendency of relatively greater intensity on the part of alternate sounds (with equal temporal intervals between the sounds) increases in a negatively accelerated fashion with increase in the difference in intensity between the more intense and the less intense sounds (Woodrow, 1909).

As regards the effect of the relative duration of the stimulus, when intensity and temporal spacing are uniform, if every second sound is longer, the probabilities are in favor of an iambic grouping, i.e. the longer sound is the second member of the group. Ordinarily this longer sound also seems to be more intense (though physically of the same intensity as the shorter one). When every third sound is longer, the series is most likely to be heard as anapestic rhythm, that is to say, in groups of three members with the longer one ending the group. In general, we may say that, with equal temporal spacing, a regularly recurring, relatively greater intensity exerts a group-beginning effect, and a regularly recurring, relatively greater duration a group-ending effect.

Objective characteristics of the stimulus series by no means completely determine the grouping. The stimulus series may induce in the subject a rhythmical series of actions on his part. The experience of these movements blends or fuses with the experience of the external stimulus series, and largely determines the nature of the perceived grouping. Even imagery of these movements, either auditory or visual, may affect the apparent rhythm. Ordinarily these subjective accompaniments of the external series are involuntary; but they may be set up intentionally. In the absence of strongly rhythmical objective characteristics, the apparent rhythm of a series of stimuli may be arbitrarily changed merely by imagining first one rhythm and then another. It is probable, however, that even where marked objective rhythmical influences are present — for example, when alternate sounds are much louder than the others — subjective factors act in cooperation with the objective to determine the nature of the perceived rhythm.

When the stimulus series is composed of stimuli that are physically identical and uniformly spaced in time, any grouping perceived must, except for the influence of the rate of sequence, be due to subjective factors. Provided the rate at which the series is run off is neither too slow nor too fast, the subject will ordinarily perceive a series of groups, with some member of each group carrying an accent. Rhythm perceived under such conditions is called subjective rhythm, and the accent is termed subjective accent. The number of members grouped together in one rhythmical measure is increased from two to six, or more, with increase in rate. In a subjective grouping by four, with the first member accented, the third member is apt to be given a lesser, secondary accent. A series heard in pronounced waltz rhythm may have a very slight accent on the third member of the group in addition to the principal accent on the first member. In general, however, subjective rhythms show considerable variation in the position of the accented members.

Subjects presented with a uniformly spaced series of clicks, all of equal loudness, may be asked to form groups containing a specified number of clicks; and for a grouping of each specified number the rate of sequence preferred by the subject may be determined. It is then found that the preferred rate increases with the number of elements grouped into one measure. The preferred rate increases less rapidly, however, than the number of elements grouped. Thus the preferred rate, indicated by the time in seconds between successive clicks, was found by Harrell (1937) to be as follows: twos, 0.63; threes, 0.79; fours, 0.97; fives, 1.14; sixes, 1.29. The grouping by fives is the most difficult.

Various theories have been proposed to account for rhythmical grouping, but they are all seriously lacking in factual support and in the precision with which the explanatory concepts are formulated. Without attempting to explain all the known facts, they endeavor to give some notion of the reason for perceived grouping. These theories usually regard grouping as determined by pulses or waves of attention or by pulses or waves of muscular contraction.

Theories of Time Perception

The duration of which one is aware is sometimes termed protensity, in order to distinguish it from physical duration. According to one view, the amount of protensity depends merely on the physical duration of the experience to which this attribute is attached, somewhat as the apparent extensity of a horizontal line varies with the physical length of the line. Protensity has often been considered an attribute of sensation. Whether this attribute could remain unitary and yet apply to a succession of sensations — for example, two short tones bounding an interval filled with strain sensations — is not altogether clear. Whatever may be the answer to this question, it is clear that protensity is a characteristic immediately given in experience.

A modification of this view holds that all sensations, perhaps all conscious processes, have an attribute of progression, and that

protensity or subjective duration is something that afterwards may or may not be added on, and does not belong to sensation as such (Curtis, 1916). The difficulty with this view is that its proponents have never clearly indicated what is added on, nor the process by which progression is integrated into protensity. The doctrine of protensity, either as an attribute of mental processes or as an integration of progression, has not led to any special theory to explain the comparison of durations. Its advocates appear to assume that the comparison of durations, like the comparison of any other attributes, is simply a matter for the general theory of successive comparison.

In the minds of a number of theorists there exists a special difficulty concerning duration. The difficulty is due to the plausible assumption that the perception of duration can arise only with change. The idea is that, if all change stops, then time stops. It would follow that a fully stable content, one that over a time remained perfectly constant, could not have any apparent duration, except by reference to other, simultaneous, changing events. This logic has been held to be incompatible with the doctrine that the duration of a uniform sensory experience can be perceived directly or immediately. It suggests that time is always judged indirectly by means of some process that serves as a cue. By a temporal cue is meant any process that changes progressively with the lapse of time.

A number of cues have been suggested. One of the earliest theories saw a temporal cue in the stage at which the image had arrived in the process of fading out. Lipps (1883), who first developed this theory, designated the various stages in the fading of the immediate memory image as temporal local signs. According to this theory, when a second momentary sensory impression follows an earlier one, the duration between the two moments is given by the degree to which the first has faded when the second occurs. James (1908) adopted the view of

Lipps, except that he restated it in terms of brain traces. The fainter the trace, he held, the longer would seem the time elapsed since the impression that originated the trace.

A second group of proposed temporal cues consists of processes connected with the activity of attention. As a result of the act of attention various feelings or sensations may be supposed to occur, and to vary with the physical time consumed by whatever is attended to. Some sort of strain, attributed to the process of attention, is the cue most commonly advanced as the basis for judgments of duration. It is held that to appreciate the duration of any interval an act of attention is required, and that this act produces strain, either directly as a central process, or, more plausibly, through the muscular tensions that accompany the direction of attention to an event. It is further supposed that the sense of strain increases with the duration of the attention. Schumann (1893) stressed not only the role of expectant attention but also that of the feeling of surprise when the terminus comes sooner than expected, and that of the feeling of intensified expectation when the terminus is delayed.

Klien (1919) attempted to summarize the whole matter of time perception by classifying the processes of judging times into two types. One of these, which he termed the S-type, refers to the use of the degree of fading of the immediate memory image as the cue for duration. The other, the P-type, refers to the use of a cue consisting of an activity feeling, which he thought of as dependent for its intensity upon an act of attention or will, conceived as a psychoenergetic process of which the subject has direct awareness. The P-mechanism may be used in perceiving any time that is long enough for the development of an activity feeling but not too long to be grasped by a unitary act of attention.

In addition to sensations or feelings of strain, various other cues are undoubtedly used, particularly for times that exceed the upper threshold of unitary duration. Münsterberg (1889) emphasized the importance of sensations from breathing. Counting to one's self is one of the commonest and most accurate ways of estimating times running into minutes. Still longer times may be estimated in terms of general bodily condition, or in terms of the known time required by the events remembered as having occurred within the period in question.

Time is not a thing that, like an apple, may be perceived. Stimuli and patterns of stimuli occupy physical time; and we react to such stimuli by perceptions, judgments, comparisons, estimates, etc. Whether some mental variable such as duration or protensity is an immediate property of our perception of temporal stimuli, or of mental processes in general, is a matter of some disagreement. If there is no such immediately given property, it follows that time is a concept, somewhat like the value of pieces of money, that attaches to perceptions only through a judgmental process. The ease and apparent immediacy of the temporal judgment in certain cases might be explained as the result of practice, much of it occurring in the first few years of life, in the interpretation in terms of physical time of the numerous alleged temporal cues.

REFERENCES

Abe, S. Neue Untersuchungen über die absoluten Eindrücke im Gebiete der wahrnehmbarren Zeit. *Tohoku psychol. Folia*, 1935, **11**, No. 3.

Benussi, V. Zur experimentellen Analyse des Zeitvergleichs. *Arch. ges. Psychol.*, 1907, **9**, 384–385.

Benussi, V. *Psychologie der Zeitauffassung.* Heidelberg: Winter, 1913. Pp. 99–122.

Blakely, W. The discrimination of short empty temporal interval. Ph.D. dissertation, University of Illinois Library, 1933. ,

Boring, L. D., and E. G. Boring. Temporal judgments after sleep. In *Studies in psychology: Titchener commemorative volume.* Worcester: Wilson, 1917. Pp. 255–279.

Curtis, J. S. Duration and the temporal judgment. *Amer. J. Psychol.*, 1916, **27**, 1–46.

Dietze, G. Untersuchungen über den Umfang des Bewusstseins bei regelmässig auf einander folgenden Schalleindrücken. *Philos. Stud.*,

1885, **2**, 362. See also James, *Principles of psychology*, Volume 1, p. 613.

Durup, G., and A. Fessard. Le seuil de perception de durée dans l'excitation visuelle. *Année psychol.*, 1930, **31**, 52–62.

Favilli, M. La percezione del tempo nell' ebbrezza mescalinica. *Rass. Studi psichiat.*, 1937, **26**, 455–462.

Ferrari, G. C. La psicologia degli scampati al terremoto di Messina. *Riv. Psicol.*, 1909, **5**, p. 95.

Fröbes, J. *Lehrbuch der experimentellen Psychologie*. Freiburg : Herder, 1923. Volume 1, pp. 379–394.

Gardner, W. A. Influence of the thyroid gland on the consciousness of time. *Amer. J. Psychol.*, 1935, **47**, 698–701.

Gulliksen, H. The influence of occupation upon the perception of time. *J. exp. Psychol.*, 1927, **10**, 52–59.

Harrell, T. W. Factors affecting preference and memory for auditory rhythm. *J. gen. Psychol.*, 1937, **16**, 427–469.

Hülser, C. Zeitauffassung und Zeitschätzung verschieden ausgefüllter Intervalle unter besonderen Berücksichtigung der Aufmerksamkeitsablenkung. *Arch. ges. Psychol.*, 1924, **49**, 363–378.

Hoagland, H. *Pacemakers in relation to aspects of behavior*. New York : Macmillan, 1935.

James, W. *Principles of psychology*. New York : Holt, 1908. Volume 1, Chapter XV, p. 635.

Kastenholz, J. Untersuchungen zur Psychologie der Zeitauffassung. *Arch. ges. Psychol.*, 1922, **43**, 171–228.

Klien, H. Beitrag zur Psychopathologie und Psychologie des Zeitsinns. *Z. Pathopsychol.*, 1919, **3**, 307–362.

Lipps, T. *Grundtatsachen des Seelenlebens*. Bonn : Max Cohen and Son, 1883, p. 589.

Münsterberg, H. *Beiträge zur Experimentellen Psychologie*. Freiburg : Mohr, 1889. Volume 2, pp. 33ff.

Omwake, K. T., and M. Loranz. Study of ability to wake at a specified time. *J. appl. Psychol.*, 1933, **17**, 468–474.

Pick, A. Psychopathologie des Zeitsinns. *Z. Pathopsychol.*, 1919, **3**, 430–441.

Quasebarth, K. Zeitschätzung und Zeitauffassung optisch und akustisch ausgefüllter Intervalle. *Arch. ges. Psychol.*, 1924, **49**, 379–432.

Schaefer, V. G., and A. R. Gilliland. The relation of time estimation to certain physiological changes. *J. exp. Psychol.*, 1938, **23**, 545–552.

Schumann, F. Ueber die Schätzung kleiner Zeitgrössen. *Z. Psychol.*, 1893, **4**, 1–69.

Stalnaker, J. M., and M. W. Richardson. Time estimation in the hypnotic trance. *J. gen. Psychol.*, 1930, **4**, 362–366.

Stott, L. H. The discrimination of short tonal durations. Ph.D. dissertation, University of Illinois Library, 1933. P. 64.

Stott, L. H. Time-order errors in the discrimination of short tonal durations. *J. exp. Psychol.*, 1935, **18**, 741–766.

Titchener, E. B. *A text-book of psychology*. New York : Macmillan, 1923. P. 340.

Vierordt, K. *Der Zeitsinn nach Versuchen*. Tübingen : H. Laupp, 1868.

Woodrow, H. A quantitative study of rhythm. *Arch. Psychol., N. Y.*, 1909, **18**, No. 1.

Woodrow, H. Behavior with respect to short temporal stimulus forms. *J. exp. Psychol.*, 1928, **11**, p. 174.

Woodrow, H. The reproduction of temporal intervals. *J. exp. Psychol.*, 1930, **13**, 473–499.

Woodrow, H. Individual differences in the reproduction of temporal intervals. *Amer. J. Psychol.*, 1933, **45**, 271–281.

Woodrow, H. The temporal indifference interval determined by the method of mean error. *J. exp. Psychol.*, 1934, **17**, 167–188.

Woodrow, H. The effect of practice upon time-order errors in the comparison of temporal intervals. *Psychol. Rev.*, 1935, **42**, 127–152.

Wundt, W. *Grundzüge der physiologischen Psychologie* (5th Ed.). Leipzig : Wilhelm Engelmann, 1903. Volume 3, p. 46.

Zoethout, W. D. *Physiological optics*. Chicago : Professional, 1947. P. 191.

33.

Selection

HAROLD P. BECHTOLDT

The State University of Iowa

The development of techniques and procedures to be used in selecting individuals for various jobs, training opportunities, or forms of therapy has become a major activity for many psychologists, and has resulted in an extensive body of knowledge, a multitude of techniques, and a few generalizations of theoretical value.

The objective of this discussion is to summarize the current work in this field and to present some of the general problems and theoretical considerations. No attempt will be made to list the various devices used in selection, to review the literature, or to treat the standardization of tests, the preparation of norms, or the office procedures required for the proper protection and utilization of classification materials. Statistical procedures will be discussed, but the formulas and computing procedures have been omitted.

Definition of Selection

Selection is defined by Warren (1934) as "the picking out or emergence of a character, an object, or a phenomenon from a group of alternatives in accordance with some standard or principle," and vocational selection is presented as "the process of choosing from a group of applicants for a vocation those most likely to succeed in that vocation."

Four characteristics of selection may be distinguished.

The writer gratefully acknowledges the extensive assistance and constructive criticisms given by Dewey B. Stuit, State University of Iowa.

First, selection of a few individuals from among many is a *process*. This process may be applied only once, as in the selection of a given number of punch-press operators for an individual plant, or it may be a recurring process, as in the periodic grading and elimination of graduate students. The process either may be formalized, with definitely stated critical levels of performance, or it may appear only as an attitude indicative of continuous scrutiny of an individual's behavior.

Second, the selection process always involves selection for some purpose: for speed of response, for capacity to lead men, or for any of the nearly limitless activities of human beings.

Third, selection requires procedures for assigning individuals into classes appropriate to the objective of the selection process. The development of these procedures constitutes the *classification problem*. The classifications may be made in terms of any *relevant* attribute of the individual. The procedures utilized may require (1) the obtaining of responses, verbal or nonverbal, from an individual, (2) reports from observers or "judges," (3) records of past performances, or (4) direct observation by the experimenter.

Fourth, selection implies prediction. The goal of a selection process is the prediction of an individual's "success" or his behavior at some future time. Success, of course, must be defined in terms of attributes other than those used in the "sorting" operations of the selection process. The forecasting of future behavior constitutes the *prediction problem*.

Selection typically involves two independent assessments separated by a temporal interval. On the basis of the first assessment we set up "predictor categories." The second assessment leads to "criterion categories." The problem, then, is to predict the criterion categories. The predictions represent *estimates* of the *expected values,* and the estimates are determined from empirical investigations of the relations between the two sets of categories. From these investigations we determine the *most probable* criterion categories corresponding to the various predictor categories.

Because the behavior of the individual is continuously modified by external events, predictions of future behavior are usually made conditional upon the occurrence of a specific state of affairs. When predictions are hedged in this manner, they are said to be conditional predictions (Horst, 1941). For example, predictions of parole success may be conditional upon whether or not the parolees return to their previous environment. The isolation of the conditional factors that are relevant to the criterion classifications is a crucial problem in prediction. The relations between such factors and the "success" categories are analogous to the stimulus-response "laws" sought in experimental studies.

The criterion category is a classification based on a performance characteristic. In contrast, the predictor category may represent *any* attribute of the individual, defined by how he appears to others, what he can do, or what he has done. Either of the two classifications (predictor or criterion) may be expressed in terms of a single characteristic or in terms of a set of measures, as in a multiple regression problem. However, the criterion attributes are usually combined to provide a single composite "measure of success" in terms of which the prediction statements are tested. When the selection process is a recurrent one, the criterion classification at an intermediate stage may be considered a predictor category for a later stage, and the final measure of success is then designated the "ultimate" criterion.

SELECTION AS AN ASPECT OF PERSONNEL PSYCHOLOGY

Unfortunately, there are few occasions in personnel selection when ready-made techniques can be applied. The personnel psychologist must meet most situations armed only with a method of approach. He must first study the problem in terms of the purpose of the selection, then formulate working hypotheses, devise the necessary procedures, try them out experimentally, check on the validity of his hypotheses, and finally revise his procedures in accordance with his findings. Each of these steps is a separate problem to be solved before the actual selection of individuals is undertaken.

The psychological analysis of behavior has not progressed to the point where direct application of general laws to the "engineering problems" of selection can be made. Each new problem has a few elements in common with old ones, plus a number of novel aspects, the effects of which can rarely be accurately predicted. Hence there is a demand for continued patient research in the applied field — a demand that usually runs counter to the demands for immediate results. This conflict is probably responsible for a concentration of effort on formalized tests of aptitude and achievement, and for the use of linear prediction equations.

Individual differences, which are often assumed to be a mere source of error in other problems, are the meat of the selection business. If individuals are homogeneous with respect to the predictor attributes, no *differential* classification in terms of these attributes can be made. If individuals are homogeneous with respect to the criterion categories, there is no selection problem.

Individual prediction, it should be pointed out, is to some extent a misnomer. Predictions are properly applied to classes of individuals homogeneous (within limits) with respect to a set of characteristics (Sarbin, 1944). The personnel psychologist is concerned with assigning individuals to classes and with making statements about the expected performances of members of the classes.

Similarity of selection research to other psychological research. Between selection and other areas of psychological endeavor there is a similar objective and a similar point of view. The objective is the formulation of empirical rules based upon observed consistencies in the attributes of individuals, and in the effects upon behavior of various stimulus conditions. The point of view is a behavioristic one in the sense that observations of overt behavior, verbal and nonverbal, and discriminable attributes of individuals are the terms related.

In pushing toward this objective of discovering relations among variables, personnel psychologists are tending to consider their problems strictly in empirical terms. This extreme empiricism is largely a reflection of the specific problems formulated in selection studies, and a reaction against the unwarranted generalizations frequently used in the past. The typical selection project has some specific purpose, and its success is evaluated strictly in terms of the accuracy of its predictions. The empirical relations between the criterion and predictor categories are the pertinent observations; no abstract or theoretical constructs need appear in the expression of these relations. If the procedures work, they are accepted. This justification of selection techniques by a pragmatic criterion may explain Guthrie's characterization of the test movement in applied psychology as ". . . highly useful and practical work, but it has not contributed to psychological theory" (1946).

This is not to suggest, however, that the applied psychologist can make no theoretical contributions and achieve no important generalizations. He appeals to psychological principles when he chooses predictor variables and estimates the effects of situational factors. The agreement between the obtained and predicted observations constitutes a partial test of these principles. Furthermore the applied psychologist accumulates observations on the empirical regularities in human behavior. These regularities may form the basis for useful hypotheses and generalizations.

Both trait concepts and descriptions of stimulus conditions are used by the personnel psychologist, but trait concepts are probably given the greater emphasis in selection because of the difficulty of manipulating environmental conditions.

Trait concepts develop from the obvious fact of conspicuous individual differences. "Few jobs exist which can be performed equally well by practically all of the participants" (Flanagan, 1948). Although some differences among individuals are subject to change, other differences are quite stable. Furthermore, a high degree of specificity is found in the traits associated with the performance of various tasks. This specificity in performance is not explicable in terms of some unreliability of evaluation, for a high degree of consistency within each single area of activity can often be demonstrated.

Consistency of performance in a given domain and independence of performances in different areas have given rise to the notion of functional unities, i.e. traits expressed as abilities, motives, interests, and temperamental variables. The provision for more adequate operational definitions of these postulated traits is one of the outcomes of the factorial approach. It has been suggested that the number of traits necessary to account for the various occupational performance measures may be relatively large (Flanagan, 1947a). It should perhaps be noted also that the factorial methods do **not** always sustain the initial hypotheses concerning the characteristics of a given trait; as often as not these hypotheses are subject to drastic modification in the light of the intercorrelations obtained among the tasks selected to represent the trait (Thurstone, 1947).

The definition of these traits by a set of test situations involves no assumptions about the origins of the traits; their source may lie in the social or in the physiological structure. The traits may be acquired or inherited, easily modifiable or resistant to change, specific to a given situation or common to many situations. Traits having the greatest stability and generality are of the greatest interest, of course, and the personnel psychologist seeks to isolate and define them and to establish relations among them.

Steps in Selection Research

The preceding discussion has emphasized two operations: the classification of behavior and the prediction of behavior. Before these operations can be carried out it is necessary that certain basic research be completed. The following five steps, modified from those listed by Horst (1941) and Sarbin (1944), represent the tasks involved in selection research:

1. The establishment of the criterion categories of "success," which involves the definition of the behavior to be predicted and the development of procedures for the classification of performance.

2. The selection of the attributes on which prediction is to be based, and the establishment of the several predictor categories for each of the attributes (for a representative sample of the population). These prediction attributes are those that are expected to have significant relations with the criterion attributes.

3. The determination of the relations between the criterion categories and the several predictor categories. These empirical relations are then used to predict the criterion category for each individual.

4. The verification of the relations determined on the basis of the original sample by the application of the classification procedures to a new sample of the population. This verification, or cross-validation, constitutes a crucial step that is too often omitted.

5. The application of the selection procedures in the routine situations for which they were developed, provided the stability of the prediction in the cross-validation step has been sustained.

Simplifying assumptions. In carrying out the selection process, we make certain assumptions for the purpose of simplifying the operational procedures. The first of these is that *human attributes that differ in magnitude can be represented by numbers.* Certainly numerical operations are used in the statistical procedures of selection, but are these statistics justified? Two replies have been given to this question. The first answer is based upon the logical implications of measurement in science: that the representation of empirical magnitudes by numbers requires that certain empirical operations be performed (see Chapter 1). "Additive" (or ratio) scales exist for some of the physical properties of responses but not for the more ubiquitous aspects known as qualitative attributes because the operations for the determination of zero and for the process of addition are not available (Bergmann and Spence, 1944; Richardson, 1941b). Psychological scales that are more than simple rank-order scales (Gulliksen, 1946; Stevens, 1946) can be constructed for some psychological properties, but they are rarely used in selection problems.

The second answer is that the use of numerals to represent the discriminal differences in attributes serves a practical purpose. Qualitative dichotomous attributes are often assigned numbers, as 0 and 1, and various statistics are computed. Multiple-category qualitative variables representing intensive dimensions are "scaled" in various ways, and numerical scores are determined.

Since the results are useful, these practices will continue. And the continued search for operations that will meet the logical requirements of measurement may eventually place these procedures on a sound basis.

The second of the simplifying assumptions is that *attributes differing in magnitude can be considered as continuous variables.* Classification categories are considered to represent intervals along a continuum. Of course, there is no assurance that the phenomena under consideration are continuous and not discrete. For example, only completed responses on a test are scored. Such responses are usually discussed, however, as though any given response might be represented by some value between zero and one.

The third simplifying assumption current in selection work is *that the criterion magnitudes can be expressed as linear functions of the predictor variables.* Horst (1941) has pointed out that increased accuracy of prediction may require the use of nonlinear relations. Such functions are current in the formulations of other psychological problems, for example, in the various mathematically stated learning theories. However, for a variety of monotonic functions within the range of values conventionally used, a linear equation provides a useful first approximation. For selection purposes, nonlinearity of relations is not crucial since linearity can often be secured by a modification of the measuring devices or by a transformation of the scales or scores. Furthermore, empirical evidence indicates that sampling fluctuations of regression parameters are of such magnitude that very large representative samples would be required to provide accurate estimates of nonlinearity (Flanagan, 1948).

Necessary Characteristics of Classification Procedures

An acceptable categorizing procedure is one that provides stable differentiations between individuals with respect to a characteristic of performance. Differentiations with respect to a single variable are desired, but for many selection purposes complex "multidimensional" sets of attributes are useful. In every case, however, the classification procedures are expected to show *discrimination* and *reliability* (Adkins, 1947; Thorndike, 1949).

Discrimination is the aspect of a classification procedure that is reflected in the number of categories to which significant proportions of individuals are assigned. A procedure that assigns all individuals to a single class fails to discriminate. If each individual is assigned to a separate class, discrimination is maximal. Most classification procedures exhibit a discrimination intermediate between these two extremes.

An index of discrimination has been developed in terms of the obtained number of differentiations between *pairs* of individuals (Ferguson, 1949). The number of possible differentiations is the number of combinations, $n(n-1)/2$. The index δ, derived in terms of s different *possible* score categories, ranges from zero for the test on which everyone has the same score to unity for the test providing a rectangular distribution extending over the entire range of scores. The formulation is

$$\delta = \frac{s}{s-1}\left(1 - \sum_{j=1}^{s} p_j{}^2\right)$$

where s = the number of possible score categories, and p_j = the proportion of individuals in the jth category, j ranging from 1 to s.

The effectiveness of the classification procedure can also be considered in terms of the possible number of differentiations, i.e. when each individual is assigned to a separate class. In this case, an index δ' is provided by

$$\delta' = \frac{n}{n-1}\left(1 - \sum_{j=1}^{s} p_j{}^2\right)$$

where n = number of individuals in the sample, and the other symbols have the same meaning as before. A value of unity for δ' is obtained only when $s = n$ and

$p_j = 1/n$. The index δ' expresses the proportion of the total possible number of discriminations that is provided by the classification procedure.

If the number of discriminations made by a classification procedure is used as a criterion of "goodness of discrimination," the best procedure is one that provides a rectangular distribution of scores (or categorizations) for the group. Since a single item, scored correct or incorrect, can be considered as a "test," the most discriminating item ($\delta = 1.00$) is one that has 50 per cent of the cases in each of the two categories (Adkins, 1947). For sets of two or more items, however, the maximum number of discriminations made by the s total test scores (each item scored 0 or 1) may or may not be obtained with items at the 50-per-cent level of difficulty. The intercorrelations of the items and their reliabilities, as well as the difficulty level of each item, must be considered (Brogden, 1946b; Carroll, 1945; Flanagan, 1939b; Gulliksen, 1945; Richardson, 1941a). It has been shown that the variance of the total score (the score defined as the sum of unit-weighted items scored 0 or 1) varies directly with the average intercorrelation of the items and with the average item variance, and varies inversely with the variance of the distribution of item difficulty values. Since a large variance is associated with a flat distribution of test scores, the relations that tend to maximize the test variance will also tend to increase the index of discrimination of the test. A decrease in the average interitem correlation for a given difficulty distribution will lead to a more nearly unimodal distribution of scores and to a smaller test-score variance and fewer discriminations. When the maximum discrimination is desired, a "cut and try" test building procedure to balance low item intercorrelations with a range of item difficulty values may be necessary (Adkins, 1947; Loevinger, 1947).

If the function of a test is to measure some hypothetical trait or "ability" common to its several items, the difficulty level of the test providing the maximum discrimination will vary with the ability of the subjects. Easy items ($\bar{p} \geq 0.70$) will give the greater number of discriminations for subjects having low ability, and difficult items ($\bar{p} \leq 0.30$) will be more appropriate for subjects having high ability (Adkins, 1947; Richardson, 1936a).

The fineness of discrimination required may, however, vary from time to time, depending primarily upon the purpose to be accomplished. If the problem is simply one of accepting or rejecting each individual on the basis of some requirement, only a dichotomous classification is needed. In this case the test-score distribution would be bimodal or U-shaped. When fine discriminations are desired only among individuals at either extreme of the range of ability, the test-score distributions can be definitely skewed or J-shaped, with the flat section of the distribution occurring in the region where the differentiations are to be made. Rectangular distributions are the goal when the number of classes desired is limited only by the errors of measurement and by the range of the sample.

It should be emphasized that this concept of discrimination does *not* refer to the relation between the assessments of two independent classification procedures. Such relations are used to provide an indication of the "validity" of one of the classifications. A classification procedure may discriminate without being valid (for a given criterion).

Reliability is the consistency or stability of the evaluations obtained from repeated observations. Repetitions of a reliable procedure lead to similar scores. Either the score (or classification) can be shown to be "essentially" the same on repeated trials, or the position of the individual relative to the group remains "relatively" constant. The terms "essentially" and "relatively" indicate that some variation is always expected. The nonsystematic or "chance" variations in repeated observations are termed "errors of measurement." If only a small fraction of the total variance of the scores is associated with these errors, the test is reliable; if the fraction is large, the test is less reliable.

Two common indices of reliability are used in selection studies, the *standard error of measurement* and the *reliability coefficient*. The square of the standard error of measurement is an estimate of the variance of the repeated measurements (error variance) of the same individual's performance. The reliability coefficient is defined as one minus the ratio of the average error variance (estimated from the entire set of observations) to the total variance of the test. This coefficient, ranging between zero and unity, is an index of the stability of a classification relative to the classifications of a group of individuals. The standard error of measurement, at least for a given score or classification, is independent of the range of performance in the sample of individuals (Adkins, 1947; Cronbach, 1947; Jackson and Ferguson, 1941; Thorndike, 1949).

The basic assumption made in estimating the reliability of a procedure is that the repeated observations can be considered as measures of the "same thing." The behavior observed is assumed to remain constant; variations are attributed to extraneous factors that operate in a nonsystematic fashion. The definition of the sources of error variance, the development of experimental procedures for securing the relevant data, and the formulation of statistical techniques for the evaluation of the error variance are three general problems of test reliability.

Since the variance included as "error" by the psychologist may arise from many sources, there are several different reliability concepts. They concern repeated measurements in situations involving (1) samples of the individual's behavior, (2) samples of the tasks or operations, and (3) samples of the performance of observers or scorers evaluating a given behavior or attribute. Estimates of the stability of classifications (relative to the variability of the group), over a sample of similar tasks, over a period of time, or over both, are provided by three coefficients: (1) *equivalence*, (2) *stability*, and (3) *stability and equivalence* (Cronbach, 1947).

Three different experimental procedures are used to obtain the data for these three coefficients. The coefficient of *equivalence* is estimated from the data obtained with a single sample of items presented at one time to a group of individuals. The coefficient of *stability* is determined from the results of two or more administrations of the same test at different times. The coefficient of *stability and equivalence* is estimated from two or more samples of items (parallel forms representing samples from the same universe of items) presented at various intervals of time. As the time interval decreases, the coefficient of stability and equivalence for two or more tests approaches the coefficient of equivalence for a single measurement consisting of the combined samples of items.

The statistical operations used to compute these various coefficients stem from the assumption that the error factors are independent of the systematic factors, or that the responses to any item on any trial are independent of the responses to other items on other trials. The mathematical details are presented by various writers (Adkins, 1947; Cronbach, 1947; Guttman, 1945, 1946; Horst, 1949; Hoyt, 1941; Kuder and Richardson, 1937; Jackson and Ferguson, 1941; Loevinger, 1947; Rulon, 1939).

The pertinent sources of variance can be classified in terms of the duration and generality of their influence. These factors may operate in a *persistent* or in a *temporary* fashion (duration) and may be *specific* to one task or *common* to two or more tasks (generality). All reliability formulations consider the systematic nonerror (true) variance to include common persistent factors such as general skills and abilities. Such factors as luck in guessing or the influence of momentary stimulus conditions are assigned to the error variance. The three formulations of reliability, however, assign different combinations of the remaining factors to the error variance.

The *coefficient of equivalence* assigns all the specific-factor variance, either temporary or persistent, to the error variance. The specific factors include all characteristics of the individual (skills or information) or of the task (form of item or terminology) that may cause the performance on *one* item alone to be more or less satisfactory. Since the data are obtained in a single test administration of the sample of items, the true variance will include any common factors that persist over the time required for the test. The Kuder-Richardson (1937) formulation of the reliability concept (and its variants) provides an exact estimate of the coefficient of equivalence if the specified assumptions are met. If the assumptions are not sustained, the Kuder-Richardson formulas provide conservative estimates of this coefficient. The coefficient of equivalence is often determined by splitting the test into halves (as odd versus even items). The estimate obtained from the Spearman-Brown formula in this case may provide either an overestimate or an underestimate of the coefficient, depending upon the comparability of the halves (Kuder and Richardson, 1937). All these estimates assume that all items of the test have been attempted, and they are not applicable to time-limit testing procedures.

This general equivalence formulation of the problem of the consistency of responses to a given set of items has been termed the *internal consistency hypothesis* and is utilized in the factorial methods, in the principal-axes solutions for combining measures, in the definitions of homogeneous tests, as well as in the estimation of a reliability coefficient (Burt, 1936; Horst, 1941; Loevinger, 1947; Wherry and Gaylord, 1943). The concept of a homogeneous test as developed by Loevinger (1947) provides an alternative formulation of the internal consistency of the responses to a single sample of items ordered with respect to the proportion of correct responses to the items. An index of homogeneity is then provided by the ratio of the obtained interitem covariances to the maximum interitem covariances for an ordered arrangement of the items. For both the Kuder-Richardson and the Loevinger formulations the concept of the total variance of the scores, as a function of the item variances and the interitem correlations, is important; these functions also provide an indication of the close relation between discrimination and reliability.

The error variance for the *coefficient of stability* includes all temporary sources of variance; these are the common and specific factors that do not persist from one test administration to another. The temporary factors may include the individual's degree of motivation, health, or degree of skill in the mechanics of taking the test. An estimate of this coefficient is provided by the correlation between repeated presentations of the same test. The estimates tend to vary with the time interval between test administrations. Guttman's (1945, 1946) formulations are based on this concept, although he provides estimates of the lower limits of this reliability coefficient from a single trial. Two of his estimates are comparable to those secured from the more precise of the several Kuder-Richardson formulas.

All temporary factors, common and specific, as well as the persistent specific factors, are included as error variance in the *coefficient of stability and equivalence*. This coefficient is estimated from the correlations between two (or preferably three) parallel or comparable tasks separated by a time interval. The coefficient is affected by the length of the time interval as well as by the degree of comparability of the forms of the test. This coefficient has been considered most appropriate for evaluating the reliability of the classification procedures used for selection purposes.

Basic Concepts of Prediction

In their prediction procedures, psychologists have made extensive use of the concepts of *probability* and of *validity*. The *relative-frequency* concept of probability provides the basis for the mathematical procedures used to forecast future behavior and to evaluate these forecasts.

Probability. A degree of probability attaches to any estimate of future behavior. The best estimate is the one yielding the least error, i.e. the most probable values, for the population as a whole (Bridgman, 1932; Guttman, 1941). For qualitative data these estimates are the criterion categories having modal frequencies at each predictor category in the bivariate or multivariate distribution. For quantitative data the most probable criterion values are the arithmetic means of the criterion variables determined for each predictor interval (Guttman, 1941). These mean values are computed from the line of regression of the criterion on the predictor variable. When the linearity assumption is accepted, these means are determined from the usual single or multiple regression equations. When the criterion represents a dichotomized variable (scored 0 or 1), the linear prediction equation (for quantitative variables) is Fisher's discriminant function (Garrett, 1943; Travers, 1939).

Because predictions are always inexact, an estimate of the error of prediction is required. This takes the form of a probability statement expressing a relation between a proposition and a set of data (Jeffreys, 1937; Sarbin, 1944). The data are the criterion classes into which the individuals fall; the proposition is the statement that such and such criterion classes are associated with each of the various predictor measures. The relative frequencies of the *successes* of these *propositions* then provide an index of the accuracy of the prediction.

These probability statements properly refer to predictions made about members of classes. A class may be defined, for example, by the consistent behavior of an individual in a given situation over a period of time or by the similar behaviors of the individuals in a group (Sarbin, 1944). The statement that the probability of John Brown's success is 80 per cent is inappropriate; the probability properly refers to the accuracy of our predictions about individuals in the same class as John Brown, say Class X, rather than to John Brown himself. Verification of probability statements is possible only in terms of relative frequencies. If additional *relevant* data are available, a more useful designation of John Brown may be as a member of Class Y rather than X, where the relative frequency of successes may be different for the two classes. A class designation for an individual can be modified by extending or reducing the attributes used to define the class. Augmented class definitions are of value if the additional data are relevant to the criterion measures (Sarbin, 1944).

Validity. The discussions of validity by Mosier (1947), Rulon (1947), and Thorndike (1949), among others, have differentiated among several different concepts of validity encountered in selection.

The first of these has been termed "validity by definition" (Mosier, 1947). It requires a judgment concerning the pertinence and comprehensiveness of the operations used to define the characteristic to be measured (Bechtoldt, 1947; Rulon, 1947). This concept of validity involves the *acceptance* of a set of operations as an adequate definition of whatever is to be measured. The concept appears in two logically similar phases of selection research, namely, in the choice of an ultimate criterion measure and in the development of tests for a specified trait or quality of performance. If the criterion is defined as the ability to use a lathe to machine a steel screw within a given period of time, a work sample involving exactly this task would be an "obviously" *valid* measure of the skill, although it might not necessarily be a reliable one. A valid test of skill in arithmetic could be defined, likewise, as one requiring the execution of addition, subtraction, multiplication, and division. In selection studies that use criteria such as these, agreement among competent observers constitutes a measure of the validity of the criterion.

The second type of validity concerns the agreement between evaluations of the same individuals by two nonequivalent measures, one of which is termed the criterion (dependent) variable and the other the predictor measure. The basic similarity between the statistical concepts of validity and reliability is evident in this formulation; the difference between them rests with whether the measures are nonequivalent or equivalent.

Obviously the statistical concept of validity, since it refers to a relation between a criterion measure and some other assessment, is dependent upon the particular criterion used. For each different objective or purpose a different criterion is required. The statistical validity of a measure varies then from one activity to the next. In this sense a test has no intrinsic validity; it has as many validities as there are criterion measures to be predicted.

Validity by assumption, involving "common-sense" judgments about the abilities measured by the test, is both common and dangerous in selection (Mosier, 1947). The blithe disregard of empirical evidence of validity in favor of the appearance, the title, or the reported factorial composition of the test and of the criterion is seen too frequently. Tests entitled "mechanical ability," that have proved useful in selecting lathe operators, may, for example, be applied to the selection of engineering students under the *assumption* that they are valid for that purpose also, but this assumption must be verified.

Still another type of validity has been termed "palatability," or "face validity" (when the term does not refer to validity by definition) (Mosier, 1947). Since this concept concerns the way in which the respondents react to the appearance of the test, it is not an important phase of validity, as the concept is used here.

Validity coefficients. When two variables are continuous and linearly related, the product-moment correlation coefficient is the index of validity most frequently used. The multiple correlation coefficient is used for the index of validity of sets of predictor variables under similar conditions. When the relations are to be determined between attributes and between both qualitative and quantitative variables, agreement as to the appropriate statistic is not so widespread.

When there are artificial or true dichotomies in the criterion and predictor variables, the point biserial, the biserial, the *phi*, the *phi* biserial, or the tetrachoric correlation coefficients are used. The point biserial and *phi* coefficients represent the product-moment correlations for true dichotomies (scored zero and one) for the cases of one and of two dichotomous measures, respectively. The biserial and tetrachoric coefficients represent estimates of the product-moment correlations under the assumptions of continuous and normal distributions and linear relations for the cases of one and of two artificial dichotomous variables, respectively. The *phi* biserial coefficient is derived for the case of one artificial and one true dichotomy scored 0 and 1, using the assumptions required for the biserial coefficient (Thorndike, 1949).

The point biserial and *phi* coefficients are regarded as the appropriate statistics for the determination of regression coefficients, in place of the biserial and tetrachoric coefficients, even for artificial dichotomies, since these coefficients indicate what the effective relation is for the case of linear prediction (Wherry and Taylor, 1946). The magnitude of the point biserial coefficient, however, is a function of the proportions in each part of the dichotomy (e.g. the difficulty level of a test at the point of division). This characteristic has led some workers to prefer the biserial, tetrachoric, and *phi* biserial co-efficients for those cases involving artificial dichotomies (Burt, 1944; Thorndike, 1949). If the analysis is concerned with the homogeneity or factorial complexity of a set of observations, the dependence of the point biserial and *phi* coefficients upon the difficulty level may lead to the appearance of "difficulty" factors if the measures are not homogeneous with respect to proportion passing (Carroll, 1945; Ferguson, 1941; Wherry and Gaylord, 1944). For purposes of item analysis or of analysis of the interrelations of measures in a single sample, the biserial or tetrachoric coefficients are more appropriate, since the difficulty of the items can be established by the proportion of correct responses.

When the qualitative predictor variable contains three or more categories, the multiserial *eta* coefficient, with the categories assigned scale values equal to their means on the continuous criterion variable, is recommended for purposes of prediction (Bittner, 1945; Wherry and Taylor, 1946). When these scale values are used, this coefficient is equal to the product-moment correlation between the two variables. One degree of freedom for each category is lost, provided the categories are ordered and weighted in terms of the differences in the criterion means of the category samples.

THE CLASSIFICATION PROBLEM

In the preceding sections selection has been treated as two interrelated activities: classification and prediction. The present section is concerned with the specific aspects of the classification problem as they arise in the development of the criterion and of the predictor "variables."

Detailed discussion of the development of classification procedures for educational, governmental, and military applications have been presented by Adkins (1947), Crawford and Burnham (1946), Davis

(1947a), Flanagan (1948), Guilford and Lacey (1947), Melton (1949), Stead, Shartle, et al. (1940), Stuit (1947a), and Thorndike (1949). Earlier and somewhat more general discussions by Bingham (1937), Horst (1941), Hull (1928), Symonds (1931), and Viteles (1932) provide valuable reference materials. Additional publications of special interest, other than the numerous journal articles, include the critical reviews in the several *Mental Measurement Yearbooks* (Buros, 1949), the *Manual of Examination Methods* (Board of Examinations, 1937), and the *Assessment of Psychological Qualities by Verbal Methods* (Vernon, 1938).

Statement of objectives. A first step in selection is the determination of the characteristics to be used in classifying individuals. For each classification we must determine (1) what traits or performance characteristics are to be evaluated, (2) what standards of success are to be used, (3) what attributes should be present or absent, and (4) what relative importance is to be assigned to the characteristics. When these aims have been defined by the pooled judgments of competent persons, general agreement can be expected on the areas of performance to be included in the success continuum (Flanagan, 1948).

For simple activities the problem of selection is straightforward enough. But when success is defined as a "flying officer competent as a leader and as a pilot or navigator," we face a difficult problem of analysis. Success so defined, although considered as a unitary variate, is actually multi-dimensional (Bechtoldt, 1947; Horst, 1941; Toops, 1944). It is rare, therefore, that assessments on a single trait will provide the required ranking of the individual with respect to the total success variable.

Job analyses. In locating the areas of performance to be assessed, the selection psychologist uses several methods to secure the information he requires. These methods of analyzing an activity are discussed in detail by Horst (1941, Chapter III), Hull

(1928, Chapter IX), Stead, Shartle, et al. (1940, Chapter X), Thorndike (1949, Chapter II), and Viteles (1932, Chapter IX).

The major hazards of job analysis are (1) the possible omission of relevant aspects of the activity, (2) the introduction of extraneous factors through the biases of observers, (3) the inability of the observers to make accurate descriptive observations, (4) the differential effect of experience or training on the performances of successful and unsuccessful individuals, and (5) the relative contributions of previous training to the performances of novices and experienced personnel.

The methods of collecting the data required for job analyses may be grouped, for convenience of exposition, into (1) those based on the judgments of individuals other than the investigator, and (2) those involving direct observations by the investigator.

Sources of information concerning an activity include the published literature on the problem, records of performances of individuals, reports of causes of failure and of common complaints, formal job classification materials, and technical or training manuals. Other sources include interviews with experts, supervisors, and independent observers. Valuable data are often had from interviews with individuals engaging in the activity, including those just entering the field, those still in the learning phase, and those who have been judged relatively successful or unsuccessful. These sources must not be used uncritically.

Of more value are the direct observations by trained persons of individuals engaged in the activity and of situations characteristic of the activity. Systematic, recorded observations directed by a variety of hypotheses are usually necessary to determine those traits or characteristics in which the successful and unsuccessful individuals differ most significantly. Participation in the activity is often helpful to the investigator.

General forms for the summarizing of job duties, essential knowledges, specific information, characteristic activities, and typical inadequacies have been described (Adkins, 1947; Stead, Shartle, et al., 1940). Such forms or trait lists may prove to be deceptively exact, because operational definitions of traits such as initiative or emotional stability are by no means precise.

Tests of ability and skill. A test is defined as one or more tasks presented to the individual, together with the method of appraising the response (Thurstone, 1947). For each task some standard is provided by which to appraise the performance and in terms of which the individual is assigned to a specified class. In the testing procedures used in selection, research workers sometimes concentrate so exclusively on the "accuracy" of a response that they ignore other relevant properties. Such matters as variability, speed, frequency of omissions, frequency of wrong responses, and the ratio of correct to total responses may be indicative of behavior tendencies important in prediction (Coombs, 1948; Guilford and Lacey, 1947).

Tests are most frequently presented in printed form. They may utilize photographs, drawings, maps, etc., as well as verbal symbols, and may require that the subject provide definitions, state purposes, indicate causes or effects, recognize errors, evaluate alternatives, point out differences, rearrange materials according to some requirement, or indicate a common principle (Adkins, 1946; Mosier, Myers, and Price, 1945). Examples of the printed aptitude and achievement tests are provided by Brigham (1932), Crawford and Burnham (1946), Davis (1947a), Guilford and Lacey (1947), and by the publications of the several commercial testing organizations.

For large-scale testing programs, items calling for a limited response or a simple recognition are favored over items that require an essay type of answer. The limited response makes scoring objective; it minimizes the possible effects of fluency; and it reduces the ambiguity of the task set for the subject. The construction of such items is discussed by Adkins (1947) and by the staff of the Board of Examinations (1937). Considerable ingenuity, experience, and technical preparation, bolstered by a thoroughly systematic procedure is necessary for the development of items that require more than trite verbalizations and the parroting of definitions.

Apparatus tests of the work-sample type are utilized whenever the trait to be measured is defined in terms of manipulatory skill. Examples of apparatus tests are those that require the manipulation of peg or form boards, the solution of mazes and assembly tasks, or the judgment of speed and direction of movement. The tasks may require the use of slide or motion-picture projectors, reaction-time equipment, complex "training devices," or actual pieces of military or industrial equipment. Instructions on the development of apparatus tests are presented by Adkins (1947), Melton (1949), and Stuit (1947a).

The demands of expediency and convenience in large-scale testing are such that apparatus tests tend to be used only when forms that are easier to administer and to score are unacceptable. The problems of large-scale administration of apparatus tests were solved fairly satisfactorily, however, by the military services (Flanagan, 1948; Thorndike, 1947a; Stuit, 1947a). The military testers found it necessary to coordinate the testing sessions, to duplicate apparatus, to centralize controls and recording devices, and to standardize instructions.

Attitude and interest questionnaires. Considerable attention has been paid to attitude questionnaires and preference inventories because of the administrative convenience of these devices. The development of such questionnaires is discussed by Maller (1944), Symonds (1931), and Vernon (1938). Pertinent triennial reviews of the general topic of "Psychological Tests and Their Uses" are provided by the *Review of Educational Research.*

Ellis (1946) has pointed out that the validity studies of these questionnaires are equivocal. The authors of the devices usually find their instruments useful, but other investigators often fail to confirm their utility. Some success in military screening, where a psychiatric diagnosis was employed as the criterion, has been reported for several types of items (Ellis and Conrad, 1948; Guilford and Lacey, 1947; Wexler, 1947). However, the usefulness of questionnaires as measures of psychological variables has been questioned by Maller (1944) and by a sample of 79 psychologists polled by Kornhauser (1945), among others. The major objections to these devices appear to be the lack of internal consistency in the set of items, the influence of changes in mental set on the part of the subjects, the instability of the responses over samples of items and periods of time, and the absence of significant relations between such devices and other aspects of behavior.

Improvements designed to reduce the ease with which the "best" responses can be determined by the subject include the use of "forced-choice" items, with elements from two or more different continua presented in pair or triad form, and the application of empirical scoring weights based upon the performances of unlike groups (Fowler, 1947; Horst, 1941; Jurgensen, 1944; Meehl, 1945; Sisson, 1949; Wexler, 1947). Improvements in the stability of the validation data can be expected from the consistent use of cross-validation procedures. Modification of the usual criterion measures, so that they may be made to include evaluations of social and personal "adjustment" and of job satisfaction, may result in increased validity indices for these devices (Maller, 1944).

Biographical or personal history forms. Previous experiences of the subjects are often collected by self-rating or biographical data sheets as well as by the case history and interview methods to be considered later. Although administratively convenient, these self-rating procedures have been characterized by low validity in cross-validation. However, biographical items have proved moderately useful in the prediction of success in selling life insurance, in the selection of army officers and pilots, and in the admission of students to some educational institutions (Bittner, 1945; Guilford and Lacey, 1947; Kurtz, 1941; Richardson, 1947). The importance of the empirical determination of the weights to be assigned to the items and the establishment of their stability on new samples should be stressed, for there is a widespread uncritical use of biographical items scored on the basis of small-sample results or *a priori* judgments.

Personal history data can be criticized on two counts: (1) the ease with which the responses may be biased to the advantage of the respondent; and (2) the inability of the individual, even when favorably disposed, to recall accurately his past experiences. The procedure is most successful when the probability of falsification is low, when the responses are not regarded as accurate sources of personal history data, and when item-scoring weights are empirically determined.

Ratings. In selection, we usually want classifications based on the attributes of the subject and not on those of a rater observing the subject. In the rating processes, however, the data obtained are the responses of an observer to a situation of which the subject and his behavior are only a part. The observer, furthermore, is a complex mechanism subject to both systematic and variable errors. In spite of these weaknesses, ratings of one type or another are widely used in the development of criterion and predictor categories. Even such matters as salary and academic grades are basically ratings (Jenkins, 1946; Patterson, 1946).

Two different functions may be served by raters, namely, recording and evaluation. The recording function is of particular importance in tasks that leave no permanent record as, for example, in interpersonal situations or complex performance tasks. The function of evaluation is less straightforward. Here the rater serves as a computer presumed to possess the ability to synthesize nonlinear data and to determine what sorts of observations are to be included. These synthetic evaluations, characteristic of summary ratings and clinical judgments, are apt to be affected by the biases of the observers (Thorndike, 1949).

A variety of methods are used to secure an analytical judgment of some aspect of a performance or of a single trait, or to obtain a summary evaluation of the individual. These methods include paired comparisons, rank orders, and designations of position on a scale. Also, check lists on which specific aspects of the performance are marked as present or absent are used in rating a sequence of operations. The voting or nominating technique, as one form of rating device has been called, may be used when a number of judges are available for evaluating complex traits.

The problems involved in rating procedures are mainly those of securing discriminating, valid, and reliable measures. Discussions of the problems of developing such rating measures are contained in Symonds (1931) and Vernon (1938). For additional phases of the problems associated with ratings of limited behavior units and summary ratings used as criterion measures, see Adkins (1947), Cooper (1940), Flanagan (1948), Stuit (1947a) and Thorndike (1949).

The observer's biases pose the most difficult problem in the rating techniques. It is possible to reduce these biases by training the raters, by providing detailed descriptions of the performance to be evaluated, by specifying the standards to be used in the evaluation, and by indicating the ways in which the separate aspects are to be combined. Pooling the independent observations of several raters and securing repetitions of the evaluations are other means of counteracting bias.

Special mention should be made of the synthetic evaluations characteristic of clinical situations and interviews. The interview routinely used in selection is an extremely complex activity in which the interviewer can be considered as (1) a variable part of the social situation, (2) a recorder of the specific types of behavior being evaluated, and (3) an interpreter of the observations (Flanagan, 1948; Rundquist, 1947; Sarbin, 1944). In the interview, the problems of variability between individuals over samples of behavior and over a period of time may be entirely insignificant compared to the variability attributable to the situation and to the interviewer.

Adequate studies have not been made of the contribution of the evaluative type of interview to the efficiency of the selection process. Those that have been made indicate that the interview contributes relatively little to the other available techniques unless it is carefully standardized, uses trained interviewers, and is directed toward traits not otherwise evaluated (Davis, 1947b; Flanagan, 1948; Rundquist, 1947; Sarbin, 1944; Stuit, 1947a).

For vocational and military selection, there is little evidence of a significant increase in accuracy of prediction because of the addition of clinical judgments. Davis (1947b) summarized a number of studies using clinical tests and case history materials by saying that the subjective evaluation of empirical data appears to add little or nothing to the accuracy with which personnel can be classified for selection on the basis of suitable objective tests. The studies he reviewed include those made for the Coast Guard, the Army Air Forces, the Navy, and the Civil Aeronautics Authority. These studies utilized the Rorschach test, various work methods, and clinical evaluations of other types. A number of other investigators, working in situations in which the accuracy of their predictions could be tested, have likewise concluded that clinical judgments are of little use in classification techniques (Sarbin, 1944; Stuit, 1947a; Wallin, 1941).

It should not be inferred, however, that the interview is valueless in the selection process. The interview is a method of collecting biographical and preference data; it also provides an opportunity to evaluate the voice, the manner of expression, and the poise of an individual. Whether the interview is the most economical, efficient, and accurate method of securing such data depends upon the situation and upon the skill of the interviewer. It may also provide an opportunity for the interviewer to explain matters to those being selected, and to establish desirable personnel relations.

CRITERION MEASURES

An acceptable criterion of success is crucial because it constitutes the basis for validation. It provides the standard in terms of which the relevant predictor variables can be isolated, the efficient testing procedures separated from the inefficient, and the relative weights determined for use in predicting future performances and in combining sets of observations. The criterion must provide an adequate definition of the success continuum for the activity in question.

The success measure is usually assumed to lie on a single continuum. However, as Toops (1944) has demonstrated, success is not unitary; an analysis of any but the simplest activity will indicate that success is often the resultant of a large number of separate abilities, traits, skills, and knowledges. We can resolve this difficulty if we express the success continuum as a multidimensional variable, with each dimension an independent component. The success measure can then be defined by (1) a single overall evaluation, (2) a weighted composite of the separately measured components, and (3) a pattern or profile of these several variables (Adkins, 1937; Bechtoldt, 1947; Horst,

1941; Toops, 1944). The first two procedures are the ones most used.

The merits of criterion measures are judged
in terms of their validity, reliability, and
discrimination.

The validity of sets of criterion measures
is evaluated in terms of statistical evidence
of positive intercorrelations among the measures. The presence of significant correlations cannot safely be assumed; some of the
psychologists working on military and industrial selection have found that individual
criteria may be quite independent of one
another, or, what is more pertinent, even
independent of, if not negatively related to,
the ultimate criterion (Flanagan, 1948; Jenkins, 1946; Stuit, 1947a).

The reliability and discrimination of criterion measures are evaluated in terms of
statistical evidence of consistencies over periods of time and over samples of situations
and by the distributions of the assigned
values. Although no test can consistently
predict a criterion that has zero reliability,
high reliability in a criterion is desirable but
not necessary. Low reliability introduces
chance factors that attenuate the relations
but do not introduce systematic irrelevant
variables (Thorndike, 1949). Likewise, multiple classification categories of success permit improvements in prediction, but a dichotomous criterion, if relevant and reliable, will
be superior, for validation purposes, to a
multiple-category criterion that is either less
valid or less reliable. An acceptable working procedure seems to be to utilize all the
categories that (1) are necessary for the purpose of the selection situation, (2) can be
shown to be reliably discriminated, and (3)
meet the demands for accuracy of representation of the data.

THE PREDICTION PROBLEM

After the criterion and predictor classifications have been established, the next phase
is the determination of the empirical relations between them and the verification on a

new sample of the forecasts based upon these
relations. These matters have been discussed
by Adkins (1947), Flanagan (1948), Horst
(1941), Hull (1928), Stead, Shartle, et al.
(1940), Stuit (1947a), and Thorndike (1949).
These general references form the basis for
the following discussion of three major topics,
namely: (1) the evaluation of prediction
statements, (2) the factors influencing the
accuracy of prediction, and (3) differential
prediction.

Evaluation of Prediction Statements

Since predictions are based on probability
estimates, errors of prediction are to be expected. For the *qualitative* case, the efficiency of prediction can be expressed in
terms of the proportion of individuals correctly assigned (Guttman, 1941). The accuracy of *quantitative* predictions, on the
other hand, is usually expressed as a function of the correlation between the criterion
and the predictor measures.

The effectiveness of a given value of a correlation coefficient is usually expressed in
terms of k, the coefficient of alienation, and
E, the index of forecasting efficiency (Hull,
1928; Horst, 1941). Validity coefficients,
corrected for attenuation, of less than 0.45
or 0.50 evaluated in terms of these indices
are considered by some workers to be of
little value in prediction unless a favorable
selection ratio is obtained.

This conservative view is appropriate when
a criterion value is to be predicted for each
individual and the accuracy of the prediction
for all cases is to be evaluated. However,
for selection purposes, the utility of a prediction may be assessed in terms of the relative number of correct predictions and in
terms of attaining or exceeding some critical
value of the criterion (Horst, 1941). A
higher validity coefficient means an increase
in the proportion of cases scoring above some
arbitrary criterion value. The magnitude of
this increase for the special case of linear
relations in a normal bivariate distribution
can be estimated from the tables provided

by Peters and Van Voorhis (1940). The correlation coefficient can be regarded as a direct index of the efficiency of prediction, according to Brogden (1946a). He shows that, when the regression is linear and the frequency distributions are similar, the correlation coefficient represents the ratio of the mean criterion score of the group selected from the top portion of the "combined predictor" distribution to the mean value that would be obtained by selecting a group of similar size by means of the *criterion* itself. Still another method of indicating the effectiveness of a selection device is provided by Richardson (1944), who defines predictive efficiency in terms of the increase in efficiency due to the use of a selection device, as compared with selecting the cases at random (Jarrett, 1948).

These measures refer to the accuracy of prediction in the original sample and not necessarily to the accuracy of the procedure when applied to a new sample. The value of a prediction procedure must be demonstrated on the new sample (Horst, 1941). The ratio of the quadratic mean of the errors of prediction in the new sample (based on the regression weights from the initial sample) to the standard error of estimate of the original sample provides an estimate of the accuracy in new samples. The quadratic mean of the errors is used, since both additive and multiplying constants based on the original sample are required. The correlation between predicted and obtained scores in the new sample is a less effective measure of accuracy because variations in the means and standard deviations are automatically corrected by the correlation coefficient (Horst, 1941).

The use of a cross-validation sample for the evaluation of the stability of a prediction equation is desirable because of the often unwarranted assumptions of (1) random sampling, (2) normality of the distribution, (3) independent errors, and (4) constant marginal frequency distributions on the predictor variables that are used to pro-

vide estimates of the sampling fluctuations of various regression statistics (Guttman, 1941). The mathematical solutions for non-normal population distributions are not yet available.

Factors Influencing the Accuracy of Prediction

The accuracy of predictions is affected by a number of factors other than the intrinsic relation (validity) between the predictor variables and the criterion. In addition to the reliability of the classification procedures, such factors include (1) the selection ratio, (2) the difficulty level of the activity, (3) the method of selection, (4) the method of evaluation, (5) the representativeness of the sample, and (6) the number of measures used.

Selection ratio. No selection problem exists unless some individuals are to be chosen and some rejected. The ratio of the number chosen to the number available is the *selection ratio*. The effectiveness of a selection procedure in terms of the performance level of those accepted will be *inversely* related to the magnitude of this ratio. When the selection ratio is low (when only a few individuals are to be accepted), moderate to low validity coefficients may prove useful. On the other hand, if only a few individuals can be *rejected*, a much higher validity would be required for the same effectiveness.

Difficulty level of activity. The possible advantage of selection over nonselection varies *inversely* with the proportion of satisfactory individuals in a random sample. If, for example, 80 per cent of the candidates can be expected to succeed anyhow, there is little value in a selection program unless the proportion of successful individuals among those selected can be significantly increased over the 80-per-cent value (Toops, 1945b). When, however, the proportion of successful candidates in a nonselected group is 50 per cent or less, measures having validity coefficients as low as 0.30 may prove valuable.

The theoretical effectiveness of a selection procedure as determined by difficulty level, selection ratio, and obtained validity has been investigated by Taylor and Russell (1939) both in terms of the expected proportions of successful candidates among those selected and under the assumption of linear relations and normally distributed variables. Their results indicate that acceptable efficiency can be achieved even though the index of forecasting efficiency is below the 10-per-cent point recommended by Hull (1928) as a critical level.

Method of selection. Selection may involve a single hurdle or successive hurdles. In the single-hurdle method, all individuals are evaluated on all the selection devices; with successive hurdles, the number of applicants is reduced successively by separate operations until at the final hurdle only a few individuals need be considered. Successive hurdles are often found in educational programs where there are periodic rejections for unsatisfactory performance. This procedure can be criticized, however, when there is a drastic use of cutting scores on separate tasks. It is sometimes assumed that failure to perform well on each task warrants elimination, and that high performance on one measure cannot compensate for failure on another. As Toops (1932) has pointed out, this disadvantage can be overcome to some extent by a proper arrangement of the tasks and the use of relatively high cutting scores in the first measures. The tasks should be arranged in decreasing order of validity, the most valid first, etc. At the final stage, the selection problem may be of little consequence, since the group may by then be quite homogeneous.

Method of evaluation. The predicted criterion scores may be obtained in terms of formal measures (linear regression equations, cutoff scores, matched profiles) or in terms of a clinical evaluation of the available data.

The more efficient procedures utilize all available data, and the predictions are made by a formal method. The linear regression equation and the multiple correlation technique are usually applicable (Thorndike, 1949). Since this process is basically one of determining the "best" weights in a linear equation, the special problems of this process will be considered later in the section on the combining of measures.

The methods of successive and multiple cutting scores and of matched profiles have been recommended for use whenever (1) the relations between the criterion and predictor measures are conspicuously nonlinear, (2) competence in one area cannot compensate for weakness in another, or (3) a specified pattern of desirable and undesirable traits has been established (Ruch, 1945; Toops, 1945b). A convenient method of utilizing these nonlinear relations or critical values, in case they exist, is to establish a cutting score on each of the crucial attributes. Individuals who fall below the success score are then automatically eliminated, regardless of their standing on other variables. The multiple-cutting-score method selects the most efficient pattern of cutoff values from a series of possible combinations and eliminates individuals falling outside this pattern.

These cutoff methods and the linear regression techniques may not result in the selection of the same individuals (Thorndike, 1949). Individuals barely above the cutting score on each of two predictor variables may be rejected by the linear regression or "summation of traits" method. Those below the cutting score on one of the variables, but who score high on the other measure, may be accepted by some linear composite selection method, but rejected by the successive cutoff procedure.

Additional work needs to be done on the relative accuracy of the predictions made by the methods described above. For large-scale selection problems in which approximately linear relations can be found, the composite score method is probably most appropriate. Critical cutting scores on the composite criterion are of greatest value when the proportion of individuals to be selected and the proportion above a given point on the composite score distribution can be determined.

Representativeness of samples studied. Perhaps the most insidious factor in selection is the nonrepresentativeness of the validity relations determined on a sample of individuals (Burt, 1944; Marks, 1947; Flanagan, 1948; Thorndike, 1949). Systematic biases may be introduced by the sampling procedure. The ideal sampling procedures may be difficult to formulate, however, because of the uncertainty in the definition of the population from which the selection is to be made. The population to be sampled includes not only those individuals available at the moment but also those who will engage in the activity in the future. When the population cannot be defined accurately, an estimate of the sampling variability may be secured, with some degree of accuracy, from the empirical results of successive large samples.

Since the relations determined on a sample are to be applied to some type of population in a selection process, the heterogeneity of the sample as compared with that of the population is important, especially when successive hurdles are used. As long as the obtained coefficients are to be used with the sample or with similar samples, no correction for heterogeneity is necessary. However, if the selection procedure is to be applied to a more heterogeneous population, an estimate is required of the correlation that would have been obtained had the total population been permitted to reach the final stage of performance. The general formulation of this problem has been presented by Burt (1943), by Kelley (1947), and by Thorndike (1949).

Another sampling question arises from the use of special groups for validation purposes and from the effects of experience on performance. This type of sampling may introduce irrelevant factors into the prediction equation. Since training may modify differentially many of the traits used for prediction, it cannot be assumed that performances before and after a given amount of experience are comparable. A similar questionable assumption is frequently made in the validation of personality tests and questionnaires through the use of hospitalized and nonhospitalized groups (Wexler, 1947). These assumptions should not be made unless there exists positive evidence of their validity.

Number of predictor variables. The stability of predictions for new samples tends to decrease with an increase in the number of predictor variables in the original sample when the regression weights are determined by least squares. The addition of variables to the original set of predictors will not, however, reduce the accuracy of prediction in the original sample (Horst, 1941; Reed, 1941). In an effort to increase the stability of their predictions, psychologists try to reduce the number of predictor variables to a minimum. Two different procedures have been used for this purpose. For the prediction of a single complex criterion, batteries of two to five complex predictor variables of the broad "aptitude" type are developed. For the prediction of several criteria, different aptitude batteries would be required. Another solution attempts to develop relatively "pure" measures of the separate criterion "traits" and to combine in various ways the several tests from the single pool of predictor measures. This second procedure is defended on the basis of the increased probability of differential prediction (see the next section) as well as on the basis of general efficiency in test construction.

The importance of comprehensive coverage of all the relevant criterion traits, however, runs counter to the desirability of reducing the number of variables. The effectiveness of a selection procedure will be lessened if any significant aspect of the criterion is omitted from the predictor variables. This has been one of the frequent sources of inaccuracies of prediction (Horst, 1941).

Differential Prediction

Selection can be extended to the situation in which each individual is considered for assignment to one of several activities. This more general selection process has been variously termed *multiple selection, classification and differential prediction*, or *placement*. The present discussion will review the major points regarding this problem that have been raised by Brogden (1946c), Burt (1943), Flanagan (1947a, 1948), Horst (1941), and Thorndike (1949); namely, (1) the characteristics of the predictor variables used in differential prediction, and (2) the procedures used in effecting such classifications.

The basic assumption here is that a restricted set of trait measurements, differentially weighted, can be used to predict success in two or more areas of activity. For reasons of parsimony, the number of these fundamental measures should be as small as possible, and each one should be significantly related to only a few criterion measures (Horst, 1941).

From this general point of view, the tests developed for the prediction of single and multiple criteria can be contrasted. For the prediction of single criterion measures, complex tests of the miniature job-sample type resembling the criterion in content, materials, type, and complexity of task have proved efficient. These are designed to measure the hypothetical traits of the criterion in combinations resembling those found in the activity itself (Thorndike, 1949). The tests recommended for use in differential prediction, on the other hand, tend to be more nearly homogeneous measures of a single functional unity and have the advantage that, in combination, the proper weight of each trait for the prediction of each criterion can be determined. Such measures usually represent performances on thoroughly learned materials.

At the present time, two methods are used to determine the functional unities to be represented by these homogeneous tests. One involves the appraisal of the test materials by sophisticated individuals. The other method utilizes the intercorrelations among the measures and defines the functional unities in terms of high intercorrelations among those measures that may be combined, and low correlations between sets of such combined measures.

After the measures have been assembled and the regression weights for the prediction of each of the several criteria determined, the problem of the most efficient assignment of the individuals arises. The objective is to maximize the selection efficiency for the available group in terms of performance in the several activities (Brogden, 1946c; Thorndike, 1949). The attainment of this objective involves consideration of (1) the reliability of the differentiation between predicted scores as a function of the reliabilities of the measures and their intercorrelations, (2) the selection ratio and critical rejection scores, and (3) the relative importance of the activities.

For an accurate differentiation between activities to which individuals are assigned, the reliabilities of the separate scores should be comparable and as high as possible, and the intercorrelations of the measures should be minimized. If significant differences are to be located, the chance variations in individual scores should be small in relation to the between-score differences for the average individual. If the obtained differences are relatively small, as would be the case with correlated composite scores or with uniformly low multiple correlations, then relatively high reliability is required (Thorndike, 1949). The ratio of the standard deviation of a difference (in standard score form) for a given *individual* to the standard deviation of standard score differences for the *group* has been suggested for the evaluation of pairs of profile differences used in differential prediction (Kelley, 1947; Bennett and Doppelt, 1948).

Although the validity of each composite score for its associated criterion should be as high as possible, only one of the several validity coefficients (for the different composite scores) for a single activity should be high, and all the other coefficients should be as low as possible (Thorndike, 1949). The highest coefficient should be that between the criterion measure of an activity and the composite score used to select individuals for that activity.

When the selection ratio is favorable and critical rejection scores can be established, a successive-approximation procedure for maximizing the overall effectiveness of selection is applicable. Brogden (1946c) has demonstrated that, in the linear case, efficient differentiation can be effected by establishing, first, a set of critical rejection composite scores for each activity in terms of the number to be accepted, and, second, a set of critical assignment scores equal, in each case, to the differences between the critical rejection scores. For the individuals above the critical values in two or more activities, the assignment is made to the activity for which the difference in predicted standard score units is greatest in terms of the critical difference scores. As the number of activities is increased, the complexity of this successive-approximation solution is increased.

A solution has been proposed for several special cases in which all individuals are to be assigned and no screening can be accomplished (Flanagan, 1948). Whenever individuals are to be assigned in equal numbers to equally important and equally difficult activities involving independent sets of predictor traits, each individual is assigned to the position for which his composite aptitude score is the highest. If cutting scores can be used, say, at the mean of the predicted scores, then for the case of three independent activities, seven-eighths of the individuals could be assigned to one activity with the expectation that their performance would be average or better. If some selection can take place, the individuals above the rejection values on two or more composite scores are assigned to the position for which their predicted scores are highest.

In the practical situation involving differences in the difficulty levels and in the relative importance of the activities, as well as in the number of individuals required, successive selection in terms of the importance of the activity may be sufficiently accurate (Flanagan, 1948). This general problem, however, has not yet been solved.

THE COMBINING OF MEASURES

In the selection process it is often necessary to combine several measures for the purpose either of defining a single composite criterion or of obtaining predictions of future performance. The solutions to this problem can be classified as: (1) the weighting of predictor (independent) variables given some single criterion (dependent) variate, which is the ordinary multiple-correlation procedure; (2) the weighting of measures when there is no dependent variable and the multiple-correlation procedures are inappropriate; (3) the simultaneous weighting of sets of predictor measures and sets of criterion measures to effect the maximum correlation between two composite variables. The first two of these solutions are those most frequently used in selection problems. The third procedure has been criticized as inappropriate for practical selection problems (Horst, 1941; Thorndike, 1949).

Weighting with the use of a dependent variable. Two situations that can be considered as a single problem are: (1) the prediction of a single criterion measure from a set of predictor variables, and (2) the combination of sets of partial criterion measures when an ultimate criterion is available. The general solution is to weight the several measures in such a way that the weighted linear composite will conform as closely as possible to the values of the single criterion observations. If the single criterion is a quantitative one, the theoretically best solution under the least-squares principle leads to a multiple-regression equation. If the criterion is a qualitative variate, the "best" combination in the same sense is provided by Fisher's discriminant function which, for a dichotomous criterion scored 0 and 1, can be regarded as a regression-equation problem. These techniques take into consideration the intercorrelations of the measures as well as their correlations with the criterion.

The computational difficulties of multiple correlation tend to restrict the applicability of this method. Dwyer (1945), Guttman (1941), and Hoel (1947), however, provide both theoretical and computational simplifications that should extend the usefulness of the technique. Rapid approximations to the exact solutions are provided by a modification of the Kelley-Salisbury iterative solution of the regression weights developed for use in the Army Air Forces research program (Thorndike, 1949). In practice, the exact weights determined by these methods may be modified for computational convenience.

Sets of more or less arbitrary, or intuitive, weights representing the judgments of experts have been used in combining predictor or criterion measures. In spite of the "subjectivity" of such weights, the stability of these solutions, as shown by the effectiveness in new samples, may be comparable to that of the more rigorous techniques (Reed, 1941). In any case the effectiveness in prediction rather than the method of obtaining the weights is the crucial point at issue.

Another important problem associated with the multiple-correlation technique is the "regression" effect in new samples as the ratio of the number of predictor variables to the number of cases in the samples increases (see above). The generality of this fact, together with the absence of a suitable criterion for the number of variables to be used, has led to the "rule of thumb" that multiple-correlation problems should be restricted to fewer than six predictor variables

and that the regression coefficients, in any case, should be based upon large samples of individuals (Horst, 1941; Adkins, 1947; Thorndike, 1949). The actual determination of the stability of regression weights on new samples will provide the evidence for the justification of a larger number of variables.

The multiple-correlation techniques, or approximations thereto, also provide a basis for deciding which are the more "efficient" items of a test (Richardson, 1936b; Adkins and Toops, 1937; Flanagan, 1939b; Horst, 1941). The dependent variable may be either the total test score or an "external criterion" measure. For computational convenience, an assumption of equal or zero interitem correlations is often introduced, although the adequacy of the solution is thereby reduced. Detailed discussions of these techniques are given by Adkins (1947), Conrad (1944), Davis (1946a), Horst (1934b), and Toops (1941). The main objectives of item analysis are (1) to increase the internal consistency, as measured by the average interitem correlation, of the set of items, (2) to increase the predictive efficiency of some external criterion by a set of items, and (3) to locate specific faults in the construction of the test items.

Whenever the purpose is to secure an internally consistent set of items, as in the development of a measure of a single trait, the dimensionality of the set of item intercorrelations and the "homogeneity" of the responses should be considered. For the practical purposes of selection, useful approximations to this objective are obtained from the correlation of the item with the total score, since this coefficient is proportional to the average correlation of the item with all the items in the set (Richardson, 1941a). Rejection of items with low item-test coefficients will increase the average intercorrelation and, in this sense, the homogeneity of the set.

If the original set of items measures two or more factors, however, the final set of items selected on the basis of high item-test correlations may contain one, two, or more factors, depending on the number of items representing each factor in the original collection. There is no assurance that the final set of items will measure only a single trait (Mosier, 1936; Sletto, 1937). If the item selection is to be accomplished through the use of the item-test coefficient, an efficient solution would be realized if the homogeneous subsets of items representing the different factors in the test were first determined, and then the several scores on the subsets and the item-subtest correlation were used for the selection of the items (Wherry and Gaylord, 1943; Davis, 1947a).

For purposes of prediction, the relation between the items used as predictors and an external criterion is determined. This relation is usually represented either by one of the correlation coefficients or an approximation thereto, or by some type of regression coefficient (Davis, 1946a; Adkins, 1947; Thorndike, 1949). One procedure treats each item as an individual test and neglects the interitem correlations. More efficient procedures using all the relevant data have been developed by Horst (1934b) and Toops (1941).

The sampling variation in item-discrimination statistics is appreciable even for samples as large as 400 cases, although the difficulty indices of items may be fairly stable (Davis, 1946b; Travers, 1942). Furthermore, unless the distribution of validity coefficients is significantly greater than that expected by chance, there is little reason to select any particular sample of items from the total test (Merrill, 1937). These sampling problems are sufficiently serious to warrant a questioning of the often mechanical application of item-analysis techniques in test construction.

Weighting without the use of a dependent variable. The basic discussions of this linear weighting problem are presented by Burt (1936), Kelley (1947), Richardson (1941a), and Wilks (1938). In general, there is no one "best" method of weighting; the differ-

ent methods accomplish different objectives. The methods may involve the simple addition of arbitrary numerical values, the use of values representing the judgments of experts, or some function of the intercorrelations of the scores and of their reliability coefficients.

The distinction between effective and nominal weights is important to the weighting problem. The nominal weights are the coefficients, W_j, of the variables in the linear equation, $T_i = \sum_j W_j X_{ji}$. The effective (or functional) weights have been defined as "the proportion of the total variance of the composite T_i that is contributed by the particular (weighted) variable $W_j X_{ji}$" (Richardson, 1941a). The effective weight of a variable depends upon the nominal weight of that variable and its standard deviation as well as upon the weighted correlations of the variable with each measure (including itself) in turn. The correlations are weighted by the dispersions of the several measures, and the self-correlation is defined as unity.

The simple addition of scores, as in the case of a set of test items, is sufficiently accurate for the combining of large numbers of variates. The rationale for this simple procedure is that, as the number of positively correlated variables increases, the correlation between any two sets of weighted scores approaches unity and the effect of differential weighting tends to disappear. However, if the number of measures to be added together is not large, the dispersions and intercorrelations of the measures will influence significantly the effective weighting.

The method of weighting scores inversely as their standard deviations is a common practice. If the tests are considered to be of equal importance and the dispersions to be artifacts of the arbitrary characteristics of the test, then the addition of the *standard scores* of the individuals is appropriate. Richardson (1941a) has pointed out two important characteristics of this method. In the first place, if the number of variables is three, or greater, the variance contributions of the several variables to the composite are not necessarily equal, even though standard scores are added (i.e. the nominal weights are unity). Differential weighting will occur unless the variables are equally correlated. The second point is that, in so far as the differences in the variances of the measures reflect differences in internal consistency (and reliability, in this sense), the addition of standard scores will, in effect, increase the relative weight of the less reliable tests, since the variance of the composite scores is directly related to the internal consistency of the set of measures.

If the set of measures can be regarded as parallel forms of a single test, such that the intertest correlations corrected for attenuation are unity, the measures may be weighted in terms of a function of their respective reliabilities (Kelley, 1947). This procedure is justified on the grounds that an increase in the size of the sample increases the reliability of the composite. The effective contribution of each measure so weighted to the composite is directly proportional to its reliability coefficient and inversely proportional to its error variance (Richardson, 1941a).

A related problem is that of weighting the measures so that the reliability of the *composite* will be maximal. The solution, which deals with a property of the composite, is not the same, however, as that obtained when the assumption is made that the intrinsic correlation coefficients are unity. Thomson (1940) has shown that weighting for the case of maximum battery reliability is a function of the reliabilities and of the intercorrelations of the measures.

Another theoretically important method of determining a set of weights is applicable to the combination of positively correlated attributes that are considered as separate aspects of a single variable. The same solution can be arrived at through three approaches; the scores may be weighted so that: (1) the dispersion of the composite is

as large as possible (Horst, 1936); (2) the variations between the weighted scores for each individual are minimized (Edgerton and Kolbe, 1936), and (3) the composite score for each individual best represents his standing on all the measures of the composite (Burt, 1936; Hotelling, 1933). Horst (1941) indicates that the units of measurement must be considered in these (principal axes) solutions. Since the least-squares determination of the principal axes requires the solution of the characteristic equation, the problem becomes computationally cumbersome for more than five or six measures. However, this weighting procedures has a sound rationale and is considered appropriate for the combination of a series of measures that represent different aspects of the underlying variable.

The computational difficulties associated with the principal-axes solution have led to the introduction of weighting in terms of the correlation of the variable with the average centroid axis of the system or according to the contribution to the total variance of the composite (Burt, 1936; Richardson, 1941a). Burt (1936) points out that another approximation can be secured by assuming that only one variable is being measured and by using a single-factor solution for the weights. These solutions will not differ greatly, but the accuracy of the centroid weighting as an approximation to the method of maximum variance may not be close (Edgerton and Kolbe, 1936). The centroid method is computationally feasible for relatively large numbers of variables for which either the intercorrelations of the measures or their correlations with the sum of the variables are available. The item-analysis procedures, using the item-test correlation coefficient (an internal criterion), represent applications of this method (Richardson, 1941a).

Another method of weighting measures representing various aspects of success utilizes the judgment of a "competent" group of individuals regarding the relative importance of the several elements (Horst, 1941;

Toops, 1945b). These judgments can be expressed in a number of ways. If there are two or more judges, each may be required to apportion among the several components of the activity a given set of numbers or "bids." The number assigned to each element represents the judge's evaluation of the importance of that aspect. The judges, in turn, can be weighted by some estimate of their competence or experience. The final set of weights can then be reduced proportionately to any desired total. The bids, in turn, may be adjusted for the intercorrelations and reliabilities of the measures. These "rational" weights can now be considered as representing the desired effective contributions of the separate measures to the composite value, but the nominal weights must still be determined. The determination of the nominal weights requires the analysis of a set of simultaneous equations that express the nominal weights as a function of the dispersions and intercorrelations of the variables and of the effective or rational weights (Horst, 1941; Bechtoldt, 1947). The error often made in the use of rational or intuitional weights lies in considering these judgments as nominal weights rather than as the effective weights.

REFERENCES *

The following references were selected on the basis of accessibility to students, recency of publication, and completeness of treatment; priority of publication was not considered.

Adkins, D. C. Test construction in public personnel administration. *Educ. psychol. Measmt.*, 1944, 4, 141–160.

Adkins, D. C. Construction and analysis of written tests for predicting job performance. *Educ. psychol. Measmt.*, 1946, 6, 195–211.

Adkins, D. C. *Construction and analysis of achievement tests.* Washington, D. C.: Superintendent of Documents, 1947.

* Reports prepared under contract with the Office of Scientific Research and Development usually bear an OSRD number. In addition, many carry a PB number, which indicates that they may be obtained from the Office of Technical Services, U. S. Department of Commerce, Washington 25, D. C.

Adkins, D. C. Needed research on examining devices. *Amer. Psychologist*, 1948, 3, 104–106.

Adkins, D. C., and H. A. Toops. Simplified formulas for item selection and construction. *Psychometrika*, 1937, 2, 165–171.

Alexander, H. W. The estimation of reliability when several trials are available. *Psychometrika*, 1947, 12, 79–99.

Anastasi, A. The nature of psychological 'traits.' *Psychol. Rev.*, 1948, 55, 127–138.

Babitz, M., and N. Keys. A method for approximating the average intercorrelation coefficient by correlating the parts with the sum of the parts. *Psychometrika*, 1940, 5, 283–288.

Baier, D. E. Selection and evaluation of West Point cadets. *Educ. psychol. Measmt.*, 1948, 8, 193–199.

Bechtoldt, H. P. Problems in establishing criterion measures. In D. B. Stuit (Ed.), *Personnel research and test development in the Bureau of Naval Personnel.* Princeton: Princeton University Press, 1947.

Bechtoldt, H. P., J. W. Maucker, and D. B. Stuit. The use of order of merit rankings. In *New methods in applied psychology.* College Park: University of Maryland, 1947. Pp. 26–33.

Bellows, R. M. Procedures for evaluating vocational criteria. *J. appl. Psychol.*, 1941, 25, 499–513.

Bennett, G. K., and J. E. Doppelt. The evaluation of pairs of tests for guidance use. *Educ. psychol. Measmt.*, 1948, 8, 319–325.

Bergmann, G., and K. W. Spence. The logic of psychophysical measurement. *Psychol. Rev.*, 1944, 51, 1–24.

Bingham, W. V. *Aptitudes and aptitude testing.* New York: Harper, 1937.

Bingham, W. V., and B. V. Moore. *How to interview.* (Revised Ed.) New York: Harper, 1941.

Bittner, R. H. Quantitative prediction from qualitative data: Predicting college entrance from biographical information. *J. Psychol.*, 1945, 19, 97–108.

Board of Examinations. *Manual of examination methods.* Chicago: University of Chicago, 1937.

Bordin, E. S. A theory of vocational interests as dynamic phenomena. *Educ. psychol. Measmt.*, 1943, 3, 49–65.

Bridgman, P. W. *The logic of modern physics.* New York: Macmillan, 1932.

Brigham, C. C. *A study of error.* Princeton: College Entrance Examination Board, 1932.

Brogden, H. E. On the interpretation of the correlation coefficient as a measure of predictive efficiency. *J. educ. Psychol.*, 1946a, 37, 65–76.

Brogden, H. E. Variation in test validity with variation in the distribution of item difficulties, number of items, and degree of their intercorrelation. *Psychometrika*, 1946b, 11, 197–214.

Brogden, H. E. An approach to the problem of differential prediction. *Psychometrika*, 1946c, 11, 139–154.

Buros, O. K. (Ed.). *The third mental measurements yearbook.* New Brunswick: Rutgers University Press, 1949.

Burt, C. The analysis of examination marks, memorandum I. In P. Hartog, E. C. Rhodes, and C. Burt, *The marks of examiners.* London: Macmillan, 1936. Pp. 245–314.

Burt, C. Validating tests for personnel selection. *Brit. J. Psychol.,* 1943, **34,** 1–19.

Burt, C. Statistical problems in the evaluation of army tests. *Psychometrika,* 1944, **9,** 219–235.

Burt, C. The reliability of teachers' assessment of their pupils. *Brit. J. educ. Psychol.,* 1945, **15,** 80–92.

Burt, C. Symposium on the selection of pupils for different types of secondary schools. I. A general survey. *Brit. J. educ. Psychol.,* 1947, **17,** 57–71.

Carroll, J. B. The effect of difficulty and chance success on correlations between items or between tests. *Psychometrika,* 1945, **10,** 1–19.

Carter, L. F., and F. J. Dudek. The use of psychological techniques in measuring and critically analyzing navigators' flight performance. *Psychometrika,* 1947, **12,** 31–42.

Conrad, H. S. Characteristics and uses of item-analysis data. OSRD Report 4034, Aug. 1944 (PBL 13296).

Coombs, C. H. Some hypotheses for the analysis of qualitative variables. *Psychol. Rev.,* 1948, **55,** 167–174.

Cooper, J. H. Rating forms. In W. H. Stead, C. L. Shartle, et al., *Occupational counseling techniques.* New York: American, 1940.

Crawford, A. B., and P. S. Burnham. *Forecasting college achievement.* New Haven: Yale University Press, 1946.

Cronbach, L. J. Response sets and test validity. *Educ. psychol. Measmt.,* 1946, **6,** 475–494.

Cronbach, L. J. Test reliability: Its meaning and determination. *Psychometrika,* 1947, **12,** 1–16.

D'Abro, A. *The decline of mechanism (in modern physics).* New York: Van Nostrand, 1939.

Darley, J. G. A study of clinical predictions of student success or failure in professional training. *J. educ. Psychol.,* 1938, **29,** 335–354.

Davis, F. B. *Item analysis data: Their computation, interpretation, and use in test construction.* Cambridge: Harvard Graduate School of Education, 1946a.

Davis, F. B. Notes on test construction: The reliability of item analysis data. *J. educ. Psychol.,* 1946b, **37,** 385–390.

Davis, F. B. *The AAF qualifying examination.* Army Air Forces Aviation Psychology Program Research Report 6. Washington, D. C.: U. S. Government Printing Office, 1947a.

Davis, F. B. *Utilizing human talent.* Washington, D. C.: Commission on Implications of Armed Services Educational Programs, American Council on Education, 1947b.

Deemer, W. L. *Records, analyses and test procedures.* Army Air Forces Aviation Psychology Program Research Report 18. Washington, D. C.: U. S. Government Printing Office, 1947.

DuBois, P. H. *The classification program.* Army Air Forces Aviation Psychology Program Research Report 2. Washington, D. C.: U. S. Government Printing Office, 1947.

Dvorak, B. J. The new USES general aptitude test battery. *J. appl. Psychol.,* 1947, **31,** 372–376.

Dwyer, P. S. Recent developments in correlational technique. *J. Amer. statist. Ass.,* 1942, **37,** 441–460.

Dwyer, P. S. The square root method and its use in correlation and regression. *J. Amer. statist. Ass.,* 1945, **40,** 493–503.

Dyer, H. S. The differential prediction of college achievement. In *Exploring individual differences.* Washington, D. C.: American Council on Education, Series 32, 1948, **12,** 80–87.

Edgerton, H., and L. E. Kolbe. The method of minimum variation for the combination of criteria. *Psychometrika,* 1936, **1,** 183–187.

Ellis, A. The validity of personality questionnaires. *Psychol. Bull.,* 1946, **43,** 385–440.

Ellis, A. A comparison of the use of direct and indirect phrasing in personality questionnaires. *Psychol. Monogr.,* 1947, **61,** No. 284.

Ellis, A., and H. S. Conrad. The validity of personality inventories in military practice. *Psychol. Bull.,* 1948, **45,** 385–426.

Eysenck, H. J. Student selection by means of psychological tests—a critical survey. *Brit. J. educ. Psychol.,* 1947, **47,** Pt. I, 20–39.

Fearing, F., and F. M. Fearing. Factors in the appraisal interview considered with particular reference to the selection of public personnel. *J. Psychol.,* 1942, **14,** 131–153.

Ferguson, G. A. The factorial interpretation of test difficulty. *Psychometrika,* 1941, **6,** 323–329.

Ferguson, G. A. On the theory of test discrimination. *Psychometrika,* 1949, **14,** 61–68.

Festinger, L. The treatment of qualitative data by "scale analysis." *Psychol. Bull.,* 1947, **44,** 149–161.

Flanagan, J. C. *The Cooperative achievement tests: A bulletin reporting the basic principles and procedures used in the development of their system of scaled scores.* New York: Cooperative Test Service of the American Council on Education, 1939a.

Flanagan, J. C. General considerations in the selection of test items and a short method of estimating the product-moment coefficient from data at the tails of the distribution. *J. educ. Psychol.,* 1939b, **30,** 674–680.

Flanagan, J. C. Current trends in psychology. Paper presented at the Conference on Current Trends in Psychology. University of Pittsburgh, Mar. 6, 1947a.

Flanagan, J. C. Units and norms in educational measurement. In *National project in educational measurement.* American Council on Education, Series 28, 1947b, **11,** 8–12.

Flanagan, J. C. *The aviation psychology program in the Army Air Forces.* Army Air Forces Aviation Psychology Program Research Report 1. Washington, D. C.: U. S. Government Printing Office, 1948.

Fowler, H. M. The consistency of items of an activity preference blank. *Psychometrika,* 1947, **12,** 221–232.

Freeman, G. L. Using the interview to test stability and poise. *Publ. Person. Rev.,* 1944, **5,** 89–94.

Garrett, H. E. The discriminant function and its use in psychology. *Psychometrika,* 1943, **8,** 65–79.

Guilford, J. P. New standards for test evaluation. *Educ. psychol. Measmt.,* 1946, **6,** 427–438.

Guilford, J. P. The discovery of aptitude and achievement variables. *Science,* 1947, **106,** 279–282.

Guilford, J. P., and J. I. Lacey. *Printed classification tests.* Army Air Forces Aviation Psychology Program Research Report 5. Washington, D. C.: U. S. Government Printing Office, 1947.

Guilford, J. P., C. Lovell, and R. M. Williams. Completely weighted versus unweighted scoring in an achievement examination. *Educ. psychol. Measmt.,* 1942, **2,** 15–21.

Gulliksen, H. The content reliability of a test. *Psychometrika,* 1936, **1,** 189–194.

Gulliksen, H. The relation of item difficulty and inter-item correlation to test variance and reliability. *Psychometrika,* 1945, **10,** 79–91.

Gulliksen, H. Paired comparisons and the logic of measurement. *Psychol. Rev.,* 1946, **53,** 199–213.

Guthrie, E. R. Psychological facts and psychological theory. *Psychol. Bull.,* 1946, **43,** 1–20.

Guttman, L. Mathematical and tabulation techniques. Supplementary study B. In P. Horst, *The prediction of personal adjustment.* New York: Social Science Research Council Bulletin 48, 1941.

Guttman, L. A basis for scaling qualitative data. *Amer. sociol. Rev.,* 1944, **9,** 139–150.

Guttman, L. A basis for analyzing test-retest reliability. *Psychometrika,* 1945, **10,** 255–282.

Guttman, L. The test-retest reliability of qualitative data. *Psychometrika,* 1946, **9,** 81–95.

Guttman, L. Scale and intensity analysis for attitude, opinion, and achievement. In *New methods in applied psychology.* College Park: University of Maryland, 1947. Pp. 173–180.

Hoel, P. G. *Introduction to mathematical statistics.* New York: Wiley, 1947.

Horst, P. Increasing the efficiency of selection tests. *Person. J.,* 1934a, **12,** 254–259.

Horst, P. Item analysis by the method of successive residuals. *J. exp. Educ.,* 1934b, **2,** 229–244.

Horst, P. Obtaining a composite measure from a number of different measures of the same thing. *Psychometrika,* 1936, **1,** 53–60.

Horst, P. *The prediction of personal adjustment.* New York: Social Science Research Council Bulletin 48, 1941.

Horst, P. A generalized expression for the reliability of measures. *Psychometrika,* 1949, **14,** 21–32.

Hotelling, H. Analysis of a complex of statistical variates into principal components. *J. educ. Psychol.,* 1933, **24,** 417–441, 498–520.

Hotelling, H. The most predictable criterion. *J. educ. Psychol.,* 1935, **26,** 139–142.

Hotelling, H., P. A. Sorokin, L. Guttman, and E. W. Burgess. The prediction of personal adjustment: A symposium. *Amer. J. Sociol.,* 1942, **48,** 61–86.

Hoyt, C. Test reliability obtained by analysis of variance. *Psychometrika,* 1941, **6,** 153–160.

Hull, C. L. *Aptitude testing.* New York: World, 1928.

Hull, C. L. *Principles of behavior.* New York: Appleton-Century-Crofts, 1943.

Jackson, R. W. B., and G. A. Ferguson. *Studies on the reliability of tests.* Toronto: Department of Educational Research, University of Toronto, 1941.

Jackson, R. W. B., and G. A. Ferguson. A plea for a functional approach to test construction. *Educ. psychol. Measmt.,* 1943, **3,** 23–28.

Jarrett, R. F. Per cent increase in output of selected personnel as an index of test efficiency. *J. appl. Psychol.,* 1948, **32,** 135–145.

Jeffreys, H. *Scientific inference.* Cambridge: Cambridge University Press, 1937.

Jerkins, J. G. *Psychology in business and industry.* New York: Wiley, 1935.

Jenkins, J. G. Validity for what. *J. consult. Psychol.,* 1946, **10,** 93–98.

Jurgensen, C. E. Report on the 'classification inventory,' a personality test for industrial use. *J. appl. Psychol.,* 1944, **28,** 445–460.

Kelley, T. L. *Fundamentals of statistics.* Cambridge: Harvard University Press, 1947.

Klein, G. S. Self-appraisal of test performance as a vocational selection device. *Educ. psychol. Measmt.,* 1948, **8,** 69–84.

Kogan, L. S. Analysis of variance—repeated measurements. *Psychol. Bull.,* 1948, **45,** 131–143.

Kornhauser, A. Replies of psychologists to a short questionnaire on mental test developments, personality inventories, and the Rorschach test. *Educ. psychol. Measmt.,* 1945, **5,** 3–15.

Kuder, G. F. The stability of preference items. *J. soc. Psychol.,* 1939, **19,** 41–50.

Kuder, G. F. Note on 'classification of items in interest inventories.' *Occupations,* 1944, **22,** 484–487.

Kuder, G. F., and M. W. Richardson. The theory of the estimation of test reliability. *Psychometrika,* 1937, **2,** 151–160.

Kurtz, A. K. Recent research in the selection of life insurance salesmen. *J. appl. Psychol.,* 1941, **25,** 11–17.

Kurtz, A. K.   A research test of the Rorschach test. *Personnel Psychol.*, 1948, 1, 41–51.

Loevinger, J.   A systematic approach to the construction and evaluation of tests of ability. *Psychol. Monogr.*, 1947, 61, No. 285.

Maller, J. B.   Personality tests.   In J. McV. Hunt (Ed.), *Personality and the behavior disorders*. New York : Ronald, 1944.

Mandell, M.   Testing for administrative and supervisory positions. *Educ. psychol. Measmt.*, 1945, 5, 217–228.

Marks, E. S.   Selective sampling in psychological research. *Psychol. Bull.*, 1947, 44, 267–275.

McGehee, W.   The prediction of differential achievement in a technological college. *J. appl. Psychol.*, 1943, 27, 88–92.

McNemar, Q.   Opinion—attitude methodology. *Psychol. Bull.*, 1946, 43, 289–374.

McPherson, M. W.   A method of objectively measuring shop performance. *J. appl. Psychol.*, 1945, 29, 22–26.

Meehl, P. E.   The dynamics of "structured" personality tests. *J. clin. Psychol.*, 1945, 1, 296–303.

Meehl, P. E., and S. R. Hathaway.   The K factor as a suppressor variable in the Minnesota multiphasic personality inventory. *J. appl. Psychol.*, 1946, 30, 525–564.

Melton, A. W.   *Apparatus tests*.   Army Air Forces Aviation Psychology Research Report 4. Washington, D. C. : U. S. Government Printing Office, 1947.

Merrill, W. M.   Sampling theory in item analysis. *Psychometrika*, 1937, 2, 215–224.

Mosier, C. I.   A note on item analysis and the criterion of internal consistency. *Psychometrika*, 1936, 1, 275–282.

Mosier, C. I.   On the reliability of a weighted composite. *Psychometrika*, 1943, 8, 161–168.

Mosier, C. I.   Rating of training and experience in public personnel selection. *Educ. psychol. Measmt.*, 1946, 6, 313–329.

Mosier, C. I.   A critical examination of the concepts of face validity. *Educ. psychol. Measmt.*, 1947, 7, 191–205.

Mosier, C. I., M. C. Myers, and H. G. Price. Suggestions for the construction of multiple choice items. *Educ. psychol. Measmt.*, 1945, 5, 261–271.

Munroe, R. L.   Prediction of the adjustment and academic performance of college students by a modification of the Rorschach method. *Appl. psychol. Monogr.*, 1945, No. 7, 1–104.

Munroe, R. L.   Academic success and personal adjustment in college.   In *Exploring individual differences*.   Washington, D. C. : American Council on Education, Series 1, 1948, 12, No. 32, 30–42.

Odell, C. W.   The scoring of continuity or rearrangement tests. *J. educ. Psychol.*, 1944, 35, 352–356.

Otis, J. L.   The criterion.   In H. W. Stead, C. L. Shartle, et al., *Occupational counseling techniques*.   New York : American, 1940.

Owens, W. A.   An empirical study of the relationship between item validity and internal consistency. *Educ. psychol. Measmt.*, 1947, 7, 281–288.

Patterson, C. H.   On the problem of the criterion in prediction studies. *J. consult. Psychol.*, 1946, 10, 277–280.

Peters, C. C., and W. R. Van Voorhis. *Statistical procedures and their mathematical bases*. New York : McGraw-Hill, 1940.

Pockrass, J. H.   Common fallacies in employee ratings. *Person. J.*, 1940, 18, 262–267.

Ramsperger, A. G.   *Philosophies of science*.   New York : Crofts, 1942.

Rao, C. R.   A statistical criterion to determine the group to which an individual belongs. *Nature, Lond.*, 1947, 160, 835–836.

Reed, R. R.   An empirical study in the reduction of the number of variables used in prediction, supplementary study C.   In P. Horst, *The prediction of personal adjustment*.   New York : Social Science Research Council Bulletin 48, 1941.

Richardson, M. W.   The relation of difficulty to the differential validity of a test. *Psychometrika*, 1936a, 1, 33–49.

Richardson, M. W.   Notes on the rationale of item analysis. *Psychometrika*, 1936b, 1, 69–75.

Richardson, M. W.   Combination of measures, supplementary study D.   In P. Horst, *Prediction of personal adjustment*.   New York : Social Science Research Council Bulletin 48, 1941a.

Richardson, M. W.   The logic of age scales. *Educ. psychol. Measmt.*, 1941b, 1, 25–34.

Richardson, M. W.   The interpretation of a test validity coefficient in terms of increased efficiency of a selected group of personnel. *Psychometrika*, 1944, 9, 245–248.

Richardson, M. W.   Selection of Army officers. In *New methods in applied psychology*.   College Park : University of Maryland, 1947. Pp. 79–85.

Richardson, M. W., and G. F. Kuder.   Making a rating scale that measures. *Person. J.*, 1933, 12, 36–40.

Ruch F. L.   The comparative efficiency of the multiple-cutting-score method and the Wherry-Doolittle method in selecting winch operators. OSRD, 1945 (PB 15820).

Ruch, F. L.   A comparative study of the predictive efficiency of batteries of tests selected by the Wherry-Doolittle and a multiple-cutting-score method. (Abstract.) *Amer. Psychologist*, 1948, 3, 291.

Rulon, P. J.   A simplified procedure for determining the reliability of a test by split halves. *Harv. educ. Rev.*, 1939, 9, 99–103.

Rulon, P. J.   Validity of educational tests.   In *National project in educational measurement*. American Council on Education, Series 1, 1947, 11, No. 28, 13–20.

Rundquist, E. A.   Development of an interview for selection purposes.   In *New methods in ap-*

plied *psychology*. College Park: University of Maryland, 1947. Pp. 85–95.

Sarbin, T. R. The logic of prediction in psychology. *Psychol. Rev.*, 1944, **51**, 210–228.

Sarbin, T. R., and E. S. Bordin. New criteria for old. *Educ. psychol. Measmt.*, 1941, **1**, 173–186.

Segel, D. *Differential diagnosis of ability in school children.* Baltimore: Warwick and York, 1934.

Sells, S. B., and R. M. W. Travers. Observational methods of research. *Rev. educ. Res.*, 1945, **15**, 394–407.

Shartle C. L. *Occupational information.* New York: Prentice-Hall, 1946.

Shartle, C. L. Developments in occupational classification. *J. consult. Psychol.*, 1946, **10**, 81–92.

Shartle, C. L., B. J. Dvorak, C. A. Heinz, et al. Ten years of occupational research, 1934–1944. *Occupations*, 1944, **7**, 387–446.

Shipley, W. C., et al. The personal inventory — its derivation and validation. *J. clin. Psychol.*, 1946, **4**, 318–322.

Sisson, E. D. Forced Choice — the new Army rating. *Person. Psychol.*, 1949, **1**, 365–379.

Sletto, R. Construction of personality scales by the criterion of internal consistency. Hanover, N. H., and Minneapolis: Sociological Press, 1937.

Spence, K. The postulates and methods of behaviorism. *Psychol. Rev.*, 1948, **55**, 67–78.

Staff, Division of Occupational Analysis, War Manpower Commission. Factor analysis of occupational aptitude tests. *Educ. psychol. Measmt.*, 1945, **5**, 147–155.

Staff, Personnel Research Section, Personnel Research and Procedure Branch, The Adjutant General's Office. The forced choice technique and rating scales. (Abstract.) *Amer. Psychologist*, 1946, **1**, 267.

Stalnaker, J. M. Personnel placement in the armed forces. *J. appl. Psychol.*, 1945, **29**, 338–345.

Stalnaker, J. M., and M. W. Richardson. A note concerning the combination of test scores. *J. gen. Psychol.*, 1933, **8**, 460–463.

Stead, W. H., C. L. Shartle, et al. *Occupational counseling techniques.* New York: American, 1940.

Stevens, S. S. On the theory of scales of measurement. *Science*, 1946, **103**, 677–680.

Stewart, N. Relationship between military occupational speciality and army general classification test score. *Educ. psychol. Measmt.*, 1947, **7**, 677–693.

Strong, E. K. *Vocational interests of men and women.* Stanford: Stanford University Press, 1943.

Stuit, D. B. (Ed.). *Personnel research and test development in the Bureau of Naval Personnel.* Princeton: Princeton University Press, 1947a.

Stuit, D. B. The effect of the nature of the criterion upon the validity of aptitude tests. *Educ. psychol. Measmt.*, 1947b, **7**, 671–676.

Stuit, D. B., and J. T. Wilson. The effect of an increasingly well defined criterion on the prediction of success at Naval Training School (Tactical Radar). *J. appl. Psychol.*, 1946, **30**, 614–623.

Super, D. E. The validity of standard and custom-built personality inventories in a pilot selection program. *Educ. psychol. Measmt.*, 1947, **7**, 735–744.

Symonds, P. M. *Diagnosing personality and conduct.* New York: Century, 1931.

Taylor, H. C., and J. T. Russell. The relationship of validity coefficients to the practical effectiveness of tests in selection: Discussion and tables. *J. appl. Psychol.*, 1939, **13**, 565–578.

Thomson, G. H. Weighting for battery reliability and prediction. *Brit. J. Psychol.*, 1940, **30**, 357–366.

Thorndike, E. L. The future of measurement of abilities. *Brit. J. educ. Psychol.*, 1948, **18**, 21–25.

Thorndike, R. L. *Research problems and techniques.* Army Air Forces Aviation Psychology Program Research Report 3. Washington, D. C.: U. S. Government Printing Office, 1947a.

Thorndike, R. L. Logical dilemmas in the estimation of reliability. In *National Project in Educational Measurement*, American Council on Education, Series 28, 1947b, **11**, 21–30.

Thorndike, R. L. *Personnel selection.* New York: Wiley, 1949.

Thurstone, L. L. *Multiple-factor analysis.* Chicago: University of Chicago Press, 1947.

Thurstone, L. L. Psychophysical methods. In T. G. Andrews (Ed.), *Methods of psychology.* New York: Wiley, 1948a.

Thurstone, L. L. Psychological implications of factor analysis. *Amer. Psychologist*, 1948b, **3**, 402–408.

Toops, H. A. The selection of graduate students. *Person. J.*, 1928, **6**, 470–471.

Toops, H. A. The successive hurdles method. *Person. J.*, 1932, **11**, 216–218.

Toops, H. A. The L-Method. *Psychometrika*, 1941, **6**, 249–266.

Toops, H. A. The criterion. *Educ. psychol. Measmt.*, 1944, **4**, 271–297.

Toops, H. A. Some concepts of job families and their importance in placement. *Educ. psychol. Measmt.*, 1945a, **5**, 195–216.

Toops, H. A. Philosophy and practice of personnel selection. *Educ. psychol. Measmt.*, 1945b, **5**, 95–124.

Travers, R. M. W. The use of the discriminant function in the treatment of psychological group differences. *Psychometrika*, 1939, **4**, 25–32.

Travers, R. M. W. A note on the value of customary measures of item validity. *J. appl. Psychol.*, 1942, **26**, 625–632.

Tucker, L. R. Maximum validity of a test with equivalent items. *Psychometrika*, 1946, **9**, 1–13.

Tucker, L. R. The problem of differential criteria. In *Exploring individual differences.* American Council on Education, Series 32, 1948, **12**, 30–42.

Turnbull, W. W. A normalized graphic method of item analysis. *J. educ. Psychol.*, 1946, **37**, 129–141.

VanDusen, A. C. Importance of criteria in selection and training. *Educ. psychol. Measmt.*, 1947, **7**, 498–504.

Vaughn, C. L. The nominating technique. In *New methods in applied psychology.* College Park: University of Maryland, 1947. Pp. 22–26.

Vernon, P. E. *The assessment of psychological qualities by verbal methods.* London: Medical Research Council Industrial Health Research Board Report 83, 1938.

Viteles, M. S. *Industrial psychology.* New York: Norton, 1932.

Wallin, P. The prediction of individual behavior from case studies, supplementary study A. In P. Horst, *The prediction of personnel adjustment.* New York: Social Science Research Council Bulletin 48, 1941.

Warren, H. C. *Dictionary of psychology.* Boston: Houghton Mifflin, 1934.

Weider, A., K. Brodman, B. Mittelmann, D. Wechsler, and H. G. Wolff. Cornell service index: A method for quickly assaying personality and psychosomatic disturbances in men in the armed forces. *War med.*, 1945, **7**, 209–213.

Wexler, M. Measures of personal adjustment. In D. B. Stuit (Ed.), *Personnel research and test development in the Bureau of Naval Personnel.* Princeton: Princeton University Press, 1947.

Wherry, R. J. An approximation method for obtaining a maximized multiple criterion. *Psychometrika,* 1940, **5**, 109–115.

Wherry, R. J. Maximal weighting of qualitative data. *Psychometrika,* 1944, **9**, 263–266.

Wherry, R. J. Test selection and suppressor variables. *Psychometrika,* 1946, **11**, 239–247.

Wherry, R. J., and R. H. Gaylord. The concept of test and item reliability in relation to factor pattern. *Psychometrika,* 1943, **8**, 247–264.

Wherry, R. J., and R. H. Gaylord. Factor pattern of test items and tests as a function of the correlation coefficient: Content, difficulty and constant error factors. *Psychometrika,* 1944, **9**, 237–244.

Wherry, R. J., and R. H. Gaylord. Test selection with integral gross score weights. *Psychometrika,* 1946, **11**, 173–183.

Wherry, R. J., and E. K. Taylor. The relation of multiserial eta to other methods of correlation. *Psychometrika,* 1946, **11**, 155–161.

Wilks, S. S. Weighting systems for linear functions. *Psychometrika,* 1938, **3**, 23–40.

Williams, S. B., and H. J. Leavitt. Methods of selecting Marine Corps officer candidates. In *New methods in applied psychology.* College Park: University of Maryland, 1947. Pp. 96–99.

Wolf, R. R. Differential forecasts of achievement and their use in educational counselling. *Psychol. Monogr.,* 1939, **51**, No. 1.

Wolfle, D. L. Factor analysis in the study of personality. *J. abnorm. soc. Psychol.,* 1942, **37**, 393–397.

Zerga, J. E. Job analysis, a résumé and bibliography. *J. appl. Psychol.,* 1943, **27**, 249–267.

34.

Training

DAEL WOLFLE
American Psychological Association

The psychology of training is the applied psychology of learning. If an investigator's primary interest is in the processes by which knowledge or skill is acquired, then his studies are classified under the heading of *learning*. But, if his purpose is to investigate the teaching that goes on in school, in industry, or in a military establishment, his work is classified under the heading of *training*. Since training is the applied aspect of learning, much that is pertinent to this chapter has already been discussed in other chapters (see especially Chapter 17).

There are several excellent sources of information about learning and training. Hunter (1934) and McGeoch (1931, 1933, 1942) provide a systematic background and extensive bibliographies. Viteles (1949) discusses industrial training. Henmon (1930) and Stroud (1940) have reviewed the literature on learning in school situations. Bray (1948) and several of the reports of the Army Air Forces Aviation Psychology Program (see Flanagan, 1948) give information about military training programs of World War II. Flanagan and a number of collaborators (1948) have reviewed the literature on training in World War II, and Wolfle (1946) has summarized the principles of learning that were most useful in the training of military specialists.

FACTORS DETERMINING THE EFFECTIVENESS OF TRAINING

A number of general principles of learning have emerged from laboratory studies and from industrial, military, and school experience. Six of them are discussed in this chapter. These six principles are concerned with variables that can be manipulated under practical training conditions. They are:

1. Knowledge of results.
2. Avoidance of habit interference.
3. Variety of practice materials.
4. Methods used in training.
5. Knowledge of principles involved.
6. Effectiveness of guidance.

Knowledge of Results

Laboratory studies are unequivocal in emphasizing the importance of giving a subject as specific and as immediate information as possible concerning the outcome of his efforts. An excellent illustration of this principle is found in a study by Trowbridge and Cason (1932). In a repetition of one of Thorndike's line-drawing experiments, they found no improvement in 100 attempts to draw a 3-inch line unless the subjects were told whether or not their attempts had been satisfactory. The results are given in Table 1. These data also demonstrate the value of making the information as exact as

TABLE 1

Effect on Learning of Giving Subjects Different Amounts of Information about Results on Each Trial (after Trowbridge and Cason, 1932)

Information Given Subjects after Each Trial	Average Errors in Inches		
	First 30 Trials	Middle 40 Trials	Last 30 Trials
None (control group)	0.75	0.86	0.80
Nonsense syllables	1.11	1.07	1.05
"Right" or "wrong"	0.92	0.67	0.49
Exact information	0.24	0.14	0.12

possible. Subjects who were told the amount and direction of error in each trial improved much more than did subjects told simply that each trial was "right" or "wrong."

learning situations the relation between length of delay and effectiveness is described by an exponential or negative growth function.

There is good evidence that knowledge of results can be as valuable in acquiring industrial or other practical skills as in learning laboratory problems. Biel et al. (1944), in training men to use Army gun directors, found it desirable to use a checksight through which an instructor could follow the target and know at all times how accurately the tracker was keeping the gun on target. When the instructor sounded an electric buzzer to indicate that the tracker was off target, men learned to track more

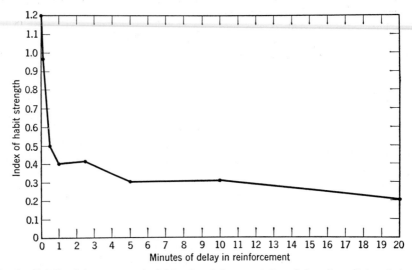

Fig. 1. Relation between amount of delay in reinforcement (knowledge of results) and strength of habit formed. The points represent the amount of learning for constant numbers of reinforcements. The delay in reinforcement was different for each of eight groups of albino rats. As the delay increased, the amount of learning decreased. (After Hull, 1943; data from Wolfe, 1934.)

The subject should be told his results not only as precisely as possible, but also as soon after each trial as possible. This principle applies to both animals and men. Thus the data for rats shown in Fig. 1 demonstrate a rapid loss in effectiveness as the delay increases. Hull (1943) analyzed a number of studies on this problem and came to the general conclusion that in typical

accurately than when they were not told their results. The experimental data are presented in Fig. 2. Lindsley (1943) reports that a group of radar operators who were not enlightened about their progress on successive trials became less and less accurate as practice went on for 6 days.

The knowledge of results in training programs should be automatic, immediate, and meaningfully related to the task being learned. Two studies of the learning of radio code illustrate how this kind of information can be given to men in training.

A man's first task in becoming a radio operator is to learn the sound patterns (dots and dashes) that represent the 10

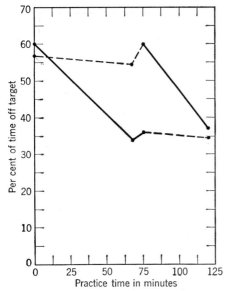

FIG. 2. Effect of knowledge of results in learning tracking. The solid lines represent practice given with knowledge of results (a buzzer sounding whenever the tracker was off target); the dashed lines represent practice given without knowledge of results. With both groups of subjects improvement occurred when knowledge of results was provided; practically no improvement occurred without it. (After Biel et al., 1944.)

digits and the 26 letters of the alphabet. In the past, many methods have been used to teach this basic information. Keller (1943, 1945) developed an improved method based on the assumption that learning would proceed most rapidly if the learner was told immediately after hearing each character just what that character was.

A double row of squares (see Fig. 3) was provided for each set of characters. When the first character was sent, for example *R*, the student wrote its name in the first box of the upper row. Three seconds later when the first character was sent, for example *R*, the student wrote its name in the first box of the upper row. Three seconds later when

the instructor named the character, the student did nothing if he had written *R*. Then, having heard the character, having tried to name it, and having been told what it was, he heard it, and named it, again. When the student did not recognize a letter, as in the third box, or made a mistake, as in the fifth, the instructor's naming of the letter allowed immediate correction. This was called the code-voice method of teaching radio code.

The code-voice method also capitalized on the superiority of whole over part methods

R	R	–	V	F	L				
		V		L					

FIG. 3. Sample row of the record sheet used in the code-voice method of teaching radio code. When the trainee hears a letter, he writes it in the upper box. If he makes an error or does not recognize a letter, he writes the correct letter in the lower box when the instructor names it 3 seconds later. (After Keller, 1945.)

by including "whole-learning" as one of its features. The previous Army method had divided the 36 characters into several groups. One group was learned, then a second, and so on, until all were mastered.

The superiority of the code-voice method of teaching the characters over the method previously used in the Army is evident in Table 2. Instead of requiring an average of

TABLE 2

Superiority of Code-Voice Method of Teaching International Morse Code over Previous Army Method (after Keller, 1945)

Training Method	Number of Men	Hours Required to Pass 5 Words per Minute		Per Cent Who Failed to Pass 5 Words per Minute
		Mean	S.D.	
Code-voice	253	26.57	7.93	3.4
Standard Army (Z-tape)	74	34.78	15.47	15.0
Standard Army (Z-tape)	446	40.87	22.78	

35 or 40 hours of practice to attain a speed of 5 words per minute, men trained by the code-voice method averaged less than

27 hours of drill. Instead of 15 per cent of them failing altogether to attain this speed, only 3.4 per cent failed to qualify.

An excellent demonstration of a teaching device that automatically informs the learner of his correct and incorrect responses is the code-actuated typewriter devised by Bennett and Langmuir (Bennett, 1945). This typewriter prints in ordinary type exactly what the student radio operator sends in code. The letter M, for example, consists of two dashes. If the operator sends two dashes of the correct length with a pause between them approximately one-third as long as the dashes, the typewriter prints M. The absolute length of these dashes is unimportant. The typewriter records accurately so long as the dots, and the pauses within a letter, are one-third as long as the dashes.

When the student operator makes an error, the typewriter tells him just what he has done wrong. If his first dash for an M is too short, the typewriter prints A, the symbol for which is a dot and a dash. If the second dash, instead of the first one, is too short, the typewriter prints N. If the space between the two dashes is too long, the typewriter prints $T\ T$. If the operator makes both the first dash too short and the pause too long, the typewriter prints $E\ T$. When the pauses, the dots, and the dashes of any character are all correct, the operator has the immediate satisfaction of seeing the correct letter appear.

The use of this typewriter illustrated another desirable feature of training devices: radio men accepted it and liked to practice on it.

The illustrations used so far have dealt with the acquisition of skill. In some training the major emphasis is not on skill but on acquiring a body of knowledge. In such cases examinations are useful. To be of greatest aid to learning, examinations should give precise information regarding the nature of errors. The better tests used to diagnose difficulties in the learning of school

subjects attempt to provide this kind of information.

In constructing either an examination or a scoring device, it is necessary to consider the purpose for which it will be used. Sometimes motivation of the learner is of primary importance. Successive scores should then show improvement. Sometimes the major purpose is to discriminate accurately among a group of trainees in terms of the level of skill that each has attained. It is well known that, when discrimination among different ability levels is the purpose, the difficulty of the examination should be set at the point where the average member of the group receives a score of 50 per cent. The same principle applies to scoring devices: they should be so set that the average member of the group gets a score of 50 per cent. By making the scoring device adjustable, as Kappauf (1945b) did in designing a photoelectric instrument for measuring the accuracy of gunners in training, it is possible to adjust scoring limits to secure an average score of 50 per cent for any group of trainees.

The two objectives of motivating the men and discriminating among them may sometimes conflict. If successive scores are obtained on a group that is learning a task, higher scores on later examinations show the trainees that they are improving. But higher average scores (above 50 per cent) decrease the accuracy with which various levels of skill can be differentiated. Both objectives can sometimes be achieved by giving the trainees examinations of increasing difficulty but reporting to them increasingly higher scores. In other situations, requiring the same level of accuracy at successively higher speeds may satisfy both objectives.

Avoidance of Habit Interference

Learning is always slower if one has to learn several alternative responses to approximately the same situation. This interference with learning has been experimentally studied under the headings of habit interference, negative transfer, and proactive and retroactive interference. The interference may occur in the learning of what is usually thought of as a single task, or it may arise in the successive learning of similar tasks.

Viteles gives an interesting personal account of habit interference. In preparation for research on the selection of streetcar motormen, he took the normal training given to new men. After preliminary schoolroom training, he was sent out on a regular run with an experienced motorman as his tutor. The next day he had a different tutor. For 10 days he continued, each day with a different motorman teaching his own preferred methods of handling the streetcar controls. The effect of being taught to respond to similar situations in a variety of ways, some of which were wholly antagonistic to each other, was, as Viteles summarized, "to create interference in habit formation — a condition which retards the development of skill, lengthens the training period, and promotes an uncertainty of response which continues after the close of the training period" (1932, pp. 396–397).

Habit interference arises when partially overlapping stimulus patterns are expected to elicit different responses. If a situation containing elements $a, b, c, \cdots, n$ is intended to elicit one response and a situation containing elements $h, i, j, \cdots, z$ is supposed to elicit another, confusion arises because of the presence of the common elements $h \cdots n$ in the two situations; either situation may lead to either response. Whether the two "responses" constitute alternative methods of performing an act, as in Viteles' experience, or are different acts with different purposes, depends upon one's definition of *response* and is irrelevant for this discussion.

The amount of overlap between the two stimulus situations may vary between complete identity and complete dissimilarity. Likewise, the degree of similarity in the two responses may range from identity to complete dissimilarity. No thorough research analysis of all interrelations of these two variables has been made. But the study by Bruce (1933), coupled with the other work that has led to the principles of stimulus generalization and response generalization, justify the following hypotheses:

1. The greater the similarity between the two stimulating situations, the greater should be the similarity between the two responses if habit interference is to be avoided.

2. The greater the similarity between the two responses, the greater should be the similarity between the two stimulating situations if habit interference is to be avoided.

From these hypotheses it follows that both the stimulating situations and their responses should be made either as little alike as possible or as much alike as possible. In the first case, the absence of overlap will mean that two noninterfering, and also nonreinforcing, habits will be learned. In the second case, the similarities between the two stimulus-response situations will mean that the principles of generalization and positive transfer will facilitate learning. An outstanding example is the adoption of the standard gearshift in automobiles of different makes. The resulting ease with which a driver can switch from one make of car to another should serve as a lesson for industrial designers.

McGeoch (1942) concluded that habit interference is greatest when the learning of the second habit system is incomplete. It is then in competition with a well-established habit elicited by a similar stimulus situation. Under these conditions the old instead of the new response may occur.

The amount of interference between two activities is in part a function of the degree of proficiency attained in both of them. Negative transfer appears to be at a maximum when the degrees of learning of the first and second activities are similar (Siipola and Israel, 1933). The little experimental evidence on this point is in agreement with the experience of airplane pilots that they are not disturbed by the different locations and operations of the controls when they first start to fly a new type of plane, but that interference, occasionally with disastrous results, is more likely to occur after they think they have become thoroughly accustomed to the second set of controls.

The reason for greater interference when both sets of habits are of about equal strength is obscure. Apparently minor factors can shift the balance from one habit system to another when the two are of nearly equal potency.

If training goes on long enough, habit interference may completely disappear (McGeoch, 1942, p. 429). Harlow (1949) has demonstrated this point in training a group of monkeys on a long series of similar visual discrimination problems. After learning a number of such problems, many subjects needed only one trial to find out which object was correct in any new problem; subsequent trials were then made correctly until another new problem was introduced.

In training situations in which habit interference is likely to develop, certain safeguards may be used to minimize its disturbing effects:

1. Careful analysis of the skill to be learned and indoctrination of all teachers in the same methods of teaching will eliminate part of the interference of the kind described by Viteles.

2. Beginning training on a later habit system only after the preceding ones are fairly well established will reduce the amount of interference.

3. Either standardizing both the stimulating situations and the responses as much as possible or making them as different as possible will eliminate interference.

Variety of Practice Material

Variation of stimulus conditions has regularly been employed in learning experiments to prevent the subjects from learning something in which the experimenter was not interested. In discrimination studies the correct stimulus appears sometimes on the right and sometimes on the left in order to keep the subject from learning a position habit. The order of pairs of words in a paired-associates study is varied to keep the subjects from learning on the basis of position in the series. For the same reason, practice material used in training typists or radio operators is varied. In all these illustrations, variation of irrelevant parts of the task forces the learner to respond to the critical aspects of the stimulating situation.

A number of military schools violated this rule during World War II. Men in training were given an inadequate variety of targets to track, casualties to repair, messages to record, or radar images to interpret. The result was that, although they learned to respond correctly to the particular materials used in training, they were not able to respond adequately to the somewhat different situations encountered later on the job. As a general rule, practice materials should vary in as many dimensions and over approximately as wide a range as will the situations to be encountered when the learning is to be applied.

Although emphasis is here placed upon the importance of varying practice material, it must be recognized that variation decreases the speed of learning. Wolfle (1935) has demonstrated that the speed of learning decreases regularly as the extent of variation in the practice material increases. Figure 4, curve A, plots the slopes of the learning curves for five groups of subjects learning a high-relief finger maze. All trials given group 1 were on the same maze. Subjects in group 2 were presented with two mazes. The alleys of one were 10 per cent longer than the corresponding alleys of the other. Variation in size increased until group 5 had randomly arranged trials on mazes of five different sizes. The learning curves for each group were plotted on semilogarithmic paper and were fitted by the equation $Y = a - bX$, in which Y represented the error scores, and X the trial number. The slopes of these curves, the *b* values, are plotted in Fig. 4.

Curves *B* and *C* show comparable data for two other experiments of the same type. Curve *B* summarizes an experiment by Grether and Wolfle (1936) in which groups of rats learned a visual brightness discrimi-

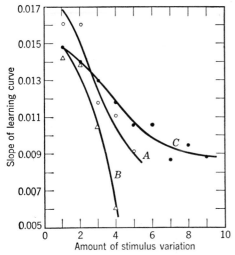

Fig. 4. Relation between amount of stimulus variation and rate of learning. In each of three experiments, different groups of subjects were taught essentially the same problem. Each group learned the problem with different amounts of stimulus variation during the learning trials. The ordinate values are slopes of the learning curves ($Y = a - bX$). (The slopes plotted in curve *B* were divided by 10.) (After Wolfle, 1935, 1936; and Grether and Wolfle, 1936.)

nation problem under different degrees of stimulus variation. Curve *C* (Wolfle, 1936) is from a study in which human subjects learned paper-and-pencil mazes in which the pathway within each unit of the maze was systematically varied.

All three curves demonstrate that increasing the amount of stimulus variation decreases the rate of learning.

On the other hand, if training is prolonged and monotonous, variety in the practice materials may speed up learning instead of retarding it. Seashore et al. (1944) attempted to combat monotony in the training of radio operators by using a great va-

riety of drill materials. Men trained under these conditions learned more rapidly than did men having less varied drills.

Relatively little consideration has been given the problem of how variation of practice material influences the transfer of a learned response to new situations. Luborsky (1945) found in an aircraft recognition class that previously unseen and briefly exposed silhouettes of airplanes were recognized more accurately if five different silhouettes were used during training than if only three were used. It seems probable that variation of the material used during learning will generally increase the range of conditions under which the learned act can be correctly applied.

All stimuli on any continuum may be represented by points on a line such as that drawn in Fig. 5. The curve above the line represents the likelihood that any given stimulus will elicit the response being learned. This curve will be at a maximum for the stimulus used during training. How it falls off on either side of its maximum is the problem of stimulus generalization, which has been investigated systematically by Hovland (1937a, b). The data of Hov-

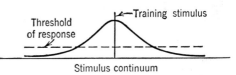

Fig. 5. Curve of stimulus generalization. The height of the curve shows the likelihood that a response will be given to stimuli, on the stimulus continuum, that are different from the one used during training.

land's experiments were well fitted by curves concave upward, similar to the traditional forgetting curve. His data, however, do not warrant the conclusion that the curve on each side of the training stimulus is concave upward over its entire course. The closest point to the stimulus that Hovland investigated was 25 jnd away. What shape the curve takes within the range between 1 and 25 jnd is still unknown. A wealth of psychophysical experiments suggests that the complete curve is probably inflected on each side. It has therefore been given a bell-shaped form in Fig. 5.

If training is given at several points on the stimulus continuum, there will be several curves of stimulus generalization. Exactly how they will reinforce one another has not been carefully investigated. As a starting point, we may assume that the several curves will summate, approximately as is

Methods Used in Training

In any learned act there is both a method of doing the job and a product or end result of the work. Under many circumstances learning proceeds more rapidly if emphasis is placed upon the process to be learned rather than upon the product to be achieved. Athletic coaches pay attention to this distinction and customarily emphasize correct *form* in athletic skills. Despite occasional unorthodox champions, it is generally as-

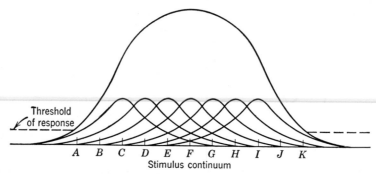

FIG. 6. Summation of several response generalization curves to produce a superthreshold response tendency over a wide range of the stimulus continuum. The upper curve is the summation of the individual curves of stimulus generalization.

shown in Fig. 6.* This figure indicates that the response tendency remains above the threshold level over a wider portion of the stimulus continuum than it does when training is confined to a single point, the condition represented in Fig. 5.

The optimal range of variation to employ during training is unknown, but well worth investigating. Until experimental results provide information, it is probably safe to advise variation over a major portion — but not over the entire extent nor at every point within it — of the range within which generalization is desired. For example, if Fig. 6 is used as an illustration, practice given at several places within the range from point *C* to point *I* should prove satisfactory if application over the range from *A* to *K* is desired.

* Hull (1943, p. 195) has used a similar curve to explain how several subthreshold stimuli may summate to superthreshold values.

sumed that the best performance can be achieved by athletes who use the "proper" muscular coordination. The difference between product and process is especially clear in swimming, where a number of different strokes have been developed and where races are run and records kept in terms of each. A swimmer who used the crawl would be disqualified in a breaststroke event, even if he won the race.

The kinds of learning in which it is advantageous to emphasize the methods used and those in which it is advantageous to emphasize the end products have never been clearly differentiated. However, in tasks that depend to a considerable extent upon symbolic or intellectual components, it is usually advantageous to give the learner information about the best methods of working on his task.

Woodrow (1927) measured the memory span of three groups of subjects and the ability of each group to memorize poetry, prose, a set of facts, a list of historical dates, and words from a Turkish-English vocabulary. Four weeks later all three groups were given a parallel set of tests of ability to memorize. During the intervening weeks one of the groups served as a control and received no training or practice. The second (practice) group was given 90 minutes of practice in memorizing poetry and 87 minutes of practice in memorizing nonsense syllables. The third (training) group was given 76 minutes of instruction on effective methods of learning, 25 minutes of practice in memorizing nonsense syllables, and 76 minutes of practice in memorizing poetry.

The practice group did not surpass the control group by a significant amount on any of the final tests. On the other hand, the group given training in how to memorize surpassed both of the other groups on every test by amounts that gave p values at the 1-per-cent level or better.

The method of learning a maze was found by Husband (1931) to influence the rate of improvement and by Wolfle (1935) to influence the extent to which variation interfered with learning. A comparison of "verbal" and "motor" learners is given in Fig. 7. When the same maze was used on every trial, verbal learners progressed about one-and-a-half times as rapidly as motor learners. When mazes of five different sizes were used in training, verbal learners progressed two or three times as rapidly as motor learners. It is a plausible hypothesis, and one worth testing, that the savings to be gained by employing better methods of learning increase with an increase in the difficulty of the task.

Lindahl (1945) has demonstrated that careful analysis of an industrial process may improve the learning of beginners as well as the production of experienced workers. The task studied was that of contact disc cutting in which a thin abrasive wheel in the cutoff machine is used to slice thin discs from the end of a tungsten rod.

The cutoff machine depends for successful operation upon the speed, form, rhythm, and pressure pattern of the hand and foot action of the operator. Failure to apply foot pressure properly results in damage to the discs, excessive breakage and use of wheels, and wastage of material. [1945, pp. 420–421.]

By comparing paper tape recordings of the foot movements of individual operators with their work records, he selected the pat-

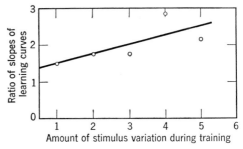

FIG. 7. The relation between amount of stimulus variation and relative efficiency of verbal and motor learning methods. The ordinate values represent the ratios of the slope of the learning curve for verbal learners divided by the slope of the learning curve for motor learners. Greater ordinate values represent relatively greater superiority of verbal over motor methods. (After Wolfle, 1935.)

tern of foot movement shown in Fig. 8 as a standard to be taught to new workers.

Figure 9 shows the course of improvement of a sample worker; after 239 hours of supervised operation his foot action closely approximated the standard pattern.

Weekly production records for new employees trained by this method were compared with production records of older employees. With 11 weeks of training the new employees reached the level of performance of those who had been on the job for 5 months. After 10 weeks of operation the newer trainees were breaking fewer wheels than were other operators with an average of 9 months of experience.

English (1942) reported an experiment conducted in 1918 on one of the factors involved in success at rifle shooting.

Recruits are instructed to squeeze the stock of the rifle as well as the trigger, the whole hand participating in the movement as if in squeezing a sponge. Unfortunately, they do not adequately respond to these excellent and clear verbal instructions. [1942, p. 3.]

The stock of a rifle was hollowed out at the place where the last three fingers should

his squeeze reaction. This continued until he could fire invariably with a proper squeeze. [1942, p. 4.]

Concentrated training on the proper method of squeezing the trigger produced satisfactory learning in subjects who had failed to learn when attention was directed at the target.

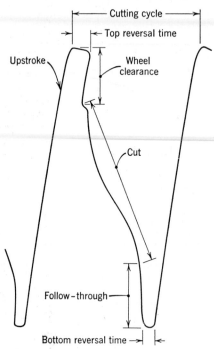

FIG. 8. A view of the disk-cutting cycle. (From Lindahl, 1945.)

press. A rubber bulb and tube were inserted and covered with a wooden plate supported by springs. To casual inspection the stock appeared normal. But a correct squeeze depressed the wooden plate. Air forced out of the bulb activated a tambour on a kymograph or changed the level of liquid in a U-tube.

The recruit was thus enabled to compare visually his own squeeze with that of an expert. If his squeeze was inadequate, he continued to practice firing, at first watching the tube, then aiming at a target without watching the tube but informed each time of

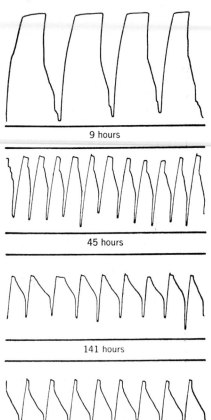

FIG. 9. Disk cutter foot-action patterns of a trainee, showing improvement with training. The records were made after 9, 45, 141, and 239 hours of supervised operation. (From Lindahl, 1945.)

The advantage of teaching correct processes may also show up when workers are transferred to new jobs. When he later tested their ability to work on a somewhat different assembly task, Cox (1934) found that specialized training designed to teach effective work methods to lampsocket assemblers was more effective than an equal amount of time spent in unguided practice.

It cannot be concluded, however, that emphasis on process is always desirable.* A skilled act involves both motor and sensory components. On the motor side, skill consists of precise timing, coordination, and control of effort. On the sensory side, it requires a response to small changes in stimulation. In some acts the controlling stimuli are self-initiated. The cutoff operators studied by Lindahl and the riflemen studied by English are examples. Although these subjects utilized other sensory data, their skill consisted of precise movements that were in large part controlled by the kinesthetic impulses aroused by the movements.

In some other acts the controlling stimuli are not self-initiated. Examples are: learning to follow in ballroom dancing, learning to parry an opponent in boxing or fencing, or learning the pointer-matching skills required by some kinds of military fire-control equipment. Skill in these acts consists of coordinating one's movements with cues that are not self-initiated.

The way in which we learn these two kinds of skill and the best methods of teaching each may be quite different. Careful experimentation in this area is needed before we can know the best methods of teaching all possible skills.

Knowledge of Principles Involved

Learning is generally faster and transfer is generally greater if the learner understands the principles underlying the task on which he is working.

In a frequently cited experiment Judd (1908) trained two groups of boys to shoot at a submerged target. Boys given an explanation of refraction did not learn any

* Renshaw and Postle (1928) reported that detailed instructions on a pursuitmeter task interfered with learning.

more rapidly than did boys not given that explanation, but they adapted more quickly to a change in the depth of the target.

Hendrickson and Schroeder (1941) have reported a similar experiment. Three groups of 14-year-old boys (thirty in each group) learned to shoot an air rifle at a submerged target, 6 inches below the surface of the water. After satisfactory performance was achieved, the target was raised to a point 2 inches below the surface. Further trials were given until a satisfactory score was achieved. Scoring was lenient enough so that, once they discovered the fact that a correction for refraction was necessary, all the boys were able to achieve good scores. Marksmanship was not involved, in other words.

The control group was given no information concerning refraction. A second group (experimental group A) was given a written explanation of refraction. The third group (experimental group B) was given the same explanation plus the specific information that changing the depth of the water changed the amount of refraction.

The results in terms of the mean number of trials required to make a satisfactory score are given in Table 3. The amount of

TABLE 3

EFFECT OF KNOWLEDGE OF PRINCIPLE INVOLVED ON RATE OF LEARNING AND AMOUNT OF TRANSFER (FROM HENDRICKSON AND SCHROEDER, 1941)

	Mean Number of Trials Required		Gain in Trials	Per Cent Improvement
Group	At 6 in.	At 2 in.		
Control	9.10	6.03	3.07	34.1
Experimental A	8.50	5.37	3.13	36.5
Experimental B	7.73	4.63	3.10	40.3

transfer from the 6- to the 2-inch depth is shown for each group by the average number of trials saved and by the percentage of improvement. None of the differences was large enough to be taken with complete confidence (critical ratios varied from 0.49 to 2.34), but all were in the direction expected on the assumptions (1) that providing the boys with information about the principle of refraction would speed up learning and (2) that, the more specific their knowledge, the more effectively would it aid learning and transfer.

Waters (1928) and Katona (1940) investigated the relative value of different methods of teaching college students to solve simple reasoning problems. Showing the student the solution to one or two of the problems aided him very little in the solution of subsequent ones. Telling him the general principle upon which the problems were based aided somewhat more. Giving him a selected series of problems that enabled him to work out the principle for himself resulted in the most rapid learning or the greatest amount of transfer to later problems.

The findings of Waters and Katona point out a difficulty with the experiments of Judd and Hendrickson and Schroeder: knowledge of the principle upon which a problem is based does not mean that the subject can proceed to employ the knowledge successfully. The principle must be in a form and at a level the learner can comprehend.

McGeoch concludes a summary of the transfer of general principles from one activity to another with the statement:

> General principles are one of the most important vehicles of transfer, but the acquisition of a principle does not guarantee that it will be used wherever it is applicable. . . . The probability that [it] will is much higher if the subject is taught, or given a *set*, to apply the principles learned and is taught to analyze similarities between old and new situations. [1942, pp. 422–23.]

The Effectiveness of Guidance

Does it help a person to learn a motor task if he is guided through it several times during the early stages of learning? This question was investigated by Carr and several of his students, using both human and

animal subjects on several different tasks. Various kinds of guidance were given in different amounts and at different places in the series of learning trials. Guidance was found to be an aid, provided it was not overdone. Two to four guided runs through a maze aided learning if given early in the series of training trials. The effectiveness of guidance decreased as its amount increased and as its point of introduction got farther away from the beginning stages of practice. This reduction in effectiveness was great enough that, if given at the wrong time or in too large amounts, guidance interfered with learning. Sample results from Koch (1923) and Ludgate (1923) are presented in Figs. 10 and 11.

An interesting result of these studies was the finding that giving guidance in the learning of one maze increased the amount of transfer to a second maze. Whether this result would appear with other learning materials is unknown.

Two conclusions from the studies on guidance are probably applicable to a wide variety of situations: (1) "The most effective results were generally secured by giving a small amount of tuition relatively early in the process of learning" (Carr, 1930, p. 204); (2) all the experiments showed that, despite its benefits, guidance cannot completely replace actually doing the job to be learned. If a trainee is to acquire skill, he must perform the task himself without outside aid.

Interaction among the factors determining the effectiveness of training. The factors influencing the effectiveness of training are many. A change in motivation may completely nullify the effects of an improved instructional method, or it may overcome the effects of less satisfactory teaching methods. Differences in the way men are selected for a task may require radical changes in the kind and amount of instruction necessary to prepare them for useful work. Changes in the design of the equipment they use may alter selection requirements and necessitate changes in the kind of instruction. The industrial worker's motivation is partially determined by the whole social situation of employee-employer relations and of labor union attitudes and regulations.

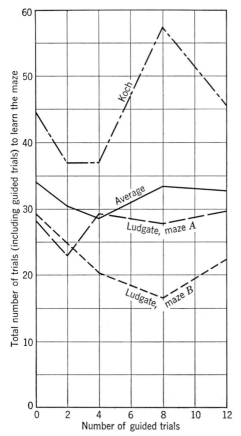

FIG. 10. Effects of guidance on number of trials required to learn a maze. In general, two or four guided trials given at the beginning of training decreased the total number of trials required to master the maze. (After Koch, 1923; Ludgate, 1923.)

The interaction of all these factors frequently makes it difficult to determine the effect of changing a single feature of the whole training situation. As reported above, Keller (1945) found that a change in the method of teaching International Morse Code produced substantially fewer failures and more rapid learning. Taylor (1943), in contrast, found that the specific method of teaching did not matter. Keller was using a normal Army population being trained under Army conditions. Taylor was teaching a group of very superior civilian volunteers. The average level of ability, the distribution of practice, and the motivation were quite different for the two groups of subjects. What a student learns is partly determined by his teachers and their teaching methods, but probably to a much greater

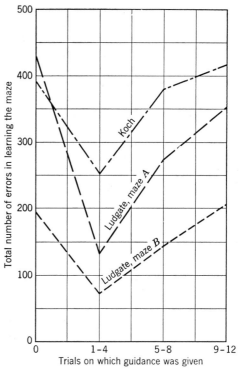

FIG. 11. Effect of location of four guided trials on the number of errors made in learning a maze. In all three studies, guidance given on trials 1 to 4 resulted in fewer errors than when no guidance was given and fewer than when the guidance was introduced later in the series. (After Koch, 1923; Ludgate, 1923.)

extent his learning is determined by his ability, motivation, and work habits. The variance of performance due to these differences may be great enough to mask small effects due to different teaching methods.

In spite of the fact that interaction is the rule rather than the exception, appropriately designed experiments can provide a good deal of information on the nature of different kinds of learning — information that will permit the planning of more effective training programs for industrial and military personnel.

ADMINISTRATION OF A TRAINING PROGRAM

An effective training program requires the solution of both administrative and psychological problems. Ghiselli and Brown (1948) and Viteles (1949) provide a general introduction to these problems and discuss a number of the social and personal adjustment aspects of industrial training that are not touched on in this chapter. Two publications of the War Manpower Commission (1945a, b) are based upon extensive experience in training war workers. Brief guides by Gardiner (1943) and Maxcy (1943) on how to train workers quickly illustrate the type of literature prepared for industrial use. Cushman (1940) and Hayes (1940) discuss the problems of teaching foremen or other industrial workers to serve as instructors of new employees. Hayes' paper discusses methods by which foremen can enhance morale, motivation, and cooperation within the plant. Morgan (1945) has outlined what he considers the most desirable organization for the training department of an industry.

Three problems of administering a training program that can in large part be answered by psychological techniques are:

1. What should be taught?
2. What teaching aids can be usefully employed?
3. How long should formal training continue?

Determination of what is to be taught. Selection of what to teach obviously depends upon what the learners are to do with the skill or knowledge acquired. Unless this information is available, trainees are likely to be given too much training on some points, not enough on others, and inappropriate instruction on still others. In order to avoid giving inappropriate training, job analyses have frequently been made to obtain exact descriptions of the duties to be performed and hence the skills to be acquired. Zerga's bibliographies (1943, 1944) on job analysis and on motion and time study can be used as a starting point for investigating the literature in this field.

Whether information on job analysis is used in planning training or not, the training is likely to get out of date unless constant effort is made to modify the training course to correspond with changes in the job. The introduction of new equipment or new work methods should lead to immediate examination of the training program to see what changes should be made in it.

The typical job analysis is made by a job analyst who observes the worker and records what he does and how he does it. It is, in a sense, an external description of the work being performed. As such, it supplies useful information on which skills are used most frequently, which sequences of movements are most economical, and what the trainee will be called upon to do at the conclusion of his formal training.

From the standpoint of research on training, a different kind of job analysis, one that describes the task in terms of its psychological components instead of in terms of its work units, could frequently contribute additional information of value. By making such analyses psychologists were able to suggest a number of improvements in the training of World War II military specialists. Lindsley's work on Navy radar-operator training is an example (Lindsley, 1945, and quoted in detail by Bray, 1948).

The use of training aids. Blackboards, models, book illustrations, lantern slides, and demonstrations have long been used as training aids. Since in the judgment of hundreds of teachers these devices are important aids to learning, World War II with its tremendous pressure to save training time saw the development of a great variety of more elaborate aids: working models, cutaway models, multicolored charts with transparent overlays, electric circuits spread out on large panels, and many, many motion pictures. There had been a few research studies, but the wartime development was founded more on enthusiasm than on evidence. That enthusiasm, however, provided the stimulus for postwar research on the usefulness of training aids. When the reports of these studies become available, we should begin to have more systematic knowledge of how best to include training aids in a training program.

Dale and Gibbony (1948) and the American Council on Education catalogue (1948) list a number of references useful to anyone seeking either specific audiovisual aids or information about the use of such materials.

A second kind of teaching aid is a synthetic trainer, a device that provides a substitute for practice under actual operating conditions. Perhaps the best known example is the Link Instrument Trainer which provides an airplane pilot with an opportunity to gain experience in controlling an airplane without leaving the ground. Other synthetic trainers have been designed to train aircraft pilots, bombardiers, navigators, gunners, radar operators, submarine crews, and other types of military specialists. Some of these trainers have peacetime applications to justify their continued use and development.

A synthetic trainer involves many of the problems of an entire training program. Kappauf (1945a), Viteles (1945), and Wolfle (1945) have discussed the psychological factors involved in the design and use of synthetic trainers. It is necessary to include a scoring system that will provide a trainee with knowledge of the results of his practice. It is necessary to avoid habit interference. It is necessary to provide an adequate variety of practice materials.

A synthetic trainer should keep the trainee informed of his progress. Automatic counters, tape records, timers, photoelectric scorers, and similar devices usually make it possible to provide knowledge immediately upon the conclusion of each trial or practice period. Ideally, the scoring device should provide specific information concerning the nature of the pupil's errors.

The scoring system should be so designed that the tolerance limits of acceptable performance can be adjusted to the level of skill of the man being trained, as noted previously.

A trainer should present the same psychological problems that the learner will encounter later in performing his task. If it does not, the validity of the trainer will be low and the trainee will experience habit interference when he transfers from the trainer to the supposedly similar equipment he is being taught to handle.

A synthetic trainer must provide an adequate variety of practice material. This requirement is not difficult to meet if its importance is recognized when the trainer is being designed. For then it is easy to prepare a sufficient number of alternative templates, cams, films, or other devices for controlling the tasks set by the trainer. Variety can sometimes be provided by making it possible to begin practice at any point within the problem or sequence of problems set by a particular cam, film, or other controlling device.

The validity of a synthetic trainer can never be taken for granted, but must always be determined experimentally. Determination of the validity of a trainer follows the methods for measuring transfer of training from one situation to another. (Gagné, Foster, and Crowley, 1948, have systematically compared these methods.) If there is positive and appreciable transfer from the trainer to the actual situation, the validity of the trainer is established. The value of practice on the trainer need not be so great as the value of an equal amount of time spent in practicing on the actual equipment, for frequently that equipment is unavailable or is too expensive or too dangerous to be used by beginners. But, unless there is some transfer, the trainer has no value.

A number of studies of trainers and training aids are now being conducted in university and other research laboratories under the auspices of the United States Navy's Special Devices Center (Mead, 1949).

The duration of training. Accurate performance records may be used to determine the appropriate time at which to stop training. In some situations formal training can be stopped before the learning curve reaches an asymptote because an acceptable level of proficiency has been reached or because the men will be put onto productive work where learning can continue. Ghiselli and Brown (1947), for example, found in a study of accident records of streetcar motormen and motor coach operators that accident rates continued to decline steadily throughout the first 17 months of operation. The men had all had from 2 to 4 weeks of training before being put onto regular runs and were, at the end of that time, judged ready for regular operation. Yet learning continued; the average number of accidents at the end of 17 months was less than half the average for the first month of regular operation.

Performance records may show that an inadequate amount of time has been devoted to training. Baldwin and Lindsley (quoted by Bray, 1948) studied the Army Air Force training program for radar bombing operators. They found that giving between three and four times the customary amount of training resulted in a large increase in bombing accuracy.

In general, a learning curve for a group as a whole or for each individual shows when an acceptable level has been reached. Men can then be transferred from a training to a production status.

PROBLEMS OF CONDUCTING RESEARCH ON TRAINING

In planning research on training, the investigator encounters all the problems of laboratory research and more besides. Thorndike (1947) has discussed these problems under the headings used below.

Defining the research problem. In research on a practical training problem, the problem itself should be sharply defined. Will x hours of such-and-such kind of practice on trainer A produce a higher or lower average score on criterion y than will an equal amount and distribution of practice on trainer B? Will trainees who see this motion picture spoil less material than trainees who spend that hour in normal shop work?

Precise definition of the research problem to be studied is necessary in order to determine:

1. What criterion will be most appropriate.

2. What administrative difficulties are likely to interfere with the study and how they can be circumvented.

3. What experimental design will secure the maximum amount of information concerning the question at issue.

Criteria of training success. If research on training is to be conducted, the effects of training must be measured. Two general types of criteria may be used — a criterion internal to the training, or one external to it. An internal criterion is one that measures improvement or changes within the course itself. The examinations in academic courses, the learning scores in most laboratory experiments, or skill in using a synthetic trainer are internal criteria. An external criterion is one that is outside the course itself. The combat efficiency of military personnel is an external criterion of the adequacy of the preliminary military training. Success on the job is an external criterion of industrial training.

Research on training is frequently planned in coordination with research on selection.

In both cases a criterion is necessary. Frequently the same criterion can be used to measure the efficiency of a selection device and the effectiveness of a training program. The ultimate aim of both selection and training is job proficiency. Consequently, the external criterion of success on the actual job is always to be preferred as a criterion. There are, however, two situations in which an internal criterion may be justified.

1. Sometimes the training situation corresponds so exactly to later work situations that an internal criterion is the equivalent of an external one. This is the case in a test of typewriting speed; whether the test is given one day on a school typewriter or the next day on an employer's typewriter is of relatively little moment.

The equivalence of internal and external criteria must always be demonstrated. It cannot be assumed.

2. Sometimes no satisfactory external criterion is available. Trainees scatter to a variety of jobs. They work under different supervisors. Different conditions determine how well they succeed in their work. Any of these factors may make the use of an external criterion extremely difficult. Under such circumstances, the experimenter may have to use an internal criterion. If he does, he must recognize it as a substitute that allows him to measure the effects of whatever factors he has studied on the training itself. It does not allow any measurement of their effects on later performance.

Whichever type of criterion is employed, it must be made as free as possible from systematic bias. As Thorndike (1947) writes:

> Since . . . a comparison is being made of the systematic effect of two or more distinct procedures, it is imperative that the criterion measure be unbiased. That is, there must be no possibility that the criterion test is being administered under conditions which permit one group to have an advantage relative to the other. . . . Any biases associated with a particular school, a particular flight, a particular group of instructors, or the attitude of the group of instructors toward the two groups are likely to affect the groups differentially. The biases may become systematic rather than random. When this happens, the validity of the experimental results is lost. Measures of proficiency based upon subjective ratings and evaluations are particularly suspect from the point of bias. Changes from time to time and place to place are the rule rather than the exception. Furthermore, in an experiment being carried on at a given time and place it is entirely possible that raters may be biased in favor of one rather than the other of the methods under study and that they may prejudice their ratings accordingly. One is led to conclude that it is particularly in training experiments that complete objectivity is needed in the criterion measure. [P. 145.]

It is possible to use a variety of criteria that satisfy Thorndike's statement concerning objectivity. The most valuable criterion depends upon the particular circumstances of each study and the nature of the task being investigated. A few examples will illustrate the range of possibilities. Total number of units of work accomplished in a given time is a standard scoring method. Stopwatch timing, photoelectric timers, and other mechanical or electrical timing devices provide objective scores that for many tasks are obviously related to success. The percentage of total time that an operation is being correctly done can be fairly well approximated in many instances by using the percentage of a periodic series of short samples during which the operation is being performed correctly. Comparisons of the path of arm or foot movements with a standard obtained by kymographic or similar recording methods is sometimes useful. Specially constructed gauges, templates, or similar devices for measuring specific aspects of work turned out are objective and easy to use. Check lists of specific items done or omitted, objective scales for rating performance, and many of the measuring devices developed by test experts are useful in measuring performance.

Having adequate criteria against which to evaluate training research is so essential that, unless criteria will be available at the end of the experiment, research should be dropped.

Administrative problems of training research. A psychologist engaging in research on training in an industrial or military setting encounters many more problems of administrative coordination than does the laboratory investigator.

Sometimes there is difficulty in explaining the purposes of the study to the supervisors and in enlisting their support for it. An unsympathetic officer or a foreman who feels that his status is being threatened by the investigator's work can ruin a research study.

The cooperation of the trainees must be secured. Properly motivated and instructed, laboratory subjects are usually willing to do a great variety of things that they might not otherwise do. But industrial workers are working in a world of pay rates, union rules, complexly determined attitudes toward management, seniority rights, and other personal, social, and economic factors that determine how they will respond to the experimenter's instructions and requests.

Overcoming these administrative problems requires cooperation on the part of the investigator, strict honesty with the men regarding the uses to be made of the findings, and sometimes a high order of selling ability. It is usually easier to enlist the necessary cooperation, as McQuitty (1948) and Taft (1946) have pointed out, if the investigator knows a good deal about the total working situation. A period of indoctrination into the problems, customs, regulations, and working habits of the plant may frequently be a desirable prelude to any research; a period of military indoctrination may be advantageous as a background for engaging in military research.

Despite the difficulties faced by a psychologist conducting research on training, he can proceed with the knowledge that if his studies are properly designed they will have two values. The first is practical: research can increase the effectiveness of specific training programs. The second value is more fundamental. Present knowledge of the principles of learning is largely of a qualitative sort. Properly conducted research will contribute quantitative information on the limits of each principle, its optimal conditions of application, and the nature of its interaction with others.

REFERENCES *

American Council on Education. *Publications of the American Council on Education.* Washington, D. C.: American Council on Education, 1948.

Bennett, George K. Development of Morse-code-actuated printer. OSRD Report 6233, The Psychological Corporation, 1945 (PBL 15808).

Biel, W. C., G. E. Brown, R. M. Gottsdanker, and R. C. Hall. The effectiveness of a check sight technique for training 40-mm gun pointers. OSRD Report 4054, Tufts College, 1944.

Bray, C. W. *Psychology and military proficiency.* Princeton: Princeton University Press, 1948.

Bruce, R. W. Conditions of transfer of training. *J. exp. Psychol.,* 1933, **16,** 343–361.

Carr, H. A. Teaching and learning. *J. genet. Psychol.,* 1930, **37,** 189–218.

Cox, J. W. *Manual skill: Its organization and development.* Cambridge: Cambridge University Press, 1934.

Cushman, F. Training trainers to train. *Employm. Secur. Rev.,* 1940, **7,** 3–8.

Dale, E., and H. L. Gibbony (Eds.). *The news letter.* 1948, **13,** No. 4. Columbus, Ohio: Ohio State University Bureau of Educational Research.

English, H. B. How psychology can facilitate military training — a concrete example. *J. appl. Psychol.,* 1942, **26,** 3–7.

Flanagan, J. C. *The aviation psychology program in the Army Air Forces.* Army Air Forces, Aviation Psychology Program Research Report 1. Washington, D. C.: U. S. Government Printing Office, 1948.

* Reports prepared under contract with the Office of Scientific Research and Development usually bear an OSRD number. In addition, many carry a PB number, which indicates that they may be obtained from the Office of Technical Services, U. S. Department of Commerce, Washington 25, D. C.

Flanagan, J. C., et al. Psychological research in the Armed Forces. *Rev. educ. Res.*, 1948, **18**, 528–655.

Gagné, R. M., H. Foster, and M. E. Crowley. The measurement of transfer of training. *Psychol. Bull.*, 1948, **45**, 97–130.

Gardiner, G. *How to train workers quickly.* New York: Elliott Service Co., 1943.

Ghiselli, E. E., and C. W. Brown. Learning in accident reduction. *J. appl. Psychol.*, 1947, **31**, 580–582.

Ghiselli, E. E., and C. W. Brown. *Personnel and industrial psychology.* New York: McGraw-Hill, 1948.

Grether, W. F., and D. Wolfle. The relative efficiency of constant and varied stimulation during learning. II. White rats on a brightness discrimination problem. *J. comp. Psychol.*, 1936, **22**, 365–374.

Harlow, H. F. The formation of learning sets. *Psychol. Rev.*, 1949, **56**, 51–65.

Hayes, R. D. How to teach foremen to teach. *Person. Ser., Amer. Mgmt. Assn.*, 1940, **42**, 20–28.

Hendrickson, G., and W. H. Schroeder. Transfer of training in learning to hit a submerged target. *J. educ. Psychol.*, 1941, **32**, 205–213.

Henmon, V. A. C. Educational psychology. *Psychol. Bull.*, 1930, **27**, 417–430.

Hovland, C. I. The generalization of conditioned responses: I. The sensory generalization of conditioned responses with varying frequencies of tone. *J. gen. Psychol.*, 1937a, **17**, 125–148. II. The sensory generalization of conditioned responses with varying intensities of tone. *J. genet. Psychol.*, 1937b, **51**, 279–291.

Hull, C. L. *Principles of behavior.* New York: Appleton-Century-Crofts, 1943.

Hunter, W. S. Learning: IV. Experimental studies of learning. In C. Murchison (Ed.), *Handbook of general experimental psychology.* Worcester: Clark University Press, 1934. Pp. 497–570.

Husband, R. W. Comparative behavior on different types of mazes. *J. gen. Psychol.*, 1931, **5**, 234–244.

Judd, C. H. The relation of special training to general intelligence. *Educ. Rev.*, 1908, **36**, 28–42.

Kappauf, W. E. Notes on the desired characteristics of trainers. Project Memorandum 7, Service Project N-111, U. S. Navy Department, Advanced Fire Control, and Brown University, 1945a.

Kappauf, W. E. Notes on the design of phototube scoring devices for tracking trainers. Informal Memorandum 9, Service Project N-111, Brown University, 1945b.

Katona, G. *Organizing and memorizing: Studies in the psychology of learning and teaching.* New York: Columbia University Press, 1940.

Keller, F. S. Studies in International Morse Code. I. A new method of teaching code reception. *J. appl. Psychol.*, 1943, **27**, 407–415.

Keller, F. S. The radio code research project: Final report of Project SC-88. OSRD Report 5379, The Psychological Corporation, 1945 (PBL 12154).

Koch, H. L. The influence of mechanical guidance upon maze learning. *Psychol. Monogr.*, 1923, **32**, No. 5.

Lindahl, L. G. Movement analysis as an industrial training method. *J. appl. Psychol.*, 1945, **29**, 420–436.

Lindsley, D. B. Radar operator training: Results of study of SCR-270–271 operators at Drew Field. OSRD Report 1737, Yerkes Laboratories of Primate Biology, 1943 (PBL 18367).

Lindsley, D. B. Final report in summary of work on the selection and training of radar operators. OSRD Report 5766, Yerkes Laboratories of Primate Biology, 1945 (PBL 12165).

Luborsky, L. F. Aircraft recognition: 1. The relative efficiency of teaching procedures. *J. appl. Psychol.*, 1945, **29**, 385–398.

Ludgate, K. E. The effect of manual guidance upon maze learning. *Psychol. Monogr.*, 1923, **33**, No. 1.

Maxcy, E. C. How people learn: A guide for teachers in industry. *Personnel*, 1943, **19**, 706–721.

McGeoch, J. A. The acquisition of skill. *Psychol. Bull.*, 1931, **28**, 413–466.

McGeoch, J. A. The psychology of human learning: A bibliography. *Psychol. Bull.*, 1933, **30**, 1–62.

McGeoch, J. A. *The psychology of human learning: An introduction.* New York: Longmans, Green, 1942.

McQuitty, L. L. Developing applied psychologists. *Amer. Psychologist*, 1948, **3**, 16–19.

Mead, L. C. Psychology at the Special Devices Center: Office of Naval Research. *Amer. Psychologist*, 1949, **4**, 97–103.

Morgan, H. K. *Industrial training and testing.* New York: McGraw-Hill, 1945.

Renshaw, S., and D. K. Postle. Pursuit learning under three types of instruction. *J. gen. Psychol.*, 1928, **1**, 360–367.

Seashore, H. G., A. K. Kurtz, H. Kendler, S. E. Stuntz, and C. Rappaport. Variation of activities in code classes: An experimental study of the problem of monotony in code learning. OSRD Report 4082, The Psychological Corporation, 1944 (PBL 12173).

Siipola, E. M., and H. E. Israel. Habit-interference as dependent upon stage of training. *Amer. J. Psychol.*, 1933, **45**, 205–227.

Stroud, J. B. Experiments on learning in school situations. *Psychol. Bull.*, 1940, **37**, 777–807.

Taft, R. The staff psychologist in industry. *Amer. Psychologist*, 1946, **1**, 55–61.

Taylor, D. W. The learning of radiotelegraphic code. *Amer. J. Psychol.*, 1943, **56**, 319–353.

Thorndike, R. L. *Research problems and techniques.* Army Air Forces, Aviation Psychology

Program Research Report 3. Washington, D. C.: U. S. Government Printing Office, 1947.

Trowbridge, M. H., and H. Cason. An experimental study of Thorndike's theory of learning. *J. gen. Psychol.*, 1932, **7**, 245–258.

Viteles, M. S. *Industrial psychology.* New York: Norton, 1932.

Viteles, M. S. Psychological principles in the design and operation of synthetic trainers with particular reference to antiaircraft gunnery. Memorandum 19, Project N-105, University of Pennsylvania, 1945.

Viteles, M. S. *Industrial psychology.* New York: Norton, 1949.

War Manpower Commission. *Training within industry materials.* Washington, D. C.: U. S. Government Printing Office, 1945a.

War Manpower Commission. *Training within industry service.* Washington, D. C.: U. S. Government Printing Office, 1945b.

Waters, R. H. The influence of tuition upon ideational learning. *J. gen. Psychol.*, 1928, **1**, 534–549.

Wolfe, J. B. The effect of delayed reward upon learning in the white rat. *J. comp. Psychol.*, 1934, **17**, 1–21.

Wolfle, D. The relative efficiency of constant and varied stimulation during learning. *J. comp. Psychol.*, 1935, **19**, 5–27.

Wolfle, D. The relative efficiency of constant and varied stimulation during learning. III. The objective extent of stimulus variation. *J. comp. Psychol.*, 1936, **22**, 375–381.

Wolfle, D. The use and design of synthetic trainers for military training. OSRD Report 5246. Washington, D. C., 1945.

Wolfle, D. Military training and the useful parts of learning theory. *J. consult. Psychol.*, 1946, **10**, 73–75.

Woodrow, H. The effect of type of training upon transference. *J. educ. Psychol.*, 1927, **18**, 159–172.

Zerga, J. E. Job analysis: A résumé and bibliography. *J. appl. Psychol.*, 1943, **27**, 249–267.

Zerga, J. E. Motion and time study: A résumé and bibliography. *J. appl. Psychol.*, 1944, **28**, 477–500.

35

Engineering Psychology and Equipment Design

PAUL M. FITTS
Ohio State University

Traditionally the design of machines has been a responsibility of engineers, and the discovery of the most effective procedures for selecting and training men to use them has been a task for psychologists. The demands of World War II, however, raised many unusual problems of equipment design — problems that drew experimental psychologists into active collaboration with physicists and engineers (cf. Stevens, 1946). By the end of the war psychologists were assisting in the design of such varied equipments as radar consoles and scope faces, instrument dials, binoculars, stereoscopic height-finders, gunsight reticles, underwater sound-detection devices, voice communication systems, signal systems, gunsight controls, aircraft cockpits, combat information centers, and synthetic training devices. Since the war, research of this nature has continued on a relatively large scale. Much of the material in the present chapter is taken from this recent work.

Psychological research on equipment design has been identified by various names: applied experimental psychology, applied psychophysiology, man-machine systems research, biotechnology, psychotechnology, human engineering, and engineering psychology. Convention favors the name *engineer-*

ing psychology, since it conforms to the practice followed in naming other specialized areas such as educational, clinical, personnel, and industrial psychology. Hereafter, engineering psychology and equipment-design research will be used synonymously.

It is the purpose of the present chapter to summarize psychological facts and principles of particular significance for equipment design and to indicate theoretical questions raised by the study of man's behavior in using the mechanical devices of our technological society.*

PROBLEMS AND METHODS

The methods employed in research on equipment problems are primarily those of experimental psychology. Problems of method peculiar to this new research field are far too numerous to permit even a listing here. They range from criterion problems to problems of electronic circuitry, from questions of how to handle skewed distributions of error frequencies in dial reading studies to questions of how to measure stimulus-response relations in continuous tasks.

This chapter was written while the author was Chief of the Psychology Branch, Aero Medical Laboratory, USAF Air Materiel Command.

* Since this chapter was written there has been published a volume, *Human Factors in Undersea Warfare,* by the Panel on Psychology and Physiology, Committee on Undersea Warfare, National Research Council, which treats some of the problems here presented.

Many areas of equipment-design research call for systematic, large-scale programs planned to attack problems of demonstrated importance. Several effective survey techniques are now available for discovering and assessing these problems. These survey techniques are not procedures that one would use in carefully controlled experiments so much as techniques for identifying, analyzing, and defining problems within the field of engineering psychology.

The discovery and definition of critical problems in designing man-machine systems. Different elements in a complex man-machine system contribute to the overall error variance of the system in accordance with a well-known statistical relation (Chapanis, 1949). If the total variable error in a system is represented by σ_T, then additive components $a, b, c, \cdots$ of the system contribute to this total in accordance with the relation

$$\sigma_T{}^2 = \sigma_a{}^2 + \sigma_b{}^2 + \sigma_c{}^2 + \cdots \qquad (1)$$

provided the errors contributed by each of the components are uncorrelated. Otherwise the relation is

$$\sigma_T{}^2 = \sigma_a{}^2 + \sigma_b{}^2 + \sigma_c{}^2 + \cdots \pm 2r_{ab}\sigma_a\sigma_b$$
$$\pm 2r_{ac}\sigma_a\sigma_c \pm 2r_{bc}\sigma_b\sigma_c \pm \cdots \quad (2)$$

It is apparent that the relative importance of the root-mean-square error contributed by any component increases quadratically with its relative size. It follows that improvement in the more accurate elements of a system will produce only a negligible reduction in the total variable error of the system. For example, if the machine components of a particular man-machine system contribute a root-mean-square error of 10 and the human components contribute an error of 50, and the two are unrelated, the variable error of the total system is only 51. In this case only a 2-per-cent improvement in the system would be gained by eliminating all the variable errors of the machine components. It is possible, in other words, to analyze the errors in complex

machine operations and industrial processes, and to determine the relative size of the error variance contributed by men, by machines, and by interaction effects.

Similarly, correlation techniques can be used to identify sources of difficulty in technical tasks. Carter and Dudek (1947), for example, secured records from standardized navigation flights. Applying factor-analysis and multiple-correlation techniques, they found that three principal factors — heading, speed, and wind effect — determined the accuracy of navigators' position reports. The most important single source of error lay in the determination of compass deviation. This error was then traced to a particular instrument, the astrocompass.

An activity-sampling technique can sometimes be used to advantage in analyzing the activities of men engaged in complex tasks. In one instance Christensen (1949) recorded at 5-second intervals the operations performed by aerial navigators and radar operators during 15-hour flights. An analysis of the resulting data enabled him to determine where the greatest amount of time could be saved by new equipment and by revised operating procedures.

Another useful procedure is the critical-incident technique. This technique was used by Fitts and Jones (1947a, b) in surveying psychological problems relating to aircraft equipment. They asked pilots for descriptions of specific errors or difficulties experienced in operating controls and in responding to instruments. These descriptions of critical experiences were classified and enumerated. The results for instrument-reading errors are given in Table 1. Findings from several experimental studies of problems revealed by this survey will be discussed later. A procedure similar to the critical-incident technique is that of analyzing errors in equipment use. Reports by Ford (1949) and Grether (1949) illustrate this approach.

As a further step in defining problems, it is desirable at times to ask experienced persons to rate the importance and fre-

TABLE 1

CLASSIFICATION OF 270 ERRORS MADE BY AIRCRAFT PILOTS IN RESPONDING TO INSTRUMENTS AND SIGNALS (MODIFIED SLIGHTLY FROM FITTS AND JONES, 1947b)

	Relative Frequency
1. *Misinterpreting multi-revolution instruments.* Mistakes in comprehending information presented by two or more pointers or by a pointer plus a rotating dial viewed through a "window."	18
2. *Misinterpreting direction of indicator movement (reversal errors).* Improper interpretation of an instrument indication with the result that subsequent actions increase rather than reduce an undesirable condition.	17
3. *Misinterpreting visual and auditory signals.* Failing to respond appropriately to hand signals, warning lights or sounds, or radio range signals.	14
4. *Errors involving poor legibility.* Difficulty in seeing numerals, scale markings, or pointers clearly enough to permit quick and accurate reading.	14
5. *Failing to identify a display.* Mistaking one instrument for another or confusing pointers on a multiple-pointer display.	13
6. *Using an inoperative instrument.* Accepting as valid the indication of an instrument that is inoperative or operating improperly.	9
7. *Misinterpreting scale values.* Difficulty in interpolating between numbered scale graduations or failure to assign the correct value to a numbered graduation.	6
8. *Errors associated with illusions.* Difficulties arising out of a conflict between body sensations and information given by visual displays.	5
9. *Omitting the reading of an instrument.* Failing to refer to an instrument at the proper time.	4
Total	100

quency of use of different components, processes, or 'links' in a system.

Much emphasis has been given in recent years to systems research. Systems studies have often been concerned with such practical problems as the optimum number of human operators that should be assigned to work in a particular system, the optimum number and kind of equipment components, and the optimum arrangement of men and machines. Motion and time engineers, attempting to discover the most efficient methods of work, have collected similar data and reported "link values," "therblig values," process charts, and time charts for many industrial tasks. For the most part, systems studies such as these are relevant to experimental psychology only in so far as they indicate problems for experimental study. In this respect, however, they have made an important contribution to research on equipment design.

Numerous authors have attempted to classify and assign importance to problems within the field of engineering psychology. Representative discussions are found in publications by Bartlett (1947), Bray (1948), Brown and Jenkins (1947), Chapanis, Garner, and Morgan (1949), Fitts (1947), Grether (1947a), Kappauf (1949), McFarland (1946), Mead (1948), and Morgan (1947).

The major distinction made by the present writer is between display problems, i.e. questions of how best to present information to the senses, and problems of the design of control systems, i.e. questions of how best to utilize human motor output, and how to secure good dynamic characteristics in complete controller systems.

One further point should be emphasized. Research in engineering psychology must concern itself with the behavior of individuals in complex and continuous tasks, particularly tasks in which skill is exercised in the rapid interpretation of instruments or signals and in the accurate control over sources of external power. Furthermore, machines usually must be designed with reference to many complex and sometimes conflicting considerations. In the present chapter, therefore, emphasis is given to experimental data relating to complex skills, to interaction effects, and to human performance in a variety of different tasks.

DESIGN OF VISUAL DISPLAYS

A display is any device that can be used for presenting information to individuals by visual, auditory, tactual, or other exteroceptive channels. The requirements of good visual displays are the matters with which we are here concerned.

Significance of different visual discrimination processes. The literature on visual discrimination includes reports of performance in many different tasks, varying from the detection of light energy to the recognition of complex patterns. Performance on these visual tasks is influenced by many parameters. This is illustrated by a study of highway signs by Forbes and Holmes (1939). After determining the maximum distance at which 24-inch-roadside warning symbols could be recognized with unlimited time, they had subjects drive along an unfamiliar road and call out all signs as soon as they were observed. Calls occurred at distances of from 200 to 400 feet, in contrast with the 800 or more feet at which similar symbols were recognized on the previous tests.

It is important to distinguish two aspects of visual discrimination. One concerns the *time* required for the completion of discrimination and response. In *visibility* studies the subjects are allowed to take as much time as they desire before responding, and accuracy alone is the criterion of efficiency. In *legibility* studies the subjects are instructed to minimize the overall time required to complete a response, and effectiveness is judged by speed as well as by accuracy.

The second aspect concerns the *nature* of the discriminatory response. *Detectability* studies require only detection of the presence of a stimulus. *Identifiability* studies require identification of the stimulus object. Detection of a stimulus is sometimes the only requirement in visibility studies; at other times identification is required. Identification is generally required in legibility studies.

In engineering psychology legibility and the identification of complex patterns are usually of greater interest than are visibility and detectability. However, in the interest of the systematic organization of topics, the simpler processes will be considered first.

Design Problems Involving Visibility

Since adequate visibility is a prerequisite for all visual displays, a few illustrations will be given to show the application of visibility data to equipment-design problems.

Size, brightness, and contrast. The design of radar (radio detection and ranging) equipment raises many problems of visual discrimination. Radar operators are often forced to search for weak signals at near-threshold levels where such factors as the size, brightness, and contrast are critical. Pulses of electrical energy are sent out by the radar and reflected back by the distant target, whereupon they are amplified and usually made to modulate the intensity of a beam of electrons in a cathode-ray tube (CRT) in such a way that corresponding to each target there appears a bright spot or a 'pip' on the face of the tube. In practice, radar reflections are almost always accompanied by 'noise,' so that the real targets are partially or completely obscured by a background of random brightness variations on the face of the CRT.

The visibility of radar signals, either with or without a noise background, has been shown to vary with CRT brightness in about the same manner as does the visibility of laboratory test objects (Williams, Bartlett, and King, 1948). A slight loss in visibility was found for small values of CRT bias (bright traces), but it was discovered that this was due to loss of sensitivity of the phosphor screen with resulting loss of contrast at higher beam intensities.

The brightness adaptation of the eye and the level of brightness of the area surrounding the target are factors that influence the visibility of displays such as those on a radar scope. Hanes and Williams (1948) found that for weak radar signals the lowest contrast thresholds and the shortest detection times occurred when the test and adapting illuminations were approximately equal in brightness. These results were obtained for adapting brightness levels ranging from 0 to

1858 foot-lamberts and for screen intensities ranging from 0.00009 to 0.204 foot-lambert. Similar results have been reported from several related studies. For optimum detection of low-contrast 'pips' the CRT should be adjusted until the background brightness of the tube is in the neighborhood of 0.1 foot-lambert. Interestingly enough, ambient illumination as bright as the screen background has no detrimental effect on CRT target visibility and may actually improve it, by permitting the maintenance of relatively uniform retinal adaptation at a level near the optimum.

A preliminary study of visibility of CRT signals as a function of their size was made by Bartlett and Williams (1947). The smallest image size employed subtended 1 minute by 12 degrees of visual angle at a viewing distance of 12 inches. It was found that very dim targets could be discriminated more readily if the eyes were near the scope face (6 inches) than if they were farther away (24 inches). This finding was true for dark or moderately bright CRT backgrounds but did not hold when noise was present. Detection of targets viewed against a noise background involves pattern perception, of course, rather than simple brightness discrimination. The role of stimulus size apparently varies, therefore, depending on whether the task involves the visibility or the identifiability of a target.

The detection of a low-intensity image that is viewed amid a cluster of relatively bright noise pips is much more difficult than the identification of the same image when it is seen against a uniform background. Payne-Scott (1948) discussed the importance of this point and suggested procedures for simplifying the radar operator's tasks. One of her suggestions was to increase the number (N) of samples of noise per unit of time, thereby obtaining a more even distribution of noise over the surface of the tube face. Engineers can vary approximately fifteen design characteristics that have an effect on the sampling rate of a radar set or

on the size, brightness, or contrast of the blip.

Although the ability of an operator to detect radar images can be predicted fairly well from existing visibility data, it is often advisable to determine visibility under conditions that permit the study of the special interaction effects and the limiting conditions peculiar to radar displays.

Color. The wavelength of the light reflected by a display is sometimes an important design factor. Monochromatic red light is especially advantageous when it is necessary to read instruments and at the same time to preserve dark adaptation. This is true because the visual receptor elements that mediate night vision are relatively insensitive to red light (see Chapter 24). It was not until late in World War II, however, that red light came into general use for the illumination of instrument panels.

Since the eye is not color corrected it cannot bring all wavelengths of light into simultaneous focus on the retina. This suggests that monochromatic light should give better visibility than light of mixed wavelength. Kappauf (1949) concluded that the evidence on this point is contradictory. Of monochromatic lights, however, yellow provides the best acuity.

Visibility of numerals and letters printed in various color combinations has been found to depend primarily on brightness and contrast, rather than on color (Sumner, 1932; Preston, Schwankel, and Tinker, 1932). Data collected by Eastman Kodak Company (1944) now make it possible to compute the equivalent brightness contrast of two monochromatic fields that are of the same apparent brightness. Thus color differences can be expressed as equivalent brightness differences.

Pattern discrimination is a function of the ability to detect gradients of brightness, color, and saturation. Few displays except those employed in color motion pictures and color television, however, employ all three factors. The science of camouflage, of course, makes extensive use of all three factors in attempting to destroy pattern vision for objects by making them blend in with their background or assume deceptive configurations.

Discrimination of velocity and acceleration. If an individual can respond to the velocity and acceleration of a moving object,

Discrimination of three coordinates from cues on a cathode-ray tube. Numerous efforts have been made to obtain more than two parameters of information from a single image on a CRT, particularly the location of objects in three-dimensional space.

Any two of the three coordinates necessary to locate an object in space can be

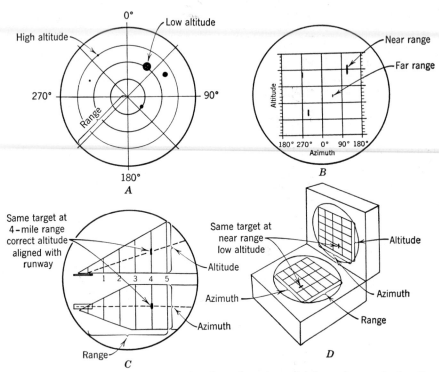

Fig. 1. Four possible ways of displaying three dimensions of information on the two-dimensional surfaces of cathode-ray tubes. In *A* and *B* the size and length, respectively, of the blip are utilized to indicate the relative magnitude of the third dimension; in *C* and *D* two separate coordinate systems are employed.

i.e. respond in anticipation of its future course, he can perform many perceptual-motor tasks much more effectively than if he responds only to the object's position from moment to moment. Hick (1948b) found that the ability to detect a sudden change in the velocity of a moving spot on a CRT obeys Weber's law approximately; the mean threshold was about 12 per cent of the initial velocity under favorable conditions.

represented by the position of the CRT image with reference to a polar or rectangular grid system superimposed on the tube face. Difficulties arise, however, when we try to add the third dimension. The use of stereoscopic devices has been considered, but most efforts to solve this problem have made use of changes imposed on the image itself, such as changes in its size, brightness, color, or pattern, or variation in its temporal characteristics, such as flicker rate. Several of the many possibilities are illustrated in Fig. 1. Thus we see that man's ability to make relative or absolute discriminations of stimulus values can be utilized in the design of 'three-dimensional' displays.

Discrimination of angular position. On many circular instruments, values are indicated by the angular position of a hand or cursor. Sometimes it is necessary for individuals to judge directly the angle formed by two such objects or lines, or by one object with respect to the vertical and horizontal. This ability has been studied with the aid of lines projected on a large unstructured circular screen (Kaufman et al., 1947; Rogers et al., 1947; Reese et al., 1948).

The average error of 33 subjects in judging the bearing of a line of light was 2.8 degrees. Subjects adjusted a marker to a designated bearing more accurately than they estimated the bearing of a marker that had already been adjusted; but adjustment required more time than estimation.

The introduction of a known reference line enabled observers to reduce their errors in estimating bearings that were as far as 20 to 30 degrees from the reference line. When no visual reference was provided, observers relied on subjective estimates of the vertical and horizontal. Estimates were most accurate at the 0- and 90-degree points, and somewhat better at 45 degrees than at other bearings in the 0- to 90-degree sector. On the basis of these and related findings, a grid system of 24 bearing markers spaced 15 degrees apart was recommended for use on large display screens (Kaufman et al., 1947). Such a grid system includes all the salient or 'natural' anchor points (0, 30, 45, 60, 90, etc., degrees).

Problems Related to Pattern Discrimination

Standards for legibility studies. The lack of standard procedures and standard units has seriously limited the generality of the results from legibility studies. Fortunately, however, agreement has been reached regarding certain units of measurement and conditions of experimentation, through the work of a subcommittee of the Armed Forces–NRC Vision Committee (1947). The recommendations formulated by this subcommittee are summarized in Table 2.

Size of numerals and letters. Burnham, in 1892, concluded that printed characters should have a minimum height of 1.5 millimeters. This is equivalent to the size of small letters printed in 10-point type. Interestingly enough, subsequent work supports this early observation. Paterson and Tinker (1940), for example, found that the use of 6- and 8-point type retards speed of reading, but that 9-, 10-, 11-, and 12-point type are about equally legible when each is used with an appropriate line width. Most journals and textbooks are printed in 10- or 11-point type. Readers have been found to prefer this size.

Reading speed is retarded if type is too large (Buckingham, 1931). Paterson and Tinker (1942, 1943, 1944) have shown that the average number of words covered per eye fixation is less for very large type than for type of an optimum size. Although fixations are somewhat shorter for large than for small type, the net result in one study comparing 10-point and 14-point type was found to be a 14-per-cent increase in perception time for the larger type. This is not strange when it is considered that 14-point type occupies 87 per cent more printing space than 10-point type.

Paterson and Tinker, who have systematically investigated such typographic variables as size, style of type, width of line, space between lines, margins, columnar arrangement, space between columns, color of print and paper, and paper surface, stress the importance of interactions between these variables. They emphasize that interaction is the rule rather than the exception, and they caution against drawing conclusions about optimum values for any variable that has been studied in isolation.

Size of instrument dials and cathode-ray tubes. The question of optimum size arises

TABLE 2

STANDARDS RECOMMENDED BY THE ARMED FORCES–NRC VISION COMMITTEE FOR USE IN RESEARCH
ON VISUAL DISPLAYS

A. Subject Variables

Variable	Unit of Measurement	Standard	Remarks
1. Visual acuity		20/20 or better	Follow testing manual issued by AF–NRC Vision Committee.
2. Color vision		'Normal'	Use any standard pseudo-isochromatic chart.
3. Mental ability		None specified	Define population used with respect to sex, age, education, work experience, intelligence scores, and measures of perceptual, verbal, numerical, and motor abilities.

B. Stimulus ('Controlled') Variables

Variable	Unit of Measurement	Standard	Remarks
4. Distance	Feet and inches	13 inches	Representative of normal reading distance.
		28 inches	Representative of instrument-reading distance.
		20 feet	Standard distance for visual acuity measurements.
5. Size	Visual angle		Express in degrees, minutes, and seconds.
6. Height of numerals	Inches	$\frac{3}{32}$, $\frac{1}{8}$, $\frac{3}{16}$	For minor, intermediate, and major numerals and letters on instruments to be viewed at 28 inches.
7. Stroke width of numerals	Inches	0.015, 0.020, 0.025	For minor, intermediate, and major numerals and letters on instruments to be viewed at 28 inches.
8. Length of scale graduations	Inches	$\frac{3}{32}$, $\frac{5}{32}$, $\frac{7}{32}$	For minor, intermediate, and major graduations on instruments to be viewed at 28 inches.
9. Width of scale graduations	Inches	0.015, 0.020, 0.025	For minor, intermediate, and major graduations on instruments to be viewed at 28 inches.
10. Pointer length	Inches		Tip should reach the inner end of minor scale graduations.
11. Pointer width	Inches	$\frac{3}{32}$	
12. Style of numerals and letters		Aeronautical Design Standard No. AND 10400	Wrico or LeRoy lettering guides are acceptable substitutes.
13. Color or hue	Millimicrons		Specify dominant wavelength if possible; otherwise match with Munsell scale.
14. Saturation	Millimicrons		Specify wavelength distribution if possible, otherwise match with Munsell scale.
15. Brightness	Foot-lambert	30 foot-lamberts for day simulation; 0.1 foot-lambert for night simulation	Use MacBeth Illuminometer or comparable photometric instrument. Brightness should be specified for the white area, whether figure or ground.
16. Illumination	Foot-candle		
17. Color of figure and ground		(1) Black on white, (2) white on black	(1) For general use. (2) For instruments designed for night lighting.
18. Contrast	$\dfrac{DI}{I + DI}$		Maximum possible contrast is recommended. I in this case is the lesser of the two brightnesses.
19. Adaptation level		Sufficient time for eyes to adapt to test level	See Hecht, Haig, and Chase, 1937.
20. Exposure time	Seconds	0.1 second	When a single eye fixation is desired.
21. Style of type			Follow recommendations in Paterson and Tinker (1940), pages 156–157.

also in the design of scale markings, numerals, pointers, overlays, radar scopes, and many other items. Here an important consideration is whether the operator has plenty of time for reading, or whether he must check a display very quickly.

Check-reading requires rapid inspection in order to detect deviations outside the normal range. Under conditions that permitted subjects to respond to the patterns formed by a group of instruments, White (1949) found that a panel containing 16 instruments of 1¾-inch diameter was check-read somewhat more rapidly and accurately than panels of either larger or smaller instruments. Results for 24 subjects are given in Table 3.

TABLE 3

Size of Individual Dials in Inches	Average Check-Reading Time in Seconds	Per Cent of Trials in Error
1	0.67	5
1¾	0.65	3
2¾	0.69	6

The differences between the 1¾- and 2¾-inch dials were significant at better than the 5-per-cent level. Eye-movement records also indicated that fewer fixations were required to check the dials of intermediate size.

Studies of the size of radar scopes in relation to speed of target detection have also indicated an optimum size range. This size is considerably less than that employed in some present-day radar sets (Horton, 1949). Where the use of a larger scope results only in distributing the existing signal over a larger surface, little gain in legibility is to be expected with scopes larger than about 6 inches in diameter. However, if CRT displays are designed to be viewed from a distance, or by several observers at once, as in the case of home television, larger sizes are often desirable.

Sleight (1948), using a 0.12-second exposure time, determined errors in reading linear, circular, and other types of scales to the nearest graduation mark. All scales covered

a range of from 0 to 10, and the distance between adjacent scale division marks was constant. The average number of errors made by 60 subjects and the maximum visible dimensions of each scale are given in Table 4. All differences in error frequency

TABLE 4

Type of Scale	Maximum Dimension in Inches	Per Cent of Trials in Error
Open window	1⅔	0.5
Round dial	2⅙	10.9
Semicircular	4⅓	16.6
Linear-horizontal	7	27.5
Linear-vertical	7	35.5

were significant at the 1-per-cent level. It can be seen that there was a close relation between the maximum visible dimension of a scale and the observer's ability to read it during an exposure shorter than the time required for an average eye fixation. For such short exposures it appears that the best scale is the one that enables the reader to anticipate most precisely where to find the pointer.

Grether and Williams (1947) reported that there was no systematic relation between speed of reading and dial size for dials ranging in diameter from 1 to 4 inches when subjects had to call out numerical values. Kappauf and associates (1947, 1948) found no significant differences in quantitative-reading speed between 1.4- and 2.8-inch dials, but they reported a marked loss of speed for a 0.7-inch dial. They also found that a general slowing of response accompanied any increase in the overall range of values depicted on a scale. For rapid detection of pattern changes or rapid reading of scales, it can be concluded that there is generally an optimum size of display.

A different principle holds when reading speed is not important. If similar information is presented on a large and on a small dial, then more accurate readings can usually be made from the larger dial. The precision of reading is then primarily a function of the

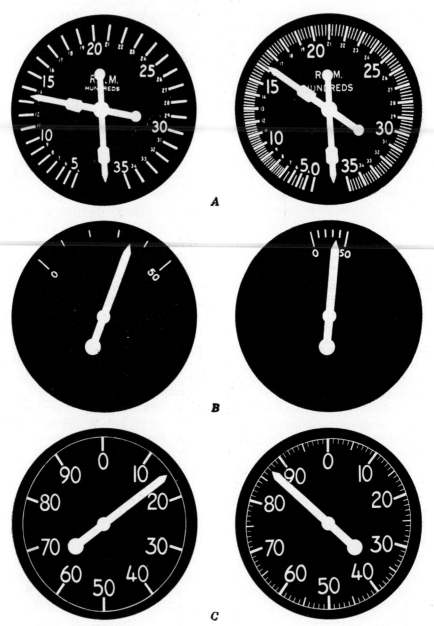

FIG. 2. Instrument dials employed in studies of legibility as a function of the spacing between scale markings by (A) Loucks (1944a), (B) Grether and Williams (1947), and (C) Kappauf, Smith, and Bray (1947).

arc distance separating each unit of the scale.

Spacing of scale marks. It is possible to vary the distance between scale marks as well as the overall size of a display (cf. Fig. 2).

Errors in reading a scale to an exact numerical value have been expressed (1) as

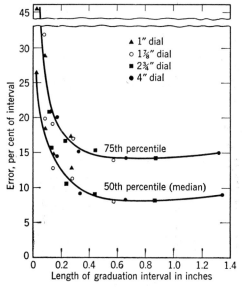

FIG. 3. Dial-reading errors for various scale intervals expressed as a relative valve. Data are for 20 subjects at each point. (From Grether and Williams, 1947.)

a percentage of the distance between scale divisions, (2) as an average error computed as arc distance along the scale, reported either in inches or in the units represented by the scale, and (3) as the proportion of readings in error by more than some arbitrary amount. The first of these measures indicates relative accuracy of interpolation between two scale marks. Results from Grether and Williams' study (1947), in which subjects read dials to the nearest tenth of an interval, have been plotted in Fig. 3 to reveal accuracy of interpolation. Relative errors of interpolation are much greater for very small intervals. The minimum relative error was reached at about 0.5 inch per scale

division. Weber's law holds approximately over the range of graduation intervals from this point on. Once Weber's law becomes operative, of course, nothing is to be gained by making divisions any larger. In fact, the data suggest that relative accuracy may actually become somewhat poorer with very large separation between scale marks.

Accuracy relative to the distance between scale marks, however, is not so important for practical purposes as is the problem of minimizing the absolute size of the reading error. The question here is, given a dial of a particular size, how close together should scale marks be placed to provide maximum reading precision? When absolute accuracy is the criterion, and adequate reading time is permitted, best results are achieved by the use of closely spaced scale marks, such as those used on a slide rule.

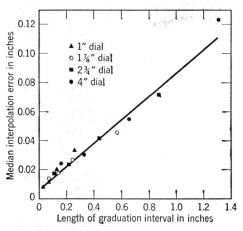

FIG. 4. Dial-reading error for various scale intervals expressed as an absolute value. (From Grether and Williams, 1947.)

Grether and Williams (see Fig. 4) found that absolute accuracy increased down to the most closely spaced scale tried. Kappauf and his associates obtained similar results, but they found evidence for a loss in absolute accuracy for very small graduation intervals. It appears that maximum relative precision in reading circular scales increases as arc distance between scale marks increases, up to a scale separation of about 0.5 inch for instrument-panel (28-inch) reading distance. But maximum absolute accuracy increases as the distance between marks decreases down to approximately 0.05 inch (about 6 minutes of visual angle). These specific values are undoubtedly subject to considerable variation with changes in pointer design, lighting, the thickness and length of scale marks, the range of values covered by the scale, and other factors. Maier (1931), for example, reported greatest accuracy when graduation marks were 25 per cent as thick as the interval between marks.

In several instances Loucks (1944a, b, d), using a short-exposure technique, found a significant advantage in favor of dials on which some of the scale division marks had been removed. For example, of the two dials shown in Fig. 2A with 0.05- and 0.25-inch separation between scales, the one with the fewer scale marks gave significantly fewer reading errors. He also found that a dial with numerals at every scale division was superior to one with every fifth division numbered, provided the dial was viewed for as long as 1.5 seconds, but that the opposite was the case when 0.75-second exposures were used. This is consistent with Ford's (1949) discovery that the introduction of fine scaling on a CRT display resulted in an increase in scale-interpretation errors but a reduction in precision errors when readings were made in moderately rapid succession.

Patterns for signs and geometrical symbols. Geometrical figures differ considerably in legibility. Straight lines have been found to be more legible than curved ones (Mackworth, 1944). The triangle, the rectangle, and the square have been reported to be more easily recognized under conditions of low illumination and in peripheral vision than circular and hexagonal forms (Collier, 1931; Helson and Fehrer, 1932; and Whitmer, 1933).

The use of geometrical symbols and pictographic markers in place of verbal symbols often improves legibility and interpretability. Arrows indicating directions, for example, are better than RIGHT and LEFT, since many individuals are momentarily nonplussed when asked to turn to the right or left. Symbols must be chosen carefully, however. For example, Lauer (1947) found that under average daylight conditions the word STOP on a standard octagonal highway marker could be recognized before the shape was identified, whereas square or diamond-shaped highway signs could be identified from nearly twice the distance at which legends on them could be read.

Optimal form of letters and numerals. Studies of the visibility and legibility of isolated letters have given varied results. For example: Webster and Tinker (1935) found that American Typewriter type was visible at a greater distance than Scotch Roman type, but that the latter could be read about 5 per cent faster. They attributed this to the fixed spacing of typed copy, rather than to the style of individual characters.

There is little difference in the legibility of lower-case Roman and lower-case italic type, but most readers prefer the former. All-capital printing, however, results in about 12-per-cent slower reading than lower-case printing (Paterson and Tinker, 1940). In spite of this fact most decals and emergency instructions on instrument panels and machines are printed in all-capital type.

Studies of the relative visibility of different letters of the alphabet were undertaken as early as 1881 by Javal, a French oculist, who was interested in selecting characters to be used in testing eyesight. Roethlein (1912) carried out a very extensive study of the visibility of isolated characters, using sixteen different type faces. The results of all her work gave the following average rank order to the various upper- and lower-case letters of the alphabet, from most to least legible: WMLJI ATCVQ PDOYU FHXGN ZKERBS, and mwdjl pfqyi hgbkv rtncu oxaezs. Tinker (1928) reported that the correlations between results from thirteen different studies of the legibility of upper-case letters ranged from -0.58 to $+0.89$. For lower-case letters the range was $+0.48$ to $+0.88$. The letter L was frequently at or near the top in legibility, and the letter G was frequently at the bottom. Tinker concluded that the maximum of legibility is represented by the old Roman capitals, which are made up almost entirely of straight lines and sharp angles.

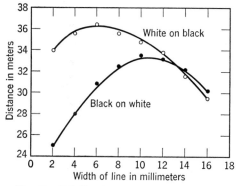

FIG. 5. Relation between stroke-width of numerals and the distances at which they can be read for two contrast relations. Data are for two observers. Note that relatively narrow white-on-black strokes gave optimum visibility. (From Berger, 1944a.)

The relative legibility of different numerals depends on the criterion employed as a legibility measure, the style of the numerals, and the figures with which they are associated. The numerals 0, 3, 6, and 9, all of which have curved outlines, are often confused with one another. In most studies the numeral 7 has been reported to have good legibility and visibility.

In the well-known Snellen test chart, the width of strokes is the same as the width of enclosed white spaces. Several investigations (Aldrich, 1937; Berger, 1944b; Bartlett, 1947; Lauer, 1947) have shown that a narrower stroke than this is desirable for best visibility. Recommendations for the width of strokes have varied from about 12 per cent to 25 per cent of the width of the letter or from approximately 8 per cent to 17 per cent of letter height. Aeronautical

standards for white-on-black numerals now call for a line width equal to 12.5 per cent of the numeral height when numerals are over $\frac{1}{8}$ inch in height, and a line width of 16.7 per cent of the height for smaller numerals. Berger (1944a) showed clearly that the stroke-width ratio giving maximum visibility varies considerably between white-on-black and black-on-white (see Fig. 5), and that white letters should have narrower strokes than black letters. Widths of lines for maximum visibility under the two contrast relations were 7.7 and 12.5 per cent, respectively, of numeral height. Loucks (1944b) found that for best legibility the stroke thickness should be increased for low brightness levels.

Designs specified for white numerals used on aircraft instruments are shown in Fig. 6C. Also shown are a set of black numerals

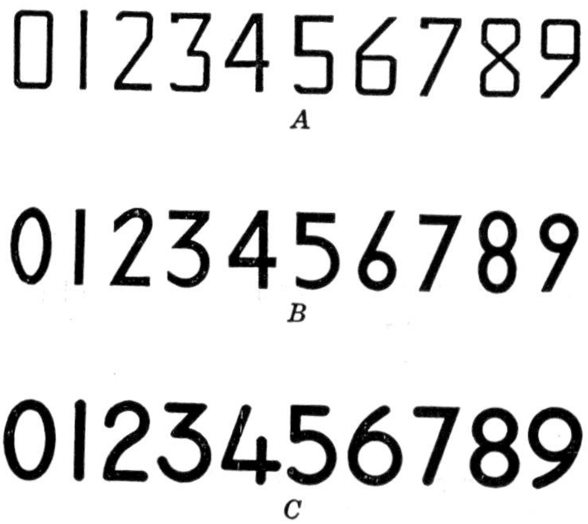

0123456789
A

0123456789
B

0123456789
C

FIG. 6. Numeral designs recommended for optimum legibility by (A) Berger (1944a), (B) Mackworth (1944), and (C) the Aeronautical Board.

developed during the war by Mackworth (1944) for use on air-raid plotting boards, and numerals designed and patented by Berger (1944a). Berger's numerals shown in Fig. 6A were designed to give optimum and equal visibility at a distance, when printed with white lettering on black, and diffusely lighted from the front. Both Mackworth and Berger made greater use of straight strokes than is customary in commonly used numeral forms. The slanting lines of Berger's numerals are usually at approximately 45 degrees.

The ratio of height to width of letters and numerals has been the subject of a few studies. Lauer (1947) concluded that block letters of equal height and width have best visibility. It is generally agreed that, when available width is limited, little or nothing is gained by using very tall characters. Aeronautical design standards, which require

Carmichael and Dearborn (1947) and will not be discussed here.

The role of meaning in the recognition of all types of patterns must not be overlooked. Words can be identified more quickly than single letters (Luckiesh and Moss, 1937), for example, and common first names can be read at distances where last names cannot be recognized (Walls, 1943).

Pointer position pattern as an aid to improved check-reading. Warrick and Grether

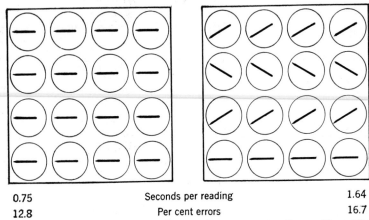

| 0.75 | Seconds per reading | 1.64 |
| 12.8 | Per cent errors | 16.7 |

Fɪɢ. 7. Instrument-panel arrangements that gave short check-reading times. (From White, 1949.)

a height-width ratio of 1 to 1 for the letter *W*, a ratio of 1.3 to 1 for *A*, *M*, and *4*, and a ratio of 1.5 to 1 for all other letters and numerals, appear to represent sound practice.

Proper spacing between letters is important for good visibility. A distance between letters equal to about half the average width of a letter was found to be optimum in one case (Lauer, 1947). Forbes and Holmes (1939) advocated graded spacing, depending on whether strokes of adjacent characters paralleled each other as in *NM* or *VA*, one stroke diverged as in *VN*, or both strokes diverged as in *VT* or *AA*.

Other problems involving pattern arrangement of printing, such as line width, spacing between lines, width of margins, and columnar arrangement, have been treated in detail by Paterson and Tinker (1940) and by

(1948) have shown that a significant gain in speed of check-reading results from patterned arrangement of instrument pointers. They found that if 16 instruments were arranged in a rectangular pattern, with the pointers of all instruments aligned at some cardinal position (such as 9 o'clock), as is shown in Fig. 7, the entire panel could be checked for deviations and a response switch operated in ¾ second. When the pattern was broken up into subgroupings of 4 instruments, response times increased to approximately 1.6 seconds. However, the latter condition still represents a marked gain over most present-day instrument panel arrangements.

Pointer design. Loucks (1944c), using standard black aircraft instrument dials with 1⅛-inch pointers, tried painting various lengths of the tip white. A pointer ³⁄₃₂ inch in width and painted white for nearly its full length was found to give fewer dial-reading errors for short exposure intervals than pointers with $\frac{7}{16}$-inch and $\frac{9}{16}$-inch white tips. Loucks also found that a standard $\frac{1}{18}$-inch long pointer could be reduced in width from $\frac{3}{32}$ inch to $\frac{1}{32}$ inch with no loss in legibility. The narrower pointer actually gave somewhat fewer errors when made to fluoresce under ultraviolet low-level illumination. This finding agrees with an earlier report by Maier (1931) who recommended that the pointer of stop-watch dials be narrower than the width of the scale marks. A narrow pointer has the further advantage that it covers up a smaller portion of any numeral that happens to lie beneath it.

The amount by which a pointer should overlap the scale, especially when scale-division marks are of different lengths, is a further problem. Vernon (1946) reported that dial-reading errors increased when the tip of the pointer was more than 0.5 inch from the scale. Parallax resulting from the height of the pointer above the scale is an additional factor that may lead to errors.

Number preferences. Kappauf (1949) has pointed out that strong preferences seem to exist for certain numbers and that this carries over into scale-reading tasks, especially if subjects must interpolate between scale divisions. Individuals appear to favor readings of 0, 2, 5, and 8 when interpolation is by tenths. Preferences can be controlled to some extent by training, and by designing displays that require a minimum of interpolation.

Black-on-white versus white-on-black. The relative merits of black characters on a light background, versus the converse arrangement, have been variously reported by investigators employing different criteria and different values for the interacting variables. The majority of studies employing visibility criteria have yielded results favoring the use of dark numerals on a bright background (Holmes, 1931; Lauer, 1933; Sumner, 1932; Taylor, 1934). However, Berger

(1944a, b) found that, if strokes of optimal width were used, bright numerals could be recognized under daylight illumination at about 9-per-cent greater distance by his 4 subjects than could dark numerals. Starch (1914) and Paterson and Tinker (1931, 1940) found faster reading with black print on white, and Taylor (1934) found that the use of black print led to fewer eye fixations per line than did the less familiar white type.

Two factors that influence the relative visibility and legibility of bright and dark characters are (1) irradiation and (2) the level of adaptation of the eye. Of course, width of lines interacts with the black-white relation.

Meaning and familiarity also play an important role in determining the relative superiority of dark versus bright stimulus objects. The factor of familiarity would be expected to favor black-on-white. Taylor (1934), using a visibility criterion, found that, the less meaningful the stimulus material, the more marked was the superiority of black-on-white printing, as indicated in Table 5. Thus it appears that familiarity

TABLE 5

Stimulus Material	Per Cent Superiority of Black-on-White
Words in sentences	11
Isolated words	17
Nonsense words	23
Isolated capitals	24
Combinations of letters i and l	33

with a particular stimulus pattern partially cancels out the advantage of the more familiar contrast relation.

Design of Quantitative Displays

The equipment-design problems considered in the preceding sections have been primarily concerned with visual discrimination processes. We turn now to questions that involve the ability to comprehend, interpret, or understand the information presented by visual displays. Errors of interpretation result from many complex and interacting factors, and they arise to some extent in the use of all types of displays. They are frequently large in magnitude and serious in consequence. Their elimination is often the most important consideration in the design of a display.

Direct display of numerical data. Quantitative data are commonly displayed either by means of counters and other devices that present numerical symbols directly, or by the position of a pointer on a scale. The advantages of the first of these methods are so obvious as scarcely to require elaboration. Whenever direct-reading displays have been compared with scale-and-pointer combinations, it has been found that individuals can obtain numerical information more rapidly from direct numerical displays. The latter are also relatively free from interpretation errors.

Why then does the design of quantitative displays present a problem? It is because displays must often serve multiple functions. Displays must be designed so that, in addition to being easy to read quantitatively, they will show the rate and direction of change of a variable, and will provide the sensory cues necessary for the performance of psychomotor tasks. For such multiple purposes a pointer-scale indication is often superior to a direct-reading numerical display. For example, it was found that an indicator could be turned to a new bearing more quickly when the cue for the response was the position of a cursor on a scale than when it was the value shown by a counter (Chapanis, Garner, and Morgan, 1949).

Interpretation of scales. Vernon (1946) investigated several systems for marking off scales. Errors in reading appeared to be influenced more by the values represented by major scale divisions (the modulus chosen for the scale) than by the values represented by the minor scale divisions. Relatively few interpretation errors arose when a scale modulus of 1, 10, 100, etc., was used. An optimum scale design was found

to be one with a major numbered graduation mark at each ten, and minor unnumbered division marks at each unit; or else one graduated by 100's and 10's or by some equivalent ratio. In a study of clock dials Grether (1948a) found that omission of numerals at any of the hour positions led to an increase in comprehension errors. It can be concluded that all major scale divisions should be numbered if possible.

Vernon found that scales having a modulus of 4 gave many errors. So did those with a modulus of 2 or 20, if the intervening spaces were marked off into fifths. Minor graduations that represented units of 2 were found to be satisfactory when the modulus of the scale was 10 and each major division was numbered. Other studies, however, have revealed that individuals may confuse minor scale divisions that increase by 2's with those that increase by 1's, particularly when minor division lines change in values from one part of the scale to another or when different scales are read in rapid succession. Chapanis (1947), using a polar-coordinate presentation, had subjects interpolate between range rings when values from 1000 to 10,000 yards were assigned to each ring. Readings with the 1000, 2000, and 10,000 scales were most accurate; those with the 3000 and 6000 scales were least accurate.

Scales that increase from right to left, or counterclockwise, are particularly susceptible to directional errors, such as reading 21 in place of 19 or reading 22 in place of 18. Christensen (1948) found that the use of a 'staircase' scale, on which the lengths of minor scale graduation marks increased in proportion to their numerical values, reduced the frequency of this particular error significantly. Whenever possible, however, counterclockwise scales should be avoided.

Interpretation of wide-range instruments. Instruments can be arranged on a continuum with respect to the number of discriminable differences they provide. At one end are the all-or-none indicators, such as *stop* or *go* signs, which provide only two categories of information. At the other end are displays, such as watches, that can be read in thousands of discrete steps. A watch, for example, if read to the nearest second, indicates a total of 43,200 different time steps during a 12-hour period.

read with an error of exactly 1000 feet. Bray (1948) reports that a serious error made in directing artillery fire was one of exactly 100 mils. Both these errors occurred because observers had to make a gross and then a vernier reading, in one

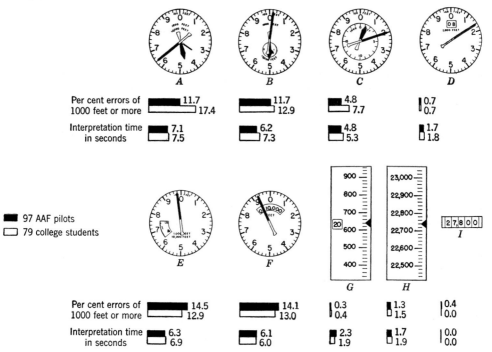

FIG. 8. Nine instrument designs for indicating quantitative values over a wide range. Some results are given for speed and accuracy of reading by two groups of subjects differing widely in experience. (From Grether, 1949.)

Devices for displaying large ranges of information include single dials with several concentric pointers, e.g. watches with sweep second hands, several one-pointer dials with different sensitivity, e.g. gas, water, and electric meters, and long scales affixed to moving tapes. Most of these devices use broken or divided scales that require the reader to combine data obtained from several sources, and they all are subject to errors of comprehension. It will be recalled (see Table 1) that the type of error described most frequently by aircraft pilots was one of misreading multiple-pointer instruments. The aircraft altimeter, for example, was often

case from separate moving pointers, in the other case from separate moving scales.

Following up the results of the critical-incident study described earlier, Grether (1949) investigated nine different designs (see Fig. 8) for presenting wide-range data in an effort to improve the altimeter. It is obvious from Fig. 8 that the differences between designs as revealed by group performance were much greater than the differences produced by several years of experience in using particular instruments.

Errors in reading the conventional three-pointer altimeter were classified into seven categories. These categories are given in

Table 6, together with the frequency counts for each in the pilot and college populations. Specific errors illustrating each category are

TABLE 6

CLASSIFICATION OF ERRORS MADE IN READING A MULTIPLE-POINTER INSTRUMENT *

N = 97 USAF PILOTS AND 79 MALE COLLEGE STUDENTS (SEE FIG. 9 FOR EXAMPLES)

Type of Error †	Per Cent of Errors	
	Pilots	College Men
A. Misinterpreting the value of a scale division.	5.8	7.1
B. Interchanging numerals.	4.0	5.5
C. Reading a value from a major scale division before it is reached.	4.4	3.7
D. Omitting the value indicated by one of several pointers.	0.3	2.3
E. Reading a value from a major scale division after that division has been passed.	0.3	2.3
F. Repeating the value indicated by a pointer.	1.0	0.8
G. Other complex, unclassified errors.	0.9	1.5

* Subjects read a sensitive aircraft altimeter, on which three concentric pointers represented hundreds, thousands, and tens of thousands of feet, respectively.

† Error descriptions have been modified slightly from those used by Grether (1949).

shown in Fig. 9. In only two of the seven types of errors was the frequency substantially less for the experienced pilot group. This finding demonstrates that design is often more important than training as a factor in instrument reading.

In the study under discussion the fastest and most accurate quantitative readings were made from the direct numerical display. The two designs that permitted the next best performances were the one combining a single pointer and a counter, and the one using a movable tape.

In practical situations the choice among designs will depend on considerations in addition to those of speed and accuracy in quantitative reading — considerations such as suitability for 'check-reading' and for quick detection of rate of change or direction of change of a variable.

Graphs and tables. Relative speed and accuracy in reading values from graphs, double scales, and tables are dependent upon factors that are similar to the ones discussed in the preceding sections. Reading a graph is similar in many respects to interpreting the value shown by a pointer on a scale. Table reading resembles the reading of a direct numerical display, although at times it may also require interpolation.

Carter (1947) had subjects work identical problems with various kinds of tables and graphs. The type of problem was found to interact significantly with the type of display. Problems requiring no interpolation were in all cases solved more quickly by the use of a table, regardless of the complexity of the numerical function. Problems requiring single or double interpolation, on the other hand, were solved much more rapidly by the use of graphs. Results for the function $y = x^2/c$, with c taking on four values, are given in Table 7. Note that

TABLE 7

Type of Problem	Problems Solved per Minute	
	Graphs	Tables
No interpolation	5.5	11.32
Single interpolation	4.4	2.6
Double interpolation	3.8	0.8

interpolation problems required very little more time than noninterpolation problems when subjects used a graph, but required fourteen times as long as noninterpolation problems when they used a table.

Characteristics of good quantitative displays. The foregoing facts support the hypothesis that the probability of an error in comprehension increases directly with the number of separate stimulus-response operations required of the subject.* Such an hypothesis has already been proposed to ac-

* A specific theory relating error frequency and number of S—R connections was proposed by W. F. Grether in a staff meeting of the Psychology Branch, USAF Aero Medical Laboratory.

count for the differential effect of short exposures on the legibility of instrument scales. It also offers a plausible explanation for the based on units, tens, hundreds, or thousands, rather than on intermediate values, and the large number of errors made in

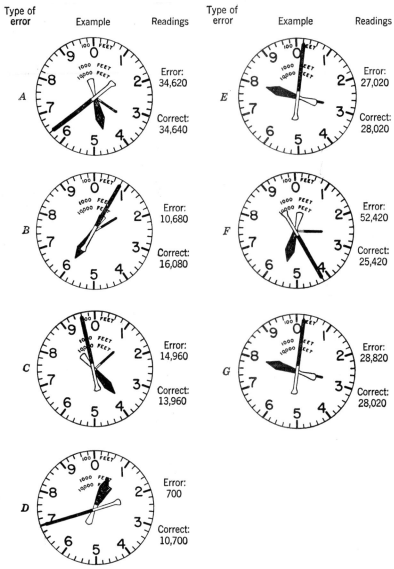

FIG. 9. Types of errors made in reading a three-pointer instrument (see Table 6). (From Grether, 1949.)

superiority of counters over scale-pointer combinations, the superiority of uniform over logarithmic or other nonlinear scales, the advantage of scales having a modulus reading instruments that require a synthesis of information from several sources. Grether (1948b) has suggested that absolute errors in interpolating between modulus points on a scale often increase inversely with the number of minor scale divisions, and that errors of comprehension increase directly with the number of minor divisions. Ford (1949) has reported experimental evidence that this happens. In a good all-purpose display we must compromise between these two opposed considerations, remembering that comprehension errors are usually large, whereas interpolation errors are usually small.

Displays for Spatial Relations

The advent of the air age with its tremendous speeds has made the display of spatial information of critical importance. The designing of displays to represent spatial relations such as direction, distance, and relative motion is, however, one of the most complex problems in engineering psychology. Numbers can be used to represent altitude, distance, and other spatial relations, of course, but there are many situations in which an overall 'pictorial' display is needed, rather than sets of numbers. Displays are needed to provide cues for the direct perception of spatial relations and for the performance of perceptual-motor tasks, such as the flying of an aircraft without any vision outside the cockpit.

Although it might seem that an ideal display would be one that exactly reproduced all the cues normally utilized in space perception, such a display would be difficult, if not impossible, to devise. And even if a complete situation display were provided, in some situations the unaided human eye would not be able to make all the necessary discriminations without supplemental information. An automobile driver, for example, relies on his speedometer for an indication of speed even when visibility is perfect.

Two solutions are possible. One is to provide both pictorial displays and supplemental quantitative displays. The other is to depict the essential spatial relations in a way that provides more precise information than is gained through unaided vision. One aspect of this second problem is to determine whether a schematic display gives a 'natural' indication, i.e. an indication to which the correct response is a *population stereotype* as demonstrated by its frequency of occurrence in the general population.

Population stereotypes in responding to directional cues. Several studies of direction-of-motion stereotypes have been carried out at Cambridge University (Vince, 1944; Vince and Mitchell, 1946; Mitchell, 1947, 1948). The motions of displays and controls were those made by pivoted pointers and levers. Responses were made to discrete stimuli appearing in rapid succession. When the operator tried to cause the display to move upward, it was found that the control movements from most to least effective were upward, forward, right or left, backward, and downward. Similar results were obtained when the operator's task was complicated by requiring him to carry on two concurrent activities. In general the effect of direction-of-motion relations was less marked in continuous than in discontinuous tasks, and less marked for the preferred than for the nonpreferred hand. Experimental

TABLE 8

RELATIVE EFFICIENCY OF DIFFERENT MOVE-MENTS OF A CONTROL LEVER IN RESPONSE TO AN UP-AND-DOWN DISPLAY MOVEMENT (FROM MITCHELL, 1947)

$N = 10$ SUBJECTS FOR EACH RELATION

	Average Number of Errors during 60 Trials	
Relation between Control Lever and Marker	In a One-Hand Task	In a Two-Hand Task
1. Upward control movement caused marker to move upward.	3.0	4.2
2. Forward (away from body) control movement caused marker to move upward.	4.5	5.3
3. Rightward control movement caused marker to move upward, combined with results obtained when a leftward control movement caused marker to move upward.	7.0	9.2
4. Backward (toward body) control movement caused marker to move upward.	6.8	11.1
5. Downward control movement caused marker to move upward.	8.0	11.9

results from one study are summarized in Table 8.

Fitzwater (1948) discovered that, when a clockwise movement of a control lever resulted in clockwise rotation of a pointer (in studied by Warrick (1947a, b). In one experiment responses were recorded while subjects were attempting to move a light to a center position on a display. All responses

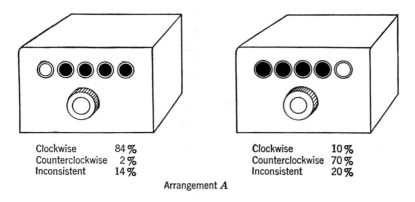

Clockwise 84%
Counterclockwise 2%
Inconsistent 14%

Clockwise 10%
Counterclockwise 70%
Inconsistent 20%

Arrangement A

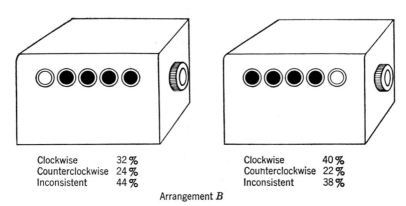

Clockwise 32%
Counterclockwise 24%
Inconsistent 44%

Clockwise 40%
Counterclockwise 22%
Inconsistent 38%

Arrangement B

Fig. 10. Population stereotypes for movements made in centering a light on a linear display by means of a rotary control. In arrangement A the control was in the same plane as the display; in B the control and display were in different planes. The light could be centered by turning the knob in either direction. The directions actually used by the subjects are tabulated. Note the preponderance of clockwise responses. (From Warrick, 1947a.)

sulted in clockwise rotation of a pointer (in the 12 o'clock sector), a significantly higher score was obtained in a continuous compensatory-pursuit task than when the same control movement caused a counterclockwise rotation of the pointer.

Population stereotypes in the operation of a variety of rotary controls in response to both linear and circular displays have been were rewarded, because the light could be centered by movement of the control in either direction. The apparatus and the results are shown in Fig. 10. Similar stereotypes were recorded by Carter and Murray (1947) for responses made in controlling the movements of a spot on an oscilloscope tube.

When controls and their associated displays were located on panels at right angles to each other, as shown in Fig. 10*B*, many individuals reacted to the same stimulus sometimes with a clockwise response, sometimes with a counterclockwise response. When displays were made in the shape of an arc, the subjects adjusted the controls more rapidly when they were required to rotate them clockwise in order to move the displays in a clockwise direction around the arc. For example, if it were desired to move

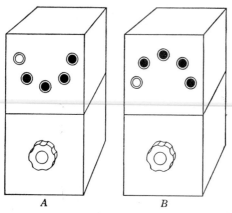

A   *B*

FIG. 11. Apparatus for studying the stereotypes of subjects in adjusting different arrangements of rotary controls and semicircular displays. (From Warrick, 1947*b*.)

the light on the display shown in Fig. 11*A* to the right (counterclockwise), the control was moved counterclockwise by most individuals. However, performance was not so stereotyped with this arrangement as it was with that shown in Fig. 11*B*.

Responses to directional cues are determined in part by configurational properties of the total visual field. Responses may depend upon whether the control is located to the right or left of the display, whether the control and display movements can be projected onto the same plane in space, whether control and display movements are rotary or translatory, and upon the dominance of various parts of the visual field. Duncker (1939), for example, showed that if a fixed point of light is observed within an oscillating rectangular frame, ob-

servers usually attribute motion to the light rather than to the frame and report that the direction of motion is opposite to what really exists.

Figure-ground relations. It is known that figure and ground relations sometimes become reversed. Such a reversal apparently occurs when an aircraft pilot switches from "contact" to "instrument" flight. As long as the pilot can see the earth, he perceives his own aircraft to be banking, climbing, or diving with respect to the stationary earth below. However, as soon as outside vision is excluded, the visible parts of his own aircraft, such as the instrument panel and cockpit enclosure, become the fixed background with reference to which the small moving parts of the instrument displays appear as figures.* He now responds in terms of an 'aircraft reference' principle.

Several observers have reported figure-ground reversals when watching the ground from a banking aircraft (MacLeod, 1940; Moore, 1940; Webster, 1940). When the earth was viewed through a near-by window, so that it subtended a relatively large visual angle, the aircraft was perceived to be in a bank; however, when a relatively small area of the earth was seen through a distant window, the aircraft was perceived to be level and the earth tilted.

The original flight attitude indicator, which was the prototype of most attitude instruments still in use, was designed with an "artificial horizon" bar that remained parallel to the earth's horizon during the roll of the aircraft (Fig. 12). It was thought that this use of the external-reference principle would give the pilot the impression that he was actually looking at the horizon and thereby reduce his "mental effort" (Poppen, 1936). It turns out that if the horizon bar is perceived as figure (instead of as part of the background) and is responded to in accordance with the population stereotype,

* Some experienced pilots, however, state that they have succeeded in preventing this reversal from taking place.

the pilot will move his control in the wrong direction and make a reversal error. Pilot reports show that this frequently happens during the early stages of flying training (Fitts and Jones, 1947b). Similar errors have been reported by men operating submarine diving controls where the same principle is used. Furthermore, two experimental studies (Browne, 1945; Loucks, 1947), agreed in showing that novices make fewer errors in responding to an artificial

Fig. 12. An artificial horizon used to give orientation information to pilots. The indication shown is that of a diving turn to the right. The long white line is a gyro-stabilized bar that represents the position of the earth's horizon.

horizon that must be interpreted in accordance with the aircraft-reference principle than to an indicator that must be perceived as a part of the background and interpreted in accordance with the external-reference principle.

Set and change of set in responding to directional indications. The important role of "set" in the interpretation of directional cues can be illustrated by one of the conditions investigated by Warrick (1947b). Subjects alternately adjusted two rotary controls, each of which governed a related semi-circular display. When clockwise rotation of the controls resulted in clockwise movement of the controlled objects, performance was superior to that recorded when clockwise control movements gave counterclockwise display movements. However, when a mixed arrangement was used, i.e. when a change of set was required between successive responses to the two controls, overall performance was inferior to that recorded under either of the two uniform conditions. Interestingly enough the greater number of errors in the change-of-set task was made in adjusting the control that operated in accordance with the population stereotype. An obvious conclusion from this finding is that all controls that must be operated in a rapid sequence should conform to a uniform direction-of-motion principle.

It must not be overlooked, however, that certain shifts in set can be made with little or no confusion if the total situation is favorable. For example, an individual who knows he is steering with a wheel seldom experiences any difficulty when he shifts his hand from the top to the bottom of the wheel, even though this requires a right-left reversal of his control movements.

Error information versus correction information. It has been proposed that a display should indicate how to correct an error rather than indicate the nature of the error itself. This proposition implies that behavioral processes are simplified if attention is directed to the movement to be made rather than to the error to be corrected.* This hypothesis has not been verified, however. Evidence cited earlier indicates that most individuals habitually respond to the movement of an indicator by executing a movement in the opposite direction. The typical individual apparently interprets a display as if it were an indication of error and responds to it as if to drive the error in the opposite direction. As a result of long experience it has been decided that the Landing Signal Officer on an aircraft carrier, for example, should hold his signal flags up when the approaching pilot is too high. Displays in most cases should indicate the direction of the error, not the direction of the movement to be made in correcting it.

Ambiguity of directional cues from circular displays. Rapid and accurate direc-

* This distinction is not comparable to that traditionally made between sensory and motor set.

tional responses cannot be made equally well to indications from all sectors of a rotary display. Warrick and Grether (1948) studied the ability of subjects to check-read panels of 16 circular instruments and to interpret as too much or too little the deviations shown by any instrument that deviated from a normal reading. When the normal pointed position was at 9 o'clock on the dial, performance was superior to that recorded when the normal position was at 3 o'clock.

Fitts and Simon (1950), utilizing a compensatory dual-pursuit apparatus, required subjects to keep the pointers of two instruments centered by operating two rotary controls. Pointer alignments at the 12, 3, 6, and 9 o'clock positions were compared. In the case of horizontal and vertical separation of the two circular instruments, the 9 and 12 o'clock positions, respectively, were found to give consistently higher performance scores than the 3 and 6 o'clock positions. Likewise, Connell and Grether (1948) and Long and Grether (1949) found a greater number of errors in verbal reports of the direction of change represented by a pointer movement when the movement occurred in the right or bottom quadrants of a circular dial than when it took place in the left or top quadrants. The inferiority of the right and bottom quadrants, as revealed by such findings, may be due to the conflict, in this part of a circular dial, between the principle of up or right to indicate an increase, and the principle of clockwise to represent an increase.

Moving pointer versus moving scale. A change in the magnitude of a value can be shown by movement of a pointer, by movement of a scale behind a fixed lubber line, or by simultaneous movement of both pointer and scale. The problem of designing a compass for use on a vertical instrument panel will serve to illustrate some of the directional ambiguities that are met in connection with each type of display.

A scale that moves behind a window or fixed lubber line permits the operator always to look at the same point in making a reading. An instrument designed in this way cannot be check-read easily, however, because the numbers on the scale must always be read before a response can be made. Furthermore, if scale values increase in a clockwise direction, then the scale must move in a counterclockwise direction in order to indicate an increase, whereas, if the scale is designed so that it rotates clockwise to indicate an increase, then values on it must increase in a counterclockwise direction. Neither alternative is a satisfactory one.

It is easy to check-read a moving-pointer instrument when the pointer is in the left or upper parts of the dial, but when the pointer is in the bottom or right quadrants reversal errors may sometimes occur, as was shown in the preceding section. Long and Grether (1949) and Loucks (1949a), assessing verbal and motor responses, respectively, to moving dials, moving scales, and moving pointers, found that a moving pointer in the upper half of a compass-type dial results in the fewest ambiguous responses.

Grid and coordinate systems. Two-dimensional coordinate systems are used on maps, graphs, television screens, and many other projection surfaces. Rectangular and polar coordinates are most common, but other systems are possible. Few studies have been made of the ability of individuals to interpret these various systems.

Compasses, maps, and terrain displays can be azimuth-stabilized; i.e. north can be made to appear always at the same point, such as the top; or they can be heading- or course-stabilized; i.e. the direction in which the reader is traveling or looking can be made to appear always at the same point, such as the top. Maps can be used with north at the top, or they can be rotated as the user turns. The advantages of the two systems with respect to the maintenance of orientation are still not clearly defined. Loucks

(1949*b*) found that novices became more seriously disoriented when using a rotatable map with a fixed-scale compass indicator than when using a fixed map. Much may depend on which principle one has been trained to use, and on whether an immediate motor reaction or a deliberate intellectual response is required.

Variations in magnitude. It is generally accepted that an increase in magnitude or a change from "off" to "on" should be represented by movement of an indicator or of a control device in a clockwise direction if motion is rotary; if motion is translatory, then by movement of the display or control upward, forward, or to the right. Although little experimental work is available on this topic, common practice seems to be sound. Clocks, thermometers, speedometers, and nearly all types of scales follow this convention. The directions employed in control movements are not so well standardized, however. Controls that follow opposite principles can be found on radios, stoves, locks, and many other common devices. These exceptions often lead to confusion. Switch positions on central telephone switchboards and in electrical substations, on the other hand, are standardized. Here one of the most useful principles is the use of the center or neutral position for "off."

Characteristics of good qualitative displays. Qualitative displays should conform to population stereotypes. The required interpretation should be in harmony with the configurational properties of the environment in which the display is to be used. The display should also conform to the sets required in interpreting related displays. The movement of a display should correspond wherever possible to the direction taken by the error and not the direction appropriate for corrective action.

Undoubtedly these requirements reflect the nature of the processes by means of which men orient themselves. In the design of qualitative displays, as was true for quantitative ones, the best display is one in which the fewest processes must intervene between the stimulus and the appropriate response. This topic is too complex, and too little is known of the processes involved in maintaining orientation, to permit formulation of any general theory to guide display design. There is need for a theory of spatial orientation that will synthesize the various findings in this area and provide a basis for a deductive approach to future design studies.

AUDITORY DISPLAYS

An on-off or pulsed signal, such as that produced by a policeman's whistle, is the simplest type of auditory display. It is possible, however, to transmit quite complex information by means of a temporal pattern of these on-off signals. Information may also be transmitted by amplitude, frequency, phase, or some other type of modulation of a carrier signal. Auditory signal systems make use of all these possibilities.

Auditory signals are almost always accompanied by other sounds (noise) that carry no useful information. Signal-to-noise ratio is the commonly used measure of the amount of noise interference present. In terms of statistical concepts of communication theory, noise level can be thought of as the probability that any discriminable signal does not represent transmitted information but is simply a fluctuation in the background. Because of the pervasiveness of unwanted sounds, the following discussion will deal primarily with auditory discrimination in the presence of noise.

As a means of introducing some of the design factors that influence signal intelligibility, it will be of advantage to take as an example a particular signal system. The low-frequency radio range will serve this purpose.

Discrimination of aural radio range signals. Radio range signals are produced by beamed radio signals modulated at 1020 cps and turned periodically on and off. The signal in one beam is on when that in the other is off, in such a way that, where the beams are of equal strength, a steady tone is heard. American radio ranges use the code letters *A* (dot-dash) and *N* (dash-dot) to identify the two beams. Pilots fly at assigned alti-

somewhat with the level of background noise.

The meaning of such data for a pilot flying a radio range is represented graphically in Fig. 13. Under the ideal conditions of no static, a pilot with normal hearing should be able to fly a course that would deviate

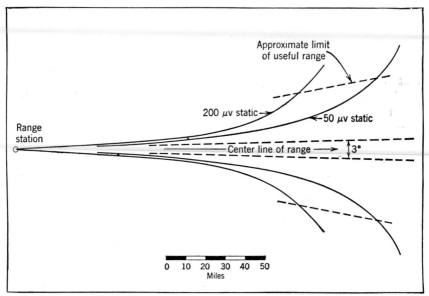

Fig. 13.   The effect of static on the effective width of the aural radio range.   (From Flynn et al., 1945.)

tudes along the edge of an air lane at a position where they are just able to detect the *A* or the *N* signal. They are separated from aircraft going in the opposite direction by the zone of steady tone, the width of which is inversely proportional to their ability to discriminate auditory signals.

Signal-to-noise ratio is one of the principal factors determining the discriminability of auditory signals. In one study (Flynn et al., 1945) the minimum intensity difference that permitted discrimination between *A* and *N* signals was found to vary from about 0.5 decibel at a favorable signal-to-noise ratio (50 decibels) to about 2.5 decibels at an unfavorable ratio (−10 decibels). The optimum signal intensity, however, varied

approximately 1.5 degrees from the center of the beam. This course is represented by dotted lines. At 150 miles from the range station he should be 4 miles off course. The solid lines in Fig. 13 represent the extent to which he might be driven off course by the presence of static. Thus at 150 miles with 50 microvolts of static he would have to be 16 rather than 4 miles off course in order to be sure that he was flying on the correct side of the beam.

It has been reported (Flynn et al., 1945) that a suitable filter permits a pilot to follow radio range signals in approximately 10 decibels more static than is possible without the filter (see Fig. 14). When a circuit is to be used for both code and voice reception, the best practice is to provide for the optional use of a band-pass filter for attenuating frequencies other than the code frequency, and a narrow band-elimination filter for attenuating the code sound when it is desired to use the system for voice communication.

Effect of signal pattern. Another way to improve signal intelligibility is to choose signal patterns that can be discriminated easily from one another. At one time an *E* (dot)

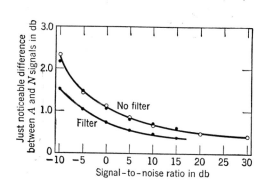

Fig. 14. Mean threshold values for discriminating *A* and *N* code as a function of signal-to-noise ratio. Note the superior performance resulting from the use of a selective filter. (From Flynn et al., 1945.)

and *T* (dash) keying system was employed on radio ranges used in Great Britain. Browne (1943) compared the number of errors made in recognizing the British *E-T* signals with the errors made with the American *A-N* system and found the latter to be superior. He also concluded that there is an optimum speed of transmission (approximately 24 letters per minute) above or below which accuracy of recognition suffers. The speed with which an individual can interpret code sounds, rather than speed of sending, is the factor that usually limits transmission rates.

Seashore and Kurtz (1944) analyzed 29,000 errors made by students in copying dot-dash code and determined the order of difficulty of code characters and the frequency of confusion between different pairs of characters. As was shown to be the case

with numbers, Seashore and Kurtz found definite preferences or population stereotypes for copying certain characters. Students tended also to write letters in place of numbers. It is of interest to note that the *E-T* pair was found to be more frequently confused than was the *A-N* pair.

Flybar. An interesting attempt has been made to devise auditory signals that can be substituted for visual cues in complex perceptual-motor tasks. The system has been called "Flybar" — flying by auditory reference — because of its application to aviation. It was first demonstrated as feasible in flight by de Florez (1936). Further research was undertaken at the Harvard Psycho-Acoustic Laboratory in order to determine how well continuous control adjustments could be made in response to different signal combinations, and how many simultaneous auditory signals could be responded to successfully (Forbes, 1946).

Various complex auditory signals were tried. Combinations of separate tones proved to be unsatisfactory, since subjects often become engrossed with one signal to the exclusion of the others. One moderately successful complex signal was devised. It combined the following three indications: (1) a "turn" signal that could be made to appear to sweep from right to left, or vice versa, by reason of an intensity shift between the two ears; (2) a "bank" signal that could be made to appear to tilt by means of a change in pitch of the carrier tone during each sweep; (3) an "air speed" signal that took the form of a "beep" at a rate that varied from 2 to 22 per second. This three-in-one signal was reported to be realistic and relatively easy to interpret. Subjects successfully 'flew' a Link instrument trainer on a straight course with only these auditory cues for guidance.

Voice communication systems. A great many psychological considerations enter into the design of equipment used for the detection, transmission, and reproduction of human speech sounds. In fact, this is the most important area in the design of auditory displays. But since the factors that influence the intelligibility of speech have been covered in earlier chapters, discussion of voice communication systems is omitted from the present chapter. For a further summary of research on a great variety of psycho-acoustic problems in the design of communication systems, the reader is referred to Miller, Wiener, and Stevens (1946).

Visual versus Auditory Displays

Developments such as Flybar, which substitutes auditory for visual cues, and new devices such as television and facsimile, which substitute visual displays for speech sounds, raise the question of the relative advantages of visual and of auditory displays. This general problem touches the display of all types of information.

Each sense modality has certain inherent advantages and disadvantages for the detection and analysis of different kinds of information. Audition is more nearly a continuous sense than vision; vision is basically selective and intermittent. As a consequence, audition is well adapted for the detection of warning stimuli that may arise at any moment from one of a variety of sources, whereas vision is well suited to the selection of and concentration on particular stimuli to the exclusion of others. Many other differences exist. Craik (1947), for example, pointed out that the ear is better than the eye in distinguishing a constant pattern from a varying background, such as the beating of a submarine's propellers in the total pressure pattern picked up by a sonar device.

Simultaneous use of two sense modalities. There are some tasks, such as the search for weak radar signals, in which simultaneous use of both visual and auditory displays may provide mutual reinforcement. The display of different information to different sense modalities, either simultaneously or in alternation, has been suggested by various writers. One of the chief arguments advanced in favor of this idea is that use of auditory cues in complex control tasks should lighten the heavy work load often carried by the eyes. This contention is plausible, but experimental data are lacking on important assumptions underlying it. In particular it has not been demonstrated in perceptual-motor tasks that it is easier to respond to a combination of visual and auditory data presented simultaneously, than to respond to the same information presented entirely by means of visual displays. Display systems employing two sense modalities may necessitate rapid fluctuation of attention between the two sense fields. If this is true, and if human perception is essentially a one-channel system, then the use of a mixed system may actually increase rather than reduce the load on the operator, at least for tasks that profit from continuous attention. However, once a skill reaches the level at which it becomes essentially automatic, it is possible that bimodal sensory control may become quite efficient. The hypothesis of a psychological refractory period, discussed in a later section, proposes that central or motor processes, rather than receptor processes, limit the speed of responses in continuous tasks. If this is true it is a further reason for doubting the advantage of bimodal displays. The judicious combination of visual and auditory displays in various kinds of tasks remains, however, an interesting, if relatively unexplored, possibility.

Visible speech. Recent developments indicate that it is feasible to transform electrical patterns of speech into two-dimensional visual intensity patterns (and perhaps patterns of color) which can be 'read.' This development is discussed in Chapter 26.

The converse of visible speech is the conversion of visual stimuli into an auditory pattern so that the blind can read or find their way about by the use of auditory cues. Considerable research is being directed at this problem.

TACTUAL DISPLAYS

Many of the skilled movements made in machine operation are guided by touch. It is desirable, therefore, to improve tactual displays as well as visual and auditory ones. One of the most obvious possibilities is to provide machine controls with knobs of distinctive shapes. Studies have been conducted to determine the advantages of shape coding and to discover what shapes provide adequate recognition cues.

Shape coding of control knobs. It has been shown (Weitz, 1947) that use of shape-coded control knobs lessens the amount of interference between conflicting position habits when an operator changes from one arrangement of controls to another. It is an advantage in this situation for the same knobs to be used on corresponding controls in the new arrangement as were used in the old one.

In order for coding to be effective, shapes must be used that can be distinguished easily from one another. An investigation by Jenkins (1947a) revealed some of the factors affecting recognition of control knobs.

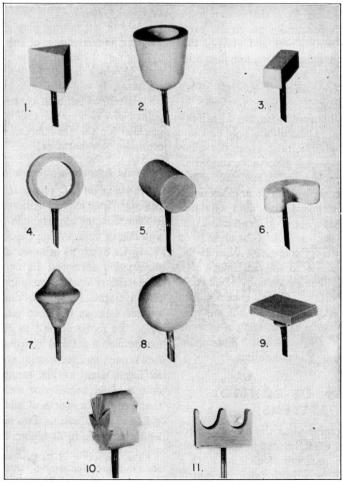

FIG. 15. Eleven knob shapes that are readily identified by touch. (From Jenkins, 1947a.)

If two objects of the same shape are mounted differently — for example, if one cube is mounted with a flat side up and another cube is mounted so that a corner is up — the two are often confused. The orientation of a shape by itself, it appears, is not a distinctive tactual cue.

It was also found that there are families of shapes, the members of which are frequently confused with one another, although they may be distinguished readily from shapes belonging to other families. For example, most shapes with sharp corners and plane surfaces, regardless of the exact number of sides, apparently belong to the same family. Eleven knob shapes that were recognized with practically no errors, even when subjects wore gloves and grasped the knob for only a second or so, are shown in Fig. 15.

Size and color coding of controls. Size and color coding have been proposed as further means for facilitating the identification of controls. Although multiple cues are theoretically desirable, neither size nor color offers a very practical means of coding controls. Size is a less useful cue than shape because one can recognize a great many more shapes of a standard size than one can identify different sizes of a standard shape. The use of color is limited because it is effective only when the operator looks at the control he is about to use, and then only when levels of illumination are sufficient to permit cone vision. Color, however, has many uses in coding both displays and controls as to function. The location of controls and their mode of actuation also serve as an important means of identification.

DESIGN OF CONTROL SYSTEMS

Man has progressed in the art of control from a state in which he used hand-held tools to fashion the products of civilization to a stage in which, by adjusting delicate control devices, he directs complex machine processes and governs the flow of energy to distant places. Man's role in a technological society is thus becoming more and more one of guiding and directing. Although the tools and simple machines employed by craftsmen can probably be improved somewhat, engineering psychology today should concern itself in large measure with the design of devices that permit individuals to exercise precise control over large sources of energy.

It is fitting, therefore, that psychological problems in the design of controls be introduced by a discussion of the transfer and application of force through mechanical and electrical systems. This brief excursion into the field of engineering may give the reader a better understanding of the problems met by engineers who must design control systems in which human beings perform critical acts. It will also introduce the reader who is unfamiliar with control theory to a point of view that holds considerable promise for the fundamental study of perceptual-motor behavior.

Dynamic Aspects of Mechanical Systems *

Transmission of forces through elastic bodies. The characteristics of an elastic system that are important in absorbing, dissipating, or transmitting the forces acting on it are its mass, its stiffness or rigidity, and the friction developed during its movement. These characteristics are referred to as system constants. The behavior of an elastic system depends on these constants as well as on the forces applied to it. This is true for simple mechanical systems that transmit forces only, and for control systems in which an input signal of low energy governs the output of an amplifier or some other device that provides a source of additional energy.

Lag and oscillation. Two important problems that arise in designing control systems

* The assistance of R. C. Gibson, Department of Electrical Engineering, USAF Institute of Technology, in formulating this section is acknowledged.

are lag and oscillation. Lag is evidenced by a time delay between the input and output sides of a transmission or control system. In systems subjected to cyclical inputs delay time often is expressed as the fraction of the cycle by which the output lags behind the input (phase lag). Lag is a universal characteristic of human motor behavior. It

The relation between the input and the output of a control system can be expressed as a function of time by means of a *system equation*. If such an equation is available, then the amount of lag and oscillation can be determined for any specified input. System equations can be employed to describe the behavior of large, complex systems, or of

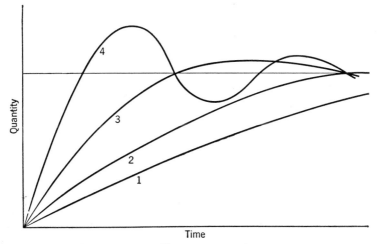

Fig. 16. Response curves illustrating different amounts of oscillation due to different damping ratios. Curve 1 illustrates overdamping, curve 2 critical damping, and curves 3 and 4 underdamping.

consists of reaction time plus movement time.

Oscillation is evidenced by an output that overshoots the correct position one or more times before it settles down. Oscillation, or "hunting," often results when high corrective forces are developed by or act upon members with large effective mass and relatively small energy-dissipating elements. As lag is reduced by the use of large initial forces, application of the exact amount of braking force needed to stop the movement at a precise point becomes more difficult and therefore oscillation tends to increase. If, after the initial disturbance, oscillation builds up in a control system, then the system is unstable. Response curves with different amounts of oscillation are illustrated in Fig. 16.

small units of a system. Often these equations can be determined for a total system even though the characteristics of some of its units are unknown.

System equations. A diagram of a simple system containing a mass, a spring, and a damper is given in Fig. 17A. If a time-varying force $f(t)$ is applied to the mass M, the internal opposing forces in the system may be equated to the applied force as

$$Kx + F\frac{dx}{dt} + M\frac{d^2x}{dt^2} = f(t) \qquad (3)$$

where x represents the position of the mass with respect to its rest position, dx/dt the velocity of the mass, and d^2x/dt^2 the acceleration of the mass at any instant. A special case, often called the transient solution, results if the mass is displaced from its rest position and released at a time arbitrarily called zero. Then the subsequent behavior of the system can be described by an equation of the form

$$Kx + F\frac{dx}{dt} + M\frac{d^2x}{dt^2} = 0 \qquad (4)$$

The mass may overshoot its rest position and proceed to oscillate with a decreasing

miliarly known as current. The transient performance of the mechanical system can be duplicated in the electrical circuit by making $e(t) = 0$ and placing an initial charge across the condenser at $t = 0$.

Once a system equation is set up, it can be solved by two general types of operations. One is to measure directly each of the constants in the system. This is not always

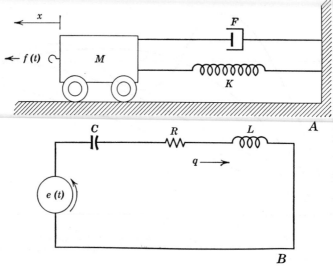

Fɪɢ. 17. Diagrams of (*A*) a simple elastic mechanical system, and (*B*) an analogous electrical circuit.

amplitude but a constant frequency (as a car does after hitting a single bump), or it may return to its former position slowly without oscillation, depending upon the relative values of the system constants of K, F, and M.

The dynamic behavior of a simple electrical circuit such as that shown in Fig. 17B can be described by the equation

$$Cq + R\frac{dq}{dt} + L\frac{d^2q}{dt^2} = e(t) \qquad (5)$$

in which K, F, M, x, and $f(t)$ are respectively replaced by capacitance C, resistance R, inductance L, electric charge q, and electromotive force $e(t)$. The term dq/dt then represents the time rate of change of electric charge and is more fa-

possible. The other approach is to apply known inputs to the system, to record the resulting outputs, and to infer the relative magnitudes of the system constants from these input-output data. In practice it is convenient to determine certain ratios between the system constants, such as the undamped natural frequency $\sqrt{K/M}$, and the damping ratio $F/2\sqrt{KM}$. Response curve 2 in Fig. 16, for example, has a damping ratio of 1 and is said to be critically damped. Curves 3 and 4 have damping ratios of less than 1 and are said to be underdamped. At present the methods commonly used by engineers in the determination of system equations from analysis of the relation between input and output depend upon an assumption of linearity. The concept of linearity as it applies to the human being is discussed in a later section.

Attempts have been made to describe the behavior of isolated muscle preparations and of intact human limbs by system equations (see Gilson, Walker, and Schoepfle, 1944; Fenn, 1938). The homeostatic processes and general neural activities of the body are also subject to analysis as rhythmic, dynamic processes (see Hoagland, 1949; McCulloch, 1949); so are certain aspects of receptor processes (see Main, 1950).

We have considered a few of the dynamic characteristics of simple physical systems and have seen that certain aspects of human behavior can to some extent be described in a manner analogous to that followed for physical systems. It may be possible, therefore, to analyze the total complex of human perceptual-motor behavior in this way. The human organism is a most complex example of a dynamic system combining electrical, chemical, and mechanical elements. As Searle and Taylor (1948) point out, it is likely that present equations, complex as they are, are still too simple to represent the processes involved in perceptual-motor tasks. Nevertheless the physical systems just described provide a suggestive model for the dynamic aspects of human controller tasks.

Control systems with feedback. The transmission links and control systems discussed thus far have been 'open' or one-way systems. To use a human analogy, these open systems resemble a patient with *tabes dorsalis* who can send signals to his arm muscles but, unless he watches the resulting movement, receives no return signals to tell him what his arm is doing. The most important, and for psychologists the most interesting control systems, however, are those with feedback loops. These are commonly called servo or slave systems. The behavior of a servo is governed, not by the input signal alone, but by the difference between the input and some function of the output. Before considering servo systems and the

dynamic aspects of total human controller tasks, however, it will be well to examine some of the more limited aspects of human motor behavior relating to the design of control systems.

Time and Force Patterns of Human Motor Responses

Every human motor response involves a distribution of force in time and space. This force is generated in the muscles and is transmitted to tools, levers, switches, steering wheels, and other objects by elastic transmission systems, the limbs. If we include only the limbs, the system is an open one that can be described adequately by reference to its equivalent mass, damping and stiffness. When we add sensory and neural processes the system becomes one with complex feedback loops. It is relatively simple to eliminate exteroceptive sensory feedback during motor performance, but it is exceedingly difficult to eliminate interoceptive feedback. Proprioceptive feedback loops are always active during normal motor responses.

Discrete corrective movements. If an individual moves his arm quickly from one point to another, he may undershoot or overshoot the point of aim. If the arm is carrying a heavy load, if damping or braking force is inadequate, or if the tenseness (gain or stiffness) of the muscles is too great, the time plot of the response may reveal a series of underdamped oscillations such as are shown in curves 3 and 4 in Fig. 16. The corrective responses made by skilled subjects to discrete stimuli may resemble curve 2 of Fig. 16, which shows no oscillation. But usually there is a succession of more-or-less discontinuous movements. Each movement may represent a separate effort to reduce the error to a subthreshold magnitude. Woodworth (1899) called the first of such a series of corrective movements an "initial impulse" and found that it lasted about 0.2 second. The phase during which discrete secondary corrective movements were made he called "current control." Most subsequent investigators have made a similar classification of the elements in adjustive movements. Woodworth reported a value of about 0.5 second for the interval between the initiation of successive adjustments during current control in a one-dimensional task. This figure agrees with later findings on the frequency characteristics of successive corrections during continuous one-dimensional tracking tasks.

Movements during continuous perceptual-motor tasks. Stetson (1905) classified rhythmical movements as slow or fast. In slow movements, groups of opposing muscles contract with uneven tension. In fast movements, both groups of opposing muscles may be under tension ("moving fixation"), or they may contract in alternation or "ballistically." When ballistic movements are made at a maximum rate the limb is literally thrown back and forth, single muscle contractions serving to check one movement and to initiate the next. Stetson and McDill pointed out that slow or controlled movements can be modified at any point in their course, but that this is not true for fast movements, especially ballistic or free movements like beating time with a baton. They observed that ". . . such a rapid movement cannot be subject to control after it is once started; movement elements occurring at the rate of 10 per second are the units; at most then movements can be modified not oftener than ten times in a second" (1923, p. 23). They concluded further that fast movements are predetermined by the preliminary adjustment or set of the individual.

Peters and Wenborne (1936), studying the time patterns of rapid arm movements executed in moving a stylus along a spiral path, concluded that control was accomplished by means of a series of more or less separate and successive variations in rate, and that these separate "motor impulse effects" were completely determined by processes that preceded each phase of the movement.

In certain situations a sequence of several movements appears to be released as a unit. Dodge (1907) thought that several eye movements were triggered off as a unit when one was reading, and Woodworth (1899) concluded that the same was true of arm movements in a dotting task. Barnes and others (1940), recording eye movements during the performance of skilled factory work, observed that, in acts ("therbligs") requiring visual guidance, the eyes left the scene of action 0.06 to 0.24 second before the action was completed.

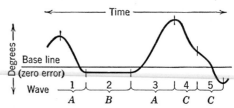

FIG. 18. Section of a tracking record showing three types of responses to a continuously moving target. *A* and *C* are successive position corrections; *B* is a 'rate tracking' response. (From Ellson, Hill, and Gray, 1947.)

Visually controlled aiming and tracking behavior usually shows a cyclic pattern with a mean frequency of about 2 responses or half-cycle waveforms per second when the tracking is in one dimension (Bates, 1947; Craik, 1947; Ellson, Hill, and Gray, 1947; Hick, 1948a; Tustin, 1947; Vince, 1948a).

Ellson, Hill, and Gray (1947) identified two types of tracking in a one-dimensional following-pursuit task in which the subject used a position control system. "Rate-tracking responses" appeared after the operator had achieved a relatively small position error, and they were evidenced by a rate of movement of the control handle that approximately matched that of the target (see Fig. 18). "Position-tracking responses" were evidenced by single or successive half-cycle waveforms, which were taken to be indicative of discrete control movements. It would appear, then, that skilled movements in continuous tasks are not under continuous visual control but, like the elements in discrete corrective movements, are triggered off in units.

Acceleration patterns during rapid control movements. Acceleration records sometimes reveal fluctuations in force that are too small or too rapid to be detected from simple

Smoothed samples of typical records of position, rate, acceleration, and rate of change of acceleration ("jerk") for a 9-inch movement to the right are shown in Fig. 19. The essential nature of the movement, which was initiated after a reaction-time lag of 0.44

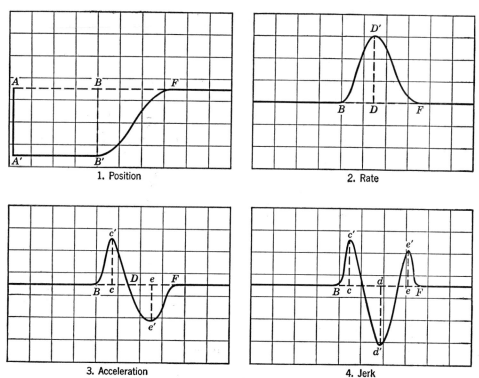

Fig. 19. Smoothed records of the (1) position, (2) rate, (3) acceleration, and (4) jerk (rate of change of acceleration) of a hand control for rapid corrections made in a tracking task. *A-B* is reaction time; *B-F* is movement time. (From Taylor and Birmingham, 1948.)

position curves. For this reason Taylor and Birmingham (1948) recorded the output from an accelerometer that was mounted on a relatively long (76-inch) control lever. Subjects watched a spot of light on an oscilloscope and tried to keep it centered by compensatory movement of the control lever. The spot jumped to one side or the other by an amount equal to 1.5, 3, or 6 degrees of visual angle; the appropriate response was a movement of 2¼, 4½ or 9 inches, respectively, in the opposite direction.

second and lasted for about 0.34 second, was described as follows:

. . . For approximately the first 0.07 sec. force in the direction of motion was applied at an increasing rate, then it was applied at a decreasing rate for another 0.07 sec., then braking force was applied at an increasing rate during the next 0.10 sec. and finally the negative force was applied at a decreasing rate for the last 0.19 sec. of the response. [P. 793.]

There were no ballistic-type movements in which agonists and antagonists showed short bursts of activity with intervening periods of no applied force. Movements appeared instead to be guided by continuously varying forces. Ellson and Hill (1947) likewise found no evidence of ballistic-type movements in muscle potential records taken during tracking. Evidence from several studies (de Montpellier, 1937; Taylor and Birmingham, 1948) indicates that the time devoted to the positive and negative phases of the acceleration curve varies with the nature of the control task, such as the relative importance of starting a movement quickly or of stopping it accurately.

Reaction time in perceptual-motor tasks. The delay time before a movement is initiated by a trained subject in response to a stimulus has been found to be independent of the rate, extent, or direction of the specific movement required by the stimulus, and also to be independent of speed-up instructions. It is difficult to measure the reaction time to particular stimuli occurring during continuous tasks, but reaction times to discrete stimuli in a series have been reported at values ranging from 0.23 to 0.50 second (Brown and Slater-Hammel, 1949; Ellson and Hill, 1948; James, Nichols, and Phillips, 1947, p. 360; Taylor and Birmingham, 1948; Tustin, 1947).

Proprioceptive reaction time is of particular interest here. Craik (1947) reported an experiment in which a lever had to be moved rapidly against a stiff spring so as to correct a misalignment. After individuals had learned the 'feel' of the control and were making fairly accurate movements, the spring tension was altered between responses so that they would tend to over- or undershoot. Under these conditions about 0.15 second elapsed after the beginning of a movement before the individual modified his response pattern to meet the changed resistance. Vince (1948b) obtained a figure of 0.16 second for proprioceptive reaction time in a somewhat similar experiment. Hick (1949), however, has questioned these short times and has shown that the inertia and elasticity of the limb are important factors whenever force must be increased in response to a second stimulus.

In many perceptual-motor tasks, especially those in which information must be secured from several different displays, the latency and perceptual span of vision are important factors. Dodge (1907) postulated the necessity of a "clearing-up" process which he believed precluded a succession of adequate visual fixations under 0.1 second each. Eye fixations in reading seldom are shorter than 0.2 second. More difficult discriminations than those made in reading impose even slower rates on the visual sampling process. Fitts, Jones, and Milton (1950), for example, found that aircraft pilots fixated individual instruments for 0.6 second on the average when making a blind landing. Travis (1936) found that the mean latency of eye movements in following a suddenly-appearing target was 0.20 second with a standard deviation of 0.02.

In general, then, it appears that responses to proprioceptive stimuli and simple following movements of the eyes take place in an interval approximately that required by simple sensory reactions, but that eye fixations and muscular responses during perceptual-motor tasks are often longer.

Psychological refractory phase. The hypothesis of a psychological refractory phase has been developed in reports from Cambridge University (Craik, 1947, 1948; Hick, 1948a; Vince, 1948a) and by some earlier workers (see Telford, 1931). For tasks requiring rapid corrective movements, this hypothesis holds that if two stimuli, S_1 and S_2, occur in rapid sequence, then the response called for by S_2 cannot be initiated until the primary movement in response to S_1 has been completed or until an appropriate time interval has elapsed. The exception has been proposed, however, that if S_1 and S_2 occur nearly together in time they may be responded to as a pair. The fact of cyclic motor responses in continuous tracking tasks has been cited as indirect evidence in support of this hypothesis. The most direct evidence, however, comes from experiments in which two discrete stimuli have been presented in rapid sequence.

Measuring the time required to initiate movements in each of two directions, and using stimuli separated by intervals varying from 0.05 to 1.6 seconds, Vince (1948a) found that responses to S_2 were delayed when S_2 followed S_1 by less than 0.3 second (approximately the reaction time). Ellson and Hill (1948), however, repeated Vince's study without finding support for the hypothesis.

It appears from the scanty data now at hand that there is often a real refractoriness when two stimuli occur closer together than a tenth of a second. At these very short intervals acceleration records reveal no changes in the typical force patterns elicited by S_1 for periods of at least $\frac{1}{10}$ second, regardless of the time of occurrence of S_2 (Warrick, 1948, unpublished data).

It is interesting to speculate that a refractory phase of greater than $\frac{1}{10}$ second may be a necessary condition for the learning of certain tasks. On the one hand, discontinuity and refractoriness may be characteristic of situations that favor the modification of behavior. For example, while an individual is learning a new skill he may respond, wait for knowledge of results, then respond again. On the other hand, in situations in which habitual modes of response are utilized he may respond continuously or nearly so. This point is also germane to the topic of linearity, to be discussed later.

Optimum Rates and Forces of Movements

Some tentative conclusions may be drawn regarding the optimum rates of movement and the optimum forces to be employed in operating controls. With the present state of knowledge, however, generalizations in this area must be made with caution.

Proprioceptive feedback. The ability of individuals to produce or discriminate variations in force, extent, and duration of movements, and in particular to utilize proprio-ceptive feedback, underlies their ability to insert these functions into a control task. Fullerton and Cattell (1892) concluded that the extent of a movement is more accurately judged than its force, and that force in turn is judged more accurately than duration. Woodworth (1901) found that discrimination of force and of extent, although related, are separate functions. Hollingworth (1909) found that the discrimination of extent and duration are also independent.

Others have suggested that one type of proprioceptive feedback is primary, and others secondary. Morgan (1917) reported that force applied in pulling a weight was judged in terms of the duration of the movement. Hick (1945b) suggested that, when an individual is operating a tracking control against viscous friction or its equivalent, better performance may result if he concentrates on generating a constant force rather than a constant rate. It has been proposed by Bates (1947) that force can be looked upon as the body's basic output quantity. In accordance with this hypothesis, he reasoned, velocity should be considered the single integral and displacement the second integral of force, and hence to generate a given velocity or a given displacement should in theory be a more complex operation than to generate a desired force.

The question of the body's basic output quantity has an important bearing on the design of control systems that provide optimum proprioceptive feedback: whether, for example, it is better to require large displacements with small variations in force, large variations in force with small displacements, or large variations in the duration of control acts without reference to their extent or force. Examples of each principle and of combinations of these can be found in many common control devices. Of even more general significance is the question of the relative importance of interoceptive versus exteroceptive feedback in control tasks and the optimum combination of the two. Visual control probably is very important while an individual is learning a new perceptual-motor task. As performance becomes habitual, however, it is likely that proprioceptive feedback or 'feel' becomes the more important.

Aeronautical engineers have followed the rule of thumb that 2 to 8 pounds of force applied to the controls should produce a maneuver involving an acceleration of $1g$. The gradient by which back pressure in a control system increases is especially critical in flying high-speed aircraft where a power boost is added to the controls and where there is a lag before the aircraft responds to the control movements (Orlansky, 1949).

Relation between speed and accuracy. Woodworth (1899) studied the relation between speed of movements and the accuracy with which they could be executed. When less than 0.5 second per movement was permitted, responses made with the eyes closed were about as accurate as those made with the eyes open. Slower speeds gave greater accuracy but about 1.5 seconds per response was sufficient for the completion of all secondary corrections. Still slower speeds failed to increase accuracy. Movements controlled by internal feedback alone (eyes closed) were about equally accurate at all speeds. In this case accuracy was determined chiefly by the initial response rather than by secondary adjustments. When the rate of each movement was constant, accuracy diminished as the interval between movements was increased. This was attributed to the fact that the delay between movements led to greater variability of the primary response and hence to a loss in accuracy. For stereotyped, repetitive movements, shortening the interval between responses resulted in increased uniformity. Woodworth concluded, "the path to skill lies in increasing the accuracy of the initial adjustment" (1899, p. 59). Vince (1948b) repeated and amplified Woodworth's study with similar results.

When subjects were urged to respond quickly but were allowed sufficient time to complete all secondary adjustments, Brown and Slater-Hammel (1948) found that the time for the initial movement was decreased, the time for secondary movements in some cases was significantly increased, and the correlation between primary and secondary movement times was negative. In subsequent studies by Brown et al. it was found that left-right movements gave shorter primary movement times than did inward-outward movements, but gave longer secondary movement times. These results confirm the assumption, based on the analogy of the mechanical system discussed earlier, that there is an optimum gain or stiffness for any response and that efforts to produce higher rates may lead to unfavorable muscular tenseness and loss of fine control.

Optimum rates of movement. The optimum rates of control movements are determined in part by such factors as the maximum rate of muscle contraction, the maximum rate of innervation, and the effect of fatigue. The maximum frequency attainable in repetitive movements of single limbs (such as tapping the finger or wagging the tongue) is approximately 10 per second. Fenn (1938) pointed out that the period of reciprocal movements is similar for different parts of the body and suggested that frequency is limited by the speed with which excitation and inhibition can be made to alternate in the central nervous system without a loss of precise control over the magnitude of the force. It should also be noted that an appreciable time — about 0.04 second in the human arm — is required for maximum tension to develop in a muscle.

High rates of movement are commonly required by handwheel controls. Winding movements are a combination of reciprocal movements properly distributed in phase. Their maximum rate is approximately half that of simple back-and-forth movements of similar amplitude. The rate that results in most accurate control depends on handwheel diameter, inertia, friction, and other design features, and on the type of target course.

Helson and Howe (1943a, b) concluded that there is always an optimum maximum speed. The maximum speeds recommended for different types of handwheels varied from 140 to 200 rpm. Some relations between tracking accuracy and speed of turning are shown in Fig. 20 for handwheels of 2.25 inches and 4.5 inches radius. Error in performance was measured in terms of the time that would be required for the target to move from the point of aim to its actual po-

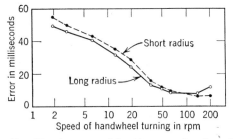

FIG. 20. Accuracy of tracking as a function of speed of handwheel turning. The two curves are for handwheels of 4.5- and 2.25-inch radii and are based on data from 14 subjects. (From Helson and Howe, 1943a.)

sition. Accuracy improved steadily with increasing handwheel speeds up to near the human breakdown point. The effect of handwheel diameter was relatively small. This finding agrees with the observation that variations in the amplitude of rhythmical movements have only a small effect on rate (Bryan, 1892; Stetson, 1905).

Optimum gear ratios. The ratio between the amplitude of movement of a control and that of its related display is important for tasks in which a control is adjusted intermittently. Jenkins and Connor (1949) investigated different gear ratios, using an apparatus that permitted variation in amplification over a range of 350 to 1 as well as variation both in control knob diameter and in the accuracy required in the adjustment of a pointer. Time was measured for the initial movement * (called "travel time") and for

* The time measurement was taken from the beginning of the pointer movement to the point

secondary movements (called "adjusting time").

The duration of the initial movement decreased as the gear ratio increased, until an optimum was reached where the pointer movement was large relative to that of the control wheel. Secondary adjustment time was at a minimum, however, when the pointer movement was small relative to that of the control wheel. The form of these relations (Fig. 21) was such that a ratio could usually be chosen to minimize the overall time required for primary plus secondary adjustments. This optimum ratio was approximately 1 revolution of the control knob for 1 inch of pointer movement. Variations in knob diameter made little difference in time scores. It should be men-

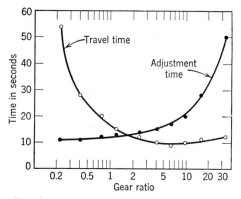

FIG. 21. Travel time and adjustment time for making discrete settings of a pointer by means of a rotary control, as a function of gear ratio. Points are the means of three subjects. Gear ratio is here defined as the pointer movement, in inches, per revolution of the control wheel. Minimum overall time was obtained for ratios between 1 and 2. (From Jenkins and Connor, 1949.)

tioned that quite different gear ratios may be optimum for other control tasks.

Searle and Taylor (1948) found that, when the ratio of hand movement to pointer movement in a linear tracking task was changed, individuals tended to compensate for the

where it reached the correct position, regardless of whether or not the correct position was overshot; thus underdamped responses gave the shortest time.

change and to produce a constant rate of pointer movement; i.e. they moved the control at a much higher rate when it was less sensitive.

Friction and inertia in controls. Friction that is independent of the speed of control motion (coulomb friction) often has an adverse effect on performance, particularly if it is large in relation to the mass, stiffness, and viscous friction in the system, but it

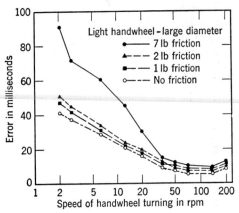

Fig. 22. Effect of friction on accuracy of tracking with a light handwheel of large diameter (six subjects). Other results indicate that the effect of friction is less marked when a heavy handwheel is used. (From Helson and Howe, 1943*b*.)

can seldom, if ever, be eliminated entirely. Helson and Howe (1943*b*) showed that coulomb friction increased the irregularity and average error of handwheel tracking. The effect was least pronounced when high velocities and large inertias were involved. Typical results are given in Fig. 22. For situations involving jolting, there is some evidence that coulomb friction actually has a beneficial effect (Hick, 1945*a*).

Friction that is proportional to the rate of movement (viscous friction) has been found, in contrast to coulomb friction, to be of advantage in many control systems. Inertia, in the form of either a heavy control or a heavy load moved directly by the human operator, may also improve performance in many situations. Some typical results from

Helson and Howe's studies of handwheel tracking are given in Table 9. Character-

TABLE 9

EFFECTS OF INERTIA AND HANDWHEEL DIAMETER ON TIME-ERROR SCORES IN TRACKING (FROM HELSON AND HOWE, 1943*b*)

N = 12 Operators

Handwheel Speed in Rpm	Large, Light Handwheel, 21 Psi	Large, Heavy Handwheel, 200 Psi	Small, Light Handwheel, 25 Psi	Small, Heavy Handwheel, 197 Psi
2.0	10.7	6.6	11.1	6.8
2.8	9.4	5.6	8.9	4.9
6.2	7.3	4.4	6.7	4.0
12.0	6.4	4.0	5.4	3.4
20.0	8.0	4.8	5.3	3.5

istic tracking records with different inertias are shown in Fig. 23. Accuracy improved as inertia was increased over a wide range of values. The limit to this favorable in-

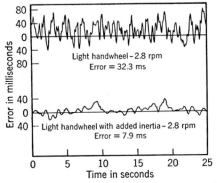

Fig. 23. Two typical tracking-error records, showing the smoothing effect of inertia. (From Helson and Howe, 1943*b*.)

crease was reached sooner for small handwheels, presumably because excessive force was required to accelerate loads with a control of small radius.

The beneficial results of viscous friction and of inertia are due to several factors. Friction and inertia tend to minimize the effects of small fluctuations in force and to damp out high-frequency oscillations. This effect becomes especially important under conditions of jolting and vibration. The operation of a control against viscous friction and inertia also provides a basis for discriminating small changes in the rate and acceleration of the load. This corresponds to the feedback of first- and second-derivative information, respectively, and enables the human controller to detect smaller variations in the position of the load than would otherwise be possible.

An open rotary transmission system is shown for comparison in Fig. 24B. The torque developed in this open system by the spring when θ_i is turned is equal to $K(\theta_i - \theta_o)$. This torque is opposed by the load and the viscous damping, J and F, so that

$$K(\theta_i - \theta_o) = F\frac{d\theta_o}{dt} + J\frac{d^2\theta_o}{dt^2} \qquad (8)$$

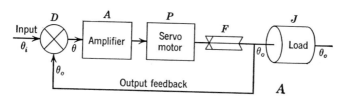

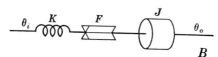

Fig. 24. Diagram of (A) a servo system with a single feedback loop, and (B) an open rotary transmission.

Operational Analysis of Motor Behavior

For some of the dynamic aspects of complete perceptual-motor processes, a simple servo system with feedback will serve as a model (see also Chapter 5).

A diagram of a servo system is shown in Fig. 24A. K and F represent stiffness and damping and J is the moment of inertia of the load. Energy for the servo motor P is supplied by the amplifier A. The error signal θ, which goes to the amplifier, is the difference between the input θ_i and the output feedback θ_o, i.e. $\theta = \theta_i - \theta_o$. The torque developed by the motor is equal to $AP\theta$. This torque is opposed by the load and the damping, J and F, on the output so that

$$AP\theta = F\frac{d\theta_o}{dt} + J\frac{d^2\theta_o}{dt^2} \qquad (6)$$

or, since $\theta = \theta_i - \theta_o$,

$$AP\theta_i = AP\theta_o + F\frac{d\theta_o}{dt} + J\frac{d^2\theta_o}{dt^2} \qquad (7)$$

Note that equations 7 and 8 are identical if $AP = K$. The amplifier and motor of the servo are, therefore, mathematically equivalent to a spring, except that the servo utilizes an external power source that is governed by the error. Note further that equations 7 and 8 are identical in form to those written for the systems in Fig. 17. It should not be construed from this, however, that all control or transmission systems are governed by this simple equation, but only that systems that are physically quite different, such as systems with and without feedback, may be mathematically identical.

As is true of the open transmission system considered earlier, a servo system is subject to lag and oscillation. If feedback is continuous, however, the amplifier is kept informed of the lag and oscillation in the output, and it governs the power supplied to the motor accordingly.

Servos may be continuous, as the one just described, or they may be intermittent. A special case of the intermittent system is the definite-correction or sampling servo, which measures the error at regular intervals and after each measurement applies a correction proportional to the error. Servos can be designed to act on different characteristics of the error signal. One possibility is to make the signal to the amplifier include integrals of the error as well as the error itself. This would predispose a system to disregard sudden changes in input and cause it to respond in part to the past history of the error. Another possibility is to make the input include derivatives of the error. This would predispose the system to respond to rates of change of the error and thereby cause it to anticipate the future course of the error. (For further discussions of servomechanisms see Brown and Campbell, 1948; James, Nichols, and Phillips, 1947; Lauer, Lesnick, and Matson, 1947; MacColl, 1945).

If we now substitute the human sense receptors, nervous system, and muscles in place of the servo, we have a somewhat analogous system. Input is the desired condition that the individual sets himself to achieve. Feedback is provided through the eyes, the ears, and the interoceptive channels from muscles, tendons, and joints. Error is the difference between the desired and the observed condition.

Linearity. The mathematical procedures for treating linear physical systems are widely used, but the mathematical treatment of nonlinear systems is so laborious that it is common practice to employ linear approximations provided the output of a system contains less than 10 per cent nonlinear elements. Consequently a practical consideration in applying operational analysis to human behavior is the question of the linearity of the human system. This is also a question of general theoretical interest.

For the present purpose it will suffice to define a linear system as one for which the superposition theorem holds. This theorem states that the response to any complex input is equivalent to the sum of the separate responses that would be made to the components of that input. In other words, it is possible to predict the response curve of a linear system to a complex time-varying input by summating the response curves given to separate components of the complex input (see Ellson, 1949).

It is well known that the human being is basically a nonlinear system. Among the most marked nonlinearities of human responses are the discontinuities associated with learning and change of set. A human being can adjust many of his 'system constants' to suit the task at hand. He can set himself to use different kinds of feedback. He can vary the tenseness of his muscles, the range of forces employed, and the timing of his responses. Phenomena such as sensory thresholds, sensory adaptation, and fluctuations in attention and motivation introduce still other nonlinearities. In spite of these obvious exceptions, however, there appear to be some situations in which human motor output is approximately linearly related to input.

It has long been known that some quick corrective movements require approximately the same time, regardless of their extent (see Stetson and McDill, 1923). For example, it requires about the same time for a man to write his name, regardless of whether he uses large or small strokes of the pen. We have already seen that the time required for successive movement responses in tracking is relatively independent of their amplitude. Some data illustrating this relation are shown in Fig. 25. These facts are consistent with the hypothesis of linearity, since response curves for the execution of large movements have a form approximately equivalent to that obtained by superimposing curves made in executing movements of smaller extent.

In testing for linearity it is common practice to record the output of a system in response to sinusoidal inputs. In a linear physical system, such as an alternating-current amplifier, the output contains only those frequencies that exist in the input. Ellson and Gray (1948) recorded human motor responses in following a simple sinusoidal stimulus motion. Subjects were able to match both the frequency and the amplitude of the stimulus up to a breakdown point in the neighborhood of 3 or 4 cps. Up to this point, therefore, human responses are essentially linear.

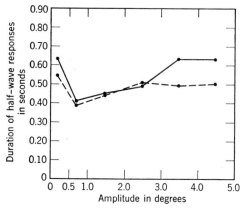

FIG. 25. Relation between duration and amplitude of control movements in a continuous pursuit task. Data are for 10 subjects. (From Ellson, Hill, and Gray, 1947.)

Experiments with discrete responses, of either a following or a compensatory nature, also throw light on the question of linearity. Large movements usually require somewhat more time to complete than do small movements (Brown and Slater-Hammel, 1949; Taylor and Birmingham, 1948). In the strict sense, therefore, these responses are nonlinear. It has also been noted that individuals tend to overcorrect for small distances or forces and undercorrect for large ones. This has been called the range effect. In a statistical sense individuals appear to cause the amplitude of responses to regress toward the mean of the range of responses of which they are members. Woodworth (1899) concluded that constant errors in judging the extent of a movement are minimal when several movements of similar extent are made in sequence, and Ellson and Wheeler (1949) showed that the direction

of the constant error is determined by whether the response is larger or smaller than other responses in the series.

Ellson and Gray (1948) made the interesting suggestion that human responses may be more linear for complex and unpredictable inputs than for simple and predictable ones.

In summary, successive responses made during continuous tracking are approximately linear in the sense that they have an approximately constant duration. Responses to simple sinusoidal target motions are approximately linear as long as the frequency does not exceed about 3 cps. (With these simple repetitive inputs, however, the results are probably accounted for by the subject's ability to recognize and compensate for repetitive stimulus patterns.) Discrete corrective responses, in contrast to continuous ones, have been found to be definitely nonlinear, movement time increasing somewhat as the extent of the movement increases.

System equations for the human controller. An objective of the study of human control dynamics is the determination of mathematical expressions for the stimulus-response relations in continuous sensory-motor tasks. Psychologists have not yet attempted this quantitative formulation of human behavior in controller tasks, but several engineers have proposed tentative system equations of this nature.

Raggazini (1948) and his associates required subjects to try to keep a spot centered on an oscilloscope by moving a set of control handles. In this type of compensatory-pursuit task the stimulus contains two components — the predetermined motion imposed on the target by the experimenter, and the motion produced by the tracker as he moves the control handles. At intervals, unknown to the tracker, Raggazini stopped the movement of the spot on the oscilloscope, opened the circuit so that the tracker had no control over the spot, and recorded the movements imparted to the control handle by the tracker during the next few seconds. In this 'open-loop' situation the stimulus remained fixed, but the subject presumably continued for a short time to behave as he would in a continuous 'closed-loop' control task. Raggazini decided on the basis of data obtained in this way that human tracking responses can be approximated by linear equations.

The equation proposed by Raggazini to describe the human response in this particular tracking task is

$$H = \left[\left(ap + b + \frac{c}{p} \right) e^{-p\tau} \right] A \qquad (9)$$

where A is the position of the stimulus as a function of time, and H is the motion of the operator's limb as a function of time. Equation 9 is written in operational form and is equivalent to the following equation written in a form more familiar to psychologists.

$$H = \left(a \frac{dA}{dt} + bA + c \int A \, dt \right)$$

delayed by one reaction time τ (10)

Equation 10 is a differential equation similar to equation 3 for the simple mechanical system. In the differential form there is no convenient notation for expressing the time delay introduced by the operator's response time, which makes the operational form of equation 9 preferable if an actual solution is desired. The terms a, b, and c are proportionality constants. Their relative values indicate the extent to which subjects respond to target rate, target position, and the integral of target position, respectively. Although his equation contains both derivative and integral terms, Raggazini concluded that derivative control is more difficult for individuals to develop than integral or proportional control and that orders of derivative control higher than the first are probably negligible.

This equation, then, states simply that the position of the operator's control handle at any moment is a function of target rate, target position, and the integral of target motion, all at some instant τ seconds earlier in time.

It has been proposed by Tustin (1947) that human responses contain basic elements that are linear or nearly so, plus subsidiary elements that take the form of random disturbances. If these disturbances are in fact random, then a "nearest linear law" may be determined. In order to arrive at a first approximation of this law, Tustin employed a following-pursuit task in which he imposed on the target a complex motion consisting of a fundamental frequency and two higher harmonics. This complex motion was

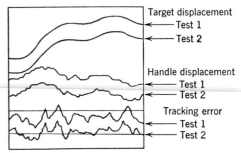

Fig. 26. Records of target displacement, control-handle displacement, and tracking error during two successive test runs by the same subject. (After Tustin, 1947.)

used in the hope that the subjects would not recognize the repetitive nature of the task. The subjects sat in a rotatable power-driven turret and operated three different types of rate-tracking controls. Simultaneous records of the target motion, the displacement of the operator's control handles, and the tracking error (discrepancy between turret and target) were obtained.

Records of control-handle movements for repeated segments of the same target motion were found to be quite similar. In Fig. 26 the target course, handle motion, and error curves are indicated for two successive runs by the same tracker. The similarity of successive records of handle movement is striking when it is remembered that the target error, to which the tracker was presumably responding, contained all the random elements that he himself had inserted, plus discrepancies introduced by the gun turret's servo system.

Records of handle position $h(t)$ and of error $e(t)$ were analyzed to determine the amplitude and phase differences of the subject's responses to the three frequencies contained in the complex target motion. For each frequency the ratio of amplitude of handle motion to amplitude of error signal was determined as well as the associated phase difference between handle motion and error. As a matter of convenience Tustin here considered the velocity of the tracker's hand motion rather than its position. He concluded that handle velocity was related to the stimulus, or error, in the following manner:

$$ph = [K(pT + 1)\epsilon^{-0.3p}]e \quad (11)$$

or when expressed in differential notation

$$\frac{dh(t)}{dt} = \left(KT \frac{de(t)}{dt} + Ke(t) \right)$$

$$\text{delayed by 0.3 second} \quad (12)$$

Integrating equation 12 we obtain

$$h(t) = [KTe(t) + K\int e(t)\, dt]$$

$$\text{delayed by 0.3 second} \quad (13)$$

which agrees with equation 10 if we let $b = KT$, $c = K$, $\tau = 0.3$ second, $A(t) = e(t)$ and $a = 0$, remembering that Raggazini felt that the derivative term in equation 10 was unimportant.

The fact that two engineers, using different tasks and analyzing their data by different techniques (transient and frequency analysis) reached similar conclusions is an encouraging indication that some aspects of behavior may be amenable to mathematical prediction. This approach may well be supplemented by other approaches such as that of Helson (1949) whose U-hypothesis "expresses the fact that organisms can adapt to a fairly wide range of stimulus values and function optimally within this range."

Effectiveness of Various Human Response Systems

The large differences between muscles with respect to strength, method of attachment to the limbs, and frequency of use lead us to expect significant differences in the efficiency with which various control tasks can be performed by fingers, arms, legs, or other body members. This expectation is confirmed by the finding that the arms gave higher scores than the legs in a continuous-pursuit task requiring precise and rapid compensatory movements (Grether, 1947b).

Studies of controls for computing gunsights furnish evidence that a large improvement in overall performance is possible through proper choice of the kinds of movements required for azimuth and elevation tracking, for ranging, and for triggering (Johnson and Milton, 1947; Bray, 1948). Engineers will be able to take full advantage of this freedom in designing control systems, however, only when the relative superiority of the various limbs, joints, and muscle groups has been fully determined.

The common notion that two hands are better than one is supported by data on position tracking with winding wheels (Helson and Howe, 1943c; Hick and Clarke, 1946) and for position tracking with a sight aimed directly at a moving target (Ellson and Craig, 1948). However, Brown, Slater-Hammel, and Bilodeau (1948) found that accuracy in making discrete corrective movements was not significantly different with one and with two hands, and that speed of primary movements was slightly less for both hands. The relative advantage of the independent movement of two separate controls versus the two-dimensional movement of a single control, when the task is to govern the movement of an object in two dimensions, has not been determined, although two-dimensional controls are considered to be superior and are generally used when this task must be accomplished by one man.

Controls can be designed so that their movement requires the use of different joints. Craik (1944) found that, when the amount of movement was expressed in degrees of rotation of the limb about its joint, the variable error decreased with increasing amounts of rotation up to about 2 degrees. Woodworth (1899) called attention to Goldscheider's evidence that sensitivity to angular rotation of the long and short bones is such as to give comparable thresholds for different joints when accuracy is measured in units of absolute arc distance at the extremity of the limb. According to this principle the shoulder should be able to discriminate more jnd's

right movements, however, showed little difference in accuracy.

Corrigan and Brogden (1949) required subjects to move a stylus along a horizontal slot 35 centimeters wide at the relatively slow speed of 3 centimeters per second without touching the sides of the slot and varied the starting point systematically in order to determine the accuracy for different direc

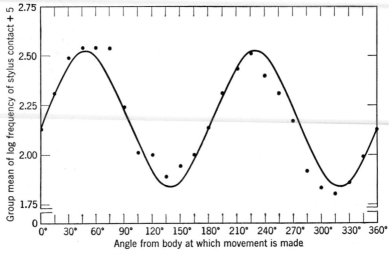

Fig. 27.   Precision with which a stylus was moved along a straight horizontal path as a function of the direction of the movement with respect to the body.   Data are for 48 subjects.   A smaller score represents greater accuracy.   (From Corrigan and Brogden, 1949.)

of angular movement than the other joints of the arm. From this it would seem that greater precision is attainable in a control properly designed for use by the entire arm than, let us say, in a control operated by the fingers alone. However, other considerations enter into such a practical question.

Accuracy of movements in relation to their origin, direction, and terminal point. When subjects moved a lightweight control along a track, movements away from the body were terminated more accurately than movements of equal extent toward the body (Brown, Knauft, and Rosenbaum, 1947). Upward movements tended to be too short in extent, whereas downward movements tended to be too long. Right-left and left-

tions of movement. Results from 48 subjects are represented graphically in Fig. 27. Movements directly away from the midline of the body are defined as being at 0 degrees (or 360 degrees). It will be seen from Fig. 27 that linear horizontal movements at 135 and at 315 degrees were made with greatest accuracy. If the marked sinusoidal relation between direction and accuracy of motion holds for other controller tasks, this finding has important implications for control design.

Accuracy in continuous-pursuit tasks, as a function of the location and orientation of the controls with respect to the body, has been studied by Grether (1947b). Fore-and-aft movements of a stick-type control and of a wheel gave a significantly better score than did side-to-side or rotary movements of the same controls. The degree of arm flexion used in operating the controls, however, was found not to be a significant variable provided the operator could move the controls without physical restraint. Thus it appears that operators can be permitted to take up any comfortable position they like in using a hand control.

Vertical, horizontal, and oblique positions of a handwheel gave equivalent efficiency in another tracking task (Helson and Howe, 1942). Similarly, it was found that accuracy in applying force against isometric controls was equivalent for four directions of arm movement (Jenkins, 1947b).

The ability to terminate a free movement with precision in three-dimensional space without visual guidance is important in many machine operations, such as in reaching for a control or an object. Fitts (1947) and Fitts and Crannell (1950) studied the accuracy of such movements as a function of the location of the reached-for object. Data were collected for 24 different targets located perpendicular to a line extending outward from the nearest shoulder and 28 inches away from the shoulder reference point. The reaching motion was initiated with the hands in a position in front of the body and slightly below shoulder height, a common starting point for many reaching movements. Results for a group of 20 college men on the last 3 days of a 12-day training session are given in Table 10. As a general rule localization was more accurate to areas toward the front, below shoulder height, and near the origin of the reaching movement. Most areas revealed distinctive constant errors in localization, the most common error being that of reaching too low.

In subsequent experiments, when reaching movements were initiated with the hands at the sides rather than in front of the body, it was found that targets directly forward were still localized most accurately, but the relative accuracy of location discrimination for various areas was considerably modified. When targets were located only 21 inches from the shoulder points, instead of 28 inches, the absolute accuracy of location discrimination was found to increase, although not by an amount sufficient to indicate that accuracy at different distances can be resolved to a constant angular error at the shoulder. . It appears, therefore, that point of origin, reaching distance, and terminal point all influence the accuracy with which a free movement can be terminated. A conclusion of practical importance is that controls ordinarily should be separated by at least 6 to 8 inches (three to four times the average error of localization) if a high degree of certainty is desired in 'reaching blind.'

Practical Problems in the Design of Controls

Many specific problems are encountered in the design of controls for various devices, and in the arrangement of controls for maximum convenience in sequential operations.

TABLE 10

Average Accuracy of 20 Practised Subjects in Reaching to Different Areas around the Body without the Aid of Vision. Accuracy is Expressed in Inches of Average Error at a Distance of 28 Inches from the Shoulder Point (from Fitts and Crannell, 1950)

| Location of Targets in an Up-and-Down Direction Relative to Shoulder Point | Location of Targets in a Left-Right Direction | | | | | | | |
| | Degrees to Left of Plane Cutting Left Shoulder Point | | | | Degrees to Right of Plane Cutting Right Shoulder Point | | | |
	135°	90°	45°	0°	0°	45°	90°	135°
Directly above the shoulder				1.9	2.0			
45° upward and outward	2.3	2.4	2.5	1.8	1.8	2.4	2.3	2.4
Level with the shoulder	2.5	2.3	2.1	1.2	1.1	2.2	2.2	2.4
45° downward and outward	2.0	2.3	2.0			1.8	2.4	2.2

No attempt will be made to deal systematically with all these questions. However, brief consideration is given to a few selected topics of practical importance in order to indicate how psychological data can be applied to practical problems.

Design of perceptual-motor tasks for efficient learning. The criterion of ease of learning is one of the most important for equipment design. According to existing facts and accepted theory, learning should progress most rapidly and reach the highest levels of efficiency when multiple feedback of information regarding the results of controller acts is provided, when discriminations are simple and interpretational processes are at their minimum, and when responses can be made directly to the stimulus position or magnitude, rather than to its integrals or derivatives. Learning should be most rapid also when the direction of movement, the mode of operation of controls, and the principles of instrument display agree with population stereotypes.

Arrangement of controls. The typewriter presents an example of a control arrangement problem. Although a standard typewriter keyboard has been in use for many years, the standard arrangement of the keys is poorly adapted to the nature of the typist's task. The work load on the different fingers varies greatly and is not related to differential finger strength or agility (Dvorak et al., 1936). Finding that 35 digraphs (two-letter combinations) account for half of all typing copy, Dvorak et al. devised an improved keyboard that permitted a maximum number of successive movements by fingers of the opposite hand or by nonadjacent fingers, and a maximum use of the "home row" of keys. This work provides an example of the use of "link values" in solving a specific design problem.

An excellent summary of principles of motion economy that can be applied in designing various controller tasks has been given by Hartson (1939) in a review of research dealing with skilled movements.

Nonlinear relations between controls and displays. In order to meet varied demands for speed and precision, adjustable or nonlinear gear ratios between controls and displays sometimes have been used. For example, low gear ratios have sometimes been provided at one end of a range of movements in order to assist the controller in executing small movements, rates, or forces, and high gear ratios have been provided at the other extreme in order to facilitate the application of large corrections. It has been shown (Vince, 1946) that, when an individual first encounters a control, he operates it as if he expects to find a linear relation between control motion and display motion. Although individuals can learn to operate nonlinear controls, considerable habit interference is experienced when it is necessary to shift rapidly between different controller tasks. Nonlinear controls should therefore be avoided whenever possible.

Tracking systems. When an individual moves a control device, such as a winding wheel, he may affect the position of the output member or the rate of its movement. In a position-control tracking system the operator must continue to move the control as long as the target moves; in a rate-control system, if he can adjust the control to a position that corresponds exactly to the target rate, he need do nothing more. Numerous other ways of utilizing human motor output are possible. In one system, known as "aided control," a given input produces both a change in output position and a change in output rate. If a watch had a single adjustment that would set the hands ahead when the watch had lost a few minutes and also cause it to run faster thereafter, the adjustment would make use of the "aiding" principle. The ratio of position to rate component in the output is known as the aided-control time constant, or aiding ratio. The optimum time constant of a system depends on the statistical distribution of rates it is called upon to follow, on the extent to which the operator can generate derivative control, i.e. respond to the rate of change of the error, and on the operator's reaction time, i.e. how large an error he allows to accumulate before he makes a corrective response. The more the operator can himself detect and respond to target rate, and the shorter his reaction time, the smaller will be the optimum time constant or aiding ratio (see James, Nichols, and Phillips, 1947, for a discussion of aiding ratio).

Stability. The problem of stability in control systems is largely that of minimizing lag (such as lag in instruments that provide visual feedback) and of adjusting the frequency characteristics of the mechanical part of the system to match the capabilities of the human operator over the expected ranges of input frequencies. Displays that combine data from several sources and show only the resultant, such as instruments that mix acceleration, rate, and position information, "aided-control" systems that utilize the position, rate, and acceleration characteristics of the controller's motor responses, and controls that provide direct (proprioceptive) feedback of information about the extent, rate, and accelerations of movements, offer promising means for increasing the inherent stability of man-machine systems. On the one side displays and proprioceptive feedback can be tailor-made to provide an input that is optimum for the operator. On the other side the control signals produced by man's muscular responses can be integrated, differentiated, or otherwise modified to produce an optimum input for the mechanical part of the system.

Time lag is closely related to instability. Lag at any point in a man-machine system increases the error in continuous control functions. For example, Warrick (1949) found that tracking accuracy decreased following the introduction of a transmission lag in the feedback of visual information, even when the lag was so slight that operators could not detect it. Considered in terms of continuous control process, time lags and inaccuracies are synonymous.

REFERENCES*

Aldrich, M. H. Perception and visibility of automobile license plates. *Highway Res. Bd. Proc.*, 1937, **18**, 393–412.

Armed Forces–NRC Vision Committee. *Standards to be employed in research on visual displays.* Ann Arbor: University of Michigan, 1947, 1–7.

Barnes, R. M., J. S. Perkins, and J. M. Juran. A study of the effect of practice on the elements of a factory operation. *Univ. Ia. Stud. Eng. Bull.* 1940, No. 22, 1–96.

Bartlett, F. C. The task of the operator in machine work. *Bull. ind. Psychol. pers. Pract., Melbourne*, 1947, **3**, 3–12.

Bartlett, N. R., and S. B. Williams. Signal mark size and visibility of radar signals on a plan position indicator. Special Devices Center, Office of Naval Research, Report 166-I-30, 1947.

Bates, J. A. V. Some characteristics of a human operator. *J. Inst. elec. Eng.*, 1947, **94**, 298–304.

Berger, Curt. Stroke-width, form and horizontal spacing of numerals as determinants of the threshold of recognition. I. *J. appl. Psychol.*, 1944a, **28**, 208–231; II. *Ibid.*, 1944b, **28**, 336–346.

Bray, C. W. *Psychology and military proficiency.* Princeton: Princeton University Press, 1948.

Brown, G. S., and D. P. Campbell. *Principles of servomechanisms.* New York: Wiley, 1948.

Brown, J. S., and W. O. Jenkins. An analysis of human motor abilities related to the design of equipment and a suggested program of research. In P. M. Fitts (Ed.), *Psychological research on equipment design.* Washington, D. C.: U. S. Government Printing Office, 1947.

Brown, J. S., E. B. Knauft, and R. Rosenbaum. The accuracy of positioning reactions as a function of direction and extent. Special Devices Center, Office of Naval Research, Report N5ori-57-1, 1947.

Brown, J. S., and A. T. Slater-Hammel. The effect of speed-up instructions upon the performance of discrete movements in the hori-

* All references cited in this chapter are unclassified. Many reports of wide psychological interest, such as those of the Applied Psychology Panel, National Defense Research Committee, and those from various Office of Naval Research contractors were still classified for military security reasons at the time this chapter was written.

Reports prepared under contract with the Office of Scientific Research and Development usually bear an OSRD Report number. In addition, many carry a PB number, which indicates that they may be obtained from the Office of Technical Services, U. S. Department of Commerce, Washington 25, D. C.

zontal plane. Special Devices Center, Office of Naval Research, Report N5ori-57-3, 1948.

Brown, J. S., and A. T. Slater-Hammel. Discrete movements in the horizontal plane as a function of their length and direction. *J. exp. Psychol.*, 1949, **39**, 84–95.

Brown, J. S., A. T. Slater-Hammel, and E. A. Bilodeau. Characteristics of discrete movements in the horizontal plane when executed with one and with two hands. Special Devices Center, Office of Naval Research, Report N5ori-57-5, 1948.

Browne, R. C. Comparison of British and American beam keying systems. British Flying Personnel Research Committee Report 418a, 1943.

Browne, R. C. Comparative trial of two attitude indicators. British Flying Personnel Research Committee Report 611a, 1945.

Bryan, W. L. On the development of voluntary motor ability. *Amer. J. Psychol.*, 1892, **5**, 128–204.

Buckingham, B. R. New data on the typography of textbooks. In *The thirtieth yearbook*. National Society for the Study of Education. Bloomington, Ill.: Public School Publishing, 1931. Part 2, pp. 93–125.

Carmichael, L., and W. F. Dearborn. *Reading and visual fatigue*. New York: Houghton Mifflin, 1947.

Carter, L. F. An experiment on the design of tables and graphs used for presenting numerical data. *J. appl. Psychol.*, 1947, **31**, 640–650.

Carter, L. F., and F. J. Dudek. The use of psychological techniques in measuring and critically analyzing navigators' flight performance. *Psychometrika*, 1947, **12**, 31–42.

Carter, L. F., and N. L. Murray. A study of the most effective relationships between selected control and indicator movements. In P. M. Fitts (Ed.), *Psychological research on equipment design*. Washington, D. C.: U. S. Government Printing Office, 1947.

Chapanis, A. Accuracy of interpolation between scale markers as a function of scale interval number. *Amer. Psychologist*, 1947, **2**, 346.

Chapanis, A. Theory and methods for analyzing errors in man-machine systems. *Ann. N. Y. Acad. Sci.*, 1949, **51**, No. 6.

Chapanis, A., W. R. Garner, and C. T. Morgan. *Applied experimental psychology*. New York: Wiley, 1949.

Christensen, J. M. The effect of a staircase scale on dial-reading accuracy. USAF Air Materiel Command Memorandum Report MCREXD-694-1P, 1948.

Christensen, J. M. A method for the analysis of complex activities and its application to the job of the arctic aerial navigator. *Mech. Engng.*, 1949, **71**, 11–16, 20.

Collier, R. M. An experimental study of form perception in indirect vision. *J. comp. Psychol.*, 1931, **11**, 281–289.

Connell, Shirley, and W. F. Grether. Psychological factors in check reading single instruments.

USAF Air Materiel Command Memorandum Report MCREXD-694-17A, 1948 (PB 95009).

Corrigan, R. E., and W. J. Brogden. The trigonometric relationship of precision and angle of linear pursuit movements. *Amer. J. Psychol.*, 1949, **62**, 90–98.

Craik, K. J. W. The psychological and physiological aspects of control mechanisms with special reference to tank gunnery. Unpublished report from the Applied Psychology Unit, Cambridge University, 1944.

Craik, K. J. W. Theory of the human operator in control systems. I. The operator as an engineering system. *Brit. J. Psychol.* (Gen. Sect.), 1947, **38**, 56–61; II. Man as an element in control systems. *Ibid.*, 1948, **38**, 142–148.

Dodge, R. An experimental study of visual fixation. *Psychol. Monogr.*, 1907, **8**, No. 4.

Duncker, K. Induced motion. In W. D. Ellis (Ed.), *Source book of Gestalt psychology*. New York: Harcourt, Brace, 1939.

Dvorak, A., N. I. Merrick, W. L. Dealey, and G. C. Ford. *Typewriting behavior*. New York: American, 1936.

Eastman Kodak Co. Influence of color contrast on visual acuity. OSRD Report 4545, 1944 (PB 33247).

Ellson, D. G. The application of operational analysis to human motor behavior. *Psychol. Rev.*, 1949, **56**, 9–17.

Ellson, D. G., and D. R. Craig. A comparison of a two-handed and several one-handed control techniques in a tracking task. USAF Air Materiel Command Memorandum Report MCREXD-694-2L, 1948.

Ellson, D. G., and Florence Gray. Frequency responses of human operators following a sine wave input. USAF Air Materiel Command Memorandum Report MCREXD-694-2N, 1948.

Ellson, D. G., and H. Hill. Action potentials during tracking. USAF Air Materiel Command Memorandum Report TSEAA-694-2I, 1947.

Ellson, D. G., and H. Hill. The interaction of step function stimuli: I. Opposed steps of constant amplitude. USAF Air Materiel Command Memorandum Report MCREXD-694-2P, 1948.

Ellson, D. G., H. Hill, and Florence Gray. Wave length and amplitude characteristics of tracking error curves. USAF Air Materiel Command Memorandum Report TSEAA-694-2D, 1947.

Ellson, D. G., and L. Wheeler. The range effect. USAF Air Materiel Command Technical Report 5813, 1949.

Fenn, W. O. The mechanics of muscular contraction in man. *J. appl. Physics*, 1938, **9**, 165–177.

Fitts, P. M. (Ed.). *Psychological research on equipment design*. Washington, D. C.: U. S. Government Printing Office, 1947.

Fitts, P. M., and C. Crannell. Location discrimination. II. Accuracy of reaching movements to twenty-four different areas. USAF Air Materiel Command Technical Report 5833, 1950.

Fitts, P. M., and R. E. Jones. Analysis of factors contributing to 460 "pilot-error" experiences in operating aircraft controls. USAF Air Materiel Command Memorandum Report TSEAA-694-12, 1947a.

Fitts, P. M., and R. E. Jones. Psychological aspects of instrument display. I : Analysis of 270 "pilot-error" experiences in reading and interpreting aircraft instruments. USAF Air Materiel Command Memorandum Report TSEAA-694-12A, 1947b.

Fitts, P. M., R. E. Jones, and J. L. Milton. Eye movements of aircraft pilots during instrument-landing approaches. Aero Eng. Rev., 1950, 9, 1–16.

Fitts, P. M., and C. W. Simon. The arrangement of instruments, the distance between instruments, and the position of instrument pointers as determinants of performance in an eye-hand coordination task. USAF Air Materiel Command Technical Report 5832, 1950.

Fitzwater, J. T. A study of the effects of rest pauses in perceptual-motor learning involving compensatory pursuit. Master's thesis, Ohio State University, 1948.

Florez, Luis de. True blind flight. J. aero. Sci., 1936, 3, 168–170.

Flynn, J. P., I. P. Truscott, S. J. Goffard, and T. W. Forbes. Auditory factors in the discrimination of radio range signals : Collected informal reports. OSRD Report 6292, Psycho-Acoustic Laboratory, Harvard University, 1945 (PB 19811).

Forbes, T. W. Auditory signals for instrument flying. J. aero. Sci., 1946, 13, 255–258.

Forbes, T. W., and R. S. Holmes. Legibility distance of highway designation signs in relation to letter height, letter width, and reflectorization. Highway Res. Bd. Proc., 1939, 321–335.

Ford, A. Types of errors in location judgments on scaled surfaces : II. Random and systematic errors. J. appl. Psychol., 1949, 33, 382–394.

Fullerton, G. S., and J. McK. Cattell. On the perception of small differences, with special reference to the extent, force and time of movement. Philadelphia : University of Pennsylvania Press, Philosophical Series, No. 2, 1892.

Gilson, A. S., S. M. Walker, and G. M. A. Schoepfle. The forms of the isometric twitch and isometric tetanus curves recorded from the frog's sartorius muscle. J. cell. comp. Physiol., 1944, 24, 185–189.

Grether, W. F. Survey of display problems in the design of aviation equipment. In P. M. Fitts (Ed.), Psychological research on equipment design. Washington, D. C. : U. S. Government Printing Office, 1947a.

Grether, W. F. Efficiency of several types of control movements in the performance of a simple compensatory pursuit task. In P. M. Fitts (Ed.), Psychological research on equipment design. Washington, D. C. : U. S. Government Printing Office, 1947b.

Grether, W. F. Factors in the design of clock dials which affect speed and accuracy of reading in the 2400-hour time system. J. appl. Psychol., 1948a, 32, 159–169.

Grether, W. F. Design of instrument dials for ease of reading. S.A.E. Quart. Trans., 1948b, 2, 539–545, 562.

Grether, W. F. Instrument reading : I. The design of long-scale indicators for speed and accuracy of quantitative reading. J. appl. Psychol., 1949, 33, 363–372.

Grether, W. F., and A. C. Williams, Jr. Speed and accuracy of dial reading as a function of dial diameter and angular spacing of scale divisions. In P. M. Fitts (Ed.), Psychological research on equipment design. Washington, D. C. : U. S. Government Printing Office, 1947.

Hanes, R. M., and S. B. Williams. Visibility on cathode-ray tube screens. The effects of light adaptation. J. opt. Soc. Amer., 1948, 38, 363–377.

Hartson, L. D. Contrasting approaches to the analysis of skilled movements. J. gen. Psychol., 1939, 20, 263–293.

Hecht, S., C. Haig, and A. M. Chase. The influence of light adaptation on subsequent dark adaptation of the eye. J. gen. Physiol., 1937, 20, 831–850.

Helson, H., and E. V. Fehrer. The role of form in perception. Amer. J. Psychol., 1932, 44, 79–102.

Helson, H. Design of equipment and optimal human operation. Amer. J. Psychol., 1949, 62, 473–497.

Helson, H., and W. H. Howe. A study of factors determining accuracy of tracking by means of handwheel control. OSRD Report 3451, The Foxboro Co., 1942 (PB 40617).

Helson, H., and W. H. Howe. Handwheel speed and accuracy of tracking. OSRD Report 3543, The Foxboro Co., 1943a (PB 40615).

Helson, H., and W. H. Howe. Inertia, friction and diameter in handwheel tracking. OSRD Report 3454, The Foxboro Co., 1943b (PB 40614).

Helson, H., and W. H. Howe. Relative accuracy of handwheel tracking with one and both hands. OSRD Report 3455, The Foxboro Co., 1943c (PB 40613).

Hick, W. E. Friction in manual controls with special reference to its effect on accuracy of corrective movements in conditions simulating jolting. Unpublished report No. 18. Applied Psychology Unit, Cambridge University, 1945a.

Hick, W. E. The precision of incremental muscular forces. Unpublished report No. 23, Applied Psychology Unit, Cambridge University, 1945b.

Hick, W. E. The discontinuous functioning of the human operator in pursuit tasks. Quart. J. exp. Psychol., 1948a, 1, 36–51.

Hick, W. E. The threshold for sudden changes in the velocity of a seen object. Unpublished report No. 88. Applied Psychology Unit, Cambridge University, 1948b.

Hick, W. E. Reaction time for the amendment of a response. Unpublished report No. 93, Applied Psychology Unit, Cambridge University, 1949.

Hick, W. E., and P. Clarke. The effect of heavy loads on handwheel tracking. Unqublished report No. 49, Applied Psychology Unit, Cambridge University, 1946.

Hoagland, H. Rhythmic behavior of the nervous system. Science, 1949, 109, 157–164.

Hollingworth, H. L. The inaccuracy of movement, with special reference to constant errors. Arch. Psychol., N. Y., 1909, 2, No. 13.

Holmes, Grace. The relative legibility of black print and white print. J. appl. Psychol., 1931, 15, 248–251.

Horton, G. P. Accuracy of reading target location and size of schematic PPI displays. USAF Air Materiel Command Technical Report 5961, 1949.

James, H. M., N. B. Nichols, and R. S. Phillips. Theory of servomechanisms. New York: McGraw-Hill, 1947.

Jenkins, W. L., and M. B. Connor. Some design factors in making settings on a linear scale. J. appl. Psychol., 1949, 33, 395–409.

Jenkins, W. O. Tactual discrimination of shapes for coding aircraft-type controls. In P. M. Fitts (Ed.), Psychological research on equipment design. Washington, D. C.: U. S. Government Printing Office, 1947a.

Jenkins, W. O. The discrimination and reproduction of motor adjustments with various types of aircraft controls. Amer. J. Psychol., 1947b, 60, 397–406.

Johnson, A. P., and J. L. Milton. An experimental comparison of the accuracy of sighting and triggering with three types of gun-sight handgrip controls. In P. M. Fitts (Ed.), Psychological research on equipment design. Washington, D. C.: U. S. Government Printing Office, 1947.

Kappauf, W. E. Studies pertaining to the design of visual displays for aircraft instruments, computers, maps, charts, tables, and graphs: A review of the literature. USAF Air Materiel Command Technical Report 5765, 1949.

Kappauf, W. E., and W. M. Smith. Design of instrument dials for maximum legibility: II. A preliminary experiment on dial size and graduation. USAF Air Materiel Command Memorandum Report MCREXD-694-1N, 1948.

Kappauf, W. E., W. M. Smith, and C. W. Bray. Design of instrument dials for maximum legibility: I. Development of methodology and some preliminary results. USAF Air Materiel Command Memorandum Report MCREXD-694-1L, 1947.

Kaufman, E. L., T. W. Reese, J. Volkmann, and S. Rogers. Accuracy, variability and speed of adjusting an indicator to a required bearing. Special Devices Center, Office of Naval Research, Report 166-I-MHC4, 1947.

Lauer, A. R. Factors which influence visibility in daylight and under artificial illumination. Proc. Ia. Acad. Sci., 1933, 40, 185.

Lauer, A. R. Certain structural components of letters for improving the efficiency of the stop sign. Highway Res. Bd. Abstracts, 1947, 17, No. 11.

Lauer, H., R. Lesnick, and L. E. Matson. Servomechanism fundamentals. New York: McGraw-Hill, 1947.

Long, G. E., and W. F. Grether. Directional interpretation of dial, scale and pointer movements. USAF Air Materiel Command Technical Report 5910, 1949.

Loucks, R. B. Legibility of aircraft instrument dials: The relative legibility of tachometer dials. AAF School of Aviation Medicine Project 265, Report 1, 1944a.

Loucks, R. B. Legibility of aircraft instrument dials: A further investigation of the relative legibility of tachometer dials. AAF School of Aviation Medicine Project 265, Report 2, 1944b.

Loucks, R. B. Legibility of aircraft instrument dials: The relative legibility of various climb indicator dials and pointers. AAF School of Aviation Medicine Project 286, Report 1, 1944c.

Loucks, R. B. Legibility of aircraft instrument dials: The relative legibility of manifold pressure indicator dials. AAF School of Aviation Medicine Project 325, Report 1, 1944d.

Loucks, R. B. An experimental evaluation of the interpretability of various types of aircraft attitude indicators. In P. M. Fitts (Ed.), Psychological research on equipment design. Washington, D. C.: U. S. Government Printing Office, 1947.

Loucks, R. B. The relative effectiveness with which various types of azimuth indicators can be interpreted by novices: I. USAF Air Materiel Command Technical Report 5957, 1949a.

Loucks, R. B. An experimental comparison of the relative effectiveness with which two types of map-reading procedures can be utilized by novices. USAF Air Materiel Command Technical Report 5963, 1949b.

Luckiesh, M., and F. K. Moss. The science of seeing. New York: Van Nostrand, 1937.

MacColl, LeRoy. Fundamental theory of servomechanisms. New York: Van Nostrand, 1945.

Mackworth, N. H. Legibility of air raid block letters and numbers. Unpublished report FPRC 423, Applied Psychology Unit, Cambridge University, 1944.

MacLeod, R. B. Spatial disorientation during landing of airplane. Science, 1940, 92, 604.

Maier, E. Zur Bestgestaltung der Zifferblatter von Stoppuhren. Industr. Psychotech., 1931, 8, 97–113.

Main, R. The dynamic characteristics of the semicircular canals. J. comp. physiol. Psychol., 1950, 43, 309–319.

McCulloch, W. S. The brain as a computing machine. Elect. Eng., 1949, 68, 492–497.

McFarland, R. A. Human factors in air transport design. New York: McGraw-Hill, 1946.

Mead, L. C. A program of human engineering. Personnel Psychol., 1948, 1, 303–317.

Miller, G. A., F. M. Wiener, and S. S. Stevens. *Transmission and reception of sounds under combat conditions.* Summary Technical Report, NDRC Division 17. Washington, D. C., 1946. Volume 3.

Mitchell, M. J. H. Direction of movement of machine controls. III. A two-handed task in a discontinuous operation. Unpublished report from the Applied Psychology Unit, Cambridge University, 1947.

Mitchell, M. J. H. Direction of movement of machine controls. IV. Right or left-handed performance in a continuous task. Unpublished report No. 85, Applied Psychology Unit, Cambridge University, 1948.

Montpellier, G. de. Note sur l'accélération dans les mouvements volontaire de la main. *Arch. Psychol., Genève,* 1937, **26,** 181–197.

Moore, A. D. Perceptual disorientation during landing of airplane. *Science,* 1940, **92,** 477–478.

Morgan, C. T. Human engineering. In W. Dennis (Ed.), *Current trends in psychology.* Pittsburgh : University of Pittsburgh Press, 1947.

Morgan, J. J. B. The speed and accuracy of motor adjustments. *J. exp. Psychol.,* 1917, **2,** 225–248.

Orlansky, J. Psychological aspects of stick and rudder controls in aircraft. *Aero. eng. Rev.,* 1949, **8,** 1–10.

Paterson, D. G., and M. A. Tinker. Studies of typographical factors influencing speed of reading. VI. Black type versus white type. *J. appl. Psychol.,* 1931, **15,** 241–247.

Paterson, D. G., and M. A. Tinker. *How to make type readable.* New York : Harper, 1940.

Paterson, D. G., and M. A. Tinker. Influence of size of type on eye movements. *J. appl. Psychol.,* 1942, **26,** 227–230.

Paterson, D. G., and M. A. Tinker. Eye movements in reading type sizes in optimal line widths. *J. educ. Psychol.,* 1943, **34,** 547–551.

Paterson, D. G., and M. A. Tinker. Eye movements in reading optimal and non-optimal typography. *J. exp. Psychol.,* 1944, **34,** 80–83.

Payne-Scott, Ruby. The visibility of small echoes on radar PPI displays. *Proc. Inst. Radio Eng.,* 1948, **36,** 180–196.

Peters, W., and A. A. Wenborne. The time pattern of voluntary movements. *Brit. J. Psychol.,* 1936, **26,** 388–406 ; **27,** 60–73.

Poppen, J. R. Equilibria functions in instrument flying. *J. aviat. Med.,* 1936, **7,** 148–160.

Preston, K., H. P. Schwankel, and M. A. Tinker. The effect of variations in color of print and background on legibility. *J. gen. Psychol.,* 1932, **6,** 459–461.

Raggazini, J. R. Engineering aspects of the human being as a servomechanism. Unpublished paper presented at the 1948 meeting of the American Psychological Association, 1948.

Reese, T. W., J. Volkmann, S. Rogers, and E. L. Kaufman. Special problems in estimation of bearing. Special Devices Center, Office of Naval Research, Report 166-I-MHC2, 1948.

Roethlein, B. E. The relative legibility of different faces of printing types. *Amer. J. Psychol.,* 1912, **23,** 1–36.

Rogers, S., J. Volkmann, T. W. Reese, and E. L. Kaufman. Accuracy and variability of direct estimates of bearing from large display screens. Special Devices Center, Office of Naval Research, Report 166-I-MHC1, 1947.

Searle, L. V., and F. V. Taylor. Studies of tracking behavior. I. Rate and time characteristics of simple corrective movements. *J. exp. Psychol.,* 1948, **38,** 615–631.

Seashore, H., and A. K. Kurtz. Analysis of errors in copying code. OSRD Report 4010, 1944 (PB 12170).

Sleight, R. B. The effect of instrument dial shape on legibility. *J. appl. Psychol.,* 1948, **32,** 170–188.

Starch, D. *Advertising.* New York : Scott, Foresman, 1914.

Stetson, R. H. A motor theory of rhythm and discrete succession. I. *Psychol. Rev.,* 1905, **12,** 250–270.

Stetson, R. H., and J. A. McDill. Mechanisms of the different types of movement. *Psychol. Monogr.,* 1923, **32,** No. 3, 18–40.

Stevens, S. S. Machines cannot fight alone. *Amer. Scientist,* 1946, **34,** 389–400.

Sumner, F. C. Influence of color on legibility of copy. *J. appl. Psychol.,* 1932, **16,** 201–204.

Taylor, C. D. The relative legibility of black and white print. *J. educ. Psychol.,* 1934, **25,** 561–578.

Taylor, F. V., and H. P. Birmingham. Studies of tracking behavior. II. The acceleration pattern of quick manual corrective responses. *J. exp. Psychol.,* 1948, **38,** 783–795.

Telford, C. W. Refractory phase of voluntary and associative responses. *J. exp. Psychol.,* 1931, **14,** 1–35.

Tinker, M. A. Relative legibility of letters and digits. *J. gen. Psychol.,* 1928, **1,** 472–496.

Travis, R. C. The latency and velocity of the eye in saccadic movements. *Psychol. Monogr.,* 1936, **47,** No. 2, 242–249.

Tustin, A. The nature of the operator's response in manual control and its implications for controller design. *J. Inst. elec. Eng.,* 1947, **94,** 190–202.

Vernon, M. D. Scale and dial reading. Unpublished report No. 49, Applied Psychology Unit, Cambridge University, 1946.

Vince, Margaret. Direction of movement of machine controls. Unpublished report FPRC 637, Applied Psychology Unit, Cambridge University, 1944.

Vince, Margaret. The psychological effect of a non-linear relation between control and display. Unpublished report SRI 2, Applied Psychology Unit, Cambridge University, 1946.

Vince, Margaret. The intermittency of control movements and the psychological refractory period. *Brit. J. Psychol.* (Gen. Sect.), 1948a, **38,** 149–157.

Vince, Margaret. Corrective movements in a pursuit task. *Quart. J. exp. Psychol.*, 1948b, **1**, 85–103.

Vince, Margaret, and M. J. H. Mitchell. Direction of movement of machine controls. II. Unpublished report from the Applied Psychology Unit, Cambridge University, 1946.

Walls, G. L. Factors in human visual resolution. *J. opt. Soc. Amer.*, 1943, **33**, 487–505.

Warrick, M. J. Direction of movement in the use of control knobs to position visual indicators. In P. M. Fitts (Ed.), *Psychological research on equipment design.* Washington, D. C.: U. S. Government Printing Office, 1947a.

Warrick, M. J. Direction of motion preferences in positioning visual indicators by means of control knobs. *Amer. Psychologist*, 1947b, **2**, 345.

Warrick, M. J. Effect of transmission-type control lags on tracking accuracy. USAF Air Materiel Command Technical Report 5916, 1949.

Warrick, M. J., and W. F. Grether. The effect of pointer alignment on check-reading of engine instrument panels. USAF Air Materiel Command Memorandum Report MCREXD-694-17, 1948.

Webster, D. L. Perceptual disorientation during landing of airplane. *Science*, 1940, **92**, 603–604.

Webster, H. A., and M. A. Tinker. Influence of type face on legibility of print. *J. appl. Psychol.*, 1935, **19**, 43–52.

Weitz, J. The coding of airplane control knobs. In P. M. Fitts (Ed.), *Psychological research on equipment design.* Washington, D. C.: U. S. Government Printing Office, 1947.

White, W. J. The effect of dial diameter on ocular movements and speed and accuracy of check-reading groups of simulated engine instruments. USAF Air Materiel Command Technical Report 5826, 1949.

Whitmer, C. Z. Peripheral form discrimination under dark-adaptation. *J. gen. Psychol.*, 1933, **9**, 405–419.

Williams, S. B., N. R. Bartlett, and E. King. Visibility on cathode-ray tube screens: Screen brightness. *J. Psychol.*, 1948, **25**, 455–466.

Woodworth, R. S. The accuracy of voluntary movement. *Psychol. Monogr.*, 1899, **3**, No. 3.

Woodworth, R. S. On the voluntary control of the force of movement. *Psychol. Rev.*, 1901, **8**, 350–359.

36

Work and Motor Performance

ROBERT H. SEASHORE

Northwestern University

The term *motor* refers primarily to action, that is, to the activity of the nerves running from the central nervous system to the muscles and glands, and particularly to the activities of the muscles and glands themselves. Behavior normally includes sensory, affective, and intellectual processes, as well as the motor activities of muscles and glands.

The term *work* is here defined as any overt motor performance, regardless of its vocational or recreational significance. Even though work and play may be the extremes of a continuum the distinction between them rests primarily upon the motivation involved rather than upon a fundamental difference between their motor aspects.

Muscular actions may be studied biophysically in terms of the physical and chemical aspects of cells, organs, and their patterns of interaction. Such studies are a joint interest shared by psychology with physiology, biochemistry, and other biological sciences, and the actual experimental literature is found in the journals of these fields. The principal interest of most psychologists lies in the biosocial or behavioral level of description of muscular activities. This interest is also shared with other sciences and technologies, such as physical education, motion-and-time study, education, and business and industry.

CLASSIFICATION OF MUSCULAR ACTIVITIES

It is useful to distinguish between the *gross* motor coordinations of athletics and certain outdoor vocations and the *finer* coordinations involved in other manual skills, because many of the experimental findings related to them differ in important ways. In fact, anyone faced with a problem of motor skill should begin by asking whether it involves predominantly gross or fine coordinations, because the answer to this question often determines what type of investigation or practical solution may be appropriate to the problem. For example, Cozens (1929) showed that there is a moderate intercorrelation between gross motor skills of athletic types, and McCloy (1935) and Wendler (1938) have further analyzed such correlations by the factorial method. The author's own data show no significant relation between gross and fine motor speed skills.

Fine motor coordinations are those in which the factor of strength is secondary to speed or precision, or both. The size of the movements is usually smaller, as in typing, and the activity is concentrated in the limbs or other small musculatures. The role of the trunk muscles is largely that of maintaining relatively stationary postures or of orienting the limbs toward the work area, which is usually a desk, a bench, or a machine.

Both gross and fine coordinations may be classified with respect to their relative emphasis on timing, spatial precision, and strength. Theoretically there could be almost any combination of these three factors, e.g. a relatively slow, nonprecise, but powerful activity, as in shoveling snow, or a very fast but not particularly precise or powerful activity, such as operating a safety control lever on a machine. In some actions, such as talking, neither rate, precision, nor strength may be crucial, whereas in still others, such as a long shot in basketball, all three factors may need to be skillfully combined. From these examples it is apparent that these aspects of movements — size, timing, precision, and strength — are really continua. It is only at the extremes that we find distinctive differences.

Within each class of motor activity we may further distinguish two types of performance, namely: *single action* in which one coordinated response follows a given stimulus pattern, and *serial action* which may involve either a chain of more or less unitary responses or a continuous "pursuit" type of coordination. An example of single action is the classical reaction-time experiment in which the carefully instructed subject awaits the stimulus that releases the response. Actually, of course, the movement of the hand in depressing the key is only the most striking part of the response, and many other background activities, such as postural tension, are involved.

Typing is an example of the chain type of serial action. It can be analyzed into a series of relatively discrete strokes upon the various keys. Such chain reactions are known as serial-discriminative responses, and they make up a large proportion of all practical skills. Differing from serial-discriminative action is the continuous or pursuit type of adjustment involved in steering a car. Actions of the pursuit type are commonly involved in piloting, whether of automobiles, airplanes, or ships. Pursuit activities are also important in many operations such as cutting or sewing cloth, painting or carving art forms, and in many athletic activities such as open-field running in a football game.

Motor Aspects of Mechanical Abilities

In considering the nature of skills we must be critical of the widely used concept of "mechanical abilities." Normally such abili-

ties are quite highly specialized. In the building of a house there are involved at least half a dozen mechanical trades: cement finishers, carpenters, lathers, plasterers, plumbers, electricians, painters, etc. We rarely find one person competent in all these skills. Nor do we expect the members of the construction trades to be particularly expert in repairing automobiles. Our industrial civilization would quickly founder without the specialized mechanical abilities of its citizens.

No doubt a great deal of this specialization in abilities is a matter of different kinds and amounts of training in the separate fields. The question then remains, are certain people significantly better qualified than others to undertake training in any one of these specialized mechanical fields because of certain aptitudes for acquiring such skills rapidly and continuing on to higher levels of attainment? There is little evidence that any particular type of physique is essential to success in the acquisition of mechanical skills, nor is there any significant amount of evidence that scores on athletic performance, or on fine motor tests that emphasize speed or precision of hand movements, are related to such mechanical skills as operating or assembling or repairing machines. Nor is there any significant evidence that general intelligence is either positively or negatively correlated with performance on mechanical tasks. The only two measurements that have been shown to be related to the acquisition of skill on even a few mechanical operations are those of spatial visualization (Paterson et al., 1930) and the comprehension of mechanical tools, parts, and mechanisms (Bennett, in Buros, 1949). A later section will review the specific findings on the measurement of the mechanical abilities.

INTERRELATIONS AMONG ABILITIES

The history of differential psychology shows a rather steady progression in the classification of human abilities away from very broad groupings of related performances. In the eighteenth century the German faculty psychologists classified human abilities under rather broad groupings such as the faculty of memory, the faculty of concentration or attention, will power, etc. These classifications had the merit of recognizing some specialization among human abilities, but the particular groupings described have since been broken down into more basic categories that are not at all closely correlated. Thus a person might be outstanding in ability to remember the names of other people, but only average, or inferior, in remembering the visual appearance of their faces or their figures. Similarly, memory span for consonants is not closely related to memory span for digits, and neither of them is closely related to other types of memory for verbal materials.

Perhaps the best summary of the actual interrelations of human abilities is given in Thorndike's sentence: "In general, desirable human characteristics are slightly, but positively, correlated." Thorndike's phrase, "in general," means that when we consider large enough groups of persons we find that desirable characteristics are slightly but positively correlated. The word "slightly" indicates that the typical coefficient of correlation between various human abilities is of the order of 0.15 to 0.25, and the phrase "but positively" indicates that good qualities tend to go together.

Thorndike's dictum leads us to expect that a prediction from one ability to another will be only slightly better than chance, a finding that has been demonstrated over and over again, ever since the first experiments of Cattell, around 1900, on the interrelations of sensory acuities, reaction time, and scholastic achievements of students at Columbia University. Failure to recognize the applicability of Thorndike's principle has resulted in much wasted effort in personnel-selection programs. Only with verbal abilities has there been any great success in the prediction of individual differences in rate or extent of acquisition of complex practical skills.

INTERRELATIONS AMONG FINE MOTOR SKILLS

In order to answer the question "What are the various kinds of motor skills, and how are they interrelated?" it is first necessary to define the four basic terms, skills, abilities, aptitudes, and capacities.

1. *Skill.* A person's effectiveness in terms of end results, e.g. speed, precision, strength, a qualitative characteristic (such as rhythm), or a combination thereof. The degree of skill is dependent upon the particular work method employed. Furthermore, of two persons attaining the same end results, the one that does so at a lower energy cost is said to be the more skillful.

2. *Ability.* What one is *able* to do in a given performance at a given time. Synonymous with present skills, but often misused in the sense of ultimate capacity.

3. *Aptitude.* An individual's probable rate, or possible ease, of learning a skill. It is to be noted that: (*a*) Aptitudes are ordinarily quite stable but may change as a result of training. (*b*) Rapidity of learning is positively correlated with high ultimate capacity. (*c*) High aptitude leads to ease in terms of low energy cost per unit of output. (*d*) Interest and satisfaction in the exercise of potential ability are easily developed. (*e*) Aptitudes are relatively specific, or, at most, are related only within small groups.

4. *Capacity.* A person's maximal *potential* effectiveness in terms of end results (i.e. speed, precision, strength, qualitative characteristic, or a combination thereof) that may be achieved by using a given work method after optimal training. Capacity further connotes that: (*a*) The functional limit is based on anatomical and physiological constants of separate organs involved in the given work method and on their integration through neural and humoral systems. (*b*) Conversely, change to a work

method involving a different set or organs would result in a different capacity. (c) A change in work methods alone, utilizing the same organs, could still change the capacity. (d) The capacity is relatively stable for each work method, owing to the stability of the anatomical and physiological characteristics involved. (e) Although there are minor variations due to age, health, and motivation, the individual tends to retain his relative ranking among others subjected to the same working conditions. (f) Optimal training includes both direct and transferred training under expert supervision. (g) Adequate tools, materials, and working conditions are assumed. (h) Since capacity refers to a *potential* limit, it can only be *inferred*. This limit can be estimated only by extrapolation of an individual's learning curve for a particular skill, on the assumption that his curve will develop in about the same way as those of other learners. These learning curves are probably asymptotic to a hypothetical ultimate level. And (i) initial *rate* of progress is thereby assumed to be significantly and positively correlated with ultimate capacity.

Capacity, then, is not a very useful concept, since a person's capacity in a given skill can only be *inferred*, and it is not defined so that it can be readily observed. In most cases the concept of aptitude is more useful.

From these definitions we see that the term "ability" is practically synonymous with level of skill, so that they may often be used interchangeably. The term "aptitude" refers to any structural or functional asset that gives a man a head start in the acquisition of a given skill, and, conversely, a low degree of aptitude may be thought of as a handicap. The term "capacity" involves so many assumptions that, aside from theoretical analyses, it is more likely to be confusing than helpful. At best, it represents a hypothetical concept that can rarely be demonstrated experimentally.

It may be appropriate to point out the fallacies commonly involved in the psychological use of the term "capacity." The term has its analogue in the physical sciences where the structure of a machine determines its maximum effectiveness. Thus a windmill pump will raise an amount of water per minute that is strictly determined by the velocity of the wind, and its capacity is readily defined. But the analogy between the human organism and a simple mechanical system overlooks the complexity and adaptability of the human machine. Our sense organs, our nervous systems, and our muscles and glands *can be used in a great variety of ways.* Furthermore these various modes of using our biological equipment result in different levels of efficiency in terms of end results. Another name for these different ways of using our physical structures is *work methods.*

It follows from the great variety of these work methods and their various efficiencies that measurements of any single aspect of structure are not very helpful in predicting the amount or quality of the work done. The greater importance of work methods, as compared to structural characteristics, is indicated by the following sets of experiments, in each of which one of the possible factors underlying individual differences is varied while the remaining factors are held constant. The reasoning is that, if variation in a given factor produces no significant change in the relative end result, then this factor does not account for individual differences in motor skills. If, on the other hand, varying a factor produces noticeable changes in an individual's performance, the factor is important in determining individual differences.

Effects of sense modality on motor skills. In this type of experiment (Seashore, Buxton, and McCollom, 1940) the individual performs the same general type of task with the same musculature but changes from one sense modality, e.g. vision, to another, e.g. audition. For example, in a simple reaction-time experiment the movement and the musculature are held constant, while the first set of trials employs a visual stimulus and the second an auditory stimulus. It is known that the split-half reliability for reactions to either visual or auditory stimuli is of the order of 0.80. Hence if the intercorrelation between visual and auditory reactions is found to be about 0.45, as is actually the case, we have evidence for the *moderate importance of the particular sense organ employed*. Since this is actually known to be a fairly representative finding for other serial motor skills, such as serial reaction times, we conclude that in general the particular sense employed in a motor skill is a moderately important variable underlying individual differences.

Effects of musculature. If, in the reaction-time experiment, we hold constant the particular movement performed and the sense employed, we may then determine the importance of the particular musculature involved. If, for example, we change from the right to the left hand we find that the intercorrelation is almost as high, $r = 0.80$ approximately, as the reliability of either the right or the left hand by itself. Since the individuals retain approximately the same relative rank with either hand, and for that matter also with either foot or with other musculatures such as the jaw, the elbow, the shoulder, or the neck (Seashore and Seashore, 1941; Reymert, 1923), we conclude that the particular musculature is not a major factor underlying individual differences in motor skills. This conclusion is further supported by the fact that similar results are found on serial reaction times (Campbell), tapping rates (Seashore, Buxton, and McCollom, 1940), and motor rhythmic coordinations (Seashore, 1940). Actually the intercorrelation between the two hands is slightly higher than between one hand and one foot, or between other dissimilar musculatures, but the difference is not great. Some experimenters (e.g. Campbell), noting this high intercorrelation between different musculatures, have con-cluded that there is a general motor ability. But this does not follow, for it has been shown that a change in the pattern of movements makes a great deal of difference.

Effects of patterns of movement. If we again study the visual reaction time of the right hand, but vary the extent of the movement from 1 millimeter to approximately 150 millimeters we find that the correlation between the two performances is approximately 0.45. In other words, a mere change in the extent of the movement causes a moderate shift in the relative ranking of individuals from one performance to the other. Furthermore if we change the pattern of the movement we are likely to find an even lower intercorrelation between the two performances: usually about $r = 0.15$, a very slight relation. Another example is the comparison between visual reaction time with the right hand and maximal tapping rate with the same hand and the same key. Seashore, Buxton, and McCollom (1940) found that even these apparently similar performances are unrelated. They also found similar low intercorrelations between most other fine motor skills in which speed was emphasized.

In summary we may say that among the factors underlying individual differences in fine motor skills the sense employed is of moderate significance, the musculature employed is of very slight significance, and the pattern of movements involved is likely to be the most important factor.

GENERAL, GROUP, AND SPECIFIC FACTORS

If there were at least moderate intercorrelations among measurements of all human abilities, we should say that there was probably one *general* ability. But since many human abilities are not significantly correlated with other abilities, the term "general ability" is not a useful one in actual practice.

Group Factors

It is still possible, however, that certain *groups* of abilities may be moderately intercorrelated, and if so we should be justified in using the name "group factors" to indicate that individuals tend to rank consistently high or low within a particular range of performances. Sometimes these group factors may be extremely narrow. Thus in a battery of tapping tests (Seashore, Buxton, and McCollom, 1940) one subgroup of related tests showed a common characteristic based on simple oscillation in one plane, either up and down, or sideways. The remaining tapping tests were intercorrelated among themselves and their common characteristic was movement through at least two dimensions, e.g. tapping alternately on two squares 6 inches apart or on three squares arranged in a triangle. This subgroup of multidimensional tests constituted a second narrow group factor. Contrary to the expectations of nearly everyone, the two subgroups showed only slight intercorrelations.

Two series of large-scale studies on the interrelations of aptitudes for fine motor skills have brought to light a number of relatively narrow group factors. The nature of these factors may be identified in the light of the various tests that show significantly high factor loadings on each factor, and, conversely, their scope may be delimited by the apparently similar tests that fail to show significant loadings on the factors. In the first series, twenty-one instrumental motor tests were employed by Seashore, Buxton, and McCollom in order to determine their interrelations.

Table 1 shows that six factors were necessary to account for the zero-order table of correlations. For convenience, loadings of 0.40 or higher were arbitrarily considered as being of probable significance and are printed in boldface. Some of the loadings are starred to indicate that in this preliminary survey they disagree somewhat with our qualitative identifications.

From previous studies we should expect that a group factor among motor tests would appear in performances involving a *similar* pattern of action, and that loadings would vary only slightly, according to the particular sense field or musculature employed. Thus we find that factor I has its most significant loadings in the four simple reaction times (tests 1–4), whether the stimulus was visual or auditory, and for both a simple 1-millimeter press reaction of the finger and hand, or a much longer (6-inch) jump-and-press reaction of the hand and forearm. It is tentatively designated "speed of single reaction." The only other significant loadings in this column are for test 7, which behaves anomalously in relation to several other axes, and the speed drill (test 15), which is a test of ability to move the hand continuously in a circle and, therefore, does not seem to resemble the simple reaction-time tests. Only a retest can check the significance of this latter relation. Each of the factors shows one or more such anomalies, which may possibly be due to statistical fluctuations from the relatively small sample of 50 cases. In a number of these instances the loadings are definitely known not to be representative of the correlational findings from previous experiments with the same tests, a matter that calls for further study.

In factor II the significant loadings fall on five tests: tests 5 and 6, tapping a telegraph key vertically (the same test was given 2 weeks in succession, which accounts for two entries in the factor table); test 7, tapping a telegraph key horizontally; test 11, the two-finger oscillometer; and test 12, the arm and hand oscillometer. All involve short oscillating movements in one plane only. Test 8, one-plate stylus tapping, fails to receive as high loadings as would be expected from our tentative identification of this factor, which is: "finger, hand, and forearm speed in restricted oscillatory move-

TABLE 1

ROTATED FACTORIAL MATRIX, GIVING TEST PROJECTIONS ON THE SIX OBLIQUE AXES (FIGURES IN BOLDFACE ARE PROBABLY SIGNIFICANT)

Test	$r_{\frac{1}{2}\frac{1}{2}}$ *	I	II	III	IV	V	VI	h^2 †	h^2 assum.†
1. Auditory simple reaction time	.63	**.65**	.01	.03	−.03	−.06	−.10	.54	.60
2. Visual simple reaction time	.90	**.64**	.15	.08	−.06	.15	.16	.82	.87
3. Auditory jump reaction time	.74	**.48**	.20	.47	−.03	−.09	−.05	.66	.78
4. Visual jump reaction time	.86	**.75**	.32	.09	.02	−.02	.01	.95	.87
5. Vertical telegraph-key tapping	.92	.03	**.89**	.04	.02	−.51 ‡	−.03	.91	.89
6. Same (2 weeks earlier)	.85	−.10	**.86**	−.10	−.08	−.05	−.39	1.09 ‡	.93
7. Horizontal telegraph-key tapping	.95	**.56**	**.51**	.04	**.74** ‡	**−.67** ‡	−.10	.93	.93
8. One-plate stylus tapping	.89	.02	.22	**.40**	.12	.38	.18	.64	.79
9. Two-plate stylus tapping	.90	−.04	.31	**.64**	.29	−.06	.11	.73	.79
10. Three-plate stylus tapping	.87	−.10	.38	**.69**	−.10	−.06	−.10	.96	.79
11. Oscillometer, two finger	.92	.03	**.70**	−.03	.25	−.01	.05	.68	.78
12. Oscillometer, arm	.85	.03	**.62**	.21	**.45**	−.02	.30	.83	.87
13. Spool-peg transfer	.89	.10	.37	**.43**	.32	.06	.11	.61	.66
14. Spool packing	.90	.01	.02	−.03	.12	.13	**−.56**	.39	.32
15. Speed drill	.81	**.54** ‡	−.03	.26	.34	−.01	.20	.44	.33
16. Serial discrimeter	.93	.07	−.04	**.69** ‡	−.06	.06	.00	.58	.77
17. Pursuit rotor	.92	−.02	.09	.19	**.44** ‡	**.44** ‡	.23	.74	.62
18. Ataxiameter, stand	.80	−.04	.09	−.09	**.75**	.05	−.08	.75	.62
19. Ataxiameter, sit	.89	.27	−.05	−.02	**.67**	−.06	−.03	.48	.57
20. Spatial relations	.82	.02	.03	.04	.01	**.58**	−.11	.53	.51
21. Assembly	.52	.00	−.08	−.01	−.03	**.53**	.37	.52	.54

I = speed of single reaction; II = finger-hand speed in restricted oscillatory movements; III = forearm and hand speed in oscillatory movements of moderate extent; IV = steadiness; V = manipulation of spatial relations; VI = unidentifiable or residual factors.

* The reliability coefficients, or correlation between the last two cycles of each test, are uncorrected for length.

† The values in h^2 and h^2 assumed are taken from the orthogonal solution.

‡ Loadings seemingly inconsistent with identifications.

ment." Note that the repetitive action tests that call for *wider* movement in two planes do not have high loadings in this factor.

Factor III shows relatively significant loadings on all three stylus-tapping tests (tests 8, 9, and 10), with the two- and three-plate stylus-tapping tests receiving definitely heavier loadings. The spool-peg transfer test (test 13), designed to involve the same distance and accuracy of movement as the two- and three-plate tests, also receives a significant weight. The ability called for seems to be "forearm and hand speed in oscillatory movements of moderate extent." These movements are nearly all in two planes, in contrast with the single plane for factor II. Two anomalous loadings are found, a moderately large one for the auditory jump reaction time (test 3) and a higher one for serial discriminative action of the four fingers (test 16).

Factor IV is best identified from the two high loadings on the standing and sitting postural sway tests (tests 18 and 19) and, on the basis of previous experiments by Seashore and Adams (1933), Buxton and Humphreys (1935), and Buxton (1938), these tests seem to be sampling a group factor having to do with steadiness or precision. It may also be related to a relaxed condition in taking the tests. The weighting of the pursuit test (test 17) seems to be logically acceptable, but it is negated by the correlational results of two previous studies. Test 7, horizontal telegraph-key tapping, is again an anomaly.

In factor V the weightings of the Minnesota spatial-relations form-board and assembly tests, together with the loading of the pursuit rotor (tests 20, 21, and 17, respectively), suggest that this factor should be designated "skill in manipulating spatial relations." This rather complex identification seems necessary because of the possibility that future experiments will show this to be largely a space-perception factor. The two negative loadings, of the vertical and horizontal telegraph-key tapping tests (tests 5 and 7), probably have to be explained again in terms of error, since no other tapping tests receive significant weights.

Factor VI seems to be a residual for this battery of tests.

The discussions contained in the papers of this series have shown that a modification of the type of interpretation given to motor factors by Buxton may be necessary. The shift probably should be from an anatomical to a functional emphasis in the identification of factors.

Specific Factors

An example of the relatively high degree of specificity to be found among many fine motor skills is afforded by the study of motor rhythm by Seashore and others.

Motor rhythm. In a previously unpublished study, Seashore found that scores on a motor-rhythm test did not correlate significantly with scores on the same apparatus when two other rhythm patterns were used as stimuli. Seashore's original study (1926) showed that motor rhythm correlated with a test for the discrimination of sensory rhythm patterns. This seems to conflict with the findings of low correlations between patterns of the same type of motor-coordination test.

Two minor studies on the relation of the Seashore motor-rhythm test to dancing ability may be mentioned as indicative of the limits of the hypothetical group factor of motor rhythm. The first, performed by the writer's students at the University of Oregon, involved the selection, by a group of fraternity students, of 50 girls who were judged distinctly superior in social dancing ability. The girls were then given C. E. Seashore's phonographic test of sensory rhythm and R. H. Seashore's test of motor

rhythm. In comparison with the norms for these tests, the average of the superior dancing group fell at the 65th percentile on the sensory-rhythm test, and at the 35th percentile on the motor-rhythm test. There is some question whether the norms used for the former test do not give results that are consistently too high. Although this result is clearly contrary to expectations based on the hypothesis of a group factor in motor rhythm, there may be several sources of error. In the first place, the men's criteria of selection may have been unduly influenced by such factors as beauty, conversational ability, and dress, and, as the girls pointed out, a girl follows her partner, not the music (!) in social dancing.

The girl selected as the outstanding dancer (both social and interpretive types) also made the best score ever reported on the motor-rhythm test.

The second study, by Childers (1937), attempted to avoid the errors of selection involved in the judgment of social dancing by studying individual tap dancing. The children studied, members of her private dancing class, were tested for the number of trials required to learn each of a series of tap routines of gradually increasing difficulty. This gave a fairly accurate estimate of their attained proficiency. No significant relation appeared between the sensory- or motor-rhythm tests and the dancing proficiency ratings.

Steadiness

An example of a somewhat broader group factor is one that was originally labeled "steadiness" by the writer and others. According to the hypothesis of a group factor for steadiness, those coordinations that emphasize accuracy (precision or steadiness), while minimizing speed and strength, should cluster together. Steadiness tests, in wide variety, should intercorrelate moderately or highly, and correlate only slightly with speed and strength tests. Actually, Spaeth and Dunham (1921) reported

$r = +0.61 \pm 0.11$ between Dunlap's test for precision in thrusting a stylus at a graded series of holes and rifle target shooting for 73 army men ranging from poor to expert marksmen. Extending this study, Seashore and Adams (1933) found that in terms of a multiple score for five steadiness tests (postural sway with eyes closed, rifle muzzle sway when sighting, hand tremor, stylus thrusting at holes, and stylus held stationary in holes) a university rifle team of 6 men was superior to all but one of the 50 unselected fellow students enrolled in R.O.T.C. They also found that in spite of several rather low test reliabilities all test intercorrelations were $+0.45$ or higher. The same trends were verified in a subsequent study of Humphreys, Buxton, and Taylor (1936) in the same laboratory.

The writer's earlier findings (1926) of an r of $+0.30 \pm 0.09$ between precision of thrust and steadiness in tracing a narrow V-slot may or may not be an exception to the above trend, depending upon the representativeness of the coefficient. In view of the encouraging findings on steadiness, which are also corroborated by a moderate correlation between various types of postural sway in later studies by H. G. Seashore

and Koch (1938) and Seashore, Buxton, and McCollom (1940), the writer has been extending and improving a battery of such tests in order to determine more accurately the range in kinds of tests, the closeness of the relation, and the significance of this factor.

In a minor experiment employing a photoelectric device for measuring steadiness of arm and hand, Katz (1935) studied a group of 25 boys in an institution for juvenile delinquency. These 25 boys were picked for "emotional instability," as evidenced by temper tantrums, and other emotional maladjustments. In comparison with 25 other less emotional boys paired for age and IQ there was no significant difference on the steadiness test. Both emotional and muscular stability have been referred to a *neural* basis, but, whatever the merits of this theory, these results indicate that they obviously do not depend on the same factors.

Subsequently this study was expanded by Seashore, Dudek, and Holtzman to test the possibility of finding more than one group factor in the general range of tests that emphasize equilibrium, precision, or steadiness in posture or in relatively slow move-

TABLE 2

FACTORIAL ANALYSIS OF ARM-HAND PRECISION TESTS (FROM SEASHORE, DUDEK, AND HOLTZMAN)

Test	Description	Trials
1. 2. } Ataxiameter	Measure of arm-hand sway. Horizontal and vertical components measured separately.	5 trials of 15 seconds each in each cycle.
3. Target register	S aimed a beam of light at a stationary target.	5 trials of 15 seconds each in each cycle.
4. Straight trace	S traced, with a stylus, a straight horizontal path toward himself.	5 trials of 10 seconds each in each cycle.
5. Curved trace	With a stylus S traced an irregular horizontal path from left to right.	10 trials of 15 seconds each in each cycle.
6. Sine trace	S moved a ring stylus along a rod that was bent vertically in the form of a sine curve.	5 trials of 30 seconds each in each cycle.
7. Three-dimensional trace	S moved a ring stylus along a rod that was bent irregularly in three dimensions.	5 trials of 40 seconds each in each cycle.
8. Thrusting steadiness	S thrust a stylus into a hole at a rate of one thrust every 2 seconds. Holes of three different diameters were used.	5 trials of 10 thrusts each in each size hole.

TABLE 3

INTERCORRELATIONS, MEANS, S.D.'S AND RELIABILITIES OF TESTS

Variable	Product-Moment r's							M	S.D.	Reliability Cycles 1 + 2 vs 3 + 4	Cycles 1 + 3 vs 2 + 4
	1	2	3	4	5	6	7				
1. Ataxiameter (horizontal)								5.19	2.91	54	67
2. Ataxiameter (vertical)	47							4.43	2.68	75	84
3. Target register	44	44						5.95	2.65	79	83
4. Straight trace	39	20	40					3.10	2.76	79	82
5. Curved trace	30	04	26	61				4.77	3.47	82	95
6. Sine trace	31	−06	26	57	72			4.43	3.12	77	89
7. 3-Dimensional trace	22	−07	34	37	72	83		4.08	3.68	85	82
8. Thrust	31	35	43	66	38	41	49	4.03	2.64	78	88

TABLE 4

FACTORIAL RESULTS

| Variable | Group 2 (N = 100) | | | | | | | | Group 1 (N = 39) | | | |
	Centroid Loadings					Rotated Loadings			Rotated Loadings			
	I	II	III	h_e^2	h_c^2	I	II	III	I	II	III	h^2
1. Ataxiameter (horizontal)	56	31	22	49	46	23	27	58	20 *	10 *	77 *	64 *
2. Ataxiameter (vertical)	37	58	24	54	53	−06	18	70				
3. Target register	60	32	25	53	52	25	27	62	22	03	77	63
4. Straight trace	78	09	−50	83	86	23	88	10	−03	66	11	45
5. Curved trace	72	−40	−09	68	68	68	46	−03	27	45	46	48
6. Sine trace	74	−53	−03	83	84	81	41	−08	84	20	29	83
7. 3-dimensional trace	72	−56	17	85	86	89	24	00	83	17	14	74
8. Thrust	69	17	−17	55	53	25	61	31	19	66	30	57

* In the data for group 1 the horizontal and vertical scores for the ataxiameter were combined into a single score.

Factor names: I = Steadiness in two- or three-dimensional space.

II = Steadiness of movement in a restricted plane.

III = Involuntary movement of the arm and hand.

Estimated correlations between factors: $r_{I\ II} = 0.47$

$r_{I\ III} = 0.00$

$r_{II\ III} = 0.24$

ments. The description of seven of these tests together with the intercorrelations, reliabilities, and factor loadings from Holtzman's experiment on 39 subjects and Dudek and Seashore's experiment on 100 men are given in Tables 2, 3, and 4.

This series of studies includes a further analysis of relatively pure tests representing each of the three factors listed in Table 4 in relation to measures of static equilibrium or postural sway (with and without visual cues), and a measure of dynamic equilibrium (a balancing chair simulating the movements of a Link trainer), a measure that does not involve bodily equilibrium but does involve the similar complex coordinations of a miniature airplane tridimensional pursuit test. Eventually there should be made available a battery of tests for primary motor abilities comparable to the primary mental abilities described by Thurstone and later extended by the AAF aircrew selection studies. The first unit of a portable battery of such tests of precision and steadiness is now nearing completion.

STUDIES IN VALIDITY

A possible hypothesis about the acquisition of complex motor skills is to assume that each person has had ample opportunity to practice many simple common skills and that if a person tended to do well on the earlier samples of this experience he would thereby be encouraged to try more skills and to perfect the skills in which he enjoys superiority. To test this hypothesis, Seashore, Jerome, and Harney, in an unpublished study, worked out a list of approximately twenty common manual skills, such as (1) bolting two boards together with a spring and washers for proper spacing, (2) making simple free-hand drawings of objects such as the covering plate of an ordinary electric switch, or of a three-dimensional object such as the paper carton for a bottle of ink, (3) handwriting (scored by the Ayres and Thorndike scales), (4) pinning two squares of cloth together with two safety pins on each side, (5) sharpening a pencil, (6) assembling a simple object with a screw driver, etc.

If there were any validity to such concepts as "manual dexterity," "being clever with one's hands," etc., it would be expected that persons who were skillful on one group of these skills would tend to be proportionately skillful on a second group. Very briefly, they weren't. One battery of ten common skills showed no significant correlation with another ten skills. Thus we have another line of evidence corroborating the previous findings on the specificity of fine motor skills. Neither on simple artificial laboratory tests where there has been no opportunity for previous practice nor on this sample of widely practiced manual skills is there any evidence for a general factor in manual coordinations. The subjects for the experiment on common motor skills were first-year high-school boys enrolled in a nonvocational shop course required of all students.

In a related experiment on the same group of subjects Harney also studied the possibility of predicting grades in the five subdivisions of this course in shopwork from a battery of tests of several fine motor skills. The five branches of the shop course included mechanical drawing, carpentry, metal work, auto mechanics, and electrical assembly and repair. Scores on the fine motor tests and on the common manual skills battery were not related significantly to a series of project scores in any of the five subdivisions of the shop course. Neither were scores on any of Holzinger's primary mental abilities tests related to success in any of the five shop scores. It is further interesting to note that the grades on the five divisions of shop work were not significantly related among themselves, except that drawing was slightly related to several. Here we have a third line of evidence against any general factor underlying motor abilities.

"MECHANICAL ABILITIES"

Closely related to such concepts as manual dexterity, being clever with one's hands, etc., is the concept of mechanical abilities. Two critical experiments may be reported here. In the first, Hazelhurst (1940) tested several hundred men who had completed a year's correspondence course on air-conditioning and refrigeration work and were undergoing a month's shop training on actual assembly and repair. Hazelhurst employed approximately fifty paper-and-pencil group tests, including a considerable number of tests that he designed and constructed himself on the basis of his own training in electrical engineering and psychology. Five criteria of success in the shop work were also obtained, and all the tests and criteria were submitted to a factorial analysis. The battery of fifty tests was analyzed to nine relatively narrow group factors of mechanical abilities; and the five success criteria were found to cluster in two groups. However, no single test nor any of the nine group factors was related to any of the success criteria. The result of this ambitious experiment should make us skeptical of any concept of a single mechanical ability or even of a series of mechanical abilities.

A parallel study by Guylee (1940) of the use of mechanical assembly tests on these same trainees showed similar negative findings. Unfortunately these careful studies have not previously been published, and personnel workers have in many instances continued to make erroneous assumptions about the nature and origin of abilities underlying the acquisition of mechanical skills.

So far as is known to the writer, there are no cases in which so-called mechanical-abilities tests have been clearly shown to be predictive of success in the acquisition of more complex mechanical skills. Isolated instances of a significant correlation need to be verified, for all such studies are subject to chance variations. This is particularly important because of the tendency of in-vestigators to consider negative findings as due to inadequacies of experimental method or as scientifically uninteresting. Even a survey of published evidences might be misleading, since there is a tendency to report only positive findings.

Prediction of success in typing. In another study Walker and Adams (1934) attempted to predict individual differences in rate of learning to typewrite among sophomore students in a commercial high school. They used the six tests of Seashore's Stanford Motor Skills Unit (1928a) (rate of tapping a telegraph key, four-finger serial visual discrimination, auditory motor rhythm, rotary wrist movement in turning a hand drill, bimanual spool packing, and eye-hand rotary pursuit). The scores were not significantly correlated with scores on speed of typing at the end of the year's training, even though each of the six motor tests had sufficient reliability to rule out this factor as a possible source of error. Incidentally, the scores for the first fifty subjects on one test, rate of tapping, were significantly correlated with the corrected number of strokes Suspecting that the very high error penalty represented a heavy chance loading of the score, the entire experiment was repeated a second year on another group of fifty subjects and no correlation was found with either the weighted or unweighted typing scores.

A review of the literature on the prediction of success in typing brought to light one study by Book (1924) in which it was shown that there are some differences between the average tapping rate of unselected university typing students, amateur champion typists, and world's champion typists. However, the size of the differences was slight in comparison with the known range of tapping rates and all three groups were near the average tapping rate for all adults.

An earlier study by Seashore (1930) on fifty male Stanford students had shown that ratings of the total amount of previous training in manual skills, such as typing and instrumental music, were not related to any of eight tests of fine motor skills, which included two other measures of eye-hand pursuit coordinations and a measure of postural sway, in addition to the types of tests included in the Stanford Motor Skills Unit. This seems to indicate again the specificity of fine motor skills, since there was apparently no cumulative transfer of training from typing and instrumental music to any of the tests of fine motor skills. Such a finding, of course, is definitely in keeping with the hypothesis that individual differences in fine motor skills are determined largely by "hitting upon" favorable work methods, which are largely specific to a particular type of operation or, at most, a relatively narrow group of operations.

Prediction of success in operating winding machines. Using the same Stanford Motor Skills Unit employed by Walker and Adams, another investigator, S. H. Seashore (1932), tested sixty apprentices of a knitting mill for any possible relation between these motor test scores and success in operating winding machines. On these machines the workers had to watch for any breakage of the wool thread, and after tying the broken ends with a weaver's knot they would loop the thread over several hooks and start the machine again. As soon as a person became reasonably proficient in operating one machine, he was given an opportunity to supervise a number of machines simultaneously, and success was measured objectively by weighing the amount of yarn wound by each worker during the first and second halves of the third month of work. Even though the range of abilities was great and the reliability of the criterion was high enough to exclude any major error from this source, there was no correlation between the criterion and any of the six motor test scores or a combined standard score from the battery of six tests.

Individual Differences as Stages of Learning

One of the peculiarities in the development of a new science seems to be the extent to which special fields are studied in isolation from related fields. This is illustrated in the field of motor skills, where an analysis of the factors underlying success has proceeded for years with very little consideration of theories about the nature of learning. It is apparent, however, that the work-methods hypothesis for the origin of individual differences in motor skills is also a hypothesis to describe the way in which successive steps in learning achieve quantitative progress in terms of end results, such as amount, rate, or accuracy of work performed.

The work-methods hypothesis states that individual differences in *any* human ability (not just motor skills) are attributable to three groups of factors: (1) the physical constants of the various organs (especially sense organs, nervous system, and musculatures) employed, (2) the general qualitative pattern of component actions involved, and (3) the refinement of these component actions with respect to both strength and timing so as to produce an optimal pattern of action. Thus it is conceivable, though rarely demonstrated, that lack of sensory acuity or reflex motor speed might handicap a person in attaining a high degree of skill in a complex motor coordination. Actually, however, the empirical evidence seems to be that skilled workers in fine manual skills rarely need to press themselves to their physiological limits and that, instead, they attain their superior results by hitting upon qualitative patterns of action, or work methods, that make the work easier. Even a person with low physiological limits can surpass one with higher physiological limits if the latter is not using an equally effective work method. A part of the process of trial-and-error practice is simply experimenting with various work methods. The sudden progress associated with insight learning is probably to be attributed very largely to the perceiving of new qualitative patterns of action. On the other hand, the relatively steady progress frequently observed in learning of all types is usually attributable to refinements within a pattern.

A hypothetical example of progress in learning to unlock the front door of a new home may illustrate the principle. The new owner will probably come up to the door, fumble in his pocket for the keys, try several keys in the hole of the lock, one of them perhaps upside down, then try both directions of turning the lock, and finally turn the door knob and push. Progress usually involves the dropping out of useless movements, such as selecting the wrong key or the wrong position or the wrong direction of turning. The remaining essential movements are made to *overlap in time,* so that on later trials as the person comes up the steps he reaches in his pocket for the key, selects the proper key *en route,* orients the key to the right position as he crosses the porch, starts turning the key immediately upon recognizing tactually the proper depth of insertion in the lock, and simultaneously twists the door knob in the proper direction. In the final stage, the component movements are essentially the same in kind as in the earlier stages, but time is saved by starting each successive step so that it is ready as soon as the preceding step is finished.

Most motor skills are developed largely by trial and error without much benefit of formal coaching or the use of scientific devices, such as slow-motion pictures, that would help the individual to understand just what he is doing in the performance, what faults need to be dropped, and where his timing could be improved. As a result, it appears that most favorable work methods are "hit upon" rather than carefully thought out or even recognized afterward. It has long been observed that a person who is himself highly skilled is not necessarily very effective in either analyzing his own performance verbally or teaching it to another person. "All-American" athletes may be quite unsuccessful as athletic coaches.

In the common absence of an analytical understanding of the methods used by a performer, it is not surprising that the quantitative individual differences observed in any particular skill are frequently quite stable. Improvement in any of these habits may easily be a matter of chance, in which a person accidentally achieves a particular improvement several times before he recognizes the nature of the change and thereby becomes better able to control it. To a certain extent the mere association in time of successive component actions tends to produce an overlapping in the timing of successive movements through the process of conditioning, in which insight may or may not be involved. Unfortunately, however, there is no automatic process by which errors are eliminated, particularly if they are only useless and not actually impediments in the performance.

Dependence of Motor Activities on Nonmotor Factors

Both observation and experiment indicate that success in complex motor activities may depend upon sensory, affective, and intellectual as well as motor factors. Thus the reports of the Army Air Forces Aviation Psychology Program (Guilford and Lacey, Eds., 1947) analyze the factorial makeup of 65 psychological tests developed to predict success in the training program for pilots, navigators, and bombardiers during World War II. Of these tests approximately 60 were objective "paper-and-pencil" tests covering every aspect believed to be significant in the learning of aircrew skills, and about 5 were individual psychomotor tests employing physical instruments. The multiple correlation between the most significant paper-and-pencil tests and a training criterion was approximately 0.50; the addition of 6 psychomotor apparatus tests raised the multiple correlation coefficient of validity to 0.70.

Among the psychological factors that were significantly related to the training criterion were those tentatively designated by the names carefulness, integration (three factors), judgment, kinesthetic (nature unknown), length estimation, memory (three factors), mathematical background, mechanical experience (interest and training), mechanical experience, perceptual speed, pilot interest, planning, reasoning (three factors), spatial relations (three factors), social science background, verbal, and visualization. Obviously, if the multiple correlation between the criterion and this group of nonmotor factors is only 0.50 it is unlikely that more than a few would be very predictive by themselves. Most of them have such slight validity that it could be detected only by using hundreds of cases in the test samples.

Of the three psychomotor factors studied, the one designated psychomotor coordination 1 seems to be somewhat similar to what we have previously designated as a pursuit or continuous coordination factor. Psychomotor precision, the second factor, was represented by only two tests, discrimination reaction time on a complex spatial pattern, and finger dexterity in turning over pegs. This factor does not appear to be very well named, since both tasks are primarily measures of speed, but at any rate it apparently does not refer to the types of factors that Seashore, Dudek, and Holtzman reported for tests involving precision in aiming or in slow movements. The third factor, psychomotor speed, likewise appears to be given much too broad a name since it is represented primarily by two paper-and-pencil tests of log book accuracy and marking accuracy, whereas the literature indicates that there is a considerable number of unrelated psychomotor factors that emphasize speed in fine motor skills.

In spite of this minor difficulty in the naming of factors, the AAF Aviation Psychology Program represents one of the largest and most successful programs of vo-cational selection ever attempted. It made possible great savings in time, machines, and man power during the war. The cost of training a pilot was an estimated $25,000 per man, but the administration of a battery of individual psychomotor tests cost only about $5.00 per man. It paid to eliminate the potential failure.

The AAF program also included tests of mechanical abilities for the selection of ground crews engaged in servicing planes, but the outcome here was not nearly so clear as in the work on aircrew selection.

Although there are relatively few published instances of the successful employment of psychomotor tests for the selection of persons to be trained in fine motor skills, this is only one use of motor tests. Actually, negative results from selection experiments may be of value if the experimenter is alert to the possibility of alternative explanations for the observed individual differences in the attainment of complex skills. Negative results on selection programs tell us that we need no longer concern ourselves about the factors tested. Instead we should turn our attention to other sources of the individual differences, for example, differences in motivation, training, health, the use of specialized tools or equipment, or simply more efficient work methods.

MOTION-AND-TIME STUDY

One of the anomalies in the development of our knowledge of psychomotor skills is the way in which the motion-and-time study methods of engineering have been neglected by psychologists and, conversely, the way in which various psychological factors in work output have been overlooked by industrial engineers. The divorcement of these two approaches is particularly striking in view of the fact that in the 1920's the work of motion-study engineers, such as Gilbreth, was quite widely known in psychology.

The basic idea of motion-and-time study is that work methods form the basis for individual differences in skills and also for differing degrees of effectiveness at successive stages of training. Differences in work methods may best be analyzed by slow-motion photography, both for finding the errors of less skilled workers and for teaching to new workers the superior methods of the most highly skilled workers. In addition to this relatively simple analysis of the specific tricks of the trade on each job, there are certain general principles and procedures that apply to all jobs. Thus any type of manual skill may be analyzed into a series of about sixteen types of actions, called "therbligs," after the approximately reverse spelling of their developer, Gilbreth (1919). The names of these units are as follows:

1. Search
2. Find
3. Select
4. Grasp
5. Position
6. Assemble
7. Use
8. Disassemble, or take apart
9. Inspect
10. Transport, loaded
11. Pre-position, for next operation
12. Release load
13. Transport, empty
14. Wait (unavoidable delay)
15. Wait (avoidable delay)
16. Rest (for overcoming fatigue)

It is further known that a working surface, such as a desk or bench, should be at a particular height for each worker, depending upon his height and whether he is sitting or standing or alternating between the two positions. The materials should be arranged in front of the worker so that he can reach each one easily with the proper hand and move it a minimal distance to the next step in the procedure. Lost motion is avoided by placing each material where it will be used. Other principles include the use of both hands simultaneously wherever possible, and the use of fixtures for the accurate placement of materials without care-

ful visual control of fine movements. Thus a person folding printed material for mailing in envelopes might find it a saving (1) to do all the folding first, then (2) to arrange all the envelopes with the flaps turned back in overlapping flat piles so that (3) he can pick up a folded letter and insert it into the adjacent envelope, (4) moisten all the gummed edges at one time, and (5) seal and *drop* (rather than place) each envelope in a hopper.

From the fact that the principal method is that of photography and the fact that one therbling, "inspect," is used to describe all activities of careful perception in placement of materials, it should be evident that motion-and-time analysis has not yet gone much beyond the study of fairly large manual skills. To supplement this method we need two parallel techniques: (1) the electrophysiological analysis of nerve and muscular activity, and (2) psychological introspection for the analysis of the sensory, affective, and intellectual aspects of the skill.

Whether or not psychologists have contributed materially to the development of motion-and-time study technique, it is apparent that they should be familiar with them in order to study psychomotor skills. The writer (1939) has in fact outlined an extension of the concept of work methods to include skill in sensory, affective, and intellectual processes. Wyatt (1945) has shown the significance of work methods in the improvement of pitch discrimination among persons who were markedly deficient in either hearing or producing fine pitch differences. The writer (1947) has outlined a classification of the principal work methods by which individuals ordinarily try to solve problems when frustrated in a conflict situation, and with Jenssen (1948) has outlined the way in which such a classification of habitual approaches to difficult problems might be made the basis for a classification of temperaments.

The basic hypothesis underlying all variations in human skills might be roughly stated: It isn't so much what kind of an organism you inherited as what you do with it. Granted that there are fairly large hereditary structural differences *between species* and that some species seem quite unable to do things that others can do easily, this does not necessarily mean that the differences of inherited structures *within a species* are equally important. Some of the world's greatest accomplishments have been by persons seriously deficient in physical endowment, e.g. Helen Keller, Steinmetz, Robert Louis Stevenson. Even champion athletes in a specialized sport, e.g. track dashes, football line play, etc., show variations in both size and proportions of body build, although these variations are not so great as those between, say, football players and high jumpers.* Football and track coaching, in fact, provides one of the best opportunities for the profitable analysis of work methods by motion pictures. The athlete who performed poorly on Saturday may, with the same physique, health, etc., on Monday show a considerable improvement simply as a result of seeing a slow motion picture of the previous game.

FATIGUE AND ALLIED PHENOMENA

The importance of work methods is by no means limited to individual differences in aptitudes or to progress in learning. Regression of behavior under unfavorable working conditions is likewise related to

* Cureton (1947) presents extensive evidence for a relation between body build (somatotype) and success in various categories of athletic endeavor. On p. 108 he concludes: "It is true that heavy athletes are relatively more mesomorphic (solid, dense muscle) ; also that track athletes run to slim body build with considerable ectomorphy (frail, linear) but with well developed musculature. Swimmers are more frequently meso-endomorphic (muscular and fat). Very seldom do men or women low in mesomorphy succeed in athletics."

An appropriate somatotype would seem to be a necessary but not a sufficient condition for success in a given athletic skill. (Ed.)

changes in method as well as to changes in bodily conditions. The volume by Bartley and Chute (1947), which systematically reviews the literature on fatigue and impairment in man, finds it necessary to distinguish among (1) physiological impairment of tissues, (2) psychological aspects of fatigue, and (3) changes in the work output of the integrated organism.

Since all three factors are important aspects of human behavior, it is desirable to know how they are interrelated. In this summary we shall follow the general analysis of Bartley and Chute. First of all, it must be recognized that the term fatigue has been commonly used in two senses, (1) a broad concept having to do with many aftereffects of work — physiological, psychological, and economic — and (2) a narrower concept having to do with some one of these aspects.

It is further apparent that the physical after-effects of work are often confused or at least intermixed with a variety of other phenomena, such as boredom and feelings of conflict, that may represent the effects of previous affective conditioning. So great is the confusion that an earlier systematic writer, Muscio (1920), proposed the abandonment of the term fatigue in favor of more specific concepts.

Bartley and Chute suggest the following distinctions in terminology:

Fatigue is regarded as an experiential pattern arising in a conflict situation in which the general alignment of the individual may be described as aversion. This particular pattern involves feelings of limpness and bodily discomfort which, besides being undesirable in themselves, are frequently taken as tokens of inadequacy for activity. The subjective constituents of this fatigue pattern are not to be taken as epiphenomena, or as symptoms of fatigue, but as fatigue itself. [Pp. 47–48.]

Impairment is a physiological change in tissue which reduces its ability to participate in the larger aspects of organic functioning. Impairment is identifiable only through the methods of physiology and biochemistry. Reduction in the ability of the organism as a whole to perform is no criterion for the presence of impairment. [P. 48.]

Work output includes all overt activity that is measured either in the laboratory or in industry. [P. 49.]

Neither fatigue nor impairment can be measured by the work output of the *intact* organism. Activity may be used as a direct measure of impairment only when such systems as isolated nerve muscle preparations are used in ergographic studies.

These three factors, fatigue, impairment, and work output, are thus semi-independent variables. As mentioned previously, the experience of fatigue (tiredness, etc.) may arise either through impairment as an immediate after-effect of exercise or as a conditioned feeling of boredom, distraction, or other conflict. In some circumstances, as in a sporting event, physiological impairment may be associated with pleasant feelings or exhilaration, very different from the feelings of tiredness and distaste for an activity.

Fatigue in the sense of an experience of aversion to further work may arise from physiological impairment of tissues during exercise, or it may be largely a conditioned response, e.g. boredom. Likewise, work output may decrease as a result of either of these two factors, or for still other reasons. Conversely, under conditions of adequate motivation, physiological impairment of tissues may not result in either feelings of fatigue or reduced work output. Under even moderate motivation, a change in the work methods may by-pass the effects of impairment in certain organs by shifting the burden to other parts of the body.

Bartley and Chute point out that visual fatigue is not necessarily due to tissue impairment through long-continued use of the eyes, but may arise as a result of a conflict or early conditioning in an unpleasant experience. Carmichael and Dearborn (1947) similarly point out that their experiments involving hours of continuous reading did not necessarily produce either the subjective effects of tiredness, discomfort, and aversion, or a decrement in work efficiency in the sense of decreased accuracy or comprehension.

Chronic fatigue is a definitely unpleasant experience that bears no consistent relation to expenditure of measureable energy. It seems to follow prolonged periods of unpleasant emotion, such as worry and uncertainty. Physical exertion may even obliterate the fatigue.

Factors compensating for fatigue and impairment in maintaining work output. One of the things that often astonishes both laymen and psychologists is the extent to which the human organism can continue to perform adequately under extremely unfavorable conditions. For example, Hovey (1928), in a study of the alleged unfavorable effects of having freshmen take intelligence tests during the excitement of the first week of college, retested some of these students under conditions of extreme distraction. Bells, buzzers, whistles, organ pipes, and a spotlight were among the distractors used. Other persons marched in step in the halls of the floor above. Shop machinery and pounding added to the noise and otherwise created disturbances without actually eliminating the possibility of continuing work in the large test room. No significant decrement in test scores was observed.

In the same laboratory the writer and his students measured the distracting effect of music from phonograph records of somewhat outdated popular songs upon the comprehension of semitechnical psychological literature. The control groups, who were initially equated with the experimental group for reading comprehension, showed no better scores under quiet conditions than did the experimental groups under conditions of musical distraction.

In Warren and Clark's study (1937) of the effects of going without sleep for 65 hours, the results likewise indicated that, although the subjects had to struggle to keep awake, their work output on a variety of psychological tests showed little or no decrement. One explanation of this is suggested by a similar experiment of Laslett in which he had no difficulty securing volunteers for the experiment but had to prevail upon his friends to go through the control series of measurements with normal amounts of sleep allowed. Evidently the motivation of being in a difficult experiment is one of the factors that helps to compensate for any deleterious effects of sleep loss or other distracting factors.

Another fairly common finding is that measures of serial or continuous performances tend to show greater decrements in output than do tests that involve momentary single actions, with an opportunity to rest in between. Evidently a person can "pull up" momentarily even when he has undergone prolonged deprivation of sleep, but he has difficulty in maintaining this alertness, even for trials lasting only a few minutes, if the test calls for practically continuous performance.

Use of psychomotor tests to measure influences on behavior. An unpublished series of experiments by Ivy and Seashore and their collaborators illustrates the use of psychomotor tests to determine the possible advantages of analeptic drugs in overcoming the effects of prolonged military operations. Moderate doses of amphetamine sulphate (benzedrine), a similar German drug Pervitin, and caffeine all tended to be effective (in that order) in relieving symptoms of fatigue and impairment on a variety of psychomotor tests. These tests measured speed of simple discriminative reaction, arm-hand steadiness, aiming, postural steadiness, and a complex coordination of operating a miniature airplane to keep it pointed level and straight ahead while it was subjected to a series of irregular movements in three dimensions comparable to the effects of a heavy storm. The possibility of serious disadvantages or "side effects" of the drugs were first ruled out by miniature experiments in laboratory rooms having artificially maintained temperature and humidity conditions comparable to desert and tropical jungle conditions, respectively. It was also shown that the drugs could be administered in moderate amounts to large groups of men under marching conditions in a temperate climate without undesirable side effects, and with a significant alleviation of various complaints common to this type of strenuous physical work. As might be expected, the administration of a neutral sugar pill or placebo produced many of the expected effects of the real drugs (through suggestion) even though all the dosages were disguised under the name of vitamins. The measures found to be most significantly affected were postural sway without vision (there was little effect with eyes open) and the airplane pursuit test. Later tests showed that similar effects were found on 24-hour truck-driving operations under black-out conditions in a moderately warm climate, and also on 20-mile night marches and 5-hour daytime tank operations under desert conditions. Commercial truck operations, up to 5 hours, did not show any significant effects, even though the drivers commented that they often had to struggle to keep alert and had various discomforts such as muscular cramps from working in one position for several hours at a time.

Psychomotor measures of efficiency under laboratory conditions of high altitude and low oxygen were found by Watson, Dunlap, and other investigators in World Wars I and II to be more sensitive indicators of impending dangerous losses in coordination than the introspective reports of difficulties as they were experienced. These and other instances indicate the possible usefulness of psychomotor tests for measuring the influence of many conditions believed to affect human behavior, e.g. the effects of age, the effects of motivation, the effects of stress, and the effects of various methods of training for motor skills.

OTHER FACTORS IN WORK OUTPUT

In our analysis of motor performances we have thus far stressed the factors inherent in the performer himself, his aptitudes and their bases in physical endowment, and the effectiveness of various work methods. It is obvious, of course, that other factors might also affect the effectiveness of the worker. Thus we have reason to believe that motivational factors, the interest of the person in his work, and group morale are relevant. Unusual neglect of, or special attention to, these factors might well alter the effectiveness of the worker, as was shown in the well-known Western Electric experiments (cf. Roethlisberger and Dickson, 1939). Physical working conditions such as temperature, ventilation, and lighting may likewise be important, as may also the design of desks, tables and benches, and specialized tools and machines.

It seems quite probable that one of the principal reasons for our relatively slight knowledge of motor abilities is the fact that industrial engineers have been so successful in designing machines to perform work that would otherwise call for high levels of dexterity. The manufacture of cigarettes, by a single machine that automatically rolls and packages the cigarettes, eliminates vast numbers of small movements of the human hand. At the other extreme, a machine stretching the entire length of a large factory can assemble heavy automobile chassis with the supervision of only five men on the whole assembly line. Even though the machine is very effective in practical operation, it is said that the designers regard the machine as a "technical failure" because it is not completely automatic!

Anyone who has carefully observed a mechanic in the process of repairing a modern automobile will realize the great importance of specialized tools and equipment in mechanical work. Of course, a knowledge of the tools and of mechanical processes is equally important. Only rarely, however, as in the complex process of coordinating hand and foot movements in piloting an airplane, are the physical endowments of the person very crucial. A person who is physically handicapped may often overcome his deficiency by using a suitable work method. Thus it is possible for a deaf man to tune a piano by using a chromatic stroboscope, and a large part of scientific research relies upon methods of amplifying, translating, or measuring stimuli that could not be observed by the unaided human senses.

It is also worth emphasizing that, if a person is not physically fitted to operate a given instrument or machine, e.g. a piano, it is often feasible to adapt the machine to the operator. Thus John B. Watson long ago pointed out that if a boy, handicapped by stubby fingers, should want to become a professional pianist, it would be possible to build a special keyboard to fit the span of his hands. We have often failed to realize that the cost of such specialized equipment may be quite reasonable in comparison to the total cost of preparation for the career in which it would be used.

By the method of work simplification, i.e. breaking down complex processes into a series of separate and simpler steps, it is possible to transform enormous numbers of inexperienced men and women into effective workers in a complex industrial process. Simplification also has its disadvantages, however, for a person may lose interest in the work because he is unable to grasp the significance of his contribution to the end result. To overcome this difficulty many manufacturers are now going back to more complex assignments for each worker so that he can have a sense of accomplishing something by himself. Where this is not feasible, a desirable substitute may be to have special days when the workers and their families can go through the whole factory and see how their own efforts fit into the total process of manufacturing an article.

Whether any one of these alternative means for improving the effectiveness of workers should be introduced, instead of a program for the selection of trainees who are personally best qualified to do the difficult performance under the old conditions, is a matter of just how far each alternative has already been taken into account. Some factories, for example, may already have good physical working conditions, and so could expect little improvement by further attention to this aspect, but they may have poor morale that could benefit by remedial efforts. The applied psychologist will presumably begin his studies of motor performance by analyzing the adequacy of each aspect of the work, and he will frequently need to call in other specialists before deciding where to place his emphasis for the improvement of efficiency.

REFERENCES

Bartley, S. H., and E. Chute. *Fatigue and impairment in man.* New York: McGraw-Hill, 1947.

Book, W. F. Voluntary motor ability of the world's champion typists. *J. appl. Psychol.,* 1924, **8**, 283–308.

Buros, O. K. *The third mental measurement book.* New Brunswick: Rutgers University Press, 1949. Pp. 720–724.

Buxton, C. E. The application of multiple factorial methods to the study of motor abilities. *Psychometrika,* 1938, **3**, 85–95.

Buxton, C. E., and L. G. Humphreys. The effect of practice upon intercorrelations in motor skills. *Science,* 1935, **81**, 441–442.

Campbell, M. Instrument for measuring the serial reaction-times of large muscle groups. *Amer. J. Psychol.,* 1934a, **46**, 481–483.

Campbell, M. The "personal equation" in serial pursuit performances. *J. appl. Psychol.,* 1934b, **18**, 785–792.

Campbell, M. The cognitive aspects of motor performances and their bearing upon general motor ability. *J. exp. Psychol.,* 1936a, **19**, 323–333.

Campbell, M. An experimental evaluation of the significance of three factors involved in motor performances for general motor ability. *J. exp. Psychol.,* 1936b, **19**, 612–620.

Carmichael, L., and W. F. Dearborn. *Reading and visual fatigue.* Boston: Houghton Mifflin, 1947.

Childers, H. The possibility of improvement in motor rhythm through training in tap dancing.

Unpublished Master's thesis, University of Southern California, 1937.

Cozens, F. W. The measurement of general athletic ability in college men. *Univ. Oreg. Publ. phys. Educ. Ser.,* 1929, **1**, 1–92.

Cureton, T. K. *Physical fitness appraisal and guidance.* St. Louis: C. V. Mosby, 1947.

Gilbreth, F. B. *Applied motion study.* New York: Macmillan, 1919.

Guilford, J. P., and J. I. Lacey (Eds.). *Printed classification tests.* Army Air Forces, Aviation Psychology Program, Research Report 5. Washington, D. C.: U. S. Government Printing Office, 1947.

Guylee, A. A study of mechanical ability tests. Unpublished Master's thesis, Northwestern University, 1940.

Hazelhurst, J. Factorial study of measures of mechanical aptitude. Unpublished Ph.D. thesis, Northwestern University, 1940.

Hovey, B. Effects of general distraction on the higher thought processes. *Amer. J. Psychol.,* 1928, **40**, 585–591.

Humphreys, L. G., C. E. Buxton, and H. R. Taylor. Steadiness and rifle marksmanship. *J. appl. Psychol.,* 1936, **20**, 680–688.

Katz, B. An experimental and clinical evaluation of the concept "nervous instability." *Psychol. Bull.,* 1935, **32**, 538–539.

McCloy, E. Factor analysis methods in the measurement of physical abilities. *Res. Quart. Amer. phys. Educ. Ass.,* 1935, **6**, 81–85.

McCollom, I. N. An analysis of factors determining individual differences in speed of simple repetitive motions of the right arm. Unpublished Master's thesis, University of Oregon Library, 1932.

Muscio, B. *Lectures on industrial psychology.* London: Routledge; New York: E. P. Dutton, 1920.

Paterson, D. G., L. D. Anderson, H. A. Toops, and E. Heidbreder. *Minnesota mechanical ability tests.* University of Minnesota, Department of Psychology, 1930.

Reymert, M. L. The personal equation in motor capacities. *Scand. Scient. Rev.,* 1923, **2**, 177–194.

Roethlisberger, F. J., and W. J. Dickson. *Management and the worker.* Cambridge: Harvard University Press, 1939.

Seashore, C. E. *Measures of musical talent* (phonograph records). New York: Columbia Phonograph Co.

Seashore, H. G., and G. Koch. Postural steadiness under conditions of muscular tension and fatigue. *Psychol. Rec.,* 1938, **2**, 319–332.

Seashore, R. H. Experimental methods in psychology. Unpublished manuscript, five chapters.

Seashore, R. H. Studies in motor rhythm. *Psychol. Monogr.,* 1926, **36**, No. 167, 142–189.

Seashore, R. H. Stanford motor skills unit. *Psychol. Monogr.,* 1928a, **39**, No. 178, 51–66.

Seashore, R. H. Techniques for measuring serial action. *J. exp. Psychol.,* 1928b, **11**, 45–55.

Seashore, R. H.   Individual differences in motor skills.   *J. gen. Psychol.*, 1930, **3**, 38–66.

Seashore, R. H.   Development of motor skills in later youth.   In *White House conference reports.* New York: Century, 1932.

Seashore, R. H.   The pyramid puzzle: A useful device in studying thought.   *Amer. J. Psychol.,* 1938, **51**, 549–557.

Seashore, R. H.   Work methods: An often neglected factor underlying individual differences. *Psychol. Rev.*, 1939, **46**, 123–141.

Seashore, R. H.   Experimental and theoretical analysis of fine motor skills.   *Amer. J. Psychol.,* 1940, **53**, 86–98.

Seashore, R. H.   Problem solving behavior in conflict situations.. *Train. Sch. Bull.*, March 1947.

Seashore, R. H., and R. D. Adams.   The measurement of steadiness: A new apparatus and results in marksmanship.   *Science*, 1933, **78**, 235.

Seashore, R. H., C. E. Buxton, and I. N. McCollom.   Multiple factorial analysis of fine motor skills.   *Amer. J. Psychol.*, 1940, **53**, 251–259.

Seashore, R. H., F. J. Dudek, and W. Holtzman. A factorial analysis of arm-hand precision tests. *J. appl. Psychol.*, 1949, **33**, 579–584.

Seashore, R. H., and W. Jenssen.   Personality classification and counseling techniques.   *Sci. Mon.*, 1948, **66**, 472–474.

Seashore, R. H., and I. N. McCollom.   Studies in motor or mechanical skills.   *Science,* 1932, **75**, 358–360.

Seashore, R. H., R. Starmann, W. E. Kendall, and J. S. Helmick.   Group factors in simple and discriminative reaction times.   *J. exp. Psychol.,* 1941, **29**, 346–349.

Seashore, S. H.   The aptitude hypothesis in motor skills.   *J. exp. Psychol.*, 1932, **14**, 555–561.

Seashore, S. H., and R. H. Seashore.   Individual differences in simple auditory reaction times of hands, feet and jaws.   *J. exp. Psychol.,* 1941, **29**, 342–345.

Spaeth, R. A., and G. C. Dunham.   The correlation between motor control and rifle shooting. *Amer. J. Physiol.*, 1921, **56**, 249–256.

Walker, R. Y., and R. D. Adams.   Motor skills: The validity of serial motor tests for predicting typewriting proficiency.   *J. gen. Psychol.,* 1934, **11**, 173–186.

Warren, N., and B. Clark.   Blocking in mental and motor tasks during a 65-hour vigil.   *J. exp. Psychol.*, 1937, **21**, 97–105.

Wendler, A. J.   A critical analysis of test elements used in physical education.   *Res. Quart. Amer. phys. Educ. Ass.*, 1938, **9**, 64–76.

Wyatt, R. F.   Improvability of pitch discrimination.   *Psychol. Monogr.*, 1945, **58**, No. 2.

Name Index

Subject Index